BOOK PRICES: USED AND RARE 1993

Edited by

**Edward N. Zempel
and
Linda A. Verkler**

THE SPOON RIVER PRESS

Published by
The Spoon River Press
2319-C West Rohmann
Peoria, IL 61604
(309) 672-2665
Fax (309) 672-7853

ISBN 0-930358-10-4

Manufactured in the United States of America

Introduction

Book Prices, Used and Rare is a reference for the secondhand and antiquarian book dealer, general and rare book librarian, and the private collector seeking to place a value on a book. The over 25,000 titles in the present volume have been selected from the 1992 catalogs of book dealers in the United States, both generalists and specialists. The dealers who provided catalogs represent a broad spectrum of the American book trade, not only geographically, but in the subject matter range and the price range of the books offered.

With a large variety of possible subject categories, we have attempted to balance the entries in this guide. Our goal has been to provide pricing information on books in those subject categories and price ranges most likely to be found in the day-to-day trade of the average generalist bookseller. This volume, then, contains entries on books in a wide variety of subject areas. Among them are modern first editions, travel, Americana and the West, science, medicine, art, architecture, children's literature, and books on books. With some exceptions, most of the titles listed in this guide are priced between $20 and $300.

Entry Alphabetizing

Entries have been alphabetized word-for-word by the author's surname. (This means, to cite just one example, that De Voto appears before DeLillo.) Every effort has been made to present the correct spelling of surnames. However, variant spellings were sometimes found, especially in names beginning with *de* and *De, le* and *Le, Mac* and *Mc*, etc. Thus, for example, while the correct entry for Peter De Vries would be De Vries, Peter, it appeared in some catalogs as DeVries, Peter. Such inconsistencies extend also to reference works and to entries in library catalog files. Please take this into consideration when searching for an entry for a particular author. If not in one place, the name may be in another.

Similarly, names preceded by *de* or *de la* should correctly be alphabetized under the family surname. For example, Simone de Beauvoir should be alphabetized under B — i.e., Beauvoir, Simone de. However, in the interests of clarity, ease of reference, and in anticipation of where many readers would first look, we have alphabetized all such names under D.

In the case of government publications such as House and Senate documents the user is advised to check for the title of the work, as well as for the work's author. Some works have been entered with the government agency as the author. For example, many publications of the Bureau of American Ethnology (BAE) have generally been alphabetized under BAE.

An entry for which the author is unknown has been entered alphabetically in the general list by its title. Pseudonymous entries give, if known, the author's real name in parentheses after the pseudonym.

Some edited works (letters, diaries, and journals, especially), were listed in catalogs under the name of the author; others were listed under the name of the editor. In looking up such titles in this guide, check first under the name of the author, and then under the name of the editor.

Translated works have generally been entered under the name of the author, not the translator.

Entry Information

When present in the catalog entry, each entry in this guide includes the following information: author's name, title of book (in CAPITAL letters), publisher and/or place and date of publication, condition, the price at which the book was cataloged, and an abbreviation identifying the dealer who cataloged the book. The key to these abbreviations is found in the listing of contributing dealers, which begins on page 7.

If the condition of a book is not noted, it may be assumed that the book is in good or better collectible condition. In the case of modern first editions, careful attention was given to noting those defects, both of the dust jacket and the book itself, affecting the book's value. The following are general definitions applying to a book's condition.

As New: In "as published" condition. The dust jacket (dj), if issued with the book, must be flawless.

Very Fine (VF): Nearly as new.

Fine: Without defect, but not "as new."

Very Good (VG): Minimal wear with no defects.

Good: In average condition.

Poor: Text complete, but book worn and binding defective.

Ex-library copies and book club editions are noted.

First editions are so noted. All titles are hardcover, unless the entry mentions otherwise. Every book is presumed to be in its original binding unless the entry mentions otherwise.

A dust jacket (dj) is mentioned when present. The dust jacket is assumed to be in the same general condition as the book unless the entry mentions otherwise. Slipcases also are noted.

In the case of certain older books, where collation is a factor in determining the book's edition, the collation (if given in the dealer's catalog) has been provided. Generally, if mentioned in the dealer's catalog description, folding maps, folding plates, and folding illustrations have been mentioned in the entry, regardless of the value of the book. In the case of entries for limited editions, the number of copies in the edition has been noted, if included in the catalog entry.

When a "point" (a typographical or binding feature bearing on the edition of the book and thus on its value) was mentioned in the bookdealer's catalog entry, we have included that "point" in our entry. For some Americana entries we have also included the Howes reference number included in the dealer's catalog entry.

For some books we have provided multiple entries, suggesting a price range, usually across a range of condition or editions. As mentioned, most of the entries provide information on books in the $20-$300 price range. Generally, then, this guide does not contain entries for unique copies, association copies, or books published in very small limited editions. The prices listed are retail prices at which the books were cataloged in 1992. While most of the books listed are hardcovers, prices on some vintage paperback first editions also have been included.

Abbreviations

To allow the inclusion of as much useful information as possible, certain standard abbreviations were used. A list of those abbreviations is on page 10.

A Caution

The prices listed in this guide are not the prices that book dealers will pay for the books listed. The prices listed are the prices at which dealers offered books for sale in 1992. The prices listed are, then, retail prices. Like any other retail business, the selling of rare, scarce, and used books depends for its profitability on a markup. The price a dealer is willing to pay for a book depends on its condition and scarcity, as well as the demand for the book.

Standing Orders

Book Prices: Used and Rare is published annually. Annual volumes may be placed on standing order at preferential discounts *well below* the post-publication price. Annual volumes on standing order will be shipped in late February each year. To place *Book Prices: Used and Rare* on standing order, contact the publisher: The Spoon River Press, 2319-C West Rohmann, Peoria, IL 61604. Send no payment. You will be billed when the book is shipped.

We are intent on making *Book Prices: Used and Rare* the most comprehensive and genuinely useful book price guide obtainable. If you have suggestions on how future annual editions might be improved regarding focus or coverage, please let us know.

Contributing Book Dealers

We are grateful to the book dealers listed below, who generously provided copies of their 1992 catalogs for our use in compiling this price guide. The name in parentheses below the name of the dealer is the name by which the dealer's catalog entries are identified in this guide.

Aardbooks
(AARD)
3026 NW 60th Street
Seattle, WA 98107

Academic Library Services
(ACADEMIC LIBRARY)
6489 S. Land Park Drive
Sacramento, CA 95831
(916) 428-2863

a/k/a Fine Used Books
(AKA)
4142 Brooklyn NE
Seattle, WA 98105
(206) 632-5870

The American Botanist
(AMERICAN BOTANIST)
P.O. Box 532
Chillicothe, IL 61523
(309) 274-5254

Archaeologia
(ARCHAEOLOGIA)
707 Carlston Avenue
Oakland, CA 94610
(510) 832-1405
Fax (510) 832-1410

Archer's Used and Rare Books
(ARCHER)
104 S. Lincoln Street
Kent, OH 44240
(216) 673-0945

Artis Books
(ARTIS)
201 N. Second Avenue
P.O. Box 822
Alpena, MI 49707
(517) 354-3401

Authors of the West
(AUTHORS OF THE WEST)
191 Dogwood Drive
Dundee, OR 97115
(503) 538-8132

Gene W. Baade
(BAADE)
1380 NW Jenne Avenue
Portland, OR 97229-4426
(503) 644-3463

Back Room Books (BACKROOM)
2 South Bridge Street
Christiana, PA 17509
(215) 593-7021

Gary Backman
(BACKMAN)
1005 Woodland Drive
Santa Paula, CA 93060

Bancroft Book Mews
(BANCROFT)
86 Sugar Lane
Newtown, CT 06470
(203) 426-6338

Beasley Books
(BEASLEY)
1533 W. Oakdale
Chicago, IL 60657

Bebbah Books
(BEBBAH)
P.O. Box 910
Gleneden Beach, OR 97388-0910

Benchmark Books
(BENCHMARK)
331 Rio Grande Street
Suite 300, P.O. Box 9027
Salt Lake City, UT 84109-0027
(801) 532-3100

Steven C. Bernard
(BERNARD)
15011 Plainfield Lane
Darnestown, MD 20874

Between the Covers
(BETWEEN COVERS)
132 Kings Highway East
Haddonfield, NJ 08033
(609) 354-7665
Fax (609) 354-7695

The Blue Dragon Book Shop
(BLUE DRAGON)
Box 216
Ashland, OR 97520
(503) 482-2142

Blue Mountain
Books & Manuscripts, Ltd
(BLUE MOUNTAIN)
P.O. Box 363
Catskill, NY 12414
(518) 943-4771

Bohling Book Company
(BOHLING)
P.O. Box 204
Decatur, MI 49045
(616) 423-8786

Nelson Bond
(BOND)
4724 Easthill Drive
Sugarloaf Farms
Roanoke, VA 24018
(703) 774-2674

The Book Block
(BOOK BLOCK)
8 Loughlin Avenue
Cos Cob, CT 06807
(203) 629-2990
Fax (203) 629-1051

The Book Broker
(BOOK BROKER)
P.O. Box 1283
Charlottesville, VA 22902

Bookcell Books
(BOOKCELL)
90 Robinwood Road
Hamden, CT 06517
(203) 248-0010
Fax (203) 230-0102

Book Finders International
(BOOKFINDERS INTL)
216 Ringwood Lane
Elgin, SC 29045

The Book Market
(BOOK MARKET)
Box 74
Altadena, CA 91003-0074

Meyer Boswell Books, Inc.
(BOSWELL)
2141 Mission Street
San Francisco, CA 94110
(415) 255-6400
Fax (415) 255-6499

Carroll Burcham, Bookseller
(BURCHAM)
5546 17th Place
Lubbock, Texas 79416
(806) 799-0419

The Captain's Bookshelf, Inc.
(CAPTAIN'S BOOKSHELF)
P.O. Box 2258
Asheville, NC 28802-2258
(704) 253-6631
(704) 254-5733

Chapel Hill Rare Books
(CHAPEL HILL)
P.O. Books 456
Carrboro, NC 27510
(919) 929-8351

Connolly & Wade Fine Books
(CONNOLLY & WADE)
P.O. Box 2309
Joplin, MO 64803-2309
(417) 624-5602

Thomas Cullen
(CULLEN)
Rockland Bookman
Box 134
Cattaraugus, NY 14719
(716) 257-5121
Fax (716) 257-9116

Dawson's Book Shop
(DAWSON'S)
535 N. Larchmont Blvd
Los Angeles, CA 90004

Joseph A. Dermont
(DERMONT)
13 Arthur Street
P.O. Box 654
Onset, MA 02558
(508) 295-4760

Harold B. Diamond
(DIAMOND)
Bookseller
Box 1193
Burbank, CA 91507
(818) 846-0342

Thomas Dorn
(DORN)
1231-P Collier Road NW
Atlanta, GA 30318
(404) 351-8652

Dramatis Personae
(DRAMATIS)
71 Lexington Avenue
New York, NY 10010
Ph/Fax (212) 679-3705

Else Fine Books
(ELSE FINE)
P.O. Books 43
Dearborn, MI 48121
(313) 834-3255

Five Quail Books
(FIVE QUAIL)
Route 1, Box 157A
Spring Grove, MN 55974

W. Bruce Fye
(FYE)
1607 N. Wood Avenue
Marshfield, WI 54449
(715) 384-8128
(715) 389-2990

Michael Gibbs
(GIBBS)
Bookseller
P.O. Box 83
West Chester, OH 45069
(513) 779-8556

Michael Ginsberg Books, Inc.
(GINSBERG)
Box 402
Sharon, MA 02067
(617) 784-8181
Fax (617) 784-1826

Great Epic Books
(GREAT EPIC)
15918 20th Place West
Alderwood Manor, WA 98037
(206) 745-3113
Fax (206) 745-9520

Great Expectations Rare Books
(GREAT EXPECTATIONS)
30 Barton Avenue
Staten Island, NY 10306

Hartfield Fine and Rare Books
(HARTFIELD)
117 Dixboro Road
Ann Arbor, MI 48105

Heinholdt Books
(HEINHOLDT)
1325 W. Central Avenue
South Egg Harbor, NJ 08215
(609) 965-2284

Josh Heller Rare Books, Inc.
(HELLER)
P.O. Box 39114
Washington, DC 20016-9114
(202) 966-9411
(202) 363-5658

Murray Hudson
(HUDSON)
Antiquarian Books and Maps
The Old Post Office
109 S. Church Street
P.O. Box 163
Halls, TN 38040

James Jaffe Rare Books
(JAFFE)
18 Haverford Station Road,
2nd Floor
P.O. Box 496
Haverford, PA 19041
(215) 649-4221
Fax (215) 649-4542

Priscilla Juvelis
(JUVELIS)
150 Huntington Avenue, Ste SDL
Boston, MA 02115
(617) 424-1895
(617) 424-7687

Kenneth Karmiole
(KARMIOLE)
P.O. Box 464
Santa Monica, CA 90406
(310) 451-4342
(310) 458-5930

Knollwood Books
(KNOLLWOOD)
Lee and Peggy Price
P.O. Box 197
Oregon, WI 53575
(608) 835-8861

Lame Duck Books
(LAME DUCK)
90 Moraine Street
Jamaica Plain, MA 02130

James and Mary Laurie
(LAURIE)
251 South Snelling Avenue
St. Paul, MN 55105
(612) 699-1114, Fax (612) 699-8088

Edward J. Lefkowicz, Inc.
(LEFKOWICZ)
P.O. Box 630
Fairhaven, MA 02719
(508) 997-6839
Fax (508) 996-6407

Ken Lopez—Bookseller
(LOPEZ)
51 Huntington Road
Hadley, MA 01035

M & S Rare Books, Inc.
(M & S)
Box 311
Weston, MA 02193
(617) 891-5650

Mad Dog and the Pilgrim
(MAD DOG)
5926 E. Colfax Avenue
Denver, CO 80220

Robert A. Madle
(MADLE)
4406 Bestor Drive
Rockville, MD 20853
(301) 460-4712

David A. McClintock
(MCCLINTOCK)
1454 Sheridan Avenue NE
Warren, OH 44483
(216) 372-4425

McGowan Book Company
(MCGOWAN)
P.O. Box 222
Chapel Hill, NC 27514
(919) 968-1121

Frank Mikesh
(MIKESH)
1356 Walden Road
Walnut Creek, CA 94596

Mordida Books
(MORDIDA)
P.O. Box 79322
Houston, TX 77279
(713) 467-4280

Howard S. Mott, Inc.
(MOTT)
Mottbooks
Sheffield, MA 01257
(413) 229-2019
Fax (413) 229-8553

Robert Mueller Rare Books
(MUELLER)
8124 W 26th Street
North Riverside, IL 60546
(708) 447-6441

Nutmeg Books
(NUTMEG)
354 New Litchfield Street
(Route 202)
Torrington, CT 06790

Oak Knoll Books
(OAK KNOLL)
414 Delaware Street
New Castle, DE 19720
(302) 328-7232
Fax (302) 328-7274

October Farm
(OCTOBER FARM)
2609 Branch Road
Raleigh, NC 27610
(919) 772-0482

The Old London Bookshop
(OLD LONDON)
P.O. Box 922
Bellingham, WA 98227-0922
(206) 733-RARE
Fax (206) 647-8946

W.B. O'Neill
(O'NEILL)
Old & Rare Books
11609 Hunters Green Court
Reston, VA 22091
(703) 860-0782
Fax (703) 620-0153

Oregon Territorial Books
(OREGON)
P.O. Box 22
Sublimity, OR 97385
(503) 769-7356

Other Worlds Bookstore
(OTHER WORLDS)
1281 N. Main Street
Providence, RI 02904-1827
(401) 331-9140

Outpost Books
(OUTPOST)
P.O. Box 697
Lake Ozark, MO 65049
(314) 348-5558

Parmer Books
(PARMER)
7644 Forrestal Road
San Diego, CA 92120-2203
(619) 287-0693
Fax (619) 287-6135

Pettler & Lieberman Booksellers
(PETTLER)
8033 Sunset Blvd #977
Los Angeles, CA 90046
(310) 474-2479

Phillip J. Pirages
(PIRAGES)
Fine Books and Manuscripts
P.O. Box 504
McMinnville, OR 97128
(800) 962-6666
Fax (503) 472-5029

R. Plapinger
(PLAPINGER)
P.O. Box 1062
Ashland, OR 97520

Polyanthos Park Avenue Books
(POLYANTHOS)
P.O. Box 343
Huntington, NY 11743
(516) 271-5558

Wallace D. Pratt, Bookseller
(PRATT)
1801 Gough Street, #304
San Francisco, CA 94109
(415) 673-0178

Alice Robbins, Bookseller
(ROBBINS)
3002 Round Hill Road
Greensboro, NC 27408
(919) 282-1964

Schoyer's Antiquarian Books
(SHOYER'S)
1404 S. Negley Avenue
Pittsburgh, PA 15217
(412) 521-8464
Fax (412) 521-8410

Second Life Books, Inc.
(SECOND LIFE)
P.O. Box 242, 55 Quarry Road
Lanesborough, MA 01237
(413) 447-8010
Fax (413) 499-1540

Flo Silver Books
(SILVER)
8442 Oakwood Court North
Indianapolis, IN 46260
(317) 255-5118

The Silver Door
(SILVER DOOR)
P.O. Box 3208
Redondo Beach, CA 90277
(310) 379-6005

Edward L. Smith
(SMITH)
P.O. Box 1183
Ojai, CA 93024
Ph/Fax (805) 646-2921

Smithfield Rare Books
(SMITHFIELD)
20 Deer Run Trail
Smithfield, RI 02917
(401) 231-8225

Monroe Stahr Books
(STAHR)
4420 Ventura Canyon
    Avenue, #2
Sherman Oaks, CA 91423
(818) 784-0870

Raymond M. Sutton, Jr.
(SUTTON)
P.O. Box 330, 430 Main Street
Williamsburg, KY 40769
(606) 549-3464
Fax (606) 549-3469

Len Unger Rare Books
(UNGER)
P.O. Box 5858
Sherman Oaks, CA 91413
(800) 990-7569

David Varner Books
(VARNER)
509 Silverado Trail
Belton, MO 64012
(816) 331-7911

Jeff Weber Rare Books
(WEBER)
P.O. Box 3368
Glendale, CA 91221-0368
(818) 848-9704

J. Howard Woolmer Rare Books
(WOOLMER)
Marienstein Road
Revere, PA 18953
(215) 847-5074

Worldwide Antiquarian
(WORLDWIDE)
P.O. Box 391
Cambridge, MA 02141
(617) 876-6220

William P. Wreden
(WREDEN)
Books & Manuscripts
206 Hamilton Avenue
P.O. Box 56
Palo Alto, CA 94302-0056
(415) 325-6851

Abbreviations

To allow us to provide the maximum amount of information, we have used the following abbreviations in editing the entries in this guide. Most of these abbreviations are standard.

4to	a book with a height of approximately 12"	lea	leather
8vo	a book with a height of approximately 9"	LEC	Limited Editions Club
		lib	library
12mo	a book with a height of approximately 7-8"	litho	lithograph, lithographic
		lrg/lg	large
aeg.	all edges gilt	ltd	limited
adv	advance	n.d.	no date
als	autograph letter, signed	n.p.	no place, no publisher
BAE	Bureau of American Ethnology	NAL	New American Library
		NF	near fine
bkpl	bookplate	NY	New York
brn	brown	o/w	otherwise
bull	bulletin	OJ	Orange Judd
cl	cloth	orig	original
comp	compiler	OUP	Oxford University Press
contemp	contemporary		
cvr	cover	pb	paperback
dec	decorative, decorated	Phila	Philadelphia
dj	dust jacket	pict	pictorial
dup	duplicate	pl/plts	plate(s)
dwgs	drawings	pg/pp	page(s)
ed	editor, edited by	prev	previous
ed(s)	edition(s)	promo	promotional
eng	paper engineer (for pop-up books)	pseud	pseudonym
		ptd	printed
engr	engraving	ptg	printing
ep(s)	endpaper(s)	pub's	publishers
esp	especially	rev	revised
et al	and others	rev copy	review copy
ex-lib	ex-library	rfep	rear free end paper
facs	facsimile	rmdr mk	remainder mark
fep	free end paper	S&S	Simon & Schuster
ffep	front free end paper	SF	San Francisco
fldg	folding	sig	signature
frontis	frontispiece	sl	slight, slightly
FSG	Farrar, Straus, and Giroux	soc	society
GC	Garden City	teg	top edges gilt
G & D	Grosset & Dunlap	tls	typed letter, signed
GPO	Government Printing Office	trans	translated, translator
		univ	university
grn	green	USGPO	United States Government Printing Office
hc/hb	hardcover		
HMSO	Her Majesty's Stationery Office		
		VF	very fine
illus	illustration(s), illustrated, illustrator	VG	very good
		vol(s)	volume(s)
imp	impression	w/	with
inscrip	inscription	w/o	without
LA	Los Angeles		

A

A BELLE OF THE FIFTIES: MEMOIRS OF MRS. CLAY....(by Virginia Clay-Clopton). Doubleday Page, 1905 (c. 1904). Fixed front, eps torn; binding weak. Good+. *BOOK BROKER.* $45

A CATALOGUE OF THE H. WINNETT ORR HISTORICAL COLLECTION AND OTHER RARE BOOKS IN THE LIBRARY OF THE AMERICAN COLLEGE OF SURGEONS. Chicago, 1960. 1st ed. Ex-lib. *FYE.* $90

A COMPLETE COLLECTION OF STATE TRIALS AND PROCEEDINGS FOR HIGH-TREASON....CRIMES AND MIS-DEMEANOURS. 4th ed. London: T. Wright, 1776-81. 2 alphabetical tables. New preface by Francis Hargrave, Esq. 12 vols in 6. Thick demy folios. Set is rebacked w/new buckram strips. Front cvr of one vol replaced w/matching board. Orig worn raised bands still present. 1st 11 lines, 10 lines of verso column of 1p in vol 10 defective. Sm inoffensive worm holes (mostly marginal) in several vols, o/w text VG. *DIAMOND.* $1,250

A CURIOUS TRAVELLER. London: J. Rowland. 1742. (4),384,(4)pp. Index. 8 copper-engr plts, incl frontis. Contemp mottled calf, rebacked; top of front hinge with 2" crack; still sound. Very scarce. *KARMIOLE.* $350

A, Dr. (pseud of Isaac Asimov). THE SENSUOUS DIRTY OLD MAN. NY: Walker, (1971). 1st ed. NF in dj (worn, frayed, head of spine). *OTHER WORLDS.* $50

A HANDBOOK FOR TRAVELLERS IN EGYPT...London: Murray; Paris: Galignani, etc., 1875. 5th ed, rev. Fldg maps. Worn, inner hinges cracked, o/w Good. *WORLDWIDE.* $30

A HISTORY OF BROWNING GUNS FROM 1831 -. St. Louis: Browning Arms Co, 1942. 1st ed. Textured, beige & brown, stapled overhanging wraps. Fine. *CONNOLLY & WADE.* $40

A LAW GRAMMAR: OR, AN INTRODUCTION TO THE THEORY AND PRACTICE OF ENGLISH JURISPRUDENCE. James Moore, No. 45, College-Green, Dublin, 1791. 2 blanks; title page; 544 starred pp (following Eng ed); 3 blanks. 8vo. The Dublin, star-paged ed, likely pirated from the sole London ed. Bound in full, contemp sheep, quite rubbed and worn; top of spine chipped, some embrowning (mainly lightish) throughout; Crisp, usable. *BOSWELL.* $350

A LETTER ADDRESSED TO TWO GREAT MEN (i.e. PITT AND THE DUKE OF NEWCASTLE), ON THE PROSPECT OF PEACE....London, 1760. 2nd ed, corrected. (4),56pp. Half morocco. Howes L276. *GINSBERG.* $125

A MEDIEVAL FEAST. Crowell, (1983). 1st ed. Illus by Aliki who has signed this copy. Fine in Fine dj. *BEBBAH.* $30

A MEMOIR TO THE ACADEMY OF SCIENCES AT PARIS ON A NEW USE OF SULPHURIC ETHER BY W.T.G. MORTON. NY, 1946. Wrappers, 24pp. Rare. *FYE.* $50

A MONOGRAPH OF THE WORK OF MELLOR, MEIGS & HOWE. NY: Architectural Bk Pub Co. 1923. 1st ed. Two-tone blue cl. Fine in sl soiled dj. *KARMIOLE.* $185

A NATURAL HISTORY OF SINGING BIRDS; AND PAR-TICULARLY, THAT SPECIES OF THEM MOST COMMONLY BRED IN SCOTLAND....Edinburgh, 1754. Frontis, 22 plain plts (some primitive coloring has occurred with a few plts). Pp(14),170,5. Recent buckram. Scattered foxing; 3 pp repaired w/tape; upper page-corners crudely cropped; ex-lib. *SUTTON.* $125

A NEW AND GENERAL BIOGRAPHICAL DICTIONARY....London: Robinson, Johnson, Nichols, and many others, 1798. New ed, greatly Enlarged and Improved, in 15 vols. 3/4 calf, marbled boards, raised bands, gilt. Some wear, but text excellent. *HARTFIELD.* $895

A RELATION OR JOURNAL OF A LATE EXPEDITION TO THE GATES OF ST. AUGUSTINE ON FLORIDA CON-DUCTED BY THE HON. GENERAL JAMES OGLETHORPE....(By Edward Kimber.) Boston: Goodspeed, 1935. Orig boards. Reprint of London, 1744, rare orig, w/biblio notes by Sidney A. Kimber. Howes K143. One of 250. *GINSBERG.* $75

A RESIDENCE OF ELEVEN YEARS IN NEW HOL-LAND...BEING THE ADVENTURES OF JAMES F. O'CONNELL. Boston: B.B. Mussey, 1841. 2nd ed. Orig cl, quite scuffed and worn, sl foxing. Scarce. *CULLEN.* $125

A SKETCH OF THE HISTORY OF SOUTH CAROLINA...REVOLUTION OF 1719. WITH AN APPEN-DIX...HITHERTO UNPUBLISHED. (By William J. River.) Charleston: McCarter, 1856. 1st ed. 470pp. Orig cl, crown of spine chipped. Howes R324. *GINSBERG.* $175

A SKETCH OF THE LIFE AND SERVICE OF GENERAL WIL-LIAM RUFFIN COX. Richmond, 1921. 1st ed. NF w/Mrs. William Ruffin Cox's card laid in. *McGOWAN.* $95

A SOUTH DAKOTA GUIDE. State of SD, 1938. 1st ed. Fldg map rear pocket. Some shelfwear; top fore-edge sl marked. Name stamp title-page. Old lib stamp, o/w VG. *DIAMOND.* $75

A STUDY OF FINGER PRINTS, THEIR USES AND CLAS-SIFICATION. Chicago: Univ of Applied Science, 1923. 5th ed. Lessons 1-10, plus Final Exam. VG. *BEASLEY.* $20

A SURGICAL PILGRIM'S PROGRESS: REMINISCENCES OF LEWIS STEPHEN PILCHER. Phila, 1925. 1st ed. *FYE.* $40

A TALE OF A TUB...(By Jonathan Swift.) London: John Nutt, 1710. 5th ed. 8vo, 344pp. Frontis, fine full-page engr. Nice later binding in 3/4 crushed morocco and brown cloth, gilt titling. Minor worming at top gutter, not affecting text. VG. *HARTFIELD.* $495

A THRILLING NARRATIVE OF THE MINNESOTA MAS-SACRE AND THE SIOUX WAR OF 1862-63...Chicago: Author, (1896). 1st ed. Cl w/gilt vignette. Minor shelfwear. Spine gilt dull, o/w VG. *DIAMOND.* $100

A TOUR ON THE PRAIRIES. (By Washington Irving.) London: John Murray, 1835. 1st British ed, precedes US ed. Orig boards, cl, spine label. VG, spine label chipped, name. *AUTHORS OF THE WEST.* $450

A TOUR THROUGH THE WHOLE ISLAND OF GREAT BRITAIN....Originally begun by the celebrated Daniel Defoe, continued by the late Mr. Richardson...and brought down to the present time by a Gentleman of Eminence in the Literary World. 7th ed. 4 vols. London: Rivington, and many others, 1769. Tall 12mo. Contemp polished calf, nicely rebacked. Handsome set. *HARTFIELD.* $495.

A TREATISE ON AGRICULTURE....BY A PRACTICAL FARMER. (By John Armstrong.) Albany: J. Buel (1820). 1st ed. 168pp. Uncut in orig linen backed boards (lacks the linen on lower 3/5's of spine; foxing, water stain on final leaf and rear blanks). VG. *SECOND LIFE.* $650

A TRUE ACCOUNT AND DECLARATION OF THE HORRID CONSPIRACY AGAINST THE LATE KING....(By Thomas Sprat.) (London:) Thomas Newcomb, 1685. 2nd ed. iv,l-167,i,ii,1-141. Fold-out plt (backed). Later full calf, name on title pg. Nice. *SECOND LIFE.* $325

A TRUE PICTURE OF EMIGRATION....(By Rebecca Burlend.) London: Berger (1848). 1st ed. 62pp. Orig ptd wraps (sl wear to spine paper, rear hinge). VG. Howes B992. *SECOND LIFE.* $300

A VIEW OF THE INTERNAL EVIDENCE OF THE CHRISTIAN RELIGION. (By Soame Jenyns.) London: J. Dodsley, 1776. 2nd ed. Small 12mo, 191pp. Orig mottled calf, raised bands, gilt lea title. Assoc copy, w/armorial bkplt of John Cator, Johnson's friend and executor. Some wear, but attractive. *HARTFIELD.* $295

A WESTERN JOURNEY WITH MR. EMERSON. (By James Bradley Thayer.) Boston: Little, Brown, 1884. 141pp. Ptd wrapper w/ptd dj. Jacket chipped, darkened & soiled, laid in fldg cl case. VG. *BO-HLING.* $200

A WESTERN TOWN. London, 1983. Illus Boggs and Svensson. Keith Moseley (eng). 2 double pop-ups front and back, 2 pull-down flaps in between, three push-pull tabs. Pop-up bk. *BOOKFINDERS INTL.* $20

A' Beckett, Gilbert Abbott. THE COMIC BLACKSTONE. Chicago: Callaghan & Cockcroft, 1870. 1st Amer ed. George Cruikshank (illus). 376pp. Orig brn bevelled cl sl worn. Spine tips defective. Sl staining on fore-edges. Minor tears pp margins, o/w text VG. *DIAMOND.* $95

Aardema, Vera and Victoria Chess (illus). PRINCESS GORILLA AND A NEW KIND OF WATER. NY: Dial, (1988). 1st ed. Fine in dj. *BETWEEN COVERS.* $45

Aardema, Verna. WHY MOSQUITOES BUZZ IN PEOPLE'S EARS. Dial, (1975). 1st ptg. Illus by Leo & Diane Dillon. Fine in Fine dj. *BEBBAH.* $90

Abbey, Edward and John Blaustein. THE HIDDEN CANYON. NY: Viking, (1978). 2nd prtg of the scarce hardcover ed. NF in dj. *LOPEZ.* $75

Abbey, Edward and Philip Hyde. SLICKROCK. SF/NY: Sierra Club, (1971). 1st ed. Fine in a dj with slight bit of offsetting to rear panel but still Fine. *LOPEZ.* $275

Abbey, Edward. A VOICE CRYING IN THE WILDERNESS. NY: St. Martin's Press, 1990. 1st ed. Fine. *SMITH.* $35

Abbey, Edward. APPALACHIAN WILDERNESS. NY: Dutton, 1970. 1st ed. Fine in sl price clipped dj w/small puncture tear on rear panel. *BETWEEN COVERS.* $275

Abbey, Edward. APPALACHIAN WILDERNESS: THE GREAT SMOKEY MOUNTAINS. NY: Dutton, 1970. 1st ed. Fine in dj. *CAPTAIN'S BOOKSHELF.* $200

Abbey, Edward. BEYOND THE WALL. NY: Holt Rinehart Winston, (1984). 1st ed. Scarce hb issue. Fine in dj w/blurb misspelling author Larry McMurtry's name on front panel. *LOPEZ.* $125

Abbey, Edward. BLACK SUN. NY: S & S (1971). 1st ed. Fine in NF price clipped dj. *DORN.* $90

Abbey, Edward. BLACK SUN. NY: Simon & Schuster, (1971). 1st ed. Fine in dj with short tear bottom edge of front panel. *LOPEZ.* $100

Abbey, Edward. BLACK SUN: A NOVEL. NY: Simon & Schuster, 1971. 1st ed. VF in dj. *ELSE FINE.* $165

Abbey, Edward. CACTUS COUNTRY. NY: Time Life Books, 1973. 1st ed. In rare dj. Fine. *SMITH.* $75

Abbey, Edward. CACTUS COUNTRY. NY: Time-Life, 1973. 1st ed. Fine in pict boards, issued w/o dj. *ELSE FINE.* $30

Abbey, Edward. DESERT IMAGES. (NY): (Harcourt Brace Jovanovich), (1979). 1st ed. Cl, cl slipcase. VF. *JAFFE.* $350

Abbey, Edward. DESERT SOLITAIRE. NY: McGraw-Hill, 1968. 1st ed, 1st bk. Fine, short tear at dj spine fold. *ELSE FINE.* $350

Abbey, Edward. DESERT SOLITAIRE. Tucson: Univ of Tucson, (1988). 20th Anniv ed, 1st thus. Signed by Abbey w/new intro. VF in VF dj. *UNGER.* $200

Abbey, Edward. DESERT SOLITAIRE....NY: McGraw Hill, (1968). 1st ed. Fine in dj (rubbing; darkening to spine). *CAPTAIN'S BOOK-SHELF.* $250

Abbey, Edward. DOWN THE RIVER. NY: Dutton, (1982). 1st ed. Fine in dj. Issued simultaneously in wraps. Hardcover ed uncommon. *CAPTAIN'S BOOKSHELF.* $300

Abbey, Edward. FIRE ON THE MOUNTAIN. London: Eyre & Spottiswoode, 1963. 1st Eng ed. NF in sl dust-soiled but still NF dj. *LOPEZ.* $375

Abbey, Edward. JONATHAN TROY. NY: Dodd, Mead, (1954). 1st ed. Abbey's first book. Minor shelfwear, spotting on rear ep, o/w NF in a dj with edge tears and chips, several of which have been internally repaired, and some foxing or spotting on the rear panel. *LOPEZ.* $650

Abbey, Edward and Philip Hyde. SLICKROCK. SF: Sierra Club, 1971. 1st ed. Fine. *SMITH.* $300.

Abbey, Edward. SLUMGULLION STEW. NY: Dutton, (1984). 1st ed. Fine in Fine dj and signed. *LOPEZ.* $125

Abbey, Edward. SLUMGULLION STEW. NY: Dutton, (1984). 1st ed. Signed. Fine in Fine dj. *UNGER.* $175

Abbey, Edward. THE BRAVE COWBOY. NY: Dodd, Mead, (1956). 1st ed. Light shelfwear, small ownership label removed from ffep, o/w VG in dj with several chips at extremities of spine, sl affecting the lettering at top and bottom, several other edge tears, and some wear along the rear flap fold. *LOPEZ.* $1500

Abbey, Edward. THE FOOL'S PROGRESS. Holt, (1988). 1st ed. Fine in Fine dj. *BEBBAH.* $28

Abbey, Edward. THE FOOL'S PROGRESS. London: Bodley Head, (1989). 1st UK ed. Fine in Fine dj. *LOPEZ.* $65

Abbey, Edward. THE FOOL'S PROGRESS. Henry Holt, 1988. 1st ed. VG in dj. Signed. Fine but for sl water damage to upper, front corners of boards and verso of dj. *STAHR.* $25

Abbey, Edward. THE JOURNEY HOME. NY: Dutton, (1977). 1st ed. Signed. Fine in Fine dj. *UNGER.* $175

Abbey, Edward. THE JOURNEY HOME. NY: Dutton (1977). 1st ed. Fine in NF dj. *LOPEZ.* $55

Abbey, Edward. THE JOURNEY HOME. NY: Dutton, 1977. 1st ed. Signed. Fine. *SMITH.* $150

Abbey, Edward. THE JOURNEY HOME: SOME WORDS IN DEFENSE OF THE AMERICAN WEST. NY: Dutton, (1977). 1st ed. Fine in dj. Signed. *CAPTAIN'S BOOKSHELF.* $175

Abbey, Edward. THE JOURNEY HOME: SOME WORDS IN DEFENSE OF THE AMERICAN WEST. NY: Dutton, 1977. 1st ed. VF in dj. *ELSE FINE.* $75

Abbey, Edward. THE MONKEY WRENCH GANG. Phila: Lippincott, (1975). 1st Amer ed. Very sm light stain bottom edge else Fine in lightly used price clipped NF dj. *DORN.* $165

Abbey, Edward. THE MONKEY WRENCH GANG. Phila: Lippincott, (1975). 1st ed. NF in like dj (a few tiny edge tears). *CAPTAIN'S BOOKSHELF.* $150

Abbey, Edward. THE MONKEY WRENCH GANG. Phila: Lippincott (1975). 1st ed. Lt stain bottom edge else Fine in sl used price clipped NF dj. *DORN.* $165

Abbey, Edward. VOX CLAMANTIS IN DESERTO. SOME NOTES.... Santa Fe: Rydal Press, 1989. 1st ed, ltd to 250 numbered. Slipcased. VF. *OREGON.* $200

Abbot, Anthony. THESE ARE STRANGE TALES. Winston, 1948, 1st ed. NF in frayed dw. *MADLE.* $15

Abbott, Bernice. CHANGING NEW YORK. Elizabeth McCausland (text). NY: Dutton, 1939. 1st ed. 96 repros of Abbott's photos. Some browning to endsheets, lt foxing to fore-edges, else Fine in dj. *CAPTAIN'S BOOKSHELF.* $350

Abbott, E.A. FLATLAND: A ROMANCE OF MANY DIMENSIONS. London: Seeley, 1884. New, rev ed. xvi,102pp. Stiff card cvrs, minor chipping front cvr, leaf margins foxed. Tight, clean. *BOOK-CELL.* $225

Abbott, Jacob. HISTORY OF CYRUS THE GREAT. NY: Harper, 1878. 1st ed. Edges rubbed, silverfished, few wormholes edge of spine, o/w Good. *WORLDWIDE.* $20

Abbott, Jacob. WAR OF THE REVOLUTION. NY: Sheldon & Co, 1864. 1st ed. Frontis, 8 plts. Name, else NF. *CONNOLLY & WADE.* $40

Abbott, James. NARRATIVE OF A JOURNEY FROM HERAUT TO KHIVA...DURING THE LATE RUSSIAN INVASION OF KHIVA. London, 1884. 3rd ed. Fldg map. 2 vols. New cl. Map neatly repaired. *O'NEILL.* $110

Abbott, John. THE HISTORY OF HERNANDO CORTEZ. NY: Harper & Brothers, 1855. 1st ed. 348pp. Marbled edges, eps, rebound. Cvr wear, contents VG+. *SILVER.* $50

Abbott, John. THE HISTORY OF MAINE. Augusta, ME, 1892, 2nd ed, rev. 53 plts. 608pp. Rebound new buckram. *HEINOLDT.* $45

Abbott, John. THE HISTORY OF NAPOLEON BONAPARTE. NY, 1883. New ed. 4 vols. Teg. Illus w/maps. NF. *POLYANTHOS.* $95

Abbott, Katharine M. OLD PATHS & LEGENDS OF NEW ENGLAND. NY: Putnam, 1909 (c. 1903). Grn cl w/gilt title, gilt top & mounted cover illus. Fep removed, front hinge cracked, bkpl. *BOHLING.* $20

Abbott, Maude. CLASSIFIED AND ANNOTATED BIBLIOGRAPHY OF SIR WILLIAM OSLER'S PUBLICATIONS. Montreal, 1939. 2nd ed. *FYE.* $100

ABC POP UP. London, 1960. Mabel Lucy Atwell, illus. Pop-up bk. *BOOKFINDERS INTL.* $60

ABC POP UP. London, 1978. Pop-up bk. *BOOKFINDERS INTL.* $25

Abdill, George B. CIVIL WAR RAILROADS. Seattle: Superior Pub Co, (1961). 1st ed. Cl, dj. *BOHLING.* $45

Abdullah, Achmed. LUTE AND SCIMITAR. NY, 1928. NF. *POLYANTHOS.* $35

Abel, Annie H. (ed). CHARDON'S JOURNAL AT FORT CLARK 1834-1839....Pierre, SD, 1932. 1st ed. 3 plts. Fine. Howes C303. *OREGON.* $125

Abella, Alex. THE KILLING OF THE SAINTS. Crown, 1991. Uncorrected proof. VG in yellow wraps. *STAHR.* $15

Abels, Robert. EARLY AMERICAN FIREARMS. Cleveland: The World Pub Co, 1950. VG. Pict cvrs. *BACKROOM.* $20

Abercrombie, John. PATHOLOGICAL AND PRACTICAL RESEARCHES...Phila: Carey, Lea & Blanchard, 1838. 3rd Amer from the 2nd London ed. 320pp. Contemp calf covers sl worn and stained, little foxing of content, o/w Good. *DIAMOND.* $45

Abercrombie, John. PATHOLOGICAL AND PRACTICAL RESEARCHES ON DISEASES OF THE BRAIN AND SPINAL CORD. Phila, 1843. Leather, 324pp. Backstrip worn, front hinge broken. *FYE.* $150

Abercrombie, Lascelles. TWELVE IDYLS AND OTHER POEMS. London: Secker, 1928. Cloth-backed boards. Pres from publisher. Fine. *MUELLER.* $35

Abernathy, Francis Edward (ed). OBSERVATIONS & REFLECTIONS ON TEXAS FOLKLORE. Austin: Encino Press, 1972. Publications of the Texas Folklore Soc. No. XXXVII. 1st ed. Mint in dj. *LAURIE.* $25

Abernethy, Francis Edward. PAISANOS: A FOLKLORE MISCELLANY. Austin: The Encino Press, 1978. 1st ed. Fine in Fine dj. *CONNOLLY & WADE.* $30

Abernethy, John. SURGICAL OBSERVATIONS ON THE CONSTITUTIONAL ORIGIN AND TREATMENT OF LOCAL DISEASES; AND ON ANEURISMS. ON DISEASES RESEMBLING SYPHILIS; AND ON DISEASES OF THE URETHRA. Phila, 1811. 1st Amer ed. Full leather, 325pp. *FYE.* $250

Abernethy, John. THE SURGICAL AND PHYSIOLOGICAL WORKS OF JOHN ABERNETHY. VOLUME 1. Hartford, 1825. Full leather, 414pp. Hinges cracked. *FYE.* $50

Abert, James W. THROUGH THE COUNTRY OF THE COMANCHE INDIANS IN THE FALL OF THE YEAR 1845....SF: John Howell, 1970. Frontis, 2 fldg maps. VF in VF dj. *OREGON.* $95

Abert, James W. THROUGH THE COUNTRY OF THE COMANCHE INDIANS IN THE FALL OF THE YEAR 1845. (SF): John Howell, 1970. One of 5000. 26 full-pg plts, 2 double-pg fldg maps. Fine in chipped dj. *LAURIE.* $100

Abert, James W. WESTERN AMERICA IN 1846-1847. THE ORIGINAL TRAVEL DIARY...John Galvin (ed). SF: John Howell, 1966. 1st ed. Frontis, 13 plts, fldg maps. Fine. *OREGON.* $85

Abetti, Giorgio. THE HISTORY OF ASTRONOMY. NY: Henry Schuman, 1952. Trans Betty Burr Abetti. Spotting, slight extremity wear, o/w VG in blue cl. *KNOLLWOOD.* $30

Abney, William de Wiveleslie. INSTRUCTION IN PHOTOGRAPHY. By Captain Abney. 8th ed. London: Piper & Carter. 1888. 1/2 maroon calf over blue cl, dec gilt spine, grn leather spine label. *KARMIOLE.* $100

ABOUT BOOKS. A GATHERING OF ESSAYS. Berkeley: Book Arts Club of the Univ of CA, 1941. 1st ed thus. One of 450 numbered. Corners worn, else Fine. *WREDEN.* $35

About, Edmond. THE KING OF THE MOUNTAINS. Chicago: Rand McNally, 1897. 1st ed. NF. *ELSE FINE.* $65

Abraham, J.J. LETTSOM: HIS LIFE....London: Heinemann, 1933. VG. *BOOKCELL.* $60

ABRAHAM LINCOLN ASSOCIATION PAPERS DELIVERED BEFORE THE MEMBERS OF THE ABRAHAM LINCOLN ASSOCIATION...FEBRUARY 12, 1932. Springfield, 1933. Pict cl. VG+. *PRATT.* $25

Abrahams, Peter. THE PATH OF THUNDER. NY: Harper & Brothers, (1948). 1st ed. VG in dj chipped at spine crown. *LOPEZ.* $40

Abram, Edward. A RIDE THROUGH SYRIA TO DAMASCUS AND BAALBEC, AND ASCENT OF MOUNT HERMON. London, 1887. Fldg frontis map. Full pebbled red morocco. 61pp. Spine rubbed, corners bumped. Presentation. *O'NEILL.* $325

ACCEPTANCE OF THE STATUE OF CHARLES M. RUSSELL...PROCEEDINGS IN THE CONGRESS AND IN THE ROTUNDA, US CAPITOL. USGPO, 1959. 1st ed. No dj as pub. Fine. *AUTHORS OF THE WEST.* $30

Achdjian, Albert. ...A FUNDAMENTAL ART: THE RUG. Paris: Editions Self, 1949. 1st ed. Wraps w/mounted color specimen pl; extrems sl chipped, lt soiling, o/w VG. *WEBER.* $100

Achebe, Chinua. HOPES AND IMPEDIMENTS. NY: Doubleday, (1989). Uncorrected proof. Fine. *LOPEZ.* $40

Achebe, Chinua. THINGS FALL APART. NY: McDowell, Obolensky, (1959). First Amer ed. NF in VG dj w/a few small edge tears. *DORN.* $40

Acier, Marcel (ed). FROM SPANISH TRENCHES. NY: Modern Age, 1937. 2nd ptg. Wraps in dj (tiny tears). VG. *AKA.* $22

Acier, Marcel (ed). FROM SPANISH TRENCHES. NY: Modern Age, 1937. 1st ed. Wraps, one corner damped, but only lightly worn. *BEASLEY.* $25

Acker, William R.B. JAPANESE ARCHERY. Rutland, VT and Tokyo: Charles E. Tuttle Co., 1965. 1st trade ed. NF in dj. *OLD LONDON.* $15

Ackerknecht, Erwin. MEDICINE AT THE PARIS HOSPITAL: 1794-1848. Baltimore, 1967. Dj. *FYE.* $40

Ackerman, Forrest. FAMOUS MONSTERS OF FILMLAND. Imagine, 1986. 1st ed. As New in wraps. *MADLE.* $18

Ackley, Mary E. CROSSING THE PLAINS AND EARLY DAYS IN CALIFORNIA. SF: Privately ptd, 1928. 1st ed. 68pp. Tipped in illus. Inscribed. Orig presentation box w/Mary Ackley's label, hand addressed. Fine. *PARMER.* $400

Ackroyd, Peter. CHATTERTON. Grove, 1988. 1st Amer ed. Advance reading copy. VF in wraps. *STAHR.* $25

Ackroyd, Peter. DICKENS. London: London Limited Editions, (1990). 1st ed. Ltd to 150 signed. Cl-backed boards, glassine dj. Mint. *JAFFE*. $150

Ackroyd, Peter. DICKENS. NY, 1990. 1st ed. Signed. Mint in dj. *POLYANTHOS*. $55

Ackroyd, Peter. THE GREAT FIRE OF LONDON. London: Hamish Hamilton, (1982). 1st ed. Fine in dj. *CAPTAIN'S BOOKSHELF*. $300

Ackroyd, Peter. THE LAST TESTAMENT OF OSCAR WILDE. Harper & Row, 1983. 1st Amer ed. VF in dj. *STAHR*. $17.50

Acosta, Oscar Zeta. THE REVOLT OF THE COCKROACH PEOPLE. (SF): (Straight Arrow), (1973). 1st ed. NF in dj. *LOPEZ*. $50

Acton, Harold. THE BOURBONS OF NAPLES (1734-1825). London: Methuen (1956). 1st ed. Fine. *WOOLMER*. $25

Adair, Gilbert. HOLLYWOOD'S VIETNAM. London: Proteus, (1981). 1st Brit ed. NF in NF dj. *AKA*. $50

Adams, A.L. FIELD AND FOREST RAMBLES, WITH NOTES AND OBSERVATIONS ON THE NATURAL HISTORY OF EASTERN CANADA. London, 1873. Orig gilt-dec cl. Bkpl, # sticker on spine; staining to gutters of 2 pp; sl inner hinge cracking. *SUTTON*. $110

Adams, Alice. FAMILIES AND SURVIVORS. NY: Knopf, 1974. 1st ed. NF in NF dj. *ROBBINS*. $35

Adams, Alice. MEXICO. SOME TRAVELS AND TRAVELERS THERE. NY: Prentice Hall (1991). Uncorrected proof. Fine in wrappers. *LOPEZ*. $45

Adams, Alice. TO SEE YOU AGAIN. NY: Knopf (1982). Uncorrected proof. Piece of wrapper missing, not affecting text. VG. *LOPEZ*. $30

Adams, Andy. A TEXAS MATCHMAKER. Boston: Houghton Mifflin, and Co, 1904. 1st ed. VG. *LAURIE*. $40

Adams, Andy. WHY THE CHISHOLM TRAIL FORKS AND OTHER TALES OF THE CATTLE COUNTRY. Austin: Univ of Texas Press, 1956. Black stamped cl in dj w/2 short tears. *DAWSON'S*. $30

Adams, Ansel. NATURAL LIGHT PHOTOGRAPHY. Hastings on Hudson: Morgan & Morgan, 1971. Ltr ed. Signed. *SMITH*. $25

Adams, Ansel. THE GLORY OF OUR WEST. GC: Doubleday, (1952). 1st ed. 50 full-pg lithogravure plts. Spiral bound. Box. VG. *LAURIE*. $40

Adams, Charles Francis (ed). MEMOIRS OF JOHN QUINCY ADAMS... PORTIONS OF HIS DIARY FROM 1795 TO 1848. Phila., 1874-1877. 12 vols. Illus, 3 ports. Orig cl, very nice. 1st ed. One of 250 sets. Howes A69. *GINSBERG*. $1000

Adams, Charles Francis. ANTINOMIANISM IN THE COLONY OF MASSACHUSETTS BAY, 1636-1638. INCLUDING THE SHORT STORY AND OTHER DOCUMENTS. Boston, Prince Soc, 1894. 415pp. Contemp half morocco. A few rubber lib stamps. 1st ed. Howes A46. One of 250. *GINSBERG*. $175

Adams, Charles Francis. RICHARD HENRY DANA: A BIOGRAPHY. Boston/NY: Houghton Mifflin, 1890. 1st ed. 2 vols. Lt wear, insect nibbles. Bkpl. Red cl, gilt spine titles. Frontis. VG. *PARMER*. $95

Adams, Douglas. DIRK GENTLY'S HOLISTIC DETECTIVE AGENCY. NY: Simon & Schuster, (1987). 1st ed. Signed. Fine in Fine dj. *AKA*. $30

Adams, Douglas. LONG DARK TEA-TIME OF THE SOUL. NY: Simon & Schuster, (1988). 1st ed. Signed. NF in NF. *AKA*. $25

Adams, Douglas. THE RESTAURANT AT THE END OF THE UNIVERSE. NY, 1980. 1st ed. Uncorrected proof in pub prtd wraps. Fine. *POLYANTHOS*. $35

Adams, Douglas. THE RESTAURANT AT THE END OF THE UNIVERSE. NY: Harmony, (1980). 1st US ed. NF in dj. Signed. *CAPTAIN'S BOOKSHELF*. $35

Adams, Edward F. THE MODERN FARMER IN HIS BUSINESS RELATIONS....SF: Stone, 1899. 1st ed. *SECOND LIFE*. $65

Adams, Edward. C.L. POTEE'S GAL. A DRAMA OF NEGRO LIFE NEAR THE BIG CONGAREE SWAMPS. Columbia, SC: The State Co, 1929. 1st ed. Orig maroon cl. #17 of 250 signed. Scarce. Fine in dj. *CHAPEL HILL*. $150

Adams, Ephraim Douglass. GREAT BRITAIN AND THE AMERICAN CIVIL WAR. 2 vols. NY, 1925. 1st Amer ed. A little apparent water damage on vol 1, confined to back cvr, chipping at spine extremities, o/w VG. *PRATT*. $50

Adams, F. Colburn. THE STORY OF A TROOPER, WITH MUCH OF INTEREST CONCERNING THE CAMPAIGN ON THE PENINSULA, NOT BEFORE WRITTEN. NY, 1865. 616pp. Feps torn along binding but still intact and o/w VG, text Fine. *PRATT*. $75

Adams, Frank. THE LONG NIGHT. London: Stanley Paul, (1932). 1st ed. Inscribed. Fine in dj w/a few tiny closed tears. *MORDIDA*. $125

Adams, Frederick Upham. PRESIDENT JOHN SMITH. Kerr, 1897. 1st ed. VG. *MADLE*. $50

Adams, George. ASTRONOMICAL AND GEOGRAPHICAL ESSAYS: CONTAINING, I. ...NEW PLAN OF THE GENERAL PRINCIPLES OF ASTRONOMY. II. THE USE OF...GLOBES... III. ...USE OF THE ARMILLARY SPHERE, PLANETARIUM, TELLURIAN, AND LUNARIUM. IV. AN INTRODUCTION...OR, THE USE OF THE QUADRANT AND EQUATORIAL. London: Pub by author, 1790. 2nd ed. VG, rebound in modern leather w/marbled eps, scattered foxing. Piece torn from top of title page not affecting contents. *KNOLLWOOD*. $550

Adams, H. Austin. THE MAN JOHN D. SPRECKELS. San Diego: Frye & Smith, 1924. 1st ed. Edges, prelims foxed; some wear, name. Good. *PARMER*. $35

Adams, H. Austin. THE MAN JOHN D. SPRECKLES. San Diego: Frye & Smith, 1924. 1st ed. Fine. *CONNOLLY & WADE*. $75

Adams, Harold. THE NAKED LIAR. NY: The Mysterious Press, (1985). Uncorrected proof. Fine in wraps. *CAPTAIN'S BOOKSHELF*. $35.

Adams, Henry Gardiner. FAVORITE SONG BIRDS. London: Groombridge and Sons, n.d. (c. 1857). 3rd ed. 192pp,12pp cat. 5 full-pg hand-colored plts. Modern brn cl, paper shelf label. Good+. *SMITHFIELD*. $120

Adams, Henry. MONT-SAINT MICHEL AND CHARTRES. With a new intro. by Francis Henry Taylor. NY: LEC, 1957. One of 1500 illus (with photos), signed by Samuel Chamberlain. Fine in slipcase. *CAPTAIN'S BOOKSHELF*. $125

Adams, Herbert. THE GOLDEN APE. Phila: Lippincott, 1930. 1st ed. NF; chips dj spine ends. *ELSE FINE*. $35

Adams, Herbert. THE MAN WHO MET THE TRAIN. NY: Mysterious Press, 1988. 1st ed. Signed. VF in dj. *SILVER DOOR*. $35

Adams, I. William. SHIBUSAWA, or THE PASSING OF OLD JAPAN. NY: G.P. Putnam's Sons. 1906. Red cl, gilt. Owner sig on title page. *KARMIOLE*. $40

Adams, James Truslow. ATLAS OF AMERICAN HISTORY. NY: Charles Scribner's Sons, 1943. 1st ed. 147 maps. Dj chipped; edge wear, age-darkening. Howes A58. *PARMER*. $175

Adams, Joey. ON THE ROAD FOR UNCLE SAM. N.p.: Bernard Geis, (1963). 1st ed. VG in worn, torn dj. *AKA*. $30

Adams, John Couch, LECTURES ON THE LUNAR THEORY. Cambridge: Univ Press, 1900. Ed by R.A. Sampson. Good. *KNOLLWOOD*. $90

Adams, John Gregory Bishop. REMINISCENCES OF THE NINETEENTH MASSACHUSETTS REGIMENT. Boston, 1899. 1st ed. NF. *McGOWAN*. $125

Adams, John Quincy. LETTERS OF JOHN QUINCY ADAMS TO EDWARD LIVINGSTON, GRAND HIGH PRIEST...Boston: Pub by Young Men's Antimasonic Assoc for Diffusion of Truth, 1833. 1st ed. 36pp, sewn. VG. *OREGON*. $95

Adams, John Quincy. ORATION ON THE LIFE AND CHARACTER OF GILBERT MOTIER DE LAFAYETTE. Washington: Gales & Seaton, 1835. 1st ed. 94pp. Orig wraps, lacking rear cover. Good+. *OREGON*. $55

Adams, John Quincy. THE JUBILEE OF THE CONSTITUTION. DISCOURSE DELIVERED AT...NY...30 APRIL 1839...50TH ANNIVERSARY OF INAUGURATION OF GEORGE WASHINGTON. NY: S. Colman, 1839. 1st ed. 136pp + frontis. Orig wraps, corners and spine chipped. VG. *OREGON*. $50

Adams, Kramer. LOGGING RAILROADS OF THE WEST. Seattle: Superior Pub Co, (1961). 1st ed. Cloth. Fine in dj. *BOHLING*. $50

Adams, Paul. ARCTIC ISLAND HUNTER. London: George Ronald, (1961). 1st ed. 45 photos, 2 maps. Fine in dj. *ARTIS*. $20

Adams, Ramon. MORE BURRS UNDER THE SADDLE: BOOKS AND HISTORIES OF THE WEST. Univ of OK Press, (1979). 1st ed. New in dj. *AUTHORS OF THE WEST*. $25

Adams, Ramon. SIX GUNS & SADDLE LEATHER. Norman: Univ Okla, (1954). 1st ed. F in F dj. *OREGON*. $150

Adams, Ramon. THE COWMAN AND HIS CODE OF ETHICS. Encino Press, (1969). 1st ltd ed of 850 numbered. Illus Remington, A.R. Collins. Signed. Pict cvr. Fine, w/o dj as issued. *AUTHORS OF THE WEST*. $50

Adams, Ramon. WESTERN WORDS. Univ of OK Press, 1946. 3rd ptg. Fine in NF dj. *VARNER*. $35

Adams, Richard. THE PLAGUE DOGS. (London): Lane/Collins, (1977). 1st ed. NF in Fine dj. *OTHER WORLDS*. $25

Adams, Richard. THE PLAGUE DOGS. London: Allen Lane, (1977). 1st ed. Fine in Fine dj. *UNGER*. $50

Adams, Richard. WATERSHIP DOWN. NY: Macmillan Publishing, (1974). 1st US ed. of 1st book. Spine sl bowed o/w VG+ in dj. *BERNARD*. $40

Adams, Samuel. THE WORLD GOES SMASH. Houghton-Mifflin, 1938. 1st ed. VG. *MADLE*. $35

Adams, W.H.D. LIFE IN THE PRIMEVAL WORLD: FOUNDED ON MEUNIER'S "LES ANIMAUX D'AUTREFOIS." London, 1872. London, 1872. Orig gilt-dec cl. Lt soiling; head of spine torn; bkpl; sm remains of paper label on spine. *SUTTON*. $65

Addams, Charles. BLACK MARIA. NY, 1960. 1st ed. Spine lightly sunned. Fine in dj (spine lightly sunned, extremities little chipped, few edge nicks, price clipped). *POLYANTHOS*. $45

Addams, Charles. BLACK MARIA. NY, 1960. Fine. *POLYANTHOS*. $45

Addams, Charles. DEAR DEAD DAYS. A FAMILY ALBUM. NY, (1959). 1st ed. Little edge rubbed. Fine in dj (small edge tear top front panel, corners little chipped, little edge rubbed and little soiled). *POLYANTHOS*. $35

Addams, Charles. HOMEBODIES. NY, 1954. 1st ed. Extremities spine sunned, little edge rubbed. NF in dj (pieces missing extremities, spine, few small edge tears, little edge rubbed). *POLYANTHOS*. $45

Addams, Charles. MONSTER RALLY. NY, (1950). Rev copy. NF. *POLYANTHOS*. $45

Addams, Jane. THE LONG ROAD OF WOMAN'S MEMORY. NY: Macmillan, 1916. 1st ed. Blue cl stamped in gilt. VG. *SCHOYER'S*. $45

Addington, Sarah. PUDDING LANE PEOPLE. Little, Brown, 1926. 1st ed. Illus by Janet L. Scott. 183pp. Slight edgewear & soil to forward edge, rear ep torn else VG. *BEBBAH*. $30

Addison, Joseph. REMARKS ON SEVERAL PARTS OF ITALY in The Years 1701, 1702, 1703. London: Tonson and Draper, 1745. Lg. 12mo, 303pp, index. Full speckled calf, rebacked w/raised bands, gilt on red lea label. Some light foxing, well-worn but attractive. *HARTFIELD*. $125

Addison, Thomas. A COLLECTION OF THE PUBLISHED WRITINGS. London, 1868. 1st ed. 242pp. Ex-lib, but Fine. *FYE*. $250

Addison, Thomas. ON THE CONSTITUTIONAL AND LOCAL EFFECTS OF DISEASE OF THE SUPRA-RENAL CAPSULES. Birmingham, 1980. Facs of 1855 ed. 4to, full lea, 43pp. 11 Fine plts. *FYE*. $75

Addison, W. EPPING FOREST: ITS LITERARY & HISTORICAL ASSOCIATIONS. London: Dent, (1947). VG. *MIKESH*. $15

Ade, George. ARTIE. A STORY OF THE STREETS AND TOWN. Chicago: Herbert S. Stone, 1896. 1st ed. Illus by John T. McCutcheon. Spine little sunned, name; uncut, Fine. 1st regularly published bk. *POLYANTHOS*. $50

Ade, George. DOC HORNE. Chicago & NY: Stone, 1899. 1st ed. McCutcheon illus. Fine. *MUELLER*. $35

Ade, George. STORIES OF THE STREETS AND OF THE TOWN: FROM THE CHICAGO RECORD 1893-1900. Ed by Franklin J. Meine. Caxton Club: Chicago, 1941. Ltd to 500. *CONNOLLY & WADE*. $85

Ade, George. THE OLD-TIME SALOON. NY: Ray Long & Richard Smith, 1931. Ltd ed, signed. In orig tattered cellophane dj. fine. *CULLEN*. $75

Adelman, Bob and Susan Hall. OUT OF LEFT FIELD. Two Continents, 1976. 1st ed. Fine in Fine dj. Inscribed by Willie Stargell. *PLAPINGER*. $60

Adelman, Bob. DOWN HOME: CAMDEN, ALABAMA. NY: McGraw-Hill, (1972). Lt edgewear. Dj edges chipped, shelfwear. VG. *AKA*. $30

Adelmann, Howard. MARCELLO MALPIGHI AND THE EVOLUTION OF EMBRYOLOGY. Ithaca, 1966. 1st ed. 5 vols. 2475pp. In slipcase. *FYE*. $200

Adler, Bill. LOVE LETTERS TO THE METS. Simon & Schuster, 1965. 1st ed. VG+ in Fine dj. *PLAPINGER*. $40

Adlington, John Henry. THE CYCLOPAEDIA OF LAW, or, THE CORRECT BRITISH LAWYER...WITH A SUPPLEMENT....London: Thomas Kelly, 1826, 1824. xxxiv,pp.(9)-688; iv,240pp+engr plts, title-pg vignette. Contemp mottled calf, sl worn, stained. Rebacked w/orig worn dec spine gilt laid down. Some staining (mostly marginal) on some pgs, o/w internally VG. *DIAMOND*. $250

Adney, E.T. and H.I. Chapelle. THE BARK CANOES & SKIN BOATS OF NORTH AMERICA. Washington, DC: Smithsonian, 1964. Illus. VG. *MIKESH*. $47.50

Adolphus, John. MEMOIRS OF JOHN BANNISTER, COMEDIAN. London: Richard Bentley, 1839. 1st ed. 2 vols. Later half red morocco; spines elaborately gilt to compartments; min rubbing to extremities; engr frontis each vol; teg. VG. *DRAMATIS PERSONAE*. $150

Adrian, E.D. THE MECHANISM OF NERVOUS ACTION, ELECTRICAL STUDIES OF THE NEURONE. London, 1932. 1st ed. 103pp. *FYE*. $100

AE (pseud of George Russell). MIDSUMMER EVE. NY: Crosby Gaige, 1928. Ltd ed of 450 signed by author. Uncut. In boards. Spine and edges sl sunned, short tear mended side spine, front panel. *POLYANTHOS*. $35

AE (pseud of George Russell). SOME PASSAGES FROM THE LETTERS OF AE TO W.B. YEATS. Dublin, Ireland: The Cuala

Press, 1936. Tan cl backed ptd blue paper covered boards (bumped). Ptd paper label on spine, part of label rubbed away. Bkpl removed from front pastedown. Title vignette. One of ltd ed of 300. NF, unopened. *BLUE MOUNTAIN.* $250

Aesop. AESOP'S FABLES. A New Translation by V.S. Vernon Jones. With an Intro by G.K. Chesterton and Illus by Arthur Rackham. London: William Heinemann. 1912. xxx,224pp. Illus w/13 color plts, incl frontis; each pl w/tissue guard. Orig dec grn cl, stamped in gold. Some lt foxing to text. *KARMIOLE.* $175

Aflalo, F.G. SUNSHINE AND SPORT IN FLORIDA AND THE WEST INDIES. Phila, PA: George W. Jacobs. N.d. (circa 1907). 46 photo plts. Orig grn cl, spine lettering sl rubbed. *KARMIOLE.* $45

Agassiz, E.C. (ed). LOUIS AGASSIZ: HIS LIFE & CORRESPONDENCE. Boston, 1885. 2 vols. Teg. VG. *MIKESH.* $55

Agassiz, Louis and A.A. Gould. PRINCIPLES OF ZOOLOGY...PART I. COMPARATIVE PHYSIOLOGY. Boston, 1848. 1st ed. 170 text-figures, 1 map. Orig cl. Spine soiled & faded; some spotting; corners missing from 2 pp w/no text loss; occasional foxing. *SUTTON.* $40

Agassiz, Louis and Mrs. Agassiz. A JOURNEY IN BRAZIL. Boston: Ticknor & Fields, 1868. 2nd ed. xix, 540pp. Orig. cl, little shelf wear. Rebacked w/new cl. Front ep repaired & reattached, o/w Good. *DIAMOND.* $50

Agassiz, Louis and Mrs. Agassiz. A JOURNEY IN BRAZIL. Boston: Ticknor and Fields, 1868. xix, 540pp. Cl hinges cracked; spine, covers discolored. *PARMER.* $115

Agassiz, Louis. A JOURNEY IN BRAZIL. Boston: Houghton Mifflin, 1886, (1867). 540pp, 20 woodcuts. Blue cl, edges rubbed, spine shipped, bkpl removed, contents VG. *SILVER.* $50

Agassiz, Louis. BIBLIOGRAPHIA ZOOLOGIAE ET GEOLOGIAE. A GENERAL CATALOGUE OF ALL BOOKS, TRACTS, AND MEMOIRS ON ZOOLOGY AND GEOLOGY. H. E. Strickland (enl, ed by). NY, 1968. Facs of 1848-1854 ed. 4 vols. *FYE.* $150

Agee, James. A DEATH IN THE FAMILY. NY: McDowell, Obolensky, (1957). 1st issue. Very slight sunning to spine, still Fine in Very NF dj w/bit of rubbing to extremities. *BETWEEN COVERS.* $85

Agee, James. A DEATH IN THE FAMILY. NY: McDowell, Obolensky (1957). First issue: "walking" on page 80. Extrems sl sunned else NF in VG dj. *DORN.* $75

Agee, James. A WAY OF SEEING. NY: Horizon, (1981). Enl ed, which corrects the text and adds 24 photos. Fine in lightly rubbed dj (a few short tears). *CAPTAIN'S BOOKSHELF.* $60

Agee, James. PERMIT ME VOYAGE. New Haven: Yale Univ Press, 1934. 1st ed. Sl sunning top edges, else Fine in dj w/chipping along upper extrems and sl darkened spine. Richard Eberhart's owner sig ffep. Very Nice. *CAPTAIN'S BOOKSHELF.* $600

Agee, James. PERMIT ME VOYAGE. New Haven: Yale Univ Press, 1934. 1st ed, 1st book. Fine in lightly chipped dj w/1" chip at head of spine, not affecting type. *BEASLEY.* $350

Agricola, G. DE RE METALLICA. Herbert Hoover & Lou Hoover (trans). London: Mining Magazine, 1912. 1st Eng ed. Good. *BOOKCELL.* $275

Aickman, Robert. PAINTED DEVILS Scribners, 1979. 1st. Notes, else VG in dj. *MADLE.* $15

Aiken, Conrad. BLUE VOYAGE. NY: Scribner, 1927. 1st ed. Fine in pict dj by Cleon (sl darkened at spine and rear panel). *CAPTAIN'S BOOKSHELF.* $125

Aiken, Conrad. GREAT CIRCLE. NY: Scribner's, 1933. 1st ed. Orig blue cl. Fine in NF dj. *CHAPEL HILL.* $225

Aiken, Conrad. KING COFFIN. NY: Scribners, 1935. 1st ed. Fine but for foxed spine in Fine dj w/short tears and barely darkened spine. *BEASLEY.* $75

Aiken, Conrad. PRELUDES FOR MEMNON. NY: Scribner's, 1931. 1st ed. NF in soiled, VG dj w/a few closed tears. Scarce in dj. *CHAPEL HILL.* $150

Aiken, Conrad. SELECTED POEMS. NY: Scribner's, 1929. 1st trade ed. Orig black cl, gilt-dec spine. Fine in VG dj (sm chip head of spine affecting no lettering). Nice. *CHAPEL HILL.* $150

Aiken, Conrad. THE CLERK'S JOURNAL, BEING THE DIARY OF A QUEER MAN. NY: The Eakins Press, 1971. 1st ed. #XCII (92) of 300 hb numbered, signed. Fine in VG ptd slipcase. *CHAPEL HILL.* $75

Aiken, Conrad. THE KID. (London): John Lehmann, 1947. 1st Eng ed. Orig grn cl. Fine, unopened in dj. *CHAPEL HILL.* $50

Aiken, Conrad. THEE. NY: George Braziller, (1967). 1st trade ed. Leonard Baskin (illus). Orig lt greenish-grey paper covered boards. NF in dj. *CHAPEL HILL.* $25

Aiken, Conrad. TOM, SUE AND THE CLOCK. Illus by Julie Maas. NY: Collier Books, (1966). 1st ed. Fine in sl soiled dj. *DERMONT.* $25

Aiken, Joan. THE GREEN FLASH. Holt, 1971. 1st ed. NF in dj. *MADLE.* $25

Aiken, Lucy. EPISTLES ON WOMEN. Boston: Wells and Wait, 1810. 1st US ed. 154pp. Little rubbed contemp sheep, front flyleaf and hinge tender. Good. *SECOND LIFE.* $225

Aikin, John. LETTERS TO A YOUNG LADY ON A COURSE OF ENGLISH POETRY. London: J. Johnson, 1807. 2nd ed, but consisting apparently of the sheets of the 1st ed. of 1804, w/cancel title page. Small 8vo, pp x, 297 (3). Half-title, and list of bks pub by Aikin family. Orig pub's boards, paper spine, label. Name on flyleaf. Nice. *HARTFIELD.* $225

Aikin, Lucy. MEMOIRS OF THE COURT OF KING JAMES THE FIRST. London: Longman, et al, 1822. 2nd ed. 2 vols. 444; 413pp. Uncut in orig paper backed boards w/paper label. VG. Some external wear. *SECOND LIFE.* $125

Aikin, Lucy. MEMOIRS OF THE COURT OF QUEEN ELIZABETH. In Two Vols. London: Longman, 1879. 3rd ed. 2 vols. Engr port frontis. Contemp 3/4 calf and marbled boards. Some wear to hinges; armorial bkpl. VG. *HARTFIELD.* $165

Aikman, Lonnelle. NATURE'S HEALING ARTS: FROM FOLK MEDICINE TO MODERN DRUGS. Washington, 1977. 1st ed. *FYE.* $25

Aimes, Hubert H.S. A HISTORY OF SLAVERY IN CUBA, 1511 to 1868. NY: G.P. Putnam's Sons. 1907. 1st ed. Orig red cloth, gilt spine. Scarce. *KARMIOLE.* $60

Ainsworth, Ed. CALIFORNIA. LA: House-Warven, 1951. 1st ed. Fine in Fine dj. *BOOK MARKET.* $18

Ainsworth, Ed. FIVE ACRES OF HEAVEN. THE STORY OF THE GREAT AMERICAN DESERT. LA, 1955. 1st ed. Fine in wraps. *BOOK MARKET.* $15

Ainsworth, Ed. GOLDEN CHECKERBOARD. Palm Desert: Desert-Southwest, (1965). 1st ed. Fine in Fine dj. *BOOK MARKET.* $125

Ainsworth, Ed. PAINTERS OF THE DESERT....Palm Desert: Desert Magazine Press, 1960. 1st ed. Fine in Fine dj. *BOOK MARKET.* $450

Ainsworth, Ed. THE COWBOY IN ART. NY: World, (1968). 1st ed. Fine in sl chipped dj. *LAURIE.* $100

Ainsworth, William Harrison. BALLADS: ROMANTIC, FANTASTICAL, AND HUMOROUS. London, 1855. 1st ed. Illus by John Gilbert. 1/2 calf, gilt spine, raised bands, teg. NF. *POLYANTHOS.* $75

Ainsworth, William Harrison. THE STAR-CHAMBER, AN HISTORICAL ROMANCE. George Routledge and Sons, London, n.d. 2 blanks;half title;frontis;title pg;leaf;(vii)-viii,296pp. 7plts; 2 blanks. 8vo. Bound in contemp, or near-contemp, 3/4 blue morocco over marbled boards. Bit rubbed but still very nice, marbled edges and eps. *BOSWELL.* $175

AIR, LAND, AND SEA. London, 1969. Pop-up bk. *BOOKFINDERS INTL.* $35

Aird, Catherine. SOME DIE ELOQUENT. London: Collins, 1979. 1st ed. VF in dj. *SILVER DOOR.* $25

Airy, George B. POPULAR ASTRONOMY, A SERIES OF LEC-TURES DELIVERED AT IPSWICH. London: Macmillan, 1868 (1849), 6th ed rev. Blindstamped red cl, faded, worn; corners bumped, worn, top of spine frayed. Fldg frontis, 69 illus. 292 pp. *KNOLLWOOD.* $50

Aitken, Robert Grant. NEW GENERAL CATALOGUE OF DOUBLE STARS WITHIN 120 OF THE NORTH POLE. 2 vols. Carnegie Institution of Washington, 1932. Ex-lib in paper wraps; stamps, o/w Good. *KNOLLWOOD.* $195

Akeley, C. and M.L.J. LIONS, GORILLAS & THEIR NEIGH-BORS. NY, 1932. 1st ed. NF. *MIKESH.* $27.50

Akeley, M.L.J. CONGO EDEN....NY, 1950. 15 plts, map. Cloth (lt wear). *SUTTON.* $23

Akin, Warren. LETTERS OF WARREN AKIN, CONFEDERATE CONGRESSMAN. Ed by Bell Irvin Wiley. Athens, GA, (1959). 1st ed. Fine. *PRATT.* $25

Akurgal, Ekrem. THE ART OF THE HITTITES. NY: Harry N. Abrams, (1962). 174 plts (26 color). Dj. Good. *ARCHAEOLOGIA.* $150

ALADDIN & THE MAGIC LAMP. NY, (1970's). Pop-up bk. *BOOK-FINDERS INTL.* $15

Alain-Fournier. THE LOST DOMAIN (LE GRAND MEAULNES). NY: Oxford, 1986. 1st Amer ed. Fine in dj. *CAPTAIN'S BOOKSHELF.* $35

ALASKA. NY, 1939. American Guide Series. WPA guide. 1st ptg. Map, dj. *SCHOYER'S.* $75

Alastos, Doros. CYPRUS IN HISTORY. London, 1955. Dj. 1st ed. *O'NEILL.* $35

Albaugh, William A. & Steuart, Richard D. THE ORIGINAL CON-FEDERATE COLT. NY (1953). 1st ed. Pict cl. Some internal water damage but not enough to seriously damage the quality or obscure the text or illus; o/w VG+. *PRATT.* $55

Albaugh, William A., III. A PHOTOGRAPHIC SUPPLEMENT OF CONFEDERATE SWORDS. Washington, 1963. 1979 reprint with addendum. Fine in dj. *PRATT.* $42.50

Albee, Edward. A DELICATE BALANCE. NY, 1966. 1st ed. Signed. Fine in like dj. *POLYANTHOS.* $75

Albee, Edward. ALL OVER. London: Jonathan Cape, (1972). 1st ed. Fine in dj. *JUVELIS.* $40

Albee, Edward. BOX AND QUOTATIONS FROM CHAIRMAN MAO. NY: Atheneum, 1969. 1st ed. Inscribed by author. Fine in Fine dj. *BEASLEY.* $125

Albee, Edward. WHO'S AFRAID OF VIRGINIA WOOLF. London: Jonathan Cape, (1964). 1st Eng ed. Fine in NF dj. *JUVELIS.* $70

Albee, Edward. WHO'S AFRAID OF VIRGINIA WOOLF? Lon-don: Cape, (1964). 1st Eng ed. NF in lightly soiled, VG dj. *LOPEZ.* $65

Albert, Lillian and Kathyrn Kent. THE COMPLETE BUTTON BOOK. GC, NY: Doubleday, 1949. 1st ed. Fine in Good dj, repaired. *WREDEN.* $85

Albion, Robert Greenhalgh. RISE OF NEW YORK PORT (1815-1860). NY, London: Scribners, 1939. 1st ed. Blue cl, gilt title. VG+. *BOHLING.* $35

Albion, Robert Greenhalgh. SEAPORTS SOUTH OF SAHARA. NY: Ap-Century-Crofts, (1959). 1st ed. Rev slip laid in. Fine in VG dj. *AARD.* $25

Albright, George Leslie. OFFICIAL EXPLORATIONS FOR PACIFIC RAILROADS 1853-1855. Berkeley: Univ of CA, 1921. Fldg map, ptd wraps. Unopened. Nice. *BOHLING.* $90

Albucasis. ON SURGERY AND INSTRUMENTS. A DEFINITIVE EDITION OF THE ARABIC TEXT WITH ENGLISH TRANS-LATION AND COMMENTARY BY M.S. SPINK AND G.L. LEWIS. London, 1973. 1st ed. Dj. *FYE.* $100

Alcock, Thomas. LECTURES ON PRACTICAL AND MEDICAL SURGERY, COMPRISING OBSERVATIONS AND REFLEC-TIONS ON SURGICAL EDUCATION. London, 1830. 1st ed. 1/2 leather, 302pp. 12 engrvd plts. Scarce. *FYE.* $200

ALCOHOLICS ANONYMOUS. NY: A.A. World Services Inc, 1955. New, rev ed. 1st ptg of 2nd ed. Fine in Fine dj. *BOOK MARKET.* $80

Alcott, A. Bronson. CONCORD DAYS. Boston: Roberts Bros., 1872. 1st ed. 8vo, 276pp, (4)pp ads. Orig terra cotta cl. Light wear to spine ends, else bright and VG. A variant binding not noted by BAL, which calls for brown or blue cl. *CHAPEL HILL.* $60

Alcott, Louisa M. AUNT JO'S SCRAP-BAG. MY GIRLS etc. Bos-ton: Roberts, 1878. 1st ed. 12mo, 229pp,adv. Grn cl, two leaves heavily oxidized, name on e.p, VG. Vol 4 in series, bound in grn cl. BAL 186. *SECOND LIFE.* $100

Alcott, Louisa M. JO'S BOYS AND HOW THEY TURNED OUT. Boston: Roberts, 1886. 1st ed, 2nd state (sheets bulk 1"). 365pp. Grn cl cocked. Good, tight. *SECOND LIFE.* $45

Alcott, Louisa. AN OLD FASHIONED GIRL. London: Sampson Low, Son and Marston, 1870. 1st ed. 12mo. 4,314,4pp. Orig cl, a lit-tle dulled, but Fine. With binder's ticket of W. Bone & Son, Lon-don. *M & S.* $750

Alcott, Louisa. HOSPITAL SKETCHES. Boston, 1863. 1st ed. Spine little sunned, top sl chipped, lower spine little rubbed. Fine. *POLYAN-THOS.* $100

Alcott, Louisa. LITTLE MEN. Winston, (1928). Illus by Clara M. Burd. Pict rubbed; marginal dampstain to frontis; corner of 1 pl torn; cvr has edgewear; lt stain to spine. Good. *BEBBAH.* $25

Alcott, Louisa. LITTLE WOMEN. Little, Brown, 1923. Illus by Alice Barber Stephens. VG w/only minor edgewear. Gilt dec spine, dec cvr in maroon, grn & yellow on olive cloth. *BEBBAH.* $25

Alcott, Louisa. LITTLE WOMEN. Little, Brown, 1938. Orchard House ed with endpaper portraying Alcott's childhood home. Variant in dark blue cloth, gilt lettering of Nudelman's A43 w/3 color full-page Jessie Wilcox Smith illus. Foxing to frontis not affect-ing illus, else VG. *BEBBAH.* $25

Aldin, Cecil. OLD INNS. NY: Doubleday Page, 1921. 1st U.S. ed. Rebacked & eps replaced, corners worn, interior tight & clean. *OC-TOBER FARM.* $68

Aldington, Richard. ALL MEN ARE ENEMIES. London, 1933. 1st ed. Dj little sunned, some edge chips. NF. *POLYANTHOS.* $30

Aldington, Richard. ALL MEN ARE ENEMIES. London: Chatto & Windus, 1933. 1st ed. DJ torn, else Fine. *WEBER.* $50

Aldington, Richard. BALLS. ANOTHER BOOK FOR SUPPRES-SION. Draguignan: The Melissa Press, 1962. 2nd ed. Orig printed as Blue Moon Booklet No 7. Printed wraps. Fine. *POLYANTHOS.* $30

Aldington, Richard. D.H. LAWRENCE: PORTRAIT OF A GENIUS BUT... NY: Duell, Sloan, & Pearce, 1950. 1st US ed. Adv rev copy w/slip laid in. Fine in lightly used dj. *BEASLEY.* $45

Aldington, Richard. FIFTY ROMANCE LYRIC POEMS. NY: Cros-by Gaige, 1928. Ltd ed of 900 on all rag paper, signed. Printed under the direction of Bruce Rogers at Printing House of William Edwin Rudge, signed by Rogers. Lakeside Press bkpl. Spine little sunned, extremities minimally rubbed, rear cover very small area rubbed. Fine. *POLYANTHOS.* $60

Aldington, Richard. LAWRENCE OF ARABIA. Chicago: Henry Regnery, 1955. 1st ed. Blindstamp. Dj. Fine. *WEBER.* $25

Aldington, Richard. REJECTED GUEST. NY: The Viking Press, 1939. 1st Amer ed. Dj edges sl worn. VG. *WEBER*. $15

Aldington, Richard. SEVEN AGAINST REEVES. London: Heinemann, (1938). Uncorrected proof. Fine in grn ptd wrappers w/light crease. *DERMONT*. $50

Aldington, Richard. STEPPING HEAVENWARD. Florence: G. Orioli, 1931. Ltd ed of 808, signed and numbered by author. Uncut, unopened. Fine in Fine dj. *POLYANTHOS*. $100

Aldiss, Brian and M. Wilks. PILE-PETALS FROM ST KLAED'S COMPUTER. Holt, 1979, 1st ed. As New. *MADLE*. $25

Aldiss, Brian. AN ISLAND CALLED MOREAU. Simon & Schuster, 1981, 1st ed. Fine on dj. *MADLE*. $20

Aldiss, Brian. BAREFOOT IN THE HEAD. Doubleday, 1970. 1st Amer ed. Fine in price-clipped dj. Rmdr spray on bottom. *STAHR*. $35

Aldiss, Brian. FRANKENSTEIN UNBOUND. Alternate Worlds Records, 1976. As New. *MADLE*. $15

Aldiss, Brian. SOLDIER ERECT. Coward-McCann, 1971, 1st US ed. Fine in sl rubbed dj. *MADLE*. $20

Aldiss, Brian. THE SALIVA TREE Gregg Press, 1981, 1st Fine. *MADLE*. $30

Aldrich, Bess Streeter. A WHITE BIRD FLYING. D. Appleton & Co., 1931. Fine; Nice dj. *AUTHORS OF THE WEST*. $50

Aldrich, Bess Streeter. MISS BISHOP. D. Appleton-Century, 1933. 1st ed. Names, else Fine; Nice dj. *AUTHORS OF THE WEST*. $40

Aldrich, Bess Streeter. SONG OF YEARS. NY: Appleton Century, 1939. 3rd prtg. Signed. Fine in dj. *ELSE FINE*. $35

Aldrich, Lorenzo D. A JOURNAL OF THE OVERLAND ROUTE TO CALIFORNIA & THE GOLD MINES. LA: Dawson's, 1950. 1st ed. Ltd to 330. Fldg pocket map. Fine. *BOOK MARKET*. $100

Aldrin, Edwin E. RETURN TO EARTH. Random House, (1973). 1st ed. Signed presentation. VG in Fine dj. *OREGON*. $95

Aleman, Mateo. THE ROGUE: OR THE LIFE OF GUZMAN DE ALFARACHE. Written in Spanish by Matheo Aleman, Servant to his Catholike Majestie, and borne in Sevill. London: Ptd for Edward Blount, 1623. 1st ed. in Eng, 2nd issue dated 1623. 2 parts in 1 vol. Small folio, (20), 267, (16), 357pp. Modern half brown morocco and marbled boards. 1st title page mounted, slight dampstaining throughout, early owners' names in ink and a few notes in pencil, final signature apparently from a smaller copy, catalogue description taped in at front, still VG. *CHAPEL HILL*. $375

Alexander, Arabel Wilbur. THE LIFE AND WORK OF LUCINDA B. HELM. Nashville: Pub House of Methodist Episcopal Church, South, 1898. 1st ed. VG. *SECOND LIFE*. $65

Alexander, Charles. THE KU KLUX KLAN IN THE SOUTHWEST. Univ of Kentucky, (1965). VG. *ARTIS*. $15

Alexander, Charles. THE LIFE AND TIMES OF CYRUS ALEXANDER. LA: Dawson's, 1967. 1st ed. 350 ptd. Fldg facs. VF. *OREGON*. $55

Alexander, Christopher et al. THE OREGON EXPERIMENT. NY: Oxford Univ Press, 1975. 1st ed. NF, owner sig, in sl chipped price-clipped dj. *CAPTAIN'S BOOKSHELF*. $30

Alexander, Christopher. THE PRODUCTION OF HOUSES. NY: Oxford Univ Press 1985. 1st ed. Fine in price-clipped dj. *CAPTAIN'S BOOKSHELF*. $30

Alexander, Frances. ORPHANS ON THE GUADALUPE. Wichita Falls, TX, (1971). 88pp. Illus by Lucile Alexander. Signed by author & illustrator. Fine in VG dj w/few closed edge tears, rubs. Publisher's material, clippings laid in. *BEBBAH*. $25

Alexander, Franz & Hugo Staub. THE CRIMINAL, THE JUDGE, AND THE PUBLIC: A PSYCHOLOGICAL ANALYSIS. Glencoe, IL, 1956. Inscribed and signed. *FYE*. $95

Alexander, J.J.G. and A.C. De La Mare. THE ITALIAN MANUSCRIPTS IN THE LIBRARY OF MAJOR J.R. ABBEY. London: Faber and Faber, (1969). 1st ed. Dj age yellowed. *OAK KNOLL*. $125

Alexander, W.D. A BRIEF HISTORY OF THE HAWAIIAN PEOPLE. NY: American Bk Co, 1891. 8 full color maps. Frontis of Queen Liliuokalani. Orig grey dec cl. Worn extremes, corners and top and bottom of spine. Internals somewhat smudgy else Good+. *GREAT EPIC*. $125

Alexander, W.D. HISTORY OF LATER YEARS OF THE HAWAIIAN MONARCHY AND THE REVOLUTION OF 1893. (Honolulu: Hawaiian Gazette), 1896. 1st ed. Oblong, 16.2 X 24.7 cm. (10), 239 pp, double-columns, + 20 plts (most from photos) + 23 ad plts (most from photos). Orig dec cl, some bad stains to front cover, else Fine. *LEFKOWICZ*. $250

Alfau, Felipe. LOCOS. NY: F&R, 1936. 1/1250 signed and numbered. 1st ptg. VG+ in dj w/2 short tears, an abrasion, and 2 scratches to spine panel. *LAME DUCK*. $225

Alfred, Cyril. JEWELS OF THE PHARAOHS. EGYPTIAN JEWELLRY OF THE DYNASTIC PERIOD. London: Thames and Hudson, (1971). 100 color illus. Good. *ARCHAEOLOGIA*. $65

Alger, Horatio. WALTER SHERWOOD'S PROBATION. Phila: Coates, 1897. 1st ed. 351pp. Little soiled grn cl. Final leaf almost separate. VG. *SECOND LIFE*. $95

Algren, Nelson (ed). NELSON ALGREN'S OWN BOOK OF LONESOME MONSTERS. NY: Bernard Geis, 1963. 1st ed thus. NF in rubbed Good to VG dj. *ARCHER*. $20

Algren, Nelson. A WALK ON THE WILD SIDE. Farrar, Straus and Cudahy, 1956. 1st ed. NF in dj (torn foot of spine; foxed on reverse side). *STAHR*. $25

Algren, Nelson. NOTES FROM A SEA DIARY: HEMINGWAY ALL THE WAY. NY: Putnam, 1965. 1st ed. NF in dj. *ELSE FINE*. $35

Algren, Nelson. OWN BOOK OF LONESOME MONSTERS. Geis, (1963). 1st ed. VG in dj with chips, light soil to rear panel. *BEBBAH*. $20

Algren, Nelson. OWN BOOK OF LONESOME MONSTERS. NY: Bernard Geis. 1963. 1st ed. VG. *SMITH*. $45

Algren, Nelson. SOMEBODY IN BOOTS. NY: Vanguard, (1935). 1st ed. Fairly grievous stain on rear cvr, underneath dj and not especially visible. Dj (shows only mild staining; missing chip at spine crown, affecting title). *LOPEZ*. $900

Algren, Nelson. THE MAN WITH THE GOLDEN ARM. GC: Doubleday, 1949. 1st ed. Fine in lightly used dj. *BEASLEY*. $75

Algren, Nelson. THE MAN WITH THE GOLDEN ARM. NY: Doubleday, 1949. 1st ed. Top edgestain faded, else Fine, somewhat worn but complete dj. *ELSE FINE*. $60

ALICE & THE MAD HATTER'S TEA PARTY. London, 1969. 3 pop-ups. Pop-up bk. *BOOKFINDERS INTL*. $45

ALICE'S ADVENTURES IN WONDERLAND. London, 1980. Roger Diaz (eng). Pop-up bk. *BOOKFINDERS INTL*. $40

Alkim, U. Bahadir. ANATOLIA I. Cleveland, NY: World Pub Co, (1968). Trans James Hogarth. Fldg chronological table. Fresh in dj. *SCHOYER'S*. $25

ALL DAY IN FERN HOLLOW. London, (1980's). 4 double-pg pop-ups. Pop-up bk. *BOOKFINDERS INTL*. $20

Allan, Elizabeth Preston. LIFE AND LETTERS OF MARGARET JUNKIN PRESTON. Boston and NY: Houghton Mifflin, 1903. Blue cl stamped in gilt, worn, rubbed and cockled. Frontis, owner inscrip. Few stains in text, o/w VG. *SCHOYER'S*. $35

Allan, P.B.M. THE BOOK-HUNTER AT HOME. London: Philip Allan & Co, (1922). 2nd ed, rev, ltd to 500 of which this is one of 50 specially bound in a different color cl and ptd on better paper. Half-cl over boards. *OAK KNOLL.* $85

Allard, William Albert. VANISHING BREED. PHOTOGRAPHS OF THE COWBOY AND THE WEST. Boston: Little, Brown, (1982). 1st ed. Fine in NF dj. *ROBBINS.* $50

Allbeury, Ted. THE ALPHA LIST. London: Granada Publishing/Hart-Davis MacGibbon, 1979. 1st ed. Light spotting on top edge o/w Fine in dj. *MORDIDA.* $35

Allbeury, Ted. THE SEEDS OF TREASON. London: NEL, 1986. 1st ed. Fine in dj. *SILVER DOOR.* $27.50

Allbeury, Ted. THE SEEDS OF TREASON. London: New English Library, 1986. 1st ed. Fine in dj with closed tear on front panel. *MORDIDA.* $30

Allegretto, Michael. BLOOD STONE. NY: Scribner's, 1988. 1st ed. Review copy, signed. Pub's slip laid in. VF in dj. *SILVER DOOR.* $35

Allegretto, Michael. DEATH ON THE ROCKS. NY: Scribner's, (1987). 1st ed. Rmdr dot, else Fine in Fine dj. *UNGER.* $40

Allen, Carroll. LOCAL AND REGIONAL ANESTHESIA. Phila, 1915. 1st ed, 2nd ptg. *FYE.* $50

Allen, Charles Dexter. AMERICAN BOOK-PLATES; A GUIDE TO THEIR STUDY....London: George Bell & Sons, 1895. 9 copperplts. Lt lt foxing. Back hinge w/2 splits at top, back inner hinge cracked, covers faded. Bkpl. *WEBER.* $75

Allen, Charles Dexter. EX LIBRIS. ESSAYS....Boston, NY: Lamson, Wolffe, 1896. Ltd ed of 800. Fine. *WEBER.* $100

Allen, Charles. NOTES ON THE BACON-SHAKESPEARE QUESTION. Boston: Houghton Mifflin, 1900. 1st ed. Signed inscrip. Presentation card laid in. Orig brn cl. Teg. Spine gilt rubbed. Minor spine tip, corner wear, else VG. Ex-libris. *DIAMOND.* $85

Allen, Charles. NOTES ON THE BACON-SHAKESPEARE QUESTION. Boston: Houghton Mifflin, 1900. Orig red cl. Teg. NF (rubbing spine tips, corners). *DIAMOND.* $45

Allen, Clifford. THE SEXUAL PERVERSIONS AND ABNORMALITIES: A STUDY IN THE PSYCHOLOGY OF PARAPHILIA. London, 1949. 2nd ed. *FYE.* $40

Allen, David Rayvern. A SONG FOR CRICKET. London: Pelham Books, 1981. 1st ed. Fine in Fine dj. *OLD LONDON.* $30

Allen, Don (ed). THE NEW AMERICAN POETRY 1945-1960. NY: Grove Press (1960). 1st ed. Simultaneous pb ed. Emb initials on cover, o/w Fine. Very Scarce. 8000 issued. *SECOND LIFE.* $75

Allen, Durward L. MICHIGAN FOX SQUIRREL MANAGEMENT. Lansing, 1943. 1st ed. VG. *ARTIS.* $39.50

Allen, F.H. (ed). BIBLIOGRAPHY OF HENRY DAVID THOREAU. Boston & NY: Houghton Mifflin Co, 1908. Ltd ed 1/530. Illus w/frontis. Uncut. Ex libris. VG. *MIKESH.* $100

Allen, Gardner W. A NAVAL HISTORY OF THE AMERICAN REVOLUTION. Boston & NY, 1913. 1st ed. 2 vols, 19.5 cm. (xiv), 365; (x), (367)-752 pp. Illus, maps. Orig cl, spines a trifle soiled. *LEFKOWICZ.* $60

Allen, Gardner W. OUR NAVAL WAR WITH FRANCE. Boston & NY, 1909. 1st ed. (xiv), 323 pp. Illus, maps. Orig cl. Fine. *LEFKOWICZ.* $60

Allen, Gardner Weld. OUR NAVY AND THE BARBARY CORSAIRS. Boston, NY & Chicago: 1905. 16 plts. 1st ed. *LEFKOWICZ.* $50

Allen, Gracie. HOW TO BECOME PRESIDENT. NY, (1940). 1st ed. Author's 1st bk. Bkpl signed by George Burns front pastedown. Spine minimally rubbed. Fine in dj, little edge chipped, rubbed. *POLYANTHOS.* $75

Allen, Harold B. COME OVER INTO MACEDONIA. New Brunswick, 1943. *O'NEILL.* $35

Allen, Hervey and Mabbot, Thomas Ollive. POE'S BROTHER. THE POEMS OF WILLIAM HENRY LEONARD POE....NY: Doran, (1926). 1st ed. #345 of 1,000. Orig grey paper-covered boards w/paper spine label, teg. Fine in NF dj (tiny chip), pub's slipcase. *CHAPEL HILL.* $85

Allen, Hervey. ACTION AT AQUILA. NY, 1938. 1st ed. VG+ in dj. *PRATT.* $42.50

Allen, Hervey. ACTION AT AQUILA. NY, 1938. 1st ed. Fine in dj (little edge torn). *POLYANTHOS.* $30

Allen, Hervey. ACTION AT AQUILA. NY: Farrar & Rinehart, (1938). 1st ed. Orig blue cl. Crown of spine lightly rubbed, but NF in pict dj. *CHAPEL HILL.* $45

Allen, Hervey. CHRISTMAS EPITHALAMIUM. Private ptg, 1925. Ltd ed of 295. Unpaginated, red text borders, red wrapper & box. VG. *BOOK BROKER.* $45

Allen, Hugh. THE HOUSE OF GOODYEAR. Akron, OH, 1936. 2nd ed. Fine in dj. *ARTIS.* $22.50

Allen, James Lane. A CATHEDRAL SINGER. NY: The Century Co, 1916. 1st ed. Orig pict lt grn cl. Fine. *CHAPEL HILL.* $25

Allen, James Lane. FLUTE AND VIOLIN AND OTHER KENTUCKY TALES AND ROMANCES. NY: Harper, 1899. Frontis, (x),308pp. Spine shows faint damp spots, else Fine. *CONNOLLY & WADE.* $35

Allen, James Lane. FLUTE AND VIOLIN AND OTHER KENTUCKY TALES AND ROMANCES. NY: Harper & Bros, 1891. 1st ed, 1st bk. 308pp. Orig terracotta cl. Couple of signatures beginning to pull, but VG. *CHAPEL HILL.* $75

Allen, James Lane. MOUNTAIN PASSES OF THE CUMBERLAND (with) Berry, Wendell. CIVILIZING THE CUMBERLANDS: A COMMENTARY. (Lexington: King Library Press/Univ of Kentucky, 1972). 1st ed. 1/100. Top corners a trifle bumped, else Fine in boards w/paper label. *CAPTAIN'S BOOKSHELF.* $300

Allen, James Lane. THE ALABASTER BOX. NY and London: Harper & Bros, 1923. 1st ed. Orig dec blue cl. NF in VG dj (1" diameter stain on rear panel, affecting no lettering). Very scarce in dj. *CHAPEL HILL.* $55

Allen, James Lane. THE CHOIR INVISIBLE. NY: Macmillan, 1897. 1st ed. 8vo, 361pp, (1)pp ads. Orig blue dec cl, teg. VG. *CHAPEL HILL.* $45

Allen, James Lane. THE DOCTOR'S CHRISTMAS EVE. NY: Macmillan, 1910. 1st ed. Orig blue cl. Fine and rare in dj. *CHAPEL HILL.* $85

Allen, James Lane. THE HEROINE IN BRONZE. NY: Macmillan, 1912. 1st ed. Orig grn cl, teg. NF in soiled, torn, VG dj. *CHAPEL HILL.* $75

Allen, James Lane. THE KENTUCKY WARBLER. GC, NY: Doubleday, Pg & Co, 1918. 1st ed. Orig grn cl. Corners, edges bumped, lt offsetting to eps. VG in lightly soiled, chipped pict dj. 1st ed. Color frontis. *CHAPEL HILL.* $60

Allen, John Houghton. SOUTHWEST. Phila: J.B. Lippincott, (1952). 1st ed. VG in dj. *LAURIE.* $20

Allen, Joseph Chase. THE WHEELHOUSE LOAFER. Ed by Colbert Smith. Boston: Little Brown and Co., 1966. Signed. Fine. *SMITH.* $25

Allen, Lawrence J. (written & produced by) with J. Malcolm Campbell, Kristina Lindbergh & Barry Provose. THE TRANS ALASKA PIPELINE. Seattle: Scribe Pub. Co, (1975). 1st ed. Folio. 3 vols. NF set in VG djs. Slipcase. *BLUE DRAGON.* $150

Allen, Lee. 100 YEARS OF BASEBALL. Bartholemew House, 1950. 1st ed. Good+ in VG+ dj. *PLAPINGER.* $40

Allen, Lee. THE CINCINNATI REDS. Putnam, 1948. 1st ed. VG. *PLAPINGER.* $45

Allen, Lee. THE HOT STOVE LEAGUE. Barnes, 1955. Good+ in VG dj. *PLAPINGER*. $165

Allen, Lee. THE NATIONAL LEAGUE STORY. Hill and Wang, 1961. 1st ed. Good in VG dj. *PLAPINGER*. $35

Allen, M.R. MALE CULTS...IN MELANESIA. Melbourne: Melbourne Univ Press, 1967. 1st ed. Black cl, gilt spine titles. 3 maps. NF in VG dj. *PARMER*. $30

Allen, Paula Gunn. THE WOMAN WHO OWNED THE SHADOWS. SF: Spinsters, (1983). 1st ed. Only issued in wrappers. *LOPEZ*. $40

Allen, R.L. HAND-BOOK OF SARATOGA, AND STRANGER'S GUIDE. NY: W.H. Arthur & Co, 1859. 1st ed. 131pp. VG. *BOOK MARKET*. $125

Allen, R.L. THE AMERICAN FARM BOOK....NY, (1849). 325pp,(48). Orig cl. Spine ends chipped away, edge of backstrip splitting; marginal dampstaining, scattered foxing; ex-lib. *SUTTON*. $45

Allen, R.L. THE AMERICAN FARM BOOK...NY: Sexton, 1852. 325pp. + 60pp. Spine absent, else clean and tight. *AMERICAN BOTANIST*. $32

Allen, Richard Hinckley, STAR NAMES AND THEIR MEANINGS. NY: Hafner, 1936 (1899). 2nd reprint. Good. *KNOLLWOOD*. $50

Allen, Robert J. THE CLUBS OF AUGUSTAN LONDON. Cambridge: Harvard Univ Press, 1933. 1st ed. Fine. *WREDEN*. $45

Allen, Thomas Gaskell Jr. and William Lewis Sachtleben. ACROSS ASIA ON A BICYCLE....NY: Century, 1903. 12mo. Grn cl stamped in white and blind, a little rubbed and discolored. Spine lettering worn away. *SCHOYER'S*. $30

Allen, W.W. and R.B. Avery. CALIFORNIA GOLD BOOK--FIRST NUGGET ITS DISCOVERY AND DISCOVERERS AND SOME OF THE RESULTS....SF and Chicago: Donohue & Henneberry, 1893. 1st ed. Lt edgewear, spine sl darkened. VG. *PARMER*. $95

Allen, William R. THE CHEQUEMEGON: SHAY-WAH-ME-GON. A NARRATIVE....NY: Wm. Frederick, 1949. 1st ed. Signed. (12), 205, (1) pp. Ivory cl, gilt. Both NF in djs. *CONNOLLY & WADE*. $40

Allen, Willis Boyd. THE RED MOUNTAIN OF ALASKA. Boston, (1889). 348pp. VG. *ARTIS*. $25

Allen, Woody. GETTING EVEN. NY: Random House, 1971. 1st ed. NF. *SMITH*. $50

Allen, Woody. THE FLOATING LIGHT BULB. NY, 1982. 1st ed. Signed. Fine in like dj. *POLYANTHOS*. $75

Allen, Woody. WITHOUT FEATHERS. NY, 1975. 1st ed. Signed. Extremities, spine minimally rubbed. Fine in price clipped dj. *POLYANTHOS*. $75

Allende, Isabel. EVA LUNA. Franklin Center: Franklin Lib, 1988. Leatherbound ltd ed. Fine. Signed. *LOPEZ*. $75

Allende, Isabel. EVA LUNA. NY: Knopf (1988). 1st ed. Signed. Fine in dj. *DORN*. $40

Allende, Isabel. THE HOUSE OF SPIRITS. NY: Knopf (1975). 1st ed, 1st bk. Signed. Fine in dj. *DORN*. $75

Allhands, J.L. GRINGO BUILDERS. (Iowa City): Privately ptd, 1931. Signed. Dull spot front cover, extremities bumped, else VG. Howes A172. *BOHLING*. $135

Allhands, J.L. GRINGO BUILDERS. Privately ptd, 1931. 283 pp. Grn cl. Inscr, dated. NF. *CONNOLLY & WADE*. $200

Allhands, J.L. URIAH LOTT. San Antonio: Naylor, 1949. 1st ed. *BURCHAM*. $65

Allingham, Margery, PEARLS BEFORE SWINE. GC: Doubleday Crime Club, 1945. 1st ed. Name. Fine, lt wear to dj extrems. *ELSE FINE*. $30

Allingham, Margery. BLACK PLUMES. GC: Doubleday Crime Club, 1940. 1st Amer.ed. Crease on fep and on first few pages o/w Fine in dj with internal reinforcing of spine, staining on back panel and minor wear at corners. *MORDIDA*. $50

Allingham, Margery. CARGO OF EAGLES. London: Chatto & Windus, 1968. 1st ed. Fine in dj. *MORDIDA*. $40

Allingham, Margery. DEADLY DUO. GC: Doubleday Crime Club, 1949. 1st Amer ed. Pp darkened, bkpl, o/w VG in dj w/chipped spine ends and wear at corners. *MORDIDA*. $30

Allingham, Margery. FLOWERS FOR THE JUDGE. Doubleday, 1936. 1st Amer ed. Edgewear. VG in dj with chips, closed tears but Good+. *BEBBAH*. $55

Allingham, Margery. THE ALLINGHAM MINIBUS. London: Chatto & Windus, 1973. 1st ed. Fine in dj. *MORDIDA*. $45

Allingham, Margery. THE BECKONING LADY. London: Chatto & Windus, 1955. 1st ed. VG in dj (internal tape mends; chipping; short closed tears, creases). *MORDIDA*. $40

Allingham, Margery. THE BLACK DUDLEY MURDER. GC, Doubleday Crime Club, 1929. 1st Amer. ed. NF in VF bright like-new dj. *MORDIDA*. $200

Allingham, Margery. THE CHINA GOVERNESS. GC: Doubleday, 1962. 1st ed. Fine in sl darkened dj with several short closed tears and wear at corners. *MORDIDA*. $35

Allingham, Margery. THE GRYTH CHALICE MYSTERY. GC: Crime Club, (1931). 1st US ed. Fine in NF dj. *UNGER*. $150

Allingham, Margery. THE MIND READERS. London: Chatto & Windus, 1965. 1st ed. Prelims faintly foxed, else Fine, minor spine fade to dj. *ELSE FINE*. $50

Allingham, Margery. THE MYSTERIOUS MR. CAMPION. London: Chatto & Windus, 1963. 1st ed. Fine, minor rubs dj spine ends. *ELSE FINE*. $35

Allingham, Margery. THE TIGER IN THE SMOKE. Doubleday, 1952. 1st Amer ed. VG+ with small cvr bump at top edge in Fair dj with pieces missing, chips, closed tear, soil to rear panel. *BEBBAH*. $18

Allingham, Margery. WANTED: SOMEONE INNOCENT. Stamford House, 1946. 1st ed. & first book pub. of the title novelette & 3 short stories. #56 Pony Book. Faintest stain to bottom of some pp, general wear & some peeling of plastic coating to wraps. *BEBBAH*. $15

Allingham, William. FISTULA, HAEMORRHOIDS, PAINFUL ULCER, STRICTURE, PROLAPSUS, AND OTHER DISEASES OF THE RECTUM. Phila, 1873. 2nd ed. 265pp. *FYE*. $100

Allis, Oscar. AN INQUIRY INTO THE DIFFICULTIES ENCOUNTERED IN THE REDUCTION OF DISLOCATIONS OF THE HIP. Phila, 1896. 1st ed. Inscribed by the Allis. *FYE*. $200

Allison, Charles E. HISTORY OF YONKERS (NY). NY, (1896). 1st ed. 454pp. Rebound in new buckram. *HEINOLDT*. $30

Allison, Dorothy. BASTARD OUT OF CAROLINA. NY: Dutton (1992). Uncorrected proof. Fine in wraps. *DORN*. $35

Allsop, Kenneth. HARD TRAVELLIN'. NY: NAL, 1967. 1st ed. Sm dj edge pieces missing. VG. *AKA*. $25

Allsopp, Fred. THE LIFE STORY OF ALBERT PIKE. Little Rock: Parke-Harper News, 1920. 1st ed. Frontis, 10 plts. Bkpl, seal. Writing on title page, o/w Fine. *OREGON*. $75

Alpert, Jane. GROWING UP UNDERGROUND. NY: Morrow, 1981. 1st ed. 372pp. About Fine in dj. *AKA*. $30

Alsberg, John L. & Rodolfo Petschek. ANCIENT SCULPTURE FROM WESTERN MEXICO. Berkeley: Nicole Gallery, 1968. 1st ed. Pict cl, silver. Fine in VG dj. *CONNOLLY & WADE*. $90

Alsop, Gulielma. HISTORY OF THE WOMAN'S MEDICAL COLLEGE, PHILADELPHIA, PENNSYLVANIA 1850-1950. Phila, 1950. 1st ed. *FYE*. $50

Alsop, Joseph and Stewart. WE ACCUSE! NY: Simon & Schuster, 1954. 1st ed. Grey, red & black wrappers. VG. *CONNOLLY & WADE.* $60

Alstrom, Carl Henry. A STUDY OF EPILEPSY IN ITS CLINICAL, SOCIAL AND GENETIC ASPECTS. Copenhagen, 1950. 1st ed. Wrappers. *FYE.* $50

Alter, J. Cecil. JAMES BRIDGER, TRAPPER, FRON-TIERSMAN...With... JAMES BRIDGER by Grenville M. Dodge. Salt Lake City: Shepard, (1925). 1st ed. Ltd to 1000, signed, numbered. Frontis, 17 plts. Simulated lea. Fine. Howes A191. *OREGON.* $250

Altgeld, John P. OUR PENAL MACHINERY AND ITS VICTIMS. Chicago, 1886. New & rev ed. NF. *POLYANTHOS.* $45

Altham, H.S. and Swanton, E.W. A HISTORY OF CRICKET. George Allen and Unwin, Ltd. 1947. 3rd ed. Bkpl. VG. *OLD LONDON.* $20

Alther, Lisa. BEDROCK. NY: Knopf, (1990). 1st Amer ed. Signed. Fine in dj. *DORN.* $35

Alther, Lisa. BEDROCK. NY: Knopf, 1990. 1st ed. New in dj. Inscribed. *CAPTAIN'S BOOKSHELF.* $30

Alther, Lisa. KINFLICKS. NY: Knopf, (1976). 1st Amer ed. Uncorrected proof. Signed. NF in wraps. Scarce. *DORN.* $125

Alther, Lisa. KINFLICKS. NY: Knopf, (1976). 1st trade ed. Signed. Fine in dj. *DORN.* $60

Alther, Lisa. ORIGINAL SINS. NY: Knopf, (1981). 1st Amer ed. Signed. Fine in NF dj. *DORN.* $45

Alther, Lisa. OTHER WOMEN. NY: Knopf, (1984). 1st Amer ed. Signed. Fine in dj. *DORN.* $40

Alton, John. PAINTING WITH LIGHT. NY: The Macmillan Co. 1949. 1st ed. Presentation note signed by Alton glued to half-title. Dj. *KARMIOLE.* $125

Altrocchi, J.C. WOLVES AGAINST THE MOON. NY, 1940. 1st ed. Fine. *VARNER.* $20

Altrocchi, Rudolph. SLEUTHING IN THE STACKS. Cambridge: Harvard Univ Press, 1944. 1st ed. Cl-backed boards, paper cover label, dj (chipped). Signed. *OAK KNOLL.* $65

Altschul, Siri von Reis. DRUGS AND FOODS FROM LITTLE KNOWN PLANTS...Cambridge: Harvard, 1973. VG in torn dj. *AMERICAN BOTANIST.* $20

Alva Ixtilixochitl, Fernando de. ALLY OF CORTES. El Paso: Texas Western Press, (1969). Douglas K. Ballentine (trans). Fine in dj. *LAURIE.* $30

Alvarez, Walter. NERVOUS INDIGESTION. NY, 1930. 1st ed. *FYE.* $50

Alvord, Clarence W. (ed). LAWS OF THE TERRITORY OF IL-LINOIS 1809-1811. Springfield, IL, 1906. 1st ed. New wraps. Orig front wrap bound in. *DIAMOND.* $25

Alvord, Clarence W. MISSISSIPPI VALLEY IN BRITISH POLITICS: A STUDY....Cleveland, Clark, 1917. 2 vols. Orig cl. 1st ed. Howes A195. *GINSBERG.* $300

Alvord, Clarence W. THE MISSISSIPPI VALLEY IN BRITISH POLITICS....A.H. Clark, 1917. 1st ed. 2 vols. 2 frontis maps, 2 plts. VF. Howes A195. *OREGON.* $175

Alvord, Clarence W. THE MISSISSIPPI VALLEY IN BRITISH POLITICS. Cleveland: A.H. Clark, 1917. 2 vols. Gilt spine titles and tops. Extensive markings of Harvard Univ Lib; extremities rubbed. *BOHLING.* $100

Amado, Jorge. GABRIELA, CLOVE AND CINNAMON. NY, 1962. 1st US ed, advance review copy. Review slip laid in, dj, ink date/place on front pastedown (hidden under dj flap), else NF. *PET-TLER.* $35

Amado, Jorge. THE MIRACLE OF THE BIRDS. Trans Barbara Shelby Merello. NY: Targ Editions, 1983. 1st ed. 1/250 signed. Fine in glassine dj. *JUVELIS.* $90

Amado, Jorge. THE MIRACLE OF THE BIRDS. Trans by Barbara Merello. NY: Targ Editions, 1983. 1st ed. One of 250 signed. Mint in dj. *JAFFE.* $100

Amado, Jorge. THE TWO DEATHS OF QUINCAS WATERYELL. NY: Knopf, 1965. 1st Amer ed. Close to Fine in similar dj. W/author's presentation inscrip. *DERMONT.* $75

Amado, Jorge. THE TWO DEATHS OF QUINCAS WATERYELL. NY: Knopf (1965). 1st ed. Fine in dj. *DORN.* $45

Amaral, Anthony. COMANCHE, THE HORSE THAT SURVIVED THE CUSTER MASSACRE. LA, 1961. 1st ed. Dj. Fine. *PRATT.* $55

Amaral, Anthony. WILL JAMES. THE GILT EDGED COWBOY. LA: Westernlore, 1967. 1st ed. VF in Fine dj. *OREGON.* $50

Ambler, Charles Henry. HISTORY OF TRANSPORTATION IN THE OHIO VALLEY WITH SPECIAL REFERENCE....Glendale: Arthur Clark, 1932. Fldg map. Orig blue cl, gilt spine title & top. VG+, corners sl bumped. *BOHLING.* $125

Ambler, Eric. A COFFIN FOR DIMITRIOS. NY: Knopf, (1939). 1st US ed. VG in VG lightly chipped dj. *UNGER.* $375

Ambler, Eric. THE ARMY OF THE SHADOWS AND OTHER STORIES. Helsinki, Finland: Eurographica, 1986. 1st of this ed. Ltd to 350 signed. Mint in ptd wraps. *JAFFE.* $175

Ambler, Eric. THE INTERCOM CONSPIRACY. Atheneum, 1969. 1st ed. VF, dj. *STAHR.* $25

AMBROSIO DE LETINEZ OR THE FIRST TEXIAN NOVEL...COUNTRIES BORDERING ON THE RIO BRAVO. Austin: Steck, (1967). Facs repro of 1842 ed. Wm. Wittliff (ed). Ltd ed. Fine in Fine slipcase. *BOOK MARKET.* $50

AMERICA AND THE AMERICANS. BY A CITIZEN OF THE WORLD. (By James Boardman.) London, Longman, 1833. 1st ed. (16),(1),430pp. Orig cl. Howes B561. *GINSBERG.* $250

AMERICA TODAY: A BOOK OF 100 PRINTS...THE AMERICAN ARTISTS' CONGRESS. NY: Equinox Cooperative Press, 1936. 1st ed. Soiled, sl stained, spine darkened. NF. *BLUE MOUNTAIN.* $125

AMERICAN CHURCH SILVER OF THE 17TH & 18TH CEN-TURIES...Boston 1911. NF. *POLYANTHOS.* $75

AMERICAN FIRE MARKS. Phila, PA. VG. Wraps. *BACKROOM.* $25

AMERICAN INDIAN CAMP. London, (1961) Artist. Kubasta. 8pp text, 2-pg pop-up of Indian Camp. Bright, in equally bright picture cvrs. Pop-up bk. *BOOKFINDERS INTL.* $150

AMERICAN SOCIETY OF LANDSCAPE ARCHITECTS, IL-LUSTRATIONS OF WORK OF MEMBERS. NY, 1934. One of 500 bound in cl. Worn dj. *SUTTON.* $125

Ames, Azel. THE MAY-FLOWER AND HER LOG. JULY 15, 1620-MAY 6, 1621. Boston/NY: Houghton, Mifflin/The Riverside Press, 1901. Facs, map. Lacks fep. *HUDSON.* $75

Ames, Azel. SEX IN INDUSTRY. Boston: Osgood, 1875. 1st ed. VG, tight. *SECOND LIFE.* $225

Ames, Blanche. ADELBERT AMES 1835-1933. GENERAL, SENATOR, GOVERNOR. THE STORY OF HIS LIFE....London: (1964). Orig cl. 1st ed. *GINSBERG.* $50

Ames, Blanche. ADELBERT AMES, GENERAL, SENATOR, GOVERNOR-1835-1933. London, (1964). 1st ed. A little dj wear, o/w Fine. *PRATT.* $35

Ames, Daniel T. AMES ON FORGERY: ITS DETECTION AND ILLUSTRATION WITH NUMEROUS CASES CELEBRES. SF: Daniel T. Ames; NY: Ames-Rollinson, 1900. 1st ed. Half title, frontis. Modern olive cl, black leather spine label. Fine. Rare. *WEBER.* $250

Ames, Fisher Jr. AMERICAN RED CROSS WORK AMONG THE FRENCH PEOPLE. NY, 1921. 1st ed. *FYE.* $40

Ames, Joseph. THE BLADED BARRIER. Century, 1929. 1st ed. VG. *MADLE.* $50

Amicis, Edmondo de. MOROCCO: ITS PEOPLE AND PLACES. Trans by C. Rollin-Tilton. NY: Putnam, 1882. 1st ed. vi,374pp. 24 plts. Contemp 1/2 morocco, marbled eps, richly gilt spine, 4 raised bands, edges rubbed, sl scuffing. Ex-lib, o/w VG. *WORLDWIDE.* $45

Amiet, Pierre. ART OF THE ANCIENT NEAR EAST. Translated from the French by John Shepley and Claude Choquet. NY: Harry N. Abrams, Inc. (1980). 1st ed. Dj. Fine. *KARMIOLE.* $125

Amis, Kingsley. ENDING UP. Harcourt Brace Jovanovich, 1974. 1st Amer Fine in dj. *STAHR.* $15

Amis, Kingsley. LUCKY JIM. GC: Doubleday, 1954. 1st US ed. Author's 1st bk. Spine sl tanned. NF in price clipped dj. *LAME DUCK.* $275

Amis, Kingsley. ONE FAT ENGLISHMAN. London: Gollancz, 1963. 1st ed. NF in dj. *SECOND LIFE.* $45

Amis, Kingsley. STANLEY AND THE WOMEN. London: Hutchinson, (1984). 1st ed. Fine in Fine dj. *ROBBINS.* $35

Amis, Kingsley. THE ALTERATION. London: Cape, (1976). 1st ed. Boards, dj. Fine. *MUELLER.* $20

Amis, Kingsley. THE CRIME OF THE CENTURY. NY: Mysterious Press, 1989. 1/100 specially bound, numbered and signed on a tipped-in leaf. Fine in Fine slipcase (issued w/o dj). *BEASLEY.* $75

Amis, Kingsley. THE GREEN MAN. London: Cape, (1969). 1st ed. Boards, dj. Fine. *MUELLER.* $35

Amis, Kingsley. THE JAMES BOND DOSSIER. London: Jonathan Cape, (1965). 1st ed. VG in dj. *JUVELIS.* $50

Amis, Kingsley. THE OLD DEVILS. Summit Books, 1986. Uncorrected proof of 1st Amer. ed. Fine in wraps. *STAHR.* $25

Amis, Kingsley. THE RIVERSIDE VILLA MURDERS. London: Cape, 1973. 1st ed. NF in dj. *SILVER DOOR.* $22.50

Amis, Kinsley. I LIKE IT HERE. NY, 1958. 1st ed. E. Gorey bkpl. Signed. Fine in dj (spine little sunned, top spine little rubbed, tiny tear rear panel). *POLYANTHOS.* $45

Amis, Martin. DEAD BABIES. NY, 1976. 1st US ed. VG in dj. *PETTLER.* $45

Amis, Martin. DEAD BABIES. NY: Knopf, 1976. 1st Amer ed. Small "skinned" spot of shelfwear rear cover, o/w Fine in a dj that has a bit of edgewear but is still NF. *LOPEZ.* $150

Amis, Martin. DEAD BABIES. NY: Knopf, 1976. 1st Amer. ed. Fine in Very NF dj sl spine faded w/small internally repaired tear. *BETWEEN COVERS.* $150

Amis, Martin. EINSTEIN'S MONSTERS. Harmony, 1987. 1st Amer. ed. VF in dj. *STAHR.* $20

Amis, Martin. EINSTEIN'S MONSTERS. London: Jonathan Cape, (1987). 1st ed. As New in dj. Signed. *CAPTAIN'S BOOKSHELF.* $75

Amis, Martin. LONDON FIELDS. London: London Ltd. Editions, 1989. 1st ed. One of 150 signed. New in glassine dj. *JAFFE.* $250

Amis, Martin. OTHER PEOPLE: A MYSTERY STORY. NY, 1981. 1st US ed, ink date/place on front pastedown, else Fine in dj. *PETTLER.* $30

Amis, Martin. OTHER PEOPLE: A MYSTERY STORY. Viking, 1981. 1st Amer ed. Fine in dj. *STAHR.* $35

Amis, Martin. OTHER PEOPLE: A MYSTERY STORY. Viking, 1981. 1st Amer ed. Fine in VG dj with touch of edgewear. *BEBBAH.* $30

Amis, Martin. SUCCESS. London: Cape, (1978). 1st ed. Fine in dj w/touch of soiling to flaps. *BETWEEN COVERS.* $200

Amis, Martin. SUCCESS. NY, 1978. 1st ed. Uncorrected proof in pub pict wraps. Fine. *POLYANTHOS.* $30

Amis, Martin. TIME'S ARROW. NY: Harmony, (1991). 1st US ed. As New in dj. Signed. *CAPTAIN'S BOOKSHELF.* $40

Amis, Martin. TIME'S ARROW. NY: Harmony (1991). Uncorrected proof. Fine in wrappers. *LOPEZ.* $40

Ammons, A.R. BRIEFINGS—POEMS SMALL & EASY. NY: Norton, (1971). 1st ed. Fine in Fine dj. *ROBBINS.* $40

AMONG THE ARABS. NY: Nelson, n.d. (c. 1877). 248pp. 12mo. Blue cloths stamped in black and gilt, a little worn. *SCHOYER'S.* $30

Amory, Thomas C. THE LIFE OF ADMIRAL SIR ISAAC COFFIN, BARONET. HIS ENGLISH AND AMERICAN ANCESTORS. Boston: Cupples, 1886. 1st ed. 141,pp. Frontis. Orig cl, light stain on blank margin. *GINSBERG.* $75

Amosoff, Nikolai. THE OPEN HEART: JOURNAL...OF A GREAT RUSSIAN SURGEON. G. St. George (trans). NY: Simon & Schuster, 1966. 1st ed in English. VG+ in Good+ dj. *SMITHFIELD.* $28

Amundsen, Roald and Lincoln Ellsworth. FIRST CROSSING OF THE POLAR SEA. NY: Doubleday Doran, 1928. Fold-out map torn loose. Cl worn. Good reading copy. *ARTIS.* $20

Amundsen, Roald and Lincoln Ellsworth. OUR POLAR FLIGHT. NY: Dodd, Mead, 1925. viii + 373pp. 1st ed. Orig gilt dec emb blue cl. Gilt titles. Fine+. *GREAT EPIC.* $175

Amundsen, Roald et al. OUR POLAR FLIGHT. NY: Dodd, Mead & Co. 1925. 1st ed. *KARMIOLE.* $75

Amundsen, Roald. MY LIFE AS AN EXPLORER. GC: Doubleday, Doran & Co, 1928. Worn at top and bottom of spine, else Good+. *BLUE DRAGON.* $30

AN ACCOUNT OF THE ROMAN ANTIQUITIES PRESERVED IN THE MUSEUM AT CHESTERS, NORTHUMBERLAND....(By E.A. Wallis Budge.) London: Gilbert & Rivington, 1907. 1 map. Good. *ARCHAEOLOGIA.* $65

AN ALPHABET OF BIRDS. Phila: Wm. White Smith, Pub. 1858 (c. 1852). 12mo. 128pp. 32 hand-colored woodcut plates, 26 hand-colored text illus. Spine extrems, corners sl frayed. *KARMIOLE.* $85

AN APOLOGY FOR THE LIFE OF MR. THEO(PHILUS) CIBBER, COMEDIAN. Supposed to be written by Himself. Dublin: George Faulkner, 1741. 1st Dublin ed. 12mo; contemp full mottled calf; foot of spine chipped, label gone, front pastedown lifted, rear pastedown lacking, lower corner torn from front eps; text VG. *DRAMATIS PERSONAE.* $95

AN ASTONISHING AFFAIR!...BY PHILANDROS. (By Samuel Arnold). Concord: Luther Roby, 1830. 1st ed. Worn lea backed boards, some foxed. Good. *SECOND LIFE.* $45

AN HISTORICAL SKETCH OF LOS ANGELES COUNTY, CALIFORNIA. LA: Louis Lewin & Co, 1876. Ptd wrappers w/spine, front wrapper, lower rt corner of first 3 leaves chipped; old owner marks front wrapper. *DAWSON'S.* $150

AN ILLUSTRATED HISTORY OF CENTRAL OREGON. Spokane: Western Hist Pub Co, 1905. Blind-and-gold stamped leather, edges gilt, spine chipped and joints starting. *DAWSON'S.* $200

Anawalt, Patricia. INDIAN CLOTHING BEFORE CORTES. Norman: Univ of OK Press, (1981). 1st ed. Dj. *SILVER.* $50

Anders, J.M. HOUSE-PLANTS AS SANITARY AGENTS....Phila, 1887 (1886). Orig gilt-dec cl. Corner, spine end wear; lt pencil marks in text, some pg browning. *SUTTON.* $45

Anders, Leslie. THE TWENTY-FIRST MISSOURI, FROM HOME GUARD TO UNION REGIMENT. Westport, (1975). 1st ed. Fine. *PRATT.* $25

Andersen, Hans Christian. FAIRY TALES. Illus by Honor C. Appleton. NY: Nelson, n.d. 1st US ed. 12 color plts. Pages beginning to brown, else NF in brown cl. *CAPTAIN'S BOOKSHELF.* $50

Andersen, Hans Christian. HANS ANDERSEN'S FAIRY TALES. Kay Nielsen. NY: George Doran, (1924). 1st US. Cl, pict paper label. 12 full-pg color plts. NF, well-preserved, silver lettering still bright. *CAPTAIN'S BOOKSHELF.* $200

Andersen, Hans Christian. TALES FROM HANS ANDERSEN. London: Etchells & Macdonald, 1929. Ltd ed, #351 of 535 numbered. 215pp. Illus Hester Sainsbury. Uncut forward edge. Age spotting to cream cl spine, bumped corners but VG+ w/dec cvrs. *BEBBAH.* $30

Andersen, Hans Christian. THE COMPLETE ANDERSEN: ALL OF THE 168 STORIES BY H.C. ANDERSEN. Jean Hersholt (trans). NY: LEC, (1949). 6 vols. One of 1500 illus, signed by Fritz Kredel and by Hersholt. Fine set in slipcase. *CAPTAIN'S BOOKSHELF.* $200

Anderson, Barry C. LIFELINE TO THE YUKON. A HISTORY OF YUKON RIVER NAVIGATION. Seattle: Superior, (1983). 1st ed. Fine in dj. *ARTIS.* $25

Anderson, C.W. A TOUCH OF GREATNESS. NY: Macmillan, 1945. 1st ed. VG+ w/tears. *ACADEMIC LIBRARY.* $28

Anderson, C.W. TOMORROW'S CHAMPION. NY: Macmillan, 1946. 1st ed. Signed. VG (loose litho) in worn dj. *ACADEMIC LIBRARY.* $45

Anderson, Carl. HENRY. NY: Greenberg, 1935. 1st ed. Somewhat soiled, w/o dj. *BEASLEY.* $50

Anderson, Chester. FOX AND HARE. Entwhistle Books, 1980. 1st ed. One of 200 numbered, signed by author & artist. Fine in dj. *MADLE.* $25

Anderson, E.T. A QUARTER-INCH OF RAIN. Emporia, KS: The author, 1962. 1st ed. Fine. *GIBBS.* $37.50

Anderson, Frank Maloy. THE MYSTERY OF "A PUBLIC MAN." Minneapolis, (1948). 1st ed. 256pp. Dj spine faded, o/w VG+. *PRATT.* $30

Anderson, Henry. THE MEDICAL AND SURGICAL ASPECTS OF AVIATION...With Chapters on Applied Physiology of Aviation by Martin Flack. London, 1919. 1st ed. Skillfully recased. Ex-lib. *FYE.* $300

Anderson, Isabel. ODD CORNERS. NY: Dodd, Mead, 1917. 1st ed. Fair in Fair but chipped dj. *AARD.* $20

Anderson, John Q. (ed). TEXAS FOLK MEDICINE: 1,333 CURES,....Texas Folklore Soc, "Paisano Book," No. 5. Austin: Encino Press, 1970. Signed. Fine in dj. *LAURIE.* $30

Anderson, Joseph L. and Donald Richie. THE JAPANESE FILM: Art and Industry. Rutland, VT: Charles E. Tuttle Co. (1959). 1st ed. Fldg chart. Presentation copy inscr by Anderson. Dj. *KARMIOLE.* $60

Anderson, Kent. SYMPATHY FOR THE DEVIL. GC: Doubleday, 1987. 1st ed. Fine in Fine dj. *AKA.* $35

Anderson, Maxwell. KEY LARGO. Washington: Anderson House, 1939. 1st ed. Owner's sig and date, else NF in dj. *LAME DUCK.* $150

Anderson, Osborne. A VOICE FROM HARPERS FERRY...Boston, privately ptd, 1861. 1st ed. 72pp. Wraps. Fine. *OREGON.* $125

Anderson, Poul. A MIDSUMMER TEMPEST. Doubleday, 1974, 1st ed. Signed. Fine in dj. *MADLE.* $50

Anderson, Poul. BRAIN WAVE. Walker, 1969. 1st US hardcover ed. VG in dj. *MADLE.* $75

Anderson, Poul. IS THERE LIFE ON OTHER WORLDS? Crowell, 1963. 1st ed. Fine dj. *MADLE.* $35

Anderson, Poul. MURDER BOUND. MacMillan, 1962. 1st ed. Ex-lib. NF in wrinkled dj. *MADLE.* $45

Anderson, Poul. TAU ZERO. Doubleday, 1970, 1st ed. VG in worn dj. *MADLE.* $100

Anderson, Poul. THE BROKEN SWORD. NY: Abelard-Schuman, 1954. 1st ed. Fine in Fine dj w/nicks. *BEASLEY.* $125

Anderson, Poul. THREE HEARTS AND THREE LIONS. Doubleday, 1961. 1st ed. VF in dj. *MADLE.* $500

Anderson, Poul. VAULT OF THE AGES. Winston, 1952. 1st ed. Signed. VG in dj. *MADLE.* $75

Anderson, R. C. THE RIGGING OF SHIPS IN THE DAYS OF THE SPRITSAIL TOPMAST 1600-1720. Salem, 1927. Pub. 14. 24 plts. Fine, dj. *LEFKOWICZ.* $95

Anderson R. G. FACES, FORMS, FILMS. Barnes, 1971. 1st ed. Fine in dj. *MADLE.* $25

Anderson, Rev. Robert. THE LIFE OF...;THE YOUNG MEN'S GUIDE OR, THE BROTHER IN WHITE. Macon, GA: The Author, 1892. Ed not stated. Photo frontis, modest foxing to eps, else Fine in orig gilt stamped cloth. *BETWEEN COVERS.* $150

Anderson, Rufus. OBSERVATIONS UPON THE PELOPONNESUS AND GREEK ISLANDS, MADE IN 1829. Boston, 1830. Fldg map, sm tear one fold. Spine cracks. 334pp, uncut. Very scarce. *O'NEILL.* $275

Anderson, Sherwood. A NEW TESTAMENT. NY: Boni & Liveright, 1927. 1st ed. Spine gilt oxidized, else Fine. *ELSE FINE.* $45

Anderson, Sherwood. ALICE AND THE LOST NOVEL. London: Elkin Mathews & Marrot, 1929. Ltd to 530 numbered, signed. Dj. *KARMIOLE.* $150

Anderson, Sherwood. HELLO TOWNS! NY: Horace Liveright, 1929. 1st ed. Orig brownish orange cl. Lt foxing to prelims as usual, else Fine in NF dj. *CHAPEL HILL.* $140

Anderson, Sherwood. HORSES AND MEN. NY: B.W. Huebsch, 1923. 1st ed, 1st issue, w/top edge stained orange. Orig orange cl, paper spine label. Fine in NF dj (with modest soiling, few short tears). Scarce in dj. *CHAPEL HILL.* $200

Anderson, Sherwood. SHERWOOD ANDERSON'S NOTEBOOK. NY: Boni & Liveright, 1926. 1st ed. VG in scarce dj w/some chipping and splitting at spine. *CHAPEL HILL.* $50

Anderson, Sherwood. THE TRIUMPH OF THE EGG: A BOOK OF IMPRESSIONS...IN TALES AND POEMS. NY: Huebsch, 1921. 1st ed, 1st issue. Fine in dj (few tiny chips, sl darkened spine). Handsome fldg slipcase. *CAPTAIN'S BOOKSHELF.* $200

Anderson, Sherwood. WINDY MCPHERSON'S SON. NY: John Lane, 1916. 1st ed, 1st bk. Fine in custom fldg slipcase w/morocco spine label. *CAPTAIN'S BOOKSHELF.* $450

Anderson, Sherwood. WINESBURG, OHIO. NY: B.W. Huebsch, 1919. 1st ed, 1st issue. Rebound in full mustard yellow morocco w/matching marbled eps. *CAPTAIN'S BOOKSHELF.* $400

Anderson, Sherwood. WINESBURG, OHIO. NY: B.W. Huebsch, 1919. 1st ed, 1st issue. NF w/faint owner's name, address. Ptd paper spine label moderately browned. *CAPTAIN'S BOOKSHELF.* $350

Anderson, Sparky and Si Burick. THE MAIN SPARK. Doubleday, 1978. Signed by Anderson. 1st ed. VG+ in VG dj. *PLAPINGER.* $40

Anderson, William Marshall. AN AMERICAN IN MAXIMILIAN'S MEXICO. 1865-1866. San Marino: The Huntington Library, 1959. Black cl. Pencil underlining o/w VG in VG dj. *PARMER.* $40

Anderson, William. MALARIAL PSYCHOSES AND NEUROSES WITH CHAPTERS MEDICO-LEGAL AND ON HISTORY, RACE DEGENERATION, ALCOHOL, AND SURGERY IN RELATION TO MALARIA. London, 1927. 1st ed. *FYE.* $75

Andral, G. MEDICAL CLINIC: DISEASES OF THE ENCEPHALON, WITH EXTRACTS FROM OLLIVIER'S WORK ON DISEASES OF THE SPINAL CORD AND ITS

MEMBRANES. Phila, 1843. 1st Eng trans. 1/2 leather, 303pp. *FYE.* $150

Andre, Major (John). JOURNAL (1777-1778). Ed by H. C. Lodge. Boston, Bibliophile Soc, 1903. 2 vols. 3 engr titles, 2 ports, 7 facs, 38 maps, some fldg. Quarto, full vellum, gold stamped. 1st ed, 1st ptg. One of 487 sets. Howes A239. *GINSBERG.* $500

ANDREANA; CONTAINING THE TRIAL, EXECUTION, AND VARIOUS MATTER...OF MAJOR JOHN ANDRE....Phila: Smith, 1865. (4),67,(4). 12 plts, 1 fldg. Contemp half morocco, raised bands, teg, bound by Chatelin. Howes A241. One of 175. *GINSBERG.* $200

Andrew, John. HISTORY OF THE WAR WITH AMERICA, FRANCE, SPAIN, AND HOLLAND. London: Published for John Fielding and John Jarvis, (1785). 3 vols (of 4). Old calf, broken. Lacks vol 4 and all plts and maps. Old ex-lib. Howes A259. *HUDSON.* $65

ANDREW MARVELL 1621-1678: TERCENTENARY TRIBUTES. London: Oxford Univ Press, 1922. 1 in ed of 1000. Fine in sl soiled dj (internally reinforced 2 places on backstrip). *HELLER.* $100

Andrews, A.T. HISTORY OF COOK COUNTY, ILLINOIS. Chicago, 1884. 1st ed. 888pp. Maps, folding, some 2pp. One 2-pp map in color. 3/4 leather, rubbed. Contents VG. *HEINOLDT.* $100

Andrews and Engel (eds). NAVY YEARBOOK I. NY: Duell, Sloan, & Pearce, (1944). 1st ed. Spine fade. Good. *ARTIS.* $45

Andrews, Clarence L. THE ESKIMO AND HIS REINDEER IN ALASKA. Caldwell: Caxton, 1939. 1st ed. VG in worn dj. *BLUE DRAGON.* $37.50

Andrews, Cyril Bruyn. THE RAILWAY AGE. NY: Macmillan Co. 1938. 1st ed. Dj sl chipped, soiled. *KARMIOLE.* $35

Andrews, Edmund & Edward. RECTAL AND ANAL SURGERY. Chicago, 1889. 2nd ed. *FYE.* $75

Andrews, Eliza Frances. THE WAR-TIME JOURNAL OF A GEORGIA GIRL 1864-1865. NY, 1908. 1st ed. 387pp + ads. Ffep torn out. Cover wear, soiling; front hinges weakened but still solid, o/w VG. *PRATT.* $75

Andrews, Jane. TEN BOYS WHO LIVED ON THE ROAD FROM LONG AGO TO NOW. Ginn, 1900. 249pp. Sm spots to edges but VG w/VG gilt dec cvr. *BEBBAH.* $25

Andrews, John. HISTORY OF THE WAR WITH AMERICA, FRANCE, SPAIN AND HOLLAND...1775 AND ENDING IN 1783. London: for John Fielding, 1785-6. 1st ed. 4 vols. 24 ports, 7 maps. 8vo, (4),448; (2)445; (2)445; (2)426(60) + subs's list. Bound in contemp chemical calf, gilt, (hinges tender, spine labels gone), name. Nice clean set. Howes A-259. *SECOND LIFE.* $750

Andrews, John. HISTORY OF THE WAR WITH AMERICA, FRANCE, SPAIN AND HOLLAND, COMMENCING IN 1775 AND ENDING IN 1783...London: 1785-1786. 1st ed. 4 vols.: (2),448; (2),445; (2),445; (2),416,(6-)pp, subscriber's list, 14pp. 31 plts, maps, some fldg. Orig boards, vol 3 marbled, paper spines, lightly cracked and worn, a few boards loose, portions of orig manuscript spine labels, entirely uncut. Howes A 259. *GINSBERG.* $1000

Andrews, Kenneth R. (ed). ENGLISH PRIVATEERING VOYAGES TO THE WEST INDIES 1588-1595. Cambridge, 1959. 1st ed. Hakluyt Society, Ser. II, 111. 4 plts, 4 maps (1 fldg). Fine, dj. *LEFKOWICZ.* $90

Andrews, L.F. PIONEERS OF POLK COUNTY, IOWA & REMINISCENCES OF EARLY DAYS. Des Moines: Baker-Tris-ler Co., 1908. 2 vols. Scuffed edges; clean and tight, unopened, some foxing. *BOHLING.* $150

Andrews, Marietta Minnegerode. SCRAPS OF PAPER. NY, (1929). 1st ed. Pict cl, dj (chipped top of spine o/w VG). *PRATT.* $45

Andrews, Matthew Page. HISTORY OF MARYLAND. PROVINCE AND STATE. GC: Doubleday, Doran, 1929. 1st ed after ltd ed of 279. Good+. *CONNOLLY & WADE.* $45

Andrews, Ralph W. INDIANS AS THE WESTERNERS SAW THEM. Seattle, (1963). 1st ed. 176pp. VG+ in dj. *PRATT.* $22.50

Andrews, Ralph W. INDIANS AS THE WESTERNERS SAW THEM. Seattle (1963), 1st ed, dj. *HEINOLDT.* $25

Andrews, Roy Chapman and Yvette Borup Andrews. CAMPS AND TRAILS IN CHINA. NY: D. Appleton & Co. 1919. (c. 1918). 58 photogr plts, 2 fldg maps. Extremities lightly rubbed, rear inner hinge partly cracked. *KARMIOLE.* $60

Andrezel, Pierre (pseud of Isak Dinesen). THE ANGELIC AVENGERS. Psued Pierre Andrezel. London: Putnam, (1946). 1st Eng ed, 1st ed in English. Top edge and fore-edge sl foxed, else Fine in sl soiled dj. *HELLER.* $60

Andrezel, Pierre (pseud of Isak Dinesen). THE ANGELIC AVENGERS. NY, 1947. 1st ed. Spine sl rubbed; dj w/small piece missing on rear panel, sl edge rubbed. *POLYANTHOS.* $50

Andric, Ivo. THE BRIDGE ON THE DRINA. NY: Macmillan (1959). 1st ed. Fine in sl used price-clipped dj. *DORN.* $50

Andric, Ivo. THE PASHA'S CONCUBINE; AND OTHER TALES. NY: Knopf (1968). 1st ed. Fine in dj. *DORN.* $30

Andrist, Ralph K. THE LONG DEATH, THE LAST DAYS OF THE PLAINS INDIANS. NY, (1964). 1st ed. Light dj wear o/w Fine. *PRATT.* $30

Andros, Edmund. THE ANDROS TRACTS. WITH NOTES AND A MEMOIR OF SIR EDMUND ANDROS BY W. H. WHIT-MORE. Boston, Prince Soc, 1868, 1869, 1874. 1st ed. 3 vols. Illus. Contemp half morocco, a few rubber library stamps. Howes A271. One of 210 sets. *GINSBERG.* $375

Andry, Nicolas. ORTHOPAEDIA. Phila, 1961. (Facs of London, 1743 ed). 2 vols. Leatherette slipcase. *FYE.* $150

ANDY PANDY & THE QUEEN OF HEARTS. London, (1970s). Pop-up bk. *BOOKFINDERS INTL.* $30

Angell, Roger. A DAY IN THE LIFE OF ROGER ANGELL. Viking, 1970. 1st ed. Good+ in Fine dj. *PLAPINGER.* $25

Angell, Roger. A DAY IN THE LIFE OF ROGER ANGELL. NY: Viking, (1970). 1st ed. Fine in VG+ dj. *AARD.* $20

Angell, Roger. FIVE SEASONS. Simon & Schuster, 1977. 1st ed. VG in Fine dj. *PLAPINGER.* $17.50

Angell, Roger. FIVE SEASONS: A BASEBALL COMPANION. Simon and Schuster, 1977. 1st ed. About Fine in price-clipped dj. Owner name ffep. *STAHR.* $30

Angell, Roger. LATE INNINGS. Simon and Schuster, 1982. Uncor-rected proof. Fine in gold wraps. *STAHR.* $30

Angell, Roger. THE SUMMER GAME. Viking, 1972. 1st ed. VG in Fine dj. *PLAPINGER.* $45

Angell, Roger. THE SUMMER GAME. Viking, 1972. 1st ed. About Fine in dj (sm chips along edges). *STAHR.* $50

Angelou, Maya. ALL GOD'S CHILDREN NEED TRAVELING SHOES. NY: Rinehart & Holt, (1986). 1st ed. Fine in dj. *LOPEZ.* $30

Angelou, Maya. ALL GOD'S CHILDREN NEED TRAVELING SHOES. NY: Random House, (1986). 1st trade ed. Orig black cl-backed boards. Fine in dj. Rev copy, slip laid in. Inscribed. *CHAPEL HILL.* $65

Angelou, Maya. HEART OF A WOMAN. NY: Random House, (1981). Stated 1st ed. Fine in Fine dj. *SCHOYER'S.* $20

Angelou, Maya. NOW SHEBA SINGS THE SONG. NY: Dut-ton/Dial, (1987). 1st ed. Inscribed by author, signed by Tom Feel-ings, artist. Fine in dj. *LOPEZ.* $65

Angelou, Maya. OH PRAY MY WINGS ARE GONNA FIT ME WELL. NY: Random House, (1975). 1st ed. Orig red cl and orange boards. Faint offsetting to fep, else Fine in dj. Inscribed. *CHAPEL HILL*. $95

Angelou, Maya. SHAKER, WHY DON'T YOU SING. NY: Random House, (1983). 1st ed. Fine in dj. *BETWEEN COVERS*. $45

Angelou, Maya. SHAKER, WHY DON'T YOU SING? NY: Random House, (1983). 1st ed. Fine in dj w/tiny traces of edgewear. *ROBBINS*. $30

Angelou, Maya. SHAKER, WHY DON'T YOU SING? Random House, 1973. 1st ed. Fine in dj. Remainder mark. *STAHR*. $25

Angelou, Maya. SINGIN' AND SWINGIN' AND GETTIN' MERRY LIKE CHRISTMAS. NY: Random House, (1976). 1st ed. Faint spotting to fore-edge, else Fine in dj. *BETWEEN COVERS*. $45

Angelou, Maya. SINGIN' AND SWINGIN' AND GETTIN' MERRY LIKE CHRISTMAS. NY: Random House, (1976). 1st ed. Orig cl backed orange boards. Fine in NF dj (minor scrapes, tears). Inscribed. *CHAPEL HILL*. $75

Angelou, Maya. THE HEART OF A WOMAN. Random House, 1981. 1st ed, Fine in price-clipped dj. Rmdr mk. *STAHR*. $30

Angle, Paul M., ed. CREATED EQUAL? THE COMPLETE LINCOLN-DOUGLAS DEBATES OF 1858. (Chicago): Univ of Chicago Press, (1958). Dj. *SCHOYER'S*. $25

Angle, Paul. HERE I HAVE LIVED. New Brunswick, NJ: Rutgers Univ Press, (1950). Fldg facs map. Sunned dj. *SCHOYER'S*. $15

ANIMAL PETS. London, (1950s). Illus Dick Eshuis. 4 picture pgs w/farm scene and animal which, when pulled out, reveals their young. Moveable bk. *BOOKFINDERS INTL*. $30

ANNALS OF PIONEER SETTLERS...IN THE VICINITY OF RICHMOND, INDIANA, FROM 1804 TO 1830. BY A NATIVE. (By John Macamy Wasson.) Richmond, 1875. 1st ed. 59pp. Orig ptd wrappers. Howes W154. *GINSBERG*. $175

Annandale, Thomas. OBSERVATIONS AND CASES IN SURGERY. Edinburgh, 1865. 1st ed. 80pp. Wrappers. Scarce. *FYE*. $200

Anno, Mitsumasa. ANNO'S U.S.A. NY: Philomel, (1983). 1st Amer ed. Pict boards. Ltd ed, #229/1000. Signed w/chop mark. Boxed. Fine in Fine dj. *ACADEMIC LIBRARY*. $45

ANNUAL MESSAGE PRESIDENT (FILLMORE). 2nd Session, 31st Congress, Dec 2, 1850. Washington, 1850. H. R. Executive Doc 7. President's message 17pp; Sect. Interior Report 444pp. Secretary of War 488pp. Rebound in new buckram. *HEINOLDT*. $20

ANNUAL OF THE UNIVERSAL MEDICAL SCIENCES. Phila, 1888. 1st ed. 5 vols. *FYE*. $75

ANNUAL REPORT OF THE ADJUTANT GENERAL OF PENNSYLVANIA FOR THE YEAR 1877. Harrisburg: Lane Hart, State Printer, 1878. 1st ed. VG (some silverfish mks). Comp slip. *BEASLEY*. $80

ANNUAL REPORT OF THE ADJUTANT GENERAL OF THE STATE OF CALIFORNIA, 1861. N.p., c. 1862. 173pp. Inscribed by the Adjutant General. VG. *PRATT*. $85

ANNUAL REPORT OF THE ADJUTANT-GENERAL OF THE COMMONWEALTH OF MASSACHUSETTS...FOR THE YEAR ENDING DECEMBER 31, 1863. Boston, 1864. 1,022pp, supplemental reports. Cover chipped at spine extremities, o/w VG. *PRATT*. $30

ANNUAL REPORT OF THE BOARD OF REGENTS OF THE SMITHSONIAN INSTITUTION. Washington, DC: GPO, 1862. Diags, tables. Orig grn cl. *HUDSON*. $75

ANNUAL REPORT OF THE COMMISSIONER OF INDIAN AFFAIRS. 1894. Washington: GPO, 1895. Fldg map. Minor shelfwear, o/w VG. *DIAMOND*. $50

ANNUAL REPORT OF THE COMMISSIONER OF INDIAN AFFAIRS. Washington, 1851. 1st ed. Bound in new wraps. Orig wraps bound in. Little soiling few pp, o/w VG. Inscribed by Henry Sibley. *DIAMOND*. $125

ANNUAL REPORT OF THE METROPOLITAN BOARD OF HEALTH 1866. NY, 1867. 1st ed. Charts and fldg tables. *FYE*. $150

ANNUAL REPORTS OF THE DEPARTMENT OF INTERIOR. INDIAN AFFAIRS. 1905. 2 vols. Washington: GPO, 1906. Fldg map. *DIAMOND*. $50

ANSEL ADAMS: IMAGES 1923-1974. Foreword by Wallace Stegner. Boston: NY Graphic Soc, (1974). 1st ed. Fine in dj and cracked slipcase. *CAPTAIN'S BOOKSHELF*. $275

Anshaw, Carol. AQUAMARINE. Boston: HMCo. (1992). Uncorrected proof. Fine in wraps. *DORN*. $35

Anson, Adrian C. A BALL PLAYER'S CAREER. New Era, 1900. 1st ed. Good+. *PLAPINGER*. $450

Anson, George, baron Anson. A VOYAGE ROUND THE WORLD, IN THE YEARS MDCCXL, I, II, III, IV. London: John and Paul Knapton, 1748. 3rd ed, w/3 fldg charts. Contemp calf, rebacked. *HUDSON*. $750

Anson, George, Baron Anson. A VOYAGE ROUND THE WORLD, IN THE YEARS MDCCXL, I, II, III, IV. London: Printed for the author, by John and Paul Knapton, 1748. 1st ed. 42 maps and plts (most fldg). Contemp calf, neatly rebacked, new eps. Some foxing and offsetting. Inscrip on title relating to dispute over editorship of Lord Anson's papers. *HUDSON*. $5,750

Anson, George. A VOYAGE ROUND THE WORLD, IN THE YEARS MDCCXL,I,III,IV. Comp by Richard Walter. London: John & Paul Knapton, 1748. 3rd ed. Contemp polished calf, gilt on spine. 3 fldg maps. *PARMER*. $650

Ansted, D.T. THE IONIAN ISLANDS IN THE YEAR 1863. London, 1863. Frontis in sepia. 5 maps on 4 plts. Full grn polished calf, gilt spine, raised bands, marbled edges. Handsome. *O'NEILL*. $475

Anstey, F. HUMOR AND FANTASY. London, 1931. 1st ed thus. VG. *MADLE*. $35

Anstie, Francis. NEURALGIA AND THE DISEASES THAT RESEMBLE IT. NY, 1882. 1st Amer ed. *FYE*. $50

Antheil, George. BAD BOY OF MUSIC. London, n.d. 1st ed. Fine in dj, reinforced internally, edge rubbed, few tiny nicks, price clipped. *POLYANTHOS*. $75

Anthony, David. THE LONG HARD CURE. London: Collins Crime Club, 1979. 1st ed. VF in dj. *MORDIDA*. $35

Anthony, Gene. THE SUMMER OF LOVE. HAIGHT-ASHBURY AT ITS HIGHEST. Millbrae: Celestial Arts, (1980). Signed by Kesey. Fine in wraps (no hb issued). *LOPEZ*. $85

Anthony, Joseph H. LAMONI'S PASSING PARADE: STORIES OF LAMONI AND LAMONI PEOPLE. Lamoni, IA: Blair, 1948. 1st ed. Frontis. Brown cl, silver letters. NF. *CONNOLLY & WADE*. $55

Anthony, Piers. TATHAM MOUND. NY: Morrow (1991). Uncorrected proof. Fine in wraps. *DORN*. $25

Anthony. E.W. HISTORY OF MOSAICS. Boston, 1935. Dj. NF. *POLYANTHOS*. $95

Anton, Ferdinand and Frederick J. Dockstader. PRE-COLUMBIAN ART AND LATER INDIAN TRIBAL ARTS. NY: Abrams, (1968). NF in sl repaired dj. *DIAMOND*. $60

Anton, Ferdinand. ANCIENT MEXICAN ART. NY: Putnam, (1969). 1st Amer ed. Chipped dj. *SILVER*. $100

Anton, Ferdinand. ART OF THE MAYA. London: Thames & Hudson, (1978). Good in dj. *SILVER*. $85

Anton, Ferdinand. ART OF THE MAYA. NY: G.P. Putnam's Sons, 1970. 1st Amer ed. NF in VG dj. *PARMER*. $75

Anton, Ferdinand. ART OF THE MAYA. NY: G.P. Putnam's Sons, 1970. 1st Amer ed. NF in VG dj. *PARMER*. $75

Antoninus, Brother. (William Everson). WHO IS SHE THAT LOOKETH FORTH AS THE MORNING. Santa Barbara: Capricorn Press, 1972. Ltd ed. 101/250 only signed. Grn leather. Handbound by Earle Gray. Title page blocks cut by Graham Mackintosh. Fine in acetate dj w/tiny piece missing top rear panel. *POLYANTHOS*. $150

Apenslak, Jacob. ARMED RESISTANCE OF THE JEWS IN POLAND. NY, (1944). Wraps. Illus. Fine. *POLYANTHOS*. $30

Apes, William. A SON OF THE FOREST. NY: Pub by author, 1829. 1st ed. 12mo, brown calf backed marble boards. Rubbed, calf split, chipped at spine. Titled & ruled in gilt on spine. 216pp, lacks eps. VG. *BLUE MOUNTAIN*. $95

Apollinaire, Guillaume. TWO NOVELS. Paris: Olympia Press, 1959. Wrappers. 1st Eng trans. Very sl edge rubbed, Fine. *POLYANTHOS*. $30

Apollonius of Rhodes. ARGONAUTICA: OR, THE QUEST FOR THE GOLDEN FLEECE. Athens: For LEC, 1957. Illus, signed by A. Tassos. 954 of 1500. Fine in slipcase. *SCHOYER'S*. $65

Appelfeld, Aharon. BADENHEIM 1939. Boston: David R. Godine, (1980). 1st ed in English. Orig rust cl. Fine in dj. *CHAPEL HILL*. $25

Appiah, Anthony, et al. POEMS OF THREE GENERATIONS. n.p., Peggy Appiah, 1977. Wraps. 1/2000 numbered . Fine. *BEASLEY*. $45

APPLE GROWING IN THE PACIFIC NORTHWEST. Portland, 1911. Cl, lt flecking front cvr; sm puncture going through front cvr, 33pp. *SUTTON*. $65

Apple, Max. THE ORANGING OF AMERICA AND OTHER STORIES. NY: Grossman Pubs, 1976. Ptd wrappers. Unrevised proofs. Author, title in ink on backstrip, otherwise NF. *HELLER*. $75

Apple, Max. THE ORANGING OF AMERICA. NY: Grossman, 1976. 1st ed. Bkpl, gift inscrip. Fine- in Fine- dj. *AARD*. $20

Applegate, Jesse A. and Lavina Honeymoon Porter. Ed by Martin Ridge. WESTWARD JOURNEYS. Chicago, 1989. 1st ed. Lakeside CLassics #87. Minor staining back cvr o/w Fine. *PRATT*. $30

Applegate, Jesse. RECOLLECTIONS OF MY BOYHOOD. Roseburg, OR: Press of Review Pub., 1914. 1st ed. 99pp. Pict wraps. Some spine end chipping and lower edge dampstain. VG. Howes A294. *OREGON*. $475

APPLETON'S ANNUAL CYCLOPAEDIA...THE YEAR (1876 THROUGH 1884) EMBRACING...New Series; Vol I through Vol IX. Whole Series; Vol XVI through Vol XXV. NY: Appleton, 1883. 9 vols. Orig 1/2 calf and marbled boards. Spine w/raised bands, blind stamped and gilt. Minimal shelf wear. NF. *CONNOLLY & WADE*. $315

APPLETON'S GENERAL GUIDE TO THE UNITED STATES AND CANADA. Part I. New England and Middle States and Canada. NY: D. Appleton and Company, 1886. Rev each year to date of issue. Maps (some fldg), charts. Old bk label. *HUDSON*. $75

APPLETON'S GENERAL GUIDE TO THE UNITED STATES AND CANADA. Part II. Western and Southern States. NY: D. Appleton, 1892. Rev each year to date of issue. Maps, 4 plans. *HUDSON*. $80

APPLETON'S HAND-BOOK OF AMERICAN TRAVEL. SOUTHERN TOUR. NY/London: D. Appleton and Company/Sampson, Low, Son, and Marston, 1876. Rev for the season of 1876. Charles H. Jones (ed). Fldg map, plans. Binding somewhat damped, pencil markings. *HUDSON*. $225

APPLETON'S HAND-BOOK OF AMERICAN TRAVEL. WESTERN TOUR. NY: D. Appleton, 1873. Rev for Autumn 1873. NY: D. Appleton, 1873. Fldg maps. Lacks fldg map of Eastern states and small one of San Francisco. *HUDSON*. $135

APPLETON'S ILLUSTRATED HAND-BOOK OF AMERICAN TRAVEL. NY/London: D. Appleton & Co, Trubner, 1857. 24pp fldg. Spine faded, split. Maps in esp Good state. *HUDSON*. $250

APPLETON'S RAILROAD AND STEAMBOAT COMPANION. NY: D. Appleton & Company, (1848). 1st ed. 30 maps on 19 fldg sheets. *HUDSON*. $325

APPOMATTOX ROSTER: A LIST OF THE PAROLES...ISSUED AT APPOMATTOX COURT-HOUSE ON APRIL 9, 1865...NY: 1962. Facsimile rprnt of 1887 orig ed. One of 750. *GINSBERG*. $35

Aptheker, Herbert. MISSION TO HANOI. NY: Internat'l Pubs, (1966). 1st ed, stated. Fine in worn dj, tape reinforced. *AKA*. $35

Apuleis, Lucius. THE TRANSFORMATION OF LUCIUS. Otherwise Known as the Golden Ass. Trans by Robert Graves. Middlesex, England: Penguin Books. 1950. Ltd to 2000, numbered, signed. Dj. Slipcase. *KARMIOLE*. $150

Aquinas, Saint Thomas. SAINT THOMAS AQUINAS. SELECTIONS...MADE BY GEORGE SHUSTER. Chatham, England: LEC, 1969. One of 1500 illus, signed by Reynolds Stone. Fine in slipcase. *CAPTAIN'S BOOKSHELF*. $125

Aquinas, Saint Thomas. THE WRITINGS OF SAINT THOMAS AQUINAS. Selected by George N. Shuster. Chatham: LEC, 1969. One of 1500. Signed by Reynolds Stone (illus). Fine in slipcase. *CAPTAIN'S BOOKSHELF*. $125

Arago, Francois. A POPULAR TREATISE ON COMETS. London: Longman et al, 1861. Adam W.H. Smyth, Robert Grant (trans, eds). Corners bumped, spine faded and frayed, wear to extremities, o/w Nice. *KNOLLWOOD*. $95

Arago, Francois. A POPULAR TREATISE ON COMETS. W.H. Smyth and R. Grant (trans). London: Longman et al, 1861. 1st Eng ed. 164pp. Fldg frontis map. Orig purple cl faded. VG. *SMITHFIELD*. $45

Aramilev, Ivan. BEYOND THE URAL MOUNTAINS. Trans, adapted by Michael Heron. London: Allen & Unwin, (1961). Dj. *SCHOYER'S*. $25

Arano, Luisa Cogliti. THE MEDIEVAL HEALTH HANDBOOK-TACUINUM SANITATIS. NY, 1976. 1st ed. 48 plts. Dj. *FYE*. $45

Arber, Agnes. HERBALS: THEIR ORIGIN AND EVOLUTION, A CHAPTER IN THE HISTORY OF BOTANY, 1470-1670. (Cambridge: The Univ Press, 1938). 2nd ed. Bkpl. Binding a little faded, jacket sl spotted and faded w/stain on backstrip, o/w Excellent. *PIRAGES*. $175

Arble, Meade. THE LONG TUNNEL: A COAL MINER'S JOURNAL. NY: Atheneum, 1976. 1st ed. Dj torn and internally mended, price-clipped. *AKA*. $25

Arcieri, John. THE CIRCULATION OF THE BLOOD IN ANDREA CESALPINO OF AREZZO. NY, 1945. 1st ed. *FYE*. $75

Arciniegas, German. GERMANS IN THE CONQUEST OF AMERICA. NY: Macmillan, 1943. 1st ed. Fine in Fine dj. *AARD*. $25

Ard, William. THE ROOT OF HIS EVIL. NY: Rinehart, 1957. 1st ed. Pages darkened o/w Fine in dj. *MORDIDA*. $25

Arden, William (Michael Collins). A DARK POWER. Dodd, Mead, 1968. 1st ed. Fine in dj w/two sm tears. Owner stamp. *STAHR*. $35

Ardizzone, Tony. HEART OF THE ORDER. Henry Holt, 1986. Ex libris. 1st ed. VG or better in dj. Glue residue on pastedowns and verso of flyleaves. *STAHR*. $15

Arelot, Henri. PHILIBERT'S BRIGHT IDEAS. Trans by Helen Hammett Owen. London: Frederick Warne & Co., Inc. (1932). 1st ed. DJ bit chipped. *KARMIOLE*. $40

Argenti, Philip P and Arnold C. Smith. THE ARCHITECTURE OF CHIOS.....London, 1962. 22 plts, 6 maps (5 fldg). Dj. Fine. *O'NEILL*. $235

Argenti, Philip P. THE EXPEDITION OF COLONEL FABVIER TO CHIOS.... London, 1933. Presentation slip laid in. The Blackmer copy, w/his bkpl. O'NEILL. $160

Ariens-Kappers, C.U. THE EVOLUTION OF THE NERVOUS SYSTEM IN INVERTEBRATES, VERTEBRATES, AND MAN. Haarlem, 1929. 1st ed. 325pp. FYE. $200

Aristophanes. THE FROGS. Illus by John Austen. NY: LEC. 1937. Ltd to 1500, signed by Austen. Pub's folder, slipcase. KARMIOLE. $75

Aristotle. POLITICS AND POETICS. Benjamin Jowett, S.H. Butcher (eds). Lunenburg, VT: LEC, 1964. One of 1500 ptd at Stinehour Press, illus, signed by Leonard Baskin. Spine sl spotted, else Fine in slipcase. CAPTAIN'S BOOKSHELF. $150

ARIZONA BRAND BOOK AND SUPPLEMENT. 1963. Arizona Livestock Sanitary Board. 1st ed. (1),118,119pp. Index. Black cl spine. Rigid brown wrappers. Fine. CONNOLLY & WADE. $30

ARIZONA NO. 3. A CHECK LIST OF ARIZONA IMPRINTS 1860-90. Chicago: Historical Records, 1938. VG in wraps. BOOK MARKET. $35

ARIZONA. A STATE GUIDE. NY: Hastings, 1947. 1st ed, 6th ptg. WPA guide. NF in chipped dj. CONNOLLY & WADE. $27.50

ARIZONA. NY, 1940. American Guide Series. WPA guide. 1st ptg. No dj. SCHOYER'S. $40

ARIZONA. NY, 1940. American Guide Series. WPA guide. 5th ptg. Lacks dj. SCHOYER'S. $15

ARIZONA'S NATIONAL MONUMENTS. Santa Fe: Southwestern Monuments Assn, Popular Series, No. 2, 1945. 1st ed. Ltd to 5,000. About Fine. CONNOLLY & WADE. $40

ARKANSAS. NY, 1941. American Guide Series. WPA guide. 1st ptg, lacks dj. SCHOYER'S. $45

Arkell, A.J. EARLY KHARTOUM: AN ACCOUNT OF THE EXCAVATION OF AN EARLY OCCUPATION SITE....London: Oxford Univ Press, 1949. 113 plts. Good. ARCHAEOLOGIA. $375

Arkell, A.J. SHAHEINAB: AN ACCOUNT OF THE EXCAVATION OF A NEOLITHIC OCCUPATION SITE....London: Oxford Univ Press, 1953. 43 plts. Good in tattered dj. ARCHAEOLOGIA. $350

Armah, Ayi Kwei. THE BEAUTYFUL ONES ARE NOT YET BORN. Boston: Houghton Mifflin, 1968. 1st ed. Fine in NF, price-clipped dj. LOPEZ. $25

Armatage, George. THE HORSEOWNER AND STABLEMAN'S COMPANION. London: Warne, 1892. 4th ed. Eps foxed, o/w VG. OCTOBER FARM. $20

Armes, George A. UPS AND DOWNS OF AN ARMY OFFICER. Wash, 1900. 1st ed. Orig pict cl, Front cover bright (sm discoloration upper right hand corner, spine faded). Back cover has small discoloration upper left corner. Howes A316. GINSBERG. $225

Armes, George A. UPS AND DOWNS OF AN ARMY OFFICER. Wash., 1900. 1st ed. Orig pict cl. Front cover bright; small discoloration upper right hand corner, spine faded, back cvr has small discoloration. Howes A31 6. GINSBERG. $225

Armistead, J.J. HANDY GUIDE TO FISH CULTURE. Scarborough, 1897. 12mo, 119pp. Boards, engr. VG+. MIKESH. $20

Armitage, Merle (ed). THE ART OF EDWARD WESTON. NY: E. Weyhe, 1932. 1st ed. Weston's 1st bk. Boards sl worn, some staining and marking. Rebacked w/sl soiled and stained title part of orig backstrip. 30 full-page Weston photos. Frontis & photos 1 & 5 have few very small tears. Recased, o/w VG. 1/550 (#147) signed by Weston. DIAMOND. $600

Armitage, Merle. A RENDEZVOUS WITH THE BOOK. Brooklyn, (1949). 1st ed. Few small cvr stains, o/w VG. DIAMOND. $45

Armitage, Merle. PAGANS, CONQUISTADORES, HEROES AND MARTYRS. Fresno: Academy Guild, (1964). Deluxe ed ltd to 1500. Fine in Fine dj. OREGON. $45

Armitage, Merle. STELLA DYSART OF AMBROSIA LAKE....NY: Duell, Sloan & Pearce, 1959. 1st ltd ed. Fine in About Fine dj. CONNOLLY & WADE. $65

Armour, J. Ogden. THE PACKERS, THE PRIVATE CAR LINES, AND THE PEOPLE. Phila: Henry Altemus, (1906). 1st ptg. 8 plts. Pict cl, sl soiling top edge, else VG. SCHOYER'S. $65

Arms, Dorothy Noyes and John Taylor Arms. CHURCHES OF FRANCE. NY: Macmillan, 1929. Blue grn cl (stained & rubbed) w/title in gilt within double gilt rules on front cover. 51 plts, each w/tissue guard. VG. BLUE MOUNTAIN. $35

Arms, Dorothy Noyes. HILL TOWNS AND CITIES OF NORTHERN ITALY. NY: MacMillan, 1932. 1st ed. Fine in dj w/shallow chipping from head of spine. CAPTAIN'S BOOKSHELF. $225.

Arms, John Taylor. AMERICAN ETCHERS. NY, 1930. 2nd prtg. Dj. 12 tipped-in plts. NF. POLYANTHOS. $30

Arms, John Taylor. HANDBOOK OF PRINT MAKING AND PRINT MAKERS. NY: MacMillan, 1934. 1st ed. Fine in price-clipped dj, few sm tears. CAPTAIN'S BOOKSHELF. $50

Armstrong, Anthony. THE SECRET TRAIL. Chicago: White House, (1927). VG in dj with slight soil, edgewear, 1 short closed tear. BEB-BAH. $18

Armstrong, Charlotte. MISCHIEF. NY: Coward-McCann, 1950. 1st ed. Fine in dj w/tiny wear at top of spine. MORDIDA. $30

Armstrong, Charlotte. THE BLACK-EYED STRANGER. NY: Coward-McCann, 1951. 1st ed. Fine in dj w/minor wear at base of spine and along folds. MORDIDA. $30

Armstrong, David A. BULLETS AND BUREAUCRATS. Westport, CT (1982). 1st ed. Fine. PRATT. $27.50

Armstrong, Dr. Nelson. NUGGETS OF EXPERIENCE. n.p., 1906. 1st ed. Pict cl. VG. PRATT. $90

Armstrong, Dr. Nelson. NUGGETS OF EXPERIENCE: NARRATIVES OF THE SIXTIES....N.p.: Times-Mirror & B. House, 1906. 1st ed. Frontis, 9 plts. Blue dec cl, gilt. VG. CONNOLLY & WADE. $65

Armstrong, Harry. PRINCIPLES AND PRACTICE OF AVIATION MEDICINE. Baltimore, 1941. 1st ed, 3rd ptg. FYE. $100

Armstrong, John. THE ART OF PRESERVING HEALTH: A POEM. IN FOUR BOOKS. London, 1748. 3rd ed. Full lea, 128pp. Front board detached, o/w VG. FYE. $150

Armstrong League of Hampton Workers. MEMORIES OF OLD HAMPTON. Hampton, VA: The Institute Press, 1909. 1st ed. 136pp. Orig cl. NF. McGOWAN. $150

Armstrong, Louis. SWING THAT MUSIC. Foreword Rudy Vallee. NY: Longman's, 1936. 1st ed. Owner sig, bkpl. VG in defective dj. Inscribed, using his real name as well as "Satchmo". CAPTAIN'S BOOK-SHELF. $450

Armstrong, Margaret. MURDER IN STAINED GLASS. NY: Random House, 1939. 1st ed, 1st mystery. Fine, minor rubs dj corners. ELSE FINE. $95

Armstrong, Martin. THE BAZAAR. Knopf, 1924. 1st ed. VG in chipped dj. MADLE. $30

Armstrong, Moses K. THE EARLY EMPIRE BUILDERS OF THE GREAT WEST. St. Paul: E.W. Porter, 1901. 23 plts. VG. SCHOYER'S. $50

Armstrong, Terence. THE RUSSIANS IN THE ARCTIC. London: Methuen, 1958. 1st ed. Fine in Fine dj. GREAT EPIC. $35

Armstrong, Thomas R. MY FIRST AND LAST BUFFALO HUNT AND A "SEQUEL." N.p.: By the author, 1918. VG in Fine dj. BO-HLING. $60

Armstrong, Walter. FENCING, BOXING, WRESTLING (BADMINTON LIBRARY) London, Bombay, Calcutta: Longmans, Green & Co., 1907. Reprint ("New Imp"). Minor wear to extremities, else VG-NF. *OLD LONDON.* $100

Arndt, Karl J.R. A DOCUMENTARY HISTORY OF THE INDIANA DECADE OF THE HARMONY SOCIETY. Indianapolis: Indiana Hist Soc 1975/1978. 1st ed. Wraps. 2 vols. NF. *BEASLEY.* $65

Arndt, Karl. A DOCUMENTARY HISTORY OF THE INDIANA DECADE OF THE HARMONY SOCIETY 1814-1824. Indianapolis, 1975. 2 fold-out maps. Wraps. VG. *ARTIS.* $22.50

Arnett, Ethel Stevens. O. HENRY FROM POLECAT CREEK. Greensboro, NC: Piedmont Press, 1962. 1st ed. Presentation, signed. Orig orange cl. Fine. *CHAPEL HILL.* $35

Arno, Peter. CARTOON REVUE. NY, 1941. 1st ed. Fine in like dj. *POLYANTHOS.* $40

Arnold, Edwin Lester. PHRA THE PHOENICIAN. London, 1893. VG. *MADLE.* $50

Arnold, Edwin Lester. THE VOYAGE OF ITHOBAL. Toronto: Briggs, 1901. 1st Canadian ed. Teg. Binding starting, some fraying, else VG+. *OTHER WORLDS.* $35

Arnold, Edwin. POEMS NARRATIVE AND LYRICAL. Oxford: Francis Macpherson, 1853. 1st ed. 174pp. Orig maroon cl. VG. *CHAPEL HILL.* $75

Arnold, Guy. LONGHOUSE AND JUNGLE: AN EXPEDITION TO SARAWAK. London: Chatto & Windus, 1959. In dj. *SCHOYER'S.* $20.

Arnold, Hugh. STAINED GLASS OF THE MIDDLE AGES IN ENGLAND AND FRANCE. London: Adam & Charles Black, 1913. Illus Lawrence B. Saint. *DAWSON'S.* $100

Arnold, Marilyn. WILLA CATHER'S SHORT FICTION. OH Univ Press, (1984). 1st ed. Fine in dj. *AUTHORS OF THE WEST.* $20

Arnold, Matthew. POETICAL WORKS OF MATTHEW ARNOLD. NY: Macmillan, 1893. 1st US ed. Prev owner's name, address, bkpl. VG+. *AARD.* $20

Arnold, Oren and J.P. Hale. HOT IRONS: HERALDRY OF THE RANGE. NY, 1940. 1st ed. Spine sunned. Fine. *VARNER.* $50

Arnold, Oren. ARIZONA UNDER THE SUN. Wheelwright, 1968. 1st ed. Fine in sl chipped dj. *VARNER.* $25

Arnold, Oren. SUN IN YOUR EYES. Univ of New Mexico, 1949. 1st ed. Fine in Fine dj. *VARNER.* $20

Arnold, Oren. THUNDER IN THE SOUTHWEST. Norman: Univ of OK, 1952. 1st ed. NF in sl chipped dj. *CONNOLLY & WADE.* $40

Arnold, Oren. THUNDER IN THE SOUTHWEST. Norman: Univ of OK, 1952. 1st ed. NF in lightly chipped dj. *CONNOLLY & WADE.* $40

Arnold, Oren. THUNDER IN THE SOUTHWEST. Univ of OK Press, 1952. 1st ed. Fine in dj, chip lower spine. *VARNER.* $25

Arnold, Thurman. THE SYMBOLS OF GOVERNMENT. Yale Univ. Press, 1935. 1st ed. Blue cl. Pencilling, else VG in chipped dj. *DIAMOND.* $75

Arnold, William Harris. VENTURES IN BOOK COLLECTING. NY: Scribner, 1923. 1st ed. Some foxing. Chipping. Fine- in VG dj. *AARD.* $35

Arnott, Henry. CANCER; ITS VARIETIES, THEIR HISTOLOGY AND DIAGNOSIS. London, 1872. 1st ed. 86pp. 21 woodcuts, 5 engrvd plts. Scarce. *FYE.* $250

Arnow, Harriette. FLOWERING OF THE CUMBERLAND. NY, (1963). 1st ed. Fine in dj. *ARTIS.* $22.50

Arnow, Harriette. FLOWERING OF THE CUMBERLAND. NY: Macmillan, 1963. 1st ed. Signed. Fine, minor edgewear to dj. *ELSE FINE.* $50

Arnow, Harriette. HUNTER'S HORN. NY: Macmillan, 1949. 1st ed, 1st novel. NF, sm chips dj spine ends. *ELSE FINE.* $50

Arnow, Harriette. THE DOLLMAKER. NY: MacMillan, 1954. Fine in sl edgeworn price-clipped dj. *CAPTAIN'S BOOKSHELF.* $100

Arruza, Carlos. MY LIFE AS A MATADOR. Boston: Houghton Mifflin, 1956. 1st ed. Chipped dj. *SILVER.* $25

Arseniev, V. K. DERSU THE TRAPPER. NY: Dutton, 1941. Trans Malcolm Burr. Some markings on the e.p. 3 line maps, number of small cuts in text. In worn badly chipped dj. *SCHOYER'S.* $45

ART IN CALIFORNIA, A SURVEY OF AMERICAN ART WITH SPECIAL REFERENCE TO CALIFORNIAN PAINTING, SCULPTURE AND ARCHITECTURE... SF: Bernier, 1916. 1st ed. 183pp. Linen-backed boards. Fine. *WEBER.* $750

ART OF MAGIC AND THE ART OF VENTRILOQUISM. NY: Dick's, n.d. (c. 1890). Small 8vo; pink, highly pict wraps; longitudinal crease. VG in wraps. *DRAMATIS PERSONAE.* $75

ARTHUR CONAN DOYLE: THE MICHAEL CROPPER COLLECTION. SF: CA Book Auction, (1984). Limited to 100 casebound, these are the auction records, w/prices realized, of an important Doyle collection. *UNGER.* $75

Arthur, William. ITALY IN TRANSITION. London: Hamilton, Adams and NY: Harper, 1860. Good only. *SCHOYER'S.* $25

ARTHUR'S ALPHABET. NY: McLoughlin Brothers, n.d. One of "Aunt Mayflower's Play Books." Pict wrappers sewn at spine. Front wrapper chipped, several long tears at margins of leaves. *JAFFE.* $50

Arthurs, Stanley C. THE AMERICAN HISTORICAL SCENE. Carlton, NY, 1936. *HEINOLDT.* $25

Artzybasheff, Boris. AS IS SEE. Dodd, Mead, 1954. 1st ed. 4to. Unpaginated. Amazing world of Artzybasheff in 4 sections. VG in VG dj. *BEBBAH.* $50

Artzybasheff, Boris. POOR SHAYDULLAH. Macmillan, 1931. 1st ed of this illustrator's 1st book as an author. Unpaginated. Illus by the author. Slight fraying top of spine, little darkened bottom of spine, toning to edges of dec cvr but VG. *BEBBAH.* $60

Artzybasheff, Boris. POOR SHAYDULLAH. NY: Macmillan, (1931). 1st ed. Cl, cvrs sunned; 1p has grey mark into text. Else VG. *ACADEMIC LIBRARY.* $30

Asch, Berta and A.R. Mangus. FARMERS ON RELIEF AND REHABILITATION. "Works Progress Administration, Division of Social Research, Research Monograph VIII." Washington: GPO. 1937. 8 photos, 15 text figures, fldg table. Pub's blue cloth, gilt. Dj. *KARMIOLE.* $50

Aschmann, Homer (trans, ed). THE NATURAL & HUMAN HISTORY OF BAJA CALIFORNIA....LA: Dawson, 1966. 1st ed. Inscr. Ltd to 600. Fine. *CONNOLLY & WADE.* $40

Ash, Brian (ed). VISUAL ENCYCLOPEDIA OF SF. Harmony Books, 1977, 1st ed. Fine in dj. *MADLE.* $25

Ashabranner, Brent. MORNING STAR, BLACK SUN: THE NORTHERN CHEYENNE INDIANS AND AMERICA'S ENERGY CRISIS. NY: Dodd, Mead, 1982. 1st ed. Fine in NF dj. *CONNOLLY & WADE.* $20

Ashbery, John. AS WE KNOW. Manchester: Carcanet (1981). 1st ed. Fine in dj. *WOOLMER.* $30

Ashbery, John. AS WE KNOW: POEMS. NY: Viking Press, (1979). 1st ed. Fine in dj. Inscribed. *CAPTAIN'S BOOKSHELF.* $100

Ashbery, John. DOUBLE DREAM OF SPRING. NY: Dutton, 1970. 1st ed, 1st issue. Fine in dj. Presentation inscrip. *CAPTAIN'S BOOKSHELF.* $175

Ashbery, John. FRAGMENT. POEM. Illus Alex Katz. LA: Black Sparrow Press, 1969. 1/250 hb signed by Ashbery and Katz. Fine in acetate dj. *CAPTAIN'S BOOKSHELF.* $150

Ashbery, John. FRAGMENT. POEM. Illus Alex Katz. LA: Black Sparrow Press, 1969. 1st ed, wrappered issue, 1/750. Top corners bumped, else Fine in wrappers. *CAPTAIN'S BOOKSHELF.* $20

Ashbery, John. HOUSEBOAT DAYS. NY: Viking, (19771. Uncorrected proof. Fine in wrappers. *CAPTAIN'S BOOKSHELF.* $50

Ashbery, John. RIVERS AND MOUNTAINS. NY: Holt, (1966). 1st ed. Fine in dj. *CAPTAIN'S BOOKSHELF.* $100

Ashbery, John. RIVERS AND MOUNTAINS. NY: Holt, (1966). 1st ed, wrappered issue. Fine. *CAPTAIN'S BOOKSHELF.* $20

Ashbery, John. RIVERS AND MOUNTAINS. NY: Holt, 1966. 1st ed, only 1,000 hardcover printed. Fine in Fine dj. *BEASLEY.* $100

Ashbery, John. SELECTED POEMS. London: Jonathan Cape, (1967). 1st ed, 3rd state w/title page corrected and integral. Fine in dj. *CAPTAIN'S BOOKSHELF.* $40

Ashbery, John. SELF-PORTRAIT IN A CONVEX MIRROR. POEMS. NY: Viking Press, (1975). 1st ed. Fine in dj w/tiny scrape. Presentation inscrip. *CAPTAIN'S BOOKSHELF.* $150

Ashbery, John. SELF-PORTRAIT IN A CONVEX MIRROR. SF: Arion Press, 1984. 1st ed. 1/175 signed. Illus w/orig signed prints by Willem de Kooning, Elaine de Kooning, Avedon, Alex Katz, Larry Rivers, Jane Freilicher and R.B . Kitaj. Circular folio, loose sheets laid into a stainless steel canister w/convex mirror inset on top. A recording of Ashbery reading his poem is incl within. VF. *CAPTAIN'S BOOKSHELF.* $7500

Ashbery, John. SHADOW TRAIN. NY: Viking, (1981). 1st ed. Fine in dj. *CAPTAIN'S BOOKSHELF.* $40

Ashbery, John. SOME TREES. W.H. Auden foreword. New Haven: Yale, 1956. 1st ed. Fine in dj. *CAPTAIN'S BOOKSHELF.* $200

Ashbery, John. THE TENNIS COURT OATH. POEMS. Middletown: Wesleyan, (1962). 1st ed, wrappered issue. Fine in sl used wrappers. *CAPTAIN'S BOOKSHELF.* $20

Ashbery, John. THE TENNIS COURT OATH. POEMS. Middletown: Wesleyan, (1962). 1st ed. Fine in spine-darkened dj w/chip from rear panel. Presentation inscrip. *CAPTAIN'S BOOKSHELF.* $125

Ashbery, John. THREE MADRIGALS. (NY: Poet's Press, 1968). 1st ed. One of 150, signed. Fine in wrappers. *JAFFE.* $125

Ashbery, John. THREE PLAYS. Calais, VT: Z Press, 1978. 1st ed. 1/26 lettered copies (out of hb ed of 500) signed. VF in dj. *CAPTAIN'S BOOKSHELF.* $250

Ashbery, John. THREE POEMS. NY: Viking, (1972). 1st ed. Fine in dj. Rev copy, slip, photo laid in. *CAPTAIN'S BOOKSHELF.* $60

Ashbrook, H. THE MURDER OF CECILY THANE. NY: Coward-McCann, 1930. 1st ed. VG in dj with some internal tape repairs and closed tears. *MORDIDA.* $35

Ashburn, P.M. A HISTORY OF THE MEDICAL DEPARTMENT OF THE UNITED STATES ARMY. Houghton Mifflin, 1929. VG. *BOOKCELL.* $40

Ashe, W.W. SHADE TREES FOR NORTH CAROLINA. Raleigh, 1908. 10 plts. Wrappers. Rear corner creased, lt marginal dampstaining. *SUTTON.* $27

Ashenback, Edward. HUMOR AMONG THE MINORS. Ed by Jack Ryder. Donahue, 1911. 1st ed. Good. *PLAPINGER.* $175

Ashley, Clifford W. THE YANKEE WHALER. Boston & NY, 1926. 1st ed. 1/1625. 16 color plts. Orig 1/4 cl, cvrs showing some sl soil, corners sl bumped, inner hinges sound. VG. *LEFKOWICZ.* $375

Ashley, Clifford W. THE YANKEE WHALER. Popular Ed. Boston: Houghton Mifflin Co. 1938. 2nd ed. Howes A356. *KARMIOLE.* $100

Ashley, Clifford W. THE YANKEE WHALER.... Boston & NY, 1926. 1st ed. One of 1,625. 16 color plts. Orig 1/4 cl, cvrs showing some very lt soil, inner hinges tender, but VG. *LEFKOWICZ.* $375

Ashley, Clifford W. WHALESHIPS OF NEW BEDFORD. Boston & NY, 1929. 1st ed. 1/1035. F.D. Roosevelt (intro). 60 plts. Orig cl, spine sl soiled. Inscribed. *LEFKOWICZ.* $350

Ashley-Montagu, M.F. COMING INTO BEING AMONG THE AUSTRALIAN ABORIGINES. London: George Routledge & Sons, Ltd, 1937. 1st ed. Blue cl. 4 plts. Dj well worn; some wear to edges of vol, else VG. *PARMER.* $95

Ashmead, Henry G. HISTORICAL SKETCH CHESTER ON DELAWARE. Chester, PA, 1883. 4, 337pp; wraps bound in 3 fldg maps. Plts. Edge of title pg and errata pg frayed. *HEINOLDT.* $50

Ashton, Dore and Denise Hare. ROSA BONHEUR. A LIFE AND A LEGEND. London: Secker & Warburg, 1981. 1st ed. VG in VG dj. *OCTOBER FARM.* $65

Ashton, Francis and Stephen. WRONG SIDE OF THE MOON. London, 1952. 1st ed. VG in frayed dj. *MADLE.* $35

Ashton, James M. ICE-BOUND. A TRADER'S ADVENTURES IN THE SIBERIAN ARCTIC. NY, 1928. 2nd prtg. Fldg map. Signed inscription. VG. *ARTIS.* $25

Ashton, John. HUMOR, WIT, & SATIRE OF THE SEVENTEENTH CENTURY. London, 1883. NF. *POLYANTHOS.* $60

Ashton, John. OLD TIMES...NY: Scribner, 1885. Large, thick 8vo, 354pp, index w/88 illus. Orig red cloth, gilt lettering and decs, top edge gilt, uncut. Rebacked, w/orig label laid down. VG. *HARTFIELD.* $125

Ashton, John. THE HISTORY OF GAMBLING IN ENGLAND. London, 1899. NF. *POLYANTHOS.* $50

Ashton, T.J. ON THE DISEASES, INJURIES, AND MALFORMATIONS OF THE RECTUM AND ANUS, WITH REMARKS ON HABITUAL CONSTIPATION. Phila, 1860. 1st Amer ed. 287pp. Woodcut illus. Exceptionally Fine. *FYE.* $200

Ashton, T.J. PROLAPSUS, FISTULA IN ANO, AND HAEMORRHOIDAL AFFECTIONS: THEIR PATHOLOGY AND TREATMENT. London, 1863. 2nd ed. VF. *FYE.* $100

Ashton, Wendell J. VOICE IN THE WEST: BIOGRAPHY OF A PIONEER NEWSPAPER. NY: Duell, Sloan & Pearce, 1950. 1st ed. Fine. *CONNOLLY & WADE.* $40

Asimov, Isaac (ed). HUGO WINNERS. VOL 2. Doubleday, 1971. 1st ed. Fine dj w/rev slip. *MADLE.* $50

Asimov, Isaac and Robert Silverberg. NIGHTFALL. NY: Foundation/Doubleday, (1990). 1st ed. One of 750 numbered, signed by both authors. Fine in slipcase w/tipped on color illus, as issued. *OTHER WORLDS.* $150

Asimov, Isaac. ASIMOV'S GUIDE TO SHAKESPEARE. Rafael Palacios (illus). GC: Doubleday, 1970. 1st ed. 2 vols. Fine in djs, slipcase. Each vol inscribed. *CAPTAIN'S BOOKSHELF.* $150

Asimov, Isaac. ASIMOV'S MYSTERIES. Doubleday, 1968. 1st ed. Signed. VG in soiled & frayed dj. *MADLE.* $35

Asimov, Isaac. EARTH IS ROOM ENOUGH: SCIENCE FICTION TALES....GC: Doubleday, 1957. 1st ed. VG+ in dj, bad snag rear spine edge. *OTHER WORLDS.* $75

Asimov, Isaac. FANTASTIC VOYAGE II: DESTINATION BRAIN. NY: Doubleday, (1987). 1st ed. One of 450 signed, numbered. Fine in slipcase, w/o dj as issued. *OTHER WORLDS.* $150

Asimov, Isaac. FOUNDATION AND EARTH. GC: Doubleday, 1986. 1st ed. Advance copy: uncorrected proof in bound ptd wrappers. Fine in trade hb ed. dj. *OTHER WORLDS.* $125

Asimov, Isaac. FOUNDATION'S EDGE. Binghamton: Whispers Press, 1982. 1st ed. One of 1000 signed, numbered. Fine w/o dj as issued. *OTHER WORLDS.* $100

Asimov, Isaac. HAVE YOU SEEN THESE? Boston: NESFA, 1974. 1st ed. One of 500 signed, numbered. Fine in Fine dj. *OTHER WORLDS.* $75

Asimov, Isaac. I ROBOT. NY: Gnome Press, (1950). 1st ed. Top of rear board, 2 corners bumped else Almost Fine in dj (worn, frayed spine ends). *OTHER WORLDS.* $300

Asimov, Isaac. IN MEMORY YET GREEN. Doubleday, 1979. 1st ed. Fine in dj. *MADLE.* $25

Asimov, Isaac. INTELLIGENT MAN'S GUIDE TO SCIENCE. Doubleday, 1960. 1st ed. 2 vols. VG. *MADLE.* $35

Asimov, Isaac. NEMESIS. NY: Doubleday, (1989). Ltd. ed. One of 500 signed, numbered. Fine in slipcase, w/o dj as issued. *OTHER WORLDS.* $125

Asimov, Isaac. NIGHTFALL AND OTHER STORIES. Doubleday, 1979. Ex-lib. VG in dj. *MADLE.* $50

Asimov, Isaac. OPUS 200. Houghton-Mifflin, 1979. 1st ed. Fine in dj. *MADLE.* $25

Asimov, Isaac. OPUS 300. Houghton-Mifflin, 1984. 1st uncorrected proof in wraps. Fine. *MADLE.* $25

Asimov, Isaac. PEBBLE IN THE SKY. Doubleday Young Moderns ed. VG in dj. *MADLE.* $25

Asimov, Isaac. PRELUDE TO FOUNDATION. NY: Doubleday, 1988. One of 500 signed, numbered, specially bound, aeg & ribbon marker. Fine in slipcase, sl bumped at corner, w/o dj as issued. *OTHER WORLDS.* $125

Asimov, Isaac. ROBOTS AND EMPIRE. Doubleday, 1985. 1st ed. NF in dj. *MADLE.* $25

Asimov, Isaac. ROBOTS AND EMPIRE. Huntington Woods: Phantasia Press, 1985. 1st ed. One of 650 signed, numbered. Fine in Fine dj in slipcase. *OTHER WORLDS.* $100

Asimov, Isaac. SECOND FOUNDATION. NY: Gnome Press, 1953. 1st binding, 1st ed. Signed bkpl. Spine sl sunned, extremities very sl rubbed. Fine in dj (5-1/2" close tear front panel, 2-1/2" tear fold front flap). *POLYANTHOS.* $150

Asimov, Isaac. TALES OF THE BLACK WIDOWERS. GC: Doubleday Crime Club, 1974. 1st ed. Fine in sl soiled dj. *MORDIDA.* $45

Asimov, Isaac. THE ASIMOV CHRONICLES: FIFTY YEARS OF ISAAC ASIMOV. Arlington Heights: Dark Harvest, 1989. 1st ed. One of 500 signed, numbered. Fine in dj, slipcase. *OTHER WORLDS.* $75

Asimov, Isaac. THE ASIMOV CHRONICLES: FIFTY YEARS OF ISAAC ASIMOV. Arlington Heights: Dark Harvest, 1989. 1st ed, trade issue. Fine in Fine dj. *OTHER WORLDS.* $30

Asimov, Isaac. THE ASIMOV CHRONICLES: FIFTY YEARS OF ISAAC ASIMOV. Arlington Heights: Dark Harvest, 1989. 1st ed. One of 52 specially bound signed, lettered. Fine (w/o dj as issued) in wooden slipcrate. *OTHER WORLDS.* $250

Asimov, Isaac. THE CURRENTS OF SPACE. GC: Doubleday, 1952. 1st ed. Some spine slant else NF in dj (worn at spine ends, short closed tear top rear panel). *OTHER WORLDS.* $100

Asimov, Isaac. THE EDGE OF TOMORROW. Tor, 1985. Uncorrected proof copy in wraps. Fine. *MADLE.* $50

Asimov, Isaac. THE END OF ETERNITY. Doubleday, 1955. 1st ed. Signed. NF in sl rubbed dj w/tape stain. *MADLE.* $225

Asimov, Isaac. THE END OF ETERNITY. GC: Doubleday, 1955. 1st ed. Light soiling to boards, owner's name on pastedown, o/w Fine in Fine dj but for a few internal reinforcements to flap fold. *BEASLEY.* $200

Asimov, Isaac. THE END OF ETERNITY. GC: Doubleday, 1955. 1st ed. Light soiling to boards, owner's name on pastedown, else Fine in Fine dj but for a few internal reinforcements to flap fold. *BEASLEY.* $200

Asimov, Isaac. THE GODS THEMSELVES. GC: Doubleday, 1972. 1st ed. Some spine cock else VG+/NF in edgeworn (mostly spine ends) dj. *OTHER WORLDS.* $75

Asimov, Isaac. THE LAND OF CANAAN. Boston: Houghton Mifflin, 1971. 1st ed. NF in sl edgeworn dj. *CAPTAIN'S BOOKSHELF.* $35

Asinof, Eliot. EIGHT MEN OUT. Holt, Rinehart & Winston, 1963. Ltr ptg. Good+ in VG+ dj. *PLAPINGER.* $25

Askins, Col. Charles. THE AMERICAN SHOTGUN. NY: Outing Publishing Company, 1910. 1st ed. Binding waterspotted. *HUDSON.* $55

Aspinall, James. ROSCOE'S LIBRARY; OR, OLD BOOKS AND OLD TIMES. London: Whittaker and Co.; Liverpool: Deighton and Laughton, 1853. 1st ed. Cvrs soiled and faded, extremities a bit worn, withal Good. *WREDEN.* $45

Asprin, Robert. THE BUG WARS. St Martins, 1979. 1st ed. Fine in sl frayed dj. *MADLE.* $25

Asquith, Cynthia (ed). NOT LONG FOR THIS WORLD. Telegraph Press, 1936. 1st US ed. VG in sl frayed dj. *MADLE.* $65

Asquith, Cynthia. A BOOK OF MODERN GHOSTS. Scribners, 1953. 1st US ed. Fine in frayed dj. *MADLE.* $35

Asquith, Cynthia. THIS MORTAL COIL. Arkham House, 1947. 1st ed. Fine in dj. *MADLE.* $75

Asquith, Lady Cynthia (ed). THE TREASURE CAVE, A BOOK OF NEW PROSE & VERSE. Scribner's, (1928). 5 tipped-in color plts by A.H. Watson, Daphne Jerrold, A.K. MacDonald. Edgewear but VG. *BEBBAH.* $25

Astley, Sir J.D. FIFTY YEARS OF MY LIFE...London: Hurst and Blackett, 1895. 4th ed (in one vol). A few minor bumps, generally VG-NF. *OLD LONDON.* $45

Atchley, S.C. WILD FLOWERS OF ATTICA. Oxford, 1938. Cl, some wear at spine ends, overall fading; lt staining. *SUTTON.* $115

Athearn, Robert G. WESTWARD THE BRITON. NY, 1953. 1st ed. Stain inside cvrs and on foldover of dj; dj has faded spine o/w VG. Ex-lib with external markings removed. *PRATT.* $35

Athearn, Robert. FORTS OF THE UPPER MISSOURI. Prentice Hall, (1967). 1st ed. Rev copy. Fine in VG dj. *OREGON.* $40

Atherton, Gertrude. ADVENTURES OF A NOVELIST. London, (1932). 1st Eng ed. Cvrs sl shelfworn, soiled. Spine soiled, o/w VG. *DIAMOND.* $25

Atherton, Gertrude. ANCESTORS. Harper, 1907. 1st ed. Crest on cvr. VG, bkpl. *AUTHORS OF THE WEST.* $25

Atherton, Gertrude. CALIFORNIA. AN INTIMATE HISTORY. NY, 1914. 1st ed. Sl cvr staining, o/w VG. *DIAMOND.* $25

Atherton, Gertrude. CALIFORNIA. AN INTIMATE HISTORY. NY: Harper, 1914. 1st ed. Red cl, uncut. VG. K-O on copyright pg. *SECOND LIFE.* $45

Atherton, Gertrude. CALIFORNIA. AN INTIMATE HISTORY. NY: Harper, 1914. 1st ed. Red cl, uncut, VG. *SECOND LIFE.* $45

Atherton, Gertrude. DIDO, QUEEN OF HEARTS. NY: Liveright, 1929. 1st ed. Name sticker o/w Fine. Uncut in dj. *SECOND LIFE.* $75

Atherton, Gertrude. GOLDEN GATE COUNTRY. NY, 1945. 3rd ptg. VG in sl chipped dj. *VARNER.* $10

Atherton, Gertrude. LIFE IN THE WAR ZONE. NY, (1916). 1st ed. Signed. Fine in glassine dj. *POLYANTHOS.* $35

Atherton, Gertrude. MY SAN FRANCISCO: A WAYWARD BIOGRAPHY. Bobbs Merrill, (1946). 1st ed. Inscribed, signed. VG+ in dj. *AUTHORS OF THE WEST.* $25

Atherton, Gertrude. SLEEPING FIRES. Frederick A. Stokes, (1922). 1st ed. Fine, name in pencil. *AUTHORS OF THE WEST.* $25

Atherton, Gertrude. THE FOGHORN. Boston: Houghton, Mifflin, 1934. 1st ed. Nice in little worn, price clipped dj. *SECOND LIFE.* $85

Atherton, Gertrude. THE JEALOUS GODS. NY: Liveright, 1928. 1st ed. Fine in dj. *SECOND LIFE.* $75

Atherton, Gertrude. THE SPLENDID IDLE FORTIES: STORIES OF OLD CALIFORNIA. NY: Macmillan, 1902. 1st ed. Red dec cl. Unfoxed, clean, VG. *CONNOLLY & WADE.* $150

Atherton, Lewis. THE CATTLE KINGS. Indiana Univ, 1961. 1st ed. Fine in VG dj. *VARNER.* $20

Atherton, William. NARRATIVE OF THE SUFFERING AND DEFEAT OF THE NORTHWESTERN ARMY, UNDER GENERAL WINCHESTER...Frankfort, Ky, author, 1842. 1st ed. 152pp. Orig leather backed marbled boards, paper label on front cvr; joints, crown, heel of spine chipped. Howes A366. *GINSBERG.* $275

Atholl, Justin. SHADOW OF THE GALLOWS. London: J. Long, 1954. 1st ed. Fine in NF dj. *ARCHER.* $15

Atkeson, Ray. THE CASCADE RANGE. Portland, OR: Belding, (1969). 1st ed. Fine- in Fine- dj (rubbing). *AARD.* $35

Atkey, Bertram. HARVEST OF JAVELINS. Brentano's, 1923. 1st ed. Proof copy in dj. *MADLE.* $25

Atkinson, E. Miles. ABSCESS OF THE BRAIN: ITS PATHOLOGY, DIAGNOSIS AND TREATMENT. London, 1934. 1st ed. *FYE.* $75

Atkinson, Mary J. CHATEAU IN BRITTANY. London: Stanley Paul & Co, n.d. (ca. 1910?). Worn dec cl. VG. *SCHOYER'S.* $20

Atkinson, Samuel C. ATKINSON'S CASKET OR GEMS OF LITERATURE, WIT AND SENTIMENT. Phila: Samuel C. Atkinson, 1836. Fldg map, engrvd plts, woodcuts. New 1/2 morocco, some foxing. *HUDSON.* $1,200

Atkinson, Thomas Witlam. ORIENTAL AND WESTERN SIBERIA. Phila: John E. Potter, n.d. (c. 1880). 483pp, 12pp pub ads. Grn cl stamped in black and gilt, a little rubbed. *SCHOYER'S.* $40

Attaway, William. LET ME BREATHE THUNDER. NY: Doubleday, Doran, 1939. 1st ed, 1st bk. Bkstore stamp front pastedown, o/w NF in VG dj. *LOPEZ.* $300

Attawy, William. CALYPSO SONG BOOK. NY: McGraw-Hill, (1957). 1st ed. Tape remnants to pastedowns and flaps of dj w/resultant offsetting, else Fine in NF dj w/tiny chips at extremities. Very uncommon. *BETWEEN COVERS.* $125

Atwood, Margaret and Catherine M. Young. TO SEE OUR WORLD. (NY): Morrow, (1980). 1st ed. NF in dj. *LOPEZ.* $85

Atwood, Margaret. BLUEBEARD'S EGG & OTHER STORIES. Boston: Houghton Mifflin, 1986. 1st US ed. Fine in Fine dj. *AKA.* $28

Atwood, Margaret. BLUEBIRD'S EGG. Boston: HM, 1986. 1st Amer ed. Fine in dj. Signed. *CAPTAIN'S BOOKSHELF.* $45

Atwood, Margaret. BODILY HARM. McClelland & Stewart, 1981. 1st ed. About Fine in lightly rubbed dj (worn at spine ends). Signed. Owner inscription. *STAHR.* $40

Atwood, Margaret. BODILY HARM. Simon and Schuster, 1982. 1st Amer ed. VF in dj. Signed. *STAHR.* $35

Atwood, Margaret. BODILY HARM. Toronto: McClelland & Stewart, 1980. 1st ed. VF in price clipped dj. Inscribed. *ELSE FINE.* $60

Atwood, Margaret. CAT'S EYE. Doubleday, 1989. Advance reading copy. VF in wraps. *STAHR.* $25

Atwood, Margaret. CAT'S EYE. NY: Doubleday, (1989). 1st ed. Fine in Fine dj. *ROBBINS.* $35

Atwood, Margaret. HURRICANE HAZEL AND OTHER STORIES. Helsinki, Finland: Eurographica, 1987. 1st of this ed. Ltd to 350 signed. Mint in ptd Roma wrappers. *JAFFE.* $175

Atwood, Margaret. LADY ORACLE. NY: Simon & Schuster, 1976. 1st ed. Remainder mark o/w NF in VG rubbed dj (1/4" tear). *ARCHER.* $20

Atwood, Margaret. LIFE BEFORE MAN. NY: Simon & Schuster, (1979). 1st US ed. Rev copy with promo material laid in. About Fine in dj. *AKA.* $35

Atwood, Margaret. POWER POLITICS. Poems. NY: Harper, (1971). 1st US ed. Fine in price-clipped dj. Signed. *CAPTAIN'S BOOKSHELF.* $75

Atwood, Margaret. SECOND WORDS. Boston: Beacon Press, n.d. 1st ed. Advance uncorrected proofs. 1st US ed. Fine in wraps w/name on bottom edge. *BEASLEY.* $30

Atwood, Margaret. SECOND WORDS... Boston: Beacon Press, (1984). 1st US ed. Tiny dent, else Fine in dj. *CAPTAIN'S BOOKSHELF.* $35

Atwood, Margaret. SURVIVAL: A THEMATIC GUIDE TO CANADIAN LITERATURE. Toronto: Anansi, 1972. 1st ed. In wraps, NF w/corner crease. *BEASLEY.* $35

Atwood, Margaret. THE ANIMALS IN THAT COUNTRY. Boston: Little Brown, (1968). 1st ed. VG in dj faintly stained near the top. *LOPEZ.* $65

Atwood, Margaret. THE JOURNALS OF SUSANNA MOODIE. Toronto: Oxford Univ Press, 1970. 1st ed. Only issued in wrappers and only published in Canada. Lightly rubbed. NF. *LOPEZ.* $50

Atwood, Margaret. TRUE STORIES. London: Cape, (1982). 1st Brit ed. Issued only in wrappers in UK. Fine. *LOPEZ.* $25

Atwood, Margaret. WILDERNESS TIPS. Doubleday, 1991. Advance Reading Copy of Amer ed. VF in dec wraps. *STAHR.* $45

Atwood, Margaret. YOU ARE HAPPY. NY: Harper, (1974). 1st US Fine in dj. Signed. *CAPTAIN'S BOOKSHELF.* $75

Auchincloss, Louis. THE INJUSTICE COLLECTORS. Boston: HM, 1950. 1st ed. NF in like dj, somewhat faded spine. *CAPTAIN'S BOOKSHELF.* $100

Auchincloss, Louis. THE INJUSTICE COLLECTORS. Boston: Houghton Mifflin Co., 1950. 1st ed. Fine in VG+ dj, a bit faded on spine, with a little spotting. *BETWEEN COVERS.* $95

Auchincloss, Louis. THE WINTHROP COVENANT. Boston: Houghton Mifflin, 1976. 1st trade ed. NF in price-clipped dj w/small abrasion on rear panel. Signed on tipped-in leaf. *CHAPEL HILL.* $40

Auden, W.H. and Christopher Isherwood. ON THE FRONTIER. London: Faber & Faber Ltd., (1938). 1st ed. F in dj w/a few short tears. *HELLER.* $125

Auden, W.H. and Louis MacNeice. LETTERS FROM ICELAND. London: Faber and Faber (1937). 1st ed. Fldg map. VG in dj, shows some minor wear. *SECOND LIFE.* $85

Auden, W.H. and Louis MacNeice. LETTERS FROM ICELAND. London: Faber, 1937. 1st ed. Sl blotching to boards, owner's name, o/w Fine in NF dj. *BEASLEY.* $100

Auden, W.H. COLLECTED POEMS. London: Faber, (1976). Uncorrected proof in proof jacket. Fine in wrappers, dj. *JAFFE.* $75

Auden, W.H. FIVE POEMS....Edward Mendelsohn (intro). Frontis by Gregory Dearth. 1/4 vellum & dec boards, linen box. (Cedar Falls, Iowa: Labyrinth Editions, 1984). 1st ed. One of 100 signed by Mendelsohn, Dearth & Richard Bigus, the printer. As New. *JAFFE.* $450

Auden, W.H. GOOD-BYE TO THE MEZZOGIORNO. Milan, 1958. 1st ed. Bilingual ed. Printed self wraps w/wraparound band. Fine. *POLYANTHOS.* $25

Auden, W.H. GOOD-BYE TO THE MEZZOGIORNO. Translated by Carlo Izzo. Milano, 1958. One of 1,000. VF w/wrap-around band. Wraps. *WOOLMER.* $65

Auden, W.H. THE CAVE OF MAKING. Frankfurt, (1965). 1st ed. Ltd ed 1500. Printed self-wraps. Fine. *POLYANTHOS*. $30

Auden, W.H. THE DANCE OF DEATH. London: Faber, (1933). 1st ed. Fine in dj. *JAFFE*. $225

Auden, W.H. THE ENCHAFED FLOOD, OR THE ROMANTIC ICONOGRAPHY OF THE SEA. NY: Random House, (c.1950). 1st ptg. Rev copy, slip laid in. Fine in sl soiled, darkened pale gray dj w/several short tears. *HELLER*. $85

Auden, W.H. THE PLATONIC BLOW. NY: Ptd by the Fuck You Press for the World Gobble Grope Fellowship, 1965. 1st trade ed. One of 300. *CHAPEL HILL*. $100

Auden, W.H. THE SHIELD OF ACHILLES. NY: Random House, (1955). 1st ed. NF in lightly soiled dj. *CHAPEL HILL*. $65

Auden, W.H. THE SHIELD OF ACHILLES. NY: Random House, (1955). 1st ed. NF in sl soiled but VG dj. *BERNARD*. $50

Auden, W.H. TWO SONGS. Phoenix Book Shop, 1968. Wraps. One of 126, this "out of series." Fine. *WOOLMER*. $50

Audsley, George Ashdown. THE ORGAN OF THE TWENTIETH CENTURY. NY: Dodd, Mead and Co, 1919. 1st ed. Blue cl w/gilt title set within double black rules on front cover & spine. Red stain at bottom of front cover. Eps soiled, sl creased. 32 plts. NF. *BLUE MOUNTAIN*. $200

Audubon, John J. A SYNOPSIS OF THE BIRDS OF NORTH AMERICA. Edinburgh 1839. 1st ed. 12,359pp. Half title (loose). Lib buckram. *M & S*. $125

Audubon, John J. and J. Bachman. THE VIVIPAROUS QUADRUPEDS OF NORTH AMERICANY, VOL. 2. NY: V.G. Audubon, 1851. Royal 8vo, 334pp+subscribers list. Orig cl w/spine label ends worn, else unfoxed, VG. *MIKESH*. $250

Audubon, John J. AUDUBON'S WESTERN JOURNAL: 1849-50....With Biographical Memoir by his Daughter, Maria R. Audubon. Intro, notes Frank Heywood Hodder. Clark, Cleveland, 1906. Lg fldg map in rear. Pub's Announcement and letter from pub acknowledging order tipped in. Edges & spine worn. # on spine. *HEINOLDT*. $150

Audubon, John J. JOURNAL OF JOHN JAMES AUDUBON MADE DURING HIS TRIP TO NEW ORLEANS IN 1820-1821 AND JOURNAL...1840-1843. H. Corning (ed). 2 vols. Cambridge, 1929. Later issue from the same type setting as the ltd ed. Discoloration spots; minor foxing; overall Nice set. *SUTTON*. $175

Audubon, John J. JOURNAL OF...MADE WHILE OBTAINING SUBSCRIPTIONS TO HIS "BIRDS OF AMERICA," 1840-1843...Cambridge, Ma, 1939. New ed. Howard Corning (ed). Orig cl boards, paper label on spine. Howes A387. *GINSBERG*. $150

Audubon, John J. LETTERS OF JOHN JAMES AUDUBON 1826-1840. 2 vols. Ed by Howard Corning. Boston: Club of Odd Volumes, 1930. One of 225. Fine in slipcase. *DERMONT*. $275

Audubon, John J. THE BIRDS OF AMERICA. NY, 1937. Frontis, 500 full-pg colored plts. Lt fading; bkpl. *SUTTON*. $55

Audubon, John J. THE ORIGINAL WATER-COLOR PAINTINGS BY JOHN JAMES AUDUBON FOR THE BIRDS OF AMERICA. NY, 1966. Colored frontis, 431 colored plts (several fldg). 2 vols. Slipcase (corners scuffed). *SUTTON*. $175

Audubon, L. THE LIFE OF JOHN J. AUDUBON, THE NATURALIST. NY: (1883). VG. *MIKESH*. $30

Audubon, L. THE LIFE OF JOHN JAMES AUDUBON THE NATURALIST. NY: G.P. Putnam's Sons, 1879. Rprnt. Boards soiled, rubbed. Bkpl, label. Accession no on title pg. Text clean. Grn cl. Frontis. Good. *PARMER*. $70

Audubon, Maria and Elliott Coues (eds). AUDUBON AND HIS JOURNALS. N.Y, 1897. 2 vols. 1st ed. Dk grn gilt cl. (ex-lib.) Howes A391. *GINSBERG*. $125

Audubon, Maria. AUDUBON AND HIS JOURNALS, with Zoological and Other Notes by Elliot Coues. 2 vols. NY: Charles Scribner's Sons, 1897. 1st ed. Owner's names. Fine, unopened set in djs (stained and chipped); of utmost rarity thus. *BLUE MOUNTAIN*. $450

Auel, Jean. THE CLAN OF THE CAVE BEAR. NY, 1980. 1st ed. Presentation inscription. Publicity photos, release. Fine in price clipped dj (extremities, spine few tiny chips, very small edge tear top spine). *POLYANTHOS*. $95

Auel, Jean. THE CLAN OF THE CAVE BEAR. NY, (1980). 1st ed. As New in dj. *BOND*. $50

Auffenberg, W. GRAY'S MONITOR LIZARD. Gainesville, 1988. 3 plts. Dj. *SUTTON*. $42

Aughey, Rev. John H. THE FIGHTING PREACHER. Chicago, 1899. 1st ed. 361pp, illus, pict cloth. VG+. *PRATT*. $185

Aughey, Rev. John H. THE IRON FURNACE: OR SLAVERY & SECESSION. William S. & Alfred Martien: Phila, 1863. Portrait, 296pp. Orig grn cl. Spine worn w/small chip. Damp stain in lower portion of pages, short-lived and not affecting text. Tight, Good+. *CONNOLLY & WADE*. $55

Aughey, Rev. John H. TUPELO. Lincoln, 1888. 595pp, ads and testimonials. Little cvr wear and soiling, o/w VG+. *PRATT*. $47.50

Augustine, Jane. LIT BY THE EARTH'S DARK BLOOD. Mt. Horeb, WI: Perishable Press, 1977. 1st ed. Ltd to 150 signed by Augustine; this also signed by Hamady. Wraps. Mint. *JAFFE*. $75

Aunt Carrie (comp). POPULAR PASTIMES FOR FIELD AND FIRESIDE. Milton Bradley, 1867. Good w/o dj in emb pict cvr. *PLAPINGER*. $250

Auslander, Joseph. MORE THAN BREAD. A BOOK OF POEMS. NY: Macmillan, 1936. 1st ed. NF. W/signed inscription. *CHAPEL HILL*. $35

Auster, Paul. MOON PALACE. NY, 1989. 1st ed. Signed. Fine in Fine dj. *POLYANTHOS*. $35

Auster, Paul. THE NEW YORK TRILOGY. London: Faber and Faber, 1987. 1st Eng. ed. Fine in dj. *MORDIDA*. $85

Auster, Paul. UNEARTH. (Weston, Connecticut): Living Hand 3, (1974). 1st ed. Presentation, inscribed. Fine. Ptd wrappers. *JAFFE*. $175

Austin, Alfred. THE GARDEN THAT I LOVE. A&C Black, 1905. 1st ed. 7s 6d Series. Minor wear to extremities, thus VG. *OLD LONDON*. $50

Austin, Gabriel (ed). FOUR OAKS LIBRARY. FOUR OAKS FARM. 2 vols. Slipcase. Somerville, NJ: (Clarke & Way), 1967. 1st ed. Ltd to 1250. VF set. *JAFFE*. $250

Austin, Mary. EARTH HORIZON. 1932. 1st ed. Spine sl stained, o/w VG. *DIAMOND*. $35

Austin, Mary. ISIDRO. Boston, 1905. 1st ed. 4 plts, 2pp ads. Cvrs sl rubbed. Top fore-edge spotted, o/w VG. *DIAMOND*. $50

Austin, Mary. LOST BORDERS. NY: Harper & Bros, 1909. 1st ed. Grn cl. VG. *SMITH*. $135

Austin, Mary. ONE-SMOKE STORIES. Boston: Houghton Mifflin, 1934. 1st ed. Fine in Fine dj. *LOPEZ*. $225

Austin, Mary. ROOM AND TIME ENOUGH: THE LAND OF MARY AUSTIN. Northland, 1979. 1st ed. New in dj. *AUTHORS OF THE WEST*. $30

Austin, Mary. THE AMERICAN RHYTHM. NY: Harcourt, (1923). 1st ed. Nice, uncut in chipped, soiled dj. *SECOND LIFE*. $75

Austin, Mary. THE FLOCK. Boston, 1906. 1st ed. Title page in red and black. Pict cl gilt. Teg. Spine soiled. Few small cvr stains. Small tear spine tip. Contents VG. *DIAMOND*. $60

Austin, Mary. THE FLOCK. Houghton Mifflin, 1906. 1st ed. Illus E. Boyd Smith. Teg. Pict cvr. VG, owner initials. *AUTHORS OF THE WEST.* $100

Austin, Mary. THE FLOCK. NY: Houghton Mifflin, 1906. 1st ed. Fine. *BOOK MARKET.* $175

Austin, Mary. THE LAND OF LITTLE RAIN. Boston: Houghton Mifflin. 1903. 1st ed, 1st bk. Orig dec grn cl, cvr stamped in 4 colors; spine somewhat spotted, rear cvr with a bit of a crease at top inch; still decent, inner hinges sound. *KARMIOLE.* $200

Austin, O.L. THE BIRDS OF NEWFOUNDLAND LABRADOR. Cambridge, 1932. Dampstaining lower edges of cvrs; dampstaining lower hinges eps, not affecting text; some cvr soiling. Inscribed. *SUTTON.* $65

AUTOBIOGRAPHY, LETTERS AND LITERARY REMAINS. (By Mrs. Hester Piozzi). Ed by A. Hayward. 2 vols. London: Longman, 1861. 1st ed, rev issue. Engr port frontis, errata sheet, half titles. 358;407pp. 24-page Longman catalog back of vol I; printed adverts each pastedown. Orig blind-stamped cloth. VG. *HARTFIELD.* $285

Avallone, Michael. LUST IS NO LADY. NY: Belmont Books, 1964. 1st ed. Pb orig. Sm scrape at top corner of front cover o/w Fine, unread in wrappers. *MORDIDA.* $25

Avallone, Michael. MEANWHILE BACK AT THE MORGUE. Greenwich: Fawcett Pubs, 1960. 1st ed. Pb orig. Gold Medal #1024. A VF unread copy in wrappers. *MORDIDA.* $30

Avallone, Michael. THE BEDROOM BOLERO. NY: Belmont Books, 1963. 1st ed. Pb orig. A Fine unread copy in wrappers. *MORDIDA.* $30

Avallone, Michael. THE SPITTING IMAGE. NY: Henry Holt, 1953. 1st ed. Fine in dj with a couple of short closed tears. *MORDIDA.* $35

Avallone, Michael. THE VIOLENT VIRGIN. London: W.H. Allen, 1960. 1st hb ed. Edges darkened o/w VG in dj (short closed tears; internal tape mend). *MORDIDA.* $25

Avary, Myrta Lockett. DIXIE AFTER THE WAR. NY, (1906). 1937 rprt. Moderate dj wear and chipping o/w VG+. *PRATT.* $42

Avedon, Richard. OBSERVATIONS. London: Weidenfeld and Nicolson, 1959. White paper boards. Cardboard case. Sm bkseller's label inside front cover. VG. *HELLER.* $250

Avedon, Richard. PORTRAITS. (NY: Farrar, Strauss & Giroux. 1977.) "2nd printing." Signed by Avedon ffep. Stiff white wrappers stamped in gray. *KARMIOLE.* $75

Aveling, T.W. VOICES OF MANY WATERS. London: Snow, 1855. 1st ed. xii,508pp. Bkpl. Orig cl rubbed, spine chipped, sl foxing, o/w Good. *WORLDWIDE.* $85

Averell, William Woods. TEN YEARS IN THE SADDLE, THE MEMOIRS OF WILLIAM WOOD AVERELL, 1851-1868. Ed by Edward K. Eckert & Nicholas J. Amato. San Rafael, (1978). 1st ed. 443pp. Dj w/light wear, faded spine; o/w Fine. *PRATT.* $30

Averill, Mary. JAPANESE FLOWER ARRANGEMENT (IKEBANA). APPLIED TO WESTERN NEEDS. London: John Lane the Bodley Head, 1914. 1st ed. Front cover a bit scuffed, corners bumped, o/w VG. *WREDEN.* $40

Averill, Naomi. CHOOCHEE, A STORY OF AN ESKIMO BOY. Grosset & Dunlap, (1937). Illus. VG, dj has tears, wrinkles, missing part of rear panel. *BEBBAH.* $35

Avey, Elijah. THE CAPTURE AND EXECUTION OF JOHN BROWN. Elgin, IL, (1906). 1st ed. NF. *McGOWAN.* $55

Ayer, Frederick . YANKEE G-MAN. Chicago, 1957. Dj. *O'NEILL.* $25

Ayres, H.B. and W.W. Ashe. THE SOUTHERN APPALACHIAN FORESTS. Washington, 1905. 37 plts; 2 folded colored maps in rear env. Encased in cl, title partially perished, corners of last few pp partially perished, 1 pp w/sm tear. Ex-lib. *SUTTON.* $125

Ayrton, Michael. BRITISH DRAWINGS. London: Collins, 1946. 1st ed. Fine. Dj. *JAFFE.* $40

B

Babcock, George. YEZAD: ROMANCE OF UNKNOWN. Cooperative Pub, 1922. 1st ed. Good. *MADLE.* $35

Babcock, Havilah. TALES OF QUAILS 'N SUCH. NY: Greenberg, (1951). 1st ed. Review copy, card laid in. Fine in dj (tiny edge tears; 2 sm chips). Signed. *CAPTAIN'S BOOKSHELF.* $150

Babcock, William. TOWER OF WYE. Coates, 1901. 1st ed. VG. *MADLE.* $35

Baber, Daisy. INJUN SUMMER, AN OLD COWHAND RIDES THE GHOST TRAILS. Caxton, 1952. 1st ed. VF in VF dj. *OREGON.* $25

Baber, Daisy. INJUN SUMMER. Caldwell, 1952. 1st ed. Minor dj wear and chipping o/w Fine. *PRATT.* $40

Baber, Daisy. INJUN SUMMER. Caxton, 1952. 1st ed. Fine in Fine dj. *VARNER.* $35

Baber, Daisy. THE LONGEST ROPE. THE TRUTH ABOUT THE JOHNSON COUNTY CATTLE WAR. Caxton, 1947. 2nd ptg. VG. *OREGON.* $40

Babson, Marian. A FOOL FOR MURDER. NY: Walker, 1983. 1st Amer ed. Advance review, slip laid in. Fine in dj. *MORDIDA.* $25

Babson, Marian. A TRAIL OF ASHES. NY: Walker, 1985. 1st Amer ed. Review copy, signed. Pub's slip laid in. Fine in dj. *SILVER DOOR.* $35

Babson, Marian. DEATH BESIDE THE SEA. NY: Walker, 1983. 1st Amer ed. Signed. VF in dj. *SILVER DOOR.* $35

Babson, Marian. ENCORE MURDER. London: Collins Crime Club, 1989. 1st ed. VF in dj. *MORDIDA.* $30

Babson, Marian. FATAL FORTUNE. London: Collins Crime Club, 1987. 1st ed. Fine in dj w/tiny wear at base of spine. *MORDIDA.* $35

Babson, Marian. REEL MURDER. London: Collins Crime Club, 1986. 1st ed. Fine in dj w/tiny tear at base of spine. *MORDIDA.* $30

Babson, Marian. WEEKEND FOR MURDER. London: Collins Crime Club, 1985. 1st ed. Adv rev copy w/slip laid in. Fine in dj. *MORDIDA.* $35

BABYLAND. Boston: D. Lothrop & Co, (1883). Editors of Wide Awake (eds). 104pp. Orig lt brn cl; cvr illus by Kate Greenaway stamped in gold and maroon. Ffep lacking, o/w very nice, clean. *KARMIOLE.* $45

Bach, Christian A. THE FOURTH DIVISION. Issued by the Division. (n.p.), 1920. Illus. 5 maps. NF. *POLYANTHOS.* $45

Bacheler, Clementine and Jessie Orr White. NUN OF THE CA'FROLLO: THE LIFE AND LETTERS OF HENRIETTA GARDNER MACY. NY: William Farquhar Payson. Sl chipped dj, VG. *SCHOYER'S.* $25

Bacheller, Irving. D'RI AND I. Boston: Lothrop Pub Co., 1901. 1st ed. Wear, some foxing. Red cl. Pict paste-on cvr. Teg. *PARMER.* $35

Bacheller, Irving. EBEN HOLDEN'S LAST DAY A-FISHING. NY: Harper & Brothers, 1907. 1st ed. Grn cl stamped in black and yellow. Fine in Rare dj. *JUVELIS.* $75

Bachman, Richard (pseud of Stephen King). THE LONG WALK. (NY): Signet Book, (1979). 1st ptg, pb orig. Bkst name, address, price stamped inside cvr, flyleaf; spine has crease lines, else VG. *BERNARD.* $40

Bachman, Richard (pseud of Stephen King). THINNER. NAL, 1984. 1st ed. Fine in dj. *MADLE.* $37

Bachman, Richard (pseud of Stephen King). THINNER. NY, 1984. 1st ed. VF in dj. *PETTLER.* $65

Bachman, Richard (Stephen King). ROADWORK. Signet, 1981. 1st ed. VG or better in pb. Spine lightly rolled & cracked. *STAHR.* $25

Backhouse, James. A NARRATIVE OF A VISIT TO THE MAURITIUS AND SOUTH AFRICA. London: Hamilton, Adams, and Co., 1844. 1st ed. xvi,648 & lvi pp. Eps chipped, ink number table of contents. 16 plts, 2 fldg maps. Presentation a.n.s from author front pastedown. VG. *BLUE MOUNTAIN.* $450

Backus, Isaac. A HISTORY OF NEW ENGLAND WITH PARTICULAR REFERENCE TO THE DENOMINATION OF CHRISTIANS CALLED BAPTISTS...WITH NOTES BY DAVID WESTON. Newton, MA., Backus Hist. Soc, 1871. 2 vols. 2nd ed. Orig cl. 1st ed was ptd 1777-1796 in 3 vols. Howes B15. *GINSBERG.* $150

Bacon, Edwin M. WALKS & RIDES IN THE COUNTRY ROUND ABOUT BOSTON...Boston: Houghton Mifflin for the Appalachian Mountain Club, 1897. vi, 419pp. 4 fldg color maps, gilt stamped grn cl, VG; name on eps. *BOHLING.* $40

Bacon, Francis. CASES OF TREASON. WRITTEN BY SIR FRANCIS BACON, KNIGHT, HIS MAJESTIES SOLICITOR GENERALL. PRINTED BY THE ASSIGNES OF JOHN MORE (ETC.), London, 1641. 1st ed. Title page; leaf; 1-35 pages. 4to. Quite pretty, definitely embrowned; still quite sound. Modern full calf, neatly gilt. *BOSWELL.* $1,250

Bacon, Francis. THE ELEMENTS OF THE COMMON LAWES OF ENGLAND, BRANCHED INTO A DOUBLE TRACT: THE ONE CONTAINING A COLLECTION OF SOME PRINCIPALL RULES AND MAXIMES OF THE COMMON LAW [AND] THE OTHER THE USE OF THE COMMON LAW (etc.). Ptd by the Assignes of Iohn More Esquire, London, 1639. 3rd and last 17th c ed; last separately pub ed of the 2 works, the 1st ed appearing in 1630, and all appearing posthumously. Blank; title pg; title pg (Maxims); 8 leaves, (1)-44, 49-94pp (irregular but complete); title page (Use); 3 leaves; 72pp. 4to. Sound, bound in full contemp sheep. Rubbed, some time rebacked, little strained, some foxing, staining and embrowning, but still quite crisp, well margined. *BOSWELL.* $850

Bacon, Francis. THE ESSAYS or Counsels, Civil & Moral... With a Table of the Colours of Good & Evil... Enlarged by the Honorable Author Himself; and Now More Exactly Published. London: T.N. for John Martyn, S. Mearne and H. Herringman. 1673. 3 parts in one. (4),254,(4);(8),32;(14),132pp+4pp. Recent full polished calf, red morocco spine label (lower spine reads "1672" in error). Some old waterstains. Wing 3287. See Gibson #23a and #23b. Our copy is #23b, with the title corrected to read "enlarged" rather than "englarged," but with the 2 cancelled (original) leaves, title and dedication leaf, bound at back. Dedication leaf has repaired tear. *KARMIOLE.* $350

Bacon, Peggy. TWO POEMS & A DRAWING. NY: The Latterday Pamphlets, Spring, 1928. 1st ed. 1/300. VG in sl chipped wrappers. *CAPTAIN'S BOOKSHELF.* $75

BAD CHILD'S POP-UP BOOK OF BEAST. London, 1987. Illus Tripp. Pop-up bk. *BOOKFINDERS INTL.* $48

Badajos, Edward. FILIPINO FOOD. LA: Feb 15, 1971. 1st ed. Wood covers. Lithogr in ed of 1,000 signed, numbered (this #289). Fine. *SMITH.* $350

Badarich, Sarah Grace. GUN SMOKE. N.p.: n.p, 1947. 1st ed. Red pict wraps, lightly spotted. Lt edge wear, else VG. *CONNOLLY & WADE.* $35

Badawy, Alexander. A HISTORY OF EGYPTIAN ARCHITECTURE....Berkeley, LA: Univ of CA Press, 1968. 16 plts. 1 corner sl bumped. Good. *ARCHAEOLOGIA.* $150

Baddeley, John F. THE RUGGED FLANKS OF THE CAUCASUS. Oxford, 1940. 1st ed. 9 maps, (8 fldg), 38 plts. 2 vols. Newly rebound in half calf. Fine set on hand-made paper, quite scarce. *O'NEILL.* $750

Bade, W.F. THE LIFE AND LETTERS OF JOHN MUIR. Boston & NY: Houghton Mifflin, 1924. 2 vols. Illus w/2 frontis gravures. Cl w/lea spine labels. VG+. *MIKESH.* $125

Bader, Barbara. AMERICAN PICTUREBOOKS FROM NOAH'S ARK TO THE BEAST WITHIN. NY: Macmillan, (1976). 1st ed. Fine in Fine dj. *ACADEMIC LIBRARY.* $60

Bader, Barbara. AMERICAN PICTUREBOOKS FROM NOAH'S ARK TO THE BEAST WITHIN. Macmillan, (1976). 1st ed. 615pp. Illus. Fine in Fine dj. *BEBBAH.* $65

Bader, Barbara. AMERICAN PICTUREBOOKS, FROM NOAH'S ARK....NY: Macmillan, (1976). 1st ed. Fine in VG dj. *WREDEN.* $50

Badger, Rev. George P. THE NESTORIANS AND THEIR RITUALS: WITH THE NARRATIVE OF A MISSION TO MESOPOTAMIA AND COORDISTAN IN 1842-1844. London, 1852. 2 frontis, 13 tinted plts and 2 b/w plans, 2 fldg maps on silk at end of vol. 1. 2 vols. xxiv,448pp; xiii,426pp. Minor binding defects, but stout. *O'NEILL.* $550

Badger, Rev. Joseph. A MEMOIR OF REV. JOSEPH BADGER. Hudson: Sawyer, Ingersoll, 1851. 1st ed. Foxed, head of spine chipped, o/w Near VG. *ARCHER.* $225

Badger, Rev. Joseph. A MEMOIR OF REV. JOSEPH BADGER...AND SELECTIONS...Hudson, Ohio: Sawyer, 1851. 1st ed. 185,(2)pp. Port. Orig cl. Howes B25, does not cite a portrait. *GINSBERG.* $175

Badura-Skoda, Paul and Eva. INTERPRETING MOZART ON THE KEYBOARD. NY: St. Martins, 1962. NF in dj. *BANCROFT.* $25

BAE FIRST ANNUAL REPORT 1879-80. J.W. Powell, Director. GPO, 1881. 1st ed. Many plts, fldg map. Lt edge and corner wear, map repaired. Good+. *OREGON.* $65

BAE. THIRD ANNUAL REPORT. 1884. lxxiv, 606pp. Newly rebound in leather and cl. *SCHOYER'S.* $65

BAE. FOURTH ANNUAL REPORT. 1886. lxiii, 532pp. Newly rebound in leather and cl. *SCHOYER'S.* $65

BAE. FIFTH ANNUAL REPORT. 1883-1884. By J.W. Powell. Washington: GPO, 1887. Complete w/both fldg maps in back pocket and color plts. Head of spine, top of front hinge somewhat torn, some signatures loosening, exterior o/w respectable and interior VG. *LAURIE.* $50

BAE. NINTH ANNUAL REPORT. 1892. xlvi, 617pp. Newly rebound in leather and cl. Subtle library markings. *SCHOYER'S.* $75

BAE. TWELFTH ANNUAL REPORT. 1894. xlviii, 742pp. Newly rebound in leather and cl. *SCHOYER'S.* $65

BAE. THIRTEENTH ANNUAL REPORT. 1896. lix, 462pp. Lib stamp. Newly rebound in leather, cl. *SCHOYER'S.* $50

BAE. FIFTEENTH ANNUAL REPORT. 1897. cxxi, 366pp. Lib stamp. Newly rebound in leather, cl. *SCHOYER'S.* $60

BAE. FIFTEENTH ANNUAL REPORT. 1893-1894. By J.W. Powell. Washington: GPO, 1897. Some spots on edges and cover, small slit on spine, else VG. *LAURIE.* $75

BAE. SIXTEENTH ANNUAL REPORT. 1897. cxix, 326pp. Lib stamp. Newly rebound in leather, cl. *SCHOYER'S.* $60

BAE. SEVENTEENTH ANNUAL REPORT. 1895-96. 2 vols. xciii,752pp. Newly rebound in leather, cl. *SCHOYER'S.* $125

BAE. TWENTIETH ANNUAL REPORT. 1898-99. ccxxiv,237pp, 177 plts. Ex lib in orig grn cl, some wear. *SCHOYER'S.* $55

BAE. TWENTY-SECOND ANNUAL REPORT, 1900-01. Part 2. Sm emb lib stamp. Orig cl. *SCHOYER'S.* $50

BAE. TWENTY-SEVENTH ANNUAL REPORT. 1905-1906. Washington: GPO, 1911. VG. *LAURIE.* $75

BAE. TWENTY-NINTH ANNUAL REPORT. 1907-1908. Washington: GPO, 1916. VG. *LAURIE.* $60

BAE. THIRTY-SECOND ANNUAL REPORT, 1910-1911. Washington: GPO, 1918. VG. *LAURIE.* $60

BAE. THIRTY-SECOND ANNUAL REPORT. Washington, D.C.: GPO, 1910-11. 1st ed. Orig olive grn cl, gilt titles. VG. *PARMER.* $65

BAE. THIRTY-SECOND REPORT, 1910-1911. GPO, 1918. Fine. *VARNER.* $50

BAE. THIRTY-FIFTH ANNUAL REPORT. 1913-1914. 2 vols. Washington: GPO, 1921. VG. *LAURIE.* $100

BAE. FORTIETH ANNUAL REPORT. 1918-1919. Emb lib stamp. Orig grn cl. *SCHOYER'S.* $50

BAE. FORTY-EIGHTH ANNUAL REPORT, 1930-1931. General index of vols 1-48. Wraps. Front wrap, 1st 5 leaves have corner damaged not affecting text. *CULLEN.* $85

Baedeker, Karl. AUSTRIA TOGETHER WITH BUDAPEST, PRAGUE, KARLSBAD, MARIENBAD. Leipzig, 1929. 86 maps, plans, 2 panoramas. 12th rev. ed. Near-mint in dj. *O'NEILL.* $40

Baedeker, Karl. AUSTRIA-HUNGARY, INCLUDING DAL-MATIA AND BOSNIA. Leipzig: Baedeker; London: Fisher Unwin; NY: Scribner, 1905. 10th ed, rev, augmented. 33 maps, 44 plans, all present. Orig cl, sl rubbed, 1 fldg color map w/slight marginal tear, not affecting image, o/w VG. *WORLDWIDE.* $45

Baedeker, Karl. BELGIUM AND HOLLAND...LUXEMBOURG. Leipsig: Baedeker and London: Dulau, 1897. 12th ed, rev, augmented. 14 maps, 21 plans. Sl soiled red cl, VG. *SECOND LIFE.* $35

Baedeker, Karl. EGYPT AND THE SUDAN. HANDBOOK FOR TRAVELLERS. Leipzig: Karl Baedeker, 1929. 106 maps and plans (many color). Signature, rubbed at extrems, 1 corner bumped, pp 301-2 repaired. Good. *ARCHAEOLOGIA.* $150

Baedeker, Karl. EGYPT AND THE SUDAN. Leipzig, 1914. Egypt and the Sudan. 22 maps, 85 plans, 55 vignettes. 7th ed. Minor stains upper edge 1st few pgs. Rare in dj. *O'NEILL.* $130

Baedeker, Karl. EGYPT, PART FIRST: LOWER EGYPT, WITH THE FAYUM AND THE PENINSULA OF SINAI. Leipzig, 1885. 16 maps, 30 plans, 7 views, 76 vignettes. 2nd ed, rev, augmented. Lt fading of spine, else Near-Mint. *O'NEILL.* $225

Baedeker, Karl. GREAT BRITAIN. Leipsig: Baedeker, 1897. 4th ed, rev, augmented. 16 maps, 30 plans, panorama. Little soiled red cl. *SECOND LIFE.* $35

Baedeker, Karl. GREAT BRITAIN. Leipzig: 1910. 28 maps, 65 plans, 1 panorama. 7th ed, rev, augmented. VF. *O'NEILL.* $40

Baedeker, Karl. GREAT BRITAIN. Leipzig: Baedeker; London: Fisher Unwin; NY: Scribner, 1910. 7th ed, rev, augmented. 8 maps, 65 plans, 1 panorama, (all present). Orig cl, extremities rubbed, lower right hand corner of back cover is bent, frontis map w/marginal tear, o/w VG. *WORLDWIDE.* $45

Baedeker, Karl. GREECE. Leipzig, 1909. 16 maps, 30 plans, 2 diagrams, 1 panorama. 4th rev ed. Spine ends worn, corners bumped. *O'NEILL.* $75

Baedeker, Karl. GREECE. PANORAMA OF ATHENS. Leipzig & Paris, 1910. 17 maps, 32 plans, 2 plts. Only ed. Fldg map in pocket. Nice. *O'NEILL.* $115

Baedeker, Karl. HOLLAND. Leipzig, 1927. 10 maps, 20 plans, 4 ground plans. 26th ed. VF. *O'NEILL.* $150

Baedeker, Karl. ITALY FROM THE ALPS TO NAPLES. Leipsic: Baedeker. London: Dulau. NY: Scribner's, 1904. Fldg frontis map torn, separated on folds; several other maps detached or with tears, w.a.f. *SCHOYER'S.* $20

Baedeker, Karl. ITALY FROM THE ALPS TO NAPLES. Leipzig, 1928. 93 maps, plans. 3rd rev ed. NF. *O'NEILL.* $30

Baedeker, Karl. ITALY. HANDBOOK FOR TRAVELLERS. SECOND PART: CENTRAL ITALY AND ROME. Leipzig: Baedeker, 1900. 13th rev ed. 11 maps, 46 plans, 1 panorama (all maps and plans present). Orig cl, edges rubbed, top and bottom of spine frayed, o/w VG. *WORLDWIDE.* $45

Baedeker, Karl. ITALY. SECOND PART: CENTRAL ITALY AND ROME. Leipzic, 1890. 10 maps, 11 plans, 1 panorama. 10th rev ed. VF in torn dj. *O'NEILL.* $60

Baedeker, Karl. ITALY...FIRST PART: NORTHERN ITALY....Leipsic: Baedeker, NY: Scribner, 1899. 25 maps, 35 plans. 11th remodelled ed. Hinge loose, Good, sl soiled. *SECOND LIFE.* $35

Baedeker, Karl. ITALY...THIRD PART. Leipsic: Baedeker, 1900. 13th rev ed. 28 maps, 19 plans. Red cl, Fine. *SECOND LIFE.* $35

Baedeker, Karl. NORTHERN FRANCE. Leipsic: Baedeker, 1899. 3rd ed. 10 maps, 34 plans. Red cl. Very Nice. *SECOND LIFE.* $35

Baedeker, Karl. NORTHERN GERMANY AS FAR AS THE BAVARIAN AND AUSTRIAN FRONTIERS. Leipsic: Baedeker; London: Dulau; NY: Scribner, 1904. 14th rev ed. 49 maps, 75 plans (all present). Orig cl, sl rubbed, half-title sl wrinkled, 1 fldg map w/marginal tear, not affecting image, o/w VG. *WORLDWIDE.* $45

Baedeker, Karl. NORWAY, SWEDEN, AND DENMARK. Bound in is complete pamphlet entitled SKETCH OF NORWEGIAN AND SWEDISH GRAMMAR, WITH VOCABULARY AND LIST OF PHRASES. Leipsic: Baedeker, 1903. 8th ed, rev, augmented. 37 maps, plans, 3 panoramas (all maps and plans present). Orig cl, sl rubbed, o/w VG. *WORLDWIDE.* $45

Baedeker, Karl. PALESTINE AND SYRIA WITH ROUTES THROUGH MESOPOTAMIA AND BABYLONIA AND THE ISLAND OF CYPRUS. Leipzig, 1912. 21 maps, 56 plans, 1 panorama. 5th ed, remodelled and augmented. Very sl rubbing of spine, else Fine. *O'NEILL.* $150

Baedeker, Karl. PARIS AND ENVIRONS....Leipzig, 1913. 14 maps, 42 plans. 18th rev ed. Fine. *O'NEILL.* $35

Baedeker, Karl. PARIS AND ITS ENVIRONS WITH ROUTES FROM LONDON TO PARIS. HANDBOOK FOR TRAVELERS. Leipzig: Baedeker; London: Dulau; NY: Scribner, 1914. 19th rev ed. Maps and plans, many fldg (all maps and plans present). Orig cl, edged sl rubbed, o/w Very God. *WORLDWIDE.* $45

Baedeker, Karl. PARIS....Leipsic: Baedeker, 1896. 12th rev ed. 12 maps, 33 plans. Last pgs sl stained. *SECOND LIFE.* $35

Baedeker, Karl. RUSSIA WITH TEHERAN, PORT ARTHUR, AND PEKING. London, 1914. 40 maps, 78 plans. Fine, bright. Minimal rubbing spine top. *O'NEILL.* $500

Baedeker, Karl. SOUTH-EASTERN FRANCE.... Leipsic: Baedeker, London: Dulau, 1898. 3rd ed. 15 maps, 14 plans, panorama. Fine. *SECOND LIFE.* $35

Baedeker, Karl. SOUTHERN BAVARIA, WITH EXCURSIONS TO INNSBRUCK AND SALZBURG. Hamburg: Baedeker; Munich: Pflaum; London: Allan & Unwin; NY: Macmillan, 1953. 1st ed. 16 maps, 133 sketches (all maps and plans present). Orig cl, sl rubbed, o/w VG. *WORLDWIDE.* $35

Baedeker, Karl. SOUTHERN FRANCE FROM THE LOIRE TO THE SPANISH AND ITALIAN FRONTIERS INCLUDING CORSICA. HANDBOOK FOR TRAVELLERS. Leipzig: Baedeker; London: Fisher Unwin; NY: Scribner, 1914. 1st (?) ed. 14 maps, 19 plans (all present). Orig cl, sl rubbed, o/w VG. *WORLDWIDE.* $45

Baedeker, Karl. SOUTHERN FRANCE INCLUDING CORSICA. HANDBOOK FOR TRAVELLERS. Leipzig: Baedeker; London: Fisher Unwin; NY: Scribner, 1914. 6th rev ed. Numerous maps and plans, some of which fold and in color (all maps and plans present).

Orig cl, sl rubbed, one leaf torn, but no loss, fldg maps sl frayed, o/w VG. *WORLDWIDE*. $45

Baedeker, Karl. SPAIN AND PORTUGAL. Leipsic: Baedeker, 1898. 1st ed. 6 maps, 46 plans. Fine. *SECOND LIFE*. $35

Baedeker, Karl. SWITZERLAND AND THE ADJACENT POR-TIONS OF ITALY, SAVOY, AND TYROL. Leipzig: Baedeker; London: Fisher Unwin; NY: Scribner, 1911. 4th ed. 75 maps, plans, 1 panorama (all maps and plans present). Orig cl, sl rubbed, o/w VG. *WORLDWIDE*. $45

Baedeker, Karl. SWITZERLAND. Leipsic: Baedeker, 1899. 18th ed. 54 maps, 12 plans, 12 panoramas. Red cl. Preliminary blank chewed. VG. *SECOND LIFE*. $35

Baedeker, Karl. THE DOMINION OF CANADA WITH NEW-FOUNDLAND AND AN EXCURSION TO ALASKA. Leipzic, 1900. 10 maps, 7 plans. 2nd rev. ed. Sl fading of spine, else Fine. *O'NEILL*. $125

Baedeker, Karl. THE DOMINION OF CANADA WITH NEW-FOUNDLAND AND AN EXCURSION TO ALASKA. Leipzig, 1907. 13 maps, 12 plans. 3rd rev, augmented ed. Clean, gilt bright. *O'NEILL*. $175

Baedeker, Karl. THE EASTERN ALPS....Leipsic: Baedeker and Lon-don: Dulau, 1891. 7th ed, rev. 34 maps, 9 plans, 7 panoramas. Front hinge loose, Good. *SECOND LIFE*. $35

Baedeker, Karl. THE MEDITERRANEAN SEAPORTS AND SEA ROUTES, INCLUDING MADEIRA, THE CANARY ISLANDS, THE COAST OF MOROCCO, ALGERIA, AND TUNISIA. HANDBOOK FOR TRAVELLERS. Leipzig: Baedeker, 1911. 1st ed. 38 maps, 49 plans (all present). Orig cl, edges a little rubbed, slight tears in spine, frontis fold map detached and marginally torn, title page sl torn, no loss of text, o/w VG. Scarce. *WORLDWIDE*. $85

Baedeker, Karl. THE RHINE FROM ROTTERDAM TO CON-STANCE. Leipsic: Baedeker and London: Dulau, 1896. 13th rev ed. 44 maps, 24 plans. VG. *SECOND LIFE*. $35

Baedeker, Karl. THE RHINE FROM THE DUTCH TO THE AL-SATIAN FRONTIER. Leipzig, 1926. 102 maps and plans. 18th rev ed. Fine. *O'NEILL*. $30

Baedeker, Karl. THE TRAVELLER'S MANUAL OF CONVERSA-TION IN FOUR LANGUAGES: ENGLISH, GERMAN, FRENCH, AND ITALIAN, WITH VOCABULARY, SHORT QUESTIONS, ETC. Leipsic: Baedeker; London: Dulau, n.d. (c. 1895). Stereotype ed. Orig cl, sl rubbed and soiled, o/w VG. *WORLDWIDE*. $65

Baedeker, Karl. THE UNITED STATES WITH AN EXCURSION INTO MEXICO. 2nd rev ed. Leipsic: Baedeker, 1899. 19 maps, 24 plans. Flexible cl. Eps sl worn o/w Fine. *SECOND LIFE*. $150

Baedeker, Karl. THE UNITED STATES WITH AN EXCURSION INTO MEXICO. Leipzig, 1904. 25 maps, 35 plans. 3rd rev ed. One map detached, but present, spine rubbed. *O'NEILL*. $150

Baedeker, Karl. THE UNITED STATES WITH AN EXCURSION INTO MEXICO. Leipzig/London/NY: Karl Baedeker/Dulau and Co./Charles Scribner's Sons, 1904. 3rd rev ed. 25 fldg maps, 35 plans. Few maps split at folds. Ex-lib. *HUDSON*. $120

Baedeker, Karl. TYROL AND THE DOLOMITES INCLUDING THE BAVARIAN ALPS. Leipzig, 1927. 65 maps, 19 plans, 11 panoramas. 13th rev ed. Near Mint in dj. *O'NEILL*. $85

Baez, Joan. DAYBREAK. Dial, 1968. 1st. NF in dj. *STAHR*. $20

Bagg, A.C. and S.A. Eliot. BIRDS OF THE CONNECTICUT VAL-LEY IN MASSACHUSETTS. Northhampton, 1937. Spine faded. Signed presentation inscrip. *SUTTON*. $145

Baggally, W.W. TELEPATHY, GENUINE & FRAUDULENT. Chicago, 1918. NF. *POLYANTHOS*. $35

Bagley, Desmond. NIGHT OF ERROR. London: Collins, 1984. 1st ed. Fine in dj. *SILVER DOOR*. $35

Bagley, Julian. CANDLE-LIGHTING TIME IN BODIDALEE. American Heritage, (1971). 128pp. Illus Wallace Tripp. Inscribed. Fine in Good+ dj w/closed tear, piece missing top of back panel. *BEBBAH*. $25

Bagnold, Enid. LETTERS TO FRANK HARRIS, & OTHER FRIENDS. Ed & with an Intro by R.P. Lister. (Gloucestershire): The Whittington Press & William Heinemann. (1980). Tipped-in color frontis and 4 tipped-in plts. Ed ltd to 400 numbered, signed by Bagnold. Slipcase. *KARMIOLE*. $75

Bagnold, Enid. NATIONAL VELVET. NY: Morrow, 1935. 1st ed. Fine; minor wear at dj spine corners. *ELSE FINE*. $50

Bagnold, Enid. NATIONAL VELVET. NY: Morrow, 1935. 1st US ed. Bkpl. VG+ in VG dj (edgewear). *AARD*. $40

Bagot, Richard. THE ITALIAN LAKES. A&C Black. 1908 reprint. NF. *OLD LONDON*. $55

Bagshawe, Thomas Wyatt. TWO MEN IN THE ANTARCTIC—AN EXPEDITION TO GRAHAM LAND 1920-1922. NY/Cambridge: Macmillan/Cambridge Univ Press, 1939. 1st ed. Ex-lib. *PARMER*. $50

Baigell, Matthew. CHARLES BURCHFIELD. NY: Watson-Guptill, (1976). 1st ed. Fine in dj. *CAPTAIN'S BOOKSHELF*. $100

Baikie, James. EGYPTIAN ANTIQUITIES IN THE NILE VAL-LEY: A DESCRIPTIVE HANDBOOK. London: Methuen, (1932). 31 plts, 107 maps and plans. 1 corner bumped. Good. *AR-CHAEOLOGIA*. $75

Baikie, James. EGYPTIAN PAPYRI AND PAPYRUS-HUNTING. London: The Religious Tract Society, 1925. Color frontis, 32 illus (3 in color). Signature. Good. *ARCHAEOLOGIA*. $65

Baikie, James. EGYPTIAN PAPYRI AND PAPYRUS-HUNTING. London: The Religious Tract Soc, 1925. 1st ed. Blue cl, gilt; spine faded. *KARMIOLE*. $50

Baikie, James. THE STORY OF THE PHARAOHS. London: Black, 1917. 2nd ed. 32 plts, 1 fldg map. Generally Good. *WORLDWIDE*. $35

Bailey, A.M. and R.J. Niedrach. BIRDS OF COLORADO. Denver, 1965. 2 vols. Name stamp on titles, lower pg edges. *SUTTON*. $125

Bailey, Alice C. THE SKATING GANDER. Wise-Parslow, (1927). 93pp. Illus by Marie H. Myers. Some cvr wear. VG+. *BEBBAH*. $30

Bailey, C.T.P. KNIVES AND FORKS. Great Britain: William Bren-don & Son, Ltd, 1927. 1st ed. VG in VG spine worn dj. *BACKROOM*. $125

Bailey, Carolyn Sherwin. TOPS AND WHISTLES. NY: Viking, 1937. 1st ed. Fine in Good dj. *AARD*. $35

Bailey, Elliot. THE SECRET VALLEY. London: Geoffrey Bles, (1927). 1st ed. VG in dj w/one-inch piece missing at top of spine, chipping at spine ends and at base of spine, and a couple of closed tears. *MORDIDA*. $45

Bailey, F.M. BIRDS OF NEW MEXICO. Albuquerque, NM: Dept. of F.& G., 1928. 1st ed. Bottom edge dampstained, else VG+. *MIKESH*. $150

Bailey, F.M. BIRDS OF NEW MEXICO. Santa Fe, 1928. 79 plts (25 in color). Spine dulled; hinges cracked; sl shaken; name. *SUTTON*. $185

Bailey, George W. A PRIVATE CHAPTER OF THE WAR (1861-5). St. Louis, 1880. 1st ed. Sl rubbed, else VG. *McGOWAN*. $125

Bailey, H.C. HONOUR AMONG THIEVES. GC: Doubleday Crime Club, 1947. 1st Amer ed. Newspaper review clipping glued to fep. VG in dj (couple short closed tears; minor wear). *MORDIDA*. $25

Bailey, H.C. HONOUR AMONG THIEVES. GC: Doubleday Crime Club, 1947. 1st ed. Pp tanning, else Fine, minor edgewear to dj. *ELSE FINE*. $25

Bailey, H.C. MEET MR. FORTUNE. Garden City Doubleday Crime Club, 1942. Omnibus ed. Fine in dj (sl faded spine; chips at corners; sl wear along folds). *MORDIDA*. $50

Bailey, H.C. MR. CLUNK'S TEXT. GC: Doubleday Crime Club, 1939. 1st ed. Fine, narrow chip at spine corner of dj. *ELSE FINE.* $40

Bailey, H.C. MR. FORTUNE FINDS A PIG. London: Victor Gollancz, 1943. 1st ed. Edges foxed o/w VG in faded and soiled dj w/several short closed tears. *MORDIDA.* $45

Bailey, H.C. NOBODY'S VINEYARD. Garden City Doubleday Crime Club, 1942. 1st Amer ed. Name, o/w VG in dj (internal tape mends; chipped, frayed spine ends; wear). *MORDIDA.* $37.50

Bailey, H.C. NOBODY'S VINEYARD. GC: Doubleday, 1942. 1st ed. NF, bkpl, in tape-mended dj. *BEASLEY.* $25

Bailey, H.C. NOBODY'S VINEYARD. GC: Doubleday Crime Club, 1942. 1st ed. Fine, minor rubs at dj spine ends. *ELSE FINE.* $45

Bailey, H.C. ORPHAN ANN. GC: Doubleday Crime Club, 1941. 1st ed. NF in pict dj. *ELSE FINE.* $45

Bailey, H.C. THE BISHOP'S CRIME. GC: Doubleday Crime Club, 1941. 1st ed. NF in dj. *ELSE FINE.* $50

Bailey, H.C. THE GARSTON MURDER CASE. GC: Doubleday Crime Club, 1930. 1st ed. Fine, minor rubs at corners of dj. *ELSE FINE.* $65

Bailey, H.C. THE RED CASTLE MYSTERY. GC: Doubleday Crime Club, 1932. 1st ed. Name; corner bump, else Fine. Sm chips at spine corners of dj. *ELSE FINE.* $125

Bailey, H.C. THE SULLEN SKY MYSTERY. GC: Doubleday Crime Club, 1935. 1st ed. Fine, some wear at spine corners of dj. *ELSE FINE.* $50

Bailey, H.C. THE TWITTERING BIRD MYSTERY. GC: Doubleday Crime Club, 1937. 1st ed. Fine, moderate edgewear, chips at spine top & one corner of dj. *ELSE FINE.* $35

Bailey, H.C. THIS IS MR. FORTUNE. Garden City Doubleday Crime Club, 1938. 1st Amer ed. Fine in price-clipped dj with minor wear at corners. *MORDIDA.* $55

Bailey, H.H. THE BIRDS OF FLORIDA....Baltimore, 1925. 76 colored plts, topographical drwg, fldg map. Scuffing; white numbers on spine; unobtrusive emb stamp on plts; bkpl; ex-lib. *SUTTON.* $115

Bailey, H.H. THE BIRDS OF VIRGINIA. Lynchburg, 1913. 14 colored plts, 1 map. Some speckling to cvrs; unobtrusive emb stamps on plts; bkpl. *SUTTON.* $60

Bailey, Hamilton. DEMONSTRATIONS OF PHYSICAL SIGNS IN CLINICAL SURGERY. NY, 1927. 1st Amer ed. 261 illus. *FYE.* $50

Bailey, Hamilton. EMERGENCY SURGERY. Bristol, 1930-31. 1st ed. 2 vols. 380, 415pp. 754 illus. *FYE.* $175

Bailey, Hamilton. SURGERY OF MODERN WARFARE. Baltimore, 1942. 2nd ed. 2 vols. *FYE.* $75

Bailey, J.W. THE MAMMALS OF VIRGINIA, AN ACCOUNT OF THE FURRED ANIMALS OF LAND AND SEA... Richmond, 1946. Portrait frontis. Cloth, (some cover spotting). Signed. *SUTTON.* $60

Bailey, L.H. CYCLOPEDIA OF AMERICAN HORTICULTURE, COMPRISING SUGGESTIONS....50 plts, 2800 engrs. 4 vols. NY, 1910. 7th ed. Orig rose-patterned grn cl, djs w/few tears, some lg pieces missing. Nice set. *SUTTON.* $250

Bailey, L.H. CYCLOPEDIA OF AMERICAN HORTICULTURE. NY: 1900. 1st ed. 4 vols. 2800 engrs. Hinge of vol I loose, bkpl, emb stamp on title pg. VG set. *SECOND LIFE.* $200

Bailey, L.H. FIELD NOTES ON APPLE CULTURE. NY: Orange Judd, 1886. 90pp. Stamp on ep, cl lightly rubbed, else VG. *AMERICAN BOTANIST.* $35

Bailey, L.H. THE GARDEN OF LARKSPURS. NY, 1939. 1st ed. 25 plts, 2 colored. Cl; some scuffing rear cvrs. *SUTTON.* $40

Bailey, Lynn R. THE LONG WALK, A HISTORY OF THE NAVAJO WARS, 1846-1868. LA, 1964. 1st ed. 254pp. Fine in dj. *PRATT.* $32.50

Bailey, Margaret Emerson. ROBIN HOOD'S BARN. NY: Doran, (1922). 1st ed. Unopened. Fine- in Fine- dj. *AARD.* $30

Bailey, Paul and Roger Holmes. FABULOUS FARMER. THE STORY OF WALTER KNOTT....LA: Westernlore, 1956. 1st ed. Lacks ffep. Good+. *CONNOLLY & WADE.* $22.50

Bailey, Paul Dayton. TYPE-HIGH: A NOVEL. NY: Suttonhouse Ltd, (1937). Gold stamped cl. Inscribed. *DAWSON'S.* $40

Bailey, Paul. A DISTANT LIKENESS. London: Cape (1973). 1st ed. Signed. Fine in dj. *WOOLMER.* $50

Bailey, Paul. A DISTANT LIKENESS. London: Cape (1973). 1st ed. Fine in dj. *WOOLMER.* $35

Bailey, Paul. A DISTANT LIKENESS. London: Cape (1973). Adv uncorrected proof in printed wrappers. Fine. *WOOLMER.* $50

Bailey, Paul. AN ENGLISH MADAM. London: Cape (1982). 1st ed. Fine in dj. *WOOLMER.* $35

Bailey, Paul. AN IMMACULATE MISTAKE: SCENES FROM CHILDHOOD AND BEYOND. London: Bloomsbury (1990). 1st ed. Fine in dj. *WOOLMER.* $35

Bailey, Paul. AT THE JERUSALEM. London: Cape (1967). 1st ed. Fine in dj. Author's 1st book. *WOOLMER.* $65

Bailey, Paul. AT THE JERUSALEM. London: Cape (1967). Uncorrected proof in wrappers. Ink markings by a reviewer. *WOOLMER.* $75

Bailey, Paul. GABRIEL'S LAMENT. London: Cape (1986). 1st ed. Fine in dj. *WOOLMER.* $35

Bailey, Paul. GABRIEL'S LAMENT. London: Cape (1986). Uncorrected proof in dj. *WOOLMER.* $50

Bailey, Paul. OLD SOLDIERS. London: Cape (1980). 1st ed. Fine in dj. *WOOLMER.* $35

Bailey, Paul. OLD SOLDIERS. London: Cape (1980). Proof copy in wrappers. *WOOLMER.* $45

Bailey, Paul. PETER SMART'S CONFESSIONS. London: Cape (1977). 1st ed. Fine in dj. *WOOLMER.* $35

Bailey, Paul. TRESPASSES. London: Cape (1970). 1st ed. Fine in dj. *WOOLMER.* $35

Bailey, Paul. TRESPASSES. London: Cape (1970). Uncorrected proof in proof dj. Signed. Fine. *WOOLMER.* $60

Bailey, Paul. WALKARA, HAWK OF THE MOUNTAINS. LA: Westernlore, (1954). 1st ed. Stated ltd ed, no limitation given. VF in VF dj. *OREGON.* $45

Bailey, Pearce. ACCIDENT AND INJURY, THEIR RELATIONS TO DISEASES OF THE NERVOUS SYSTEM. NY, 1899. 430pp. 1st ed. *FYE.* $200

Bailey, Pearl. HURRY UP, AMERICA, AND SPIT. NY: Harcourt, 1976. 1st ed. Signed. Fine in Fine dj. *BEASLEY.* $45

Bailey, Percival, Douglas Buchanan & Paul Bucy. INTRACRANIAL TUMOURS OF INFANCY AND CHILDHOOD. Chicago, 1939. 1st ed. 598pp + 23 photo plts. *FYE.* $200

Bailey, Percival. INTRACRANIAL TUMORS. Springfield, 1948. 2nd ed. 478pp + plts. Inscribed and signed. Dj. *FYE.* $200

Bailey, Robert. HELL'S CANYON: A STORY OF THE DEEPEST CANYON ON THE NORTH AMERICAN CONTINENT...Lewiston, ID: the author, 1943. 1st ed. #1304/1500 ptd, signed. *AKA.* $125

Bailey, Robert. RIVER OF NO RETURN. Lewiston: Bailey, (1947). Enl 2nd ed, ltd to 2000 signed, numbered. VG. *OREGON.* $140

Bailey, Rosalie Fellows. PRE-REVOLUTIONARY DUTCH HOUSES AND FAMILIES IN NORTHERN NEW JERSEY AND SOUTHERN NEW YORK. NY: Morrow, 1936. 1st ed, ltd issue. One of 350 . NF in cracked slipcase. *CAPTAIN'S BOOKSHELF.* $250

Baillie, Alexander F. THE ORIENTAL CLUB AND HANOVER SQUARE PHOTOGRAVURE PORTRAITS....London, 1901. Cl, gilt. Uncut. *O'NEILL.* $45

Baillie-Grohman, William A. CAMPS IN THE ROCKIES....WITH AN ACCOUNT OF THE CATTLE RANCHES OF THE WEST...New Ed. NY, 1884 (1882). Fldg map torn. Cl cvrs stained & worn. Several page corners bent, o/w VG. *DIAMOND.* $25

Baily, Francis. JOURNAL OF A TOUR IN UNSETTLED PARTS OF NORTH AMERICA IN 1796 AND 1797...WITH A MEMOIR OF THE AUTHOR. London, 1856. 1st ed. (12),439pp. Contemp half morocco. On title pg: "From Miss Baily Tavistock Sq." Howes B40. *GINSBERG.* $1000

Bain, William E. FRISCO FOLKS: STORIES OF....Denver: Sage Books; Swallow Press, 1961. 1st ed. VG in dj. *CONNOLLY & WADE.* $40

Bainbridge, George C. THE FLY FISHER'S GUIDE...Liverpool: Printed for the Author by G.F. Harris's Widow and Brothers, 1816. 1st ed. 8,150pp. Colored frontis, 7 colored plates. Old 3/4 calf, marbled boards. Very Nice. *M & S.* $550

Bainbridge, H.C. PETER CARL FABERGE. London, 1949. Plts. NF. *POLYANTHOS.* $120

Baird, G.W. A REPORT TO THE CITIZENS, CONCERNING CERTAIN LATE DISTURBANCES ON THE WESTERN FRONTIER...Ashland, Lewis Osborne, 1972. 67pp. Ltd to 600 numbered. Fine *OREGON.* $45

Baird, Joseph Armstrong, Jr. CALIFORNIA'S PICTORIAL LETTER SHEETS 1849-1869. SF: David Magee Ptd by Robert Grabhorn & Andrew Hoyem, 1967. Ltd to 475. 1st ed. Letter Sheet reprint sample in pocket. Fine in Fine unptd dj. *BOOK MARKET.* $350

Baird, Newton. A KEY TO FREDRIC BROWN'S WONDERLAND. Georgetown: Talisman Literary Research, 1981. 1st ed. 1/275 softcover, signed. VF in wrappers. *MORDIDA.* $85

Baird, S.F., T.M. Brewer, and R. Ridgway. A HISTORY OF NORTH AMERICAN BIRDS. 64 plts, 593 woodcuts. 3 vols. Boston, 1874. 1st ed. Orig gilt-stamped grn cl. Corner wear, spine ends frayed; backstrip tear to Vol 3 repaired; bkpl; white numbers on spines; unobtrusive emb stamp on plts. *SUTTON.* $295

Bakarich, Sarah. GUNSMOKE, THE TRUE STORY OF TOMBSTONE. Tombstone Press, 1954. 1st ed. Wraps. Owner name on cvr. VG. *OREGON.* $20

Bakeless, John. SPIES OF THE CONFEDERACY. Phila, (1970). 1st ed. Dj has faded spine o/w VG+. *PRATT.* $50

Baker, B. Granville. A Winter Holiday in Portugal. NY: James Pott (nd, ca 1910). Almost Fine. *AARD.* $50

Baker, Denys Val. THE FACE IN THE MIRROR. Sauk City: Arkham House, 1971. 1st ed. Fine in Fine dj, pub's $5 price sticker affixed. *OTHER WORLDS.* $35

Baker, DeVere. THE RAFT...LEHI IV: 69 DAYS ADRIFT ON THE PACIFIC OCEAN. Long Beach: Whitehorn, 1959. 1st ed. Inscr and dated. Fine in Fine dj. *CONNOLLY & WADE.* $50

Baker, E.A. THE HIGHLANDS WITH ROPE AND RUCKSACK. London: Witherby, 1923. 1st ed. Minor edgewear, else VG+. *OLD LONDON.* $50

Baker, E.W. and G.W. Wharton. AN INTRODUCTION TO ACAROLOGY. NY, 1952. 1st ed. Light wear, front hinge starting, dj worn. *SUTTON.* $45

Baker, Ernest A. CAVING: EPISODES OF UNDERGROUND EXPLORATION. London: Chapman & Hall, 1935. 2nd ed. Dj. Signed, dated. *DAWSON'S.* $50

Baker, George Pierce (ed). CHARLES DICKENS AND MARIA BEADNELL: PRIVATE CORRESPONDENCE. Boston: The

Bibliophile Society, 1908. 1st ltd ed. 8vo, ltd to 493, grey boards with vellum spine and tips, illus with tinted plts, facs letters, etc., fore-edge of front board bumped. Bkpl. Good+. *GREAT EXPECTATIONS.* $55

Baker, Howard. ORANGE VALLEY. NY: Coward-McCann, Inc., (c.1931). 1st ed. Name stamp, lt silverfish marking cvrs, o/w VG (portions of dj flaps, backstrip laid in). *HELLER.* $75

Baker, J.A. THE PEREGRINE. NY and Evanston: Harper and Row, 1967. 1st US ed. Dj. NF. *OLD LONDON.* $25

Baker, Joseph E. PAST AND PRESENT OF ALAMEDA COUNTY, CALIFORNIA. Chicago, Clarke, 1914. 1st ed. 2 vols. Orig half morocco, sm paper label on lower spine, bkpls removed. *GINSBERG.* $200

Baker, Josephine and Jo Bouillon. JOSEPHINE. NY: Harper, 1977. 1st ed. Fine in NF dj. *BEASLEY.* $30

Baker, L.C. HISTORY OF THE UNITED STATES SECRET SERVICE. Phila: L.C. Baker, 1867. 1st ed. Brn cl rubbed, stained, chipped at corners, edges of spine. 703pp,1 ad. Sl foxed, lacks eps, some damage to top inner edge of rear pastedown. VG. *BLUE MOUNTAIN.* $45

Baker, L.C. THE UNITED STATES SECRET SERVICE IN THE LATE WAR. Chicago, 1894. 1902 reprint. VG+. *PRATT.* $40

Baker, Nicholson. ROOM TEMPERATURE. NY: Grove, (1990). 1st ed. New in dj. Signed. *CAPTAIN'S BOOKSHELF.* $50

Baker, Nicholson. ROOM TEMPERATURE. NY: Grove Weidenfeld, (1990). Fine in Fine dj. *LOPEZ.* $30

Baker, Nicholson. ROOM TEMPERATURE. NY: Grove Weidenfeld (1990). 1st ed. Signed. Fine in dj. *DORN.* $50

Baker, Nicholson. THE MEZZANINE. NY: Weidenfeld & Nicolson, (1988). 1st ed, 1st book. One corner lightly bumped, else Fine in Fine dj. *ROBBINS.* $30

Baker, Nicholson. THE MEZZANINE. NY: Weidenfeld & Nicolson (1988). 1st ed, 1st bk. Signed. Fine in dj. *DORN.* $95

Baker, Nicholson. THE MEZZANINE. NY: Weidenfeld and Nicolson, (1988). 1st ed. Signed. Fine in Fine dj. *LOPEZ.* $100

Baker, Nicholson. U AND I. NY: Random House (1991). 1st ed. Signed. Fine in dj. *DORN.* $65

Baker, Nicholson. U AND I. NY: RH, (1991). 1st ed. Fine in dj. Signed. *LOPEZ.* $85

Baker, Nicholson. VOX. NY: Random House, (1992). 1st ed. Signed. VF in VF dj. *UNGER.* $45

Baker, Nicholson. VOX. NY: Random House, (1992). 1st ed. New in dj. Signed. *CAPTAIN'S BOOKSHELF.* $75.

Baker, Nicholson. VOX. NY: Random House, (1992). Advance reading copy. Fine in wraps and plain brown outer wrapper marked with an "X", as issued. *CAPTAIN'S BOOKSHELF.* $75

Baker, Richard M. DEATH STOPS THE MANUSCRIPT. NY: Charles Scribner's Sons, 1936. 1st ed. Bkpl front pastedown o/w Fine in VG dj (chips; nicked and frayed spine ends; short closed tears). *MORDIDA.* $35

Baker, Robert A. (ed). A STRESS ANALYSIS OF A STRAPLESS EVENING GOWN AND OTHER ESSAYS FOR A SCIENTIFIC AGE. Englewood Cliffs: Prentice Hall, (1963). 1st ed. Fine in sl used, price clipped dj. *CAPTAIN'S BOOKSHELF.* $75

Baker, Russell. AN AMERICAN IN WASHINGTON. NY: Knopf, 1961. 1st ed. About Fine in sl used white price-clipped dj w/several short tears. *CAPTAIN'S BOOKSHELF.* $45

Baker, Russell. SO THIS IS DEPRAVITY. NY: Congdon, (1980). 1st ed. One of 500 signed. Fine in pub's slipcase. *UNGER.* $75

Baker, S. Josephine. THE DIVISION OF CHILD HYGIENE OF THE DEPARTMENT OF HEALTH OF THE CITY OF NEW

YORK. NY, 1912. 1st ed. Wrappers, ex-lib. Fldg charts, photo illus. Scarce. *FYE.* $100

Baker, Samuel White. THE ALBERT NYANZA, GREAT BASIN OF THE NILE....London/Phila: Macmillan and Co/J. B. Lippincott and Co, 1866. xxvi,516pp. Frontis, fldg map in back, erratum slip tipped in. Dark blue binding w/gilt letters and scene. Interior hinges have been repaired as well as spine edges. Some wear to corners. In-scrip. Good+ of an early prtg. *BACKMAN.* $165

Baker, Sir S.W. ISMAILIA: A NARRATIVE OF THE EXPEDITION TO CENTRAL AFRICA, ETC. NY: Harper, 1875. 1st U.S. ed. Good+. *MIKESH.* $60

Baker, Sir Samuel. THE RIFLE AND HOUND IN CEYLON. London: Longmans Green & Co, 1908. New imp. *CULLEN.* $50

Bakewell, Peter. MINERS OF THE RED MOUNTAIN. Univ of NM Press, 1984. 1st ed. Less than 500 ptd. As New. *MAD DOG.* $25

Bakewell, Robert. AN INTRODUCTION TO GEOLOGY. New Haven: B. & W. Noyes, 1839. 3rd Amer from 5th London ed. B. Silliman (ed). 1 fldg map, 8 plts (4 fldg). Orig legal calf, foxed. Ex-collection. *HUDSON.* $125

Balaban, John. VIETNAM POEMS. (Oxford:) Carcanet Press, (1970). 1st ed. One of 600. Sm rust spot from staples used in binding, o/w Fine in ptd wrappers. *HELLER.* $65

Balaban, John. VIETNAM POEMS. (Oxford): Carcanet Press, (1970). 1st ed. One of 600 of 1st bk. VF in dj. *LOPEZ.* $85

Balch, William Ralston. LIFE AND PUBLIC SERVICES OF GENERAL GRANT; THE SOLDIER, THE STATESMEN, THE NATIONS HERO. SF, (1885). 613pp. Minor cvr wear, o/w Fine. *PRATT.* $27.50

Baldwin, Charles Sears. ANCIENT RHETORIC AND POETIC. NY: The MacMillan Co., 1924. 1st ed. Spine soiled, rubbed, else VG. *OLD LONDON.* $25

Baldwin, J.D. ANCIENT AMERICA, IN NOTES ON AMERICAN ARCHAEOLOGY. NY, (1871). NF. *ARTIS.* $25

Baldwin, James and Margaret Mead. A RAP ON RACE. Lippincott, 1971. 1st ed. About Fine in dj with small chip bottom of front panel. *STAHR.* $35

Baldwin, James and Margaret Mead. A RAP ON RACE. Phila: Lippincott, (1971) 1st ed. VG in dj. *SECOND LIFE.* $45

Baldwin, James and Margaret Mead. A RAP ON RACE. London: Michael Joseph (1971). 1st Eng ed. Copyright info blacked out, o/w Fine in Fine dj. *LOPEZ.* $25

Baldwin, James and Richard Avedon. NOTHING PERSONAL. NY: Atheneum, 1964. 1st ed. White covers lightly foxed, as is predominately white pub's slipcase. VG in Good slipcase. *LOPEZ.* $275

Baldwin, James and Yoran Corzac. LITTLE MAN LITTLE MAN. NY: Dial, (1976). 1st US ed. NF in NF dj. *ACADEMIC LIBRARY.* $45

Baldwin, James. BLUES FOR MISTER CHARLIE. A Play. NY: Dial Press, 1964. 1st ed. Signed. Orig black cl. Fine in VG dj. *CHAPEL HILL.* $175

Baldwin, James. GIOVANNI'S ROOM. NY: Dial, 1956. 1st ed. VF in dj. Rev copy w/slip loosely inserted. *WOOLMER.* $300

Baldwin, James. GO TELL IT ON THE MOUNTAIN. Franklin Center: Franklin Library, 1979. Ltd ed reissue of first novel. Leatherbound, aeg, silk marker. Fine, signed. *LOPEZ.* $150

Baldwin, James. GOING TO MEET THE MAN. Dial, 1965. 1st ed. NF. Dj rubbed at head & foot of spine. *STAHR.* $30

Baldwin, James. IF BEALE STREET COULD TALK. NY: Dial, 1974. Wraps. Adv uncorrected proof. VG. *BEASLEY.* $85

Baldwin, James. IF BEALE STREET COULD TALK. NY: Dial Press, 1974. 1st ed. Orig orange cl. Fine in dj (sm blemish). *CHAPEL HILL.* $50

Baldwin, James. JUST ABOVE MY HEAD. NY: Dial, (1979). 1/500 numbered, signed. Fine in slipcase. *LOPEZ.* $150

Baldwin, James. JUST ABOVE MY HEAD. NY: Dial, (1979). 1st ed. One of 500 numbered, signed. Burgundy cl. Fine in pub's slipcase. *UNGER.* $225

Baldwin, James. JUST ABOVE MY HEAD. NY: Dial Press, (1979). 1st ed, #196 of 500 specially bound, signed. Orig burgundy cl, aeg. Fine in pub's slipcase. *CHAPEL HILL.* $150

Baldwin, James. NO NAME IN THE STREET. London: Michael Joseph, (1972). Eng ed precedes Amer ed. Uncorrected proof. Fine in ptd wraps. *HELLER.* $75

Baldwin, James. THE DEVIL FINDS WORK. NY: Dial, 1976. 1st ed. Fine in price clipped, wrinkled dj. *SECOND LIFE.* $25

Baldwin, James. THE DEVIL FINDS WORK. NY: Dial Press, (1976). 1st ed. Orig speckled red boards. Fine in dj. *CHAPEL HILL.* $40

Baldwin, James. THE EVIDENCE OF THINGS NOT SEEN. NY: Holt, Rinehart, Winston, (1985). 1st ed. Fine in price clipped dj. *SECOND LIFE.* $35

Baldwin, James. THE EVIDENCE OF THINGS NOT SEEN. NY: Holt Rinehart Winston, (1985). Rev copy. Fine in dj w/promo sheets laid in. *LOPEZ.* $45

Baldwin, James. THE EVIDENCE OF THINGS NOT SEEN. NY: Holt, Rinehart & Winston, (1985). 1st ed. Inscribed. Orig black cl-backed boards. Fine in dj. *CHAPEL HILL.* $125

Baldwin, Joseph G. THE FLUSH TIMES OF ALABAMA AND MISSISSIPPI. SF: Bancroft-Whitney Co, 1891. 11th thousand. Shaken. Poor. *HUDSON.* $20

Baldwin, W.C. AFRICAN HUNTING, FROM NATAL TO THE ZAMBESI...FROM 1852 TO 1860. Cloth, 40 illus, 1 fold-out map. NY, 1967 (1863). Bkpl removed. *SUTTON.* $35

Baldwin, William Wright (comp). CHICAGO, BURLINGTON & QUINCY RAILROAD COMPANY. DOCUMENTARY HISTORY....2 vols. Chicago, 1928-9. 1st ed. Sl staining on margins of about 100pp at beginning & end of both vols, o/w VG set. *DIAMOND.* $150

Baljeu, Joost. THEO VAN DOESBURG. NY: Macmillan, (1974). 1st US ed. Prev owner's name ffep. Fine in Fine dj. *AARD.* $30

Ball, C.J. LIGHT FROM THE EAST. London, etc.: Eyre & Spottiswoode, 1899. 1st ed. Orig cl edge rubbed, spine faded, chipped, 1st, last few leaves sl foxed, sl shaken, o/w Good. *WORLDWIDE.* $45

Ball, Ian M. PITCAIRN: CHILDREN OF MUTINY. Boston/Toronto: Little, Brn & Co, 1973. 2nd prtg. VG in lightly worn dj. *PARMER.* $25

Ball, John. IN THE HEAT OF THE NIGHT. London: Michael Joseph, (1966). 1st Eng ed. Inscribed. Name fep, else Fine in price-clipped dj. *UNGER.* $100

Ball, John. THE COOL COTTONTAIL. NY: Harper & Row, (1966). 1st ed. Fine in dj. *LOPEZ.* $30

Ball, John. THEN CAME VIOLENCE. London: Joseph, 1981. 1st British ed. Signed. NF in dj. *SILVER DOOR.* $35

Ball, Katherine M. BAMBOO. ITS CULT AND CULTURE. Berkeley: The Gillick Press, 1945. 1st ed. One of 500 signed. Fine in VG dj. *PARMER.* $125

Ball, Katherine M. DECORATIVE MOTIFES OF MODERN ART. London: John Lane The Bodley Head/NY: Dodd, Mead, (1927). 1st ed. Bumped, rubbed, cl split top of rear joint, spine chipped. NF internally. *BLUE MOUNTAIN.* $65

Ball, Katherine M. DECORATIVE MOTIFES OF ORIENTAL ART. London: John Lane, The Bodley Head Ltd.; NY: Dodd, Mead, (1927). 1st ed. 673 illus. Spine ends a bit frayed, rubbing, o/w VG. *WEBER.* $150

Ball, Katherine M. DECORATIVE MOTIFES OF ORIENTAL ART....London: John Lane The Bodley Head, (1927). 1st ed. Orig gilt dec cl, teg. Silverfish nibbling on covers, o/w Fine. *WREDEN.* $100

Ball, Larry A. THOSE INCOMPARABLE BONANZAS. Wichita: McCormick-Armstrong, 1971. 1st ed (?). Signed. Fine in Fine dj. *AARD.* $20

Ball, Nicholas. PIONEERS OF '49. Boston: Lee & Shepard, 1891. xvi, 288pp. Frontis, engrs, ad. Dk blue cl w/gilt & black stamping. Spine ends lightly frayed. VG. Howes B67. *BOHLING.* $135

Ball, Robert Hamilton. SHAKESPEARE ON SILENT FILM. London: Allen & Unwin, (1968). 1st Eng ed. VG+ in VG- dj. *AARD.* $25

Ball, Robert Hamilton. THE AMAZING CAREER OF SIR GILES OVERREACH. Princeton & London: Princeton Univ Press, 1939. 1st ed. VG in dj. Inscribed. *DRAMATIS.* $25

Ball, Robert S. STAR-LAND, BEING TALKS WITH YOUNG PEOPLE ABOUT THE WONDERS OF THE HEAVENS. London: Cassell, 1905, (1889). VG. *KNOLLWOOD.* $25

Ball, Robert S. THE STORY OF THE HEAVENS. London: Cassell, 1897 (1885). New, rev ed. Red 1/2 leather, worn, waterstain, o/w clean. *KNOLLWOOD.* $25

Ball, W. Valentine. REMINISCENCES AND LETTERS OF SIR ROBERT BALL. Boston: Little, Brown, 1915. Good ex-lib. *KNOLLWOOD.* $55

Ballamy, Edward. EQUALITY. NY: Appleton, 1897. 1st ed. 12mo. Fine in dec cl. *CAPTAIN'S BOOKSHELF.* $60

Ballance, Charles. SOME POINTS IN THE SURGERY OF THE BRAIN AND ITS MEMBRANES. London, 1907. 1st ed. 451pp. VF. *FYE.* $500

Ballantine, Bill. HORSES AND THEIR BOSSES. Phila/NY: Lippincott, 1964. 1st ed. Signed. VG in VG+ dj. *OCTOBER FARM.* $25

Ballantine, Bill. WILD TIGERS & TAME FLEAS. NY: Rinehart, 1958. 1st ed. Signed. Spine darkened, o/w VG. *OCTOBER FARM.* $25

Ballantyne, R. M. THE GORILLA HUNTERS. Burt, n.d. VG. *MADLE.* $30

Ballard, Brigadier-General Colin R. THE MILITARY GENIUS OF ABRAHAM LINCOLN. Cleveland, (1952). 1st Amer ed. Fine in dj. *PRATT.* $35

Ballard, G.A. THE INFLUENCE OF THE SEA ON THE POLITICAL HISTORY OF JAPAN. NY: Dutton, 1921. 1st US ed. VG. *AARD.* $40

Ballard, George. MEMOIRS OF BRITISH LADIES WHO HAVE BEEN CELEBRATED FOR THEIR WRITING OR SKILL IN THE LEARNED LANGUAGES, ARTS, AND SCIENCES. London: Evans, 1775. 2nd ed. Tall 8vo, pp viii, 320 (8). Rebinding in full sprinkled calf, w/inset panel and blind tooling to front and back covers, gauffred edges, raised bands, gilt and red lea label. Title-page silked, else Fine. Scarce. *HARTFIELD.* $365.

Ballard, J. G. HIGH RISE. Holt, 1975. 1st US ed. Fine in NF dj. *MADLE.* $50

Ballard, J.G. CHRONOPOLIS AND OTHER STORIES. NY: Putnam, (1971). 1st ed. Fine in very lightly rubbed dj. *CAPTAIN'S BOOKSHELF.* $125

Ballard, J.G. CONCRETE ISLAND. NY: Farrar, 1974. 1st US ed. Fine in Fine dj. *BEASLEY.* $50

Ballard, J.G. DAY OF CREATION. London: Gollancz, 1987. 1st ed. As New in dj. Inscribed. *CAPTAIN'S BOOKSHELF.* $50

Ballard, J.G. EMPIRE OF THE SUN. London: Gollancz, 1984. 1st ed. As New in dj. *CAPTAIN'S BOOKSHELF.* $65.

Ballard, J.G. EMPIRE OF THE SUN. Simon and Schuster, 1984. 1st Amer ed. Fine in a dj (2 sm bruises flyleaf folds). *STAHR.* $25

Ballard, J.G. LOVE & NAPALM: EXPORT U.S.A. NY, 1972. 1st US ed. Dampstain to inside of dj, else NF. *PETTLER.* $40

Ballard, J.G. PASSPORT TO ETERNITY. Berkley (F823), 1963. 1st ed. Fine in wraps. *STAHR.* $15

Ballard, J.G. RUNNING WILD. NY: Farrar Straus Giroux, 1989. 1st Amer ed. VF in dj. *MORDIDA.* $25

Ballard, J.G. TERMINAL BEACH. Berkley (F928), 1964. 1st Amer. ed. VG+ in wraps. Fine but for usual reading crease on spine. *STAHR.* $10

Ballard, J.G. THE BURNING WORLD. Berkley (F961), 1964. 1st ed. NF in wraps. Reading crease. *STAHR.* $15

Ballard, J.G. THE DROWNED WORLD & THE WIND FROM NOWHERE. Doubleday, 1965. 1st ed thus. Fine in VG dj (tear front flyfold; rubbed at spine ends). 1st hb pub of THE WIND FROM NOWHERE. *STAHR.* $90

Ballard, J.G. THE IMPOSSIBLE MAN. Berkley (F1204), 1966. 1st. VF in wraps. *STAHR.* $15

Ballard, J.G. THE KINDNESS OF WOMEN. Farrar, Straus, & Giroux, 1991. Uncorrected proof of Amer. ed. Fine in pink wraps. Two corners very lightly bumped. *STAHR.* $60

Ballard, J.G. THE UNLIMITED DREAM COMPANY. London, 1979. 1st ed. Fine in dj. *MADLE.* $45

Ballard, J.G. THE VOICES OF TIME. Berkley (F607), 1962. 1st ed. VG+ in wraps. *STAHR.* $15

Ballard, J.G. THE WIND FROM NOWHERE. Berkley, 1962. 1st ed. VG in wraps. Spine chipped; small piece missing at top of spine. *STAHR.* $10

Ballard, J.G. UNLIMITED DREAM COMPANY. NY: Holt, Rinehart, Winston, (1979). 1st ed. Sticker residue, tiny tears to worn dj. *AKA.* $25

Balliett, Whitney. NEW YORK NOTES. Boston: Houghton Mifflin, 1976. 1st ed. Fine in Fine dj. *BEASLEY.* $30

Ballou, M.M. AZTEC LAND. Boston, 1890. 2nd ed. VG. *DIAMOND.* $25

Ballou, Robert. EARLY KLICKITAT VALLEY DAYS. Goldendale Sentinel, 1938. 1st ed. Fine. Howes B79. *OREGON.* $100

Balmer, Edwin. KEEBAN. Boston: Little, Brown, 1923. 1st ed. VG in dj (chipped). *BERNARD.* $75

Balneaves, Elizabeth. MOUNTAINS OF THE MURCHA ZERIN. London: John Gifford (1972). 1st ed. VG in VG dj. *AARD.* $25

Bambara, Toni Cade. GORILLA, MY LOVE. NY: Random House, (1972). 1st ed. NF in VG, edgeworn dj. *LOPEZ.* $55

BAMBI SAVES THE DAY. London, 1978. Pop-up bk. *BOOKFINDERS INTL.* $38

BAMBI. London, (1960). Illus Faith Jaques. 3 pop-ups. Pop-up bk. *BOOKFINDERS INTL.* $45

Bamburg, L. BEADS OF SILENCE. NY: E.P. Dutton, 1927. 1st Amer ed. VG in dj (internal tape repairs; chipped edges; closed tears). *MORDIDA.* $25

Bancroft, A.L. & Company. BANCROFT'S TOURIST GUIDE TO THE GEYSERS. SF: Bancroft, 1871. W/80pp ads. *HUDSON.* $125

Bancroft, Frederic & Cobb Pilcher (eds). SURGICAL TREATMENT OF THE NERVOUS SYSTEM. Phila, 1946. 1st ed. 534pp. *FYE.* $100

Bancroft, Frederic & George Humphreys (eds). SURGICAL TREATMENT OF THE SOFT TISSUES. Phila, 1946. 1st ed. 244 illus. *FYE.* $100

Bancroft, George. HISTORY OF THE UNITED STATES. NY, 1882. 6 vols. Teg. Fine. *POLYANTHOS.* $175

Bancroft, George. LITERARY AND HISTORICAL MISCEL-LANIES. NY: Harper, 1855. 1st ed. 3/4 leather. VG. *CONNOLLY & WADE.* $50

Bancroft, Hubert Howe. HISTORY OF ARIZONA AND NEW MEXICO 1530-1888. VOL. XVII OF WORKS. SF History Co, 1889. 1st ed. xxxviii,829pp. Fldg map. Full calf. VG. *OREGON.* $100

Bancroft, Hubert Howe. HISTORY OF ALASKA, 1730-1885. NY, 1959. Orig cl. Ltd ed of 750 numbered. Howes B90. *GINSBERG.* $75

Bancroft, Hubert Howe. HISTORY OF BRITISH COLUMBIA 1792-1887. SF: The History Company, 1887. Vol 32 of the series. Full lea. Spine darkened, edge wear and light spotting, interior clean and tight. *PARMER.* $75

Bancroft, Hubert Howe. HISTORY OF NEVADA, COLORADO, AND WYOMING. VOLUME XXV OF THE WORKS. SF History, 1890. 1st ed. All edges marbled, orig full calf, morocco labels, gilt. Hinges starting. Lea spine chipping. Internally Fine. Howes B91. *CONNOLLY & WADE.* $85

Bancroft, Hubert Howe. HISTORY OF UTAH, 1540-1887. SF: The History Co, 1890. xlvii,808pp. Ex-lib in orig cl. *SCHOYER'S.* $25

Bancroft, Hubert Howe. POPULAR TRIBUNALS. In 2 vols. SF: The History Co, 1887. 1st ed. Pub's notice laid in. Fldg frontis map, SF, 1854. Orig tree calf, gilt morocco labels. Chipping on upper edge of spine, else VG. *CONNOLLY & WADE.* $87.50

Bancroft, Hubert Howe. RESOURCES AND DEVELOPMENT OF MEXICO. SF: Bancroft, 1893. 1st ed. 2 fldg maps. One sig loose. Ex-lib. *HUDSON.* $50

Bancroft, Hubert Howe. THE HISTORY OF UTAH. 1540-1886. SF: The History Company, 1889. 1st ed. xlvii, 808pp. Full leather, marbled edges. Edgewear; rear hinge cracked; interior VG. *PARMER.* $50

Bancroft, Hubert Howe. THE NATIVE RACES OF THE PACIFIC STATES OF NORTH AMERICA. Vol. V. Primitive History. NY: D. Appleton, 1876. 2 fldg maps, 1/2 morocco, broken. *HUDSON.* $45

Bancroft, Hubert Howe. THE NATIVE RACES. 5 vols. SF: The History Co, 1883-1886. Approx. 850pp each vol. Fldg maps, fldg chart. All edges marbled. Orig calf binding. Black & gilt lea labels. Covers detached on 2 vols, nearly so on 2 others. Front blank lacking on vol 1. Binding somewhat scuffed, as usual. Contents exceptionally Fine. Howes B91. *CONNOLLY & WADE.* $195

Bancroft, Hubert Howe. WORKS. VOL. XVIII: HISTORY OF CALIFORNIA: VOL I 1542-1800. Santa Barbara: Wallace Hebberd, 1963. Fasc of 1st Amer ed. Fine in dj. *CONNOLLY & WADE.* $50

Bandel, Eugene. FRONTIER LIFE IN THE ARMY 1854-1861. Ralph Bieber (ed). Glendale, A.H. Clark. 1932, 1st ed. 9 plts, fldg map. Sl water spotting front cvr o/w VG. *OREGON.* $95

Bandelier, Adolf F. HISTORICAL INTRODUCTION TO STUDIES AMONG THE SEDENTARY INDIANS OF NEW MEXICO. REPORT ON THE RUINS OF THE PUEBLO OF PECOS. Boston, 1881. 1st ed. (4),133,(2)pp. Map. Few sm emb lib stamps. Howes B97. *GINSBERG.* $150

Bandelier, Adolf F. REPORT OF AN ARCHAEOLOGICAL TOUR IN MEXICO, IN 1881. Boston, 1884. 1st ed. 26 plts & drwgs. Boards soiled, shelfworn. Spine tips defective. Typed paper spine label. Contents VG. *DIAMOND.* $150

Bandelier, Adolf F. THE DELIGHT MAKERS. NY: Dodd, Mead, and Co, 1942. NF in worn dj. *PARMER.* $40

Bandelier, Adolf F. THE DELIGHT MAKERS. NY: Dodd, Mead, and Co., 1890. 1st ed. iv,490. Gold cl, some soil. Interior clean, tight. *PARMER.* $150

Bandelier, Adolf F. THE DELIGHT MAKERS. NY: Dodd, Mead, (1918). Later ed. Prev owner's pencil name fep, o/w VG in sl edgeworn dj. *LOPEZ.* $50

Bandelier, Adolph F. THE UNPUBLISHED LETTERS CONCERN-ING THE WRITING AND PUBLISHING OF "THE DELIGHT MAKERS." El Paso: Carl Hertzog, 1942. One of 295 numbered. NF in dj. *LAURIE.* $600

Bandinelli, Ranuccio Bianchi. ROME: THE LATE EMPIRE. ROMAN ART A.D. 200-400. NY: George Braziller, (1971). 74 color illus, 4 maps, 10 plans. Good in torn dj. *ARCHAEOLOGIA.* $150

Bang, Molly. THE PAPER CRANE. NY: Greenwillow, (1985). 1st ed. Slick illus boards. Unpaged. Fine in Fine dj. *ACADEMIC LIBRARY.* $35

Bangs, John Kendrick. A HOUSE-BOAT ON THE STYX: BEING SOME ACCOUNT OF THE DIVERS DOINGS OF THE AS-SOCIATED SHADES. NY: Harper & Bros., 1896. 1st ed. 12mo, 172pp, (4)pp ads. Orig pict grn cl. VG. BAL 726. *CHAPEL HILL.* $65

Bangs, John Kendrick. A LITTLE BOOK OF CHRISTMAS. Boston, Little, Brown, 1912. 1st ed. Frontis, 3 plts. Orig pict grn cl. Bright, NF in scarce, spine-faded dj (1/4" chip top of spine). BAL 793. *CHAPEL HILL.* $95

Bangs, John Kendrick. A REBELLIOUS HEROINE. NY: Harper & Brothers, 1896. 1st ed. 225p. Dec cl. VG, untrimmed and uncut. *BUR-CHAM.* $75

Bangs, John Kendrick. MR. BONAPARTE OF CORSICA. NY, 1895. 1st ed. 16mo, xii, 265pp. Pict cl. Some cover rubbing & stain-ing, o/w VG. BAL 722, 1st state. *DIAMOND.* $25

Bangs, John Kendrick. THE WATER GHOST AND OTHER STORIES. Harper, 1894. 1st ed. VG. *MADLE.* $50

Bank, Ted. BIRTHPLACE OF THE WINDS. NY: Thomas Y. Crowell Company, c. 1956. Fading to covers, soiling to fore-edge, else VG in dj. *PARMER.* $30

Banks, Charles Eugene and Opie Read. THE HISTORY OF THE SAN FRANCISCO DISASTER AND MOUNT VESUVIUS HORROR. (np: np, 1906). Pict cl, photo mounted fr cvr. *SCHOYER'S.* $20

Banks, Eleanor. WANDERSONG. Caxton, 1950. 1st ed. VG in Fine dj. *OREGON.* $45

Banks, Iain. WALKING ON GLASS. Houghton Mifflin, 1986. 1st Amer ed. Fine to VF in dj. Rear flap of dj creased. *STAHR.* $22.50

Banks, Russell. SEARCHING FOR SURVIVORS. NY and Boulder: Fiction Collective, 1975. 1st ed. Fine in Fine dj. *BEASLEY.* $50

Banks, Russell. THE BOOK OF JAMAICA. Boston: Houghton Mif-flin Co., 1980. 1st ed. Slight bend to front ep, else Fine in NF, lightly rubbed dj w/short tear front panel. Signed. *BETWEEN COVERS.* $85

Bankson, Russell THE KLONDIKE NUGGET. Caldwell, Caxton, 1935 1st ed. VG. *OREGON.* $70

Bannerman, David A. and W. Mary. BIRDS OF CYPRUS. Edin-burgh, 1958. 1st ed. D.M. Reid-Henry, Roland Green (illus). 16 plts in color, 15 in half-tone; fldg map. lxix,384pp. Dj torn at fold. *O'NEILL.* $275

Banning, George Hugh. IN MEXICAN WATERS. Boston: Charles E. Lauriat Co. 1925. 1st ed. *KARMIOLE.* $30

Banta, N. Moore. BUSY LITTLE BROWNIES. Grosset & Dunlap, (1923). 12mo. 128pp. Illus by Dorothy Dulin. Some edgewear, else VG. *BEBBAH.* $32

Banta, N. Moore. THE BROWNIES AND THE GOBLINS. Flanagan, (1915). 128pp. Illus. General wear to pict cvr, VG. *BEB-BAH.* $38

Banvard, Joseph. TRAGIC SCENES IN THE HISTORY OF MARYLAND AND THE OLD FRENCH WAR. WITH AN AC-COUNT....Boston: 1856. 1st ed. (4),239,(12)pp. 11 woodcuts. Orig cl (lax front flyleaf). *GINSBERG.* $125

BARBARA'S BIRTHDAY. NY, 1983. Pop-up bk. *BOOKFINDERS INTL.* $10

Barbauld, Anna Letitia. THE WORKS, WITH A MEMOIR by Lucy Aikin. London: Longman, 1825. 1st collected ed. 2 vols. Tall 8vo, pp 344 and 470. Full diced black, morocco, blind fillets, raised bands, gilt, gilt on red lea labels, blind inner dentelles. Silhouette port frontis. Some wear, but Excellent set. *HARTFIELD*. $295.

Barbe, Muriel Culp. A UNION FOREVER. Glendale, (1940). 1st ed. Dj has minor soiling o/w Fine. *PRATT*. $20

Barbeau, Marius. HAIDA CARVERS IN ARGILLITE. Ottawa: Nat'l Museum of Canada, 1957. 1st ed. Wraps. VG. *BLUE DRAGON*. $55

Barbeau, Marius. PATHFINDERS IN THE NORTH PACIFIC. Caldwell, ID: Caxton, 1958. 1st ed. Fine in NF dj. *GREAT EPIC*. $55

Barbeau, Marius. THE DOWNFALL OF TEMLAKAM. Toronto: Macmillan, 1928. Map dj. True 1st ed. Fine in Fine dj. *GREAT EPIC*. $145

Barber, H. THE AEROPLANE SPEAKS. NY, 1917. Bds worn. Frontis, 87 sketches & diagrams. NF. *POLYANTHOS*. $75

Barber, John W. THE HISTORY AND ANTIQUITIES OF NEW ENGLAND, NEW YORK, AND NEW JERSEY;....Worcester: Door, Howland, 1841. Early ed. Rebound in new cl. A little foxing in text, o/w VG. Howes B124. *DIAMOND*. $50

Barber, Lynn. THE HEYDAY OF NATURAL HISTORY, 1820-1870. GC, 1980. Dj. *FYE*. $30

Barber, R.H. A SUPPLEMENTARY BIBLIOGRAPHY OF HAWK-ING. Privately Ptd For The Author. (1000 only). 1st ed. Stapled ptd paper wraps. NF in custom case. *OLD LONDON*. $45

Barber, Red and Robert Creamer. RHUBARB IN THE CATBIRD SEAT. Doubleday, 1961. 1st ed. Inscribed. Good+ in VG+ dj. *PLAPINGER*. $50

Barber, Red. 1947: WHEN ALL HELL BROKE LOOSE IN BASEBALL. Doubleday, 1982. 1st ed. VG in Fine dj. Inscribed. *PLAPINGER*. $50

Barber, Red. SHOW ME THE WAY TO GO HOME. Westminster, 1971. 1st ed. Inscribed. Good+ in VG+ dj. *PLAPINGER*. $45

Barber, T.G. BYRON AND WHERE HE IS BURIED. Hucknall, 1939. 2 fldg plans, fldg pedigree. Partly unopened. *O'NEILL*. $45

Barbour, Ralph Henry and LaMar Sarra. HOW TO PLAY BETTER BASEBALL. Appleton-Century, 1935. 1st ed. VG. *PLAPINGER*. $35

Barbour, Ralph Henry. DOUBLE PLAY. Appleton, 1909. VG without dj as issued. *PLAPINGER*. $30

Barbour, T. A CONTRIBUTION TO THE ZOOEOGRAPHY OF THE WEST INDIAN, WITH ESPECIAL REFERENCE TO AM-PHIBIANS AND REPTILES. Cambridge, 1914. 1 plt, 7 fold-out tables. Wrappers very chipped, w/tears, rear wrapper loose, pp browning. *SUTTON*. $55

Barbour, T. CUBAN ORNITHOLOGY. Cambridge, 1943. 2 plts. Lt spotting rear cvr. *SUTTON*. $55

Barbour, T. NATURALIST AT LARGE. Boston, (1943). Dj worn. *SUTTON*. $25

Barbour, T. REPTILES AND AMPHIBIANS. Boston, 1934. Rev ed. Worn at corners, soiled, eps browned. *SUTTON*. $30

Barclay, G. Lippard (ed). THE LIFE AND REMARKABLE CAREER OF ADAH ISAACS MENKEN, THE CELEBRATED ACTRESS. Phila: Barclay & Co., (1868). 1st ed. Orig green pict wraps, sewn; extremities worn, light soiling of covers; with plts. VG. *DRAMATIS PERSONAE*. $110

Barclay, George. LIFE ADVENTURES, STRANGE CAREER AND ASSASSINATION OF COL. JAMES FISK, JR. Phila: Barclay (1872). Scarce. *SECOND LIFE*. $75

Barclay, Glen. ANATOMY OF HORROR. St Martins, 1978. 1st ed. Fine in dj. *MADLE*. $25

Bard, Floyd C. HORSE WRANGLER. Univ of OK Press, 1960. 1st ed. Fine in Fine dj. *VARNER*. $45

Bareis, George F. HISTORY OF MADISON TOWNSHIP INCLUD-ING GROVEPORT AND CANAL WINCHESTER, FRANKLIN COUNTY, OHIO. Canal Winchester, OH, 1902. 1st ed. fldg map, Orig cl, sm paper label on lower spine, bkpl removed. *GINSBERG*. $125

Barich, Bill. LAUGHING IN THE HILLS. NY: Viking, 1980. 1st ed. VG in Good dj. *OCTOBER FARM*. $20

Baring-Gould, S. CURIOSITIES OF OLDEN TIMES. NY, 1896. NF. *POLYANTHOS*. $30

Baring-Gould, S. CURIOUS MYTHS OF THE MIDDLE AGES. Alden, 1884. VG. *MADLE*. $75

Baringer, William E. LINCOLN'S VANDALIA. New Brunswick: Rutgers Univ/Springfield: Abraham Lincoln Assoc, 1949. 1st ed. Fine in NF dj. *CONNOLLY & WADE*. $30

Barkas, Geoffrey. THE CAMOUFLAGE STORY (FROM AINTREE TO ALAMEIN). London: Cassell, 1952. 1st ed. Fine in Near VG dj w/chips. *ARCHER*. $35

Barker, Alan. THE CIVIL WAR IN AMERICA. London, (1961). 1st ed. Fine in dj. *McGOWAN*. $35

Barker, Anthony R. HIDDEN GOLD, A BOOK OF WOODCUTS. London: Lane, (n.d.). 125pp. Slight edgewear, 1 leaf opened rough-ly, VG. *BEBBAH*. $45

Barker, Clive. BOOKS OF BLOOD (VOLUMES I-III). Santa Cruz: Scream Press, 1985. 1st US ed trade issue. Bkpl else Almost Fine (minor crimping to some pages at one corner) in dj. *OTHER WORLDS*. $125

Barker, Clive. BOOKS OF BLOOD I-III. California: Scream Press, 1985. 1st ed, 2nd ptg April 1986. Signed presentation w/full page drwg by Barker. Fine in NF dj. *POLYANTHOS*. $100

Barker, Clive. BOOKS OF BLOOD. London, 1985. 1st eds. Wraps. All 6 vols are Fine; vols 2-5 are signed. *MADLE*. $175

Barker, Clive. THE DAMNATION GAME. Ace/Putnam, 1987. 1st Amer ed. About Fine in dj. Signed and inscribed. Book dusty along top edge. *STAHR*. $45

Barker, Clive. THE DAMNATION GAME. Ace/Putnam, 1987. 1st US ed. Fine in dj. *MADLE*. $25

Barker, Clive. THE DAMNATION GAME. NY: Ace/Putnam, (1987). 1st US ed. Fine in Fine dj. *OTHER WORLDS*. $30

Barker, Clive. THE GREAT AND SECRET SHOW. Harper, 1989. 1st US ed. VG in dj. *MADLE*. $15

Barker, Clive. THE GREAT AND SECRET SHOW. London: Col-lins, 1989. 1st ed. VF in dj. *JAFFE*. $65

Barker, Clive. WEAVEWORLD. London: Collins, 1987. 1st UK ed. Almost Fine in dj. *OTHER WORLDS*. $35

Barker, Clive. WEAVEWORLD. Poseidon Press, 1987. 1st ed. As New w/scarce errata slip. *MADLE*. $30

Barker, Ethel Ross. ROME OF THE PILGRIMS AND THE MAR-TYRS. London: Methuen and NY: Doran, n.d. (ca.1913). Faded, waterstained. Fldg map, w.a.f. *SCHOYER'S*. $40

Barker, J. Ellis. BRITISH SOCIALISM. London: Smith, Elder, 1908. Bkpl, lt wear. *AKA*. $30

Barker, Joseph. RECOLLECTIONS OF THE FIRST SETTLE-MENT OF OHIO. Ed. George Blazier. Marietta: Marietta College, 1958. 1st ed. VG+. *ARCHER*. $30

Barker, Lewellys. THE NERVOUS SYSTEM AND ITS CON-STITUENT NEURONES. NY, 1899. 1st ed. 1132pp. *FYE*. $350

Barker, Nicholas. BIBLIOTHECA LINDESIANA: THE LIFE AND COLLECTIONS OF ALEXANDER WILLIAM....London: Bernard Quaritch, 1978. Fldg chart. Cloth, teg, some wear spine extrems. *DAWSON'S.* $75

Barker, Ruth. CABALLEROS. Appleton, 1931. 2nd prtg. VG. *OREGON.* $20

Barker, William Burckhardt. LARES AND PENATES, OR CILICIA AND ITS GOVERNORS. London: Ingram, Cooke & Co, 1863. Map (tear in fold). 1/2 calf, gilt dec. spine, marbled boards. Scuffed, worn on ends. *CULLEN.* $75

Barkley, Henry C. A RIDE THROUGH ASIA MINOR AND ARMENTIA...London, 1891. x,350pp. Unusually Fine. *O'NEILL.* $175

Barlow, N. (ed). CHARLES DARWIN & THE VOYAGE OF THE BEAGLE. NY: Philos Lib, 1946. Illus. VG+. *MIKESH.* $15

Barly, Joseph. JUDGING SADDLE HORSES AND ROADSTERS. Milwaukee: Barly, 1945. Good+. *OCTOBER FARM.* $45

Barly, Joseph. JUDGING SADDLE HORSES AND ROADSTERS. Milwaukee: Barly, 1945. Signed presentation. Good. *OCTOBER FARM.* $58

Barnao, Jack (pseud of Ted Wood). HAMMER LOCKE. NY: Charles Scribner's Sons, 1986. 1st ed. Fine in dj. *MORDIDA.* $25

Barnao, Jack (pseud of Ted Wood). LOCKE STEP. NY: Charles Scribner's Sons, 1987. 1st ed. Advance review copy, slip laid in. VF in dj. *MORDIDA.* $25

Barnard, Henry. SCHOOL ARCHITECTURE. NY/Cincinnati: A.S. Barnes & Co/H.W. Derby & Co, 1849. 3rd ed. Plans, tables. Lower half of spine lacking and mouse chewed. Inwardly, VG. *HUDSON.* $75

Barnard, Robert. A CORPSE IN A GILDED CAGE. London: Collins Crime Club, 1984. 1st ed. Fine in dj. *MORDIDA.* $40

Barnard, Robert. A CORPSE IN A GILDED CAGE. NY: Scribner, 1984. 1st Amer ed. Signed. VF in dj. *SILVER DOOR.* $35

Barnard, Robert. A TALENT TO DECEIVE: AN APPRECIATION OF AGATHA CHRISTIE. London: Collins, 1980. 1st ed. Signed. *SILVER DOOR.* $35

Barnard, Robert. BODIES. London: Collins Crime Club, 1986. 1st ed. Signed. Fine in dj. *MORDIDA.* $40

Barnard, Robert. DEATH IN PURPLE PROSE. London: Collins, 1980. 1st ed. Review copy, pub's slip laid in. Fine in dj. *SILVER DOOR.* $25

Barnard, Robert. DEATH IN PURPLE PROSE. London: Collins Crime Club, 1987. 1st ed. Fine in dj, minor wear spine ends. *MORDIDA.* $35

Barnard, Robert. DEATH OF A LITERARY WIDOW. NY: Scribner's, (1980). 1st US ed. Signed. Fine in Fine dj. *UNGER.* $40

Barnard, Robert. DEATH ON THE HIGH C'S. NY: Walker, 1977. 1st ed. Fine, minor rubs to dj spine corners. *ELSE FINE.* $50

Barnard, Robert. POLITICAL SUICIDE. London: Collins Crime Club, 1986. 1st ed. Fine in dj, tiny wear top corner. *MORDIDA.* $35

Barnard, Robert. THE CASE OF THE MISSING BRONTE. NY: Scribner's, (1983). 1st US ed. Review copy. Fine in Fine dj. *UNGER.* $40

Barnard, Robert. THE DISPOSAL OF THE LIVING. London: Collins Crime Club, 1985. 1st ed. VF in dj. *MORDIDA.* $35

Barnard, Robert. THE SKELETON IN THE GRASS. London: Collins Crime Club, 1987. 1st ed. Signed. Fine in dj w/wear at base of spine. *MORDIDA.* $40

Barnes, Al. VINEGAR PIE AND OTHER TALES OF THE GRAND TRAVERSE REGION. Detroit, 1959. 1st ed. Fine in dj. *ARTIS.* $25

Barnes, Carl. THE ART AND SCIENCE OF EMBALMING, DESCRIPTIVE AND OPERATIVE. Chicago, c. 1910. *FYE.* $40

Barnes, Clare Jr. JOHN F. KENNEDY SCRIMSHAW COLLECTOR. MA: Little, Brown & Co, 1969. VG in chipped dj. *BACKROOM.* $45

Barnes, Djuna. CREATURES IN AN ALPHABET. NY: Dial, (1982). 1st ed. Clean in fresh dj. *SCHOYER'S.* $30

Barnes, Djuna. JAMES JOYCE. Trans by Michael Causse. (Paris): Le Nouveau Commerce, (1984). One of 600. Wraps. Fine. *WOOLMER.* $45

Barnes, Djuna. LADIES ALMANACK. Harper & Row, (1972). Facsimile of ltd ed of 1928. Fine in NF dj. *BEBBAH.* $30

Barnes, Djuna. SELECTED WORKS. SPILLWAY....NY: Farrar, Straus & Cudahy, (1962). 1st ed. Fine in trifle rubbed dj. *JAFFE.* $65

Barnes, Djuna. THE ANTIPHON—A PLAY. London: Faber & Faber, (1958). 1st ed. Dj sl darkened at edges, else Fine. *WOOLMER.* $50

Barnes, Djuna. TO THE DOGS. (Rochester): The Press of the Good Mountain, 1982. One of 85 numbered (total ed of 110). Bound accordion-style in marbled boards, paper label; slipcase w/paper label. Fine. *CAPTAIN'S BOOKSHELF.* $300

Barnes, Harry E. HISTORY OF THE PENAL, REFORMATORY AND CORRECTIONAL INSTITUTIONS OF THE STATE OF NEW JERSEY. Trenton, NJ, 1918. 1st ed. Ex-lib. Orig buckram sl worn, spotted. Margins, corners repaired. Inner rear hinge worn, o/w VG. *DIAMOND.* $35

Barnes, Harry E. NEW HORIZONS IN CRIMINOLOGY. NY, 1950. Rev. ed. Marginal damp-staining on corners. Pencil marks on few pages. *DIAMOND.* $25

Barnes, Julian. A HISTORY OF THE WORLD IN 10 1/2 CHAPTERS. NY: Knopf, 1989. 1st Amer ed. Signed. Fine in Fine dj. *AKA.* $28

Barnes, Julian. FLAUBERT'S PARROT. London: Cape, (1984). 1st Eng ed. VF in dj. *LOPEZ.* $450

Barnes, Julian. FLAUBERT'S PARROT. NY: Knopf, 1985. 1st Amer ed. Review copy, publicity material laid in. VF in dj. *JAFFE.* $100

Barnes, Julian. FLAUBERT'S PARROT. NY: Knopf, 1985. 1st US ed. Fine in dj. *CAPTAIN'S BOOKSHELF.* $75

Barnes, Julian. FLAUBERT'S PARROT. NY: Knopf, 1985. Adv rev copy. Fine in Fine dj, promo sheet, photo, contemp rev laid in. *LOPEZ.* $65

Barnes, Julian. STARING AT THE SUN. Knopf, 1987. 1st ed. VF in dj. *STAHR.* $15

Barnes, Julian. STARING AT THE SUN. London: London Limited Editions, (1986). 1st ed. Ltd to 150, signed. VF in glassine dj. *JAFFE.* $150

Barnes, Julian. STARING AT THE SUN. London: London Limited Editions, (1986). 1st ed. 1/150, signed. VF in glassine dj. *CAPTAIN'S BOOKSHELF.* $150

Barnes, Julian. STARING AT THE SUN. NY: Knopf, 1987. 1st ed. Signed. Fine in Fine dj but for very slight rubbing. *BEASLEY.* $50

Barnes, Julian. TALKING IT OVER. NY: Knopf, 1991. Adv reading copy in pub's box. Fine in wraps, signed. *LOPEZ.* $45

Barnes, Julian. TALKING IT OVER. NY: Knopf, 1991. Uncorrected proof, pub's promo sheets stapled in. Fine. *LOPEZ.* $40

Barnes, Linda. A TROUBLE OF FOOLS. London: Hodder, 1988. 1st British ed. Signed. NF in dj. *SILVER DOOR.* $35

Barnes, Linda. A TROUBLE OF FOOLS. NY: St. Martin's Press, 1987. 1st ed. VF in dj. *MORDIDA.* $35

Barnes, Linda. BLOOD WILL HAVE BLOOD. NY: Avon, 1982. 1st ed. Pb orig. Corner torn back cvr; crease front cvr o/w VG, unread, in wrappers. *MORDIDA.* $20

Barnes, Linda. CITIES OF THE DEAD. NY: St. Martin's Press, 1986. 1st ed. Fine in dj (minor edge wear). *MORDIDA.* $30

Barnes, Linda. COYOTE. NY: Delacorte Press, 1990. 1st ed. VF in dj. *MORDIDA.* $25

Barnes, Linda. THE SNAKE TATTOO. NY: St. Martin's, 1989. 1st ed. Review copy, signed. Promo material, photo laid in. Fine in dj. *SILVER DOOR.* $35

Barnes, Linda. THE SNAKE TATTOO. NY: St. Martin's Press, 1989. 1st ed. VF in dj. *MORDIDA.* $32.50

Barnes, Melvyn. DICK FRANCIS. NY: Ungar Publishing, 1986. 1st ed. Fine in dj. *MORDIDA.* $30

Barnes, Nellie. AMERICAN INDIAN LOVE LYRICS. NY: Macmillan, 1925. 1st ed. NF in VG, sl edgeworn dj. *LOPEZ.* $45

Barnes, Trevor. A MIDSUMMER KILLING. London: NEL, 1989. 1st ed, 1st bk. About Fine in dj. *SILVER DOOR.* $22.50

Barnes, Will C. ARIZONA PLACE NAMES. Rev & Enlrgd by Byrd H. Granger. Univ of Arizona Press, (1970). 3rd ptg. Minor cvr marking, o/w NF. *DIAMOND.* $45

Barnes, Will C. ARIZONA PLACE NAMES. Tucson, 1979. 2nd ptg. Red leatherette covers. Fine. *FIVE QUAIL.* $40

Barnes, Will C. ARIZONA PLACE NAMES. Tucson: Univ of AZ, 1935. 1st ed. Fldg map. Orig ptd wrappers. VG. *CONNOLLY & WADE.* $80

Barnes, Will C. ARIZONA PLACE NAMES. Tucson: Univ of AZ, (1979). Rev, enl ed by Byrd H. Granger. Red leatherette. Fine. *CONNOLLY & WADE.* $50

Barnes, Will C. WESTERN GRAZING GROUNDS AND FOREST RANGES...Chicago: Breeders Gazette, 1913. 1st ed, errata sheet laid in. Dk grn cl. Fine. *VARNER.* $175

Barnes, Will. TALES FROM THE X-BAR HORSE CAMP. BLUE-ROAN OUTLAW & OTHER STORIES. Chicago: Breeder's Gazette, 1920. 1st ed. 217pp + 17 plts. VG. Scarce. *OREGON.* $225

Barney, Mary. A BIOGRAPHICAL MEMOIR OF THE LATE COMMODORE JOSHUA BARNEY....Boston, Gray, 1832. 1st ed. (16),238pp. Port. New cl w/leather label. Howes B160. *GINSBERG.* $150

Barney, Mary. A BIOGRAPHICAL MEMOIR OF THE LATE COMMODORE JOSHUA BARNEY....Boston: Gray, 1832. 1st ed. (16),238pp. Port. New cl w/lea label. Howes B160. *GINSBERG.* $150

Barnhill, John and William Mellinger. SURGICAL ANATOMY OF THE HEAD AND NECK. Baltimore, 1940. 2nd ed. 400+ illus. *FYE.* $50

Barnitz, Albert and Jennie. LIFE IN CUSTER'S CAVALRY, DIARIES AND LETTERS OF ALBERT AND JENNIE BARNITZ, 1867-1868. New Haven, 1977. Ed by Robert M. Utley. 1st ed. Light dj wear o/w Fine. *PRATT.* $32.50

Baron, S. THE DESERT LOCUST. NY, 1972. Light wear. *SUTTON.* $20

Baron, Stanley. BREWED IN AMERICA. Boston: Little, Brown, (1962). 1st ed. Dj. Fine. *WREDEN.* $45

Baronio, Giuseppe. ON GRAFTING IN ANIMALS (DEGLI INNESTI ANIMALI). Boston, 1985. Ltd ed, ptd at Bird & Bull Press. 1/4 lea, 87pp. *FYE.* $250

Barr, Alwyn. POLIGNAC'S TEXAS BRIGADE. Houston: Texas Gulf Coast Hist Assoc, 1964. 1st ed. Fine in wraps. *GIBBS.* $45

Barr, Harriet et al. LSD: PERSONALITY AND EXPERIENCE. NY: Wiley-Interscience, 1972. 1st ed. Close to Fine in bit worn dj. *BEASLEY.* $30

Barr, Pat. A CURIOUS LIFE FOR A LADY. THE STORY OF ISABELLA BIRD....NY: Doubleday, 1970. 1st ed. Fine in Fine dj. *BOOK MARKET.* $40

Barr, Robert. FROM WHOSE BOURNE? London, 1893. 1st ed. No title pg, else VG. *MADLE.* $50

Barrett, Joseph H. LIFE OF ABRAHAM LINCOLN...Cincinnati: Moore, Wilstach & Baldwin, 1865. 12 plts, lacks frontis. *SCHOYER'S.* $20

Barrett, Wilson and Robert Hichens. DAUGHTERS OF BABYLON. Lippincott, 1899. 1st ed. VG. *MADLE.* $25

Barrie, J. M. QUALITY STREET: A COMEDY IN FOUR ACTS. (London): Hodder & Stoughton, (1913). Color frontis, 21 tipped-in color plts. Lt purple cl over boards, pict front cvr in gold, spine stamped in gold, pict eps ptd in gray on mauve stock. Illus by Hugh Thomson. Sl wear to spine edge, some foxing. VG. *BOOKMINE.* $175

Barrie, J.M. A WINDOW IN THRUMS. London: Hodder and Stoughton, 1889. 1st ed. Navy blue buckram, teg. Bkpl of Estelle Doheny. *WEBER.* $100

Barrie, J.M. COURAGE. London: Hodder & Stoughton, n.d. (1922). 1st ed. Large paper issue, ltd. Fine. *MUELLER.* $40

Barrie, J.M. GEORGE MEREDITH. London: Constable, 1909. 1st ed. Tan calf, red morocco spine label; aeg. Orig cvrs bound in. Bkpl of Estelle Doheny. *WEBER.* $75

Barrie, J.M. MARGARET OGILVY BY HER SON J. M. BARRIE. London: Hodder & Stoughton, 1896. 1st Eng ed. Bkpl of Estelle Doheny. *WEBER.* $40

Barrie, J.M. PETER PAN. Holt, (1987). 1st ed. 158pp. Illus by Michael Hague. Fine in fine dj. *BEBBAH.* $25

Barrie, J.M. SENTIMENTAL TOMMY, THE STORY OF HIS BOYHOOD. London: Cassell and Company, 1896. 1st ed, 1st issue. viii,452pp. Navy blue buckram, teg; spine sl faded, inner hinges cracked. Bkpl of Estelle Doheny. *WEBER.* $40

Barrie, J.M. THE ADMIRABLE CRICHTON. London: Hodder & Stoughton, (1914). 1st ed. Illus Hugh Thomson. Frontis, pict title, 20 color illus tipped in. Minor wear to extrems, o/w Fine. *WREDEN.* $125

Barrie, J.M. THE LITTLE MINISTER. (London, Paris, and Melbourne: Cassell & Company, 1891) 7 1/2" x 5". 3 vols. 1st ed. Very pretty red polished calf by Bayntun, double gilt ruled borders on covers, heavily gilt spine compartments featuring intricate floral motif, raised bands, blue and green morocco labels, inner gilt dentelles, gilt edges, marbled end papers; in sl soiled and worn cloth-covered, felt-lined slipcase. Inscribed and signed by Barrie on ffep preserved from earlier binding, the sig dated by Barrie April, 1919. Approx 10 leaves in each vol creased at upper corner, o/w VF. *PIRAGES.* $650

Barrie, J.M. THE WORKS. NY: Charles Scribner's Sons, 1929-1941. 18 vols. Peter Pan Ed. Cl spines, paper spine labels. Bkpl in 1 vol. One of 1030 sets. *DAWSON'S.* $600

Barrie, J.M. WHEN A MAN'S SINGLE, A TALE OF LITERARY LIFE. London: Hodder and Stoughton, 1888. 1st ed. 289pp. Black cl, teg. Pencil name, address. Bkpl of Estelle Doheny. Fine. *WEBER.* $175

Barringer, Marie. THE FOUR AND LENA. Doubleday, Doran & Junior Literary Guild, 1938. Stated 1st ed. 216pp. Illus by Maud & Miska Petersham. Glaser lithography. VG+. *BEBBAH.* $25

Barrington-Ward, L.E. THE ABDOMINAL SURGERY OF CHILDREN. Oxford, 1928. 1st ed. *FYE.* $75

Barron, Archibald F. VINES AND VINE CULTURE. London: Journal of Horticulture, 1892. 3rd ed, rev. VG. *SECOND LIFE.* $75

Barrow, Edward and James Kahn. MY FIFTY YEARS IN BASEBALL. Coward-McCann, 1951. 1st ed. VG in VG+ dj. *PLAPINGER.* $65

Barrow, John. THE MUTINY OF THE BOUNTY. Gavin Kennedy (ed). Boston: David R. Godine, 1980. 1st Amer ed. VG in lightly worn dj. *PARMER.* $35

Barrow, John. VOYAGES OF DISCOVERY AND RESEARCH WITHIN THE ARCTIC REGIONS, FROM 1818 TO THE PRESENT TIME....London: John Murray, 1846. 1st ed. xiv,530,(6 ad)pp. Port, 2 charts (1 fldg). Later 1/4 calf over marbled boards, old faint lib stamps on title; fldg chart laid down. *LEFKOWICZ.* $150

Barrow, John. VOYAGES OF DISCOVERY...WITHIN THE ARCTIC REGIONS, FROM THE YEAR 1818 TO THE PRESENT TIME...WITH TWO ATTEMPTS TO REACH THE NORTH POLE. NY: Harper & Bros, 1846. 1st Amer ed. 2 maps, 1 fldg (creased). Nicely rebound. Lt foxing. *PARMER.* $295

Barrows, John. UBET. Caxton, 1934. 1st ed. R.H. Hall (illus). VG. Howes B185. *OREGON.* $100

Barrows, R.M. (comp). THE KIT BOOK FOR SOLDIERS, SAILORS, AND MARINES. Chicago: Consolidated Book Publishers, 1943. 1st ed, 2nd issue. Page margins browned as usual (cheap paper) o/w bright, NF; pict paper-covered boards; issued without dj. *BERNARD.* $100

Barry, Charles. DEATH OF A FIRST MATE. NY: E.P. Dutton, 1935. 1st Amer ed. VG in dj w/short closed tear and wear along spine edge which has worn through in a few spots. *MORDIDA.* $25

Barry, Florence. A CENTURY OF CHILDREN'S BOOKS. NY: George H. Doran, (ca. 1922). NF. *WREDEN.* $35

Barry, John D. THE CITY OF DOMES: A WALK WITH....SF: J.J. Newbegin, 1915. 1st ed. Frontis, x,142(4)pp + 47 plts. Cl backed boards, gilt decor, letters. About Fine in chipped, rare dj. *CONNOLLY & WADE.* $75

Barry, Julian. LENNY: A PLAY. NY: Grove Press, 1971. 1st ed. Fine, short closed tear to dj. *ELSE FINE.* $30

Barth, John. CHIMERA. NY, 1972. 1st ed, signed. Fine in dj (tiny edge stain). *POLYANTHOS.* $30

Barth, John. CHIMERA. NY: Random House, (1972). 1/300 numbered/signed. Fine in pub's slipcase. *DERMONT.* $100

Barth, John. CHIMERA. NY: Random House, (1972). 1st trade ed. Fine in dj. *JUVELIS.* $25

Barth, John. CHIMERA. NY: RH, (1972). 1st ed. Fine in sl used dj. *CAPTAIN'S BOOKSHELF.* $30

Barth, John. GILES GOAT-BOY. GC: Doubleday, 1966. 1st ed, code H18 on last page of text. Signed. Name, o/w NF in dj. *BERNARD.* $85

Barth, John. GILES GOAT-BOY. NY, 1966. 1st ed. Signed presentation. Neat name. Fine in dj (top spine sl rubbed). *POLYANTHOS.* $75

Barth, John. LETTERS. A NOVEL. NY: Putnam, (1979). 1/300 numbered/signed. Fine in slipcase. *DERMONT.* $75

Barth, John. LETTERS. NY, 1979. 1st ed. Signed presentation. Fine in silver lettered dj. *POLYANTHOS.* $40

Barth, John. LETTERS. NY, 1979. 1st ed. Signed. Fine in gold lettered dj. *POLYANTHOS.* $30

Barth, John. LETTERS. NY: G.P. Putnam's Sons, (1979). 1st ed. Signed. Fine in dj. *BERNARD.* $35

Barth, John. LETTERS. NY: Putnam's, (1979). 1st ed. One of a specially bound ltd ed, signed. Mint in pub's slipcase, orig plastic shrinkwrap. *CHAPEL HILL.* $150

Barth, John. LOST IN THE FUNHOUSE. GC: Doubleday, 1968. 1st ed. NF in NF dj, inscribed, dated. *LOPEZ.* $65

Barth, John. LOST IN THE FUNHOUSE. NY, 1968. 1st ed. Signed presentation. Bkpl, tiny area rubbed ffep. NF in dj (spine little sunned, few edges nicked). *POLYANTHOS.* $45

Barth, John. SABBATICAL. NY, 1982. One of 750 signed, numbered. Boards show lt spotting, else NF in Fine slipcase. *PETTLER.* $60

Barth, John. SABBATICAL. NY: Putnam, (1982). 1st ed. Fine in dj. *CAPTAIN'S BOOKSHELF.* $15

Barth, John. SABBATICAL: A ROMANCE. NY: Putnam, (1982). 1st ed. 1/750 specially bound, signed. Fine in slipcase. *CAPTAIN'S BOOKSHELF.* $60

Barth, John. THE FLOATING OPERA. London: Secker & Warburg, (1968). 1st UK ed. 4,000 copies of 1st book. Signed. Fine in dj. *BERNARD.* $100

Barth, John. THE FLOATING OPERA. NY, 1956. 1st ed, 1st bk. No dj, literary agent's sticker on fep, else VG. *PETTLER.* $45

Barth, John. THE FLOATING OPERA. NY: Appleton, (1956). 1st ed, 1st bk. Fine in dj (sm spot rear panel; sl darkened spine). *CAPTAIN'S BOOKSHELF.* $250

Barth, John. THE FLOATING OPERA. NY: Appleton, (1956). 1st ed. Fine in dj. *JAFFE.* $375

Barth, John. THE FLOATING OPERA. NY: Appleton-Century-Crofts, (1956). 1st ed, 1st bk. Orig brn cl. NF in sl soiled dj (some sunning to spine). *CHAPEL HILL.* $300

Barth, John. THE FLOATING OPERA. NY: Appleton-Century-Crofts, (1956). 1st ed. Signed. Orig brown cl. Nick at head of spine, sl offsetting to eps. VG in dj. *CHAPEL HILL.* $300

Barth, John. THE LAST VOYAGE OF SOMEBODY THE SAILOR. Boston, 1991. 1st ed, signed. Mint in like dj. *POLYANTHOS.* $45

Barth, John. THE SOT-WEED FACTOR. GC: Doubleday, 1960. 1st ed. NF in somewhat tattered dj. Signed. *LOPEZ.* $250

Barth, John. THE SOT-WEED FACTOR. London: Secker & Warburg, 1962. 1st Eng ed. Proof copy. VG in sl soiled ptd wraps. *HELLER.* $150

Barth, John. TODD ANDREWS TO THE AUTHOR. Northridge, CA: Lord John Press, 1979. 1 of ltd ed of 300, signed. New, issued w/o dj. *BERNARD.* $50

Bartheleme, Donald. SNOW WHITE. NY: Atheneum (1967). 1st ed. Name, else Fine in dj. *DORN.* $80

Barthelme, Donald. AMATEURS. NY: Farrar, Straus, Giroux, (1976). 1st ed. Orig orange cl. Fine in dj. *CHAPEL HILL.* $30

Barthelme, Donald. COME BACK, DR. CALIGARI. Boston: Little, Brown and Co, (c.1964). 1st ed, 1st bk. Fine in dj (sl chipped, internally reinforced top of backstrip). *HELLER.* $125

Barthelme, Donald. FORTY STORIES. Putnam's, 1987. Uncorrected Proof. About Fine in gold wraps. *STAHR.* $45

Barthelme, Donald. GUILTY PLEASURES. Farrar Straus Giroux, 1974. 1st ed. VG in VG dj. *BEBBAH.* $25

Barthelme, Donald. SADNESS. NY: Farrar, Straus, Giroux, (1972). 1st ed. Orig red cl. Fine in NF dj. *CHAPEL HILL.* $40

Barthelme, Donald. SIXTY STORIES. NY: Putnam's, (1981). 1st ed, #329 of 500 specially bound, signed. Orig plum cl. Fine in slipcase. *CHAPEL HILL.* $125

Barthelme, Donald. SNOW WHITE. NY: Atheneum, 1967. 1st ed. Fine in dj. *HELLER.* $75

Barthelme, Donald. THE DEAD FATHER. NY: Farrar, Straus & Giroux, (1975). Advance review copy (photo laid in). Signed. Fine in Fine dj. *LOPEZ.* $85

Barthelme, Donald. THE DEAD FATHER. NY: Farrar, Straus, Giroux, (1975). 1st ed. Orig black cl. NF in dj. Signed. *CHAPEL HILL.* $65

Barthelme, Donald. THE DEAD FATHER. NY: Farrar, Straus, Giroux, (1975). 1st ed. Orig black cl. NF in dj. *CHAPEL HILL.* $40

Barthelme, Frederick. TRACER. Simon and Schuster, 1985. Uncorrected proof. Fine in yellow wraps. *STAHR.* $25

Bartholow, Roberts. A PRACTICAL TREATISE ON MATERIA MEDICA AND THERAPEUTICS. NY, 1877. 1st ed. 537pp. Paper pasted over part of title page, o/w Fine. Inscription. *FYE.* $50

Bartholow, Roberts. MEDICAL ELECTRICITY: A PRACTICAL TREATISE ON THE APPLICATIONS OF ELECTRICITY TO MEDICINE AND SURGERY. Phila, 1882. 2nd ed. *FYE.* $60

Bartlett, Arthur. BASEBALL & MR. SPALDING. NY: Farrar Straus & Young, (1951). 1st ed. VG+ in Good+ dj. *AKA.* $20

Bartlett, Elisha. THE HISTORY, DIAGNOSIS, AND TREATMENT OF THE FEVERS OF THE UNITED STATES. Phila, 1856. 4th ed. 610pp. *FYE.* $125

Bartlett, Frederick Orin. THE WEB OF THE GOLDEN SPIDER. Small-Maynard, 1919, 1st ed. VG. *MADLE.* $35

Bartlett, John Russell. PERSONAL NARRATIVE OF EXPLORATIONS AND INCIDENTS IN TEXAS, NEW MEXICO, CALIFORNIA, SONORA, AND CHIHUAHUA, CONNECTED WITH THE UNITED STATES AND MEXICAN BOUNDARY COMMISSION DURING THE YEARS 1850, '51, '52, AND '53. NY, 1856. 2 vols in one: (22),506,(6)pp. 16 lithos, 94 illus, fldg map. Orig cl. Howes B201. *GINSBERG.* $500

Bartlett, John Russell. PERSONAL NARRATIVE OF EXPLORATIONS AND INCIDENTS. NY: D. Appleton, (1854). Assembled set w/bindings not uniform. Fldg map present in vol 1. 1st vol bound in blue gray embossed ribbed cl; vol 2 in brn pebbled cl and printed on better grade of paper. *HUDSON.* $425

Bartlett, John Russell. PERSONAL NARRATIVE OF EXPLORATIONS AND INCIDENTS IN TEXAS, NEW MEXICO, CALIFORNIA, SONORA, AND CHIHUAHUA. NY: D. Appleton, (1854). 1st ed in most desired binding style. 2 vols. Fldg map, fldg litho frontis plt, 15 color litho views. Hinges to vol 1 cracked, vol 2 rebacked w/spine laid down. Old names end leaves, yet Nice. *HUDSON.* $675

Bartlett, John Russell. PERSONAL NARRATIVE OF EXPLORATIONS IN TEXAS, NEW MEXICO...CONNECTED WITH THE UNITED STATES AND MEXICAN BOUNDARY COMMISSION DURING THE YEARS 1850, '51, '52, & '53. NY: D. Appleton, 1854. 1st ed. Two vols: xxii,506,(6); xviii,624pp (lacking pp xv,xvi) 16 lithos, all but one w/orig tissue guards. 94 other illus. Fldg map, short tear, expertly repaired. Vol 2's frontis and title page secured in w/vertical strip of cl tape. Occasional light foxing, spotting. Faint damp line on the edge of a few pgs in Vol. 2. Orig grn cl w/gilt cactus decs, lettering on spine. All edges showing wear w/chipping on top and bottom of backstrips. Hinges strong, unbroken. Good set. Howes B201. *CONNOLLY & WADE.* $865

Bartlett, L. ON THE OLD WEST COAST; BEING FURTHER REMINISCENCES OF A RANGER....Grosset & Dunlap, '30s rpt. Fine in Fine dj. *VARNER.* $17.50

Bartlett, Richard. GREAT SURVEYS OF AMERICAN WEST. Norman: Univ of OK, (1962). 1st ed. Fine in VG dj. *OREGON.* $50

Bartlett, Robert A. and Ralph T. Hale. THE LAST VOYAGE OF THE KARLUK. Boston, (1919). 2nd prtg. Signed presentation. Good. *ARTIS.* $35

Bartlett, W.H. WALKS ABOUT THE CITY AND ENVIRONS OF JERUSALEM. London, (late 1840s). Corrected 2nd ed. Teg. NF. *POLYANTHOS.* $125

Bartok, Bella. HUNGARIAN FOLK MUSIC. Trans M.D. Calvocoressi. London: Oxford, 1931. 1st ed in Eng. Fine. *CAPTAIN'S BOOKSHELF.* $125

Barton, Clara. THE RED CROSS IN PEACE AND WAR. Washington, DC: 1899. 1st ed. Tri-color gilt cl. Cvr worn, stained; front hinge weak, contents VG. Scarce. *SMITHFIELD.* $45

Barton, Clara. THE RED CROSS. A HISTORY....Washington, DC: Red Cross, (1898). Cvr worn, contents near VG. *SMITHFIELD.* $30

Barton, Clara. THE RED CROSS: A HISTORY OF THIS REMARKABLE INTERNATIONAL MOVEMENT IN THE INTEREST OF HUMANITY. Washington, 1898. 1st ed. *FYE.* $75

Barton, G.A.H. BACKWATERS OF LETHE (SOME ANAESTHETIC NOTIONS). NY, 1920. 1st Amer ed. *FYE.* $30

Barton, Michael. GOODMEN: THE CHARACTER OF CIVIL WAR SOLDIERS. Univ Park, PA: (1981). 1st ed. 135pp. Fine in dj. *PRATT.* $20

Barton, William E. ABRAHAM LINCOLN AND THE HOOKER LETTER. NY, 1928. 1st ed, ltd to 750. Fine. *McGOWAN.* $45

Barton, William E. THE LIFE OF ABRAHAM LINCOLN. NY, (1933). 1 vol ed. 772pp. Two small tears upper spine, o/w VG+. *PRATT.* $25

Barton, William E. THE WOMEN LINCOLN LOVED. Indianapolis, (1927). 1st ed. Minor shelf wear o/w Fine. *PRATT.* $25

Barton, William P.C. VEGETABLE MATERIA MEDICA OF THE UNITED STATES; OR MEDICAL BOTANY; CONTAINING A BOTANICAL, GENERAL, AND MEDICAL HISTORY, OF MEDICINAL PLANTS INDIGENOUS TO THE UNITED STATES. 50 hand-colored, eng plts. 2 vols in 1. Phila, 1817-18. 1st ed. Pp xv,(17-)273,(1); xvi(9-)243. 1/2 morocco. Perished backstrip replaced w/black cl tape, some soiling. Joint between title pgs completely split, lower marginal dampstaining many pp, colored plts mostly unstained, pp nearly free of foxing, some pl background contain browning and offsetting. *SUTTON.* $3,850

Bartram, John with Lewis Evans and Conrad Weister. A JOURNEY FROM PENNSYLVANIA TO ONODAGA IN 1743. Barre: Imprint Society, 1973. 1st ed thus. #12 of 1950. Fldg map. 1/4 leather. Signed by Nathan Goldstein (illus). Fine. *CONNOLLY & WADE.* $85

Bartram, John with Lewis Evans and Conrad Weister. A JOURNEY FROM PENNSYLVANIA TO ONODAGA IN 1743. Barre: Imprint Society, 1973. 1st ed thus, #12/1950. David R. Godine Press. Signed by illus Nathan Goldstein. Fldg map. 1/4 lea, marbled boards. Fine. *CONNOLLY & WADE.* $75

Bartram, William. TRAVELS THROUGH NORTH AND SOUTH CAROLINA....CONTAINING AN ACCOUNT OF THE SOIL AND NATURAL PRODUCTIONS....Dublin, 1793. 8 copper plts (1 fldg), 1 fldg map. 8vo. pp. xxiv, 520, index (8 pp. of 11). Contemp mottled calf (worn at corners and edges, piece of backstrip missing at head of spine, backstrip worn, front flyleaf partially loose, bkpl, internally, mostly clean). Rare. *SUTTON.* $950

Bashe, C.J. et al. IBM'S EARLY COMPUTERS. MIT Press, 1986. Near New in dj. *BOOKCELL.* $45

Basket, Sir James. HISTORY OF THE ISLAND OF ST. DOMINGO...TO THE PRESENT PERIOD. London, 1818, NY, 1824. 1st Amer ed. New cl & boards, lea label. viii,266pp. Browning and foxing, o/w attractive. *O'NEILL.* $200

Baskin, Leonard. ARS ANATOMICA. NY, 1972. Ltd ed. of 2500. Folio (22 1/2 x 15 1/2"). 13 separate plts w/commentary laid into cl-backed folder and slip case. Signed. *FYE.* $350

Baskin, Leonard. HOSIE'S ALPHABET. Viking, 1972. 1st ed. 4to. Unpaginated. Baskin color illus. VG in VG dj. *BEBBAH.* $30

Baskin, Leonard. THE RAPTORS AND OTHER BIRDS. NY: Pantheon, 1985. 1st ed. Color pl laid-in. Fine in Fine dj. *ACADEMIC LIBRARY.* $35

Baskin, R.N. REMINISCENCES OF EARLY UTAH. Salt Lake, 1914. 1st ed. VG+. *BENCHMARK.* $85

Basler, Roy P. (ed.) THE COLLECTED WORKS OF ABRAHAM LINCOLN. 9 vols. New Brunswick, (1953). History Bk Club Ed. *PRATT.* $125

Bass, Rick. OIL NOTES. Boston, 1989. 1st ed. Signed. Fine in like dj. *POLYANTHOS.* $30

Bass, Rick. OIL NOTES. Boston: Mifflin/Lawrence, 1989. 1st ed. Fine in NF dj. *ROBBINS.* $20

Bass, Rick. OIL NOTES. Houghton Mifflin, 1989. 1st ed. Fine in Fine dj except for spot to lower edge of book. *BEBBAH.* $18

Bass, Rick. THE WATCH. NY & London: Norton, (1989). 1st ed. New in dj. *BERNARD.* $25

Bass, William Wallace. ADVENTURES IN THE CANYONS OF THE COLORADO BY TWO OF ITS EARLIEST EXPLORERS, JAMES WHITE AND W.W. HAWKINS. Grand Canyon, 1920. Stiff wraps, illus. 38pp. Very Scarce. *FIVE QUAIL.* $200

Bassford, Amy O. and Fritiof Fryxell. HOME THOUGHTS FROM AFAR: LETTERS OF THOMAS MORAN TO MARY NIMMO MORAN. East Hampton, 1967. 1st ed. VF in Fine dj. *FIVE QUAIL.* $25

Basshe, Emjo. DOOMSDAY CIRCUS. A DRAMATIC CHRONICLE. NY, (1938). 1st ed. Signed presentation. Fine in dj (sl sunned, extremities little rubbed, tiny chip top spine). *POLYAN-THOS.* $75

Basshe, Emjo. EARTH. A PLAY IN SEVEN SCENES. NY, (1927). 1st ed. Signed. Fine in dj, spine sl sunned, chips. Owner inscrip. *POLYANTHOS.* $75

Bast, Theodore & Barry Anson. THE TEMPORAL BONE AND THE EAR. Springfield, 1949. 1st ed. *FYE.* $50

Bast, Theodore. THE LIFE & TIMES OF ADOLF KUSSMAUL. NY, 1926. 1st ed. *FYE.* $50

Bast, William. JAMES DEAN: A BIOGRAPHY. NY: Ballantine Books, (1956). 1st ptg. Pb orig. Small mark to front cover where price sticker removed, edges sl worn o/w VG ppwrps. *BERNARD.* $25

Bastin, Bruce. CRYING FOR THE CAROLINES. London: Studio Vista, 1971. 1st ed. Fine in Fine dj. The uncommon hardcover ed. *BEASLEY.* $35

Batchelder, C.F. A BIBLIOGRAPHY OF THE PUBLISHED WRITINGS OF WILLIAM BREWSTER. Cambridge, 1951. *SUTTON.* $23

Batchelder, C.F. AN ACCOUNT OF THE NUTTALL OR-NITHOLOGICAL CLUB 1873 TO 1919. Cambridge, 1937. *SUT-TON.* $27

Batchelder, George A. A SKETCH OF THE HISTORY AND RESOURCES OF DAKOTA TERRITORY. Yankton: Press Steam Printing, 1870. 56pp. Frontis map. 1/2 morocco. Howes B231. *GINSBERG.* $1750

Batchelor, John Calvin. THE FURTHER ADVENTURES OF HALLEY'S COMET. NY: Condon & Lattes, 1980. 1st ed. Very NF in light dj w/slight rubbing. *BETWEEN COVERS.* $250

Bateman, Frederic. ON APHASIA, OR LOSS OF SPEECH, AND THE LOCALIZATION OF THE FACULTY OF ARTICULATE LANGUAGE. London, 1890. 2nd ed. 420pp. *FYE.* $300

Bateman, G.C. THE VIVARIUM....London, (1897). Orig cl worn at extrems, 1" spine split, some interior joint cracking. *SUTTON.* $60

Bates, Daisy. LONG SHADOW OF LITTLE ROCK. NY: David McKay, 1962. DJ price-clipped. *AKA.* $35

Bates, Ernest Sutherland and John V. Dittemore. MARY BAKER EDDY. NY: Knopf. 1932. 1st ed. Dj bit soiled. Inscrip, signed. Suppressed by the Christian Science Church after a short period of sale. Now very scarce, particularly inscr. *KARMIOLE.* $150

Bates, H.W. THE NATURALIST ON THE RIVER AMAZONS. London & Toronto: Dent, (1930). VG. *MIKESH.* $25

Bates, H.W. THE NATURALIST ON THE RIVER AMAZONS. London, 1910. Popular Ed. Faded, soiled. *SUTTON.* $23

Bates, Joseph D., Jr. STREAMER FLY TYING AND FISHING. Harrisburg: Stackpole Co, 1966. Stated 1st ed. VG+. *BACKMAN.* $25

Bates, M. THE NATURAL HISTORY OF MOSQUITOES. NY, 1949. Light cover spotting. NY, 1949. *SUTTON.* $40

Bates, Mrs. D.B. INCIDENTS ON LAND AND WATER....Boston: Libby, 1858. 7th ed (ptg). 336pp. 4 plts. Fine. *SECOND LIFE.* $125

Bates, Mrs. D.B. INCIDENTS ON LAND AND WATER...Boston: Pub for the author, 1860. 8th ed. Plts. Black cl, gilt, crudely mended. *HUDSON.* $35

Bateson, Gregory. STEPS TO AN ECOLOGY OF MIND. SF: Chandler, (1972). 1st ed. NF in dj with couple of unobtrusive tears. *LOPEZ.* $275

Bathe, Basil W. SEVEN CENTURIES OF SEA TRAVEL. NY: Tudor Publishing Co, (1973). 30 mounted color plts. Dj. *KARMIOLE.* $45

Bathurst, C. NOTES ON NETS; or, THE QUINCUNX PRACTI-CALLY CONSIDERED, TO WHICH ARE ADDED MISC. MEMORANDA. London, 1837. VG. 1st ed. *MIKESH.* $150

Batten, H. Mortimer. INLAND BIRDS. London: Hutchinson, 1923. 1st ed. Minor wear, else VG-NF. *OLD LONDON.* $35

Battershall, Fletcher. BOOKBINDING FOR BIBLIOPHILES...TOGETHER WITH A SKETCH OF GOLD TOOLING....Greenwich: The Literary Collector Press, 1905. 1st ed, ltd to 350 numbered; this out of series. Boards, paper spine, cvr labels. *OAK KNOLL.* $250

Battie, William. A TREATISE ON MADNESS. NY, 1969. Facs of 1758 ed. 99pp. Corner clipped from fep, small gouge in head of spine. Dj. *FYE.* $30

BATTLES AND LEADERS OF THE CIVIL WAR. Peoples Pictorial Edition. NY: Century Co, (1894). Cl soiled. NF. *BLUE MOUN-TAIN.* $75

Bauer, Clyde Max. YELLOWSTONE GEYSERS. Haynes: Yellowstone, 1947. Rev ed. Tipped-in colored frontis, 2pp maps. Photgr on verso. Gilt dec cl. Fine. *CONNOLLY & WADE.* $40

Baughman, Theodore. THE OKLAHOMA SCOUT. Chicago: W.B. Conkey Co., (1886). 215 pp. Cloth, illus. VG. Howes B244. Scarce. *GIBBS.* $50

Baum, I.E. SAVAGE ABYSSINIA. NY, 1927. 32 photo plts. Rear hinge cracked. Signed. *SUTTON.* $95

Baum, L. Frank. DOROTHY AND THE WIZARD OF OZ. Reilly & Lee, (1945 format). 226pp. Illus by J.R. Neill. VG w/bright pict cvr in grn, dark blue & yellow on grn cloth. Good dj has edgewear, chips, narrow piece missing at bottom, skinned patches rear panel. *BEBBAH.* $60

Baum, L. Frank. DOROTHY AND THE WIZARD OF OZ. Reilly & Lee, (1945 format). 226pp. Illus by J.R. Neill. Beige cloth w/pict cvr pastedown in yellow, dark blue and grn. Ffep removed. VG. *BEB-BAH.* $35

Baum, L. Frank. GLINDA OF OZ. Reilly & Lee, c.1936. B/w illus by John R. Neill. Faint spotting to page edges but VG & bright in VG dj w/couple of small chips, slight spine soil. *BEBBAH.* $115

Baum, L. Frank. KABUMPO IN OZ. Reilly & Lee, (1922). Late 1930s ptg. 1 1/2" closed tear to title page; Dorothy portrait page edge small chips; edgewear; pict pastedown has rubbing but Good w/Kabumpo's smile bright. *BEBBAH.* $40

Baum, L. Frank. RINKITINK IN OZ. Rand McNally, 1939. 1st printing of Junior Edition w/CS 6-39. 16mo. 62pp. 12 color plates plus b/w illus by John R. Neill. Edgewear, rubs to color pict paper-covered boards w/tape repaired at spine. Good+. *BEBBAH.* $37

Baum, L. Frank. RINKITINK IN OZ. Rand McNally, 1939. 2nd ptg of Junior Edition w/CS 8-39. 16mo. 62pp. 12 color plates plus b/w illus by John R. Neill. Corner wear, rubs, chips, split at spine but VG. *BEBBAH.* $27

Baum, L. Frank. RINKITINK IN OZ. Reilly & Lee, (post 1935). 314pp. Illus in b/w by J.R. Neill. Illus endpaper. Faint spot of soil at front cvr hinge, bump to bottom of front cvr, else VG+. *BEBBAH.* $50

Baum, L. Frank. THE EMERALD CITY OF OZ. Reilly & Lee, (post 1960). W/no pict cvr but dec spine. 296pp. Illus by J.R. Neill, illus Endpaper. VG. *BEBBAH.* $28

Baum, L. Frank. THE LAND OF OZ. Reilly & Lee, (c. 1945). 287pp. Illus by J.R. Neill. Has some edgewear, rubbing, lacking, ffep but color pict cvr pastedown bright. VG. *BEBBAH.* $30

Baum, L. Frank. THE LAND OF OZ. Reilly & Lee, (c. 1945). Illus by J.R. Neill. 287pp. VG w/repaired inner hinges, in brown cloth w/pict cvr pastedown of Scarecrow, Tin Man & Emerald City in grn, white, dark blue, & yellow + dec spine in dj w/same color illus as cvr has chips but bright & VG. *BEBBAH.* $85

Baum, L. Frank. THE LAUGHING DRAGON OF OZ. Racine, WI, (1934). 1st ed. Big Little Book #1128. Illus by Milt Youngren. Pgs browning, lt rub around cvr edges. VG. *McCLINTOCK.* $155

Baum, L. Frank. THE LOST PRINCESS OF OZ. Chicago, (1917). Actually WWII-era later ptg after color plts had been dropped by the publisher. Illus in b & w by Neill. VF w/full color pasteplate cover. *McCLINTOCK.* $35

Baum, L. Frank. THE LOST PRINCESS OF OZ. Rand McNally, 1939. Later (CS 10-39) ptg of Junior Edition. 16mo. 62pp. 12 full-page color plus b/w illus by John R. Neill. Edgewear, some rubs to color pict paper cvrs. VG+. *BEBBAH.* $25

Baum, L. Frank. THE LOST PRINCESS OF OZ. Rand McNally, 1939. 2nd (CS 8-39) ptg of Junior Edition. 16mo. 62pp. 12 color plates plus b/w illus by John R. Neill. Corner, edgewear, chips to spine ends. VG. *BEBBAH.* $27

Baum, L. Frank. THE LOST PRINCESS OF OZ. Reilly & Lee, (post 1935). B/w illus by J.R. Niell, pict endpaper pict pastedown, red cloth. Staple holes to corner of ffep, few small spots at spine else VG. *BEBBAH.* $55

Baum, L. Frank. THE MAGIC OF OZ. Reilly & Lee, (c. 1930). 12 color plates by J.R. Neill pict endpaper. Cvr & pict pastedown have wear, shaken, few b/w illus. Much writing on ownership page. Good. *BEBBAH.* $60

Baum, L. Frank. THE NEW WIZARD OF OZ. Bobbs-Merrill, (c. 1930s). 5th ed, 2nd state. 208pp. 8 color plts. W.W. Denslow (illus). Lt grn cl, spine lettering in blue, pict pastedown (2 fine scratches) in orange, blue & olive. Scratch to rear cvr; 2 bumps to cvr edges; crimping bottom margin some pp; short closed tear margin of 1 pl not affecting illus. Sl top edge soil. Good+. *BEBBAH.* $45

Baum, L. Frank. THE NEW WIZARD OF OZ. Bobbs-Merrill, (1903). The MGM movie version pub in 1939. 8 color plts. W.W Denslow (illus). Eps depic scenes from movie in sepia. VG bright book w/VG colorful dj w/scenes from film on rear panel has some edge chipping, few crinkles but also bright. *BEBBAH.* $150

Baum, L. Frank. THE NEW WIZARD OF OZ. Bobbs-Merrill. (1920s-'30s). 5th ed, 2nd state w/8 W.W. Denslow color plts. In this ptg yellow replaces blue in pict pastedown. Page soil; 1 leaf tape repaired, 5 leaves w/tear; pastedown worn. Good. *BEBBAH.* $40

Baum, L. Frank. THE NEW WIZARD OF OZ. Bobbs-Merrill. (1920s-'30s). 5th ed., 2nd state. 8 color plates by W.W. Denslow. 1 leaf w/ragged edge, some finger soil, cvr soil, wear, VG. *BEBBAH.* $60

Baum, L. Frank. THE NEW WIZARD OF OZ. Bobbs-Merrill. (1944). Hanff, Greene. 1st ed., state 2 w/misprint p. 193, 8 color plts by Evelyn Copelman bound in. Edgewear, ink scrawls to endpaper, else VG. *BEBBAH.* $25

Baum, L. Frank. THE NEW WIZARD OF OZ. Donohue, (c. 1919). 3rd ed., 2nd state variant w/textual illus on p. 195 in brown but illus p. 261 in black; witch's hat remains on p. 137. Cvr edgewear, short closed tear to ffep, 1 page, few finger smudges, Good+. *BEBBAH.* $50

Baum, L. Frank. THE PATCHWORK GIRL OF OZ. Reilly & Lee, c. 1936. John R. Neill (illus). VG in dj (tape-repaired closed tears spine and rear panel; 2 short closed tears front panel. General wear but front pict bright. *BEBBAH.* $100

Baum, L. Frank. THE ROAD TO OZ. Rand McNally, 1939. Later (CS 10-39) ptg of Junior Edition. 16mo. 62pp. 12 full-page color plates plus b/w illus by John R. Neill. Some wear, rubs to back of pict paper-covered boards but VG+. *BEBBAH.* $25

Baum, L. Frank. THE ROAD TO OZ. Reilly & Lee, (post 1935). 261pp. Illus by J.R. Neill. Lt blue cl. VG+ w/bright color pict cvr pastedown. *BEBBAH.* $60

Baum, L. Frank. THE ROAD TO OZ. Reilly & Lee, (1964 format). 268pp. Illus J.R. Neill. White cl w/color pict on cvrs, spine. Faint cvr soil and tiny spot paint. VG. *BEBBAH.* $25

Baum, L. Frank. THE SCARECROW AND THE TIN WOODMAN OF OZ. Rand McNally, 1939. 1st ed in The Wonderful Land of Oz Library w/CS 3-39 on copyright page. 16mo. 64pp. 2 double-spread & 12 full-page color illus by John R. Neill. Wear, soil to color pict paper-covered boards & chips top, bottom of spine. Good+. Also contains Princess Ozma of Oz. *BEBBAH.* $37

Baum, L. Frank. THE SCARECROW OF OZ. Reilly & Lee, (1940). 288pp. Illus by J.R. Neill. Oversize volume w/leaf measuring 9 7/16" x 7 inches. Dec red cloth spine w/pict paper-covered board showing Scarecrow & 9 deliriously happy crows. One small skinned patch to cvr, slight rubs to cvr, rubbing to rear cvr. VG. *BEBBAH.* $70

Baum, L. Frank. THE TIN WOODMAN OF OZ. Chicago, 1918. 1st ed. 1st issue w/"Reilly & Britton" on spine. 12 full color plts, front cover paste plt by Neill. One text page scribbled in pencil, but legible; interior hinges cracking, usual light rub and soil to covers. Far better than most. *McCLINTOCK.* $125

Baum, L. Frank. THE TIN WOODMAN OF OZ. Reilly & Lee, (c. 1935). Illus by J.R. Neill. 288pp. Ownership page is split part way at gutter w/tape remains, edgewear, slight rubs to cvr pict pastedown. Good+. *BEBBAH.* $50

Baum, L. Frank. THE VISITORS FROM OZ. Reilly & Lee, (1960). 4to. Illus in color, b/w by Dick Martin. Full-color pict cvrs. VG+ in VG dj w/rubs. Based on Baum's 1904-05 newspaper series "Queer Visitors from the Marvelous Land of Oz," adapted by Jean Kellogg. *BEBBAH.* $100

Baum, L. Frank. THE WIZARD OF OZ. Reilly & Lee, (1956). 237pp. Illus by Dale Ulrey in 2 colors. Good+ w/wear. *BEBBAH.* $40

Baum, L. Frank. THE WONDERFUL WIZARD OF OZ. Geo. M. Hill, 1900. 1st ed. State Z, (Blanck's From Peter Parley to Penrod). Co. on spine is red with O within C, advertisements on verso of front fly are not bordered, typographical errors are corrected on pp. 14 & 81, 13-line colophon, type defects present on pp. 100 & 186. Front fly endpaper has been inserted in facsimile, chips to front end of title page, cvrs have wear, some soil, frayed spine ends repaired. Volume has been professionally tightened to make it a solid copy of this rare 1st ed. Interior is VG. *BEBBAH.* $800

Baum, L. Frank. THE WONDERFUL WIZARD OF OZ. Univ of CA, 1986. Stated 1st ptg. 268pp. Illus, signed by Barry Moser. Fine in Fine dj. *BEBBAH.* $45

Baum, L. Frank. TIK-TOK OF OZ. Reilly & Lee, (post 1935). 272pp. Illus by J.R. Neill. Rear endpaper removed, part of inscription on rear fixed e.p. scratched out, slight soil to rear cover, color pictorial pastedown bright. Bright cloth. VG. *BEBBAH.* $50

Baum, L. Frank. TIK-TOK OF OZ. Reilly & Lee, (c. 1935). Illus by J.R. Neill. 271pp. VG+. *BEBBAH.* $60

Baumann, John. OLD MAN CROW'S BOY. ADVENTURES IN EARLY IDAHO. Morrow, 1948. Fine in VG dj. *OREGON.* $45

Baumgardt, Carola. JOHANNES KEPLER, LIFE AND LETTERS. NY: Philosophical Library, 1951. Good in tattered dj. *KNOLLWOOD.* $25

Baumgartel, Elise J. THE CULTURES OF PREHISTORIC EGYPT. VOL. II only. Oxford: Griffith Institute, 1960. 13 plts, wraps. Signature. Good. *ARCHAEOLOGIA.* $110

Baumgartner, Leona & Fulton, John. A BIBLIOGRAPHY OF THE POEM SYPHILISSIVE MORBUS GALLICUS BY GIROLAMO

FRACASTORO OF VERONA. New Haven, 1935. 1st ed. Wraps. *FYE.* $40

Baur, John E. DOGS ON THE FRONTIER. San Antonio: The Naylor Company, (1964). Black-stamped cl in dj. *DAWSON'S.* $30

Baurmeister, Major Carl Leopold. REVOLUTION IN AMERICA: CONFIDENTIAL LETTERS AND JOURNALS 1776-1784. New Brunswick: Rutgers Univ, 1957. 1st ed. Bernard A. Uhlendorf (trans). Slight damp mark on bit of top edge of pages, light and not affecting text of condition. Some chipping on edges of dj, else Fine. *CONNOLLY & WADE.* $40

Bausch, Richard. REAL PRESENCE. NY: Dial, (1980). 1st ed. Evidence of paper clip at half title, else Fine in dj, sl faded spine. *CAPTAIN'S BOOKSHELF.* $50

Bausch, Richard. THE FIREMAN'S WIFE AND OTHER STORIES. NY: Linden, (1990). 1st Amer ed. Signed. Fine in dj. *DORN.* $30

Bausch, Richard. VIOLENCE. Boston: Houghton Mifflin Co., (1992). 1st Amer ed. Uncorrected proof. Signed. Fine in wraps. *DORN.* $45

Bausch, Robert. ON THE WAY HOME. NY: St. Martin's Press, (c.1982). 1st ed. Inscribed. Fine in sl rubbed, NF, dj. *HELLER.* $65

Bautain, M. THE ART OF EXTEMPORE SPEAKING. NY: Charles Scribner & Co., 1871. 6th ed. Good+. *OLD LONDON.* $15

Baxt, George. A QUEER KIND OF DEATH. NY: S&S, (1966). 1st ed. The first mystery in the Pharoah Love trilogy. Signed. Fine in sl soiled dj. *UNGER.* $65

Baxt, George. SWING LOW, SWEET HARRIET. NY: S&S, (1967). 1st ed. Signed. Rmdr line, else Fine in edge-rubbed dj. *UNGER.* $50

Baxt, George. THE ALFRED HITCHCOCK MURDER CASE. NY: St. Martin's, (1986). 1st ed. Signed. Fine in Fine dj. *UNGER.* $35

Baxt, George. THE ALFRED HITCHCOCK MURDER CASE. NY: St. Martin's, 1986. 1st ed. Review copy, signed. Pub's slip laid in. Fine in dj. *SILVER DOOR.* $35

Baxt, George. TOPSY AND EVIL. NY: S&S, (1968). 1st ed. Fine in NF dj, spine faded. *UNGER.* $40

Baxter, Albert. HISTORY OF THE CITY OF GRAND RAPIDS, MICHIGAN. (WITH AN APPENDIX-HISTORY OF LOWELL, MICHIGAN). NY & Grand Rapids: Munsell & Co., 1891. 1st ed. Orig 3/4 lea, aeg. Some scuffing, etching of binding. Good, sturdy. *BOHLING.* $150

Baxter, James Phinney. PIONEERS OF NEW FRANCE IN NEW ENGLAND, WITH CONTEMPORARY LETTERS AND DOCUMENTS. Albany, Munsell, 1894. 1st ed. (2),450pp. Orig ptd boards, joints worn and chipped, bkpl removed. Howes B249. *GINSBERG.* $125

Baxter, William E. IMPRESSIONS OF CENTRAL AND SOUTHERN EUROPE; BEING NOTES OF SUCCESSIVE JOURNEYS....London, 1850. Full polished calf, richly gilt. xii,388pp. *O'NEILL.* $150

Bayley, Frank W. THE LIFE AND WORKS OF JOHN SINGLETON COPLEY. Boston: The Taylor Press. 1915. 1st ed. Frontis port. Burgundy cl, gilt spine. *KARMIOLE.* $35

Bayliss, William. THE VASO-MOTOR SYSTEM. London, 1923. 1st ed. *FYE.* $100

Beach, Rex. OH SHOOT! CONFESSIONS OF AN AGITATED SPORTSMAN. NY, (1921). Sl cvr staining. Several pages badly opened, o/w VG. *DIAMOND.* $25

Beach, Sylvia. ULYSSES IN PARIS. NY: Harcourt, Brace and Co., (1956). 1st ed. 24pp. Priv prtd as a New Year's greeting. Pict paper covered boards. *BLUE MOUNTAIN.* $50

Beadle, J.H. LIFE IN UTAH; OR, THE MYSTERIES AND CRIMES OF MORMONISM....Phila: National, 1870. Frontis. Fldg map, 540,(4),pp+14 plts. Orig cl, gilt dec. Extremity wear, stains. Tight, clean, Good. *CONNOLLY & WADE.* $75

Beadle, J.H. LIFE IN UTAH; OR, THE MYSTERIES AND CRIMES OF MORMONISM. Phila: National Publishing Company, c1870. Little rubbed, but clean, tight. *HUDSON.* $85

Beadle, J.H. WESTERN WILDS AND THE MEN WHO REDEEM THEM. Cincinnati, 1879. 634pp, 3/4 lea, marbled eps. Gilt lettering on the spine faded, moderate soil and wear on covers and edges, else VG+ externally, NF internally. *FIVE QUAIL.* $115

Beadle, J.H. WESTERN WILDS, AND THE MEN WHO REDEEM THEM. Cincinnati: Jones Brothers Publishing Company, 1879. Fldg frontis map. Pub's 1/2 morocco, gilt. Top of spine pulled. Subscription bk. *HUDSON.* $110

Beadnell, H.J.L. EGYPTIAN OASIS. London: John Murray, 1909. Soiled, rubbed. Fldg map. *SCHOYER'S.* $50

Beadnell, H.J.L. THE WILDERNESS OF SINAI. London, 1927. Uncut. *O'NEILL.* $40

Beagle, Peter S. I SEE BY MY OUTFIT. NY: Viking, 1965. 1st ed. NF in dj. *ELSE FINE.* $35

Beagle, Peter S. THE LAST UNICORN. NY: Viking, 1968. 1st ed. VF in dj. *ELSE FINE.* $80

Beagle, Peter. THE LAST UNICORN. NY: Viking Press, (1968). 1st ed. Fine in sl marked black dj, 2 short tears. *HELLER.* $75

Beaglehole, J.C. THE EXPLORATION OF THE PACIFIC. London: A. & C. Black, Ltd., 1934. Fldg maps. VG in poor dj. *PARMER.* $100

Beal, M.D. A HISTORY OF SOUTHEASTERN IDAHO. Caldwell: Caxton, 1942. 1st ed. VG. *OREGON.* $70

Beal, Merrill D. THE STORY OF MAN IN YELLOWSTONE. Caldwell: Caxton Printers, 1949. 1st ed. Inscribed. VG+ in Good dj. *PARMER.* $35

Beal, Rebecca J. JACOB EICHHOLTZ 1776-1842: PORTRAIT PAINTER OF PENNSYLVANIA. Phila: Hist Soc of PA, 1969. 1st ed. NF in dj. *BACKROOM.* $30

Beale, L.S. HOW TO WORK WITH THE MICROSCOPE. London: Harrison, 1880. New end leaves. Good. *BOOKCELL.* $45

Beale, Lionel. ON SLIGHT AILMENTS: THEIR NATURE AND TREATMENT. Phila, 1880. 1st Amer ed. *FYE.* $50

Beall, John Yates. TRIAL OF JOHN Y. BEALL, AS SPY AND GUERRILLERO BY MILITARY COMMISSION. NY, 1865. 1st ed. Orig wrappers, bound in cloth. Two small lib stamps, else NF. Howes B-276. *McGOWAN.* $375

Bealle, Morris. WASHINGTON SENATORS. Columbia Pub., 1947. 1st ed. Good+ in VG+ dj. *PLAPINGER.* $150

Bean, W.J. THE ROYAL BOTANIC GARDENS, KEW: HISTORI-CAL AND DESCRIPTIVE. London, (1908). 20 colored, 40 half-tone plts. Orig cl, lt wear, soiling; sm split bottom edge of spine; sl shaken. *SUTTON.* $145

Bear, Greg. BLOOD MUSIC. Arbor House, 1985. 1st ed. As New. *MADLE.* $35

Bear, Greg. QUEEN OF ANGELS. (NY): Warner, (1990). 1st ed. Signed. Fine in Fine dj. *AKA.* $25

Bear, Greg. TANGENTS. Warner Books, 1989. 1st ed. Fine in dj. *MADLE.* $25

Bear, Greg. THE WIND FROM A BURNING WOMAN. Sauk City: Arkham House, 1983. 1st ed. As New in dj. *ELSE FINE.* $125

Beard, George & A.D. Rockwell. A PRACTICAL TREATISE ON THE MEDICAL AND SURGICAL USES OF ELECTRICITY. NY, 1871. 1st ed. 698pp. 102 Fine woodcut illus. Backstrip faded, binding water spotted, inner hinges cracked. Contents VG. Scarce. *FYE.* $200

Beard, George and A.D. Rockwell. A PRACTICAL TREATISE ON THE MEDICAL & SURGICAL USES OF ELECTRICITY. NY, 1875. 2nd ed. 794pp. Nearly 200 woodcut illus. *FYE.* $150

Beard, George. SEXUAL NEURASTHENIA (NERVOUS EXHAUSTION). NY, 1884. 1st ed. 270pp. Scarce. *FYE.* $150

Beard, George. STIMULANTS AND NARCOTICS; MEDICALLY, PHILOSOPHICALLY, AND MORALLY CONSIDERED. NY, 1871. 1st ed. 155pp. *FYE.* $200

Beard, Mary Ritter. ON UNDERSTANDING WOMEN. London & NY: Longmans, Green, 1931. 1st ed. Fairly soiled in dj. *SCHOYER'S.* $30

Beard, Peter. THE END OF THE GAME: THE LAST WORD FROM PARADISE. GC: Doubleday, 1977. 1st rev ed. Review copy, slip laid in. Fine in pict wrappers. *CAPTAIN'S BOOKSHELF.* $75

Beardsley, Harry M. JOSEPH SMITH AND HIS MORMON EMPIRE. Boston, 1931. 1st ed. VG. *DIAMOND.* $35

Beare, W. THE ROMAN STAGE: A SHORT HISTORY OF LATIN DRAMA IN THE TIME OF THE REPUBLIC. London: Methuen, (1964). 8 plts. Good in dj. *ARCHAEOLOGIA.* $45

Bearss, Edwin C. FORREST AT BRICE'S CROSS ROADS. Dayton, 1979. 1st ed. Light cover wear o/w Fine. *PRATT.* $30

Bearss, Edwin C. HARDLUCK IRONCLAD, THE SINKING AND SALVAGE OF THE CAIRO. Baton Rouge, 1966. 1st ed. Cvr soiling o/w VG+. *PRATT.* $35

Bearss, Edwin C. STEELE'S RETREAT FROM CAMDEN AND THE BATTLE OF JENKINS FERRY. Little Rock, (1967). 1st ed. Dj wear with one small piece torn from rear o/w VG+. *PRATT.* $45

Beatie, George & Helen. HERITAGE OF THE VALLEY. SAN BERNARDINO'S FIRST CENTURY. Pasadena: San Pasqual Press, 1939. 1st ed. Fldg map. Fine in heavily chipped and torn dj. *OREGON.* $125

Beatie, R.H., Jr. ROAD TO MANASSAS. N.p., 1961. 1st ed. 285pp. VG+ in dj. *PRATT.* $37.50

Beatis, Antonio de. THE TRAVEL JOURNAL OF ANTONIO DE BEATIS. GERMANY, SWITZERLAND, THE LOW COUNTRIES, FRANCE AND ITALY, 1517-1518. J.R. Hale and J.M.A. Lindon (trans). London: Hakluyt Society, 1979. Hakluyt Society, Second Series No. 150. Plts, 1 figure, 1 fldg map. Orig cl, dj. VG. *WORLDWIDE.* $45

Beaton, Cecil. THE YEARS BETWEEN. DIARIES: 1939-44. NY: Holt Rinehart Winston, 1965. 1st ed. Bkpl, else NF. *SMITH.* $30

Beaton, George (pseud of Gerald Brenan). JACK ROBINSON. A PICARESQUE NOVEL. NY, 1934. 1st Amer ed, 1st bk. Rear covers foxed. NF in dj (spine sunned, edge chipped, torn along flap folds). *POLYANTHOS.* $50

Beattie, Ann. ALEX KATZ. Abrams, 1987. 1st ed. VF in dj. Signed. *STAHR.* $40

Beattie, Ann. CHILLY SCENES OF WINTER. GC: Doubleday, 1976. Uncorrected proof. Spine sl cocked; NF in tall wraps. *LOPEZ.* $200

Beattie, Ann. CHILLY SCENES OF WINTER. GC: Doubleday, 1976. 1st ed. Fine in NF dj. *LOPEZ.* $85

Beattie, Ann. CHILLY SCENES OF WINTER. NY: Doubleday (1976). Adv copy (stamped on front pastedown). VG (some typical discoloration of spine cl) in sl chipped dj (creased front panel). *DORN.* $75

Beattie, Ann. DISTORTIONS. GC, NY: Doubleday, (1976). 1st ed, 1st bk. Orig cl-backed boards. Fine in NF dj. *CHAPEL HILL.* $125

Beattie, Ann. DISTORTIONS. NY: Doubleday (1976). 1st ed. Top, bottom of spine bumped else VG in price-clipped sl chipped dj. *DORN.* $75

Beattie, Ann. LOVE ALWAYS. Random House, 1985. 1st ed. Fine in dj. Signed. *STAHR.* $35

Beattie, Ann. PICTURING WILL. NY: RH, (1989). Uncorrected proof. NF. *LOPEZ.* $45

Beattie, Ann. WHAT WAS MINE. NY: Random House (1991). 1st ed. Signed. Fine in dj. *DORN.* $35

Beattie, Ann. WHERE YOU'LL FIND ME. Linden Press, 1986. 1st ed. VF in dj. Signed. *STAHR.* $35

Beattie, William. SWITZERLAND. Illus (views) by W.H. Bartlett. London: George Virtue. 1836. 1st ed. 2 vols. (8),188; (4),152pp. 106 steel-engr plts, fldg map. Contemp 1/2 olive morocco over marbled boards, gilt spines. Occasional foxing, mostly marginal; overall a very nice, clean set. Pls w/tissue guards. *KARMIOLE.* $850

Beattie, William. THE CASTLES AND ABBEYS; OR, ENGLAND FROM THE NATIONAL RECORDS, EARLY CHRONICLES, AND OTHER STANDARD AUTHORITIES. London: Virtue, n.d. (c. 1850). 4to, xvi,351pp. 10 engr plts. Contemp morocco, front cover detached, edges a little rubbed and scuffed, but internally VG and clean; aeg. *WORLDWIDE.* $60

Beatty, Clyde and Earl Wilson. JUNGLE PERFORMERS. NY: McBride, 1941. 1st ed. Signed. VG. *OCTOBER FARM.* $25

Beatty, David L. DON'T TREAD ON MY TIRE RUBBER SANDALS; A TALE OF VIETNAM. Boonville: Seven Oceans, (1969). 1st ed. Signed. Fine in dj. Uncommon. *DORN.* $100

Beatty, John W. THE RELATION OF ART TO NATURE. NY: William Edwin Rudge. 1922. Ltd to 950. *KARMIOLE.* $35

Beatty, John. MEMOIRS OF A VOLUNTEER 1861-1863. Cincinnati, 1879. 1946 reprint. VG in dj. *PRATT.* $50

Beatty, John. MEMOIRS OF A VOLUNTEER, 1861-1863. NY: Norton, 1946. 1st ed. Bumped, silverfishing. Dj badly silverfished, o/w Near VG. *ARCHER.* $25

Beatty, Richard Croom (ed). A VANDERBILT MISCELLANY 1919-1944. Nashville: Vanderbilt Univ Press, 1944. 1st ed. Fine (bkpl, 2 owner sigs). Sl used pict dj. Signed. *CAPTAIN'S BOOKSHELF.* $175

Beaty, Richard Edward. THE MOUNTAIN ANGELS. Front Royall: the author, (c. 1928). VG. *BOOK BROKER.* $25

BEAUCHAMPE, OR THE KENTUCKY TRAGEDY. (By William Gilmore Simms.) Phila: Lea and Blanchard, 1842. 2 vols, 1st ed. (2)pp ads,303pp; (2)pp ads,301pp,(2)pp ads. Orig purple muslin w/paper spine labels. Some fading of binding, sl rubbing of labels, but handsome set showing little wear. *CHAPEL HILL.* $600

Beaudry, Louis Napolean. HISTORIC RECORDS OF THE FIFTH NEW YORK CAVALRY, FIRST IRA HARRIS GUARD. Albany, NY, 1865. 1st ed. Orig full leather, pub's presentation binding. VG to NF. *McGOWAN.* $185

Beaufort, Emily A. EGYPTIAN SEPULCHRES AND SYRIAN SHRINES....London, 1874. Full dk blue calf, gilt. Very sl rubbing. *O'NEILL.* $50

Beaumont, Charles. THE HUNGER AND OTHER STORIES. NY: Putnam, (1957). 1st ed. 1st book. Bump to bottom edge of front cover, o/w Fine in NF dj chipped at crown. *LOPEZ.* $100

Beaumont, Charles. THE INTRUDER. NY: Putnam, 1959. 1st ed, 1st novel. NF, dj has few edgetears, chipped at upper edge. *ELSE FINE.* $55

Beaumont, Cyril W. THE BALLET CALLED SWAN LAKE. London: C.W. Beaumont. 1952. 1st ed. Fldg diagram. Presentation, signed. Cl a bit soiled. Dj. *KARMIOLE.* $60

Beaumont, Francis. SALMACIS AND HERMAPHRODITUS. Gwyn Jones (ed). (London): Golden Cockerel Press, 1951. 1st ed. 10 engr by John Buckland-Wright. Orig 1/4 blue morroco, grn cl, grn slipcase. One of 80 containing an extra plt, specially bound, signed by Buckland-Wright & Gwyn Jones. Sl foxed, spine sl dulled, o/w Fine. *JAFFE.* $650

Beaumont, William. EXPERIMENTS AND OBSERVATIONS ON THE GASTRIC JUICE, AND THE PHYSIOLOGY OF DIGESTION. Plattsburgh, 1833. 1st ed. Orig boards, rebacked, new eps. Small paper repair to upper, inner corner of title page. *FYE.* $1,750

Beaupre, Moricheau. A TREATISE ON THE EFFECTS AND PROPERTIES OF COLD, WITH A SKETCH, HISTORICAL AND MEDICAL, OF THE RUSSIAN CAMPAIGN. Trans. by John Clendinning. Edinburgh, 1826. 1st ed. 375pp. Orig boards, rebacked, w/preservation of part of ptd label. Name clipped from title page. Inscribed by trans. Scarce. *FYE.* $400

Beaver, C. Masten. FORT YUKON TRADER. THREE YEARS IN AN ALASKAN WILDERNESS. NY: Exposition Press, (1955). 1st ed. VG+ in VG- dj. *BLUE DRAGON.* $25

Beaver, Wilfred N. UNEXPLORED NEW GUINEA. Phila: J.B. Lippincott Co. 1920. 1st ed. Cl lightly stained. *KARMIOLE.* $60

Beazley, C. Raymond. THE DAWN OF MODERN GEOGRAPHY, VOL III. A HISTORY OF EXPLORATION...MIDDLE OF THE THIRTEENTH TO THE EARLY YEARS OF THE FIFTEENTH CENTURY (c. A.D. 1260-1420). Oxford: Clarendon Press, 1906. 1st ed. Maroon cl. Fine. *WEBER.* $60

Beazley, J.D. ATTIC BLACK-FIGURE VASE-PAINTERS. Oxford: Clarendon Press, 1956. Dj. Good. *ARCHAEOLOGIA.* $45

Beazley, J.D. ATTIC RED-FIGURE VASE PAINTERS. 3 vols. Oxford: Clarendon Press, 1963. 2nd ed. Dj. Good. *ARCHAEOLOGIA.* $650

Becatti, Giovani. THE ART OF ANCIENT GREECE AND ROME. John Ross (trans). NY: Abrams, n.d. (c. 1967). 1st ed. Torn dj. VG. *WORLDWIDE.* $95

Bechdolt, Frederick R. TALES OF THE OLD-TIMERS. Century, 1924. 1st ed. VG to Fine. *VARNER.* $45

Beck, L.C. BOTANY OF THE NORTHERN AND MIDDLE STATES....Albany, 1833. Pp lv,471. Contemp calf worn, backstrip mostly perished, spine reinforced w/tape, front cover partially loose. Foxing. Ex-lib. *SUTTON.* $125

Becker, Bob. THE DEVIL BIRD. Reilly & Lee, 1933. 1st ed. VG *MADLE.* $35

Becker, Ethel A. A TREASURY OF ALASKANA. Seattle: Superior, 1969. 1st ed. Fine in Fine dj. *GREAT EPIC.* $55

Becker, Ethel A. HERE COMES THE POLLY. Seattle: Superior Pub Co, 1971. 1st ed. Fine in dj. *PARMER.* $35

Becker, Friedrich. THE BREED OF THE RACEHORSE. London: British Bloodstock, 1935. 1st ed. Good+. *OCTOBER FARM.* $85

Becker, Robert (ed). THOMAS CHRISTY'S ROAD ACROSS THE PLAINS. Denver: Old West, 1969. 1st ed. Ptd in ed of 2000. Prospectus laid in. Uncut, unopened. VF in VF dj. *OREGON.* $40

Becker, Robert H. (ed) THOMAS CHRISTY'S ROAD ACROSS THE PLAINS: A GUIDE....Denver: Fred A. Rosenstock/Old West Pub. Co, 1969. Frontis, 94 maps. Bound in orig pub cl. Fine. *LAURIE.* $30

Becker, Robert. DESIGNS ON THE LAND. DISENOS OF CALIFORNIA RANCHOS & THEIR MAKERS. Bk Club of CA, 1969. 1st ed. Ltd to 500 ptd by Grabhorn-Hoyem. Unpaginated (180pp). 2 sheet prospectus laid in. VF. *OREGON.* $335

Beckett, Samuel (ed). OUR EXAGMINATION ROUND HIS FACTIFICATION FOR INCAMINATION OF WORK IN PROGRESS. Paris: Shakespeare and Co., 1929. 1st ed. Minor soiling and wear with chipping at extremities. Altogether VG. This has the scarce "Made in Great Britain" stamped on the title page. *OLD LONDON.* $200

Beckett, Samuel. ALL THAT FALL. London: Faber, 1958. 1st ed. A little rubbed at spine corners; NF in wraps. *ELSE FINE.* $40

Beckett, Samuel. ALL THAT FALL. NY: Grove (1957). 1st ed. NF in dj (wrinkled but still NF). *LOPEZ.* $125

Beckett, Samuel. COLLECTED POEMS IN ENGLISH AND FRENCH. Grove Press, 1977. 1st Amer ed. Fine in dj. *STAHR.* $25

Beckett, Samuel. DISJECTA: MISCELLANEOUS WRITINGS AND A DRAMATIC FRAGMENT. Grove Press, 1984. 1st Amer ed. Fine in dj. *STAHR.* $20

Beckett, Samuel. FIRST LOVE AND OTHER SHORTS. Grove Press, 1974. 1st Amer. ed. Fine in dj. *STAHR.* $25

Beckett, Samuel. HAPPY DAYS. A PLAY. NY: Grove Press, 1961. 1st ed. Evergreen Original. NF. *POLYANTHOS.* $20

Beckett, Samuel. HOW IT IS. NY: Grove Press, Inc, (1964). 1st Amer ed. Rev copy, slip laid in. Fine in dj. *HELLER.* $50

Beckett, Samuel. HOW IT IS. London, 1964. Ltd ed, 42/100 only on handmade paper, signed. Printed hors commerce in adv of 1st ed. Teg, uncut and partly unopened. Full morocco gilt spine. Spine very sl sunned. Fine in slipcase. *POLYANTHOS.* $400

Beckett, Samuel. HOW IT IS. Trans by the Author. London: John Calder, (1964). 1st ed. Precedes trade ed. Orig full vellum, teg. Sl bowed, but Fine, clean, untrimmed and unopened. #33 of 100 hors commerce (series A) ptd on handmade paper, signed by Beckett. *CHAPEL HILL.* $500

Beckett, Samuel. ILL SEEN, ILL SAID. CA: Lord John Press, 1982. Ltd ed of 299 signed. 1/4 leather, marbled boards. Mint. No dj, as issued. *POLYANTHOS.* $100

Beckett, Samuel. ILL SEEN, ILL SAID. Grove Press, 1981. 1st Amer ed. Fine in dj. *STAHR.* $20

Beckett, Samuel. ILL SEEN, ILL SAID. Lord John Press, 1982. 1/299 numbered/signed. As New. *DERMONT.* $125

Beckett, Samuel. ILL SEEN, ILL SAID. Northridge: Lord John Press, 1982. 1st ed. One of 299 in 1/4 leather and marbled boards. Signed. Fine. *CAPTAIN'S BOOKSHELF.* $125

Beckett, Samuel. PROUST. London: Chatto & Windus, 1931. 1st ed. 2pp ads. Dec boards in dj; minimal foxing. *DAWSON'S.* $150

Beckett, Samuel. PROUST. London: Chatto & Windus, 1931. 1st ed. Fine in dj (sl sunned spine; few tiny nicks). *CAPTAIN'S BOOKSHELF.* $250

Beckett, Samuel. PROUST. London: Chatto & Windus, 1931. 1st ed. Orig pict boards. Spine lightly sunned, else NF. *CHAPEL HILL.* $125

Beckett, Samuel. ROCKABY AND OTHER SHORT PIECES. Grove Press, 1981. 1st Amer ed. Fine in dj. *STAHR.* $20

Beckett, Samuel. THREE NOVELS BY SAMUEL BECKETT: MOLLOY, MALONE DIES, THE UNNAMABLE. NY: Grove Press, (1959). 1st ed thus. Fine in dj (some wear head of spine, few short tears). *CAPTAIN'S BOOKSHELF.* $50

Beckett, Samuel. WORSTWARD HO. Grove Press, 1983. 1st Amer ed. Fine in dj. *STAHR.* $20

Beckford, Peter. THOUGHTS UPON HARE & FOX HUNTING. NY & London: Cape, 1932. VG. *OCTOBER FARM.* $40

Beckford, William. ITALY, SPAIN, AND PORTUGAL... WITH AN EXCURSION TO THE MONASTERIES OF ALCOBACSA AND BATALHA. 2 vols. in one. NY: Wiley & Putnam, 1845. xxii, 174; xii, 256pp. Contemp 3/4 brn morocco, rubbed. Some small marginal notes in pencil. *SCHOYER'S.* $65

Beckford, William. VATHEK. London: Nonesuch Press, 1929. Ltd ed, 1146/1550. 500 of which are for sale in US. 10 illus. Uncut. Vellum spine sunned, edges rubbed, covers little soiled. Fine. *POLYANTHOS.* $60

Beckwith, John. THE ART OF CONSTANTINOPLE. AN INTRODUCTION TO BYZANTINE ART 330-1453. London, 1968. Dj. *O'NEILL.* $35

Beckworth, James P. THE LIFE AND ADVENTURES OF JAMES P. BECKWORTH AS TOLD TO THOMAS D. BONNER. Lincoln: Univ of NE, 1972. 1st ed thus. Fine in VG dj. Howes B601. *CONNOLLY & WADE.* $42.50

Beclard, P.A. ADDITIONS TO THE GENERAL ANATOMY OF XAVIER BICHAT. George Hayward (trans). Boston, 1823. 1st Eng trans. Full leather, 328pp. *FYE.* $250

Beddoes, Thomas. OBSERVATIONS ON THE NATURE AND CURE OF CALCULUS, SEA SCURVY, CONSUMPTION, CATARRH, AND FEVER: TOGETHER WITH CONJECTURES UPON SEVERAL OTHER SUBJECTS OF PHYSIOLOGY AND PATHOLOGY. Phila, 1797. 1st Amer. ed. 279pp. Full leather. Scarce. *FYE.* $175

Bedell, Mary Crehore. MODERN GYPSIES: THE STORY OF A TWELVE THOUSAND MILE MOTOR CAMPING TRIP....NY: Brentano's, (1924). 1st ed. Pict cl cvr. Signed by author's husband. VG. *SCHOYER'S.* $45

Bedford-Jones, H. D'ARTAGNAN'S LETTER. Covici-Friede, 1931. 1st ed. NF in sl chipped dj. *MADLE.* $40

Bedford-Jones, H. THE MISSION AND THE MAN. THE STORY OF SAN JUAN CAPISTRANO. Pasadena: San Pasqual Press, 1939. 1st ed. Pict cl. Fine in VG, scarce dj. *CONNOLLY & WADE.* $100

Bedichek, Roy. ADVENTURES WITH A TEXAS NATURALIST. Doubleday & Co, 1947. 1st ed. Fine in dj. *AUTHORS OF THE WEST.* $60

Bedichek, Roy. THE SENSE OF SMELL. London: Michael Joseph, (1960). 1st British ed. Fine in dj. *AUTHORS OF THE WEST.* $50

Bee, J.W. and E.R. Hall. MAMMALS OF NORTHERN ALASKA. Lawrence, KS: Univ of KS, Mar. 1956. 1st ed. Fine. *MIKESH.* $25

Beebe, C.W. TWO BIRD-LOVERS IN MEXICO. Boston, 1905. Orig orange pict cl. Good. Ex-lib. *SUTTON.* $30

Beebe, Lucius and Charles Clegg. HEAR THE TRAIN BLOW, A PICTORIAL EPIC OF AMERICA IN THE RAILROAD AGE. NY, 1952. 1st ed. Dj frayed. Folio. *HEINOLDT.* $35

Beebe, Lucius and Charles Clegg. HEAR THE TRAIN BLOW....NY: Dutton, 1952. 1st ed. VG. *ARTIS.* $35

Beebe, Lucius and Charles Glegg. LEGENDS OF THE COMSTOCK LODE. Oakland: Grahame H. Hardy, 1950. 1st ed. VF in VG dj. *CONNOLLY & WADE.* $30

Beebe, Lucius and Charles Clegg. LEGENDS OF THE COMSTOCK LODE. Carson City, NV, 1950 (1952). 4th ptg. Cvrs sl stained, soiled. Little spine tip, corner wear. Contents VG. Signed by both authors. *DIAMOND.* $45

Beebe, Lucius and Charles Clegg. RIO GRANDE, MAINLINE OF THE ROCKIES. H-North, 1962. 1st ed. Fine in Fine dj. *VARNER.* $40

Beebe, Lucius and Charles Clegg. VIRGINIA AND TRUCKEE. Oakland: Grahame H. Hardy, 1949. 1st ed, ltd to 950, signed by both authors. VG. *CONNOLLY & WADE.* $47.50

Beebe, Lucius. THE OVERLAND LIMITED. H-North, 1963. 1st ed. Fine in VG dj. *VARNER.* $30

Beebe, W.C. PHEASANTS: THEIR LIVES & HOMES. NY: Doubleday, 1926. 2 vols. 64 plts. B & w photo and map. Ex Libris. Good. *MIKESH.* $45

Beebe, William. HIGH JUNGLE. NY: Duell, Sloan & Pearce, 1949. 1st ed. 32 plts, map. NF in Good+ dj. *CONNOLLY & WADE.* $32.50

Beebe, William. JUNGLE DAYS. Putnam, 1925. 1st ed. VG. *MADLE.* $35

Beebe, William. NONSUCH: LAND OF WATER. NY, 1932. 1st ed. Bkpl. VG+. *DIAMOND.* $25

Beebe, William. THE ACTURUS ADVENTURE. NY: Putnam, 1926. 1st ed. 58 plts. Shadow from news clipping on 2pp. NF. *CONNOLLY & WADE.* $45

Beecher, Catherine E. A TREATISE ON DOMESTIC ECONOMY....NY: Harper, 1850. Rev ed. Blue cl. Sl wear. VG. *SECOND LIFE.* $75

Beecher, Harris H. RECORD OF THE 114TH REGIMENT N.Y.S.V....Norwich, NY, 1866. 1st ed. 2 engr plts. Rebacked w/orig backstrip. Little cvr wear, soiling, staining. Some age-staining in text, o/w VG. *DIAMOND.* $75

Beecher, Henry Ward. PLAIN AND PLEASANT TALK ABOUT FRUITS, FLOWERS AND FARMING. NY: Derby & Jackson, 1859. 1st ed. Fine. *JUVELIS.* $50

Beecher, Henry. RESUSCITATION AND ANESTHESIA FOR WOUNDED MEN. THE MANAGEMENT OF TRAUMATIC SHOCK. Springfield, 1949. 1st ed. *FYE.* $50

Beecher, Henry. THE PHYSIOLOGY OF ANESTHESIA. NY, 1938. 1st ed. *FYE.* $50

Beecher, Rev. Edward. NARRATIVE OF RIOTS AT ALTON; IN CONNECTION WITH THE DEATH OF REV. ELIJAH P. LOVEJOY. Alton, 1838. 1st ed. 159pp. Orig cl boards, paper label on spine, small piece missing. Howes B307. *GINSBERG.* $125

Beede, A. McG. SITTING BULL-CUSTER. Bismark, (1913). 1st ed. Orig gold stamped brown suede. Very scarce. *GINSBERG.* $150

Beeding, Frances. THE TEN HOLY HORRORS. NY: Harper & Brothers, 1939. 1st Amer ed. Bkpl on front ep o/w VG in dj w/minor wear at top of spine and at corners. *MORDIDA.* $40

Beeding, Francis. DEATH WALKS IN EASTREPPS. NY: The Mystery League, Inc, 1931. 1st US ed. Spine bowed, lower corner tips sl bumped, name o/w VG in edge worn chipped dj. *BERNARD.* $75

Beer, Thomas. HANNA. NY: Knopf, 1929. 1st ed. Lea label on linen backstrip, paper label on front cover. VG. *CONNOLLY & WADE.* $37.50

Beer, Thomas. HANNA. NY: Knopf, 1929. Lg ed, lg-paper #160/250, signed. Cl, boards. *SCHOYER'S.* $30

Beerbohm, Julius. WANDERINGS IN PATAGONIA....NY: Henry Holt and Company, 1879. Fldg map. Orig cl w/black titles, decs. Sl soiled, else VG. *PARMER.* $75

Beerbohm, Max. AND EVEN NOW. London, 1920. 1st ed. Uncut. Spine little sunned, extremities sl rubbed, 2 corners sl creased; dj spine sunned, chip, small heel piece missing, panels little dust soiled. *POLYANTHOS.* $75

Beerbohm, Max. AROUND THEATRES. NY: Knopf, 1930. 2 vols. 1st US ed. Newspaper clipping pasted inside frt cvr of vol 1; tiny nick inside frt cvr second vol. Fine. *WOOLMER.* $50

Beerbohm, Max. LYTTON STRACHEY. The Rede Lecture, 1943. C.U.P. 1943. 1st ed. Spine sl sunned. Printed wraps. Fine. *POLYANTHOS.* $25

Beerbohm, Max. OBSERVATIONS. London: Heinemann, 1923. 1st ed. Fine in dj. *JAFFE.* $250

Beerbohm, Max. THINGS NEW AND OLD. London: Heinemann, 1923. 1st ed. Fine in dj. *JAFFE.* $250

Behan, Richard. PAIN: ITS ORIGIN, CONDUCTION, PERCEPTION AND DIAGNOSTIC SIGNIFICANCE. NY, 1914. 1st ed. Exceptionally Fine. *FYE.* $100

Behn, Aphra, (trans). THE HISTORY OF THE ORACLES, AND THE CHEATS OF THE PAGAN PRIESTS BY (BOVIER DE FONTENELLE). IN TWO PARTS, MADE ENGLISH. London: 1688. 1st ed. (20),227,(5)pp. Signed A.B. Rebacked contemp calf, VG. *SECOND LIFE.* $850

Behrens, Charles (ed). ATOMIC MEDICINE. NY, 1949. 416pp. *FYE.* $150

Belcher, Captain Sir Edward et al. THE LAST OF THE ARCTIC VOYAGES; BEING A NARRATIVE OF THE EXPEDITION IN H. M. S. ASSISTANCE...SEARCH OF SIR JOHN FRANKLIN DURING THE YEARS 1852-53-54 WITH NOTES ON THE

NATURAL HISTORY. London: Lovell Reeve, 1855. Maps (3 fldg, 2 in pocket), 36 plts, 25 engr. Some rubbing to extremities; expert repair to hinge of 1 map. 2 vols bound in 1. *PARMER*. $1,150

Beldam, G.W. and Fry, C.B. GREAT BATSMEN—THEIR METHODS AT A GLANCE. London: MacMillan and Co., 1907. Reissue of 1st ed of 1905). VG. *OLD LONDON*. $150

Belden, Josiah. JOSIAH BELDEN...HIS MEMOIR AND EARLY LETTERS. Georgetown: Talisman, 1962. 1st ed, ltd to 750. Signed presentation. Fine. *OREGON*. $30

Belden, L. Burr. DEATH VALLEY HEROINE AND SOURCE ACCOUNTS OF THE 1849 TRAVELERS. San Bernardino: Inland Printing. 1st ed, ltd to 250. 78pp. Fine. *BOOK MARKET*. $38

Belden, Thomas Graham & Marva Roberts. SO FELL THE ANGELS. Boston, (1956). 1st ed. Dj wear o/w VG+. *PRATT*. $25

Beldham, G.W. and Fry, C.B. GREAT BOWLERS AND FIELDERS—THEIR METHODS AT A GLANCE. London: MacMillan and Co., 1907. Reissue of 1st ed of 1906. Vol II 2-vol series. Inscribed by Beldham. Good. *OLD LONDON*. $150

Belknap, Charles E. HISTORY OF THE MICHIGAN ORGANIZATIONS AT CHICKAMAUGA, CHATTANOOGA AND MISSIONARY RIDGE, 1863. Lansing, 1899. 2nd ed. Inscribed. Fine. *PRATT*. $60

Belknap, Waldron Phoenix Jr. AMERICAN COLONIAL PAINTING. Cambridge: Harvard Univ Press, (1959). 1st ed. (21) 377pp + 75pp of photo ports. 4to. Gilt cloth. VG to Fine. *ARTIS*. $25

Bell, A.N. CLIMATOLOGY AND MINERAL WATERS OF THE UNITED STATES. NY, 1885. 1st ed. 386pp. *FYE*. $125

Bell, Alexander Graham. ON THE NATURE AND USES OF VISIBLE SPEECH...Boston: Rand, Avery & Co., 1872. 1st ed. 8pp. Wrappers detached, soiled, worn, and repaired. Several pp almost detached, several page margins repaired. *DIAMOND*. $125

Bell, Benjamin. A SYSTEM OF SURGERY. Phila, 1791. 1st Amer ed. Full leather, xxx, 570pp. Inner hinges taped, front outer hinge cracked, 1/2 of leather backstrip missing. *FYE*. $250

Bell, Benjamin. A TREATISE ON THE THEORY AND MANAGEMENT OF ULCERS: WITH A DISSERTATION ON WHITE SWELLINGS OF THE JOINTS. TO WHICH IS PREFIXED, AN ESSAY ON THE CHIRURGICAL TREATMENT OF INFLAMMATION AND ITS CONSEQUENCES. Boston, 1797. Full leather, 264pp. *FYE*. $250

Bell, Charles. A SYSTEM OF OPERATIVE SURGERY, FOUNDED ON THE BASIS OF ANATOMY. Hartford, 1812. 1st Amer ed. 2 vols. 323, 272pp + 19 plts. Fine woodcut illus, engrvd plts. Recent leatherette w/new eps. Scarce *FYE*. $500

Bell, Charles. ENGRAVINGS OF THE ARTERIES; ILLUSTRATING THE SECOND VOLUME OF THE ANATOMY OF THE HUMAN BODY...AND SERVING AS AN INTRODUCTION TO THE SURGERY OF THE ARTERIES. London, 1801. 1st ed. Recent leatherette, 49pp. 10 hand-colored engrvd plts. Title page and half title in Xerox facsimile (bound in). O/w VG. *FYE*. $250

Bell, Charles. ENGRAVINGS OF THE BRAIN AND NERVES. Birmingham, 1982. Facs of the 1802, 1803 and 1829 eds. 1st collected ed. Full lea. Fine colored illus. *FYE*. $60

Bell, Charles. ESSAYS ON THE ANATOMY OF EXPRESSION IN PAINTING. London, 1806. 1st ed. 4to, 186pp. Engrvs. Beautifully rebound in 1/2 leather w/marbled boards, new eps. Fine, large paper, untrimmed. *FYE*. $1,500

Bell, Charles. MANUSCRIPT OF DRAWINGS OF THE ARTERIES. NY, 1971, Ltd ed. 12 colored plts. Slipcase. *FYE*. $60

Bell, Charles. THE ANATOMY AND PHILOSOPHY OF EXPRESSION AS CONNECTED WITH THE FINE ARTS. London, 1844. 3rd ed. 1/2 leather, 265pp. Fine copper plts engrvs. Scattered foxing as usual. *FYE*. $400

Bell, Charles. THE ANATOMY AND PHILOSOPHY OF EXPRESSION AS CONNECTED WITH THE FINE ARTS. London, 1888. 7th ed. 254pp. Engr plts. *FYE*. $75

Bell, Charles. THE HAND: ITS MECHANISM AND VITAL ENDOWMENTS AS EVINCING DESIGN. London, 1837. 4th ed. 368pp. Tears affecting 2 leaves w/o loss of text, o/w VF in orig binding. *FYE*. $300

Bell, Currer (pseud of Charlotte Bronte). THE PROFESSOR. A TALE. NY: Harper & Brothers, 1857. 1st Amer ed. Orig brn cl, rubbed, bumped; blind stamped dec frame, titled & ruled in gilt on spine (cloth split at rear joint, head, tail chipped). 330pp, 6 ads (lt scattered foxing). VG. *BLUE MOUNTAIN*. $75

Bell, George. ROUGH NOTES BY AN OLD SOLDIER, DURING FIFTY YEARS SERVICE, FROM ENSIGN G. B. TO MAJOR - GENERAL, C. B. London: Day, 1867. 2 vols. ed. (12),367; (8),382pp. Port, frontis. Orig gold dec red cl w/blue gilt cl spines, light tear on spine of vol 2, else attractive set. *GINSBERG*. $750

Bell, Gertrude. THE LETTERS OF GERTRUDE BELL. London: Ernest Benn, 1927. (2 Vols). Lady Bell (ed). Fldg map. Worn but complete reading copy. *GREAT EPIC*. $25

Bell, Gertrude. LETTERS OF GERTRUDE BELL. Selected and Ed. by Lady (Florence) Bell. NY: Liveright, n.d. (c. 1927). 2 vols. Blue-grey cl, spines faded and discolored. 39 illus, 2 maps, one fldg. *SCHOYER'S*. $25

Bell, Horace. ON THE OLD WEST COAST: BEING FURTHER REMINISCENCES OF A RANGER. NY: Morrow, 1930. Lanier Bartlett (ed). 1st ed, ltd to 210 signed. VF in torn glassine dj, VF slipcase. *BOOK MARKET*. $200

Bell, Horace. ON THE OLD WEST COAST: BEING FURTHER REMINISCENCES OF A RANGER. NY: Morrow, 1930. 38pp photo illus. Two-tone cl w/paper labels in dj, newspaper stain to 2pp. *DAWSON'S*. $40

Bell, Horace. REMINISCENCES OF A RANGER. OR EARLY TIMES IN SOUTHERN CALIFORNIA. LA: Primavera Press, 1933. VG. Howes B325. *OREGON*. $50

Bell, Horace. REMINISCENCES OF A RANGER....LA: Yarnell, Caystile & Mathes, 1881. 1st ed. Orig grn cl, bright, binding extrems sl rubbed, lt foxing to prelim eps o/w Fine. The 1st bk ptd, bound in LA. *BOOK MARKET*. $450

Bell, James Mackintosh. WILDS OF MAORILAND. London: MacMillan, 1914. 6 maps in text, 2 fldg maps. Blue cl stamped in gilt, scuffed and rubbed. *SCHOYER'S*. $70

Bell, John R. THE JOURNAL OF CAPTAIN JOHN R. BELL. Glendale: The Arthur H. Clark Company, 1973. 2nd ptg. Fldg map, frontis. Grn cl. Fine. *PARMER*. $85

Bell, John. DISCOURSES ON THE NATURE AND CURE OF WOUNDS. Walpole, 1807. 1st Amer ed. Recent half leather, 192, 180pp. 2 engrvd plts. *FYE*. $300

Bell, John. PRINCIPLES OF SURGERY. NY, 1810. 1st Amer ed. Full leather, 562pp. Front hinge cracked o/w Fine. Numerous Fine engrvd plts. Scarce. *FYE*. $300

Bell, John. REPORT OF THE IMPORTANCE AND ECONOMY OF SANITARY MEASURES TO CITIES. NY, 1859. 243pp. 1" piece missing from spine, fep taped. *FYE*. $200

Bell, John. THE PRINCIPLES OF SURGERY. NY, 1812. 2nd Amer ed. Full leather, 562pp. Binding scuffed, worn, front hinge broken. Contents VG. *FYE*. $150

Bell, Josephine. DEATH AT THE MEDICAL BOARD. London: Longmans Green, 1944. 1st ed. Edges spotted and covers discolored o/w VG in price-clipped dj w/one-inch piece missing from back panel and chipping at top of spine. *MORDIDA*. $45

Bell, Josephine. DOUBLE DOOM. London: Hodder and Stoughton, 1957. 1st ed. Sl cocked, o/w Fine in Fine dj. *BEASLEY*. $35

Bell, Josephine. THE HUNTER AND THE TRAPPED. London: Hodder and Stoughton, 1963. 1st ed. Sl cocked, o/w Fine in Fine dj. *BEASLEY*. $35

Bell, Lilian. THE LOVE AFFAIRS OF AN OLD MAID. NY: Harper, 1893. 1st ed, 1st bk. VG. *SECOND LIFE*. $65

Bell, Madison Smartt. SOLDIER'S JOY. NY: Ticknor & Fields, (1989). 1st Amer ed. Signed. Fine in dj. *DORN*. $35

Bell, Madison Smartt. SOLDIER'S JOY. NY: Ticknor & Fields, 1989. 1st ed. Fine in dj. Signed. *CAPTAIN'S BOOKSHELF*. $30

Bell, Madison Smartt. SOLDIER'S JOY. NY: Ticknor & Fields, 1989. 1st ed. Uncorrected proof. NF in Wraps. *SMITH*. $25

Bell, Madison Smartt. STRAIGHT CUT. NY: Ticknor & Fields, (1986). 1st Amer ed. Signed. Fine in NF dj. *DORN*. $40

Bell, Madison Smartt. STRAIGHT CUT. NY: Ticknor & Fields, 1986. 1st ed. Fine in dj. Inscribed. *CAPTAIN'S BOOKSHELF*. $40

Bell, Madison Smartt. STRAIGHT CUT. Ticknor & Fields, 1986. Advance review copy. Fine. *BEBBAH*. $25

Bell, Madison Smartt. THE WASHINGTON SQUARE ENSEMBLE. NY: Viking, (1983). 1st ed. Fine in dj. Signed. *CAPTAIN'S BOOKSHELF*. $100

Bell, Madison Smartt. THE YEAR OF SILENCE. NY: Ticknor & Fields, 1987. Proof copy. Lightly used wraps with edgewear. *ROBBINS*. $30

Bell, Madison Smartt. THE YEAR OF SILENCE. NY: Ticknor & Fields, (1987). 1st Amer ed. Signed. Fine in dj. *DORN*. $35

Bell, Madison Smartt. WAITING FOR THE END OF THE WORLD. NY: Ticknor and Fields, 1985. 1st ed. Fine in NF dj. *BEASLEY*. $40

Bell, Madison Smartt. ZERO DB AND OTHER STORIES. NY: Ticknor & Fields, 1987. Proof copy. NF in wraps. *ROBBINS*. $35

Bell, Madison Smartt. ZERO DB AND OTHER STORIES. NY: Ticknor & Fields, (1987). 1st Amer ed. Signed. Fine in dj. *DORN*. $35

Bell, Madison Smartt. ZERO DB AND OTHER STORIES. NY: Ticknor & Fields, 1987. 1st ed. Fine in dj. Inscribed. *CAPTAIN'S BOOKSHELF*. $40

Bell, Mrs. A.G. NUREMBURG. A&C Black, 1905. 1st ed. 7s 6d Series. Slight wear to extremities, else VG indeed. *OLD LONDON*. $45

Bell, Mrs. N.S. PATHWAYS OF THE PURITANS. Framingham, MA, (1930). 1st ed. Fold-out map. Slight corner wear, o/w VG. *ARTIS*. $17.50

Bell, Solomon. TALES OF TRAVELS WEST OF THE MISSISSIPPI. Boston, 1830. 1st ed. 162pp. Map, plts. Old cl. Howes S739. *GINSBERG*. $375

Bell, Thomas. A HISTORY OF BRITISH REPTILES. London, 1839. 1st ed. xxiv, 142pp. 40+ woodcuts. Lt scuffing, spine faded, bkpl. *SUTTON*. $75

Bell, Thomas. A HISTORY OF BRITISH REPTILES. London: J. Van Voorst, 1939. 1st ed. Small holes in spine, minor spine tip wear, bkpl, o/w Good. *DIAMOND*. $75

Bell, W.H. THE QUIDDITIES OF AN ALASKAN TRIP. Portland: C.A. Steel & Co, 1873. 1st ed. Sl wear to edges; overall VG. 67pp *PARMER*. $275

Bell, W.S. OLD FORT BENTON. WHAT IT WAS....Helena, 1909. 1st ed. Frontis, 1 photo, wraps. Fine. Howes B331. *OREGON*. $90

Bell, Walter George. THE GREAT PLAGUE IN LONDON IN 1665. London, 1924. 1st ed. *FYE*. $100

Bell, William A. NEW TRACKS IN NORTH AMERICA; A JOURNAL OF TRAVEL AND ADVENTURE WHILST ENGAGED IN A SURVEY FOR A SOUTHERN RAILROAD TO THE PACIFIC OCEAN DURING 1867-8. 2 vols. London, 1869. lxv,236; vii,322pp plus adverts. This set is lacking the "General Map To Face First Page of the Introduction," but incl all full-page color plts and woodcuts. Both vols attractively rebound. Repair work on some of the brittle text pages and plts. In general, good-looking. *FIVE QUAIL*. $225.

Bellairs, George. DEATH IN THE NIGHT WATCHES. Macmillan, 1946. 223pp. 1st ed. VG in Good dj with few chips, rubbing. *BEBBAH*. $20

Bellamann, Henry. KINGS ROW. NY: Simon & Schuster, 1940. 1st ed. Name stamp under front flap, else Fine in dj w/a few short edge tears. *CHAPEL HILL*. $40

Bellamy, Edward. EQUALITY. NY: D. Appleton & Co., 1897. 1st ed. 8vo, 412pp, (8)pp ads. Orig salmon cl. Small piece missing from rear ffep, adhesive remnants on rear pastedown, owner's signature, still VG. *CHAPEL HILL*. $65

Bellamy, Edward. THE DUKE OF STOCKBRIDGE. Boston: Silver, Burdett, 1900. Close to Fine. Name, price. *BEASLEY*. $75

Bellard, Alfred. Ed by David Herbert Donald. GONE FOR A SOLDIER, THE CIVIL WAR MEMOIRS OF PRIVATE ALFRED BELLARD. Boston, 1975. 1st ed. VG+. *PRATT*. $45

Belle, Francis P. LIFE AND ADVENTURES OF THE CELEBRATED BANDIT JOAQUIN MURRIETA (sic)....Frances P. Belle (trans). Chicago: Chas. T. Powner, 1937. 2nd ed, after a 1st ed of 975. Rust cl, black letters. VG. *CONNOLLY & WADE*. $35

Belloc, Hilaire. A CONVERSATION WITH A CAT AND OTHERS. NY: Harper, 1931. 1st US ed. Bkpl. VG+ in VG dj. *AARD*. $35

Belloc, Hilaire. DANTON. A STUDY. NY: Putnam, 1928. 1st Amer ed. Orig buckram. Spine faded and sl stained. Minor shelf wear, o/w VG. *DIAMOND*. $25

Bellow, Saul. HENDERSON THE RAIN KING. NY, 1959. 1st ed. Spine sl sunned. Fine in like dj. *POLYANTHOS*. $85

Bellow, Saul. HENDERSON THE RAIN KING. NY: Viking, 1959. 1st ed. Fine in Fine dj, w/few small tears at head of spine. *BEASLEY*. $125

Bellow, Saul. HERZOG. London: Weidenfeld & Nicholson, 1965. 1st ed. Fine; minor wear to dj. *ELSE FINE*. $50

Bellow, Saul. HERZOG. NY: Viking Press, (1964). 1st ed. Orig blue cl. NF in price-clipped dj. *CHAPEL HILL*. $45

Bellow, Saul. HIM WITH HIS FOOT IN HIS MOUTH....NY: Harper & Row, (1984). 1st ed. Orig blue cl. Fine in dj. *CHAPEL HILL*. $35

Bellow, Saul. HUMBOLDT'S GIFT. NY: Viking, 1975. 1st ed. Fine in Fine dj. *BEASLEY*. $45

Bellow, Saul. HUMBOLDT'S GIFT. NY: Viking Press, (1975). 1st ed. NF in dj (internally strengthened at edges). *LOPEZ*. $65

Bellow, Saul. HUMBOLDT'S GIFT. NY: Viking Press, (1975). 1st ed. Fine in dj. *JUVELIS*. $25

Bellow, Saul. HUMBOLDT'S GIFT. NY: Viking Press, (1975). Adv reading copy. VG in sl soiled yellow wrappers. *JUVELIS*. $70

Bellow, Saul. MOSBY'S MEMOIRS AND OTHER STORIES. NY: Viking, 1968. 1st ed. Fine in Fine dj. *BEASLEY*. $45

Bellow, Saul. MR. SAMMLER'S PLANET. NY: Viking, (1970). 1st ed. Orig cl-backed boards. Fine in dj. *CHAPEL HILL*. $50

Bellow, Saul. MR. SAMMLER'S PLANET. NY: Viking, 1970. 1st ed. Signed. Fine in Fine dj. *BEASLEY*. $75

Bellow, Saul. NOBEL LECTURE. (NY: Targ Editions, (1979). 1st ed. #325 of 350 signed. Orig cream cl. Fine in plain white dj. *CHAPEL HILL*. $150

Bellow, Saul. SEIZE THE DAY. London: Weidenfeld & Nicholson, (1957). 1st Eng ed. Orig grn cl. Spine somewhat faded, else VG in dj (wear to top of spine). *CHAPEL HILL*. $100

Bellow, Saul. THE ADVENTURES OF AUGIE MARCH. NY, 1953. 1st ed. 2nd issue w/Wolff imprint and top edge unstained. NF in 1st issue dj. Extremities, spine little rubbed. Few tiny edge nicks, short edge tear front panel. *POLYANTHOS.* $60

Bellow, Saul. THE LAST ANALYSIS: A PLAY. NY: Viking, 1965. 1st ed. Fine in dj. *ELSE FINE.* $95

Bellow, Saul. THE VICTIM. NY: Vanguard Press, (1947). 1st ed. Orig black cl. NF in price-clipped, VG dj. *CHAPEL HILL.* $300

Bellrose, Frank C. DUCKS, GEESE, & SWANS OF NORTH AMERICA. Harrisburg, (1976). 2nd ed. Fine in dj. *ARTIS.* $27.50

Beltrami, J. C. A PILGRIMAGE IN EUROPE AND AMERICA, LEADING TO THE DISCOVERY OF THE SOURCES OF THE MISSISSIPPI AND BLOODY RIVER: WITH A DESCRIP-TION....London, 1828. 2 vols. lxxvi,472; (525)pp. Fldg map and plans, portrait. New cl w/paper labels. The Eng ed, enl. Howes B338. *GINSBERG.* $750

Belzoni, G. NARRATIVE OF THE OPERATIONS AND RECENT DISCOVERIES WITHIN THE PYRAMIDS, TEMPLES, TOMBS, AND EXCAVATIONS, IN EGYPT AND NUBIA....Brussels: H. Remy, 1835. 4th ed. xxi + 455pp, 1/2 calf w/marbled boards and eps. Rubbed, top of spine lightly chipped, small tear on title page, comtemp signature on title page. W/notice of death of Belzoni not in earlier eds. Good. *ARCHAEOLOGIA.* $225

Bemelmans, Ludwig. LA BONNE TABLE. NY, 1964. 1st ed. VF in VF dj. *BOND.* $50

Bemelmans, Ludwig. LIFE CLASS. NY: Viking, 1938. 1st ed. NF in pict dj. Inscribed and including an orig drawing. *CHAPEL HILL.* $125

Bemelmans, Ludwig. THE DONKEY INSIDE. Illus by author. NY: Viking, 1941. 1st ed. One of 175 w/orig watercolor drwng signed. Fine in slipcase. *JAFFE.* $275

Bemelmans, Ludwig. THE WOMAN OF MY LIFE. NY: Viking, 1957. 1st ed. VG in sl worn dj. Bkpl. *SECOND LIFE.* $20

Benchley, Robert. AFTER 1903 WHAT? NY, 1938. 1st ed. Drwgs by Gluyas Williams. NF in bright orange dj. *PETTLER.* $100

Benchley, Robert. BENCHLEY OR ELSE! NY: Harper, (1947). 1st ed. VG. *SECOND LIFE.* $25

Benchley, Robert. LOVE CONQUERS ALL. NY: Holt, 1922. 1st ed. VG. *SECOND LIFE.* $35

Benchley, Robert. PLUCK AND LUCK. NY: Holt, (1925) 1st ed. VG. *SECOND LIFE.* $25

Bender, Marylin & Selig Altshul. THE CHOSEN INSTRUMENT, JUAN TRIPPE/PAN AM. NY: Simon & Schuster, (1982). 1st prtg. Fine in dj. *AKA.* $25

Benecke, Louis. SOME LIGHT UPON A CHARITON COUNTY EPISODE OF '64. (Brunswick, 1895). 1st ed. 13pp. Orig printed wrappers. Scarce. *GINSBERG.* $125

Benedict, Carl Peters. A TENDERFOOT KID ON GYP WATER. Austin: Texas Folklore Soc, 1943. One of 550 designed by Carl Hertzog. Fine in tissue wrapper. *LAURIE.* $350

Benedict, F.C. THE PHYSIOLOGY OF LARGE REPTILES. Amsterdam, 1973. *SUTTON.* $95

Benet, Stephen Vincent. JAMES SHORE'S DAUGHTER. GC: Doubleday, 1934. 1st ed. Ltd to 307 signed. Offsetting to boards from tissue jacket (discarded), o/w VG in slipcase. *JAFFE.* $45

Benet, Stephen Vincent. JOHN BROWN'S BODY. GC, NY: Doubleday, Doran, 1928. 1st trade ed. Orig black cl. VG in dj. *CHAPEL HILL.* $40

Benet, Stephen Vincent. JOHN BROWN'S BODY. NY, 1927. 1st ed. VG+. *PRATT.* $45

Benet, Stephen Vincent. THE BALLAD OF THE DUKE'S MERCY. NY: House of Books, Ltd, 1939. Issued in tissue dj (not present). #34/250 numbered, signed. NF in orig cl. *HELLER.* $100

Benet, Stephen Vincent. WESTERN STAR. Farrar & Rinehart, (1943). 1st ed. Fine in dj. *AUTHORS OF THE WEST.* $25

Benezet, Anthony A. THE FAMILY PHYSICIAN; COMPRISING RULES FOR THE PREVENTION AND CURE OF DIS-EASES...WITH A DISPENSATORY AND APPENDIX....WITH ORIGINAL REMARKS. By a Graduate of the Pennsylvania University... Cincinnati: W. Hill Woodward, (1826). 1st ed. 8vo. 562pp. Contemp boards, rebacked. Heavily foxed. Repairs to top of title and inner margin. Uncut. Very scarce. *M & S.* $550

Benford, Gregory. IN THE OCEAN OF NIGHT. Dial Press, 1977. 1st ed. Fine in dj. *MADLE.* $30

Benford, Gregory. JUPITER PROJECT. Nelson, 1975. 1st ed. NF in dj. *MADLE.* $60

Benford, Gregory. THE STARS IN SHROUD. Berkley/Putnam, 1978. 1st ed. Fine in dj. *MADLE.* $25

Benford, Gregory. TIMESCAPE. Simon & Schuster, 1980. 1st ed. Fine in dj. *MADLE.* $60

Benford, Gregory. TIMESCAPE. Simon and Schuster, 1980. 1st ed. Fine in price-clipped dj w/light wear to edges; rmdr mark. *STAHR.* $45

Benford, Robert. DOCTORS IN THE SKY. THE STORY OF THE AERO MEDICAL ASSOCIATION. Springfield, 1955. 1st ed. Dj. *FYE.* $50

Benham, Charles. THE FOURTH NAPOLEON. London, 1898. 1st British ed. VG. *MADLE.* $100

Benitez, Fernando. IN THE FOOTSTEPS OF CORTES. NY: Pantheon, 1952. Mexico, 1950. 1st Eng ed. NF in sl worn, Good dj. *CONNOLLY & WADE.* $25

Benjamin, Mary A. AUTOGRAPHS: A KEY TO COLLECTING. NY: R.R. Bowker Co., 1963. Rev ed. Cl, soiled dj. 35 plts. *OAK KNOLL.* $35

Benjamin, S.G.W. PERSIA. London, 1920. Half morocco & marbled boards. Handsome. *O'NEILL.* $70

Benner, Judith Ann. SUL ROSS, SOLDIER, STATESMAN, EDUCATOR. College Station, (1983). 1st ed. Two small tears in dj o/w Fine. *PRATT.* $30

Bennet, Edna Mae. TURQUOISE AND THE INDIAN. Denver: Sage, 1970. Rev ed. 28 plts. NF in VG dj. *CONNOLLY & WADE.* $30

Bennet, Melba Berry. THE STONE MASON OF TOR HOUSE. (LA): The Ward Ritchie Press, (1966). 1st ed. Dj. Fine. *WEBER.* $50

Bennett, A.G. WHALING IN THE ANTARCTIC. NY: Henry Holt, 1932. 1st ed. Very minor wear extrems, else NF. *GREAT EPIC.* $45

Bennett, Arnold. OUR WOMEN, CHAPTERS ON THE SEX-DIS-CORD. NY: Doran, (1920). 1st US ed. VG. *SECOND LIFE.* $45

Bennett, Arnold. THE FEAST OF ST. FRIEND. A CHRISTMAS BOOK. NY, (1911). 1st ed. Pict boards, gilt, little offsetting prelims, spine heel sl rubbed; dj sl sunned, rubbed, sl chipped. *POLYANTHOS.* $60

Bennett, Arnold. THE VANGUARD. A FANTASIA. NY: Doran, (1927). 1st Amer ed. Bkpl, else Fine in lightly used dj. *CHAPEL HILL.* $45

Bennett, Edna Mae. TURQUOISE AND THE INDIAN. Denver: Sage, 1970. Rev ed. 28 plts. NF in VG dj. *CONNOLLY & WADE.* $30

Bennett, Frank M. THE STEAM NAVY OF THE UNITED STATES. A HISTORY...Pittsburgh: Warren & Co., 1896. 1st ed. (xvi), 953 pp. 80 plts. Extremities a little worn, still acceptable. *LEFKOWICZ.* $125

Bennett, George Fletcher. THE PERENIAL APPRENTICE. Wilmington, DE: G.F. Bennett, 1977. 1st ed. VG in VG+ dj. Signed. *BACKROOM.* $55

Bennett, H.S. ENGLISH BOOKS & READERS, 1475-1557. Cambridge: at the Univ Press, 1952. Some smoke stain, else Fine. *WREDEN*. $30

Bennett, Hal. LORD OF DARK PLACES. NY: Norton, (1970). 1st ed. Fine in dj. *LOPEZ*. $35

Bennett, James Gordon. MY FATHER'S GEISHA. NY: Delacorte (1990). Uncorrected proof. Fine in wraps. *DORN*. $35

Bennett, James. OVERLAND JOURNEY TO CALIFORNIA: JOURNAL OF...WHOSE PARTY LEFT NEW HARMONY IN 1850...NY, 1932. Orig wrps. Ltd ed of 200 from New Harmony Times of 1906. Howes B357a. *GINSBERG*. $50

Bennett, Lerone. THE NEGRO MOOD AND OTHER ESSAYS. Chicago: Johnson Publishing Co, 1964. 1st ed. Fine in dj rubbed at spinal extremities. Inscribed. Short ALS from Bennett's wife laid in. *CAPTAIN'S BOOKSHELF*. $75

Bennett, Mildred R. THE WORLD OF WILLA CATHER. Dodd, Mead, (1951). 1st ed. Fine, bkpl, chipped dj. *AUTHORS OF THE WEST*. $17.50

Bennett, Patrick. TALKING WITH TEXAS WRITERS: TWELVE INTERVIEWS. Texas A & M Univ Press, (1980). 1st ed. New in dj. *AUTHORS OF THE WEST*. $17.50

Bennett, Paul A. (ed). BOOKS AND PRINTING, A TREASURY FOR TYPOPHILES. Cleveland, NY: World Pub Co, (1951). 1st ed. Cl, dj. *OAK KNOLL*. $45

Bennett, Robert Ames. INTO THE PRIMITIVE. McClure, 1908. 1st ed. VG. *MADLE*. $45

Bennett, Robert. THE WRATH OF JOHN STEINBECK, OR ST. JOHN GOES TO CHURCH. LA: Albertson Press in assoc with Bunster Creelet, 1939. Lawrence Clark Powell (foreword). Signed by Powell and Bennett. Ltd ed of 1000 numbered, signed (900 for sale). Tipped-in frontis. Red paper boards. Fine. *WEBER*. $50

Bennett, Robert. THE WRATH OF JOHN STEINBECK. LA: The Albertson Press, 1939. #572 of 1,000 numbered. Signed. Foreword by Lawrence Clark Powell with tipped in frontispiece by Artemis. Red boards with gold label, issued w/out dj. Bit scuffed & worn at edges o/w VG. *BERNARD*. $125

Bennett, William P. THE SKY-SIFTER...N.p.: Author, (1892). 1st ed. Inner hinges starting, o/w NF. *DIAMOND*. $75

Benni, Most Rev. Cyril B. THE TRADITION OF THE SYRIAC CHURCH OF ANTIOCH....London, 1871. Cover stains. *O'NEILL*. $75

Benois, Alexandre. THE RUSSIAN SCHOOL OF PAINTING. NY, 1916. 32 plts. NF. *POLYANTHOS*. $65

Benois, Alexandre. THE RUSSIAN SCHOOL OF PAINTING. NY: Alfred A. Knopf, 1916. 1st ed in Eng. 32 plts. Stained, rubbed, chipped, prelims sl foxed. Contents mostly bright, Fine. *BLUE MOUNTAIN*. $125

Benram, Anthony. THE HOUSE, A MACHINE FOR LIVING IN. London: A. & C. Black. 1935. 1st ed. Fine in dj. *KARMIOLE*. $40

Benson, A.E. HISTORY OF THE MASSACHUSETTS HORTICULTURAL SOCIETY. N.p., 1929. Cl. *SUTTON*. $60

Benson, E. F. VISIBLE AND INVISIBLE. London, n.d. VG in frayed dj. *MADLE*. $50

Benson, E.F. THE MALE IMPERSONATOR. London: Elkin Mathews & Marrot, 1929. 29 pp, unopened. One of 530 signed. Dj. *DAWSON'S*. $50

Benson, Luther. FIFTEEN YEARS IN HELL. Indianapolis: Douglass & Carlon, 1879 (c. 1877). Spine faded, edges frayed, front hinge weak, foxing. Good. *BOHLING*. $35

Benson, Lyman. THE CACTI OF ARIZONA. Tucson: Univ of AZ, 1969. Fine in Fine dj. *CONNOLLY & WADE*. $30

Benson, Robert. THE LIGHT INVISIBLE. London, 1903. 1st ed. VG. *MADLE*. $35

Benson, Stella. HOPE AGAINST HOPE AND OTHER STORIES. London: Macmillan, 1931. Unopened. Marble boards, cloth spine. Orig ptd and clear dj. One of 670 signed. *DAWSON'S*. $75

Bensusan, S.L. MOROCCO. A&C Black, 1904. 1st ed. 20s Series. VG-NF. *OLD LONDON*. $65

Bent, A. C. LIFE HISTORIES OF NORTH AMERICAN JAYS, CROWS, AND TITMICE. 1st ed. Washington, GPO, 1946. Ptd wraps. Frontis. Upper right front corner of cvr clipped. Small chip inner corner, lower left cvr, else VG. *CONNOLLY & WADE*. $52.50

Bent, A. C. LIFE HISTORIES OF NORTH AMERICAN NUTHATCHES, WRENS, THRASHERS AND THEIR ALLIES. 1st ed. Wraps. Upper right front corner of cvr clipped, else VG. *CONNOLLY & WADE*. $55

Bent, A.C. LIFE HISTORIES OF NORTH AMERICAN BIRDS OF PREY, ORDERS FALCONIFORMES AND STRIGIFORMES. Washington, 1937-38. 2 vols. 94 plts. Binder's buckram. Orig wrappers retained; soiling to wraps. *SUTTON*. $75

Bent, A.C. LIFE HISTORIES OF NORTH AMERICAN GALLINACEOUS BIRDS. With 93 plts. Washington, 1932. Recent buckram. Spine faded; orig wraps retained. *SUTTON*. $40

Bent, A.C. LIFE HISTORIES OF NORTH AMERICAN SHORE BIRDS, ORDER LIMICOLAE (PART 1). Washington, 1927. 55 plts. Wraps. Backstrip & rear wrapper missing; ex-lib. *SUTTON*. $26

Bent, A.C. LIFE HISTORIES OF NORTH AMERICAN SHORE BIRDS, ORDER LIMICOLAE (PART 2). Washington, 1929. 66 plts. Wraps (tear to front; rear missing); prelim pg foxing. *SUTTON*. $20

Bent, J. Theodore. AEGEAN ISLANDS. THE CYCLADES, OR LIFE AMONG THE INSULAR GREEKS. Chicago, 1966. Dj. *O'NEILL*. $35

Bent, N. JUNGLE GIANTS. 31 photos. Norwood, 1936. Gilt-stamped cl. Spine faded. *SUTTON*. $35

Benteen, Frederick W. CAMP TALK. Mattituck, NY, (1983). Ed by John M. Carroll. 1st ed. Dj. Fine. *PRATT*. $35

Bentley, E.C. ELEPHANT'S WORK. Knopf, 1950. 1st Amer ed. VG in VG dj with chips, edgewear. *BEBBAH*. $25

Bentley, E.C. ELEPHANT'S WORK. London: Hodder & Stoughton, 1950. 1st ed. Top edge darkened o/w Fine in dj w/tear on back panel and minor wear at spine ends and at corners. *MORDIDA*. $45

Bentley, Eric (ed). THIRTY YEARS OF TREASON. NY: Viking, (1971). 2nd ptg. Spotting top edges, name stamp. Tiny dj tear. VG. *AKA*. $26

Benton, F. THE HONEY BEE: A MANUAL.... Washington, 1896. Worn at corners, lower 1/3 of backstrip perished, fep gutter partially cracked. *SUTTON*. $45

Benton, Frank. COWBOY LIFE ON THE SIDETRACK. Denver: Western Stories Syndicate, (1903). Pict cl, rubbed. *SCHOYER'S*. $60

Benton, Frank. COWBOY LIFE ON THE SIDETRACK...Denver, (1903). 1st ed. 3pp ads. Small stain bottom page margins, o/w VG. Scarce. *DIAMOND*. $90

Benton, Joel. LIFE OF HON. PHINEAS T. BARNUM. (NY): Edgewood Publishing, 1891. 1st ed. 621pp. Dec binding. VG to Fine. *BOOK MARKET*. $200

Benwell, Gwen and Arthur Waugh. SEA ENCHANTRESS. THE TALE OF THE MERMAID AND HER KIN. London: Hutchinson, (1961). 1st ed. VG. *WREDEN*. $35

Berengario da Carpi, J. A SHORT INTRODUCTION TO ANATOMY (ISAGOGAE BREVES). Trans by L.R. Lind. Chicago, 1959. 1st Eng trans. *FYE*. $75

Berenson, Bernard. LORENZO LOTTO. COMPLETE EDITION. NY, 1956. Dj w/closed tears, small chips. NF. *POLYANTHOS.* $100

Beresford, Charles. BREAK-UP OF CHINA. NY & London: Harper & Bros, 1900. 491pp. Grn cl stamped in gilt and red. 2 fldg maps, 1 fldg chart. *SCHOYER'S.* $75

Beresford, J.D. THE HAMPDENSHIRE WONDER. Garland, 1975. 1st ed thus. As New. *MADLE.* $30

Berg, A. Scott. MAX PERKINS, EDITOR OF GENIUS. NY: Dutton, 1978. 1st ed. Uncorrected proof. NF in Wraps. *SMITH.* $40

Berg, Stephen. BEARING WEAPONS. POEMS. Cl. Iowa City: Cummington Press, 1963. 1st ed. Ltd to 250. Fine. *JAFFE.* $85

Berger, Francesco. REMINISCENCES IMPRESSIONS & ANECDOTES. London: Sampson Low, Marston, 1913. 1st ed. 12 mo, 227pp, illus. Small pict pastedown on cover, sl tear to top of spine. *GREAT EXPECTATIONS.* $35

Berger, Melvin. PREHISTORIC MAMMALS. A NEW WORLD. 1986. Illus Cremins. Keith Mosely (eng). Pop-up bk. *BOOKFINDERS INTL.* $20

Berger, Thomas. CRAZY IN BERLIN. NY: Scribners, 1958. 1st ed, 1st book. Fine in NF dj w/light wear at spine ends. *BEASLEY.* $150

Berger, Thomas. LITTLE BIG MAN. NY: Dial, 1964. 1st ed. Fine in NF dj and signed. *LOPEZ.* $250

Berger, Thomas. REGIMENT OF WOMEN. Eyre Methuen (1974). 1st UK ed. Fine in dj. *LOPEZ.* $35

Berger, Thomas. REINHART IN LOVE. NY: Scribners, 1962. 1st ed. Fine in Fine dj but for light rubbing, a few short, clean tears. *BEASLEY.* $100

Berger, Thomas. REINHART IN LOVE. Scribner's, 1962. 1st ed. Fine in dj chipped at foot of spine, front flyleaf fold; a few other small blemishes. *STAHR.* $90

Berger, Thomas. REINHART'S WOMEN. NY, 1981. 1st ed. Signed presentation. Fine in like dj. *POLYANTHOS.* $35

Berger, Thomas. SNEAKY PEOPLE. NY, 1975. 1st ed. Signed presentation. Fine in price-clipped dj (rear panel very sl soiled). *POLYANTHOS.* $35

Berger, Thomas. SNEAKY PEOPLE. NY: Simon and Schuster, (c.1975). Yellow ptd wraps. Adv uncorrected proofs in tall format. Fine. *HELLER.* $75

Berger, Thomas. THE FEUD. NY, 1983. 1st ed. Signed presentation. Fine in like dj. *POLYANTHOS.* $35

Berger, Thomas. WHO IS TEDDY VILLANOVA? (n.p.): Delacorte Press/Seymour Lawrence (1977). 1st ed. NF in dj. *LOPEZ.* $20

Berghold, Alexander. THE INDIANS REVENGE...SOME APPALLING EVENTS IN THE HISTORY OF THE SIOUX. SF: P.J. Thomas, 1891. 7 plts. VG. Howes B373. *LAURIE.* $200

Berghold, Alexander. THE INDIANS' REVENGE; OR, DAYS OF HORROR....SF, 1891. 1st Amer ed. 240pp. Orig pict cl. Howes B373. *GINSBERG.* $150

Bergmann, E. von et al. A SYSTEM OF PRACTICAL SURGERY. NY, 1904. 1st Eng trans. 5 vols. VF. *FYE.* $250

Bering, John A. and Thomas Montgomery. HISTORY OF THE FORTY-EIGHT OHIO VET. VOL. INF...FROM ITS ORGANIZATION AT CAMP DENNISON,...TO THE CLOSE OF THE WAR...AND THE CLOSING EVENTS OF THE WAR IN THE TRANS-MISSISSIPPI DEPT. Hillsboro, Ohio, Highland, 1880. 1st ed. (15),290pp. Orig cl. *GINSBERG.* $175

Beringer, Richard E. et al. WHY THE SOUTH LOST THE WAR. Athens, (1986). 1st ed. Dj. Fine. *PRATT.* $27.50

Berkeley, Anthony. A PUZZLE IN POISON. GC: Doubleday Crime Club, 1938. 1st Amer ed. Sm nick in front o/w Fine in dj (rubbing along edges; couple short, closed tears). *MORDIDA.* $150

Berkeley, Anthony. THE POISONED CHOCOLATE CASE. GC: Doubleday Crime Club, 1929. 1st Amer ed. Edges darkened, o/w Fine in dj (sl faded spine; short closed tears; wear at spine ends; internal damp stain). *MORDIDA.* $100

Berkeley, Anthony. THE SECOND SHOT. GC: Doubleday Crime Club, 1931. 1st Amer ed. Fine in bright Like New dj w/wraparound intact. *MORDIDA.* $150

Berkeley, George. PHILOSOPHICAL COMMENTARIES: GENERALLY CALLED THE COMMONPLACE BOOK. (London and elsewhere: Thomas Nelson & Sons, 1944). 1st ed of this transcription. Copy number one of 400. Transcribed and ed by A.A. Luce. Frontis facs of MS page. Extremely Fine in dj flecked with foxing, sl wrinkled, and torn at bottom of one inner flap. *PIRAGES.* $150

Berkman, Alexander. NOW AND AFTER. NY: Vanguard, 1929. 1st ed. Co-published by The Jewish Anarchist Federation. Fine but for small hole in front joint, in dj w/chip on back panel and 2" chip at foot of spine. *BEASLEY.* $100

Berkman, Alexander. PRISON MEMOIRS OF AN ANARCHIST. NY: Mother Earth, 1912. 1st ed. Little rippling and mild staining to top of margins of some pp, spine darkening at foot, else Nice. Lengthy inscription by author. *BEASLEY.* $350

Berkman, Alexander. PRISON MEMOIRS OF AN ANARCHIST. NY: Mother Earth, 1912, 1920. 2nd ed. Intro by Hutchins Hapgood. Nice w/only lt wear to edges. *AKA.* $50

Berlandier, Jean Louis. THE INDIANS OF TEXAS IN 1830. Washington: Smithsonian, 1969. 1st ed. Ed by John C. Evers. 20 plts. Fine in VG dj. *CONNOLLY & WADE.* $47.50

Berman, Henry. THE WORSHIPPERS. NY: Grafton Press, 1906. 1st ed. Pencilled names ffep, a few scattered pencillings throughout, wear to spine ends. VG. Uncommon. *BEASLEY.* $100

Bernal, Ignacio. 100 GREAT MASTERPIECES OF THE MEXICAN MUSEUM OF ANTHROPOLOGY. NY,: Abrams, (1969). 1st ed. Good in dj. *SILVER.* $50

Bernal, Ignacio. MEXICO: PRE-HISPANIC PAINTINGS. Greenwich: NY Graphic Soc, (1958). 32 color plts, dj. Good. *ARCHAEOLOGIA.* $85

Bernal, Ignacio. THE OLMEC WORLD. Berkeley: Univ of CA Press, 1969. 1st ed. Good in chipped dj. *SILVER.* $40

Bernan, Walter. (pseud of Robert Stuart Meikleham). THE HISTORY AND ART OF WARMING AND VENTILATING ROOMS AND BUILDINGS....London: George Bell, 1845. 1st ed. 2 vols. 231,335pp. Wear to cvrs, hinges loose, title pg separate. Lib discard, stamp on each title pg. *SECOND LIFE.* $125

Bernanos, Georges. A DIARY OF MY TIMES. London: Boriswood, (1938). 1st ed in English. NF, bkpl, lacking dj. *CAPTAIN'S BOOKSHELF.* $30

Bernard, Claude. AN INTRODUCTION TO THE STUDY OF EXPERIMENTAL MEDICINE. NY, 1949. Facs of 1927 ed. *FYE.* $35

Bernard, Claude. THE CAHIER ROUGE OF CLAUDE BERNARD. Trans by H.E. Hoff et al. Cambridge, 1967. 1st Eng trans. Dj. *FYE.* $25

Bernard, George Smith. THE BATTLE OF THE CRATER IN FRONT OF PETERSBURG, JULY 30, 1864. Petersburg, VA, 1890. 1st ed. Orig ptd wraps reinforced; edge chipping and soiling, else VG. *McGOWAN.* $85

Bernard, Kenneth. TWO STORIES. Illus Ellen Lanyon. Mt. Horeb: Perishable Press, 1973. 1st ed. Ltd to 150 "or less" signed by Bernard; also signed by Hamady, w/inscrip. Boards. VF. *JAFFE.* $250

Bernard, Theos. PENTHOUSE OF THE GODS. NY: Scribner's, 1939. 1st Amer ed. Dec cover. VG in G- dj. *BLUE DRAGON.* $37.50

Berneri, Marie Louise. JOURNEY THROUGH UTOPIA. Boston: Beacon, 1950. Dj edgeworn and price clipped. *AKA.* $35

Bernhard, Thomas. GATHERING EVIDENCE. NY: Knopf, 1985. 1st US ed. Adv reading copy w/slip stating such laid in. New in dj. *BERNARD*. $30

Bernhard, Thomas. THE LIME WORKS. NY: Knopf, 1973. 1st US ed. Fine in dj. *BERNARD*. $30

Bernhard, Thomas. WOODCUTTERS. NY: Knopf, 1987. 1st US ed. Adv reading copy w/slip stating such laid in. New in dj. *BERNARD*. $25

Bernhardt, C. INDIAN RAIDS IN LINCOLN COUNTY, KANSAS, 1864 AND 1869. Lincoln, KS: The Lincoln Sentinal Print, 1910. Printed wraps, nicely printed. *HUDSON*. $100

Bernhardt, C. INDIAN RAIDS IN LINCOLN COUNTY, KANSAS, 1864 AND 1869. Lincoln, KS, 1910. 1st ed. Laid in a list of subscribers to Lincoln Memorial Monument Fund. 62pp. Fldg map, pict wraps, VG. *PRATT*. $75

Bernheim, Bertram. THE STORY OF THE JOHNS HOPKINS: FOUR GREAT DOCTORS AND THE MEDICAL SCHOOL THEY CREATED. NY, 1948. 1st ed. *FYE*. $45

Bernheim, H. SUGGESTIVE THERAPEUTICS. A TREATISE ON NATURE AND USES OF HYPNOTISM. NY, 1889. 1st Eng trans. 420pp. *FYE*. $100

Bernheimer, Charles L. RAINBOW BRIDGE. CIRCLING NAVAJO MOUNTAIN AND EXPLORATIONS IN THE "BAD LANDS" OF SOUTHERN UTAH AND NORTHERN ARIZONA. GC, 1924. Stated 1st. 182pp, teg. Spine dull, former lib markings removed (no other markings), else VG. *FIVE QUAIL*. $50

Bernstein, Aline. AN ACTOR'S DAUGHTER. NY: Knopf, 1941. 1st ed. NF in sl chipped, internally mended dj. Inscribed. *CAPTAIN'S BOOKSHELF*. $150

Berra, Yogi and Ed Fitzgerald. YOGI. Doubleday, 1961. 1st ed. Good+ in VG dj. *PLAPINGER*. $20

Berrian, William. HISTORICAL SKETCH OF TRINITY CHURCH, NEW YORK. NY, 1847. 1st ed. 386pp + 8pp cat. 8 steel engr plts. Lt foxing, mostly on margins. Rebound, new buckram, old cover transposed. *HEINOLDT*. $30

Berrigan, Daniel. AMERICA IS HARD TO FIND. Doubleday, 1972. 1st ed. Owner's name. Dj. *AKA*. $35

Berrigan, Daniel. ENCOUNTERS. NY: World, (1960). 1st ed. Owner name. About Fine in lightly soiled, edge-chipped dj. *AKA*. $35

Berrigan, Daniel. LIGHTS ON IN THE HOUSE OF THE DEAD. Doubleday, 1974. 1st ed. About Fine in VG dj. *AKA*. $25

Berrigan, Daniel. NIGHT FLIGHT TO HANOI. NY: Macmillan, (1968), 1st ed. About Fine in VG+ price-clipped dj. *AKA*. $40

Berrigan, Daniel. THE GEOGRAPHY OF FAITH. Boston: Beacon, (1971). Fine in NF dj. *AKA*. $35

Berrigan, Ted. MANY HAPPY RETURNS TO DICK GALLUP. SF: Grabhorn-Hoyem, 1967. Ltd ed of 200. This copy signed. Wraps. Little edge sunned. Fine. *POLYANTHOS*. $30

Berrone, Louis (ed). JAMES JOYCE IN PADUA. NY: Random House, 1977. 1st ed. Fine in Fine dj. *OLD LONDON*. $25

Berry, Don. A MAJORITY OF SCOUNDRELS...ROCKY MOUNTAIN FUR COMPANY. Harper, (1961). 1st ed. 2 maps rear pocket. Fine in VG dj. *OREGON*. $80

Berry, Don. A MAJORITY OF SCOUNDRELS...THE ROCKY MOUNTAIN FUR COMPANY. Harper, (1961). 1st ed. Maps in pocket. Fine in dj. *AUTHORS OF THE WEST*. $75

Berry, Don. MOONTRAP. Viking, (1962). 1st ed. Fine in dj. *AUTHORS OF THE WEST*. $35

Berry, F. A. and E. Bollay, Norman R. Beers (eds). HANDBOOK OF METEOROLOGY. NY: McGraw-Hill, 1945, 1st ed, 2nd impression. Ex-lib, blue cl; crease to front board, some extremity wear, pocket, stamps, spine label, but Good. *KNOLLWOOD*. $60

Berry, R.E. YANKEE STARGAZER....Whittlesey, 1941. Signed by Louise Hall Tharp. VG. *BOOKCELL*. $25

Berry, Robert Elton. YANKEE STARGAZER. NY: Whittlesey House, 1941. 1st ed. 6 plts. Fine in edgeworn, else Good dj. *CONNOLLY & WADE*. $55

Berry, Robert Elton. YANKEE STARGAZER. NY: Whittlesey House, 1941. Ex-lib. *KNOLLWOOD*. $30

Berry, W. Turner et al. THE ENCYCLOPEDIA OF TYPEFACES. London: Blandford Press (1962). "Third Ed, Revised & Enlarged." Extrems lightly rubbed. Dj somewhat chipped. *KARMIOLE*. $40

Berry, Wendell and Gene Meatyard. THE UNFORESEEN WILDERNESS: AN ESSAY ON KENTUCKY'S RED RIVER GORGE. Lexington: Univ Press of Kentucky, 1971. 1st ed. Slight foxing to fore-edge, else Fine in dj w/small sticker shadow at base of spine, some scraping to rear panel. *BETWEEN COVERS*. $85

Berry, Wendell. A PART. POEMS. SF: North Point Press, 1980. 1st ed. Fine in VG dj. Signed. *CAPTAIN'S BOOKSHELF*. $40

Berry, Wendell. A PART. SF: North Point, (1980). 1st Amer ed. Signed. Fine in VG dj. *DORN*. $20

Berry, Wendell. A PLACE ON EARTH. NY: Harcourt, 1967. Adv rev copy w/slip laid in. Fine in Fine dj. *BEASLEY*. $175

Berry, Wendell. A PLACE ON EARTH. NY: HB&W, (1967). Small inked -out number on the dedication page, else Fine in dj (2" tear in rear panel). *CAPTAIN'S BOOKSHELF*. $100

Berry, Wendell. CLEARING. NY: Harcourt, Brace & Jovanovich, (1977). 1st Amer ed. Signed. Fine in dj. *DORN*. $45

Berry, Wendell. FINDINGS. (Iowa City): Prairie Press, 1969. 1st ed. Fine (owner sig) in dj. *CAPTAIN'S BOOKSHELF*. $100

Berry, Wendell. HORSES, A POEM. Monterey, KY: Larkspur, (1975). 1st ed. 1/949. Ptd wraps. VG. Signed. *SECOND LIFE*. $45

Berry, Wendell. HORSES. Monterey, KY: Larkspur Press, 1975. Wraps, one of 942. Fine. *BEASLEY*. $40

Berry, Wendell. NATHAN COULTER. Boston: Houghton Mifflin, 1960. 1st ed. Fine in lightly used dj (slight chipping from the spinal extremities). *CAPTAIN'S BOOKSHELF*. $150.

Berry, Wendell. NATHAN COULTER. Boston: Houghton Mifflin, 1960. 1st ed, 1st bk. Fine but for crayon piece on fep, in Fine dj but for light spine wear. *BEASLEY*. $175

Berry, Wendell. NATHAN COULTER. Boston: Houghton Mifflin Co., (1960). 1st Amer ed. Signed. NF in VG dj missing a few small chips. *DORN*. $225

Berry, Wendell. NOVEMBER TWENTY SIX NINETEEN HUNDRED SIXTY THREE. NY: Braziller, (1964). 1st, ltd issue, unnumbered. Drawings by Ben Shahn. Fine in slipcase. Signed by Berry, Shahn. *CAPTAIN'S BOOKSHELF*. $125

Berry, Wendell. NOVEMBER TWENTY SIX NINETEEN HUNDRED SIXTY THREE. Drawings by Ben Shahn. NY: Braziller, (1963). 1st Amer ed. Signed. Fine in slipcase w/sun fading else VG. *DORN*. $80

Berry, Wendell. THE BROKEN GROUND. London: Cape (1966). 1st Eng ed. Uncorrected proof in wraps. Signed. Name, title penned in on front cvr where old labels have been removed. VG. *DORN*. $150

Berry, Wendell. THE COUNTRY OF MARRIAGE, POEMS. NY: Harcourt, (1975). 1st pb ed. VG, Signed. *SECOND LIFE*. $25

Berry, Wendell. THE DISCOVERY OF KENTUCKY. (Frankfort): Gnomon, (1991). 1st ed. 1/100 in boards signed. Fine. *CAPTAIN'S BOOKSHELF*. $60

Berry, Wendell. THE GIFT OF GRAVITY. (Old Deerfield): Deerfield Press & Dublin: (Gallery Press), 1979. 1st ed. 1/300 signed. Fine in dj. *CAPTAIN'S BOOKSHELF*. $75

Berry, Wendell. THE HIDDEN WOUND. Boston: Houghton Mifflin Co., (1970). 1st Amer ed. Signed. Fine in dj. *DORN.* $65

Berry, Wendell. THE KENTUCKY RIVER: TWO POEMS. Monterey, Ky.: Larkspur Press, 1976. 14pp in fldg wraps. Ltd to 1000 numbered. VG. *OREGON.* $30

Berry, Wendell. THE MEMORY OF OLD JACK. NY: Harcourt Brace & Jovanovich, (1974). 1st ed. Fine in dj. Uncommon. *CAPTAIN'S BOOKSHELF.* $150

Berry, Wendell. THE MEMORY OF OLD JACK. NY: Harcourt, Brace & Jovanovich, (1974). Adv rev copy of trade ed with slip. (1,500 1st ptg). Signed. Fine in NF dj. *DORN.* $175

Berry, Wendell. THE RISE. (Lexington: The Univ of Kentucky Library Press, 1968). 1st ed. 1/100 signed. Fine in boards w/slightly soiled paper label. *CAPTAIN'S BOOKSHELF.* $250

Berry, Wendell. THE UNFORESEEN WILDERNESS. Lexington: Univ Press of KY, 1971. 1st ed. Sl spotting to cl but VG in dj. *LOPEZ.* $100

Berry, Wendell. THE UNSETTLING OF AMERICA. SF: Sierra Book Club, (1977). 1st Amer ed. Signed. Fine in dj. *DORN.* $60

Berry, Wendell. THE WILD BIRDS....SF: North Point, 1986. 1st ed. Fine in dj. Signed. *CAPTAIN'S BOOKSHELF.* $40

Berry, Wendell. THREE MEMORIAL POEMS. Berkeley, CA.: Sand Dollar, 1977. 1st ed. Fine in orig tissue. One of 100 numbered, signed copies bound in cl. *SECOND LIFE.* $125

Berry, Wendell. THREE MEMORIAL POEMS. Berkeley: Sand Dollar, 1977. 1st ed. 1/1OO signed. Fine in glassine dj w/tiny stain. *CAPTAIN'S BOOKSHELF.* $100

Berry, Wendell. TO WHAT LISTENS. (Crete, Nebraska: The Best Cellar Press, 1975) 1st ed. Ptd wraps, little faded, NF. Scarce early work. *SECOND LIFE.* $85

Berry, Wendell. TRAVELING AT HOME. With wood engravings by John DePol. SF: North Point, (1989). 1st Amer ed. Signed. Fine w/o dj as issued. *DORN.* $30

Berryman, John. HOMAGE TO MISTRESS BRADSTREET AND OTHER POEMS. NY: Noonday Press, (1968). 1st ed, pb orig w/new note by Berryman. Signed. Fine in ptd wrappers. *JAFFE.* $125

Berryman, John. HOMAGE TO MISTRESS BRADSTREET. NY: Farrar, Straus & Cudahy, (1956). 1st ed. Orig illus boards. Almost invisible offsetting to rear ep, but Fine in dj. *CHAPEL HILL.* $200

Berryman, John. POEMS. Norfolk, CT: New Directions, (c.1942). 1st bk. Few lt stains right edge rear wrapper, o/w NF in ptd wraps. *HELLER.* $75

Berryman, John. THE DISPOSSESSED. NY: Sloane, (1948). 1st ed. Signed. Bkpl, base of spine frayed, o/w Good in chipped, worn dj. *JAFFE.* $150

Berryman, John. THE DREAM SONGS. NY: FSG (1969). 1st ed. Fine in NF dj (sm tear). *DORN.* $50

Berton, Pierre. KLONDIKE: THE LAST GREAT GOLD RUSH, 1896-1899. Toronto: McClelland and Stewart, (1972). Rev ed. Fine in slipcase. *LAURIE.* $22.50

Berton, Ralph. REMEMBERING BIX: A MEMOIR OF THE JAZZ AGE. NY: Harper & Row, (1974). 1st ed. Fine in NF dj. *AKA.* $35

Berve, Helmut & Gottfried Gruben. GREEK TEMPLES, THEATRES AND SHRINES. London: Thames and Hudson, (1963). 154 figs, 212 plts (36 color, tipped in). Good. *ARCHAEOLOGIA.* $350

Best, Hugh. DEBRETT'S TEXAS PEERAGE. NY (1983). 1st ed. 385pp. Small tear on dj o/w Fine. *PRATT.* $30

Besterman, Theodore. A DICTIONARY OF THEOSOPHY. London, 1927. NF. *POLYANTHOS.* $40

Betenson, Lula Parker as told to Dora Flack. BUTCH CASSIDY, MY BROTHER. Provo, UT, (1975). 2nd prtg. Signed by Mrs. Betenson. Minor cvr and dj wear o/w Fine. *PRATT.* $50

Betjeman, John. COLLECTED POEMS. Comp by Lord Birkenhead. London: Murray, 1958. 1st ed. Signed. NF in VG dj. *JUVELIS.* $150

Betjeman, John. LONDON'S HISTORIC RAILWAY STATIONS. Photogr by John Gay. (London): John Murray. (1972). 1st ed. Purple cloth, gilt spine. Dj. Fine. *KARMIOLE.* $30

Betjeman, John. METRO-LAND. VERSES. (London): Warren Editions, (1977). 16 orig colored lithos by Glynn Boyd Harte. White cl w/pict label, red cl fldg box. 1st ed. One of 220 signed by Betjeman & Harte. VF. *JAFFE.* $450

Bettmann, Otto L. BETTMANN PORTABLE ARCHIVE....Picture House Press, (1966). Cl, paper label on front, slipcase. *OAK KNOLL.* $30

Betts, Doris. BEASTS OF THE SOUTHERN WILD AND OTHER STORIES. NY: Harper & Row, (1973). 1st ed. Orig cl-backed boards. About Fine in dj. *CHAPEL HILL.* $45

Betts, Doris. HEADING WEST. NY: Knopf, 1981. 1st ed. Orig cl-backed boards. Fine in dj. *CHAPEL HILL.* $30

Betts, Doris. THE GENTLE INSURRECTION AND OTHER STORIES. NY: Putnam's, (1954). 1st ed, 1st bk. Adv rev copy, slip laid in. Orig grn cl. Fore-edge a little soiled, name stamp on half-title, front flap of dj, still NF in VG dj. *CHAPEL HILL.* $100

Betts, Doris. THE GENTLE INSURRECTION. NY: Putnam, (1954). 1st ed, 1st bk. Fine, owner sig, in bright, sl edgeworn dj. Signed. *CAPTAIN'S BOOKSHELF.* $125

Betts, Doris. THE SCARLET THREAD. Harper & Row, 1964. 1st ed. Fine in price-clipped dj. *STAHR.* $45

Beurdeley, Michel. CHINESE TRADE PORCELAIN. Rutland, VT: Charles E. Tuttle. (1963). "2nd edition." 24 mounted color plts, inc frontis. Dj chipped. *KARMIOLE.* $50

Bevan, Bernard. HISTORY OF SPANISH ARCHITECTURE. NY: Scribner, 1939. 1st US ed. 2 fldg maps. Head of spine chipped, else Fine w/pencil notations in rear. *CAPTAIN'S BOOKSHELF.* $45

Beveridge, Albert J. ABRAHAM LINCOLN 1809-1858. Boston, NY: Houghton Mifflin, 1928. 1st trade. Fine set, sl edge wear. *PARMER.* $65

Beveridge, Albert. ABRAHAM LINCOLN, 1809-1858. 4 vols. Houghton Mifflin, 1928. Standard Lib ed. 32 plts. Sm cut in cl spine of vol 2; 2 nicks in vol 4; o/w Fine. Howes B408. *OREGON.* $45

Bewick, Thomas. 21 ENGRAVINGS. St. Charles, IL: Privately Ptd, 1951. 2 vols. (42;40)pp. Ed ltd to 500 sets, ptd at the Printing Office of Philip Reed, Chicago. Slipcase sl soiled. *KARMIOLE.* $175

Bewick, Thomas. A MEMOIR BY THOMAS BEWICK, WRITTEN BY HIMSELF. London: Longman, Green, Longman, and Roberts, 1862. 1st ed. xix,344 pp. 18 full-pg fish engr. Cloth, rebacked w/orig spine laid down. *DAWSON'S.* $200

Bewick, Thomas. MEMOIR OF THOMAS BEWICK WRITTEN BY HIMSELF 1822-1828. London: The Bodley Head, 1924. Grey cl boards, front cvr dec, title on spine in black. Spine faded, else VG. *HELLER.* $70

Beyer, William Gray. MINIONS OF THE MOON. NY: Gnome Press, (1950). 1st ed. Fine in NF dj (few light rub touches). *McCLINTOCK.* $30

Bezzerides, A.I. LONG HAUL. NY: Carrick & Evans, Inc, (c.1938). 1st ed, 1st bk. NF in sl rubbed, internally reinforced dj. *HELLER.* $85

Bialik, Hayyim Nahman. AND IT CAME TO PASS. Trans H. Danby. NY: Hebrew Publ. Co., (1938). 1st US ed. Owner's name. Fine in VG+ dj. *AARD.* $25

Bianchi, Martha Dickinson. THE LIFE AND LETTERS OF EMILY DICKINSON. London, 1924. 1st ed. Spine sunned and sl soiled. NF. *POLYANTHOS.* $35

Bianco, Margery (Williams). POOR CECCO. Illus Arthur Rackham. NY: Doran, (1925). 1st US ed. 7 tipped-in color plts. NF in somewhat soiled, lightly chipped dj. *CAPTAIN'S BOOKSHELF.* $150

BIBLIOGRAPHY OF THE HISTORY OF MEDICINE 1964-1969. Washington, 1971. *FYE.* $60

Bichat, Xavier. A TREATISE ON THE MEMBRANES IN GENERAL AND ON DIFFERENT MEMBRANES IN PARTICULAR. Boston, 1813. 1st Eng trans. Recent 1/4 leather, 260pp. Tall, untrimmed, w/repairs to inner and outer margins of title page which is narrower than the remaining leaves. *FYE.* $450

Bickel, Lennard. IN SEARCH OF FRANK HURLEY. Melbourne: Macmillan, 1980. 1st ed. Small bump, else VG+ in dj. *PARMER.* $40

Bickel, Lennard. MAWSON'S WILL. NY: Stein & Day, 1977. 1st Amer ed. NF in price-clipped dj. *PARMER.* $40

Bickel, Lennard. MAWSON'S WILL-THE GREATEST SURVIVAL STORY EVER WRITTEN. NY: Stein & Day, (1977). 1st ed. VG in VG- dj. *BLUE DRAGON.* $25

Bickerdyke, John et al. SEA FISHING (BADMINTON LIBRARY). Longmans, Green & Co., 1895. 1st ed. Minor bump, minor wear, else VG+. *OLD LONDON.* $55

Bickmore, Albert S. TRAVELS IN THE EAST INDIAN ARCHIPELAGO. NY: D. Appleton and Company, 1869. 553pp, ads. Fldg map. Grn cl w/gilt spine titles, cover dec. Sm repair to head of spine, some shelfwear else VG. *PARMER.* $275

Biddle, Richard. A MEMOIR OF SEBASTIAN CABOT; WITH A REVIEW OF THE HISTORY OF MARITIME DISCOVERY. London: Hurst, Chance, and Co, 1831. 1st Eng ed. Full tan calf, double-ruled, calf chipped at top of rear joint. Gilt dec spine in 6 panels w/raised bands, burgundy leather label, all edges & eps marbled. 333pp, errata slip. Ex-lib w/emb stamp, number, date. Bkpl removed from rear pastedown, bkpl on front pastedown, else Fine, bright. Very Scarce. Howes B-430. *BLUE MOUNTAIN.* $150

Biddlecomb, George. THE ART OF RIGGING...Salem, 1925. Best ed. Pub. 8. 17 plts. Fine. *LEFKOWICZ.* $95

Bidwell, John. IN CALIFORNIA BEFORE THE GOLD RUSH. LA: Ward Ritchie, 1948. 1st ed. Ltd to 1,000. 1st separate ptg of Bidwell's Memoirs. Rose cl spine. Beige pict boards. Fine. Howes B432. *CONNOLLY & WADE.* $60

Bidwell, John. IN CALIFORNIA BEFORE THE GOLD RUSH. LA: Ward Ritchie Press, 1948. 1st thus. Ltd to 1000. News clipping remnant ffep o/w VG. *OREGON.* $30

Bieber, Margarete. THE HISTORY OF THE GREEK AND ROMAN THEATER. Princeton: Princeton Univ Press, (1961). 2nd ed. Dj. Good. *ARCHAEOLOGIA.* $110

Bieber, Ralph P. & Le Roy Hafen (eds). THE SOUTHWEST HISTORICAL SERIES: HISTORICAL DOCUMENTS, HITHERTO UNPUBLISHED....Volume XII (Index). Glendale: Arthur H. Clark, 1943. Unopened. NF in dj. *LAURIE.* $100

Bien, H.M. BEN-BEOR. Friedenwald, 1891. 1st ed. Good+. *MADLE.* $50

Bienfang, Ralph. THE SUBTLE SENSE: KEY TO THE WORLD OF ODORS. Norman, OK, 1946. 1st ed. Dj. *FYE.* $40

Bierce, Ambrose. A SON OF THE GODS AND A HORSEMAN IN THE SKY. SF and NY: Paul Elder and Company, (c.1907). One of 1000. Fine in dj chipped at head and foot of backstrip, in worn pub's box. BAL 1126. *HELLER.* $75

Bierce, Ambrose. FANTASTIC FABLES. NY and London: G.P. Putnam's Sons, 1899. Backstrip darkened, cvrs sl soiled, o/w bright. BAL 1120. *HELLER.* $175

Bierce, Ambrose. NUGGETS AND DUST PANNED OUT IN CALIFORNIA BY DOD GRILE. London: Chatto & Windus, 1873. 1st ed of 2nd trade pub. Spine perished. Pict yellow wrappers, text Fine. Custom made archival box w/leather, gilt stamped labels. Never pub in America. Extremely scarce. BAL 1099. *PARMER.* $1200

Bierce, Ambrose. SHAPES OF CLAY. SF: W.E. Wood, 1903. 1st issue, in elaborate dec cover, stamped in purple and gilt. Upper front corner sl bumped but NF with the gilt still bright and clear on both front panel and spine. Signed. Nice. Scarce. *LOPEZ.* $1,250

Bierce, Ambrose. THE COLLECTED WRITINGS. Citadel, 1946. 1st ed. VG in dj. *MADLE.* $25

Bierce, Ambrose. THE DEVIL'S DICTIONARY. NY: LEC, 1972. 1074/1500, signed by illus Fritz Kredel. Fine in box. *BOOKMINE.* $85

Bierce, Ambrose. WRITE IT RIGHT: A LITTLE BLACKLIST OF LITERARY FAULTS. NY: Neale, 1910. 3rd ptg. Minimal wear. Fine. *CONNOLLY & WADE.* $35

Bierring, Walter. ONE HUNDRED YEARS OF IOWA MEDICINE. Iowa City, 1950. *FYE.* $60

Bierstadt, Edward Hale. SATAN WAS A MAN. GC: Doubleday Doran, 1935. 1st ed. Fine in dj. *MORDIDA.* $35

Bigelow, Horatio. AN INTERNATIONAL SYSTEM OF ELECTRO-THERAPEUTICS. Phila, 1895. 1st ed. 1179pp. 200+ woodcut illus. *FYE.* $250

Bigelow, Horatio. GUNNERMAN. NY: Derrydale Press, 1939. Ltd ed., #412/950. Frontis. *BACKMAN.* $150

Bigelow, Horatio. GUNNERMAN'S GOLD—MEMORIES OF FIFTY YEARS AFIELD WITH A SCATTER GUN. Huntington: Standard Publications Inc, 1943. 1st ed. Ltd, #261/1,000. Fine in VG dj. *BACKMAN.* $165

Bigelow, Jacob. A TREATISE ON THE MATERIA MEDICA, INTENDED AS A SEQUEL TO THE PHARMACOPOEIA OF THE UNITED STATES. Boston, 1822. 424pp. Recent 1/4 lea w/marbled boards and new eps. 424pp. Lib perforation stamp on title, scattered foxing. Overall, Fine. *FYE.* $300

Bigelow, Jacob. NATURE IN DISEASE, ILLUSTRATED IN VARIOUS DISCOURSES AND ESSAYS. Boston, 1854. 1st ed. 391pp. VF. Scarce. *FYE.* $200

Bigelow, John. MEMOIR OF THE LIFE...OF JOHN CHARLES FREMONT. NY: Derby & Jackson, 1856. 1st ed. Corners sl bumped. 480pp in grn cl over boards, gilt titles, frontis. VG. *PARMER.* $40

Bigelow, John. THE LIFE OF SAMUEL J. TILDEN. NY: Harper, 1895. 1st ed. 2 vols. 416;442pp. Uncut, partially unopened. *SECOND LIFE.* $50

Bigelow, Poultney. THE BORDERLAND OF CZAR AND KAISER....London, 1895. Illus F. Remington. Spine darkened, lt cover soil. Front inner hinge split. Presentation, inscribed. *O'NEILL.* $45

Biggers, Don H. GERMAN PIONEERS IN TEXAS. Fredericksburg, TX: Press of the Fredricksburg Publishing Co, 1925. 1st ed. VG. Scarce. *GIBBS.* $125

Biggers, Earl Derr. EARL DERR BIGGS TELLS TEN STORIES. Indianapolis: Bobbs-Merrill, 1933. 1st ed. Fine in VG dj (chipped, worn spine ends and corners; closed tears; wear along folds; creasing front panel). *MORDIDA.* $125

Biggle, Lloyd. THE WORLD MENDERS. Elmfield Press, 1973, 1st British ed. Fine in dj. *MADLE.* $35

Biggs, Donald C. THE PONY EXPRESS. SF: Privately ptd, 1956. 1st ed, ltd to 500. 1 pl. Untrimmed. Heavy wrappers. Fine. *CONNOLLY & WADE.* $40

Bigham, Clive. A RIDE THROUGH WESTERN ASIA. London, 1897. 4 fldg maps. Lt cover soil, else Fine. *O'NEILL.* $85

Bigham, R.W. CALIFORNIA GOLD-FIELD SCENES. Nashville: Southern Methodist Publishing House, 1886. 1st ed. Howes B444. *HUDSON.* $90

Bikelas, Demetrios. SEVEN ESSAYS ON CHRISTIAN GREECE. London, 1890. John, Marquess of Bute (trans). 1/2 calf. (6),298pp. Lib stamp, else Fine. *O'NEILL.* $85

Bill, Alfred Hoyt. THE BELEAGUERED CITY, RICHMOND 1861-1865. NY, 1946. 1st ed. Fldg map. Small piece torn from upper spine of dj, o/w VG. *PRATT.* $30

Bill, Buffalo (Hon. W.F. Cody). STORY OF THE WILD WEST.... Bridgeport: Union Pub (1888). Ptd cvrs. 1st signature almost separate. Frontis. *SECOND LIFE.* $45

Billcliffe, Roger. CHARLES RENNIE MACKINTOSH, THE COMPLETE FURNITURE, FURNITURE DRAWINGS, AND INTERIOR DESIGNS. NY: Taplinger Publishing Co. (1979). 1st ed. Dj. Fine. *KARMIOLE.* $75

Billing, Graham and Guy Mannering. SOUTH—MAN AND NATURE IN ANTARCTICA—A NEW ZEALAND VIEW. Wellington: A.H. & A.W. Reed, 1969. Rev ed. Sm spot front cvr, else VG. *PARMER.* $50

Billings, John D. HARDTACK AND COFFEE. Boston, 1887. 1960 reprint, ed by Richard Harwell. Lakeside Classic #58. Fine. *PRATT.* $37.50

Billings, John D. THE HISTORY OF THE TENTH MASSACHUSETTS BATTERY OF LIGHT ARTILLERY IN THE WAR OF THE REBELLION 1862-1865. Boston, 1881. 1st ed. 400pp, roster, index, pict cloth. Small waterstain on cover, o/w Fine. *PRATT.* $210

Billings, John S. A REPORT ON THE HYGIENE OF THE UNITED STATES ARMY WITH DESCRIPTIONS OF MILITARY POSTS. NY, 1974. Facs of 1875 ed. Plts, charts, maps. *FYE.* $150

Billings, John S. SELECTED PAPERS OF JOHN SHAW BILLINGS. Ed. by Frank B. Rogers. Chicago, 1965. 1st ed. *FYE.* $75

Billington, R.A. THE CALIFORNIA GOLD RUSH OVERLAND DIARY OF BYRON N. MCKINSTRY 1850-1852. A.H. Clark, 1975. 1st ed. Fine in Fine dj. *VARNER.* $37.50

Billroth, Theodor. GENERAL SURGICAL PATHOLOGY AND THERAPEUTICS. NY, 1874. 2nd Amer ed. Ex-lib. *FYE.* $100

Billroth, Theodor. THE MEDICAL SCIENCES IN THE GERMAN UNIVERSITIES. NY, 1924. 1st Eng trans. *FYE.* $100

Bilson, Benjamin. THE HUNTERS OF KENTUCKY; OR THE TRIALS AND TOILS OF TRAPPERS AND TRADERS. NY, 1847. 100pp., this copy lacks the adverts. Antique calf, very clean and Good. 1st pirated ed of James Ohio Pattie's narrative. Rare. *GINSBERG.* $1250

Bindman, David. THE COMPLETE GRAPHIC WORKS OF WILLIAM BLAKE. NY: G.P. Putnam's Sons, (1978). Dj. Fine. *WEBER.* $100

Binet, Alfred and Theodore Simon. THE INTELLIGENCE OF THE FEEBLE-MINDED. Baltimore, 1916. 1st Eng trans. 328pp. *FYE.* $125

Bing, Robert. COMPENDIUM OF REGIONAL DIAGNOSIS IN AFFECTIONS OF THE BRAIN AND SPINAL CORD. NY, 1909. 1st Eng trans. *FYE.* $75

Bingham, Carson. GORGO. Derby, CT, (1960). 1st ed. Wraps. Neat owner's name top edge first leaf; unread copy w/very slight touches of cover rub and barely visible crease. *McCLINTOCK.* $30

Bingham, D. THE BASTILLE. 2 vols. James B. Perkins (preface). NY: James Pott, 1901. 1st Amer ed. Plts w/red-ptd tissue guards. Spine gilt dull, minor shelf wear, else NF set. *DIAMOND.* $75

Bingham, Hiram. A RESIDENCE OF TWENTY-ONE YEARS IN THE SANDWICH ISLANDS. Hartford/NY: Hezekiah Huntington/Sherman Converse, 1847. 1st ed. Fldg map, tables. Badly water stained, not affecting map. *HUDSON.* $325

Bingham, Hiram. LOST CITY OF THE INCAS: THE STORY OF MACHU PICCHU....NY: Duell, Sloan and Pearce, 1948. 1st ed. Brn cl, gilt titles. Shelfwear, VG. *PARMER.* $45

Bingham, John. A FRAGMENT OF FEAR. London: Victor Gollancz, 1965. 1st ed. Edges sl darkened o/w Fine in dj. *MORDIDA.* $40

Bingham, John. GOD'S DEFECTOR. London: Macmillan, 1976. 1st ed. Fine in dj. *MORDIDA.* $35

Bingham, John. MURDER OFF THE RECORD. NY: Dodd Mead, 1957. 1st Amer ed. Fine in VG dj (short closed tears; wear, rubbing). *MORDIDA.* $22.50

Bingham, John. MY NAME IS MICHAEL SIBLEY. NY: Dodd, Mead, 1952. 1st ed. Store stamp bottom edge, dates rear pastedown, o/w NF in lightly used dj. *BEASLEY.* $30

Bingham, John. THE MARRIAGE BUREAU MURDERS. London: Macmillan, 1977. 1st ed. Fine in dj. *MORDIDA.* $35

Binion, Charles H. AN INTRODUCTION TO EL PASO'S SCENIC AND HISTORIC LANDMARKS. El Paso: Texas Western Press, 1970. One of 495 numbered of deluxe ed. Designed by Carl Hertzog. Signed by Binion and Hertzog. Fine. *LAURIE.* $75

Binkley, William Campbell. THE EXPANSIONIST MOVEMENT IN TEXAS, 1836-1850. Berkeley, 1925. 1st ed. Orig printed wrappers. Very Nice. *GINSBERG.* $125

Binyon, Laurence. ENGLISH WATER-COLOURS. London, 1933. Frontis, 24 photogravures. NF. *POLYANTHOS.* $45

Binyon, Lawrence. THE WONDER NIGHT. Ariel Poems No. 3. London: Faber & Gwyer, n.d. Purple paper wraps. VG. *HELLER.* $30

BIOGRAPHICAL, LITERARY AND POLITICAL ANECDOTES OF SEVERAL OF THE MOST EMINENT PERSONS OF THE PRESENT AGE... With An Appendix; Consisting of Original, Explanatory And Scarce Papers. (By John Almon.) 3 vols. London: Longman and Seeley, 1797. 1st ed. xi,408; viii,373; ii,410pp. Orig tree calf, rubbed, new polished calf spines, gilt titles. Early penciled comment on title-page. VG. *HARTFIELD.* $295

BIOGRAPHICAL RECORD AND PORTRAIT ALBUM OF TIPPECANOE COUNTY, INDIANA. Chicago: Lewis Pub Company, 1888. 93 plts, portraits. Front cover detached, backstrip torn, sound interior. *BOHLING.* $75

BIOLOGICAL LECTURES DELIVERED AT THE MARINE BIOLOGICAL LABORATORY OF WOOD'S HOLL IN THE SUMMER SESSION OF 1894. Boston, 1896. 1st ed. Scarce. *FYE.* $75

Bird, Annie Laurie. MY HOME TOWN. Caldwell: Caxton, 1968. 1st ed. Inscribed, dated. Town Plat (1886) eps. Laid in newspaper pp. Fine in Good dj. *CONNOLLY & WADE.* $65

Bird, Arthur. UTOPIAN LITERATURE. Arno, 1971 rprt of 1899. As New. *MADLE.* $25

Bird, Isabella L. A LADY'S LIFE IN THE ROCKY MOUNTAINS. London, 1879. 1st ed of 1960 Univ of OK Press ed w/intro by Daniel J. Boorstin. 252pp. Little dj wear, o/w Fine. *PRATT.* $30

Bird, Isabella. A LADY'S LIFE IN THE ROCKY MOUNTAINS. London: Murray, 1885. 5th ed. Front hinge tender. Good, clean. *SECOND LIFE.* $65

Bird, Isabella. SIX MONTHS AMONG THE PALM GROVES, CORAL REEFS, AND VOLCANOES OF THE SANDWICH ISLANDS. NY: Putnam's "Sixth Edition," 1886. Scarce US ed. 318pp. Fine. *BOOK MARKET.* $100

Bird, Yellow (J.R. Ridge). THE LIFE AND ADVENTURES OF JOAQUIN MURIETA. Univ of OK Press, 1955. 1st ptg. Fine in Fine dj. *VARNER.* $15

BIRDS IN FLORIDA. Comp by workers of the Writer's Program of the Work Projects Administration. Tallahassee, n.d. Paperbound. Scuffing, soiling. *SUTTON.* $30

Birdwell, Cleo (pseud of Don DeLillo). AMAZONS. NY: Holt, Rinehart & Winston, (1980). 1st ed. Signed. NF in NF dj. *AKA.* $40

Birge, Julius C. THE AWAKENING OF THE DESERT. Boston: Richard G. Badger, The Gorham Press, 1912. 1st ed. 24 plts, frontis. Untrimmed, neat name, Fine. Howes B463. *CONNOLLY & WADE.* $50

Birkbeck, Morris. LETTERS FROM ILLINOIS. London, 1818. 1st Eng ed. 114,(22)adv pp. Orig boards, expertly recased and mended. Howes B467. *GINSBERG.* $125

Birkbeck, Morris. LETTERS FROM ILLINOIS. Phila: M. Carey, 1818. 1st ed. 154pp incl initial ad leaves. Rebound, entirely uncut, w/orig front wrapper laid down. Map Fine, sl foxing. Howes B467. *HUDSON.* $350

Birkenhead, Earl. THE WORLD OF 2030. Brewer & Warner, 1930. 1st US ed. *MADLE.* $40

Birkenhead, Sheila. AGAINST OBLIVION—THE LIFE OF JOSEPH SEVERN. NY: Macmillan, 1944. 1st US ed. Fine in VG+ price clipped dj. *AARD.* $17.50

Birkett, John. THE DISEASES OF THE BREAST, AND THEIR TREATMENT. London, 1850. 1st ed. 264pp. 11 Fine, partially hand-colored plts. Rebacked w/new eps. Very Scarce. *FYE.* $450

Birkhimer, William E. HISTORICAL SKETCH OF THE ORGANIZATION, ADMINISTRATION...ARTILLERY, UNITED STATES ARMY. Wash: Chapman, 1884. 1st ed. 181,406. Orig full calf w/red lea labels on spine. *GINSBERG.* $175

Birkhimer, William E. HISTORICAL SKETCH OF THE ORGANIZATION, ADMINISTRATION, MATERIEL AND TACTICS OF THE ARTILLERY, UNITED STATES ARMY. Washington, DC, 1884. 1st ed. Sl shaken, else VG. *McGOWAN.* $185

Birney, Hoffman. VIGILANTES. Penn, 1929. 1st ed. VG. Spine frayed top, bottom. *VARNER.* $25

Birney, Hoffman. ZEALOTS OF ZION. Phila, 1931. 1st ed. Tan cloth. 317pp, many photo plts. VG+ in VG dj. *FIVE QUAIL.* $60

Birrell, Augustine. IN THE NAME OF THE BODLEIAN AND OTHER ESSAYS. NY: Charles Scribner's Sons, 1905. 1st US ed. Cl, teg. Spot on cvr. *OAK KNOLL.* $25

Birrell, Augustine. SEVEN LECTURES ON THE LAW AND HISTORY OF COPYRIGHT IN BOOKS. London: Cassell, 1899. 1st ed thus. Orig cl. Lt foxing. *OAK KNOLL.* $55

Bischoff, Charitas. THE HARD ROAD...AMALIE DIETRICH. NY: Hopkinson, 1931. 1st UK ed. Dj. *SECOND LIFE.* $45

Bishop, Elizabeth. POEMS. NORTH & SOUTH—A COLD SPRING. Boston: Houghton Mifflin, 1955. 1st ed. Fine in lightly used dj (short tear, sm hole). *BEASLEY.* $175

Bishop, Elizabeth. QUESTIONS OF TRAVEL. NY: Farrar, Straus & Giroux, (1965). 1st ed. Cloth. VF in dj. *JAFFE.* $75

Bishop, Elizabeth. QUESTIONS OF TRAVEL. NY: FS&G, 1965. 1st ed. Bksellers sticker. Fine in sl used price clipped dj. Inscribed. *CAPTAIN'S BOOKSHELF.* $600

Bishop, Elizabeth. SELECTED POEMS. London: Chatto & Windus, 1967. 1st ed. Fine in dj. No Amer ed. *WOOLMER.* $100

Bishop, Elizabeth. SELECTED POEMS. London: Chatto & Windus, 1967. 1st ed. Cl. Fine in dj. *JAFFE.* $125

Bishop, Ernest S. THE NARCOTIC DRUG PROBLEM. NY: Macmillan, 1921. 2nd ptg. Lightly soiled, o/w Fine in chipped, torn dj. *BEASLEY.* $25

Bishop, Henry G. THE PRACTICAL PRINTER....Oneonta, NY: Henry G. Bishop (1895). 3rd ed. Orig cl. Cvrs worn and silverfished; internally VG. *OAK KNOLL.* $45

Bishop, Isabella L. JOURNEYS IN PERSIA AND KURDISTAN. INCLUDING A SUMMER....NY & London, 1891. 2 fldg maps. 2 vols. xiv,381pp; (iii),409pp. Virtually mint. *O'NEILL.* $275

Bishop, John Peale and Edmund Wilson, Jr. THE UNDERTAKER'S GARLAND. NY: Alfred A. Knopf, 1922. 1st ed, 1st bk. Fine w/o dj. *HELLER.* $75

Bishop, John Peale. ACT OF DARKNESS. NY: Scribner's, 1935. 1st ed, 1st novel. Orig black cl. NF in Nice dj (tiny chip at head of spine, BMOC sticker on front). Scarce in dj. *CHAPEL HILL.* $225

Bishop, Morris. THE ODYSSEY OF CABEZA DE VACA. NY, 1933. Dj. NF. *POLYANTHOS.* $35

Bishop, Robert and Safford L. Carleton. AMERICAN QUILTS AND COVERLETS. NY: E.P. Dutton, 1972. VG. *BACKROOM.* $40

Bishop, S.C. THE SALAMANDERS OF NEW YORK. Albany, 1941. 66 text figures (2 fldg). Wrappers sltly smudged, name on cover, pp edges. *SUTTON.* $60

Bishop, William Henry. MEXICO, CALIFORNIA AND ARIZONA. NY: Harper & Brothers, 1889. Map. *HUDSON.* $75

Bishop, William Henry. OLD MEXICO AND HER LOST PROVINCES. A JOURNEY....NY: Harper & Brothers, 1883, (1883). 1st ed. 509pp, Orig gilt dec cl. Rubbing, rear cl cover stained, contents tight, VG. *SILVER.* $50

Bishop, Zealia. THE CURSE OF YIG. Arkham House, 1953. 1st ed. Fine in dj. *MADLE.* $175

Bissell, Richard. MY LIFE ON THE MISSISSIPPI, OR WHY I AM NOT MARK TWAIN. Little, Brown, 1973. 1st ed. Fine in NF dj. *CONNOLLY & WADE.* $25

Bisset, P. THE BOOK OF WATER GARDENING. NY, 1924. 2nd ed. 2 double-pg plts. Orig dec cl; lt dampstaining, foxing. *SUTTON.* $50

Bitschai, J. and M. Brodney. A HISTORY OF UROLOGY IN EGYPT. (Cambridge, MA), 1956. 1st ed. *FYE.* $35

Bitting, Samuel Tilden. RURAL LAND OWNERSHIP AMONG THE NEGROES OF VIRGINIA...REFERENCE TO ALBEMARLE COUNTY. Charlottesville, VA, 1915. 1st ed. Orig stiff ptd wrappers. NF. *McGOWAN.* $75

Bixby-Smith, Sarah. ADOBE DAYS...Cedar Rapids, IA: Torch Pr, 1925. 1st ed. Spine sl soiled. Small stain rear cvr & top fore-edge, o/w NF. *DIAMOND.* $25

Black, A.P. THE END OF THE LONG HORN TRAIL. Selfridge, ND: Journal, n.d. (c. 1936). 1st ed. Stiff wraps. VF. *OREGON.* $60

Black, Eleanora and Sidney Robertson (comp.) THE GOLD RUSH SONG BOOK. SF: Colt Press. 1940. 1st ed. Fine. *KARMIOLE.* $45

Black Hawk. MA-KA-TAI-SHE-KA-KIAK, AN AUTOBIOGRAPHY. Donald Jackson (ed). Univ of IL, 1955. 1st this ed. Map. Dj w/tears. *HEINOLDT.* $25

Black, Lydia. T. ALEUT ART. UNANGAN OF THE ALEUTIAN ARCHIPELAGO. Anchorage: Aleutian/Pribilof Islands Association, 1982. 1st ed. Very minor smudging, else NF. *GREAT EPIC.* $65

Black, Mrs. (M). SUPERIOR COOKERY. London & Glasgow, n.d. 25th thousand. Frontis, 7 full-pg plts. Cl, lacks front flyleaf. VG. *SECOND LIFE.* $45

Black, Robert L. LITTLE MIAMI RAILROAD. Cincinnati, n.d. (1936?). Fldg map. Orig cl, deckle edge. Dj, plastic jacket. VG+ in soiled & chipped dj. Undated, so apparently the 1st of 2 issues (1936 & 1940). *BOHLING.* $90

Blackburn, I.W. ILLUSTRATIONS OF THE GROSS MORBID ANATOMY OF THE BRAIN OF THE INSANE. Washington, 1908. 1st ed. 154pp, 75 plts. Ex-lib, inner hinges cracked, shaken. *FYE.* $125

Blackburn, I.W. INTRACRANIAL TUMORS AMONG THE IN-SANE. A STUDY OF TWENTY-NINE INTRACRANIAL TUMORS FOUND IN SIXTEEN HUNDRED AND FORTY-TWO AUTOPSIES IN CASES OF MENTAL DISEASE. Washington, 1903. 1st ed. 95pp + plts. *FYE.* $100

Blackburn, John. DEEP AMONG THE DEAD MEN. London: Cape, 1973. 1st ed. Fine in dj. *ELSE FINE.* $50

Blackburn, John. MISTER BROWN'S BODIES. London: Cape, 1975. 1st ed. Fine in dj. *ELSE FINE.* $40

Blackburn, John. THE CYCLOPS GOBLET. London: Cape, 1977. 1st ed. VF in dj. *ELSE FINE.* $35

Blackburn, John. THE FACE OF THE LION. London: Jonathan Cape, 1976. 1st ed. Fine in dj. *MORDIDA.* $37.50

Blackburn, John. THE SINS OF THE FATHER. London: Jonathan Cape, 1979. 1st ed. Fine in dj w/short hair-line scratch on back panel and minor rubbing. *MORDIDA.* $40

Blackburn, Neville. LADIES CHAIN. London: Falcon Press 1952. 1st ed. VG. *HARTFIELD.* $85

Blackburn, Paul. BROOKLYN-MANHATTAN TRANSIT: A BOU-QUET FOR FLATBUSH. NY: Totem Press (1960). 1st ed. Fine in pict wraps. *CAPTAIN'S BOOKSHELF.* $25

Blackburn, Paul. GIN: FOUR JOURNAL PIECES. Mt. Horeb: The Perishable Press. 1st ed. One of 136. Vellum-backed marbled boards. Fine. *CAPTAIN'S BOOKSHELF.* $300

Blackburn, Paul. THE DISSOLVING FABRIC. (Mallorca): Divers Press, 1955. Faint offsetting from French-fold wraps, else especially Fine. *CAPTAIN'S BOOKSHELF.* $350

Blackburn, Paul. THE JOURNALS: BLUE MOUNDS ENTRIES. (Mt. Horeb: The Perishable Press, 1971). 1st ed. One of 125. Cl-backed paperboards. Fine. *CAPTAIN'S BOOKSHELF.* $275

Blackburn, Paul. THE NETS. NY: Trobar, (1961). 1st ed. NF in wraps. *CAPTAIN'S BOOKSHELF.* $50

Blackburn, Paul. THE NETS. NY: Trobar, (1961). 1st ed. Inscribed. Owner name, o/w VG in dec wrappers. *JAFFE.* $100

Blackburn, Paul. THE OMITTED JOURNALS. Edith Jar Olim (ed). (Mt. Horeb, WI): The Perishable Press, 1983. 1st ed. One of 200. Fine in orig wraps. *CAPTAIN'S BOOKSHELF.* $125

Blacker, Irwin R. TAOS. Cleveland: World, 1959. 1st ed. Cl over boards. Fine in NF dj. *CONNOLLY & WADE.* $35

Blackmore, Richard Doddridge. FRINGILLA OR TALES IN VERSE. Cleveland: Burrows Brothers Co, 1895. 1/4 cl, pict paper boards. One of 600. Ink inscrip. Corners bumped, o/w VG. Internally Fine, no foxing. *HELLER.* $350

Blackstone, Sir William. AN ANALYSIS OF THE LAWS OF ENGLAND. Oxford: Clarendon Press, 1759. 4th ed. lxx,(vi),189,(14)pp. Fldg table. Contemp mottled calf very sl worn. Front fly almost detached, o/w text VG. *DIAMOND.* $250

Blackstone, Sir William. COMMENTARIES ON THE LAWS OF ENGLAND (ETC.). 12th ed. Ptd by A. Strahan and W. Woodfall, Law-Printers (etc.), London, 1793-95. Edward Christian (ed). 13 full-pg engrs. Quite a good set, a bit of foxing and staining but still generally fresh and crisp. Well bound in modern 1/4 speckled calf over marbled boards; spines gilt ruled and blind dec, w/crimson morocco labels, gilt; with a leaf at the end of vol 2, advertising the 17th ed of Burn's Justice and two of Burn's other works. *BOSWELL.* $1,500

Blackstone, Sir William. COMMENTARIES ON THE LAWS OF ENGLAND; IN FOUR BOOKS....2 vols. Phila: J.B. Lippincott & Co, 1858. Rubbed, front cover of vol. 1 detached, top of spine pulled, hinges cracked. xxxvi,468pp; xx,402pp. Internally Very Nice. *BLUE MOUNTAIN.* $85

Blackwood, Algernon. A PRISONER IN FAIRYLAND. MacMillan, 1913. 1st ed. Near VG. *MADLE.* $30

Blackwood, Algernon. DAY AND NIGHT STORIES. Dutton, 1917. 1st ed. Cvr soil, else VG. *MADLE.* $40

Blackwood, Algernon. EPISODES BEFORE THIRTY. NY: Dutton, (1924). 1/1550. Staining to spine heel else VG+. *OTHER WORLDS.* $75

Blackwood, Algernon. JULIUS LE VALLON. Dutton, 1916, 1st US ed. VG. *MADLE.* $40

Blackwood, Algernon. SHOCKS. Dutton, 1936. 1st ed. VG in dj, chip. *MADLE.* $50

Blackwood, Algernon. THE DOLL AND ONE OTHER. Arkham House, 1946. 1st ed. VF in dj. *MADLE.* $60

Blackwood, Algernon. THE DOLL AND ONE OTHER. Sauk City, 1946. 1st ed. Fine in dj. *McCLINTOCK.* $75

Blackwood, Algernon. THE DOLL AND ONE OTHER. Sauk City: Arkham House, 1946. 1st ed, ltd to 3490. Fine in NF dj. *ROBBINS.* $45

Blackwood, Algernon. THE EMPTY HOUSE. London, 1916. VG. *MADLE.* $35

Blackwood, Algernon. THE PROMISE OF AIR. Dutton, 1918. 1st ed. VG in sl chipped, taped dj. *MADLE.* $175

Blackwood, Algernon. THE PROMISE OF AIR. Dutton, 1938. Fine in dusty dj. *MADLE.* $50

Blades, William. THE ENEMIES OF BOOKS. London: Elliot Stock, 1902. Rev, enlrgd, the Popular ed. Cl-backed boards. Wear along edges. *OAK KNOLL.* $35

Blaine, James G. JAMES A. GARFIELD. MEMORIAL ADDRESS PRONOUNCED IN THE HALL OF REPRESENTATIVES. Washington, 1882. 87pp. Ornate engr. 4to. Gilt cl. Good. *ARTIS.* $17.50

Blaine, James G. TWENTY YEARS IN CONGRESS FROM LIN-COLN TO GARFIELD WITH A REVIEW....2 vols. Norwich, CT, 1884. Fldg map. Minor shelfwear o/w Fine. *PRATT.* $30

Blaine, James. TWENTY YEARS OF CONGRESS. Norwich: Henry Bill Pub., 1884. 2 vols. 1st ed. VG. *ARCHER.* $40

Blair, Emma. THE INDIAN TRIBES OF THE UPPER MISSISSIP-PI VALLEY AND REGION OF THE GREAT LAKES....A.H. Clark, 1911. 1st ed. 2 vols. 2 frontispieces, 13 plts. VF. Howes B498. *OREGON.* $295

Blair, Gerry. PREDATOR CALLER'S COMPANION. Tulsa: Winchester Press, 1981. 1st ed. Fine in Fine dj. *BACKMAN.* $25

Blair, Karin. MEANING IN STAR TREK. Anima Books, 1977. Fine in VG dj. *MADLE.* $25

Blair, Maria. MATTHEW FONTAINE MAURY. Richmond, 1918. 1st ed. Wrappers. Fine. *McGOWAN.* $37.50

Blair, W.F. (ed). EVOLUTION IN THE GENUS BUFO. Austin, 1972. 6 colored plts, text figures. Dj. *SUTTON.* $60

Blake, E. Vale (ed). ARCTIC EXPERIENCES. NY: Harper & Brothers, 1874. 1st ed. Spine extrems bit chipped. *KARMIOLE.* $75

Blake, E. Vale (ed). ARCTIC EXPERIENCES....NY: Harper & Bros., 1874. 1st ed. 486,(6 ad)pp. Frontis. Dampstain to cover, and fore-edge margin of text w/tide mark. *LEFKOWICZ.* $100

Blake, E. Vale (ed). ARCTIC EXPERIENCES: CONTAINING CAPT. GEORGE E. TYSON'S WONDERFUL DRIFT ON THE ICE-FLOE...NY: Harper & Bros, 1874. 1st ed. Some wear to cvrs, o/w VG. *PARMER.* $150

Blake, Forester. RIDING THE MUSTANG TRAIL. Scribner's, 1935. 1st ed. VG. *VARNER.* $30

Blake, J. M. ed. JOY OF TYROL. London: Stanley Paul & Co., n.d. (188?). 1st ed. Spotting, edgewear, binding sl shaken, else G+. *OLD LONDON.* $35

Blake, John. A SHORT TITLE CATALOG OF EIGHTEENTH CENTURY BOOKS IN THE NATIONAL LIBRARY OF MEDICINE. Bethesda, 1979. 1st ed. *FYE.* $75

Blake, Nicholas. A PENKNIFE IN MY HEART. London: Collins Crime Club, 1958. 1st ed. Pages sl darkened o/w Fine in dj w/nicks and wear at spine ends and at corners. *MORDIDA.* $40

Blake, Nicholas. A TANGLED WEB. London: Collins Crime Club, 1956. 1st ed. Fine in dj w/small chip at base of spine. *MORDIDA.* $45

Blake, Nicholas. END OF CHAPTER. London: Collins Crime Club, 1957. 1st ed. Edges sl darkened o/w Fine in VG price-clipped dj w/chipping at top of spine and at corners. *MORDIDA.* $30

Blake, Nicholas. THERE'S TROUBLE BREWING. NY: Harper & Brothers, 1937. 1st Amer ed. Feps darkened o/w VG in dj (sl faded spine; closed tears, staining). *MORDIDA.* $45

Blake, Sir Henry Arthur. CHINA. A&C Black, 1909. Scarce. VG-NF. *OLD LONDON.* $95

Blake, Vernon. THE ART AND CRAFT OF DRAWING. London, 1927. NF. *POLYANTHOS.* $60

Blakston, W.A. et al. THE ILLUSTRATED BOOK OF CANARIES AND CAGE-BIRDS, BRITISH AND FOREIGN. London, (1880). Pp. viii,448,(4 pp ads). Colored frontis, 55 colored plts, 84 wood engrs. Orig gilt-dec cl. Lower corners worn; splitting to edges of spine ends; inner hinges cracked; sm hole scraped margin of frontis; 1 signature nearly loose; lt staining to upper margins some pp, not affecting print; institutional & owner bkpls; sm number sticker on spine; pp yellowed; aeg. *SUTTON.* $265

Blalock, Alfred. PRINCIPLES OF SURGICAL CARE, SHOCK AND OTHER PROBLEMS. St. Louis, 1940. 1st ed. Myron Prinzmetal's copy. *FYE.* $100

Blanc, Louis. THE HISTORY OF TEN YEARS, 1830-1840. In Two Volumes. London: Chapman & Hall. 1st ed. 1844-45. 2 vols. Lg. 8vo. (4),viii,628; viii,656pp. Fldg map. Fine. *KARMIOLE.* $100

Blanchard, Elizabeth & Manly Wade Wellman. THE LIFE AND TIMES OF SIR ARCHIE: 1805-1833. Chapel Hill: Univ of NC, 1958. VG in Good dj. *OCTOBER FARM.* $45

Blanchard, Rufus. THE DISCOVERY AND CONQUESTS OF THE NORTHWEST. Chicago: Cushing, Thomas & Company, 1880. 2nd ed w/Chicago imprint. 7pp double pp color maps, 11 views. A little shaken. Howes B508. *HUDSON.* $125

Bland, J.O.P. & Blackhouse, E. CHINA UNDER THE EMPRESS DOWAGER...Phila: J.P. Lippincott Co, 1910. 1st Amer ed. Detailed double pg map. Lea spine and corners, marbled eps. Some wear to covers, lt foxing, else VG. *PARMER.* $125

Bland-Sutton, John. TUMOURS INNOCENT AND MALIGNANT: THEIR CLINICAL FEATURES AND APPROPRIATE TREAT-MENT. Phila, 1893. 1st Amer ed. 511pp. 250 woodcuts, 9 colored plts. VF. *FYE.* $150

Blandford, G. Fielding. INSANITY AND ITS TREATMENT: LEC-TURES ON THE TREATMENT, MEDICAL AND LEGAL, OF INSANE PATIENTS. Phila, 1871. 1st ed. 471pp. *FYE.* $200

Blanding, Don. HULA MOONS. NY: Dodd, Mead, 1930. 1st ed. Blue cl stamped in silver, a little soiled and faded on spine. Color tipped-in frontis. Inscription. *SCHOYER'S.* $25

Blanding, Don. THE REST OF THE ROAD. NY: Dodd, Mead, 1937. 1st ed. NF in NF dj. *GREAT EPIC.* $25

Blanford, W.T. OBSERVATIONS ON THE GEOLOGY AND ZOOLOGY OF ABYSSINIA...1867-68. London, 1870. 1st ed. Pp. xii,487. Fldg colored frontis, fldg geological map (colored), 6 plain plts, 6 hand-colored plts. Orig grn cl w/gilt-dec spine. Spine some-what darkened; some overall soiling; lt wear; sm nick to backstrip; paper on interior hinges broken, hinges solid; pp yellowed, o/w text, plts very clean; sm number stamp on spine, bkpl bearing withdrawal stamp. *SUTTON.* $700

Blankenship, William D. THE LEAVENWORTH IRREGULARS. Indianapolis: Bobbs-Merrill, (1974). 1st prtg. Dj edgeworn. *AKA.* $50

Blanton, Rosa A. THE MESQUITE. NY: Hobson, 1947. 1st ed. Red cl, bit of discoloration bottom edge, else VG in VG dj. *CONNOLLY & WADE.* $20

Blanton, Wyndham. MEDICINE IN VIRGINIA IN THE NINETEENTH CENTURY. Richmond, 1933. 1st ed. Scarce. *FYE.* $200

Blashfield, Edwin Howland and Evangeline Wilbour Howland. ITALIAN CITIES. 2 vols. NY: Scribner's, 1902. Partially unopened. *SCHOYER'S.* $35

Blasingame, Ike. DAKOTA COWBOY, MY LIFE IN THE OLD DAYS. Putnam, (1958). 1st ed. Fine in Good+ dj w/small ink stain on back. *OREGON.* $50

Blatty, William Peter. THE EXORCIST. Harper & Row, 1971. 1st ed. Fine. Dj (short tear; sm rubbed spot). Signed & inscribed in yr of pub. *STAHR.* $75

Blatty, William Peter. WHICH WAY TO MECCA, JACK? (NY): Bernard Geis Associates, (1960). 1st ed, 1st book. VG+ in VG price clipped dj. *BERNARD.* $35

Blatty, William. THE EXORCIST. Harper, 1971. 1st ed. VG in dj. *MADLE.* $27

Blavatsky, H.P. THE KEY TO THEOSOPHY. LA, 1920. 1st US ed. Fine. *POLYANTHOS.* $40

Blaylock, James P. HOMUNCULUS. (Bath, Avon), Morrigan, 1988. 1st hb ed. 1/700 trade copies. Fine in Fine dj. *OTHER WORLDS.* $40

Blaylock, James P. PLEASANT DREAMS. Arkham House, 1960. 1st ed. Fine in dj. *MADLE.* $125

Blazek, Doug (ed). A BUKOWSKI SAMPLER. Madison: Quixote Press, (1969). 2nd expanded ed. Fine in wraps. Signed by Blazek. *SMITH.* $50

Bleden, Theodore. THE KENSINGTON RUNE STONE. St. Paul: Minnesota Hist Soc, 1968. 1st ed. Good in chipped dj. *SILVER.* $20

Bleeck, Oliver (pseud of Ross Thomas). NO QUESTIONS ASKED. Morrow, 1976. 1st ed. Fine in dj. *STAHR.* $125

Bleeck, Oliver (pseud of Ross Thomas). NO QUESTIONS ASKED. London: Hamish Hamilton, 1976. 1st Eng. ed. Fine in dj. *MORDIDA.* $50

Bleeck, Oliver (pseud of Ross Thomas). NO QUESTIONS ASKED. NY: William Morrow, 1976. 1st ed. VF in dj. *MORDIDA.* $150

Bleeck, Oliver (pseud of Ross Thomas). PROTOCOL FOR A KID-NAPPING. NY: William Morrow, 1971. 1st ed. Fine in dj w/lamina-tion wrinkle front panel. *MORDIDA.* $185

Bleeck, Oliver (pseud of Ross Thomas). THE BRASS GO-BE-TWEEN. London: Hodder & Stoughton, 1970. 1st Eng ed. Fine in dj. *MORDIDA.* $50

Bleeck, Oliver (pseud of Ross Thomas). THE HIGHBINDERS. Mor-row, 1974. 1st ed. Fine in dj. *STAHR.* $100

Bleek, W.H.I. and L.C. Lloyd. SPECIMENS OF BUSHMAN FOLK-LORE. London: George Allen & Company, 1911. 1st ed. Minor wear extremities, corner bumped. VG. *GREAT EPIC.* $225

Bleeker, Leonard. THE ORDER BOOK OF CAPT. LEONARD BLEEKER IN THE CAMPAIGN OF 1779. NY, Sabin, 1865. Ltd to 250. 138pp. Orig ptd wrappers, rebacked in cl. Howes B532. *GINSBERG.* $125

Blegen, Theodore C. NORWEGIAN MIGRATION TO AMERICA. Northfield, MN, 1940. *ARTIS.* $30

Bleiler, Everett and T. Dikty (eds). YEAR'S BEST SF NOVELS 1952. Fell, 1952, 1st ed. VG in dj. *MADLE.* $25

Bleiler, Everett F. (ed). THE CHECKLIST OF FANTASTIC LITERATURE: A BIBLIOGRAPHY... Chicago: Shasta, 1948. 1st ed. Bkpl else VG in dj w/minor chipping. *OTHER WORLDS.* $75

Blesh, Rudi and Harriet Janis. THEY ALL PLAYED RAGTIME. NY: Knopf, 1950. 1st ed. Fine in worn dj w/chips and internal mends. *BEASLEY.* $40

Blesh, Rudi. SHINING TRUMPETS. A HISTORY OF JAZZ. London: Cassell, 1949. 1st UK ed. Owner's name, o/w Fine in Fine dj. *BEASLEY.* $45

Blesh, Rudi. THIS IS JAZZ. SF: priv ptd, 1943. 1st ed. Wraps. Fine. *BEASLEY.* $100

Blevins, Winfred. GIVE YOUR HEART TO THE HAWKS. LA, 1973. 1st prtg, 1st issue. Fine in chipped dj. *BAADE.* $55

Blevins, Winfred. THE MISADVENTURES OF SILK AND SHAKESPEARE. Jameson Bks, (1985). 1st ed. Signed. Ep erasure, else Fine in dj. *AUTHORS OF THE WEST.* $25

Blewitt, Mary. SURVEYS OF THE SEAS: A BRIEF HISTORY OF BRITISH HYDROGRAPHY. (London, 1957). 1st ed. 67 plts, 2 in color. *LEFKOWICZ.* $125

Bligh, William. A VOYAGE TO THE SOUTH SEAS. Illus by Geoffrey C. Ingleton. (LEC). Adelaide, Australia: Griffin Press, 1975. Ltd to 2000 signed by designer, illus. Slipcase. Fine. *JAFFE.* $175

Bligh, William. A VOYAGE TO THE SOUTH SEAS... Adelaide, So. Australia: The LEC. 1975. Ed ltd to 2,000, ptd at the Griffin Press, signed by Ingleton (illus), Douglas A. Dunstan (designer). Slipcase. Nice but spine dust soiled. *KARMIOLE.* $75

Bligh, William. THE BLIGH NOTEBOOK "ROUGH ACCOUNT—LIEUTENANT WM. BLIGH'S VOYAGE..." 28 APRIL TO 14 JUNE 1789 WITH A DRAFT LIST OF THE 'BOUNTY' MUTINEERS. North Sidney: Allen & Unwin, 1987. 1st ed. Fldg chart. New in dj. *PARMER.* $45

Blish, James. BLACK EASTER. Doubleday, 1968. 1st ed. Ex-lib. VG in dj. *MADLE.* $100

Blish, James. BLACK EASTER. Doubleday, 1968. 1st ed. Fine in perfect dj. (Very scarce thus). *MADLE.* $350

Blish, James. BLACK EASTER/THE DAY AFTER JUDGMENT. Gregg Press, 1980. 1st ed thus. As New. *MADLE.* $35

Blish, James. DOCTOR MIRABILIS. Dodd-Mead, 1971. 1st ed. Fine in dj. *MADLE.* $35

Blish, James. JACK OF EAGLES. Greenberg, 1952. 1st ed. VG in frayed dj. *MADLE.* $40

Blish, James. JACK OF EAGLES. NY: Greenberg Publisher, (1952). 1st ed, 1st book. Corner tips sl bumped o/w NF in dj which has few tiny, internally mended tears. *BERNARD.* $100

Blish, James. THE VANISHED JET. Weybright & Talley, 1968. 1st ed. Ex-lib, but Fine in dj. *MADLE.* $40

Bliss, Douglas Percy. A HISTORY OF WOOD ENGRAVING. London: Dutton, 1928. Frontis. Cream buckram over boards, engr in blind, titling in gilt on spine, top edge brn. Minor shelfwear. Sl spotting of prelims, end matter. VG. *HELLER.* $195

Bliss, Frederick J. THE RELIGIONS OF MODERN SYRIA AND PALESTINE. Edinburgh, 1912. *O'NEILL.* $55

Bliss, Michael. THE DISCOVERY OF INSULIN. Chicago, 1982. 1st ed. Dj. *FYE.* $45

Bliss, William (ed). THE ENCYCLOPEDIA OF SOCIAL REFORM INCLUDING POLITICAL ECONOMY, POLITICAL SCIENCE, SOCIOLOGY, AND STATISTICS... NY, 1897. 1st ed. Inner hinges cracked. *FYE.* $75

Blitz, Professor. THE BOY'S OWN BOOK OF INDOOR SPORTS AND CHOICE PARLOR GAMES...Hurst & Co. (circa 1870's). Green dec cloth w/small damp stain. *MAD DOG.* $35

Bloch, Iwan. THE SEXUAL LIFE OF OUR TIME IN ITS RELATIONS TO MODERN CIVILIZATION. NY, 1928. *FYE.* $35

Bloch, Robert. BLOOD RUNS COLD. NY: Simon and Schuster, 1961. 1st ed. Bloch's signed bkpl on fep. VG in dj (sl stained inner back flap; couple closed tears; minor wear spine ends, corners). *MORDIDA.* $45

Bloch, Robert. BLOOD RUNS COLD. Simon & Schuster, 1961. 1st ed. Fine in rubbed dj. *MADLE.* $100

Bloch, Robert. COLD CHILLS. GC: Doubleday, 1977. 1st ed. Adv review copy, slip laid in. Fine in dj. *MORDIDA.* $37.50

Bloch, Robert. LORI. Tor, 1989. 1st ed. Fine in dj. *MADLE.* $20

Bloch, Robert. NIGHT-WORLD. NY: Simon and Schuster, 1972. 1st ed. Fine in dj. *MORDIDA.* $50

Bloch, Robert. OUT OF THE MOUTHS OF GRAVES. NY: Mysterious Press, 1979. 1st ed. Fine in dj. *MORDIDA.* $45

Bloch, Robert. THE COUCH. Greenwich: Gold Medal, 1962. 1st ed. Wraps. NF but for crease to rear wrap. *BEASLEY.* $25

Bloch, Robert. THE DEAD BEAT. NY: Simon & Schuster, 1960. 1st ed. Pg edges browned, very sl cocked, bump bottom edge. Dj sl soiled. *AKA.* $65

Bloch, Robert. THE DEADBEAT. Simon & Schuster, 1960. 1st ed. Fine in dj. *MADLE.* $100

Bloch, Robert. THE DEADBEAT. Simon & Schuster, 1960. 1st ed. Ex-lib in dj w/usual markings. *MADLE.* $25

Bloch, Robert. THE EIGHTH STAGE OF FANDOM. Advent, 1962. 1st ed. Wraps ed. Fine. *MADLE.* $50

Bloch, Robert. THE KING OF TERRORS. NY: Mysterious Press, 1977. 1st ed. Inscribed. Fine in dj. *MORDIDA.* $45

Bloch, Robert. THE NIGHT OF THE RIPPER. GC: Doubleday 1984. 1st ed. Fine in dj w/stains on back panel and tiny wear at spine ends. *MORDIDA.* $35

Bloch, Robert. THE SCARF. Dial, 1947. VG in Fine dj (magic tape reinforcement to top edge). Inscribed. *MADLE.* $200

Bloch, Robert. THE SCARF. NY: Dial, 1947. 2nd ptg. Dj edgeworn w/sl trim, apparently to fit glassine cover. *AKA.* $35

Blochman, Lawrence G. BLOW DOWN. NY: Harcourt Brace, 1939. 1st ed. VG in dj (internal tape mends; sl faded spine). *MORDIDA.* $45

Blochman, Lawrence G. CLUES FOR DR. COFFEE. Phila: Lippincott, 1964. 1st ed. Sl cocked, o/w Fine in Fine dj. *BEASLEY.* $50

Blochman, Lawrence G. DIAGNOSIS: HOMICIDE. Phila: Lippincott, 1950. 1st ed. Lightly soiled, glue residue on rear pastedown, o/w Fine in lightly used dj. *BEASLEY.* $75

Block, Andrew. KEY BOOKS OF BRITISH AUTHORS, 1600-1932. London: Denis Archer, 1933. 1st ed. Dj lightly worn. *DAWSON'S.* $40

Block, Andrew. THE BOOK COLLECTOR'S VADE MECUM. London: Denis Archer, 1932. 1st ed. Dj sl worn. *DAWSON'S.* $30

Block, Eugene B. GREAT TRAIN ROBBERIES OF THE WEST. NY, (1959). 1st ed. 317pp. Little dj wear, chipping, o/w Fine. *PRATT.* $30

Block, Jean F. HYDE PARK HOUSES—AN INFORMAL HISTORY 1856-1910. Chicago: Univ of Chicago Press, (1978). 1st ed. Signed. Fine in Fine- dj. *AARD.* $30

Block, Lawrence. ARIEL. NY: Arbor House, 1980. 1st ed. Fine in dj. *MORDIDA.* $25

Block, Lawrence. FIVE LITTLE RICH GIRLS. London: Allison & Busby, 1984. 1st hb ed. Orig pub in US as Make Out With Murder. Fine in dj. *MORDIDA.* $37.50

Block, Lawrence. HERE COMES A HERO. Greenwich: Fawcett Pubs, 1968. 1st ed. Pb orig. Fine, unread, in wrappers. *MORDIDA.* $30

Block, Lawrence. IN THE MIDST OF DEATH. Dell, 1976. 1st ed. NF in wraps. Cover lightly creased. *STAHR.* $20

Block, Lawrence. LIKE A LAMB TO SLAUGHTER. NY: Arbor House, 1984. 1st ed. Signed. Fine in dj. *MORDIDA.* $30

Block, Lawrence. RANDOM WALK. NY: Tor, 1988. 1st ed. Signed. VF in dj. *SILVER DOOR.* $35

Block, Lawrence. TANNER'S TWELVE SWINGERS. Fawcett, 1967. 1st ed. About Fine in wraps. Light wear at foot of spine. *STAHR.* $20

Block, Lawrence. TANNER'S TWELVE SWINGERS. Greenwich: Fawcett Pubs, 1967. 1st ed. Pb orig. Inscribed. Fine, unread, in wrappers. *MORDIDA.* $30

Block, Lawrence. THE BURGLAR WHO PAINTED LIKE MONDRIAN. NY: Arbor House, 1983. 1st ed. Signed. VF in dj. *MORDIDA.* $30

Block, Lawrence. THE BURGLAR WHO STUDIED SPINOZA. NY: Random House, 1980. 1st ed. Fine in dj. *MORDIDA.* $30

Block, Lawrence. THE SPECIALISTS. Greenwich: Fawcett Pubs, 1969. 1st ed. Pb orig. Stamp, sm ink mk o/w Fine, unread, in wrappers. *MORDIDA.* $25

Block, Lawrence. THE TOPLESS TULIP CAPER. London: Allison & Busby, 1984. 1st hb ed. VF in dj. *MORDIDA.* $35

Block, Lawrence. WHEN THE SACRED GIN MILL CLOSES. NY: Arbor House, 1986. 1st ed. Signed. VF in dj. *MORDIDA.* $25

Blockson, Charles. THE UNDERGROUND RAILROAD. NY, (1987). 1st ed. VG+ in dj. *PRATT.* $20

Blodget, Lorin. CLIMATOLOGY OF THE UNITED STATES AND OF THE TEMPERATE LATITUDES OF THE NORTH AMERICAN CONTINENT. (Phila: J. B. Lippincott & Co., 1857) 536pp. 1st ed. Orig emb cl. Largely unopened. 12 fldg maps, 1 chart. Signed twice on front pastedown by "J. D. Graham, Lt. Colonel, U.S. Army, Stationed at Chicago, 1857." Small acid stain at extremity of one fldg map. Maps and one gathering near the end a bit foxed, o/w VF in orig sl faded cl binding. *PIRAGES.* $550

Blodgett, Rush Maxwell. LITTLE DRAMAS OF OLD BAKERSFIELD: AS SEEN BY A BOY AND TOLD IN AFTER YEARS. LA: Carl A. Bundy Quill & Press, (1932). 2nd ed. Gold-stamped boards w/fabricoid spine. Inscribed. *DAWSON'S.* $50

Blogg, Minnie. BIBLIOGRAPHY OF THE WRITINGS OF SIR WILLIAM OSLER. Baltimore, 1921. 2nd ed. *FYE.* $60

Blois, John T. GAZETTEER OF THE STATE OF MICHIGAN CONTAINING A GENERAL VIEW OF THE STATE...WITH AN APPENDIX...Detroit, Rood, 1838. 1st ed. 418pp, errata slip. Orig cl, some lt spotting on front cvr; lt tape residue on spine not affecting gold stamping. Howes B542. *GINSBERG.* $350

Blois, John T. GAZETTEER OF THE STATE OF MICHIGAN, IN THREE PARTS. Detroit: S. Rood & NY: Robinson, Pratt & Co., 1840 (c. 1838). Top half of backstrip, w/title portion, gone, edges chipped, paper darkened, stain to upper corner. *BOHLING.* $95

Blome, Richard. HAWKING OR FALCONRY. The Cresset Press, 1929. Plt, 1/4 white parchment, tan boards, teg. Ltd ed of 650 numbered. Fine, unopened. *WEBER.* $150

Bloomfield, Arthur. A BIBLIOGRAPHY OF INTERNAL MEDICINE—COMMUNICABLE DISEASES. Chicago, 1958. 1st ed. Ex-lib. *FYE.* $75

Blos, Joan. OLD HENRY. NY: Morrow, (1987). 1st ed. Pict slick boards. Inscribed. Fine in Fine dj. *ACADEMIC LIBRARY.* $25

Blount, Roy. FIRST HUBBY. NY: Villard, l990. 1st ed. Fine in dj. Inscribed. *CAPTAIN'S BOOKSHELF.* $30

Blount, Roy. IT GROWS ON YOU. GC: Doubleday, 1986. 1st ed. Fine (rmdr mk) in pict wraps. Inscribed. *CAPTAIN'S BOOKSHELF.* $30

Blount, Roy. NOT EXACTLY WHAT I HAD IN MIND. Boston: LB, (1985). 1st ed. Fine in dj. Inscribed. *CAPTAIN'S BOOKSHELF.* $40

Blount, Roy. NOW, WHERE ARE WE? NY: Villard, 1988. 1st ed. Fine in dj. Inscribed. *CAPTAIN'S BOOKSHELF.* $30

Blount, Roy. ONE FELL SOUP OR I'M JUST A BUG ON THE WINDSHIELD OF LIFE. Boston: LB, (1982). 1st ed. Fine in dj. Inscribed. *CAPTAIN'S BOOKSHELF.* $45

Blount, Roy. WHAT MEN DON'T TELL WOMEN. Boston: LB, (1984). 1st ed. Fine in dj, sm tear. Inscribed. *CAPTAIN'S BOOKSHELF.* $40

Blum, Andre. ON THE ORIGIN OF PAPER. Harry Miller Lydenberg (trans). NY: Bowker. 1934. 1st ed. Ed ltd to 1,000. *KARMIOLE.* $45

Blum, Clara. OLD WORLD LACE OR A GUIDE FOR THE LACE LOVER. NY: Dutton, (1920). 1st. Title written on spine, else NF in grn cl w/ptd paper label. *CAPTAIN'S BOOKSHELF.* $45

Blumann, Ethel. CALIFORNIA LOCAL HISTORY, A CENTENNIAL BIBLIOGRAPHY....Stanford Univ, 1950. Dj, few tears at top. *HEINOLDT.* $45

Blumberg, Rhoda. COMMODORE PERRY IN THE LAND OF THE SHOGUN. NY: Lothrop, Lee, (1985). 1st ed. Cl, boards. Signed. Fine in Fine dj. *ACADEMIC LIBRARY.* $28

Blunden, Edmund. NEAR AND FAR: NEW POEMS. London: Cobden-Sanderson, 1929. 1st ed. Offsetting to the endsheets, else Fine, bright in somewhat edgeworn and darkened example of the scarce dj. *CAPTAIN'S BOOKSHELF.* $75

Blunden, Edmund. PASTORALS: A BOOK OF VERSES. London: Erskine MacDonald, (1916). 1st ed, 1/1000. Fine in wrappers. *JUVELIS.* $140

Blunden, Edmund. RETREAT. (London:) Richard Cobden-Sanderson, (1928). 1st trade ed. Inscribed. Spine sunned, else Fine in dj w/darkened and worn spine. *JUVELIS.* $150

Blunden, Edmund. WINTER NIGHTS. A REMINISCENCE. London, 1928. 1st ed. W/drawings by Albert Rutherston. Large paper ed. Ltd ed, 352/500 signed. Fine. *POLYANTHOS.* $35

Blunden, Edmund. WINTER NIGHTS. A REMINISCENCE. London: 1928. 1st ed. Lrg-paper ed. Ltd ed. 352/500 signed. No. 17 of the Ariel Poems. Boards. Fine. *POLYANTHOS.* $45

Blunden, Edwin. CHRIST'S HOSPITAL: A RETROSPECT. London, c. 1925. 1st ed. *FYE.* $30

Blunt, Lady Anne. BEDOUIN TRIBES OF THE EUPHRATES. NY, 1879. Spine lettering rubbed. NF. *POLYANTHOS.* $100

Blunt, Reginald (ed). MRS. MONTAGU, QUEEN OF THE BLUES. Boston: Houghton Mifflin, n.d. (1923). 1st Amer ed. 2 vols. Excellent set. *HARTFIELD.* $145

Blunt, Wilfred Scawen. MY DIARIES. BEING A PERSONAL NARRATIVE OF EVENTS 1888-1914. NY, 1921. 2 vols. Uncut. 1st ed, ltd to 1500. Fine. *O'NEILL.* $110

Blunt, Wilfrid and Sandra Raphael. THE ILLUSTRATED HERBAL. NY, 1979. 1st ed. Dj. *FYE.* $75

Bly, Robert (ed). THE WINGED LIFE: THE POETIC VOICE OF HENRY DAVID THOREAU. Sierra Club, (1986). 1st ed. Review copy, slips laid in. Fine in dj. *AUTHORS OF THE WEST.* $50

Bly, Robert and David Ray (eds). A POETRY READING AGAINST THE VIETNAM WAR. Madison: Sixties Press & American Writers Against the Vietnam War, 1966. 1st ed. Blue-green wraps. NF. *AKA.* $60

Bly, Robert. CHRYSANTHEMUMS. Wisconsin: Ox Head Press, 1967. Ltd ed 179/350. Printed wrappers. Fine. *POLYANTHOS.* $20

Bly, Robert. OLD MAN RUBBING HIS EYES. POEMS. North Carolina: Unicorn Press, 1974. 1st ed. Signed. Pict wraps. Fine. *POLYANTHOS.* $30

Bly, Robert. SELECTED POEMS. Harper & Row, (1986). 1st ed. Fine in dj. *AUTHORS OF THE WEST.* $20

Bly, Robert. THE MAN IN THE BLACK COAT TURNS. Dial, 1981. 1st ed. VF in dj. *STAHR.* $30

Bly, Robert. THIS BODY IS MADE OF CAMPHOR AND GOPHERWOOD: PROSE POEMS. Harper, (1977). 1st ed. Boards. Fine in dj. *AUTHORS OF THE WEST.* $35

Bly, Robert. THIS TREE WILL BE HERE FOR A THOUSAND YEARS. Harper, (1979). 1st ed. Fine in dj. *AUTHORS OF THE WEST.* $35

Boaden, James. THE LIFE OF MRS. JORDAN. London: Edward Bull, 1831. 1st ed. 2 vols. Contemp half calf, quite rubbed; engr frontispieces, morocco labels worn, two lacking; upper hinge of one vol starting; marbled edges. Fldg facs plt of handwriting. VG. *DRAMATIS PERSONAE.* $50

Boardman, John and David Finn. THE PARTHENON AND ITS SCULPTURES. Austin, 1985. Dj. *O'NEILL.* $30

Boardman, John. ATHENIAN BLACK FIGURE VASES. NY: Oxford Univ. Press, 1974. 1st ed. Covers sl faded, corners sl frayed, o/w NF. *WORLDWIDE.* $25

Boardman, John. GREEK GEMS AND FINGER RINGS. EARLY BRONZE AGE TO LATE CLASSICAL. London: Thames and Hudson, (1970). 51 color plts. Fine in dj. *ARCHAEOLOGIA.* $150

Boardman, John. GREEK GEMS AND FINGER RINGS. NY: Harry N. Abrams, (1972). 1st ed. Orig blue cl. Good in dj. *KARMIOLE.* $185

Boardman, R.C. LILIES AND ORCHIDS. NY, 1906. 24 colored plts. Cloth. Corners worn, spine ends frayed; stain back cover, edge of spine, some soiling. *SUTTON.* $65

Boardman, Samuel L. MAINE CATTLE....Augusta: for the author, 1875. 1st ed. 48pp. Sl worn printed paper wraps. VG. *SECOND LIFE.* $75

Boas, Franz. ETHNOLOGY OF THE KWAKIUTL—BRITISH COLUMBIA. Washington, DC: GPO, 1913-14. BAE, 35th Annual Report, 2 vols. 1st ed. Orig olive cl, gilt titles. VG. *PARMER.* $195

Boas, Franz. HANDBOOK OF AMERICAN INDIAN LANGUAGES. Washington: GPO, 1911. 2 vols. Very Nice, clean set. *PARMER.* $250

Boas, Franz. KATHLAMET TEXTS. BAE, Bulletin 26. Washington: GPO, 1901. VG. *LAURIE.* $30

Boas, Franz. TSIMSHIAN TEXTS. BAE, Bulletin 27. Washington: GPO, 1902. Some water staining on cover, else VG. *LAURIE.* $30

Boas, Franz. TSIMSHIAN TEXTS. Washington: GPO, 1902. 1st ed. Fine. *KARMIOLE.* $40

Boatright, Hudson and Maxwell. FOLK TRAVELERS, BALLADS, TALES, AND TALK. Texas Folklore Society Publications Number XXV. Austin: SMU Press, 1953. 1st ed. VF in VG dj. *OREGON.* $30

Boatright, Mody C. (ed). MEXICAN BORDER BALLADS AND OTHER LORE. Texas Folklore Soc, 1946. 1st ed. Fine. *AUTHORS OF THE WEST.* $60

Boatright, Mody C. et al (eds). A GOOD TALE AND A BONNIE TUNE. Pubs of Texas Folklore Soc, No. XXXII. Dallas: Southern Methodist Univ Press, (1964). Fine in dj. *LAURIE.* $20

Boatright, Mody C. GIB MORGAN: MINSTREL OF THE OIL FIELDS. Texas Folklore Soc, Publication XX. (El Paso): (Carl Hertzog), 1945. One of 1,000. Bound in orange cl. VG. *LAURIE.* $60

BOBBY BEAR. "Magic-Action" Book. Whitman, 1935. Pop-up bk. *BOOKFINDERS INTL.* $65

Boccaccio. THE DECAMERON. Edward Hutton (trans). NY: LEC, (1940). 2 vols. Fritz Kredel (illus and signed by). Scarce. One of 530 ptd. Fine set in sl worn, split slipcase. *CAPTAIN'S BOOKSHELF.* $350

Bock, C.E. ATLAS OF THE HUMAN ANATOMY, WITH EXPLANATORY TEXT. NY: William Wood & Co., 1881. 38 color plts. Fine. *WREDEN.* $85

Bodde, Derek. PEKING DIARY—YEAR OF REVOLUTION. NY: H. Schuman (1950). 1st ed. Almost Fine in Almost Fine dj. *AARD.* $15

Bodenheim, Maxwell. MY LIFE & LOVES IN GREENWICH VILLAGE. NY: Bridgehead, 1954. 1st ed. Bit of ink marginalia throughout & touch musty. Good in worn dj. *AKA.* $25

Bodley, R.V.C. ADMIRAL TOGO. London: Jarrolds Pubs, 1935. 1st ed. Spine a bit faded. *KARMIOLE.* $40

Boehn, Max Von. DOLLS AND PUPPETS. London: Bombay and Sidney, George Harrap & Co, (1932). 1st Eng ed. 30 color plts. Unusually Fine condition in dj. *CULLEN.* $175

Boelter, Homer and S.E. Hussey. THE DESERT THEMATIC PORTRAIT. Hollywood, 1945. 1st ed. Fine. *BOOK MARKET.* $25

Boelter, Homer H. PORTFOLIO OF HOPI KACHINAS. Hollywood: Homer H. Boelter Lithography, (1969). One of 1000. 2 of prospectus laid in. 16 color plts and accompanying explanation. Add'l plts in stiff paper folder. Grn-stamped cl in slipcase, tail of spine sl bumped. *DAWSON'S.* $200

Boessenecker, John. BADGE AND BUCKSHOT, LAWLESSNESS IN OLD CALIFORNIA. Norman, (1988). 1st ed. 333pp. Two small tears on dj o/w Fine. *PRATT.* $22.50

Boethius, Axel. THE GOLDEN HOUSE OF NERO: SOME ASPECTS OF ROMAN ARCHITECTURE. Ann Arbor: Univ of Michigan Press, (1960). 109 figs. Tattered dj. Good. *ARCHAEOLOGIA.* $85

Boger, Louise Ade and H. Batterson. THE DICTIONARY OF ANTIQUES AND THE DECORATIVE ARTS. NY: Scribners, (1957). 1st ed. Fine in dj (stain verso of spine; few sm chips). *CAPTAIN'S BOOKSHELF.* $75

Bogert, Mayor Frank M. PALM SPRINGS FIRST HUNDRED YEARS. Palm Springs Heritage Associates, Pub, (1987). 1st ed. Fine in Fine dj. *BOOK MARKET.* $60

Boggs, K.D. PRINTS AND PLANTS OF OLD GARDENS. Richmond, 1932. 39 plts. Orig dec cl, upper edges worn, corners and fore-edges bumped. Cvrs faded, some staining. Ink inscription. *SUTTON.* $75

Boggs, Mae H. B. MY PLAYHOUSE WAS A CONCORD COACH: AN ANTHOLOGY OF NEWSPAPER CLIPPINGS AND DOCUMENTS...DURING THE YEARS 1822-1888. (Oakland, Howell-North, 1942). 1st ed. 763pp. 8 fldg maps, plts. Orig 4to blue cl. Howes B570. *GINSBERG.* $500

Bogle, Donald. TOMS, COONS, MULATTOES, MAMMIES, & BUCKS. NY: Viking, (1973). 2nd ptg. Pgs bumped bottom corner. NF in NF dj. *AKA.* $50

Bohart, R.M., A.S. Menke et al. SPHECID WASPS OF THE WORLD. Berkeley, 1976. Name on ep. *SUTTON.* $85

Bohn, Dave (photos & text). GLACIER BAY: THE LAND AND THE SILENCE. SF: Sierra Club, (1967). VG in VG dj. *BLUE DRAGON.* $35

Bohr, Neils. ATOMIC PHYSICS AND HUMAN KNOWLEDGE. NY, 1958. 1st ed. Dj. *FYE.* $35

Bois, E. ROSES. London, 1962. 1st Eng ed. 60 tipped-in colored plts. Cl, some darkening around edges; lt overall soiling. *SUTTON.* $45

Bolander, Henry N. A CATALOGUE OF THE PLANTS GROWING IN THE VICINITY OF SAN FRANCISCO. SF: A. Roman & Co, 1870. 43pp. Wrappers. Cvrs detached, somewhat soiled, o/w Good. *WREDEN.* $35

Boles, Robert. CURLING. Boston: Houghton Mifflin, 1968. 1st ed. Fine in NF dj. *LOPEZ.* $45

Bolin, Major C. NARRATIVE OF THE LIFE...OF MAJOR C. BOLIN...AS RELATED...TO A.A. SARGENT. Palo Alto: Lewis Osborne, 1966. Grn cl. Laid-in a fldg facs of newspaper report. Plain dj soiled. VG. *PARMER*. $50

Bolinder, Gustaf. INDIANS ON HORSEBACK. London: Dobson (1957). 1st Eng ed. Fine in VG dj. *AARD*. $17.50

Bolitho, William. MURDER FOR PROFIT. London: Dennis Dobson, (1953). John Arlott (intro). 1st ed thus. VG in soiled dj. *DIAMOND*. $12.50

Boll, Heinrich. ACQUAINTED WITH THE NIGHT. NY: Holt (1954). 1st Amer ed. Fine in Fine price-clipped dj. *DORN*. $100

Boll, Heinrich. TOMORROW AND YESTERDAY. NY: Criterion, 1957. 1st US ed. Fine in VG spine sunned torn dj. *ARCHER*. $17.50

Bollaert, William. WILLIAM BOLLAERT'S TEXAS. Norman: Univ of OK, 1956. 1st ed. Cloth. About Fine. *CONNOLLY & WADE*. $75

Boller, Henry. AMONG THE INDIANS. EIGHT YEARS IN THE FAR WEST: 1858-1866....SKETCHES OF MONTANA AND SALT LAKE. Phila., 1868. 428pp. 1st ed. Fldg map. Orig cl, few chips and nicks on spine, 2 rubber lib stamps. Howes B579. *GINSBERG*. $750

Boller, Henry. AMONG THE INDIANS. EIGHT YEARS IN THE FAR WEST, 1858-1866. Lakeside Classic 1959. Fldg maps. Fine. *OREGON*. $35

Bolton, Ethel Stanwood and Eva Johnston Coe. AMERICAN SAMPLERS. MA: MA Society of Colonial Dames, 1921.1st ed. VG. *BACKROOM*. $200

Bolton, Herbert (ed). SPANISH EXPLORATION IN THE SOUTH-WEST, 1542-1706. NY: Scribner's, 1916. 1st ptg. 3 fldg maps. Ex-lib in orig cl. Clean. *SCHOYER'S*. $65

Bolton, Herbert. ATHANASE DE MEZIERES AND THE LOUISIANA-TEXAS FRONTIER, 1768-1780....NY, 1970. 1st ed. 2 vols, bound in one vol. Orig cl. Howes B584. *GINSBERG*. $45

Bolton, Herbert. CORONADO—KNIGHT OF PUEBLOS AND PLAINS. Albuquerque and NY, (c) 1949. VG+ in Good+ repaired dj. *FIVE QUAIL*. $40

Bolton, Herbert. FONT'S COMPLETE DIARY: A CHRONICLE OF THE FOUNDING OF SAN FRANCISCO...Berkeley, 1933. 20 maps, plts, facs. Howes B585. *GINSBERG*. $85

Bolton, Herbert. PAGEANT IN THE WILDERNESS. Salt Lake City: Utah Hist Soc, 1950. 1st ed in book form. Fldg maps in rear pocket. VF. *FIVE QUAIL*. $75

BOMBA'S ADVENTURE. London, 1967. 3D Pop-Up Book. Pulls out from spine for 3-D effect. Pop-up bk. *BOOKFINDERS INTL*. $50

Bombal, Maria Luisa. NEW ISLANDS AND OTHER STORIES. NY: FSG (1982). 1st Amer ed. Fine in dj. *DORN*. $20

Bonadio, Felice A. NORTH OF RECONSTRUCTION, OHIO POLITICS, 1865-1870. NY, 1970. 1st ed. Two small tears in dj o/w VG+. *PRATT*. $17.50

Bonar, Andrew A. and R.M. McCheyne. NARRATIVE OF A MISSION OF INQUIRY TO THE JEWS FROM THE CHURCH OF SCOTLAND IN 1839. Phila, 1845. Fldg map. 1/4 calf, worn at joints. *O'NEILL*. $85

Bonavia, Duccio. MURAL PAINTING IN ANCIENT PERU. Bloomington: IU Press, (1985). 1st ed. 16 color plts. Good in dj. *SILVER*. $50

Bond, Harold L. AN ENCYCLOPEDIA OF ANTIQUES. NY, 1946. NF. *POLYANTHOS*. $30

Bond, James. BIRDS OF THE WEST INDIES. Boston: Houghton Mifflin, (1971). 2nd US ed. Color plts. Fine in VG+ dj. *MIKESH*. $25

Bond, James. FIELD GUIDE TO BIRDS OF THE WEST INDIES. NY, 1947. Dj. Lt scuffing. *SUTTON*. $25

Bond, James. FIELD GUIDE TO BIRDS OF THE WEST INDIES. NY: Macmillan, 1947. 1st ed. Sm stain, o/w Fine in VG dj with rubbing along folds, spine ends and corners. *MORDIDA*. $75

Bond, Michael. MONSIEUR PAMPLEMOUSSE AND THE SECRET MISSION. London: Hodder & Stoughton, 1984. 1st ed. VF in dj. *MORDIDA*. $30

Bond, Michael. MONSIEUR PAMPLEMOUSSE RESTS HIS CASE. London: Headline, 1991. 1st ed. VF in dj. *MORDIDA*. $35

Bond, Michael. MONSIEUR PAMPLEMOUSSE TAKES THE CURE. NY: Random House, 1988. 1st Amer ed. VF in dj. *MORDIDA*. $25

Bond, Nelson. NIGHTMARES AND DAYDREAMS. Sauk City (WI): Arkham House, (1968). 1st ed. 1/2000. Fine in sl rubbed dj. *SECOND LIFE*. $25

Bond, Nelson. NIGHTMARES AND DAYDREAMS. Sauk City, 1968. 1st ed. Fine in VG dj w/shelfwear to edges. *McCLINTOCK*. $35

Bond, Nelson. NIGHTMARES AND DAYDREAMS. Sauk City: Arkham House, 1968. 1st ed. NF in spine rubbed else NF dj (in dj protector neatly taped to bk). *OTHER WORLDS*. $30

Bond, Nelson. THE THIRTY-FIRST OF FEBRUARY. Gnome Press, 1949. One of 112 numbered, signed. Fine (the only ltd ed Gnome Press) *MADLE*. $350

Bond, Nelson. THE THIRTY-FIRST OF FEBRUARY. NY, (1949). 1st ed. Fine in VG dj (one chip bottom of spine). *McCLINTOCK*. $20

Bond, Nelson. THE THIRTY-FIRST OF FEBRUARY. NY: Gnome, (1949). 1st ed. VG+ in VG+ dj. *AARD*. $30

Bond, Nelson. THE THIRTY-FIRST OF FEBRUARY. NY: Gnome Press, (c.1949). 1st ed. Inscribed. Fine in dj (few sm soil spots back panel). *HELLER*. $125

Bond, Simon. HAVE A NICE DAY. London, 1986. Pop-up bk. *BOOKFINDERS INTL*. $25

Bond, W.H. (ed). THE HOUGHTON LIBRARY, 1942-1967. A SELECTION OF BOOKS AND MANUSCRIPTS IN HARVARD COLLECTIONS. Cambridge, 1967. 1st ed. *FYE*. $100

Bond, William R. PICKETT OR PERRIGREW? AN HISTORICAL ESSAY (REVISED AND ENLARGED). Scotland Neck, NC, c. 1888. 2nd ed. Wrappers. NF. *McGOWAN*. $150

Bonelli, William G. BILLION DOLLAR BLACKJACK. Beverly Hills, CA: Civic Research Press. (1954). 1st ed. Blue cl. Dj. Apparently this book was suppressed; many copies were destroyed. *KARMIOLE*. $30

Bonestell, Chesley. WORLDS BEYOND: THE ART OF....Donning, 1983, 1st ed. One of 300 numbered, signed in slipcase. As New. *MADLE*. $130

Bonhote, J. Lewis. BIRDS OF BRITAIN. A&C Black. 1917 reprint. 20s Series. VG-NF. *OLD LONDON*. $95

Bonker, Frances & John J. Thornber. THE SAGE OF THE DESERT AND OTHER CACTI...Boston, (1930). 1st ed. Color prints of cactus attached to pastedown & blank fly. Minor spine tip wear, o/w VG+. *DIAMOND*. $25

Bonnell, James Francis. DEATH FLIES WEST. NY: Scribner's, 1941. 1st ed. Fine in dj w/minor wear. *MORDIDA*. $40

Bonnell, James Francis. DEATH OVER SUNDAY. NY: Charles Scribner's Sons, 1940. 1st ed. Edges darkened o/w Fine in dj w/minor wear. *MORDIDA*. $40

Bonner, M.G. and Alan Gould. THE BIG BASEBALL BOOK FOR BOYS. McLoughlin Bros., 1931. Presumed 1st. Good. *PLAPINGER*. $50

Bonner, T.D. THE LIFE AND ADVENTURES OF JAMES P. BECKWOURTH....Harper, 1856. 1st ed. 537pp. Frontis, 12 plts. Some corners, spine end. VG. Howes B601. *OREGON*. $250

Bonner, T.D. THE LIFE AND ADVENTURES OF JAMES P. BE-CKWOURTH. NY: Harper & Bros. 1856. 1st ed. 538pp+(2)pp of ads. Frontis, 11 plts. Orig dec brn cl, blindstamped, gilt spine. Fine. *KARMIOLE.* $350

Bonner, Thomas. THE KANSAS DOCTOR, A CENTURY OF PIONEERING. Lawrence, 1959. *FYE.* $30

Bonnet, Theodore. THE REGENERATORS. SF: Pacific Printing, 1911. VG. *AKA.* $35

Bonneval, Claude-Alexandre, Comte de. MEMOIRS OF THE BASHAW COUNT BONNEVAL, AFTERWARDS AHMED PASHA. FROM HIS BIRTH TO HIS DEATH...London: E. Withers, 1750. 1st Eng ed. Engr frontis. Contemp calf, rubbed. *O'NEILL.* $850

Bonney, Cecil. LOOKING OVER MY SHOULDER. SEVENTY FIVE YEARS IN THE PECOS VALLEY. Roswell, NM: Hall-Poorbaugh Press, 1971. 1st ed. VF in Fine dj. *OREGON.* $75

Bonney, Cecil. LOOKING OVER MY SHOULDER. SEVENTY-FIVE YEARS IN THE PECOS VALLEY. Rosewell, NM, 1971. 1st ed. Fine. *GIBBS.* $45

Bonney, T.G. VOLCANOES, THEIR STRUCTURE AND SIG-NIFICANCE. NY: Putnam's, 1899. 1st ed. 332pp. Fldg map. Gilt grn cl. NF. *SMITHFIELD.* $25

Bonomi, Joseph. NINEVEH AND ITS PALACES. THE DIS-COVERIES OF BOTTA AND LAYARD....London: Bell & Daldy, 1865. New ed, rev. xviii,537pp. 272 illus. 1/2 morocco, marbled eps, edges rubbed, gilt spine, 4 raised bands, all edges marbled. Ex-lib, # on spine. VG. *WORLDWIDE.* $75

Bontemps, Arna. STORY OF THE NEGRO. NY: Knopf, 1948. 1st ed. Inscribed. Bottom portion of cvrs, pp dampstained, o/w VG. *LOPEZ.* $150

Bontemps, Arna. STORY OF THE NEGRO. NY: Knopf, 1955. 2nd enlrgd ed. Spine frayed and faded. Signed, dated. VG lacking dj. *LAME DUCK.* $85

Bontemps, Arna. WE HAVE TOMORROW. Boston: Houghton Mif-flin, 1945. 1st ed. Thin paper browned o/w VG in thin paper dj chipped at heel, moderately edgeworn, but still Good. *LOPEZ.* $65

Bonvalot, Gabriel. ACROSS THIBET. NY, 1892. C.B. Pitman (trans). Pict cl, spine numbering, spine ends sl chipped. Uncut. Fldg map front pocket. Excellent. *O'NEILL.* $100

BOOK OF TRAVELS OF A DOCTOR OF PHYSIC...(By William Henry Taylor) Phila: J. B. Lippincott, 1871. 373pp,10pp pub ads. Blue cl stamped in black and gilt, rubbed at head and foot of spine, one signature pulled. *SCHOYER'S.* $85

BOOKS AND MANUSCRIPTS ON OLD MEDICINE, AL-CHEMY, WITCHCRAFT, PHARMACY, COOKERY, TOBAC-CO, (ARRANGED CHRONOLOGICALLY). London, Maggs Bros, 1926. Wrappers. *FYE.* $50

Boole, George. AN INVESTIGATION OF THE LAWS OF THOUGHT, ON WHICH ARE FOUNDED THE MATHEMATI-CAL THEORIES OF LOGIC AND PROBABILITIES. London: Macmillan, 1854. 8vo, (2),v,(5),(numbered "iv" on verso), 424pp. Does not incl errata leaf, which represents the probable 1st issue of the bk. Orig grn pebbled cl, brn endleaves; extrems worn, corners showing, inner hinges cracked, but untouched. Bkpl, sig. *WEBER.* $3,500

Boone, J. Allen. LETTERS TO STRONGHEART. Englewood Cliffs, NJ: Prentice Hall, 1939. 1st ed. Well closed 2" tear, scuff to rear of dj o/w Fine in VG- dj. *AARD.* $60

Booth, Charles. ZACHARY MACAULAY: HIS PART IN THE MOVEMENT FOR THE ABOLITION OF THE SLAVE TRADE & OF SLAVERY. NY: Longmans & Green, 1934. 117pp. *AKA.* $25

Booth, E.S. BIRDS OF THE WEST. Stanford, (c. 1950). Chipped dj. *SUTTON.* $30

Booth, John. THE BATTLE OF WATERLOO...London: Ptd for J. Booth; and T. Egerton, 1815. 3rd ed. xcviii,116pp. Fldg frontis map, 2 facing panoramic plts. Few spots, else entirely clean. Modern 1/4 grn cl, grn marbled boards. Fine. *WEBER.* $250

Booth, Martin. HIROSHIMA JOE. London: Hutchinson, (1985). 1st ed. Fine in close to Fine dj. *WOOLMER.* $35

Booth, William Stone. SOME ACROSTIC SIGNATURES OF FRANCIS BACON..TOGETHER WITH SOME OTHERS.... Bos-ton: Houghton Mifflin, 1909. 1st ed. 1/150 lg paper. Cl-backed boards. Spine and paper label a bit soiled, else Fine in worn slipcase. *CAPTAIN'S BOOKSHELF.* $125

Boothby, Guy. PHAROS, THE EGYPTIAN. NY: Appleton, 1899. 1st ed. Owners' names. VG. *NUTMEG.* $25

Boraston, J.H. (ed). SIR DOUGLAS HAIG'S DESPATCHES DECEMBER 1915-APRIL 1919. London & Toronto, 1919. 10 fldg maps, slipcase vol 2. VG. *CULLEN.* $160

Borchgrevink, C.E. FIRST ON THE ANTARCTIC CON-TINENT...THE BRITISH ANTARCTIC EXPEDITION 1898-1900. London: George Newnes, 1901. 1st ed. Blue dec cl. Frontis lacking, rebacked w/orig spine laid down, bright, tight, clean. *PARMER.* $225

Borden, W.C. THE USE OF THE ROENTGEN RAY BY THE MEDICAL DEPARTMENT OF THE UNITED STATES ARMY IN THE WAR WITH SPAIN. Washington, 1900. 1st ed. 98pp + 38 x-ray plts. Inner hinges cracked, front board sl stained, shaken, some sections starting. Overall, VG. *FYE.* $400

BORDER BEAGLES; A Tale of Mississippi. (By William Gilmore Simms.) Phila: Carey & Hart, 1840. 2 vols. 1st ed. 300; 337pp. Orig purple cl w/paper spine labels. Spines sunned as usual, edges less so, some pencilled marginalia, few traces of foxing, else VG. Nice set. *CHAPEL HILL.* $650

BORDER LANDS OF SPAIN AND FRANCE...London: Chapman & Hall, 1856. Rubbed on edges, head and foot of spine. Lacks fron-tis. *SCHOYER'S.* $45

Borges, Jorge Luis. A PERSONAL ANTHOLOGY. Anthony Ker-rigan (ed, foreword). NY: Grove Press, (1967). 1st ed. Fine in very sl used price-clipped dj w/short tear. Rev copy, slip laid in. *CAPTAIN'S BOOKSHELF.* $75

Borges, Jorge Luis. A PERSONAL ANTHOLOGY. NY: Grove, 1967. 1st ed. Fine in Fine dj. *BEASLEY.* $50

Borges, Jorge Luis. AN INTRODUCTION TO AMERICAN LITERATURE. (Lexington): Univ Press of Kentucky, (1971). 1st US ed. Fine in Fine dj. *LOPEZ.* $65

Borges, Jorge Luis. IN PRAISE OF DARKNESS. Bilingual ed. NY: Dutton, 1974. 1st US ed. Fine in dj. *CAPTAIN'S BOOKSHELF.* $60

Borges, Jorge Luis. LABYRINTHS. (NY): New Directions, (1964). 2nd ed, expanded. Two small accession labels on dj spine, o/w Fine in dj. *LOPEZ.* $150

Borges, Jorge Luis. TEXAS. Mark Strand (trans). Austin: Univ of Texas, (1975). 1st ed. 1/295. Lower corner bumped, else Fine in wraps. *CAPTAIN'S BOOKSHELF.* $100

Borland, J. Nelson and David Cheever. FIRST MEDICAL AND SURGICAL REPORT OF THE BOSTON CITY HOSPITAL. Boston, 1870. 1st ed. Rear inner hinge cracked, few sections start-ing. *FYE.* $325

Borman, Frank with Robert J. Serling. COUNTDOWN, AN AUTOBIOGRAPHY. NY: Wm. Morrow, 1988. 1st ed. VG in dj. *KNOLLWOOD.* $25

Borneman, Henry. PENNSYLVANIA GERMAN BOOKPLATES. Phila: Phila German Society, 1953. VG+. *BACKROOM.* $150

Borrow, George. CELEBRATED TRIALS AND REMARKABLE CASES...FROM EARLIEST RECORDS TO THE YEAR 1825. NY, 1928. Newly rev ed. 2 vols. NF. *POLYANTHOS.* $95

Borsook, Eve. THE MURAL PAINTERS OF TUSCANY. (London): Phaidon Pubs, Inc. 1960. 1st ed. 118 plts (one mounted color). Gray cl, gilt. Dj. *KARMIOLE.* $60

Borthwick, J.D. THREE YEARS IN CALIFORNIA. Oakland: Biobooks, 1948. One of 1,000. 1st pub in 1857. Fine. Howes B-622. *LAURIE.* $50

Borup, George. A TENDERFOOT WITH PEARY. NY: Stokes, 1911. VG (wear to edges, front hinge cracked). *PARMER.* $55

Bosanquet, Mary. SADDLEBAGS FOR SUITCASES: ACROSS CANADA ON HORSEBACK. NY: Dodd, Mead, 1942. 1st prtg. VG. *OCTOBER FARM.* $18

Bosqui, Edward. MEMOIRS OF EDWARD BOSQUI. Oakland, CA: The Holmes Book Co. 1952. Ltd to 350, ptd by the Grabhorn Press. *KARMIOLE.* $100

Bosqui, Edward. MEMOIRS OF EDWARD BOSQUI. Oakland: Holmes, 1952. Orig prospectus laid in. Orig cl backed boards, plain dj. One of 350 ptd by Grabhorn Press. Intro by Henry R. Wagner. Orig pub in 1904 in ed of 50. Howes B623. *GINSBERG.* $150

Boston, Charles K. (pseud of Frank Gruber). THE SILVER JACKASS. NY: Reynal & Hitchcock, 1941. 1st ed. Inscription, o/w Fine in dj. *MORDIDA.* $90

Boston, David M. PRE-COLUMBIAN POTTERY OF THE AMERICAS. NY: Kodansha, (1980). 121 full pp color plts. Masterpieces of Western & Near Eastern Ceramics, Vol. III. Boxed. Good. *ARCHAEOLOGIA.* $350

Boston, Noel. OLD GUNS AND PISTOLS. London: Ernest Benn, (1958). 1st ed. 159pp. VG in torn dj. *WEBER.* $25

Boswell, James. AN ACCOUNT OF CORSICA, THE JOURNAL OF A TOUR TO THAT ISLAND; and MEMOIRS OF PASCAL PAOLI. Illus With a New and Accurate Map of Corsica. 2nd ed. London: for Edw. and Chas. Dilly, 1768. Tall 8vo; pp xxii, 384. Fldg map frontis and half-title. Early lea covers, nicely rebacked w/tooled spine and lea label, gilt. Tape marks on blank prelims, bookseller's ticket front paste-down. Some wear, internally Fine. *HARTFIELD.* $395

Boswell, James. BOSWELL'S JOURNAL OF A TOUR TO THE HEBRIDES with Samuel Johnson. NY: The Viking Press. 1936. Fldg map, tipped-in facs. Ed ltd to 790 numbered. Red cl over red boards, in slipcase. *KARMIOLE.* $75

Boswell, James. LIFE OF JOHNSON. London: John Murray, 1835. 1st illus ed. 10 vols. Small 8vos. Bound by Zaehnsdorf in full polished calf, gilt, lea labels, floral endpapers, top edges gilt. Spines sl but uniformly darkened, front hinge Vol 10 repaired, but an Excellent set. *HARTFIELD.* $985

Boswell, James. LIFE OF SAMUEL JOHNSON. London: T. Cadell, 1804. 4th ed. 4 vols. Tall 8vo, with engr port and 2 fldg facsimiles (Sl waterstain at bottom edge of portrait page, not affecting engr). Contemp polished calf, rebacked: elaborately gilt in panels, red and green lettering pieces. Knowledgeable annotations. Bkpl. Part of pastedown torn away, else a handsome set. *HARTFIELD.* $595

Boswell, James. THE JOURNAL OF A TOUR TO THE HEBRIDES WITH SAMUEL JOHNSON, L.L.D. London: Chas. Dilly, 1785. 2nd ed, Revised and Corrected. Tall 8vo. pp xxii, 534, 1 p. advert. (for Boswell's Life of Johnson). Extra-illus w/engr portraits of Johnson and Boswell. Nicely rebound in polished morocco, gilt, and marbled boards, w/orig label laid down. Excellent. *HARTFIELD.* $495

Boswell, James. THE LIFE OF SAMUEL JOHNSON, LL. D. (London: Printed for J. Richardson et al., 1823). 4 vols. Contemp half calf, marbled paper sides, spine gilt in compartments with stylized tulip ornament in center, double morocco labels. Engraved frontis and 2 fldg facs of handwriting. Armorial bkpl. Corners just sl worn,

a little variation in the color of the lea, otherwise virtually no wear at all. End sheets as well as engr leaves and facing pages somewhat foxed, o/w extremely clean and smooth internally. *PIRAGES.* $450

Boswell, James. THE LIFE OF SAMUEL JOHNSON, LL.D....5th ed, rev, augmented. 4 vols. London: T. Cadell & W. Davies. 1807. Frontis port in vol 1; fldg facs vols 2 and 3. 19th-c grn morocco, gilt cvrs and spines w/red morocco spine labels; extrems sl rubbed. *KARMIOLE.* $200

Boswell James. THE LIFE OF SAMUEL JOHNSON. Newly edited by Roger Ingpen. NY: Sturgis and Walton, 1909. 1st Amer ed. 2 vols. Gravure port frontis each vol, 306 illus, 4 other gravure plts. Light wear, spine gilt somewhat faded but VG. *HARTFIELD.* $165

Boswell, James. THE LIFE OF SAMUEL JOHNSON...London: Ptd by Henry Baldwin, for Charles Dilly, 1791. 4to. 2 vols. 1st ed, 1st issue, w/"gve" in the couplet on p.135 in vol 1. xii,(16),516pp.; (1)f.,588 (i.e. 586)pp. 19th century Russia morocco; rebacked w/orig back-strip laid down. Fldg drop-back boxes. Title-pg sig of M. Bower. Fine. *WEBER.* $4000

Boswell, Thomas. HOW LIFE IMITATES THE WORLD SERIES. Doubleday, 1982. 1st ed. VG+ in Fine dj. *PLAPINGER.* $40

Botkin, B.A. and Alvin Harlow (eds). A TREASURY OF RAILROAD FOLKLORE. NY: Crown, 1953. 1st ed. Gilt cl. Fine in dj (faint discoloration bottom of backstrip), o/w bright, Fine. *CONNOLLY & WADE.* $35

Botkin, B.A. SIDEWALKS OF AMERICA. Indianapolis: Bobbs Merrill, 1954. 1st ed. Fine in Good dj. *CONNOLLY & WADE.* $37.50

Bott, Alan. THIS WAS ENGLAND: MANNERS AND CUSTOMS OF THE ANCIENT VICTORIANS. GC, NY: Doubleday, Doran & Co, 1931. 1st ed. Cvrs a bit dust marked, o/w VG. *WREDEN.* $25

Botta, Carlo. ITALY, DURING THE CONSULATE & EMPIRE OF NAPOLEON BUONAPARTE. 2 vols in 1. Phila: Towar & Hogan, 1829. 1st Amer ed. xv,392pp. Contemp full calf covers sl worn. Text foxed, o/w Good. *DIAMOND.* $45

Bottoms, David. ANY COLD JORDAN. Atlanta: Peachtree, (1987). 1st Amer ed. Signed. *DORN.* $30

Bottoms, David. SHOOTING RATS AT THE BIBB COUNTY DUMP. NY: Morrow, (1980). 1st Amer ed. Signed. Name ffep else Fine in dj. *DORN.* $45

Boucher, Anthony. BEST FROM F & SF. 5TH SERIES. Doubleday, 1956. 1st ed. Fine in dj. *MADLE.* $30

Boucher, Anthony. THE COMPLEAT WEREWOLF. NY: S&S, (1969) 1st ed. Fine in lightly rubbed dj. *UNGER.* $75

Boucher, Francois. 20,000 YEARS OF FASHION. NY: Harry N. Abrams, Inc. (1966). 1st ed. Dj. *KARMIOLE.* $60

Boudreau, Lou with Ed Fitzgerald. PLAYER-MANAGER. Little Brown, 1949. Signed by Boudreau. 1st ed. VG+ in Fine dj. *PLAPINGER.* $50

Boudreau, Lou. GOOD INFIELD PLAY. Ziff-Davis, 1948. 1st ed. Signed by Boudreau. VG with minor spine wear, without dj as issued. *PLAPINGER.* $65

Boughton, F.E. FLEXOGRAPHIC PRINTING. Chicago: F.E. Boughton, 1958. *OAK KNOLL.* $25

BOULDER DAM. CONSTRUCTION OF BOULDER DAM. Boulder City, NV: The Boulder Dam Service Bureau, c1936. 17th ed. Wraps. Issued w/o title page. Cover somewhat soiled. *HUDSON.* $25

Boule, T.C. DESCENT OF MAN. London: Gollancz, (1981). 1st Eng ed, 1st bk. Signed. Fine in NF dj w/1 minute rub at top of spine. *DORN.* $125

Boulenger, E.G. CATALOGUE OF THE BATRACHIA GRADIENTIA S. CAUDATA AND BATRACHIA APODS IN

THE COLLECTION OF THE BRITISH MUSEUM. 1966 (1882). 2nd ed. 9 plts. *SUTTON.* $30

Boulenger, E.G. REPTILES AND BATRACHIANS. London & NY, (1914). Colored frontis. Lt wear, sl joint cracking. *SUTTON.* $100

Boulenger, G.A. CATALOGUE OF THE BATRACHIA SALIENTIA S. ECAUDATA IN THE COLLECTION OF THE BRITISH MUSEUM. 1966 (1882). 2nd ed. 30 plts. *SUTTON.* $85

Boulenger, G.A. CATALOGUE OF THE CHELONIANS, RHYNCHOCEPHALIANS AND CROCODILES IN THE BRITISH MUSEUM. 1966 (1889). 2nd ed. 6 plts, 73 text-figures. *SUTTON.* $45

Boulenger, G.A. CATALOGUE OF THE LIZARDS IN THE BRITISH MUSEUM. 1965 (1885-87). Reprint. 3 vols in 2. 96 plts. xii,436pp; xiii,497pp; xii,575pp. *SUTTON.* $280

Boulle, Pierre. NOT THE GLORY. NY: Vanguard, 1955. 1st ed. As New, minor rubs at dj folds. *ELSE FINE.* $35

Boulle, Pierre. PLANET OF THE APES. NY: Vanguard, 1963. 1st ed. Name. Fine in dj. *ELSE FINE.* $50

Boulton, Major. REMINISCENCES OF THE NORTH-WEST REBELLIONS...AND A CHAPTER ON CANADIAN SOCIAL & POLITICAL LIFE. Toronto, 1886. 1st ed. 531pp. Fldg map. Orig cl, stained at edges of covers. *GINSBERG.* $75

Bouquet, A.G. CAULIFLOWER AND BROCCOLI CULTURE. NY: Orange Judd, 1929. VG ex-lib. *AMERICAN BOTANIST.* $20

Bourgery, D.M.T. A TREATISE ON LESSER SURGERY, OR, THE MINOR SURGICAL OPERATIONS. NY, 1834. 1st Eng trans. Orig cloth, half of spine label missing, front outer hinge torn. Contents Fine. *FYE.* $150

Bourjaily, Vance. THE END OF MY LIFE. NY: Scribner's, 1947. 1st ed, 1st bk. NF in Near VG chipped dj. *ARCHER.* $60

Bourjaily, Vance. THE GREAT FAKE BOOK. Franklin Center: Franklin Library, 1986. 1st ed. One of an unspecified number signed. Fine in full lea. *BETWEEN COVERS.* $45

Bourke, John G. AN APACHE CAMPAIGN IN THE SIERRA MADRE. NY: Scribner's, 1886. 1st ed. 112pp, plus ads. Frontis. Orig brown pict cl. Howes B652. *GINSBERG.* $500

Bourke, John G. ON THE BORDER WITH CROOK. NY: Scribner's, 1892. 2nd ed. 491pp, cloth. New paste downs, literary label removed, water ring on cover, cover worn. *GIBBS.* $65

Bourke, John G. ON THE BORDER WITH CROOK. Rio Grande, (1962). VG. Howes B654. *OREGON.* $35

Bourke, John G. SCATALOGIC RITES OF ALL NATIONS. Washington: W. H. Lowdermilk & Co, 1891. x, 11, 496pp. Brn cl. Front hinge cracked but well held, modest edge wear, rubbing. *PARMER.* $300

Bourke, John G. THE SNAKE DANCE OF THE MOQUIS OF ARIZONA. Chicago: Rio Grande, (1962). 31 full page engr. Plts. Fine. *MIKESH.* $40

Bourke, John G. THE SNAKE DANCE OF THE MOQUIS OF ARIZONA. Chicago: Rio Grande Press, 1962. 1st ed thus. 31 plts. Facsimile of 1884 ed. Cl. Fine. *ARTIS.* $35

Bourke, John G. WITH GENERAL CROOK IN THE INDIAN WARS. Palo Alto: Lewis Osborne, 1968. 2 fldg maps. Ltd to 2100. First pub in March 1891 Century mag. VF. *OREGON.* $45

Bourke, John G. WITH GENERAL CROOK IN THE INDIAN WARS. Palo Alto, 1968. #433/2100 of 1st ed in book form. 59pp, fldg map. Fine. *PRATT.* $45

Bourke-White, Margaret and Erskine Caldwell. SAY IS THIS THE U.S.A. NY: Duell, Sloan & Pearce. 1941. 1st ed. Cl bit soiled; spine extrems, corner bit frayed. *KARMIOLE.* $60

Bourne, Geoffrey and Nelly Golarz (eds). MUSCULAR DYSTROPHY IN MAN AND ANIMALS. NY, 1963. 1st ed. Ex-lib. *FYE.* $75

Bourne, Lawrence. THE RADIUM CASKET. London: Milford, 1929. 1st ed. Fine, pict dj chipped at spine ends. *ELSE FINE.* $45

Bourne, Randolph S. YOUTH AND LIFE. Boston/NY: Houghton Mifflin, 1913. 1st ed, 1st bk. Grn cl stamped in gold on backstrip, front cvr. Unopened. Front hinge beginning to crack. NF. *HELLER.* $100

Bouton, Jim. BALL FOUR. World, 1970. Leonard Schecter (ed). 1st ed. VG+ in Fine dj. Signed by Bouton. *PLAPINGER.* $50

Bouton, John. THE ENCHANTED. Cassell, 1891. 1st ed. VG. *MADLE.* $50

Bouvier, Hannah M. BOUVIER'S FAMILIAR ASTRONOMY.... Phila: Sower, Barnes & Potts, (1857). Two corners and spine worn, o/w Good. *KNOLLWOOD.* $42

Bova, Ben (ed). THE SCIENCE FICTION HALL OF FAME. Doubleday, 1973, 1st ed. 2 vols. Fine in sl frayed djs. *MADLE.* $75

Bova, Ben. CYBORGS. Tor, 1989. 1st ed. Fine in dj. *MADLE.* $20

Bova, Ben. STAR WATCHMAN. NY: HRW, 1964. 1st ed. Brief inscription. Corners sl bumped, else Fine, light edgewear to dj. *ELSE FINE.* $70

Bowden, J. THE NATURALIST IN NORWAY OR, NOTES ON THE WILD ANIMALS BIRDS, FISHES, AND PLANTS, OF THAT COUNTRY PRINCIPAL SALMON RIVERS. 8 plts (7 tinted & 1 colored). London, 1869. xiii,263pp. Orig gilt-dec cl. Some chipping & wear at spine ends & corners; backstrip faded; remains of paper label on spine; pp yellowed. *SUTTON.* $95

Bowden, Keith Macrae. GEORGE BASS 1771-1803. Melbourne: Oxford Univ Press, (1952). Dj. *SCHOYER'S.* $25

Bowditch, Heng I. (ed). FIRST ANNUAL REPORT OF THE STATE BOARD OF HEALTH, LUNACY AND CHARITY OF MASSACHUSETTS, 1879. A SUPPLEMENT CONTAINING THE REPORTS AND PAPERS ON PUBLIC HEALTH. Boston, 1880. 1st ed. Fldg maps. *FYE.* $150

Bowditch, N. T. SUFFOLK SURNAMES (MASS). London, 1861. 3rd ed. Rebound. *HEINOLDT.* $45

Bowditch, Nathaniel Ingersoll. MEMOIR OF NATHANIEL BOWDITCH. ...3rd ed. Cambridge, 1884. 29 cm. (4),178 pp. 8 plts. *LEFKOWICZ.* $200

Bowditch, Nathaniel. THE NEW AMERICAN PRACTICAL NAVIGATOR....30th new stereotype ed. NY: E.& G.W. Blunt, 1861. (2),8,(iii-xx)1-289,(1 blank),460 tables,(2 ads)pp. 14 charts and plts. Orig calf, cvrs showing some wear, a few gatherings started, tear to chart fold, dampstains, lt foxing. Better than average. Bkpl. Scarce. *LEFKOWICZ.* $225

Bowditch, Nathaniel. THE NEW AMERICAN PRACTICAL NAVIGATOR. NY: Blunt, 1853. 23rd new stereotype ed. (2),4,(iii-xx),319,(1 blank),460, 2 ads. 14 charts & plts, incl uncalled-for pl facing p452. Orig calf, worn. *LEFKOWICZ.* $175

Bowditch, Nathaniel. THE NEW AMERICAN PRACTICAL NAVIGATOR. NY: Blunt, 1847. 17th new stereotype ed. (xvi),318,(2 blank)451,(1 blank,2 ads). 13 charts and plts. Orig calf, front cvr loose, some foxing. *LEFKOWICZ.* $200

Bowen, Dana Thomas. SHIPWRECKS OF THE LAKES. Daytona Beach, (1952). 2nd ptg. Dj. *ARTIS.* $17.50

Bowen, Elizabeth. COLLECTED IMPRESSIONS. NY: Knopf, 1950. 1st US ed. Fine in lightly worn dj (sl darkened spine). Signed. *CAPTAIN'S BOOKSHELF.* $175

Bowen, Elizabeth. EVA TROUT. London: Cape, (1969). 1st ed. Just About Fine in like dj w/wrinkle. *CAPTAIN'S BOOKSHELF.* $60

Bowen, Elizabeth. THE HOTEL. NY: Dial, 1928. 1st ed. Former owner's name in two places, NF in VG+ dj. *LAME DUCK*. $100

Bowen, Elizabeth. TO THE NORTH. NY: Knopf, 1933. 1st ed. Fine in Fine dj w/minor fading, a few tiny tears. *BEASLEY*. $150

Bowen, Frank C. THE GOLDEN AGE OF SAIL. London: Halton & Truscott Smith, Ltd. 1925. 91 plts (11 tipped-in color plts) and tipped-in color frontis. Ltd to 1500 numbered. Dj. Fine. *KARMIOLE*. $200

Bowen, Frank C. THE GOLDEN AGE OF SAIL: INDIAMEN, PACKETS AND CLIPPER SHIPS. London & NY, 1925. 1st ed. One of 1,500. 91 plts. Fine. *LEFKOWICZ*. $175

Bowen, George Ferguson. MOUNT ATHOS, THESSALY, AND EPIRUS: A DIARY OF A JOURNEY FROM CONSTANTINOPLE TO CORFU. London, 1852. vii,253pp. Fine. *O'NEILL*. $200

Bowen, Helen Gilman. MOUNT SHASTA OR BUST: A FAMILY TRAVELOGUE IN THE 1890's. LA: Plantin Press, 1978. 1st ed. Signed. Grn cl, gilt decor. VF in dj. *CONNOLLY & WADE*. $45

Bowen, James L. HISTORY OF THE THIRTY-SEVENTH REGIMENT MASS...1861-1865. Holyoke and NY: Bryan, 1884. 1st ed. Lacks rear ep, hinge little tender, VG. *SECOND LIFE*. $75

Bowen, W.H. CHARLES DICKENS AND HIS FAMILY. Cambridge: W. Heffer & Sons, 1956. 1st ed. 8vo, 182pp, green cloth, spine sunned. VG. *GREAT EXPECTATIONS*. $25

Bower, B.M. CABIN FEVER. Little, Brown, 1918. 1st ed. Frontis. Pict cvr. Fine. *AUTHORS OF THE WEST*. $25

Bower, B.M. CHIP OF FLYING-U. NY: G.W. Dillingham, April, 1906. 1st ed. 3 color. Red pict dec boards. About Fine. *CONNOLLY & WADE*. $95

Bower, B.M. THE EAGLE'S WING: A STORY OF THE COLORADO. Little, Brown, 1924. 1st ed. Frontis, dec cover. Fine, stamp. *AUTHORS OF THE WEST*. $17.50

Bower, B.M. THE FLYING U'S LAST STAND. Little, Brown, 1915. 1st ed. Frontis, dec cover. VG. *AUTHORS OF THE WEST*. $20

Bower, B.M. THE GRINGOS: A STORY OF THE OLD CALIFORNIA DAYS IN 1849. Little, Brown, 1913. 1st ed. VG. *AUTHORS OF THE WEST*. $20

Bower, B.M. THE PHANTOM HERD. Little, Brown, 1916. 1st ed. Frontis. VG+. *AUTHORS OF THE WEST*. $20

Bower, B.M. THE RANGE DWELLERS. Dillingham, (1907). 1st Dillingham ed. Spine faded, else VG+. *AUTHORS OF THE WEST*. $25

Bowers, C.G. RHODODENDRONS AND AZALEAS....NY, 1960. 2nd ed. 28 colored plts. Cl, chipped dj. *SUTTON*. $95

Bowie, Henry P. ON THE LAWS OF JAPANESE PAINTING. SF: Paul Elder, (1911). Largely unopened. *SCHOYER'S*. $45

Bowie, Theodore and Diether Thimme (eds). THE CARREY DRAWINGS OF THE PARTHENON SCULPTURES. Bloomington: Indiana Univ Press, (1971). Good. *ARCHAEOLOGIA*. $200

Bowles, Jane. IN THE SUMMER HOUSE. NY: Random House, (c1954). 1st ed, 1st play. NF in price clipped dj, few short tears. *HELLER*. $60

Bowles, Jane. IN THE SUMMER HOUSE. NY: Random House. (1954). 1st ed. Mounted photo top cvr. Dj. *KARMIOLE*. $45

Bowles, Jane. OUT IN THE WORLD: SELECTED LETTERS OF JANE BOWLES, 1935-1970. Santa Barbara: Black Sparrow, 1985. Millicent Dillon (ed). Fine in plain acetate dj. One of 500 of trade hb. *LOPEZ*. $35

Bowles, Jane. PLAIN PLEASURES. London: Peter Owen, (1966). 1st ed. Sm stain top edge, else Fine in dj (sl fading of spine lettering). *CAPTAIN'S BOOKSHELF*. $75

Bowles, Jane. THE COLLECTED WORKS OF JANE BOWLES. NY: Farrar, Straus & Giroux, (1966). 1st ed. Fine in price-clipped dj. *LOPEZ*. $60

Bowles, Jane. TWO SERIOUS LADIES. London: Peter Owen, (1965). 1st UK ed. Fine in sl used dj, sm tears. *CAPTAIN'S BOOKSHELF*. $60

Bowles, Jane. TWO SERIOUS LADIES. NY: Knopf, 1943. 1st ed. NF in bright, VG dj (tiny bit of chipping at extremities of spine). *LOPEZ*. $850

Bowles, Paul Frederic and Gertrude Stein. SCENES FROM THE DOOR. (NY): Editions de la Vipere, (1933). Bowles' 1st pub music, w/lyrics by Stein. Issued in ed of 100. NF. *LOPEZ*. $1500

Bowles, Paul. A HUNDRED CAMELS IN THE COURTYARD. (SF): City Lights, (1962). 1st ed. Only issued in wrappers. Small strip of surface peel on rear cover, o/w Fine. *LOPEZ*. $75

Bowles, Paul. A LITTLE STONE. London: Lehmann, (1950). 1st ed. 1st issue binding (according to Lepper: light grn cl). Fine in dj (minute wear at heel, o/w Fine). *LOPEZ*. $225

Bowles, Paul. COLLECTED STORIES 1939-1976. Gore Vidal (intro). Santa Barbara: Black Sparrow Press, 1979. One of 300 clbound, signed by Bowles. Fine in dj. *CAPTAIN'S BOOKSHELF*. $175

Bowles, Paul. COLLECTED STORIES 1939-1976. Gore Vidal (intro). Santa Barbara: Black Sparrow Press, 1979. 1st ed. #99 of 300 signed. Orig dec cream boards w/purple cl spine, paper spine label. As New in orig acetate jacket. *CHAPEL HILL*. $200

Bowles, Paul. LET IT COME DOWN. NY: Random House, 1952. 1st ed. VG. *ARCHER*. $25

Bowles, Paul. MIDNIGHT MASS. Santa Barbara: Black Sparrow, 1981. One of 350 numbered, signed. Fine in pub's acetate dj. *LOPEZ*. $100

Bowles, Paul. MOHAMMED MRABET: LOOK AND MOVE ON. London: Owen (1989). 1st Eng ed. Fine in Fine dj. *LOPEZ*. $45

Bowles, Paul. NEXT TO NOTHING. Santa Barbara: Black Sparrow, 1981. One of 300 numbered, signed. Fine in pub's acetate dj. *LOPEZ*. $100

Bowles, Paul. NEXT TO NOTHING. Starstreams 5. Nepal, 1976. Ltd ed, 102/500. Pict wraps. NF. *POLYANTHOS*. $75

Bowles, Paul. SCENES. LA: Black Sparrow Press, 1968. 1st ed. Bowles 1st signed ltd ed, with a ptg of 300 of which this is one of 50 bound in hb and signed. Exceedingly scarce in hb issue. Edges of boards sl faded, rear cover has sunned area, o/w Fine. *LOPEZ*. $750

Bowles, Paul. THE BIG MIRROR. London: Owen (1989). 1st Eng ed. Only issued in wrappers. Fine. *LOPEZ*. $45

Bowles, Paul. THE HOURS AFTER NOON. London: Heinemann, (1959). 1st ed. Slight soiling to top edge of pages o/w VG in a dj that has two internal repairs. *LOPEZ*. $250

Bowles, Paul. THE SHELTERING SKY. (NY): New Directions, 1949. 1st US ed. VG in dj (lightly chipped at extrems of spine). *LOPEZ*. $300

Bowles, Paul. THE SHELTERING SKY. (NY): New Directions, (1949). 1st ed. US. Fine in very lightly used dj (1/4" by 3/4" stain fore-edge of front panel). *CAPTAIN'S BOOKSHELF*. $300

Bowles, Paul. THE SHELTERING SKY. London: John Lehmann, (1949). 1st ed. Orig grey cl. Bkseller's label, else VG in price-clipped pict dj. *CHAPEL HILL*. $450

Bowles, Paul. THE SPIDER'S HOUSE. NY: Random House, (1955). 1st ed. Fine in sl rubbed dj. Signed. *CAPTAIN'S BOOKSHELF*. $225

Bowles, Paul. THE TIME OF FRIENDSHIP. NY: Holt Rinehart Winston, (1967). 1st ed. Fine in sl spine-darkened dj (bit of wear at extrems), overall VG. *LOPEZ*. $55

Bowles, Paul. THE TIME OF FRIENDSHIP. NY: Holt, Rinehart, & Winston, (1967). 1st ed. Orig dec white cl. VG in dj (sunned spine, 1/4" piece lacking top of front panel). *CHAPEL HILL.* $65

Bowles, Paul. THEIR HEADS ARE GREEN AND THEIR HANDS ARE BLUE. NY, 1963. 1st ed. NF in VG dj. *PETTLER.* $45

Bowles, Paul. TWO YEARS BESIDE THE STRAIT. TANGIER JOURNAL 1987-1989. London: Peter Owen, (1990). Fine in dj. One of 75 signed by author. *WOOLMER.* $125

Bowles, Paul. UP ABOVE THE WORLD. NY: Simon & Schuster (1966). 1st ed. Adv rev copy. Fine in Fine dj, rev slip laid in. *LOPEZ.* $100

Bowles, Samuel. ACROSS THE CONTINENT. Springfield, MA/NY: Samuel Bowles & Company/Hurd & Houghton, 1865. 1st ed. Fldg map. *HUDSON.* $100

Bowles, Samuel. ACROSS THE CONTINENT: A SUMMER'S JOURNEY TO THE ROCKY MOUNTAINS, THE MORMONS, AND THE PACIFIC STATES, WITH SPEAKER COLFAX. Springfield, Ma, 1865. 1st ed, 1st issue. 452pp. Fldg map. Orig cl. Howes 1089. *GINSBERG.* $125

Bowles, Samuel. ACROSS THE CONTINENT; A SUMMER'S JOURNEY TO THE ROCKY MOUNTAINS... NY, 1866. 452pp, ads. Fldg map, hinges cracked, spine sunned, external wear, respectable. *BENCHMARK.* $35

Bowles, Samuel. OUR NEW WEST. Hartford, 1869. 1st ed. 524pp, map. At least VG. *FIVE QUAIL.* $115

Bowles, Samuel. OUR NEW WEST. Hartford, CT, 1869. 1st ed thus. Orig maroon cl, complete w/map, portraits, many illus. Very Nice. W/pencil sig of John T. Jones. *HUDSON.* $95

Bowles, Samuel. OUR NEW WEST...Hartford, CT, 1869. 1st ed. Contemp full lib calf. Little cvr staining & repair. Front cvr reattached. Little fore-edge staining, o/w VG. *DIAMOND.* $45

Bowles, Samuel. OUR NEW WEST: RECORDS OF TRAVEL BETWEEN THE MISSISSIPPI RIVER AND THE PACIFIC OCEAN. Hartford: Hartford Pub Co, 1869. 1st ed. 524pp incl 14 full-pg plts. Gold-stamped cl, light wear to extremities, some silver-fishing to covers, inner hinges weak. *DAWSON'S.* $75

Bowles, Samuel. THE SWITZERLAND OF AMERICA: COLORADO ITS PARKS & MOUNTAINS. Springfield/Boston/NY, 1869. 1st ed. 166pp+ads. Spine faded w/some chipping, else VG+. *FIVE QUAIL.* $65

Bowman, John E. A PRACTICAL HANDBOOK OF MEDICAL CHEMISTRY. London: John Churchill, 1862 (1850). 4th ed. Front joint split, extremities worn, corners bumped. *KNOLLWOOD.* $35

Bowman, John E. A PRACTICAL HANDBOOK OF MEDICAL CHEMISTRY. Phila: Lea and Blanchard, 1850. 1st Amer ed. 288pp, cat. Emb black cl cvr very worn. Contents VG. *SMITHFIELD.* $35

Bowman, S.M. and R.B. Irwin. SHERMAN AND HIS CAMPAIGNS: A MILITARY BIOGRAPHY. NY, 1865. 1st ed. VG. *DIAMOND.* $45

Bownas, Samuel. AN ACCOUNT OF THE LIFE, TRAVELS, AND CHRISTIAN EXPERIENCES IN THE WORK OF THE MINISTRY OF...Stanford, NY, 1805. 306,(2)pp. Orig boards, expertly rehinged and mended. Howes B668. *GINSBERG.* $125

BOY'S OWN BOOK OF INDOOR GAMES & RECREATIONS. Lippincott, 1888. 528pp. VG dec cvr, sl edgewear. *BEBBAH.* $50

Boyce, Rubert. MOSQUITO OR MAN? THE CONQUEST OF THE TROPICAL WORLD. London, 1910. 2nd ed. Head of tail chipped. *FYE.* $100

Boyd, C.R. RESOURCES OF SOUTH-WEST VIRGINIA. NY: Wiley, 1881. 1st ed. Woodcut plts, tables. Rebacked w/new cl. Small stain margins of 40pp; slight cover wear, staining, o/w Good. *DIAMOND.* $45

Boyd, Ernest A. IRELAND'S LITERARY RENAISSANCE. Dublin: Maunsel & Co., 1916. 1st ed. Thumb-size ripple to grn cl on front panel, else Fine, fresh. Signed. *CAPTAIN'S BOOKSHELF.* $60

Boyd, J. R. ELEMENTS OF RHETORIC AND LITERARY CRITICISM. NY: Harper & Bros., 1845. Good+. *OLD LONDON.* $35

Boyd, James P. RECENT INDIAN WARS UNDER THE LEAD OF SITTING BULL AND OTHER CHIEFS: WITH A FULL ACCOUNT OF THE MESSIAH CRAZE AND GHOST DANCES. N.p., 1891. 1st ed. 320pp. VG. *PRATT.* $55

Boyd, James. MARCHING ON. NY, 1927. 1st ed. 426pp. VG+. *PRATT.* $40

Boyd, John. THE GIRL WITH THE JADE GREEN EYES. Viking, 1973. 1st ed. Fine. Dj (2 sm tears). *STAHR.* $20

Boyd, Robin. KENZO TANGE. NY: Braziller, 1962. 1st ed. Fine in VG+ dj. *AARD.* $20

Boyd, William. A GOOD MAN IN AFRICA. Morrow, 1982. 1st Amer ed. Fine in dj. *STAHR.* $40

Boyd, William. A GOOD MAN IN AFRICA. NY: Morrow, 1982. 1st US ed, 1st bk. Fine in dj. *CAPTAIN'S BOOKSHELF.* $50

Boyd, William. A GOOD MAN IN AFRICA. NY: Morrow, (1982). 1st US ed. Fine in Fine dj. *UNGER.* $45

Boyd, William. AN ICE CREAM WAR. London, 1982. 1st UK ed. Fine in dj. *PETTLER.* $75

Boyd, William. AN ICE CREAM WAR. London: Hamish Hamilton, (1982). 1st ed. As New in dj. Als laid in. *CAPTAIN'S BOOKSHELF.* $125

Boyd, William. AN ICE-CREAM WAR. Morrow, 1983. 1st Amer ed. VF in dj. *STAHR.* $15

Boyd, William. AN ICE-CREAM WAR. Morrow, 1983. Uncorrected proof of Amer ed. VG or better in gold wraps. Sm spot on spine; lightly soiled. *STAHR.* $35

Boyd, William. AN ICE-CREAM WAR. NY: Morrow, 1983. 1st US ed. Fine in NF dj. *LOPEZ.* $45

Boyd, William. BRAZZAVILLE BEACH. Cl backed marbled boards, glassine dj. London: London Limited Editions, (1990). 1st ed. Ltd to 150, signed. Mint. *JAFFE.* $100

Boyd, William. BRAZZAVILLE BEACH. Morrow, 1991. Advance reading copy. VF in dec wraps. *STAHR.* $20

Boyd, William. BRAZZAVILLE BEACH. NY, 1991. 1st ed. Uncorrected bound galleys in pub's printed wraps. Fine. *POLYANTHOS.* $35

Boyd, William. BRAZZAVILLE BEACH. NY: Morrow, (1991). Adv reading copy of 1st Amer ed. Fine in pict wraps. *LOPEZ.* $30

Boyd, William. ON THE YANKEE STATION. Morrow, 1984. 1st Amer ed. VF in dj.*STAHR.* $15

Boyd, William. ON THE YANKEE STATION. Morrow, 1984. Uncorrected proof of 1st Amer ed. VF in wraps. *STAHR.* $35

Boyd, William. PHYSIOLOGY AND PATHOLOGY OF THE CEREBRO-SPINAL FLUID. NY, 1920. 1st ed. *FYE.* $50

Boyd, William. SCHOOL TIES. Morrow, 1986. Uncorrected proof of Amer ed. VF in gold wraps. *STAHR.* $25

Boyd, William. STARS AND BARS. NY: Morrow, (1985). Uncorrected proof of 1st Amer ed. VG in wraps. *LOPEZ.* $40

Boyd, William. STARS AND BARS. Hamish Hamilton, 1984. 1st ed. Fine in price clipped dj. Signed & inscribed. *STAHR.* $45

Boyd, William. STARS AND BARS. London: Hamish Hamilton, 1984. 1st ed. Fine in lightly used dj. *DERMONT.* $20

Boyd, William. STARS AND BARS. Morrow, 1985. Uncorrected proof of 1st Amer ed. VF in wraps. Signed. *STAHR.* $60

Boyd, William. THE NEW CONFESSIONS. Hamish Hamilton, 1987. 1st ed. Fine in dj. Signed & inscribed. *STAHR.* $45

Boyd, William. THE NEW CONFESSIONS. Morrow, 1988. Adv reading copy of Amer ed. Fine in dec wraps. *STAHR.* $15

Boyd, William. THE NEW CONFESSIONS. NY, 1988. 1st ed. Signed presentation. Fine in like dj. *POLYANTHOS.* $50

Boyd, William. THE NEW CONFESSIONS. NY: Morrow (1988). Adv rev copy of 1st Amer ed. Fine in dj. *LOPEZ.* $35

Boyer, Alexis. A TREATISE ON SURGICAL DISEASES, AND THE OPERATIONS SUITED TO THEM. NY, 1815-1816. 1st Eng trans. 2 vols. Full leather, 415, 395pp. VF. Rare. *FYE.* $1,000

Boyer, Mary Joan. THE OLD GRAVOIS COAL DIGGINGS. Private, 1952. 1st ed. Autographed. Fine. *VARNER.* $125

Boyer, Mary. ARIZONA IN LITERATURE. Clark, Glendale, 1935. Frontis. Front hinge weak. *HEINOLDT.* $40

Boyer, Rick. BILLINGSGATE SHOAL. Boston: Houghton Mifflin, 1982. 1st ed. Fine in dj, closed tear; scrape on spine. *MORDIDA.* $35

Boykin, Edward. BEEFSTEAK RAID. NY, (1960). 1st ed. 305pp. VG+ in dj. *PRATT.* $45

Boykin, Edward. GHOST SHIPS OF THE CONFEDERACY. NY, (1957). 1st ed. 404pp. VG. *PRATT.* $25

Boylan, Grace Duffie. YAMA YAMA LAND. Illus by Edgar Keller. Chicago: The Reilly & Britton Co. N.d. (circa 1909). 13 full-pg color plts (2 double-pg). Blue paper-cvred boards w/mounted color cvr illus. Extrems bit rubbed. *KARMIOLE.* $75

Boyle, F. THE CULTURE OF GREENHOUSE ORCHIDS, OLD SYSTEM AND NEW. London, 1902. 3 colored plts. Cl, cvr fading. *SUTTON.* $95

Boyle, Kay. THE CRAZY HUNTER. THREE SHORT NOVELS. NY: Harcourt, Brace and Company, (1940). 1st ed. Inscribed. VG in lightly used dj. *JUVELIS.* $125

Boyle, Kay. THE WHITE HORSES OF VIENNA AND OTHER STORIES. NY: Harcourt, Brace, (1936). 1st ed. Sensitive blue cl typically faded, thus VG in bright pict dj (light edge wear). Attractive. Inscribed. *CAPTAIN'S BOOKSHELF.* $125

Boyle, T. Coragahessan. BUDDING PROSPECTS. NY: Viking, 1984. 1st ed. Fine. *SMITH.* $40

Boyle, T. Corgahessan. BUDDING PROSPECTS. Viking, 1984. Signed 1st ed. Fine in Fine dj. *BEBBAH.* $50

Boyle, T. Coraghessan. BUDDING PROSPECTS. NY: Viking, (1984). Fine in dj. Signed. *LOPEZ.* $85

Boyle, T. Coraghessan. DESCENT OF MAN. 1st Eng ed. (London: Gollancz, 1980). Fine in Fine dj. *LOPEZ.* $75

Boyle, T. Coraghessan. DESCENT OF MAN. Boston: Little, Brown (1979). 1st ed. Fine in NF dj (bit of edgewear at extrems of spine). Signed. *LOPEZ.* $225

Boyle, T. Coraghessan. DESCENT OF MAN. London, 1980. 1st British ed, 1st bk. Inscribed, signed, dj. Fine. *PETTLER.* $65.

Boyle, T. Corgahessan. DESCENT OF MAN. NY: Atlantic Monthly Press, 1979. 1st ed, 1st bk. Review copy. NF, wrinkles to dj. *SMITH.* $175

Boyle, T. Coraghessan. DESCENT OF MAN. London: Victor Gollancz Ltd, 1980. 1st Eng ed, 1st bk. Fine in dj, short tear back panel. *HELLER.* $100

Boyle, T. Coraghessan. EAST IS EAST. (NY): Viking (1990). 1st ed. As New. Inscribed. *LOPEZ.* $65

Boyle, T. Coraghessan. EAST IS EAST. Adv reading copy. 1st ed. Fine in wraps. Inscribed. *LOPEZ.* $75

Boyle, T. Coraghessan. EAST IS EAST. NY: Viking, (1990). 1st ed. Signed. VF in VF dj. *UNGER.* $50

Boyle, T. Coraghessan. GREASY LAKE & OTHER STORIES. NY, 1985. 1st ed. VF in dj. *PETTLER.* $35

Boyle, T. Coraghessan. GREASY LAKE. (NY): Viking (1985). 1st ed. Sl shelfwear to cl, sm sticker fep. Signed. *LOPEZ.* $75

Boyle, T. Coraghessan. IF THE RIVER WAS WHISKEY. (NY): Viking (1989). 1st ed. Fine in Fine dj. Inscribed. *LOPEZ.* $75

Boyle, T. Coraghessan. IF THE RIVER WAS WHISKEY. 1st ed. Fine in Fine dj. *LOPEZ.* $30

Boyle, T. Coraghessan. IF THE RIVER WAS WHISKEY. 1st ed. Fine in Fine dj. Signed. *LOPEZ.* $65

Boyle, T. Coraghessan. IF THE RIVER WAS WHISKEY. Uncorrected proof. Fine in wraps. *LOPEZ.* $60

Boyle, T. Coraghessan. WATER MUSIC. 1st Eng ed. (London: Gollancz, 1982). Fine in Fine dj. *LOPEZ.* $45

Boyle, T. Coraghessan. WATER MUSIC. Boston, 1981. 1st ed. Fine in dj. *PETTLER.* $75

Boyle, T. Coraghessan. WATER MUSIC. Boston, 1981. 1st ed. Ink date on front pastedown (hidden under dj flap), else NF in Fine dj. No remainder mark. Inscribed, signed. *PETTLER.* $90

Boyle, T. Coraghessan. WATER MUSIC. Boston: Little, Brown, (1981). 1st ed. Signed. Fine in very lightly soiled dj. *UNGER.* $100

Boyle, T. Coraghessan. WORLD'S END. (NY): Viking (1987). 1st ed. Signed. Fine in Fine dj. *LOPEZ.* $85

Boyle, T. Coraghessan. WORLD'S END. Uncorrected proof. Fine in wrappers. *LOPEZ.* $50

Boyle, Thomas. POST-MORTEM EFFECTS. NY: Viking, 1987. 1st ed. Signed. VF in dj. *SILVER DOOR.* $35

Boyle, Virginia Frazier. THE OTHER SIDE. Cambridge (MA), 1893. 1st ed. 12mo, 64pp. Orig cl. Lib bkpl, blindstamp, else NF. *CHAPEL HILL.* $30

Boynton, C.B. and T.B. Mason. A JOURNEY THROUGH KANSAS; WITH SKETCHES OF NEBRASKA. Moore, Wilstach, Keys & Co, 1855. Fldg map. Blue buckram, orig wrappers preserved. At head of front wrapper, "Sixth thousand." Howes B677. *HUDSON.* $450

Boynton, Charles B. THE HISTORY OF THE NAVY DURING THE REBELLION. NY: Appleton, 1867-68. 1st ed. 2 vols. 576; (580),(8 ads)pp. 30 plts. Pubr's sheep, bindings bit dried. *LEFKOWICZ.* $300

Boynton, Henry Van Ness. CHATTANOOGA AND CHICK-AMAUGA. REPRINT OF GEN. H.V. BOYNTON'S LETTERS TO THE CINCINNATI COMMERCIAL GAZETTE, AUGUST, 1888. Washington, 1891. 2nd ed. Wrappers. VG. *McGOWAN.* $45

Boynton, Henry W. BRET HARTE. McClure, Phillips & Co, 1903. 1st ed. Frontis. VG+. *AUTHORS OF THE WEST.* $17.50

Boynton, Percy H. THE REDISCOVERY OF THE FRONTIER. Univ of Chicago Press, (1931). 1st ed. Boards. VG+, corners scuffed. *AUTHORS OF THE WEST.* $25

Braathen, Sverre. TY COBB—IDOL OF BASEBALL FANDOM. Avondale, 1928. 1st ed. VG. *PLAPINGER.* $650

Braby, Dorothy. THE WAY OF WOOD-ENGRAVING. London: Studio Publications, 1953. Frontis. Red case, titling in black on spine. Minor wear, Fine in dj. *HELLER.* $85

Brace, Charles Loring. THE DANGEROUS CLASSES OF NEW YORK, AND TWENTY YEARS' WORK AMONG THEM. NY: Wynkoop & Hallenbeck, 1872. 12 plts. 1st ed. Presentation, inscribed "The Author." Burgundy cl bumped, gilt on spine sl faded, sm chip to top of front fly leaf, front edge 2 leaves, minor foxing. VG. *BLUE MOUNTAIN.* $100

Bracken, Henry. FARRIERY IMPROV'D. London: for J. Clarke, 1738. 2nd ed. (2), 363pp + 35pp index. Vol. I only of 2 vols. Contemp calf covers sl worn, stained; bottom of title page shaved, cutting bottom of date and 11 letters. *DIAMOND.* $95

Bracken, Henry. FARRIERY IMPROVED: OR, A COMPLEAT TREATISE UPON THE ART OF FARRIERY. Dublin, 1737. 382pp. Leatherbound 1st ed. Last 4 pp of index have been removed; binding worn on edges. *OCTOBER FARM.* $195

Brackenridge, Hugh Henry. INCIDENTS OF THE INSURRECTION IN THE WESTERN PARTS OF PENNSYLVANIA, IN THE YEAR 1794. Phila: John M'Culloch, 1795. 1st ed. Comtemp calf, front hinge cracked. Irregular pagination. *HUDSON.* $575

Brackett, Leigh. SILENT PARTNER. NY: G.P. Putnam's Sons, 1969. 1st ed. Fine in dj, tiny wear at base of spine. *MORDIDA.* $65

Brackett, Leigh. SWORD OF RHIANON. Gregg Press, 1979. 1st US hb ed. Fine. *MADLE.* $45

Brackett, Leigh. THE LONG TOMORROW. Doubleday, 1955. 1st ed. VG in frayed dj. *MADLE.* $70

Brackett, Leigh. THE STARMEN. Gnome Press, 1952. 1st ed. NF in tape-stained dj. *MADLE.* $100

Brackett, Oliver (ed). AN ENCYCLOPEDIA OF ENGLISH FURNITURE. NY, (1927). NF. *POLYANTHOS.* $150

Brackett, Oliver. ENGLISH FURNITURE ILLUSTRATED. London: Spring Books, 1958. 2nd ed. Rev, enl ed. VG. *BACKROOM.* $45

Bradbury, Jim. THE MEDIEVAL ARCHER. NY: St. Martin's Press, 1985. 1st U.S. ed. NF in dj. *OLD LONDON.* $25

Bradbury, Ray. BEYOND 1984: REMEMBRANCE OF THINGS FUTURE. (NY: Targ Editions, (1979). 1st ed. #125 of 350 signed. Orig red cl, pict charcoal paper-covered boards. *CHAPEL HILL.* $125

Bradbury, Ray. DARK CARNIVAL. Arkham House, 1947. Near VG in worn dj. *MADLE.* $375

Bradbury, Ray. DARK CARNIVAL. Sauk City: Arkham House, 1947. 1st ed, 1st bk. 3000 copies. Signed, dated. Lower corner very sl creased, extremities, spine minimally bumped. Fine in dj (extremities, spine and folds flaps strengthened internally, top spine very sl frayed, lower spine little creased, rear panel little soiled). *POLYANTHOS.* $550

Bradbury, Ray. DEATH HAS LOST ITS CHARM FOR ME. Northridge: Lord John Press, 1987. 1st ed, trade issue. Signed. Corners bumped else Fine w/o dj as issued. *OTHER WORLDS.* $25

Bradbury, Ray. DEATH IS A LONELY BUSINESS. Franklin Center: Franklin Library, 1985. 1st ed. One of an unspecified number signed. Fine in full lea. *BETWEEN COVERS.* $75

Bradbury, Ray. FAHRENHEIT 451. London, 1954. 1st British ed. VG in dj. *MADLE.* $125

Bradbury, Ray. FAHRENHEIT 451. NY: Ballantine, (1953). Hardcover ed. Tiniest bit of shelf rubbing near the spine, o/w Fine. Dj has one unobtrusive tear top of front panel, is practically unfaded on the spine, and very scarce thus. *LOPEZ.* $750

Bradbury, Ray. FAHRENHEIT 451. NY: Ballantine Books, (1953). 1st ed. Pb orig. Orig illus wraps. VG. *CHAPEL HILL.* $50

Bradbury, Ray. HALLOWEEN TREE. Knopf, 1972. 1st ed. NF in dj. Inscribed. *MADLE.* $90

Bradbury, Ray. LONG AFTER MIDNIGHT. Knopf, 1976. 1st ed. Fine in frayed dj. *MADLE.* $25

Bradbury, Ray. LONG AFTER MIDNIGHT. NY, 1976. 1st ed. Signed, dated presentation. 11 line holograph excerpt from bk. Extremities, spine very sl bumped. Fine in like dj. *POLYANTHOS.* $75

Bradbury, Ray. S IS FOR SPACE. Doubleday, 1966. 1st ed. Fine in sl chipped dj. *MADLE.* $75

Bradbury, Ray. SOMETHING WICKED THIS WAY COMES. Simon & Schuster, 1962. 1st ed. Fine in worn dj. *MADLE.* $120

Bradbury, Ray. THE GHOSTS OF FOREVER. Rizzoli, 1980. 1st ed. Fine in dj. *MADLE.* $50

Bradbury, Ray. THE ILLUSTRATED MAN. Doubleday, 1951. 1st ed. Good+. *MADLE.* $25

Bradbury, Ray. THE ILLUSTRATED MAN. GC, NY: Doubleday, 1951. 1st ed. Orig tan cl. Sl discoloration top edge of cl, else VG in spine-faded dj. *CHAPEL HILL.* $250

Bradbury, Ray. THE LAST CIRCUS & THE ELECTROCUTION. Northridge, CA: Lord John Press, 1980. 1st trade ed. New in dj. *BERNARD.* $25

Bradbury, Ray. THE MARTIAN CHRONICLES. GC: Doubleday, 1950. 1st ed, 1st binding. Spine sl sunned, else Fine lacking dj. *CAPTAIN'S BOOKSHELF.* $75

Bradbury, Ray. THE MARTIAN CHRONICLES. Martin Gardner (intro). Avon: LEC, 1974. One of 2000 illus, signed by Joseph Mugnaini and Bradbury. Fine in sl bumped slipcase. *CAPTAIN'S BOOKSHELF.* $275

Bradbury, Ray. THE OCTOBER COUNTRY. Ballantine, 1955. 1st ed. Ex-lib in worn, faded dj. *MADLE.* $25

Bradbury, Ray. THE STORIES OF RAY BRADBURY. Knopf, 1980. 1st ed. NF in dj. *MADLE.* $40

Bradbury, S. BERTRAM DOBELL, BOOKSELLER AND MAN OF LETTERS. London: Bertram Dobell, 1909. 8vo, paper wrappers (worn). 32pp. *OAK KNOLL.* $25

Braddock, Gordon. REX KINDGON OF RIDGEWOOD HIGH. Al Burt, 1914. Ltr. prtg. VG in Good dj. *PLAPINGER.* $50

Bradfield, Scott. THE HISTORY OF LUMINOUS MOTION. (London): Bloomsbury, (1989). 1st ed. VF. *JAFFE.* $40

Bradfield, Scott. THE HISTORY OF LUMINOUS MOTION. Knopf, 1989. Advance reading copy. Fine in wraps; promo letter laid in. *STAHR.* $25

Bradford, Roark. JOHN HENRY. NY & London: Harper & Bros., 1931. 1st ed. Light offsetting to one pp, else NF in sl browned, VG dj. *CHAPEL HILL.* $75

Bradford, Roark. JOHN HENRY. NY & London: Harper & Bros, 1931. 1st ed. Orig grn patterned cl w/gold paper spine label. Lt offsetting to one pg, else NF in sl browned, VG dj. *CHAPEL HILL.* $75

Bradford, Roark. JOHN HENRY. Play by Roark Bradford, music by Jacques Wolfe, sets by Albert Johnson. NY & London: Harper & Bros, 1939. 1st ed. Orig pict beige cl. Owner inscrip, else Fine in VG dj. *CHAPEL HILL.* $45

Bradford, Roark. THE GREEN ROLLER. NY: Harper, (1949). 1st ed. NF in dj. *LOPEZ.* $30

Bradford, Roark. THE THREE-HEADED ANGEL. NY & London: Harper & Bros, 1937. 1st ed. Fine in price-clipped pict dj. *CHAPEL HILL.* $65

Bradford, Roark. THIS SIDE OF JORDAN. NY & London: Harper & Bros, 1929. 1st ed. Orig cl-backed patterned boards. NF in pict dj (very shallow chipping at spine ends affecting no lettering). *CHAPEL HILL.* $125

Bradford, Roark. THIS SIDE OF JORDAN. NY: Harper, 1929. 1st ed. NF in dj. *LOPEZ.* $45

Bradford, William. HISTORY OF PLYMOUTH PLANTATION. Boston, 1856. 1st ed. (20),476,(1)pp. Orig cl w/paper label on spine. Charles Deane (ed). Mass. Hist. Soc. Colls. 4th Series Vol 3. Howes B703. *GINSBERG.* $75

Bradley, A.G. THE GATEWAY OF SCOTLAND—EAST LOTHIAN, LAMMERMOOR AND THE MERSE. Boston: Little, Brown, 1912. 1st US ed. VG. Bkpl. *AARD.* $25

Bradley, A.G. THE RIVERS AND STREAMS OF ENGLAND. A&C Black, 1909. 1st ed. 20s Series. Top and bottom of spine somewhat frayed, else VG. *OLD LONDON.* $45

Bradley, A.G. THE WYE. A&C Black, 1910. 1st ed. 7s 6d Series. Very minor wear extremities, else VG-NF. *OLD LONDON.* $60

Bradley, A.G. WORCESTERSHIRE. A&C Black, 1909. 1st ed. 7s 6d Series. Minor cl tear at cover fold bottom. Minor wear, else VG indeed. *OLD LONDON*. $50

Bradley, Cuthbert. THE FOXHOUND OF THE TWENTIETH CENTURY. London: George Routledge & Sons, 1914. 1st ed. Half lea over bds. Minor fade line front cover, else NF. *OLD LONDON*. $125

Bradley, David. SOUTH STREET. NY: Grossman Viking, 1975. 1st ed, 1st bk. Large owner name and date ffep, o/w NF in dj. *LOPEZ*. $100

Bradley, David. THE CHANEYSVILLE INCIDENT. Harper, 1981. 1st ed. About Fine in dj. *STAHR*. $15

Bradley, John L. (ed). ROGUE'S PROGRESS. THE AUTOBIOGRAPHY OF "LORD CHIEF BARON" NICHOLSON. Boston, 1965. Frontis. Spine faded, gilt rubbed, o/w VG. *DIAMOND*. $25

Bradley, O.C. THE STRUCTURE OF THE FOWL. T. Grahame (rev). London, 1950. 3rd ed. 23 plts. Cl, faded dj. *SUTTON*. $35

Bradley, Richard. NEW IMPROVEMENTS OF PLANTING AND GARDENING....London: Mears, 1717. 1st ed. (12),70,(i)pp. Title ptd in red and black, I engr plt, lt staining. Bound in recent 1/4 sheep. VG. *SECOND LIFE*. $750

Bradley, Ruth. DELLIE. A LOTUS IN THE DUST. Berkeley: Ber-Cal, 1967. 1st ed. Inscribed, dated. Fine in NF dj. *CONNOLLY & WADE*. $35

Bradley, Van Allen. MUSIC FOR THE MILLIONS, THE KIMBALL PIANO AND ORGAN STORY. Chicago: Henry Regnery Co., 1957. 1st ed. Dj rubbed. *OAK KNOLL*. $25

Bradley, Van Allen. MUSIC FOR THE MILLIONS. Chicago: Regnery, 1957. 1st ed. VG+ in VG- dj. *AARD*. $15

Bradna, Fred with Hartzell Spence. THE BIG TOP: MY FORTY YEARS WITH THE GREATEST SHOW ON EARTH. NY: Simon & Schuster, 1952. 1st ed. VG+ in VG+ dj. *OCTOBER FARM*. $25

Bradshaw, Gillian. HAWK OF MAY. Simon & Schuster, 1980. 1st ed. Fine in dj. *MADLE*. $30

Brady, Charles. SEVEN GAMES IN OCTOBER. Little, Brown, 1979. 1st ed. Fine in dj with the lightest of wear. *STAHR*. $25

Brady, Cyrus Townsend. SECRET SERVICE. NY, 1912. 1st ed. Light cvr wear o/w Fine. *PRATT*. $25

Brady, Cyrus Townsend. THE TRUE ANDREW JACKSON. Phila/London: J.B. Lippincott Company, 1906. Partly unopened. *HUDSON*. $25

Brady, William. THE KEDGE-ANCHOR; OR, YOUNG SAILOR'S ASSISTANT....Eight (sic) edition....NY: By the Author, 1855. 400 pp. 32 plts. Orig cl, some minor binding chips, but attractive, w/contemp bkseller's ticket. *LEFKOWICZ*. $175

Bragadin, Marc Antonio. THE ITALIAN NAVY IN WORLD WAR II. Annapolis, 1957. Dj. *O'NEILL*. $30

Brailsford, H.N. MACEDONIA: ITS RACES AND THEIR FUTURE. London, 1906. 2 maps (1 fldg). *O'NEILL*. $55

Brainard, David L. SIX CAME BACK. Indianapolis: Bobbs-Merrill, (1940). Maps. Inscribed. VG in VG dj. *BLUE DRAGON*. $45

Brainard, General David L. THE OUTPOST OF THE LOST. Indianapolis: Bobbs-Merrill Company, c. 1929. 1st ed. Light specks, else VG+. *PARMER*. $75

Braine, John. LIFE AT THE TOP. London, 1962. 1st ed. Fine in dj, sl edge sunned, tiny nick. *POLYANTHOS*. $30

Braine, John. ROOM AT THE TOP. Boston, 1957. 1st ed. Spine sl rubbed; dj w/chips, sl edge rubbed, sl soiled. *POLYANTHOS*. $35

Braine, John. THE VODI. (London): Eyre & Spottiswoode, (1959). 1st UK ed. NF in dj. *BERNARD*. $50

Brainerd, C(hauncey) N(iles). MY DIARY: OR THREE WEEKS ON THE WING. NY: Egbert, Bourne & Co, 1868. 45pp, ptd wraps. Wraps lightly soiled & quite chipped along spine. *BOHLING*. $125

Brake, Brian, James McNeish, David Simmons. ART OF THE PACIFIC. NY: Abrams, (1980). Fine in Fine dj. *ACADEMIC*. $85

Brake, Hezekiah. ON TWO CONTINENTS. A LONG LIFE'S EXPERIENCE. Topeka, 1896. 1st ed. 240pp. 2 ports. Orig cl, spine lightly discolored. Howes B718. *GINSBERG*. $85

Bramah, Ernest. EYES OF MAX CARRADOS. NY, (1924). 1st ed. Spine sl soiled. Stain on rear cvr. Small bump at bottom corner. *DIAMOND*. $75

Bramah, Ernest. KAI LUNG UNROLLS HIS MAT. Doubleday, 1928. 1st ed. Fine in sl rubbbed dj. *MADLE*. $150

Bramah, Ernest. KAI LUNG UNROLLS HIS MAT. Doubleday, 1928. 1st ed. VG. *MADLE*. $40

Bramah, Ernest. KAI LUNG'S GOLDEN HOURS. Doran, 1923. 1st ed. VG. *MADLE*. $60

Bramah, Ernest. THE MIRROR OF KONG HO. Doubleday, 1930. 1st ed. Chip to dj, else VG. *MADLE*. $150

Bramwell, Byrom. DISEASES OF THE SPINAL CORD. Edinburgh, 1895. 3rd ed. 659pp. *FYE*. $75

Bramwell, Byrom. DISEASES OF THE SPINAL CORD. NY, 1882. 1st Amer. ed. 300pp. Morton Prince's copy w/his autograph. *FYE*. $250

Branch, E. Douglas. THE HUNTING OF THE BUFFALO. NY: Appleton, 1929. 1st ed. Frontis, 15 plts. Cl, paper cover, spine labels. VF in VG dj. *OREGON*. $75

Branch, Louis Leon (ed). LOS BILITOS: THE STORY OF BILLY THE KID...TOLD BY CHARLES FREDERICK RUDULPH. NY: Carleton Press Inc, (1980). Presentation, signed. VG in edge chipped dj. *OUTPOST*. $75

(Brand Book). 1941 BRAND BOOK OF THE STATE OF KANSAS. Topeka: State Brand Commissioner, 1941. Gold-stamped fabricoid. *DAWSON'S*. $40

BRAND BOOK: CAMAS AND BLAINE COUNTIES, STATE OF IDAHO, 1921. N.p.: Farm Bureau of Camas and Blaine Counties, (1921). Ptd wrappers, tape on rear wrapper, sticker on corner of front wrapper. *DAWSON'S*. $35

Brand, Christianna. CAT AND MOUSE. NY: Alfred A. Knopf, 1950. 1st Amer ed. Fine in dj, minor corner wear. *MORDIDA*. $35

Brand, John. OBSERVATIONS ON POPULAR ANTIQUITIES....Arranged and Revised, With Additions, by Henry Ellis, Keeper of the Manuscripts In the British Museum. 2 vols. London: Rivington, etc., 1813. 1st ed. Large paper ed w/half-titles and index. Very tall, wide quarto; pp xxvi, 486 and xi, 731. Bound in full tan polished calf, gilt extra, gauffred edges, gilt-paneled spine in compartments, w/gilt crests of the Earl of Minto on front and back covers of both vols. Marbled edges and endpapers. Spines rehinged, but a very handsome set. *HARTFIELD*. $695.

Brand, John. OBSERVATIONS ON POPULAR ANTIQUITIES...London: Chatto & Windus, 1900. VG. *WEBER*. $25

Brand, Max (pseud of Frederick Faust). ALCATRAZ. G.P. Putnam's, 1923. 1st ed. VG+. *AUTHORS OF THE WEST*. $25

Brand, Max (pseud of Frederick Faust). LOST WOLF. Dodd, Mead, (1953). Fine in dj. *AUTHORS OF THE WEST*. $15

Brand, Max (pseud of Frederick Faust). MAX BRAND'S BEST STORIES. Dodd, Mead, (1967). 1st ed. Robert Easton (ed). VG+ in dj. *AUTHORS OF THE WEST*. $17.50

Brand, Max (pseud of Frederick Faust). THE GUN TAMER. NY: Dodd, Mead, (1929). 1st ed. A touch foxed, else Fine in brightly illustrated dj. *UNGER*. $250

Brand, Max (pseud of Frederick Faust). THE SEVENTH MAN. NY, 1921. 1st ed. Cvrs sl stained, o/w VG. *DIAMOND.* $25

Brand, Millen. THE OUTWARD ROOM. NY: Simon Schuster, 1937, 1st ed, 1st bk. Fine in NF dj. *SECOND LIFE.* $45

Brandau, R. S. (ed). HISTORY OF HOMES AND GARDENS OF TENNESSEE. (Nashville, TN): Pub for the Garden Study Club by the Parthenon Press, 1936. Lt foxing. 1st ed. #633 of 1,500. Frontis. NF. *CHAPEL HILL.* $250

Brandau, R.S. (ed). HISTORY OF HOMES AND GARDENS OF TENNESSEE. Nashville, 1964. 2nd ed. Cloth. Chipped, stained dj. *SUTTON.* $190

Brande, W.T. MANUAL OF CHEMISTRY. London: Parker, 1836. 1317pp. Rebacked w/orig backstrip label. Tight, clean. *BOOKCELL.* $40

Brandeis, Louis D. JEWISH UNITY AND THE CONGRESS. NY: Jewish Congress Organization Committee, 1915. 4pp (one sheet, folded); 8vo. Somewhat embrowned and chipped; ink stamp, but sound. *BOSWELL.* $225

Brandes, Ray. FRONTIER MILITARY POSTS OF ARIZONA. Globe, AZ: Dale Stuart King, 1960. 1st ed. No dj, as issued. Fine. *CONNOLLY & WADE.* $35

Brandes, Ray. TROOPERS WEST: MILITARY & INDIAN AF-FAIRS ON THE AMERICAN FRONTIER. San Diego: Frontier Heritage Press, 1970. 1st ed, ltd to 1000. Illus by Ted De Grazia. Presentation inscrip, signed by Brandes and a contributor. VG in Good dj. *CONNOLLY & WADE.* $95

Brandon, William. THE MEN AND THE MOUNTAIN—FREMONT'S FOURTH EXPEDITION. NY: William Morrow, 1955. 1st ed. Black cl. NF, rubbed dj. *PARMER.* $45

Brandt, H. ARIZONA AND ITS BIRD LIFE, A NATURALIST'S ADVENTURES....Cleveland, 1951. 20 colored plts. Lt scuffing to spine ends. *SUTTON.* $195

Brann, Eva T.H. LATE GEOMETRIC AND PROTOATTIC POT-TERY, MID 8TH TO LATE 7TH CENTURY, B.C. Princeton: ASCSA, 1962. 9 figs, 40 plts. The Athenian Agora, Vol. VIII. Good. *ARCHAEOLOGIA.* $150

Branson, H.C. THE PRICKING THUMB. NY: Simon & Schuster, 1942. 1st ed. Fine; minor wear at dj spine corners. *ELSE FINE.* $20

Braque, Georges. THE INTIMATE SKETCHBOOKS OF G. BRA-QUE. Texts by Will Grohmann and Antoine Tudal; apprec by Rebecca West. NY: Harcourt, Brace & Co. (1955). 1st ed. Amer ed of Verve #31-32. *KARMIOLE.* $300

Brasher, Rex. BIRDS & TREES OF NORTH AMERICA. 875 full-color plts. Lisa McGaw (ed). NY: Rowman and Littlefield, 1961. 1st, the Memorial ed, regular issue. 4 vols. Bound in 1/4 black Fabrikoid over heavy red boards. Fine. *CAPTAIN'S BOOKSHELF.* $300

Brashear, John A. JOHN A. BRASHEAR, THE AUTOBIOG-RAPHY. Boston: Houghton Mifflin, 1925. W. Lucien Scaife (ed). Spine lettering faded, corners bumped, some extremity wear, o/w Good in blue cl. Frontis, 22 plts. *KNOLLWOOD.* $60

Brassey, Lady. SUNSHINE AND STORM IN THE EAST...NY: Holt, 1890. *SCHOYER'S.* $35

Brassey, Lady. THE LAST VOYAGE. London: Longmans, Green and Co., 1889. Some rubbing; 3/4 leather. 2 fldg maps. *PARMER.* $125

Brassey, Lady. VOYAGE IN THE YACHT "SUNBEAM." Chicago: J.W. Henry, (1879). 30 full page engr. Lacks map, else VG+. *MIKESH.* $35

Bratton, Fred Gladstone. A HISTORY OF EGYPTIAN AR-CHAEOLOGY. NY: Thomas T. Crowell, (1968). Brn cl. VG. *WEBER.* $25

Braudel, Fernand. THE MEDITERRANEAN...IN THE AGE OF PHILIP II. NY, Evanston, SF, London: Harper and Row, (1972-73). 1st Amer ed. 2 vols. Djs. VG. *WEBER.* $40

Braun, Alfred & Isadore Friesner. THE LABYRINTH: AN AID TO THE STUDY OF INFLAMMATIONS OF THE INTERNAL EAR. NY, 1913. *FYE.* $50

Braun, Ernest. GRAND CANYON OF THE LIVING COLORADO. Sierra Club, 1970. NF in NF dj. *FIVE QUAIL.* $25

Braun, Heinrich. LOCAL ANAESTHESIA, ITS SCIENTIFIC BASIS AND PRACTICAL USE. Phila, 1914. 1st Eng trans. 399pp. *FYE.* $250

Braune, Wilhelm. AN ATLAS OF TOPOGRAPHICAL ANATOMY AFTER PLANE SECTIONS OF FROZEN BODIES. Phila, 1877. 1st Eng trans. 200pp + 31 plts. VF. *FYE.* $300

Brautigan, Richard. A CONFEDERATE GENERAL FROM BIG SUR. NY: Grove, (1964). 1st ed. Just About Fine in dj. *CAPTAIN'S BOOKSHELF.* $150

Brautigan, Richard. DREAMING OF BABYLON. Delacorte, (1977). 1st ed. VG in VG dj. *BEBBAH.* $30

Brautigan, Richard. DREAMING OF BABYLON. NY, 1977. 1st ed. NF in dj. *PETTLER.* $35

Brautigan, Richard. REVENGE OF THE LAWN. STORIES 1962-1970. NY: Simon & Schuster, 1971. 1st ed. Sm tear dj, bkpl o/w Fine. *SMITH.* $75

Brautigan, Richard. ROMMEL DRIVES DEEP INTO EGYPT. NY: Delacorte, 1970. 1st ed. Fine. *SMITH.* $75

Brautigan, Richard. THE ABORTION: AN HISTORICAL ROMANCE 1966. NY: Simon & Schuster, 1971. 1st ed. Spine on dj sl sunned, bkpl o/w Fine. *SMITH.* $75

Brautigan, Richard. THE PILL VERSUS THE SPRINGHILL MINE DISASTER. London: Cape, (1970). Uncorrected proof, paper label. Fine in wraps. *CAPTAIN'S BOOKSHELF.* $125

Brautigan, Richard. THE TOKYO-MONTANA EXPRESS. NY: Targ, (1979). 1st ed. One of 350 signed. Fine in tissue, issued w/o dj. *UNGER.* $185

Brautigan, Richard. TROUT FISHING IN AMERICA. London: Cape, (1970). Uncorrected proof of 1st Eng ed. Fine in wraps. *CAPTAIN'S BOOKSHELF.* $175

Brautigan, Richard. TROUT FISHING IN AMERICA. London: Cape, 1970. 1st UK ed, 1st hb ed. Fine in Fine dj starting to curl bot-tom edge. *BEASLEY.* $150

Brautigan, Richard. WILLARD AND HIS BOWLING TROPHIES. NY: Simon & Schuster, 1975. 1st ed. Fine in Fine dj. *BEASLEY.* $35

Bray, Mary Matthews. SEA TRIP IN CLIPPER SHIP DAYS. Bos-ton: Richard G. Badger, (1920). 1st ed. Red cl. Some pages roughly opened. Inscrips, owner marks, o/w VG. *SCHOYER'S.* $20

Bray, Mrs. (Anna Eliza Stothard). A DESCRIPTION OF THE PART OF DEVONSHIRE BORDERING ON THE TAMAR AND TAVY....London: John Murray. 1836. 3 vols. Later 19th-c 1/2 brn calf over marbled boards, gilt; extrems bit rubbed. *KARMIOLE.* $125

Brayton, Matthew. INDIAN CAPTIVE. A NARRATIVE OF AD-VENTURES AND SUFFERINGS OF MATTHEW BRAYTON....Cleveland, 1860. 68pp. 1st ed. Orig ptd boards w/cl spine. Howes B736. *GINSBERG.* $3000

Brazier, Mary (ed). BRAIN FUNCTION. 2 Vols. Berkeley, 1963-1964. 1st ed. Ex-lib. *FYE.* $75

Brazier Mary. A BIBLIOGRAPHY OF ELECTROENCEPHALOG-RAPHY 1875-1948. Montreal, 1950. 1st ed. Ex-lib. *FYE.* $85

BREAD AND ROSES...TWO EVENTFUL YEARS 1933-1934. NY: Amalgamated Clothing Workers of America, (1935). 1st ed. Pict wraps. VG. *SECOND LIFE.* $50

Bready, James. THE HOME TEAM. Self-pub, 1959. 1st ptg, 2nd ed. Good in VG dj. *PLAPINGER.* $125

Breakenridge, William M. HELLDORADO. BRINGING THE LAW TO THE MESQUITE. Boston: Houghton Mifflin, 1928. 1st ed. VG. *BOOK MARKET.* $50

Brearley, Mary. HUGO GURGENY, PRISONER OF THE LISBON INQUISITION. London: Jonathan Cape (1948). 2nd prtg. Dj chipped. *SCHOYER'S.* $20

Breasted, James H. Jr. EGYPTIAN SERVANT STATUES. Washington, DC: Bollingen Foundation, 1948. 99 plts. Good in dj. *ARCHAEOLOGIA.* $275

Breasted, James Henry. A HISTORY OF EGYPT. NY: Scribner's, 1912 (1929). 2nd rev ed. Bright dec cover. VG+. *BLUE DRAGON.* $60

Brebner, Percy. KNIGHT OF THE SILVER STAR. Fenno. 1907, 1st ed. VG. *MADLE.* $35

Brecher, Ruth & Edward. THE RAYS: A HISTORY OF RADIOLOGY IN THE UNITED STATES AND CANADA. NY, 1969. 1st ed. *FYE.* $100

Breck, Joseph. THE FLOWER-GARDEN....Boston: Jewett et al, 1856. New ed, rev. Lt water staining to title pg, o/w Nice, tight. *SECOND LIFE.* $45

Breen, John L. TOUCH OF THE PAST. NY: Walker, 1988. Review copy, signed. Pub's slip laid in. VF in dj. *SILVER DOOR.* $35

Breen, John L. TRIPLE CROWN. NY: Walker, 1985. 1st ed. Fine in dj. *MORDIDA.* $30

Bregenzer, Don and Samuel Loveman. A ROUND-TABLE IN POICTESME. A Symposium. Cleveland: Privately Ptd by Members of the Colophon Club. 1924. Ltd to 774 numbered. Brown cl, in ptd dj (somewhat chipped). Bkpl. *KARMIOLE.* $75

Breihan, Carl W. THE COMPLETE AND AUTHENTIC LIFE OF JESSE JAMES. NY, (1953). 1st ed. Dj wear o/w Fine. *PRATT.* $30

Breihan, Carl W. YOUNGER BROTHERS; COLE, JAMES, BOB, JOHN. Naylor, 1972. 2nd ptg. Fine in NF dj. *VARNER.* $27.50

Bremer, Frederika. THE HOMES OF THE NEW WORLD. Mary Howitt (trans). 2 vols. NY: Harper, 1853. 1st US ed. 651; 654pp. Sl worming to cl on front hinge, some soiling internally, but generally VG. Howes B-745. *SECOND LIFE.* $325

Brenan, Gerald. THE LITERATURE OF THE SPANISH PEOPLE. Cambridge: At the Univ Press, 1951. 1st ed. Owner sig. Fine in dj, sl sunned spine. *CAPTAIN'S BOOKSHELF.* $75

Brenan, Gerald. THE LITERATURE OF THE SPANISH PEOPLE. Cambridge: Cambridge Univ Press, 1951. 1st ed. Owner sig, o/w Fine in very sl rubbed dj. *JAFFE.* $45

Brenn, George J. VOICES. NY: Century, 1923. 1st ed. Edges darkened, spine faded, bkpl o/w VG in darkened dj w/piece missing; chipping. *MORDIDA.* $25

Brennan, Joseph Payne. CREEP TO DEATH. West Kingston: Grant, 1981. 1st ed. One of 750 signed. Fine in Fine dj. *OTHER WORLDS.* $35

Brennan, Joseph Payne. NINE HORRORS AND A DREAM. Arkham House, 1958. 1st ed. Fine in dj. *MADLE.* $150

Brennan, Joseph Payne. SCREAM AT MIDNIGHT. New Haven: Macabre House, 1963. 1st ed. One of 250 signed. Lower corners bumped else Fine w/o dj as issued. *OTHER WORLDS.* $225

Brennan, Joseph Payne. STORIES OF DARKNESS AND DREAD. Sauk City: Arkham House, 1973. 1st ed. Just short of Fine in dj. *OTHER WORLDS.* $22.50

Brennan, Joseph Payne. THE BORDERS JUST BEYOND. West Kingston: Grant, (1986). 1st ed. One of 750 signed. Fine in dj. *OTHER WORLDS.* $35

Brennan, Joseph Payne. THE DARK RETURNERS. New Haven: Macabre House, 1959. 1st ed. One of 150 signed, numbered.

Bumped near spine heel else almost Fine w/o dj as issued. *OTHER WORLDS.* $300

BRER RABBIT & THE TAR BABY. London, 1980. Pavlin and Seda. 6 double-pg pop-ups. Pop-up bk. *BOOKFINDERS INTL.* $20

Brereton, Austin. THE LIFE OF HENRY IRVING. London: Longmans Green and Company, 1908. 1st ed. 2 vols. Spine ends rubbed, else Fine. *DRAMATIS PERSONAE.* $30

Brereton Capt F. S. THE GREAT AEROPLANE. London, n.d. 1st ed. Sl cvr wear. VG. *MADLE.* $60

Breton, Andre. WHAT IS SURREALISM? London: Faber and Faber, (1936). 1st ed. 4 full-pg illus; wrappers, spine and upper wrappers sunned. *DAWSON'S.* $100

Brett, Simon. CAST, IN ORDER OF DISAPPEARANCE. NY: Scribners, 1975. 1st ed. VF in dj. *ELSE FINE.* $25

Brett, Simon. DEAD GIVEAWAY. London: Gollancz, 1985. 1st ed. Signed. Fine in dj. *SILVER DOOR.* $37.50

Brewer, Gil. PLAY IT HARD. Derby, CT: Monarch Books, 1964. 1st ed. Pb orig. Monarch #444. Writing; crease front cvr o/w VG in wrappers. *MORDIDA.* $25

Brewer, William H. UP AND DOWN CALIFORNIA IN 1860-1864. New Haven: Yale Univ Press, 1930. 1st ed. Blue cl, gilt spine titles. Lt edge wear. VG. *PARMER.* $165

Brewer, William H. UP AND DOWN CALIFORNIA IN 1860-1864: THE JOURNAL OF WILLIAM H. BREWER. Francis P. Farquhar (ed). New Haven: Yale Univ Press, 1930. Folding map, cl in dj. *DAWSON'S.* $150

Brewer, William Henry. SUCH A LANDSCAPE! N.p.: Yosemite Assoc, Sequoia Natural History Assoc, 1987. 1st ed, ltd to 500 numbered. As New. Signed. *WREDEN.* $125

Brewerton, George D. OVERLAND WITH KIT CARSON, EDITED BY STALLO VINTON. NY: Coward McCann, 1930. 1st ed. VG in VG dj. *BOOK MARKET.* $45

Brewington, Marion V. THE PEABODY MUSEUM COLLECTION OF NAVIGATING INSTRUMENTS....Salem, 1963. 1st ed, never reprinted. One of 1,000. Frontis, 56 plts. NF. *LEFKOWICZ.* $350

Brewster, F(rederick) Carroll. FROM INDEPENDENCE HALL AROUND THE WORLD. Phila: Levytype Co. 1895. 214pp. Greygrn cl stamped in brown and gilt, spine darkened. Presentation copy. *SCHOYER'S.* $30

Brians, Paul. NUCLEAR HOLOCAUSTS. Kent State Univ Press, 1987. 1st ed. As New. *MADLE.* $30

Brickwork in Italy: A BRIEF REVIEW FROM ANCIENT TO MODERN TIMES. Chicago: American Face Brick Assoc, 1925. 1st ed. Tinted map of Italy at rear. NF in 1/4 leather. *CAPTAIN'S BOOKSHELF.* $100

Bridenbaugh, Carl. PETER HARRISON, FIRST AMERICAN ARCHITECT. Chapel Hill: Univ of NC Press. 1949. 1st ed. Red cloth, dj. *KARMIOLE.* $45

Bridenbaugh, Carl. PETER HARRISON, FIRST AMERICAN ARCHITECT. Chapel Hill: Univ of North Carolina Press, 1949. 1st ed. Fine-. *AARD.* $25

Bridgeman, Thomas. THE YOUNG GARDENER'S ASSISTANT, IN THREE PARTS, CONTAINING CATALOGUES....NY: by the author, et al, 1845. 164,189pp. Pub's cl (little worn, nicked), some foxed, VG. Frontis. *SECOND LIFE.* $95

Bridges, Robert. THE NECESSITY OF POETRY. Oxford: Clarendon Press, 1918. Edges worn, lt spotting to edges. Fine. *HELLER.* $45

Bridges, Robert. THE TESTAMENT OF BEAUTY. London: Oxford, 1929. 1st trade ed. Sl soiled white boards. *CULLEN.* $40

Bridges, Victor. THE GULLS FLY LOW. London: Hodder & Stoughton, 1943. 1st ed. Inscribed. VG in dj w/chipped spine ends; short closed tears. *MORDIDA.* $45

Bridgman, Frederick A. WINTERS IN ALGERIA. NY, 1890. NF. *POLYANTHOS*. $45

Bridgman, L.J. MOTHER GOOSE AND HER WILD BEAST SHOW. Boston, 1900. 1st ed. Sl rubbing to edges, else Fine. *McCLINTOCK*. $22.50

Bridgman, P. W. DIMENSIONAL ANALYSIS. New Haven, CT: Yale Univ Press, 1922 (1922). Good in blue cl; top of spine fraying, bkpl. Author's card laid. *KNOLLWOOD*. $29

Brier, Warren J. and Nathan B. Blumberg. A CENTURY OF MONTANA JOURNALISM. Mountain Press, (1971). 1st ed. Fine in dj. *AUTHORS OF THE WEST*. $25

Briffault, Robert. THE MOTHERS. A STUDY OF THE ORIGINS....3 vols. NY: Macmillan, 1927. 1st ed. VG. *SECOND LIFE*. $175

Briggs, Ellis O. SHOTS HEARD ROUND THE WORLD. NY: Viking, 1957. 1st ed. Fine in VG dj. *AARD*. $15

Briggs, Harold. FRONTIERS OF THE NORTHWEST, A HISTORY OF THE UPPER MISSOURI VALLEY. Peter Smith, 1950. 2nd ed. 7 maps, 31 plts. Fine. *OREGON*. $30

Briggs, Henry George. THE PARSIS; OR, MODERN ZERDUSTHIANS. Bombay: Dunlop, 1852. 1st ed. xi,146pp. Orig cl, sl rubbed and silverfished, minor wormholes, some foxing, o/w Good. *WORLDWIDE*. $75

Briggs, Jean L. NEVER IN ANGER. Cambridge: Harvard Univ Press, 1970. 1st ed. Fine in VG dj. *AARD*. $20

Briggs, L. Vernon. AROUND THE HORN TO HONOLULU ON THE BARK "AMY TURNER" IN 1880. Boston: Charles Lauriat Co, 1926. Good. *CULLEN*. $75

Brigham, Clarence. PAUL REVERE'S ENGRAVINGS. NY, 1969. 77 full-pg plts. 2 color fold-outs. Fine. *POLYANTHOS*. $125

Brigham, William T. GUATEMALA. THE LAND OF THE QUETZAL. NY: Scribner's, 1887. 1st ed. 453pp. Fldg map, 25 b/w plates. Grn dec cl, gilt lettering. Lt cvr wear, soil, rubbing. Contents tight, VG+. *SILVER*. $85

Bright, Richard. CLINICAL MEMOIRS ON ABDOMINAL TUMOURS AND INTUMESCENCE. London, 1860. 1st ed. 326pp. Outer hinges torn. *FYE*. $250

Brightwell, Cecilia L. MEMORIALS OF THE LIFE OF AMELIA OPIE. Norwich, 1854. 3/4 lea. Teg. *POLYANTHOS*. $100

Brigs, L. Vernon. HISTORY OF SHIPBUILDING ON NORTH RIVER, PLYMOUTH COUNTY, MASSACHUSETTS...1640-1872. NY, (1970). Orig cl. Facsimile rprt of scarce 1889 orig. Howes B774. *GINSBERG*. $30

Brillat-Savarin, Jean Anthelme. THE PHYSIOLOGY OF TASTE OR, MEDITATIONS ON TRANSCENDENTAL GASTRONOMY. Trans M.F.K. Fisher. NY: LEC, 1949. One of 1500. Spine sl darkened, else Fine in slipcase. *CAPTAIN'S BOOKSHELF*. $150

Brillat-Savarin. THE HANDBOOK OF DINING....NY: Appleton, 1865. 200pp, ads (4)pp. L.F. Simpson (trans). Orig dk grn pebbled cl. Owner sig. Fine. *WEBER*. $175

Brininstool, E.A. A TROOPER WITH CUSTER....Columbus: Hunter-Trader-Trapper, 1926. 2nd ed. The Frontier Series, Vol 1. Gold, blue dec cl. VG. *CONNOLLY & WADE*. $35

Brininstool, E.A. FIGHTING RED CLOUD'S WARRIORS. Columbus, 1926. 1st ed. 241pp + ads. Cvr wear o/w Fine. *PRATT*. $55

Brininstool, E.A. TRAIL DUST OF A MAVERICK...2nd ed. LA, 1921. Cl w/small photo pasted on. Little cvr wear. Stain on bottom of cvrs, bottom fore-edges. Foxing on few pp o/w VG. Inscribed. *DIAMOND*. $50

Brink, Carol R. MADEMOISELLE MISFORTUNE. Macmillan, 1936. 1st ed. 267pp. 12 full-page illus by Kate Seredy. Some edgewear, VG. *BEBBAH*. $30

Brinnin, John M. SWAY OF THE GRAND SALOON. NY, (1971), 1st ed. Marbled end papers, dj. *HEINOLDT*. $25

Brinton, Henry. NOW LIKE TO DIE. London: Hutchinson, 1955. 1st ed. VG in VG dj with tiny spine scratches, light wear. *BEBBAH*. $20

Bristol, Roger P. MARYLAND IMPRINTS, 1801-1810. Pub. by Univ of VA Press from the Bibliographical Soc of Univ of VA, 1953. Ltd to 300. *HEINOLDT*. $25

BRITISH PHARMACOPOEIA, 1867. London, 1880. 4th rpt w/additions made in 1874. Orig cl worn at corners, spine ends frayed; eps stained, inner hinges cracked; ex-lib. *SUTTON*. $45

Brittain, Vera. HUMILIATION WITH HONOR. NY: Fellowship, (1943) 1st ed. Review copy. Nice in little browned dj. *SECOND LIFE*. $45

Brittain, Vera. TESTAMENT OF EXPERIENCE. NY: Macmillan, 1957. 1st ed. Shelfworn dj with sunning, tears. Signed. *AKA*. $30

Brittain, Vera. TESTAMENT OF YOUTH....NY: Macmillan, 1933. (4th ptg). Inscribed. VG, no dj. *SECOND LIFE*. $45

Brittain, Vera. THE WOMEN AT OXFORD. NY: MacMillan, (1960). 1st US ed. Fine in sl used dj. *CAPTAIN'S BOOKSHELF*. $25

Brittain, Vera. THRICE A STRANGER. NY: Macmillan, 1938. 1st ed. Sl soiled cl. *SCHOYER'S*. $12.50

Britton, Christopher. PAYBACKS. NY: Donald Fine, (1985). 1st ed. Fine in lightly used dj. *AKA*. $35

Britton, Lionel. SPACETIME INN. London, 1932. 1st ed. VG in wraps. *MADLE*. $75

Britton, N.L. and A. Brown. AN ILLUSTRATED FLORA OF THE NORTHERN UNITED STATES, CANADA, AND THE BRITISH POSSESSIONS. NY: Scribner's, 1896-1898. 3 vols. Grn cl moderately worn; front hinge vol I weak; contents VG. *SMITHFIELD*. $72

Britton, N.L. and A. Brown. AN ILLUSTRATED FLORA OF THE NORTHERN UNITED STATES, CANADA AND THE BRITISH POSSESSIONS. NY: Scribner's, 1896-1898. 3 vols. Blind-stamped grn cl sl worn; front hinge vol 1 weak. Contents VG. *SMITHFIELD*. $60

Broadbent, William. SELECTIONS FROM THE WRITINGS MEDICAL AND NEUROLOGICAL OF SIR WILLIAM BROADBENT. London, 1908. 1st ed. *FYE*. $100

Brock, Rose (Joseph Hansen). LONGLEAF. NY: Harper & Row, 1974. 1st ed. VF in dj. *MORDIDA*. $45

Brockett, L.P. EPIDEMIC AND CONTAGIOUS DISEASES: THEIR HISTORY, SYMPTOMS, AND TREATMENT....A BOOK FOR THE FAMILY AND HOME. NY, 1873. 1st ed. Full lea, rubbed. *FYE*. $250

Brockett, L.P. HANDBOOK OF THE UNITED STATES OF AMERICA. NY: Gaylord Watson, 1886. (Cover title: "Government statistics"). Tables. Aeg. *HUDSON*. $95

Brocklehurst, Thomas. MEXICO TODAY: A COUNTRY WITH A GREAT FUTURE....London: John Murray, 1883. 1st ed. 259pp, 56 plates incl 15 color lithos (2 missing). Rubbing, chipping, outer spine hinge broken, interior, plts clean and VG. *SILVER*. $75

Brodeur, Paul. DOWNSTREAM. NY: Atheneum, 1972. 1st ed. VF in dj. Bkpl. *ELSE FINE*. $25

Brodeur, Paul. THE SICK FOX. Boston: A-LB, 1963. 1st ed. VF, dj sl darkened. *ELSE FINE*. $35

Brodhead, L.W. DELAWARE WATER GAP, ITS SCENERY, ITS LEGENDS AND EARLY HISTORY. Phila, 1870. 2nd enl ed, addt'l material. 12,276pp. Colored litho frontis. Edges top & bottom spine worn, contents clean & tight. Custom made slipcase. *HEINOLDT.* $25

Brodie, Benjamin C. (THREE MONOGRAPHS) 1) CLINICAL LECTURES ON SURGERY. 352pp. 2) SURGICAL OBSERVATIONS ON THE DISEASES OF JOINTS. 172pp. 3) LECTURES ON THE DISEASES OF THE URINARY ORGANS. 194pp. Phila, 1846-1847. Full leather. *FYE.* $125

Brodkey, Harold. FIRST LOVE AND OTHER SORROWS. NY, 1957. 1st ed, rare 1st bk. Fine in bright, VG+ price-clipped dj. *PETTLER.* $200

Brodkey, Harold. THE RUNAWAY SOUL. NY: Farrar, Straus, Giroux (1991). Uncorrected proof. Fine in wraps. *LOPEZ.* $50

Brodman, Estelle. THE DEVELOPMENT OF MEDICAL BIBLIOGRAPHY. Baltimore, 1954. *FYE.* $75

Brodsky, Joseph. SELECTED POEMS. George L. Kline (trans). NY: Harper & Row, (1973). 1st Amer ed. Orig purple cl, black boards. Fine in price-clipped dj. Signed. *CHAPEL HILL.* $100

Brodzky, Horace. HENRI GAUDIER-BRZESKA. London: Faber & Faber Ltd, 1933. Frontis. Bound in red cl over boards, engr stamped on front cvr, title in gilt on spine. Spine faded, lt spotting eps, VG. *HELLER.* $80

Brogan, Phil F. EAST OF THE CASCADES. L.K. Phillips (ed). Portland: Binfords & Mort, 1964. 1st ed. Fine in VG dj. *CONNOLLY & WADE.* $30

Bromell, Henry. THE SLIGHTEST DISTANCE. Boston: Houghton Mifflin Company, 1974. 1st ed, 1st bk. Fine in dj. *HELLER.* $50

Bromfield, Louis. EARLY AUTUMN. NY: Frederick Stokes, 1926. 1st ed. One corner bumped, o/w VF in dj chipped at crown and reinforced internally; still VG. *LOPEZ.* $65

Bromfield, Louis. FROM MY EXPERIENCE...NY: Harper, (1955). 1st ed. VG in worn dj. Inscribed. *SECOND LIFE.* $45

Bromfield, Louis. MR. SMITH. NY, 1951. Ltd ed, 600 specially autographed. NF in sl chipped dj. *POLYANTHOS.* $30

Bromley, George Tisdale. LONG AGO AND THE LATER ON OR RECOLLECTIONS OF EIGHTY YEARS. SF, 1904. Red cl w/black stamping. VG, lt wear. *BOHLING.* $40

Bromley, George Tisdale. THE LONG AGO AND THE LATER ON: OR RECOLLECTIONS OF EIGHTY YEARS. SF: A.M. Robinson, 1904. 1st ed. Frontis. Deckle edges. Red cl, black decs. NF. *CONNOLLY & WADE.* $50

Bronaugh, W.C. THE YOUNGERS' FIGHT FOR FREEDOM. Columbia, MO, 1906. 1st ed. VG. Spine sl rubbed. *VARNER.* $110

Bronson, Edgar. REMINISCENCES OF A RANCHMAN. McClure, 1908. 1st ed. VG. Howes B802. *OREGON.* $120

Bronson, Edgar. REMINISCENCES OF A RANCHMAN. NY: The McClure Company, (1907). 1st ed. Grn cl faded. *HUDSON.* $35

Bronson, Wilfrid. WATER PEOPLE. NY: Wise-Parslow, (1935). Cl, pict boards. Lt wear along edges. Dj w/tears along top. Else VG. *ACADEMIC LIBRARY.* $30

Bronson, Wilfrid. WATER PEOPLE. Wise-Parslow (1935). 104pp. Illus by author. Slight wear, VG+. *BEBBAH.* $25

Bronte, Emily. WUTHERING HEIGHTS. London: Duckworth, 1931. Clare Leighton (illus). Frontis. Red maroon buckram over boards, title in gilt on spine, red top edge. Edges of cvrs sl faded. VG. *HELLER.* $250

Bronte Sisters. NOVELS OF THE SISTERS BRONTE. Temple Scott (ed). "Thornton Edition." Edinburgh: John Grant, 1905. Complete set in 12 vols. Each vol w/frontis portrait + plates. Grn cl w/dec gilt spines. *KARMIOLE.* $300

Bronte Sisters. THE NOVELS OF THE BRONTE SISTERS. Temple Scott and B.W. Willett (intro, notes). Edinburgh: (John Grant), 1924. 12 vols. Pub's sage grn cl w/gilt dec and titling, teg. Very nice set (minor wear; few tiny splits at heads of some vols). No foxing. *BOOK BLOCK.* $275

Brooke, Rupert. LETTERS FROM AMERICA. NY, 1916. 1st ed. NF. *POLYANTHOS.* $25

Brookner, Anita. A MISALLIANCE. Jonathan Cape, 1986. 1st ed. Fine in dj. *STAHR.* $45

Brookner, Anita. BRIEF LIVES. NY: RH (1990). Uncorrected proof of 1st Amer ed. Fine in wraps, promo sheet laid in. *LOPEZ.* $30

Brookner, Anita. FAMILY AND FRIENDS. London: London Limited Editions, (1985). 1st ed. Ltd to 250 signed. VF. *JAFFE.* $125

Brookner, Anita. FAMILY AND FRIENDS. London: London Limited Editions, (1985). One of 250 specially bound, signed. Fine in glassine dj. *CAPTAIN'S BOOKSHELF.* $125

Brookner, Anita. INGRES. (London): (Knowledge Publications), (1965). 1st ed. Wrappers, yapped edges a bit worn o/w Fine. *LOPEZ.* $75

Brookner, Anita. LEWIS PERCY. London: Cape, (1989). 1st ed. Mint. *JAFFE.* $45

Brookner, Anita. PROVIDENCE. NY: Pantheon, (1982). 1st Amer ed. Orig cl backed boards. Fine in dj. *CHAPEL HILL.* $30

Brookner, Anita. THE DEBUT. Linden, 1981. 1st Amer ed. VF in dj. *STAHR.* $20

Brooks, (Charles William) Shirley. THE GORDIAN KNOT: A STORY OF GOOD AND OF EVIL. London: Richard Bentley, 1860. 1st book ed of author's 2nd novel. 8vo, 376pp. Frontis, 21 engrvd plts. ALS tipped in. 19th century full mottled calf, rebacked with orig spine laid down. Orig grn cl cvr and spine are bound in at rear. VG. *CHAPEL HILL.* $150

Brooks, A.H. BLAZING ALASKA'S TRAILS. Fairbanks, 1953. Illus. Ex libris. VG+. *MIKESH.* $17.50

Brooks, Alfred Hulse. BLAZING ALASKA'S TRAILS. Univ of AK, 1953. 1st ed. VG. *ARTIS.* $35

Brooks, Alfred Hulse. BLAZING ALASKA'S TRAILS. Univ of Arkansas, 1953. 1st ed. Presentation card laid in. VG in worn dj. *ARTIS.* $50

Brooks, Cleanth. A SHAPING JOY: STUDIES IN THE WRITER'S CRAFT. NY: Harcourt, Brace & Jovanovich, (1971). 1st Amer ed. Signed. Fine in dj. *DORN.* $45

Brooks, Cleanth. THE WELL-WROUGHT URN: STUDIES IN THE STRUCTURE OF POETRY. NY: Reynal & Hitchcock, (1947). 1st ed. Fine in price-clipped dj (few small chips and tears). *CAPTAIN'S BOOKSHELF.* $45

Brooks, George (ed). THE SOUTHWEST EXPEDITION OF JEDEDIAH S. SMITH, HIS PERSONAL ACCOUNT....1826-1827. A.H. Clark, 1977. 1st ed. 3 maps. Prospectus sheet. Fine. *OREGON.* $150

Brooks, George R. (ed). THE SOUTHWEST EXPEDITION OF JEDEDIAH S. SMITH: HIS PERSONAL ACCOUNT....1826-1827. Glendale: Arthur Clark, 1977. 1st ed. Fine. *BOOK MARKET.* $150

Brooks, Gwendolyn. A STREET IN BRONZEVILLE. NY: Harper, 1945. 1st ed, 1st bk. Brief gift inscrip. VF in dj. *ELSE FINE.* $375

Brooks, Gwendolyn. BLACKS. Chicago: The David Company, 1987. 1st ed. Inscribed. Issued w/o dj. NF (2 ink notes). *BEASLEY.* $45

Brooks, Gwendolyn. THE TIGER WHO WORE WHITE GLOVES. Chicago: Third World Press, 1974. 1st ed. Wraps. Fine but for crease on rear wrap. Also issued in cloth. *BEASLEY.* $100

Brooks, Juanita. JOHN D. LEE—ZEALOT, PIONEER, BUILDER, SCAPEGOAT. Glendale, 1973. New ed w/corrections. Fine in VG+ dj. *FIVE QUAIL.* $55

Brooks, Juanita. JOHN DOYLE LEE, ZEALOT, PIONEER BUILDER, SCAPEGOAT. A.H. Clark, 1973. 2nd ptg, 2nd ed. VG in VG dj. *OREGON.* $45

Brooks, Juanita. JOHN DOYLE LEE, ZEALOT—PIONEER BUILDER—SCAPEGOAT. Glendale, 1961. 1st ed. Port. Lt hand soiling to cover. VG. *BENCHMARK.* $245

Brooks, Juanita. THE MOUNTAIN MEADOWS MASSACRE. Stanford, 1950. 1st ed. Some cover soil and gentle bumps, o/w VG to VG+. *FIVE QUAIL.* $65

Brooks, Juanita. THE MOUNTAIN MEADOWS MASSACRE. Stanford, 1950. 1st ed. Sl worn dj, o/w VG. *BENCHMARK.* $85

Brooks, Juanita. THE MOUNTAIN MEADOWS MASSACRE. Stanford: Stanford Univ, 1950. 1st ed. Inscr. Fine in VG dj. *CONNOLLY & WADE.* $125

Brooks, Juanita. THE MOUNTAIN MEADOWS MASSACRE. Stanford: Stanford Univ, 1950. 1st ed. Inscribed. Fine in VG dj. *CONNOLLY & WADE.* $125

Brooks, Noah. MR. LINCOLN'S WASHINGTON, THE CIVIL WAR DISPATCHES OF NOAH BROOKS. Ed by P.J. Straudenraus. NY, (1967). 1st ed. 481pp. VG+ in dj. *PRATT.* $25

Brooks, Noah. THE BOY SETTLERS. NY: Scribner's, 1919. Frontis. Red cl, Fine in VG dj. *CONNOLLY & WADE.* $30

Brooks, Terry. THE SWORD OF SHANNARA. Random House, 1977. Adv copy in wraps. VG. *MADLE.* $35

Brooks, Thomas. PICKET LINES & BARGAINING TABLES. NY: Grosset & Dunlap, 1968. 1st ed. Ink spot bottom edges. Price-clipped dj. *AKA.* $30

Brooks, Van Wyck. A CHILMARK MISCELLANY. NY: Dutton, 1948. 1st ed. Fine in Fine dj. *BOOK MARKET.* $38

Brooks, William E. GRANT OF APPOMATTOX. Indianapolis (1942). 1st ed. Ex-lib; no external, minimal internal markings. Dj wear, chipping o/w Fine. *PRATT.* $40

Brooks, William E. LEE OF VIRGINIA. Bobbs-Merrill, (c. 1932). 1st ed. Ex-lib, remnants of labels. Good+. *BOOK BROKER.* $30

Brophy, John. A MINER'S LIFE. Madison: Univ of WI, 1964. 1st ed. Dj worn, sunned. VG. *AKA.* $20

Brosnan, Jim. PENNANT RACE. Harper & Row, 1962. Ltr ptg. Signed. VG+ in Fine dj. *PLAPINGER.* $50

Brosnan, John. JAMES BOND IN THE CINEMA. London: Tantivy Press, 1972. 1st Eng. ed. Fine in dj. *MORDIDA.* $35

Brossard, Chandler. THE BOLD SABOTEURS. Farrar, Straus & Young, 1953. 1st ed. VG in dj with skinned patches, edgewear, chips. *BEBBAH.* $25

Brossard, Chandler. WHO WALKS IN DARKNESS. (NY): New Directions, (1952). 1st ed. Beautiful in pict dj (touch of wear to head of spine). *CAPTAIN'S BOOKSHELF.* $75

Brotherhead, William. FORTY YEARS AMONG THE OLD BOOKSELLERS OF PHILADELPHIA, WITH BIBLIOGRAPHICAL REMARKS. Phila: A.P. Brotherhead, 1891. 1st ed. Cvrs soiled, spine sl chipped, tear. Withal Good, almost entirely unopened. *WREDEN.* $60

Brotherhead, William. FORTY YEARS AMONG THE OLD BOOKSELLERS OF PHILADELPHIA, WITH BIBLIOGRAPHICAL REMARKS. Phila: A.P. Brotherhead, 1891. 122pp. Orig red cl, paper cvr label. VG. *WEBER.* $90

Broughton, James. MUSICAL CHAIRS: A SONGBOOK....SF: Centaur Press, 1950. 1st ed. One of 500. Fine in dj, sm chips, tears. Signed. *CAPTAIN'S BOOKSHELF.* $65

Broussais, F.J.V. HISTORY OF CHRONIC PHLEGMASIAE, OR INFLAMMATIONS FOUNDED ON CLINICAL EXPERIENCE AND PATHOLOGICAL ANATOMY. Phila, 1831. 1st Eng trans.

2 vols. Full leather, 497, 403pp. Hinges cracked, labels missing. *FYE.* $125

Brower, (Jacob) V. MEMOIRS OF EXPLORATIONS IN THE BASIN OF THE MISSISSIPPI. Volume I: QUIVIRA. St. Paul: (H.L. Collins), 1898. One of 300 numbered, this out of series. 4 maps, 25 plts. Some wear at extremities, else VG. *LAURIE.* $90

Brower, Brock. THE LATE GREAT CREATURE. Atheneum, 1971. 1st ed. VG in dj. *MADLE.* $30

Brower, J.V. and N.H. Winchell. MEMOIRS OF EXPLORATIONS IN THE BASIN OF THE MISSISSIPPI. Volume V: KAKABIKANSUNG. St. Paul, (H.L. Collins), 1902. One of 300 numbered. 30 plts, incl 5 maps and charts. Front inner hinge weak, some wear at extremities, else VG. *LAURIE.* $90

Brower, Jacob V. KANSAS. MONUMENTAL PERPETUATION OF ITS EARLIEST HISTORY. 1541-1896. Memoirs of Explorations in the Basin of the Mississippi, vol. VII. St. Paul: Privately printed, 1903. One of 300 numbered, signed. 2 double-pg fldg maps, 1 color fldg railroad map of Kansas pasted inside the rear cover. Bound in orig pub's cl. Box. Spine worn, interior Fine. *LAURIE.* $90

Brown, A. B. SKETCH OF THE LIFE AND WRITINGS OF A. B. BROWN,....EDITED BY DR. AND MRS. WM. E. HATCHER. Baltimore, Wharton, 1886. 1st ed. 351pp. Orig cl. *GINSBERG.* $75

Brown, Abram English. FANEUIL HALL AND FANEUIL HALL MARKET. Boston: Lee and Shephard. 1901. 1st ed. Maroon cl, gilt. *KARMIOLE.* $30

Brown, Adna. FROM VERMONT TO DAMASCUS RETURNING BY WAY OF BEYROUT, SMYRNA...AND ENGLAND. Boston: Ellis, 1895. 1st ed. 4,209pp. 16 pls. Orig cl, sl rubbed, o/w VG; aeg. *WORLDWIDE.* $65

Brown, Adna. FROM VERMONT TO DAMASCUS....Boston, 1895. Presentation. *O'NEILL.* $45

Brown, Alfred. OLD MASTERPIECES IN SURGERY. Omaha: Privately ptd, 1928. 1st ed. 57 plts. Very Scarce. *FYE.* $225

Brown, Alice. MEADOW-GRASS. Boston: Copeland and Day, 1895. 1st ed. 12mo, 315pp. Nice, untrimmed. *SECOND LIFE.* $65

Brown, Alonzo Leighton. HISTORY OF THE FOURTH REGIMENT OF MINNESOTA INFANTRY VOLUNTEERS DURING THE GREAT REBELLION 1861-1865. St. Paul, MN, 1892. 1st ed. Inner hinges starting, minor wear to spine ends, corners scuffed, else VG. *McGOWAN.* $275

Brown, Basil. LAW SPORTS AT GRAY'S INN (1594). NY, Privately ptd, 1921 1st ed. Cl & boards. Board corners & edges sl worn, o/w VG. *DIAMOND.* $45

Brown, Cecil. THE LIFE AND LOVES OF MR. JIVEASS NIGGER. NY: Farrar Straus Giroux, (1969). 1st ed. Fine in Fine dj. *LOPEZ.* $40

Brown, Cecil. THE LIFE AND LOVES OF MR. JIVEASS NIGGER. NY: Farrar, 1969. 1st ed. Fine in Fine dj but for one tiny tear. *BEASLEY.* $40

Brown, Claude. MANCHILD IN THE PROMISED LAND. NY: Macmillan, (1965). Adv reading copy. NF in wrappers. *LOPEZ.* $75

Brown, Claude. MANCHILD IN THE PROMISED LAND. NY: Macmillan, (c1965). 1st bk. Adv copy in darkened white ptd wrappers. *HELLER.* $85

Brown, D. Alexander. GRIERSON'S RAID. Urbana, 1954. 2nd prtg. Dj worn, chipped o/w VG+. *PRATT.* $35

Brown, D.C. JOURNEY FROM THE ARCTIC. NY, 1956. 1st Amer ed. Fine in dj. *ARTIS.* $15

Brown, Dee and M.F. Schmitt. TRAIL DRIVING DAYS. Scribner's, 1952. 1st ed. Fine in Fine dj. *VARNER.* $75

Brown, Dee. BURY MY HEART AT WOUNDED KNEE. NY, (1970). 1st ed. Dj has small tears o/w VG. *PRATT.* $25

Brown, Dee. FORT PHIL KEARNEY: AN AMERICAN SAGA. NY, 1962. 1st ed. 251pp. VG in dj. *PRATT.* $37.50

Brown, Dee. HEAR THAT LONESOME WHISTLE BLOW. NY: Holt, Rinehart & Winston, 1977. 1st ed. VF in Fine dj. *CONNOLLY & WADE.* $30

Brown, Dee. THE GENTLE TAMERS. Lincoln, (1958). 1st ed. Dj. VG. *PRATT.* $20

Brown, Dee. THE GENTLE TAMERS. NY: Putnam, 1958. 1st ed. VF in VG dj. *CONNOLLY & WADE.* $30

Brown, Dee. WOUNDED KNEE. AN INDIAN HISTORY OF THE AMERICAN WEST. NY: HRW, (1974). "Adapted for Young Readers by Amy Ehrlich from Dee Brown's Bury My Heart at Wounded Knee." Fine in Fine dj. *LOPEZ.* $50

Brown, F.M. and B. Heineman. JAMAICA AND ITS BUT-TERFLIES. London, 1972. Colored frontis, 10 colored plts. Dj. *SUTTON.* $95

Brown, Fredric. ANGELS & SPACESHIPS. NY: Dutton, 1954. 1st ed. Fine in dj. *ELSE FINE.* $225

Brown, Fredric. BEFORE SHE KILLS. San Diego: Dennis McMillan Publications, 1984. 1st ed. Vol. 2 of collected short stories. 1/350 numbered, signed by author of intro, William F. Nolan. VF in dj. *MORDIDA.* $75

Brown, Fredric. DEATH HAS MANY DOORS. NY: Dutton, 1951. 1st ed. Fine; rear panel of dj dusty, minor edgewear. *ELSE FINE.* $165

Brown, Fredric. DEATH HAS MANY DOORS. NY: Dutton, 1951. 1st ed. Store stamp bottom edge, dates rear pastedown, o/w NF in lightly used dj w/separating front flap. *BEASLEY.* $85

Brown, Fredric. HAPPY ENDING. Missoula: Dennis McMillan Publications, 1990. 1st ed. Vol. 16 of collected short stories. 1/450 numbered. VF in dj. *MORDIDA.* $35

Brown, Fredric. HOMICIDE SANITARIUM. San Antonio: Dennis McMillan Publications, 1984. 1st ed. Vol. 1 of collected short stories. 1/300 numbered, signed by author of intro, Bill Pronzini. VF in dj. *MORDIDA.* $85

Brown, Fredric. MARTIANS GO HOME. Dutton, 1955. 1st ed. Fine in sl soiled dj. *MADLE.* $175

Brown, Fredric. MRS. MURPHY'S UNDERPANTS. NY: E.P. Dutton, 1963. 1st ed. Small date stamp and crease on rear pastedown o/w Fine in dj w/wear at spine ends and at corners. *MORDIDA.* $85

Brown, Fredric. MURDER CAN BE FUN. NY: E.P. Dutton, 1948. 1st ed. Fine in VG price-clipped dj (sl faded spine; wear at spine ends, corners; couple short closed tears). *MORDIDA.* $95

Brown, Fredric. NIGHTMARES AND GEEZENSTACKS. NY: Bantam, 1961. 1st ed. Wraps. NF w/cover creases. *BEASLEY.* $15

Brown, Fredric. PARADOX LOST. Random House, 1973. 1st ed. Ex-lib in unmarked NF dj. *MADLE.* $22

Brown, Fredric. ROGUE IN SPACE. Dutton, 1957. 1st ed. Fine in dj. *MADLE.* $250

Brown, Fredric. ROGUE IN SPACE. NY: Dutton, 1957. 1st ed. Fine, minor wear at dj extrems. Scarce. *ELSE FINE.* $200

Brown, Fredric. SEX LIFE ON THE PLANET MARS. Charles Willeford intro. Miami Beach: Dennis McMillan, 1986. 1st ed. One of 400 numbered, signed by Willeford. VF in dj. *MORDIDA.* $85

Brown, Fredric. SPACE ON MY HANDS. Chicago: Shasta Press, 1951. 1st ed. Fine, dj worn at corners, spine ends, some soiling to rear panel. *ELSE FINE.* $150

Brown, Fredric. THE MURDERERS. NY: Dutton, 1961. 1st ed. Fine, light wear to dj edges. *ELSE FINE.* $90

Brown, Fredric. THE OFFICE. Miami Beach: Dennis McMillan, 1987. 1st ed of orig draft. One of 425 numbered, signed by the author of intro, Philip Jose Farmer. VF in dj. *MORDIDA.* $45

Brown, Fredric. THE OFFICE. NY: E.P. Dutton, 1958. 1st ed VF in dj w/trace of soiling on back panel. *MORDIDA.* $250

Brown, Fredric. THE OFFICE. NY: E.P. Dutton, 1958. 1st ed. VF in dj, trace of soiling back panel. *MORDIDA.* $250

Brown, Fredric. THE SHAGGY DOG & OTHER STORIES. London: T.V. Boardman, (1963). 1st UK ed. Close to Fine sl scuffed, price clipped dj. *AKA.* $75

Brown, Fredric. THE SHAGGY DOG & OTHER STORIES. London: T.V. Boardman & Company Ltd., (1963). 1st UK ed. NF in lightly scuffed dj. *AKA.* $75

Brown, Fredric. WHAT MAD UNIVERSE. Dutton, 1949. 1st ed. Fine in edge-rubbed dj. *MADLE.* $175

Brown, Fredric. WHISPERING DEATH. (Vol. 15). MT: McMillan, 1989. 1st ed. Ltd to 450. VF in dj. *SILVER DOOR.* $40

Brown, George MacKay. A TIME TO KEEP AND OTHER STORIES. London: Hogarth Press, 1969. 1st ed. Fine in dj (bit of light spotting on rear panel). *CAPTAIN'S BOOKSHELF.* $45

Brown, George W. REMINISCENCES OF GOV. R.J. WALKER...Rockford, IL: Author, 1902. 1st ed. Cl cvrs sl stained, spine faded, o/w VG. *DIAMOND.* $35

Brown, Henry. NARRATIVE OF THE ANTI-MASONICK EX-CITEMENT IN THE WESTERN PART OF THE STATE OF NEW YORK DURING THE YEARS 1826, '7, '8 AND PART OF 1829. Batavia, NY, 1829. 1st ed. 244pp. Contemp full calf, raised bands, leather label on spine. Howes B840. *GINSBERG.* $275

Brown, Ina Corinne. THE STORY OF THE AMERICAN NEGRO. NY: Friendship, (1936). 1st ed. VG in dec wrappers w/ephemeral pub's booklist laid in. *LOPEZ.* $30

Brown, J. Ross. ADVENTURES IN THE APACHE COUNTRY: A TOUR THROUGH ARIZONA AND SONORA, WITH NOTES ON THE SILVER REGIONS OF NEVADA. NY: Harper, 1869. 1st ed. 535pp. Unusually Fine in orig cl. *BOOK MARKET.* $300

Brown, J. Wood. THE BUILDERS OF FLORENCE. London: Methuen & Co. (1907). 1st ed. Blue cl, gilt. *KARMIOLE.* $65

Brown, James Berry. JOURNAL OF A JOURNEY ACROSS THE PLAINS IN 1859. Bk Club of CA, 1970. 1st ltd ed of 450. George R. Stewart (ed). Pict boards. Fine in dj. *AUTHORS OF THE WEST.* $75

Brown, James. LIFE OF A PIONEER—BEING AN AUTOBIOG-RAPHY OF...Salt Lake, 1900. 1st ed. Ex-lib. No exterior markings. Scar from pocket removal, number on title page, front hinge loose, o/w VG. *BENCHMARK.* $200

Brown, Jennifer S.H. STRANGERS IN BLOOD. Vancouver, (1980). 1st ed. 255pp. Small tear in dj o/w VG+. *PRATT.* $35

Brown, John Henry EARLY DAYS OF SAN FRANCISCO, CALIFORNIA. Oakland, Biobooks, 1949. 1 color pl, 1 fldg map. Ltd to 500. Howes B853. Fine. *OREGON.* $45

Brown, John P. THE DERVISHES; OR, ORIENTAL SPIRITUALISM. Phila, 1868. *O'NEILL.* $75

Brown, John. SPARE HOURS. FIRST SERIES. RAB AND HIS FRIENDS AND OTHER PAPERS. Boston, 1883. 1st Amer ed. *FYE.* $45

Brown, John. SPARE HOURS. THIRD SERIES. LOCKE AND SYDENHAM AND OTHER PAPERS. Boston, 1883. 1st Amer ed. *FYE.* $45

Brown, John. THE NORTH-WEST PASSAGE, AND THE PLANS FOR THE SEARCH FOR SIR JOHN FRANKLIN. London: E. Stanford, 1860. 2nd ed. Report concerning M'Clintock's expedition incl this ed. Prelims foxed; bk VG+. Bkpl. *PARMER.* $650

Brown, Lady Richmond. UNKNOWN TRIBES, UNCHARTED SEAS. NY: D. Appleton and Co, 1925. Blue cl, gilt spine titles. Offset to eps. NF. *PARMER.* $50

Brown, Larry. BIG BAD LOVE. Chapel Hill: Algonquin, (1990). 1st Amer ed. Signed. Fine in dj. *DORN.* $35

Brown, Larry. DIRTY WORK. Chapel Hill, NC: Algonquin, 1989. 1st ed. Fine in dj. Promo letter from pub laid in. *STAHR.* $25

Brown, Larry. DIRTY WORK. Chapel Hill: Algonquin, (1989). 1st Amer ed. Signed. Fine in dj. *DORN.* $40

Brown, Larry. DIRTY WORK. Chapel Hill: Algonquin, 1989. Adv reading copy. Fine in wrappers. *CAPTAIN'S BOOKSHELF.* $75

Brown, Larry. DIRTY WORK. Chapel Hill: Algonquin Books, 1989. Adv reading copy of 1st novel. Inscribed. Orig ptd dk blue wraps. Fine. *CHAPEL HILL.* $55

Brown, Larry. FACING THE MUSIC. Chapel Hill: Algonquin, (1988). 1st trade ed. Signed. Fine in dj. *DORN.* $60

Brown, Larry. FACING THE MUSIC. Chapel Hill: Algonquin, (1988). Uncorrected proof. Signed. NF in wraps. *DORN.* $175

Brown, Larry. FACING THE MUSIC. Chapel Hill: Algonquin Books, 1988. 1st ed, 1st bk. Orig black cl. Fine in dj. *CHAPEL HILL.* $50

Brown, Larry. JOE. (Chapel Hill): Algonquin Books of Chapel Hill, 1991. Adv reading copy. Fine in wraps w/promo brochure laid in. *LOPEZ.* $40

Brown, Larry. JOE. Chapel Hill: Algonquin, (1991). 1st Amer ed. Signed. Fine in dj. *DORN.* $30

Brown, Larry. JOE. CHAPEL HILL: Algonquin (1991). Adv rev copy. Fine in wraps. *DORN.* $35

Brown, Larry. JOE. Chapel Hill: Algonquin, 1991. Advance reading copy. Fine in ptd wrappers. *CAPTAIN'S BOOKSHELF.* $50

Brown, Lloyd L. IRON CITY. NY: Masses & Mainstream, 1951. 1st ed, 1st bk. Signed. Fine in pict wraps. *ELSE FINE.* $75

Brown, Lloyd L. IRON CITY. NY: Masses & Mainstream, 1951. 1st ed, 1st bk, wrappered form. Fine in ptd wraps. *HELLER.* $50

Brown, Louise Norton. BLOCK PRINTING AND BOOK ILLUSTRATION IN JAPAN. London: George Routledge & Sons, Ltd. 1924. 1st ed. Orig tan cloth over grn boards, green calf spine label. Unusually Fine in dj. *KARMIOLE.* $500

Brown, Marion T. LETTERS FROM FORT SILL: 1886-1887. Austin: Encino Press, 1970. C. Richard King (ed). Cloth spine and paper boards. Fine. *LAURIE.* $30

Brown, Mark H. and W.R. Felton. BEFORE BARBED WIRE. NY, 1956. 1st ed. Bkpl. VG in moderately edgeworn dj. *BAADE.* $47.50

Brown, Mark H. and W.R. Felton. BEFORE BARBED WIRE: L.A. HUFFMAN, PHOTOGRAPHER ON HORSEBACK. NY: Henry Holt, (1956). 1st ed. VG in dj. *LAURIE.* $50

Brown, Mark. THE PLAINSMEN OF THE YELLOWSTONE. A HISTORY OF YELLOWSTONE BASIN. Putnam, (1961). 1st ed. VG in VG dj. *OREGON.* $40

Brown, Merle Blinn. EIGHT RATTLES AND A BUTTON. San Antonio, (1967). 1st ed. Inscribed. Fine in dj. *PRATT.* $25

Brown, Moses True. THE SYNTHETIC PHILOSOPHY OF EXPRESSION Boston: Houghton, Mifflin, 1886. 5th ed. Ink notations. Overall VG. *OLD LONDON.* $20

Brown, Mrs. Hugh. LADY IN BOOMTOWN. Palo Alto, (1968). 1st ed. Dj. VG+. *PRATT.* $32.50

Brown, Paul. INSIGNIA OF THE SERVICES. NY, 1941. NF. *POLYANTHOS.* $30

Brown, R. Shepard. STRINGFELLOW OF THE FOURTH. NY, (1960). 1st ed. 307pp. VG in dj. *PRATT.* $40

Brown, Rita Mae and Sneaky Pie Brown. WISH YOU WERE HERE. NY: Bantam, (1990). 1st Amer ed. Signed. Fine in dj. *DORN.* $30

Brown, Rita Mae. BINGO. Bantam, 1988. 1st ed. Fine in dj. Signed & inscribed. *STAHR.* $30

Brown, Rita Mae. BINGO. NY: Bantam, (1988). 1st Amer ed. Signed. Fine in dj. *DORN.* $35

Brown, Rita Mae. HIGH HEARTS. NY: Bantam, (1986). Uncorrected proof. NF in wrappers. *LOPEZ.* $25

Brown, Rita Mae. IN HER DAY. Plainfield: Daughters, (1976). 1st Amer ed. Pb orig. Signed. Name on ffep else VG+. *DORN.* $60

Brown, Rita Mae. RUBYFRUIT JUNGLE. Plainfield: Daughters, Inc., (1973). 1st ed. Only issued in pb. Very scarce. Spine sl cocked. NF. *LOPEZ.* $150

Brown, Rita Mae. SIX OF ONE. NY: Harper & Row, (1978). 1st Amer ed. Signed. NF in price-clipped VG+ dj. *DORN.* $45

Brown, Rita Mae. SOUTHERN DISCOMFORT. NY: Harper & Row, (1982). 1st Amer ed. Signed. NF in dj. *DORN.* $35

Brown, Rita Mae. STARTING FROM SCRATCH: A DIFFERENT KIND OF WRITER'S MANUAL. NY: Bantam, (1988). 1st Amer ed. Signed. Fine in dj. *DORN.* $35

Brown, Rita Mae. SUDDEN DEATH. NY: Bantam, (1983). 1st Amer ed. Signed. Fine in lightly used NF dj. *DORN.* $35

Brown, Rosellan. SOME DEATHS IN THE DELTA & OTHER POEMS. N.p.: Univ of MA Press, (1970). New in dj. 1st ed, 1st book. New in price clipped dj. *BERNARD.* $40

Brown, Roselle G. SYBIL SUE BLUE. Doubleday, 1966, 1st ed. Fine in rubbed dj. *MADLE.* $35

Brown, Roselle G. WATERS OF CENTAURUS. Doubleday, 1970. 1st ed. Fine in dj. *MADLE.* $30

Brown, Rosellen. THE AUTOBIOGRAPHY OF MY MOTHER. GC: Doubleday, 1976. 1st ed. New in dj. *BERNARD.* $20

Brown, T. Allston. HISTORY OF THE AMERICAN STAGE. NY: Dick and Fitzgerald, (1872). Engr portraits. End chipped, sl shaken. Good. *CULLEN.* $130

Brown, T. Graham and Gavin de Beer. THE FIRST ASCENT OF MONT BLANC. London, NY, and Toronto: Oxford Univ Press, 1957. 1st ed. Dj. Fine. *WEBER.* $45

Brown, T. THE TAXIDERMIST'S MANUAL. London & Edinburgh, A. Fullarton, (n.d.). 28th ed. VG. *MIKESH.* $55

Brown, T. THE TAXIDERMIST'S MANUAL. NY, O. Judd (n.d.). Rev ed from 20th UK ed. VG+. *MIKESH.* $47.50

Brown, Thomas. AN ACCOUNT OF THE PEOPLE CALLED SHAKERS...Troy, NY: Parker & Bliss, 1812. Leather scuffed, front hinge split, front cover nearly detached; tight interior, paper little darkened w/some staining; very tired. *BOHLING.* $150

Brown, Warren. THE CHICAGO CUBS. Putnam, 1946. 1st ed. Good+ in VG+ dj. *PLAPINGER.* $40

Brown, Warren. THE CHICAGO WHITE SOX. Putnam, 1952. 1st ed. VG. *PLAPINGER.* $30

Brown, William Edgar. ECHOES OF THE FOREST: AMERICAN INDIAN LEGENDS. Boston: Richard G. Badger, 1918. The Gorham Press. 1st ed. Signed. Frontis. VG. *CONNOLLY & WADE.* $30

Brown, Wm. Compton. THE INDIAN SIDE OF THE STORY. Spokane, 1961. 1st ed. 469pp. VG+. *PRATT.* $50

Brown-Sequard, C.E. COURSE OF LECTURES ON THE PHYSIOLOGY AND PATHOLOGY OF THE CENTRAL NERVOUS SYSTEM. Phila, 1860. 1st ed. 276pp. Wear to head and tail of spine, o/w Fine. *FYE.* $750

Brown-Sequard, C.E. LECTURES ON THE DIAGNOSIS AND TREATMENT OF PRINCIPAL FORMS OF PARALYSIS OF THE LOWER EXTREMITIES. Phila, 1861. 1st ed. 118pp. Name clipped from top of title, wear to head and tail of spine. Contents Fine. Scarce. *FYE.* $500

Browne, Belmore. THE FROZEN BARRIER. NY, 1921. 1st ed. Pict cl. Edgewear. *ARTIS.* $22.50

Browne, C.R. MAORI WITCHERY: NATIVE LIFE IN NEW ZEALAND. London: Dent, (1920). 1st ed. VG. *ACADEMIC.* $25

Browne, Edgar. PHIZ AND DICKENS AS THEY APPEARED TO EDGAR BROWNE. London: James Nisbet, 1913. 1st ed. Large 8vo, 320pp, illus by the author's father mostly from hitherto un-published work. (From the Dickens House Library with their bkpl and identifying stamps.) Blue cloth. Good+. *GREAT EXPECTATIONS.* $25

Browne, Edward Granville. A YEAR AMONGST THE PERSIANS. Cambridge: Univ Press; NY: Macmillan, 1926. New ed. Frontis, fldg map. Recent cl, frontis sl dampstained, o/w VG. Bkpl. *WORLDWIDE.* $125

Browne, Francis I. (ed). BUGLE-ECHOES. NY, 1886. 1st ed. Gilt edges, pict cl. Cvr wear o/w Fine. *PRATT.* $30

Browne, G. Waldo & Nathan Haskell Hole. THE NEW AMERICA AND THE FAR EAST. 9 VOLS. Boston, (1910). 2pp color map each vol. Gilt cl. VF. *ARTIS.* $125

Browne, Howard. HALO IN BLOOD. England: No Exit Press, 1988. 1st British ed. Fine in dj. *SILVER DOOR.* $35

Browne, Howard. RETURN OF THARN. Providence, RI: Grandon Company Pubs, 1956. 1st ed. Signed. VG in sl soiled dj. *HELLER.* $125

Browne, Howard. WARRIOR OF THE DAWN. Reilly & Lee, 1943. 1st ed. Fine in dj, sl wear to spine. *MADLE.* $125

Browne, J. Ross. A PEEP AT WASHOE OR, SKETCH OF ADVEN-TURE IN VIRGINIA CITY. Palo Alto: Lewis Osborne, 1968. 1st ed thus. Ltd to 1,400, this being #385. Grn cl w/silver decs. Slight fading on spine and upper front corner else VG+. *CONNOLLY & WADE.* $45

Browne, J. Ross. ADVENTURES IN THE APACHE COUNTRY. NY, 1974. Reprint of 1874 ed. Fine in VG dj. *FIVE QUAIL.* $25

Browne, J. Ross. ADVENTURES IN THE APACHE COUNTRY...NY: Harper, 1869. 1st ed. Binding little worn, soiled; spine ends, lower corners frayed; overall Nice. Howes B875. *BO-HLING.* $350

Browne, J. Ross. HIS LETTERS, JOURNALS AND WRITINGS. Univ of Mexico Press, (1969). 1st ed. Lina Fergusson Browne (ed). Fine. *AUTHORS OF THE WEST.* $30

Browne, J. Ross. WASHOE REVISITED. NOTES ON THE SIL-VER REGIONS OF NEVADA. Biobooks, (1957). Ltd to 500. Fine. *OREGON.* $45

Browne, J. Ross. YUSEF; OR THE JOURNEY OF THE FRANGI. A CRUSADE IN THE EAST. Harper, 1853. 1st ed. 421pp + 6pp ads. Illus. Pict glt stamped cl. Corners worn o/w fine. VG. *OREGON.* $175

Browne, John. MYOGRAPHIA NOVA: OR, A GRAPHICAL DESCRIPTION OF ALL THE MUSCLES IN THE HUMANE BODY, AS THEY ARISE IN DISSECTION. NY, c. 1970. Fac-simile of London 1697 ed. *FYE.* $60

Browne, Junius Henri. THE GREAT METROPOLIS. Hartford, 1869. 700pp. Rubbed top, bottom spine. *HEINOLDT.* $20

Browne, Peter. TRICHOLOGIA MAMMALIUM; OR, A TREATISE ON THE ORGANIZATION, PROPERTIES AND USES OF HAIR AND WOOL...Phila: J.H. Jones, 1853. 1st ed. 179,(1)pp. Errata leaf. Plts. Contemp 3/4 calf, marbled boards, rubbed. Lib stamps on title. *M & S.* $225

Browne, Thomas. HYDRIOTAPHIA. URNE-BURIALL. (Boston: Houghton Mifflin) 1907. 108 in ed of 385. Bkpl, o/w immaculate in pub's box. *HELLER.* $150

Browne, Thomas. MISCELLANEOUS WRITINGS. Ed by Geoffrey Keynes. London: Faber, 1946. 8vo, 473pp,index. Brown linen, gilt, uncut. Orig issued as Vol V of the 1931 Keynes edition of The Col-lected Works. The remaining stocks of vols I through IV were destroyed by enemy action in 1941; this volume reprints the scarce survivors, w/the addition of a few errata. *HARTFIELD.* $95

Browne, Thomas. RELIGIO MEDICI, A LETTER TO A FRIEND, CHRISTIAN MORALS, URN-BURIAL, AND OTHER PAPERS. Boston, 1862. 440pp. W/Fine engr port of Browne which is often lacking. Fine. *FYE.* $250

Browne, Thomas. RELIGIO MEDICI. Ed by Geoffrey Keynes. Eugene: Univ of Oregon. Ptd for the LEC by John Henry Nash, 1939. 1st ed. 1/1500 signed by Nash. NF in moderately worn slip-case. *CAPTAIN'S BOOKSHELF.* $65

Browne, Thomas. RELIGIO MEDICI. NY, 1903. Ltd ed, ptd on hand-made paper. *FYE.* $100

Browne, Thomas. THE WORKS. Edinburgh: John Grant, 1927. Ed by Charles Sayle. 3 vols. First this edition. Excellent condition. *HARTFIELD.* $165

Browning, D.M. ANNUAL REPORT OF THE COMMISSIONER OF INDIAN AFFAIRS, 1896. Washington: GPO, 1896. Fldg map at back. Faint lib marks on spine. Head and heel of spine taped, o/w tight. *LAURIE.* $75

Browning, Elizabeth Barrett. POEMS BEFORE CONGRESS. Lon-don: Chapman & Hall. 1860. 1st ed. viii,(2),66pp+(2)pp ads. With half title. Orig red cl, gilt; spine extrems lightly frayed, cloth bit soiled. *KARMIOLE.* $200

Browning, Robert. PARLEYINGS WITH CERTAIN PEOPLE OF IMPORTANCE IN THEIR DAY. London: Smith, Elder & Co., 1887. 1st ed. 8vo; pp 268 (2 adverts). Orig terra-cotta cloth, dec in blind and black, gilt spine titles. Bkpls, else Nice. *HARTFIELD.* $85

Browning, Robert. THE PIED PIPER OF HAMELIN. Rand Mc-Nally, (1910). Illus by Hope Dunlap. VG+ w/color pict cvr pas-tedown & gilt lettering on blue cloth. *BEBBAH.* $35

Brownlee, Richard S. GRAY GHOSTS OF THE CONFEDERACY. Baton Rouge, (1958). 1st ed. Signed. VG in dj. *PRATT.* $50

Brownlow, Kevin. THE PARADE'S GONE BY.... NY: Knopf, 1968. 1st ed. Errata slip laid in. Fine in very lightly used dj. *CAPTAIN'S BOOK-SHELF.* $50

Brownlow, W.G. SKETCHES OF THE RISE, PROGRESS AND DECLINE OF SECESSION;...Phila, 1862. 1st ed. "Parson Brownlow's Book" on spine. Dampstaining on few pp, lacks frontis tissue guard, o/w VG. *DIAMOND.* $35

Brownlow, W.G. SKETCHES OF THE RISE...OF SECESSION; G.W. Childs, 1862. 1st ed. Fair. *BOOK BROKER.* $25

Bruccoli, Matthew. ROSS MACDONALD. NY: Harcourt Brace Jovanovich, 1984. 1st ed. Fine in dj. *MORDIDA.* $35

Bruce, Edward and Forbes Watson. ART IN FEDERAL BUILD-INGS...VOLUME I: MURAL DESIGNS. 1934-1936. Washington, DC: Art in Federal Buildings Inc, 1936. Ed of 1000. Bumped, rubbed, stained, chipped at extrems, cl splitting at joints, pp dampstained and soiled, some leaves creased. Good. *BLUE MOUN-TAIN.* $235

Bruce, George A. THE CAPTURE AND OCCUPATION OF RICH-MOND. (N.p., n.d., ca. 1925?). 1st ed. Orig cl. *GINSBERG.* $75

Bruce, John. GAUDY CENTURY. NY: Random, 1948. 1st ed. Cloth. Fine in NF dj. *CONNOLLY & WADE.* $35

Bruce, Philip Alexander. ECONOMIC HISTORY OF VIRGINIA IN THE SEVENTEENTH CENTURY. Macmillan, 1896. 1st ed. 2 vols. Good+. *BOOK BROKER.* $45

Bruce, Robert. THE FIGHTING NORTHS AND PAWNEE SCOUTS, NARRATIVES AND REMINISCENCES OF MILITARY SERVICE ON THE OLD FRONTIER. Lincoln, NE, 1932. 1st ed. 73pp. VG+ in pict wraps. *PRATT.* $37.50

Bruce, Robert. THE FIGHTING NORTHS AND PAWNEE SCOUTS. Lincoln: Nebraska State Hist Soc, 1932. 1st ed. Pict wraps, some wear, soiling. *SCHOYER'S.* $30

Bruce, Thomas. SOUTHWEST VIRGINIA AND SHENANDOAH VALLEY. J.L. Hill, 1891. 259pp Orig brn cl (rubbed, flecked). Pencil marks, pp browned throughout, front fly present but detached. Good. *BOOK BROKER.* $100

Bruce-Mitford, R.L.S. (ed). RECENT ARCHAEOLOGICAL EXCAVATIONS IN BRITAIN. Selected Excavations, 1939-1955. NY: The Macmillan Co. (1956). 1st ed. Dj (back cvr chipped). *KARMIOLE.* $30

Bruchac, Joseph. SURVIVAL THIS WAY. Tucson: Sun Tracks and Univ of Arizona Press, (1987). Fine in Fine dj. *LOPEZ.* $50

Bruckner, W.H. and J.B. Chynoweth. AMERICAN MANURES....Phila, 1872. 2nd ed. Orig cl, spine ends chipped; backstrip, edges faded; prelim pp foxed. *SUTTON.* $45

Brugsch-bey, Heinrich. EGYPT UNDER THE PHARAOHS. London: John Murray, 1891. Frontis, 9 illus, 4 maps. Bkpl, owner's ink stamp. Good. *ARCHAEOLOGIA.* $125

Brunhouse, Robert L. FRANS BLOM. MAYA EXPLORER. Albuquerque: Univ of NM Press, 1976. 1st ed. Fine in VG dj. *PARMER.* $30

Brunhouse, Robert. FRANS BLOM, MAYA EXPLORER. Albuquerque: Univ. of NM Press, (1976). 1st ed. Good in chipped dj. *SILVER.* $25

Brunner, John. THE WRONG END OF TIME. Doubleday, 1971. 1st ed. Fine in soiled dj. *MADLE.* $27

Bruno, Anthony. BAD GUYS. NY: Putnam, 1988. 1st ed. Review copy, signed. Promo material laid in. Fine in dj. *SILVER DOOR.* $35

Bruno, Giordano. THE EXPULSION OF THE TRIUMPHANT BEAST. New Brunswick: Rutgers Univ Press, (1964). 1st ed. Arthur D. Imerti (trans, ed). VG. *BLUE DRAGON.* $35

Brunton, T. Lauder. MODERN DEVELOPMENTS OF HARVEY'S WORK. London, 1894. Scarce. *FYE.* $75

Brunton, T. Lauder. PHARMACOLOGY AND THERAPEUTICS; OR, MEDICINE PAST AND PRESENT. London, 1880. 1st ed. Scarce. *FYE.* $125

Bryan, C.D.B. FRIENDLY FIRE. NY: Putnam, (1976). 1st ed. NF in NF dj, tiny edge tear. *AKA.* $35

Bryan, Daniel. THE MOUNTAIN MUSE COMPRISING THE ADVENTURES OF DANIEL BOONE....Ptd for the author by Davidson & Bourne: Harrisburg, 1813. 1st ed. 252,12pp. 16mo. Orig mottled sheep. Upper third of front hinge starting; paper browned and fragile; Ffep and half title removed. Red morocco label. Clamshell box of brown cl in matching slipcase w/full lea spine of raised bands and gilt. *CONNOLLY & WADE.* $300

Bryan, Daniel. THE MOUNTAIN MUSE. Harrisonburg (VA): Ptd for author by Davidson & Bourne, 1813 . 1st ed. 252pp, list of subscribers. Bound in full contemp calf (warped). VG (some foxing). *SECOND LIFE.* $325

Bryan, John. THE DIFFERENCE TO ME. London: Faber and Faber Ltd., (1957). 1st ed. Minor spine fading. *OAK KNOLL.* $30

Bryan, Julien. SIEGE. NY: Doubleday, Doran & Co, Inc, 1940. 48 photo plts. Faded dj. *KARMIOLE.* $40

Bryan, Michael. BRYAN'S DICTIONARY OF PAINTERS AND ENGRAVERS. New Edition Revised and Enlarged Under the Supervision of George C. Williamson. London: George Bell & Sons. 1903-1905. 5 vols. *KARMIOLE.* $175

Bryan, W.A. KEY TO THE BIRDS OF THE HAWAIIAN GROUP. Honolulu, Bishop Museum, 1901. 15 full pg photo plts. VG. *MIKESH.* $60

Bryan, William Alanson. NATURAL HISTORY OF HAWAII. Honolulu, 1915. 1st, only ed. (Some front matter bound out of order.) Attractive. *LEFKOWICZ.* $200

Bryan, William Jennings. THE OLD WORLD AND ITS WAYS....St. Louis: Thompson, 1907. 1st ed. VG. *AARD.* $50

Bryant, Dorothy. THE KIN OF ATA ARE WAITING FOR YOU. Berkeley/NY: Moon Books/Random House, (1976). 1st ed thus, one of 1,500. Name. Dj edgewear, tiny snag. Signed. VG. *AKA.* $25

Bryant, Joseph. MANUAL OF OPERATIVE SURGERY. NY, 1884. 1st ed. 2 vols. 593pp. 705 woodcut illus. *FYE.* $125

Bryant, Louise. SIX RED MONTHS IN RUSSIA. AN OBSERVER'S ACCOUNT....NY, 1918. *O'NEILL.* $50

Bryant, Thomas. A MANUAL FOR THE PRACTICE OF SURGERY. Phila, 1879. 2nd Amer ed. Full leather, 945pp. 672 Fine woodcut illus. *FYE.* $50

Bryant, Thomas. THE DISEASES OF THE BREAST. 1889, pp. 33-322, IN: WMSM (Vol. 4). NY, 1889. 1st Amer ed. 8 color lithographs. *FYE.* $75

Bryant, William Cullen (ed). PICTURESQUE AMERICA. NY, 1872. 2 vols. Illus w/full-pg steel & wood engr. Vol 1 professionally rebacked. Aeg. Full lea bindings. NF. *POLYANTHOS.* $350

Bryant, William Cullen (ed). PICTURESQUE AMERICA...2 Vols. NY: Appleton, (1872-4). 1st 2 vol ed. Cvrs reattached. Some cvr wear. Very sl fraying of corners of pp 561-8, Vol. I, w/sl crease corner of 1 plate. New spine labels. Small old lib stamp on copyright pages covered over. Ex-lib stamp on blank rears (only) of all 49 steel-engr plts, o/w contents VG. *DIAMOND.* $200

Bryant, William Cullen (trans). THE ILIAD OF HOMER. Boston: Fields, Osgood, 1870. 1st ed. 4to, 2vols. 398,426pp. Fine. BAL 1724. *SECOND LIFE.* $100

Bryant, William Cullen. LETTERS FROM THE EAST. NY: G.P. Putnam & Son, 1869. 1st (gilt) ed. Purple cl, aeg, spine faded and sl soiled. Good+. *JUVELIS.* $15

Bryce, George. THE REMARKABLE HISTORY OF THE HUDSON'S BAY COMPANY. NY: Burt Franklin, 1968. Fine. *BLUE DRAGON.* $25

Bryce, George. THE REMARKABLE HISTORY OF THE HUDSON'S BAY COMPANY. INCLUDING THAT OF THE FRENCH TRADERS....London: Sampson Low Marston & Co, 1902. 2nd issue. Some back hinge deterioration, else VG. *BLUE DRAGON.* $65

Bryce, George. THE REMARKABLE HISTORY OF THE HUDSON'S BAY COMPANY. NY: Scribner's, (1910). Good copy. *BLUE DRAGON.* $35

Bryce, James. THE AMERICAN COMMONWEALTH. 3 vols. London, 1888. 1st ed, 1st issue, containing Chapter 88, "The Tweed Ring in New York City" in vol 3, which was suppressed in later issue. Fldg color map, vol 1. Contemp 3/4 black polished calf, marbled boards & eps. Teg. Slight cover wear. Interiors VG. *DIAMOND.* $300

Bryden, H.A. HORN AND HOUND. London: Methuen & Co., 1927. 1st ed. VG-NF. *OLD LONDON.* $50

Bryers, Paul. COMING FIRST. London: Bloomsbury, (1987). 1st ed. Fine in dj. *WOOLMER.* $35

Bryers, Paul. HOLLOW TARGET. (London): Andrew Deutsch, (1976). 1st ed. Fine in dj. *WOOLMER.* $45

Bryher, Winifred, trans. THE LAMENT FOR ADONIS BION THE SMYNAEAN. London: Humphreys, 1918. 1st ed. Wraps have a sl crease on top cover caused when binding, else Fine. *WOOLMER.* $450

Bryk, Felix. VOODOO-EROS. NY: Privately Ptd for Subscribers, 1933. 1st Amer ed, ltd to 495 numbered. Trans by Mayne R. Sexton. *WREDEN.* $90

BUBBLES AND BLAST. (By Mary E. Bouligny.) Baltimore: Kelly, Piet and Co, 1871. Grn cl stamped in black, blind and gilt, silver-fished, chipped. Good only. *SCHOYER'S.* $25

Buber, Martin. I AND THOU. Edinburgh: Clark, 1937. 1st ed in English. VG+ in self wraps. Cvrs tanned. Scarce. *LAME DUCK.* $150

Buchan, John and George Adam Smith. THE KIRK IN SCOTLAND, 1560-1929. London: Hodder & Stoughton, (1930). 1st Eng. ed. Pencil gift inscription ffep. Fine in VG dj. *AARD.* $50

Buchan, John. A PRINCE OF THE CAPTIVITY. Boston & NY, 1933. 1st ed. Fine. *McCLINTOCK.* $10

Buchan, John. THE ISLAND OF SHEEP. London: Hodder and Stoughton, (1936). 1st ed. Fine in lightly used dj. *JUVELIS.* $200

Buchan, John. THE MAN FROM THE NORLANDS. Boston: Houghton Mifflin, (1936). 1st Amer ed of THE ISLAND OF SHEEP. Tan cl, pict dj by N.C. Wyeth. Fine in NF dj. *JUVELIS.* $200

Buchan, John. THE THIRTY-NINE STEPS. Edinburgh & London, 1915. 1st ed. Orig. light blue cloth. Spine soiled. Slight cvr soiling, staining, and shelfwear. Inner front hinge starting. Little bumping at spine tips. Slight yellowing at page margins, o/w VG. *DIAMOND.* $150

Buchan, William. DOMESTIC MEDICINE: OR, A VALUABLE TREATISE ON THE PREVENTION AND CURE OF DISEASES BY REGIMEN AND SIMPLE MEDICINES. Leominster, MA: Isaiah Thomas, Jr., 1804. 484pp. Full lea. Fep missing, foxed. Scarce. *FYE.* $100

Buchanan, A. WILD LIFE IN CANADA. London: J. Murray, (Jun 1920). 2nd ptg. VG+. *MIKESH.* $27.50

Buchanan, James. MESSAGE OF THE PRESIDENT OF THE UNITED STATES, Communicating...information in relation to the massacre at Mountain Meadows...36th Congress 1st Session, Ex Doc 42. 139pp, May 4, 1860. Disbound, and attractively rebound. Light dampstaining on many pages, not affecting legibility of text o/w generally VG. *FIVE QUAIL.* $190

Buchanan, James. THE UTAH EXPEDITION. MESSAGE FROM...Wash., HD71, 1858. 1st ed. 215pp. Buckram, rubber lib stamp. Howes U33. *GINSBERG.* $150

Buchanan, R. THE CULTURE OF THE GRAPE, AND WINEMAKING....Cincinnati, 1856. 5th ed. Orig cl very worn, scuffed. Foxed; ex-lib. *SUTTON.* $45

Buchanan, Thomas G. WHO KILLED KENNEDY? London: Secker & Warburg, (1964). 2nd UK ptg. About Fine in very bright dj. *AKA.* $25

Buchele, William. RECREATING THE KENTUCKY RIFLE. York, PA: Shumway, 1967. 2nd ed of 500. 2 detached, fldg sheets of details laid in. Fine. *CONNOLLY & WADE.* $35

Bucher, Elmer E. VACUUM TUBES IN WIRELESS COMMUNICATION. NY: Wireless Press, 1919. Owner's name, o/w Fine. *MAD DOG.* $40

Buchner, Alexander. MUSICAL INSTRUMENTS THROUGH THE AGES. London: Spring Books, n.d. Fine in sl rippled dj. *BANCROFT.* $28.50

Buck, Albert. A TREATISE ON HYGIENE AND PUBLIC HEALTH. 2 vols. London, 1879. 1st British ed. London ed, ptd on thicker paper. Scarce. *FYE.* $250

Buck, Daniel. INDIAN OUTBREAKS. Mankato, MN., 1904. 1st ed. Frontis, plts. Orig orange cl w/title in gilt on spine, some discoloration to spine. Overall VG, clean, tight. Howes B914. *GINSBERG.* $250

Buck, Daniel. INDIAN OUTBREAKS. Ross & Haines, 1965. 1st ptg. Fine in Fine dj. *VARNER.* $25

Buck, F. with C. Weld. ANIMALS ARE LIKE THAT! NY: McBride, 1939. VG. *MIKESH.* $30

Buck, F. with F. Fraser. FANG & CLAW. NY: Simon & Schuster, (1935). VG. *MIKESH.* $30

Buck, Franklin. A YANKEE TRADER IN THE GOLD RUSH. THE LETTERS OF....Houghton Mifflin, 1930. 1st ed. 7 plts. VG in VG dj. *OREGON.* $50

Buck, Fraser and George Thompson. TREASURE MOUNTAIN HOME. Salt Lake: Deseret, 1968. 1st ed. Fine in Fine dj. *OREGON.* $35

Buck, Irving A. CLEBOURNE AND HIS COMMAND; PAT CLEBOURNE, STONEWALL JACKSON OF THE WEST. Rd by Thomas Robson Hay. Jackson, 1959. (CLEBOURNE AND HIS COMMAND orig issued in 1908). VG. *PRATT.* $35

Buck, Pearl S. THE GOOD EARTH. NY: John Day, (1931). 1st issue. Gilt lettering on spine a touch tarnished, else Fine in about VG dj darkened on spine, has a few dampspots and a few small chips, also on spine. Very scarce. *BETWEEN COVERS.* $500

Buck, Pearl S. THE GOOD EARTH. NY: John Day, (1931). Advance reading copy of her first book. VG in wrappers, with promo info tipped in. *LOPEZ.* $850

Buck, Pearl S. THE GOOD EARTH. NY: John Day (1931). 1st ed, 1st issue, NF in dj (internally strengthened w/tape but still at least VG). Very Nice. *LOPEZ.* $750

Buck, Solon J. THE GRANGER MOVEMENT: A STUDY OF AGRICULTURAL ORGANIZATION...1870-1880. Cambridge, 1913. 1st ed. Orig cl. (emb lib stamp, bkpl removed). Howes B916. *GINSBERG.* $75

Buck, William J. HISTORY OF MONTGOMERY COUNTY WITHIN THE SCHUYLKILL VALLEY...FROM THE EARLIEST PERIOD TO THE PRESENT TIME....Norristown: Acker, 1859. 1st ed. 124,(4)pp. Old cl, paper label on lower spine; bkpl removed; some marginal staining, no text affected. Howes B918. *GINSBERG.* $85

Buckbee, Edna Bryan. PIONEER DAYS OF ANGEL'S CAMP. Calaveras Californian, (1932) 80pp + 12 plts. Pict wraps. Ltd ed. VG. *OREGON.* $60

Buckingham, James S. TRAVELS IN ASSYRIA, MEDIA, AND PERSIA, INCLUDING A JOURNEY FROM BAGDAD...AND THE RUINS OF PERSEPOLIS. London, 1830. 2nd ed. 2 vols. Fldg map, 26 plts. Newly bound in 1/4 calf, marbled boards, raised bands. xxvii,508pp; 466pp. Attractive. Few sm rubber stamps do not detract. *O'NEILL.* $300

Buckingham, James S. TRAVELS IN PALESTINE, THROUGH THE COUNTRIES OF BASHAN AND GILEAD...INCLUDING A VISIT TO THE CITIES OF GERAZA AND GAMALA, IN THE DECAPOLIS. London, 1821. Frontis, fldg map, 7 plts. New 1/2 calf, marbled boards. xxvii,553pp. VF (very lt foxing). *O'NEILL.* $650

Buckingham, Nash. DE SHOOTINEST GENT'MAN. NY: Scribners, 1941. 1st separate ed. Fine in sl used dj, short tears. Tls laid in. *CAPTAIN'S BOOKSHELF.* $175

Buckland, F. LOG-BOOK OF A FISHERMAN AND ZOOLOGIST. London, c. 1880's. 5th thousand. Pp xiv,(1),339. Half morocco. Lt scuffing; bkpl. *SUTTON.* $28

Buckland, F.T. CURIOSITIES OF NATURAL HISTORY. Frontis, 33 plts & 22 text drawings. London, 1903. New ed. Gilt-dec cl. Lt foxing; ex-lib. *SUTTON.* $30

Buckle, Henry Thomas. ESSAYS WITH A BIOGRAPHICAL SKETCH OF THE AUTHOR. NY: Appleton, 1863. 1st US ed. 209pp. Orig tipped-in photogr port. Lib bkpl. VG. *SECOND LIFE.* $125

Buckle, Richard. DIAGHILEV. NY: Atheneum, 1979. 1st Amer. ed. Fine in sl chipped dj. *BANCROFT.* $20

Buckley, A.K. THE KEENELAND ASSOCIATION LIBRARY, A GUIDE TO THE COLLECTION (OF BOOKS ON HORSES). Lexington: Univ of Kentucky, 1958. VG+. *MIKESH.* $65

Buckley, J.M. TRAVELS IN THREE CONTINENTS....NY, 1895. Orig dec cl, gilt. Uncut. *O'NEILL.* $25

Buckley, W. BIG GAME HUNTING IN CENTRAL AFRICA. London: Cecil Palmer, 1930. Stated 1st ed. VG. *BACKMAN.* $175

Buckley, William F. MARCO POLO, IF YOU CAN. GC: Doubleday, 1982. 1st ed. Inscribed on tipped-in photo. Fine in dj. *ELSE FINE.* $35

Buckley, William F. SAVING THE QUEEN. GC: Doubleday, 1976. 1st ed. Fine, minor edgewear to dj. *ELSE FINE.* $30

Buckley, William F. STAINED GLASS. GC: Doubleday, 1978. 1st ed. VF, minor rubbing dj spine ends. *ELSE FINE.* $25

Buckley, William F. THE STORY OF HENRY TODD. NY: Franklin Library, 1984. 1st ed. Signed. VF in black leather. *ELSE FINE.* $60

Buckman, J. WHERE TOWN AND COUNTRY MEET. Cincinnati & NY, 1903. VG+. *MIKESH.* $27.50

BUCKSKIN MOSE. Ed and with illus by C.G. Rosenberg. NY: Henry L. Hinton, 1873. 1st ed. Orig dec cloth, somewhat dusty and worn, bit shaken; 12 engr plts. Signed inscrip. VG. *DRAMATIS PERSONAE.* $135

Buckton, A. THROUGH HUMAN EYES: POEMS. Oxford: Daniel Press, 1901. 1st ed. One of 130 numbered. Edge worn orig wrappers. Fine. *MUELLER.* $50

Budd, George. ON THE ORGANIC DISEASES AND FUNCTIONAL DISORDERS OF THE STOMACH. NY, 1856. 1st Amer ed. *FYE.* $125

Budge, E.A. Wallis (ed). BOOK OF THE DEAD. CHAPTERS OF COMING FORTH BY DAY OR THE THEBAN RECENSION. London, 1910. 3 vols. NF. *POLYANTHOS.* $250

Budge, E.A. Wallis. AN EGYPTIAN HIEROGLYPHIC DICTIONARY. NY: Frederick Ungar, (1960). 2 vols, complete. Signature. Good. *ARCHAEOLOGIA.* $200

Budge, E.A. Wallis. EGYPTIAN SCULPTURES IN THE BRITISH MUSEUM. London: British Museum, 1914. 54 photo plts. Repaired tears to spine, spine rubbed. Good. *ARCHAEOLOGIA.* $275

Budge, E.A. Wallis. FACSIMILES OF EGYPTIAN HIERATIC PAPYRI IN THE BRITISH MUSEUM....London: British Museum, 1923. Second Series (only). 51pp + 128 photo plts, lrg folio, 1/2 grn calf. Rubbed, top and bottom of spine lightly chipped. Good. Rare. *ARCHAEOLOGIA.* $1,500

Budge, E.A. Wallis. FACSIMILES OF THE PAPYRI OF HUNEFOR, ANHAI, KARASHER AND NETCHEMET....London: British Museum, 1899. xi + 64pp, 94 plts (20 in color, 15 fldg, 63 autographic), atlas folio, 3/4 calf antique. Rebacked w/orig spine laid down and modern boards. Good. *ARCHAEOLOGIA.* $1,250

Budge, E.A. Wallis. THE LITURGY OF FUNERARY OFFERINGS. London: Kegal Paul, Trench, Trubner, 1909. Bkpl, signature. Good. *ARCHAEOLOGIA.* $95

Budge, E.A. Wallis. THE NILES. London: Thos. Cook, 1892. 2nd ed. Orig dec cl. G+. *BLUE DRAGON.* $35

Budgen, Frank. JAMES JOYCE AND THE MAKING OF ULYSSES. NY: Smith & Haas, 1934. 1st ed. Sl darkening at edges, else Fine in worn dj. *WOOLMER.* $75

Budker, Paul. WHALES AND WHALING. London: George G. Harrap & Co. Ltd, 1958. Black cl, gilt spine titles. 32 plts. Some foxing to edges, prelims, else VG. *PARMER.* $50

Buechner, Thomas S. NORMAN ROCKWELL: ARTIST AND ILLUSTRATOR. NY: Abrams, (1970). 1st ed. Fine in dj. *CAPTAIN'S BOOKSHELF.* $200

Buel, J.W. (ed). LOUISIANA AND THE FAIR. St. Louis, 1905. 10 vols. NF *POLYANTHOS.* $200

Buel, J.W. HEROES OF THE PLAIN, OR LIVES AND WONDERFUL ADVENTURES OF....NY: Parks Brothers, 1882. Brn cl rubbed and bumped, shaken, several signatures pulled. Good. Scarce. *BLUE MOUNTAIN.* $50

Buel, J.W. THE BORDER OUTLAWS. Chicago: M.A. Donahue & Co, n.d. Cloth. Reprint. Small hole lower margin first 35pp. Good. *GIBBS.* $20

Buel, Jesse. THE FARMER'S COMPANION....NY: Harper, 1854. 6th ed, rev, enl. 336pp. Bound in worn full calf. Lib bkpl. Water spotting 1st few leaves. VG. *SECOND LIFE.* $85

Buell, Augustus C. THE MEMOIRS OF CHARLES H. CRAMP. Phila: 1906. 1st ed. Orig cl. *GINSBERG.* $75

Buff, Mary and Conrad. KOBI, A BOY OF SWITZERLAND. Viking, 1939. 1st ed. Illus by Conrad Buff. VG+ in VG dj w/chips, pieces missing top, bottom of spine. *BEBBAH.* $55

Buff, Mary and Conrad. THE COLORADO: RIVER OF MYSTERY. Ward Ritchie Press, 1968. Fine copy in Fine dj. *FIVE QUAIL.* $45

Buffon, George Louis Le Clerc. BUFFON'S NATURAL HISTORY...In Ten Vols. London: For The Proprietor, 1797. 83 fine copper-plate engrs. Contemp tree calf, gilt dec spines, double green and black morocco labels, elegantly dec spine compartments. Fine set. *HARTFIELD.* $985.

Buffum, E. Gould. SIX MONTHS IN THE GOLD MINES: FROM A JOURNAL...IN UPPER AND LOWER CALIFORNIA 1847-8-9. N.p.: Ward Ritchie Press, 1959. John W. Caughey (ed). Fine. *LAURIE.* $35

BUGS BUNNY. London, 1974. 3 good pop-ups. Pop-up bk. *BOOKFINDERS INTL.* $35

Buhler, Curt F. THE FIFTEENTH-CENTURY BOOK....Phila: Univ of PA Press, (1961). 1st ed. Cl, dj. *OAK KNOLL.* $60

Buhler, Kathryn C. AMERICAN SILVER 1655-1825 IN THE MUSEUM OF FINE ARTS BOSTON. Boston: Museum of Fine Arts, 1972. 1st ed. VG. 2 vols. *BACKROOM.* $175

Buick, T. Lindsay. THE MOA-HUNTERS OF NEW ZEALAND. New Plymouth, New Zealand: T. Avery, 1937. 1st ed. NF. *ACADEMIC.* $20

Buist, R. THE ROSE MANUAL....Phila, 1847. 2nd ed, w/additions. 192pp. Orig gilt dec cl worn at corners; cvr edge nicked, spine ends frayed; 1/2" split, soiled. *SUTTON.* $145

Buist, Robert. THE FAMILY KITCHEN GARDENER....NY: C.M. Saxton, Barker; SF: H.H. Bancroft, 1860. vi,216,10pp. Engr. Grn cl, stamped, bit rubbed. VG. *WEBER.* $75

Bukofzer, Manfred F. STUDIES IN MEDIEVAL AND RENAISSANCE MUSIC. NY: W.W. Norton. (1950). 1st ed. Dj chipped. *KARMIOLE.* $30

Bukowski, Charles. A LOVE POEM. Santa Barbara: Black Sparrow, (1979). One of 150 numbered, signed by Bukowski. In plain dw, as issued. Fine. *SMITH.* $60

Bukowski, Charles. AFRICA, PARIS, GREECE. LA: Black Sparrow, (1975). 1st ed. Issued as Sparrow #30. Signed. NF in wraps. *SMITH.* $45

Bukowski, Charles. ALL THE ASSHOLES IN THE WORLD AND MINE. Bensenville: Open Skull, 1966. 1st ed. Pub in ed of 400. Fine in pict wrappers. *SMITH.* $300

Bukowski, Charles. ALL THE ASSHOLES IN THE WORLD AND MINE. Bensenville: Open Skull Press, (1966). 1st ed. Pict wrappers. Pub in an ed. of 400. Fine. *SMITH.* $275

Bukowski, Charles. ALL THE ASSHOLES IN THE WORLD AND MINE. (Bensenville, IL: Open Skull Press, 1966). 1st ed. 1/400. Spine sl faded else Fine in wrappers. *CAPTAIN'S BOOKSHELF.* $225

Bukowski, Charles. ALONE IN A TIME OF ARMIES. Santa Barbara: Black Sparrow, 1985. 1st ed. Wraps, not published commercially. Fine. *BEASLEY*. $25

Bukowski, Charles. COLD DOGS IN THE COURTYARD. (Chicago: Literary Times-Cyfoeth, 1965). 1st ed. 1/500. Fine in wrappers. *CAPTAIN'S BOOKSHELF*. $250

Bukowski, Charles. COLD DOGS IN THE COURTYARD. Chicago: Literary Times-Cyfoeth, (1965). 1st ed. Pict wrappers, pub in an ed of 500. Owner sig of Doug Blazek. Fine. *SMITH*. $350

Bukowski, Charles. CONFESSIONS OF A MAN INSANE ENOUGH TO LIVE WITH BEASTS. Bensenville: Mimeo Press, 1965. 1st ed, One of 500. Fine in wraps. *BEASLEY*. $350

Bukowski, Charles. CONFESSIONS OF A MAN INSANE ENOUGH TO LIVE WITH BEASTS. Bensenville: Mimeo Press, (1965). 1st ed. Pict wrappers. One of about 475 (of total ed of 500). Signed by the publisher Blazek. Fine. *SMITH*. $350

Bukowski, Charles. CONFESSIONS OF A MAN INSANE ENOUGH TO LIVE WITH BEASTS. Bensenville, IL: Mimeo Press, 1965. One of 500. Fine in pict wraps. *CAPTAIN'S BOOKSHELF*. $375

Bukowski, Charles. CRUCIFIX IN A DEATHHAND: NEW POEMS. NY: Loujon Press & Lyle Stuart, (1965). 1st ed. One of 3100. Noel Rockmore (illus). Signed. VF w/fragile wraparound band still present. *CAPTAIN'S BOOKSHELF*. $250

Bukowski, Charles. ERECTIONS, EJACULATIONS, EXHIBITIONS AND GENERAL TALES OF ORDINARY MADNESS. SF: City Lights, (1972). 2nd ed. VG in wraps. *SMITH*. $35

Bukowski, Charles. FACTOTUM. Santa Barbara: Black Sparrow, (1975). 1st ptg, in wraps. Fine. *SMITH*. $20

Bukowski, Charles. FACTOTUM. Santa Barbara: Black Sparrow, (1975). 1st ed. One of 1,000 hb trade copies, pub's promo flyer laid in. Fine. *SMITH*. $45

Bukowski, Charles. GOLD IN YOUR EYE. Santa Barbara: Black Sparrow (1986). 1st ed. One of 226 signed. Fine w/o dj as issued. *DORN*. $55

Bukowski, Charles. GOLD IN YOUR EYE. Santa Barbara: Black Sparrow, (1986). 1-226 signed. Issued as New Year's Greeting for friends of the press. Fine w/o dj as issued. *DORN*. $55

Bukowski, Charles. GOLD IN YOUR EYE. Santa Barbara: Black Sparrow, 1986. 1st ed. Fine, wraps. Not issued commercially. *BEASLEY*. $25

Bukowski, Charles. IF WE TAKE. Santa Barbara: Black Sparrow, (1970). One of 100 numbered, signed. Fine. *SMITH*. $125

Bukowski, Charles. IN THE MORNING AND AT NIGHT AND IN BETWEEN. Santa Rosa: Black Sparrow, (1991). 1st ed. Issued as a New Year's greeting from the press. Fine in wraps. Untrimmed. *SMITH*. $20

Bukowski, Charles. IN THE MORNING AND AT NIGHT AND IN BETWEEN. Santa Rosa: Black Sparrow, 1991. 1st ed. Not commercially issued. Fine in wraps. *BEASLEY*. $20

Bukowski, Charles. IN THE MORNING AND IN THE NIGHT AND IN BETWEEN. Santa Rosa: Black Sparrow (1991). 1st ed. One of 226 signed. Fine w/o dj as issued. *DORN*. $50

Bukowski, Charles. LONGSHOT POEMS FOR BROKE PLAYERS. NY: 7 Poets Press, (1962). 1st ed. Pub in an ed of 200. Fine in pict wrappers. Ownership sig of Douglas Blazek, early pub of Buk's. *SMITH*. $1,200

Bukowski, Charles. LUCK. Santa Rosa: Black Sparrow (1987). 1st ed. One of 226 signed. Fine w/o dj as issued. *DORN*. $55

Bukowski, Charles. LUCK. Santa Rosa: Black Sparrow, (1987). 1st ed. Issued as New Year's greeting from the press. One of 200 numbered, signed. Fine in boards. *SMITH*. $40

Bukowski, Charles. MAYBE TOMORROW. Santa Barbara: Black Sparrow, (1977). 1st ed. Issued as Sparrow #54. Fine in wraps. *SMITH*. $20

Bukowski, Charles. NOW. Santa Rosa: Black Sparrow, 1992. 1st ed. Issued as a New Year's greeting by the press. One of 200 numbered, signed. Fine. *SMITH*. $25

Bukowski, Charles. NOW. Santa Rosa: Black Sparrow, 1992. Wraps, one of an unspecified number as New Year's Greeting & not for sale. Fine. *BEASLEY*. $20

Bukowski, Charles. NUDE. LA: Illuminati, 1986. 1st ed. Fine. Scarce. *SMITH*. $30

Bukowski, Charles. PEACE AMONG THE ANTS. SF: Nevada/Tattoo, 1969. 1st ed. Fine in paper portfolio and orig mailing carton, with note from the pub. Rare. *SMITH*. $300

Bukowski, Charles. PLAY THE PIANO DRUNK LIKE A PERCUSSION INSTRUMENT....Santa Barbara: Black Sparrow, 1979. 1st trade ed. 1/500. Owner name fep. Signed. NF in rubbed, orig acetate. *AKA*. $45

Bukowski, Charles. POEMS WRITTEN BEFORE JUMPING OUT OF AN EIGHT STORY WINDOW. Glendale Poetry Xchange, (1968). 1st ed. NF in wraps. Untrimmed. *SMITH*. $150

Bukowski, Charles. POEMS WRITTEN BEFORE JUMPING OUT OF AN 8 STORY WINDOW. (Glendale: Poetry X/Change, n.d.). 1st ed. Bottom corners sl bumped, else Fine in wrappers. *CAPTAIN'S BOOKSHELF*. $150

Bukowski, Charles. RELENTLESS AS THE TARANTULA. Planet Detroit, (1986). 1st ed. Signed. Fine in wraps. *SMITH*. $35

Bukowski, Charles. RUN WITH THE HUNTED. Chicago/Midwest Poetry Chapbooks, (1962). 1st ed. Pub in ed of 300. Ptd wraps. Lightly sunned, title page sl rumpled, evidence of extensive pencilled notes erased (title pg), but presentable. *SMITH*. $325

Bukowski, Charles. SEPTUAGENARIAN STEW. Stories and Poems. Santa Rosa, CA: Black Sparrow Press. 1990. With photo of author. One of 500 numbered, signed by Bukowski, from ed of 1751. *KARMIOLE*. $85

Bukowski, Charles. SHAKESPEARE NEVER DID THIS. City Lights, 1979. 1st ed. NF in pb. *STAHR*. $25

Bukowski, Charles. THE DAY IT SNOWED IN L.A. Sutton West & Santa Barbara: Paget Press, (1986). One of 200 numbered, signed. Fine. *SMITH*. $100

Bukowski, Charles. THE MOVIE CRITICS. Santa Rosa: Black Sparrow (1988). 1st ed. One of 226 signed. Fine w/o dj as issued. *DORN*. $50

Bukowski, Charles. THERE'S NO BUSINESS. Santa Barbara: Black Sparrow, (1984). One of 400 numbered, signed by Bukowski and R. Crumb, illus. Fine. *SMITH*. $125

Bukowski, Charles. THREE BY BUKOWSKI. Santa Rosa: Black Sparrow, 1992. 1st ed. One of unspecified number pub and not offered for sale. Wraps. *BEASLEY*. $20

Bukowski, Charles. TOUGH COMPANY AND THE LAST POEM. Santa Barbara: Black Sparrow, (1976). Bukowski and Diane Wakoski. Signed by both writers. One of 150 numbered in boards and unptd dj, as issued. Fine. *SMITH*. $100

Bukowski, Charles. WE AIN'T GOT NO MONEY, HONEY, BUT WE GOT RAIN. Santa Rosa: Black Sparrow, 1990. 1st ed. Fine in wraps. Not offered commercially. *BEASLEY*. $20

Bukowski, Charles. WE'LL TAKE THEM. Santa Barbara: Black Sparrow, (1978). 1st ed. Issued as Sparrow #72. Fine in wraps. *SMITH*. $20

Bukowski, Charles. WOMEN. London: W.H. Allen, 1981. 1st Eng ed. Fine in dj. *LOPEZ*. $45

Bukowski, Charles. WOMEN. Sydney: Wild and Woolley, (1979). 1st Australian ptg, in wraps. Fine. *SMITH.* $20

Bukowski, Charles. YOU KISSED LILY. Santa Barbara: Black Sparrow, (1978). One of 200 numbered, signed. Fine in boards. *SMITH.* $100

Bulatovic, Miodrag. A HERO ON A DONKEY. World, 1969. 1st ed. NF in dj. *STAHR.* $15

Bulau, Alwin E. FOOTPRINTS OF ASSURANCE. NY: Macmillan Co, 1953. 1st ed. VG. *BACKROOM.* $50

Buley, R. Carlyle. THE OLD NORTHWEST, PIONEER PERIOD, 1815-1840. Bloomington: Indiana Univ Press, (1962). 3rd ptg, c. 1950. 2 vols. VG to Fine in worn slipcase. *BOHLING.* $35

Bulfinch, S.G. POEMS. Charleston, (SC): James S. Burges, 1834. 1st ed. 12mo, 108pp. Orig cl w/paper spine label. Lt shelfwear, else VG. *CHAPEL HILL.* $85

Bulkeley, Benjamin Reynolds. THE SHIFTING WIND & OTHER POEMS. Chicago: (Stone & Kimball), 1895. Pp 2 and 3 darkened from clipping formerly laid in, else Fine in orig blue cl stamped in gold. *HELLER.* $85

Bullchild, Percy. THE SUN CAME DOWN. SF: H&R, (1985). Rev copy. Fine in dj. *LOPEZ.* $30

Bullett, Gerald. THE JURY. London: J.M. Dent & Sons, 1935. 1st ed. Fine in VG dj (chipping, tears, 1" piece missing back panel). *MORDIDA.* $35

Bullins, Ed. FIVE PLAYS. Indianapolis: Bobbs-Merrill, (1969). 1st ed. NF in price-clipped dj. *LOPEZ.* $45

Bulloch, James D. SECRET SERVICE OF THE CONFEDERATE STATES IN EUROPE: OR, HOW THE CONFEDERATE CRUISES WERE EQUIPPED. NY: Putnam, 1884. 1st Amer ed. 2 vols. (10),460; (6),438pp. Orig cl, paper labels on spines worn. Howes B949. *GINSBERG.* $200

Bulloch, James D. SECRET SERVICE OF THE CONFEDERATE STATES....2 vols. NY, (1959). Boxed. *HEINOLDT.* $27

Bulloch, James D. THE SECRET SERVICE OF THE CONFEDERATE STATES IN EUROPE....2 vols. NY, 1884-1959 rprt; new intro by Philip Van Doren Stern. Slipcase. Minor wear to box o/w Fine. *PRATT.* $60

Bullock, Barbara. WYNN BULLOCK. With notes. (SF): Scrimshaw Press, 1971. 1st ed. Fine in sl used acetate dj. *CAPTAIN'S BOOKSHELF.* $175

Bullock, Helen. THE WILLIAMSBURG ART OF COOKERY....2ND ED. Williamsburg: Ptd for Colonial Williamsburg, Incorporated, on the press of August Dietz and his son, 1939. Full calf, gilt ruled red leather label on spine, raised bands. Scratches on rear cover, o/w Fine. *WREDEN.* $40

Bumgardner, Ed. THE LIFE OF EDMUND G. ROSS. Kansas City, MO, 1949. 1st ed. Fine. *VARNER.* $17.50

Bump, Darrow, Edminster and Crissey. THE RUFFED GROUSE. NY, State Game Comm., 1947. 1st ed. VG+. *MIKESH.* $100

Bump, G. et al. THE RUFFED GROUSE....Albany, 1947. 4 colored plts. Lt scuffing to extrems; bkpl; ex-lib. Signed presentation. 2 signed letters tipped in. *SUTTON.* $185

Bundy, G., R.J. Connor and J.O. Harrison. BIRDS OF THE EASTERN PROVINCE OF SAUDI ARABIA. London, 1989. Dj. *SUTTON.* $75

Bunim, Miriam Schild. SPACE IN MEDIEVAL PAINTING AND THE FORERUNNERS OF PERSPECTIVE. NY: Columbia Univ Press, 1940. 1st ed. Cl spotted. Dj. Scarce. *KARMIOLE.* $100

Bunn, Alfred. THE STAGE: BOTH BEFORE AND BEHIND THE CURTAIN....Phila: Lea & Blanchard, 1840. 1st Amer ed. 2 vols. Cl soiled, rubbed; extrems and leather labels worn, frayed; contents VG. *DRAMATIS.* $75

Bunn, Matthew. JOURNAL OF THE ADVENTURES OF....Chicago, 1962. Orig ptd wrappers. Facsimile reprint. Foreword by Colton Storm. One of 2000. *GINSBERG.* $15

Bunnell, Lafayette. DISCOVERY OF THE YOSEMITE AND THE INDIAN WAR OF 1851 WHICH LED TO THAT EVENT. LA: Gerlicher 1911. 4th ed. Fldg map. Howes B954. VG. *OREGON.* $75

Bunting, Basil. COLLECTED POEMS. (London): Fulcrum Press, (1968). 1st ed. Fine in dj. *CAPTAIN'S BOOKSHELF.* $100

Bunting, Basil. FIRST BOOK OF ODES. London: Fulcrum Press, (1966). 1st ed. One of 175 numbered cl-bound. VF. *JAFFE.* $450

Bunting, Basil. LOQUITUR. London: Fulcrum Press, (1965). 1st ed. One of 200 hardbound. Bottom corner sl bumped, else Fine. *CAPTAIN'S BOOKSHELF.* $175

Bunting, Basil. LOQUITUR. London: Fulcrum Press, (1965). 1st ed. One of 774 bound in boards. Fine. *JAFFE.* $225

Bunting, Basil. LOQUITUR. London: Fulcrum Press, (1965). 1st ed. One of 200 clbound. VF. *JAFFE.* $450

Bunting, Basil. THE SPOILS. Newcastle upon Tyne: Morden Tower Book Room, (1965). 1st ed. Signed. Fine. *JAFFE.* $250

Bunting, Basil. TWO POEMS. Unicorn Press, 1967. Ltd ed, 250 only. Signed presentation. Printed wraps. Fine. *POLYANTHOS.* $100

Bunting, Basil. WHAT THE CHAIRMAN TOLD TOM. Cambridge, MA: Pym-Randall Press, (1967). 1st ed. One of 200 signed. VF. *JAFFE.* $250

Bunting, Eve. DEMETRIUS AND THE GOLDEN GOBLET. NY: Harcourt Brace, (1980). 1st ed. Michael Hague (illus). Signed by Hague. Inscribed by Bunting. Fine in Fine dj. *ACADEMIC LIBRARY.* $35

Bunyan, John. PILGRIM'S PROGRESS. Stokes, 1939. 1st ed. Illus by Robert Lawson. Near 4to. 120pp. VG+. *BEBBAH.* $68

Bunyan, John. PILGRIMS PROGRESS. (London): Essex House Press, 1899. Ltd to 750. Bound in full white vellum, lt soil. VG. *CULLEN.* $300

Bunyan, John. THE PILGRIM'S PROGRESS. 118 illus by Charles H. Bennett. London: Gibbings, 1897. VG. *HARTFIELD.* $55

Bunyan, John. THE PILGRIM'S PROGRESS. G.B. Harrison (ed). NY: The Spiral Press for LEC, 1941. 1st ed. One of 1500. 29 illus by William Blake. Gutters browned, else NF w/sl discolored spine in moderately worn slipcase. *CAPTAIN'S BOOKSHELF.* $80

Bunzel, Ruth L. ZUNI KATCINAS, paper from the BAE annual report, BAE. Glorietta, NM, (1973). 1st this ptg. 61 plts. *HEINOLDT.* $40

Burbank, Addison. GUATEMALA PROFILE. NY: Coward-McCann, Inc., 1939. VG in lightly worn and soiled dj. *PARMER.* $65

Burbank, E.A. BURBANK AMONG THE INDIANS. As told by Ernest Royce. Caldwell: Caxton Printers, 1946. 2nd prtg. 56 full-pg plts. Black-stamped cl in lightly chipped dj. *DAWSON'S.* $60

Burbank, L. PARTNER OF NATURE. NY & London: 1939. 1st ed. VG+ in Good+ dj. *MIKESH.* $30

Burberry, H.A. THE AMATEUR ORCHID CULTIVATOR'S GUIDE BOOK. Liverpool, 1900. 3rd ed. 4 colored plts. Cl worn and faded, inner hinges cracked. Lt foxing, ink notations. *SUTTON.* $40

Burbidge, F.W. COOL ORCHIDS, AND HOW TO GROW THEM....London, 1874. Cl, some wear to corners, spine, hinges cracked. *SUTTON.* $135

Burch, John P. CHARLES W. QUANTRELL (sic), A TRUE HISTORY OF HIS GUERRILLA WARFARE ON THE MISSOURI AND KANSAS BORDER...(Vega, TX, 1923). 1st ed. Little bumping of corners. Few small cvr stains, o/w NF. *DIAMOND.* $45

Burch, John P. CHARLES W. QUANTRELL, A TRUE HISTORY OF HIS GUERILLA WARFARE ON THE MISSOURI AND

KANSAS BORDER....(Vega, TX: by the author, 1923) 1st ed. VG. *SECOND LIFE.* $75

Burchell, Sidney Herbert. JACOB PEEK, ORANGE GROWER....London: Gay and Hancock, 1915. 2nd ed. White stamped cl. Hinges weak, some binding wear, 2 nicks cvr, 1st 2 leaves stuck together. *DAWSON'S.* $45

Burchett. Wilfred. FURTIVE WAR. NY: International, (1963). About Fine in price-clipped, tape-reinforced dj. *AKA.* $45.

Burckhardt, John Lewis. TRAVELS IN NUBIA. London: Murray, 1822. 3 maps (2 fldg). Frontis. Recent 1/2 calf, marbled boards, raised bands. xcviii,498pp. Uncut, partly opened. *O'NEILL.* $900

Burden, W.D. DRAGON LIZARDS OF KOMODO, AN EXPEDITION TO THE LOST WORLD OF THE DUTCH EAST INDIES. NY & London: Putnam, 1927. Illus. Ex libris. Good. *MIKESH.* $30

Bureau of American Ethnology. See BAE.

Buret, F. SYPHILLIS IN ANCIENT AND PREHISTORIC TIMES. Volume 1. Phila, 1891. 1st Eng trans. *FYE.* $75

Burger, Nash K. and Bettersworth, John K. SOUTH OF APPOMATTOX. NY, (1959). 1st ed. Fine. *PRATT.* $30

Burgess, Anthony. A CLOCKWORK ORANGE. London: Heinemann, (1962). 1st ed. Beautiful in dj w/new price sticker on flap. *CAPTAIN'S BOOKSHELF.* $1500

Burgess, Anthony. A VISION OF BATTLEMENTS. London: Sidgwick & Jackson, (1965). 1st ed. VF in like dj. *CAPTAIN'S BOOKSHELF.* $100

Burgess, Anthony. A VISION OF BATTLEMENTS. NY, (1965). 1st ed. Fine in dj (spine sl sunned, 2 small edge tears, few tiny edge chips). *POLYANTHOS.* $35

Burgess, Anthony. A VISION OF BATTLEMENTS. NY: Norton, 1965. 1st ed. VF in dj. *ELSE FINE.* $40

Burgess, Anthony. DEVIL OF A STATE. London: Heinemann, (1961). 1st ed. Fine in sl used dj w/small stain front flap. *CAPTAIN'S BOOKSHELF.* $125

Burgess, Anthony. ENDERBY'S DARK LADY. London: Hutchinson, 1984. 1st ed. VF in dj. *ELSE FINE.* $40

Burgess, Anthony. ERNEST HEMINGWAY AND HIS WORLD. London: Thames & Hudson, (1978). 1st ed. Fine in dj. *CAPTAIN'S BOOKSHELF.* $75

Burgess, Anthony. HONEY FOR THE BEARS. London: Heinemann, (1963). 1st ed. Fine in sl used dj. *CAPTAIN'S BOOKSHELF.* $65

Burgess, Anthony. HONEY FOR THE BEARS. NY: Knopf, 1964. 1st ed. VF in dj. *ELSE FINE.* $45

Burgess, Anthony. LITTLE WILSON & BIG GOD. Franklin Center: Franklin Lib, 1987. Leatherbound ltd ed, true 1st ed. Fine. Signed. *LOPEZ.* $75

Burgess, Anthony. M/F. NY: Knopf, 1971. 1st ed. Fine in dj. *ELSE FINE.* $30

Burgess, Anthony. M/F. NY: Knopf, 1971. 1st US ed. Fine in dj. *CAPTAIN'S BOOKSHELF.* $30

Burgess, Anthony. NAPOLEON SYMPHONY. London: Cape, 1974. 1st ed. VF in price clipped dj. *ELSE FINE.* $65

Burgess, Anthony. NAPOLEON SYMPHONY. NY: Alfred Knopf, 1974. 1st Amer ed. Fine in dj, tiny tear. *CAPTAIN'S BOOKSHELF.* $30

Burgess, Anthony. NAPOLEON SYMPHONY. NY: Knopf, 1974. 1st US ed. Fine in dj. Signed. *CAPTAIN'S BOOKSHELF.* $75

Burgess, Anthony. NOTHING LIKE THE SUN. London: Heinemann, (1964). 1st ed. Fine in like dj. *CAPTAIN'S BOOKSHELF.* $100

Burgess, Anthony. ON MOZART. A PAEAN FOR WOLFGANG. NY: T&F, 1991. Uncorrected proof. Fine. *LOPEZ.* $40

Burgess, Anthony. THE CLOCKWORK TESTAMENT OR ENDERBY'S END. NY, 1975. 1st ed. Fine in price clipped dj. *POLYANTHOS.* $25

Burgess, Anthony. THE END OF THE WORLD NEWS. NY, 1983. 1st ed. Signed, presentation. Fine in Fine dj. *POLYANTHOS.* $40

Burgess, Anthony. THE END OF THE WORLD NEWS. NY, 1983. 1st ed. Signed presentation. Fine in like dj. *POLYANTHOS.* $40

Burgess, Anthony. THE ENEMY IN THE BLANKET. London: Heinemann, (1958). 1st ed. Fine in sl soiled dj w/short tear. Inscribed. Bkpl. *CAPTAIN'S BOOKSHELF.* $275

Burgess, Anthony. THE EVE OF SAINT VENUS. London: Sidgwick and Jackson, (1964). 1st ed. Price sticker pasted over price on dj. Fine in dj. *HELLER.* $50

Burgess, Anthony. THE LONG DAY WANES. A MALAYAN TRILOGY. NY, (1964). 1st ed. Top spine very sl rubbed, dj spine sl sunned, few tiny chips. *POLYANTHOS.* $30

Burgess, Anthony. THE WANTING SEED. London: Heinemann, (1962). 1st ed. VF in dj. *CAPTAIN'S BOOKSHELF.* $150

Burgess, Anthony. THE WANTING SEED. NY: Norton, (1963). 1st US ed. Fine in price-clipped dj. *CAPTAIN'S BOOKSHELF.* $40

Burgess, Anthony. THE WANTING SEED. NY: Norton, 1963. 1st US ed. Fine in NF dj w/tears. *BEASLEY.* $60

Burgess, Anthony. THE WANTING SEED. NY: Norton, 1963. 1st US ed. Fine in NF dj w/tears. *BEASLEY.* $60

Burgess, Anthony. TREMOR OF INTENT. London, 1966. 1st ed. Minimal edge rubbed. Fine in dj (few very small edge tears, little edge rubbed). *POLYANTHOS.* $35

Burgess, Anthony. TREMOR OF INTENT. Norton, 1966. 1st. Fine in VG+, price-clipped dj. Spine of dj darkened. *STAHR.* $15

Burgess, Anthony. URGENT COPY. LITERARY STUDIES. London, 1968. 1st ed. Traces of small label removed inside front cvr; price clipped dj spine sl sunned, tiny stain. *POLYANTHOS.* $30

Burgess, Eric. AN INTRODUCTION TO ROCKETS AND SPACEFLIGHT. London: Hodder & Stoughton, 1956. VG in dj. *KNOLLWOOD.* $30

Burgess, Eric. ROCKET PROPULSION, WITH AN INTRODUCTION TO THE IDEA OF INTERPLANETARY TRAVEL. London: Chapman & Hall, 1954 (1952). VG in dj. *KNOLLWOOD.* $36

Burgess, G.H.O. THE ECCENTRIC ARK. NY: Horizon, (1967). 1st US ed. Fine in VG dj. *AARD.* $20

Burgess, Robert. THE CAVE DIVERS. NY: Dodd, Mead (1976). 1st ed. Fine in VG dj. *AARD.* $15

Burgess, Thornton and Thora Stowell. THE BOOK OF ANIMAL LIFE. Little, Brown, 1937. 1st ed. 315pp. Many photos, drawings. VG+. *BEBBAH.* $35

Burgess, Thornton. BIRDS YOU SHOULD KNOW. Little, Brown, 1933. 24mo. 256pp. in leatherette cvrs. Louis Agassiz Fuertes color paintings. VG w/gilt dec cvr. *BEBBAH.* $60

Burgess, Thornton. BUSTER BEAR'S TWINS. Grosset & Dunlap, (1923). 207pp. Illus Harrison Cady. Edgewear, VG+ in VG dj w/wear, chips. *BEBBAH.* $27

Burgess, Thornton. MOTHER WEST WIND'S CHILDREN. Boston: Little, Brown, 1911. 1st ed. Bright and Nearly Fine in lightly soiled pict dj w/a few chips and tears. *CHAPEL HILL.* $200

Burgess, Thornton. THE ADVENTURES OF BUSTER BEAR. Little, Brown, 1946. 96pp. Illus Harrison Cady, inscribed by Burgess. Slight edgewear, VG+. *BEBBAH.* $85

Burgess, Thornton. THE ADVENTURES OF GRANDFATHER FROG. Little, Brown, 1946. 96pp. Illus Harrison Cady, inscribed by

Burgess. Slight fading to cloth spine, edgewear but VG+ w/bright pict paper-covered boards. *BEBBAH.* $85

Burgess, Thornton. THE ADVENTURES OF JOHNNY CHUCK. Grosset & Dunlap, (1941). 191pp. Illus Harrison Cady. NF in VG+ dj. *BEBBAH.* $35

Burgess, Thornton. THE ADVENTURES OF MR. MOCKER. Grosset & Dunlap, (1942). 188pp. Illus Harrison Cady. VG+ in Fair dj w/large piece missing back panel, wear, chips. *BEBBAH.* $30

Burgess, Thornton. THE ADVENTURES OF OLD MAN COYOTE. Little, Brown, 1923. 16mo. 120pp. Illus Harrison Cady. Little edgewear, VG. Pict cvr in red, black on tan cloth. *BEBBAH.* $40

Burgess, Thornton. THE ADVENTURES OF PADDY THE BEAVER. Grosset & Dunlap, (1945). 180pp. Illus Harrison Cady. VG+ in Fair dj w/piece missing, small tape repairs. *BEBBAH.* $30

Burgess, Thornton. THE ADVENTURES OF POOR MRS. QUACK. Little, Brown, 1919. 16mo. 119pp. Illus Harrison Cady. Edgewear, slight cvr soil, VG. Cvr pict in orange, black on grey cloth. *BEBBAH.* $30

Burgess, Thornton. THE ADVENTURES OF SAMMY JAY. Little, Brown, 1925. 16mo. 119pp. Illus Harrison Cady. Pict cvr in red, black on tan cloth. VG+. *BEBBAH.* $40

Burgess, Thornton. THE BURGESS ANIMAL BOOK FOR CHILDREN. Boston: Little, Brown, (1950). 48 b & w repros by L.A. Fuertes. Dec cl. VG+. *MIKESH.* $25

Burgess, Thornton. THE BURGESS BIRD BOOK FOR CHILDREN. Illus Louis Agassiz Fuertes. Boston: Little Brown, 1919. 1st ed. Dec blue cloth w/pict paper label. Fine in chipped dj. *CAPTAIN'S BOOKSHELF.* $60

Burgess, Thornton. THE BURGESS BIRD BOOK FOR CHILDREN. Little, Brown, 1919. 1st ed. 353pp. Illus by Louis Agassiz Fuertes. VG w/only slightest wear to color pict pastedown of meadowlark. *BEBBAH.* $40

Burgess, Thornton. THE BURGESS FLOWER BOOK FOR CHILDREN. Little, Brown, 1923. 1st ed. 350pp. 47 color plates. VG+ w/pict cvr in grn gilt w/pict pastedown. *BEBBAH.* $45

Burgess, Thornton. THE BURGESS FLOWER BOOK FOR CHILDREN. Little, Brown, 1923. 1st ed. Illus color plates. Edgewear, scratches to pict pastedown. VG. *BEBBAH.* $40

Burgoyne, (John). A STATE OF THE EXPEDITION FROM CANADA, AS LAID BEFORE THE HOUSE OF COMMONS. London: J. Almon, 1780. 2nd ed. ix,(2),191,cixpp,6 fldg maps, 8 3/8" x 5". New marbled boards w/gilt leather spine and vellum tips. Howes B966. *DAWSON'S.* $1,250

Burke, Fielding (pseud of Olive Tilford Dargan). A STONE CAME ROLLING. NY, Toronto: Longmans, Green and Co, 1935. 1st ed. Fine in dj sl chipped top, bottom edges. *HELLER.* $75

Burke, James Lee. A MORNING FOR FLAMINGOS. Boston: Little, Brown, (1990). 1st Amer ed. Signed. Fine in dj. *DORN.* $40

Burke, James Lee. A MORNING FOR FLAMINGOS. Boston: Little, Brown, (1990). 1st ed. Signed. VF in VF dj. *UNGER.* $40

Burke, James Lee. A MORNING FOR FLAMINGOS. Boston: Little Brown, 1990. 1st ed. Fine in price-clipped dj. *MORDIDA.* $25

Burke, James Lee. A STAINED WHITE RADIANCE. NY: Hyperion, (1992). 1st ed. Signed. VF in VF dj. *UNGER.* $40

Burke, James Lee. A STAINED WHITE RADIANCE. NY: Hyperion, 1992. 1st ed. Signed. Fine in Fine dj. *BEASLEY.* $45

Burke James Lee. BLACK CHERRY BLUES. Boston: Little, Brown (1989). 1st ed. Signed. Fine in dj. *DORN.* $45

Burke, James Lee. BLACK CHERRY BLUES. Boston: Little Brown, 1989. 1st ed. VF in dj. *MORDIDA.* $35

Burke, James Lee. BLACK CHERRY BLUES. Boston: Little Brown, 1989. 1st ed. Rmdr mk. Signed. As new in dj. *ELSE FINE.* $70

Burke, James Lee. BLACK CHERRY BLUES. Boston: Little Brown, 1989. 1st ed. Adv reading copy. Fine in wraps. *SMITH.* $60

Burke, James Lee. BLACK CHERRY BLUES. Boston: Little Brown, 1989. 1st ed. Rmdr mark, o/w Fine. *SMITH.* $25

Burke, James Lee. HALF OF PARADISE. Boston: Houghton Mifflin Company, 1965. 1st ed, 1st bk. Fine in sl chipped dj, few short tears. *HELLER.* $200

Burke, James Lee. HALF OF PARADISE. Boston: Houghton Mifflin, 1965. 1st ed. of scarce 1st book. VG+ in dj which has 2 very unobtrusive, internally mended tears on rear flap & 2 abrasions on plain white portion of rear panel—a quite attractive copy. *BERNARD.* $500

Burke, James Lee. HALF OF PARADISE. Houghton Mifflin, 1956. 1st ed. Fine in dj (lightly worn & rubbed at head of spine and front flyleaf fold). 1st novel. *STAHR.* $450

Burke, James Lee. HEAVEN'S PRISONERS. NY, (1988). 1st ed. Fine (rmdr mk) in dj. Inscribed. *CAPTAIN'S BOOKSHELF.* $40

Burke, James Lee. HEAVEN'S PRISONERS. NY: Henry Holt, 1988. 1st ed. VF in dj. *MORDIDA.* $30

Burke, James Lee. HEAVEN'S PRISONERS. NY: Henry Holt, 1988. 1st ed. Signed. As New. *SMITH.* $75

Burke, James Lee. HEAVEN'S PRISONERS. NY: Holt, (1988). 1st ed. Signed. Fine in Fine dj. *UNGER.* $65

Burke, James Lee. TEXAS CITY, 1947. Northridge: Lord John Press, 1992. 1st ed. 1/275 numbered, signed. VF w/o dj as issued. *MORDIDA.* $75

Burke, James Lee. THE LOST GET-BACK BOOGIE. Baton Rouge: Louisiana State Univ, 1986. 1st ed. VF in price-clipped dj. *MORDIDA.* $75

Burke, James Lee. THE LOST GET-BACK BOOGIE. Baton Rouge: Louisiana State Univ, 1986. 1st ed. VF in dj.dj. *CAPTAIN'S BOOKSHELF.* $75

Burke, James Lee. THE NEON RAIN. NY, 1987. 1st ed. Inscribed, signed. Remainder line. VF in dj. *PETTLER.* $75

Burke, James Lee. THE NEON RAIN. NY: Henry Holt, 1987. 1st ed. Signed. Fine. *SMITH.* $75

Burke, James Lee. THE NEON RAIN. NY: Henry Holt, (1987). 1st ed. Fine in Fine dj. *LOPEZ.* $65

Burke, James Lee. THE NEON RAIN. NY: Holt, 1987. 1st ed. Review copy, signed. Pub's slip laid in. VF in dj. *SILVER DOOR.* $95

Burke, James Lee. TWO FOR TEXAS. NY: Pocket Books, 1982. 1st ed. Pb orig. Short creases on back cover o/w Fine unread copy. *MORDIDA.* $65

Burke, Martyn. LAUGHING WAR. GC: Doubleday, 1980. 1st ed. Fine in rubbed dj w/wear at edges. *BEASLEY.* $50

Burke, Thomas. EAST OF MANSION HOUSE. Doran, 1926. 1st ed. NF in chipped dj. *MADLE.* $50

Burke, Thomas. EAST OF MANSION HOUSE. London, 1928. 1st ed. Spine sl bumped; dj spine sl sunned, 2 pieces missing, small chips, front flap torn along fold. *POLYANTHOS.* $50

Burke, Thomas. EAST OF MANSION HOUSE. London: Cassell, 1928. 1st ed. Fine in VG dj (darkened spine; chipping; closed tears). *MORDIDA.* $75

Burke, Thomas. MORE LIMEHOUSE NIGHTS. Doran, 1921. 1st ed. VG in chipped, worn dj. *MADLE.* $30

Burke, Thomas. THE ENGLISH INN. London: Longmans, Green & Co. 1931. 1st ed. *KARMIOLE.* $30

Burke, Thomas. THE SONG BOOKS OF QUONG LEE OF LIMEHOUSE. NY, 1920. 1st ed. NF. *POLYANTHOS.* $25

Burke, Thomas. THE SUN IN SPLENDOUR. London: Constable, 1927. 1st ed. Bkpl on front. Fine in dj. *MORDIDA.* $75

Burke, Thomas. THE WIND AND THE RAIN. London: Thornton Butterworth, 1924. 1st ed. Edges foxed o/w Fine in dj with several tiny tears. *MORDIDA.* $85

Burke, W.S. OFFICIAL MILITARY HISTORY OF THE KANSAS REGIMENTS DURING THE WAR FOR THE SUPPRESSION OF THE GREAT REBELLION. Leavenworth: W.S. Burke, 1870. Modern 1/2 morocco, gilt stamps on spine. Scarce. *HUDSON.* $575

Burke, William. THE MINERAL SPRINGS OF VIRGINIA. Richmond, VA: Morris & Brother, 1851. 1st ed w/this title. Fldg map. Corners, spine ends bit worn, o/w very clean; map torn at inner margin (no loss), some foxing, consistent offsetting. Still VG. *PIRAGES.* $75

Burkhart, Charles. CHARLOTTE BRONTE: A PSYCHOSEXUAL STUDY... London: Gollancz, 1973. 1st ed. Just About Fine in like dj. *CAPTAIN'S BOOKSHELF.* $25

Burks, Arthur J. BLACK MEDICINE. Arkham House, 1966, 1st ed. VF in dj. *MADLE.* $60

Burland, C.A. & Walter Forman. FEATHERED SERPENT AND SMOKING MIRROR. NY: G.P. Putnam's Sons, 1975. 4to. VG+ in dj. *PARMER.* $35

Burleigh, T.D. GEORGIA BIRDS. Norman, 1958. 1st ed. 35 colored plts. Lower corner spine frayed; lt ep foxing; name stamp. *SUTTON.* $85

Burlend, Rebecca. A TRUE PICTURE OF EMIGRATION; OR, FOURTEEN YEARS IN THE INTERIOR OF NORTH AMERICA....London, (1848). 64pp. Orig ptd wrappers. Howes B992. *GINSBERG.* $250

Burley, W.J. WYCLIFFE & THE TANGLED WEB. London: Gollancz, 1988. 1st ed. Review copy, pub's slip laid in. Fine in dj. *SILVER DOOR.* $25

Burlington Fine Arts Club. EXHIBITION OF A COLLECTION OF SILVERSMITHS' WORK OF EUROPEAN ORIGIN. London, 1901. 1st ed. Chipped at head, cvrs soiled. Lt foxing. VG. *BACKROOM.* $600

Burn, Lucilla. THE MEIDIAS PAINTER. Oxford: Clarendon Press, 1987. 52 plts. Corner bumped. Dj. Good. *ARCHAEOLOGIA.* $85

Burnaby, Frederick (Gustavus). ON HORSEBACK THROUGH ASIA MINOR. London: Sampson, Low, 1877. 2 vols. xxxii, 352, 24pp pub cat; (xx), 399pp. Grn cl stamped in black and gilt. Corners bumped, rubbed, scuffed, somewhat shaken but sturdy. Tipped-on photo frontis; 3 detailed fldg maps, 2 colored. *SCHOYER'S.* $325

Burne, Alfred H. LEE, GRANT AND SHERMAN. Aldershot, England, 1938. 1st ed. 207pp, fldg maps. VG. *PRATT.* $75

Burnett, Frances Hodgson. EDITHA'S BURGLAR. Boston, 1888. 1st US ed, 1st state. Illus by Henry Sandham. Gilt pict boards, name stamp, extrems sl rubbed. NF. *POLYANTHOS.* $45

Burnett, Frances Hodgson. HAWWORTH'S. NY: Scribner, 1879. 1st ed. 374pp,adv. Brown cl. VG. BAL 2051. *SECOND LIFE.* $35

Burnett, Frances Hodgson. LOUISIANA. NY: Scribner, 1880. 1st ed. 163pp,adv. Bound in blue cl w/brown coated eps. Contemp owner comment on ep. VG. BAL 2053. *SECOND LIFE.* $35

Burnett, Frank. SUMMER ISLES OF EDEN. NY: Putnam's, 1923. Blue-grn cl stamped in gilt, a bit worn and spotted, chipped at head and foot of spine. Fldg map. *SCHOYER'S.* $25

Burnett, W.R. BITTER GROUND. NY: Knopf, 1958. 1st ed. Fine in sl chipped and sunned at spine dj. *LAURIE.* $35

Burnett, W.R. THE ASPHALT JUNGLE. NY: Knopf, (1949). 1st ed. VG+ in VG edge-nicked dj. *UNGER.* $75

Burnett, W.R. THE ASPHALT JUNGLE. NY: Knopf, 1949. 1st ed. Lt wear bottom edge, else Fine in Fine dj (sm tear back panel). *HELLER.* $110

Burnett, Whit. THE MAKER OF THE SIGNS. NY: Harrison Smith & Robert Haas, 1934. 1st ed of 1st bk. Edges shelf-worn, spine browned. VG in bright, NF dj. *BERNARD.* $50

Burnette, Robert. THE TORTURED AMERICANS. Englewood Cliffs: Prentice-Hall, (1971). 1st ed. VG in spine-faded dj. *LOPEZ.* $45

Burney, Fanny. DIARY AND LETTERS... Rev, ed by Sarah Chauncey Woolsey. 2 vols. Boston: Little Brown, 1910. Spines sl darkened. Frontis ports. *SCHOYER'S.* $35

Burney, James. THE PRIVATE JOURNAL OF JAMES BURNEY. Ed by Beverly Hooper. Canberra: National Library of Australia, 1975. 1st ed. As New in dj. *PARMER.* $55

Burnham, Frederick. SCOUTING ON TWO CONTINENTS. Doubleday, 1926. 1st ed. VG. *OREGON.* $45

Burnham, Frederick. SCOUTING ON TWO CONTINENTS. LA: Haynes Corp, 1942. Gold stamped cl in dj (frayed). Inscribed by Burnham and Mary Nixon Everett (ed). Card photo laid in. *DAWSON'S.* $50

Burns, Amy & Ken. THE SHAKERS....NY: Portland House, 1st ed. VG in dj. *BACKROOM.* $30

Burns, E. Bradford. EADWEARD MUYBRIDGE IN GUATEMALA, 1857. Berkeley: Univ of CA Press, (1986). 1st ed. Dj. *SILVER.* $45

Burns, John. DISSERTATIONS ON INFLAMMATION. 2 vols in 1. Albany, NY: E.F. Backus, 1812. 1st Amer ed. 213, 214pp. Contemp calf covers sl worn, stained; o/w Good. *DIAMOND.* $75

Burns, John. PRINCIPLES OF MIDWIFERY. London: Longman, Hurst, 1814. 3rd ed, enl. 639pp. New cl and marbled boards. Some age staining in text, o/w Good. *DIAMOND.* $75

Burns, Rex. THE ALVAREZ JOURNAL. NY: Harper & Row, 1975. 1st ed. Fine in dj. *MORDIDA.* $35

Burns, Rex. THE FARNSWORTH SCORE. NY: Harper & Row, 1977. 1st ed. Fine in dj. *MORDIDA.* $30

Burns, Robert Homer, Andrew Springs Gillespie and Willing Gay Richardson. WYOMING'S PIONEER RANCHES. Laramie, WY: Top-of-the-World Press, 1955. 1st ed, signed by Burns & Gillespie. #207 of 1,000. Announcement laid-in. Very scarce. *GIBBS.* $300

Burns, Robert. THE JESUITS AND THE INDIAN WARS OF THE NORTHWEST. Yale, (1966). 1st ed. Frontis, 3 fldg maps. VG in VG dj. *OREGON.* $50

Burns, Robert. THE WORKS...WITH HIS LIFE, by Allan Cunningham. London: (J. Cochrane), 1834-1835-1836. 8 vols. Full contemp brn calf w/single gilt fillet border both cvrs. Vols have all been rehinged, virtually invisibly, at a much earlier date. Very attractive set. *BOOK BLOCK.* $375

Burns, Ruby. JOSEPHINE CLARDY FOX: TRAVELER, OPERA-GOER, COLLECTOR OF ART, BENEFACTOR. El Paso: Texas Western Press, 1973. Bound in full cl. Fine in dj. *LAURIE.* $60

Burns, Thomas. OLD SCOTTISH COMMUNION PLATE. Edinburgh: R & R Clark, 1892. 1st ed. #312/500. Corners bumped and head worn. VG. *BACKROOM.* $100

Burns, Walter Noble. A YEAR WITH A WHALER. NY, 1913. 1st ed. Orig cl. Fine in dj. *LEFKOWICZ.* $100

Burns, Walter Noble. THE SAGA OF BILLY THE KID. Doubleday, 1926. 1st ed. VG. *OREGON.* $35

Burns, Walter Noble. THE SAGA OF BILLY THE KID. NY: Grosset & Dunlap, (c. 1940's). Dj. *OUTPOST.* $25

Burns, Walter Noble. THE SAGA OF BILLY THE KID. GC: Garden City Pub Co, (c. 1940's). Dj, minor chips. *OUTPOST.* $25

Burns, Zed H. CONFEDERATE FORTS. Natchez, 1977. 1st ed. Fine in dj. *PRATT.* $32.50

Burr, Anna R. WEIR MITCHELL, HIS LIFE AND LETTERS. NY, 1929. 1st ed. *FYE*. $60

Burr, Anna R. WEIR MITCHELL. HIS LIFE AND LETTERS. NY: Duffield, 1929. 1st ed. Slight cover wear, corners chipped. Contents Good. *DIAMOND*. $35

Burr, Frank A. and Richard J. Hinton. THE LIFE OF GEN. PHILIP H. SHERIDAN. Providence, 1888. 445pp. A little cvr wear, o/w Fine. *PRATT*. $35

Burrage, Henry S. THOMAS HAMLIN HUBBARD...N.p. 1923. Ex-lib; markings ltd to 2 sm stamps fep. Minor cover wear o/w Fine. *PRATT*. $25

Burrage, Henry Sweetser. GETTYSBURG AND LINCOLN, THE BATTLE, THE CEMETERY, AND THE NATIONAL PARK. NY, 1906. 1st ed. Minor cvr wear o/w Fine. *PRATT*. $45

Burrell, Charles E. A HISTORY OF PRINCE EDWARD COUNTY VIRGINIA...1753, TO THE PRESENT...MAINLY FROM ORIGINAL RECORDS...Richmond, 1922. 1st ed. Orig cl, sm paper label on spine, bkpl removed. *GINSBERG*. $100

Burroughs, Edgar Rice. A FIGHTING MAN OF MARS. Tarzana, CA: ERB, Inc, (1948). Reissue. Frontis. VG+ in rubbed dj. *BERNARD*. $45

Burroughs, Edgar Rice. CARSON OF VENUS. ERB Inc, 1939. 1st ed. Nick to dj, else Fine. *MADLE*. $350

Burroughs, Edgar Rice. ESCAPE ON VENUS. ERB Inc, 1946. 1st ed. Fine in dj (2 chips out of front). *MADLE*. $150

Burroughs, Edgar Rice. JUNGLE TALES OF TARZAN. Chicago, 1919. 1st ed, 1st binding (orange cloth). Usual medium soil to cloth. Good. *McCLINTOCK*. $45

Burroughs, Edgar Rice. LLANA OF GATHOL. ERB Inc, 1948. 1st ed. Fine in dj. *MADLE*. $145

Burroughs, Edgar Rice. LOST ON VENUS. ERB Inc, 1935. 1st ed. VG in sl frayed, somewhat soiled dj. *MADLE*. $375

Burroughs, Edgar Rice. SWORDS OF MARS. ERB Inc, 1936. 1st ed. NF in tape reinforced dj. *MADLE*. $50

Burroughs, Edgar Rice. SYNTHETIC MEN OF MARS. Tarzana, California: Edgar Rice Burroughs, Inc, c1940. 1st ed. Blue cl over boards, cvr and spine lettered in red-orange. Ink name ffep. Fine dj. *BOOKMINE*. $500

Burroughs, Edgar Rice. TARZAN AND THE ANT MEN. NY, (1924). 2nd G&D issue. (1st was G&D cloth on McClurg sheets). Fine. *McCLINTOCK*. $20

Burroughs, Edgar Rice. TARZAN AND THE CASTAWAYS. NY: Canaveral Press, 1975. Reissue of 1964 ed. New in dj. *BERNARD*. $50

Burroughs, Edgar Rice. TARZAN AND THE FORBIDDEN CITY. ERB Inc, 1938. 1st ed. VF in dj. *MADLE*. $500

Burroughs, Edgar Rice. TARZAN AND THE FOREIGN LEGION. ERB Inc, 1948, 1st ed. VG in frayed, soiled dj. *MADLE*. $80

Burroughs, Edgar Rice. TARZAN AND THE JEWELS OF OPAR. G & D, 1920s. NF in dj. *MADLE*. $100

Burroughs, Edgar Rice. TARZAN AND THE JEWELS OF OPAR. Chicago, April 1918. 1st ed. Fresh, clean, tight copy with bright gilt lettering. VF. *BOND*. $85

Burroughs, Edgar Rice. TARZAN AND THE LION MAN. NY, (1934). 1st reprint (G&D) ed. Fine copy w/nice copy of the St. John dj (lightly soiled, shallowly chipped spine ends). *McCLINTOCK*. $45

Burroughs, Edgar Rice. TARZAN AND THE MADMAN. NY: Canaveral Press, 1974. Reissue of 1964 ed. New in dj. *BERNARD*. $50

Burroughs, Edgar Rice. TARZAN THE INVINCIBLE. Tarzana: Burroughs (1931). 16th Tarzan bk, 1st to be pub by Burrough's pub co. 1st ed. Fine in dj (few tiny edge tears). *POLYANTHOS*. $300

Burroughs, Edgar Rice. TARZAN THE MAGNIFICENT. Tarzana, CA, (1939). 2nd ed (actually published in 1948 despite copyright date). Fine in dj; 1/2" chip bottom dj spine. *McCLINTOCK*. $35

Burroughs, Edgar Rice. TARZAN TRIUMPHANT. Tarzana, 1932. 1st ed. Fine in dj (2 short tears front panel, spine sl sunned). *POLYANTHOS*. $200

Burroughs, Edgar Rice. TARZAN TRIUMPHANT. Tarzana, California: Edgar Rice Burroughs, Inc, 1932. Plts, blue cl over boards, front cvr and spine letter in crimson, top edge red, dj. Inscription on ffep, edges stained, ink and pencil notes on dj, some wear to edges of dj. *BOOKMINE*. $85

Burroughs, Edgar Rice. THE BANDIT OF HELL'S BEND. London, (1926). 1st Eng ed. Cvrs sl soiled, stained, worn. Pages repaired. Lacks half-title page. Little soiling and staining in text. New ffep. Text Good. *DIAMOND*. $35

Burroughs, Edgar Rice. THE BEASTS OF TARZAN. Burt, 1917. NF in repaired dj. *MADLE*. $75

Burroughs, Edgar Rice. THE BEASTS OF TARZAN. Chicago: A.C. McClurg, 1916. 1st ed. Name front pastedown, o/w VG. *BERNARD*. $500

Burroughs, Edgar Rice. THE BEASTS OF TARZAN. NY, (1916). 1st (Burt) reprint ed. Good. *McCLINTOCK*. $10

Burroughs, Edgar Rice. THE ETERNAL LOVER. NY: Grosset-Dunlap, n.d. (1927). Early rprt. Frontis. Bit frayed; faded w/vertical crease down center, else VG. *BERNARD*. $60

Burroughs, Edgar Rice. THE GIRL FROM FARRIS'S. (Tacoma): (Wilma), (1959). 1st ed. Of 250, 1/150 numbered, w/blue-taped spine and (dark red) paper-covered boards. Almost Fine. *OTHER WORLDS*. $250

Burroughs, Edgar Rice. THE GIRL FROM FARRIS'S. (Tacoma): (Wilma), (1959). 1st ed. Of 250, 1/150 numbered w/(red) taped spine and (tan/brown) paper-covered boards. Fine. *OTHER WORLDS*. $250

Burroughs, Edgar Rice. THE GIRL FROM HOLLYWOOD. NY: The Macauley Co, (1923). 1st ed, 1st issue. Frontis. Tiny hole; sl frayed, else VG. *BERNARD*. $75

Burroughs, Edgar Rice. THE GODS OF MARS. Tarzan, CA, (1940). 1st ERB, Inc. ed (actually published 1948 despite copyright date). Fine in NF dj. *McCLINTOCK*. $35

Burroughs, Edgar Rice. THE LAND OF TERROR. Canaveral, 1963. Fine in dj. *MADLE*. $50

Burroughs, Edgar Rice. THE MONSTER MEN. NY, (1929). 1st reprint (and only G&D) ed. VG. *McCLINTOCK*. $15

Burroughs, Edgar Rice. THE MOON MEN. NY: Canaveral Press, 1975. Reissue of 1962 ed. Orig pub by McClurg in 1926 as The Moon Maid. New in dj. *BERNARD*. $35

Burroughs, Edgar Rice. THE PIRATES OF VENUS. ERB Inc, 1934. 1st ed. NF in sl frayed dj. *MADLE*. $500

Burroughs, Edgar Rice. THE RETURN OF TARZAN. NY: Burt, (1916). Early rprt. VG in dj (faded, sl soiled). *BERNARD*. $65

Burroughs, Harry E. TALE OF A VANISHED LAND. Boston: Houghton Mifflin Co. 1930. 1st ed. Dj. Fine. *KARMIOLE*. $35

Burroughs, John Rolfe. GUARDIAN OF THE GRASSLANDS. Cheyenne, 1971. 1st ed. Fine in dj. *ARTIS*. $45

Burroughs, John. BIRD AND BOUGH. Boston: Houghton Mifflin, 1906. 1st trade. Fine. *MUELLER*. $15

Burroughs, John. CAMPING AND TRAMPING WITH ROOSEVELT. Boston, 1907. 1st ed. Name label, spine and edges sl sunned. Fine. *POLYANTHOS*. $35

Burroughs, John. FAR AND NEAR. Boston, 1904. 1st ed. Frontis. Extremities, spine minimally rubbed. NF. *POLYANTHOS*. $30

Burroughs, John. THE BREATH OF LIFE. Boston: Houghton Mifflin, 1915. 1st ed. Fine in sl chipped dj. *SECOND LIFE.* $85

Burroughs, John. THE LAST HARVEST. Boston, 1922. 1st ed. Extremities, spine minimally rubbed. Fine in dj (little edge torn strengthened internally, little edge chipped and soiled, piece missing center spine). *POLYANTHOS.* $30

Burroughs, John. WAKE-ROBIN. NY: Hurd & Houghton, 1871. 1st ed. Bright, VG. Binding A, w/triple-rule frame blindstamped on back cvr. BAL 2135. *CHAPEL HILL.* $90

Burroughs, Raymond. THE NATURAL HISTORY OF THE LEWIS AND CLARK EXPEDITION. MI State Univ, (1961). 1st ed. VG in VG dj. *OREGON.* $95

Burroughs, Stephen. MEMOIRS OF THE NOTORIOUS STEPHEN BURROUGHS OF NEW HAMPSHIRE. NY: Lincoln MacVeagh, the Dial Press, 1924. 1st ed thus. Lightly shelfworn, owner sig, else Good+. Howes 1022. *CONNOLLY & WADE.* $65

Burroughs, William and Charles Gatewood. SIDETRIPPING. (NY: Derbibooks, 1975). 1st ed. NF in pict wraps. Signed by Burroughs and Gatewood. *CAPTAIN'S BOOKSHELF.* $125

Burroughs, William S. and Allen Ginsberg. THE YAGE LETTERS. SF: City Lights, (1963). 1st ed. This copy specially signed by Ginsberg. Bkpl signed by Burroughs. Pict wraps. Fine. *POLYANTHOS.* $45

Burroughs, William S. and Brion Gysin. THE THIRD MIND. NY: Viking, (1978). 1st ed. Fine in dj. Presentation inscrip. Additionally signed by both authors. *CAPTAIN'S BOOKSHELF.* $200

Burroughs, William S. APO-33. BULLETIN. A METABOLIC REGULATOR. CA: Beach Books, 1968. 2nd ptg. Ptd wraps. NF. *POLYANTHOS.* $35

Burroughs, William S. CITIES OF THE RED NIGHT. NY, 1981. 1st ed. This copy specially signed. Fine in like dj. *POLYANTHOS.* $40

Burroughs, William S. CITIES OF THE RED NIGHT. NY: Holt, Rinehart & Winston, (1981). 1st ed. One of a specially bound, ltd ed, signed. Mint in pub's slipcase, orig plastic shrinkwrap. *CHAPEL HILL.* $150

Burroughs, William S. CITIES OF THE RED NIGHT. NY: Holt, Rinehart & Winston, (1981). 1st trade ed. Orig terra-cotta cl, grey boards. Fine in dj. Signed. *CHAPEL HILL.* $85

Burroughs, William S. et al. MINUTES TO GO. (Paris): Two Cities Editions, (1960). 1st ed. Orig ptd blue wraps. Wraps faded, else VG. Signed by Burroughs and Gysin. *CHAPEL HILL.* $175

Burroughs, William S. EXTERMINATOR! Viking, 1973. 1st ed. Fine in dj. Corner of ffep has been clipped. *STAHR.* $25

Burroughs, William S. KENTUCKY HAM. NY: Dutton, 1973. 1st ed. Fine in Fine dj. *BEASLEY.* $50

Burroughs, William S. NOVA EXPRESS. Grove, (1964). 1st prtg. NF in dj with rubs, wear. VG+. *BEBBAH.* $40

Burroughs, William S. NOVA EXPRESS. NY: Grove Press, (1964). 1st ed. Orig red-orange cl. NF in dj. Signed. *CHAPEL HILL.* $100

Burroughs, William S. NOVA EXPRESS. NY: Grove Press, (1964). 1st ed. Fine in dj. *CAPTAIN'S BOOKSHELF.* $75

Burroughs, William S. NOVA EXPRESS. NY: Grove Press, (1964). 1st ed. Fine. *JAFFE.* $45

Burroughs, William S. NOVA EXPRESS. NY: Grove Press, 1964. 1st ed. VF in dj. *ELSE FINE.* $55

Burroughs, William S. ROOSEVELT AFTER INAUGURATION. (NY): (Fuck You Press) (1964). One of approximately 500. Stapled wraps. Fine. *LOPEZ.* $150

Burroughs, William S. ROOSEVELT AFTER INAUGURATION. NY: Fuck You Press, 1964. 1st ed. Crudely mimeographed. Lightly used copy with few wrinkles in wraps. *BEASLEY.* $250

Burroughs, William S. SINKI'S SAUNA. NY: Pequod Press, (1982). Ltd ed, 100/500. This copy specially signed. Pict wraps. Fine. *POLYANTHOS.* $50

Burroughs, William S. THE ADDING MACHINE. SELECTED ESSAYS. NY, 1986. 1st ed. Signed. Fine in like dj. *POLYANTHOS.* $85

Burroughs, William S. THE BOOK OF BREETHING. Ingatestone, Essex, U.K.: H. Chopin, 1974. 1st ed. In Fr, Dutch, and Eng. This copy specially signed. Ltd ed, of 350 in pict wraps. Fine. *POLYANTHOS.* $100

Burroughs, William S. THE CAT INSIDE. With 8 Drawings by Brion Gysin. Folio, 1/4 vellum & boards. NY: Grenfell Press, 1986. 1st ed. One of 115 (entire ed of 133) signed by Burroughs & Gysin. Mint. *JAFFE.* $450

Burroughs, William S. THE LAST WORDS OF DUTCH SCHULTZ. London: Cape Goliard Press, 1970. 1st ed. Fine in dj (tiny edge nick top rear panel). *POLYANTHOS.* $45

Burroughs, William S. THE SOFT MACHINE. NY: Grove Press, (1966). 1st ed. Orig red cl. NF in sl soiled dj. Signed. *CHAPEL HILL.* $100

Burroughs, William S. THE TICKET THAT EXPLODED. Grove, 1967. 1st Amer ed. Fine in dj. Ffep clipped. *STAHR.* $45

Burroughs, William S. THE TICKET THAT EXPLODED. NY, 1967. 1st US ed. Fine in dj. *PETTLER.* $50

Burroughs, William S. THE TICKET THAT EXPLODED. NY: Grove Press, (1967). 1st ed. VF in dj. *ELSE FINE.* $50

Burroughs, William S. THE WESTERN LANDS. NY: Viking, (1987) 1st ed. Fine in dj. *SECOND LIFE.* $35

Burrows and Colton. CONCISE INSTRUCTIONS IN THE ART OF RETOUCHING. With Lithographic Illustrations and Negatives, Which may be Detached and Printed From as Examples. London: Marion & Co. 1876. 1st ed. viii,66pp. 4 plts and text figures. 1/2 maroon calf over maroon cl, dec gilt spine, grn leather spine label; spine faded. The 2 example negatives are lacking, as would be expected. *KARMIOLE.* $100

Burrows, George. ON DISORDERS OF THE CEREBRAL CIRCULATION, AND ON THE CONNECTION BETWEEN AFFECTIONS OF THE BRAIN AND DISEASES OF THE HEART. Phila, 1848. 1st Amer ed. 6 hand colored illus. Ffep lacking. 1/4 inch cut from top of title page. Rare. *FYE.* $400

Burstyn, Harold L. AT THE SIGN OF THE QUADRANT....Mystic, CT, 1957. Marine Hist Assoc Pub 32. 1st ed. Wraps. *LEFKOWICZ.* $30

Burt, (Maxwell) Struthers. THE DIARY OF A DUDE WRANGLER. NY: Scribner's, 1924. 1st ed. VG. *CONNOLLY & WADE.* $45

Burt, Olive W. (compiler). AMERICAN MURDER BALLADS AND THEIR STORIES. NY, 1958. Boards sl shelfworn, o/w VG. Ex-lib. *DIAMOND.* $12.50

Burt, Struthers. ENTERTAINING THE ISLANDERS. NY: Scribner's, 1933. 1st ed. Orig dec silver cl. Fine in very scarce glassine dj w/ptd paper flaps. *CHAPEL HILL.* $60

Burt, Struthers. POWDER RIVER. (Rivers of Am). 6th ptg, (1938). Fine in VG dj. *VARNER.* $17.50

Burt, Struthers. POWDER RIVER. Farrar & Rinehart, (1938). 1st ed. Sl soiled; tear, chip back of dj. VG in dj. *OREGON.* $50

Burt, W.H. MAMMALS OF THE GREAT LAKES REGION. Ann Arbor, 1957. Cloth. *SUTTON.* $25

Burt, William H. THE MAMMALS OF MICHIGAN. Ann Arbor: Univ of Michigan, 1948. Rev ed. VG. *CONNOLLY & WADE.* $40

Burton, E. Milby. CHARLESTON FURNITURE 1700-1825. Charleston: Charleston Museum, 1955. 1st ed. Fine in orig glassine dj. *CAPTAIN'S BOOKSHELF.* $125

Burton, E. Milby. SOUTH CAROLINA SILVERSMITHS 1690-1860. Charleston: The Charleston Museum, (1968). 1st ed. VF in dj. *CAPTAIN'S BOOKSHELF.* $125

Burton, Gideon. REMINISCENCES OF....Cincinnati: G.P. Houston, 1895. 152pp. Frontis. Orig cl, gilt title & top. Nice w/new end leaves. *BOHLING.* $65

Burton, Harley T. A HISTORY OF THE J.A. RANCH. Austin, 1928. 1st ed. Fine. *VARNER.* $650

Burton, Isabel Lady and W.H. Wilkins. THE ROMANCE OF ISABEL LADY BURTON. NY: Dodd, Mead, 1904. 8 plts. 1/2 morocco, sl rubbed, cover a little silverfished, o/w VG, teg. *WORLDWIDE.* $85

Burton, Miles (pseud of John Rhode). A WILL IN THE WAY. NY: Doubleday Crime Club, 1947. 1st ed. Fine in sl edgeworn dj. *ELSE FINE.* $25

Burton, Miles (pseud of John Rhode). LEGACY OF DEATH. London: Collins Crime Club, 1960. 1st ed. VG in dj with sl faded spine. *MORDIDA.* $25

Burton, Miles (pseud of John Rhode). THE HARDWAY DIAMONDS MYSTERY. NY: Mystery League, 1930. 1st ed. Discreet owner stamp. VF; faint age darkening spine of dj. *ELSE FINE.* $85

Burton, R.W. TIGERS OF THE RAJ. Gloucester: Allan Sutton Pub, 1987. 1st ed. Fine in Fine dj. *BACKMAN.* $25

Burton, Richard F. ABEOKUTA AND THE CAMAROONS MOUNTAINS. London: Tinsley Brothers, 1863. 1st ed. 2 vols, orig cl. Subscript lib bkpl front pastedown vol I, o/w NF in gilt-stamped grn cl, w/gilt stamping still bright. Vol II mildly frayed along top edge of front cover, spotted on top page edges but still at least VG. *LOPEZ.* $2500

Burton, Richard F. PERSONAL NARRATIVE OF A PILGRIMAGE TO EL MEDINAH AND MECCAH. NY: Putnam, 1856. 1st Amer ed, abridged and condensed (pub in Eng in 1855-56 in 3 vols). Fldg map of Arabia. Binding professionally restored. VG in orig cl, sl frayed. *LOPEZ.* $850

Burton, Richard F. SELECTED PAPERS ON ANTHROPOLOGY, TRAVEL & EXPLORATION. London: A.M. Philpot Ltd, 1924. 1st ed. N.M. Penzer (ed). Half title, index, later full tan calf, two maroon morocco spine labels, marbled eps. VG. *WEBER.* $200

Burton, Richard F. SELECTED PAPERS ON ANTHROPOLOGY, TRAVEL & EXPLORATION BY SIR RICHARD BURTON, K.C.M.G. London, 1924. 1st ed. N.M. Penzer (ed). Orig maroon ribbed cl, spine sunned, occasional lt foxing. *BOOK BLOCK.* $75

Burton, Richard F. SELECTED PAPERS ON ANTHROPOLOGY, TRAVEL & EXPLORATION. London: A.M. Philpot Ltd., 1924. Ed by N.M. Penzer. 1st ed. Fine. *WEBER.* $200

Burton, Richard F. THE ARABIANS NIGHTS ENTERTAINMENTS...THE DEFINITIVE AND ALL-INCLUSIVE BURTON TRANSLATION, ETC.. Ipswich: LEC, 1954. 4 vols. Fine in slipcases. *CAPTAIN'S BOOKSHELF.* $225

Burton, Richard F. THE BOOK OF THE SWORD. London: EP Publishing, 1972. Rprt of 1884 ed. 1st ed thus. Fine in price-clipped dj. *CAPTAIN'S BOOKSHELF.* $50

Burton, Richard F. THE CITY OF THE SAINTS, AND ACROSS THE ROCKY MOUNTAINS TO CALIFORNIA. NY, 1862. 1st Amer ed. 574pp. Cl worn at edges, spine worn, frt hinge loose, lacks map, some red-pencil marking in text. Acceptable. *BENCHMARK.* $125

Burton, Richard F. THE GUIDE BOOK. A PICTORIAL PILGRIMAGE TO MECCA AND MEDINA. London: William Clowes, 1865. 1st ed. Small, fragile vol in wrappers, few have survived over the years. Tiny nick at crown of spine, o/w Fine in orig wrappers, exceedingly scarce thus. Encl in quarter-morocco folding chemise. *LOPEZ.* $7500

Burton, Richard F. THE KASIDAH OF HAJI ABDU EL-YEZDI. Phila: David McKay, 1931. 1st ed. VG w/wear foot of spine; marker price front board. *BEASLEY.* $60

Burton, Richard F. THE LAND OF MIDIAN (REVISITED). London, 1879. 1st ed. Fldg map. 6 chromolitho plts. 2 vols. Tops of spines heavily chipped. xxxviii,338pp; vii,319pp. *O'NEILL.* $325

Burton, Robert F. THE ANATOMY OF MELANCHOLY....London: J. Walker et al, 1813. 2 vols. 416pp, cat, 612pp. 3/4 leather over marbled boards. Vol 1 rebacked w/orig backstrip laid down; discrete lib stamp; else near VG. *SMITHFIELD.* $80

Burton, Robert. THE ANATOMY OF MELANCHOLY, WHAT IT IS, WITH ALL THE KINDS CAUSES, SYMPTOMS, PROGNOSTICS, AND SEVERAL CURES OF IT. London, 1891. 747 pp. Fine engr frontis. *FYE.* $75

Burton, Robert. THE ANATOMY OF MELANCHOLY, WHAT IT IS, WITH ALL THE KINDS CAUSES, SYMPTOMS, PROGNOSTICS & SEVERAL CURES OF IT. Boston, 1859. 3 vols. VF. Fine engr frontis. *FYE.* $200.

Burton, Robert. THE ANATOMY OF MELANCHOLY. London: J. Walker et al, 1813. 2 Vols. 416pp,cat; 612pp. 3/4 leaf over marbled boards. Vol I rebacked, orig backstrip laid down; lib stamp. Near VG. *SMITHFIELD.* $90

Bury, G. Wyman. ARABIA INFELIX OR THE TURKS IN YEMEN. London, 1915. 29 illus. 3 maps. VF. *O'NEILL.* $150

Bury, Richard de. THE PHILOBIBLON OF RICHARD DE BURY. Trans by Andrew Fleming West. NY: Philip C. Duschnes, 1945. Ed ltd to 600. Slipcase. *KARMIOLE.* $75

Busbey, Hamilton. THE TROTTING AND PACING HORSE IN AMERICA. NY: Macmillan, 1904. 1st ed. Good. *OCTOBER FARM.* $35

Busby, J. JOURNAL OF A RECENT VISIT TO THE PRINCIPAL VINEYARDS OF SPAIN AND FRANCE....NY, 1835. Pp 166, (2pp-ads). 1/2 leather very worn, scuffed; top 1/3 spine missing; outer hinges splitting. Dampstain top 1st 4pp, edges of last 13pp, o/w Very Nice internally. *SUTTON.* $325

Busch, Briton (ed). ALTA CALIFORNIA 1840-1842. THE JOURNAL AND OBSERVATIONS OF WILLIAM DANE PHELPS, MASTER OF THE SHIP 'ALERT.' A.H. Clark, 1983. 1st ed. 3 maps. Fine. *OREGON.* $30

Busch, Francis X. IN AND OUT OF COURT. Chicago, 1942. 1st ed. NF in chipped, soiled dj. *DIAMOND.* $25

Busch, Gregory James. LAKE HURON'S DEATH SHIP (PEWABIC). Saginaw: Busch Oceanographic, (1975). 1st ed. VG in dj. *ARTIS.* $20

Busch, Niven. THE ACTOR. NY: Dial Press, 1955. 1st ed. Fine, minor edgewear to dj. *ELSE FINE.* $30

Busch, Niven. THE FURIES. NY: Dial Press, 1948. 1st ed. Fine in dj. *ELSE FINE.* $45

Bush, Christopher. THE PERFECT MURDER CASE. GC: Doubleday Crime Club, 1929. 1st ed. Fine, dj worn at corners, sm chip at spine head. *ELSE FINE.* $30

Bush, Lewis. THE LIFE AND TIMES OF THE ILLUSTRIOUS CAPTAIN BROWN. London, 1876. Tokyo: The Voyagers' Press, Ltd. and Charles E. Tuttle. (1969). 1st ptg. Fldg map. Dj. Slipcase. Fine. *KARMIOLE.* $65

Bush, M.D, I.J. GRINGO DOCTOR. Caldwell: Caxton Printers, 1939. NF in VG dj. *PARMER.* $35

Bush, Martin H. BEN SHAHN: THE PASSION OF SACCO AND VANZETTI. NY: Syracuse Univ, 1968. 1st ed. Pict dj. NF. *BLUE MOUNTAIN.* $45

Bushnell, G.H.S and Adrian Digby. ANCIENT AMERICAN POTTERY. London: Farber, (1955). 1st ed. 3 color, 80 b/w plts. Good in chipped dj. *SILVER.* $40

Bushnell, Horace. WOMEN'S SUFFRAGE. NY: Scribner, 1869. Brn cl rubbed on edges. Marginal pencil notations. SCHOYER'S. $50

Bushnell, Vivian (ed). SCIENTIFIC STUDIES AT FLETCHER'S ICE ISLAND, T-3, 1952-1955. 3 vols. Bedford, MA, 1959. Wraps. VG. ARTIS. $45

Bussey, George Moir and Thomas Gaspey. THE PICTORIAL HISTORY OF FRANCE AND THE FRENCH PEOPLE. 2 vols. London: Orr, 1843. 1st ed. iv,640pp; iv,644pp. 400 engr, (74 full-pg). Full morocco, marbled eps, edges rubbed, spinal labels missing, top and bottom of spine chipped, joints tender, o/w VG. WORLDWIDE. $30

BUSY TIMES IN FERN HOLLOW. London, (1980's). John Patience. BOOKFINDERS INTL. $20

Buten, Harry M. WEDGEWOOD RARITIES. Merion, PA: Buten Museum of Wedgewood, 1960. 1st ed. VG. BACKROOM. $30

Butler, Benjamin F. AUTOBIOGRAPHY AND PERSONAL REMINISCENCES...BUTLER'S BOOK...Boston, 1892. 1st ed. Spine gilt rubbed off, sl cvr staining, o/w VG. DIAMOND. $45

Butler, Benjamin F. PRIVATE AND OFFICIAL CORRESPONDENCE...DURING THE PERIOD OF THE CIVIL WAR. Privately issued, (Norwood, Ma, Plympton Press), 1917. 1st ed. 5 vols. Orig cl, bkplts removed, paper lib slip pasted to verso of title pp; some light discoloration lower spines. GINSBERG. $300

Butler, Frances Anne (Late Fanny Kemble). POEMS. London: Washbourne, et. al, 1844. 1st UK ed. 144,16pp of adv. Orig cl, little faded, Nice. Signed William Honyman. Rare. SECOND LIFE. $175

Butler, Jack. JUJITSU FOR CHRIST. (Little Rock): August House, (1986). 1st ed. Fine in dj which has small crease at front flap edge. BERNARD. $30

Butler, John C. HISTORICAL RECORD OF MACON AND CENTRAL GEORGIA...Macon, GA, 1879. 1st ed. 351,(28ads)pp. Orig dec cl. Howes B1056 w/inserted slip at p.348. Scarce. GINSBERG. $300

1Butler, John. SKETCHES OF MEXICO....NY: Hunt & Eaton, 1894. 1st ed. Frontis. Lt cvr wear; contents VG. SILVER. $30

Butler, Joseph T. CANDLEHOLDERS IN AMERICA. NY: Crown, 1967. 1st ed. VG. BACKROOM. $45

Butler, Mann. A HISTORY OF THE COMMONWEALTH OF KENTUCKY. Louisville, Ky.: for the author by Wilcox, Dickerman, 1834. 1st ed. 396pp. Contemp calf, sl loose at hinges. Good. Howes B-1059. Lacks portrait. Sylvester Judd's copy w/holograph. SECOND LIFE. $125

Butler, Marvin Benjamin. MY STORY OF THE CIVIL WAR AND THE UNDERGROUND RAILROAD. Huntington, IN, 1914. 1st ed. NF. McGOWAN. $165

Butler, Octavia. WILD SEED. Doubleday, 1980. 1st ed. Fine in dj. MADLE. $45

Butler, Robert Olen. A GOOD SCENT FROM A STRANGE MOUNTAIN. NY: Holt, (1992). 1st ed. Signed. VF in VF dj. UNGER. $35

Butler, Robert Olen. COUNTRYMEN OF BONES. NY: Horizon, (1983). 1st ed. Signed. Fine in Fine dj. LOPEZ. $65

Butler, Robert Olen. SUN DOGS. NY: Horizon, (1982). 1st ed. Signed. Fine in NF dj, lightly rubbed. LOPEZ. $50

Butler, Samuel. HUDIBRAS: IN THREE PARTS. WRITTEN IN THE TIMES OF THE LATE WARS. WITH A LIFE OF THE AUTHOR. Edinburgh: James Watson, 1797. 12mo. Contemp calf, rubbed, burgundy morocco spine label. VG. CAPTAIN'S BOOKSHELF. $100

Butler, Samuel. THE AUTHORESS OF THE ODYSSEY. London: Longmans, Green, & Co, 1897. 1st ed. Presentation, inscribed. Gilt dec cl. Faint marginal darkening of cl, o/w Fine in red 1/2 morocco slipcase. JAFFE. $750

Butler, William Francis. THE WILD NORTH LAND. London, 1907. NF. POLYANTHOS. $35

Butler, William Francis. THE WILD NORTH LAND. Toronto: Musson Book Co, 1924. Reprint ed. VG. BLUE DRAGON. $40

Butler, William Francis. THE WILD NORTH LAND....London: Sampson, Low, 1884. 9th ed. xi,358pp. Frontis, 15 plts, fldg map. VG. OREGON. $35

Butler, William Francis. THE WILD NORTHLAND. NY: Allerton Book Company, 1922. Fldg map. VG+. PARMER. $25

Butor, Michel. INVENTORY. London: Cape (1970). 1st Eng ed. Fine in dj. DORN. $35

Butor, Michel. PASSING TIME. London: Faber (1961). 1st Eng ed. Top edge foxed else tight, Fine in Fine dj. DORN. $50

Butor, Michel. PASSING TIME. Trans by Jean Stewart. London: Faber, (1961). 1st Eng ed. Top edge foxed else tight, Fine,in Fine dj. DORN. $50

Butterfield, Daniel. MAJOR-GENERAL JOSEPH HOOKER AND THE TROOPS FROM THE ARMY OF THE POTOMAC AT WAUTCHIE, LOOKOUT MOUNTAIN AND CHATTANOOGANY, 1896. 1st ed. Wrappers, spine reinforced, few edge chips, else VG. McGOWAN. $27.50

Butterworth, Hezekiah. ZIGZAG JOURNEYS IN AUSTRALIA...Boston: Estes & Lauriat. (1891). 320pp+8pp ads. Orig beige paper-covered boards, color ptd. KARMIOLE. $75

Butterworth, Hezekiah. ZIGZAG JOURNEYS IN THE WHITE CITY...Boston: Estes and Lauriat, (1894). 320pp. Pict cl. SCHOYER'S. $45

Butterworth, Hezikiah. ZIGZAG JOURNEYS IN CLASSIC LANDS; OR, TOMMY TOBY'S TRIP TO MOUNT PARNASSUS. Boston: Estes and Lauriat, 1882. 318pp. Red cl stamped in black and gilt. Spine soiled. SCHOYER'S. $20

Buttles, Janet R. THE QUEENS OF EGYPT. London: Archibald Constable, 1908. 20 plts (2 in color), teg. Good. ARCHAEOLOGIA. $150

Butts, Mary. IMAGINARY LETTERS. Paris: Titus, 1928. 1st ed. Ltd to 250. Cl w/ptd label, glassine dj, boxed. VF in damaged box. JAFFE. $150

Buxton, Thomas Fowell, Charles Buxton (ed). MEMOIRS OF SIR THOMAS FOWELL BUXTON...FROM HIS CORRESPONDENCE. EDITED BY HIS SON. Phila, 1849. 1st Amer ed. 510pp. Orig cl, slight wear to spine extremities, corners scuffed, yet VG to NF. McGOWAN. $150

Byatt, A.S. DEGREES OF FREEDOM. NY, 1965. 1st US ed, 2nd bk. Fine in NF dj. PETTLER. $100

Byatt, A.S. POSSESSION. London: Chatto & Windus, (1990). 1st ed. Fine in NF dj. UNGER. $75

Byatt, A.S. POSSESSION: A ROMANCE. NY: Random House, (1990). 1st US ed. VF in dj. CAPTAIN'S BOOKSHELF. $50

Byatt, A.S. THE GAME. NY: Scribner's, (1967). 1st Amer ed. Small, faint ink offsetting on front fly, a little bending to first couple of pages, else NF in price-clipped dj. BETWEEN COVERS. $150

Byatt, A.S. THE GAME. NY: Scribner's, (1967). 1st US ed. NF in NF dj. UNGER. $60

Byatt, A.S. THE GAME. NY: Scribners, (1967). 1st Amer ed. Fine in dj, few tears. CAPTAIN'S BOOKSHELF. $75

Bykov, Constantine. THE CEREBRAL CORTEX AND THE INTERNAL ORGANS. NY, 1957. 1st Eng trans. FYE. $50

Bynner, Witter (trans). THE JADE MOUNTAIN. A CHINESE ANTHOLOGY. NY: Knopf, 1929. 1st ed. Covers darkened at edges; clippings pasted in. WOOLMER. $35

Bynner, Witter. INDIAN EARTH. Knopf, 1929. 1st ed. Fine. AUTHORS OF THE WEST. $40

Bynner, Witter. JOURNEY WITH GENIUS: RECOLLEC-TIONS...CONCERNING THE D.H. LAWRENCES. London: Peter Nevill, (1953). 1st British ed. VG, lower spine faded, clean chipped dj. *AUTHORS OF THE WEST.* $35

Bynum, Lindley and Idwal Jones. BISCAILUZ: SHERIFF OF THE NEW WEST. NY: Morrow, 1950. 1st ed. Inscribed by Biscailuz. Signed by authors. 16 plts. Fine in Good+ dj. *CONNOLLY & WADE.* $60

Byrd, Max. FINDERS WEEPERS. London: Allison & Busby, 1985. 1st hardcover ed. VF in dj. *MORDIDA.* $35

Byrd, Richard E. ALONE. NY, 1938. 1st ed. (11), 296pp. Signed. Fine in chipped dj. *ARTIS.* $37.50

Byrd, Richard E. DISCOVERY. NY: Putnam, 1935. 1st ed. Hinges beginning, spine faded; an Average copy. *PARMER.* $25

Byrd, Richard E. DISCOVERY. NY: Putnam, 1935. 1st ed. VG except for sl spine fade. Dj worn. *PARMER.* $35

Byrd, Richard E. LITTLE AMERICA. AERIAL EXPLORA-TION....NY: Putnam, 1930. 4 maps, 2 fldg maps. NF. *CONNOLLY & WADE.* $28.50

Byrd, Richard E. LITTLE AMERICA. NY, London: G.P. Putnam's Sons, 1930. Fldg map. Author's Autograph Ed. One of 1000 signed by pub and author. VG. *WEBER.* $150

Byrd, Richard E. LITTLE AMERICA. NY: G.P. Putnam's, 1930. 1st ed. VG clean. Byrd "Prize Letter Contest" announcement laid in. *PARMER.* $35

Byrd, Richard E. SKYWARD. Chicago: R.R. Donnelly, 1981. Lakeside Classic. Prior owner's inscrip ffep, else Fine. *PARMER.* $30

Byrd, William. HISTORIES OF THE DIVIDING LINE BETWIXT VIRGINIA AND NORTH CAROLINA. Raleigh, 1929. Fldg map, facs. Orig cl. Intro, notes by William K. Boyd. Howes B1077. *GINSBERG.* $50

Byrd, William. THE WRITINGS OF....NY, 1901. 4 plts. One quarter art vellum, boards, cl, dj, worn. One of 500. Howes B1077. *GINSBERG.* $175

Byrne, Donn. A PARTY OF BACCARAT. NY, 1930. 1st ed. Traces of removed tape inside cvrs and ffep. Dj spine sl sunned, traces of removed tape inside flaps. *POLYANTHOS.* $35

Byrne, Edward. ALONG THE DARK SHORE. POEMS. John Ashbery (foreword). Brockport, NY: Boa Editions, 1977. 1st ed. One of 26 signed by Ashbery & Byrne. Mint. *JAFFE.* $75

Byrne, J.F. SILENT YEARS. AN AUTOBIOGRAPHY WITH MEMOIRS OF JAMES JOYCE AND OUR IRELAND. NY: FS&Y, (1953). 1st ed. Spine of dj darkened, else Fine. *WOOLMER.* $50

Byrnes, Gene. A COMPLETE GUIDE TO PROFESSIONAL CAR-TOONING. Drexel Hill: Bell, 1950. 1st ed. Cloth. VG. *ARTIS.* $25

Byron, (George Gordon Noel), Lord. SARDANAPALUS, A TRAGEDY. THE TWO FOSCARI, A TRAGEDY. CAIN, A MYSTERY. London: John Murray, 1821. 1st ed. Contemp half calf and boards. Boards worn and rehinged, scattered foxing and dampstain, but untrimmed, VG w/binder's ticket of W. Rayment, Kennington. *CHAPEL HILL.* $175

Byron, George Gordon Noel, Lord; and Samuel Rogers. LARA, A TALE. (By Byron). JACQUELINE, A TALE. (By Rogers). London: J. Murray, 1814. 1st eds. of both works as issued together in single vol. Contemp full sprinkled calf by A. Milne. Light wear at base of spine, but Very Nice. Scarce. *CHAPEL HILL.* $250

Byron, Lord G.G.N. THE PRISONER OF CHILLON, AND OTHER POEMS. London: Murray, 1816. Dk maroon morocco, gilt. 1st ed, 1st issue. Splendid, w/adverts on verso of leaf E8 (recto blank). *O'NEILL.* $150

Byron, Lord. CHILDE HAROLD'S PILGRIMAGE. Paris: Harrison of Paris, 1931. 1/660 on Montgolfier Freres vellum from total issue of 725. Slipcase. Fine. *JUVELIS.* $100

Byron, Robert. IMPERIAL PILGRIMAGE. London: London Passenger Transport Board, 1937. 1st ed. NF in stiff wraps in dj w/chipping to base of spine and sm hole rubbed from rear panel. *LAME DUCK.* $165

Byron, Robert. THE STATION ATHOS: TREASURES AND MEN. NY, 1949. 263pp. Dj. *O'NEILL.* $35

Byron, Robert. THE STATION. ATHOS: TREASURES AND MEN. NY, 1949. 1st ed. Fine in dj (spine sunned, extremities sl chipped, little dust soiled). *POLYANTHOS.* $30

Byron-Curtiss, A.L. THE LIFE AND ADVENTURES OF NAT FOSTER....Utica, NY: Griffiths, 1897. 286pp. 1st ed. Orig pict cl. *GINSBERG.* $125

C

Cabanes, Augustin. CURIOUS BY-PATHS OF HISTORY. Engr frontis. Paris: Charles Carrington. 1898. xxiv,370pp. Index. Frontis. Ed ltd to 500 numbered. Orig black cl, gilt; somewhat worn and faded. *KARMIOLE.* $100

Cabell, James Branch. A ROUND-TABLE IN POICTESME: A SYMPOSIUM. Don Bregenzer, Samuel Loveman (eds). Cleveland: Privately Ptd by Members of The Colophon Club, 1924. 1st ed. One of 774. One corner bumped, else Fine in a lightly edgeworn dj. *CAPTAIN'S BOOKSHELF.* $75

Cabell, James Branch. FIGURES OF EARTH: A COMEDY OF AP-PEARANCES. NY, 1925. 1st ed. Uncut. Fine in dj (top spine sl frayed). *POLYANTHOS.* $50

Cabell, James Branch. GALLANTRY: AN ENGLISH CENTURY DIZAIN IN TEN COMEDIES WITH AN AFTERPIECE. NY: Harpers, 1907. 1st ed. 4 tipped-in color plts. Dec cl. Fine. *CAPTAIN'S BOOKSHELF.* $100

Cabell, James Branch. JURGEN AND THE LAW. NY, 1923. Guy Holt, ed. 1st ed. Ltd to 1080 numbered. VG in dj (chip top dj spine). *McCLINTOCK.* $37.50

Cabell, James Branch. JURGEN. London, 1921. 1st Eng & 1st illus ed. Plts by Pape. Ltd to 3000. Spine ends lightly worn, one snag top edge of spine. VG. *McCLINTOCK.* $75

Cabell, James Branch. JURGEN. NY, 1919. 1st ed, 2nd ptg. Very commonly mistaken for the 1st bk, but has top rule w/small break on page 144 and is sl thicker than the 1st ptg. Light stain to part of binding. VG. *McCLINTOCK.* $12.50

Cabell, James Branch. JURGEN. NY, 1926. 2nd ptg of 1st Amer illus ed. Illus by Ray F. Coyle. VG. *McCLINTOCK.* $10

Cabell, James Branch. PREFACE TO THE PAST. McBride, 1936. VG in rubbed dj. *MADLE.* $35

Cabell, James Branch. QUIET, PLEASE. Gainesville: Univ. of Florida Press, 1952. 1st ed. Adv rev copy, slip laid in. Orig beige cl. Fine in NF dj, lightly browned spine. *CHAPEL HILL.* $50

Cabell, James Branch. SOMETHING ABOUT EVE. McBride, 1927. VG in chipped dj. *MADLE.* $40

Cabell, James Branch. SOMETHING ABOUT EVE. NY, 1927. 1st ed. 1/850 numbered, signed. Large paper issue. Vellum spine mottled. Fine. *McCLINTOCK.* $55

Cabell, James Branch. SOMETHING ABOUT EVE. NY: McBride, 1927. 1st trade ed. Orig brown cl. Spine lettering dulled, else Fine in NF dj w/one small chip. Scarce in dj. *CHAPEL HILL.* $50

Cabell, James Branch. SOMETHING ABOUT EVE. NY: McBride, 1927. 1st ed. #702 of 850 lg paper, signed. Orig half vellum and boards. Fine. *CHAPEL HILL.* $85

Cabell, James Branch. SONNETS FROM ANTAN. NY: The Fountain Press, 1929. 1st ed. Fine. #443 of 718 signed. *CHAPEL HILL.* $75

Cabell, James Branch. TABOO. NY, 1921. 1st ed. Trade issue. 1/820 numbered. NF. Scarce. *McCLINTOCK.* $50

Cabell, James Branch. THE EAGLE'S SHADOW. Intro. by Edwin Bjorkman. NY: McBride, 1923. 1st rev ed of 1st bk. Fine, bright in price-clipped dj. *CHAPEL HILL.* $60

Cabell, James Branch. THE MUSIC FROM BEHIND THE MOON. NY, 1926. Ltd ed, 3000, printed by W.E. Rudge. Prospectus laid in. 8 engr by Leon Underwood. Extremities, spine very sl rubbed. Fine in Fine glassine dj in Fine box. *POLYANTHOS.* $75

Cabell, James Branch. THE SILVER STALLION. A Comedy of Redemption. NY: Robert McBride, (1928). 1st illus ed. Orig pict black cl. Fine, unopened in gilt-stamped dj. *CHAPEL HILL.* $40

Cabell, James Branch. THE SILVER STALLION. NY, 1926. 1st ed. Large paper issue. Ltd to 850 numbered, signed. Some of the gilt has flaked, else VG. *McCLINTOCK.* $30

Cabell, James Branch. THE SOUL OF MELICENT. Stokes, (1913). 1st ed w/Howard Pyle color plates. 216pp. VG+. *BEBBAH.* $40

Cabell, James Branch. THE WAY OF ECBEN. NY: McBride, 1929. 1st ed. #235 of 850 lg paper, signed. Orig blue boards w/parchment spine, corner tips. Spine a trifle soiled, else Fine. *CHAPEL HILL.* $75

Cabell, James Branch. THE WHITE ROBE. McBride, 1928. Ltd ed in slipcase, Fine. *MADLE.* $75

Cabell, James Branch. THESE RESTLESS HEADS. NY: McBride, 1932. 1st ed. #203 of 410, signed. Orig silver boards w/parchment spine, corner tips. Fine, unopened in chipped glassine jacket, lightly worn pub's slipcase. *CHAPEL HILL.* $95

Cable, George W. BYLOW HILL. NY: Scribner's, 1902. 1st ed, 1st prtg. Orig dec red cl, teg. Owner name, sm spot on front cover, else bright, Almost Fine. *CHAPEL HILL.* $40

Cable, George W. GIDEON'S BAND. NY: Scribner's, 1914. 1st ed. VG. 1st ed. BAL 2381. *CHAPEL HILL.* $35

Cable, George W. MADAME DELPHINE. NY: Charles Scribner's Sons, 1881. 1st Amer ed. 125pp, 2pp ads. Orig dec olive grn cl. Sm lib mark stamp, couple of small check marks on title pg, else a Nice, VG . *CHAPEL HILL.* $30

Cable, George W. THE AMATEUR GARDEN. NY: Scribner, 1914. 1st ed. Fine. BAL 2382. *SECOND LIFE.* $45

Cabrera Infante, G. THREE TRAPPED TIGERS. NY: Harper & Row et al, (1971). 1st US ed, 1st book. New in dj. *BERNARD.* $125

Cackler, Christian. "RECOLLECTIONS OF AN OLD SETTLER." Republished by the Kent Courier, 1904. Recent black cloth binding w/title in gilt on front cover. Pulp paper very darkened and fragile, last leaf loose. Howes C13. *BOHLING.* $45

Cadieux, Charles L. PRONGHORN—NORTH AMERICA'S UNIQUE ANTELOPE. Harrisburg: Stackpole Books, 1986. 1st ed. Fine in Fine dj. *BACKMAN.* $25

Cadwallader, Sylvanus. THREE YEARS WITH GENERAL GRANT. NY, 1955. Ed by Benjamin J. Thomas. 2nd prtg. Minor dj wear o/w Fine. *PRATT.* $30

Cady, John H. ARIZONA'S YESTERDAY: BEING THE NARRATIVE OF JOHN H. CADY, PIONEER. (Patagonia, Arizona, 1916). Orig ptd pict wrappers, mended. Howes ClB. *GINSBERG.* $100

Caesar, Julius. THE GALLIC WARS. John Warrington (trans), Bruno Bramanti (illus). Cl-backed dec boards, dj, slipcase. Verona: LEC, 1954. One of 1500 ptd at the Officina Bodoni & signed by Giovanni Mardersteig & Bramanti. VF. *JAFFE.* $150

Cage, John. FOR THE BIRDS. JOHN CAGE IN CONVERSATION WITH DANIEL CHARLES. Boston, 1976. 1st ed. Signed. Fine in Fine dj. *POLYANTHOS.* $50

Cage, John. SILENCE. LECTURES AND WRITINGS. Wesleyan Univ Press, 1961. 1st ed. Bkpl. Fine in dj (little edge rubbed, one short edge tear). *POLYANTHOS.* $35

Cage, John. SILENCE. Middletown: Wesleyan Univ Press, (1961). 1st ed. Fine in dj. *CAPTAIN'S BOOKSHELF.* $75

Cagle, Malcolm W. and Frank A. Manson. THE SEA WAR IN KOREA. Annapolis, MD: US Naval Institute. (1957). 1st ed. Dj. Fine. *KARMIOLE.* $40

Cahan, A. Yekl. A TALE OF THE NEW YORK GHETTO. NY: Appleton, 1896. 1st ed. 1st book. NF. *BEASLEY.* $150

Cahill, Mary. CARPOOL. NY: Random House (1991). Adv rev copy in ptd wraps. Fine. *DORN.* $30

Caidin, Martin. ROCKETS BEYOND THE EARTH. NY: McBride, 1952. 1st prtg. VG in plastic protected dj. *KNOLLWOOD.* $28

Caidin, Martin. VANGUARD. NY: Dutton, 1957. 1st ed. Fine in Good dj. *AARD.* $20

Caidin, Martin. WAR FOR THE MOON. NY: E.P. Dutton, 1959. 1st ed. Good in sl worn dj. *KNOLLWOOD.* $20

Caiger, G. DOLLS ON DISPLAY: JAPAN IN MINIATURE. Tokyo: Hokuseido Press, (1933). xi,141pp. Color frontis and plts (incl 2 fldg). Ptd tissue guards. Fine in sl worn box repaired w/tape. *WREDEN.* $95

Caille, Augustus. DIFFERENTIAL DIAGNOSIS AND TREATMENT OF DISEASE. NY, 1906. 1st ed. 1/2 leather, 867pp. 228 illus. *FYE.* $100

Cain, George. BLUESCHILD BABY. NY: McGraw-Hill, (1970). 1st ed. Fine in dj. *LOPEZ.* $30

Cain, James M. GALATEA. NY: Alfred A. Knopf, 1953. 1st ed. Signed. VG+ in dj. *BERNARD.* $300

Cain, James M. GALATEA. NY: Knopf, 1953. 1st ed. Fine in Fine dj w/two tiny rubs and few tiny tears. Bright, Fine. *BEASLEY.* $50

Cain, James M. GALATEA. NY: Knopf, 1953. 1st ed. Fine; light wear at spine ends, chip to rear of dj. *ELSE FINE.* $30

Cain, James M. LOVE'S LOVELY COUNTERFEIT. NY: Knopf, 1942. 1st ed. Tiny corner bump, else VF, minor rubbing spine ends of price clipped dj. *ELSE FINE.* $200

Cain, James M. MILDRED PIERCE. NY: Knopf, 1941. 1st ed. Advance prepub in stiff wraps w/dj attached to spine by pub. Spine cocked & worn at edges, else VG. *BERNARD.* $375

Cain, James M. SINFUL WOMAN. Cleveland: World, 1948. 1st hrdcvr ed. Fine in lightly used dj. *BEASLEY.* $75

Cain, James M. THE MOTH. NY: Alfred A. Knopf, 1948. 1st ed. Signed. VG in dj. *BERNARD.* $400

Cain, James M. THE MOTH. NY: Knopf, 1948. 1st ed. NF in price-clipped, VG dj. *CHAPEL HILL.* $65

Cain, Paul. SEVEN SLAYERS. England: No Exit Press, 1988. 1st British ed. Fine in dj. *SILVER DOOR.* $35

Cain, Paul. SEVEN SLAYERS. NY: Avon, 1950. Wraps. 1st ed. Paperback orig, preceded by digest-size edition. VG+. *BEASLEY.* $45

Caine, W. Ralph Hall. ISLE OF MAN. A&C Black, 1909. 1st ed. 7s 6d Series. Repair bottom of spine, else VG-NF. *OLD LONDON.* $60

Cairis, Nicholas T. PASSENGER LINERS OF THE WORLD SINCE 1893. NY: Bonanza Books, 1979. Rev ed. Front hinge cracked, else VG in worn dj. *PARMER.* $30

Cairnes, J. W. THE SLAVE POWER: ITS CHARACTER, CAREER, AND PROBABLE DESIGNS.... Carleton, NY, 1862. 2nd ed. 171pp. Spine faded & worn. *HEINOLDT.* $20

Calder, Ritchie. MEN AGAINST THE FROZEN NORTH. London: George Allen & Unwin Ltd., 1957. 1st ed. Good+ in worn dj. *PARMER.* $20

Caldwell, Alfred Betts. NO TEARS SHED. Garden City: Doubleday Crime Club, 1937. 1st ed. Fine in dj with minor wear. *MORDIDA*. $35

Caldwell, Charles. ELEMENTS OF PHRENOLOGY. (2nd ed. greatly enl). WITH A PRELIMINARY DISCOURSE IN VINDICATION OF THE SCIENCE, AGAINST AN ATTACK OF IT BY FRANCIS JEFFREY, ESQ.: AND A CONCLUDING ESSAY IN PROOF OF ITS USEFULNESS. Lexington, 1827. 279pp. Orig cloth-backed boards. Front board and ffep detached, spine worn. Scarce. *FYE*. $250

Caldwell, E.N. ALASKA TRAIL DOGS. NY: R.R. Smith, 1945. Photos. VG+ in Fair dj. *MIKESH*. $17.50

Caldwell, Elsie Noble. ALASKA TRAIL DOGS. NY, 1945. 1st ed. Shelfwear, o/w VG. *ARTIS*. $17.50

Caldwell, Erskine. ALL NIGHT LONG. NY: Duell, Sloan & Pearce, (1942). 1st ed. Orig blue cl. VG in dj (chipped at spine ends, 3" x 2" chip rear panel). *CHAPEL HILL*. $25

Caldwell, Erskine. ALL-OUT ON THE ROAD TO SMOLENSK. NY: Duell, Sloan & Pearce, (1942). 1st ed. Fine in bright dj, only a trace of wear. *CHAPEL HILL*. $80

Caldwell, Erskine. CLOSE TO HOME. NY: Farrar, Straus & Cudahy, (1962). 1st ed. Orig cl-backed boards. Fine in price-clipped, NF dj (very short tear on rear panel). *CHAPEL HILL*. $30

Caldwell, Erskine. HAMRICK'S POLAR BEAR AND OTHER STORIES. Helsinki, Finland: Eurographica, 1984. 1st of this ed. Ltd to 350 signed. Ptd wraps. Mint. *JAFFE*. $175

Caldwell, Erskine. JOURNEYMAN. NY: Viking, 1935. One of 1475 numbered. Fine w/lightly sunned spine, in worn and bit soiled. Slipcase. *BEASLEY*. $45

Caldwell, Erskine. KNEEL TO THE RISING SUN AND OTHER STORIES. NY: Viking, 1935. 1st ed. #137 of 300 specially bound, signed. Orig reddish br buckram w/morocco labels, teg. Fine in sl used pub's slipcase. *CHAPEL HILL*. $200

Caldwell, Erskine. PLACE CALLED ESTHERVILLE. NY: Duell, Sloan & Pearce, (1949). 1st ed. VG in dj (sm chip in front panel). *CHAPEL HILL*. $35

Caldwell, Erskine. SAY, IS THIS THE U.S.A. NY: Duell, Sloane and Pearce, 1941. 1st ed. Bourke-White photos. NF. *CAPTAIN'S BOOKSHELF*. $100

Caldwell, Erskine. SOUTHWAYS. NY: Viking, 1938. 1st ed. Orig blue cl. Slight fading to edges of cl, o/w Fine in lightly used dj. *CHAPEL HILL*. $60

Caldwell, Erskine. THE COURTING OF SUSIE BROWN. NY: Duell, Sloan & Pearce; Boston: Little, Brown, (1952). 1st ed. NF in VG dj. *CHAPEL HILL*. $25

Caldwell, Erskine. THIS VERY EARTH. NY: Duell, (1948). 1st ed. NF in price-clipped dj with several edge nicks. Signed on bkpl. *UNGER*. $75

Caldwell, Erskine. TOBACCO ROAD. NY: Scribner's, 1932. 1st ed. Orig brownish orange cl. VG in pict dj. *CHAPEL HILL*. $650

Caldwell, Erskine. WE ARE THE LIVING. BRIEF STORIES. NY, 1933. Ltd ed, 7/250 only. Signed. Teg, uncut. Spine little sunned, Fine. *POLYANTHOS*. $60

Caldwell, Erskine. WE ARE THE LIVING. NY: Duell, Sloan & Pearce; Boston: Little, Brown, (ca. 1953). Reprint. Right pg of this ptg states "First Edition," there is no statement of ed in the true 1st prtg. (1933). Orig grey boards. As New in lightly rubbed, price-clipped dj (few minor tape reinforcements on verso). *CHAPEL HILL*. $20

Caldwell, Erskine. WITH ALL MY MIGHT. (Atlanta: Peachtree Publishers, 1987). Uncorrected proof. Fine in wrappers. Signed. *CAPTAIN'S BOOKSHELF*. $50

Caldwell, J.F.J. THE HISTORY OF A BRIGADE OF SOUTH CAROLINIANS KNOWN FIRST AS "GREGG'S" AND SUBSEQUENTLY AS "MCGOWAN'S BRIGADE." Phila, 1866. 1951 rprt. Dj chipped o/w VG+. *PRATT*. $47.50

Caldwell, Steven (ed). THE ASTOUNDING S-F ANTHOLOGY. Simon & Schuster, 1952. 1st ed. NF in sl frayed dj. *MADLE*. $30

Caldwell, W.V. LSD PSYCHOTHERAPY. NY: Grove, (1968). 1st ed. NF in dj. *LOPEZ*. $35

Calhoun, Alfred R. LOST IN THE CANON. NY: Burt, 1888. Grn cloth with red and yellow designs. 288pp, plus 32pp adverts. Very early ed, perhaps the 1st. Modest cover soil and wear, spine sunburned, overall at least VG. *FIVE QUAIL*. $35

Calhoun, Mary. MEDICINE SHOW, CONNING PEOPLE AND MAKING THEM LIKE IT. NY, 1976. 1st ed. Dj. *FYE*. $35

Calhoun, William Lowndes. HISTORY OF THE 42ND REGIMENT, GEORGIA VOLUNTEERS, CONFEDERATE STATES ARMY. Atlanta, 1900. 1st ed. Wrappers. NF. *McGOWAN*. $375

CALIFORNIA CLIPPER CARDS. Bk Club of CA, (1949). 1st ed of 850. 12 cards, each in brochure w/text. Cl folder in slipcase w/gilt-stamped leather labels on spine. VG. *AUTHORS OF THE WEST*. $60

California Club, (comp). WAR POEMS, 1898. Irving M. Scott (intro). SF: Murdock Press, (1898). 1st ed. 147pp, 1/4 cl and pict boards. *DIAMOND*. $25

CALIFORNIA THREE HUNDRED AND FIFTY YEARS AGO. MANUELOS' NARRATIVE. TRANSLATED FROM THE PORTUGUESE BY A PIONEER (ascribed to Cornelius C. Cole). SF: Samuel Carson, 1888. 1st ed. 333pp. 12mo. First 2 blanks show light foxing, soiling. Orig gilt dec cl. VG. *CONNOLLY & WADE*. $95

CALIFORNIA THREE HUNDRED AND FIFTY YEARS AGO— MANUELO'S NARRATIVE. SF/NY: Samuel Carson & Co, 1888. 1st ed. VG, aging paper, slt rubbing. Bk review laid in. *PARMER*. $50

CALIFORNIA. NY, 1939. American Guide Series. WPA guide. 1st ptg, map, lacks dj. *SCHOYER'S*. $45

CALIFORNIA: A GUIDE TO THE GOLDEN STATE. Compiled and Written by the Federal Writers' Project. NY: Hastings House, 1939. 1st ed, 1st state. Map in rear pocket. Grn stamped cl in dj (lacks rear flap). *DAWSON'S*. $40

CALIFORNIA: A GUIDE TO THE GOLDEN STATE. NY: Federal Writer's Project of the W.P.A. Hastings, 1947. Fldg map in rear pocket. Cloth. NF in VG dj. *CONNOLLY & WADE*. $30

Calisher, Hortense. IN THE ABSENCE OF ANGELS. Boston: Little, Brown, 1951. 1st ed, 1st bk. Rev copy, slip laid in. Corners sl bumped, else Fine in dj (lt chipping top and bottom of backstrip, single short tear). *HELLER*. $75

Calkins, Alonzo. OPIUM AND THE OPIUM-APPETITE. Phila, 1871. 1st ed. 390pp. Ex-lib. *FYE*. $100

Calkins, Clinch. LADY ON THE HUNT. NY: Harper, 1950. 1st ed, 1st novel. Fine, sm chips at dj extrems. *ELSE FINE*. $25

Calkins, Frank. JACKSON HOLE. NY: Knopf, 1973. 1st ed. Fine in Good+ dj. *CONNOLLY & WADE*. $35

Callado, Antonio. QUARUP. NY: Knopf, 1970. 1st Amer ed. Fine in Fine dj. *LOPEZ*. $25

Callaghan, Morley. MORE JOY IN HEAVEN. NY: Random House (1937). 1st ed. Fine in VG dj, chips, edgewear. *DORN*. $70

Callaghan, Morley. MORLEY CALLAGHAN'S STORIES. Toronto: Macmillan (1959). 1st Canadian ed. Fine in VG dj. *DORN*. $50

Callaghan, Morley. STRANGE FUGITIVE. NY: Scribners (1928). 1st ed, 1st bk. NF w/o dj. *DORN*. $90

Callaghan, Morley. THE VARSITY STORY. Toronto: Macmillan, (1948). 1st Canadian ed. Fine in dj missing small piece from bottom of front panel and top of spine, About VG. Uncommon. *DORN*. $60

Callahan, James D. (ed). JAYHAWK EDITOR. A BIOGRAPHY OF A.Q. MILLER, SR. LA: Sterling, 1955. 1st ed. Fine in Good+ dj. Inscribed. *CONNOLLY & WADE.* $25

Callis, Jo Ann. OBJECTS OF REVERIE: SELECTED PHOTOGRAPHS 1977-1989. With poems by Raymond Carver. Des Moines: Des Moines Art Center/Black Sparrow Press, 1989. 1st ed. #1/1000 . Fine in wrappers. *ROBBINS.* $25

Calloway, Cab. OF MINNIE THE MOOCHER AND ME. NY: Crowell, 1976. 1st ed. Fine in worn dj. *BEASLEY.* $25

Calthrop, Dion Clayton. ENGLISH COSTUME. A&C Black. 1923 Reprint. 61 illus in color; red and grn dec plum cl. VG-NF. *OLD LONDON.* $65

Calthrop, Dion Clayton. ENGLISH COSTUME: I Early English. A&C Black, 1906. 1st ed. 7s 6d Series. Minor wear top and bottom spine, else VG-NF; ENGLISH COSTUME: II Middle Ages. A&C Black, 1906. 1st ed. 7s 6d Series. Minor wear top and bottom spine. else VG-NF; ENGLISH COSTUME: III Tudor and Stuart. A&C Black, 1906. 1st ed. 7s 6d Series. Some wear top and bottom of spine, else VG; ENGLISH COSTUME: IV Georgian. A&C Black, 1906. 1st ed. 7s 6d Series. Minor edgewear, else VG-NF. All four vols as a set. *OLD LONDON.* $175

Calthrop, Dion Clayton. THE CHARM OF GARDENS. A&C Black, 1910. 1st ed. 7s 6d Series. Minor wear to extremities, thus VG. *OLD LONDON.* $45

Calvert, Henry Murray. REMINISCENCES OF A BOY IN BLUE. NY, 1920. 1st ed. Presentation copy. 347pp. Front hinges weakened, still VG. *PRATT.* $110

Calvery, A.S. and P.P. Calvery. A YEAR OF COSTA RICAN NATURAL HISTORY. NY, 1917. Frontis, fldg map. Some wear, rear hinge partially cracked, front hinge taped, light foxing few pp. *SUTTON.* $90

Calvin, Ross. RIVER OF THE SUN: STORIES OF THE STORIED GILA. Albuquerque: Univ of NM Press, 1946. 1st ed. Fine in dj. *LAURIE.* $40

Calvino, Italo. THE CASTLE OF CROSSED DESTINIES. NY: HBJ (1977). 1st Amer ed. Fine in NF dj (chip, sm tear back panel). *DORN.* $65

Calvino, Italo. THE SILENT MR. PALOMAR. Trans by William Weaver. NY: Targ Editions. 1981. Frontis. Ed ltd to 250 numbered, signed. Glassine dj. Fine. *KARMIOLE.* $100

Calvino, Italo. THE SILENT MR. PALOMAR. Trans by William Weaver. Targ, 1981. 1/250 numbered/signed. Fine in orig parchment dj. *DERMONT.* $100

Calvino, Italo. THE WATCHERS. NY: Harcourt, 1971. 1st ed. Fine in Fine dj w/two tiny tears. *BEASLEY.* $40

Cambridge Cross, Ada. A MARKED MAN: SOME EPISODES IN HIS LIFE. NY: John W. Lovell, (1890). 1st Amer ed. Tan cl stamped in black and gilt. Clean. *SCHOYER'S.* $25

Camehl, Ada Walker. THE BLUE CHINA BOOK. NY, (1916). VG. *NUTMEG.* $30

Cameron, Ian. ANTARCTICA—THE LAST CONTINENT. London: Cassell & Company, 1974. NF in VG dj. *PARMER.* $30

Camm, Dom Bede. PILGRIM PATHS IN LATIN LANDS. St. Louis: B. Herder; London: MacDonald and Evans. n.d. (ca. 1923). Teg. 63 plts. *SCHOYER'S.* $40

Cammell, Charles Richard. ALEISTER CROWLEY: The Man: The Mage: The Poet. NHP: Univ Books, (1962). VG+ in VG dj. *BLUE DRAGON.* $30

Camp, Charles (ed). GEORGE C. YOUNT AND HIS CHRONICLES OF THE WEST....Denver: Old West, 1966. 1st ed. 1250 copies. Frontis, 3 plts. Fldg map tipped in at rear. Uncut, unopened. VF. *OREGON.* $95

Camp, Charles (ed). JAMES CLYMAN, AMERICAN FRONTIERSMAN, 1792-1881, ADVENTURES OF....DIARIES. Portland: Champoeg, (1960). 1st ed. Frontis, 2 fldg maps. Gilt stamped cl. VF. Howes C81. *OREGON.* $150

Camp, Charles (ed). JAMES CLYMAN, AMERICAN FRONTIERSMAN. Portland: Champoeg Press, 1960. 1st ed, ltd to 1,450. Fine. *BOOK MARKET.* $150

Camp, Charles. MUGGINS THE COW HORSE. Denver: Welch-Haffner Printing Co, 1928. 1st ed. Fine in extended wraps. *GIBBS.* $95

Camp, John M. THE ATHENIAN AGORA: EXCAVATIONS IN THE HEART OF CLASSICAL ATHENS. London: Thames and Hudson, (1986). 11 color illus. Dj. Good. *ARCHAEOLOGIA.* $300

Camp, Walter. Ed by Kenneth Hammer. CUSTER IN '76, WALTER CAMP'S NOTES ON THE CUSTER FIGHT. Provo, (1976). 2nd prtg. Dj. VG+. *PRATT.* $30

Camp, Walter. WALTER CAMP'S BOOK OF COLLEGE SPORTS. Century, 1893. 1st ed. VG. *PLAPINGER.* $50

Camp, William. SAN FRANCISCO: PORT OF GOLD. Doubleday, 1947. Presentation copy. Marginal dampstaining. 1st ed. G+ in G+ Dj. *OREGON.* $20

CAMPAIGNS OF THE CIVIL WAR. 16 vols. NY: 1881-1885. 1st "Subscription Edition." Some cvrs have bleach spots, one spine has sm tear, but o/w solid copies w/tight hinges and virtually unblemished interiors. Overall VG. *PRATT.* $375

Campan, Madame. MEMOIRS OF THE COURT OF MARIE ANTOINETTE...FROM THE THIRD LONDON EDN....Phila: Parry & McMillan, 1854. 2 vols. New ed, w/3 add chapters. Port vol 1. Cvrs discolored, extrems of spine worn, water mark vol I. VG. *SECOND LIFE.* $85

Campbell, Donald. ARABIAN MEDICINE AND ITS INFLUENCE ON THE MIDDLE AGES. London, 1926. 1st ed. 2 vols. VF. *FYE.* $250

Campbell, Elizabeth Crozer. THE DESERT WAS HOME: ADVENTURES AND TRIBULATIONS....LA: Westernlore Press, 1961. 1st ed. Fine in VG to Fine dj. *BOOK MARKET.* $45

Campbell, Harry Modean. WARREN AS PHILOSOPHER IN WORLD ENOUGH AND TIME. Offprint from The Hopkins Review, Baltimore, MD. Winter, 1953. NF in wraps. Inscribed. *CAPTAIN'S BOOKSHELF.* $60

Campbell, Iain. IAN FLEMING: A CATALOGUE OF A COLLECTION. Liverpool: Iain Campbell, 1978. 1st ed. Signed. VF in stiff wrappers. *MORDIDA.* $65

Campbell, John W. INVADERS FROM THE INFINITE. Hicksville (NY): Gnome Press, (1961). 1st ed. Dj torn, else Fine. *WEBER.* $32.50

Campbell, John W. ISLANDS OF SPACE. Reading, PA: Fantasy Press, (1956). 1st ed. Fine in dj. *McCLINTOCK.* $65

Campbell, John W. THE BLACK STAR PASSES. Fantasy Press. 1953. 1st ed. Fine in dj. *MADLE.* $90

Campbell, John W. THE INCREDIBLE PLANET. Reading, PA: Fantasy Press, 1949. 1st ed. Fine in sl rubbed dj chipped top, bottom edge. *HELLER.* $75

Campbell, John W. THE MIGHTIEST MACHINE. Providence, RI: Hadley Pub Co, (c1947). Red pebbled boards. 1st ed. NF in soiled dj, sl chipped head, foot of backstrip. *HELLER.* $100

Campbell, John W. THE MOON IS HELL. Fantasy Press, 1951. 1st ed. One of 500 numbered, signed. Fine in Mint dj. *MADLE.* $200

Campbell, John W. THE MOON IS HELL! Reading: Fantasy Press, 1951. 1st ed. One of 500 signed. Bkpl, name, date else Almost Fine in perfect As New dj. *OTHER WORLDS.* $125

Campbell, John. LIVES OF THE ADMIRALS, AND OTHER EMINENT BRITISH SEAMEN; CONTAINING THEIR PERSONAL HISTORIES...3rd ed. London: For T. Osborne (a.o.),

1761. 4 vols. (8),587; (2),579; (2),488; (2),519 pp. 6 fldg maps, 6 engr ports. (incl Drake and Raleigh). Contemp calf, gilt, spine ends rubbed, but Fine set. *LEFKOWICZ.* $450

Campbell, M.J. RIVERS OF AMERICA: THE SASKATCHEWAN. NY & Toronto: Rinehart, 1950. Fine in VG+ dj. *MIKESH.* $35

Campbell, Mary. NEW ENGLAND BUTT'RY SHELF ALMANAC. World, 1970. 1st ed. 302pp. Illus by Tasha Tudor. Inscribed by author who has also pasted on half title a package of rosemary. NF in NF dj. *BEBBAH.* $60

Campbell, Patrick. TRAVELS IN THE INTERIOR INHABITED PARTS OF NORTH AMERICA IN THE YEARS 1791 AND 1792. Toronto: Champlain Soc., 1937. Rprt of rare 1793 orig ed, w/new material. One of 550. H.H.Langton (ed). (21),326,(12)pp. Orig cl. Champlain Soc. Pubs 23. Howes C101. *GINSBERG.* $300

Campbell, R. Wright. FAT TUESDAY. New Haven: Ticknor & Fields, 1983. 1st ed. Fine in sl rubbed dj (wear at spine ends; tear front panel). *MORDIDA.* $25

Campbell, R. Wright. HONOR. NY: Tor, 1987. 1st ed. Fine in dj. *MORDIDA.* $25

Campbell, Ramsey (ed). NEW TALES OF THE CTHULHU MYTHOS. Arkham House, 1980. 1st ed. VF in dj. *MADLE.* $125

Campbell, Ramsey (ed). NEW TALES OF THE CTHULHU MYTHOS. (Sauk City): Arkham House, 1980. 1st ed. Fine in Fine dj. *OTHER WORLDS.* $60

Campbell, Ramsey. DEMONS BY DAYLIGHT. Sauk City: Arkham House, 1973. 1st ed. Almost Fine in dj (red lettering on spine sl faded); pub's *OTHER WORLDS.* $6 price sticker affixed. *OTHER WORLDS.* $20

Campbell, Ramsey. THE HEIGHT OF THE SCREAM. Sauk City: Arkham House, 1976. 1st ed. Fine in dj. *OTHER WORLDS.* $20

Campbell, Ramsey. THE HUNGRY MOON. MacMillan, 1986. 1st ed. Fine in dj. *MADLE.* $25

Campbell, Ramsey. THE INFLUENCE. NY: Macmillan, 1988. 1st US ed. Advance uncorrected proofs. Fine in wraps. *BEASLEY.* $35

Campbell, Ramsey. THE INHABITANT OF THE LAKE & LESS WELCOME TENANTS. Sauk City, WI: Arkham House, 1964. 1 of 2,009 of 1st book. NF in dj which is very sl worn at bottom spine edge. *BERNARD.* $125

Campbell, Ramsey. THE INHABITANT OF THE LAKE AND LESS WELCOME TENANTS. Sauk City: Arkham House, 1964. 1st ed, 1st bk. Spine heel waterstained, else Fine in heavily browned dj (some light edgewear). *OTHER WORLDS.* $100

Campbell, Ramsey. THE INHABITANT OF THE LAKE. Arkham House, 1964. 1st ed. Fine in dj. *MADLE.* $150

Campbell, Ramsey. THE PARASITE. MacMillan, 1980. 1st ed. Fine in dj. *MADLE.* $30

Campbell, Reau. CAMPBELL'S NEW REVISED COMPLETE GUIDE...OF MEXICO. Chicago: Pub by author, 1907. 2nd updated ed. Though contents page lists maps on pg 345, they are not there nor is there evidence of removal. Map on pg 325 is listed as being elsewhere. Fine. *CONNOLLY & WADE.* $40

Campbell, Robert. ALICE IN LA-LA LAND. NY: Poseidon Press, 1987. 1st ed. Fine in dj. *MORDIDA.* $25

Campbell, Robert. IN LA-LA LAND WE TRUST. NY: Mysterious Press, 1986. 1st ed. Fine in dj. *MORDIDA.* $25

Campbell, Robert. ROCKY MOUNTAIN LETTERS. Yale Univ, ptd for Frederick Beinecke, Christmas, 1955. Tie in blue wrappers w/title label. VG+. *BOHLING.* $35

Campbell, Robert. THINNING THE TURKEY HERD. NY: NAL, 1988. 1st ed. Signed. VF in dj. *SILVER DOOR.* $35

Campbell, Roy. THE GEORGIAD. London: Boriswood, (1931). 1st ed. One of 170 signed. Cl backed dec boards, glassine dj. VF. *JAFFE.* $175

Campbell, Sheldon. LIFEBOATS TO ARARAT. London: Weidenfeld, (1979). Foreword by Gerald Durrell. Signed by both Durrell and Campbell, inscribed by Campbell and hand illus by Durrell. 1st ed. Fine in Fine dj. *BOOK MARKET.* $50

Campbell, Thomas Monroe. THE MOVABLE SCHOOL GOES TO THE NEGRO FARMER. Tuskegee Institute, AL, (1936). 1st ed. Orig cl, minor cover speckling. VG. *McGOWAN.* $165

Campbell, Thomas. GERTRUDE OF WYOMING; A PENNSYL-VANIA TALE, and Other Poems. London: Longman, 1809. 1st ed. Wide folio; pp 134, uncut. Orig pub's boards, spine renewed. Some wear to edges, old sig on paste-down, contents excellent. Exceedingly rare errata slip present. *HARTFIELD.* $245

Campbell, W.S. (Stanley Vestal). THE BOOK LOVER'S SOUTHWEST. Univ of OK Press, 1955. 1st ed. Fine in Fine dj. *VARNER.* $135

Campbell, Walter. THE BOOK LOVER'S SOUTHWEST. Norman: Univ of OK Press, 1955. 1st ed. Ex-lib. Head of spine faded o/w VG+. *ARCHER.* $15

Campbell, Will D. BROTHER TO A DRAGONFLY. NY: Seabury, (1977). 1st Amer ed. Signed. Top edge sl sunned else Fine in price-clipped NF dj. *DORN.* $50

Campbell, Will D. FORTY ACRES AND A GOAT. Atlanta: Peachtree (1986). Uncorrected proof. Sl used in wraps. *DORN.* $25

Campbell, Will D. THE CONVENTION: A PARABLE. Atlanta: Peachtree Publishers, (1988). 1st Amer ed. Signed. Fine in dj. *DORN.* $30

Campbell, Will D. THE GLAD RIVER. NY: Holt, Rinehart and Winston, (1982). 1st Amer ed. Signed. Fine in dj. *DORN.* $35

Campbell, William C. A COLORADO COLONEL....Topeka: Crane & Co, 1901. Pict cl, VG. *SCHOYER'S.* $40

Campbell, William C. FROM THE QUARRIES OF LAST CHANCE GULCH...HELENA AND ITS MASONIC LODGES....With Vol II: 1890— 1900. Helena: Prvt ptd. (1951) 2 vols. 1st ed. Gilt stamped pict cl (vol 1 blue, vol 2 red). Scarce. Couple spots underlining in vol 2. VG. *OREGON.* $100

Campbell, William C. FROM THE QUARRIES OF LAST CHANCE GULCH... HELENA AND ITS MASONIC LODGES... FROM DISCOVERY OF GOLD—1864 TO STATEHOOD— 1889. Helena: Priv ptd, (1951). 1st ed. Signed presentation. VG. Scarce. *OREGON.* $70

Campbell, William W. AN HISTORICAL SKETCH OF ROBIN HOOD AND CAPTAIN KIDD. NY: Scribner, 1853. 1st ed. 12mo. Brown cl tooled in blind. Spine a bit dull. VG. *CAPTAIN'S BOOKSHELF.* $75

Camus, Albert. THE STRANGER. NY: Knopf, 1946. 1st Amer ed. Sl dust soiling; NF in dj. *LOPEZ.* $125

Canby, Courtlandt (ed). LINCOLN AND THE CIVIL WAR, A PROFILE AND A HISTORY. NY, 1960. Dj a little worn, repaired, o/w Fine. *PRATT.* $20

Canetti, Elias. AUTO-DA-FE. NY: Stein and Day (1964). Orig pub as The Tower of Babel, this ed uses the orig Eng title. First thus. NF in VG+ dj missing a few chips. *DORN.* $50

Canfield, Dorothy. HOME FIRES IN FRANCE. NY: Holt, 1918. 1st ed. Owner's name, small bookseller's label, else Nearly Fine. *CHAPEL HILL.* $35

Canfield, Gae Whitney. SARAH WINNEMUCCA OF THE NORTHERN PIUTES. Norman, (1983). 1st ed. 306pp. Fine in dj. *PRATT.* $25

Canfield, Thomas Hawley. LIFE OF THOMAS HAWLEY CAN-FIELD, HIS EARLY EFFORTS TO OPEN A ROUTE....Burlington, VT, 1889. 48pp, double column. Frontis. Orig dk grn cl, presentation copy. VG or better. Howes C113. *BOHLING.* $450

Canin, Ethan. EMPEROR OF THE AIR. Boston: Houghton Mifflin, 1988. 1st ed, 1st book. Inscribed. Fine in Fine dj. *BEASLEY.* $60

Cannon, Curt (pseud of Ed McBain). I'M CANNON FOR HIRE. Greenwich: Fawcett Publications, 1958. 1st ed. Pb orig. Gold Medal no. 814. Fine, unread, in wrappers. *MORDIDA.* $35

Cannon, Frank. BRIGHAM YOUNG AND HIS MORMON EMPIRE. NY, 1913. 1st ed. Faint staining on spine, front hinge loose, o/w VG. *BENCHMARK.* $35

Cannon, J. Vennerstrom. WATERSHED DRAMA. BATTLE LAKE MINNESOTA. Berkeley, privately ptd, 1942. Signed presentation. 1st ed. G+. *OREGON.* $30

Cantor, Eddie. BETWEEN THE ACTS. NY: Simon & Schuster. 1930. 1st ed. Dj. Fine. *KARMIOLE.* $40

Cantor, Eddie. CAUGHT SHORT! NY: Simon & Schuster. 1929. 1st ed. Dj. Fine. *KARMIOLE.* $40

Cantor, Eddie. THE WAY I SEE IT. Ed by Phyllis Rosenteur. Englewood Cliffs, NJ: Prentice Hall. (1959). 1st ed. Signed. Dj. *KARMIOLE.* $45

Cantor, Meyer. INTESTINAL INTUBATION. Springfield, 1949. Dj. *FYE.* $75

Cantril, Hadley. THE INVASION FROM MARS. Princeton U. Press, 1947 VG. *MADLE.* $25

Cantwell, J. (John) C. REPORT OF THE OPERATIONS OF THE U.S. REVENUE STEAMER NUNIVAK...1899-1901. Wash: GPO, 1902. 1st ed. Scuffing to cvrs; else NF. Inscrip, bkplt. *PARMER.* $250

Cantwell, J.S. THIRTY DAYS OVER THE SEA. Cincinnati: Williamson & Cantwell, 1873. 1st ed. Light foxing, cloth faded. *PARMER.* $20

Cantwell, Robert. LAUGH AND LIE DOWN. Farrar & Rinehart, (1931). 1st ed. VG+. *AUTHORS OF THE WEST.* $75

Cantwell, Robert. LAUGH AND LIE DOWN. NY: Farrar, 1931. 1st ed. 1st book. Fine but for barely faded spine in dj. *BEASLEY.* $150

Canuck, Janey. SEEDS OF PINE. Toronto: Hodder & Stoughton, (1914). 1st ed. Color frontis. Gilt, emb cl. Fine. *ARTIS.* $35

Capa, Robert. SLIGHTLY OUT OF FOCUS. 1st ed. Dj (sl crease), o/w Fine, bright. *SMITH.* $150

Capablanca, Jose R. A PRIMER OF CHESS. NY, 1935. NF. *POLYANTHOS.* $40

Capart, Jean. LECTURES ON EGYPTIAN ART. Chapel Hill, NC: Univ of South Carolina Press, 1928. 1st ed. VG ex-lib w/o lib markings on outside. *WORLDWIDE.* $65

Capek, Karel. KRAKATIT. MacMillan, 1925. 1st ed. VG. *MADLE.* $40

Capek, Karel. KRAKATIT: AN ATOMIC PHANTASY. NY: Arts, Inc. 1951. VF, dj has sm edge peel, remains on upper rear edge of asphalt tape from a previous protector. Fresh copy. *ELSE FINE.* $65

Capek, Karel. LETTERS FROM SPAIN. NY: Putnam's, 1932. 1st ed. Spine darkened o/w VG in dj which has open tiny chip at bottom spine corner. *BERNARD.* $50

Capell, Richard. SIMIOMATA. A GREEK NOTE-BOOK 1944-1945. London, (1945). Dj. *O'NEILL.* $45

Capers, Gerald M. THE BIOGRAPHY OF A RIVER TOWN. MEMPHIS...Chapel Hill: Univ of North Carolina Press, 1939. 1st ed. Dj repaired. Pres copy. *HUDSON.* $75

Capote, Truman. A TREE OF NIGHT AND OTHER STORIES. NY: Random House, (1949). 1st ed. Faintest of soiling, but Nearly Fine in dj. *CHAPEL HILL.* $150

Capote, Truman. ANSWERED PRAYERS. NY: Random House, (1987). Uncorrected proof of the 1st Amer. ed. Orig ptd yellow

wraps. Pub's slip taped to front wrap, as issued, else NF. *CHAPEL HILL.* $125

Capote, Truman. BREAKFAST AT TIFFANY'S. NY: Random House, (1958). 1st ed. Orig yellow cl. Offsetting to fep where something was laid in (affecting edge of jacket flap), else NF in dj (spine sunned, as usual, slight darkening at edges). *CHAPEL HILL.* $150

Capote, Truman. I REMEMBER GRANDPA. Peachtree, (1987). 1st ed with watercolor paintings by Barry Moser. Small greenish smudges to ffep. NF in NF dj. *BEBBAH.* $25

Capote, Truman. IN COLD BLOOD. NY: Random House, (1965). 1st ed. Dj. VF. *WREDEN.* $45

Capote, Truman. IN COLD BLOOD. NY: Random House, (1965). Adv reading copy of 1st ed. One of 500. Orig ptd wraps. Fine with no soiling or wear. *CHAPEL HILL.* $200

Capote, Truman. IN COLD BLOOD. NY: Random House, (1966). 1st trade ed. Orig maroon cl. Fine in NF dj. *CHAPEL HILL.* $45

Capote, Truman. IN COLD BLOOD. NY: Random House, (1966). 1st ed. #409 of 500 specially ptd and bound , signed. Orig black cl. Fine in orig. acetate jacket and pub's slipcase. *CHAPEL HILL.* $400

Capote, Truman. IN COLD BLOOD. NY: RH, (1965). Adv reading copy. NF in ptd wraps. *CAPTAIN'S BOOKSHELF.* $125

Capote, Truman. IN COLD BLOOD. Random House, 1966. 1st ed. Dj worn at head and foot of spine. *STAHR.* $25

Capote, Truman. LOCAL COLOR. NY: RH, (1950). 1st ed. Fine (neat bkpl under flap) in sl used dj (sm chips). Review copy, slip laid in. *CAPTAIN'S BOOKSHELF.* $150

Capote, Truman. MUSIC FOR CHAMELEONS. NEW WRITING. NY: Random House, (1980). 1st ed. Ltd to 350 signed. Slipcase. VF. *JAFFE.* $350

Capote, Truman. MUSIC FOR CHAMELEONS. NY: Random House, (1980). Fine in red ptd wraps w/label taped to front wrapper reading "Advance Proofs (Uncorrected)". Pasted label soiled; chipped at lower left corner. The proof itself reads "Uncorrected First Proof" at top of front wrapper. *HELLER.* $100

Capote, Truman. MUSIC FOR CHAMELEONS. NY: Random House, (1980). 1st ed. One of 350 specially bound, signed. Orig brn cl. Mint in pub's slipcase, orig plastic shrinkwrap. *CHAPEL HILL.* $325

Capote, Truman. MUSIC FOR CHAMELEONS. NY: Random House, (1980). 1st ed. #34 of 350 numbered and signed. Fine in pub's slipcase. *UNGER.* $250

Capote, Truman. MUSIC FOR CHAMELEONS. Random House, 1980. 1st trade. Fine in dj. *STAHR.* $15

Capote, Truman. OTHER VOICES, OTHER ROOMS. NY: Random House, (1948). 1st ed, 1st bk. Orig tan cl. Fine in dj. *CHAPEL HILL.* $300

Capote, Truman. OTHER VOICES, OTHER ROOMS. NY: Random House, 1948. 1st ed, 1st bk. VG in lightly used dj. *JUVELIS.* $125

Capote, Truman. THE DOGS BARK. NY, 1973. 1st ed. Dj has closed slit on front panel, else NF. *PETTLER.* $30

Capote, Truman. THE GRASS HARP. (NY): Random House, (1951). 1st ed, 1st issue. Orig rough tan cl. Spine dulled, thus VG in price-clipped, NF dj (1" tear on front panel mended on verso). *CHAPEL HILL.* $150

Capote, Truman. THE GRASS HARP. A Play. NY: Random House, (1952). 1st ed. Orig tan cl w/paper cover label. Sm abrasion on front cover, else Fine in price-clipped dj (couple of short closed tears).*CHAPEL HILL.* $275

Capote, Truman. THE GRASS HARP. London: Heinemann, (1952). 1st UK. Fine in dj (tiny chip, two short tears). *CAPTAIN'S BOOKSHELF.* $50

Capote, Truman. THE GRASS HARP: A PLAY. NY, 1952. 1st ed. Fine in dj w/very shallow chipping to top edge. *PETTLER.* $150

Capote, Truman. THE MUSES ARE HEARD. NY: Random House, 1956. 1st ed. Rev copy w/slip laid in. NF in VG+ dj. *LAME DUCK.* $150

Capote, Truman. THE MUSES ARE HEARD. NY: Random House, (1956). 1st ed. Former owner's name, else Fine in dj w/minimal rubbing. *CHAPEL HILL.* $95

Capote, Truman. THE MUSES ARE HEARD. NY: Random House, (1956). 1st ed. Inscribed. Inside back panel dj stained, not affecting book cvrs, sl worn at head of spine, o/w VG. *JAFFE.* $350

Capote, Truman. THE MUSES ARE HEARD. NY: Random House, (1956). 1st ed. Orig black cl. Owner sig, date, else Fine in VG dj. *CHAPEL HILL.* $75

Capote, Truman. THE MUSES ARE HEARD. NY: RH, (1956). Advance review. Fine in NF dj, with review slip laid in. *LOPEZ.* $125

Capote, Truman. THE THANKSGIVING VISITOR. NY: Random House, (1967). 1st trade ed. Cl-backed boards, slipcase. Fine. *JAFFE.* $100

Cappel, Jeanne L'Strange. CHIPPEWA TALES RETOLD BY WA-BE-NO O-PEE-CHEE JEANNE L'STRANGE CAPPEL. LA: Wetzel, 1928. 1st ed. Frontis tipped in. Ptd boards. NF. Inscribed. Scarce. *CONNOLLY & WADE.* $30

Capps, Benjamin. THE WARREN WAGONTRAIN RAID. NY, 1974. 1st ed. 304pp. VG+ in dj. *PRATT.* $25

Capron, E.S. HISTORY OF CALIFORNIA, FROM ITS DISCOVERY TO THE PRESENT TIME. Boston: Jewett, Proctor and Worthington, 1854. Fldg map, carefully repaired. Howes C127. *HUDSON.* $175

Capron, J. Rand. PHOTOGRAPHED SPECTRA. London: E. & F.N. Spon, 1877. Good in orig illus red cl. *KNOLLWOOD.* $120

Capstick, Peter Hathaway. DEATH IN THE LONG GRASS. NY: St. Martin's Press, 1977. 1st ed. Fine in Fine dj. *GREAT EPIC.* $45

Caputo, Philip. HORN OF AFRICA. Holt, 1980. Advance reading copy. Fine in wraps. *STAHR.* $15

Caputo, Philip. INDIAN COUNTRY. Bantam, 1987. Advance reading copy. NF in wraps. Signed w/promo letter. Lightly bumped. *STAHR.* $25

Caras, R.A. NORTH AMERICAN MAMMALS, FUR-BEARING ANIMALS OF THE U.S. & CANADA. NY, 1967. 1st ed. VG+ in Fine dj. *MIKESH.* $27.50

Caras, Roger A. ANTARCTICA—LAND OF FROZEN TIME. Phila: Chilton, 1962. Stated 1st ed. Average very worn dj. *PARMER.* $25

Caras, Roger. MONARCH OF DEADMAN BAY: THE LIFE AND DEATH OF A KODIAK BEAR. Boston: Little Brown, 1969. 1st ed. Fine in Fine dj. *CONNOLLY & WADE.* $25

Card, Orson Scott. A PLANET CALLED TREASON. St Martins, 1979. 1st ed. Fine in dj. *MADLE.* $85

Card, Orson Scott. CARDOGRAPHY. Eugene: Hypatia Press, 1987. 1st ed. 1/750 signed, numbered. Fine in Fine dj. *OTHER WORLDS.* $60

Card, Orson Scott. ENDER'S GAME. (NY): Tor, (1985). 1st ed. Inscribed. Trace of shelfwear, else Fine in dj. *OTHER WORLDS.* $275

Card, Orson Scott. SPEAKER FOR THE DEAD. London, 1987. 1st British hb ed. As New. *MADLE.* $50

Card, Orson Scott. SPEAKER FOR THE DEAD. NY: Tor, 1986. 1st ed. VF in dj. *ELSE FINE.* $100

Cardan, Jerome. THE BOOK OF MY LIFE. NY, 1930. 1st ed. *FYE.* $40

Cardigan, Earl of. THE WARDENS OF SAVERNAKE FOREST. London: Routledge & Kegan Paul. (1949). 1st ed. Fldg plate. Dj. *KARMIOLE.* $30

Carell, Paul. HITLER MOVES EAST 1941-1943. Boston: Little, Brown, (1964). 1st US ed. Fldg map in rear. A few closed dj tears. VG. *AKA.* $100

Carew, Thomas. A RAPTURE. The Golden Cockerel Press. (Waltham Saint Lawrence). 1928. 1/4 cl, dec paper boards. #68/375. Fine in sl soiled cream dj. *HELLER.* $125

Carey, Charles H. (ed). THE OREGON CONSTITUTION AND PROCEEDINGS...CONSTITUTIONAL CONVENTION OF 1857. Salem, OR, (1926). 1st ed. TLS attached. NF. *DIAMOND.* $75

Carey, Edith F. THE CHANNEL ISLANDS. A&C Black, 1904. 1st ed. 20s Series. Minor ex-lib markings, else VG. *OLD LONDON.* $75

Carey, Peter. ILLYWHACKER. NY: Harper, 1985. 1st ed. As New in jacket. *ELSE FINE.* $45

Carey, Peter. OSCAR & LUCINDA. (Queensland): Univ of Queensland Press, (1988). True 1st ed, Australian. Paper sl yellowed with age. NF in dj. Signed. *LOPEZ.* $185

Carey, Peter. OSCAR & LUCINDA. (Queensland): Univ of Queensland Press, (1988). True 1st ed, Australian. Fine in dj. *LOPEZ.* $125

Carey, Peter. OSCAR & LUCINDA. Harper & Row, 1988. 1st Amer ed. VF in dj. Signed & inscribed. *STAHR.* $35

Carey, Peter. THE FAT MAN IN HISTORY AND OTHER STORIES. NY: Random House, 1980. 1st ed., 1st bk. Fine in NF dj. *ELSE FINE.* $65

Carey, Peter. THE TAX INSPECTOR. NY: Knopf, 1992. Signed. 1st US ed. Fine in Fine dj. *BEASLEY.* $40

Carkeet, David. THE GREATEST SLUMP OF ALL TIME. Harper and Row, 1984. 1st ed. Fine in dj. *STAHR.* $35

Carl, Louis and Petit, Joseph. MOUNTAINS IN THE DESERT. GC: Doubleday, 1954. 1st ed. Fine in VG dj. *AARD.* $15

CARL WERNER...WITH OTHER TALES....(By William Gilmore Simms.) NY: George Adlard, 1838. 2 vols, 1st ed. 243; 208pp,(4)pp ads. Orig plum cl w/paper spine labels. Cl faded as usual, spine label rubbed on Vol 11, few traces of foxing, else VG+. Nice set. *CHAPEL HILL.* $675

Carleton, George. OUT ARTIST IN PERU...1865-6. NY: Carleton Pub, 1886. 1st ed. Orig grn cl w/gilt. Lt soiling, wear, 1" paint spot on cl cover, foxing on plts, Good in Good- dj. *SILVER.* $40

Carleton, Lieutenant J. Henry. THE PRAIRIE LOGBOOKS: DRAGOON CAMPAIGNS TO THE PAWNEE VILLAGES IN 1844, AND TO THE ROCKY MOUNTAINS IN 1845...EDITED WITH AN INTRODUCTION BY LOUIS PELZER. Chicago: Caxton, 1943. 1st ed. One of 350. Orig cl backed boards. Boxed. 1st pub of all letters in 1 vol. Howes C146. *GINSBERG.* $150

Carley, Kenneth. MINNESOTA IN THE CIVIL WAR. Minneapolis, (1961). 1st ed. 168pp. Dj. Minor cvr soiling o/w Fine. *PRATT.* $32.50

Carling, John. THE VIKING'S SKULL. Little-Brown, 1904. 1st ed. Near VG. *MADLE.* $35

Carlisle, Bill. BILL CARLISLE, LONE BANDIT. Pasadena: Trail's End (1946). 1st ed. Deluxe ltd ed. Padded leatherette. Ltd to 650 signed, numbered. VG. *OREGON.* $80

Carlisle, Bill. BILL CARLISLE LONE BANDIT. Trail's End, 1950. 2nd ed. Fine in VG sl chipped dj. *VARNER.* $45

Carlisle, Lilian Baker. PIECED WORK AND APPLIQUE QUILTS. Shelburne, VT: The Shelburne Museum, 1957. VG. Wraps. *BACKROOM.* $45

Carlisle, Lilian Baker. VERMONT CLOCK AND WATCHMAKERS, SILVERSMITHS AND JEWELERS. Burlington, VT: The Author, 1970, 1st ed. Ltd to 1000. NF in NF dj. *BACKROOM.* $60

Carlisle, Robert. AN ACCOUNT OF BELLEVUE HOSPITAL WITH A CATALOGUE OF THE MEDICAL AND SURGICAL STAFF FROM 1736-1894. NY, 1893. 1st ed. *FYE.* $150

Carlock, William B. A COMPILATION OF THE HISTORICAL AND BIOGRAPHICAL WRITINGS OF WILLIAM B. CAR-LOCK. ALSO OF THE CEREMONIES ATTENDING THE DEDICATION OF THE LINCOLN TRAIL MONUMENT, ON THE LINE BETWEEN MCLEAN AND WOODFORD COUN-TIES. (N.p.), 1923. *GINSBERG.* $125

Carlquist, Sherwin. HAWAII: A NATURAL HISTORY. NY: The Natural History Press, 1970. 1st ed. Fine in Fine dj. *BOOK MARKET.* $150

Carlson, Helen S. NEVADA PLACE NAMES: A GEOGRAPHI-CAL DICTIONARY. Reno: Univ of NV Press, 1974. 1st ed. Fine in Fine dj. *CONNOLLY & WADE.* $35

Carlson, Raymond. GALLERY OF WESTERN PAINTINGS. Mc-Graw-Hill, 1951. 1st ed. Fine in chipped dj. *VARNER.* $45

Carlyle, Thomas. REMINISCENCES. London: Longmans, Green, 1881. 2 vols. 1st ed. Ed by James Anthony Froude. 3/4 tan calf, cl, green leather labels on paneled spines, teg. Generally Fine. *WREDEN.* $75

Carlyon, Richard. THE DARK LAND OF PENGERSICK. Farrar, 1980. 1st ed. Fine in dj. *MADLE.* $20

Carmichael, John et al. MY GREATEST DAY IN BASEBALL. Bar-nes, 1945. 2nd prtg. Signed by Hubbell on his photo. VG in Good dj. *PLAPINGER.* $75

Carnac, Carol. A DOUBLE FOR DETECTION. London: Mac-donald, (1945). 1st ed. Minor spotting on fore-edge o/w Fine in dj w/tiny wear at base of spine. *MORDIDA.* $75

Carnegie, Andrew. AN AMERICAN FOUR-IN-HAND IN BRITAIN. NY: Scribner, 1914. Later prtg. Spine quite dull, else VG. Inscribed. *CAPTAIN'S BOOKSHELF.* $225

Carnell, John (ed). NO PLACE LIKE EARTH. London, 1952. 1st ed. Signed. Fine in chipped dj. *MADLE.* $25

Carothers, Alva. STEVENSON'S ISLES OF PARADISE....Santa Bar-bara, CA: Alva Carothers, 1931. 2nd ed. Red cl stamped in gilt. Lacks ffep. Illus. *SCHOYER'S.* $20

Carp, Augustus. AUGUSTUS CARP, ESQ. Boston: Houghton Mif-flin Co., 1924. 1st US ed. VG+ in VG dj. *AARD.* $25

Carpenter, Edmund. ESKIMO REALITIES. NY: Holt, Rinehart & Winston, (1973). 1st ed. VG+ in VG- dj. *BLUE DRAGON.* $25

Carpenter, Edward. THE SIMPLIFICATION OF LIFE. CT: The Hil-lacre Bookhouse, 1912. Ltd ed of 1000. Wraps. Fine. *POLYANTHOS.* $25

Carpenter, F.B. THE INNER LIFE OF ABRAHAM LIN-COLN....NY: Hurd & Houghton, 1868. vii,359pp. 12mo. Black peb-bled cl exposed to damp. Slight wave to rear pages, no mustiness, not affecting text. Else VG. *CONNOLLY & WADE.* $45

Carpenter, Frank D.Y. ROUND ABOUT RIO. Chicago: Jansen, Mc-Clurg, 1884. 1st ed. 415pp. Dk grn pict cl, stamped in black, gilt. VG. *WEBER.* $22.50

Carpenter, Frank G. ALASKA OUR NORTHERN WONDER-LAND. NY, 1926. VG. *ARTIS.* $18.50

Carpenter, John A. SWORD AND OLIVE BRANCH, OLIVER OTIS HOWARD. Pittsburgh, (1964). 1st ed. VG+ in dj. *PRATT.* $45

Carpenter, Kenneth. THE HISTORY OF SCURVY & VITAMIN C. Cambridge, 1987. *FYE.* $50

Carpenter, Kinchen Jahu. WAR DIARY OF KINCHEN JAHU CARPENTER...Rutherfordton, NC, 1955. 1st ed. Wrappers. NF. *McGOWAN.* $75

Carpenter, P.P. THE MOLLUSKS OF WESTERN NORTH AMERICA. Washington, 1872. Half leather (worn, w/outer hinge splitting, tears to last page repaired, bkplt). *SUTTON.* $115

Carpenter, W. THE MICROSCOPE & ITS REVELATIONS. Lon-don: Churchill, 1881. 6th ed. 26 plts, frontis. Some plts dampstained; rebacked w/orig backstrip. Tight, clean. *BOOKCELL.* $50

Carpenter, W.B. INTRODUCTION TO THE STUDY OF FOR-MAMINIFERA. London: Ray Society, 1862. 22 plts. Orig boards (some staining and edge wear, spine chipped, pp yellowed). *SUTTON.* $135

Carpenter, William. ON THE USE AND ABUSE OF ALCOHOLIC LIQUORS, IN HEALTH AND DISEASE. Phila, 1866. 1st Amer ed. *FYE.* $75

Carpenter, William. PRINCIPLES OF HUMAN PHYSIOLOGY, WITH THEIR CHIEF APPLICATIONS TO PSYCHOLOGY, PATHOLOGY, THERAPEUTICS, HYGIENE, AND FOREN-SIC MEDICINE. Phila, 1853. 5th Amer ed. 300 woodcut illus. *FYE.* $35

Carpentier, Alejo. EXPLOSION IN A CATHEDRAL. Boston: Lit-tle, Brown (1962). 1st Amer ed. Lt foxing top edge else Fine in VG dj. *DORN.* $45

Carpentier, Alejo. REASONS OF STATE. NY: Knopf (1976). 1st Amer ed. Fine in VG+ dj. *DORN.* $30

Carpentier, Alejo. THE KINGDOM OF THIS WORLD. NY: Knopf (1957). 1st Amer ed. Lt damp stain top edge else Fine in Fine dj. *DORN.* $50

Carpentier, Alejo. THE KINGDOM OF THIS WORLD. Roberto Juarez (illus). Harriet De Onis (trans), John Hersey (intro). 1/2 morocco & cl, slipcase. (NY): LEC, (1987). Ltd to 750 signed by Jaurez & Hersey. Mint. *JAFFE.* $450

Carpentier, Alejo. THE LOST STEPS. Trans by Harriet de Onis. NY: Knopf, (1956). 1st Amer ed. Fine in NF spine sun darkened, price-clipped dj. *DORN.* $125

Carpentier, Alejo. WAR OF TIME. London: Gollancz (1970). 1st Eng ed. Fine in a dust soiled dj (sm price sticker shadow, or VG). *DORN.* $40

Carpentier, Alejo. WAR OF TIME. NY: Knopf (1970). 1st Amer ed. Name partially erased else Fine in dj. *DORN.* $50

Carr, A. HANDBOOK OF TURTLES. Ithaca, 1952. 1st ed. 82 plts, 32 text figures, 15 tables, 23 maps. Name stamp on ep, some edge scuffing. *SUTTON.* $65

Carr, Harry. THE WEST IS STILL WILD. Houghton Mifflin, 1932. 1st ed. Signed. Portions of another dj pasted to rear eps, inside edges of dj reinforced w/masking tape. Good+ in Good+ dj. *OREGON.* $25

Carr, John Dickson. DARK OF THE MOON. Harper & Row, 1967. 1st ed. Fine in NF price-clipped dj w/lt wear head, foot of spine. *STAHR.* $30

Carr, John Dickson. DEATH TURNS THE TABLES. NY: Harper & Brothers, 1941. 1st ed. Bkpl, o/w Fine in dj (several tiny closed tears; tiny wear top of spine). *MORDIDA.* $400

Carr, John Dickson. HE WHO WHISPERS. NY, 1946. 1st Amer ed. Extremities, spine minimally rubbed. Fine in dj (extremities little rubbed, few tiny edge nicks). *POLYANTHOS.* $50

Carr, John Dickson. HE WHO WHISPERS. NY: Harper, 1946. 1st ed. Fine; minor edgewear to dj. *ELSE FINE.* $60

Carr, John Dickson. HE WHO WHISPERS. NY: Harper, 1946. 1st ed. Head and foot of spine frayed, o/w VG in chipped dj w/internal mends. *BEASLEY.* $45

Carr, John Dickson. IN SPITE OF THUNDER. NY: Harper, 1960. 1st ed. Fine in NF dj (lt wear at spine head). *BEASLEY.* $50

Carr, John Dickson. MOST SECRET. NY: Harper & Row, 1964. 1st ed. Spotting on top edge o/w Fine in price-clipped dj. *MORDIDA.* $25

Carr, John Dickson. THE CASE OF THE CONSTANT SUICIDES. NY: Harper, 1941. 1st ed. Fine. *ELSE FINE.* $45

Carr, John Dickson. THE DEVIL IN VELVET. NY: Harper, 1951. 1st ed. Fine but for sunned edges, in Fine dj. *BEASLEY.* $40

Carr, John Dickson. THE DOOR TO DOOM & OTHER DETECTIONS. London: Hamilton, 1980. 1st British ed. Douglas G. Greene (ed). VF in dj. *SILVER DOOR.* $35

Carr, John Dickson. THE EMPEROR'S SNUFF BOX. NY: Harper & Brothers, 1942. 1st ed. Bkseller's stamp o/w Fine in price-clipped dj (sm chip top front panel; several short closed tears). *MORDIDA.* $350

Carr, John Dickson. THE FOUR FALSE WEAPONS. NY: Harper & Brothers, 1937. 1st ed. Fine in dj (sl faded spine; tiny nicks, tears at spine ends, wear at corners; sm piece missing lower corner back panel). *MORDIDA.* $350

Carr, John Dickson. THE HOUSE AT SATAN'S ELBOW. NY: Harper, 1965. 1st ed. Fine in Fine dj. *BEASLEY.* $35

Carr, John Dickson. THE LIFE OF SIR ARTHUR CONAN DOYLE. London: John Murray, 1949. 1st ed. Initials on fep and foxing on edges o/w VG in dj with internal tape mends. *MORDIDA.* $55

Carr, John Dickson. THE LIFE OF SIR ARTHUR CONAN DOYLE. NY: Harper & Bros., 1949. 1st Amer ed. VG in dj w/minor wear at spine ends. *MORDIDA.* $45

Carr, John Dickson. THE PROBLEM OF THE GREEN CAPSULE. NY: Harper, 1939. 1st ed. Tape shadows on cover & endpapers, Good. Chips at spine top, minor edgewear to bright dj. *ELSE FINE.* $75

Carr, John Dickson. THE SLEEPING SPHINX. NY: Harper, 1947. 1st ed. Fine in NF dj (tiny chips head of spine). *BEASLEY.* $75

Carr, John Dickson. THE WITCH OF THE LOW-TIDE. NY: Harper & Brothers, 1961. 1st ed. VF in dj. *MORDIDA.* $35

Carr, John Dickson. THE WITCH OF THE LOW-TIDE. NY: Harper, 1961. 1st ed. Fine in Fine dj but for few short tears. *BEASLEY.* $45

Carr, John. A VULCAN AMONG THE ARGONAUTS: BEING VIVID EXCERPTS....Robin Lampson (ed, signed by). SF: George Fields, 1936. 1st ed, ltd to 500. VF. *CONNOLLY & WADE.* $75

Carr, John. PIONEER DAYS IN CALIFORNIA...HISTORICAL AND PERSONAL SKETCHES. Eureka, Ca., 1891. 452pp. Orig cl, spine faded. 1st ed. Howes C167. *GINSBERG.* $250

Carr, Joseph Baker. THE MAN WITH BATED BREATH. NY: Viking Press, 1934. 1st ed. Covers spotted o/w VG in dj w/internal spotting and spotting on flaps. *MORDIDA.* $37.50

Carr, Michael H. THE SURFACE OF MARS. New Haven, CT: Yale Univ Press, 1981. VG in worn dj. *KNOLLWOOD.* $55

Carrel, Alexis and G. Dahelly. THE TREATMENT OF INFECTED WOUNDS. NY, 1917. 1st Eng trans. *FYE.* $150

Carrell, Gladys Hasty. AS THE EARTH TURNS. NY: Macmillan, 1933. 1st ed. Signed. Fine- in VG dj. *AARD.* $50

Carrick, Alice Van Leer. A HISTORY OF AMERICAN SILHOUETTES: A COLLECTOR'S GUIDE 1790-1840. Rutland: Tuttle, (1968). 1st Tuttle ed. Fine in dj. *CAPTAIN'S BOOKSHELF.* $50

Carrighar, Sally. ONE DAY AT TETON MARSH. NY: Knopf, 1947. 1st ed. Gilt cl. NF in Good+ dj. *CONNOLLY & WADE.* $30

Carrington, Frances C. MY ARMY LIFE AND THE FORT PHIL KEARNEY MASSACRE. Phila, 1910. 1st ed. 318pp. A little of the color on cover has been rubbed off, o/w VG. *PRATT.* $135

Carrington, General Henry B., U.S.A. THE INDIAN QUESTION. Boston, 1884. 1st ed. 32pp, fldg map. VG in wraps. *PRATT.* $300

Carrington, Thomas. TUBERCULOSIS HOSPITAL AND SANITORIUM CONSTRUCTION. NY, 1914. 3rd ed. *FYE.* $75

Carroll, Daniel B. HENRI MERCIER AND THE AMERICAN CIVIL WAR. Princeton, 1971. 1st ed. Fine in Fine dj. *PRATT.* $25

Carroll, H. Bailey and J. Villasana Haggard (eds, trans). THREE NEW MEXICO CHRONICLES: THE EXPOSICION...1812; THE OJEADA...1832; AND THE ADDITIONS...1849. Quivira Society Publications, vol. XI. Albuquerque: Quivira Society, 1942. One of 550 numbered. 2 fold out maps. Ex-lib, bound in pub orig 1/4 cl and paper boards. Slight wear to cover, interior Fine. *LAURIE.* $100

Carroll, H. Bailey. GUADAL P'A. THE JOURNAL OF LIEUTENANT J.W. ABERT FROM BENT'S FORT TO ST. LOUIS IN 1845. Canyon, TX: Panhandle Plains Hist Soc, 1941. Frontis, 1 pl, fldg map tipped to rear. Spine discolored o/w VG. Howes A10. *OREGON.* $100

Carroll, John M. (ed). BLACK MILITARY EXPERIENCE IN THE AMERICAN WEST. NY, (1971). 1st ed. 591pp. Light dj wear o/w Fine. *PRATT.* $75

Carroll, John M. CUSTER IN TEXAS. NY, 1975. 1st ed. Fine. *PRATT.* $40

Carroll, John M. CUSTER IN TEXAS: AN INTERRUPTED NARRATIVE. NY: 1975. 1st ed. Orig cl, dj. *GINSBERG.* $30

Carroll, John M. THE ARREST AND KILLING OF SITTING BULL. A DOCUMENTARY. Hidden Springs of Custeriana series vol X. A.H. Clark, 1986. Ltd to 350. VF. *OREGON.* $75

Carroll, Jonathan. THE LAND OF LAUGHS. NY: Viking, (1980). 1st ed, 1st bk. NF (upper corners bumped) in dj. *OTHER WORLDS.* $85

Carroll, Jonathan. VOICE OF OUR SHADOW. NY: Viking (1983). 1st ed. Fine in NF dj, a few edge tears. *LOPEZ.* $45

Carroll, Jonathan. VOICE OF OUR SHADOW. NY: Viking, 1983. 1st ed, Fine, minor wear to top edge of dj. *ELSE FINE.* $75

Carroll, Jonathan. VOICE OF OUR SHADOW. Viking, 1983. 1st Amer ed. Fine in dj (2 short, closed tears on front panel). *STAHR.* $80

Carroll, Lewis (pseud of Charles L. Dodgson). ALICE'S ADVENTURES IN WONDERLAND & THROUGH THE LOOKING-GLASS. Heritage, 1941. Illus John Tenniel. Boxed ed. NF in slipcase w/scuffs. *BEBBAH.* $30

Carroll, Lewis (pseud of Charles L. Dodgson). ALICE'S ADVENTURES IN WONDERLAND. St. Martin's, 1977. 206pp. 15 color plts. Pict cvr in red, black on grn cl, color pict ep. Fine in Fine dj w/gold seal of 125th anniversary of publication of Alice. *BEBBAH.* $25

Carroll, Lewis (pseud of Charles L. Dodgson). FOR THE TRAIN. London: Denis Archer, (1932). 1st ed. Fine in dj, 2 short tears. *CHAPEL HILL.* $200

Carroll, Lewis (pseud of Charles L. Dodgson). FURTHER NONSENSE VERSE AND PROSE. Appleton, 1926. 1st ed. Dec papercovered board has edgewear; overall VG. *BEBBAH.* $35

Carroll, Lewis (pseud of Charles L. Dodgson). LEWIS CARROLL'S THE HUNTING OF THE SNARK. (By Charles Lutwidge Dodgson.) Illus by Henry Holiday. The annotated Snark by Martin Gardner. The designs for the Snark by Charles Mitchell. The listing of the Snark by Selwyn H. Goodacre. Ed by James Tanis and John Dooley. Los Altos, CA: William Kaufmann, Inc, in cooperation with Bryn Mawr College Library, (1981). One of 395 numbered ptd at the Stinehour Press. Signed by Gardner, Goodacre, Mitchell and Roderick Stinehour. With extra set of plts loose as issued in portfolio. In orig cl backed box. Mint. *WREDEN.* $395

Carroll, Lewis (pseud of Charles L. Dodgson). PHANTASMAGORIA AND OTHER POEMS. London: Macmillan, 1869. 1st ed. 202pp. Stamped blue cl (spine soiled), Bkpls both eps, Nice, tight w/minor external wear; aeg. *SECOND LIFE.* $425

Carroll, Lewis (pseud of Charles L. Dodgson). SYLVIE AND BRUNO. London: Macmillan, 1889. 1st ed. 8vo, 400pp, (3)pp ads. Org red cl, aeg. Hairline crack in hinges, some soiling, but VG. *CHAPEL HILL.* $85

Carroll, Lewis (pseud of Charles L. Dodgson). THE LETTERS OF LEWIS CARROLL. Morton N. Cohen, Roger Lancelyn Green (eds). NY: Oxford Univ Press, 1979. 2 vols. Boxed. As New. *WEBER.* $60

Carroll, Lewis (pseud of Charles L. Dodgson). THROUGH THE LOOKING GLASS AND WHAT ALICE FOUND THERE. Illus John Tenniel. NY: LEC, 1935. One of 1500. Dec leather. Without sig of orig Alice. Fine in slipcase. *CAPTAIN'S BOOKSHELF.* $275

Carroll, Lewis (pseud of Charles L. Dodgson). THROUGH THE LOOKING GLASS AND WHAT ALICE FOUND THERE. Altemus, (1899). John Tenniel illus, color frontis by another illus. Some faint cvr soil but gilt dec cvr w/pict pastedown. VG+ overall. *BEBBAH.* $25

Carroll, Lewis (pseud of Charles L. Dodgson). THROUGH THE LOOKING-GLASS AND WHAT ALICE FOUND THERE. Peter Newell (illus). NY: Harper, 1902. 1st ed, thus. NF in red cl, teg; in ptd linen dj. *CAPTAIN'S BOOKSHELF.* $175

Carroll, Lewis (pseud of Charles L. Dodgson). THROUGH THE LOOKING-GLASS, AND WHAT ALICE FOUND THERE. By Lewis Carroll, with Fifty Illus by John Tenniel. NY and London: Macmillan and Co., 1872. 1st Amer ed, with the misprint of p. 21. 8vo. 6 leaves; 224pp. Orig brown cloth, stamped at top in gilt with title only. Sl damage to outer hinges, and a trifle bit of staining on front cover. Text foxed. VG with reddish salmon endleaves. Quite possibly a trial binding. *M & S.* $1500

Carruth, Hayden. CONTRA MORTEM. Johnson, VT: Crow's Mark Press, (1967). 1st ed. One of 250 ptd. Signed. Ptd wraps. VF. *JAFFE.* $125

Carruth, Hayden. JOURNEY TO A KNOWN PLACE. Norfolk, CT: New Directions, 1961. 1st ed. Ltd to 300 ptd by Harry Duncan & Kim Merker. Cl-backed boards. Fine in chipped glassine dj. *JAFFE.* $275

Carruth, Hayden. NORTH WINTER. Cl-backed boards, dj. Iowa City: Prairie Press, (1964). 1st ed. Signed. VF. *JAFFE.* $100

Carruth, Hayden. THE CLAY HILL ANTHOLOGY. Iowa City: Prairie Press, (1970). 1st ed. Signed. Cl-backed dec boards, dj. VF. *JAFFE.* $100

Carruth, Hayden. THE NORFOLK POEMS. Cl-backed boards, dj. Iowa City: Prairie Press, (1962). 1st ed. Signed. VF. *JAFFE.* $100

Carruthers, Douglas (ed). THE DESERT ROUTE TO INDIA, BEING THE JOURNALS OF FOUR TRAVELLERS....London: Hakluyt Society, 1928. xxxvi,196pp. Uncut. *O'NEILL.* $35

Cars, A. Des. A TREATISE ON PRUNING FOREST AND OR-NAMENTAL TREES. Charles S. Sargent (trans). Boston: A. Williams, 1900. 4th ed. Sl cvr soil. VG. *SECOND LIFE.* $50

Carse, Robert. BLOCKADE. THE CIVIL WAR AT SEA. NY, 1958. 1st ed. NF in sl worn dj. *McGOWAN.* $45

Carson, Christopher. KIT CARSON'S AUTOBIOGRAPHY. Chicago: Lakeside Classic, 1935. Ed by Milo M. Quaife. Fine. *OREGON.* $35

Carson, Christopher. KIT CARSON'S OWN STORY OF HIS LIFE. Grant, Blanche C. (ed). 1926. 13pp photo illus. Wraps. *DAWSON'S.* $75

Carson, Gerald. ONE FOR A MAN, TWO FOR A HORSE...PATENT MEDICINE. NY, 1961. 1st ed. Dj. *FYE.* $50

Carson, Gerald. THE SOCIAL HISTORY OF BOURBON. NY: Dodd, Mead & Company, (1963). 16pp of photo illus. Cl in lightly chipped dj, one small nick to bottom edge of front cover. *DAWSON'S.* $30

Carson, James. THE SADDLE BOYS IN THE GRAND CANYON, or, The Hermit of the Cave. NY: Cupples & Leon, 1913. Probable 1st ed. Two-color covers of Saddle Boys on the trail. 204pp, plus adverts. Silverfish marks bottom edges of covers, else NF. *FIVE QUAIL.* $25

Carson, Michael. BROTHERS IN ARMS. NY: Pantheon, 1988. 1st US ed. of Sucking Sherbet Lemons. Fine in dj. *WOOLMER.* $35

Carson, Michael. COMING UP ROSES. London: Gollancz, 1990. 1st ed. Fine. *WOOLMER.* $30

Carson, Michael. COMING UP ROSES. London: Gollancz, 1990. Proof copy in wrappers and dj. *WOOLMER.* $40

Carson, Michael. FRIENDS AND INFIDELS. London: Gollancz, (1989). Adv proof in wrappers and dj. Fine. *WOOLMER.* $40

Carson, Michael. FRIENDS AND INFIDELS. London: Gollancz, (1989). 1st ed. Fine in dj. *WOOLMER.* $30

Carson, Michael. SUCKING SHERBET LEMONS. London: Gollancz, 1988. Adv proof in wrappers. *WOOLMER.* $60

Carswell, John. THE ROMANTIC ROGUE. NY: Dutton, (1950). 1st US ed. 7 plts. VG in VG dj. *AARD.* $25

Carter, Angela. BLACK VENUS. London: Chatto & Windus/Hogarth Press, (1985). 1st ed. Fine in dj. *LOPEZ.* $45

Carter, Angela. FIREWORKS. Harper, 1981. 1st Amer ed. VF in dj. *STAHR.* $15

Carter, Angela. FIREWORKS. NY: Harper, 1981. 1st ed. Fine in price clipped dj. *ELSE FINE.* $30

Carter, Angela. HONEYBUZZARD. NY: Simon & Schuster, (1966). 1st Amer ed. Sm black remainder stripe bottom edge of pages, o/w VG in VG dj. *LOPEZ.* $85

Carter, Angela. MISS Z: THE DARK YOUNG LADY. (NY): Simon & Schuster, 1970. 1st Amer ed. Fine in dj with a little rubbing and tiny nick at base of spine. *BETWEEN COVERS.* $125

Carter, Angela. NIGHTS AT THE CIRCUS. Viking, 1985. 1st Amer ed. VF in dj. *STAHR.* $10

Carter, Boake. BLACK SHIRT, BLACK SKIN. Harrisburg, PA: Telegraph, 1935. Signed. 1/3 ffep missing. *AKA.* $23

Carter, Charles Franklin. STORIES OF THE OLD MISSIONS OF CALIFORNIA. SF: Paul Elder, 1917. Pict cl. Fine in dj. *PARMER.* $45

Carter, Forrest. THE EDUCATION OF LITTLE TREE. (N.p.): Delacorte/Friede, (1976). 1st ed. VF copy of uncommon 1st ed, in VF dj. *LOPEZ.* $350

Carter, Forrest. WATCH FOR ME ON THE MOUNTAIN. (NY): Delacorte/Friede, (1978). 1st ed. Rmdr mark bottom edge of pages, o/w Fine in dj. *LOPEZ.* $85

Carter, Harvey Lewis. "DEAR OLD KIT," THE HISTORICAL CHRISTOPHER CARSON. Norman, (1968). 1st ed. VG+ in dj. *PRATT.* $55

Carter, Harvey. DEAR OLD KIT. Norman: Univ of OK, (1968). 1st ed. VF in Fine dj. *OREGON.* $55

Carter, Hodding. LOWER MISSISSIPPI. NY/Toronto: Rinehart & Company, c1942. Map. Spine faded. *HUDSON.* $25

Carter, Hodding. THE ANGRY SCAR....GC, 1959. 1st ed. Dj. VG. *PRATT.* $27.50

Carter, Howard. THE TOMB OF TUT-ANKH-AMEN DIS-COVERED BY THE LATE EARL OF CARNARVON AND HOWARD CARTER. 3 vols. complete. London: Cassell. 1923-33. 1st ed, 1st issue. Signatures. Good. *ARCHAEOLOGIA.* $750

Carter, John (ed). NEW PATHS IN BOOK COLLECTING, ES-SAYS....London: Constable & Co, (1934). 1st ed. Cloth. Spine very faded; foxed. *OAK KNOLL.* $45

Carter, John and Muir, Percy H. (eds). PRINTING AND THE MIND OF MAN. London: Cassell & Co.; NY: Holt, Rinehart &

Winston, (1967). 1st ed. Orig red cl. Marginal tear one leaf, else Fine in dj. *CHAPEL HILL.* $350

Carter, John and Percy Muir. PRINTING AND THE MIND OF MAN. Munchen: Karl Pressler, 1983. 2nd ed, rev, enl. As New. *WEBER.* $130

Carter, John and Sadleir, Michael. VICTORIAN FICTION. An Exhibition of Original Editions at 7 Albemarle Street, London. January to February 1947. Cambridge: Univ Press, 1947. 1st ed. Tall 8vo; pp xiii, 50, index of authors and 16 photo plates of books. Excellent. *HARTFIELD.* $145

Carter, John. BOOKS AND BOOK-COLLECTORS. Cleveland: World Pub, (1957). 1st US ed. Cl, dj (pieces missing). *OAK KNOLL.* $50

Carter, John. SPECIMENS OF THE ANCIENT SCULPTURE AND PAINTING NOW REMAINING IN ENGLAND. London: Henry G. Bohn, 1887. Contemp red half morocco, marbled eps. 2 frontispieces, 2 engr titles, 115 plts (2 folding, 1 double-pg). Back hinge broken, lea sl scuffed, abraded. Sm tears from sewing thread at inner margins, o/w Fine internally. *PIRAGES.* $250

Carter, L. J. (ed). REALITIES OF SPACE TRAVEL, SELECTED PAPERS....London: Putnam, 1957. Paragr underlined in pen, marginal pencil notes, o/w VG. *KNOLLWOOD.* $40

Carter, Lin. DREAMS FROM R'LYEH. Sauk City: Arkham, 1975. 1st ed. Fine in Fine dj. *OTHER WORLDS.* $25

Carter, Paul A. LITTLE AMERICA: TOWN AT THE END OF THE WORLD. NY: Columbia Univ Press, 1979. 1st ed. Autographed. NF in lightly worn dj. *PARMER.* $30

Carter, Peter. MIES VAN DER ROHE. NY: Praeger, (1974). 1st Amer ed. NF in like price-clipped dj. *CAPTAIN'S BOOKSHELF.* $60

Carter, Russell. THE WHITE PLUME OF NAVARRE. Volland, (1928). 1st ed. Illus by Beatrice Stevens. Slight cvr edgewear, couple of spots. VG+. *BEBBAH.* $45

Carter, Samuel III. THE FINAL FORTRESS, THE CAMPAIGN FOR VICKSBURG, 1862-1863. NY, (1980). 1st ed. Light dj wear, o/w Fine. *PRATT.* $27.50

Carter, Samuel, III. THE LAST CAVALIERS, CONFEDERATE AND UNION CAVALRY IN THE CIVIL WAR. NY, (1979). 1st ed. Light dj wear o/w Fine. *PRATT.* $25

Carter, Samuel. COWBOY CAPITAL OF THE WORLD. THE SAGA OF DODGE CITY. GC: Doubleday & Co, 1973. 1st ed. VF in dj. *GIBBS.* $20

Carter, William. GHOST TOWNS OF THE WEST. Menlo Park: Lane, (1971). 1st deluxe ed. Fine in Fine slipcase. *BOOK MARKET.* $35

Cartwright, D.W. NATURAL HISTORY OF WESTERN WILD ANIMALS AND GUIDE FOR HUNTERS, TRAPPERS, AND SPORTSMEN...Written by M.F. Bailey. 19 illus. Toledo, 1875. 2nd ed. Pp x,(1),280. Recent buckram Some pp tanned; institutional bkpl. *SUTTON.* $175

Cartwright, David W. and Mary F. Bailey. NATURAL HISTORY OF WESTERN WILD ANIMALS AND GUIDE FOR HUNTERS...ALSO, NARRATIVES OF PERSONAL ADVENTURE. Toledo: Blade Printing and Paper, 1875. 2nd ed. Wear at head and heel of spine, else VG. Howes C-205 *LAURIE.* $125

Cartwright, Frederick. DISEASE AND HISTORY, THE INFLUENCE OF DISEASE IN SHAPING THE GREAT EVENTS OF HISTORY. NY, 1972. 1st ed. Dj. *FYE.* $35

Cartwright, Frederick. THE DEVELOPMENT OF MODERN SURGERY. NY, 1968. *FYE.* $60

Cartwright, Julia. JEAN FRANCOIS MILLET: HIS LIFE AND LETTERS. NY, 1896. NF. *POLYANTHOS.* $60

Carus-Wilson, Mrs. Ashley. IRENE PETRIE. London: Hodder & Stoughton, 1901. 4th ed. Nice. Unopened. *SECOND LIFE.* $45

Caruthers, William. LOAFING ALONG DEATH VALLEY TRAILS. Ontario, CA: Death Valley, 1951. Fine. Deluxe 2nd ed. Ltd to 100. *CONNOLLY & WADE.* $75

Caruthers, William. LOAFING ALONG DEATH VALLEY TRAILS....Palm Desert: Desert Magazine, 1951. 1st ed. Signed by Senator Charles Brown. Red cl w/gilt. Fine in NF dj. *CONNOLLY & WADE.* $95

Carvalho, S.N. INCIDENTS OF TRAVEL AND ADVENTURE IN THE FAR WEST. NY: Derby & Jackson, 1857. Issue w/NY/Cincinnati imprint and frontis showing Fremont and author taking astronomical observations. Broken covers loose, spine lacking. Howes C213. *HUDSON.* $95

Carvalho, Solomon Nunes. INCIDENTS OF TRAVEL AND ADVENTURE IN THE FAR WEST; WITH COL. FREMONT'S LAST EXPEDITION ACROSS THE ROCKY MOUNTAINS: INCLUDING THREE MONTHS' RESIDENCE IN UTAH, AND A PERILOUS TRIP ACROSS THE GREAT AMERICAN DESERT, TO THE PACIFIC. (New York: Derby & Jackson; Cincinnati: H. W. Derby & Co., 1857) xvi, 17-380pp, (2) leaves. Missing the suppressed dedication leaf (pp v & vi) to Mrs. Fremont which was cut out of all early editions. 1st ed (according to Howes). Orig emb cl. Frontis. Ownership sig of Noah A. Elder, Jr., on front fly. Tiny tears in cloth at spine ends, corners somewhat worn, a few spots on spine, o/w quite Fine. Occas minor foxing, but excellent internally. *PIRAGES.* $275

Carver, Raymond. A NEW PATH TO THE WATERFALL. NY: Atlantic Monthly Press (1989). 1/200 numbered, specially bound, signed by Tess Gallagher (ed). Spine gilt flaking a bit as is common o/w Fine in slipcase. *LOPEZ.* $100

Carver, Raymond. CATHEDRAL. Knopf, 1983. 1st ed. VF in dj. *STAHR.* $25

Carver, Raymond. CATHEDRAL. NY: Knopf, 1983. Uncorrected proof. Fine in ptd wraps. *CAPTAIN'S BOOKSHELF.* $100

Carver, Raymond. CATHEDRAL. Stories. NY: Knopf, 1983. 1st ed. Fine in dj w/a few tiny edge tears. Rev copy, photo, publicity material laid in. Signed. *CAPTAIN'S BOOKSHELF.* $175

Carver, Raymond. ELEPHANT AND OTHER STORIES. London, 1988. 1st ed. Fine in like dj. *POLYANTHOS.* $40

Carver, Raymond. FIRES. ESSAYS, POEMS, STORIES. London: 1985. 1st ed. Fine in like dj. *POLYANTHOS.* $40

Carver, Raymond. FIRES. London: Collins Harvill, 1985. 1st UK ed. Deletes 2 pieces from the US ed. and adds 2 not in the US ed. Fine in price clipped dj. *BERNARD.* $65

Carver, Raymond. FIRES. Santa Barbara: Capra, 1983. Hb trade ed, which was apparently a print overrun for the ltd ed, and is thus scarcer (according to the pub) than the signed, ltd issue, i.e., fewer than 250 copies. Fine w/o dj, as issued. *LOPEZ.* $100

Carver, Raymond. FURIOUS SEASONS AND OTHER STORIES. Santa Barbara: Capra Press, 1977. 1st ed. NF in wrappers. *ROBBINS.* $150

Carver, Raymond. FURIOUS SEASONS AND OTHER STORIES. Santa Barbara: Capra Press, 1977. 1st ed. One of 1200. Fine in ptd wraps. *CAPTAIN'S BOOKSHELF.* $125

Carver, Raymond. MY FATHER'S LIFE. Derry: Babcock & Koontz, (1986). One of 40 signed by author and artist in total limitation of 240. Wraps. Fine. *WOOLMER.* $235

Carver, Raymond. NO HEROICS, PLEASE. (London): Harvill, (1991). 1st Eng ed. Fine in Fine dj. *LOPEZ.* $75

Carver, Raymond. NO HEROICS, PLEASE. UNCOLLECTED WRITINGS. NY: Knopf, 1992. Advance uncorrected proofs. Fine in wraps, in Fine ptd cardboard slipcase. *BEASLEY.* $100

Carver, Raymond. PUT YOURSELF IN MY SHOES. Santa Barbara: Capra Press, 1974. One of 75 numbered in pict boards signed. *CAPTAIN'S BOOKSHELF.* $450

Carver, Raymond. THE STORIES OF RAYMOND CARVER. (London): Picador/Pan, (1985). 1st ed. Fine in pict wraps. *CAPTAIN'S BOOKSHELF.* $300

Carver, Raymond. THOSE DAYS. EARLY WRITINGS. Frontis, marbled wraps. Elmwood, CT: Raven Editions, 1987. 1st ed. One of 100, signed. Mint. *JAFFE.* $150

Carver, Raymond. THOSE DAYS. Elmwood: Raven Editions, 1987. 1st ed. #1/100 signed. Fine in marbled wrappers. *ROBBINS.* $200

Carver, Raymond. ULTRAMARINE. NY: Random House, (1986). Uncorrected proof. Ptd wraps. VF. *JAFFE.* $125

Carver, Raymond. ULTRAMARINE. NY: Random House, 1986. 1st ed. Fine in dj. *ARCHER.* $20

Carver, Raymond. WHAT WE TALK ABOUT WHEN WE TALK ABOUT LOVE. NY: Knopf, 1981. 1st ed. Signed. Small ink spots on top edge which have bled into the top of a few pages, o/w NF in NF dj. *ROBBINS.* $150

Carver, Raymond. WHAT WE TALK ABOUT WHEN WE TALK ABOUT LOVE. NY: Knopf (1981). 1st ed. Sm date stamp else Fine in NF dj. *DORN.* $80

Carver, Raymond. WHERE I'M CALLING FROM. Franklin Center, PA.: Franklin Library, 1988. Correct 1st ed, w/special preface incl only this ed. Signed. Full gilt dec leather. Mint. *JAFFE.* $175

Carver, Raymond. WHERE I'M CALLING FROM. NY: Atlantic Monthly, (1988). 1st ed. One of 250 signed. Cl, slipcase. Mint. *JAFFE.* $150

Carver, Raymond. WHERE I'M CALLING FROM: NEW & SELECTED STORIES. NY: Atlantic Monthly Press, (1988). 1st ed. Fine in dj. Signed. *CAPTAIN'S BOOKSHELF.* $175

Carver, Raymond. WHERE WATER COMES TOGETHER WITH OTHER WATER. NY: Random House, (195). 1st ed. Fine in dj. *ROBBINS.* $60

Carver, Raymond. WILL YOU PLEASE BE QUIET, PLEASE?. NY: McGraw-Hill, (1976). 1st ed. Fine in NF dj (short tear at crown). *LOPEZ.* $450

Carvic, Heron. PICTURE MISS SEETON. London: Geoffrey Bles, 1968. 1st ed. Fine in dj. *MORDIDA.* $50

Cary, Elisabeth. THE ART OF WILLIAM BLAKE. NY: Moffat, Yard and Co, 1907. 1st ed. Illus grn cl. Corner bump, some loose pp. VG. *SMITH.* $50

Cary, Elizabeth L. EMERSON: POET AND THINKER. NY: Putnam's, (1904). 1st ed. NF. Gilt cl binding initialled by Margaret Armstrong. *CAPTAIN'S BOOKSHELF.* $75

Cary, John. CARY'S NEW ITINERARY: OR AN ACCURATE DELINEATION OF THE GREAT ROADS...10th ed. London: G. & J. Cary, 1826. 2 vols in 1. 8 fldg plts. Modern 1/4 brn calf, orig marbled boards, modern red morocco spine label. Bkpl. *WEBER.* $375

Cary, Joyce. THE HORSE'S MOUTH. (London): George Rainbird/Michael Joseph, 1957. #401/1500 (#300-500 reserved for friends of George Rainbird Ltd.). Fine in sl rubbed pub's box. *HELLER.* $95

Casanova. THE MEMOIRS OF CASANOVA DE SEINGALT. Subscribers' Ed. London, 1929. 12 vols. 550 sets. Teg. NF. *POLYANTHOS.* $175

Case, David. FENGRIFFEN. Hill & Wang, 1970. 1st ed. Fine in rubbed dj. *MADLE.* $75

Casey, John. AN AMERICAN ROMANCE. NY: Atheneum, 1977. Uncorrected proof. Erasure front cvr, sm surface gouge on (blank) rear panel, o/w Fine. *LOPEZ.* $150

Casey, John. SPARTINA. NY: Knopf, 1989. 1st ed. Fine in price-clipped dj. *CAPTAIN'S BOOKSHELF.* $40

Casey, Michael. OBSCENITIES. New Haven: Yale Univ Press, 1972. 1st ed, 1st bk. Fine in dj. *LOPEZ.* $75

Casey, Michael. OBSCENITIES. New Haven: Yale Univ Press, 1972. 1st ed. Fine in Fine dj. *BEASLEY.* $75

Casey, Robert J. THE BLACK HILLS AND THEIR INCREDIBLE CHARACTERS. Indianapolis: Bobbs Merrill, (1949). 1st ed. Pamphlet in rear pocket. VG. *SCHOYER'S.* $30

Casey, Robert J. THE LOST KINGDOM OF BURGUNDY. NY: Century Co, 1923. 1st ed. Almost Fine in nearly Fine dj. Bkpl. *AARD.* $30

Cash, W.J. THE MIND OF THE SOUTH. NY: Knopf, 1941. 1st ed. Few small tape marks on eps, but NF in dj with a couple of chips. Nice. Scarce in dj. *CHAPEL HILL.* $200

Casler, Melyer. A JOURNAL GIVING THE INCIDENTS OF A JOURNEY TO CALIFORNIA IN THE SUMMER OF 1859, BY THE OVERLAND ROUTE. Fairfield, WA: Ye Galleon Press, 1969. 1st ed, thus, ltd to 488; this is #164. Orig title pp. Page centers pink w/sepia dec borders. Fine. Howes C220. *CONNOLLY & WADE.* $75

Cass, Lewis. LETTER FROM...TRANSMITTING DOCUMENTS IN RELATION TO HOSTILITIES OF CREEK INDIANS. Wash., HD276, 1836. 1st ed. 413pp. Half morocco. Howes C877. *GINSBERG.* $150

Cassady, Neal. THE FIRST THIRD. (SF): City Lights, (1971). 1st ed. NF in wrappers. *LOPEZ.* $85

CASSELL'S COMPLETE BOOK OF SPORTS & PASTIMES BEING A COMPENDIUM....Cassell, 1896. New ed. 2 vols. Good. *BOOKCELL.* $60

Cassidy, John. A STATION IN THE DELTA. NY: Scribner's, (1979). 1st ed. NF in NF dj. *AKA.* $40

Cassidy, John. A STATION IN THE DELTA. Scribner's 1979. 1st ed. VF in dj. *STAHR.* $15

Casson, Michael. POTTERY IN BRITAIN TODAY. London: Titanti, 1967. 1st ed. Fine in VG+ dj. *AARD.* $20

Castaneda, Carlos. TALES OF POWER. Simon and Schuster, 1974. 1st ed. Fine in dj. *STAHR.* $25

Castaneda, Carlos. THE EAGLE'S GIFT. Simon and Schuster, 1981. Uncorrected proof. VF in pale yellow wraps. *STAHR.* $25

Castel, Albert. GENERAL STERLING PRICE AND THE CIVIL WAR IN THE WEST. Baton Rouge, (1968). 1st ed. 300pp. Dj wear, o/w Fine. *PRATT.* $60

Castel, Albert. WILLIAM CLARKE QUANTRILL, HIS LIFE AND TIMES. NY, (1962). 1st ed. NF in dj. *PRATT.* $30

Castiglioni, Arturo. A HISTORY OF MEDICINE. NY, 1941. 1st ed. Backstrip dull. *FYE.* $150

Castle, Cora. A STATISTICAL STUDY OF EMINENT WOMEN. 1913. 1st ed. *FYE.* $75

Castle, Egerton. ENGLISH BOOK-PLATES. London: George Bell & Sons, 1893. Rev and enlarged ed. Covers rubbed, cl worn along hinges. *OAK KNOLL.* $55

Castle, Henry A. MINNESOTA, ITS STORY & BIOGRAPHY. Chicago & NY: Lewis Publishing Company, 1915. 3 vols. VG. *BOHLING.* $150

Castle, Henry Anson. THE ARMY MULE AND OTHER WAR SKETCHES. Indianapolis, 1898. 1st ed. Inner hinge starting, else NF. *McGOWAN.* $60

Castleman, Harvey N. THE TEXAS RANGERS. Girard, Kansas: Haldeman-Julius, 1944. 1st ed. Fine in wraps. *GIBBS.* $25

Castlereagh, Viscount Frederick. A JOURNEY TO DAMASCUS THROUGH EGYPT, NUBIA, ARABIA PETRAEA, PALESTINE, AND SYRIA. London, 1847. 10 plts. 2 vols. New 1/2 calf, raised bands. viii,291pp; vi,308pp, 8pp of ads. Very attractive. O'NEILL. $575

Caswell, John E. ARCTIC FRONTIERS. Norman: Univ of Oklahoma Press, (1956). 1st ed. Fine in VG dj. BLUE DRAGON. $25

CATALOGUE OF THE AMERICAN LIBRARY OF THE LATE SAMUEL LATHAM MITCHILL BARLOW. Cl backed boards, morocco corners, morocco label on spine, w/orig ptd front wrapper bound in. Corners and label worn, cvrs a bit rubbed, else VG, w/prices realized neatly noted in outer margins. WREDEN. $150

CATALOGUE OF THE LIBRARY OF THOMAS JEFFERSON. E. Millicent Sowerby (comp). Charlottesville: (Univ Press of VA), 1983. 5 vols. Pub in ed of 400. Pub's black cl, burgundy spine labels. In as published condition. BOOK BLOCK. $250

Cather, Thomas. VOYAGE TO AMERICA. THE JOURNALS OF THOMAS CATHER. Thomas Yoseloff (ed). NY: Yoseloff, 1961. 1st ed. Fine in VG dj. CONNOLLY & WADE. $25

Cather, Willa. A LOST LADY. (LEC, 1983). One of 1500, signed by the artist, William Bailey. VF in slipcase. PIRAGES. $350

Cather, Willa. A LOST LADY. Knopf, 1923. 1st trade ed. On pg 174, line 19, "af" for "of." Fine. AUTHORS OF THE WEST. $50

Cather, Willa. A LOST LADY. NY: Knopf, 1923. Name, address under flap, else Fine in NF dj. 1st ed, 1st ptg, with "of" correctly ptd in line 19 of page (174). Very Scarce in this ed. CHAPEL HILL. $175

Cather, Willa. COLLECTED SHORT FICTION. Lincoln: Univ of Nebraska Press, 1965. 1st ed. NF in like dj (spine internally reinforced). BEASLEY. $75

Cather, Willa. DEATH COMES FOR THE ARCHBISHOP. Knopf, 1927. 1st trade ed. Fine, gift message. AUTHORS OF THE WEST. $65

Cather, Willa. DEATH COMES FOR THE ARCHBISHOP. NY: Alfred Knopf, 1927. 1st ed. Grn cl w/paper labels on front covers and spine, light wear to extremities, spine label lightly sunned. DAWSON'S. $75

Cather, Willa. DEATH COMES FOR THE ARCHBISHOP. NY: Knopf, 1927. 1st ed. Owner's gift inscrip, o/w NF in dj (chipped at crown; 1" tear bottom front spine fold; minor edge tears). LOPEZ. $450

Cather, Willa. DEATH COMES FOR THE ARCHBISHOP. NY: Knopf, 1929. Cvrs sl spotted, bkpl removed, 2" crack at top of front inner hinge, but VG lacking slipcase. 1st ed. #13 of 170 specially bound, ptd on Rives Cream Plate Paper, signed. CHAPEL HILL. $550

Cather, Willa. DECEMBER NIGHT, A SCENE FROM ..DEATH COMES FOR THE ARCHBISHOP. (NY: Knopf, 1933) 1st ed this format. Illus. Fine in dj. SECOND LIFE. $35

Cather, Willa. DECEMBER NIGHT: A SCENE FROM "DEATH COMES FOR THE ARCHBISHOP". Knopf, 1933. 1st ed. Fine, clean chipped dj. AUTHORS OF THE WEST. $40

Cather, Willa. LUCY GAYHEART. Knopf, 1935. 1st ed. VG with sunned spine. BEBBAH. $25

Cather, Willa. LUCY GAYHEART. Knopf, 1935. 1st trade ed. Fine, spine faded some. AUTHORS OF THE WEST. $35

Cather, Willa. LUCY GAYHEART. NY, 1935. 1st ed. Bkpl, spine sunned unevenly. NF in dj (little torn, extremities, spine chipped). POLYANTHOS. $25

Cather, Willa. LUCY GAYHEART. NY: Alfred A. Knopf, 1935. Ltd ed. Signed. Dj has chip top edge of rear panel & a few internally mended tears; in moderately worn slipcase. VG+ in VG dj. BERNARD. $325

Cather, Willa. LUCY GAYHEART. NY: Knopf, 1935. 1/749 numbered, signed. Owner name, bkpl, o/w this is NF (sl spine sunned),

lacking dj, in VG pub's box w/sl splitting along top edge. LOPEZ. $275

Cather, Willa. LUCY GAYHEART. NY: Knopf, 1935. 1st ed. Spine sl faded underneath the dj, spot on feps, o/w NF in VG dj (few short edge tears; minor chip). LOPEZ. $75

Cather, Willa. NOT UNDER FORTY. London: Cassell and Company Ltd, (1936). 1st Eng ed. Fine in dj w/few very small tears. HELLER. $125

Cather, Willa. SAPPHIRA AND THE SLAVE GIRL. Knopf, 1940. 1st trade ed. Fine in dj. AUTHORS OF THE WEST. $75

Cather, Willa. SAPPHIRA AND THE SLAVE GIRL. NY: Knopf, 1940. 1st ed. One of 520 specially-bound, signed. Fine in ptd French-fold dj sl browned at spine and moderately worn slipcase. CAPTAIN'S BOOKSHELF. $425

Cather, Willa. SAPPHIRA AND THE SLAVE GIRL. NY: Knopf, 1940. 1st ed. Orig grn cl with paper labels. NF in dj. CHAPEL HILL. $125

Cather, Willa. THE OLD BEAUTY AND OTHERS. Knopf, 1948. 1st ed. NF in VG dj. BEBBAH. $40

Cather, Willa. THE OLD BEAUTY AND OTHERS. NY: Knopf, 1948. 1st ed. VG. SMITH. $35

Cather, Willa. THE OLD BEAUTY AND OTHERS. NY: Knopf, 1948. 1st ed. Fine in NF dj. LOPEZ. $65

Cather, Willa. THE PROFESSOR'S HOUSE. Knopf, 1925. 1st ed. Light spots to front edge, faintest soil to orange covers else VG. BEBBAH. $35

Cather, Willa. THE PROFESSOR'S HOUSE. Knopf, 1925. 1st trade ed. Name, date, spine darkened but readable, else Fine. AUTHORS OF THE WEST. $50

Cather, Willa. WILLA CATHER IN EUROPE: HER OWN STORY OF THE FIRST JOURNEY. Knopf, 1956. 1st ed. Fine in dj. AUTHORS OF THE WEST. $25

Catich, Edward M. LETTERS REDRAWN FROM THE TRAJAN INSCRIPTION IN ROME. Davenport, IA: St. Ambrose College, 1961. 93 plts. Pocketed case and bk in orange buckram, alphabetical device in gilt on front covers, title in gilt on spine. Edges sl worn. VG. HELLER. $250

Catich, Edward M. THE ORIGIN OF THE SERIF. BRUSH WRITING & ROMAN LETTERS. Davenport, Iowa: Catfish Press, (1968). 1st ed. Owner sig, o/w Fine in laminated dj. JAFFE. $225

Catlin, George. CATLIN'S NOTES OF EIGHT YEARS' TRAVELS AND RESIDENCE IN EUROPE, WITH HIS NORTH AMERICAN INDIAN COLLECTION. NY: Burgess, Stringer & Co, 1848. 1st ed. 24 Fine illus. Tops and foot of spines chipped. HUDSON. $375

Catlin, George. GEORGE CATLIN. EPISODES FROM LIFE AMONG THE INDIANS.... Norman: Univ of OK, (1959). Marvin C. Ross (ed). 1st ed. Fine in VG dj. OREGON. $60

Catlin, George. GEORGE CATLIN. EPISODES FROM LIFE...AND LAST RAMBLES. Marvin C. Ross (ed). Univ of OK, (1959). 1st ed. VF in VG dj. OREGON. $65

Catlin, George. ILLUSTRATIONS OF THE MANNERS, CUSTOMS & CONDITION OF THE NORTH AMERICAN INDIANS. WITH LETTERS AND NOTES, WRITTEN DURING EIGHT YEARS OF TRAVEL AND ADVENTURE AMONG THE WILDEST AND MOST REMARKABLE TRIBES NOW EXISTING. (London: Chatto & Windus, 1876). viii,264pp; viii,266pp. 2 vols. Recent 3/4 morocco, marbled paper sides, raised bands, morocco labels. 180 colored plts after paintings by Catlin (inc a fldg map). First title and each plate with small embossed oval library stamp (withdrawn stamp on verso of both titles). Fldg map repaired, final leaf of first volume and penultimate leaf in second torn and silked on verso, frontis in second volume neatly repaired at inner margin, one unrepaired closed tear into text, some short marginal tears well away from text; text very sl darkened at extreme edge and w/minor smudging; generally, very smooth and clean set. *PIRAGES.* $750

Catlin, George. LETTERS AND NOTES ON THE MANNERS, CUSTOMERS....Minneapolis: Ross and Haines, 1965. (1841) 2 vols. Ltd to 2000 sets. Grn cl. Slipcase somewhat worn, yet both vols in VF condition. Howes C241. *CONNOLLY & WADE.* $150

Catlin, George. LIFE AMONG THE INDIANS. London & Edinburgh: Gall & Inglis, n.d. Pictorial red cl, 352pp, 7 plts, aeg. Bumped, cl sl split along joint. Contents NF. *BLUE MOUNTAIN.* $85

Catlin, George. LIFE AMONG THE INDIANS. London: Gall & Inglis, n.d. (1890). 352pp. Frontis, 3 plts. VG. *OREGON.* $60

Catlin, George. NORTH AMERICAN INDIANS. Edinburgh: John Grant, 1903. 2 vols. 298;303pp, maps, 400 illus. 25.1 cm, burgundy cl w/elaborate black, gilt cvr and spine dec. Modest shelfwear; covers bright; partially unopened. Inscrip, pencil notation. *PARMER.* $500

Caton, J.D. THE ANTELOPE AND DEER OF AMERICA, A COMPREHENSIVE SCIENTIFIC TREATISE UPON THE NATURAL HISTORY...OF THE ANTILOCAPRA AND CERVIDAE OF NORTH AMERICA. Portrait frontis, 54 wood engr. NY, 1877. 1st ed. xvi,426pp. Orig gilt-stamped cl. Head of spine and rear corner perished; some overall wear & soiling; # sticker on spine; institutional bkpl. *SUTTON.* $75

Caton-Thompson, G. KHARGA OASIS IN PREHISTORY. London: Univ of London, The Athlone Press, 1952. 128 plts. Signature. Good. *ARCHAEOLOGIA.* $350

Cattell, Henry. POST-MORTEM PATHOLOGY: A MANUAL OF POST-MORTEM EXAMINATIONS AND THE INTERPRETATIONS TO BE DRAWN THEREFROM. Phila, 1905. 2nd ed. 183 illus. Scarce. *FYE.* $100

Catton, Bruce. GRANT TAKES COMMAND. Boston, (1968). 1st ed. A little cover wear o/w Fine in dj. *PRATT.* $25

Catton, Bruce. THE COMING FURY. GC: Doubleday, 1961. 1st ed. 5 plts. Fine in NF dj. *CONNOLLY & WADE.* $37.50

Catton, Bruce. THE WAR LORDS OF WASHINGTON. NY: Harcourt, (1948). 1st ed, 1st bk. VG in chipped dj. *ARTIS.* $25

Catton, Bruce. WAITING FOR THE MORNING TRAIN. GC, 1972. 1st ed after ltd ed of 250. Some dj wear o/w Fine. *PRATT.* $35

Catton, William and Bruce. TWO ROADS TO SUMTER. NY, (1963). 1st ed. Fine in dj with some wear and 1" tear. *PRATT.* $20

Caudwell, Sarah. THE SHORTEST WAY TO HADES. NY: Charles Scribner's Sons, 1985. 1st Amer ed. Fine in price-clipped dj. *MORDIDA.* $25

Caudwell, Sarah. THE SIRENS SANG OF MURDER. London: Collins Crime Club, 1989. 1st ed. VF in dj. *MORDIDA.* $40

Caudwell, Sarah. THE SIRENS SANG OF MURDER. London: Collins, 1989. 1st ed. Fine in dj. *SILVER DOOR.* $25

Caudwell, Sarah. THUS WAS ADONIS MURDERED. NY: Scribner's, (1981). 1st ed. Signed. Fine in Fine dj. *UNGER.* $50

Caudwell, Sarah. THUS WAS ADONIS MURDERED. NY: Scribners, 1981. 1st Amer ed. Fine in dj. *MORDIDA.* $35

Cauffman, Stanley. THE WITCHFINDERS. Penn, 1934. 1st ed. Near VG. *MADLE.* $20

Caughey, John W. GOLD IS THE CORNERSTONE. Univ CA, 1948. 1st ed. Fine in VG dj. *OREGON.* $45

Caughey, John Walton. THE AMERICAN WEST: FRONTIER & REGION....Ward Ritchie Press, (1969). 1st ed. Norris Hundley, Jr John A. Schutz (eds). Frontis. Fine in dj. *AUTHORS OF THE WEST.* $25

Caunitz, William J. ONE POLICE PLAZA. NY: Crown, 1984. 1st ed. VF in dj. *ELSE FINE.* $35

Cauthorn, Henry S. A HISTORY OF THE CITY OF VINCENNES, INDIANA FROM 1702 TO 1901. (Terre Haute, 1902). Binding bit soiled, spotted. VG. *BOHLING.* $50

Cautley, Marjorie S. GARDEN DESIGN. NY: Dodd, Mead & Co., 1935. 1st ed. 312pp. Illus. *AKA.* $30

Cavafy, (Constantine P.) THE COMPLETE POEMS OF CAVAFY. NY: Harcourt, Brace & World, (1961). 1st ed. Orig tan cl. VG in dj. *CHAPEL HILL.* $45

CAVALCADE OF THE AMERICAN NEGRO. Chicago: Diamond Jubilee Exposition, 1940. 1st ed. Wraps. Fine. *BEASLEY.* $45

Cave, F.O. and J.D. Macdonald. BIRDS OF THE SUDAN, THEIR IDENTIFICATION AND DISTRIBUTION. 12 full-pg colored plts. London, 1955. Lt rubbing; inner hinge reinforced, o/w Very nice. *SUTTON.* $325

Cave, Hugh B. DISCIPLES OF DREAD. Tor, 1988. 1st ed. As New (special ed w/tipped-in signature pg). *MADLE.* $50

Cave, Hugh B. MURGUNSTRUMM AND OTHERS. Chapel Hill: Carcosa, 1977. 1st ed. NF to Fine in dj. *OTHER WORLDS.* $50

Cave, Hugh B. MURGUNSTRUMM AND OTHERS. Chapel Hill: Carcossa, 1977. 1st ed. VF in dj. *ELSE FINE.* $40

Cave, Nick. AND THE ASS SAW THE ANGEL. (London: Black Spring, 1989). 1st ed. Fine in dj. Author's 1st novel. *WOOLMER.* $35

Cawadias, A.P. HERMAPHRODITOS. London: William Heinemann Medical Books Ltd, 1946. Good. *WREDEN.* $35

Cazin, Achille. THE PHENOMENA AND LAWS OF HEAT. NY: Charles Scribner, 1869. Elihu Rich (ed). Ex-lib, blindstamped red cl, gilt dec spine; stamp, bumping, wear; foxing to frontis, o/w Good. *KNOLLWOOD.* $40

Cecil, Henry. ALIBI FOR A JUDGE. London: Michael Joseph, 1960. 1st ed. Inscribed. Fine in dj w/crease-tear on back panel, several short closed tears and minor wear at corners. *MORDIDA.* $40

Cecil, Henry. CROSS PURPOSES. London: Michael Joseph, 1976. 1st ed. Fine in price-clipped dj w/couple of tiny tears. *MORDIDA.* $40

Cecil, Henry. DAUGHTERS IN LAW. London: Michael Joseph, 1961. 1st ed. Inscribed. Fine in dj w/short closed tear. *MORDIDA.* $50

Cecil, Henry. THE ASKING PRICE. London: Michael Joseph, 1966. 1st ed. Inscribed. Fine in dj. *MORDIDA.* $50

Cela, Camilo Jose. MRS. CALDWELL SPEAKS TO HER SON. Ithaca: Cornell (1968). 1st Amer ed. Rmdr mk top edge else Fine in VG price-clipped dj. *DORN.* $25

Cela, Camilo Jose. THE HIVE. NY: FSY (1953). 1st Amer ed. VG in VG edgeworn dj. *DORN.* $50

Celiere, Paul. THE STARTLING EXPLOITS OF DR J. B. QUIES. Harper, 1887, 1st US ed. Fine. *MADLE.* $100

Cell, Gillian T. NEWFOUNDLAND DISCOVERED. ENGLISH ATTEMPTS AT COLONISATION, 1610-1630. London: The Hakluyt Society, 1982. 1st ed. Fine in lightly rubbed dj. *PARMER.* $35

Cellini, Benvenuto. THE LIFE OF BENVENUTO CELLINI. John Addington Symonds (trans). London: John C. Nimmo, 1889. Full crushed morocco, paneled spine, teg. Fine, partially unopened. *WREDEN.* $150

Cellini, Benvenuto. THE LIFE OF BENVENUTO CELLINI...Trans by John Addington Symonds (trans), Thomas Craven (intro), Fritz Kredel (illus). Dec cl. Verona: LEC, 1937. Ltd to 1500 ptd by Hans Mardersteig at the Officina Bodoni & signed by Kredel. VF in sl worn dj, slipcase. *JAFFE.* $175

Cendrars, Blaise. PANAMA, OR THE ADVENTURES OF MY SEVEN UNCLES. Illus. and trans. by John Dos Passos. NY & London: Harper & Bros., 1931. 12 color illus. Fine in chipped glassine and Good publisher's slipcase lacking top quarter of spine. 1st ed. in Eng. #262 of 300 signed by Dos Passos and Cendrars. *CHAPEL HILL.* $225

CENTURY WAR BOOK. BATTLES AND LEADERS OF THE CIVIL WAR. NY, (1894). 323pp. Some wear to spine. 2 spots on front cover. *HEINOLDT.* $60

Ceram, C.W. ARCHAEOLOGY OF THE CINEMA. NY, (1965). 1st US ed. Dj. NF. *POLYANTHOS.* $50

Ceram, C.W. ARCHAEOLOGY OF THE CINEMA. NY: Harcourt, Brace & World, n.d. (c. 1965). 264pp. Stated 1st US ed. VG+ in torn dj. *AKA.* $30

Cervantes, Maria Antonieta. TREASURES OF AN ANCIENT MEXICO FROM THE NATIONAL ANTHROPOLOGICAL MUSEUM. NY: Crescent Books, 1978. 2nd ed. VG in dj. *PARMER.* $25

Cervantes. DON QUIXOTE DE LA MANCHA. Motteaux' Trans Revised Anew (1743). Illus E. McKnight Kauffer. 2 vols. Full calf w/morocco labels on spines, marbled board slipcase. (Cambridge): Nonesuch Press, (1930). 1st of this ed. Ltd to 1475. Spines sl darkened, o/w a Fine set in sl edge-worn slipcase. *JAFFE.* $450

Cervantes. DON QUIXOTE. THE INGENIOUS GENTLEMAN OF LA MANCHA. John Ormsby (trans). Irwin Edman (intro), Edy Legrand (illus). 2 vols. Cl-backed marbled boards, glassine djs. (Mexico City): LEC, 1950. Ltd to 1500. VF set in slipcase w/worn label. *JAFFE.* $125

Cesaire, Aime. STATE OF THE UNION. n.p. Caterpillar, 1966. 1st ed. Wraps, owner's name. NF w/light curvature. *BEASLEY.* $40

Cescinsky, Herbert. ENGLISH FURNITURE FROM GOTHIC TO SHERATON. NY, 1937. Some staining to bds. NF. *POLYANTHOS.* $75

Cescinsky, Herbert. ENGLISH FURNITURE OF THE EIGHTEENTH CENTURY. 3 VOLS. NY: Funk & Wagnalls Co, 1909. 1st Amer ed. Foxing title pp o/w VG. Small cut one spine. *BACKROOM.* $300

Cescinsky, Herbert. THE OLD WORLD HOUSE. NY: Macmillan, 1924. 1st ed. 2 vols. VG. *BACKROOM.* $110

Chaber, M.E. HANGMAN'S HARVEST. Henry Holt, 1952. 1st ed. Fine in dj (worn). *STAHR.* $25

Chabon, Michael. A MODEL WORLD & OTHER STORIES. Morrow, 1991. Advance reading copy. VF in dec wraps. *STAHR.* $30

Chabon, Michael. THE MYSTERIES OF PITTSBURGH. NY, 1988. 1st ed, 1st bk. Signed bkpl. Fine in like dj. *POLYANTHOS.* $30

Chabon, Michael. THE MYSTERIES OF PITTSBURGH. NY: Morrow, (1988). 1st ed. Signed. Fine in Fine dj. *UNGER.* $60

Chace, Elizabeth Buffum and Lucy Buffum Lovell. TWO QUAKER SISTERS FROM THE ORIGINAL DIARIES OF... NY, (1937). 1st ed. Orig cl. VG. *McGOWAN.* $75

Chacon, Rafael. LEGACY OF HONOR, THE LIFE OF RAFAEL CHACON. Ed by Jacqueline Dorgan Meketa. Albuquerque, (1986). 1st ed. VF in dj. *PRATT.* $25

Chadwick, Douglas H. A BEAST THE COLOR OF WINTER— THE MOUNTAIN GOAT OBSERVED. SF: Sierra Club Books, 1983. 1st ed. Fine in VG+ dj. *BACKMAN.* $30

Chadwick, French E. THE RELATIONS OF THE UNITED STATES AND SPAIN: THE SPANISH-AMERICAN WAR. NY: 1911. 1st ed. 2 vols. Orig cl. *GINSBERG.* $150

Chalfant, W.A. DEATH VALLEY. THE FACTS. Stanford/London: Stanford Univ Press/Oxford Univ Press, 1930. 1st ed. Orig dec cl. Spine has darkened; some edge wear; overall VG. *PARMER.* $45

Chalfant, W.A. GOLD, GUNS, & GHOST TOWNS. Stanford Univ Press, 1954. Pict cl. Frontis. Inscription, else VF in VG dj. *CONNOLLY & WADE.* $27.50

Chalfant, W.A. THE STORY OF INYO. Chicago: Published by author, 1922. Burgundy cl. Errata rear pastedown, fldg sketch map. Slight wear to spine; else VG+. *PARMER.* $60

Chalfant, W.A. THE STORY OF INYO. N.p, 1933. 1st rev ed. Map frontis. Cloth. Inscrip on rear fly, else VF in scarce, VG dj. *CONNOLLY & WADE.* $80

Chalmers, Harvey II. THE LAST STAND OF THE NEZ PERCE, DESTRUCTION OF A PEOPLE. NY, (1962). 1st ed. 288pp. VG+. *PRATT.* $45

Chalmers, Patrick R. THE HORN. London: Collins, 1937. 1st ed. Minor edgewear, else VG. *OLD LONDON.* $40

Chamberlain, Samuel E. MY CONFESSION. NY: Arizona Silhouettes, (1956). 1st ed, ltd to 500 signed, in buckram. Fine in Fine dj. *BOOK MARKET.* $50

Chamberlain, Samuel Emery. MY CONFESSION. NY, (1956). VG in dj. *DIAMOND.* $20

Chamberlayne, Edwin Harvie, Jr. (comp). RECORD OF THE RICHMOND CITY AND HENRICO CO. VIRGINIA TROOPS, CONFEDERATE STATES ARMY. Series No. 1, 2 and 6. Richmond, 1879. 3 vols. Wrappers. VG+. *McGOWAN.* $150

Chamberlin, Ethel. THE AMAZING ADVENTURES OF KERMIT THE HERMIT CRAB. Sully, (1930). Illus by author, color frontis. Cvrs have wear, fading else VG. *BEBBAH.* $35

Chambers, Raymond Wilson. THOMAS MORE. London and Toronto: Jonathan Cape, (1935). 1st ed. Frontis, plts, brn cl. VG. *WEBER.* $50

Chambers, Robert W. IN SEARCH OF THE UNKNOWN. NY & London, 1904. 1st ed. Color frontis. Light rub touches to cover. VG. *McCLINTOCK.* $55

Chambers, Robert W. QUICK ACTION. Appleton, 1914. 1st ed. Good. *MADLE.* $23

Chambers, Robert W. THE KING IN YELLOW. Harper, 1907 VG. *MADLE.* $30

Chambers, Robert W. THE TALKERS. Doran. 1923. 1st ed. VG *MADLE.* $25

Chambers, Robert W. THE TREE OF HEAVEN. Appleton, 1907. VG. *MADLE.* $30

Chambers, William. AMERICAN SLAVERY AND COLOUR. London, 1861. 2nd Eng ed, enl. Orig cl, slight wear to spine ends, else VG. *McGOWAN.* $150

Chambliss, Rev. J.E. THE LIFE AND LABORS OF DAVID LIVINGSTONE COVERING HIS ENTIRE CAREER IN SOUTHERN AND CENTRAL AFRICA. Phil: Hubbard Bros., 1875. 1st ed. Very minor wear top/bottom spine. Interior tight, clean. NF. *GREAT EPIC.* $95

Champion, F.W. THE JUNGLE IN SUNLIGHT & SHADOW. NY: Scribner, (1934). 1st US ed. 95 full page photos. VG. *MIKESH.* $47.50

Champion, F.W. WITH A CAMERA IN TIGER-LAND. NY: Doubleday, 1928. 1st US ed. 73 full page photos. VG. *MIKESH.* $37.50

Champney, Elizabeth W. ROMANCE OF THE FEUDAL CHATEAUX. NY, London: G. P. Putnam's Sons, 1906. 1st Amer ed. Newspaper offset browning 1p, o/w VG. *WEBER.* $45

Chance, Frank. THE BRIDE AND THE PENNANT. Laird & Lee, 1910. Rare 1st novel. VG without dj, as issued. *PLAPINGER.* $950

Chandler, Allison. TROLLEY THROUGH THE COUNTRYSIDE. Denver: Sage Books, (1963). Buckram dj. VG in soiled & frayed dj. *BOHLING.* $75

Chandler, Frank Wadleigh. THE LITERATURE OF ROGUERY. 2 vols. Boston: Houghton Mifflin, 1907. 1st ed. Laid in is handwritten letter signed. Fine w/o dj. *MORDIDA.* $125

Chandler, Lt. Col. Melbourne C. OF GARRY OWEN IN GLORY, THE HISTORY OF THE 7TH U.S. CAVALRY. N.p., (1960). 1st ed. Fldg maps. Little dj wear o/w Fine. *PRATT.* $105

Chandler, Raymond. FAREWELL MY LOVELY. NY: Knopf, 1940. 1st ed. A small discoloration on top edge o/w Fine, bright w/o dj. *MORDIDA.* $250

Chandler, Raymond. FAREWELL, MY LOVELY. NY: Knopf, 1940. 1st ed. Rebound in full medium brown leather w/striking marbled eps by W.W. Streeter. Handsomely preserved. *CAPTAIN'S BOOKSHELF.* $500

Chandler, Raymond. FAREWELL, MY LOVELY/THE LADY IN THE LAKE. Modern Library, 1967. 1st thus. VG or better in price-clipped dj (worn,internally reinforced at spine ends). Owner's name twice on front matter. *STAHR.* $20

Chandler, Raymond. FIVE SINISTER CHARACTERS. NY: Avon Book Company, (1945). 1st ed. Wrappers, some soiling. *JUVELIS.* $90

Chandler, Raymond. KILLER IN THE RAIN. London: Hamish, (1964). 1st ed. NF in NF, partly sunfaded dj. *UNGER.* $350

Chandler, Raymond. PLAYBACK. Boston: Houghton Mifflin, 1958. 1st US ed. NF in VG dj. *LOPEZ.* $125

Chandler, Raymond. PLAYBACK. London: Hamish Hamilton, (1958). 1st ed, preceding the US pub. Spine very sl cocked, o/w Fine in NF dj. *LOPEZ.* $150

Chandler, Raymond. PLAYBACK. London: Hamish Hamilton, 1958. 1st ed. Fine in dj (sl spine fading; wear top of spine; short closed tears; minor wear, sm stain inner front flap). *MORDIDA.* $85

Chandler, Raymond. SPANISH BLOOD, A COLLECTION OF SHORT STORIES. Cleveland, NY: World Pub Co, (1946). Tower Books ed. Paper sl browning, else Fine in dj. *HELLER.* $85

Chandler, Raymond. SPANISH BLOOD. Cleveland and NY: World, (1946). 1st ed thus. VG in lightly chipped, soiled dj w/internal tape repairs. *JUVELIS.* $40

Chandler, Raymond. SPANISH BLOOD. NY & Cleveland: World, (1946). 1st ed. Pages browned as usual this book (cheap paper) o/w NF in bright, attractive dj. *BERNARD.* $65

Chandler, Raymond. SPANISH BLOOD. NY: World, (1946). 1st ed. Fine in Fine dj. *UNGER.* $75

Chandler, Raymond. THE BIG SLEEP. Cleveland: World, 1946. 1st ed thus. Motion picture ed. 2 water spots on front cover, browning pp, VG+ in Good+ dj (creased, chipped). *ARCHER.* $15

Chandler, Raymond. THE BIG SLEEP. NY: Alfred A. Knopf, 1939. 1st ed. VG in a Fine, restored dj that has a sl darkened spine and back panel. *MORDIDA.* $2250

Chandler, Raymond. THE BIG SLEEP. NY: Knopf, 1939. 1st ed. VG without dj. *MORDIDA.* $150

Chandler, Raymond. THE BIG SLEEP. World, 1946. 1st movie ed. 165pp. Slight edgewear, pp browning but VG. *BEBBAH.* $20

Chandler, Raymond. THE HIGH WINDOW. NY, 1942. 1st ed. Minor shelfwear. Beginning of small chew mark at upper corner, o/w VG. *DIAMOND.* $45

Chandler, Raymond. THE HIGH WINDOW. NY: Knopf, 1942. 1st ed. NF lacking dj. *CAPTAIN'S BOOKSHELF.* $200

Chandler, Raymond. THE HIGH WINDOW. NY: Knopf, 1942. 1st ed. VG w/o dj. *MORDIDA.* $100

Chandler, Raymond. THE LADY IN THE LAKE. Stockholm, London: Zephyr Books, (c1943). Rprt. VG in sl soiled dj, edge tears. *BERNARD.* $85

Chandler, Raymond. THE LITTLE SISTER. Boston: Houghton Mifflin, 1949. 1st Amer ed. Fine in dj (spine fading; closed tears; minor wear top of spine). *MORDIDA.* $350

Chandler, Raymond. THE SECOND CHANDLER OMNIBUS. London: Hamish Hamilton, (1962). 1st UK ed. Fine in VG+ dj (chipped, soiled). *BERNARD.* $90

Chandler, Raymond. THE SIMPLE ART OF MURDER. Boston: Houghton Mifflin, 1950. 1st ed. Fine in dj (sl faded spine; short closed tears; short crease-chip lower corner front panel). *MORDIDA.* $400

Chandler, Raymond. THE SIMPLE ART OF MURDER. London: Hamish, (1950). 1st English ed. VG in VG, lightly chipped dj. *UNGER.* $350

Chapel, Charles Edward. GUNS OF THE OLD WEST. NY, (1961). 1st ed. Light dj wear o/w Fine. *PRATT.* $40

Chapelle, Howard I. THE BALTIMORE CLIPPER. Salem, MA: The Marine Research Society. 1930. 1st ed. Textured blue cloth, gilt spine. Fine. *KARMIOLE.* $125

Chapelle, Howard I. THE BALTIMORE CLIPPER; ITS ORIGIN AND DEVELOPMENT. Salem, 1930. Pub. 22. One of 97 lg paper copies. Tear to head of spine. *LEFKOWICZ.* $225

Chapelle, Howard I. THE HISTORY OF AMERICAN SAILING SHIPS. NY, W.W. Norton, 1935. 2nd prtg. Spine age darkened; light soil, else VG. *PARMER.* $50

Chapelle, Howard I. THE HISTORY OF THE AMERICAN SAILING NAVY. NY: W.W. Norton, 1949. 1st ed. VG in chipped and worn dj. *PARMER.* $75

Chapin, Elisabeth Leonard. EXPERIENCES OF A LITTLE TRAVELER: EXTRACTS...EDITED BY HER SISTER. Chicago: Geo. E. Marshall, 1898. Turquoise cl stamped in gilt, rubbed. Portrait. Owner sigs, o/w VG. *SCHOYER'S.* $45

Chapin, Eugene. BY-GONE DAYS OR THE EXPERIENCES OF AN AMERICAN. Boston, 1898. 3 plts. Spine ends rubbed, bkpl. VG. *BOHLING.* $65

Chapin, Howard M. THE TARTAR: THE ARMED SLOOP OF THE COLONY OF RHODE ISLAND IN KING GEORGE'S WAR...Providence, 1922. 1st ed. Fldg plt. Orig cl. *GINSBERG.* $35

Chaplin, Ralph. WOBBLY. Chicago: Univ of Chicago, 1948. 1st ed. 8 photo plts. Fine in Good bright red dj. *CONNOLLY & WADE.* $55

Chapman, A.P.F. THE GAME OF CRICKET. Seeley, Service & Co., 1930. 1st ed. (The Lonsdale Library, Vol VI). VG. *OLD LONDON.* $50

Chapman, Abel. ON SAFARI: BIG GAME HUNTING IN BRITISH EAST AFRICA...London, 1908. 1st ed. Ex-lib, some markings, front hinge repaired w/lib tape. Top of spine cl chipped. Bkpl. VG. *McCLINTOCK.* $45

Chapman, Ervin S. PARTICIPS CRIMINIS. NY: Revell, (1910). Port, 7 photos, pict cl. *SCHOYER'S.* $30

Chapman, F. Spencer. NORTHERN LIGHTS—THE OFFICIAL ACCOUNT OF THE BRITISH ARCTIC AIR-ROUTE. NY: Oxford Univ Press, 1933. 1st Amer ed. Chipped dj. Lt foxing lower boards, edges. *PARMER.* $75

Chapman, F.M. AUTOBIOGRAPHY OF A BIRD LOVER. NY & London: Appleton, 1933. VG. *MIKESH.* $50

Chapman, F.M. COLOR KEY TO NORTH AMERICAN BIRDS....NY, 1912. Rev ed. Lt scuffing, soiling; scattered pencil checks in text. *SUTTON.* $35

Chapman, F.M. THE WARBLERS OF NORTH AMERICA. NY, 1907. 1st ed. 24 colored plts. Some foxing on title; ex-lib. *SUTTON.* $55

Chapman, John A. HISTORY OF EDGEFIELD COUNTY FROM THE EARLIEST SETTLEMENTS TO 1897. BIOGRAPHICAL AND ANECDOTAL....Newberry, SC, 1897. 1st ed. 521,(6)pp. Orig cl, sm paper label on spine, bkpl removed. Howes C294. *GINSBERG.* $150

Chapman, John Mitchel. CORSICA: AN ISLAND OF REST. London: Edward Stanford, 1908. Little faded, soiled, light foxing. *SCHOYER'S.* $20

Chapman, N. LECTURES ON THE MORE IMPORTANT DISEASES OF THE THORACIC AND ABDOMINAL VISCERA.

Phila, 1844. 1st ed. Full leather, 383pp. Title page and prelim leaves waterstained, recent label, o/w VG. *FYE.* $75

Chapman, Olive Murray. ACROSS LAPLAND WITH SLEDGE AND REINDEER. London, (1932). 1st ed. Minor shelfwear. *ARTIS.* $35

Chapman, R. A. REVIEW OF RIPLEY'S "DEFENCE,"...ESQ. COUNSEL FOR THE ACCUSED MARCH 16, 1846. Springfield, 1846. 1st ed. 30pp. Contemp plain wrappers. *GINSBERG.* $50

Chapman, Victor (Emmanuel). VICTOR CHAPMAN'S LETTERS FROM FRANCE. WITH A MEMOIR BY JOHN JAY CHAPMAN. NY: McMillan, 1917. 8 plts. Orig boards, cl spine w/paper labels on backstrip and front cover. *GINSBERG.* $75

Chapman, W. and L. WILDERNESS WANDERERS, ADVENTURES AMONG WILD ANIMALS IN ROCKY MOUNTAIN SOLITUDES. NY, 1937. Cloth. 3 scars on spine, dj worn. *SUTTON.* $35

Chappell, Fred. BRIGHTEN THE CORNER WHERE YOU ARE. NY: St. Martin's, (1989). 1st Amer ed. Signed. Fine in dj. *DORN.* $35

Chappell, Fred. BRIGHTEN THE CORNER WHERE YOU ARE. NY: St. Martin's Press, (1989). Uncorrected proof. Fine in wrappers. *CAPTAIN'S BOOKSHELF.* $50

Chappell, Fred. BRIGHTEN THE CORNER WHERE YOU ARE. NY: St. Martin's, (1989). 1st ed. New in dj. Signed. *CAPTAIN'S BOOKSHELF.* $40

Chappell, Fred. I AM ONE OF YOU FOREVER. Baton Rouge & London: Louisiana State Univ. Press, 1985. Uncorrected proof of 1st ed. Orig spiral-bound blue wraps w/ptd cvr label. Leaves ptd on rectos only. A few instances of reviewer's marginalia. VG. *CHAPEL HILL.* $85

Chappell, Fred. IT IS TIME, LORD. NY: Atheneum, 1963. 1st ed, 1st bk. Signed. Orig cl-backed charcoal boards. Bright, NF in dj (very modest wear around head of spine). *CHAPEL HILL.* $125

Chappell, Fred. MIDQUEST: A POEM. Baton Rouge: Louisiana State Univ Press, 1981. 1st ed. Fine in dj. Signed. *CAPTAIN'S BOOKSHELF.* $50

Chappell, Fred. MOMENTS OF LIGHT. LA: The New South Co, (1980). 1st ed. Fine in dj. Signed. *CAPTAIN'S BOOKSHELF.* $100

Chappell, Fred. MORE SHAPES THAN ONE. NY: St. Martin's (1991). Uncorrected proof. Fine in wraps. *DORN.* $30

Chappell, Fred. MORE SHAPES THAN ONE. NY: St. Martin's, (1991). 1st Amer ed. Signed. Fine in dj. *DORN.* $30

Chappell, Fred. THE GAUDY PLACE. NY: Harcourt Brace Jovanovich, (1973). 1st ed. Orig orange cl. Fine in dj. *CHAPEL HILL.* $40

Chappell, Fred. THE INKLING. London: Chapman & Hall, (1965). 1st UK ed. Signed. Fine in price-clipped sl sunned dj. *ROBBINS.* $60

Chappell, Fred. THE INKLING. NY: Harcourt, (1965). 1st ed. Fine in dj w/two short tears. Signed. *CAPTAIN'S BOOKSHELF.* $75

Chappell, Fred. THE WORLD BETWEEN THE EYES. Baton Rouge: LSU Press, 1971. 1st ed. Fine in price-clipped dj, sticker removal front flap. Signed. *CAPTAIN'S BOOKSHELF.* $75

Chappell, Fred. THE WORLD BETWEEN THE EYES. Baton Rouge: Louisiana State Univ, 1971. 1st ed. Signed. Fine in Fine dj. *ROBBINS.* $50

Chappell, Warren. A SHORT HISTORY OF THE PRINTED WORD. NY: Knopf, 1970. 1st ed. Fine. *OAK KNOLL.* $35

Chaptal, J.A. CHYMISTRY APPLIED TO AGRICULTURE. Hilliard, Gray, 1835. 1st Amer ed. 365pp. Leather cvrs, modern paper label, usual foxing o/w Good+. *BOOKCELL.* $50

Chaput, Donald. FRANCOIS X. AUBRY, TRADER, TRAILMAKER...1846-1854. A.H. Clark, 1975. 1st ed. VF. *OREGON.* $30

Char, Rene. HYPNOS WALKING; POEMS AND PROSE. NY: Random House (1956). 1st ed. Bilingual ed. VF in sl used NF dj. *DORN.* $65

Charbonneau, Andre et al. QUEBEC, THE FORTIFIED CITY: FROM THE 17TH CENTURY TO THE 19TH CENTURY. (Ottawa, 1982). 1st ed. Fldg maps in rear pocket. Orig printed wraps. *GINSBERG.* $50

Charbonneaux, Jean (ed). ARCHAIC GREEK ART (620-480 B.C.). NY: George Braziller, (1971). 106 color illus, 31 plans, 4 maps. Dj. Good. *ARCHAEOLOGIA.* $150

Charbonneaux, Jean et al. ARCHAIC GREEK ART (620-480 B.C.). NY: Braziller, 1971. 1st ed. Fldg color plan. Dj torn. VG. *WORLDWIDE.* $65

Charcot, J.M. CLINICAL LECTURES ON THE DISEASES OF OLD AGE. NY, 1881. 1st Eng trans. 280pp. *FYE.* $150

Charcot, J.M. LECTURES ON LOCALISATION OF CEREBRAL AND SPINAL DISEASES. London, 1883. 1st Eng trans. 341pp. *FYE.* $300

Chard, Thomas S. CALIFORNIA SKETCHES. Chicago, n.p., 1888. VG. *LAURIE.* $125

Chardin, Sir John. SIR JOHN CHARDIN'S TRAVELS IN PERSIA. London: Argonaut Press, 1927. 3rd ed. #694 of ed ltd to 975. 7 plts (2 fldg), 2 textual illus. Orig cl w/vellum spine, sl rubbed, o/w VG untrimmed, unopened. *WORLDWIDE.* $225

Chardin, Sir John. TRAVELS IN PERSIA. WITH AN INTRODUCTION BY BRIG-GEN SIR PERCY SYKES... London: Argonaut Press, 1927. Uncut. Ltd to 975. *O'NEILL.* $125

Charhardi, Driss ben Hamed. A LIFE FULL OF HOLES. NY: Grove, (1964). Paul Bowles, trans. 1st ed. Owner stamp, o/w Fine in dj. *LOPEZ.* $35

CHARLES M. RUSSELL CATALOGUE OF KARL YOST. Weatherford, Southworth, Wash. n/d (c. 1987) 138pp. Wraps. *HEINOLDT.* $35

Charles, Mrs. Tom. TALES OF THE TULAROSA. Alamogordo: Privately ptd for author, 1959. 3rd prtg of rev ed of 1954. Full cl. Fine in dj. *LAURIE.* $40

Charley, Irene. THE BIRTH OF INDUSTRIAL NURSING: ITS HISTORY AND DEVELOPMENT IN GREAT BRITAIN. London, 1954. 1st ed. Signed. *FYE.* $75

Charlot, Jean. ART FROM THE MAYANS TO DISNEY. NY: Sheed & Ward, 1939. 1st ed. 27 plts. Cl cvrs, dj soiled. Writing on fly. Fore-edges soiled, else VG. *DIAMOND.* $75

Charlot, Jean. CHARLOT MURALS IN GEORGIA. Univ of Georgia Press, (1945). 1st ed. Fine in price clipped dj. *POLYANTHOS.* $75

Charlot, Jean. THE MEXICAN MURAL RENAISSANCE 1920-1925. New Haven: Yale, 1963. 1st ed. Spine somewhat faded, else NF in price-clipped dj (short tear). *CAPTAIN'S BOOKSHELF.* $75

Charlton, Robert M. and Thomas J. Charlton. POEMS. Boston: Charles C. Little and James Brown, 1839. 1st ed. 12mo, 174pp. Orig emb cl. Lib bkpl, blindstamp, rear flyleaf lacking, else VG. *CHAPEL HILL.* $125

Charlton, Thomas V. P. THE LIFE OF MAJOR-GENERAL JAMES JACKSON. Augusta, GA, 1809. (Atlanta, 1896). 215pp. 13 ports, 2 plts. Orig cl (frayed at top of front cover; spine a little faded). Ltd to 250. Reprint of rare orig ed. Howes C309. *GINSBERG.* $125

Charnas, Suzy McKee. THE VAMPIRE TAPESTRY. NY: Simon & Schuster, 1980. 1st ed. VF in dj. *ELSE FINE.* $100

Charnwood, Lady (Dorothea Mary Benson). AN AUTOGRAPH COLLECTION, AND THE MAKING OF IT. London: Ernest Benn, 1930. 1st ed. Fine. *WREDEN.* $30

Charnwood, Lord. ABRAHAM LINCOLN. London: Constable & Co, 1919. 5th ptg of 2nd ed. Frontis, fldg map. Wear spine, ends. *SCHOYER'S*. $12.50

Charteris, Leslie. CALL FOR THE SAINT. GC: Doubleday, 1948. 1st ed. Fine. Minor edgewear; sm chips spine ends of dj. *ELSE FINE*. $50

Charteris, Leslie. COUNT ON THE SAINT. GC: Doubleday Crime Club, 1980. 1st ed. VF in dj. *ELSE FINE*. $25

Charteris, Leslie. ENTER THE SAINT. Doubleday, Doran, (1931). 1st Amer ed. 320pp. Good+ with general cvr wear. *BEBBAH*. $12

Charteris, Leslie. SENOR SAINT. London, H & S, 1948. 1st ed. Fine; slight dust soiling to rear of dj. *ELSE FINE*. $90

Charteris, Leslie. THE SAINT IN EUROPE. London, H & S, 1954. 1st ed. Fine; light wear to dj extremities. *ELSE FINE*. $75

Charteris, Leslie. THE SAINT ON GUARD. GC: Doubleday Crime Club, 1944. 1st ed. Fine in VG+ dj, lt edgewear; sm chips. *ELSE FINE*. $25

Charteris, Leslie. THE SAINT SEES IT THROUGH. GC: Doubleday Crime Club, 1946. 1st ed. Fine. Dj has lt edgewear, sm chips upper corners. *ELSE FINE*. $40

Charteris, Leslie. THIEVES' PICNIC. GC: Doubleday Crime Club, 1937. 1st ed. Fine, moderate wear to extrems; chip at spine heel of dj. *ELSE FINE*. $45

Charters, Ann. KEROUAC. (London): Deutsch, (1974). 1st Eng ed. This is the issue in wrappers. Fine in dj. *LOPEZ*. $50

Charyn, Jerome. AMERICAN SCRAPBOOK. NY: Viking, 1969. 1st ed. Inscribed. Fine in Fine dj. *BEASLEY*. $150

Charyn, Jerome. EISENHOWER, MY EISENHOWER. NY: Holt, 1971. 1st ed. Inscribed. Fine in Fine dj. *BEASLEY*. $100

Charyn, Jerome. GOING TO JERUSALEM. NY: Viking, 1967. 1st ed. Inscribed. Fine in Fine dj. *BEASLEY*. $125

Charyn, Jerome. ON THE DARKENING GREEN. NY: McGraw-Hill, 1965. 1st ed. Inscribed. Fine in Fine dj but for light wear at spine ends. *BEASLEY*. $125

Charyn, Jerome. ONCE UPON A DROSHKY. NY: McGraw Hill Book Company, (c1964). 1st ed, 1st bk. Small abrasion on back cover, else Fine in dj w/small snag on back panel and a few light soil marks. *HELLER*. $55

Charyn, Jerome. ONCE UPON A DROSHKY. NY: McGraw-Hill, 1964. 1st ed, 1st bk. Inscribed. Fine in Fine dj w/few little tears. *BEASLEY*. $125

Charyn, Jerome. THE MAN WHO GREW YOUNGER. NY: Harper, 1966. 1st ed. Inscribed. Fine in Fine dj but for lamination creasing. *BEASLEY*. $100

Charyn, Jerome. THE SEVENTH BABE. Arbor House, 1979. 1st, Fine in a dj with small chip rear panel. *STAHR*. $25

Chase, Borden. BLAZING GUNS ON THE CHISHOLM TRAIL. NY, 1948. 1st ed. Missing ffep o/w VG. *VARNER*. $25

Chase, Edward. THE MEMORIAL LIFE OF GENERAL WILLIAM TECUMSEH SHERMAN. Chicago: Peale, 1891. 1st ed. Pict red cl, gilt. NF. *CONNOLLY & WADE*. $85

Chase, Ernest Dudley. THE ROMANCE OF GREETING CARDS. Rust Craft, 1956. 1st ed. Fine in dj. Signed. *ARTIS*. $25

Chase, George H. CATALOGUE OF ARRETINE POTTERY. Boston: Riverside Press, 1916. NF. *POLYANTHOS*. $75

Chase, Heber. THE FINAL REPORT OF THE COMMITTEE OF THE PHILADELPHIA MEDICAL SOCIETY ON THE CONSTRUCTION OF INSTRUMENTS, AND THEIR MODE OF ACTION IN THE RADICAL CURE OF HERNIA. Phila, 1837. Cloth-backed boards, 243pp. Front outer hinge worn, label missing, contents Fine. Untrimmed and uncut. Scarce. *FYE*. $200

Chase, J.H. CLOCHE GARDENING. London: Faber, 1954. 4th prtg. As New in dj. *AMERICAN BOTANIST*. $32

Chase, James Hadley. STRICTLY FOR CASH. London: Robert Hale, 1951. 1st ed. VG in dj (chipping, closed tears). *MORDIDA*. $25

Chase, James Hadley. THERE'S ALWAYS A PRICE TAG. London: Robert Hale, 1956. 1st ed. Pp darkened o/w VG in dj (crease-tear front panel; wear). *MORDIDA*. $25

Chase, James Hadley. YOU'VE GOT IT COMING. London: Robert Hale, 1955. 1st ed. Pp darkened o/w VG in dj (closed tears; chipping). *MORDIDA*. $25

Chase, Joan. DURING THE REIGN OF THE QUEEN OF PERSIA. Harper, 1983. 1st. Fine, dj. *STAHR*. $35

Chase, Lucy and Sarah. DEAR ONES AT HOME, LETTERS FROM CONTRABAND CAMPS. Selected and ed by Henry L. Swint. Nashville, 1966. 1st ed. Map. Fine in Fine dj. *PRATT*. $32.50

Chase, Owen et al. NARRATIVES OF THE WRECK OF THE WHALE SHIP ESSEX. London: Golden Cockerel Press, 1935. Ltd ed, #259 of 275. 12 Robert Gibbings engr. Issued w/o dj. Fine-. *AARD*. $400

Chase, Salmon P. INSIDE LINCOLN'S CABINET, THE CIVIL WAR DIARIES OF SALMON P. CHASE. NY, 1954. Ed by David Donald. 1st ed. Dj. VG+. *PRATT*. $30

Chase, Will H. PIONEERS OF ALASKA: THE TRAIL BLAZERS OF BYGONE DAYS. Kansas City, 1951. 1st ed. Fine. *ARTIS*. $20

Chase-Riboud, Barbara. FROM MEMPHIS AND PEKING. NY: Random House, 1974. 1st ed. Fine but for discount mark on bottom edge, in Fine dj. 1st book. *BEASLEY*. $40

Chase-Riboud, Barbara. SALLY HEMINGS. NY: Viking, 1979. 1st ed. Close to Fine w/owner name and date, in used dj w/tears. *BEASLEY*. $45

Chase-Riboud, Barbara. SALLY HEMINGS. NY: Viking, 1979. 1st ed. Fine in NF dj, 2 tiny tears. *BEASLEY*. $50

Chatterton, E. Keble. KING'S CUTTERS AND SMUGGLERS. Phila: J.B. Lippincott, 1912. Corners bumped, some shelfwear. Overall VG. *PARMER*. $75

Chatterton, E. Keble. SAILING MODELS ANCIENT AND MODERN. London, 1934. 1st ed. 7 fldg plans. Orig cl, expertly rebacked. *LEFKOWICZ*. $120

Chatwin, Bruce and Paul Theroux. PATAGONIA REVISITED. (Wiltshire): Michael Russell, (1985). One of 250 numbered, signed by both authors. Fine w/o dj, as issued. *LOPEZ*. $300

Chatwin, Bruce and Paul Theroux. PATAGONIA REVISITED. (Great Britain): Michael Russell, (1985). One of 250 numbered, signed by both authors. Fine w/o dj, as issued. *LOPEZ*. $350

Chatwin, Bruce and Paul Theroux. PATAGONIA REVISITED. Houghton Mifflin, 1986. 1st Amer ed. Fine in Fine dj. *BEBBAH*. $35

Chatwin, Bruce. IN PATAGONIA. London: Cape, (1977). Uncorrected proof. According to the bibliographer, only 55 copies of the proof were produced. Faint stain along fore-edge of first dozen leaves; overall VG. *LOPEZ*. $1,500

Chatwin, Bruce. IN PATAGONIA. NY: Summit Books, (1978). 1st Amer ed. Fine in Fine dj. *LOPEZ*. $225

Chatwin, Bruce. LADY LISA LYON. NY: St. Martin's, (1983). 1st ed. Mapplethorpe photos. VF in dj. Hardcover issue uncommon. *CAPTAIN'S BOOKSHELF*. $375

Chatwin, Bruce. ON THE BLACK HILL. London: Cape, (1982). Uncorrected proof. Spine sl rubbed, o/w Fine. Ptd wraps. *JAFFE*. $100

Chatwin, Bruce. ON THE BLACK HILL. NY: Viking, (1983). 1st Amer ed. Orig cl-backed boards. Fine in dj. Signed in grn ink. *CHAPEL HILL*. $150

Chatwin, Bruce. ON THE BLACK HILL. NY: Viking Press, (1983). 1st US ed. Fine in dj. Rev copy w/publicity sheet, author's photo. Signed. *CAPTAIN'S BOOKSHELF*. $250

Chatwin, Bruce. ON THE BLACK HILL. Viking, 1983. 1st Amer. ed. Fine in dj. Price sticker on ffep. *STAHR*. $15

Chatwin, Bruce. THE SONGLINES. Franklin Center: Franklin Library, 1987. True 1st Amer ed. Black leather binding, stamped in orange and gold. Gilt page edges, marbled eps, silk ribbon marker. Fine, signed. *LOPEZ*. $275

Chatwin, Bruce. THE SONGLINES. Franklin Center: Franklin Library, 1987. 1st ed (with 2-pg intro esp for this ed). Full dec leather. VF. Signed. *CAPTAIN'S BOOKSHELF*. $250

Chatwin, Bruce. THE SONGLINES. Franklin Center: Franklin Lib, 1987. True 1st Amer ed. Fine. Signed. *LOPEZ*. $250

Chatwin, Bruce. THE SONGLINES. London: Cape, (1987). 1st ed. Boards, dj. Mint. *JAFFE*. $100

Chatwin, Bruce. THE SONGLINES. London: Cape, (1987). One of 150 numbered, specially bound, signed. Fine in NF glassine dj. *LOPEZ*. $650

Chatwin, Bruce. THE SONGLINES. London: London Limited Editions, (1987). One of 150 specially bound, signed. Fine in glassine dj. *CAPTAIN'S BOOKSHELF*. $400

Chatwin, Bruce. THE VICEROY OF OUIDAH. Jonathan Cape, 1980. 1st ed. VF in dj. *STAHR*. $60

Chatwin, Bruce. THE VICEROY OF OUIDAH. London: Jonathan Cape, (1980). 1st ed. VF in dj. *CAPTAIN'S BOOKSHELF*. $125

Chatwin, Bruce. THE VICEROY OF OUIDAH. NY: Summit, 1980. 1st ed. Fine. *SMITH*. $30

Chatwin, Bruce. UTZ. London: Cape, (1988). 1st ed. Boards, dj. Mint. *JAFFE*. $50

Chatwin, Bruce. UTZ. London: Jonathan Cape, (1988). 1st Eng ed. Advance review copy. Spine sl cocked, o/w Fine in Fine dj. *LOPEZ*. $75

Chatwin, Bruce. UTZ. NY, 1988. Unrevised and unpublished proofs in pub's printed wraps. Fine. *POLYANTHOS*. $30

Chatwin, Bruce. WHAT AM I DOING HERE? London: Cape, (1989). 1st ed. Boards, dj. Mint. *JAFFE*. $50

Chaucer, Geoffrey. THE CANTERBURY TALES. By the late Thomas Tyrwhitt. The 2nd ed. Oxford: (Clarendon Press), 1798. 2 vols. Contemp diapered calf. Both vols rebacked; aeg. This is a corrected and sl expanded ed. Very handsome ed. *BOOK BLOCK*. $575

Chaucer, Geoffrey. THE COMPLETE WORKS OF GEOFFREY CHAUCER. Rev. Walter W. Skeat (ed). 2nd ed. Oxford: The Clarendon Press, 1898-97. 7 vols. Bound in 1/4 brn morocco, 5 raised hands, gilt spine, brn marbled boards, morocco corners, teg. VG. *WEBER*. $850

Cheatle, George and Max Cutler. TUMORS OF THE BREAST. THEIR PATHOLOGY SYMPTOMS, DIAGNOSIS AND TREATMENT. Phila, 1931. 1st Amer ed. 596pp. 468 illus. *FYE*. $100

Checkley, John. JOHN CHECKLEY; OR THE EVOLUTION OF THE RELIGIOUS TOLERANCE IN MASSACHUSETTS BAY...1719-1774. Boston: Prince Soc, 1897. 2 vols. 1/250 sets. Unopened, untrimmed. Fine. *BOHLING*. $90

Cheever, Henry T. LIFE IN THE SANDWICH ISLANDS. NY: A.S. Barnes & Co, 1851. (iv),355pp +3pp ads, 5 full pg plts. Blind and gold stamped cl, front inner hinge weak, lt wear to spine. *DAWSON'S*. $250

Cheever, Henry T. THE WHALE AND HIS CAPTORS....NY: Harper, 1850. 1st ed. 314pp. 17 engrs. Worn, sl foxed. *SECOND LIFE*. $150

Cheever, John. BULLET PARK. NY Knopf, 1969. 1st ed. Orig burgundy cl. Dusty, else Fine in dj. *CHAPEL HILL*. $35

Cheever, John. BULLET PARK. NY: Knopf, 1969. 1st ed. NF in dj. Signed. *CHAPEL HILL*. $95

Cheever, John. EXPELLED. Foreword: Malcolm Cowley. Afterword: John Updike. Decs: Warren Chappell. A miniature, 2 7/8 x 2 1/8", cl w/pict label, cl slipcase. (LA): Sylvester & Orphanos, (1987). 1st ed. One of 150 numbered (the entire ed) signed by Updike, Cheever, Cowley & Chappell. Mint. *JAFFE*. $350

Cheever, John. FALCONER. NY: Knopf, 1977. 1st ed. Fine in dj. Signed. *CHAPEL HILL*. $125

Cheever, John. FALCONER. NY: Knopf, 1977. 1st ed. Orig owner's name, else Fine in price-clipped, NF dj. *CHAPEL HILL*. $35

Cheever, John. HOMAGE TO SHAKESPEARE. Stevenson, CT: Country Squires Book, (1968). 1st ed, 1/150 numbered, signed. Fine in Fine dj. *ROBBINS*. $250

Cheever, John. HOMAGE TO SHAKESPEARE. Stevenson, CT: Country Squires Books, (1968). 1st ed. #56 of 150 signed. Orig blue cl. Fine in lavender dj, paper label. *CHAPEL HILL*. $300

Cheever, John. OH WHAT A PARADISE IT SEEMS. NY: Knopf, 1982. 1st ed. Fine in Fine dj. Signed. *LOPEZ*. $100

Cheever, John. SOME PEOPLE, PLACES, AND THINGS THAT WILL NOT APPEAR IN MY NEXT NOVEL. London: Victor Gollancz, 1961. 1st Eng ed. Fine in dj. *HELLER*. $75

Cheever, John. SOME PEOPLE, PLACES, AND THINGS THAT WILL NOT APPEAR IN MY NEXT NOVEL. London: Gollancz, 1961. 1st Eng ed. Fine in dj. *CHAPEL HILL*. $75

Cheever, John. THE BRIGADIER AND THE GOLF WIDOW. NY: Harper & Row, (1964). 1st ed. NF in dj. *CHAPEL HILL*. $35

Cheever, John. THE DAY THE PIG FELL INTO THE WELL. Northridge, CA: Lord John Press, 1978. 1st ed. Ltd to 275 signed. Cl-backed dec boards. VF. *JAFFE*. $125

Cheever, John. THE DAY THE PIG FELL INTO THE WELL. Northridge: Lord John Press, 1978. 1st ed. One of 275 signed. Fine in cl-backed patterned boards w/paper spine label. *CAPTAIN'S BOOKSHELF*. $100

Cheever, John. THE ENORMOUS RADIO AND OTHER STORIES. London: Victor Gollancz, Ltd, 1953. 1st Eng ed. Fine in lightly soiled yellow dj darkened on backstrip and chipped at head and foot of backstrip and at corners. *HELLER*. $75

Cheever, John. THE ENORMOUS RADIO AND OTHER STORIES. NY: Funk & Wagnalls, 1953. 1st ed. Fine in NF dj w/minimal rubbing and closed tear on rear panel. *CHAPEL HILL*. $225

Cheever, John. THE ENORMOUS RADIO AND OTHER STORIES. NY: Funk & Wagnalls, 1953. 1st ed. VG in price-clipped dj. *CHAPEL HILL*. $195

Cheever, John. THE HOUSEBREAKER OF SHADY HILL & OTHER STORIES. NY: Harper & Bros., (1958). 1st ed. Spine faded o/w VG in VG+ price clipped dj which has a small abrasion on spine. *BERNARD*. $60

Cheever, John. THE HOUSEBREAKER OF SHADY HILL AND OTHER STORIES. NY: Harper & Bros., (1958). 1st ed. Gift inscription, else VG in dj. *CHAPEL HILL*. $75

Cheever, John. THE HOUSEBREAKER OF SHADY HILL AND OTHER STORIES. NY: Harper, (1958). 1st ed. NF in dj beginning to show wear on folds and spine edges. *ROBBINS*. $65

Cheever, John. THE HOUSEBREAKER OF SHADY HILL AND OTHER STORIES. Harper & Brothers, (1958). 1st ed. NF in price-clipped dj (sm, closed tear). Lt rubbing. *STAHR*. $85

Cheever, John. THE JOURNALS OF JOHN CHEEVER. NY: Knopf, 1991. Uncorrected proof. Fine in wraps. *LOPEZ*. $85

Cheever, John. THE STORIES OF JOHN CHEEVER. London: Jonathan Cape, (1979). 1st Eng ed. Few tiny pinholes in front board, else Fine in 2 djs, one price-clipped. *CHAPEL HILL*. $50

Cheever, John. THE STORIES OF JOHN CHEEVER. NY: Knopf, 1978. 1st ed. Fine in NF dj. *JUVELIS.* $40

Cheever, John. THE STORIES OF JOHN CHEEVER. NY: Knopf, 1978. 1st ed. Fine in Fine dj. *LOPEZ.* $75

Cheever, John. THE STORIES OF JOHN CHEEVER. NY: Knopf, 1978. 1st ed. Orig black cl. Fine in dj. Signed. *CHAPEL HILL.* $150

Cheever, John. THE WAPSHOT CHRONICLE. NY, 1957. 1st ed. National Book Award sticker on dj front panel, VG+. *PETTLER.* $50

Cheever, John. THE WAPSHOT SCANDAL. NY: Harper & Row, (1964). 1st ed. Fine in dj. *CHAPEL HILL.* $40

Cheever, John. THE WORLD OF APPLES. Knopf, 1973. 1st ed. Fine in price clipped dj. Rmdr mark. *STAHR.* $20

Cheever, John. THE WORLD OF APPLES. NY: Knopf, 1973. 1st ed. Fine in dj. Signed. *CHAPEL HILL.* $125

Cheever, Susan. A HANDSOME MAN. Simon and Schuster, 1981. Uncorrected proof. Fine in pale yellow wraps. *STAHR.* $25

Cheever, Susan. DOCTOR'S & WOMEN. NY: Potter, (1987). Fine in dj. 1st ed. *CHAPEL HILL.* $25

Cheever, Susan. HOME BEFORE DARK. London: Weidenfeld & Nicolson, (1985). Fine in dj, virtually as New. 1st Eng ed. Advance review copy w/publisher's slip laid in. *CHAPEL HILL.* $45

Cheever, Susan. LOOKING FOR WORK. London: Weidenfeld & Nicolson, 1979. 1st UK ed, 1st bk. Fine in Fine dj. *ARCHER.* $15

Cheever, Susan. THE CAGE. London: Weidenfeld & Nicolson, (1983). Fine in dj. 1st Eng ed. *CHAPEL HILL.* $25

Cheim, John (ed, designer). BRUCE WEBER. (NY): Knopf, (1988). 1st ed. NF in dj (outer, ptd glassine dj being lightly chipped). *CAPTAIN'S BOOKSHELF.* $100

Cheiro. TRUE GHOST STORIES. London Pub. Co, 1928. 1st ed. VG in chipped dj. *MADLE.* $35

Chekhov, Anton. NOTE-BOOK OF ANTON CHEKHOV. S.S. Koteliansky and Leonard Woolf (trans). NY: B.W. Huebsch, 1921. 1st US ed. Fine in lightly soiled dj w/tear rear panel. *CAPTAIN'S BOOK-SHELF.* $90

Cheney, Brainard. DEVIL'S ELBOW. NY: Crown, 1969. 1st ed. Fine (small bump to top edge), in close to Fine dj. *BEASLEY.* $25

Cheney, Brainard. THIS IS ADAM. NY: McDowell, Obolensky, (1958). 1st ed. Fine in dj, sm tears. Inscribed. *CAPTAIN'S BOOKSHELF.* $75

Cherkovski, Neeli. HANK. NY: Random House, (1991). Review copy. Signed by the author. Fine in dj. *SMITH.* $40

Cherkovski, Neeli. HANK. Santa Rosa: Black Sparrow, (1991). 1st ed. One of 200 numbered, signed by author and Bukowski. Fine. *SMITH.* $100

Cherkovski, Neeli. HANK: THE LIFE OF CHARLES BUKOWSKI. Santa Rosa: Black Sparrow (1991). 1st ed. One of 200 numbered, signed by Bukowski and Cherkovski. Fine in acetate. *DORN.* $60

Chernichewski, Vladimir. ANTHROPOLOGICAL REPORT ON A LONDON SUBURB. London: Grayson & Grayson, (1935). 1st ed. Charles Duff (ed). NF in sl worn dj. *WREDEN.* $25

Cherry, Kelly. AUGUSTA PLAYED. Boston: Houghton Mifflin, 1979. Adv rev copy w/slip. Fine in NF dj but for short tears. *BEASLEY.* $30

Chesbro, George C. CITY OF WHISPERING STONE. NY: Simon and Schuster, 1978. 1st ed. Rmdr stamp, o/w Fine in dj, couple short closed tears. *MORDIDA.* $35

Chesbro, George C. SHADOW OF A BROKEN MAN. NY: Simon & Schuster, 1977. 1st ed. Small light stain on top edge o/w Fine in dj. *MORDIDA.* $45

Chesbro, George C. SHADOW OF A BROKEN MAN. Simon and Schuster, 1977. 1st ed. Fine in dj (2 short tears). Rmdr stamp. *STAHR.* $25

Chesbro, George C. THE COLD SMELL OF SACRED STONE. NY: Atheneum, 1988. 1st ed. Signed. Fine in dj. *MORDIDA.* $45

Chesbro, George C. THE GOLDEN CHILD. London: Severn House, 1987. 1st hb ed. VF in dj. *MORDIDA.* $45

Chesbro, George. C. TWO SONGS THIS ARCHANGEL SINGS. NY: Atheneum, 1986. 1st ed. VF in dj. *MORDIDA.* $35

Cheselden, William. ANATOMY OF THE HUMAN BODY. Boston: David West, 1806. 2nd Amer ed. 352 pp; 40 plts. Full calf, worn but sound. Ex-lib marks, some foxing. Solid, tight. *SMITHFIELD.* $180

Cheselden, William. THE ANATOMY OF THE HUMAN BODY. Boston, 1806. 2nd Amer ed. 1/2 leather, 352pp. 40 Fine full page engrvd plts. *FYE.* $400

Cheselden, William. THE ANATOMY OF THE HUMAN BODY. The XIth Edition. London: J.F. & C. Rivington, et al. 1778. vi,334,(16)pp. + 40 copper-engr, incl frontis. Orig brown calf, rebacked, w/old calf label laid down. Contemp ownership sig. *KARMIOLE.* $285

Cheshire, Frank. THE SCIENTIFIC TEMPERANCE HAND-BOOK. FOR TEMPERANCE TEACHERS AND ADVOCATES. London, c. 1890. 1st ed. 285pp. *FYE.* $60

Chesley, Larry. SEVEN YEARS IN HANOI. Salt Lake City: Bookcraft, (1973). 1st ed. Fine in NF price-clipped dj. *AKA.* $45

Chesney, Alan. THE JOHNS HOPKINS HOSPITAL AND THE JOHNS HOPKINS UNIVERSITY SCHOOL OF MEDICINE. VOLUME 1. 1867-1893. Baltimore, 1943. 1st ed. *FYE.* $75

Chesnut, Mary. MARY CHESNUT'S CIVIL WAR. New Haven (1981). 1st ed. C. Vann Woodward (ed). Dj. *PRATT.* $40

Chesnutt, Charles Waddell. THE COLONEL'S DREAM. NY: Doubleday, Pg & Co, 1905. 1st ed. Orig red cl. VG+. *CHAPEL HILL.* $325

Chesnutt, Charles Waddell. THE CONJURE WOMAN. Boston & NY: Houghton, Mifflin, 1899. 1st trade ed. 12mo, 229pp. Orig pict brown cl. Bkpl, owner signature, spine sl darkened. VG. *CHAPEL HILL.* $500

Chester, George. FIVE THOUSAND AN HOUR. Syndicate Pub, n.d. VG in chipped dj. *MADLE.* $40

Chester, Giraud. EMBATTLED MAIDEN. NY, (1951). 1st ed. Dj chipped o/w VG. *PRATT.* $25

Chester, Jonathan. GOING TO EXTREMES: PROJECT BLIZZARD AND AUSTRALIA'S ANTARCTIC HERITAGE. Sydney/Auckland: Doubleday, 1986. 1st ed. Fine in dj. *PARMER.* $45

Chester, S.B. LIFE OF VENIZELOS....NY: 1921. Uncut, unopened. 1st ed. *O'NEILL.* $35

Chesterfield, Philip Dormer Stanhope, Earl of. THE POETICAL WORKS. London: Officina Bodoni for Elkin Mathews & Marrot Ltd, 1927. One of 250 numbered in patterned paper boards, paper spine label. Bottom corners bumped, some rubbing. VG. *CAPTAIN'S BOOKSHELF.* $275

CHESTERFIELD TRAVESTIE....(by George Moutard Woodward). Phila: M. Carey, 1812. Thomas Rowlandson (illus). 1st Amer ed. Orig ptd paper boards. In morocco folder and slipcase w/cl label. 1/2 spine paper perished, front board wobbly (cords intact); front cvr stained, but quite good. Noticeable offsetting; marginal foxing. *PIRAGES.* $200

Chesterton, G.K. CHAUCER. NY: Farrar, Rinehart, (1932). 1st US ed. NF in lightly soiled and chipped pict dj. *CAPTAIN'S BOOKSHELF.* $60

Chesterton, G.K. FIVE TYPES. A BOOK OF ESSAYS. London: Arthur L. Humphries, 1910. 1st ed. Fine in French-fold dj, sl browned; broken slipcase. Uncommonly Nice. *CAPTAIN'S BOOKSHELF.* $60

Chesterton, G.K. GLORIA IN PROFUNDIS. Wood engr by Eric Gill. (London: Faber & Gwyer, Ltd. N.d., circa 1927). Ltd to 350 numbered. Number 5 of "The Ariel Poems." *KARMIOLE.* $50

Chesterton, G.K. THE COLOURED LANDS. London: Sheed & Ward, 1938. 1st trade ed. Fine in Fine dj. *JUVELIS.* $80

Chesterton, G.K. THE SCANDAL OF FATHER BROWN. London: Cassell, 1935. 1st ed. Fine in VG dj (1" V-shaped piece missing front panel; chipping back panel; sm chip, minor wear). *MORDIDA.* $285

Chetwynd, George, Sir. RACING REMINISCENCES AND EXPERIENCES OF THE TURF. London: Longman's, Green, and Co., 1891. 2nd ed. 2 vols. Spines a bit darkened, a few ballpoint numbers on flyleaves. NF. *CHAPEL HILL.* $125

Cheuse, Alan. FALL OUT OF HEAVEN: AN AUTOBIOGRAPHICAL JOURNEY. Salt Lake City: Peregrine, (1987). 1st Amer ed. Signed. Fine in dj. *DORN.* $35

Cheuse, Alan. THE GRANDMOTHER'S CLUB. Salt Lake City: Peregrine, (1986). 1st Amer ed. Signed and dated in the year of pub. Fine in dj. *DORN.* $35

Cheuse, Alan. WALTZ AND OTHER STORIES. Salt Lake City: Peregrine, (1990). 1st Amer ed. Signed. Fine in dj. *DORN.* $30

Chevigny, Hector. LORD OF ALASKA. Portland, 1951. VG in dj. *ARTIS.* $12.50

Chevigny, Hector. LORD OF ALASKA. Portland: Binfords & Mort, 1965. Fine in sl chipped, else Good dj. *CONNOLLY & WADE.* $20

Chevigny, Hector. LORD OF ALASKA—THE STORY OF BARANOV AND THE RUSSIAN ADVENTURE. London: Robert Hale, 1946. 1st ed. Top/bottom of spine sunned. Dj chipped, else NF. *GREAT EPIC.* $45

Cheyne, George. AN ESSAY OF HEALTH AND LONG LIFE. London, 1725. 4th ed. Recent 1/4 leather, 232pp. Title page wrinkled, stained, old repair of tear rather carelessly done, contents Fine. *FYE.* $150

Cheyne, George. AN ESSAY ON REGIMEN. TOGETHER WITH FIVE DISCOURSES, MEDICAL, MORAL, AND PHILOSOPHICAL. London, 1740. 1st ed. 344pp. Recent 1/4 leather w/marbled boards. *FYE.* $300

Cheyney, Peter. CAN LADIES KILL? London: Collins, 1937. 1st ed. Special gift ed. Inscribed. VG in price-clipped dj (chipping; piece missing back panel; corner wear). *MORDIDA.* $60

Cheyney, Peter. DARK DUET. NY: Dodd, 1943. 1st ed. Fine, lt wear extrems of pict dj. *ELSE FINE.* $35

Cheyney, Peter. I'LL SAY SHE DOES! Dodd, Mead, 1946. 1st ed. VG in VG dj with few chips, light soil. *BEBBAH.* $18

Chickering, Carol. FLOWERS OF GUATEMALA. Norman: Univ of OK Press, (1973). 1st ed. 50 full-pg color plts. Chipped dj. *SILVER.* $45

Child, Andrew. OVERLAND ROUTE TO CALIFORNIA. Intro by Lyle H. Wright. LA: N.A. Kovach, 1946. One of 750. Fldg map, 5pp photo illus. Gold-stamped cl in lightly chipped dj. *DAWSON'S.* $30

Child, Lydia Maria (Francis). HOBOMOK, A TALE OF EARLY TIMES. BY AN AMERICAN. Boston: Cummings, Hilliard, & Co, 1824. 1st ed. 8vo, orig boards (rebacked). Light foxing some leaves, fep wanting. Orig printed paper label, uncut, ex-libris. In brown cl clamshell box. Rare. *JUVELIS.* $1400

Child, Lydia Maria. ISAAC T. HOPPER. Boston: Jewett, 1853. 1st ed. 2nd ptg w/sheets bulking 1-1/16". Foxed, worn cl, Good. BAL 3174. *SECOND LIFE.* $25

Child, Lydia Maria. LETTERS OF...Boston: Houghton Mifflin, 1883. 1st ed. Water mark, o/w Good. BAL 3220. *SECOND LIFE.* $35

CHILD'S BOOK OF THE NATIVITY. NY: Triad, (1960's). Robert Osborne. Spiral binding which has, as usual, caused some wear on spine. Internally sound, couple sm childish scribbles. Stand up bk. *BOOKFINDERS INTL.* $40

CHILD'S GARDEN OF VERSES. London, (1960s) A Jolly Jump-Ups book. 6 double pg pop-ups (sm repair to 1st one). Pop-up bk. *BOOKFINDERS INTL.* $50

CHILDREN OF ALL NATIONS, THEIR HOMES, THEIR SCHOOL-ROOMS & THEIR PLAYGROUNDS. London: Cassell (n.d.). 254pp. Lt wear, few lt scratches to dec gilt cvr, brown & black on grn cloth. VG. *BEBBAH.* $35

Childress, Alice. A HERO AIN'T NOTHIN' BUT A SANDWICH. NY: Coward, (1973). 1st ed. Fine in Fine sl spine faded dj. *BETWEEN COVERS.* $75

Childress, Alice. A SHORT WALK. NY: Coward, (1979). 1st ed. Fine in dj w/short tear rear panel. *BETWEEN COVERS.* $55

Childress, Alice. LIKE ONE OF THE FAMILY. Brooklyn: Independence Publishers, (1956). 1st ed. Top edge of rear cover has 2 bumps o/w VG+ in VG lightly soiled dj sl chipped at spine ends & w/several internally mended edgetears. *BERNARD.* $100

Childress, Mark. A WORLD MADE OF FIRE. Knopf, 1984. 1st ed. About Fine in dj. *STAHR.* $35

Childress, Mark. TENDER. NY: Harmony, (1990). 1st Amer ed. Signed. Fine in dj. *DORN.* $35

Childress, Mark. TENDER. NY: Harmony (1990). Uncorrected proof. Fine in wraps. *DORN.* $30

Childs, Mary Fairfax. DE NAMIN' OB DE TWINS, and Other Sketches from the Cotton Land. NY: B.W. Dodge & Co, 1908. 1st ed. Orig pict blue-grey cl. VG. *CHAPEL HILL.* $85

Childs, Timothy. COLD TURKEY. Harper & Row, 1979. 1st ed. Fine, dj. Signed. *STAHR.* $25

Chilton, Eleanor Carroll and Herbert Agar. THE GARMENT OF PRAISE. GC: Doubleday, Doran, 1929. 1st ed. NF in somewhat soiled, chipped dj. *CAPTAIN'S BOOKSHELF.* $50

CHINESE SECRET SOCIETIES IN SINGAPORE. Singapore: Criminal Investigation Dept, 1958. 94pp. Stapled in ptd boards. *AKA.* $25

Chipman, Donald E. NUNO DE GUZMAN AND THE PROVINCE OF PANUCO IN NEW SPAIN. 1518-1533. Glendale: The Arthur C. Clark Company, 1967. 1st ed. As New. *PARMER.* $35

Chipman, Donald. NUNO DE GUZMAN AND THE PROVINCE OF PANUCO IN NEW SPAIN 1518-1533. Glendale: Arthur Clarke Co, 1967. 1st ed. *SILVER.* $35

Chipman, Gen. N. P. THE TRAGEDY OF ANDERSONVILLE: TRIAL OF CAPTAIN HENRY WIRZ, THE PRISON KEEPER. (Sacramento, 1911). 2nd ed, rev, enlgd. *GINSBERG.* $50

Chipman, Nathaniel. PRINCIPLES OF GOVERNMENT: A TREATISE ON FREE INSTITUTIONS. Burlington, VT: Edward Smith, 1833. Rebound. Name; hand-written outline attached. Much foxing in text, inner hinges cracking o/w text VG. *DIAMOND.* $250

Chipman, Nathaniel. PRINCIPLES OF GOVERNMENT; A TREATISE ON FREE INSTITUTIONS. INCLUDING THE CONSTITUTION OF THE UNITED STATES. Burlington, (VT), 1833. Rev ed of rare 1793 orig. (8),330pp. Cl w/leather label. Howes C389. *GINSBERG.* $175

Chisholm, Daniel. THE CIVIL WAR NOTEBOOK OF DANIEL CHISHOLM. Ed by W. Springer Menge & J. August Shimrack. NY, (1989). 1st ed. 202pp. Fine in dj. *PRATT.* $20

Chisholm, Joe. BREWERY GULCH. San Antonio: Naylor, 1949. VG in Good dj. *PARMER.* $55

Chittenden, Hiram M. HISTORY OF EARLY STEAMBOAT NAVIGATION ON THE MISSOURI RIVER. Minneapolis: Ross & Haines, 1962 reprint of 1903 ed. 2 vols in one. Cl. One of 1500. Fine in dj. Howes C391 reprint. *BOHLING.* $40

Chittenden, Hiram M. HISTORY OF EARLY STEAMBOAT NAVIGATION ON THE MISSOURI RIVER. LIFE & ADVENTURES OF JOSEPH LA BARGE...NY: Harper, 1903. Ltd to 950. 2 vols. 1st ed. Frontis, 9 plts vol 1; frontis, 5 plts vol 2. Bkpls neatly removed o/w Fine. Howes C391. *OREGON.* $395

Chittenden, Hiram M. HISTORY OF EARLY STEAMBOAT NAVIGATION ON THE MISSOURI RIVER; LIFE AND ADVENTURES OF JOSEPH LA BARGE. NY, 1903. 1st ed. 2 vols. 16 maps and plts. Orig cl, bkpls removed. One of 950 sets. Howes C391. *GINSBERG.* $350

Chittenden, Hiram M. THE AMERICAN FUR TRADE OF THE FAR WEST: A HISTORY OF THE PIONEER TRADING POSTS & FUR COMPANIES....Press of the Pioneers, 1935. 2 vols. Frontis, 7 plts vol 1; 8 plts, rear pocket fldg map vol 2. VF in VG slipcase. Howes C390. *OREGON.* $225

Chittenden, Hiram M. THE AMERICAN FUR TRADE OF THE FAR WEST. Two Vols. NY: The Press of the Pioneers. 1935. 2nd ed. 16 plts, fldg map in a rear pocket. Spines sl faded. *KARMIOLE.* $150

Chittenden, Lucius E. INVISIBLE SHIELD, THE JOURNAL OF LUCIUS E. CHITTENDON, APRIL 15, 1861-JULY 14, 1861. San Diego, (1969). 1st ed. Ltd to 1500. Fine in slipcase. *PRATT.* $15

Chittenden, Lucius E. INVISIBLE SIEGE....San Diego: Americana Exchange Press, 1969. 1st ed, ltd to 1500; this is #1341. Signed by pub. Untrimmed. Fine in Fine slipcase. *CONNOLLY & WADE.* $65

Chittenden, Lucius E. RECOLLECTIONS OF PRESIDENT LINCOLN AND HIS ADMINISTRATION. NY: Harper & Brothers, (1891). Frontis. Cl w/shelf wear. *SCHOYER'S.* $12.50

Chittenden, Russell. HISTORY OF THE SHEFFIELD SCIENTIFIC SCHOOL OF YALE UNIVERSITY, 1846-1922. New Haven, 1928. Ltd ed. 2 vols. 1/2 lea. Signed. *FYE.* $125

CHITTY CHITTY BANG BANG. Random House, 1968. Abridged by Albert Miller. Gwen Gordon, Dave Chambers (illus). Designed by Paul Taylor. Excellent condition. Scarce. Pop-up bk. *BOOKFINDERS INTL.* $75

Choate, Joseph Hodges. THE BOYHOOD AND YOUTH OF JOSEPH HODGES CHOATE. NY: privately ptd, 1917. 1st ed. #537/600 of Ltd. ed. w/visiting card of Mabel Choate tipped in. Unopened. Fine. *AARD.* $35

Choate, Rufus. DISCOURSE DELIVERED BEFORE FACULTY, STUDENTS, AND ALUMNI OF DARTMOUTH COLLEGE. Boston, 1853. NF. *POLYANTHOS.* $45

Cholmondeley-Pennell, H. FISHING. PIKE AND OTHER COARSE FISH. Boston & London: Little, Brown & Longmans Green/The Badminton Library, 1885. 1st U.S. ed. VG. *OCTOBER FARM.* $58

Chopin, Kate. BAYOU FOLK. Boston and NY: Houghton Mifflin, 1894. 1st ed. Hinges cracked, covers intact. VG in orig grn, gold stamped cl. BAL 3244. *HELLER.* $175

Chopin, Kate. THE AWAKENING. Chicago: Herbert Stone, 1899. 1st ed. Lt sunning, soiling. VG. *LOPEZ.* $1,000

Chopping, Richard. THE FLY. NY: Farrar Straus Giroux, (1965). 1st ed. Fine in Fine dj. *DERMONT.* $25

Chopra, R.N. et al. POISONOUS PLANTS OF INDIA. 2 vols. New Delhi, 1965. 2nd ed. Cloth. Inner hinges of Vol I open, corners bumped. *SUTTON.* $90

Chorao, Kay. MAUDIE'S UMBRELLA. Dutton, (1975). 1st ed. Unpaginated. Illus by author. VG+ in VG+ dj. *BEBBAH.* $20

Chorao, Kay. THE CHILD'S STORY BOOK. Dutton, (1987). 1st ed. 63pp. Illus Kay Chorao. Signed. Fine in Fine dj. *BEBBAH.* $25

Choukas, Michael. BLACK ANGELS OF ATHOS. Brattleboro, 1935. 327pp. Dj. *O'NEILL.* $35

Chrisman, Harry E. FIFTY YEARS ON THE OWL HOOT TRAIL. Chicago: Sage Books, 1969. 1st ed. VF. *GIBBS.* $45

Christ-Janer, Albert. BOARDMAN ROBINSON. (Chicago): The Univ of Chicago Press. (1946). 1st ed. Dj. *KARMIOLE.* $45

Christ-Janer, Albert. BOARDMAN ROBINSON. Chicago: The Univ of Chicago Press, (1946). 1st ed. Tan cl bumped, in pict dj soiled, chipped at edges. NF in VG dj. *BLUE MOUNTAIN.* $75

Christ-Janer, Albert. GEORGE CALEB BINGHAM: FRONTIER PAINTER OF MISSOURI. NY: Abrams. VF in VF dj. *BOOK MARKET.* $125

Christensen, Erwin. PRIMITIVE ART. NY: Bonanza Books, (1955). Good. *SILVER.* $30

Christensen, Paul. MINDING THE UNDERWORLD: CLAYTON ESHLEMAN & LATE POSTMODERNISM. Santa Rosa: Black Sparrow (1991). 1st ed. One of 100 numbered, signed. Fine in acetate. *DORN.* $40

Christian, George Llewellyn. OFFICIAL REPORT OF THE HISTORY COMMITTEE OF THE GRAND CAMP...A CONTRAST BETWEEN THE WAY THE WAR WAS CONDUCTED BY THE FEDERALS AND THE WAY IT WAS CONDUCTED BY THE CONFEDERATES. Richmond, 1901. 1st ed. Wrappers, chipping along backstrip, else VG. *McGOWAN.* $37.50

Christian, George Llewellyn. OFFICIAL REPORT OF THE HISTORY COMMITTEE OF THE GRAND CAMP C...ON THE TREATMENT AND EXCHANGE OF PRISONERS. Pulaski, VA, 1902. 1st ed. Wrappers, shows crease where folded, else NF. *McGOWAN.* $45

Christian, W. Asbury. RICHMOND HER PAST AND PRESENT. Richmond: L.H. Jenkins, 1912. 1 fldg illus. Shaken, binding loose. *HUDSON.* $45

Christie, Agatha. 4.50 FROM PADDINGTON. Collins, (1957). 1st ed. 256pp. VG+ in VG+ dj. *BEBBAH.* $65

Christie, Agatha. A CARIBBEAN MYSTERY. NY: Dodd-Mead, 1964. Advance copy. Owner's label. Fine, pages bound in the dj. *ELSE FINE.* $120

Christie, Agatha. A MURDER IS ANNOUNCED. Dodd, Mead, (1950). 1st US ed. Advance prepub in stiff wraps w/dj attached by pub. Spine wrinkled, worn, else VG+. *BERNARD.* $175

Christie, Agatha. APPOINTMENT WITH DEATH. Dodd, Mead, 1938. 1st Amer ed. 301pp. VG+ with few flecks of soil to cvr. *BEBBAH.* $45

Christie, Agatha. APPOINTMENT WITH DEATH. NY: Dodd Mead, 1938. 1st Amer ed. Lg label removed fep o/w Fine in dj (minor wear spine ends, corners; couple short closed tears; sl soiled back panel). *MORDIDA.* $250

Christie, Agatha. BY THE PRICKING OF MY THUMBS. London: Collins, (1963). 1st ed. Fine in lightly rubbed dj. *UNGER.* $35

Christie, Agatha. CARDS ON THE TABLE. Dodd, Mead, 1937. 1st Amer ed. 262pp. Edgewear, faint dampstain to rear cvr. Good. *BEBBAH.* $20

Christie, Agatha. DEATH COMES AS THE END. London: Collins Crime Club, 1945. 1st Eng. ed. Top edge sl spotted o/w Fine in dj w/sl faded spine and closed tear. *MORDIDA.* $150

Christie, Agatha. DEATH ON THE NILE. London: Collins, 1937. 1st ed. 284pp. VG with slight edgewear. *BEBBAH.* $40

Christie, Agatha. DESTINATION UNKNOWN. London: Collins Crime Club, 1954. 1st ed. Fine in dj. *MORDIDA.* $135

Christie, Agatha. ELEPHANTS CAN REMEMBER. London: Collins, (1972). 1st ed. Fine in lightly rubbed dj. *UNGER.* $35

Christie, Agatha. FUNERALS ARE FATAL. NY: Dodd Mead, 1953. 1st ed. VF in lightly used dj. *ELSE FINE.* $60

Christie, Agatha. HICKORY DICKORY DOCK. London: Collins, 1955. 1st ed. NF in dj. *ELSE FINE.* $50

Christie, Agatha. MRS. MCGINITY'S DEAD. London: Collins Crime Club, 1952. 1st ed. VG in dj w/sl faded spine and internal tape mends. *MORDIDA.* $45

Christie, Agatha. MURDER AT THE VICARAGE. NY: Dodd Mead, 1930. 1st Amer ed. Fading top of spine o/w VG in dj (long tear front panel; 1/2" piece missing top of spine; chip back panel). *MORDIDA.* $115

Christie, Agatha. N OR M? NY: Dodd, 1941. 1st US ed. Fine in NF dj w/small snag on lightly sunned spine, w/little wear at spine head. *BEASLEY.* $200

Christie, Agatha. N OR M?. NY: Dodd Mead, 1941. 1st Amer ed. Edges sl darkened o/w Fine in price-clipped dj (couple short closed tears, minor wear spine ends, corners, along folds). *MORDIDA.* $200

Christie, Agatha. ORDEAL BY INNOCENCE. London: Collins, 1958. 1st ed. Fine, minute corner rubs to dj. *ELSE FINE.* $40

Christie, Agatha. PERIL AT END HOUSE. Dodd, Mead, 1932. 1st Amer ed. 270pp. NF. *BEBBAH.* $25

Christie, Agatha. SLEEPING MURDER, MISS MARPLE'S LAST CASE. London: Collins, 1976. 1st ed. 224pp. VG with small split at spine top in VG dj with 1 short closed tear. *BEBBAH.* $20

Christie, Agatha. TAKEN AT THE FLOOD. London: Collins Crime Club, 1948. 1st ed. VG in dj w/small chips at top of spine, several short closed tears and a crease on front panel. *MORDIDA.* $60

Christie, Agatha. TEN LITTLE NIGGERS. London: Collins Crime Club, 1939. 1st ed. Some light spotting on edges and slight darkening at spine corners o/w VG in dj (chipped spine ends; crease-tears back panel; chipped corners; wear along flap folds). *MORDIDA.* $850

Christie, Agatha. THE MIRROR CRACK'D FROM SIDE TO SIDE. London: Collins Crime Club, 1962. 1st ed. Fine in Fine dj but for short tear at spine fold, tiny chip. *BEASLEY.* $65

Christie, Agatha. THE MOUSETRAP. London: French, c. 1954. Fine in wrappers. *SILVER DOOR.* $25

Christie, Agatha. THE MYSTERY OF THE BLUE TRAIN. NY: Dodd Mead, 1928. 1st Amer ed. Pages soiled and stamps on two pages o/w VG in dj w/crease on spine, several nicks along bottom edge and slight spine fading. *MORDIDA.* $250

Christie, Agatha. THE PALE HORSE. London: Collins, 1961. 1st ed. Fine in dj. *ELSE FINE.* $40

Christie, Agatha. THE PALE HORSE. NY: Dodd, Mead, 1962. 1st US ed. Fine and bright in NF dj (few sm tears). *BEASLEY.* $25

Christie, Agatha. THEY DO IT WITH MIRRORS. Collins, 1952. 1st ed. 192pp. VG+ in VG dj with small stains to rear panel. *BEBBAH.* $70

Christie, Agatha. THIRD GIRL. Dodd, Mead, 1967. 1st Amer ed. 248pp. VG+ with slight edgewear in VG dj with edgewear, small chips, crinkle. *BEBBAH.* $18

Christie, Agatha. THIRTEEN AT DINNER. NY: Dodd, 1933. 1st US ed. Fine in lightly used dj w/a little wear and tear at ends of bit dulled spine. *BEASLEY.* $275

Christie, Agatha. TOWARDS ZERO. London: Collins Crime Club, 1944. 1st ed. NF w/sl soiling, in VG dj w/tears, quarter-size chip rear panel. *BEASLEY.* $65

Christie, Agatha. TOWARDS ZERO. London: Collins Crime Club, 1944. 1st ed. Pages sl darkened, o/w Fine in sl darkened dj w/short closed tear. *MORDIDA.* $250

Christie, Grace. SAMPLERS AND STITCHES: A HANDBOOK OF THE EMBROIDERER'S ART. London: B.T. Batsford, (1950). 5th ed. Fine in VG dj. *WREDEN.* $25

CHRISTMAS SURPRISE BOOK. NY, 1950. Illus Irma Wilde. Animation A. Schenk. 6 pop-up Christmas scenes, 10 stories. Intri-cate double-pg pop-ups—viewed from both sides. Pop-up bk. *BOOK-FINDERS INTL.* $65

Chrysler, C. Donald and Donald L. Chaffee. ...ON COURSE TO THE STARS....Grand Rapids, MI: Kregel Pubs, 1968, 1st ed. VG in very sl worn dj. Signed. *KNOLLWOOD.* $36

Chuinard, Eldon. ONLY ONE MAN DIED. THE MEDICAL ASPECTS OF THE LEWIS AND CLARK EXPEDITION. A.H. Clark, 1979. 1st ed. Signed presentation. Frontis. Fine in VG dj. *OREGON.* $135

Chujoy, Anatole (ed). THE DANCE ENCYCLOPEDIA. NY. (1949). NF. *POLYANTHOS.* $35

Church, Albert Cook. WHALE SHIPS AND WHALING. NY, (1938). 1st ed. Orig pict cl. Fine. *LEFKOWICZ.* $135

Church, Archibald (ed). DISEASES OF THE NERVOUS SYSTEM. NY, 1910. 1st Eng trans, 2nd prtg. *FYE.* $75

Churchill, Frank G. HORSESHOEING. Fort Riley, KS: The Cavalry School, 1933. Cl backed wraps. *SECOND LIFE.* $25

Churchill, Sam. BIG SAM. GC: Doubleday, 1965. 1st ed. Fine in VG dj. *CONNOLLY & WADE.* $25

Churchill, Winston S. MARLBOROUGH, HIS LIFE AND TIMES. London: George G. Harrap, (1933-1938). 1st eds. 4 vols. Gold-stamped cl, teg, spines faded. *DAWSON'S.* $350

Churchill, Winston S. MEMOIRS OF THE SECOND WORLD WAR. AN ABRIDGEMENT. Cl, dj. Boston: Houghton Mifflin, 1959. 1st ed. Fine. *JAFFE.* $75

Churchill, Winston S. WHILE ENGLAND SLEPT. NY: G.P. Putnam's Sons. 1938. 1st Amer ed. Blue cloth stamped in red and silver. Dj lightly chipped. *KARMIOLE.* $75

Churchill, Winston. MAXIMS AND REFLECTIONS. Boston: HM, 1947. 1st US ed. One pg roughly opened, else About Fine in edgeworn dj (tear). *CAPTAIN'S BOOKSHELF.* $40

Churchman, John. THE MAGNETIC ATLAS, OR VARIATION CHARTS OF THE WHOLE TERRAQUEOUS GLOBE; COMPRISING A SYSTEM...BY WHICH...THE LONGITUDE MAY BE ASCERTAINED. London: For the Author, by Darton and Harvey, 1796. 1st ed. 28.4 cm., (viii),80pp. 2 engr charts. Contemp 1/2 calf, cvrs rubbed, expertly rebacked; perforated lib stamp on title, last leaf, some foxing, but VG. *LEFKOWICZ.* $1250

Churchward, James. LOST CONTINENT OF MU. Washburn, 1944. VG in sl frayed dj. *MADLE.* $20

Chute, Carolyn. THE BEANS. London: Chatto & Windus/Hogarth Press, (1985). 1st Eng ed. Fine in dj. *CAPTAIN'S BOOKSHELF.* $85

Chute, Carolyn. THE BEANS. London: Chatto & Windus (1985). 1st Eng ed. Fine in dj. *DORN.* $50

Chute, Carolyn. THE BEANS OF EGYPT, MAINE. Ticknor & Fields, 1985. 1st ed. Inside boards show narrow remains of rubber cement. VG in VG dj with edgewear. *BEBBAH.* $35

Cibber, Colley. A LETTER FROM MR. CIBBER TO MR. POPE. London: W. Lewis, 1742. 2nd ed. Modern cloth and marbled boards; half-title browned somewhat. VG. *DRAMATIS PERSONAE.* $100

Cibber, Colley. AN APOLOGY FOR THE LIFE OF MR. COLLEY CIBBER, COMEDIAN. London: for the author, 1740. 2nd ed. Later half calf, rubbed; morocco label; title in red and black. VG. *DRAMATIS PERSONAE.* $80

Cicellis, Kay. THE EASY WAY. NY, (1950). 1st ed, 1st bk. Foreword by V. Sackville-West. NF in price clipped dj (spine sunned, sl edge rubbed). *POLYANTHOS.* $30

CINDERELLA OR THE LITTLE GLASS SLIPPER. NY: Mc-Loughlin Brothers, n.d. A "Pantomime Toy Book." Cl backed pict boards. Spine & corners worn, contents lightly dust-soiled, o/w Good. *JAFFE.* $100

CINDERELLA. Collins, (1920). Illus Eulalie. A Panorama Book that folds out into "Six Magnificent Scenes". Extraordinarily Fine condition. Pop-up bk. *BOOKFINDERS INTL.* $280

CINDERELLA. London, (1970's). Sl wear top, bottom spine, pop-ups OK. Pop-up bk. *BOOKFINDERS INTL.* $15

CINDERELLA. London, 1980. Illus Griffith. Tor Lokvig (eng). A moveable bk. *BOOKFINDERS INTL.* $40.

CINDERELLA. London, 1989 (Prague). Illus Pamela Storey. Pop-up bk. *BOOKFINDERS INTL.* $20

Cintron, Conchita. MEMOIRS OF A BULLFIGHTER. NY: Holt, (1968). 1st ed. Chipped dj. *SILVER.* $25

CIRCUS FUN. NY: McLoughlin Bros, 1890. Color pict self-wraps (sl creased, 3 sm stains), w/pub, date bottom right. Very Nice. *BLUE MOUNTAIN.* $100

Cisneros, Sandra. WOMAN HOLLERING CREEK. NY: Random House, (1991). 1st ed. Signed. VF in VF dj. *UNGER.* $60

Cisneros, Sandra. WOMAN HOLLERING CREEK. NY: Random House, 1991. Fine. *SMITH.* $35

Cist, Charles. CINCINNATI IN 1841: ITS EARLY ANNALS AND FUTURE PROSPECTS. Cincinnati, ptd and published for the author, 1841. 1st ed. 300pp. Frontis, 4 steel plts. Orig cl. Howes C412. *GINSBERG.* $150

Cist, Henry M. THE ARMY OF THE CUMBERLAND. NY: Scribner's, 1882. 1st ed. Fldg frontis map. NF. *CONNOLLY & WADE.* $35

Cist, Henry M. THE ARMY OF THE CUMBERLAND-CAMPAIGNS OF THE CIVIL WAR, VOL. VII. NY, 1882. 1st ed. Minor cvr wear o/w VG+. *PRATT.* $35

Claiborne, J.F.H. LIFE AND TIMES OF GEN. SAM DALE, THE MISSISSIPPI PARTISAN. NY, 1860. 1st ed. 233,161pp. 13 plts incl in pagination. Orig cl, chipped at crown, heel and rear joint edges wearing. Howes C417. *GINSBERG.* $175

Claiborne, J.F.H. LIFE AND TIMES OF GEN. SAM. DALE, THE MISSISSIPPI PARTISAN. NY: Harper & Brothers, 1860. Black 1/2 sheep, raised bands. Ex-lib. Hinges rubbed. Howes C417. *HUDSON.* $75

Claiborne, J.F.H. MISSISSIPPI, AS A PROVINCE, TERRITORY, AND STATE. Vol 1. Jackson: Power & Barksdale, 1880. 1st ed. 6 plts. Fine. *OREGON.* $225

Clampitt, Amy. THE KINGFISHER. NY: Knopf, 1983. 1st ed. Fine in Fine dj. *DERMONT.* $35

Clampitt, Amy. THE KINGFISHER. POEMS. Cl, dj. NY: Knopf, 1983. 1st ed. Mint. *JAFFE.* $35

Clampitt, Amy. WESTWARD. POEMS. NY: Knopf, 1990. Uncorrected proof. Ptd wraps. VF *JAFFE.* $45

Clancy, Tom. PATRIOT GAMES. NY, 1987. Adv reading copy. Pub's pict wraps. Fine. *POLYANTHOS.* $40

Clancy, Tom. PATRIOT GAMES. NY: G.P. Putnam's Sons, 1987. 1st ed. Errata slip laid in. VF in dj. *MORDIDA.* $45

Clancy, Tom. PATRIOT GAMES. NY: Putnam, 1987. 1st ed. Fine in dj. *ELSE FINE.* $35

Clancy, Tom. RED STORM RISING. NY: Putnam, 1986. 1st ed. Fine in dj. *ELSE FINE.* $50

Clancy, Tom. THE CARDINAL OF THE KREMLIN. NY: G.P. Putnam's Sons, 1988. 1st ed. Advance reading copy. Fine in pict wrappers. *MORDIDA.* $50

Clancy, Tom. THE HUNT FOR RED OCTOBER. Annapolis, 1984. 1st ed. VF in dj. Rare. *PETTLER.* $750

Clancy, Tom. THE SUM OF ALL FEARS. NY: Putnam, (1991). Uncorrected proof. NF. *LOPEZ.* $100

Clap, Roger. MEMOIRS OF CAPTAIN ROGER CLAP RELATING TO SOME OF GOD'S REMARKABLE PROVIDENCES TO HIM, IN BRINGING HIM INTO NEW ENGLAND....Boston: Clap, 1807. 39pp. Orig ptd wrappers. Howes C422, orig ed 1731. *GINSBERG.* $250

Clapp, William W. A RECORD OF THE BOSTON STAGE. Boston: James Munroe, 1853. 1st ed. Slight shelf wear. *DRAMATIS.* $80

Clappe, Louise. CALIFORNIA IN 1851 (V.l)-& 1852 (V.2). THE LETTERS OF DAME SHIRLEY. Grabhorn Press, 1933. 2 vols. Ltd to 500. 1st ed. VG. *OREGON.* $160

Claretie, Jules. CAMILLE DESMOULINS AND HIS WIFE. Trans. by Mrs. Cashel Hoey. London: Smith, Elder, 1876. 1st ed. Royal 8vo, xiii, 480pp, frontis, plt, cloth. Some spine wear and repair. Little shelf wear. Rear cover reattached, o/w VG. Ex-lib. *DIAMOND.* $35

Clark, A.H. A MONOGRAPH OF THE EXISTING CRINOIDS. Parts 1, 2, 3, 4a, 4b, 4c and 5 (complete). Washington, 1915-67. 292 plts. Binder's buckram (Pts. 1 & 2) and original wrappers (some chipping & soiling, some bowing to Pt. 3). Ex-lib. *SUTTON.* $235

Clark, A.H. THE BUTTERFLIES OF THE DISTRICT OF COLUMBIA AND VICINITY. Washington, 1932. 64 plts. Wrappers (light wear). Washington, 1932. *SUTTON.* $40

Clark, Allen C. ABRAHAM LINCOLN IN THE NATIONAL CAPITAL. Washington, 1925. 1st ed. 179pp. A little cover wear, o/w Fine. *PRATT.* $25

Clark, Ann Nolan. IN MY MOTHER'S HOUSE. NY: Viking, (1941) 1948. VG in Good+ dj. *ACADEMIC LIBRARY.* $25

Clark, Ann Nolan. SECRET OF THE ANDES. Viking, 1952. 1st ed. VG. *BEBBAH.* $40

Clark, Badger. SUN AND SADDLE LEATHER. Boston: Gorham, 1922. 6th enl ed. Good+; dj though worn and chipped, very scarce in any condition. Contents Fine. *CONNOLLY & WADE.* $45

Clark, Badger. SUN AND SADDLE LEATHER. Boston: Richard C. Badger, (1920). 5th ed. *SCHOYER'S.* $20

Clark, C. M. A TRIP TO PIKE'S PEAK AND NOTES BY THE WAY. Chicago, 1861. 1st ed. 134, errata pp. Frontis, woodcut plts on tinted paper. Orig black cl, title in gilt on front cover, blind embossed corner ornaments. Presentation copy. 1st ed. Howes C430. *GINSBERG.* $1250

Clark, Cumberland. DICKENS AND TALFOURD WITH AN ADDRESS AND THREE UNPUBLISHED LETTERS TO TALFOURD, THE FATHER OF THE FIRST COPYRIGHT ACT WHICH PUT AN END TO THE PIRACY OF DICKENS' WRITINGS. London: Chiswick Press, 1919. 1st ed. 8vo, 43pp, red cloth, deckle edged paper unopened. Bkpl. Top of rear board sl shaved. VG+. *GREAT EXPECTATIONS.* $40

Clark, Daniel. PROOFS OF THE CORRUPTION OF GEN. JAMES WILKINSON, AND OF HIS CONNEXION WITH AARON BURR....Phila., 1809. 1st ed. 150,199pp. Half calf. Nice. Howes C431. *GINSBERG.* $850

Clark, Douglas. PLAIN SAILING. London: Victor Gollancz, 1987. 1st ed. Fine in dj. *MORDIDA.* $25

Clark, Douglas. ROAST EGGS. London: Victor Gollancz, 1981. 1st ed. VF in dj. *MORDIDA.* $30

Clark, Douglas. STORM CENTRE. London: Victor Gollancz, 1986. 1st ed. VF in dj. *MORDIDA.* $30

Clark, Douglas. THE BIG GROUSE. London: Gollancz, 1986. 1st ed. VF in dj. *SILVER DOOR.* $25

Clark, Douglas. THE BIG GROUSE. London: Victor Gollancz, 1986. 1st ed. VF in dj. *MORDIDA.* $30

Clark, Edna Maria. OHIO ART AND ARTISTS. Richmond: Garret & Massie, (1932). 1st ed. 142 b/w plts. Fine in VG dj (title ptd by hand on spine). Signed. *CAPTAIN'S BOOKSHELF.* $125

Clark, Edward L. DALETH, OR THE HOMESTEAD OF THE NATIONS. Boston: Ticknor & Fields, 1864. 1st ed. x,289 pp. 15 plts. Orig cl, edges sl rubbed, spine frayed, o/w VG. *WORLDWIDE.* $95

Clark, Edward L. RECORD OF THE INSCRIPTIONS ON THE TABLETS AND GRAVESTONES IN THE BURIAL GROUNDS OF CHRIST CHURCH, PHILADELPHIA. Phila, 1864. 1st ed. Rebound. *HEINOLDT.* $25

Clark, Eleanor. ROME AND A VILLA. GC, NY: Doubleday, 1952. 1st ed. Ptd on browning paper. Dj chipped. *SCHOYER'S.* $30

Clark, Ellery H. Jr. RED SOX FOREVER. Exposition Press, 1977. 1st ed. VG+ in Fine dj. *PLAPINGER.* $30

Clark, Francis E. OUR JOURNEY AROUND THE WORLD. Hartford, CT: Worthington, 1895. 641pp. Fldg color map. Orig cl, sl rubbed. VG. *WORLDWIDE.* $50

Clark, Galen. INDIANS OF THE YOSEMITE VALLEY AND VICINITY. Yosemite: Galen Clark, 1907. 3rd ed. Signed. 10pp ads, 25 full-pg illus. Lt wear to dec wrappers; sm holes in margins of front cover not affecting design, paper flaw affecting pages 3-6. *DAWSON'S.* $60

Clark, J.L. THE GREAT ARC OF THE WILD SHEEP. Norman, OK: Univ of OK, (1978). NF. *MIKESH.* $35

Clark, James A. and T. Halbouty Michel. SPINDLETOP. NY, 1952. 1st prtg. Former owner inscrip. Fine in sl worn dj. *BAADE.* $75

Clark, John Mason. THE HEART OF THE GASPE. NY: Macmillan, 1913. 1st ed. VG, some foxing. Hinges starting. *AARD.* $20

Clark, John Spencer. THE LIFE AND LETTERS OF JOHN FISKE. 2 vols. Boston, 1917. 1st ed. VG. *ARTIS.* $17.50

Clark, Kenneth. LEONARDO DA VINCI, ANATOMICAL DRAWINGS AT WINDSOR CASTLE. NY, 1969. 2nd ed. Dj. *FYE.* $50

Clark, Kenneth. THE GOTHIC REVIVAL. London, 1928. Teg. NF. *POLYANTHOS.* $75

Clark, Mary Higgins. THE ANASTASIA SYNDROME & OTHER STORIES. London: Century, 1990. 1st British ed. Review copy, signed. Pub's slip laid in. Sl bumped cvr tip o/w Fine in dj. *SILVER DOOR.* $35

Clark, Mary Higgins. WHILE MY PRETTY ONE SLEEPS. NY: Simon and Schuster, 1989. 1st ed. Signed. Fine in Fine dj. *BEASLEY.* $35

Clark, Paul. PIONEER MICROBIOLOGISTS OF AMERICA. Madison, 1961. *FYE.* $50

Clark, Thomas Dunlop Douglas. RHYTHMIC RAMBLINGS IN BATTLE SCARRED MANASSAS. Phila, 1905. 1st ed. NF. *McGOWAN.* $37.50

Clark, Tom. KEROUAC'S LAST WORD: JACK KEROUAC IN ESCAPADE. Sudbury: Water Row Press, 1986. One of 500 numbered in wrappers. NF. *LOPEZ.* $30

Clark, Tom. THE WORLD OF DAMON RUNYON. NY: Harper & Row, 1978. 1st ed. VF in dj. *ELSE FINE.* $40

Clark, Walter (ed). HISTORIES OF THE SEVERAL REGIMENTS AND BATTALIONS FROM NORTH CAROLINA IN THE GREAT WAR 1861-'65. 5 vols. Raleigh, 1901. 1st ed. A little cvr wear and spotting but VG. *PRATT.* $800

Clark, Walter Van Tilberg. THE CITY OF TREMBLING LEAVES. Random House, (1945). 1st ed. Fine. *AUTHORS OF THE WEST.* $30

Clark, Walter Van Tilberg. THE TRACK OF THE CAT. London: Victor Gollancz, 1950. 1st British ed. VG in dj, blotched. *AUTHORS OF THE WEST.* $20

Clark, Walter Van Tilberg. THE WATCHFUL GODS AND OTHER STORIES. Random House, (1950). 1st ed. VG+, owner initials. *AUTHORS OF THE WEST.* $25

Clark, Walter Van Tilburg. THE WATCHFUL GODS AND OTHER STORIES. NY: Random House, 1950. 1st ed. Fine w/owner name, in NF dj. *BEASLEY.* $50

Clark, William G. GREECE AND THE GREEKS. PELOPONNESUS: NOTES OF STUDY AND TRAVEL. London, 1858. Frontis plt, 5 maps (1 fldg). New cl, aeg. VF. *O'NEILL.* $175

Clark, William. WESTWARD WITH DRAGOONS...Fulton, MO: Ovid Bell Press, 1937. Gregg, Kate (ed). 1st ed. Frontis, fldg map. Signed presentation. Fine. *OREGON.* $35

Clark-Kennedy, A.E. STEPHEN HALES, D.D, F.R.S. Cambridge: at the Univ Press, 1929. 1st ed. VG, w/remnant of dj laid in. *WREDEN.* $30

Clarke, Arthur C. (ed). COMING OF THE SPACE AGE. Meredith, 1967. 1st ed. Signed. Fine in dj. *MADLE.* $50

Clarke, Arthur C. 2001: A SPACE ODYSSEY. NAL, 1968. 1st ed. VG in frayed dj. *MADLE.* $150

Clarke, Arthur C. 2001: A SPACE ODYSSEY. NY: NAL, 1968. 1st ed, 1st ptg. Small stain to upper left front cvr, two edges yellowed, small tear to o/w bright dj. *BOOKMINE.* $150

Clarke, Arthur C. 2010: ODYSSEY TWO. NY, 1982. 1st ed. Uncorrected proof. Fine in pub printed wraps. *POLYANTHOS.* $75

Clarke, Arthur C. 2010: ODYSSEY TWO. NY: Ballantine Books, 1985. 1st ed. Fine in dj. *SECOND LIFE.* $45

Clarke, Arthur C. ACROSS A SEA OF STARS. NY: HB, 1959. 1st ed. VF, small chip rear panel of dj. *ELSE FINE.* $95

Clarke, Arthur C. EXPEDITION TO EARTH. London, 1955. 1st British ed. Fine in dj. *MADLE.* $100

Clarke, Arthur C. IMPERIAL EARTH. London, 1975. 1st ed. Fine in dj, tear. *MADLE.* $35

Clarke, Arthur C. PROFILES OF THE FUTURE. Harper, 1962. 1st ed. NF in frayed dj. *MADLE.* $25

Clarke, Arthur C. PROMISE OF SPACE. Harper, 1968. Fine in dj, signed. *MADLE.* $45

Clarke, Arthur C. TALES OF TEN WORLDS. NY: HBW, 1962. 1st ed. Fine in dj. *ELSE FINE.* $60

Clarke, Arthur C. THE CITY AND THE STARS. NY: Harcourt, Brace & Co., (1956). 1st ed. Rev. & expanded version. NF in price clipped dj which has one chip at lower right corner of rear panel. *BERNARD.* $150

Clarke, Arthur C. THE OTHER SIDE OF THE SKY. Harcourt, 1957. 1st ed. VG in tape-stained dj. *MADLE.* $100

Clarke, Arthur C. THE SONGS OF DISTANT EARTH. Random House, 1986. One of 500 numbered, signed. As New. *MADLE.* $100

Clarke, Donald Henderson. MAN OF THE WORLD. NY, (1951). 304pp. Cloth. NF in dj. *DIAMOND.* $25

Clarke, Dwight L. WILLIAM TECUMSEH SHERMAN: GOLD RUSH BANKER. SF: CA Hist Soc, 1969. 1st ed. Fine in Fine dj. *CONNOLLY & WADE.* $45

Clarke, Edward. THE RELATION OF DRUGS TO TREATMENT. Boston, 1856. 1st ed. Front wrapper detached, rear wrapper lacking. *FYE.* $40

Clarke, Edward. VISIONS: A STUDY OF FALSE SIGHT (PSEUDOPIA) WITH AN INTRODUCTION AND MEMORIAL SKETCH BY OLIVER WENDELL HOLMES. Boston, 1878. 1st ed. 315pp. Lacks frontis, o/w VG. *FYE.* $75

Clarke, Edwin (ed). MODERN METHODS IN THE HISTORY OF MEDICINE. London, 1971. 1st ed. Dj. *FYE.* $90

Clarke, Eleanor P. DESIGNS ON THE PREHISTORIC POTTERY OF ARIZONA. Tucson: Univ of AZ, 1935. Color illus, wrappers. *DAWSON'S.* $35

Clarke, James. HISTORY OF CRICKET IN KENDAL. Thompson Bros. Duckett Works, Kendal printers priv pub, 1906. 1st ed. Good. *OLD LONDON.* $50

Clarke, M.U. NATURE'S OWN GARDENS. London, 1907. 51 colored plts. Orig dec cl. *SUTTON.* $50

Clarke, Mary Cowden. THE GIRLHOOD OF SHAKESPEARE'S HEROINES. 1st and 2nd series. NY: Putnam, 1878. 1st US ed. 2 vols. 489pp; 473. Engr frontis each vol. Hinge tender vol 1, else VG. *SECOND LIFE.* $75

Clarke, Mary Whatley. DAVID G. BURNET. Austin: The Pemberton Press, 1969. 1st ed. Fine. Fldg map. *GIBBS.* $30

Clarke, O.P. GENERAL GRANT AT MOUNT MACGREGOR. Saratoga, NY, 1895. 1st ed. Wrappers. NF. *McGOWAN.* $37.50

Clarke, S.J. HISTORY OF MCDONOUGH COUNTY, IL-LINOIS...Springfield, IL: D.W. Lusk, 1878. Worn, frayed, chipped, some looseness. Good. *BOHLING.* $125

Clarke, S.J. HISTORY OF MCDONOUGH COUNTY, ILLINOIS, ITS CITIES....Springfield: Lusk, 1878. 1st ed. 692pp + plts, etchings. Orig black blindstamped lea, raised bands, gilt dec cover. NF. Scarce. *CONNOLLY & WADE.* $385

Clarke, Somers and R. Engelbach. ANCIENT EGYPTIAN MASONRY: THE BUILDING CRAFT. London: Oxford Univ Press, 1930. 1st ed. Frontis. 2 small ink stamps of previous owner. Good in dj. *ARCHAEOLOGIA.* $475

Clarke, William M. MINOR ENGLISH DOMESTIC ARCHITECTURE. In Three Volumes. LA: Pub by LA Pressed Brick Co. (1923-1925). Each vol has 25 mounted gravures w/preliminary text. Sheets loose within two-tone cl portfolios with ties. *KARMIOLE.* $300

Clarkson, L. INDIAN SUMMER, AUTUMN POEMS AND SKETCHES. Dutton, 1883. 4to. 12 full-pg color plts; 2 duotone plts. Interior NF. Cvr w/wear, soil. VG. *BEBBAH.* $25

Clason, Clyde B. BLIND DRIFTS. GC: Doubleday, 1937. 1st ed. Fine, bright, in lightly used dj w/spine chips. *BEASLEY.* $50

Claudy, C.H. THE BATTLE OF BASEBALL. Bell & Cockburn, 1912 (1st Canadian ed of orig published by Century in the same year). Good. *PLAPINGER.* $200

Claudy, Carl. THE LAND OF NO SHADOW. Grosset, 1933. 1st ed. Good. *MADLE.* $25

Clavir, Judy and John Spitzer (eds). THE CONSPIRACY TRIAL. THE EXTENDED EDITED TRANSCRIPT. Indianapolis: Bobbs-Merrill, 1970. Wraps, only lightly worn. Also issued in cloth. *BEASLEY.* $40

Clay, John. MY LIFE ON THE RANGE. NY, 1961. Reprt ltd to 750. Fine. *VARNER.* $45

Clay, John. MY LIFE ON THE RANGE. NY: Antiquarian Press, 1961. Orig cl. Intro by E. E. Dale. One of 750. Howes C478. *GINSBERG.* $75

Clay, Reginald and Thomas Court. THE HISTORY OF THE MICROSCOPE. London, 1975. 1st ed, reprtd. 164 illus. *FYE.* $75

Clayton, Henry H. WORLD WEATHER....NY: Macmillan, 1923., 1st ed. Spots to front board, o/w Good in blue cl. *KNOLLWOOD.* $30

Clayton, Michael. THE COLLECTOR'S DICTIONARY OF THE SILVER AND GOLD OF GREAT BRITAIN AND NORTH AMERICA. NY: World Pub, 1971. 1st ed. VG. *BACKROOM.* $125

Clayton, Victoria V. WHITE AND BLACK UNDER THE OLD REGIME. Milwaukee, (1899). 1st ed. NF. *McGOWAN.* $150

Clayton, W. THE LATTER-DAY SAINTS' EMIGRANTS' GUIDE: BEING A TABLE OF DISTANCES.... Reprint pub by Latter-day Saints, ca. 1930, from the photo plts of orig pub in St. Louis at MO Republican Steam Power Press-Chambers & Knapp in 1848. Bound in full grn cl, gilt stamped. VG. *LAURIE.* $100

Cleary, Jon. PETER'S PENCE. NY: William Morrow, 1974. 1st Amer ed. Couple tiny spots on edges o/w Fine in dj. *MORDIDA.* $37.50

Cleaton, Irene and Allen. BOOKS AND BATTLES. AMERICAN LITERATURE, 1920-1930. Boston: Houghton Mifflin, 1937. 1st ed. VG in frayed dj. *WREDEN.* $35

Cleaveland, Agnes M. NO LIFE FOR A LADY. Houghton Mifflin, 1941. 1st ed. VG in Good+ tape repaired dj. *OREGON.* $60

Cleaveland, Agnes M. SATAN'S PARADISE. FROM LUCIEN MAXWELL TO FRED LAMBERT. Houghton Mifflin, 1952. 1st ed. Fine in Good+ dj. *OREGON.* $35

Cleaveland, Agnes M. SATAN'S PARADISE. Houghton Mifflin Co., 1952. 1st ed. Fine in sl chipped dj. *VARNER.* $25

Cleaveland, Agnes Morley. NO LIFE FOR A LADY. Boston: Houghton Mifflin, 1941. 1st ed. Cover sl worn, interior VG. *LAURIE.* $50

Cleaver, Eldridge. ELDRIDGE CLEAVER. NY: RH, (1969). 1st ed. NF in dj. *LOPEZ.* $35

Cleeves, Ann. A BIRD IN THE HAND. London: Century Publishing, 1986. 1st ed. Signed. Fine in dj. *MORDIDA.* $50

Cleeves, Ann. COME DEATH AND HIGH WATER. London: Century, 1987. 1st ed. Signed. VF in dj. *MORDIDA.* $40

Clegg, Charles and Duncan Emrich (eds). THE LUCIUS BEEBE READER. GC: Doubleday, 1967. 1st ed. Fine in Good+ dj. *CONNOLLY & WADE.* $35

Cleland, Robert (ed). APRON FULL OF GOLD. Huntington Lib, 1949. 1st ed. F in G+ dj. *OREGON.* $35

Cleland, Robert and Juanita Brooks. A MORMON CHRONICLE: THE DIARIES OF JOHN D. LEE — 1848-1876. The Huntington Library, 1955. 1st ed. 2 vols. (Vol I) xxvi,344pp; (Vol II) 480pp. VF in NF djs. *FIVE QUAIL.* $125

Cleland, Robert Glass. CALIFORNIA IN OUR TIME (1900-1940). NY: Knopf, 1947. 1st ed. Fine. *CONNOLLY & WADE.* $40

Cleland, Robert Glass. THE CATTLE ON A THOUSAND HILLS, SOUTHERN CALIFORNIA 1850-1870. San Marino: Huntington, 1951. 2nd ed. VF. Howes C477. *OREGON.* $55

Cleland, Robert Glass. THE IRVINE RANCH OF ORANGE COUNTY 1810-1950. Huntington, 1952. 1st ed. Tape marks on fep, o/w VF in VF dj. *OREGON.* $60

Cleland, Robert Glass. THE IRVINE RANCH OF ORANGE COUNTY. 1810-1950. San Marino: Huntington Lib, 1962. Rev. Blue grn cl, gilt spine titles. VG, worn dj. *PARMER.* $45

Cleland, Robert Glass. THE IRVINE RANCH OF ORANGE COUNTY. 1810-1950. San Marino: Huntington Lib, 1953. 2nd ed. VG in worn dj. *PARMER.* $30

Cleland, Robert Glass. THIS RECKLESS BREED OF MEN. Knopf, 1950. 1st ed. Frontis. VF in VG dj. *OREGON.* $40

Cleland, Robert Glass. THIS RECKLESS BREED OF MEN. NY, 1952. 3rd ptg. NF in VG dj. *FIVE QUAIL.* $30

Cleland, Robert. FROM WILDERNESS TO EMPIRE. HISTORY OF CALIFORNIA 1542-1900. Knopf, 1944. 1st ed. 20 plts. VG in VG dj. *OREGON.* $35

Cleland, T.M. THE DECORATIVE WORK OF T.M. CLELAND. NY: Pynson Printers. 1929. Ed ltd to 1200. Dj chipped. *KARMIOLE.* $125

Clemenceau, Georges. AMERICAN RECONSTRUCTION. NY, 1928. 1st ed. Dj wear and chipping, o/w VG+. *PRATT.* $27.50

Clemens, Will M. MARK TWAIN: HIS LIFE AND WORK, A BIOGRAPHICAL SKETCH. SF: The Clemens Publishing Co., 1892. 1st ed. 211pp, grn cl, stamped in black and gold. *BOOKMINE.* $225

Clement, Clara Erksine. THE QUEEN OF THE ADRIATIC; OR, VENICE, MEDIAEVAL AND MODERNS. Boston: Estes & Lauriat, 1893. 1st ed. (vi),380pp. Orig cl, richly gilt, in cl dj, sl shaken, o/w VG; teg. *WORLDWIDE.* $18

Clement, Hal. ICEWORLD. (NY: Gnome Press, 1953). 1st ed. Fine in dj. *McCLINTOCK.* $100

Clement, Hal. ICEWORLD. Gnome Press, 1953. 1st ed. Fine in dj. Inscribed. *MADLE.* $200

Clement, Hal. MISSION OF GRAVITY. Doubleday, 1954. 1st ed. VG in frayed, sl chipped dj. Signed. *MADLE.* $225

Clement, Hal. NEEDLE. Doubleday, 1950. 1st ed. VG. Signed. *MADLE.* $35

Clement, Maud C. THE HISTORY OF THE PITTSYVANIA COUNTY, VIRGINIA. Lynchburg, VA, Bell, 1929. 1st ed. 23 maps, ports. and plts. Orig cl, sm paper label on spine, bkpl removed. *GINSBERG.* $75

Clements, Edith S. FLOWERS OF COAST AND SIERRA. NY: H.W. Wilson Co, 1928. 1st ed. 32 color plts. Sl water damage bottom of pp not affecting text. VG. *SMITH.* $40

Clemons, Walter. THE POISON TREE AND OTHER STORIES. Boston: Houghton Mifflin, 1959. 1st ed, 1st bk. Inscribed. VG in soiled, rubbed, chipped dj. *HELLER.* $75

Clendening, Logan. A HANDBOOK TO THE PICKWICK PAPERS. NY: Knopf, 1936. 1st ltd ed. 8vo, 156pp, 25 illus, 2 maps, grey boards, dj torn at bottom of spine lacking 2" wedge, one of 2000. Fine in Good+ dj. *GREAT EXPECTATIONS.* $27.50

Clendening, Logan. BEHIND THE DOCTOR. NY, 1933. 1st ed. *FYE.* $40

Clerke, Agnes M. THE SYSTEM OF THE STARS. London: A & C Black, 1905 (1890). 2nd ed. Fldg chart. Good. *KNOLLWOOD.* $50

Clifford, D. A HISTORY OF GARDEN DESIGN. London, 1966. 2nd ed. Cl, dj. *SUTTON.* $95

Clifford, D. PELARGONIUMS....London, 1970. 2nd ed. Cl, chipped dj. *SUTTON.* $35

Clifford, Henry. HENRY CLIFFORD V.C. HIS LETTERS AND SKETCHES FROM THE CRIMEA. NY, 1956. 1st ed. Orig cl, Fine in NF dj. *McGOWAN.* $45

Clifford, Sir Hugh. THE FURTHER SIDE OF SILENCE. Doubleday, 1916. 1st ed. Fine. *MADLE.* $50

Clifford, W.G. BOOKS IN BOTTLES. London: Geoffrey Bles, (1926). 1st ed. VG. *WREDEN.* $25

Clifton, Lucille. GENERATIONS. A MEMOIR. NY: Random House, 1976. 1st ed. Fine in NF dj. *BEASLEY.* $45

Clifton, Lucille. GENERATIONS. NY: Random House, (1976). 1st ed. Fine in very sl spine-tanned dj. Errata slip laid in. Scarce. *BETWEEN COVERS.* $60

Clifton, Lucille. GOOD TIMES. NY: Random House, (1969). 1st ed. Couple spots fore-edge, else NF in NF white dj darkened at extremities. Uncommon. *BETWEEN COVERS.* $125

Clifton, Lucille. GOOD TIMES. POEMS. NY: Random House, (1969). 1st ed. Cl-backed boards. Fine in dj. *JAFFE.* $175

Clifton, Lucille. GOOD TIMES: POEMS. NY: Random House, n.d. Uncorrected proof. Spiral bound. Pgs browning, short tear in title pg. NF, scarce. *CAPTAIN'S BOOKSHELF.* $150

Clifton, Lucille. TEN OXHERDING PICTURES. (Santa Cruz: Moving Parts Press, 1988). 1st ed. One of 30 specially bound, signed by Clifton. 4to, 1/4 calf & boards. Mint in glassine dj. *JAFFE.* $275

Clifton, Mark and Frank Riley. THEY'D RATHER BE RIGHT. Gnome Press, 1957. 1st ed. Dj spine sl darkened, else Fine. *MADLE.* $100

Clinton, Catherine. THE PLANTATION MISTRESS. NY, (1982). 1st ed. Light dj wear o/w Fine. *PRATT.* $25

Clinton, Henry. OBSERVATIONS ON EARL CORNWALLIS' ANSWER. Phila: Campbell, 1866. 1st Amer ed. 35,116pp. Fldg table, orig printed wrappers. One of 250 printed. Reprint of London 1783 orig ed. Howes C499. *GINSBERG.* $75

Clinton, Lieut. Gen. Sir Henry. NARRATIVE OF LIEUT.-GEN. SIR HENRY CLINTON, K.B. RELATIVE TO HIS CONDUCT....Phila: 1866. (4), 115pp. Orig printed wrappers. Reprint of London 1783 orig ed. One of 250 printed. Howes C496. *GINSBERG.* $75

Clinton, Thomas P. THE MILITARY OPERATIONS OF GEN. JOHN T. CROXTON IN WEST ALABAMA, 1865. Montgomery, AL, 1904. 1st separate ed. Wrappers. VG. *McGOWAN.* $37.50

Clissold, Stephen. CONQUISTADOR. THE LIFE OF DON PEDRO SARMIENTO DE GAMBOA. London: Derek Verschoyle Ltd, 1954. 1st ed. VG. *PARMER.* $30

Clock, Herbert and Eric Boetzel. THE LIGHT IN THE SKY. Coward-McCann, 1929. 1st ed. VG. *MADLE.* $60

Cloete, Stuart. THE AFRICAN GIANT THE STORY OF A JOURNEY. London, 1956. 1st ed. Orig cl, minor scattered foxing, else VG. *McGOWAN.* $45

Clopper, Edward N. AN AMERICAN FAMILY...THROUGH EIGHT GENERATIONS...FROM 1650 TO 1880. (Huntington, WV: 1950). 1st ed. Orig cl, dj. *GINSBERG.* $35

Cloquet, M. Jules. RECOLLECTIONS OF THE PRIVATE LIFE OF GENERAL LAFAYETTE. London: Ptd for Baldwin and Cradock, by G. Woodfall, 1835. 1st ed in English. xxx,339pp & 8pp catalog. 3/4 black calf and marbled boards, sl rubbed, teg. Very attractive. *BLUE MOUNTAIN.* $75

Closson, Ernest. HISTORY OF THE PIANO. London: Paul Elek, 1947. 1st Eng ed. Delano Ames (trans). 1/4 black cl and red boards; a bit rubbed, o/w VG. *WEBER.* $25

Clouston, J. Storer. THE MAN FROM THE CLOUDS. Doran, 1919. VG. *MADLE.* $25

Coast, John. DANCERS OF BALI. NY: Putnam (1953). 1st ed. VG in VG dj. *AARD.* $25

COASTAL COMMAND. The Air Ministry Account of the Part Played by Coastal Command in the Battle of the Seas, 1939-1942. NY: The Macmillan Co, 1943. 1st ed. Dj. *KARMIOLE.* $30

Coates, James. HUMAN MAGNETISM OR HOW TO HYPNOTISE. London, 1897. 1st ed. 253pp. *FYE.* $125

Coates, Robert M. BEYOND THE ALPS. NY: William Sloane, 1961. 1st ed. Owner marks. Dj chipped. *SCHOYER'S.* $20

Coates, Robert M. SOUTH OF ROME. NY: Morrow, 1965. 1st ed. Dj sl chipped. *SCHOYER'S.* $15

Coats, Alice M. THE QUEST FOR PLANTS. London: Studio Vista, (1969). 1st ed. Dj. Fine. *WREDEN.* $35

Coatsworth, Elizabeth. MOUSE CHORUS. Pantheon, (1955). 1st ed. Unpaginated. Illus Genevieve Vaughan-Jackson. VG w/wear. *BEBBAH.* $25

Cobb, Bert (artist). HUNTING DOGS BY BERT COBB. NY: The Crafton Collection Inc, 1931. 1st trade ed. Owner inscrip. Fine in VG dj. *BACKMAN.* $65

Cobb, J.H. A MANUAL CONTAINING INFORMATION RESPECTING THE GROWTH OF THE MULBERRY TREE...IN THREE PARTS. Boston: Carter, Hendee, 1833. New ed. 98pp. Worn linen backed ptd boards. 3 plts, 2 hand colored. Lt foxing, scribbling on eps, o/w VG. *SECOND LIFE.* $85

Cobb, Thomas R.R. AN INQUIRY INTO THE LAW OF NEGRO SLAVERY,...TO WHICH IS PREFIXED AN HISTORICAL

SKETCH OF SLAVERY. Vol 1 (all pub). Phila & Savannah, 1858. 1st ed. Rebound. *DIAMOND.* $150

Cobb, Ty with Al Stump. MY LIFE IN BASEBALL—THE TRUE RECORD. Doubleday, 1961. Book club ed. Good+ in VG+ dj. *PLAPINGER.* $40

Cobbett, William. COTTAGE ECONOMY: CONTAINING INFOR-MATION...RELATIVE TO OTHER MATTERS DEEMED USE-FUL IN THE CONDUCTING OF THE AFFAIRS OF A LABOURER'S FAMILY...NY: Stephen Gould and Son, 1824. 125 (126), pub's ads. 4pp. Inserted frontis, pp77 & 78 bound upside down, p75 w/closed tear, orig boards and spine label, sl rubbed, otherwise VG. Contemporary Inscription. Rare. *WEBER.* $500

Cobbett, William. LIFE AND ADVENTURES OF PETER POR-CUPINE. London: Nonesuch Press, 1927. Ltd ed, 469/1800 for England and America, on Arches paper. Colored frontis. Uncut, un-opened. Extremities, spine little rubbed, few tiny spots, sl edge rubbed. Fine. *POLYANTHOS.* $75

Cobbett, William. THE AMERICAN GARDENER....NY: Turner & Hayden, 1844. Later ptg. 230pp. Foxed, but Very Nice, tight. *SECOND LIFE.* $125

Cobbett, William. THE ENGLISH GARDENER....London: Cobben, 1838. Cl backed boards (lacking paper label). Lt foxing throughout. Fold-out plt. VG. *SECOND LIFE.* $235

Cobden-Sanderson, T.J. THE ARTS AND CRAFTS MOVEMENT. Hammersmith: Hammersmith Publishing Society, 1905. Small 8vo, parchment backed boards. 39+(1)pp. Parchment spine somewhat yellowed and spotting along inner margins. *OAK KNOLL.* $75

Cobden-Sanderson, Thomas James. THE JOURNALS OF THOMAS JAMES COBDEN-SANDERSON: 1879-1922. NY: The Macmillan Co. 1926. 1st ed. 2 vols. Ed ltd to 1050 numbered sets. Fine set in seldom seen djs. *KARMIOLE.* $275

Cobham, Alan. TWENTY THOUSAND MILES IN A FLYING-BOAT. Phila: David McKay Co. (1930). 1st ed. Dj extrems rubbed. *KARMIOLE.* $45

Coblentz, Stanton A. THE WONDER STICK. NY: Cosmopolitan, 1929. 1st ed, 1st bk. Fine, pict dj has minor edge wear, sm chips at spine ends. *ELSE FINE.* $85

Coblentz, Stanton A. VILLAINS AND VIGILANTES: THE STORY OF JAMES KING OF WILLIAM AND PIONEER JUSTICE IN CALIFORNIA. NY: Wilson-Erickson, 1936. 1st ed. VG. *LAURIE.* $35

Coblentz, Stanton A. VILLAINS AND VIGILANTES: THE STORY OF JAMES KING OF WILLIAM AND PIONEER JUSTICE IN CALIFORNIA. NY, 1936. 1st ed. Bkpl front pastedown (slight of-fset on opposite front fly). Fine in dj. *BAADE.* $50

Coblentz, Stanton. FROM ARROW TO ATOM BOMB. Beech-churst, 1953. 1st ed. VG. *MADLE.* $20

Coblentz, Stanton. INTO PLUTONIAN DEPTHS. Avon, 1950. Wraps. VG. *MADLE.* $30

Coblentz, Stanton. THE DECLINE OF MAN. Minton-Balch, 1925. 1st ed. VG. *MADLE.* $35

Coburn, Jesse L. LETTERS OF GOLD: CALIFORNIA POSTAL HISTORY THROUGH 1869. (Canton): U.S. Philatelic Classics Soc, 1984. Illus, fabricoid in dj. *DAWSON'S.* $60

Cochran, John H. DALLAS COUNTY A RECORD OF ITS PIONEERS AND PROGRESS. Dallas: Arthur S. Mathis Service Publishing Co, 1928. 1st ed. VF. *GIBBS.* $125

Cochrane, Ben and William Coldiron. DISILLUSION: A STORY OF THE LABOR STRUGGLE IN THE WESTERN WOOD-WORKING MILLS. Portland: Binfords & Mort, (1939). 279pp. Edgeworn dj. *AKA.* $30

Cochrane, Hamilton. NOTED AMERICAN DUELS AND HOS-TILE ENCOUNTERS. Phila: Chilton Books, (1963). 1st ed. Dj. *SCHOYER'S.* $15

Cochrane, Mickey. BASEBALL—THE FAN'S GAME. Funk & Wagnall's, 1939. 1st ed. VG with minor cover wear. *PLAPINGER.* $70

Cockcroft, G. L. INDEX TO THE WEIRD FICTION MAGAZINES. Arno, 1975, 1st hb ed. VG. *MADLE.* $50

Cockerell, Douglas. BOOKBINDING, AND THE CARE OF BOOKS, A TEXT-BOOK FOR BOOKBINDERS AND LIBRARIANS. London: John Hogg, 1906. 2nd ed. Covers spotted, staining to page tops. *OAK KNOLL.* $20

Cockrum, Col. William M. HISTORY OF THE UNDERGROUND RAILROAD....Oakland City, IN: Cockrum Printing Co., 1915. 1st ed. Frontis. 13 plts. Map. Edge wear, w/gilt worn on spine and front cover. Front inner hinge cracking. Else Good. *CONNOLLY & WADE.* $45

Cockton, Henry. THE LIFE AND ADVENTURES OF VALEN-TINE VOX, VENTRILOQUIST. London: Robert Tyas, 1840. 620pp. 1st bk ed. Frontis, engr title, 58 plts. Modern full polished tan calf, gilt tooled spine panels, morocco spine label, gilt fillets and inner dentelles, aeg. Few dots of foxing to engr title, but Fine. *CHAPEL HILL.* $200

Cocteau, Jean. PARIS ALBUM. 1900-1914. London, 1956. 1st ed. Name. Fine in dj (spine little sunned). *POLYANTHOS.* $30

Cocteau, Jean. THE WHITE PAPER BY ANONYMOUS. Paris: The Travelers Companion, Olympia Press, 1957. 1st ed. Printed wraps. Fine. *POLYANTHOS.* $30

Codman, E. A. A STUDY IN HOSPITAL EFFICIENCY AS DEMONSTRATED BY THE CASE REPORT OF THE SECOND TWO YEARS OF A PRIVATE HOSPITAL. Boston, 1915. 44pp. Wrappers. *FYE.* $200

Codman, John Thomas. BROOK FARM, HISTORIC & PER-SONAL MEMOIRS. Boston: Arena Publishing Company, 1894. Upper extremities frayed, rear hinge cracked. VG. *BOHLING.* $65

Codman, John Thomas. BROOK FARM. HISTORIC AND PER-SONAL MEMOIRS. Boston: Arena, 1894. 1st ed. Fine but for light wear to spine ends. Correct 1st ptg w/pict of Brook Farm on title page. *BEASLEY.* $100

Codman, John. THE ROUND TRIP BY WAY OF PANAMA THROUGH CALIFORNIA...NY, 1879. 1st ed. New rear cvr. Lit-tle shelfwear, o/w VG. Scarce. *DIAMOND.* $35

Codrington, R.H. THE MELANESIANS: ANTHROPOLOGY & FOLK-LORE. Oxford, 1891. Fldg map & illus. NF. *POLYANTHOS.* $100

Cody, Iron Eyes. IRON EYES. NY: Everest, (1982). 1st ed. VG in sl rubbed dj, few edge tears. *LOPEZ.* $40

Cody, Liza. HEAD CASE. London: Collins Crime Club, 1985. 1st ed. VF, price-clipped dj has minor rubs at spine ends. *ELSE FINE.* $35

Cody, Liza. HEAD CASE. London: Collins Crime Club, 1985. 1st ed. Signed. VF in dj. *MORDIDA.* $35

Cody, Liza. HEAD CASE. London: Collins Crime Club, 1985. 1st ed. Signed. As New in dj. *ELSE FINE.* $45

Cody, Liza. RIFT. London: Collins Crime Club, 1988. 1st ed. VF in dj. *ELSE FINE.* $30

Cody, Liza. UNDER CONTRACT. London: Collins Crime Club, 1986. 1st ed. VF in price-clipped dj. *ELSE FINE.* $30

Cody, Liza. UNDER CONTRACT. London: Collins Crime Club, 1986. 1st ed. VF in dj. *MORDIDA.* $30

Cody, Louisa Frederick. MEMORIES OF BUFFALO BILL, BY HIS WIFE,...NY, 1920. 2nd ed. Sl shelfwear, cvr staining, o/w VG. *DIAMOND.* $45

Cody, William F. AN AUTOBIOGRAPHY OF BUFFALO BILL. Cosmopolitan, 1923. VG. *VARNER.* $20

Cody, William F. LIFE AND ADVENTURES OF "BUFFALO BILL." Chicago: Stanton and Van Vliet, (1917). Cl w/rubbed photo mounted on fr cvr. *SCHOYER'S.* $35

Cody, William F. STORY OF THE WILD WEST AND CAMP-FIRE CHATS BY BUFFALO BILL (Hon W.F. Cody)...(Richmond, VA: B.F. Johnson & Co, 1888). 1st ed. 766pp, color frontis. Pict brown cl gilt cvrs sl worn & repaired. Cvr gilt dull. Small hole in rear cvr. Small hole in pastedown. Frontis & front ep sl chipped & repaired. Ink name on bottom fore-edge. Recased, o/w VG. *DIAMOND.* $250

Coe, Tucker. DON'T LIE TO ME. Random House, 1972. 1st ed. Fine in dj. *STAHR.* $35

Coe, Tucker. KINDS OF LOVE, KINDS OF DEATH. Random House, 1966. 1st ed. About Fine. Dj has a small chip at front flyleaf fold. *STAHR.* $30

Coe, Urling. FRONTIER DOCTOR. Macmillan, 1940. 2nd prtg. VG. *OREGON.* $25

Coe, Wilbur. RANCH ON THE RUIDOSO. STORY OF A PIONEER FAMILY IN NEW MEXICO, 1871-1968. 1st ed. Frontis, 2 color portraits, 4 maps. VG in Good+ dj. *OREGON.* $55

Coe, Wilbur. RANCH ON THE RUIDOSO: THE STORY OF A PIONEER FAMILY IN NEW MEXICO, 1871-1968. NY: Knopf, 1968. Fine in dj. *LAURIE.* $75

Coetzee, J.M. IN THE HEART OF THE COUNTRY. London: Secker & Warburg, (1977). 1st Eng ed. Fine in lightly rubbed dj w/short tear. *CAPTAIN'S BOOKSHELF.* $100

Coetzee, J.M. LIFE & TIMES OF MICHAEL K. Johannesburg: Ravan Press, (1983). 1st ed. Fine in dj. *CAPTAIN'S BOOKSHELF.* $90

Coffey, Brian (pseud of Dean R. Koontz). THE VOICE IN THE NIGHT. GC: Doubleday, 1980. 1st ed. Fine in dj w/wear along top edge front panel; chipping, wear. *MORDIDA.* $150

Coffey, Brian. (pseud of Dean R. Koontz). FACE OF FEAR. Bobbs-Merrill, 1977. 1st ed. Tear in dj, else Fine. *MADLE.* $250

Coffin, Charles Carleton. ABRAHAM LINCOLN. NY: Harper, 1899. Bright pict cl. *SCHOYER'S.* $15

Coffin, Charles Carleton. OUR NEW WAY AROUND THE WORLD. Boston: Fields, Osgood, 1869. 1st ed. xviii,524pp. Orig cl, edges rubbed, spine frayed, foxing, o/w Good. *WORLDWIDE.* $22

Coffin, Charles Carleton. THE BOYS OF '61, OR FOUR YEARS OF PERSONAL FIGHTING. Boston: Page, 1925. New ed, rev, enl. VG. *CONNOLLY & WADE.* $45

Coffin, Charles Carleton. THE SEAT OF EMPIRE. Boston: Fields, Osgood, & Co, 1870. Lacks map, western plts. *HUDSON.* $50

Coffin, Margaret. THE HISTORY & FOLKLORE OF AMERICAN COUNTRY TINWARE 1700-1900. Camden: Thos. Nelson, 1968. 1st ed. 8 plts. Discreet underlining on few lines, notation. Else Fine in Fine dj. *CONNOLLY & WADE.* $27.50

Coffin, Margaret. THE HISTORY & FOLKLORE OF AMERICAN COUNTRY TINWARE 1700—1900. NJ: Thomas Nelson & Sons, 1968. 1st ed. VG. *BACKROOM.* $35

Coffin, Peter (pseud of Jonathan Latimer). THE SEARCH FOR MY GREAT-UNCLE'S HEAD. GC: Doubleday Crime Club, 1937. 1st ed. VG+, lacking dj. Scarce. *ELSE FINE.* $65

Coffin, Robert P. Tristram. SALTWATER FARM. NY: The Macmillan Co., 1937. 1st ed. Illus. with 5 woodcuts by J.J. Lankes. Bookplate o/w VG in dj which is chipped at top of spine. *BERNARD.* $30

Coffin, Tristam Potter. THE ILLUSTRATED BOOK OF BASEBALL FOLKLORE. Seabury, 1975. 1st ed. VG+ in Fine dj. *PLAPINGER.* $35

Cofield, Jack. WILLIAM FAULKNER: THE COFIELD COLLECTION. Oxford, MS: Yoknapatawpha Press, (1978). 1st ed. Orig brn cl. Fine in NF dj. *CHAPEL HILL.* $55

Cogswell, E.C. MEMOIR OF THE REV. SAMUEL HIDDEN. Boston: Crocker, 1842. 1st ed. 332pp. Orig cl. *GINSBERG.* $75

Cohen, I.B. SOME EARLY TOOLS OF AMERICAN SCIENCE...COLLECTIONS IN HARVARD UNIVERSITY. Harvard Univ Press, 1950. VG+ in dj. *BOOKCELL.* $40

Cohen, Leonard. THE FAVORITE GAME. NY, 1963. 1st ed. Fine in Fine dj. *POLYANTHOS.* $60

Cohen, Leonard. THE SPICE-BOX OF EARTH. NY, (1961). 1st ed. Fine in dj w/nick, tiny tear. *POLYANTHOS.* $60

Cohen, Octavus Roy. BIGGER AND BLACKER. Boston, 1925. 1st ed. Inscribed by author and son. VG. *McCLINTOCK.* $75

Cohen, Octavus Roy. THE TOWNSEND MURDER MYSTERY. NY: Appleton Century, 1933. 1st ed. Signed. VF, small chip, minor wear top edge of silver pict dj. *ELSE FINE.* $125

Cohn, Alfred and Joe Chisholm. "TAKE THE WITNESS!". NY, 1934. 3rd ptg. Frontis. Cl sl stained. Spine tip wear, o/w VG. *DIAMOND.* $25

Cohn, William. CHINESE PAINTING. London: Phaidon, (1950). 2nd rev ed. 224 plts; several tipped-in color plts. Corners bumped. *ARTIS.* $25

Cohnheim, Julius. LECTURES ON GENERAL PATHOLOGY. 3 vols. London, 1889, 1890. 1st Eng trans. 1434pp. Minimal lib markings. Overall, Fine. *FYE.* $300

Coke, Roger. A DETECTION OF THE COURT AND STATE OF ENGLAND DURING THE FOUR LAST REIGNS, AND THE INTERREGNUM...The Second Edition Corrected....London: N.p., 1696. 2 vols in one. (42),134,200; (2),88,208,78pp. Recent black calf, old red leather spine label laid down. *KARMIOLE.* $300

Colby, Merle. A GUIDE TO ALASKA. NY, 1943. 7th prtg. Fold-out map in packet. VG in Good dj. *ARTIS.* $20

Cole, Adeline P. (comp). NOTES ON THE COLLECTION OF DOLLS AND FIGURINES AT THE WENHAM MUSEUM, CLAFLIN-RICHARDS HOUSE...Wenham, MA: Wenham Historical Association, 1951. 1st ed. Signed by the compiler. Paper label laid down on ffep stating that "This book is no. 407." Fine. *WREDEN.* $65

Cole, E.B. THE PHILOSOPHICAL CORPS. Hicksville, NY: Gnome Press, (1961). 1st ed. Fine in dj. *McCLINTOCK.* $20

Cole, Ernest. HOUSE OF BONDAGE. NY: Random House, (1967). 1st ed. NF in dj. *LOPEZ.* $65

Cole G.D.H. and Margaret. COUNTERPOINT MURDER. NY: Macmillan, 1941. 1st Amer ed. Advance review, slip laid in. VG in dj (dampstain back panel; wear; short closed tears). *MORDIDA.* $45

Cole, G.D.H. and Margaret. DEAD MAN'S WATCH. GC: Doubleday Crime Club, 1932. 1st Amer ed. VG in dj (extensive internal tape reinforcing, sm color restoration base of spine; long crease). *MORDIDA.* $45

Cole, G.D.H. and Margaret. THE BROTHERS SACKVILLE. NY: Macmillan, 1937. 1st Amer ed. Eps darkened, erasures on fep o/w VG in dj (wear; couple short closed tears). *MORDIDA.* $40

Cole, G.D.H. and Margaret. TOPER'S END. NY: Macmillan, 1942. 1st Amer ed. NF in dj (chipped; wear; couple short closed tears). *MORDIDA.* $40

Cole, George E. EARLY OREGON 1850 TO 1860. JOTTINGS OF PERSONAL RECOLLECTIONS OF A PIONEER OF 1850. Spokane: Privately Ptd. 1st ed. Red cl, white titles. Frontis. NF. *PARMER.* $55

Cole, George E. EARLY OREGON, JOTTINGS...OF A PIONEER OF 1850. Spokane: Shaw & Borden, (1905). 1st ed. VG. *OREGON.* $60

Cole, George E. EARLY OREGON; JOTTINGS OF PERSONAL RECOLLECTIONS OF A PIONEER OF 1850. Spokane: Publ by author, (1905). 1st ed. Ex-lib, stamped withdrawn. VG. *LAURIE.* $60

Cole, Harry Ellsworth. STAGECOACH & TAVERN TALES OF THE OLD NORTHWEST. Cleveland: Arthur Clark, 1930. Double map frontis. Navy cl, gilt top. VG+. *BOHLING.* $75

Cole, R.V. BRITISH TREES, DRAWN AND DESCRIBED. D. Kempe (rev). 2 vols. London, 1907. Orig cl, spine ends frayed, 1 tear; edge wear Vol 2. Soiling, insect tracings, eps browned, inner hinges open; nice internally. *SUTTON.* $95

Cole, S.W. THE AMERICAN FRUIT BOOK. Boston: Jewett, 1849. 288pp. Cloth light wear, contents VG. *AMERICAN BOTANIST.* $80

Cole, S.W. THE AMERICAN FRUIT BOOK....Boston: Jewen, 1849. 1st ed. Orig sheep, little scuffed. Very Nice. *SECOND LIFE.* $65

Cole, Timothy. ART BY THE WAY. NY: William Edwin Rudge, 1925. Frontis woodcut signed by Cole. Ed ltd to 750. Spine bit soiled. Dj. *KARMIOLE.* $35

Coleman, A.P. ICE AGES, RECENT & ANCIENT. NY, (1929). VG. *MIKESH.* $20

Coleman, A.P. ICE AGES RECENT AND ANCIENT. NY, 1926. Illus. Shelfwear spine top. NF. *POLYANTHOS.* $65

Coleman, Elliott. THE POEMS OF ELLIOTT COLEMAN. NY: Dutton, (c1936). 1st ed. NF in dj, few short tears. *HELLER.* $50

Coleman, Emily Holmes. THE SHUTTER OF SNOW. NY: Viking, 1930. 1st ed. NF in dj, few short tears. *HELLER.* $75

Coleman, James M. AESCULAPIUS ON THE COLORADO....(Austin): Encino Press, (1971). Fine. *LAURIE.* $20

Coleman, Max M. FROM MUSTANGER TO LAWYER. Lubbock, TX: The author, 1952. Book One. 1st ed, ltd to 500, signed. Fine. *GIBBS.* $30

Coleman, Max. FROM MUSTANGER TO LAWYER. BOOK ONE, PART B, FROM 1890 TO 1910. San Antonio: Carleton Ptg., (1953). 1st ed. Ltd. to 500 numbered and signed. Fine. *OREGON.* $50

Coleman, R.V. THE FIRST FRONTIER. NY: Scribners, 1948. 1st ed. NF in sl chipped and faded dj. *CONNOLLY & WADE.* $45

Coleman, W.S. BRITISH BUTTERFLIES. London, 1860. 1st ed. Worn & scuffed, some inner joint splitting, one being nearly separated, some foxing of plts). *SUTTON.* $37

Coleman, William and Camille Limoges (eds). STUDIES IN THE HISTORY OF BIOLOGY. Volumes 1-7 (All Published). Baltimore, 1977-1984. 1st ed. *FYE.* $150

Coleridge, Samuel Taylor. AIDS TO REFLECTION...FOURTH EDITION WITH THE AUTHOR'S LAST CORRECTIONS. London: William Pickering, 1839. ix,315pp. Full calf, leather labels on paneled spine, gilt, inside gilt dentelles. Small chip in head of spine, else VG. *WREDEN.* $40

Coleridge, Samuel Taylor. BIOGRAPHIA LITERARIA; OR, BIOGRAPHICAL SKETCHES OF MY LITERARY LIFE AND OPINIONS. Vol. I-(II, in one). NY: Kirk and Mercein, 1817-17. 1st Amer ed. 12mo. 183;196pp. Contemp 3/4 calf, leather label. Very nice. Two title pages with separate pagination. On each title is the 1820 sig of Mitchell King, probably a judge. *M & S.* $450

Coleridge, Samuel Taylor. BIOGRAPHIA LITERIA; OR, BIOGRAPHICAL SKETCHES....NY: Kirk and Mercein, 1817. 1st USed. 2 vols. Scattered light foxing, but NF. Rebound in modern black 1/4 leather over marbled boards. *CAPTAIN'S BOOKSHELF.* $125

Coleridge, Samuel Taylor. THE COMPLETE POETICAL WORKS. Edited by Ernest Hartley Coleridge. Oxford: Clarendon Press,

1912. 1st ed. 2 vols. Portrait. Errata slips. Typed bibliographical note pasted inside frt cvr of vol 1; spine labels a bit rubbed, else a Very Nice set. *WOOLMER.* $75

Coleridge, Samuel Taylor. THE RIME OF THE ANCIENT MARINER. WITH TEN ENGRAVINGS ON COPPER AND WITH A FOREWORD BY DAVID JONES. NY: Chilmark Press, 1964. 1st ed. 1/200. Bound in cl. In pub's box. VG. *SECOND LIFE.* $125

Coleridge, Samuel Taylor. THE RIME OF THE ANCIENT MARINER. Bristol: Douglas Cleverdon, 1929. 1st ed. One of 400 numbered. 10 engr by David Jones. Orig cl-backed boards. Cvrs darkened & lightly soiled, corners a bit rubbed, o/w VG. *JAFFE.* $550

Coleridge, Sar. PHANTASM. Roberts Brothers, 1874. Good. *MADLE.* $150

Coles, Manning. A TOAST TO TOMORROW. GC: Doubleday Crime Club, 1941. 1st Amer ed. Fine in dj w/tiny internal tape mends. *MORDIDA.* $65

Coles, Manning. BASLE EXPRESS. London: Hodder & Stoughton, 1956. 1st ed. Fine in VG dj w/internal tape mends; nicks. *MORDIDA.* $40

Coles, Manning. DRINK TO YESTERDAY. NY: Knopf, 1941. 1st Amer ed. Edges sl darkened and stained o/w VG in dj. *MORDIDA.* $85

Coles, Manning. LET THE TIGER DIE. London: Hodder & Stoughton, 1948. 1st ed. VG in price-clipped dj w/frayed spine ends, chips, short closed tears. *MORDIDA.* $35

Coles, Manning. THE FIFTH MAN. GC: Doubleday Crime Club, 1946. 1st ed. Fine, dj lt wear. *ELSE FINE.* $30

Coles, Manning. THE FIFTH MAN. London: Hodder & Stoughton, 1946. 1st ed. Spine faded o/w VG in dj w/small dampstain; chipping, wear at corners. *MORDIDA.* $40

Coles, Manning. THE HOUSE AT PLUCK'S GUTTER. London: Hodder & Stoughton, 1963. 1st ed. Fine in VG dj (sl faded spine; stain back panel; minor wear). *MORDIDA.* $45

Coles, Manning. THEY TELL NO TALES. GC: Doubleday Crime Club, 1942. 1st Amer ed. Fine in bright unfaded dj w/minor wear. *MORDIDA.* $45

Coles, Manning. THEY TELL NO TALES. GC: Doubleday Crime Club, 1942. 1st ed. Fine, lt edgewear pict dj. *ELSE FINE.* $50

Coles, Manning. TOAST TO TOMORROW. GC: Doubleday Crime Club, 1941. 1st ed. Fine, light edgewear to dj. *ELSE FINE.* $85

Coles, Robert. THE LAST AND FIRST ESKIMOS. Boston: NY Graphic Soc, 1978. 1st ed. Rubber stamp, else VG in rubbed dj. *PARMER.* $40

Coles, Robert. WALKER PERCY: AN AMERICAN SEARCH. Boston: Little, Brown, (1978). 1st ed. Fine in dj. Signed. *CAPTAIN'S BOOKSHELF.* $75

Colette (Sidonie-Gabrielle). CLAUDINE MARRIED. Farrar, Straus and Cudahy, 1960. 1st Amer. ed. Fine in VG dj. Spine of dj darkened; large chip missing at foot. *STAHR.* $20

Colette (Sidonie-Gabrielle). MY MOTHER'S HOUSE AND SIDO. NY: Farrar, Straus and Young, 1953. 1st US ed. Fine in dj. *SECOND LIFE.* $25

Colette (Sidonie-Gabrielle). THE VAGABOND. NY: Farrar, Straus, and Young. 1955. 1st US ed. Fine in dj. *SECOND LIFE.* $25

COLLECTIONS OF THE STATE HISTORICAL SOCIETY OF NORTH DAKOTA. VOLUME 1. Bismark Tribune, 1906. 1st ed. 27 plts. Fine. *OREGON.* $75

Colledge, Malcolm A.R. THE ART OF PALMYRA. London: Thames and Hudson, (1976). 66 figs. Dj. Good. *ARCHAEOLOGIA.* $95

Colles, Abraham. SELECTIONS FROM THE WORKS OF ABRAHAM COLLES . Ed by Robert McDowell. London, 1891. 1st ed. 431pp. *FYE.* $150

Collias, J.G. THE LAST OF STEAM. H-North, 1960. 1st ed. Fine in chipped dj. *VARNER.* $35

Collias, J.G. THE SEARCH FOR STEAM. H-North, 1972. 1st ed. Fine in Fine dj. *VARNER.* $35

Collie, John. MALINGERING AND FEIGNED SICKNESS. London, 1913. 1st ed. Ex-lib. *FYE.* $125

Collier and Westrate. DAVE COOK OF THE ROCKIES....NY: R.R. Wilson, 1936. 1st ed. Fine in VG dj. *OREGON.* $90

Collier, Jeremy. A SHORT VIEW OF THE IMMORALITY AND PROFANESS OF THE ENGLISH STAGE...London: Keble, Sare, Hindmarsh, 1698. 2nd ed, same year as 1st. Small 8vo; pp xvi, 288. Full calf, rebacked, w/raised bands and orig label laid down. Minor foxing, considerable wear to covers but text VG. *HARTFIELD.* $295

Collier, John. THE JOHN COLLIER READER. Knopf, 1973. NF in dj. *MADLE.* $20

Collier, Richard. THE RIVER THAT GOD FORGOT. NY: Dutton, 1968. 1st ed. Fine in VG dj. *AARD.* $17.50

Collings, E. & A.M. England. THE 101 RANCH. Univ of Oklahoma Press, 1938. 1st ed. NF. *VARNER.* $75

Collins, (Jacob C.). COLLINS' POEMS. Memphis: Rogers & Co, printers and bk publishers, 1883. 1st ed. 296pp. Orig blue cl. Lib bkpl, blindstamp, lt rubbing, spotting, spine and edges a little darkened. VG. *CHAPEL HILL.* $55

Collins, John S. ACROSS THE PLAINS IN '64...Omaha, NE, 1904. 151pp. 1st ed. Orig cl, new front ep, few ink stains on cvrs. Inscribed presentation. Howes C594. *GINSBERG.* $200

Collins, Max Allan and Ed Gorman. THE KILLER INSIDE HIM. Cedar Rapids: Fedora Press, 1983. 1st ed. One of 425 numbered. Fine in wrappers. *MORDIDA.* $85

Collins, Max Allan. A SHROUD FOR AQUARIUS. NY: Walker, 1985. 1st ed. Inscribed. VF in dj. *MORDIDA.* $35

Collins, Max Allan. KILL YOUR DARLINGS. NY: Walker, 1984. 1st ed. VF in dj. *MORDIDA.* $30

Collins, Max Allan. KILL YOUR DARLINGS. NY: Walker, 1984. 1st ed. Signed. Fine in dj. *SILVER DOOR.* $35

Collins, Max Allan. NO CURE FOR DEATH. NY: Walker, 1983. 1st ed. Fine in dj, tiny tear. *MORDIDA.* $30

Collins, Max Allan. SPREE. NY: Tor, 1987. 1st ed. Adv rev copy w/sheet laid in. VF in dj. *MORDIDA.* $25

Collins, Max Allan. THE BABY BLUE RIP-OFF. NY: Walker, 1983. 1st ed. Fine in dj. *MORDIDA.* $40

Collins, Max Allan. THE MILLION-DOLLAR WOUND. NY: St. Martin's Press, 1986. 1st ed. Inscribed. Fine in dj w/scrape on back panel. *MORDIDA.* $30

Collins, Max Allan. TRUE CRIME. NY: St. Martin's Press, 1984. 1st ed. Inscribed. Adv rev copy w/sheet laid in. VF in dj. *MORDIDA.* $37.50

Collins, Max Allan. TRUE DETECTIVE. NY: St. Martin's Press, 1983. 1st ed. Inscribed. VF in dj. *MORDIDA.* $35

Collins, Michael. FREAK. NY: Dodd Mead, 1983. 1st ed. Inscribed. Adv rev copy w/slip laid in. Fine in dj. *MORDIDA.* $35

Collins, Michael. MINNESOTA STRIP. NY: Donald I. Fine, 1987. 1st ed. VF in dj. *MORDIDA.* $25

Collins, Michael. RED ROSA. NY: Donald I. Fine, 1988. 1st ed. VF in dj. *MORDIDA.* $22.50

Collins, Michael. THE BLOOD-RED DREAM. NY: Dodd , Mead, 1976. 1st ed. Signed. Fine in rubbed dj. *MORDIDA.* $25

Collins, Michael. THE NIGHTRUNNERS. NY: Dodd Mead, 1978. 1st ed. Fine in sl rubbed dj. *MORDIDA.* $25

Collins, Michael. THE SLASHER. NY: Dodd Mead, 1980. 1st ed. Signed by Collins and Dennis Lynds. VF in dj. *MORDIDA.* $35

Collins, Perry McDonough. A VOYAGE DOWN THE AMOOR. NY: D. Appleton & Co. 1860. 1st ed. (4),390pp+(2)pp ads. Frontis, 3 plts. Cl bit soiled. Ex-lib w/small spine label, rear pocket. *KARMIOLE.* $75

Collins, Robert, A PRACTICAL TREATISE ON MIDWIFERY....Boston: Ticknor, 1841. 1st US ed. Foxed, lacks much of cl on spine, tight. *SECOND LIFE.* $45

Collins, Wilkie. MISS OR MRS? AND OTHER STORIES. Phila: T.B. Peterson & Bros., (1872). 1st US ed. Stain & chip on rear cover, top 1" of spine chipped, edges a bit ragged o/w Good ppwrps. *BERNARD.* $200

Collins, Wilkie. NO NAME. NY, 1863. 1st ed. Spine sl sunned, extremities little chipped, sl edge rubbed. NF. *POLYANTHOS.* $100

Collins, Wilkie. THE MOONSTONE. Illus by Dignimont. NY: LEC, 1959. Fine in NF box. Ltd to 1500 signed by Dignimont (#197). *DIAMOND.* $75

Collins, Wilkie. THE WOMAN IN WHITE. NY: Harper, 1860. 1st Amer ed. Tall 8vo. 260pp, (6 pub's ads). Orig blind-stamped cloth gilt, text in double columns. Some darkening of text, but VG. *HARTFIELD.* $195

Collins, Winfield Hazlitt. THE TRUTH ABOUT LYNCHING AND THE NEGRO IN THE SOUTH IN WHICH THE AUTHOR PLEADS THAT THE SOUTH BE MADE SAFE FOR THE WHITE RACE. NY: Neale Pub. Co, 1918. 1st ed. Orig. cl. Ex libris, bkpl, small blindstamp, else NF. *McGOWAN.* $250

Collins. G. E. P. EAST MONSOON. NY: Scribner's, 1937. 288pp. 1st Amer ed. Somewhat soiled. Fldg line map. In dj. *SCHOYER'S.* $20

Collinson, Clifford W. LIFE AND LAUGHTER 'MIDST THE CANNIBALS. London: Hurst & Blackett, 1926. 4th ed. Spine faded, foxed. *PARMER.* $30

Collinson, Frank. LIFE IN THE SADDLE. Illus. by Harold Bugbee, ed. by Mary Whatley Clarke. Univ of OK, (1963). 1st ed. One of few true 1st eds in Western Frontier Library Series. VG. *OREGON.* $17.50

Collinson, Richard. JOURNAL OF H.M.S. ENTERPRISE...IN SEARCH OF SIR JOHN FRANKLIN'S SHIPS BY BEHRING STRAIT, 1850-55. WITH A MEMOIR....London: Sampson Low, Marston, Searle & Rivington, 1889. 1st ed. 8vo, xi,(1),531,32 ad pp. Color litho frontis, photogravure port, 6 fldg color maps. Orig blue cl w/gilt title, vignette front cvr. Spine sl darkened, ends frayed, hinges expertly reinforced, some chipping to leading edges of some fldg maps. *PARMER.* $900

Collis, Maurice. FOREIGN MUD....NY: Knopf, 1947 (46). 1st US ed. Fine in Good dj. *AARD.* $25

Collis, Septima M. A WOMAN'S TRIP IN ALASKA. NY: Cassell, (1890). Red and slate-blue cl stamped in gilt and brown, a little faded and rubbed. Map. VG. *SCHOYER'S.* $65

Collis, Septima M. A WOMAN'S TRIP TO ALASKA. NY: Cassell Pub Co, (1890). (xii),194pp. Map; lacks half of fldg plt, pict cl. VG. *SCHOYER'S.* $50

Collis, Septima. A WOMAN'S TRIP TO ALASKA. NY, 1890. VG-NF. *POLYANTHOS.* $95

Collison, W.H. IN THE WAKE OF THE WAR CANOE. London: Seeley, Service & Co. Ltd, 1915. 1st ed. 18 photo plts, map. Pub's emb stamp "Presentation Copy" on title page. *KARMIOLE.* $60

Colman, George. THE IRON CHEST: A PLAY... WITH A PREFACE. London: for Cadell and Davies, 1796. 1st ed. Disbound; fresh copy. VG. *DRAMATIS PERSONAE.* $85

Colman, H. EUROPEAN AGRICULTURE AND RURAL ECONOMY FROM PERSONAL OBSERVATION. Boston, 1851. 4th ed, w/additions. 5 engr plts (foxed). Full, ornately tooled leather. Spine edge split, very rubbed, worn; front hinge weak; ex-lib. *SUTTON.* $55

COLOR ATLAS OF PATHOLOGY: HEMATOPOETIC SYSTEM, RETICULOENDOTHELIAL SYSTEM, RESPIRATORY TRACT, CARDIOVASCULAR SYSTEM, LIVER ALIMENTARY TRACT KIDNEY AND URINARY TRACT, MUSCULOSKELETAL SYSTEM. Phila, c. 1950. 1st ed. 365 color plts. *FYE.* $50

COLORADO TOURIST AND ILLUSTRATED GUIDE TO THE ROCKY MOUNTAIN RESORTS...PUBLISHED BY THE...UNION PACIFIC RAILWAY. (By Stephen F. Smart.) Kansas City: Ramsey, 1880. 3rd ed. 80pp. Fldg map, woodcuts. Orig ptd pict wrappers. Howes S563. *GINSBERG.* $250

COLORADO. NY, 1941. American Guide Series. WPA guide. 1st ptg, sl worn dj. *SCHOYER'S.* $60

Colquhoun, Archibald R. THE "OVERLAND" TO CHINA. London/NY: Harper & Brothers, 1900. 4 fldg maps. Some shelfwear. *PARMER.* $125

Colquhoun, John. THE MOOR AND THE LOCH. Edinburgh and London: Blackwood & Sons, 1851. 3rd ed. Minor bumps and wear, but overall VG+. *OLD LONDON.* $85

Colson, Elizabeth and Max Gluckman. SEVEN TRIBES OF BRITISH CENTRAL AFRICA. London: Oxford Univ Press, 1951. NF in Good dj. *GREAT EPIC.* $45

Colt, Mrs. Miriam Davis. WENT TO KANSAS: BEING A THRILLING ACCOUNT...Watertown, 1862. 1st ed. 294pp. Orig cl, lacks front flyleaf. Howes C616. *GINSBERG.* $450

Colter, Cyrus. THE HIPPODROME. Chicago: Swallow, 1973. 1st ed. 213pp. NF in VG dj. Signed. *AKA.* $28

Colton, Harold S. A SURVEY OF PREHISTORIC SITES IN THE REGION OF FLAGSTAFF, ARIZONA. Tan cloth, 68pp, 10 plts incl 4 maps, some fldg. 21 figures. Fine. *FIVE QUAIL.* $40

Colton, Harold S. POTSHERDS: AN INTRODUCTION TO THE STUDY OF PREHISTORIC SOUTHWESTERN CERAMICS AND THEIR USE IN HISTORIC RECONSTRUCTION. Flagstaff: Northern Arizona Society of Science and Art, 1953. Good in tattered dj. *ARCHAEOLOGIA.* $45

Colton, James (pseud of Joseph Hansen). THE OUTWARD SIDE. NY: Traveller's Companion, 1971. 1st ed. VG+ in wraps. *LAME DUCK.* $85

Colton, Walter. DECK AND PORT: OR, INCIDENTS OF A CRUISE IN THE UNITED STATES FRIGATE CONGRESS TO CALIFORNIA. NY: A.S. Barnes & Co, 1854. Frontis portrait, 4 color lithos. *HUDSON.* $75

Colton, Walter. LAND AND LEE IN THE BOSPHORUS AND AEGEAN: OR, VIEWS....NY, 1851. Spine chipped. *O'NEILL.* $60

Colton, Walter. SHIP AND SHORE, IN MADEIRA, LISBON AND THE MEDITERRANEAN. NY, 1851. Frontis, 1 plt. Fine (lt foxing). *O'NEILL.* $85

Colton, Walter. THE CALIFORNIA DIARY BY REV. WALTER COLTON....Oakland: Biobooks, 1948. One of 1,000. Reprint of THREE YEARS IN CALIFORNIA. Fine. Howes C-625. *LAURIE.* $50

Colton, Walter. THE CALIFORNIA DIARY BY...LATE ALCALDE OF MONTEREY. Biobooks, 1948. Ltd to 1000. 6 plts, map, fldg facs. Fine. *OREGON.* $50

Colton, Walter. THE CALIFORNIA DIARY. Oakland: Biobooks, 1948. 1/1000. Map, 6 plts. Fldg facs. Gilt faded, else NF. *PARMER.* $65

Colton, Walter. THREE YEARS IN CALIFORNIA. NY: A.S. Barnes, 1850. 1st ed. Binding worn at extremities, lacks fldg plt. Howes C-626. *LAURIE.* $150

Colton, Walter. THREE YEARS IN CALIFORNIA. TOGETHER WITH EXCERPTS FROM THE AUTHOR'S 'DECK AND PORT'...Stanford Univ, 1949. Fine in Good dj. *CONNOLLY & WADE.* $47.50

Colum, Padraic. BALLOON: A COMEDY IN FOUR ACTS. Illus by Boris Artzybasheff. 1st ed. Signed. Fine, dj chipped at top edge & spine ends. *ELSE FINE.* $60

Colum, Padraic. THE FRENZIED PRINCE, HEROIC STORIES OF ANCIENT IRELAND. McKay, (1943). 1st ed. 196pp. Illus by Willy Pogany. VG+ in dj w/edgewear, chips, short closed tear w/tape discoloration. Glaser lithography. *BEBBAH.* $90

Colum, Padraic. THE PEEP-SHOW MAN. Macmillan, 1924. 1st ed. 16mo. 65pp. Illus by Lois Lenski. NF w/dec cvr in VG+ dj w/chips at spine, 1 short closed tear. *BEBBAH.* $50

Colum, Padraic. A BOY IN EIRINN. NY, (1913). 1st ed. Spine little sunned, extremities minimally rubbed, ffep little stained. NF. *POLYANTHOS.* $35

Colum, Padraic. CREATURES. Macmillan, (1927). 56pp. Illus by Boris Artzybasheff. VG+ w/small scuff to rear endpaper. *BEBBAH.* $50

Colum, Padraic. CREATURES. NY, 1927. 1st ed. Names, part of dj pasted to ffep. NF. *POLYANTHOS.* $30

Columbus, Christopher. THE VOYAGES OF CHRISTOPHER COLUMBUS BEING THE JOURNALS OF HIS FIRST AND THIRD, AND THE LETTERS CONCERNING HIS FIRST AND LAST VOYAGES, TO WHICH IS ADDED THE ACCOUNT OF HIS SECOND VOYAGE WRITTEN BY ANDRES BERNALDEZ. Cecil Jane (trans, ed). London: Argonaut Press, 1930. One of 1,050 (this copy unnumbered). 5 fldg maps. VF, bright. 1st ed thus. *LEFKOWICZ.* $250

Colville, Mrs. E. POEMS AND SONGS ON HOME AND ABROAD. Kilmarnock: Dunlap & Drennan, 1905. 1st ed. Soiled cl. Good, tight. *SECOND LIFE.* $25

Colwin, Laurie. DANGEROUS FRENCH MISTRESS & OTHER STORIES. London: Chatto & Windus, 1975. 1st ed. Fine in Fine dj. *ARCHER.* $20

Colwin, Laurie. DANGEROUS FRENCH MISTRESS AND OTHER STORIES. London: Chatto & Windus, 1975. 1st UK ed, 1st book. Fine in Fine dj. *ROBBINS.* $40

Colwin, Laurie. HAPPY ALL THE TIME. Knopf, 1978. 1st ed. Fine in dj. *STAHR.* $20

Colwin, Laurie. PASSION AND AFFECT. Viking, 1974. 1st ed. Fine in dj. *STAHR.* $45

Colwin, Laurie. THE LONE PILGRIM. STORIES. NY: Knopf, 1981. 1st ed. NF in NF dj. *ROBBINS.* $20

Colyar, A. S. LIFE AND TIMES OF ANDREW JACKSON....Nashville, 1904. Orig cl. 1st ed. *GINSBERG.* $75

Colyer, Vincent. PEACE WITH THE APACHES OF NEW MEXICO AND ARIZONA...1871. Washington, 1872. 58pp. Fine. *PRATT.* $45

Colyer, William H. SKETCHES OF THE NORTH RIVER. NY, 1838. Fldg map. Blue silk, rebacked in matching leather, new endsheets. Ex-lib. *HUDSON.* $150

Coman, Katherine. ECONOMIC BEGINNINGS OF THE FAR WEST. VOL. 1: EXPLORERS AND COLONIZERS. VOL. 2: AMERICAN SETTLERS. Macmillan, 1912. 1st ed. 2 frontis, 48 plts, fldg map. Bkpls removed o/w VG. Howes C637. *OREGON.* $100

Combe, A. THE PRINCIPLES OF PHYSIOLOGY APPLIED TO THE PRESERVATION OF HEALTH. Edinburgh: 1835. 3rd ed. 404pp. 3/4 leather, cvr wear. VG. *BOOKCELL.* $40

Combe, Andrew. THE PRINCIPLES OF PHYSIOLOGY APPLIED TO THE PRESERVATION OF HEALTH....NY: Harper & Bros., 1843. Family Library Series. 396pp. Foxing, Good+. *SMITHFIELD.* $30

Combe, George. A SYSTEM OF PHRENOLOGY. NY: S.R. Wells, 1897. 2nd ed. Over 100 engr. G+. *BLUE DRAGON.* $20

COMBINATION ATLAS MAP OF KANE COUNTY, ILLINOIS. Geneva, IL: Thompson & Everts, 1872. 88,(4)pp + 2 lg tissue-paper maps. Blind and gold stamped cl, neatly rebacked and retipped. Lt wear and spotting to cvrs, short marginal tears (a few affecting the edges of text or images), long tears to 3 pp, tear and creasing to 1 tissue map. *DAWSON'S.* $500

Combs, B.B. WESTWARD TO PROMONTORY. Palo Alto, 1969. 2nd ptg. Pb. VG. *VARNER.* $12.50

Combs, Barry B. WESTWARD TO PROMONTORY, BUILDING THE UNION PACIFIC ACROSS THE PLAINS AND MOUNTAINS. Palo Alto, CA (1969). 1st ed. Name stamp title pg. *HEINOLDT.* $20

Comet, Joseph. A SURVEY OF ZAIRIAN ART. Raleigh, NC: North Carolina Museum of Art. 1978. 1st ed. Black and gold cl, a bit spotted. *KARMIOLE.* $65

COMIC TRAGEDIES. (By Louisa May Alcott.) Boston: Roberts, 1893. 1st ed. 317pp,adv. Brown cl, Fine. BAL 224. *SECOND LIFE.* $85

Comin, Donald. ONION PRODUCTION. NY: Orange Judd, 1946. VG. *AMERICAN BOTANIST.* $25

Commager, Henry Steele (ed). THE BLUE AND THE GRAY, THE STORY OF THE CIVIL WAR AS TOLD BY PARTICIPANTS. NY, (1950). 1st ed of 1 volume ed. VG in dj. *PRATT.* $30

Commager, Henry Steele. THE BLUE AND THE GRAY. NY, Indianapolis: Bobbs-Merrill, (1950). 1st ed. 2 vols. Djs. Box. *WEBER.* $100

Compton-Burnett, Ivy. A HERITAGE AND ITS HISTORY. London: Gollancz, 1959. 1st ed. Fine in dj (sl faded spine, tiny tear). Comp copy, slip laid in. *CAPTAIN'S BOOKSHELF.* $50

Comstock, Helen. THE LOOKING GLASS IN AMERICA 1700-1825. Viking, 1968. 1st ed. Fine in VG dj. *MAD DOG.* $17.50

Comstock, J.H. THE SPIDER BOOK. GC, 1913 (1912). Half leather. Ex-lib. *SUTTON.* $40

Comstock, John L. HISTORY OF THE GREEK REVOLUTION: COMPILED FROM OFFICIAL DOCUMENTS...TO WHICH IS ADDED AN APPENDIX AND AN ADDENDUM. Hartford, 1853. Top of spine chipped. *O'NEILL.* $100

Comstock, John L. HISTORY OF THE GREEK REVOLUTION; COMPILED FROM OFFICIAL DOCUMENTS....NY, 1828. 2 engrs, sm piece missing from corner of one. Full contemp calf. Title pg refers to map, which was never included. *O'NEILL.* $85

Comstock, Sarah. OLD ROADS FROM THE HEART OF NEW YORK. NY, 1915. Pull-out map. NF. *POLYANTHOS.* $50

Comstock, William T. MODERN ARCHITECTURAL DESIGNS AND DETAILS... NY: William T. Comstock, (1881). 1st ed. (viii)pp, 80ff, ads. (xiii)pp. 80 plts, pl of paint samples inside rear cvr. Orig deep mustard cl, stamped in black, gold on upper cvr and in blind on back cvr. Corners showing, rubbed; silverfish trailings along edges, but internally VG. *WEBER.* $250

Conant, R. A FIELD GUIDE TO REPTILES AND AMPHIBIANS. Boston, (1958). 40 plts (many colored). Chipped dj. *SUTTON.* $23

Conard, Howard L. UNCLE DICK WOOTEN. PIONEER FRONTIERSMAN OF ROCKY MOUNTAIN REGION....Chicago: Lakeside Classic, 1957. 3rd ptg, 1st annotated ed. Fine. *OREGON.* $35

Conard, Howard L. UNCLE DICK WOOTEN. PIONEER FRONTIERSMAN OF ROCKY MOUNTAIN REGION...Chicago: W.E. Dibble, 1890. 474pp, frontis, 31 plts. Gilt stamped pict cl. Front hinge cracked & glued, eps cracking at hinges, corners worn, o/w VG. Good+. Howes C659. *OREGON.* $175

Conard, Howard Louis. UNCLE DICK WOOTON, PIONEER FRONTIERSMAN OF THE ROCK MOUNTAIN REGION. Ed by Milo Milton Quaife. Chicago, 1890 (1957 reprint). Lakeside Classic #55. VG+. *PRATT.* $37.50

Conder, Claude R. TENT WORK IN PALESTINE. London: Palestine Exploration Fund, 1879. 9 plts (one fldg). 2 vols. Cl, recased, new eps. xxvi,381pp; viii,352pp. Sound, attractive. *O'NEILL.* $175

Conder, Claude Reignier. TENT WORK IN PALESTINE. NY: D. Appleton, 1878. 2 vols (complete). Lightly rubbed at extremities, bkpls. Good. *ARCHAEOLOGIA.* $200

Conder, Josiah. LANDSCAPE GARDENING IN JAPAN. With Numerous Illustrations. (Supplement to Landscape Gardening in Japan. With Collotypes by K. Ogawa). Tokyo: Kelly & Walsh, Ltd. 1893. 2 vols. Folio. xii,162;(8)pp. + 40 collotype plts, each w/leaf of description. 37 plts vol 1. Orig grn cl, dec gilt; spine extrems, corners bit rubbed; 2" crack vol 1 hinge. *KARMIOLE.* $500

Condon, Edward U. FINAL REPORT OF THE SCIENTIFIC STUDY OF UNIDENTIFIED FLYING OBJECTS. NY: Dutton, 1969. Ex-lib. *KNOLLWOOD.* $40

Condon, Richard. THE MANCHURIAN CANDIDATE. NY: McGraw Hill, (1959). 1st ed. About Fine (owner sig) in sl edgeworn price-clipped, faded dj. *CAPTAIN'S BOOKSHELF.* $100

Condon, Richard. THE MANCHURIAN CANDIDATE. NY: McGraw-Hill, 1959. 1st ed. Fine; minor wear to dj corners. *ELSE FINE.* $100

Condon, Richard. THE MANCHURIAN CANDIDATE. NY-Toronto-London: McGraw-Hill Book Co., (1959). 1st ed, 2nd book. Spine a bit cocked, name stamped upper right corner of flyleaf o/w VG+ in dj. *BERNARD.* $125

Condon, Thomas. THE TWO ISLANDS & WHAT CAME OF THEM. Portland: J.K. Gill, 1902. 1st ed. 30 plts. VG. *OREGON.* $50

Cone, Mary. TWO YEARS IN CALIFORNIA. Chicago: Griggs, 1876. 1st ed. 15 plts, fldg map. Lt corner wear. VG. *OREGON.* $60

Conger, A.L. THE RISE OF U.S. GRANT. NY, (1931). 1st ed. Fine. *PRATT.* $25

Conklin, E. PICTURESQUE ARIZONA. NY: The Mining Record Printing Establishment, 1878. Map. Very Scarce. Not in Howes. *HUDSON.* $275

Conklin, Groff (ed). A TREASURY OF S-F. Crown, 1948. 1st ed. Fine in dj. *MADLE.* $40

Conklin, Groff (ed). THE OMNIBUS OF S-F. Crown, 1952. 1st ed. Fine in sl frayed dj. *MADLE.* $27

Conkling and Jackman. STEENS MOUNTAINS IN OREGON'S HIGH DESERT COUNTRY. Caldwell: Caxton, 1967. 1st ed. VF in VF dj, in orig shipping carton. *OREGON.* $125

Conlan, Jocko and Robert Creamer. JOCKO. Lippincott, 1967. 1st ed. VG in Fine dj. *PLAPINGER.* $35

Conn, George. THE ARABIAN HORSE IN FACT, FANTASY AND FICTION. NY: Barnes, 1959. 1st ed. VG. *OCTOBER FARM.* $30

Connell, Evan S. A LONG DESIRE. NY: Holt, Rinehart & Winston, 1979. 1st ed. VF in Fine dj. *CONNOLLY & WADE.* $25

Connell, Evan S., Jr. THE ANATOMY LESSON....NY: Viking, 1957. 1st ed, 1st bk. Orig cl-backed brn boards. Fine in NF dj (sl faded spine). *CHAPEL HILL.* $100

Connell, Evan S. MR. BRIDGE. NY: Knopf, 1969. 1st ed. Fine in price clipped dj. *ELSE FINE.* $35

Connell, Evan S. MR. BRIDGE. NY: Knopf, 1969. 1st ed. Fine in very lightly used dj. *CAPTAIN'S BOOKSHELF.* $50

Connell, Evan S. MRS. BRIDGE. NY: Viking, 1959. 1st ed, 1st novel. Orig two toned cl. NF in sl soiled dj. *CHAPEL HILL.* $150

Connell, Evan S. POINTS FOR A COMPASS ROSE. NY: Knopf, 1973. 1st ed. Fine in sl edgeworn dj. *CAPTAIN'S BOOKSHELF.* $40

Connell, Evan S. SAINT AUGUSTINE'S PIGEON. SF: North Point, 1982. 1st ed. Fine in wraps & dj. *ELSE FINE.* $20

Connell, Evan S. SON OF THE MORNING STAR. SF: North Point, (1984). 1st ed. Fine in Fine dj. *UNGER.* $150

Connell, Evan S. SON OF THE MORNING STAR: CUSTER AND THE LITTLE BIGHORN. SF: North Point Press, 1984. 1st ed. VF in dj. *ELSE FINE.* $135

Connell, Evan S. SON OF THE MORNING STAR, CUSTER AND THE LITTLE BIG HORN. SF, 1984. 1st ed. Dj. Fine. *PRATT.* $55

Connell, Evan S. SON OF THE MORNING STAR. SF: North Point Press, 1984. 1st ed. Cl-backed boards, dj. Fine. *JAFFE.* $150

Connell, Evan S. THE ANATOMY LESSON AND OTHER STORIES. NY: Viking, 1957. 1st ed, 1st bk. Fine in very lightly used dj. *CAPTAIN'S BOOKSHELF.* $100

Connell, Evan S. THE ANATOMY LESSON. NY: Viking, 1957. 1st ed. Tape residue from sm price sticker on front flap of dj has "shadowed" onto ffep, o/w Fine in lightly worn dj somewhat faded at the spine. *CAPTAIN'S BOOKSHELF.* $50

Connell, Evan S. THE DIARY OF A RAPIST. NY: S & S, (1966). 1st ed. VF in dj. *CAPTAIN'S BOOKSHELF.* $50

Connell, Evan S. THE DIARY OF A RAPIST. NY: Simon & Schuster, 1966. 1st ed. NF in dj. *ELSE FINE.* $25

Connell, Evan S. THE WHITE LANTERN. NY: Holt, (1980). 1st ed. Fine in dj. Review copy, slip laid in. *CAPTAIN'S BOOKSHELF.* $40

Connell, Evan S. THE WHITE LANTERN. NY: Holt, Rinehart & Winston, 1980. 1st ed. VF in Fine dj. *CONNOLLY & WADE.* $25

Connelley, William Elsey. DONIPHAN'S EXPEDITION AND THE CONQUEST OF NEW MEXICO AND CALIFORNIA. WAR WITH MEXICO, 1846-1847. Kansas City, MO: Bryant & Douglas Book and Stationery Co., 1907. 1st ed. Incl reprint of Work of Col. John T. Hughes. 2 fldg maps. Pres copy. Mounted b/w plate front cvr. Howes C688. *KARMIOLE.* $185

Connelley, William Esley. QUANTRILL AND THE BORDER WARS. Cedar Rapids, 1910. 1st ed. Cvr wear o/w VG +. *PRATT.* $165

Conner, Daniel Ellis. A CONFEDERATE IN THE COLORADO GOLD FIELDS. Norman, OK, (1970). 1st ed. Fine in NF dj. *McGOWAN.* $35

Conner, Daniel Ellis. A CONFEDERATE IN THE COLORADO GOLD FIELDS. Donald Berthrong, Odessa Davenport (eds). Univ of OK, (1970). 1st ed. VF in Fine dj. *OREGON.* $27.50

Conner, Daniel. JOSEPH REDDEFORD WALKER AND ARIZONA ADVENTURE. Norman: Univ of OK, (1956). 1st ed. 8 plts. VG in Good+ dj. *OREGON.* $50

Conner, Philip S. P. HOME SQUADRON UNDER COMMODORE CONNER IN THE WAR WITH MEXICO.... (WITH AN ADDENDUM....) 1846-1847. (Phila: Conner), 1896. 1st ed. 84pp. Orig tall 8vo cloth, outer marginal staining. *GINSBERG.* $75

Connett, Eugene V. (ed). AMERICAN SPORTING DOGS. NY: D. Van Nostrand Co, Inc, 1948. Stated 1st ed. VG (sm stain back edge). *BACKMAN.* $55

Connett, Eugene V. DUCK SHOOTING ALONG THE ATLANTIC TIDEWATER. NY: Morrow, 1947. VG in worn dj. *CULLEN.* $100

Connold, E.T. BRITISH VEGETABLE GALLS. NY, 1902. 130 full-pg plts. Light scuffing, name on eps & occasionally in text. *SUTTON.* $67

Connolly, Cyril. IDEAS AND PLACES. London: Weidenfeld & Nicolson, (1953). 1st ed. Cl, dj. Fine. *JAFFE.* $65

Connolly, Cyril. THE CONDEMNED PLAYGROUND. ESSAYS 1927-1944. NY, 1946. 1st ed. Offsetting 2pp. Extremities, spine very sl rubbed. Fine in dj (little soiled, creased, edge chipped). *POLYANTHOS.* $25

Connolly, Cyril. THE EVENING COLONNADE. London: David Bruce & Watson, (1973). 1st ed. Fine in dj. *CAPTAIN'S BOOKSHELF.* $60

Connolly, Cyril. THE MODERN MOVEMENT. London: Andre Deutsch/ Hamish Hamilton, (1965). 1st ed. Fine (owner sig) in dj. *CAPTAIN'S BOOKSHELF.* $175

Connolly, Cyril. THE MODERN MOVEMENT. ONE HUNDRED KEY BOOKS....1880-1950. Boards. London: Deutsch/Hamilton, (1965). 1st ed. Short closed tear in dj, lamination somewhat lifted, o/w Fine. *JAFFE.* $125

Connolly, James B. MASTER MARINER. THE LIFE AND VOYAGES OF AMASA DELANO. GC: Doubleday, Doran, 1943. 1st ed. Fine in bright, attractive dj. *CONNOLLY & WADE.* $25

Connor, D. Russell and Warren H. Hicks. BG ON THE RECORD. New Rochelle: Arlington House, 1969. Fine. *BANCROFT.* $32

Connor, Ralph. THE ROCK AND THE RIVER: A ROMANCE OF QUEBEC. McClelland & Stewart, (1931). 1st Canadian ed. Inscribed, signed. VG +, foxed dj. *AUTHORS OF THE WEST.* $25

Conover, Chris. THE ADVENTURES OF SIMPLE SIMON. FSG, 1987. 1st ed. Illus by author. Inscribed. Fine in Fine dj. *BEBBAH.* $30

Conrad, Barnaby. ENCYCLOPEDIA OF BULLFIGHTING. Boston: Houghton Mifflin, 1961. 1st ed. Chipped dj. *SILVER.* $25

Conrad, Barnaby. GATES OF FEAR. NY: Crowell, (1957). 1st ed. Chipped dj. *SILVER.* $25

Conrad, Jessie. A HANDBOOK OF COOKERY FOR A SMALL HOUSE. Joseph Conrad (preface). London: Heinemann, (1923). 1st ed. 135pp. Ptd cl. Sl browned eps. VG, tight. *SECOND LIFE.* $200

Conrad, Joseph and Ford Madox Ford. THE NATURE OF A CRIME. NY, 1924. 1st ed. Lower spine and corners little rubbed. NF in dj (spine sunned, extremities chipped, edge tears and edge chips, front panel 1 small edge chip, 2 edge tears). *POLYANTHOS.* $25

Conrad, Joseph and Ford Madox Hueffer. THE NATURE OF A CRIME. London: Duckworth, (1924). 1st ed. Some offsetting on eps from jacket flaps, else Nice in dj w/single short tear. Scarce in dj. *CHAPEL HILL.* $125

Conrad, Joseph and Ford Madox Hueffer. THE NATURE OF A CRIME. London: Duckworth & Co., (1924). 1st UK ed. Some general fading of red/pink binding, eps partially browned o/w VG in moderately soiled dj. *BERNARD.* $100

Conrad, Joseph. AN OUTCAST OF THE ISLANDS. NY: Appleton, 1896. Pub's presentation ed, in 3/4 leather, marbled paper boards, teg. Chipping at spine crown, o/w attractive, NF. *LOPEZ.* $450

Conrad, Joseph. AN OUTCAST OF THE ISLANDS. NY: Appleton, 1896. Trade ed in cl. Small smudge front cover; tiny tear top of fep; 1p ads in back roughly opened, o/w NF. *LOPEZ.* $225

Conrad, Joseph. LETTERS, JOSEPH CONRAD TO RICHARD CURLE. Richard Curle (ed). NY: Crosby Gaige, 1928. NF in chipped orig tissue dj and somewhat soiled custom folder and slipcase. 1st ed. One of 850. *CHAPEL HILL.* $125

Conrad, Joseph. LORD JIM, A ROMANCE. GC: Doubleday Page, 1922. Early American reprint. Blue cl. NF. Inscribed in 1923. *CAPTAIN'S BOOKSHELF.* $500

Conrad, Joseph. NOSTROMO. London & NY: Harper & Bros., 1904. 1st ed. Orig blue cl. Crown of spine nicked, dots of foxing, but NF. *CHAPEL HILL.* $400

Conrad, Joseph. NOTES ON MY BOOKS. London: Heinemann, 1921. One of 250 numbered, signed. Parchment spine sl darkened. NF. *LOPEZ.* $450

Conrad, Joseph. ONE DAY MORE. GC: Doubleday, 1920. 1st US ed. One of 377 numbered, signed. Vellum spine sl darkened, else Fine. *CAPTAIN'S BOOKSHELF.* $300

Conrad, Joseph. SOME REMINISCENCES. London: Nash, 1912. 1st published ed. Fine. *MUELLER.* $100

Conrad, Joseph. SUSPENSE. London & Toronto: J.M. Dent & Sons, 1925. 1st Eng ed, pub one day after Amer 1st trade ed. Orig maroon cl, spine sl cocked. Book and dj show light wear. Good+ *JUVELIS.* $100

Conrad, Joseph. SUSPENSE. London, 1925. 1st ed. Frontis. Spine sl rubbed, little foxing prelims. Bright, fresh. *POLYANTHOS.* $75

Conrad, Joseph. TALES OF HEARSAY. GC, NY: Doubleday, 1925. 1st Amer ed, pub simultaneously w/Eng ed. Fine in dj. *JUVELIS.* $60

Conrad, Joseph. TALES OF HEARSAY. London: T. Fisher Unwin Ltd., 1925. 1st ed. Dj torn. VG. *WEBER.* $45

Conrad, Joseph. THE ARROW OF GOLD. GC, NY: Doubleday, Page, 1919. Name, small bkseller's label, else VG. 1st ed, 1st issue, w/"credentials and apparently" in lines 16-17 on pg 5. Precedes Eng ed by 4 months. *CHAPEL HILL.* $120

Conrad, Joseph. THE MIRROR OF THE SEA. NY: Harpers, 1906. 1st US ed. Beautiful in pict cl (delicate white lettering still bright). *CAPTAIN'S BOOKSHELF.* $125

Conrad, Joseph. THE ROVER. GC: Doubleday, 1923. 1st US trade ed. Spine sl cocked, edges a bit rubbed o/w VG. *BERNARD.* $35

Conrad, Joseph. THE ROVER. London: T. Fisher Unwin, (1923). 1st Eng ed. Spine dull and minor foxing of prelims. VG. *WOOLMER.* $35

Conrad, Joseph. THE ROVER. London: T. Fisher Unwin, (1923). 1st Eng ed. Grn cl; hinges cracked, else VG in lightly used white dj. *JUVELIS.* $150

Conrad, Joseph. THE ROVER. London: Unwin, (1923). 1st ed. NF in lightly soiled dj (few shallow chips). Uncommon in dj. *CAPTAIN'S BOOKSHELF.* $125

Conrad, Joseph. THE SECRET AGENT, A DRAMA IN THREE ACTS. London: Privately ptd for Subs by T. Werner Laurie, 1923. Ltd ed of 1,000. Signed. Dj (spine sl darkened; unopened). Bkpl of Estelle Doheny. *WEBER.* $350

Conrad, Joseph. THE SECRET AGENT. London: Werner Laurie, 1923. "Privately ptd for Subscribers only." One of unspecified number (1000), w/port frontis, signed. Boards, parchment spine w/paper spine label, in heavy paper dj, also w/spine label. Dj repaired on verso, laminated on verso. Extra paper label tipped in. Very Nice. *LOPEZ.* $500

Conrad, Joseph. THE SISTERS. NY: Crosby Gaige, 1928. 1st ed. 1/926. Fine in very lightly rubbed marbled boards w/morocco spine label. *CAPTAIN'S BOOKSHELF.* $100

Conrad, Joseph. THE TREMOLINO. NY: Duschenes, 1942. Ltd ed of 1000. Wood engr. by G.A. Wilson. Signed by Wilson. Teg, uncut. Fine in like box. *POLYANTHOS.* $35

Conrad, Joseph. UNDER WESTERN EYES. London: Methuen, (1911). 1st ed. Short tear in rear joint at head of spine, offsetting to eps, bkpl, else NF. *CAPTAIN'S BOOKSHELF.* $275

Conrad, Joseph. UNDER WESTERN EYES. NY: Harper, 1911. 1st US ed. VG, clean. *SECOND LIFE.* $65

Conrad, Joseph. VICTORY: AN ISLAND TALE. London: Methuen, (1915). 1st ed, 1st issue w/35pp ads. Rose cl somewhat faded but VG. 2pp Author's Note not found in US ed, which precedes. *CAPTAIN'S BOOKSHELF.* $100

Conrad, Joseph. YOUTH. A NARRATIVE AND TWO OTHER STORIES. Edinburgh and London: William Blackwood & Sons, 1902. 1st ed. With ads dated 10/02. Grn cl, back hinge starting, minor wear to spine. Good+. *JUVELIS.* $225

Conrad, Joseph. YOUTH. NY: McClure Phillips, 1903. 1st Amer ed. Sl soiling to grn cvrs, but still NF. *LOPEZ.* $150

Conrotto, Eugene L. LOST DESERT BONANZAS. Palm Desert: Southwest Publishing. 1st ed. 278pp. Fine in Fine dj. *BOOK MARKET.* $85

Conroy, Frank. STOP-TIME. NY: Viking Press, (1967). 1st ed. of his 1st book. Adv prepub copy in stiff ppwrps with dj attached to spine by pub. VG+. *BERNARD.* $45

Conroy, Jack. A WORLD TO WIN. NY, Covici Friede, 1935. 1st ed. NF in dj (spine little sunned, extremities little chipped little edgeworn). *POLYANTHOS.* $45

Conroy, Pat. CONROY'S WORLD. Bantam, 1987. Fine in wraps. *STAHR.* $15

Conroy, Pat. THE BOO. Atlanta: Old New York Book Shop, 1988. One of 250 w/new intro by Conroy, Lt. Colonel Nugent Courvoisie (The Boo) and Col. Donald Conroy (The Great Santini) and signed by each. VF in slipcase. *CAPTAIN'S BOOKSHELF.* $300

Conroy, Pat. THE BOO. Verona: McClure, (1970). 1st ed, 1st bk. Fine in very sl soiled white dj. Scarce. *CAPTAIN'S BOOKSHELF.* $1650

Conroy, Pat. THE GREAT SANTINI. Boston: Houghton Mifflin, 1976. 1st ed. Signed. Fine in dj. *ELSE FINE.* $125

Conroy, Pat. THE LORDS OF DISCIPLINE. Boston: Houghton Mifflin, 1980. 1st ed. Fine in dj. Signed. *CAPTAIN'S BOOKSHELF.* $85

Conroy, Pat. THE PRINCE OF TIDES. Boston, 1986. 1st ed. VF in dj. *PETTLER.* $45

Conroy, Pat. THE PRINCE OF TIDES. Boston: HMCo. (1986). Adv reading copy. NF in wraps. *DORN.* $50

Conroy, Pat. THE PRINCE OF TIDES. Boston: Houghton Mifflin Company, 1986. 1st ed. Fine in dj. *JUVELIS.* $35

Conroy, Pat. THE PRINCE OF TIDES. Houghton Mifflin, 1986. Advance reading copy. Fine in wraps. *STAHR.* $30

Constantine, K.C. THE ROCKSBURG RAILROAD MURDERS. NY: Saturday Review Press, 1972. 1st ed, 1st bk. Fine in dj. *ELSE FINE.* $250

Constantine, K.C. THE ROCKSBURG RAILROAD MURDERS. NY: Saturday Review Press, 1972. 1st ed. Erasure front pastedown o/w Fine in price-clipped dj. *MORDIDA.* $175

CONTRIBUTIONS TO THE MONTANA HIST. SOCIETY. VOL. 1. Helena, 1902. 2nd prtg. Frontis, 1 pl. Fine. *OREGON.* $80

CONTRIBUTIONS TO THE MONTANA HIST. SOCIETY. VOL. III. Helena, 1900. 1st ed. Frontis, 13 plts. Fine. *OREGON.* $100

CONTRIBUTIONS TO THE MONTANA HIST. SOCIETY. VOL. 4. Helena, 1903. 1st ed. Frontis, 50 plts. Fine. *OREGON.* $75

CONTRIBUTIONS TO THE MONTANA HIST. SOCIETY. VOL. 10. Helena, 1940. 1st ed. Frontis, 17 plts. Fine. *OREGON.* $90

CONVERSATIONS ON POLITICAL ECONOMY IN WHICH THE ELEMENTS OF THAT SCIENCE ARE FAMILIARLY EXPLAINED. (By Jane Marcet.) London: Longman et al, 1817. 2nd ed. xi,486pp. Orig half lea over marbled boards, well worn, hinges reinforced, end matter sl foxed, interior near VG. *SMITHFIELD.* $205

CONVICT LABOR. 20th Annual Report of Commissioner of Labor. Washington: GPO, 1906. House of Rep Doc 906. Contemp calf sl worn. Rebacked. Text VG. Ex-lib 59th Congress. *DIAMOND.* $35

Conway, J. Gregory. CONWAY'S TREASURY OF FLOWER ARRANGEMENTS. NY: Alfred A. Knopf, 1953. 1st ed. Fine in sl worn dj. *WREDEN.* $60

Conway, Moncure D. AUTOBIOGRAPHY: MEMORIES & EXPERIENCES. Boston, 1904. 2 vols. Signed. Fine. *POLYANTHOS.* $95

Conway, Sir Martin. THE BOLIVIAN ANDES. NY/London: Harper & Brothers, 1901. Grey cl. Photo plts. Spine lightly darkened, else NF. *PARMER.* $125

Conway, W. Martin. THE ALPS. A&C Black, 1904. 1st ed. 20s Series. Front eps replaced, slight edgewear, else VG. *OLD LONDON.* $50

Conwell, Russell H. HISTORY OF THE GREAT FIRE IN BOSTON, NOVEMBER 9 AND 10, 1872. Boston: B.B. Russell. 1873. 1st ed. 312pp. Frontis, 9 plts. Orig grn cl, gilt; spine extrems sl rubbed. *KARMIOLE.* $30

Cook, Bruce. LISTEN TO THE BLUES. NY: Scribners, 1973. 1st ed. Fine in Fine dj. *BEASLEY.* $35

Cook, C.H. AMONG THE PIMAS OR THE MISSION TO THE PIMA AND MARICOPA INDIANS. Albany, 1893. 136pp. *CULLEN.* $50

Cook, D.J. HANDS UP; or, THIRTY-FIVE YEARS OF DETECTIVE LIFE IN THE MOUNTAINS AND ON THE PLAINS. Denver, 1897. 1st ed. 442pp. Unusually Fine. Scarce this ed. *BOOK MARKET.* $200

Cook, David J. HANDS UP. Denver, 1897. Enl ed. 442pp. Port. Orig cl. Howes C728. *GINSBERG.* $175

Cook, Earnshaw. PERCENTAGE BASEBALL. Waverly, 1964. 1st ed. VG. *PLAPINGER.* $85

Cook, Fannie. MRS. PALMER'S HONEY. GC: Doubleday, 1946. 1st ed. Fine in lightly used dj w/small chip. Inscribed by author year of pub. *BEASLEY.* $125

Cook, Frederick A. MY ATTAINMENT OF THE POLE. NY, 1913. 3rd ed. Signed inscription. Shelfwear. Good, sound. *ARTIS.* $50

Cook, James H. FIFTY YEARS ON THE OLD FRONTIER. New Haven: Yale Univ Press, 1925. 3rd prtg. 31pp photo illus. Cl, light spotting, light wear to extremities, bkpl. *DAWSON'S.* $35

Cook, James H. FIFTY YEARS ON THE OLD FRONTIER. AS COWBOY, HUNTER, GUIDE, SCOUT, AND RANCHMAN. New Haven: Yale Univ Press, 1923. 2 fldg plts. VG. *CONNOLLY & WADE.* $45

Cook, James. CAPTAIN COOK'S ORIGINAL VOYAGES, ROUND THE WORLD...CONTAINING THE WHOLE OF HIS DISCOVERIES...AND PARTICULARS RELATIVE TO HIS UNFORTUNATE DEATH. Woodbridge: B. Smith, (1815). Frontis, engr title pg, (2 preface), 798 pp. 10 plts. Antique-style 1/4 calf. *LEFKOWICZ.* $500

Cook, James. THE EXPLORATIONS OF CAPTAIN JAMES COOK IN THE PACIFIC...1768-1779. A. Grenfell Price (ed). Illus Geoffrey C. Ingleton. NY: LEC. 1957. Ed ltd to 1,500 numbered, signed by artist, Ingleton, and Douglas A. Dunstan, ptr. Slipcase. *KARMIOLE.* $150

Cook, John A. PURSUING THE WHALE, A QUARTER-CENTURY OF WHALING IN THE ARCTIC. Boston & NY, 1926. 1st ed VG+. *MIKESH.* $45

Cook, John A. PURSUING THE WHALE. London: J. Murray, 1926. 1st British ed. Good+. *BLUE DRAGON.* $45

Cook, Joseph. HEREDITY, WITH PRELUDES ON CURRENT EVENTS. Boston, 1879. 1st ed. Exceptionally Fine. *FYE.* $75

Cook, Marc. THE WILDERNESS CURE. NY, 1881. 1st ed. Scarce. *FYE.* $75

Cook, Robert M. and Robert J. Charleston. GREEK AND ROMAN POTTERY. NY: Kodansha, (1979). 122 color plts. Boxed. Mint. *ARCHAEOLOGIA.* $350

Cook, Roy Bird. THE FAMILY AND EARLY LIFE OF STONEWALL JACKSON. Richmond, 1925. 1st ed. Fine. *McGOWAN.* $75

Cook, Theodore Andrea. THE SUNLIT HOURS. London: Nisbet & Co., 1925. 1st ed. Some wear to extremities, else VG. *OLD LONDON.* $40

Cook, Thomas H. BLOOD INNOCENTS. NY: Playboy Press, 1980. 1st ed. Signed. Pb orig. Fine unread copy in wrappers. *MORDIDA.* $75

Cook, Thomas H. FLESH AND BLOOD. NY: G.P. Putnam's Sons, 1939. 1st ed. Advance review copy, slip and flyer laid in. VF in dj. *MORDIDA.* $30

Cook, Thomas H. NIGHT SECRETS. NY: Putnam, (1990). 1st ed. Signed. Fine in Fine dj. *UNGER.* $40

Cook, Thomas H. STREETS OF FIRE. NY: Putnam, (1989). 1st ed. Signed. Fine in Fine dj. *UNGER.* $40

Cook, Thomas H. TABERNACLE. Boston: Houghton Mifflin, 1933. 1st ed. Fine in dj, couple short closed tears. *MORDIDA.* $25

Cook, Thomas H. THE ORCHIDS. Boston: Houghton Mifflin, (1982). 1st ed. Inscribed. Fine in sl edge-rubbed dj. *UNGER.* $40

Cook, Thomas H. THE ORCHIDS. Boston: Houghton Mifflin, 1982. 1st ed. Fine in dj. *MORDIDA.* $30

Cook, Wesley. PRACTICAL LESSONS IN HYPNOTISM AND AUTOSUGGESTION. NY: Willey Book Company, (1927). Dj chipped. VG. *DRAMATIS PERSONAE.* $35

Cooke, George Willis. JOHN SULLIVAN DWIGHT, BROOK-FARMER, EDITOR AND CRITIC OF MUSIC. Boston: Small, Maynard, 1898. 1st ed. Lightly worn. *BEASLEY.* $100

Cooke, Grace M. SON RILEY RABBIT AND LITTLE GIRL. London: Chambers (n.d., c. 1900). VG w/sl edgewear & soil but ring of yellow rabbits around oval photo of girl holding sketched-in rabbit Good w/2 tiny skinned patches, 1 scratch. *BEBBAH.* $55

Cooke, Hereward L. and James D. Dean. EYEWITNESS TO SPACE: PAINTINGS AND DRAWINGS....NY: Harry N. Abrams, n.d. (circa 1976). VG in repaired dj (5" tear clumsily repaired w/tape; unrepaired 1" tear), top edge of pgs sl yellowed. *KNOLLWOOD.* $125

Cooke, John (ed). THE DUBLIN BOOK OF IRISH VERSE, 1728-1909. Dublin: Hodges, Figgis, and Co., and London: Henry Frowde, OUP, 1909. (Prints three orig Joyce poems for 1st time.) Ex-lib with very minor markings. W/o dj (probably as issued). NF. *OLD LONDON.* $60

Cooke, John Esten. Ed by Richard Barksdale Harwell. STONEWALL JACKSON AND THE OLD STONEWALL BRIGADE. Charlottesville, (1954). 1st ed. VG+ in dj. *PRATT.* $47.50

Cooke, John Esten. SURRY OF EAGLE'S NEST OR THE MEMOIRS OF A STAFF-OFFICER SERVING IN VIRGINIA. NY, 1866. Undated reprint (circa 1894). 484pp. Dj wear and chipping o/w VG. *PRATT.* $35

Cooke, M.C. VEGETABLE WASPS AND PLANT WORMS. London, 1892. 4 plts. Lt foxing. *SUTTON.* $30

Cooke, Nicholas. A TREATISE ON ANTISEPTIC MEDICATION OR DECLAT'S METHOD. Chicago, 1882. 1st ed. *FYE.* $75

Cooke, William. MEMOIRS OF SAMUEL FOOTE, ESQ. NY: for Peter A. Mesier, 1806. 1st Amer ed. 2 vols. 12mo; contemp tree calf, quite rubbed; morocco labels, lettered in gilt; occas spotting. VG. *DRAMATIS PERSONAE.* $65

Cooley, Dale and Mary Owen. WHERE THE WAGONS ROLLED. Topeka, 1976. 1st ed. VG. *OREGON.* $40

Coolidge, Calvin. THE AUTOBIOGRAPHY. NY: Cosmopolitan Book Corp, 1929. 1st ed, ltd to 1,000, numbered, signed. This #193. Fine in Fine slipcase. *BOOK MARKET.* $375

Coolidge, Dane and Mary Roberts. THE NAVAJO INDIANS. Boston: Houghton Mifflin, 1930. 1st ed. VG, lacking dj. *LOPEZ.* $65

Coolidge, Dane. FIGHTING MEN OF THE WEST. NY: Dutton, (1932). Stated 1st ed. 20 plts, Sun marks rear cvr. *SCHOYER'S.* $35

Coolidge, Dane. SILVER HAT. NY: Dutton, 1934. 1st ed. VG to Fine in VG, torn dj. *BOOK MARKET.* $50

Coolidge, Richard. STATISTICAL REPORT ON THE SICKNESS AND MORTALITY IN THE ARMY OF THE UNITED STATES, COMPILED FROM THE RECORDS OF THE SURGEON GENERAL'S OFFICE; EMBRACING A PERIOD OF SIXTEEN YEARS, FROM JANUARY, 1839 TO JANUARY, 1855. Washington, 1856. 1st ed. 703pp. Skillfully rebacked w/lea label. *FYE.* $275

Coolidge, Richard. STATISTICAL REPORT ON THE SICKNESS AND MORTALITY IN THE ARMY OF THE UNITED STATES, COMPILED FROM THE RECORDS OF THE SUR-

GEON GENERAL'S OFFICE; EMBRACING A PERIOD OF FIVE YEARS, FROM JANUARY, 1855, TO JANUARY, 1860. Washington, 1860. 1st ed. 515pp. Fldg map. *FYE.* $250

Cooling, Benjamin Franklin. FORTS HENRY AND DONELSON, THE KEY TO THE CONFEDERATE HEARTLAND. Knoxville, (1987). 1st ed. 354pp. VF in VF dj. *PRATT.* $25

Coombs, Charles. SKYROCKETING INTO THE UNKNOWN. NY: Wm. Morrow, 1954. Minor extremity wear, o/w VG in torn dj. *KNOLLWOOD.* $35

Coonts, Stephen. FLIGHT OF THE INTRUDER. Annapolis, 1986. 1st ed, 1st bk. VF in dj. *PETTLER.* $40

Coonts, Stephen. FLIGHT OF THE INTRUDER. Annapolis: Naval Institute Press, (1986). 1st ed, 1st book. Fine in Fine dj. *ROBBINS.* $25

Cooper, Astley. THE ANATOMY AND SURGICAL TREATMENT OF ABDOMINAL HERNIA. Phila, 1844. 1st Amer ed. Full leather, 427pp + 26 Fine engrvd plts. Name clipped from upper corner of title page, o/w Fine. *FYE.* $350

Cooper, Clarence L. Jr. THE FARM. NY: Crown 1967. Fine in NF dj. *LOPEZ.* $40

Cooper, Clarence L. Jr. THE SCENE. NY: Crown, (1960). 1st ed. NF in sl spine-sunned dj. *LOPEZ.* $45

Cooper, Frederic Taber. RIDER'S CALIFORNIA. A GUIDEBOOK FOR TRAVELERS WITH 28 MAPS AND PLANS. NY/London: Macmillan/George Allen, Unwin, 1925. Color maps (some missing). Ex-lib. *HUDSON.* $25

Cooper, Gordon. ISLES OF ROMANCE AND MYSTERY. London: Lutterworth (1949). 1st. Almost Fine in VG dj. *AARD.* $25

Cooper, J. California. HOMEMADE LOVE. NY: St. Martin's Press, (1986). 1st ed. Fine in dj w/short tear on rear panel. *BETWEEN COVERS.* $45

Cooper, J.W. THE EXPERIENCED BOTANIST OR INDIAN PHYSICIAN...Lancaster, PA: Printed for the Author and Publishers, 1840. First pub in 1833. 16mo. 303pp. Old tree calf, bottom of spine chipped. *M & S.* $225

Cooper, James F. TECHNIQUE OF CONTRACEPTION....NY: Day-Nichols, 1928. 3rd ptg. Dust soiled cl. VG. *SECOND LIFE.* $35

Cooper, James Fenimore. THE CHRONICLES OF COOPERSTOWN. Cooperstown, NY: Phinney, 1883. 1st ed. 100pp. Orig cl, boards, paper label on front cover, front hinges mended, chipping at rear joint. Howes C747. *GINSBERG.* $150

Cooper, James Fenimore. THE HISTORY OF THE NAVY OF THE UNITED STATES OF AMERICA. Phila: Lea & Blanchard, 1839. 2 vols. 1st ed. 2 maps. Orig cl, rebacked, orig spines preserved. Cvrs bit stained and bubbled; some foxing within. Owner sig. *LEFKOWICZ.* $250

Cooper, James Fenimore. THE PATHFINDER. Richard M. Powers (illus). Lunenberg, VT: LEC, 1965. Ed ltd to 1500 numbered, signed by Powers. Slipcase. *KARMIOLE.* $50

Cooper, James Fenimore. THE PATHFINDER....Phila: Lea and Blanchard, 1840. 2 vols. 1st Amer ed. Orig purple cl, paper labels. Spines faded, one label half gone. Else NF set, Nice double cl slipcase. *AUTHORS OF THE WEST.* $275

Cooper, James Fenimore. THE PILOT. Robert M. Quackenbush (illus). (Baltimore): LEC, at the Garamond Press. 1968. Ed ltd to 1500 numbered, signed by Quackenbush. Slipcase. *KARMIOLE.* $35

Cooper, James Fenimore. WYANDOTTE, OR THE HUTTED KNOLL: A TALE (ANON.). NY: Stringer & Townsend, 1851. 2 vols bound together. 237pp,(1)p ad; 201pp,2pp ads. 12 mo. 1/2 lea w/marbled boards. Orig binding, worn and cracking yet tight, clean. *CONNOLLY & WADE.* $75

Cooper, John M. ANALYTICAL AND CRITICAL BIBLIOGRAPHY OF THE TRIBES OF TIERRA DEL FUEGO AND AD-

JACENT TERRITORY. BAE Bull 63. Washington: GPO, 1917. 1st ed. Fldg map. Grn cl w/gilt. VG+. *CONNOLLY & WADE.* $35

Cooper, Samuel. A DICTIONARY OF PRACTICAL SURGERY...With notes and additions by John Syng Dorsey. Phila, 1816. 2 vols. 2nd Amer ed. Full leather, 531, 522pp. *FYE.* $325

Cooper, Samuel. A DICTIONARY OF PRACTICAL SURGERY: COMPREHENDING ALL THE MOST INTERESTING IMPROVEMENTS, FROM THE EARLIEST TIMES DOWN TO THE PRESENT: FORMING A "CATALOGUE RAISONNE" OF SURGICAL LITERATURE FROM THE 6TH LONDON EDITION. Notes and additions by David Reese. NY, 1830. Full leather, 2 vols. *FYE.* $150

Cooper, Samuel. THE FIRST LINES OF THE PRACTICE OF SURGERY. Phila, 1830. 3rd ed. 2 vols. Full leather, 460, 484pp. Fine steel engrvd plts. *FYE.* $150

Cooper, Susan. MANDRAKE. London: H & S, 1964. 1st ed, 1st bk. Fine, lt wear at dj corners. *ELSE FINE.* $85

Cooper, William. SCENES FROM PROVINCIAL LIFE. Malcolm Bradbury (intro). (London): MacMillan, (1969). 1st ed, thus. Fine in lightly rubbed dj. Inscribed 1969 using his real name Harry (Hoff). *CAPTAIN'S BOOKSHELF.* $65

Coover, Robert. A THEOLOGICAL POSITION. NY: Dutton, (1972). 1st ed. Fine in dj. *CAPTAIN'S BOOKSHELF.* $125

Coover, Robert. AFTER LAZARUS. Bloomfield Hills: Bruccoli Clark, 1980. 1st ed, One of 450 numbered and signed. Fine, issued w/o dj. *BEASLEY.* $35

Coover, Robert. GERALD'S PARTY. London, 1986. 1st ed. Signed, presentation. Fine in Fine dj. *POLYANTHOS.* $35

Coover, Robert. PRICKSONGS AND DESCANTS. NY: Dutton (1969). 1st ed. NF in VG sl used dj. *DORN.* $75

Coover, Robert. PRICKSONGS AND DESCANTS. NY: Dutton, (1969). 1st ed. Fine in dj. *CAPTAIN'S BOOKSHELF.* $75

Coover, Robert. THE ORIGIN OF THE BRUNISTS. NY: G.P. Putnam's Sons, (1966). 1st ed. Signed. Fine in dj. *BERNARD.* $200

Coover, Robert. THE ORIGIN OF THE BRUNISTS. NY: Putnam, (1966). 1st ed, 1st bk. Fine in dj (trace of edgewear, two small tears). *CAPTAIN'S BOOKSHELF.* $150

Coover, Robert. THE ORIGIN OF THE BRUNISTS. NY: Putnam's, (1966). 1st ed. Cl, dj. Fine. *JAFFE.* $175

Coover, Robert. THE ORIGIN OF THE BRUNISTS. Putnam, 1966. 1st ed. Fine. Dj worn at spine ends and soiled on rear panel. *STAHR.* $140

Coover, Robert. THE PUBLIC BURNING. Viking, 1977. 1st ed. VF in dj. *STAHR.* $15

Coover, Robert. THE UNIVERSAL BASEBALL ASSOCIATION, INC. Henry Waugh, Prop. NY: Random House, (1968). 1st ed. Fine in dj. *CAPTAIN'S BOOKSHELF.* $175

Coover, Robert. THE UNIVERSAL BASEBALL ASSOCIATION INC., J. HENRY WAUGH, PROP. Random House, 1968. 1st ed. Fine in a price-clipped dj that is lightly nicked at the edges. *STAHR.* $75

Cope, E.D. THE CROCODILIANS, LIZARDS, AND SNAKES OF NORTH AMERICA. Washington, 1900. 36 plts, 347 text-figures. Orig cl w/some scuffing, bkpl, ex-lib. *SUTTON.* $95

Cope, Harley F. SERPENT OF THE SEAS. THE SUBMARINE. NY: Funk & Wagnalls Co. 1942. 1st ed. Dj sl chipped. *KARMIOLE.* $30

Cope, Z. THE ROYAL COLLEGE OF SURGEONS OF ENGLAND. London: Anthony Blond, (1959). 1st ed. VG. *SMITHFIELD.* $35

Cope, Zachary. SOME PRINCIPLES OF MINOR SURGERY. London, 1929. 1st ed. *FYE.* $75

Copeland, R.M. COUNTRY LIFE: A HANDBOOK....Boston, 1859. 1st ed. Orig cl w/lt staining. Bkpl removed, faint dampstaining top edge of few pp; only occasional foxing. *SUTTON.* $335

Copeland, Thomas. OBSERVATIONS ON THE PRINCIPAL DISEASES OF THE RECTUM AND ANUS-PARTICULARLY STRICTURE OF THE RECTUM, THE HAEMORRHOIDAL EXCRESCENCE, AND FISTULA IN ANO. London, 1824. 3rd ed. 1/2 leather, 178pp. Boards detached, backstrip missing. *FYE.* $200

Copeman, W.S.C. A SHORT HISTORY OF THE GOUT AND THE RHEUMATIC DISEASES. Berkeley, 1964. 1st ed. Dj. *FYE.* $75

Coplan, Maxwell Frederick. PINK LEMONADE. NY: Whittlesey, (1945). 1st ed. Cloth. VG. *ARTIS.* $30

Coppard, A.E. EMERGENCY EXIT. NY: Random House, (1934). 1/350 numbered, signed. About Fine. *DERMONT.* $40

Coppard, A.E. FEARFUL PLEASURES. Arkham House, 1946. 1st ed. NF in NF dj. *MADLE.* $100

Coppard, A.E. FEARFUL PLEASURES. Sauk City: Arkham House, 1946. One of 4,033. 1st ed. Fine, lt wear to dj spine ends. *ELSE FINE.* $60

Coppard, A.E. PINK FURNITURE. London: Jonathan Cape, (1930). 1st ed. NF in lightly soiled dj w/paper remnant on front flap. Signed. *CHAPEL HILL.* $55

Coppard, A.E. SILVER CIRCUS: TALES....(London): Cape, (1928). 1st ed. Shelfwear, some browning/minor tape marks to first/last few pgs, else VG. *OTHER WORLDS.* $35

Coppens, Charles. MORAL PRINCIPLES AND MEDICAL PRACTICE, THE BASIS OF MEDICAL JURISPRUDENCE. Cincinnati, 1897. 1st ed. *FYE.* $100

Copper, Basil. FROM EVIL'S PILLOW. Sauk City: Arkham House, 1973. 1st ed. Fine in dj. *ELSE FINE.* $30

Copper, Basil. HERE BE DAEMONS. NY: St. Martin's, 1978. 1st ed. As New in dj. *ELSE FINE.* $40

Copper, Basil. NECROPOLIS (A NOVEL OF GOTHIC MYSTERY). (Sauk City): Arkham House, (1980). 1st ed. NF in dj. *OTHER WORLDS.* $45

Copper, Basil. NECROPOLIS. Arkham House, 1980. 1st ed. Fine in dj. *MADLE.* $60

Copper, Basil. THE CURSE OF THE FLEERS. NY: St. Martin's, 1976. 1st ed. As New in dj. *ELSE FINE.* $35

Copper, Basil. WHEN FOOTSTEPS ECHO. NY: St. Martin's, 1975. 1st ed. Fine in dj. *ELSE FINE.* $50

COPPER CAMP: STORIES OF THE WORLD'S GREATEST MINING TOWN, BUTTE, MONTANA. Comp by the Writer's Program, W.P.A. NY: Hastings House, 1943. 1st ed, 1st ptg. NF in bright, sl chipped dj. *CONNOLLY & WADE.* $60

Copper River Joe. A GOLDEN CROSS (?) ON TRAILS FROM THE VALDEZ GLACIER. LA: White-Thompson Pub, 1939. 1st ed. VG. *BACKMAN.* $40

Copsey, W.G. (ed.). THE PRACTICAL GROCER. Written by Specialist Contributors. London: The Gresham Pub Co, (1933). 2nd ptg. 2 vols. 6 fldg tables back of vol 2. Djs sl chipped. *KARMIOLE.* $60

Corbet, G.B. THE MAMMALS OF THE PLAEARCTIC REGION. London & Ithaca, NY: Brit. Museum, (1980) w/amend. Fine in Fine dj. *MIKESH.* $35

Corbett, James. THE GHOST PLANE. London: Herbert Jenkins, 1939. 1st ed. Edges lightly spotted o/w Fine in dj with minor wear, couple closed tears. *MORDIDA.* $45

Corbett, James. THE WHITE ANGEL. London: Herbert Jenkins, 1931. 1st ed. Newer eps. Edges darkened, pp somewhat spotted o/w VG in dj (sl faded spine; chipped, short closed tears, wear). *MORDIDA.* $35

Corbett, Jim. MAN-EATERS OF INDIA. NY: Oxford Univ Press, 1957. 1st ed. VG+ in VG dj (chipping to corners). *BACKMAN.* $65

Corbett, Jim. THE MAN-EATING LEOPARD OF RUDRAPRAYAG. NY & Bombay: Oxford, (1948). Photos, map ep. VG. *MIKESH.* $30

Cordasco, Francesco. AMERICAN MEDICAL IMPRINTS, 1820-1910, A CHECKLIST OF PUBLICATIONS ILLUSTRATING THE HISTORY AND PROGRESS OF MEDICAL SCIENCE, MEDICAL EDUCATION AND THE HEALING ARTS IN THE UNITED STATES. Totowa, 1985. 2 vols. *FYE.* $250

Cordell, Eugene Fauntleroy. THE MEDICAL ANNALS OF MARYLAND, 1799-1899. Baltimore: (Medical & Chirurgical Faculty of Maryland), 1903. 1st ed. Fine. *KARMIOLE.* $75

Cordell, Eugene. THE MEDICAL ANNALS OF MARYLAND 1799-1899. Baltimore, 1903. 1st ed. *FYE.* $40

Corder, E.M. THE DEER HUNTER. NY: Exeter, (1979). 1st hb ed. In dj. *AKA.* $40

Cordry, T.A. THE STORY OF THE MARKING OF THE SANTA FE TRAIL. By the DAR, Topeka, 1915. 1st ed. Fine. *VARNER.* $50

Coren, Alan (comp). THE PUNCH BOOK OF SHORT STORIES 3. (London): Robson Books, (1981). 1st ed. Fine in dj. *CAPTAIN'S BOOK-SHELF.* $45

Coren, Michael. GILBERT: THE MAN WHO WAS G.K. CHESTERTON. London: Jonathan Cape, 1989. 1st ed. Fine in dj. *MORDIDA.* $35

Corkran, David. THE CREEK FRONTIER, 1540-1783. Univ of OK, (1967). 1st ed. Rev copy card laid in. VG in Good+ dj. *OREGON.* $35

Corle, Edwin (ed) IGOR STRAVINSKY. (NY: Duell, Sloan & Pearce. 1949.) 1st ed. *KARMIOLE.* $60

Corle, Edwin. BILLY THE KID. NY: Duell, (1953). 1st ed. Signed. Fine in NF price-clipped dj bumped at spine. *UNGER.* $75

Corle, Edwin. BILLY THE KID: A NOVEL. NY: Duell, Sloan & Pearce, (1953). 1st ed. Dj. *OUTPOST.* $25

Corle, Edwin. BURRO ALLEY. NY, 1946. Ltd ed, 977/1500 signed. This ed designed by Merle Armitage. Rear cover little spotted, lower edge rubbed, one corner creased. Fine in dj (spine little sunned, few edge chips, 1 small edge tear). *POLYANTHOS.* $65

Corle, Edwin. BURRO ALLEY. NY: Random House, (1938). 1st trade ed. Fine in VG dj. *BOOK MARKET.* $35

Corle, Edwin. DESERT COUNTRY. NY: Duell, Sloan, (1941). 1st ed. Fine in VG to Fine dj. *BOOK MARKET.* $48

Corle, Edwin. FIG TREE JOHN. LA: Ward Ritchie Press, 1955. Ltd ed of 550 numbered. Fine in slipcase. *WEBER.* $100

Corle, Edwin. LISTEN, BRIGHT ANGEL. NY, 1946. 1st ed. Spine sl dull, else VG. *FIVE QUAIL.* $30

Corle, Edwin. LISTEN, BRIGHT ANGEL. NY: Duell, Sloan (1946). 1st ed. Fine in VG dj. *BOOK MARKET.* $35

Corle, Edwin. PEOPLE ON THE EARTH. NY: Random House, 1937. 1st ed. Fine but for sl darkened spine, in lightly used dj. *BEASLEY.* $75

Corle, Edwin. THE GILA. (Rivers of Amer) Rinehart, 1951. 1st ed. Fine in Fine dj. *VARNER.* $40

Corle, Edwin. THE GILA: RIVER OF THE SOUTHWEST. NY: Rinehart, 1951. 1st ed. Fine in VG dj. *CONNOLLY & WADE.* $45

Corle, Edwin. THE ROYAL HIGHWAY (EL CAMINO REAL). Indianapolis: Bobbs-Merrill, 1949. 1st ed. 22pp plts. NF in VG dj. *CONNOLLY & WADE.* $45

Corley, Donald. THE HAUNTED JESTER. NY: McBride, 1931. 1st ed. Fine, minor edgewear to fragile gold foil dj. *ELSE FINE.* $85

Corley, Donald. THE HOUSE OF LOST IDENTITY. McBride, 1927. VG *MADLE*. $25

Corliss, Carlton J. MAINLINE OF MID-AMERICA: THE STORY OF THE ILLINOIS CENTRAL. Creative Age: NY, 1950. 1st ed. VF in NF dj. *CONNOLLY & WADE*. $35

Corman, Cid. BE QUEST. Elizabeth Press, 1972. One of 300 printed in Japan. Wraps. Signed. Fine. *WOOLMER*. $45

Corman, Cid. NONCE. (Elizabeth Press, 1965). One of 500 printed in Japan. Wraps. Fine. *WOOLMER*. $45

Corman, Cid. STANCES & DISTANCES. Origin Press, 1957. 1st ed. Wrappers. Fine. *WOOLMER*. $75

Corman, Cid. STEAD. (New Rochelle: The Elizabeth Press, 1966). One of 500 printed in Japan. Wrappers. Fine. *WOOLMER*. $45

Corn, Alfred. ALL ROADS AT ONCE. NY: Viking, (1976). 1st ed, 1st bk. Orig blue boards. Fine in dj. *CHAPEL HILL*. $30

Cornelius, Brother. KEITH, OLD MASTER OF CALIFORNIA BY BROTHER CORNELIUS. NY: Putnam/Fresno: Academy Library Guild, (1942) & (1957). 2 vols. Both 1st eds. Signed & inscribed. Fine in Fine dj. Several associate items. *BOOK MARKET*. $450

Corney, Peter. VOYAGES IN THE NORTHERN PACIFIC. NARRATIVES OF SEVERAL TRADING VOYAGES FROM 1813 TO 1818...INTERESTING EARLY ACCOUNT OF KAMEHAMEHA'S REALM; MANNERS AND CUSTOMS OF THE PEOPLE, ETC. AND SKETCH OF A CRUISE IN THE SERVICE OF THE INDEPENDENTS OF SOUTH AMERICA IN 1819. Honolulu: Thos. G. Thrum, 1896. 1st separate ed. 18.5 x 11.6 cm in orig. ptd wrapper. 1st published in the London Literary Gazette. Repaired tear to front wrapper and spine, some soiling; still unusually Good. *PARMER*. $595

Cornford, L. C. THE LORD HIGH ADMIRAL AND OTHERS. London, 1915. VG. *MADLE*. $40

Corning, Howard (ed). JOURNAL OF JOHN JAMES AUDUBON MADE DURING HIS TRIP TO NEW ORLEANS IN 1820-21. Cambridge, MA, 1929. 1st ed. Uncut. Orig cl, lightly spotted on cvrs near edges. Howes A387. One of 225. *GINSBERG*. $125

Corning, Howard (ed). LETTERS OF JOHN JAMES AUDUBON 1826-1840. N.Y, 1969. Cloth. Rprnt of 1930 ed. Howes A387. *GINSBERG*. $30

Corning, Howard McKinley. WILLAMETTE LANDINGS: GHOST TOWNS OF THE RIVER. OR Hist Soc, Binfords & Mort, 1947. 1st ed. Inscription by Capt. George Jerome's granddaughter. Fine in Good+ dj. *CONNOLLY & WADE*. $30

Cornish, Dudley Taylor and Virginia Jeans Laas. LINCOLN'S LEE, THE LIFE OF SAMUEL PHILIPS LEE, UNITED STATES NAVY, 1812-1897. Lawrence, (1986). 1st ed. VF in dj. *PRATT*. $25

Cornplanter, Jesse. LEGENDS OF THE LONGHOUSE. Phila: Lippincott, (1938). 1st ed. VG in lightly edgeworn, VG dj. *LOPEZ*. $85

Cornwallis, Earl. ANSWER TO SIR HENRY CLINTON'S NARRATIVE OF THE CAMPAIGN IN 1781 IN NORTH AMERICA. Phila: Campbell, 1866. 1st Amer ed. (16),260pp. Orig ptd wrappers. Reprint of London 1783 orig ed. One of 250. Howes C781. *GINSBERG*. $100

Cornwell, Bernard. SHARP'S HONOUR. London: Collins, 1985. 1st ed. Fine in price clipped dj. *ELSE FINE*. $35

Cornwell, Bernard. SHARPE'S EAGLE. NY: Viking, (1981). 1st ed. VF in VF dj. *UNGER*. $60

Cornwell, Bernard. SHARPE'S EAGLE. NY: Viking, 1981. 1st ed. Fine in dj. *ELSE FINE*. $45

Cornwell, Patricia D. BODY OF EVIDENCE. NY: Scribner's, 1991. 1st ed. VF in dj. *MORDIDA*. $35

Cornwell, Patricia D. POSTMORTEM. NY: Charles Scribner's Sons, 1990. 1st ed. Fine in dj. *MORDIDA*. $125

Cornwell, Patricia D. POSTMORTEM. NY: Charles Scribner's Sons, 1990. 1st ed. Uncorrected proof. VF in ptd wraps. *MORDIDA*. $150

Cornwell, Patricia D. POSTMORTEM. NY: Scribner's, 1990. 1st ed. Signed. VF in dj. *MORDIDA*. $250

CORONATION TRANSFER PICTURE BOOK. 1952. 2pp transfers, numbered and, when used, can be placed on corresponding numbers of the story pages. All transfers in Mint condition. Pop-up bk. *BOOKFINDERS INTL*. $90

Correll, D.S. and H.B. Correll. AQUATIC AND WETLAND PLANTS OF SOUTHWESTERN UNITED STATES. Washington, 1972. 1st ptg. Cl, lt speckling, soiling; lt foxing. *SUTTON*. $85

Correll, D.S. and M.S. Johnston. MANUAL OF THE VASCULAR PLANTS OF TEXAS. Richardson, 1979 (1970). Cloth. 3 maps. *SUTTON*. $100

Correll, Donovan. POTATO AND ITS WILD RELATIVES. Texas: TX Res. Found, 1962. As New in dj. *AMERICAN BOTANIST*. $45

Corsaro, Frank. THE LOVE FOR THREE ORANGES. FSG, 1984. 1st Amer ed. 125pp. Illus by Maurice Sendak. NF; corner bumps. *BEBBAH*. $30

Corser, H.P. SEVENTY-SIX PAGE HISTORY OF ALASKA. (n.p.): 1927. 1st ed. Some wear to orig wraps; overall VG. *PARMER*. $65

Cortazar, Julio. 62: A MODEL KIT. NY: Pantheon (1972). 1st Amer ed. Fine in dj. *DORN*. $35

Cortazar, Julio. A CERTAIN LUCAS. NY: Knopf, 1984. Uncorrected proof of 1st US ed. Fine in wraps. *CAPTAIN'S BOOKSHELF*. $35

Cortazar, Julio. ALL FIRES THE FIRES; AND OTHER STORIES. NY: Pantheon (1973). 1st Amer ed. in Fine price clipped dj. *DORN*. $25

Cortazar, Julio. END OF THE GAME AND OTHER STORIES. NY, 1967. 1st ed. NF in NF dj. *POLYANTHOS*. $30

Cortazar, Julio. END OF THE GAME AND OTHER STORIES. Paul Blackburn (trans). NY: Pantheon, (1967). 1st US ed. Fine in dj w/somewhat faded spine. *CAPTAIN'S BOOKSHELF*. $75

Cortazar, Julio. END OF THE GAME. NY: Pantheon, (1967). 1st Amer ed. Fine in Fine dj. *LOPEZ*. $125

Cortazar, Julio. END OF THE GAME; AND OTHER STORIES. London: Collins and Harvill (1968). 1st Eng ed. Fine in dj. *DORN*. $75

Cortazar, Julio. HOPSCOTCH. London: Collins and Harvill (1967). 1st Eng ed. Fine in dj. *DORN*. $85

Cortazar, Julio. HOPSCOTCH. NY: Pantheon (1966). 1st Amer ed. VG (ink underlining few pp) in Near VG dj. *DORN*. $35

Cortazar, Julio. THE WINNERS. NY: Pantheon (1965). 1st Amer ed, 1st bk. NF in VG+ dj. *DORN*. $60

Cortissoz, Royal. AUGUSTUS SAINT-GAUDENS. Boston: Houghton Mifflin Co. 1907. 1st ed. Illus. 24 photogravure pl, each w/tissue guard. Extremities sl worn and a bit soiled. *KARMIOLE*. $65

Corvo, Baron. NICHOLAS CRABBE OR THE ONE AND THE MANY. New Directions, (1958). 1st US ed. Fine in dj w/small note inked on front flap. *WOOLMER*. $40

Corvo, Frederick Baron. ABERDEEN INTERVAL: SOME LETTERS...TO WILFRID MEYNELL. Edinburgh: Tragara, 1975. 1st ed. Wrappers. From 140, 1 of 120 numbered. Fine. *MUELLER*. $30

Corvo, Frederick Baron. DIFFERENT ASPECTS:...& THE FOREIGN OFFICE. Edinburgh: Tragara, 1976. 1st ed. Wrappers. One of 125 numbered. *MUELLER*. $35

Corvo, Frederick Baron. LETTERS TO HARRY BAINBRIDGE. London: Enitharmon, 1977. 1st ed. From 395, one of 350 numbered. Fine. *MUELLER*. $40

Corvo, Frederick Baron. LETTERS TO HARRY BAINBRIDGE. Mariam Benkovitz, ed. London: Enitharmon Press, 1977. One of 350. Fine in orig glassine dj. *WOOLMER*. $45

Corvo, Frederick Baron. See also Rolfe, Frederick.

Corvo, Frederick Baron. STORIES TOTO TOLD ME. London: Collins, 1969. 1st thus. Dj. Fine. *MUELLER*. $30

Corvo, Frederick Baron. TARCISSUS: THE BOY MARTYR OF ROME. London: Victim Press, 1972. Oversized wrappers over facs of 1st ptg. Fine. *MUELLER*. $20

Corvo, Frederick Baron. THE RUBAIYAT OF UMAR KHAIYAM. London & NY: Bodley Head, 1903. 1st ed. Cl-backed boards. Inked tp, lib and owner's name, front board stained. *MUELLER*. $100

Cory, C.B. HOW TO KNOW THE SHORE BIRDS OF NORTH AMERICA Bound With HOW TO KNOW THE DUCKS, GEESE AND SWANS OF NORTH AMERICA. Boston, 1897. 2 frontispieces. Roan. Worn, chipped edges, ex-lib. *SUTTON*. $95

Cory, C.B. THE BIRDS OF EASTERN NORTH AMERICA KNOWN TO OCCUR EAST OF THE NINETIETH MERIDIAN. Boston, 1900. 2nd ed. Spine ends frayed, pp yellowed; o/w nice ex-lib. *SUTTON*. $45

Cory, C.B. THE BIRDS OF EASTERN NORTH AMERICA. PART I. WATER BIRDS. PART II. LAND BIRDS. 2 vols in 1. Chicago, 1899. Special ed ptd for the Field Columbian Museum. Front hinge starting; some smudging & yellowing of pp; ex-lib. *SUTTON*. $55

Cory, H.T. THE IMPERIAL VALLEY AND THE SALTON SINK. SF: John J. Newbegin, 1915. Fldg maps, gold-stamped cl, lt wear to extrems. *DAWSON'S*. $75

Cossio del Pomar, Felipe. THE ART OF ANCIENT PERU. NY: Wittenborn & Co, (1971). Good in dj. *SILVER*. $75

Cossley-Batt, Jill L. THE LAST OF THE CALIFORNIA RANGERS. NY: Funk & Wagnalls, 1928. Front hinge beginning to separate, o/w VG. *LAURIE*. $75

Cotlow, Lewis. ZANZABUKU. NY: Rinehart & Co, Inc, 1956. 1st ed. Inscribed, signed. Good+ in Good dj. *BACKMAN*. $25

Cottam, Clarence and James B. Trefethen (eds). WHITE-WINGS—THE LIFE HISTORY, STATUS AND MANAGEMENT OF THE WHITE-WINGED DOVE. Princeton: D. Van Nostrand Co, Inc, 1968. 1st ed. VG in VG dj. *BACKMAN*. $35

Cotteral, Bonnie and Donnie Cotteral. TUMBLING, PYRAMID BUILDING AND STUNTS FOR GIRLS AND WOMEN. NY: A.S. Barnes & Co. 1926. (14),144pp. Brn cl. *KARMIOLE*. $30

Cotterell, H.H. NATIONAL TYPES OF OLD PEWTER. Boston, 1925. NF. *POLYANTHOS*. $60

Cotterill, George F. THE CLIMAX OF A WORLD QUEST. Seattle, 1927 (?). 1st ed. Inscribed. Fine. *VARNER*. $35

Cotterill, R.S. THE SOUTHERN INDIANS. The Civilization of the American Indian Series, vol 38. Norman: Univ of OK Press, (1954). 1st ed. VG in dj. *LAURIE*. $50

Cotton, Charles. THE COMPLEAT GAMESTER. Barre: Imprint Society, 1970. Cowhide binding by Robert F. Lewis, spine lettered in gilt. Fine in marbled slipcase. *DRAMATIS PERSONAE*. $75

Cottrell, Leonard. MADAME TUSSAUD. London: Evans, (1951). 1st ed. Fine in VG+ dj (price-clipped). *AARD*. $30

Couderc, Paul. THE EXPANSION OF THE UNIVERSE. London: Faber & Faber, 1952. 1st Eng lang ed. Good in frayed dj. *KNOLLWOOD*. $25

Coues, Elliot (trans, ed). ON THE TRAIL OF A SPANISH PIONEER: THE DIARY AND ITINERARY OF FRANCISCO GARCES (MISSIONARY PRIEST)....1775-1776. 2 vols. NY: Francis Harper, 1900. 1st ed, ltd to 950. VG to Fine set. *BOOK MARKET*. $250

Coues, Elliott (ed and trans). ON THE TRAIL OF A SPANISH PIONEER, THE DIARY AND ITINERARY OF FRANCISCO GARCES. (1775-1776). 2 vols. NY: Francis P. Harper, 1900. xxx, 312; vii, 313-608pp; 3 maps (some folding), photo plts and 5 facsimiles. 1st ed in orig cloth. Ltd ed, #395 of 950. Mostly unopened. From Diocesan Lib of Catholic Bishop of Providence. Moderate cover wear/soil, some of the usual lib markings, o/w VG set. *FIVE QUAIL*. $275

Coues, Elliott. BIRDS OF THE NORTH-WEST, A HAND-BOOK OF AMERICAN ORNITHOLOGY....Boston, 1877. One of 214 of 1874 ed, rebound and reissued, with new title pg. Orig gilt-stamped cl. Soiled; worn at extrems, spine ends frayed; inch split to edge of backstrip; inner hinges cracked, although vol is solid; institutional bkpl, call numbers on spine. Rare. *SUTTON*. $67

Coues, Elliott. BIRDS OF THE NORTH-WEST... Boston: Estes and Lauriat, 1877. 791pp,index. Emb brn cl, sl worn, spine label half gone. Interior VG, no foxing. *SMITHFIELD*. $45

Coues, Elliott. FORTY YEARS A FUR TRADER ON THE UPPER MISSOURI. NY: Francis P. Harper, 1898. 2 vols. One of 950. 18 plts. Cl, unopened, sm nick to spine of one vol. *DAWSON'S*. $250

Coues, Elliott. HISTORY OF THE EXPEDITION UNDER THE COMMAND OF LEWIS AND CLARK. NY: Francis P. Harper, 1893. One of 1000. 4 vols, 2 ports, 2 facs letters, 8 maps (3 fldg, in pocket), and 2 tables. Cl, clean 3" cut bottom of one rear cvr. *DAWSON'S*. $250

Coues, Elliott. KEY TO NORTH AMERICAN BIRDS, CONTAINING A CONCISE ACCOUNT...INCLUSIVE OF GREENLAND AND LOWER CALIFORNIA. Boston, 1887. 3rd ed. Orig cl. Some wear corners, spine ends; sm nick to spine; pp yellowed; institutional bkpl; no. sticker on spine. *SUTTON*. $75

Coues, Elliott. ON THE TRAIL OF A SPANISH PIONEER: THE DIARY...OF FRANCISCO GARCES. NY: Francis P. Harper, 1900. One of 950. 2 vols, 20 plts. Cl, sl wear to one tip, unopened. *DAWSON'S*. $250

Coues, Elliott. THE EXPEDITIONS OF ZEBULON MONTGOMERY PIKE TO HEADWATERS OF THE MISSISSIPPI RIVER...1805-6-7, Minneapolis, MN, (1965). Ltd ed. One of 2000 sets, 3 vols. in 2. VF in Fine dj in box. *MIKESH*. $57.50

Coues, Elliott. THE EXPEDITIONS OF ZEBULON MONTGOMERY PIKE. NY: Francis P. Harper, 1895. One of 1150. 3 vols. Port, facs letter, 7 maps (6 fldg, in pocket). *DAWSON'S*. $250

Coues, Elliott. THE JOURNAL OF JACOB FOWLER....1821-22. NY: Francis P. Harper, 1898. One of 950. xxiv,183pp + 1p ad. Facs letter. Unopened. *DAWSON'S*. $75

Coughlin, Jack. GROTESQUES: ETCHINGS. Baltimore: Aquarius Press, (1970). 1st ed. 1/165 signed. 20 etchings. Fine in orig slipcase. *CAPTAIN'S BOOKSHELF*. $250

Coulson, T. JOSEPH HENRY....Princeton Univ Press, 1950. VG+ in dj. *BOOKCELL*. $28

Coulter, E. Merton. THE CONFEDERATE STATES OF AMERICA 1861-1865. (Baton Rouge): Louisiana State Univ Press, 1950. 1st ed. Bumped o/w Fine in VG+ torn dj. *ARCHER*. $27.50

Coulter, E. Merton. THE CONFEDERATE STATES OF AMERICA. Baton Rouge, 1950. 1st ed. Dj worn and chipped o/w VG+. *PRATT*. $37.50

Coulter, Ellis Merton. THE CIVIL WAR AND READJUSTMENT IN KENTUCKY. Chapel Hill, (1926). 1st ed. Dj chipped o/w VG. *PRATT*. $85

Coulter, Ellis Merton. TRAVELS IN THE CONFEDERATE STATES: A BIBLIOGRAPHY. Norman, 1948. 1st ed. Orig cl, F in dj. *McGOWAN*. $150

Courtenay, Bryce. THE POWER OF ONE. Random House, 1989. Advance reading copy. VF in wraps. Promo letter laid in. *STAHR.* $25

Courtney, W.L. THE SOUL OF A SUFFRAGETTE AND OTHER STORIES. London: Chapman and Hall, 1913. 1st ed. Tear to the cl along rear hinge. Good. *SECOND LIFE.* $65

Courville, Cyril. BIRTH AND BRAIN DAMAGE. Pasadena, 1971. *FYE.* $75

Courville, Cyril. COMMOTIO CEREBRI: CEREBRAL CONCUSSION AND THE POSTCONCUSSION SYNDROME IN THEIR MEDICAL AND LEGAL ASPECTS. LA, 1953. 1st ed. Dj. *FYE.* $100

Courville, Cyril. INTRACRANIAL TUMORS. Providence, 1931. 1st ed. Wrappers. Ink underlining throughout. *FYE.* $50

Cousins, Norman. MODERN MAN IS OBSOLETE. NY: Viking (1945). 1st ed. NF in VG dj. *DORN.* $50

Coutant, C.G. HISTORY OF WYOMING & THE FAR WEST....Argonaut, (1966). Frontis, 26 plts. Fine. Howes C810. *OREGON.* $50

Couteau, Paul. OBSERVING VISUAL DOUBLE STARS. Cambridge, MA: MIT Press, 1981. 1st ed. Trans Alan H. Batten. VG in torn dj. *KNOLLWOOD.* $25

Couts, Cave Johnson. HEPAH, CALIFORNIA! Henry F. Dobyns (ed). Tucson, AZ: Pioneer Hist Soc, 1961. 1st ed, ltd to 650. 8 plts, fldg map. Uncut, unopened. Fine. *OREGON.* $65

Coutts, J. et al. THE COMPLETE BOOK OF GARDENING. London, 1930. Cl. 16 colored plts. *SUTTON.* $50

Covarrubias, Miguel. INDIAN ART OF MEXICO AND CENTRAL AMERICA. NY: Knopf, 1954. 1st ed. Chipped dj. 12 color plts, 64 b/w. *SILVER.* $85

Covarrubias, Miguel. ISLAND OF BALI. NY: Knopf, 1937. 1st ed. Lt wear along edges, dj chipped, lt yellowing along inside front cvrs, o/w VG. *ACADEMIC.* $68

Covarrubias, Miguel. MEXICO SOUTH. NY: Knopf, 1954. 4th prtg. Fldg map, 8 color plts. Pink cl faded, contents VG in chipped dj. *SILVER.* $25

Covarrubias, Miguel. MEXICO SOUTH—THE ISTHMUS OF TEHUANTEPEC. NY: Alfred A. Knopf, 1946. 427pp + linguistic chart + index. 1st ed. Fine in NF dj. *GREAT EPIC.* $95

Covarrubias, Miguel. THE EAGLE, THE JAGUAR, AND THE SERPENT....NY: Alfred A. Knopf, 1954. 1st ed. 12 full-color plts. VG in worn dj. *PARMER.* $100

Covarrubias, Miguel. THE EAGLE, THE JAGUAR, AND THE SERPENT. Knopf, 1954. 1st ed. 12 plts. Fine in VG dj. *OREGON.* $125

Coville, F.V. BOTANY OF THE DEATH VALLEY EXPEDITION. Washington, 1893. 21 tinted lithos, fold out map. Glued into manilla wrappers (orig wrappers missing). Marginal dampstain on frontis. *SUTTON.* $115

Cowan, James. DAYBREAK, A ROMANCE OF AN OLD WORLD. Richmond, 1896, 1st ed. Near VG. *MADLE.* $50

Cowan, James. TRAVEL IN NEW ZEALAND. Melbourne & London: Whitcombe & Tombs Ltd, n.d. (1927). 2 vols. (265): 178pp. Vol I in blue cl stamped in blind, w/dj.; Vol. 2 in brown cl stamped in gilt, somewhat worn, w/no dj. Some foxing. *SCHOYER'S.* $40

Cowan, John F. NEW INVASION OF THE SOUTH, BEING A NARRATIVE OF THE EXPEDITION OF THE SEVENTY FIRST INFANTRY....NY: 1881. 1st ed. 103,24,(3)pp. Orig cl, lightly worn on gold stamped front cover. *GINSBERG.* $150

Cowan, Robert Ernest, Anne Bancroft, and Addie L. Ballou. THE FORGOTTEN CHARACTERS OF OLD SAN FRANCISCO....The Ward Ritchie Press, c. 1964. VG lt worn, soiled dj. *PARMER.* $27.50

Cowan, Robert. RANCHOS OF CALIFORNIA, A LIST OF SPANISH CONCESSIONS 1775-1822 & MEXICAN GRANTS 1822-1846. Historical Society of Southern California, 1977. 1st ed. Signed. Fine. *OREGON.* $27.50

Coward, Noel. PRESENT INDICATIVE. GC: Doubleday, (1937). 1st US ed. One of 301 numbered and signed. Virtually mint unopened in pub's slipcase. *UNGER.* $325

Coward, T.A. THE BIRDS OF THE BRITISH ISLES & THEIR EGGS; ETC. MIGRATION & HABITS. London & NY, (1930); (1929); (1929). 3 vols. 1st, 2nd, & 3rd series. Fine in VG dj. *MIKESH.* $100

Cowell, Roberta. ROBERTA COWELL'S STORY. NY: British Book Centre, (1954). 1st US ed. Fine in Good+ dj. *AARD.* $25

Cowles, Harry. THE ART OF SQUASH RACQUETS. NY, 1935. NF. *POLYANTHOS.* $30

Cowley, Hannah. THE RUNAWAY, A COMEDY. As It Is Acted at The Theatre-Royal in Drury Lane.London: for the Author and sold by Mr. Dodsley, 1776. 1st ed. 8vo; pp viii, 72. Recent marbled boards, printed label. Excellent. *HARTFIELD.* $175

Cowley, Malcolm and Bernand Smith (eds). BOOKS THAT CHANGED OUR MINDS: A SYMPOSIUM. NY: Doubleday, Doran, 1939. 1st ed. Fine in lightly used price-clipped dj. *CAPTAIN'S BOOKSHELF.* $50

Cowley, Malcolm. BLUE JUNIATA: COLLECTED POEMS. NY: Viking, (1968). 1st ed. NF in price-clipped dj. *CHAPEL HILL.* $35

Cowley, Malcolm. EXILES RETURN. A LITERARY ODYSSEY OF THE 1920'S. Cl-backed boards, glassine dj, slipcase. NY: LEC, 1981. 1st of this ed. Ltd to 2000 signed by Cowley & Berenice Abbott (photos). Mint. *JAFFE.* $150

Cowper, Richard. THE WEB OF THE MAGI. London, 1980. 1st ed. Fine in dj. *MADLE.* $40

Cowtan, Charles W. SERVICES OF THE TENTH NEW YORK VOLUNTEERS (NATIONAL ZOUAVES), IN WAR OF THE REBELLION. NY, 1882. 1st ed. Fine. *McGOWAN.* $350

Cowtan, Robert. MEMORIES OF THE BRITISH MUSEUM. London: Richard Bentley and Son, 1872. 1st ed. Orig photo frontis. Cover soil, rear hinge cracked, else VG. *WREDEN.* $45

Cox, Harding and Gerald Lascelles. COURSING AND FALCONRY. Boston: Little, Brown, & Co. and London: Longmans, Green & Co., 1892. 1st Amer ed. VG-NF. *OLD LONDON.* $100

Cox, James M. JOURNEY THROUGH MY YEARS. NY, 1946. 1st ed. Signed. VG. *ARTIS.* $25

Cox, James. HISTORICAL AND BIOGRAPHICAL RECORD OF THE CATTLE INDUSTRY AND THE CATTLEMEN OF TEXAS AND ADJACENT TERRITORY. NY: Antiquarian, 1959. 2 vols. Frontis, 8 plts. 294 & 295-743pp. VF in VF slipcase. *OREGON.* $300

Cox, Rev. John E. FIVE YEARS IN THE UNITED STATES ARMY. Owensville, IL, 1892. 1973 reprint (ed ltd to 500). Fine. *PRATT.* $30

Cox, Samuel S. A BUCKEYE ABROAD; OR WANDERINGS....NY, 1852. Front hinge loose. Presentation inscrip. *O'NEILL.* $55

Cox, Samuel S. DIVERSIONS OF A DIPLOMAT IN TURKEY. NY, 1887. Orig dec cl, soiled. *O'NEILL.* $35

Cox, Samuel S. WHY WE LAUGH. NY, 1876. NF. *POLYANTHOS.* $60

Cox, Samuel S(ullivan). SEARCH FOR WINTER SUNBEAMS...NY: Appleton, 1870. (xiv),442pp. 2 chromolithos (incl frontis). Presentation inscrip dated 1870. *SCHOYER'S.* $60

Cox, Sandford C. RECOLLECTIONS OF THE EARLY SETTLEMENT OF THE WABASH VALLEY. Lafayette, IN: Courier

Steam Book & Job Printing House, 1860. Orig cloth w/cover title "Old Settlers." Lower front corner frayed. Nice. *BOHLING*. $150

Cox, Sidney. ROBERT FROST: ORIGINAL ORDINARY MAN. NY: Henry Holt, (1929). 1st ed. One of 1000 signed. Parchment-backed boards, teg. Fine in chipped, internally mended dj. *CAPTAIN'S BOOKSHELF*. $100

Cox, W.W. HISTORY OF SEWARD COUNTY, NEBRASKA, TOGETHER WITH...REMINISCENCES OF...LANCASTER COUNTY. Lincoln, NE: State Journal, 1888. 1st ed. Sm break in cl bottom of each board, minor spotting, o/w Fine. *OREGON*. $100

Cox, Warren E. LIGHTING AND LAMP DESIGN. NY: Crown. (1952). 1st ed. Dj. *KARMIOLE*. $30

Cox, Warren E. THE BOOK OF POTTERY AND PORCELAIN. NY, (1944). 2 vols. Fine. *POLYANTHOS*. $55

Cox, Warren E. THE BOOK OF POTTERY AND PORCELAIN. NY: Crown Publ, 1970. 2 vols, slipcased. VG. *BACKROOM*. $40

Cox, William D. THE ETCHING HOBBY. NY: William Farquhar Payson, 1932. 3rd ed. Dj. VG. *WEBER*. $75

Cox, William R. LUKE SHORT AND HIS ERA. NY, (1961). 1st ed. 214pp. VG+ in dj. *PRATT*. $20

Cox, William. THE METS WILL WIN THE PENNANT. Putnam, 1964. 1st ed. VG+ in VG+ dj. *PLAPINGER*. $45

Coxe, John Redman. THE PHILADELPHIA MEDICAL DICTIONARY: CONTAINING A CONCISE EXPLANATION OF ALL THE TERMS USED IN MEDICINE, SURGERY, PHARMACY, BOTANY, NATURAL HISTORY, CHEMISTRY, AND MATERIA MEDICA. Phila, 1808. 1st ed. 433pp. Full lea, scattered foxing and staining, binding rubbed. *FYE*. $200

Coxe, John Redman. THE PHILADELPHIA MEDICAL MUSEUM. VOLUME 1. Phila, 1805. 1st ed. Leather, 488pp. *FYE*. $200

Coxere, Edward. ADVENTURES BY SEA OF EDWARD COXERE—A RELATION OF THE SEVERAL...NY/London: Oxford Univ, 1946. 1st Amer ed. Fldg map. VG in dj. *PARMER*. $25

Coy, Owen C. IN THE DIGGINGS IN '49. LA: CA State Hist Assoc, 1948. 1st ed. Plts. Maps. Several pp in biblio and index left blank by printers, apparently a common malady of 1st prtg. Fine in edge chipped, fragile dj. *CONNOLLY & WADE*. $57.50

Coyen, William. ARTHUR BOND. Palaemon, (1979). Wrappers. 1/200 numbered/signed. As New. *DERMONT*. $35

Coyne, John. HOBGOBLIN. Putnam, 1981. 1st ed. Fine in dj. Inscribed. *MADLE*. $40

Coyne, John. THE PIERCING. Putnam, 1979. 1st ed. Fine in dj. Inscribed. *MADLE*. $40

Coyner, David. THE LOST TRAPPERS...ALSO, SOME ACCOUNT OF FUR TRADE....Cincinnati: J.A. James, 1847. 255pp, 7pp ads. Crack in cl at upper front spine edge. VG. Howes C836. *OREGON*. $750

Cozzens, Frederic S. YACHTS AND YACHTING....New and rev ed. NY: Cassell & Co, (1888). Edition De Luxe, One of 250 numbered. 1st ed. Spine ends chipped, still VG. *LEFKOWICZ*. $300

Cozzens, Frederick S. THE SPARROWGRASS PAPERS: OR....Derby & Jackson: NY, 1856. Rare 1st ed, 1st issue. Illus by Darley. 328,(8)pp. Orig emb cl, ornate spine, gilt. VG, tight. *CONNOLLY & WADE*. $85

Cozzens, James Gould. CONFUSION. Boston: B.J. Brimmer Company, 1924. 1st ed. Good. *JUVELIS*. $75

Cozzens, James Gould. GUARD OF HONOR. NY: Harcourt, Brace, (1950). 1st ed. Fine in lightly rubbed dj. Cloth. *JAFFE*. $65

Cozzens, James Gould. GUARD OF HONOR. NY: Harcourt, Brace, (1948). 1st ed. Fine in dj (internally strengthened), o/w NF. *LOPEZ*. $45

Cozzens, Samuel W. THE MARVELLOUS COUNTRY; OR, THREE YEARS IN ARIZONA AND NEW MEXICO. London: Sampson, Low, Marston, Searle & Rivington, 1890. Reprint of Howes C838. *HUDSON*. $85

Cozzens, Samuel W. THE MARVELLOUS COUNTRY; OR, THREE YEARS IN ARIZONA AND NEW MEXICO, THE APACHE'S HOME. Boston: James M. Piper and Company, 1875. Maps. Grn pict cl, top of spine torn. Howes C838. *HUDSON*. $175

Crabb, Richard. EMPIRE ON THE PLATTE. Cleveland, 1967. 1st ed. Fine in price clipped dj. *BAADE*. $47.50

Crabbe, George II. THE LIFE OF GEORGE CRABBE. Intro by E. Blunden. London: Cresset Press, 1947. 1st ed thus. Fine in NF dj. *ARCHER*. $12.50

Crabbe, Rev. George. THE WORKS. In Five Volumes. London: John Murray, 1823. Tall 8vos. Full tan polished calf, gilt panels, gauffred edges, spines heavily gilt in compartments, double lea labels, marbled edges and eps. Handsome library set. *HARTFIELD*. $450

Crabtre, A.D. THE FUNNY SIDE OF PHYSIC; OR, THE MYSTERIES OF MEDICINE, PRESENTING THE HUMOROUS AND SERIOUS SIDES OF MEDICAL PRACTICE. Hartford, 1880. 1st ed. *FYE*. $225

Crackanthorpe, Hubert. WRECKAGE. SEVEN STUDIES. London, 1893. 1st ed, 1st bk. Uncut. Spine sunned, extremities little rubbed, spine sl cocked. Dec. covers. NF. Scarce. *POLYANTHOS*. $85

Craddock, Charles Egbert (pseud of Mary N. Murfree). IN THE CLOUDS. Boston & NY: Houghton, Mifflin, 1887. 1st ed, 1st prtg. 452pp, 12pp ads. Orig br cl. Owner name, address, else VG. *CHAPEL HILL*. $35

Craddock, Charles Egbert (pseud of Mary N. Murfree). IN THE TENNESSEE MOUNTAINS. Houghton Mifflin & Co. 1886. 12th ed. Minor shelfwear, else VG-NF. *OLD LONDON*. $15

Craddock, Charles Egbert (pseud of Mary N. Murfree). IN THE "STRANGER PEOPLE'S" COUNTRY. NY: Harper & Bros., 1891. 1st ed, 1st ptg. Orange dec cl. Fine. *CHAPEL HILL*. $45

Craddock, Charles Egbert (pseud of Mary N. Murfree). IN THE TENNESSEE MOUNTAINS. Boston, 1884. 1st ed, 1st bk. Rear fep little rubbed, lower rear cover little edge rubbed. Fine. Scarce. *POLYANTHOS*. $60

Craddock, Charles Egbert (pseud of Mary N. Murfree). THE PHANTOMS OF THE FOOT-BRIDGE AND OTHER STORIES. NY: Harper & Bros, 1895. 1st ed. 353pp, (4)pp ads. Orig grn cl. Owner sig, top edge trifle soiled, else Fine in bright, VG ptd dj (chipped head of spine; tape repair on verso). An unrecorded variant binding, w/pine cones on spine stamped in blue. BAL 14809 calls for black or blindstamped pine cones. *CHAPEL HILL*. $350

Craddock, Charles Egbert (pseud of Mary N. Murfree). THE PROPHET OF THE GREAT SMOKY MOUNTAINS. Boston & NY: Houghton, Mifflin, 1885. 1st ed. 308pp, 12pp ads. Orig cl. VG. *CHAPEL HILL*. $40

Craddock, Charles Egbert (pseud of Mary N. Murfree). THE WINDFALL. NY: Duffield & Co, 1907. 1st ed. Orig dec dark blue cl. Inscription; eps sl foxed; couple of leaves carelessly opened; white lettering flaked on spine. Nice, VG. *CHAPEL HILL*. $35

Craddock, Charles Egbert (pseud of Mary N. Murfree). THE STORY OF DUCIEHURST. NY: Macmillan, 1914. 1st ed. Binding A. Orig dec blue cl. Fine. *CHAPEL HILL*. $50

Craddock, Charles Egbert (pseud of Mary N. Murfree). THE STORY OF KEEDON BLUFFS. Boston & NY: Houghton Mifflin, 1888. 1st ed, 1st prtg. One of 3,060. 257pp, 14pp ads. Orig grn cl. Bright, NF. *CHAPEL HILL*. $40

Craddock, Charles Egbert (pseud of Mary N. Murfree). THE CHAMPION. Boston & NY: Houghton, Mifflin, 1902. 1st ed. Light offsetting to eps, else NF in exceptionally bright pict dj w/2" x 1/2" piece lacking from top edge (affecting title on spine), 3" split along hinge of rear panel, and minor edgewear. Rare in dj. BAL 14815. *CHAPEL HILL.* $250

Crahs, Wilbur. INTOXICANTS & OPIUM IN ALL LANDS AND TIMES. Washington, 1900. 6th ed. Wrappers. *FYE.* $50

Craig, Alisa. MURDER GOES MUMMING. GC: Doubleday Crime Club, 1981. 1st ed. VF in dj. *MORDIDA.* $30

Craig, Alisa. THE GRUB-AND STAKERS QUILT A BEE. GC, Doubleday Crime Club, 1985. 1st ed. VF in dj. *MORDIDA.* $25

Craig, Colin. A SUITOR FROM THE STARS. Baltimore: Thomas & Evans, 1928. 1st ed. Fine, minor edgewear to dj. Scarce. *ELSE FINE.* $95

Craig, E. Gordon. SCENE. London: (H. Milford), 1923. 1st trade ed, pub simultaneously w/ltd ed bound differently. Pub's blue-gray boards w/black lettering on cvr, spine. Head, foot of spine bit rubbed; spine, edges of boards sl sunned. 19 full-pg plts. *BOOK BLOCK.* $95

Craig, Edward Gordon. BOOKS AND THEATRES. London: J.M. Dent & Sons. 1925. 1st ed. 164pp. 32 plts. Spine, extrems sl discolored. *KARMIOLE.* $40

Craig, Edward Gordon. ELLEN TERRY AND HER SECRET SELF. London: Sampson Low, Marston & Co., Ltd. N.d. (circa 1931). 1st ed. Pamphlet in pocket inside rear cvr, "Annex: A Plea for G.B.S." Yellow cl, gilt; sl soiled. Dj chipped. *KARMIOLE.* $60

Craig, Edward Gordon. INDEX TO THE STORY OF MY DAYS. 1st ed. Fine in dj, chipped. *POLYANTHOS.* $30

Craig, Edward Gordon. ON THE ART OF THE THEATRE. London, 1911. 1st ed. 16 illus. Uncut. Some scattered light foxing, extremities little rubbed, covers little soiled. VG. *POLYANTHOS.* $45

Craig, Edward Gordon. PARIS DIARY 1932-1933. Colin Franklin (ed). North Hills, PA.: Bird & Bull Press, 1982. 1st ed. Ltd to 350. 1/4 morocco & boards. Mint in acetate dj. *JAFFE.* $200

Craig, Gerald (ed). EARLY TRAVELLERS IN THE CANADAS...1791-1867. Toronto, 1955. 1st ed. VF in dj. *ARTIS.* $25

Craig, Reginald S. THE FIGHTING PARSON: BIOGRAPHY OF COL. JOHN M. CHIVINGTON. LA, 1959. 1st ed. Fine in dj. *BAADE.* $47.50

Craighead, F.C. INSECT ENEMIES OF EASTERN FORESTS. Washington, 1950. Bkplt, light wear. *SUTTON.* $45

Craighead, Frank C, Jr. TRACK OF THE GRIZZLY. SF: Sierra Club, 1979. 1st ed. Signed by John Craighead. Fine in Good dj. *BACKMAN.* $25

Craik, D.M. THE LITTLE LAME PRINCE AND HIS TRAVELING CLOAK. Crowell, (1893). 197 dec pp. Frontis. Some wear to board, spine dec. VG+. *BEBBAH.* $30

Craik, D.M. THE LITTLE LAME PRINCE AND HIS TRAVELING CLOAK. McLoughlin, (n.d.). Frontis. Edgewear, few faint spots to dec cvr. VG. *BEBBAH.* $25

Crais, Robert. STALKING THE ANGEL. NY: Bantam, 1989. 1st ed. Signed. VF in dj. *SILVER DOOR.* $35

Crais, Robert. STALKING THE ANGEL. NY: Bantam Books, 1989. 1st ed. VF in dj. *MORDIDA.* $30

Crais, Robert. THE MONKEY'S RAINCOAT. (London): Piatkus, (1987). 1st UK ed. & 1st hardcover of 1st book. New in dj. *BERNARD.* $60

Crais, Robert. THE MONKEY'S RAINCOAT. London: Piatkus, (1989). 1st English ed. Signed. Fine in Fine dj. *UNGER.* $50

Crais, Robert. THE MONKEY'S RAINCOAT. London: Piatkus, 1989. 1st hardcover ed. VF in dj. *MORDIDA.* $45

Crais, Robert. THE MONKEY'S RAINCOAT. NY: Bantam Books, 1987. 1st ed. Pb orig. Reading crease on spine o/w VG in wrappers. *MORDIDA.* $25

Cram, Thomas J. TOPOGRAPHICAL MEMOIR OF THE DEPARTMENT OF THE PACIFIC...RELATIVE TO THE TERRITORIES OF OREGON AND WASHINGTON....Washington, HD114, 1859. 1st ed. 126pp. New cl w/leather label. Howes C853. *GINSBERG.* $150

Cramer, John H. LINCOLN UNDER ENEMY FIRE. Baton Rouge, (1948). 1st ed. Dj chipping o/w VG+. *PRATT.* $25

Cramer, Maurice. PHOENIX IN EAST HADLEY. Houghton, 1941. 1st ed. VG in frayed dj. *MADLE.* $30

Cramp, Arthur. NOSTRUMS AND QUACKERY: ARTICLES ON THE NOSTRUM EVIL, QUACKERY AND ALLIED MATTERS AFFECTING THE PUBLIC HEALTH; REPRINTED, WITH OR WITHOUT MODIFICATIONS, FROM THE JOURNAL OF THE AMERICAN MEDICAL ASSOCIATION. VOLUME 2. Chicago, 1921. 1st ed. *FYE.* $75

Cramp, Leonard G. SPACE, GRAVITY AND THE FLYING SAUCER. NY: British Bk Centre. (1955). 1st ed. Yellow cl. Dj. *KARMIOLE.* $30

Crandall, L.S. THE MANAGEMENT OF WILD MAMMALS IN CAPTIVITY. Chicago, 1964. 1st ptg. Cloth, chipped dj. Signed, inscribed. *SUTTON.* $65

Crane, Charles E. WINTER IN VERMONT. NY: Knopf, 1941. 1st ed. Fine in VG to Fine dj. *BOOK MARKET.* $30

Crane, Frances. MURDER IN BLUE STREET. NY: Random House, (1951) 1st ed. Fine, VG price clipped dj. *SECOND LIFE.* $35

Crane, Frances. THE ULTRAVIOLET WIDOW. NY: Random House, 1956. 1st ed. Fine in price-clipped dj. *ELSE FINE.* $35

Crane, Hart. THE COLLECTED POEMS. Waldo Frank (ed). London: Boriswood, (1938). 1st Eng ed, differing from Amer ed. Cl, dj. VF. *JAFFE.* $450

Crane, Hart. THE LETTERS OF HART CRANE 1916-1932. Ed Brom Weber. NY: Hermitage, (1952). 1st ed. Bkpl. NF in sl worn dj. *CAPTAIN'S BOOKSHELF.* $25

Crane, Hart. VOYAGES: SIX POEMS. Leonard Baskin (illus). NY: Museum of Modern Art, 1957. 1st ed. #487 of 975 signed by Baskin. Illus (some fldg). Orig plain blue wraps, paper label. Fine in pub's protective folder (few splits along folds). *CHAPEL HILL.* $300

Crane, J. FIDDLER CRABS OF THE WORLD (OCYPODIDAE: GENUS UCA). Princeton, 1975. 50 plts. Dj. *SUTTON.* $95

Crane, Newton. BASEBALL. Geo. Bell & Sons, 1891. Good+ without dj. *PLAPINGER.* $850

Crane, Robert. HERO'S WALK. Ballantine, 1954. 1st ed. Fine in dj. *MADLE.* $27

Crane, Stephen and Robert Barr. THE O'RUDDY. NY: Stokes, (1903). 1st ed. NF in pict cl. *CAPTAIN'S BOOKSHELF.* $90

Crane, Stephen. GEORGE'S MOTHER. NY & London: Edward Arnold, 1896. 1st ed. 12mo, 177pp, (8)pp ads. Orig tan cl. Round inkstamp erased from fep and half-title, small bkseller's label, still nice, VG. *CHAPEL HILL.* $125

Crane, Stephen. THE OPEN BOAT. NY: Doubleday & McClure, 1898. 12mo, 336pp. Orig grn cl, pict stamped in silver and black. Small bkplate, else Excellent. 1st ed. One of approximately 1500 . BAL 4079. *CHAPEL HILL.* $350

Crane, Stephen. THE RED BADGE OF COURAGE: AN EPISODE OF THE AMERICAN CIVIL WAR. NY: Appleton and Company, 1895. 1st ed, 1st state. (4) 233 (1) pp + (4) pp of ads, title page in red and black. Pale yellow buckram over boards, dec front cvr and spine in red, black and gold, tan eps, top edge stained yellow, in leatherbound box. Lid to box has been repaired. Small chunk missing from edge of page 233, o/w NF. *BOOKMINE*. $2000

Crane, Stephen. THE WORK OF STEPHEN CRANE. Wilson Follett (ed). 12 vols. Cl, glassine djs, slipcases. NY: Random House, (1925-1926). 1st ed. Ltd to 750 sets. Fine in lightly worn slipcases. *JAFFE*. $475

Crane, W.J.E. BOOKBINDING FOR AMATEURS...Illus with 156 Engravings. London: L. Upcott Gill, n.d. (circa 1895), 8vo., stamped cloth binding decorated in gilt and black. viii,184,14pp. Reprt of 1885 ed. *OAK KNOLL*. $75

Crankshaw, Edward. GESTAPO: INSTRUMENT OF TYRANNY. London: Putnam, 1956. 1st ed. 275pp. NF in NF dj. *AKA*. $27

Craster, Sir Edmund. HISTORY OF THE BODLEIAN LIBRARY 1845-1945. Oxford: Clarendon Press, 1952. 1st ed. Navy blue cloth. Fine. *WEBER*. $200

Cravath, Prosper, et al. EARLY ANNALS OF WHITEWATER, 1837-1867...Whitewater, WI, 1906. 1st ed. 22 ports. Orig cl, sm paper label on lower spine, bkpl removed. *GINSBERG*. $75

Craven, Thomas. TREASURY OF AMERICAN PRINTS, A SELECTION OF ONE HUNDRED ETCHINGS AND LITHOGRAPHS BY THE FOREMOST LIVING AMERICAN ARTISTS. NY: Simon and Schuster, (1939). Spiral bound paper over boards, slipcase. Not paginated. *OAK KNOLL*. $95

Craven, W. and J. Cate (eds). THE ARMY AIR FORCES IN WORLD WAR II. Vol. VII: Service Around the World. Chicago: Univ of Chicago Press, 1958. 1st ed. NF. *ARCHER*. $40

Cravens, Gwyneth. HEART'S DESIRE. Knopf, 1986. Uncorrected proof. NF in wraps. Light rubbing on fore edge. *STAHR*. $25

Cravens, Gwyneth. LOVE AND WORK. Knopf, 1982. 1st ed. VF in dj. *STAHR*. $25

Cravens, Gwyneth. SPEED OF LIGHT. NY: Simon & Schuster, (1979). 1st ed. Fine in NF dj. *LOPEZ*. $40

Crawford, F. A LADY OF ROME. MacMillan, 1906. 1st ed. VG. *MADLE*. $25

Crawford, F. Marion. CONSTANTINOPLE. NY: Charles Scribner's Sons. 1895. 1st ed. 80pp. Frontis. Dec beige cl stamped in 3 colors; edges sl darkened. Note laid in w/signed presentation inscrip. *KARMIOLE*. $50

Crawford, F. Marion. KHALED, A TALE OF ARABIA. London, 1891. 1st VG. *MADLE*. $40

Crawford, F. Marion. MAN OVERBOARD! NY, 1903. 1st ed. Extremities minimally rubbed. Fine. *POLYANTHOS*. $50

Crawford, F. Marion. THE RULERS OF THE SOUTH: SICILY, CALABRIA, MALTA. London & NY, 1900. VG. *NUTMEG*. $25

Crawford, F. THE WITCH OF PRAGUE. MacMillan, 1891. 1st US ed. NF. *MADLE*. $50

Crawford, F. WANDERING GHOSTS. MacMillan, 1911. 1st ed. VG. *MADLE*. $45

Crawford, J.R. WITCHCRAFT AND SORCERY IN RHODESIA. London: OUP, 1967. 1st ed. NF in VG dj. *ACADEMIC*. $25

Crawford, Lewis F. (ed). REKINDLING OF CAMP FIRES. Bismarck, ND: Capital Book Co, (1926). 1st trade ed. Map, 10 plts. Old, minor watermarks. *SCHOYER'S*. $50

Crawford, Lewis F. REKINDLING CAMP FIRES. Bismarck, ND, (1926). 1st ed. Ex-lib. Shelfwear. 2pp badly opened, o/w VG. *DIAMOND*. $45

Crawford, Lewis. BADLANDS AND BRONCHO TRAILS. Bismark, ND: Capital Book, (1922). 1st ed. 6 plts. Inscription on recto of frontis, o/w Fine. *OREGON*. $75

Crawford, Lewis. THE MEDORA-DEADWOOD STAGE LINE. Bismark, ND, Capital Book, 1925. 4 plts. Wraps. 1st ed. VG. *OREGON*. $45

Crawford, Mary. ROMANCE OF OLD NEW ENGLAND ROOFTREES. Boston: Page, 1903. Light wear, contents VG. *AMERICAN BOTANIST*. $28

Crawford, Medorem. JOURNAL OF MEDOREM CRAWFORD...Eugene: Star Job Office, 1897. Fine. Howes C874. *OREGON*. $65

Crawley, Ernest. THE MYSTIC ROSE. A STUDY OF PRIMITIVE MARRIAGE....Theodore Besterman (rev, enl by). NY: Boni & Liveright, 1927. 2 vols. VG. *OREGON*. $60

Crawshay-Williams, Elliot. MAN WHO MET HIMSELF. London, 1947. 1st ed. VG in chipped dj. *MADLE*. $15

Creasey, John. ALIAS BLUE MASK. Phila: Lippincott, 1939. 1st ed. VF, minor edgewear to dj. *ELSE FINE*. $60

Creasey, John. THE FOOTHILLS OF FEAR. London: Hodder & Stoughton, 1961. 1st ed. 190pp. VG+ in VG+ dj with edgewear, light rear panel soil. *BEBBAH*. $20

Creed, Perry (ed). THE BOSTON SOCIETY OF NATURAL HISTORY 1830-1930. Boston: The Society, 1930. 1st ed. Teg, 117pp, green cloth & brown paper over boards, sunned. VG. *ARCHER*. $25

Creed, R.S. et al. REFLEX ACTIVITY OF THE SPINAL CORD. Oxford, 1938. 1st ed., 2nd prtg. *FYE*. $100

Creeley, Robert. 1.2.3.4.5.6.7.8.9.0. Drawings Arthur Okamura. Berkeley: Shambala & SF: Mudra, 1971. 1st ed. 1/200 signed by Creeley and Okamura. Fine in ptd yellow acetate dj (offset onto first few preliminary leaves). *CAPTAIN'S BOOKSHELF*. $100

Creeley, Robert. A FORM OF WOMEN. (Highlands): Jargon, (1959). 1st ed. NF in pict wraps. Pub as Jargon 33. *CAPTAIN'S BOOKSHELF*. $75

Creeley, Robert. A QUICK GRAPH: COLLECTED NOTES & ESSAYS. Donald Allen (ed). SF: Four Seasons Foundation, 1970. 1st ed. Issued as Writing 22. Fine in dj. *CAPTAIN'S BOOKSHELF*. $50

Creeley, Robert. AWAY. Illus Bobbie Creeley. Santa Barbara: The Black Sparrow Press, 1976. 1st ed. 1/50 in boards and w/orig color print by the artist. Signed by both Creeleys. Fine. *CAPTAIN'S BOOKSHELF*. $75

Creeley, Robert. AWAY. Santa Barbara: Black Sparrow (1976). 1st ed. One of 200 numbered, signed. Fine in acetate. *DORN*. $45

Creeley, Robert. DIVISIONS & OTHER EARLY POEMS. (Madison): Perishable Press, 1968. 1st ed. 1/110 numbered ptd on Shadwell and sewn into brn Fabriano cover. Fine. *CAPTAIN'S BOOKSHELF*. $250

Creeley, Robert. DIVISIONS & OTHER EARLY POEMS. Mt. Horeb, Wisconsin: Perishable Press, 1968. 1st ed. Ltd to 110 ptd. Ptd wraps. VF. *JAFFE*. $275

Creeley, Robert. FOR MY MOTHER: GENEVIEVE JULES CREELEY 8 APRIL 1887 7 OCTOBER 1972. Northamptonshire: The Sceptre Press, (1973). 1st ed. 1/150. Fine in wrappers. *CAPTAIN'S BOOKSHELF*. $45

Creeley, Robert. FOUR POEMS FROM A FORM OF WOMEN. Ptd blue wrappers. NY: Eighth Street Bookshop, 1959. 1st ed, privately ptd. Fine in 1/4 morocco fldg box. *JAFFE*. $150

Creeley, Robert. HELLO: POEMS. (Christchurch, New Zealand): Hawk Press, 1976. 1st ed. 1/50 numbered, signed. Fine in wrappers. *CAPTAIN'S BOOKSHELF*. $50

Creeley, Robert. IN LONDON. Bolinas: Angel Hair Books, 1970. 1st ed. 1/200 ptd by Grabhorn-Hoyem. Fine in wrappers w/paper label. *CAPTAIN'S BOOKSHELF*. $75

Creeley, Robert. INSIDE OUT. (LA): Black Sparrow Press, 1973. 1st ed. Fine in wrappers. Pub as Sparrow 14. *CAPTAIN'S BOOKSHELF*. $15

Creeley, Robert. LE FOU. Columbus: Golden Goose Press, 1952. 1st ed, 1st bk. Some soiling to edges, else Fine in wrappers and most of the rare orig cellophane dj. Signed. *CAPTAIN'S BOOKSHELF.* $500

Creeley, Robert. LE FOU. POEMS. Columbus: Golden Goose Press, 1952. 1st ed, 1st bk. Stapled dec wrappers. Fine. *DERMONT.* $400

Creeley, Robert. LISTEN. Monoprints by Bobbie Creeley. LA: Black Sparrow Press, 1972. 1st ed. 1/150 specially-bound, signed by both Creeleys. Fine in acetate dj w/orig monoprint tipped in as frontis. *CAPTAIN'S BOOKSHELF.* $75

Creeley, Robert. MARY'S FANCY. (NY: Bouwerie Editions, 1970). 1st ed. 1/100 (total ed 402) signed. Illus w/photo by William Katz. Fine in ptd wrappers, ptd brn paper outer wrapping. *CAPTAIN'S BOOK-SHELF.* $75

Creeley, Robert. PIECES. Collages by Bobbie Creeley. LA: Black Sparrow Press, 1968. 1st ed. 1/150 specially bound, signed by both Creeleys. Fine. *CAPTAIN'S BOOKSHELF.* $75

Creeley, Robert. POEMS 1950-1965. London: Calder & Boyars, (1966). 1st ed. Fine in dj. *CAPTAIN'S BOOKSHELF.* $50

Creeley, Robert. QUICK GRAPH: COLLECTED NOTES AND ESSAYS. SF: Four Seasons Foundation, 1970. 1st ed. Fine in wrappers. Published as Writing 22. *CAPTAIN'S BOOKSHELF.* $15

Creeley, Robert. THE CHARM: EARLY AND UNCOLLECTED POEMS. (Mt. Horeb): Perishable Press, 1967. 1st ed. 1/250 signed. Fine in 1/4 leather and cl. *CAPTAIN'S BOOKSHELF.* $150

Creeley, Robert. THE CHARM: EARLY AND UNCOLLECTED POEMS. (Mt. Horeb, Wisconsin): Perishable Press, 1967. 1st ed. One of 250 signed. 1/4 leather, cl. VF. *JAFFE.* $250

Creeley, Robert. THE FINGER. Collages by Bobbie Creeley. LA: Black Sparrow Press, 1968. 1st ed. 1/250 signed. Fine in wrappers. *CAPTAIN'S BOOKSHELF.* $50

Creeley, Robert. THE GOLD DIGGERS. (Palma de Mallorca): The Divers Press, 1954. 1st ed. Fine in very sl soiled wrappers. *CAPTAIN'S BOOKSHELF.* $150

Creeley, Robert. THE ISLAND. NY: Scribners, (1963). 1st ed., 2nd issue. Fine in dj w/some discoloration. *CAPTAIN'S BOOKSHELF.* $30

Creeley, Robert. THE KIND OF ACT. (Palma de Mallorca): The Divers Press, 1953. 1st ed, scarce 2nd bk. Poet Ronald Johnson's sig on ffep. Wrappers sl foxed, else Fine. Signed. *CAPTAIN'S BOOKSHELF.* $750

Creeley, Robert. THE WHIP. (Worcester): Migrant Books, 1957. 1st ed. Ptd at the Divers Press. Fine in wrappers. *CAPTAIN'S BOOKSHELF.* $75

Creeley, Robert. THIRTY THINGS. LA: Black Sparrow, 1974. 1/250 signed. Fine in cl-backed boards, paper label and acetate dj. *CAPTAIN'S BOOKSHELF.* $50

Creighton, Wilbur Foster. THE LIFE OF MAJOR WILBUR FISK FOSTER A CIVIL ENGINEER, CONFEDERATE SOLDIER, BUILDER, CHURCHMAN AND FREE MASON WITH PERSONAL RECOLLECTIONS. N.p., n.d. 1st ed. NF. Scarce. *McGOWAN.* $75

Cremer, W.H. (ed). THE MAGICIAN'S OWN BOOK. Edinburgh: John Grant, n.d. (1871). Orig pict cloth, spine lettered in gilt, rubbed, joints rubbed, edges foxed as usual. VG. *DRAMATIS PERSONAE.* $40

Cremony, John C. LIFE AMONG THE APACHES. NY: Time-Life, 1981. Marbled eps. Aeg. Ribbon marker. Emb lea, gilt. Fine. *CONNOLLY & WADE.* $25

Cressy-Marcks, Violet. JOURNEY INTO CHINA. NY: Dutton, 1942. Grn cl, a little faded, scuffed at head and foot of spine. *SCHOYER'S.* $35

Creston, Lan. LIEUTENANT LSD. (Richmond/Berkeley): (Creston/The Book People), (1971). Softcover orig. VG. *LOPEZ.* $125

Crews, Harry. 2 BY CREWS. Northridge: Lord John Press, 1984. One of 200 numbered, signed. Fine. *CAPTAIN'S BOOKSHELF.* $150

Crews, Harry. A CHILDHOOD: THE BIOGRAPHY OF A PLACE. NY: Harper & Row (1978). 1st ed. Fine in VG dj (sm tear). *DORN.* $80

Crews, Harry. A CHILDHOOD: THE BIOGRAPHY OF A PLACE. NY: Harper & Row, (1978). Uncorrected proof. Fine in wrappers. *CAPTAIN'S BOOKSHELF.* $125

Crews, Harry. A FEAST OF SNAKES. NY: Atheneum, 1976. Uncorrected proof. Fine in wrappers. *CAPTAIN'S BOOKSHELF.* $250

Crews, Harry. ALL WE NEED OF HELL. NY: Harper & Row (1987). 1st ed. Signed. Fine in dj. *DORN.* $60

Crews, Harry. BODY. NY: Poseidon, (1990). 1st ed. Fine in dj. Inscribed. *CAPTAIN'S BOOKSHELF.* $40

Crews, Harry. CAR. London: Secker & Warburg, (1973). 1st UK ed. Fine in dj. *CAPTAIN'S BOOKSHELF.* $100

Crews, Harry. CAR. NY: Morrow, 1972. 1st ed. Fine in wrinkled dj. Signed. *CAPTAIN'S BOOKSHELF.* $300

Crews, Harry. CAR. NY: Morrow, 1972. 1st ed. Fine, minor wear to jacket spine ends. *ELSE FINE.* $85

Crews, Harry. CAR. NY: Wm. Morrow & Co., 1972. 1st ed of 5,005. Fine in price clipped dj. *BERNARD.* $175

Crews, Harry. FLORIDA FRENZY. Gainesville: Univ of FL Press (1982). 1st ed. Lt stain on fore-edge of front panel, else Fine in pict wraps. Signed. *CAPTAIN'S BOOKSHELF.* $35

Crews, Harry. FLORIDA FRENZY. Gainesville: Univ Presses of FL, (1982). Rev copy with slip laid in. In very lightly used pict wrappers. *ROBBINS.* $50

Crews, Harry. KARATE IS A THING OF THE SPIRIT. NY: Morrow, 1971. 1st ed. Fine, one very minor wrinkle to dj laminate. Uncommon, first ptg was fewer than 6,000. *ELSE FINE.* $110

Crews, Harry. KARATE IS A THING OF THE SPIRIT. NY: William Morrow, 1971. 1st ed. Traces of tape residue on front and rear eps, else NF in Fine dj. Inscribed. *CAPTAIN'S BOOKSHELF.* $250

Crews, Harry. NAKED IN GARDEN HILLS. Morrow, 1969. 1st ed. About Fine. Dj shows yellowing to the edges of the white dj. Book has red star on ffep. First issue dj, with reviews of THE GOSPEL SINGER on rear panel. *STAHR.* $200

Crews, Harry. NAKED IN GARDEN HILLS. NY: Morrow (1969). Signed. 1st state in 1st state dj. Corner fep cut away else sl used VG in VG dj, sm closed tear back gutter. *DORN.* $195

Crews, Harry. NAKED IN GARDEN HILLS. NY: Morrow, 1969. 1st ed, 2nd issue w/the 2 strange dots at the bottom of the copyright pg, but in sl used, 1st issue dj w/o reviews for this bk on rear panel. *CAPTAIN'S BOOKSHELF.* $125

Crews, Harry. NAKED IN GARDEN HILLS. NY: Morrow, 1969. 2nd ed. 5,500 copies, 2nd book. Signed. Bottom edge a bit shelf-worn o/w VG+ in lightly soiled dj. *BERNARD.* $125

Crews, Harry. SCAR LOVER. NY: Poseidon (1992). 1st ed. Signed. Fine in dj. *DORN.* $45

Crews, Harry. SCAR LOVER. NY: Poseidon, (1992). 1st ed. Rev copy. Fine in dj. *CAPTAIN'S BOOKSHELF.* $25

Crews, Harry. THE GOSPEL SINGER. NY: Morrow, 1958. 1st ed, 1st bk. Endsheets sl discolored, else Fine in dj. Review copy, slip laid in. Signed. *CAPTAIN'S BOOKSHELF.* $800

Crews, Harry. THE GOSPEL SINGER. NY: Morrow, 1968. 1st ed, 1st bk. Orig grn cl. Eps discolored as is common, probably from acid content of binder's glue, front cover sl affected o/w About Fine in bright dj. *CHAPEL HILL.* $500

Crews, Harry. THE GYPSY'S CURSE. NY: Knopf, 1974. 1st ed. Orig yellow cl. Virtually As New in dj. *CHAPEL HILL.* $75

Crews, Harry. THE KNOCKOUT ARTIST. 1st trade ed. Signed. Fine in dj. *DORN.* $60

Crews, Harry. THE KNOCKOUT ARTIST. Harper & Row, (1988). 1st ed. Fine in Fine dj. *BEBBAH.* $30

Crews, Harry. THE KNOCKOUT ARTIST. NY: Harper & Row (1988). Uncorrected proof. Signed. Fine in wraps. *DORN.* $125

Crews, Harry. THIS THING DON'T LEAD TO HEAVEN. NY: Wm. Morrow & Co., 1970. 1st ed. 7,500 copies. Fine in VG+ dj which has a 3/4" internally mended tear at top edge of rear panel & at top right corner fold of front panel. *BERNARD.* $150

Crews, Harry. THIS THING DON'T LEAD TO HEAVEN. NY: Morrow, 1970. 1st ed. Just About Fine in like dj (2 internally-mended tears on front panel). *CAPTAIN'S BOOKSHELF.* $125

Crichton, Kyle S. LAW AND ORDER LTD. Santa Fe, 1928. 1st ed. Fine in Fine dj. *VARNER.* $65

Crichton, Kyle S. LAW AND ORDER, LTD....Santa Fe: New Mexican Pub Corp, 1928. 1st ed. Ports. Orig cl. VG. *OUTPOST.* $50

Crichton, Michael. JASPER JOHNS. NY: Harry N. Abrams, Inc. in association with the Whitney Museum of American Art, (1977). Pict white wraps, spine sl darkened. Fine. *BLUE MOUNTAIN.* $75

Crichton, Michael. JURASSIC PARK. Knopf, 1990. Advance reading copy. Fine in dec. wraps. *STAHR.* $15

Crichton, Michael. RISING SUN. Knopf, 1992. Advance reading copy. Fine in dec. wraps. *STAHR.* $25

Crichton, Michael. TRAVELS. Franklin Center: Franklin Lib, 1988. Leatherbound ltd ed, true 1st. Signed. Fine. *LOPEZ.* $45

Crickett, W.S. ABBOTSFORD. A&C Black, 1912. 1st ed (this series). Good, lacking dj. *OLD LONDON.* $15

Crider, Bill. DYING VOICES. NY: St. Martin's, 1989. 1st ed. Review copy, signed. Pub's slip laid in. VF in dj. *SILVER DOOR.* $35

Crile, George Washington. AN AUTOBIOGRAPHY. Grace Crile (ed). Phila: J.B. Lippincott, 1947. 1st ed. NF in Good+ dj. *SMITHFIELD.* $30

Crile, George. ANEMIA AND RESUSCITATION: AN EXPERIMENTAL AND CLINICAL RESEARCH. NY, 1914. 1st ed. Recent 1/4 leather, 305pp. Scarce. *FYE.* $200

Crile, George. ANOCI-ASSOCIATION. Phila, 1914. 1st ed, 1st prtg. Scattered pencil notations. *FYE.* $100

Crile, George. DISEASES PECULIAR TO CIVILIZED MAN, CLINICAL MANAGEMENT AND SURGICAL TREATMENT. NY, 1934. 1st ed. *FYE.* $50

Crile, George. GEORGE CRILE. AN AUTOBIOGRAPHY. Grace Crile (ed). 2 vols. Phila: Lippincott, 1947. 1st ed. Inscription. News clippings laid in. VF in Good dj, worn slipcase. *CONNOLLY & WADE.* $45

Crile, George. HEMORRHAGE AND TRANSFUSION: AN EXPERIMENTAL AND CLINICAL RESEARCH. NY, 1909. 1st ed. In leather, 560pp. VF. *FYE.* $300

Cripps, Harrison. THE PASSAGE OF AIR AND FECES FROM THE URETHRA. London, 1888. 1st ed. *FYE.* $75

Cripps, Wilfred J. OLD ENGLISH PLATE, ECCLESIASTICAL, DECORATIVE & DOMESTIC: ITS MAKERS & MARKS. London, 1906. Later ed. NF. *POLYANTHOS.* $35

Crisp, N.J. THE LONDON DEAL. London: Raven Books, 1978. 1st ed. Signed. Fine in dj. *MORDIDA.* $35

Crisp, N.J. THE ODD JOB MAN. London: Raven Books, 1977. 1st ed. Signed. Fine in dj. *MORDIDA.* $35

Crispin, Edmund. FEN COUNTRY: TWENTY-SIX STORIES. Walker, (1979). 1st Amer ed. 160pp. NF in NF dj. *BEBBAH.* $15

Crispin, Edmund. SUDDEN VENGEANCE. NY: Dodd, Mead, 1950. 1st US edition. NF in worn, chipped dj. *BEASLEY.* $25

Crispin, Edmund. THE LONG DIVORCE. Phila: J.B. Lippincott, 1951. 1st Amer ed. Fine in VG dj w/wear at spine ends, along top of front panel, and at corners. *MORDIDA.* $45

Crispin, Edmund. THE MOVING TOYSHOP. Lippincott, (1946). 1st Amer ed. Cvr edgewear, fading lower spine, bookshop label ffep. VG in Fair to Good dj with edgewear, creases, largish chips at spine. *BEBBAH.* $40

Critchley, Macdonald. SHIPWRECK-SURVIVORS, A MEDICAL STUDY. London, 1943. Scarce. *FYE.* $50

Crockett, David. THE LIFE OF MARTIN VAN BUREN. Phila: Robert Wright, 1835. 1st ed. Lib stamp (only marking); part of front ad leaf missing; signatures pulled. Orig pink cl, many stains, sunned, most of paper spine label gone. Text foxing. Fair. Howes C-899. *SCHOYER'S.* $60

Crockett, W.S. ABBOTSFORD. A&C Black, 1905. 1st ed. 7s 6d Series. VG-NF. *OLD LONDON.* $37.50

Crockett, Walter Hill. HISTORY OF LAKE CHAMPLAIN, THE RECORD OF THREE CENTURIES, 1609-1909. Burlington, VT, (1909). Lightly soiled, some creased corners. Wraps. *BOHLING.* $45

Crockett, William Day and Sarah Gates Crockett. A SATCHEL GUIDE TO EUROPE. 53rd ed. London: George Allen, 1937. 7 fldg maps. Sig. Dj. VG. *WEBER.* $25

Croffut, W. A. and Morris, John M. THE MILITARY AND CIVIL HISTORY OF CONNECTICUT...1861-65. NY: Ledyard and Bill, 1868. 1st ed. VG. *SECOND LIFE.* $75

Crofts, Freeman Wills. DARK JOURNEY. NY: Dodd, Mead, 1951. 1st US ed. Store stamp bottom edge, dates rear pastedown, o/w nice in NF dj w/old traces of damp. *BEASLEY.* $40

Crofts, Freeman Wills. DEATH OF A TRAIN. London, 1946. 1st ed. Fine in dj (few tiny tears, minimally edge rubbed). TLS laid in. *POLYANTHOS.* $75

Crofts, Freeman Wills. MYSTERY ON SOUTHAMPTON WATER. London: Hodder & Stoughton, 1934. 1st ed. Spine sl faded, edges lightly spotted, inscription, o/w VG in dj with 3/4" V shaped piece missing at top of spine, several closed tears and wear at corners. *MORDIDA.* $275

Crofts, Freeman Wills. SILENCE FOR THE MURDERER. London: Hodder & Stoughton, 1949. 1st ed. Minor spotting on edges o/w Fine in dj w/some internal spotting, several tiny closed tears, and nicks at spine ends. *MORDIDA.* $75

Crofts, Freeman Wills. THE SEA MYSTERY. NY: Harper & Brothers, 1928. 1st Amer ed. VG in dj (darkened spine; chipped, frayed spine ends). *MORDIDA.* $45

Crofut, William. TROUBADOUR: A DIFFERENT BATTLEFIELD. NY: Dutton, 1968. Stated 1st ed. 283pp. VG+ in edge-rubbed, torn, price-clipped dj. *AKA.* $40

Crofutt, George A. CROFUTT'S NEW OVERLAND TOURIST AND PACIFIC COAST GUIDE....Vol. 1, 1878-9. Chicago: Overland Pub. Co, 1878. (6),(25)-322pp. 18 engr double views; ads, maps. Paging irregular. Orig cl. Lt wear, spine a little soiled & frayed, no foxing. Good in VG dj. *BOHLING.* $150

Crofutt, George A. CROFUTT'S NEW OVERLAND TOURIST, AND PACIFIC COAST GUIDE. Omaha/Denver: The Overland Publishing Co, 1884. Plts, maps in text. *HUDSON.* $85

Croghan, George. ARMY LIFE ON THE WESTERN FRONTIER. Norman, (1958). Ed by Francis Paul Prucha. 1st ed. 187pp. Ex-lib w/no external markings. VG. *PRATT.* $25

Croll, James. CLIMATE AND TIME IN THEIR GEOLOGICAL RELATIONS: A THEORY OF SECULAR CHANGES OF THE EARTH'S CLIMATE. Edinburgh: Adam & Charles Black, 1885 (1875). 8 color plts (2 fldg), 12 text illus. Good in brown cl; corners bumped & a bit worn, front hinge tender, occasional pencil notes & underlining. *KNOLLWOOD.* $95

Croly, David G. MISCEGENATION; THE THEORY OF THE BLENDING OF THE RACES APPLIED TO THE AMERICAN WHITE MAN AND NEGRO. NY: Dexter, 1864. 1st ed. (2),72pp. Orig printed wrappers. Howes C909. *GINSBERG.* $275

Cromer, Earl of (Evelyn Baring). MODERN EGYPT. NY: Macmillan, 1908. 2 vols. Vol 1, 1st prtg; vol 2, 2nd prtg. Bright, though a little rubbed. Frontis port, 1 fldg map. *SCHOYER'S.* $50

Crone, J.O. THE MAGNETIC HEALER'S GUIDE OR PERSONAL EXPERIENCES IN MAGNETIC AND SUGGESTIVE HEALING. Kansas City, MO, 1903. 1st ed. *FYE.* $40

Cronin, Vincent. LAST MIGRATION. London: Rupert Hart Davis, 1957. 343pp. One map. In faded dj. *SCHOYER'S.* $25

Cronise, T.F. THE NATURAL WEALTH OF CALIFORNIA, COMPRISING EARLY HISTORY...GEOLOGY, ZOOLOGY, AND BOTANY...TOGETHER WITH A DETAILED DESCRIPTION OF EACH COUNTY...16 plts. SF, 1868. 1st ed. xvi,696pp. Orig grn clh w/title in gilt. Some wear at corners & spine ends; several brown stains on front cover; inner hinges restored; pp yellowed & with occasional brown spots. *SUTTON.* $200

Cronise, Titus. NATURAL WEALTH OF CALIFORNIA. SF: Bancroft, 1868. 1st ed. Ex-lib. 696pp. Good to VG. *BOOK MARKET.* $60

Cronkhite, Daniel. DEATH VALLEY'S VICTIMS: A DESCRIPTIVE CHRONOLOGY 1849-1966. Nevada: Sagebrush, 1968. 1st ed, ltd to 225 hb copies, signed. Fine in Fine dj. *BOOK MARKET.* $40

Cronkhite, Daniel. RECOLLECTIONS OF A YOUNG DESERT RAT... NEVADA AND DEATH VALLEY. Nevada: Sagebrush, 1972. 1st ed, ltd to 777, signed. 102pp. Fine in Fine dj. *BOOK MARKET.* $40

Cronwright-Schreiner, S.C. LIFE OF OLIVE SCHREINER. Boston: Little, Brown, n.d. Grn cl a little faded, few leaves roughly opened. *SCHOYER'S.* $20

Crookes, W. (ed). MITCHELL'S MANUAL OF PRACTICAL ASSAYING. London: Longmans Green, 1888. Good+. *BOOKCELL.* $60

Crosby, Alexander L. (ed). STEAMBOAT UP THE COLORADO. From the Journal of Lt. Joseph Christmas Ives...1857-1858. Boston, 1965. 1st ed. Spine sunfaded, else VG. *FIVE QUAIL.* $45

Crosby, Caresse. THE PASSIONATE YEARS. NY: Dial, 1953. 1st ed. Plates. Rev copy, slip inserted. VF in dj. *WOOLMER.* $75

Crosby, Edward. RADIANA. Ivy Press, 1906. 1st. VG. *MADLE.* $40

Crosby, Elisha O. MEMOIRS...1849-1864. San Marino: Huntington Lib, 1945. 1st ed. Fine in Fine dj. *BOOK MARKET.* $15

Crosby, Frank(lin?). EVERYBODY'S LAWYER AND COUNSELLOR IN BUSINESS. Pub by John E. Potter, No. 617 Sansom Street, Phila, 1860. 2 blanks; half title; title pg; 5-384pp; 10 advertising leaves; 2 blanks. 8vo. Bound in orig brn, diced calf-backed ptd boards. Rubbed and showing wear, but quite sound and very clean. *BOSWELL.* $175

Crosby, Harry. SIX POEMS. NY: The Latterday Pamphlets, Spring, 1928. 1st ed. One of 225 ptd by Paul Johnston. VG in sl chipped wrappers. *CAPTAIN'S BOOKSHELF.* $300

Crosby, Harry. THE KING'S HIGHWAY IN BAJA CALIFORNIA. Copley Press, 1974. 1st ed. Fine in VG dj. *CONNOLLY & WADE.* $35

Cross, Amanda. IN THE LAST ANALYSIS. NY: Macmillan, 1964. 1st ed, 1st bk. Owner's name & critique on endpaper. VG, sm spine chips, lt wear to dj. *ELSE FINE.* $35

Cross, Amanda. THE JAMES JOYCE MURDER. NY: Macmillan, 1967. 1st ed. Fine in 1st state dj. *MORDIDA.* $85

Cross, Amanda. THE JAMES JOYCE MURDER. NY: Macmillan, 1967. 1st ed. Fine in price-clipped dj. *MORDIDA.* $50

Cross, John Keir. THE OTHER PASSENGER. Phila: Lippincott, 1946. 1st US ed. Fine in NF dj w/light wear at spine head. *BEASLEY.* $45

Cross, M.I. and Martin J. Cole. MODERN MICROSCOPY, A HANDBOOK...London: Bailliere, Tindall, and Cox, 1903. 3rd ed. Cover discolored, top of spine deteriorated, name. *KNOLLWOOD.* $34

Cross, Osborn. A REPORT, IN THE FORM OF A JOURNAL, TO THE QUARTERMASTER GENERAL, OF THE MARCH OF THE REGIMENT OF MOUNTED RIFLEMEN TO OREGON, FROM MAY 10 TO OCTOBER 5, 1849....Washington: SD1, 1850. Pp127-244. 36 plts. Contemp full calf. Howes C923. *GINSBERG.* $450

Crossette, George (ed). SELECTED PROSE OF JOHN WESLEY POWELL. Boston, 1970. Ltd ed 1500. VG+ to NF, in Good dj with dampstain along upper edge (not affecting book or text). *FIVE QUAIL.* $35

Crossley, Fred H. ENGLISH CHURCH MONUMENTS, A.D.1150-1550. London, (1921). One closed tear 1st fep, folds bottom edge of title pg. NF. *POLYANTHOS.* $60

Crothers, Samuel M. THE CHILDREN OF DICKENS. Scribner's, 1944. 259pp. 10 Jessie Wilcox illus and pict cvr pastedown. VG. *BEBBAH.* $35

Crothers, Samuel M. THE CHILDREN OF DICKENS. Scribner's, 1946. 259pp. 10 full-page Jessie Wilcox illus + pict pastedown. VG in dj w/wrinkles, closed tears, some rubbing, slight soil. *BEBBAH.* $45

Crotti, A. DISEASES OF THE THYROID, PARATHYROIDS AND THYMUS. Phila, 1938. 3rd ed. 262 illus. *FYE.* $50

Crouse, Nellis M. IN QUEST OF THE WESTERN OCEAN. NY: Wm. Morrow, (1928). 1st ed. Name stamped on fore-edge, else VG in Good- dj. *BLUE DRAGON.* $40

Crouse, Nellis M. IN QUEST OF THE WESTERN OCEAN. NY: William Morrow, 1928. 1st ed. Minor fore-edge foxing. Dj has sunned spine, minor chips, else NF dj. *GREAT EPIC.* $75

Crow, Vernon H. STORM IN THE MOUNTAINS. Cherokee, NC, (1982). #120 of 1st ed, ltd to 1,000. 273pp. Signed. Fine. *PRATT.* $30

Crowe, Earle. MEN OF EL TEJON: EMPIRE IN THE TEHACHAPIS. LA: Ward Ritchie, 1957. 1st ed, ltd to 2000. Fine in NF dj. *CONNOLLY & WADE.* $45

Crowe, Robert. CLYDE MONSTER. Dutton, (1976). Unpaginated. Illus & signed by Kay Chorao. Fine in Fine dj. *BEBBAH.* $27

Crowfoot, J.W. EARLY CHURCHES IN PALESTINE. London, 1941. 30 plts & figures (1 fldg). *O'NEILL.* $55

Crowl, Philip. THE WAR IN THE PACIFIC: CAMPAIGN IN THE MARIANAS. Washington: Dept Army, 1960. 1st ed. Fldg maps. NF. *ARCHER.* $20

Crowley, Aleister. THE CONFESSIONS OF ALEISTER CROWLEY. NY: Hill & Wang, (1970). 1st Amer ed, 2nd ptg. John Symonds & Kenneth Grant (eds). VG in VG- dj. *BLUE DRAGON.* $50

Croy, Homer. JESSE JAMES WAS MY NEIGHBOR. NY, (1949). 1st ed. 313pp. Dj wear o/w Fine. *PRATT.* $45

Crozier, Emmet. YANKEE REPORTERS 1861-1865. NY: Oxford, 1956. 1st ed. NF in tape repaired dj. *ARCHER.* $25

Crozier, R.H. GOLDEN RULE A TALE OF TEXAS. Richmond, VA: Whittet & Shepperson, 1900. 1st ed. VG. *GIBBS.* $25

Cruickshank, H.G. BIRD ISLANDS DOWN EAST. NY, 1941. Worn dj. *SUTTON.* $28

Cruickshank, H.G. FLIGHT INTO SUNSHINE, BIRD EXPERIENCES IN FLORIDA. NY, 1948. Dj worn. *SUTTON.* $25

Cruikshank, George. ILLUSTRATIONS OF TIME. London: Published..by the artist, 1827. 6 plts. 3/4 maroon morocco, red morocco label w/gilt lettering on front cvr. Extrems a bit scuffed, front cvr stained, scattered foxing, else Good. *WREDEN.* $150

Crum, Josie Moore. THE RIO GRANDE SOUTHERN STORY. Durango: Railroadiana, Inc, 1957. Gilt titled black cl. Dj, Fine. BO-HLING. $75

Crumley, James. DANCING BEAR. Random House, 1983. 1st ed. Fine in dj. STAHR. $35

Crumley, James. ONE TO COUNT CADENCE. NY: Random House, (1969). 1st ed. Fine in dj. CAPTAIN'S BOOKSHELF. $250

Crumley, James. ONE TO COUNT CADENCE. NY: Random House, 1969. 1st ed, 1st bk. Water drop to top-edge has rippled top edge of the last few pgs, o/w close to Fine in Fine dj but for a short tear. BEASLEY. $125

Crumley, James. ONE TO COUNT CADENCE. NY: Random House, 1969. 1st ed, 1st bk. Fine in dj. MORDIDA. $300

Crumley, James. THE LAST GOOD KISS. NY: Random House, (1978). 1st ed. Fine (rm) in dj. CAPTAIN'S BOOKSHELF. $40

Crumley, James. THE LAST GOOD KISS. NY: Random House, 1978. 1st ed. Signed. VF in dj. MORDIDA. $65

Crumley, James. THE LAST GOOD KISS. Random, 1978. 1st ed. Fine in dj. Remainder mark. STAHR. $25

Crumley, James. THE MUDDY FORK AND OTHER THINGS. Livingston, MT: Clark City Press, 1991. Advance uncorrected proofs. Fine in wraps. BEASLEY. $50

Crumley, James. THE MUDDY FORK AND OTHER THINGS. Livingston: Clark City Press, 1991. 1st ed. One of 125 numbered, signed. VF slipcase w/o dj as issued. MORDIDA. $150

Crumley, James. THE MUDDY FORK. Northridge: Lord John Press, 1984. 1st ed. 1/200 numbered, signed. VF w/o dj as issued. MORDIDA. $125

Crumley, James. THE PIGEON SHOOT. Santa Barbara: Neville, 1987. 1st ed. 1/350 numbered, signed. VF w/o dj as issued. MORDIDA. $75

Crumley, James. THE WRONG CASE. London: Hart-Davis, 1976. 1st British ed. Signed. Sl spine crease o/w NF in dj, lt wear. SILVER DOOR. $275

Crumley, James. THE WRONG CASE. NY: Random House, (1975). 1st ed. Edges of boards beginning to fade, else Fine in dj, sm tears. Presentation inscrip. CAPTAIN'S BOOKSHELF. $400

Crumley, James. THE WRONG CASE. NY: Random House, 1975. 1st ed. Fine w/rmdr mk top edge and lightly sunned edges, in lightly used dj. BEASLEY. $200

Crumley, James. THE WRONG CASE. Random House, 1975. 1st ed. About Fine in dj. Boards sunned at edges, rmdr mark, name ffep. Dj has w/small chip, short closed tear, sl wear head of spine. STAHR. $250

Crumley, James. WHORES. (Missoula, MT), 1988. 1st ed, 1/475 numbered, signed. VF in dj. McCLINTOCK. $145

Crumley, James. WHORES. Missoula: Dennis McMillan, 1988. 1st ed. 1/450, signed. VF in dj. ELSE FINE. $85

Crumley, James. WHORES. Missoula: Dennis McMillan, 1988. 1st ed. 1/475 numbered, signed. VF in dj. MORDIDA. $100

Cruso, Solomon. MESSIAH ON THE HORIZON. Audubon, 1940. 1st ed. Fine in dj. MADLE. $45

Cruso, Solomon. THE LAST OF THE JAPS AND THE JEWS. Lefkowitz, 1933. 1st ed. VG. MADLE. $75

Cudworth, R. THE TRUE INTELLECTUAL SYSTEM OF THE UNIVERSE...ATHEISM CONFUTED. London, 1778. Engr frontis. Half lea and marbled boards. Fine. POLYANTHOS. $500

Cudworth, Warren H. HISTORY OF THE FIRST REGIMENT (MASSACHUSETTS INFANTRY)...Boston, 1866. 1st ed. Rebacked w/part of orig backstrip. Sl cvr wear and staining. Cvr gilt rubbed, minor text staining, o/w VG. DIAMOND. $75

Culbertson, Thaddeus A. et al. JOURNAL OF AN EXPEDITION TO THE MAUVAISES TERRES AND THE UPPER MISSOURI IN 1850. Washington, 1952. Orig ptd wraps. BAE, Bulletin 147. Howes C941. GINSBERG. $50

Culbertson, Thaddeus A. JOURNAL OF AN EXPEDITION TO THE MAUVAISES TERRES AND THE UPPER MISSOURI IN 1850. Washington: GPO, 1952. John Francis McDermott (ed). BAE, Bulletin 147. 2 fldg facs maps. Ptd wraps. VG. SCHOYER'S. $40

Culbertson, Thaddeus. JOURNAL OF EXPEDITION TO MAUVAISES TERRES & UPPER MISSOURI IN 1850. J.F. McDermott (ed). 2 fldg maps. BAE Bull. 147, 1952. VG. Howes C941. OREGON. $65

Culbreth, David M.R. THE UNIVERSITY OF VIRGINIA: MEMOIRS....Neale, 1908. BOOK BROKER. $85

Cullen, Countee (ed.). CAROLING DUSK: AN ANTHOLOGY OF VERSE BY NEGRO POETS. NY: Harper, (1927). 3rd ptg. Dj spine faded, 2 tears, tiny chips. AKA. $65

Cullen, Countee. COPPER SUN. NY: Harper & Row, 1927. 1st ed. Fine & bright cover, cl-backed marbled boards w/paper labels. Bkpl, penciled name. Short edgetears to 3pp, (2 appear professionally repaired). Overall Very Nice in dj w/chips; extremities, pieces missing head, foot of spine. AKA. $300

Cullen, Countee. ON THESE I STAND. NY: Harper, (1947). 1st ed. NF in about VG dj w/some wear to extremities. BETWEEN COVERS. $125

Cullen, Countee. ON THESE I STAND. NY: Harper, (1947). 1st ed. VG in dj missing 2 large pieces from front panel. LOPEZ. $25

Cullen, William. FIRST LINES OF THE PRACTICE OF PHYSIC. WITH NOTES AND OBSERVATIONS, PRACTICAL AND EX-PLANATORY AND A PRELIMINARY DISCOURSE, IN DEFENCE OF CLASSICAL MEDICINE BY CHARLES CALDWELL. Phila, 1816. 1st ed. w/Caldwell's contributions. 2 vols. Full leather, 550, 456pp. FYE. $300

Cullimore, Clarence. OLD ADOBES OF FORGOTTEN FORT TEJON. Bakersfield: Kern County Hist Soc, 1941. 1st ed. Inscr. Dj over matching pict stiff wrappers, Fine. CONNOLLY & WADE. $35

Cullimore, Clarence. SANTA BARBARA ADOBES. 1st ed. Santa Barbara: Santa Barbara Bk Pub Co. (1948). KARMIOLE. $35

Cullingford, Guy. POST MORTEM. Phila: Lippincott, 1953. 1st ed. Store stamp bottom edge, dates on rear pastedown, o/w nice in NF dj but for tear at head of spine. BEASLEY. $40

Cullingford, Guy. THIRD PARTY RISK. London: Geoffrey Bles, 1962. 1st ed. Fine in price-clipped dj w/rubbing on front panel. MOR-DIDA. $35

Culp, Ed. STATIONS WEST, THE STORY OF THE OREGON RAILWAYS. Caldwell: Caxton, 1972. 265pp. 1st ed. VF in F dj. OREGON. $45

Cuming, E. D. (ed). THE HUNTING TOURS OF SURTEES. Edinburgh and London: William Blackwood & Sons and NY: Charles Scribner's Sons, 1927. Ltd ed (1 of 230) Minor shelfwear, else VG-NF. OLD LONDON. $150

Cuming, E.D. (ed). SQUIRE OSBALDESTON: HIS AUTOBIOG-RAPHY. London & NY, 1926. 16 color plts, 75 b/w, map. NF. POLYANTHOS. $75

Cumming, C.F. Gordon. AT HOME IN FIJI. NY: Armstrong, 1882. New ed. (xii),(366)pp, fldg map, 2pp pub ads. Teal cl stamped in black, soiled and w/repairs where binding was damaged on upper edge. Frontis, 2 illus. SCHOYER'S. $40

Cumming, C.F. Gordon. TWO HAPPY YEARS IN CEYLON. NY: Charles Scribner's Son. 1892. 1st ed. 2 vols. vi,(4),438; (8),442pp. In both vols, fldg map ptd in red and black and 17 plts. Orig dec blue cl stamped in 3 colors; rear cvr vol 2 w/small waterstain. KARMIOLE. $175

Cumming, John (ed). THE GOLD RUSH. LETTERS....1849-1851. Mount Pleasant, MI: Cumming Press, (1974). 1st ed, ltd to 487. Fine. *OREGON*. $35

Cumming, Primrose. BEN: THE STORY OF A CART-HORSE. NY: Dutton, 1940. 1st US ed. VG. *OCTOBER FARM*. $25

Cummings, Byron. KINISHBA. A PREHISTORIC PUEBLO OF THE GREAT PUEBLO PERIOD. Tucson, Hohokam Museum & Univ Arizona, (1940). 1st ed. 26 color plts, 3 fldg maps incl 1 in rear pocket. VG. *OREGON*. $75

Cummings, E. E. THE ENORMOUS ROOM. NY: Boni and Liveright, c1922. 1st ed, 2nd state. Mustard cl over boards, spine and front cvr stamped in black; "shit" inked out p219. *BOOKMINE*. $125

Cummings, E.E. 73 POEMS. (New York: Harcourt, Brace & World, [1963]). 1st ed. Mint with 2 djs, the outer one VF, the extra one, underneath, pristine. *PIRAGES*. $150

Cummings, E.E. COMPLETE POEMS OF E.E. CUMMINGS 1913-1962. NY: Harcourt Brace & Jovanovich, (1972). 1st ed. Fine in dj. *CAPTAIN'S BOOKSHELF*. $50

Cummings, E.E. POEMS 1905-1962. AN AUTHORIZED TYPEWRITER ED....George James Firmage (notes). 3/4 calf & cl, acetate dj. London: Marchim Press, 1973. 1st ed. One of 225. VF. *JAFFE*. $150

Cummings, E.E. PUELLA MEA. (n.p.): Golden Eagle Press, (1923). Date refers to 1st pub. of poems in Tulips and Chimneys. This is the 1st separate prtg. in 1949. Orig. illus. by Kurt Roesch & drawing by Cummings produced for this ed. Fine with gilt dec. cvr in NF dec. dj with faint sunning & barest of chipping at top of spine & corners. Very scarce in dj. *BEBBAH*. $300

Cummings, E.E. TULIPS AND CHIMNEYS. NY, 1923. 1st ed. Little offsetting inside cover and ffep. Fine in dj (spine sunned, extremities little chipped, small edge tear, few edge nicks, sl edge sunned). *POLYANTHOS*. $200

Cummings, Homer. THE TIRED SEA. Baltimore, (1939). #115/300, signed. VG. *NUTMEG*. $30

Cummings, Ray. THE GIRL IN THE GOLDEN ATOM. Harper, 1923. 1st ed. VG. *MADLE*. $75

Cummings, Ray. THE MAN WHO MASTERED TIME. McClurg, 1929. 1st ed. VG. *MADLE*. $45

Cummings, Ray. THE SEA GIRL. McClurg, 1930. 1st ed. VG. Inscribed. *MADLE*. $125

Cummings, Ray. THE SHADOW GIRL. London, 1946. 1st ed. Fine in dj. *MADLE*. $45

Cummins, Ella. THE STORY OF THE FILES, A REVIEW OF CALIFORNIAN WRITERS & LITERATURE. SF, 1893. 1st ed. Orig pict boards, rebacked w/cloth spine. VG. *OREGON*. $150

Cummins, Sarah J. AUTOBIOGRAPHY AND REMINISCENCES. N.p., (1914). Walla Walla Bulletin. Orig wraps. VF. Howes C952. *OREGON*. $50

Cunard, Nancy. PARALLAX. London: Hogarth Press, 1925. 1st ed, one of 420. Fine w/sl darkened edges and few signs of foxing internally. *BEASLEY*. $400

Cunard, Nancy. RELEVE INTO MAQUIS. U.K.: Grasshopper Press, 1944. 1st ed. Single leaf folded. Ltd ed, 250. Scarce in such Fine condition. *POLYANTHOS*. $45

Cunard, Nancy. THOUGHTS ABOUT RONALD FIRBANK. Marbled wrappers. NY: Albondocani Press, 1971. 1st ed. One of 200 numbered. VF. *JAFFE*. $75

Cundall, H.M. A HISTORY OF BRITISH WATER COLOUR PAINTING. WITH BIOGRAPHICAL LIST OF PAINTERS. NY, 1908. Teg. NF. *POLYANTHOS*. $75

Cunnimgton, Phillis, and Mansfield, Alan. ENGLISH COSTUME FOR SPORTS AND OUTDOOR RECREATION. NY: Barnes and Noble, 1969. 1st US ed. W/o dj, as issued. Slight shelfwear, else VG-NF. *OLD LONDON*. $25

Cunningham, E.V. THE CASE OF THE ONE-PENNY ORANGE. Holt, 1977. 1st ed. Fine in dj. *STAHR*. $15

Cunningham, E.V. THE CASE OF THE RUSSIAN DIPLOMAT. Holt, 1978. 1st ed. VF in dj. *STAHR*. $15

Cunningham, Eugene. RIDING GUN: A BUSCADERO NOVEL. Houghton Mifflin, 1956. 1st ed. Fine, clean chipped dj. *AUTHORS OF THE WEST*. $25

Cunningham, Eugene. TRIGGERNOMETRY, A GALLERY OF GUNFIGHTERS. Caldwell, 1975. 11th ptg. Some dj wear o/w VG+. *PRATT*. $37.50

Cunningham, Frank. BIG DAN: THE STORY OF A COLORFUL RAILROADER. Salt Lake City: Deseret News Press, 1946. Pict ep. Lengthy inscrip. Gilt titled blue cl. VG or better. *BOHLING*. $50

Cunningham, Imogen. PHOTOGRAPHS. Margery Mann (text). Seattle: Univ of WA Press, 1970. 1st ed. Illus. Signed by Cunningham. Fine. *SMITH*. $300

Cunningham, J.T. SEXUAL DIMORPHISM IN THE ANIMAL KINGDOM. London: A&C Black, 1900. Illus. Neville Chamberlain's copy w/his bkpl. VG. *MIKESH*. $60

Cunningham, J.V. SELECTED POEMS. 1/4 morocco & marbled boards. Mt. Horeb, WI: Perishable Press, 1971. 1st ed. One of 120 signed. VF. *JAFFE*. $400

Cunningham, J.V. SOME SALT. POEMS AND EPIGRAMS. The Perishable Press, 1967. One of 200. Wrappers. Fine. *WOOLMER*. $125

Cunningham, Joe Anderson. THE BLUE AND THE GRAY AND OTHER POEMS AND SONGS. Nashville: McQuiddy Printing Co, 1903. 2nd ed. Orig blue cl. Slight spotting on cover, but VG+. *CHAPEL HILL*. $30

Cunninghame Graham, Gabriela and R.B. FATHER ARCHANGEL OF SCOTLAND AND OTHER ESSAYS. London, 1896. 1st ed. xi,227pp. 2 sm cvr stains; several pp badly opened, o/w VG. *DIAMOND*. $45

Cunninghame Graham, R.B. BIBI. London: Heinemann, 1929. Traces of light foxing, else Nearly Fine in dj. 1st ed. #18 of 250 signed. *CHAPEL HILL*. $120

Cunninghame Graham, R.B. CARTAGENA AND THE BANKS OF THE SINU. London, 1920. 1st ed. Good. *DIAMOND*. $20

Cunninghame Graham, R.B. MOGREB-EL-ACKSA: A JOURNEY IN MOROCCO. NY: Viking, 1930. 1st Amer ed. Spine faded. *SCHOYER'S*. $15

Cunninghame Graham, R.B. THE DREAM OF THE MAGI. London: William Heinemann, Ltd. 1923. Ltd to 280 numbered, signed. *KARMIOLE*. $60

Cunninghame Graham, R.B. THE IPANE. London, 1899. 1st ed. 273pp, frontis port. Dec wraps sl chipped, repaired. Inner front hinge cracking, o/w VG. *DIAMOND*. $45

Curle, Richard. COLLECTING AMERICAN FIRST EDITIONS. Indianapolis: Bobbs-Merrill, (1930) 1st ed. Ltd to 1250 numbered, signed. Exceptionally Fine in sl worn slipcase. *WREDEN*. $60

Curle, Richard. INTO THE EAST: NOTES ON BURMA AND MALAYA. London: Macmillan, 1923. 1st ed. Fine. *MUELLER*. $30

Curle, Richard. JOSEPH CONRAD: A STUDY. London: Kegan Paul, 1914. 1st ed. With frontis tag. Fine. *MUELLER*. $35

Curley, Edwin A. NEBRASKA: ITS ADVANTAGES, RESOURCES, AND DRAWBACKS. (NY: The Amer and Foreign Pub Co, 1875). 1st ed. 8 color maps (2 fldg), 12 plts (1 fldg). Covers a bit rubbed and marked, hinges partly cracked, but binding rather clean. Bkpl removed, 3 short tears, a few spots, o/w Fine. *PIRAGES*. $250

Curling, T. B. OBSERVATIONS ON THE DISEASES OF THE RECTUM. London, 1851. 1st ed. 123pp. Backstrip chipped. Scarce. *FYE*. $150

Curran, Dale. PIANO IN THE BAND. NY: Reynal and Hitchcock, 1940. 1st ed. Fine in NF dj w/light wear at head of spine and tiny abrasion on front panel. *BEASLEY*. $35

Curran, W. Tees and Calkins, H. A. IN CANADA'S WONDERFUL NORTHLAND. NY/London: G.P. Putnam's Sons, 1917. Fldg map. Lt wear, bumping. *PARMER*. $75

Currey, Lloyd. SCIENCE FICTION AND FANTASY AUTHORS: A BIBLIOGRAPHY....Hall, 1979. 1st ed. As New. *MADLE*. $68

Currie, Barton. FISHERS OF BOOKS. 2 vols. Boston: Little, Brown, 1931. 1st ed. One of 365 numbered sets signed by author. *OAK KNOLL*. $95

Currie, Barton. FISHERS OF BOOKS. Boston, 1931. 2 vols. Ltd ed 242/365 sets signed. Uncut. Spine sl rubbed, sl sunned. Fine. *POLYANTHOS*. $85

Currie, Barton. FISHERS OF BOOKS. Boston: Little, Brown, 1931. 1st trade ed. Fine in sl rubbed dj. *JAFFE*. $35

Currie, Barton. THE TRACTOR AND ITS INFLUENCE UPON THE AGRICULTURAL IMPLEMENT INDUSTRY. Phila: Curtis, 1916. Paper covered boards, light wear. *AMERICAN BOTANIST*. $50

Currie, George E. WARFARE ALONG THE MISSISSIPPI, THE LETTERS OF LIEUTENANT COLONEL GEORGE E. CURRIE. Mount Pleasant, MI, (1960). Ed by Norman E. Clarke. 1st ed. Ltd to 1000. Minor cover staining o/w VG+. *PRATT*. $25

Curry, J.L.M. CIVIL HISTORY OF THE CONFEDERATE STATES WITH SOME PERSONAL REMINISCENCES. Richmond, 1900. 1st ed. 318pp. VG+. *PRATT*. $47.50

Curry, Manfred. BEAUTY OF FLIGHT. NY: The John Day Co. N.d. (circa 1932). Spine faded. Bkpl. *KARMIOLE*. $40

Curson, Louis Henry. THE BLUE RIBBON OF THE TURF. Phila: Gebbie & Co., 1891. 1st ed. Some wear to extremities, else a nice tight copy of a scarce book. VG. *OLD LONDON*. $75

Curti, Merle Eugene. THE AMERICAN PEACE CRUSADE, 1815-1860. Durham, Duke, 1929. 1st ed. Orig cl, defective dj. *GINSBERG*. $30

Curtis, Edward S. IN THE LAND OF THE HEAD-HUNTERS. Yonkers-on-Hudson: World Book, 1919. VG. *LAURIE*. $20

Curtis, George William. NILE NOTES OF A HOWADJI. NY, 1856. VF. *O'NEILL*. $45

Curtis, Joseph Henry. LIFE OF CAMPESTRIS ULM—THE OLDEST INHABITANT OF BOSTON COMMON. Boston: W.B. Clarke, 1910. 1st ed. Presentation inscrip. Wear to spine. VG. *AARD*. $40

Curtis, Leslie. RENO REVERIES, IMPRESSIONS OF LOCAL LIFE. Reno, 1924. 1st ed. Pict cl. Fine. *CONNOLLY & WADE*. $25

Curtis, Mattoon M. SNUFF AND SNUFF BOXES. NY, 1930. NF. *POLYANTHOS*. $35

Curtis, Newton Martin. FROM BULL RUN TO CHANCELLORSVILLE. NY, 1906. 1st ed. Signed. 384pp. VG+. *PRATT*. $85

Curtis, Paul A. GUNS AND GUNNING. Phila: Penn. Pub. Co, 1934. 1st ed. VG. *BACKMAN*. $25

Curtis, W.H. THE ELEMENTS OF WOOD SHIP CONSTRUCTION. NY: McGraw Hill, 1919. 1st ed. Orig cl. Owner stamp, o/w Fine. *LEFKOWICZ*. $95

Curtis, William E. AROUND THE BLACK SEA. ASIA MINOR, ARMENIA, CAUCASUS...ROUMANIA. NY, 1911. Fldg map. *O'NEILL*. $65

Curtis, William E. THE TURK AND HIS LOST PROVINCES....Chicago, 1903. Fine. *O'NEILL*. $47.50

Curtiss, Daniel S. WESTERN PORTRAITURE, AND EMIGRANT'S GUIDE: A DESCRIPTION OF WISCONSIN, ILLINOIS, AND IOWA....NY: J.H. Colton, 1852. Fldg map. Hinge split. Ex-lib but generally sound. Howes C967. *HUDSON*. $250

Curtiss, Daniel S. WESTERN PORTRAITURE AND EMIGRANT'S GUIDE...NY, 1852. 351pp,18pp ads. Fldg map. Repairable tear. Scarce. *CULLEN*. $150

Curtiss, Mina. BIZET AND HIS WORLD. NY: Knopf, 1958. 1st ed. Fine in VG dj. *AARD*. $25

Curtiss, Richard D. THOMAS E. WILLIAMS & THE FINE ARTS PRESS. LA: Dawson's Book Shop, 1973. One of 400 ptd by Richard J. Hoffman. Dec boards w/cl spine. *DAWSON'S*. $50

Curtiss, Richard D. THOMAS E. WILLIAMS & THE FINE ARTS PRESS. LA: Dawson's, 1973. 1st ed. Ltd to 400. Printer's note laid in. VF. *CONNOLLY & WADE*. $75

Curtiss, Ursula. THE BIRTHDAY GIFT. NY: Dodd Mead, 1976. 1st ed. Name on first page of text o/w Fine in dj. *MORDIDA*. $25

Curwen, Henry. A HISTORY OF BOOKSELLERS, THE OLD AND THE NEW. London, (1873). 1st ed. Dec cvrs gilt, top spine little chipped, sl foxing some pages, front hinge started. Fine. *POLYANTHOS*. $75

Curwood, James Oliver. THE ALASKAN. Cosmopolitan, (1928). 1st ed. Corner of front cvr dampstained. VG in clean dj. *AUTHORS OF THE WEST*. $25

Curwood, James Oliver. THE DANGER TRAIL. Bobbs Merrill, (1910). 1st ed. VG. *AUTHORS OF THE WEST*. $30

Curwood, James Oliver. THE VALLEY OF SILENT MEN. Cosmopolitan, (1920). 1st ed. 7-line review stamp. VG. *AUTHORS OF THE WEST*. $25

Cushing, Frank H. THE NATION OF WILLOWS. Flagstaff, 1965. Light soil and spine fade to dj, else VF in VG+ dj. *FIVE QUAIL*. $35

Cushing, Frank Hamilton. ZUNI BREADSTUFF. NY: Museum of the American Indian, Heye Foundation. 1920. 1st ed. 674pp. Frontis, 26 plates. Scarce. *KARMIOLE*. $85

Cushing, Frank. MY ADVENTURES IN ZUNI. Palo Alto: Am. West, (1970). Ltd to 1950. VG. *OREGON*. $40

Cushing, Harvey. CONSECRATIO MEDICI AND OTHER PAPERS. Boston, 1928. 1st ed, 1st ptg. *FYE*. $150

Cushing, Harvey. FROM A SURGEON'S JOURNAL, 1915-1918. Boston, 1936. NF. *POLYANTHOS*. $50

Cushing, Harvey. FROM A SURGEON'S JOURNAL. Boston 1936. 1st ed., 1st prtg. *FYE*. $50

Cushing, Harvey. FROM A SURGEON'S JOURNAL. London, 1936. 1st British ed. Scarce. *FYE*. $100

Cushing, Harvey. PAPERS RELATING TO THE PITUITARY BODY, HYPOTHALAMUS AND PARASYMPATHETIC NERVOUS SYSTEM. Springfield, 1932. 1st ed. 234pp. *FYE*. $450

Cushing, Harvey. THE HARVEY CUSHING COLLECTION OF BOOKS AND MANUSCRIPTS. NY, 1943. 1st ed. *FYE*. $175

Cushing, Harvey. THE LIFE OF SIR WILLIAM OSLER. London: Oxford Univ Press, 1940. Red cl. Spine sl faded, sl stain inside back cvr, contents VG. *SMITHFIELD*. $40

Cushing, Harvey. THE LIFE OF SIR WILLIAM OSLER. Oxford, 1926. 1st ed., 4th prtg. 2 vols. 685pp, 728pp. W/the very rare Corrigenda and Addenda pub. in 1936. *FYE*. $250

Cushing, Harvey. THE LIFE OF SIR WILLIAM OSLER. Oxford, 1925. 1st ed.. 1st prtg. 2 vols. 685, 728pp. Binding rubbed. *FYE*. $200

Cushing, Harvey. THE LIFE OF SIR WILLIAM OSLER. Oxford, 1925. 1st ed., 3rd prtg. 2 vols. 685, 728pp. *FYE*. $125

Cushing, Harvey. THE LIFE OF SIR WILLIAM OSLER. Oxford, 1940. Complete in 1 vol. *YE*. $45

Cushing, Harvey. THE LIFE OF SIR WILLIAM OSLER. Oxford Univ, 1940. One vol reprint of 1925 2-vol work. 10 plts. VG. *OREGON.* $35

Cushing, Harvey. THE MEDICAL CAREER. Hanover, 1930. 1st ed. in book form. Ltd. ed. ptd at the press of Ichabod Crane. *FYE.* $100

Cushing, Harvey. THE PERSONALITY OF A HOSPITAL. Boston, 1930. 1st ed. in book form. *FYE.* $75

Cushing, Henry. THE PITUITARY BODY AND ITS DISORDERS. Phila, 1912. 1st ed., 1st prtg. 341pp. Fine. *FYE.* $600

Cushman, Dan. THE GREAT NORTH TRAIL. NY: McGraw-Hill, 1966. 1st ed. VG in lt worn dj. *PARMER.* $30

Cussler, Clive. CYCLOPS. NY: Simon & Schuster, 1986. 1st ed. Fine in dj. *MORDIDA.* $25

Cussler, Clive. DRAGON. NY: Simon & Schuster, 1990. 1st ed. Inscribed. VF in dj. *MORDIDA.* $35

Cussler, Clive. NIGHT PROBE! NY: Bantam Books, 1981. 1st ed. Fine in dj w/couple of internal tape mends, crease-tear on back panel and minor wear at corners. *MORDIDA.* $25

Cussler, Clive. RAISE THE TITANIC! NY: Viking Press, 1976. 1st ed. Signed. Fine in dj w/tiny closed tear. *MORDIDA.* $45

Cussler, Clive. TREASURE. NY: Simon & Schuster, 1988. 1st ed. Fine in dj. *MORDIDA.* $25

Cussler, Clive. VIXEN 03. NY: Viking Press, 1978. 1st ed. Fine in dj w/minor wear at spine ends and several short closed tears. *MORDIDA.* $35

Cust, Lionel. THE CENCI: A STUDY IN MURDER. London: Mandrake, 1929. 1st ed. Black cl & snakeskin paper over boards. Spine label chipped, edgeworn, Good+. *ARCHER.* $15

Custer, Elizabeth B. "BOOTS AND SADDLES" OR LIFE IN DAKOTA WITH GENERAL CUSTER. NY: Harper & Brothers, 1885. 1st ed, ltr state w/portrait and map added. Bkpl. *HUDSON.* $75

Custer, Elizabeth B. BOOTS AND SADDLES OR LIFE IN DAKOTA WITH GENERAL CUSTER. NY: Harper, 1885. 1st ed. Frontis. 312 pp. Orig gilt-stamped pict brn cl. Sl edge wear. NF. Howes C980. *CONNOLLY & WADE.* $100

Custer, Elizabeth B. BOOTS AND SADDLES OR LIFE IN DAKOTA WITH GENERAL CUSTER. NY: Harper, 1885. 1st ed. Variant issue w/map. Orig gilt-stamped pict cl. Frontis added. Howes C980. NF. *CONNOLLY & WADE.* $75

Custer, Elizabeth B. FOLLOWING THE GUIDON. NY, 1890. 1st ed. 341pp. Illus pict cloth. Ex-lib, but no external markings and evidenced only by bookplate. A little cvr wear o/w VG+. *PRATT.* $110

Custer, G.A. MY LIFE ON THE PLAINS....London: Folio Society, 1963. 1st FS ed. Gilt-stamped leather spine label. Fine in slipcase. *AUTHORS OF THE WEST.* $40

Custer, Mrs. E. TENTING ON THE PLAINS OR GENERAL CUSTER IN KANSAS AND TEXAS. NY: Chas. L. Webster, 1887. 1st ed. Frontis, xii,(4),702pp. Illus A. Berghaus, F. Remington. Orig pict cl, beveled edges, gilt. NF. *CONNOLLY & WADE.* $200

Custer, Mrs. E. TENTING ON THE PLAINS. NY: Harper, 1895 (1887). Later ed. Spine sl soiled. Small smudge title-page verso, o/w VG. *DIAMOND.* $35

Cutbush, James. THE AMERICAN ARTIST'S MANUAL, OR DICTIONARY OF PRACTICAL KNOWLEDGE IN THE APPLICATION OF PHILOSOPHY TO THE ARTS AND MANUFACTURES... Phila, 1814. 1st ed. Scarce. 39 full-page engr plts. 2 vols. Full contemp calf; 1 sig sl shaken, some foxing, but Very Nice. *M & S.* $375

Cuthbert, Norma B. (ed). LINCOLN AND THE BALTIMORE PLOT, 1861. San Marino, CA, 1949. 1st ed. 161pp. VG+ in dj. *PRATT.* $32.50

Cutler, Carl C. A DESCRIPTIVE CATALOGUE OF THE MARINE COLLECTION AT INDIA HOUSE. Middleton: India House, 1973. 2nd ed, ltd to 1250. As new in slipcase. *PARMER.* $125

Cutler, Carl C. QUEENS OF THE WESTERN OCEAN. Annapolis: U.S. Naval Institute, 1961. 1st ed. Frontis, 32 plts, 15 plans. Fine in VG dj. *CONNOLLY & WADE.* $75

Cutler, Elliott and Robert Zollinger. ATLAS OF SURGICAL OPERATIONS. NY, 1940. 1st ed., 3rd prtg. *FYE.* $35

Cutler, Julia P. LIFE AND TIMES OF EPHRIAM CUTLER PREPARED FROM HIS JOURNAL AND CORRESPONDENCE...WITH BIOGRAPHICAL SKETCHES....Cincinnati, Clarke, 1890. 1st ed. 141,353pp. 3 plts. Orig cl. Howes C985. *GINSBERG.* $150

Cutler, Max. TUMORS OF THE BREAST. Phila, 1962. 1st ed. Signed. *FYE.* $75

Cutright Paul R. and M.J. Brodhead. ELLIOTT COUES, NATURALIST AND FRONTIER HISTORIAN. Univ of IL, (1981). 1st ed. VF in VF dj. *OREGON.* $35

Cutright, Paul R. LEWIS AND CLARK: PIONEERING NATURALISTS. Univ of IL, 1969. 1st ed. Fine. *OREGON.* $100

Cutten, George. THREE THOUSAND YEARS OF MENTAL HEALING. NY, 1911. 1st ed. *FYE.* $100

Cutting, C.L. FISH SAVING: A HISTORY OF FISH PROCESSING FROM ANCIENT TO MODERN TIMES. NY: Philos Library, 1956. Plts. Fine in VG dj. *MIKESH.* $37.50

CYCLOPEDIA OF CIVIL ENGINEERING. 9 vols. Chicago, 1916. 1/4 leather chipped. Good. *ARTIS.* $125

D

D., H. (Hilda Doolittle, trans). CHORUSES FROM IPHIGENEIA IN AULIS. (London: Egoist, 1915.). Self-wrappers. Author's 1st bk. Wraps sl soiled, else NF. *HELLER.* $200

D., H. (Hilda Doolittle). HIPPOLYTUS TEMPORIZES. A PLAY IN THREE ACTS. Boston, 1927. Ltd ed, 500/550. Name. Uncut. Fine in NF box. *POLYANTHOS.* $150

D., H. (Hilda Doolittle). HIPPOLYTUS TEMPORIZES: A PLAY IN THREE ACTS BY H.D. Boston: Houghton Mifflin, 1927. One of 550. NF in worn slipcase. Bkpl. *CAPTAIN'S BOOKSHELF.* $250

D., H. (Hilda Doolittle). PALIMPSEST. Boston: HM, (1926). 1st Amer ed, One of 700. Lt shelfwear. NF in VG dj. *LOPEZ.* $300

D.H. LAWRENCE, A PERSONAL RECORD by E.T. NY: Knight, 1936. 1st US ed. Fine in close to Fine dj. *WOOLMER.* $35

D'Annunzio, Gabriele. FRANCESCA DA RIMINI. NY: Stokes, (1902). 1st US ed. Fine-. *AARD.* $35

D'Aulaire, Ingri and Edgar Parin. BENJAMIN FRANKLIN. Doubleday, (1950). 1st ed. 4to. Unpaginated. Illus by the d'Aulaires. VG+ in VG+ dj. *BEBBAH.* $45

D'Aulaire, Ingri and Edgar Parin. D'AULAIRES' TROLLS. Doubleday, (1972). 1st ed. Illus, signed by authors. Fine in NF dj. *BEBBAH.* $85

D'Aulaire, Ingri and Edgar Parin. EAST OF THE SUN AND WEST OF THE MOON. Viking, 1938. 1st ed. Illus by the d'Aulaires. VG in VG dj w/chips, wear. *BEBBAH.* $85

D'Aulaire, Ingri and Edgar Parin. OLA. Doubleday, Doran, 1932. 1st ed. 4to. Unpaginated. Illus by the d'Aulaires. Interior VG in dj w/paper-covered pict boards w/edgewear, abraded spots but presentable. *BEBBAH.* $60

D'Aulaire, Ingri and Edgar Parin. OLA. NY: Doubleday Doran, 1932. Extrems worn. Inside Good+. *ACADEMIC LIBRARY.* $35

D'Aulaire, Ingri and Edgar Parin. POCAHONTAS. NY: Doubleday & Co., 1946. 1st ed. Minor edgewear; dj, some tears. *ACADEMIC LIBRARY.* $45

D'Aulaire, Ingri and Edgar Parin. THE TERRIBLE TROLL BIRD. Doubleday, (1976). Stated 1st ed. Illus by the authors. VG+ in VG+ dj w/short closed tear rear panel. *BEBBAH.* $30

D'Auvergne, Edmund B. SWITZERLAND IN SUNSHINE AND SNOW. London: T. Werner Laurie, n.d. (1921?). 1st ed. Minor bumps and shelfwear, else VG. *OLD LONDON.* $40

D'Israeli, Isaac. ROMANCES. London: Cadell and Davies, 1799. 1st this ed. (Contains an additional novella and a new preface.) 8vo; pp xix, 314 (2), w/errata sheet and engr frontis. Orig lea boards, later cloth re-backing, lea label, marbled eps. Armorial bkpl, inner hinges reinforced, else VG. *HARTFIELD.* $325

D'Orgeix, Le Chavalier. HORSE IN THE BLOOD. A SHOW JUMPER'S WORKING NOTEBOOK. London: Kaye, 1951. 1st Eng ed. Some shelfwear, o/w VG. *OCTOBER FARM.* $25

Da Vinci, Leonardo. LEONARDO DA VINCI'S NOTE-BOOKS ARRANGED AND RENDERED INTO ENGLISH WITH INTRODUCTIONS BY MCCURDY. NY, 1935. Dj. *FYE.* $50

Dabbs, James McBride. THE SOUTHERN HERITAGE. NY: Knopf, 1958. NF in dj. *LAURIE.* $25

Dabney, Owen P. THE LOST SHACKLE....(Salem, Oregon:) 1897. 1st ed. 98pp. Blue ptd wraps, Closed tear on cvr, some blue faded out, o/w Excellent. Howes 2527. *SECOND LIFE.* $350

Dabney, Owen P. TRUE STORY OF THE LOST SHACKLE, OR SEVEN YEARS WITH THE INDIANS. Salem, OR: Capital Printing, 1897. 1st ed. VG. *OREGON.* $60

Dabney, Virginius. PISTOLS & POINTED PENS, THE DUELING EDITORS OF OLD VIRGINIA. Chapel Hill, 1987. 1st ed. 193pp. Fine in dj. *PRATT.* $20

Dacus, J. A. ANNALS OF THE GREAT STRIKES IN THE UNITED STATES: A RELIABLE HISTORY....Chicago: Palmer, 1877. 1st ed. 480pp. Orig pict cl. Howes D5. *GINSBERG.* $150

Dagmar, Peter. ALIEN SKIES. Arcadia, 1967. 1st ed. VG in dj. *MADLE.* $25

Dahl, Kai R. THE "TEDDY" EXPEDITION AMONG THE ICE FLOES OF GREENLAND. NY/London: D. Appleton, 1925. 1st ed. Bkpl. book description tipped in ffep. NF. *PARMER.* $65

Dahl, Roald. CHARLIE AND THE GREAT GLASS ELEVATOR. Illus Joseph Schindelman. NY: Knopf, (1972). 1st ed. Just About Fine in like dj. *CAPTAIN'S BOOKSHELF.* $75

Dahl, Roald. SOME TIME NEVER: A FABLE FOR SUPERMEN. NY: Scribner, 1948. True 1st ed. Fine in very sl rubbed dj w/very short tear. *BETWEEN COVERS.* $350

Dahl, Roald. SOMEONE LIKE YOU. NY: Knopf, 1953. 1st ed. Fine in Fine dj (spine very faintly sunned). *ARCHER.* $125

Dahl, Roald. SWITCH BITCH. NY, 1974. 1st ed. Fine in like dj. *POLYANTHOS.* $30

Dahl, Roald. THE TWITS. NY: Knopf, 1981. 1st Amer ed. Fine in Fine dj. *DERMONT.* $25

Dahlberg, Edward. DO THESE BONES LIVE. NY: Harcourt Brace, (1941). 1st ed. Fine- in dj w/tape repaired tear top spine. *AARD.* $35

Dahlberg, Edward. THE CONFESSIONS OF EDWARD DAHLBERG. NY, 1971. #166 of 200 signed, numbered. Linen covered boards. Fine in slipcase. *PETTLER.* $60

Dahlberg, Edward. THE CONFESSIONS OF EDWARD DAHLBERG. NY: George Braziller, (1971). 1/200 numbered, signed. Fine in slipcase. *DERMONT.* $100

Dahlberg, Edward. THE CONFESSIONS OF EDWARD DAHLBERG. NY: George Braziller, (1971). 1st ed. 1/200 specially-

bound. Signed on tipped in leaf. Fine in slipcase. *CAPTAIN'S BOOK-SHELF.* $125

Dahlberg, Edward. THE FLEA OF SODOM. London, NY: Peter Nevill Ltd, (1950). 1st ed. Signed. Fine w/o dj. *HELLER.* $65

Dahlberg, Edward. THE SORROWS OF PRIAPUS. CT: New Directions, (1957). 1st ed. Ben Shahn illus. Tiny nick top spine. Fine in dj (spine little sunned, extremities rubbed, few edge nicks). *POLYAN-THOS.* $25

Dahlberg, Edward. THOSE WHO PERISH. NY: Day, (1934). 1st ed. Spine rubbed, else Fine in sl rubbed dj, sm chips. Inscribed. *CAPTAIN'S BOOKSHELF.* $175

Dailey, Abram. MOLLIE FANCHER, THE BROOKLYN ENIGMA. Brooklyn, 1894. 1st ed. Ex-lib. *FYE.* $50

Dailey, Gardner A. THE MEMORIAL GARDENS FOR THE MANILA CEMETERY. SF: American Battle Monuments Commission, (c. 1954). Fldg frontis plan view. Orig brown wraps. VG with only moderate soiling. *PARMER.* $50

Dain, Phyllis. THE NEW YORK PUBLIC LIBRARY, A HISTORY OF ITS FOUNDING AND EARLY YEARS. (New York): The New York Public Library, 1972. 1st ed. *OAK KNOLL.* $55

Daken, S.B. THE LIVES OF WILLIAM HARTNELL. Univ of Stanford, 1949. 1st ed. Fine. *VARNER.* $15

Dale, Edward E. COW COUNTRY. Univ of OK, 1942. 1st ed. VG. *OREGON.* $60

Dale, Edward E. COW COUNTRY. Univ of OK Press, 1945. 3rd ptg. Fine in NF dj. *VARNER.* $60

Dale, Edward Everett. THE INDIANS OF THE SOUTHWEST: A CENTURY OF DEVELOPMENT UNDER THE UNITED STATES. Norman: Univ of OK, 1949. 1st ed. Fine in Fine dj. *BOOK MARKET.* $60

Dale, Harrison (ed). GREAT GHOST STORIES. London, 1931. VG. *MADLE.* $45

Dale, Harrison (ed). MORE GREAT GHOST STORIES. London, 1932. 1st ed. VG. *MADLE.* $45

Dale, Harrison C. THE ASHLEY-SMITH EXPLORATIONS AND THE DISCOVERY OF A CENTRAL ROUTE TO THE PACIFIC, 1822-1829. A.H. Clark, 1918. 1st ed. 750 ptd. Frontis, 4 plts. VG. Howes D21. *OREGON.* $225

Dale, Harrison C. THE ASHLEY-SMITH EXPLORATIONS AND THE DISCOVERY OF A CENTRAL ROUTE TO THE PACIFIC, 1822-1829. A.H. Clark, 1941. 1st ed, revised. Fine. *OREGON.* $175

Dale T.F. FOX HUNTING IN THE SHIRES (THE HUNTING LIBRARY). London: Grant Richards, 1903. 1st ed. Minor shelfwear, else VG-NF. *OLD LONDON.* $45

Dali. 50 SECRETS OF MAGIC CRAFTSMANSHIP. NY, 1948. Bds faded, rubbed & worn at spine extremities. VG-NF. *POLYANTHOS.* $100

Dali. LES DINERS DE GALA. Trans Captain J. Peter Moore. NY: Felicie, (1973). Pict cl, gold pict wrapper. VG. *WEBER.* $75

Dall, Caroline H. THE COLLEGE, THE MARKET AND THE COURT. Boston: Lee & Shepard, 1867. 1st ed. Ex-lib. Good. *SECOND LIFE.* $125

Dallas, Francis Gregory. PAPERS OF FRANCIS GREGORY DALLAS....Ed by Gardiner W. Allen. NY: Naval Hist. Soc, 1917. 1st ed. Orig boards vellum spine. One of 750 numbered. Naval Hist Soc Pubs Vol. 8. *GINSBERG.* $75

Dallas, Paul. THE LOST PLANET. Winston, 1956. 1st ed. VG in Fine dj. *MADLE.* $70

Dallas, R.C. RECOLLECTIONS OF THE LIFE OF LORD BYRON, FROM THE YEAR 1808 TO THE END OF 1814. London: Ptd for Charles Knight, 1824. 1st ed. Contemp dark grn cl. Untrimmed, VG. *CHAPEL HILL.* $65

Dally, Nathan. TRACKS AND TRAILS; OR, INCIDENTS IN THE LIFE OF A MINNESOTA TERRITORIAL PIONEER. Walker, MN, (1931). 1st ed. Frontis, map, plts. Orig cl, gilt faded, lax flyleaf. Howes D31. *GINSBERG.* $150

Dalrymple, Major William. TRAVELS THROUGH SPAIN AND PORTUGAL, IN 1774: WITH A SHORT ACCOUNT OF THE SPANISH EXPEDITION AGAINST ALGIERS, IN 1775. London: Ptd for J. Almon, 1777. 1st London ed. 4to. iv, 187pp. Recent 3/4 morocco and marbled-paper binding. Frontis engr, fldg map. Early leaves, frontis and map badly dampstained in gutter. Rest of text clean. *SCHOYER'S.* $300

Dalrymple, Margaret. THE MERCHANT OF MANCHAC. THE LETTERBOOKS OF JOHN FITZPATRICK, 1768-90. LA State Univ, (1978). 1st ed. VF in VF dj. *OREGON.* $35

Dalton, David. JAMES DEAN: THE MUTANT KING. SF: Straight Arrow, 1974. 1st ed. Owner's name. About Fine in dj w/lt edgewear. *AKA.* $35

Dalton, John. HISTORY OF THE COLLEGE OF PHYSICIANS AND SURGEONS IN THE CITY OF NEW YORK: MEDICAL DEPARTMENT OF COLUMBIA COLLEGE. NY, 1888. Scarce. *FYE.* $100

Dalton, O.M. EAST CHRISTIAN ART. A SURVEY OF MONUMENTS. Oxford, 1925. Cl, rebacked, orig back retained. xv,396pp. *O'NEILL.* $175

Daly, Cesar. HISTORICAL MOTIFS OF ARCHITECTURE AND SCULPTURE IN FRANCE...INTERIOR WORK. EPOCHS FRANCIS I TO LOUIS XVI. 2 vols. NY: Wm. Helburn, n.d. (c. 1920). 148 plts. Black calf backed cl rubbed, corners worn, top and bottom of spines chipped. Signed by Marcus Reynolds (arch). Very Nice. *BLUE MOUNTAIN.* $125

Daly, Elizabeth. SOMEWHERE IN THE HOUSE. NY: Rinehart, 1946. 1st ed. Name. Fine, light wear at dj corners. *ELSE FINE.* $85

Daly, Elizabeth. SOMEWHERE IN THE HOUSE. NY: Rinehart, 1946. 1st ed. Fine, minor rub at upper spine corner of dj. *ELSE FINE.* $95

Daly, Elizabeth. THE BOOK OF THE DEAD. NY: Farrar, 1944. 1st ed. Fine in lightly used dj w/chips and internally strengthened separation of rear panel from spine. *BEASLEY.* $75

Daly, Elizabeth. THE BOOK OF THE LION. NY: Rinehart, 1948. 1st ed. Fine in lightly worn dj. *ELSE FINE.* $65

Daly, Elizabeth. THE STREET HAS CHANGED. NY: Farrar, 1941. 1st ed. Fine in NF dj but for light chipping at head of spine. *BEASLEY.* $85

Dana, Charles A. RECOLLECTIONS OF THE CIVIL WAR, WITH THE LEADERS AT WASHINGTON AND IN THE FIELD IN THE SIXTIES. NY, 1898. 1902 rpt. Minor cover staining and wear o/w Fine. *PRATT.* $27.50

Dana, Charles. TEXT-BOOK OF NERVOUS DISEASES. NY, 1892. 1st ed. 524pp. Part of leather label chipped, o/w VG. *FYE.* $150

Dana, Charles. THE PEAKS OF MEDICAL HISTORY. NY, 1926. 1st ed. *FYE.* $50

Dana, Freeman (pseud of Phoebe Atwood Taylor). MURDER AT THE NEW YORK WORLD'S FAIR. NY: Random House, 1938. 1st ed. NF, minor wear to extrems of the dj. *ELSE FINE.* $350

Dana, J.D. CORALS AND CORAL ISLANDS. NY, 1872. 2 fldg maps. Orig dec cloth (worn at edges & corners, rebacked, 4 lib stamps in margins, inner hinges repaired, bkpls. & lib sheet removed from eps), NY, 1872. *SUTTON.* $145

Dana, J.D. CORALS AND CORAL ISLANDS. NY, 1879 (1872). 2 fldg maps. Spine ends worn, some spotting & fading, inscrip contents page. *SUTTON.* $95

Dana, J.D. MANUAL OF GEOLOGY. NY, 1862. Rev ed. NF. *POLYANTHOS.* $75

Dana, J.D. MANUAL OF MINERALOGY, INCLUDING OBSERVATIONS....Durrie & Peck, 1855. 432pp, rebacked, new end leaves. Good+. *BOOKCELL.* $50

Dana, Richard Henry, Jr. TO CUBA AND BACK. A VACATION VOYAGE. Boston: Ticknor & Fields, 1859. 1st ed. viii, 288pp + 16pp publ. ads dated April, 1859. Dec. blind-stamped brown cl. Spine gilt and spine tip & corners rubbed. New front eps. Dana's sig. attached to paste down. BAL 4447 *DIAMOND.* $75

Dana, Richard Henry Jr. TWO YEARS BEFORE THE MAST. NY: Harper & Brothers, (copyright 1840). Orig black roan-backed cl, very worn. Scarce early ed, c1855. *HUDSON.* $125

Dana, Richard Henry, Jr. TWO YEARS BEFORE THE MAST. Chicago: Lakeside Press, 1930. Ltd ed, 1000. Illus Edward A. Wilson. Spine sl sunned. Fine in box (spine and top edge sunned). Publicity bklet laid in. *POLYANTHOS.* $100

Dana, Richard Henry, Jr. TWO YEARS BEFORE THE MAST. London: The Folio Society, 1986. 1st folio ed. New in slipcase. *AUTHORS OF THE WEST.* $40

Dana, Richard Henry. TWO YEARS BEFORE THE MAST: A PERSONAL NARRATIVE OF LIFE AT SEA. Chicago: The Lakeside Press, 1930. 1st, thus w/illus by Edward A. Wilson. One of 1000. Handsome two-toned cl w/gilt nautical devices. Spine sl darkened, else Fine in slipcase. Inscribed. Very attractive. *CAPTAIN'S BOOK-SHELF.* $200

Dana, Samuel L. A MUCK MANUAL FOR FARMERS. Lowell, MA: D. Bixby, 1842. 1st ed. 244pp. Spine tips defective, spine label sl worn, spine soiled, little cover staining. Contents Good. *DIAMOND.* $75

DANCING CHARLIE. London, (30s or 40s). Lacking Confidential and Secret Instructions in brn paper bag w/Charlie. Doll in Fine condition—5 components—joined with studs. *BOOKFINDERS INTL.* $40

Dandy, Walter. BENIGN TUMORS IN THE THIRD VENTRICLE OF THE BRAIN, DIAGNOSIS AND TREATMENT. Springfield, 1933. 1st ed. 171pp. Dj. VF. *FYE.* $350

Dandy, Walter. INTRACRANIAL ARTERIAL ANEURYSMS. Ithaca, 1944. 1st ed. 147pp + numerous fldg charts. Head and tail of spine and corners rubbed and torn, spine dull. Contents VG. Very Scarce. *FYE.* $250

Dane, G. Ezra and Beatrice J. Dane. GHOST TOWN. NY: Tudor Pub Co, 1948. 2nd prtg. VG, very chipped, worn dj. *PARMER.* $35

DANIEL BERKELEY UPDIKE AND THE MERRYMOUNT PRESS. NY: The Grolier Club. 1940. Ed ltd to 1000, this being one of 150 ptd for the Grolier Club by the Pynson Printers. Signed by Updike. *KARMIOLE.* $75

Daniel, Dan. BABE RUTH: THE IDOL OF THE AMERICAN BOY. Racine: Whitman, (1930). 1st ed. Bumped and rubbed; NF internally. *BLUE MOUNTAIN.* $150

Daniel, Dan. BABE RUTH—IDOL OF THE AMERICAN BOY. Whitman, 1930. 1st ed. Good without dj as issued. *PLAPINGER.* $45

Daniel, Dave. THE REAL BABE RUTH. Spink Pub, 1963. 3rd ptg, 2nd ed. Fine. The book was published only in a trade pb ed, then bound into hardcvrs w/o dj, but with orig pb cvrs intact. *PLAPINGER.* $65

Daniel, J.C. THE BOOK OF INDIAN REPTILES. Bombay, 1983. 54 plts (41 colored). Dj. *SUTTON.* $33

Daniel Mallory (comp, ed). THE LIFE AND SPEECHES OF THE HON. HENRY CLAY. 2 vols. Hartford: S. Andrus, (1853). Frontis, vol 1. Dec blind-stamped covers sl repaired. Two pp badly opened o/w text VG. *DIAMOND.* $75

Daniels, Les (ed). DYING OF FRIGHT. NY: Scribner's, (1976). 1st ed. Rear board nicked else VG+/NF in NF dj. *OTHER WORLDS.* $50

Daniels, Les. THE BLACK CASTLE. NY: Charles Scribner's Sons, 1978. 1st ed. VF in dj. *MORDIDA*. $35

Daniels, Les. THE BLACK CASTLE. Scribners, 1978. 1st ed. NF in dj. *MADLE*. $35

Daniels, Les. THE BLACK CASTLE: A NOVEL OF THE MACABRE. NY: Scribner's, (1978). 1st ed. Signed. Almost Fine in Fine dj. *OTHER WORLDS*. $45

Daniels, Les. THE SILVER SKULL. NY: Charles Scribner's Sons, 1979. 1st ed. Advance review copy, slip laid in. Fine in dj. *MORDIDA*. $35

Daniels, Les. THE YELLOW FOG. West Kingston: Grant, (1986). 1st ed. One of 800 signed by author, artist. Fine in dj. *OTHER WORLDS*. $35

Dannett, Sylvia G.L. (comp, ed). NOBLE WOMEN OF THE NORTH. NY, (1959). 1st ed. Fine ex-lib in dj. *PRATT*. $20

Dannett, Sylvia G.L. A TREASURY OF CIVIL WAR HUMOR. NY, (1963). 1st ed. VG+ in dj. *PRATT*. $35

Dannett, Sylvia G.L. and Rosamond H. Burkart. CONFEDERATE SURGEON, ARISTIDES MONTEIRO. NY, (1969). 1st ed. Light dj wear o/w Fine. *PRATT*. $35

Dannett, Sylvia. SHE RODE WITH THE GENERALS. NY: Thos. Nelson, 1960. 1st ed. Fine in NF dj. *ARCHER*. $30

Dante. THE DIVINE COMEDY OF DANTE ALIGHIERI. Melville Best Anderson (trans), Arthur Livingston (intro). Verona: LEC, 1932. Ltd to 1500 ptd by the Officina Bodoni & signed by Hans Mardersteig. Dj. Exceptionally Fine in sl soiled slipcase. *JAFFE*. $350

Danzig, Allison and Joe Reichler. THE HISTORY OF BASEBALL. Prentice-Hall, 1959. 1st ed. Good+. *PLAPINGER*. $35

Danzig, Allison and Joe Reichler. THE HISTORY OF BASEBALL. Prentice-Hall, 1959. 1st ed. Signed by sportswriter Bill Bryson. VG in Good dj. *PLAPINGER*. $55

Darby, John Curtis. SCIENCE AND THE HEALING ART, OR A NEW BOOK ON OLD FACTS. Louisville, KY, 1880. 1st ed. Scarce. *FYE*. $100

Darby, John. BRUSHLAND. NY, 1882. 1st ed. Shelfwear. VG. *ARTIS*. $15

Darby, Ruth. DEATH BOARDS THE LAZY LADY. GC: Doubleday Crime Club, 1939. 1st ed, 1st bk. VF, minor wear to corners of dj. *ELSE FINE*. $35

Darby, William. A TOUR FROM THE CITY OF NEW YORK, TO DETROIT, IN MICHIGAN TERRITORY. NY: Kirk & Mercein, 1819. 1st ed. 3 fldg maps. Some foxing, 1 map misfolded. Howes D66. *HUDSON*. $765

Darling, William Young. THE PRIVATE PAPERS OF A BANKRUPT BOOKSELLER. NY: D. Appleton and Co, 1932. 1st Amer ed. Rubbed, a few pp carelessly opened, else VG. *WREDEN*. $15

Darlington, William. AMERICAN WEEDS AND USEFUL PLANTS...SECOND AND ILLUSTRATED ED...REVISED, WITH ADDITIONS BY GEORGE THURBER. NY: Moore, 1859. 1st thus. Worn. VG. *SECOND LIFE*. $75

Darrah, William Culp. POWELL OF THE COLORADO. Princeton, 1969. 2nd ed. Fine in lightly sunburned jacket. *FIVE QUAIL*. $30

Darrah, William Culp. POWELL OF THE COLORADO. Princeton Univ Press, 1951. 1st ed. Review copy, slip laid in. Fine in chipped dj. *AUTHORS OF THE WEST*. $30

Darrow, Clarence S. FARMINGTON. Chicago: McClurg, 1904. 2nd ed. Fine w/one tiny break at cloth at base of spine. Signed. *BETWEEN COVERS*. $350

Darton, F.J. Harvey. DICKENS: POSITIVELY THE FIRST AP-PEARANCE, A CENTENARY REVIEW. London: Argonaut Press, 1933. 1st ed. 8vo, 145pp, illus, green cloth spine over boards, bkpl. Dj sl chipped. Fine in VG dj. *GREAT EXPECTATIONS*. $27.50

Darton, N.H. et al. GUIDEBOOK OF THE WESTERN UNITED STATES, WITH A SIDE TRIP TO THE GRAND CANYON. 1915. 1st ed. Brown wraps, 194pp, 25 colored fldg maps. VG+ w/modest ex-lib marking. *FIVE QUAIL*. $35

Darton, N.H. STORY OF THE GRAND CANYON OF ARIZONA, A POPULAR ILLUSTRATED ACCOUNT OF ITS ROCKS & ORIGIN. Fred Harvey, Jan. 1920. 3rd ed. Wraps bit edge worn. VG. *BOHLING*. $35

Dartt, Mary. ON THE PLAINS AND AMONG THE PEAKS...Phila: Claxton, et al, 1879. 2nd ed. Sl warped, worn, lacks front flyleaf. Good. *SECOND LIFE*. $75

Darwin, Bernard (ed). THE DICKENS ADVERTISER. London: Elkin Mathews, 1930. 1st ed. Tall 8vo, 208pp, illus, pict boards. VG. *GREAT EXPECTATIONS*. $35

Darwin, Charles. GEOLOGICAL OBSERVATIONS ON THE VOL-CANIC ISLANDS AND PARTS OF SOUTH AMERICA VISITED DURING THE VOYAGE OF THE H.M.S. 'BEAGLE'. NY, 1897. 3rd ed. 1/2 lea. *FYE*. $60

Darwin, Charles. JOURNAL OF RESEARCHES INTO NATURAL HISTORY & GEOLOGY...London: Murray, 1845. 2nd ed. 520pp. 3/4 leather, gilt dec backstrip, minor backstrip wear. Lacks adverts removed when leather bound. Usually seen w/red cl binding. VG. *BOOKCELL*. $160

Darwin, Charles. JOURNAL OF RESEARCHES INTO THE NATURAL HISTORY & GEOLOGY OF THE COUNTRIES VISITED DURING THE VOYAGE OF THE H.M.S. BEAGLE UNDER THE COMMAND OF CAPT. FITZ ROY, R.N. NY: The Heritage Press, c. 1957. VG+ in similar slipcase. *PARMER*. $40

Darwin, Charles. JOURNAL OF RESEARCHES INTO THE NATURAL HISTORY AND GEOLOGY OF THE COUNTRIES VISITED DURING THE VOYAGE OF H.M.S. BEAGLE ROUND THE WORLD. NY, 1896. 519pp. *FYE*. $75

Darwin, Charles. ON THE ORIGIN OF SPECIES BY MEANS OF NATURAL SELECTION, OR, THE PRESERVATION OF FAVOURED RACES IN THE STRUGGLE FOR LIFE. (NY): LEC, 1963. Paul Landacre, illus. Wood veneer boards, leather spine, slipcase. One of 1500. *DAWSON'S*. $200

Darwin, Charles. ON THE ORIGIN OF SPECIES....Paul Landacre (illus). Adelaide, South Australia: LEC, at the Griffin Press. 1963. Ed ltd to 1500. Slipcase. *KARMIOLE*. $200

Darwin, Charles. ON THE ORIGIN OF THE SPECIES BY MEANS OF NATURAL SELECTION. Paul Landacre (illus). Adelaide: Ptd for LEC by Griffin Press, 1963. Ltd to 1500. Slipcase. Fine. *WEBER*. $250

Darwin, Charles. THE DESCENT OF MAN & SELECTION IN RELATION TO SEX. NY: Appleton, 1871. 2 vol. VG. *MIKESH*. $150

Darwin, Charles. THE DESCENT OF MAN, AND SELECTION IN RELATION TO SEX. London: John Murray, 1871. 1st ed, 2nd issue. 2 vols. viii,423; viii,475pp (incl index). Illus. 3/4 tan calf, buck-ram, green leather label on paneled spine, teg. Lacking ads, else VG. *WREDEN*. $160

Darwin, Charles. THE DESCENT OF MAN AND SELECTION IN RELATION TO SEX. Adelaide, South Australia: LEC at Griffin Press, 1971. One of 1500 illus, signed by Fritz Kredel.1/4 grn leather a bit discolored at the spinal extremities, else Fine in lightly rubbed slipcase. *CAPTAIN'S BOOKSHELF*. $225

Darwin, Charles. THE DESCENT OF MAN AND SELECTION IN RELATION TO SEX. Illus by Fritz Kredel. (LEC). 1/4 grn leather, boards, slipcase. Adelaide, Australia: The Griffin Press, 1971. Ltd to 1500 signed by Kredel. Extrems of spine sl darkened, o/w Fine. *JAFFE*. $225

Darwin, Charles. THE DESCENT OF MAN...With Drawings by Fritz Kredel. Adelaide, South Australia: LEC, at the Griffin Press. 1971. Ed ltd to 1500 numbered, signed by Kredel. Wood veneer slipcase (partly cracked). *KARMIOLE.* $150

Darwin, Charles. THE EXPRESSION OF THE EMOTIONS IN MAN AND ANIMALS...NY: Appleton, 1873. 1st Amer ed. 7 heliotype plts. Orig brown cl dec in black, rebacked w/part of orig backstrip. Some shelfwear, rubbing, very slight repair to 1 plt and pp corner, lib stamp on title page, o/w Contents Good. *DIAMOND.* $125

Darwin, Charles. THE EXPRESSION OF THE EMOTIONS IN MAN AND ANIMALS. NY, 1897. 1/2 leather, 372pp. VF. *FYE.* $125

Darwin, Charles. THE FORMATION OF VEGETABLE MOULD, THROUGH THE ACTION OF WORMS, WITH OBSERVATIONS OF THEIR HABITS. NY: Appleton, 1897. Auth ed. VG+. *MIKESH.* $30

Darwin, Charles. THE FORMATION OF VEGETABLE MOULD. London: John Murray, 1881. 5th thousand (corrected). Orig grn cl covers worn, paper cover and spine labels removed. Contents Good. *DIAMOND.* $45

Darwin, Charles. THE LIFE AND LETTERS OF CHARLES DARWIN. INCLUDING AN AUTOBIOGRAPHICAL CHAPTER. NY: D. Appleton and Company, 1898. Authorized ed. 2 vols in burgundy cl w/gilt spine titles. Spot front cvr 1st vol; overall VG set. *PARMER.* $95

Darwin, Charles. THE ORIGIN OF SPECIES BY MEANS OF NATURAL SELECTION WITH ADDITIONS AND CORRECTIONS FROM SIXTH AND LAST ENGLISH EDITION. NY, 1898. 1/2 lea, 2 vols. 365pp,338pp. *FYE.* $125

Darwin, Charles. THE POWER OF MOVEMENT IN PLANTS. NY: Harper, 1881. 1st US ed. 592pp, ads. Pub's cl, name on ep, o/w Fine. *SECOND LIFE.* $150

Darwin, Charles. THE POWER OF MOVEMENT IN PLANTS. NY: Appleton, 1881. 1st Amer ed. Shelfwear, lib stamp, bkpl, o/w Good. *DIAMOND.* $35

Darwin, Charles. THE STRUCTURE AND DISTRIBUTION OF CORAL REEFS. NY, 1897. 3rd ed. 1/2 lea, 344pp. 1 fldg map torn with some loss of content. *FYE.* $45

Darwin, Charles. THE VARIOUS CONTRIVANCES BY WHICH ORCHIDS ARE FERTILISED BY INSECTS. NY: Appleton, 1877. 2nd ed, rev 1st Amer ed. A little shelfwear, lib bkpl, blind-stamp, o/w Good. *DIAMOND.* $45

Darwin, Charles. THE VARIOUS CONTRIVANCES BY WHICH ORCHIDS ARE FERTILISED BY INSECTS. London, 1904. Popular ed. Cl, lt wear to extrems, sm split to spine repaired, hinge cracked. Lt foxing. *SUTTON.* $45

Darwin, F. (ed). THE LIFE & LETTERS OF CHARLES DARWIN, INCLUDING AN AUTOBIOGRAPHICAL CHAPTER. NY: Appleton, (1897). 2 vols. 558pp; 562pp. Illus. Good+. *MIKESH.* $45

Darwin, F. (ed). THE LIFE & LETTERS OF CHARLES DARWIN. 2 vols. Basic Books, 1959. Backstrips sunned o/w VG+. *BOOKCELL.* $32

Dasent, G.W. EAST O' THE SUN AND WEST O' THE MOON. McKay, (1921). 289pp. Illus Edna Cooke. Sl edgewear, minor scratches to color pict pastedown. VG. *BEBBAH.* $30

Daubeny, C. LECTURES ON ROMAN HUSBANDRY....Oxford, 1857. Fldg plan w/tear to 1 fold. 12 plts (1 colored). Cl, some corner wear. Sm tear edge of spine; hinges reinforced. Pencil marks, underlinings. *SUTTON.* $90

Daugherty, James. ABRAHAM LINCOLN. Viking, 1943. 1st ed, inscribed. VG in VG dj. *BEBBAH.* $45

Daugherty, James. LINCOLN'S GETTYSBURG ADDRESS. Chicago: Whitman, (1947). 2nd ed. Cl, gold lettering. NF, sm tears to dj. *ACADEMIC LIBRARY.* $30

Daugherty, James. POOR RICHARD. Viking, 1941. 1st ed. Daugherty illus. VG in VG dj w/some chips, small closed edge tears. *BEBBAH.* $35

Davenent, William. SELECTED POEMS OF SIR WILLIAM DAVENENT. Cambridge, MA: Ptd at the Willow Press, 1943. Ltd to 190. *KARMIOLE.* $40

Davenport, Charles. HEREDITY IN RELATION TO EUGENICS. NY, 1915. 1st ed., 1st prtg. *FYE.* $50

Davenport, Cyril. BEAUTIFUL BOOKS. London: Methuen & Co, (1929). 1st ed. Orig stiff wrappers, dj. Exceptionally Fine. *WREDEN.* $35

Davenport, Cyril. BYWAYS AMONG ENGLISH BOOKS. London: Methuen, (1927). 1st ed. Navy blue cl. Bkpl of John Stockbridge Barrows. Fine. *WEBER.* $50

Davenport, Cyril. ROGER PAYNE. ENGLISH BOOK-BINDER....Chicago: The Caxton Club, 1929. 1st ed. Ltd to 250 ptd on Eng hand-made paper. Spine a bit faded, o/w Fine in worn slipcase. *JAFFE.* $475

Davenport, Guy. ECLOGUES. SF: North Point, 1981. 1st ed. Fine in Fine dj. *BEASLEY.* $25

Davenport, Guy. FLOWERS AND LEAVES. Highlands: Jargon, 1966. 1st ed. Wraps. Fine. *BEASLEY.* $100

Davenport, Guy. GOLDFINCH THISTLE STAR. Np: Red Ozier Press, (1968). One of 45 special hb (from ed of 200) signed. Cl-backed patterned boards, paper label. Fine. *CAPTAIN'S BOOKSHELF.* $100

Davenport, Guy. THE BOWMAN OF SHU. NY: Grenfell Press, 1983. 1st ed. One of 115 signed. 1/4 grn morocco, dec boards. Mint. *JAFFE.* $175

Davenport, John. APHRODISIACS AND ANTI-APHRODISIACS: THREE ESSAYS ON THE POWERS OF REPRODUCTION. London, 1869. 1st ed. 1/4 leather, 154pp + 7 plts. Hinges cracked, two 1" pieces missing from spine. Contents Fine. *FYE.* $150

Davenport, John. CURIOSITATES EROTICAE PHYSIOLOGIAE; OR, TABOOED SUBJECTS FREELY TREATED. IN SIX ESSAYS, VIZ., 1. GENERATION. 2. CHASTITY AND MODESTY. 3. MARRIAGE. 4. CIRCUMCISION. 5. EUNICHISM. 6. HERMAPHRODITISM. AND FOLLOWED BY A CLOSING ESSAY ON DEATH. London, 1875. 1st ed. Privately ptd on fine paper. 1/4 lea rubbed. Scarce. *FYE.* $200

DAVID AND GOLIATH. Random House, (1960s). Illus Svenson. Pop-up bk. *BOOKFINDERS INTL.* $35

David, R.B. FINN BURNETT, FRONTIERSMAN. A.H. Clark, 1937. 1st ed. Fine. *VARNER.* $125

David, Robert. MALCOLM CAMPBELL, SHERIFF. Casper, WY: Wyomingana, Inc., (1932). 1st ed. 19 plts. VG. Howes D85. *OREGON.* $150

David-Neel, Alexandra. INITIATIONS AND INITIATES IN TIBET. London: Rider & Co, (1958). 2nd ed. *BLUE DRAGON.* $25

David-Neel, Alexandra. MAGIC AND MYSTERY IN TIBET. NY: Univ Books, (1958). VG in VG- dj. *BLUE DRAGON.* $30

David-Neel, Alexandra. MAGIC AND MYSTERY IN TIBET. University Books, 1958. 1st ed. About Fine in spine darkened dj. *STAHR.* $45

Davidge, William. FOOTLIGHT FLASHES. NY: The American News Company, 1866. 1st ed. Orig patterned cloth; illus. VG. *DRAMATIS PERSONAE.* $55

Davidoff, Leo. BRAIN TUMORS: THEIR PATHOLOGY, SYMPTOMATOLOGY, DIAGNOSIS AND PROGNOSIS. Utica, NY, 1931. 1st ed. Wrappers. 62 illus. Scarce. *FYE.* $100

Davids, Thaddeus. THE HISTORY OF INK, INCLUDING ITS ETYMOLOGY, CHEMISTRY, AND BIBLIOGRAPHY. NY: Thaddeus Davids, (1860). 72, 4pp. Chromolitho half title, 17 plts (1 color), orig brn cl, gilt, aeg, sm dampstain rear upper corner, o/w Fine. *WEBER.* $200

Davidson, A. and G.L. Moxley. FLORA OF SOUTHERN CALIFORNIA. LA, 1923. Cl, gilt titles dulled. *SUTTON.* $45

Davidson, Angus. MISS DOUGLAS OF NEW YORK. NY: Viking, 1953. 1st US ed. VG+ in VG- dj. *AARD.* $15

Davidson, Diane Mott. CATERING TO NOBODY. NY: St. Martin's, (1990). 1st ed. Signed. Fine in Fine dj. *UNGER.* $40

Davidson, Donald. AN OUTLAND PIPER. Boston: Houghton Mifflin Co., (1924). 1st Amer ed. Inscribed. Fine in Fine dj. *DORN.* $425

Davidson, Donald. THE LONG STREET. Illus. by Theresa S. Davidson. Nashville: Vanderbilt Univ Press, 1961. 1st ed. Fine. Issued w/o dj. Inscribed. *WOOLMER.* $75

Davidson, Donald. THE LONG STREET. Nashville: Vanderbilt Univ. Press, 1961. 1st ed. Inscribed. 7 woodcuts. Orig cream paper-covered boards. Fine in pub's slipcase w/paper label. *CHAPEL HILL.* $100

Davidson, Donald. THE TENNESSEE. NY: Rinehart (1946 & 1948). 1st eds. 2 vols. Both vols inscribed. Both NF, both djs spine-faded and sl used. *DORN.* $150

Davidson, Donald. THE TENNESSEE; THE NEW RIVER: CIVIL WAR TO TVA. (Rivers of Amer). Rinehart, 1948. 1st ed. Fine in Fine dj. *VARNER.* $30

Davidson, H. M. FOURTEEN MONTHS IN SOUTHERN PRISONS; BEING A NARRATIVE....Milwaukee, 1865. 1st ed. 393pp. Fldg plan. Orig cl. *GINSBERG.* $375

Davidson, Homer K. BLACK JACK DAVIDSON, A CAVALRY COMMANDER...Glendale, CA: Arthur Clark, 1974. 1st ed. *HEINOLDT.* $25

Davidson, Homer K. BLACK JACK DAVIDSON, A CAVALRY COMMANDER ON THE WESTERN FRONTIER. Glendale, 1974. 1st ed. Fldg map. Dj. Fine. *PRATT.* $35

Davidson, Joe. THE ART OF THE CIGAR LABEL. Stamford: Longmeadow, (1989). 1st ed. Actual litho cigar label in front. VF in dj. *ARTIS.* $25

Davidson, L. SMITH'S GAZELLE. NY: Knopf, 1971. NF. *MIKESH.* $20

Davidson, Levette J. (ed). POEMS OF THE OLD WEST.... Univ of Denver Press, (1951). 1st ed. Fine in chipped dj. Names. *AUTHORS OF THE WEST.* $25

Davidson, Lionel. THE CHELSEA MURDERS. London: Cape, 1978. 1st ed. Fine in dj. *ELSE FINE.* $40

Davidson, Lionel. THE MENORAH MEN. NY: Harper, 1966. 1st ed. As New in dj. *ELSE FINE.* $40

Davidson, Marshall B. THE ORIGINAL WATERCOLOR PAINTINGS FOR THE BIRDS OF AMERICA. NY: American Heritage Pub. Co, 1966. 1st ed. 2 vol boxed set. VG. *BACKROOM.* $160

Davidson, Maurice. THE ROYAL SOCIETY OF MEDICINE, THE REALIZATION OF AN IDEAL (1805-1955). London, 1955. 1st ed. *FYE.* $50

Davie, O. EGG CHECK LIST & KEY TO THE NESTS & EGGS OF NORTH AMERICAN BIRDS. Columbus, OH, (1886). 2nd ed. rev. & eng. Rubbed, else Good+. *MIKESH.* $45

Davie, O. NESTS AND EGGS OF NORTH AMERICAN BIRDS. Phila, (1898). 5th ed. Minor dampstaining to edges of cvrs, margins of preliminary pp; pp browned. *SUTTON.* $45

Davies, A. Mervyn. STRANGE DESTINY. NY: Putnam, (1935). 1st US ed. Fine- in Fine- dj. *AARD.* $45

Davies, Charles. A TREATISE ON SHADES AND SHADOWS, AND LINEAR PERSPECTIVE. New York: A.S. Barnes & Co. 1855. 1st ed. 160 pp. 21 fldg plts. Black calf over brown cloth, a bit

worn; spine extremities chipped, outer hinges partly cracked but still quite sound. First pub in 1832. *KARMIOLE.* $60

Davies, E.W.L. A MEMOIR OF THE REV. JOHN RUSSELL AND HIS OUT-OF-DOOR LIFE. London: Bentley, 1878. Half leather. 1st ed. Edges of binding much worn & both hinges cracking. *OCTOBER FARM.* $125

Davies, J.J.(comp). HISTORY AND BUSINESS DIRECTORY OF MADISON COUNTY, IOWA. CONTAINING A COMPLETE HISTORY OF THE COUNTY...Des Moines, 1869. 1st ed. 254pp. Fldg map. Orig cl faded. Howes D98. *GINSBERG.* $150

Davies, James. RELATION OF A VOYAGE TO SAGADAHOC. Cambridge: John Wilson and Son, 1880. One of a "small ed...for private distribution." 3/4 leather, marbled eps, orig front wrap bound in. 25.2 cm. 43pp. *PARMER.* $250

Davies, John. PHRENOLOGY: FAD AND SCIENCE, A 19TH CENTURY AMERICAN CRUSADE. 1971, 1st ed, reprinted. *FYE.* $50

Davies, L.P. ASSIGNMENT ABACUS. London: Barrie & Jenkins, 1975. 1st ed. Fine in price-clipped dj. *MORDIDA.* $25

Davies, L.P. THE SHADOW BEFORE. London: Barrie & Jenkins, 1971. 1st Eng. ed. Fine in price-clipped dj w/minor wear at spine ends, along top edge and at corners. *MORDIDA.* $25

Davies, L.P. WHAT DID I DO TOMORROW? Barrie & Jenkins: London, 1972. 1st ed. Fine in dj. *MORDIDA.* $25

Davies, N. De Garis. THE TOMB OF ANTEFOKER, VIZIER OF SESOSTRIS I, AND OF HIS WIFE, SENET. London: George Allen & Unwin, 1920. 1st ed. Color frontis, 30 plts (5 color). Signature. Good. *ARCHAEOLOGIA.* $250

Davies, Nina M. and Alan H. Gardiner. ANCIENT EGYPTIAN PAINTINGS. 3 vols. complete. Chicago: Chicago Univ Press, 1936. Ltd ed. Lrg folio, 8vo, full pigskin expertly rebacked. Text xlviii + 209pp. Plts (2 vols) 104 color plts. Good. Rare. *ARCHAEOLOGIA.* $5,000

Davies, Robertson et al. RENOWN AT STRATFORD. Toronto: Clarke, Irwin, 1953. 1st ed. VG+ in VG dj w/chips and tears. *LAME DUCK.* $50

Davies, Robertson et al. THRICE THE BRINDLED CAT HATH MEWED. Toronto: Clarke Irwin, 1955. 1st ed. Bookplate. Fine, dj has a few chips, some edgewear. *ELSE FINE.* $70

Davies, Robertson et al. THRICE THE BRINDLED CAT HATH MEWED. Toronto: Clarke, Irwin, 1955. 1st ed. NF in VG dj/few tears and chip to front panel. *LAME DUCK.* $45

Davies, Robertson et al. TWICE HAVE THE TRUMPETS SOUNDED. Toronto: Clarke Irwin, 1954. 1st ed. Color illus. by Grant MacDonald. Fine, sm chips at dj spine ends. *ELSE FINE.* $65

Davies, Robertson et al. TWICE THE TRUMPETS HAVE SOUNDED. Toronto: Clarke, Irwin, 1954. 1st ed. Dj flaps taped to pastedowns, overall VG. *LAME DUCK.* $40

Davies, Robertson. A JIG FOR THE GYPSY. Toronto: Clarke Irwin, 1954. 1st ed. Bkpl, o/w NF in VG dj. *LOPEZ.* $100

Davies, Robertson. A MIXTURE OF FRAILTIES. NY: Scribner's, (1958). 1st Amer ed. Owner name, address, o/w Fine in sl spine-sunned dj, but still at least VG. *LOPEZ.* $75

Davies, Robertson. A MIXTURE OF FRAILTIES. Scribner's, 1958. 1st Amer ed. Fine in dj w/darkened spine, lt chips. *STAHR.* $60

Davies, Robertson. A VOICE FROM THE ATTIC. NY: Knopf (1960). 1st ed. Fine in NF dj. *DORN.* $60

Davies, Robertson. A VOICE FROM THE ATTIC. NY: Knopf, 1960. 1st US ed. Rev copy w/slip laid in. NF in VG+ price clipped dj w/few short edge tears. *LAME DUCK.* $85

Davies, Robertson. FIFTH BUSINESS. NY: Viking, (1970). 1st US ed. Just About Fine in like dj. *CAPTAIN'S BOOKSHELF.* $45

Davies, Robertson. FIFTH BUSINESS. Toronto: Macmillan (1970). 1st Canadian ed. Name, else NF in torn dj (nearly closed) at fold of front flap (does not detract); lt chipping. *DORN.* $70

Davies, Robertson. MURTHER & WALKING SPIRITS. NY: Viking, (1991). Uncorrected proof of 1st Amer ed. Fine in wraps. *LOPEZ.* $45

Davies, Robertson. MURTHER & WALKING SPIRITS. Viking, 1991. Advance reading copy of Amer ed. Fine in dec wraps. One corner bumped. *STAHR.* $45

Davies, Robertson. ONE HALF ROBERTSON DAVIES. NY, (1978). 1st ed. Fine in like dj. *POLYANTHOS.* $25

Davies, Robertson. THE LYRE OF ORPHEUS. Pennsylvania: Franklin Library, 1988. 1st ed. VF in dec. leather binding, aeg, ribbon marker. Signed & ltd. *ELSE FINE.* $55

Davies, Robertson. THE MANTICORE. NY: Viking (1972). 1st ed. Fine in dj. *DORN.* $50

Davies, Robertson. THE MANTICORE. Toronto: Macmillan, 1972. 1st ed. Fine in dj. *JUVELIS.* $100

Davies, Robertson. THE PERSONAL ART: READING TO GOOD PURPOSE. London: S & W, (1961). 1st ed. Pub only in England. Fine in price-clipped NF dj, a little tanned at spine, w/slight soiling. *BETWEEN COVERS.* $125

Davies, Robertson. THE REBEL ANGELS. Toronto: Macmillan of Canada, (1981). 1st ed. Fine in lightly rubbed dj. *CAPTAIN'S BOOKSHELF.* $60

Davies, Robertson. THE REBEL ANGELS. Toronto: Macmillan of Canada, 1981. 1st ed. Fine in dj. *JUVELIS.* $40

Davies, Robertson. THE TABLE TALK OF SAMUEL MARCHBANKS. London, 1951. 1st UK ed. NF in NF dj but for some spine darkening. *PETTLER.* $75

Davies, Robertson. WORLD OF WONDERS. NY: Viking (1975). 1st ed. Fine in dj. *DORN.* $40

Davies, Robertson. WORLD OF WONDERS. NY: Viking, 1976. 1st US ed. Fine in NF dj. *ARCHER.* $30

Davies, Robertson. WORLD OF WONDERS. NY: Viking Press, (1975). Adv reading copy of 1st US ed. Fine in wrappers (touch of spine fading). *CAPTAIN'S BOOKSHELF.* $40

Davis, Angela. AN AUTOBIOGRAPHY. Random House, 1974. 1st ed. About Fine in dj. *STAHR.* $30

Davis, Audrey and Mark Dreyfuss. THE FINEST INSTRUMENTS EVER MADE: A BIBLIOGRAPHY OF MEDICAL, DENTAL, OPTICAL, AND PHARMACEUTICAL COMPANY TRADE LITERATURE; 1700-1939. Arlington, MA, 1986. 1st ed. *FYE.* $50

Davis, Barbara A. EDWARD S. CURTIS: THE LIFE AND TIMES OF A SHADOW CATCHER. (SF): Chronicle Books, (1985). 1st ed. Price clipped. Fine in Fine dj. *AKA.* $75

Davis, Britton. THE TRUTH ABOUT GERONIMO. Milo Milton Quaife (ed). New Haven: Yale Univ, 1929. 1st ed. 12 plts (incl 1 map). Fine. *OREGON.* $75

Davis, Britton. THE TRUTH ABOUT GERONIMO. New Haven: Yale Univ Press, 1929. 1st ed. Fine. *LAURIE.* $100

Davis, Burke. OUR INCREDIBLE CIVIL WAR. NY, (1960). 1st ed. Small piece torn from dj o/w VG+. *PRATT.* $30

Davis, Burke. THE BILLY MITCHELL STORY. Phila: Chilton Book Co, 1969. 1st ed. VG. *BURCHAM.* $25

Davis, Burke. WHISPER MY NAME. NY: Rinehart & Co, Inc, (c1949). 1st ed, 1st bk. Inscribed. VG in soiled, torn dj. *HELLER.* $75

Davis, C.M. and T. Newman. LOS ANGELES ILLUSTRATED. (LA): Kingsley-Barnes & Neuner Co, (c. 1898). Ptd on rectos only. Recent gold-stamped cl w/string binder, final 2 leaves chipped and repaired by lamination. *DAWSON'S.* $175

Davis, Carl L. ARMING THE UNION. Port Washington, 1973. 1st ed. Fine in Fine dj. *PRATT.* $35

Davis, Charles G. SHIP MODELS: HOW TO BUILD THEM. Salem, 1925. Pub. 11. 16 plts, fldg plans in pocket. Fine, dj. Prospectus laid in. *LEFKOWICZ.* $95

Davis, Charles G. SHIPPING & CRAFT IN SILHOUETTE. Salem, 1929. Pub. 20. VF. dj. *LEFKOWICZ.* $65

Davis, Charles G. SHIPS OF THE PAST. Salem, 1929. Pub. 19. Fine. Worn dj. *LEFKOWICZ.* $125

Davis, Charles G. THE BUILT-UP SHIP MODEL. Salem, 1933. Pub. 25. 37 plts. Dj. *LEFKOWICZ.* $95

Davis, Charles G. THE SHIP MODEL BUILDER'S ASSISTANT. Salem, 1926. Pub 12. Fine. Worn dj. Prospectus laid in. *LEFKOWICZ.* $85

Davis, Charles H.S. (ed). THE EGYPTIAN BOOK OF THE DEAD. THE MOST ANCIENT...NY & London: Putnam, 1901. 99 plts. Orig cl, worn, edges rubbed, spine torn; sl shaken, o/w Good. *WORLDWIDE.* $195

Davis, David. ACUTE HYDROCEPHALUS, OR WATER IN THE HEAD, AND INFLAMMATORY DISEASE, AND CURABLE EQUALLY BY THE SAME MEANS WITH OTHER DISEASES OF INFLAMMATION. Phila, 1840. 1st Amer ed. Stiff wrappers, 126pp. *FYE.* $75

Davis, Dorothy Salisbury. THE HABIT OF FEAR. NY: Scribner's, (1987). 1st ed. Signed. Fine in Fine dj. *UNGER.* $35

Davis, Duke. FLASHLIGHTS FROM MOUNTAIN AND PLAIN. Bound Brook, NJ: The Pentecostal Union, 1911. 4 color plts, 3pp ads. Black and gold stamped cl. *DAWSON'S.* $75

Davis, Edward. OPERATIVE OBSTETRICS INCLUDING THE SURGERY OF THE NEWBORN. Phila, 1911. 1st ed. 264 illus. *FYE.* $50

Davis, Elmer O. (comp). THE FIRST FIVE YEARS OF THE RAILROAD ERA IN COLORADO, JUNE 19, 1867 TO JUNE 19, 1872....(Denver): Sage Books, (1948). Maps on eps, cl, signed twice. VG+ in chipped dj. *BOHLING.* $65

Davis, George. RECOLLECTIONS OF A SEA WANDERER'S LIFE....NY, 1878. 1st ed. 181.408Pp. Orig pict cl (spine faded). Howes D111. *GINSBERG.* $200

Davis, H.L. BEULAH LAND. London: Cassell & Company, (1950). 1st British ed. Map. Fine, clean chipped dj. *AUTHORS OF THE WEST.* $35

Davis, H.L. HARP OF A THOUSAND STRINGS. William Morrow & Co., 1947. 1st ed. Fine, name, Nice dj, chipped. *AUTHORS OF THE WEST.* $25

Davis, H.L. HONEY IN THE HORN. NY: Harper, 1935. 1st ed. VG in dj (internally repaired, strengthened w/tape). Only Good. *LOPEZ.* $50

Davis, H.L. KETTLE OF FIRE. Morrow, 1959. 1st ed. Fine in dj. *AUTHORS OF THE WEST.* $15

Davis, H.L. TEAM BELLS WOKE ME AND OTHER STORIES. Morrow, 1953. 1st ed. Fine, Nice sl chipped dj. *AUTHORS OF THE WEST.* $50

Davis, H.L. THE DISTANT MUSIC. William Morrow, 1957. 1st ed. Fine, clean chipped dj. *AUTHORS OF THE WEST.* $35

Davis, Henry T. SOLITARY PLACES MADE GLAD...Cincinnati, 1890. 422pp. Orig cl, rubber lib stamp. Frontis, port. Howes D114. *GINSBERG.* $100

Davis, Jefferson. THE PAPERS OF JEFFERSON DAVIS. Baton Rouge, 1971. Monroe, Haskell M., Jr. and James T. McIntosh, (eds). 1st ed. 2 vols. Orig cl. Dj. *GINSBERG.* $65

Davis, John. TRAVELS OF FOUR YEARS AND A HALF IN THE UNITED STATES OF AMERICA DURING 1798, 1799, 1800, 1801, AND 1802. NY: Henry Holt, 1909. *HUDSON*. $45

Davis, John. TRAVELS OF JOHN DAVIS IN THE UNITED STATES OF AMERICA 1798 TO 1802. Boston: Bibliophile Soc, 1910. 2 vols. J. V. Cheney (ed). Orig boards, vellum spines, boxed. One of 487 sets. *GINSBERG*. $175

Davis, Keith. DESIRE CHARNAY. Albuquerque: Univ of NM Press, (1981). 1st ed. Good in dj. *SILVER*. $30

Davis, Lindsey. SHADOWS IN BRONZE. London: Sidgwick & Jackson, 1990. 1st ed. Signed. VF in dj. *MORDIDA*. $50

Davis, Lindsey. SILVER PIGS. NY: Crown Pubs, 1989. 1st Amer ed. VF in dj. *MORDIDA*. $25

Davis, Lindsey. THE IRON HAND OF MARS. London: Hutchinson, 1992. 1st ed. Signed. VF in dj. *MORDIDA*. $45

Davis, Lindsey. VENUS IN COPPER. London: Hutchinson, 1991. 1st ed. Signed. VF in dj. *MORDIDA*. $45

Davis, Loyal. NEUROLOGICAL SURGERY. Chicago, 1936. 1st ed. 172 illus. *FYE*. $100

Davis, Loyal. THE PRINCIPLES OF NEUROLOGICAL SURGERY. Phila, 1946. 3rd ed. *FYE*. $50

Davis, Martha Ann. POEMS OF LAURA; An Original American Work. Petersburg, (VA): (Whitworth & Yancey, printers), 1818. 1st ed. 12mo, 106,(4)pp. Orig full calf. Boards rather bowed and lightly rubbed, occasional lt dampstain, front fly lacking. VG. *CHAPEL HILL*. $375

Davis, Mary Lee. SOURDOUGH GOLD. W.A. Wilde: Boston, 1933. Fldg map. Blue cl, VG. *CONNOLLY & WADE*. $45

Davis, Matthew L. MEMOIRS OF AARON BURR. NY 1837. 2 vols. Frontis, fold-out letter. 3/4 lea. NF. *POLYANTHOS*. $150

Davis, Rear-Admiral C.H. NARRATIVE OF THE NORTH POLAR EXPEDITION, U.S. SHIP POLARIS. Washington, 1876. Many tissue-covered engr, 6 maps, 2 photo-lithos. Large 4to. Emb cl. Shelfwear. Good. *ARTIS*. $150

Davis, Richard Harding. ABOUT PARIS. NY: Harper & Bros., (1895). NF in lightly soiled, VG dj w/minor edgewear and a small piece lacking from bottom edge of rear panel. 2nd prtg. Very Scarce in dj. BAL 4519 (1st prtg.). *CHAPEL HILL*. $50

Davis, Richard Harding. CUBA IN WAR TIME. NY: R.H. Russell, 1897. 1st ed. Glt top. *HUDSON*. $75

Davis, Richard Harding. IN THE FOG. NY, 1901. 1st ed. Illus by Thomas Mitchell Pierce & F.D. Steele. VG. *McCLINTOCK*. $10

Davis, Richard Harding. NOTES OF A WAR CORRESPONDENT. NY, 1912. Fine. *O'NEILL*. $25

Davis, Richard Harding. RULERS OF THE MEDITERRANEAN. NY: Harper, 1894. x,228pp. 1st ed, 1st state. Dec grn cl. Lacks ffep. BAL 4515. *SCHOYER'S*. $15

Davis, Richard Harding. THE SCARLET CAR. Scribner's, 1907. 1st ed. Illus Frederic Steele. NF. *BEBBAH*. $25

Davis, Richard Harding. THE WEST FROM A CAR-WINDOW. London: Harper & Brothers, c1892. 1st ed. Cover spotted. *HUDSON*. $65

Davis, Richard Harding. THE WEST FROM A CAR-WINDOW. NY: Harper, (1892). Early ed. Spine soiled. Spine tip & little corner wear, o/w VG. *DIAMOND*. $25

Davis, Richard Harding. VAN BIBBER AND OTHERS. NY: Harper & Bros., 1892. Owner's name, tiny bkseller's label, else NF. 1st ed, 1st prtg, w/no ads at rear. BAL 4512. *CHAPEL HILL*. $45

Davis, Stephen Chapin. CALIFORNIA GOLD RUSH MERCHANT, THE JOURNAL OF STEPHEN CHAPIN DAVIS. San Marino: The Huntington Lib, 1956. Owner inscrips. Half cl. VG. *PARMER*. $25

Davis, Varina Howell. JEFFERSON DAVIS...A Memoir by His Wife. In Two Vols. NY: Belford Co. (1890). 1st ed. Thick 8vo. xviii,700; xxxii, 940pp. 2 fldg maps, frontis each vol. Orig blue cl, gilt. Back cover of vol 2 bit soiled. *KARMIOLE*. $175

Davis, W. W. H. THE SPANISH CONQUEST OF NEW MEXICO. Doylestown, Pa, 1869. 1st ed. 483pp. Port, fldg map. Orig cl w/title in gilt on spine, minor foxing. Inscr. Howes D141 (aa). Rare. Privately printed in sm ed. *GINSBERG*. $750

Davis, William C. (ed). SHADOWS OF THE STORM. Vol. 1 of THE IMAGE OF WAR: 1861-1865. GC, 1981. 1st ed. Light dj wear o/w Fine. *PRATT*. $35

Davis, William C. BATTLE FOR NEW MARKET. GC, (1975). 1st ed. Signed. Dj torn o/w VG. *PRATT*. $30

Davson, Hugh. THE PHYSIOLOGY OF THE EYE. London, 1949. 1st ed. Scarce. *FYE*. $50

Davy, Humphrey. ELEMENTS OF AGRICULTURAL CHEMISTRY....London: Longman, et al, 1814. 2nd ed. 479pp, index. Worn calf backed boards, 9 fldg plts. *SECOND LIFE*. $225

Davy, John. NOTES AND OBSERVATIONS ON THE IONIAN ISLANDS AND MALTA....London, 1842. 6 engr plts, table, half-titles. (Lacks preface and fldg map, almost always missing). 2 vols. Orig dec cl, recased, new eps. 436; 500pp. Sound, tight. *O'NEILL*. $550

Davy, Norman. BRITISH SCIENTIFIC LITERATURE IN THE SEVENTEENTH CENTURY. London, 1953. 1st ed. Dj. *FYE*. $25

Daws, Gavan. SHOAL OF TIME: A HISTORY OF THE HAWAIIAN ISLANDS. NY: Macmillan, (1968). 1st ed. Fine in Fine dj. *BOOK MARKET*. $50

Dawson, Fielding and Jack Boyd. 2 & 4 POEMS. (Black Mountain, NC: Fielding Dawson, 1950). 1st ed. One of 250. Signed by both poets. Stapled self-wrappers. VF. *JAFFE*. $350

Dawson, Fielding. A SIMPLE WISH FOR A SINCERE AND MEANINGFUL CHRISTMAS. Black Mountain, NC: Black Mountain College Print Shop, (1950). 1st ed. Signed. VF. *JAFFE*. $375

Dawson, Fielding. KRAZY KAT/THE UNVEILING AND OTHER STORIES FROM 1951-1968. LA: Black Sparrow, 1969. Ltd ed, 1000 in paper wrappers. This copy signed. Fine in acetate dj. *POLYANTHOS*. $30

Dawson, Fielding. MAN STEPS INTO SPACE. NY: Shortstop, 1965. Wraps. 1/500. Fine. *BEASLEY*. $35

Dawson, Fielding. THE BLACK MOUNTAIN BOOK. New ed, rev, enl. (Rocky Mount): NC Wesleyan College Press, (1990). Uncorrected proof. Fine. *CAPTAIN'S BOOKSHELF*. $75

Dawson, Fielding. THE MANDALAY DREAM. Indianapolis, 1971. 1st Amer ed. Signed presentation. Fine in like dj. *POLYANTHOS*. $40

Dawson, George M. THE JOURNALS OF GEORGE M. DAWSON: BRITISH COLUMBIA, 1875-1878. Vancouver: Univ of British Columbia Press, 1989. Review copy. As New in slipcase. 2 vol set. *PARMER*. $65

Dawson, Janet. KINDRED CRIMES. London: Macmillan, 1990. 1st British ed. Signed. Sl spine crease o/w Fine in dj. *SILVER DOOR*. $30

Dawson, Janet. KINDRED CRIMES. NY: St. Martin's, (1990). 1st ed. Signed. Fine in Fine dj. *UNGER*. $35

Dawson, W.L. THE BIRDS OF OHIO, A COMPLETE, SCIENTIFIC AND POPULAR DESCRIPTION OF THE 320 SPECIES....L. Jones (intro). 80 colored plts. 2 vols. Columbus, 1903. Blue buckram. Corners, spine ends scuffed & fraying; hinges cracked; bkpls. *SUTTON*. $95

Dawson, W.R. A LEECHBOOK OR COLLECTION OF MEDICAL RECIPES OF THE FIFTEENTH CENTURY. London: Macmillan, 1934. VG. *BOOKCELL*. $45

Dawson, W.R. THE HUXLEY PAPERS, A DESCRIPTIVE CATALOGUE OF THE CORRESPONDENCE...OF THE RIGHT HON. THOMAS HENRY HUXLEY. London: Macmillan, 1946. NF. *MIKESH.* $65

Day, A. Grove. HAWAII AND ITS PEOPLE. NY: Duell, Sloan & Pearce, (1955). 1st ed. Good+ in chipped dj. *ACADEMIC.* $27

Day, A.M. NORTH AMERICAN WATERFOWL. Harrisburg, 1949. Eps tanned. *SUTTON.* $40

Day, Beth. GLACIER PILOT. NY: Holt & Co, (1957). 1st ed. VG in Good+ dj. *BLUE DRAGON.* $27.50

Day, Donald (ed). THE AUTOBIOGRAPHY OF WILL ROGERS. Houghton Mifflin/Riverside Press, 1949. 1st ed. VG. *CONNOLLY & WADE.* $20

Day, Donald. BIG COUNTRY TEXAS. NY: Duell, Sloan & Pearce, 1947. 1st ed. Fine in Good+ dj. *CONNOLLY & WADE.* $35

Day, J.W. COASTAL ADVENTURE, A BOOK ABOUT MARSHES AND THE SEA; SHOOTING AND FISHING...London: Harrap, 1949. Fine in VG+ dj. *MIKESH.* $35

Day, J.W. FARMING ADVENTURE. London: Harrap, (1949). Photos, plts. Fine in VG dj. *MIKESH.* $25

Day, Jeremiah. AN INTRODUCTION TO ALGEBRA. New Haven: Durrie and Peck, 1839. 332pp, 2 fldg plts. Full lea. Front cvr loose, foxing, lt pencilling. Good. *SMITHFIELD.* $45

Day Lewis, C. SELECTED POEMS. New Hogarth Library II, 1940. 1st ed. Cocked, else Fine in dj. *WOOLMER.* $35

Day, Lewis F. ALPHABETS OLD & NEW, CONTAINING OVER ONE HUNDRED AND FIFTY COMPLETE ALPHABETS, THIRTY SERIES OF NUMERALS... London: B.T. Batsford: 1902. Covers rubbed. *OAK KNOLL.* $45

Dazai, Osamu. NO LONGER HUMAN. Trans by Donald Keene. Norfolk: New Direction, (1958). 1st Amer ed. NF in VG dj. *DORN.* $45

De Arment, Robert, KNIGHTS OF THE GREEN CLOTH. Univ Okla, (1982). 1st ed. VF in VF dj. *OREGON.* $30

de Beauvoir, Simone. MEMOIRS OF A DUTIFUL DAUGHTER. Cleveland: World, 1959. 1st ed. VG in dj. *LOPEZ.* $35

de Beauvoir, Simone. THE MANDARINS. Cleveland & NY: The World Publishing Co., (1956). Fine in VG pict dj. 1st Amer ed. *CHAPEL HILL.* $35

de Beauvoir, Simone. THE SECOND SEX. NY: Knopf, 1953. 1st Amer ed. Little musty, in faded sl chipped dj. *SCHOYER'S.* $35

De Blois, Austen Kennedy. THE PIONEER SCHOOL: A HISTORY OF SHURTLEFF COLLEGE....Chicago: Fleming H. Revell, 1900. 1st ed. VG. *LAURIE.* $22.50

de Brunhoff, Jean. BABAR THE KING. Harrison Smith & Haas, 1935. 1st Amer ed. Fraying to top, bottom of spine, pict boards worn, soil, ffep missing. Good. Scarce. *BEBBAH.* $50

de Brunhoff, Jean. BABAR THE KING. NY: Random House, (1935). 1st Amer ed. Orig pict boards. Remnants of stickers, sl rubbed, else VG. *CHAPEL HILL.* $150

de Brunhoff, Laurent. BABAR'S COUSIN, THAT RASCAL ARTHUR. NY: Random House, (1946). 1st Amer ed. Orig pict boards. Rear fep pasted to pastedown, else VG. *CHAPEL HILL.* $75

de Camp, L. Sprague (ed). SPRAGUE DE CAMP'S NEW ANTHOLOGY. Panther Books, 1953. 1st ed. Staining to cvrs, else VG. *MADLE.* $40

de Camp, L. Sprague and Fletcher Pratt. THE CASTLE OF IRON. NY: Gnome Press, (1950). 1st ed. Some soiling to top, else NF in worn dj. *OTHER WORLDS.* $35

de Camp, L. Sprague and P. Schuyler Miller. GENUS HOMO. Reading: Fantasy Press, 1950. 1st ed. One of 500 numbered, signed by both authors. Bkpl, name, date else NF in Fine (as New) dj. *OTHER WORLDS.* $125

de Camp, L. Sprague and Catherine C. de Camp. ANCIENT RUINS AND ARCHAEOLOGY. GC, 1964. 1st ed. Faint rubber stamp across top closed edges of pages. Fine in VG dj. *McCLINTOCK.* $27.50

de Camp, L. Sprague and Fletcher Pratt. LAND OF UNREASON. Holt, 1942. 1st ed. VG. *MADLE.* $45

de Camp, L. Sprague and Fletcher Pratt. WALL OF SERPENTS. NY: Avalon Books, (1960). 1st ed. Fine in VG+ dj. *BERNARD.* $150

de Camp, L. Sprague and Willy Ley. LANDS BEYOND. Rinehart, 1952. 1st ed. NF in dj. *MADLE.* $20

de Camp, L. Sprague. DIVIDE AND RULE. Fantasy Press, 1948. 1st ed. One of 500 numbered, signed. NF in dj. *MADLE.* $175

de Camp, L. Sprague. DIVIDE AND RULE. Reading: Fantasy Press, 1948. 1st ed. One of 500 signed, numbered. Bkpl, name, date. Lt edgewear, sl fading of red lettering on spine, else VG+ in dj. *OTHER WORLDS.* $65

de Camp, L. Sprague. GREAT CITIES OF THE ANCIENT WORLD. GC: Doubleday, 1972. 1st ed. 136 illus, 14 maps. VG in VG dj. *BLUE DRAGON.* $20

de Camp, L. Sprague. LEST DARKNESS FALL. Holt, 1941. 1st ed. Good+. *MADLE.* $65

de Camp, L. Sprague. LOVECRAFT: A BIOGRAPHY. GC: Doubleday, 1975. 1st ed. VG+ in NF dj. *OTHER WORLDS.* $40

de Camp, L. Sprague. ROGUE QUEEN. Doubleday, 1951. 1st ed. Fine in dj. Inscribed. *MADLE.* $125

de Camp, L. Sprague. THE BRONZE GOD OF RHODES. Doubleday, 1960. 1st ed. NF in dj. *MADLE.* $75

de Camp, L. Sprague. THE CONTINENT MAKERS. Twayne, 1953. 1st ed. Fine in sl frayed dj. *MADLE.* $45

de Camp, L. Sprague. THE DRAGON OF THE ISHTAR GATE. GC: Doubleday, 1961. 1st ed. VF in dj. Corrected map laid in. *ELSE FINE.* $145

de Camp, L. Sprague. THE HEROIC AGE OF AMERICAN INVENTION. Doubleday, 1961. 1st ed. Fine in dj. *MADLE.* $50

de Camp, L. Sprague. THE TOWER OF ZANID. NY: Avalon, 1958. 1st ed. Fine; minor wear at dj extremities. *ELSE FINE.* $50

de Camp, L. Sprague. THE TRITONIAN RING. Twayne, 1953. 1st ed. VG in dj. *MADLE.* $40

de Camp, L. Sprague. WALL OF SERPENTS. HW: Phantasia Press, 1978. 1st ed. VF in dj, slipcase. 1/200 signed. *ELSE FINE.* $125

De Chair, Somerset. THE FIRST CRUSADE. THE DEEDS OF THE FRANKS AND OTHER JERUSALEMITES...The Golden Cockerel Press, 1945. Ltd ed of 500. *WEBER.* $300

De Chamerlat, Christian Antoine. FALCONRY AND ART. London: Sotheby's, 1987. 1st ed. NF in dj. *OLD LONDON.* $95

De Costa, B.F. LAKE GEORGE; ITS SCENES....NY: Anson D.F. Randolph & Co. 1869. 186pp, frontis, 10 plts. Teg. Fine. *KARMIOLE.* $75

De Fonvielle, W. THUNDER AND LIGHTNING. NY: Charles Scribner, 1869. T.L. Phipson (ed). Ex-lib in worn red cl (fraying, foxing, ink name of lib, o/w tight). *KNOLLWOOD.* $40

De Forest, Emily J. JAMES COLLES, 1788-1883:LIFE AND LETTERS. NY: privately printed, 1926. 1st ed. Orig dec cl backed boards. One of 400. *GINSBERG.* $75

De Forest, John W. HISTORY OF THE INDIANS OF CONNECTICUT FROM THE EARLIEST KNOWN PERIOD TO 1850. Hartford: Wm. Jas. Hamersley, 1852. 509pp. Cloth. Partial map. Spine missing, minor foxing. *GIBBS.* $37.50

De Forest, John William. A UNION OFFICER IN THE RECONSTRUCTION. Ed by James H. Croushore and David M. Potter. New Haven, 1948. 1st ed. 211pp. VG+ in dj. *PRATT.* $50

de Francesco, Grete. THE POWER OF THE CHARLATAN. New Haven, 1939. 1st ed. Backstrip faded. Scarce. *FYE.* $50

De Gaury. Gerald. TRAVELLING GENT. THE LIFE OF ALEXANDER KINGLAKE (1809-1891). London, 1972. Dj. *O'NEILL.* $25

de Hegermann-Lindencrone, Lillie. IN THE COURTS OF MEMORY 1858-1875, FROM CONTEMPORARY LETTERS. NY: Harper, 1912. 1st US ed. VG. *AARD.* $25

De Jesus, Carolina Maria. CHILD OF THE DARK. NY: Dutton, 1962. 1st ed. VG in dj. *LOPEZ.* $25

De Kay, I.E. ZOOLOGY OF NEW-YORK, OR THE NEW-YORK FAUNA. Part V. Mollusca. Part VI. Crustacea. Albany, 1843-44. 2 vols in 1. 53 hand-colored plts. 2 vols in 1. Wear to corners & spine ends, light foxing, plts clean, except for 2 which contain a tarnish wash background.) Ex-lib. *SUTTON.* $265

De La Cierva, Juan and Don Rose. WINGS OF TOMORROW: THE STORY OF THE AUTOGIRO. (N.p.): Brewer, Warren & Putnam, (1931). 1st ed. Small spot fore-edge, former owner's sig, name stamp, else tight. Scarce. Lacking dj. *BETWEEN COVERS.* $150

de la Mare, Walter. BELLS AND GRASS. Dorothy Lathrop (illus). NY: Viking, 1942. 1st ed. Cl w/pict inset. Edgewear. Sm tear, soil to dj. VG. *ACADEMIC LIBRARY.* $30

de la Mare, Walter. DING DONG BELL. NY: Knopf, 1924. 1st ed. Fine; small chip spine top, dj lightly aged. *ELSE FINE.* $20

de la Mare, Walter. EIGHT TALES. Sauk City: Arkham House, 1971. 1st ed. Fine in dj. *OTHER WORLDS.* $30

de la Mare, Walter. LISPET, LISPETT AND VAINE. London, 1923. Ltd. to 200 numbered and signed. This copy marked "Specimen copy" and is signed. 3 orig wood-blocks designed and engr by W.P. Robins. Hand set, printed on handmade paper. Bound in full vellum. Fine. *POLYANTHOS.* $65

de la Mare, Walter. STUFF AND NONSENSE AND SO ON. London: Constable & Co., 1927. 1st ed. Dj edgeworn. *DAWSON'S.* $150

de la Mare, Walter. THE CONNOISSEUR AND OTHER STORIES. London, (1926). Ltd ed, 243/250 only. Signed. Uncut and mostly unopened. Spine sunned. Fine. *POLYANTHOS.* $60

de la Mare, Walter. THE VEIL AND OTHER POEMS. London, 1921. 1st ed. Ltd ed. 115/250 only. Signed. Uncut and partly unopened. Spine and label sunned, little edge sunned. Fine. *POLYANTHOS.* $50

de la Torre, Lillian. DR. SAM: JOHNSON, DETECTOR. NY: Alfred A. Knopf, 1946. 1st ed. Fine in dj. *MORDIDA.* $45

De la Torre, Lillian. VILLAINY DETECTED. NY: D. Appleton-Century, 1947. 1st ed. VG in price-clipped dj w/soiled back panel, internal spotting and several nicks and tiny tears. *MORDIDA.* $35

De Laurence, L.W. THE GREAT BOOK OF MAGICAL ART, HINDU MAGIC, AND EAST INDIAN OCCULTISM. AND THE BOOK OF SECRET HINDU, CEREMONIAL, AND TALISMANIC MAGIC. In One Volume. Chicago: The De Laurence Co. Inc, (1939). "14th ed." *KARMIOLE.* $60

De Lerma, Dominique-Rene, ed. REFLECTIONS ON AFRO-AMERICAN MUSIC. Kent: Kent State Univ Press, 1973. 1st ed. Fine in sl rubbed dj. *BEASLEY.* $35

De Lint, J.G. ATLAS OF THE HISTORY OF MEDICINE, ANATOMY. NY, 1926. 1st ed. Folio, 96pp. Scarce. *FYE.* $200

De Long, Emma Wotton. EXPLORER'S WIFE. NY: Dodd, Mead, 1938. Good; spine faded; text clean, tight, brds sl rubbed, cvr edges faded. *PARMER.* $60

De Long, Emma Wotton. EXPLORER'S WIFE. NY: Dodd, Mead, 1938. Spine faded, text clean, tight, boards sl rubbed, cover edges faded. Good. *PARMER.* $60

De Manaceine, Marie. SLEEP: ITS PHYSIOLOGY, PATHOLOGY, HYGIENE, AND PSYCHOLOGY. London, 1897. 1st Eng trans. *FYE.* $60

De Mille, James. A STRANGE MANUSCRIPT FOUND IN A BOTTLE. Harper, 1900. VG. *MADLE.* $35

De Mille, James. A STRANGE MANUSCRIPT FOUND IN A COPPER CYLINDER. NY: Harper & Bros., 1888. 1st ed. Illus. by Gilbert Gaul. Navy, gold & silver dec. binding. Bright, beautiful copy. *BERNARD.* $150

de Monberaut, Chevalier Montault. THE MEMOIARE JUSTIFICATIF OF THE CHEVALIER MONTAULT DE MONBERAUT. University of AL, (1965). Milor B. Howard, Robert E. Rea (trans). 1st ed. Dj (lt wear, faded spine) o/w Fine. *PRATT.* $22.50

De Monfried, Henride. PEARLS, ARMS AND HASHISH. Collected by Ida Treat. NY: McBride, 1930. 1st ed. Dj torn. VG. *WORLDWIDE.* $35

De Morgan, A. AN ESSAY ON PROBABILITIES & ON THEIR APPLICATION TO...INSURANCE OFFICES. London: Longman, Orme...1838. Cvrs worn, o/w tight, clean internally. *BOOKCELL.* $85

de Ona, Pedro. ARANCO TAMED. Charles Maxwell Lancaster and Paul Thomas Manchester (trans). Albuquerque: Univ of NM, 1948. 1st ed. Frontis. 1st Eng trans. VG. *CONNOLLY & WADE.* $75

de Poncins, Gontram. THE GHOST VOYAGE: OUT OF ESKIMO LAND. London: Victor Gollancz, 1955. 1st ed. Fine in NF dj. *GREAT EPIC.* $35

De Quille, Dan (W. Wright). THE BIG BONANZA. NY, 1947. 1st Borzoi ed. Fine. *VARNER.* $25

de Rachewiltz, Boris. BLACK EROS. NY: Lyle Stuart, (1964). Emb stamp ffep. VG in dj. *SCHOYER'S.* $35

De Ricci, Seymour. LOUIS XIV AND REGENCY, FURNITURE AND DECORATION. NY: William Helburn. (1929). 1st ed. *KARMIOLE.* $75

De River, J. Paul. THE SEXUAL CRIMINAL. Springfield, 1949. 1st ed. 281pp. *FYE.* $100

De Roo, P. HISTORY OF AMERICA BEFORE COLUMBUS, According to Documents and Approved Authors. Volume I: American Aborigines. (Volume II: European Immigrants). Phila: J.B. Lippincott Co., 1900. 1st ed. 2 vols. 5 maps (one fldg). Ltd to 1500. Bit rubbed. *KARMIOLE.* $75

De Rosier, Arthur H. THE REMOVAL OF THE CHOCTAW INDIANS. Knoxville: Univ of TN, 1970. 1st ed. As New in dj. *CONNOLLY & WADE.* $30

de Ross, Robert. THE THIRSTY LAND. Stanford Univ Press, 1948. 1st ed. Fine in VG dj. *CONNOLLY & WADE.* $42.50

De Sommieres, Colonel L.V. Vialla. TRAVELS IN MONTENEGRO; CONTAINING A TOPOGRAPHICAL, PICTURESQUE....London, 1820. 8 full-pg plts. Modern boards, cl spine. iv,108pp. Excellent. *O'NEILL.* $125

De Stael, Baroness. CONSIDERATIONS OF THE PRINCIPAL EVENTS OF THE FRENCH REVOLUTION. Posthumous work ed by The Duke de Broglie and the Baron de Stael. NY: James Eastburn, 1818. 1st US ed. 2 vols. 404; 344pp. Orig boards, uncut, hinges loose, spines worn. Upper blank margin title pg repaired where it had been cut off. Owner sigs. *SECOND LIFE.* $250

De Takats, Geza. VASCULAR SURGERY. Phila, 1959. 1st ed. *FYE.* $75

De Varigny, Charles. FOURTEEN YEARS IN THE SANDWICH ISLANDS 1855-1868. Honolulu: Univ Press of Hawaii/Hawaiian Historical Society, 1981. 1st Eng ed. New in dj. *PARMER.* $24.95

de Vaucouleurs, G. DISCOVERY OF THE UNIVERSE. NY: Macmillan, 1957, 1st ptg. VG in sl chipped dj (price-clipped). *KNOLLWOOD.* $25

De Vinne, Theodore L. THE INVENTION OF PRINTING, A COLLECTION OF FACTS AND OPINIONS...London: Trubner & Co., 1877. 2nd ed. Literary Society ink stamp first six pages. *OAK KNOLL.* $225

De Vinne, Theodore L. THE INVENTION OF PRINTING: A COLLECTION OF FACTS AND OPINIONS. NY: Francis Hart & Co, 1876. Frontis. 556pp. Bound in 3/4 brown leather, marbled paper over boards, titling in gilt on spine between raised bands, teg. Presentation, inscribed. Fly-leaf corner torn, edges of cvrs shelf worn, VG. *HELLER.* $350

De Voto, Bernard. ACROSS THE WIDE MISSOURI. Boston: Houghton Mifflin Company, 1947. 1st ed. NF in dj. *JUVELIS.* $50

De Voto, Bernard. ACROSS THE WIDE MISSOURI....Houghton Mifflin, (1947). 81 plts. VG in dj. *OREGON.* $30

De Voto, Bernard. THE CHARIOT OF FIRE. Macmillan, 1926. 1st ed. Eps foxed, else Fine. *AUTHORS OF THE WEST.* $20

De Voto, Bernard. THE CROOKED MILE. Minton, Balch & Co, 1924. 1st ed, 1st bk. Fine. *AUTHORS OF THE WEST.* $35

De Voto, Bernard. THE EASY CHAIR. Houghton Mifflin, 1955. 1st ed. Boards. Fine in dj. *AUTHORS OF THE WEST.* $20

De Voto, Bernard. THE HOUR. Houghton Mifflin, 1951. 1st ed. Signed, inscribed pres. Fine in VG dj. *MAD DOG.* $25

De Voto, Bernard. THE HOUSE OF SUN-GOES-DOWN. Macmillan, 1928. 1st ed. Fine, bkpl. *AUTHORS OF THE WEST.* $20

De Voto, Bernard. THE WORLD OF FICTION. Houghton Mifflin, 1950. 1st ed. VG in dj. *AUTHORS OF THE WEST.* $20

De Voto, Bernard. WE ACCEPT WITH PLEASURE. Little, Brown & Co, 1934. 1st ed. VG+. *AUTHORS OF THE WEST.* $17.50

De Voto, Bernard. WESTWARD THE COURSE OF EMPIRE. London: Eyre & Spottiswoode, 1954. 1st British ed. Fine in dj. *AUTHORS OF THE WEST.* $35

De Vries, Peter, and Joseph Fields. THE TUNNEL OF LOVE. Boston: Little, Brown, 1957. 1st ed. Fine in lightly used dj w/sunned spine. *BEASLEY.* $65

De Vries, Peter. INTO YOUR TENT I'LL CREEP. Boston, 1971. 1st ed. Signed presentation. Fine in like dj. *POLYANTHOS.* $35

De Vries, Peter. MRS. WALLOP. Boston: Little, Brown, (1970). 1st ed. NF in like dj. Signed. *CAPTAIN'S BOOKSHELF.* $75

De Vries, Peter. NO BUT I SAW THE MOVIE. Boston: Little, Brown, (1952). 1st ed. NF in VG dj (few short tears and a sm chip). Inscribed. *CAPTAIN'S BOOKSHELF.* $350

De Vries, Peter. REUBEN, REUBEN. Boston, 1964. 1st ed. Signed presentation. Extremities, spine minimally rubbed. Fine in dj (extremities, spine very sl frayed, few tiny edge tears). *POLYANTHOS.* $35

De Vries, Peter. SAUCE FOR THE GOOSE. Boston: Little, Brown, (1981). 1st ed. Fine in dj. Signed. *CAPTAIN'S BOOKSHELF.* $50

De Vries, Peter. THE CAT'S PAJAMAS & WITCH'S MILK. Boston: LB, (1968). 1st ed. NF in like dj. Signed. *CAPTAIN'S BOOKSHELF.* $75

De Vries, Peter. THE GLORY OF THE HUMMINGBIRD. Boston: LB, (1974). 1st ed. Fine in dj. Inscribed. *CAPTAIN'S BOOKSHELF.* $60

De Vries, Peter. THE VALE OF LAUGHTER. Boston, 1967. 1st ed. Signed presentation. Fine in like dj. *POLYANTHOS.* $35

De Vries, Peter. THROUGH THE FIELDS OF CLOVER. Boston, 1961. 1st ed. Signed presentation. Fine in price clipped dj (spine little sunned, top chipped). *POLYANTHOS.* $30

De Waal, Ronald Burt. THE WORLD BIBLIOGRAPHY OF SHERLOCK HOLMES AND DR. WATSON. Boston, (1974). 1st ed. Spine dulled. Fine in Fine dj. Fine slipcase. *McCLINTOCK.* $85

De Windt, Harry. THROUGH THE GOLD-FIELDS OF ALASKA TO BERING STRAITS. NY: Harper & Bros. 1898. 1st ed. x,(2),314pp+(2)pp of ads. Fldg map, 32 plts. Spine soiled. *KARMIOLE.* $150

De Witt, C. Chipman. BEYOND THE VERGE. Boston: Jas. H. Earle, 1896. Inner hinges cracking. *NUTMEG.* $37.50

De Zemler, Charles. ONCE OVER LIGHTLY. THE STORY OF MAN AND HIS HAIR. NY: No pub, 1939. Dj chipped. *KARMIOLE.* $30

Deacon, A. BERNARD. MALEKULA—A VANISHING PEOPLE IN THE NEW HEBRIDES. London: George Routledge & Sons, 1934. 1st ed. Orig. blue cl, very minor foxing prelims and edges. All errata slips tipped-in place. Very rare dj has sunned spine and minor chips else NF in VG+ dj. *GREAT EPIC.* $325

Deaderick, Barron. STRATEGY IN THE CIVIL WAR. Harrisburg: Military Service, 1946. 1st ed. NF. Scarce. *CONNOLLY & WADE.* $55

Dean, Henry Clay. CRIMES OF THE CIVIL WAR AND CURSE OF THE FUNDING SYSTEM. Baltimore, 1868. 1st ed. 512pp. Faded spine, a little wear and spotting, but sound and o/w VG. *PRATT.* $50

Dean, Robert George. MURDER THROUGH THE LOOKING GLASS. GC: Doubleday Crime Club, 1940. 1st ed. Fine, chips at dj spine corners. *ELSE FINE.* $25

Dean, Robert George. MURDER THROUGH THE LOOKING GLASS. GC: Doubleday Crime Club, 1940. 1st ed. Fine in dj w/chipped spine ends and corners. *MORDIDA.* $35

DeAndrea, William L. FIVE O'CLOCK LIGHTNING. St. Martin's, 1982. 1st ed. About Fine in dj. Book has small chip from boards; dj rubbed at spine. *STAHR.* $35

DeAndrea, William. KILLED IN PARADISE. NY: Mysterious Press, 1988. 1st ed. Signed. VF in dj. *SILVER DOOR.* $35.

DeAngulo, Jaime. INDIAN TALES. NY: AA Wyn, (1953). 1st ed. Fine in NF dj. Scarce. *LOPEZ.* $150

Deans, R. Storry. THE TRIALS OF FIVE QUEENS. NY: Brentano's, 1910. 1st ed. Lacks rfep, spine sunned & stained, o/w Near VG. *ARCHER.* $25

Dearborn, Henry. REVOLUTIONARY WAR JOURNALS OF...1775-1783. Chicago, Caxton Club, 1939. Orig cl boards. 1st ed. One of 350. Lloyd A. Brown and Howard H. Peckham (eds). *GINSBERG.* $150

DEATH VALLEY: A GUIDE. Boston: Houghton Mifflin, (1939). WPA Guide. Tipped in fldg map, cl w/dj. Fine. *SCHOYER'S.* $20

Deatherage, Charles. EARLY HISTORY OF GREATER KANSAS CITY, MISSOURI AND KANSAS. Vol. 1 (all pub) EARLY HISTORY TO 1870. Kansas City, 1928, Diamond Jubilee Edition. Fldg map tipped in at rear. Howes D178. VG. *OREGON.* $75

Deatherage, Charles. STEAMBOATING ON MISSOURI RIVER IN THE SIXTIES. Kansas City, (1924). 1st ed. VG. *OREGON.* $25

Deatherage, Charles. STEAMBOATING ON THE MISSOURI RIVER IN THE 'SIXTIES. (Kansas City, MO, 1924). Ptd wraps. 39pp. VG+. 2 illus. *BOHLING.* $45

Deaver, Jeffery Wilds. MANHATTAN IS MY BEAT. NY: Bantam Books, 1989. 1st ed. Pb orig. VF, unread, in wrappers. *MORDIDA.* $20

DeBarthe, Joe (ed). LIFE AND ADVENTURES OF FRANK GROUARD. Norman, (1958). 1st ed. VG+ in dj. *PRATT.* $50

DeBerg, Jean. THE IMAGE. NY: Grove, 1966. Fine in Fine dj. *BEASLEY.* $30

Debo, Angie (ed). THE COWMAN'S SOUTHWEST BEING THE REMINISCENCES OF OLIVER NELSON. Glendale, CA: The Arthur H. Clark Co, 1953. 1st ed. VF. *GIBBS.* $95

Debo, Angie (ed). THE COWMAN'S SOUTHWEST; BEING THE REMINISCENCES OF OLIVER NELSON. A.H. Clark, 1953. 1st ed. Fine. *VARNER.* $175

Debus, Allen (ed). MEDICINE IN SEVENTEENTH CENTURY ENGLAND. Berkeley, 1974. 1st ed. Dj. *FYE.* $75

DeCarava, Roy. PHOTOGRAPHS. Carmel: Friends of Photography, 1981. 1st ed. 82 photos. VG. Member's ed. *SMITH.* $60

Decatur, Stephen, Jr. PRIVATE AFFAIRS OF GEORGE WASHINGTON. Boston: Houghton Mifflin, 1933. 17 plts. Untrimmed, partially unopened. Ltd ed #35/160. Inscribed. Cl and boards, w/paper spine label. Bright. *SCHOYER'S.* $75

Decker, Amelia Stickney. THAT ANCIENT TRAIL (THE OLD MINE ROAD) (Trenton), 1942. Orig cl. Signed. VG. *BOHLING.* $45

Decker, Robert Owen. THE WHALING CITY: A HISTORY OF NEW LONDON. Chester, CT: (1976). 1st ed. Dj. Signed. *LEFKOWICZ.* $50

deCoccola, Raymond and Paul King. AYORAMA. NY: Oxford Univ Press, 1956. 1st ed. Light wear to dj and book, else VG. *PARMER.* $35

Dedmon, Emmett. FABULOUS CHICAGO. NY: Random House, 1953. 1st ed. Fine in VG dj. *CONNOLLY & WADE.* $27.50

Deering, John R. LEE AND HIS CAUSE; OR, THE WHY AND THE HOW OF THE WAR BETWEEN THE STATES. NY: Neale, 1907. 1st ed. Orig cl, light wear. *GINSBERG.* $100

Dees, Jesse Walter, Jr. FLOPHOUSE. Francestown, NH: Marshall Jones, 1948. 1st ed. 170pp. Worn dj. *AKA.* $28

Defoe, Daniel. THE FORTUNES AND MISFORTUNES OF THE FAMOUS MOLL FLANDERS. Reginald Marsh (illus). NY: LEC, 1954. One of 1500 ptd by Peter Beilenson, signed by Marsh. Dec satin. Fine, foil slipcase worn. *JAFFE.* $125

Defoe, Daniel. THE LIFE AND ADVENTURES OF ROBINSON CRUSOE. Ithaca, NY: Mack, Andrus & Woodruff, n.d. Later navy blue calf, gilt, red and grn morocco spine labels. *WEBER.* $75

Defoe, Daniel. THE LIFE AND STRANGE SURPRISING ADVENTURES...ROBINSON CRUSOE. Boston: Houghton, 1907. 1st, this ed w/illus from designs of Thomas Stothard. 2 vols. NF in cl-backed boards w/paper labels. *CAPTAIN'S BOOKSHELF.* $60

Defoe, Daniel. THE LIFE AND STRANGE SURPRISING ADVENTURES OF ROBINSON CRUSOE...London, 1791. 2 vols. 17th ed. Rebound in brown lea w/raised bands and gilt decs. *BOOKMINE.* $500

Defoe, Daniel. THE LIFE AND STRANGE SURPRISING ADVENTURES OF ROBINSON CRUSOE OF YORK, MARINER. Illus Richard Floethe. NY: Peter Pauper Press, Mount Vernon, (c. 1970). 1st ed. 284pp. End papers and edges, hand-marbled. Mint. *BOOK MARKET.* $300

DeHass, Frank S. BURIED CITIES RECOVERED. Phila: Bradley; Boston: Gurnsey, 1883. 5th ed, w/appendix. 525pp. Rebound. Ex-lib. Good. *WORLDWIDE.* $32

Dehn, Paul. QUAKE, QUAKE, QUAKE. A LEADEN TREASURY OF ENGLISH VERSE. NY, 1961. Illus by Edward Gorey. 1st ed. NF in dj (3 tiny edge tears, little edge rubbed). *POLYANTHOS.* $30

Deighton, Len. AIRSHIPWRECK. London: Jonathan Cape, 1978. 1st ed. Fine in dj w/single zeppelin postcard laid in. *MORDIDA.* $45

Deighton, Len. AIRSHIPWRECK. London: Cape, 1978. 1st ed. VF in price-clipped dj. *ELSE FINE.* $60

Deighton, Len. ACTION COOKBOOK. London: Jonathan Cape (for the Cookery Book Club), 1967. 1st thus. Minor bumping at corners & spine ends. NF, issued w/o dj. *ELSE FINE.* $45

Deighton, Len. AN EXPENSIVE PLACE TO DIE. London: Cape, (1967). 1st ed. Top secret transit docket w/documents laid in. Fine in dj nicked at spine ends. *UNGER.* $100

Deighton, Len. AN EXPENSIVE PLACE TO DIE. London: Cape, 1967. 1st ed. NF, light edgewear to dj. Lacks docket. *ELSE FINE.* $40

Deighton, Len. AN EXPENSIVE PLACE TO DIE. London: Jonathan Cape, 1967. 1st Eng ed. "In Transit" Document laid in. Fine in dj, tiny wear top of spine. *MORDIDA.* $85

Deighton, Len. AN EXPENSIVE PLACE TO DIE. NY: Putnam, 1967. 1st ed. Fine in price clipped dj w/"In Transit Docket" present. Precedes Brit ed. *ELSE FINE.* $125

Deighton, Len. BERLIN GAME, MEXICO SET & LONDON MATCH. 3 vols. NY: Alfred A. Knopf, 1984-85. 1st Amer eds. All 3 vols Fine in djs. *MORDIDA.* $50

Deighton, Len. BERLIN GAME. London: Hutchinson, 1983. 1st ed. As New in dj. *ELSE FINE.* $30

Deighton, Len. BERLIN GAME. NY: Knopf, 1983. Advance uncorrected proofs, 1st US ed. Bump and light fold, thus VG+ to NF in wraps. *BEASLEY.* $25

Deighton, Len. BILLION DOLLAR BRAIN. London: Cape, 1966. 1st ed. Fine, dj price clipped, very sl rubbed. *ELSE FINE.* $135

Deighton, Len. BILLION DOLLAR BRAIN. London: Jonathan Cape, 1966. 1st Eng ed. Fine in dj (several nicks, short closed tears; wear; creases inner flaps). *MORDIDA.* $85

Deighton, Len. BOMBER. London: Cape, 1970. 1st ed. Name. Fine, minor edgewear to jacket. *ELSE FINE.* $65

Deighton, Len. FUNERAL IN BERLIN. London: Jonathan Cape, 1964. 1st ed. Fine in dj, sm scrape near base of spine. *MORDIDA.* $85

Deighton, Len. HORSE UNDER WATER. London: Jonathan Cape, 1963. 1st ed. Crossword competition slip laid in. Fine in dj w/some tiny wear spine ends. *MORDIDA.* $150

Deighton, Len. LEN DEIGHTON'S CONTINENTAL DOSSIER. London: Michael Joseph, 1968. 1st ed. Fine in pict boards, issued w/out dj. Cloth map & ribbon markers present. *ELSE FINE.* $90

Deighton, Len. LEN DEIGHTON'S LONDON DOSSIER. London: Cape, 1967. 1st ed. Fine in dj. *ELSE FINE.* $135

Deighton, Len. LONDON MATCH. London: Hutchinson, 1985. 1st ed. VF in dj. *ELSE FINE.* $30

Deighton, Len. ONLY WHEN I LARF. London: Sphere, 1967. 1st ed. Pb orig. NF, minor rubs, faint creases to cover. *ELSE FINE.* $65

Deighton, Len. OU EST LE GARLIC. London: Penguin Books, 1963. 1st ed. NF in stiff wrappers w/light rubbing along spine edges. *MORDIDA.* $75

Deighton, Len. OU EST LE GARLIC: FRENCH COOKING IN 50 LESSONS. NY: Harper & Row, 1977. 1st hc ed. VF, issued w/o dj. *ELSE FINE.* $100

Deighton, Len. SPY HOOK. London: Hutchinson, 1988. 1st ed. VF in dj. *ELSE FINE.* $30

Deighton, Len. SPY SINKER. NY: Harper, 1990. Advance reading copy. Fine in wraps. *BEASLEY.* $30

Deighton, Len. SPY STORY. London: Jonathan Cape, 1974. 1st ed. VF in dj. *MORDIDA.* $75

Deighton, Len. SS-GB. London: Cape, (1978). 1st ed. Fine in dj. *CAPTAIN'S BOOKSHELF.* $40

Deighton, Len. THE IPCRESS FILE. NY: Simon and Schuster, 1963. 1st Amer ed. VG in dj (wear at corners; short closed tears). *MORDIDA.* $100

Deighton, Len. WINTER. London: Hutchinson, 1987. 1st ed. Fine in dj w/short closed tear. *MORDIDA*. $65

Deighton, Len. XPD. London: Hutchinson, (1981). 1st ed. Fine in dj. *CAPTAIN'S BOOKSHELF*. $35

Deighton, Len. XPD. London: Hutchinson, 1981. 1st ed. Fine in price-clipped dj. *MORDIDA*. $35

Dejerine, Joseph and E. Gauckler. THE PSYCHONEUROSES AND THEIR TREATMENT BY PSYCHOTHERAPY. Phila, 1913. 1st Eng trans. 395pp. Front cover spotted, front inner hinge cracked. *FYE*. $100

Dekens, Camiel. RIVERMAN, DESERTMAN: THE RECOLLECTIONS...AS TOLD TO TOM PATTERSON. Riverside: Press-Enterprise Co, (1963). 2nd ptg. Pict wraps. *DAWSON'S*. $25

Del Rey, Lester. ATTACK FROM ATLANTIS. NY: Winston, 1953. 1st ed. Name. Fine; dj w/minor wear, fading to spine. *ELSE FINE*. $45

Del Rey, Lester. STEP TO THE STARS. Winston, 1954. 1st ed. VG in chipped dj. *MADLE*. $35

Del Rey, Lester. THE INFINITE WORLDS OF MAYBE. Holt, 1966. 1st ed. Fine in soiled dj. *MADLE*. $35

Delabarre, Edmund Burke. DIGHTON ROCK; A STUDY OF THE WRITTEN ROCKS OF NEW ENGLAND. NY: Neale Pub. Co., 1928. 1st ed. NF in NF dj. *McGOWAN*. $150

Delafield, Francis and Charles F. Stillman. A MANUAL OF PHYSICAL DIAGNOSIS. NY: William Wood, 1878. 1st ed. 4to. 30pp, plus interleaving. 2 plts w/overlays. Orig cloth, some staining. *M & S*. $150

Delafresnaye, J.F. (ed). BRAIN MECHANISMS AND LEARNING, A SYMPOSIUM. Oxford, 1961. 1st ed. *FYE*. $50

Deland, Margaret. FLORIDA DAYS. Boston, 1889. 3/4 lea. Binding rubbed. VG-NF. *POLYANTHOS*. $75

Deland, Margaret. THE OLD GARDEN. Boston 1894. 1st Amer ed. Illus by Walter Crane. NF. *POLYANTHOS*. $50

Deland, Margaret. THE VOICE. NY: Harper, 1912. 1st ed. VG in stamped binding. *SECOND LIFE*. $35

Delaney, Ed. BOBBY SHANTZ. Barnes, 1953. VG in VG+ dj. *PLAPINGER*. $45

Delano, Alonzo. A SOJOURN WITH ROYALTY AND OTHER SKETCHES BY "OLD BLOCK" COLLECTED AND EDITED BY G. EZRA DANE. SF: George Fields, 1936. Ltd ed of 500. *WEBER*. $50

Delany, Samuel R. CITY OF A THOUSAND SUNS. NY: Ace, (1965). Pb orig. NF. *LOPEZ*. $30

Delany, Samuel R. NOVA. GC: Doubleday, 1968. 1st ed. Spine mottled from dampstaining else VG+ to NF in NF dj w/traces of edgewear. *OTHER WORLDS*. $40

Delany, Samuel R. STARS IN MY POCKET LIKE GRAINS OF SAND. Bantam, 1984. 1st ed. Fine in dj. *MADLE*. $30

Delany, Samuel R. STARS IN MY POCKETS LIKE GRAINS OF SAND. NY: Bantam, (1984). 1st ed. Fine in dj. *LOPEZ*. $30

Delany, Samuel R. THE BRIDGE OF LOST DESIRE. Arbor House, 1987. 1st ed. Fine in dj. *MADLE*. $20

Delany, Samuel R. THE MOTION OF LIGHT IN WATER. (Ultramarine Press, 1988). Ltd ed. One of 50 signed, this being One of 40 in 1/2 lea. Fine at orig list price. *LOPEZ*. $200

Delany, Samuel R. THE MOTION OF LIGHT IN WATER. NY: Arbor House/Morrow, (1988). 1st ed. Fine in Fine dj. *LOPEZ*. $25

Delavan, James. NOTES ON CALIFORNIA AND THE PLACERS. Biobooks, 1956. Ltd to 700. Fine. *OREGON*. $40

DeLillo, Don. AMERICANA. Boston: Houghton Mifflin, 1971. 1st ed, 1st bk. Orig blue cl, red boards. Almost Fine in dj. *CHAPEL HILL*. $125

DeLillo, Don. AMERICANA. Boston: Houghton Mifflin, 1971. 1st ed. Fine in dj. Signed. *CAPTAIN'S BOOKSHELF*. $300

DeLillo, Don. END ZONE. Boston: HMCo. (1972). 1st ed. 6000 ptd. Signed. VG in fragile dj (chipping, sm fold tear back panel or About VG). *DORN*. $100

DeLillo, Don. GREAT JONES STREET. Boston: HMCo. (1973). 1st ed. Signed. NF in VG rubbed price-clipped edgeworn dj. *DORN*. $90

DeLillo, Don. GREAT JONES STREET. Boston: Houghton Mifflin, 1973. Uncorrected proof. Fine in ptd wraps. *CAPTAIN'S BOOKSHELF*. $250

DeLillo, Don. GREAT JONES STREET. Boston: Houghton Mifflin, 1973. 1st ed. Fine in NF price-clipped dj. *LOPEZ*. $75

DeLillo, Don. RATNER'S STAR. NY: Knopf (1976). 1st ed. Signed. Fine in NF dj. *DORN*. $90

DeLillo, Don. RATNER'S STAR. NY: Knopf, 1976. Uncorrected proof. NF in wraps. Uncommon. *CAPTAIN'S BOOKSHELF*. $125

DeLillo, Don. RUNNING DOG. NY: Alfred A.Knopf, 1978. 1st ed. Fine in dj. Signed. *CAPTAIN'S BOOKSHELF*. $75

DeLillo, Don. THE DAY ROOM. NY: Knopf, (1987). 1st ed. Signed. *DORN*. $50

DeLillo, Don. THE DAY ROOM: A PLAY. NY: Knopf, 1987. 1st ed. As New in dj. Signed. *CAPTAIN'S BOOKSHELF*. $50

DeLillo, Don. THE NAMES. NY: Knopf (1982). 1st ed. Signed. Fine in dj. *DORN*. $75

DeLillo, Don. THE NAMES. NY: Knopf, 1982. 1st ed. As New in like dj. *DERMONT*. $35

DeLisle, General Sir Beauvoir. REMINISCENCES OF SPORT AND WAR. London: Eyre & Spottiswoode, 1939. 1st ed. Minor shelfwear, else VG+. *OLD LONDON*. $55

Dell, Anthony. LLAMA LAND. NY: Doran, (1927). 1st ed. 24 b/w plts. Cl bright, gilt, spine chipped. Contents VG+. *SILVER*. $45

Dell, Floyd. HOMECOMING. AN AUTOBIOGRAPHY. NY: Farrar, 1933. 1st ed. NF w/bit darkened spine, in lightly used dj. *BEASLEY*. $75

Dell, Floyd. JANET MARCH. London: Bodley Head, (1924). 1st UK ed. Sl soiled pub's cl, some foxing to top of leaves. *SECOND LIFE*. $45

Dell, Floyd. LOVE IN THE MACHINE AGE, A PSYCHOLOGICAL STUDY....NY, (1930). 1st ed. VG. *SECOND LIFE*. $45

Dellenbaugh, Frederick S. A CANYON VOYAGE. The Narrative of the Second Powell Expedition down the Green-Colorado River from Wyoming, and the Explorations on Land 1871 and 1872. Yale, 1926. 1st thus. VG. *FIVE QUAIL*. $40

Dellenbaugh, Frederick S. FREMONT AND '49. NY: G.P. Putnam's Sons, 1914. Blue cl. Fldg maps. Light wear, bkpl. Fldg maps. VG. *PARMER*. $75

Dellenbaugh, Frederick S. THE ROMANCE OF THE COLORADO RIVER. NY, 1903. 2nd ed. Orig pict cl, teg; xxxv,399pp. Some cover soil/fade, else Good+ to VG. *FIVE QUAIL*. $65

Deloria, Ella Cara. SPEAKING OF INDIANS. NY: Friendship Press, (1944). 1st ed. VG in sl edgeworn wrappers. *LOPEZ*. $50

Deloria, Vine Jr. INDIANS OF THE PACIFIC NORTHWEST. GC: Doubleday, (1977). 1st ed. Owner initials fep o/w Fine in VG, price-clipped dj. *LOPEZ*. $55

Deloria, Vine Jr. WE TALK, YOU LISTEN. (NY): Macmillan, (1970). 1st ed. Fine in dj. *LOPEZ*. $45

Delving, Michael. THE DEVIL FINDS WORK. NY: Charles Scribner's Sons, 1969. 1st ed. Fine in dj. *MORDIDA*. $35

DeMarthold, Jules. THE HISTORY OF A BEARSKIN. From the French... NY: Dodd, Mead & Co, (1893). Pict tan cl, triple ruled in red & black, gilt title outlined in red. Gilt title, vignette on spine, front hinge sl cracked. 190pp. Frontis (starting). J.O.B. (illus). NF. *BLUE MOUNTAIN*. $75

Demby, William. THE CATACOMBS. NY, 1965. 1st ed. Fine in dj (extremities, spine little chipped. Few tiny edge tears, little piece missing lower edge rear panel). *POLYANTHOS*. $75

Demeny, Jabos. BELA BARTOK LETTERS. NY: St. Martin's Press, 1971. 1st ed. As New in dj. *BANCROFT*. $30

Demijohn, Thom with John Sladek. BLACK ALICE. GC: Doubleday, 1968. 1st ed. (Thom Demijohn is pseud of Thomas Disch.) VF, dj has tiny, invisible closed tear. *ELSE FINE*. $150

Demijohn, Thom. BLACK ALICE. GC: Doubleday, 1968. 1st ed. Pseudonymous collaboration between Thomas Disch and John Sladek. NF in like dj. *LOPEZ*. $100

Deming, Alden O. MANABOZHO, THE INDIAN STORY OF HIAWATHA. Phila, 1938. 1st ed. 87pp, illus in color. Dj chipped and cvr stained o/w VG+. *PRATT*. $35

DEMONS, IMPS & FIENDS. Leonard Baskin (illus). Northampton, 1976. One of 450. Marbled paper over boards w/full-length morocco spine label, gilt stamped (by Gray Parrot). Fine. *BOOK BLOCK*. $245

DeMonvel, M.B. JOAN OF ARC. McKay, 1918. Unpaginated. Illus by DeMonvel. Cvr wear, lt chips to color cvr illus but VG. *BEBBAH*. $35

Demus, Otto. ROMANESQUE MURAL PAINTING. NY: Harry N. Abrams. (1970). 1st ed. 324 plts, incl 102 in color (most tipped-in). Fine in dj. *KARMIOLE*. $150

DeNevi, Don. THE WESTERN PACIFIC; FEATHER RIVER ROUTE. Superior, 1978. 1st ed. Fine in VG dj. *VARNER*. $30

Denham, Bertie. THE MAN WHO LOST HIS SHADOW. London: Macmillan, 1979. 1st ed, 1st bk. Signed. NF in dj. *SILVER DOOR*. $35

Denison, Merrill. KLONDIKE MIKE—AND ALASKAN ODYS-SEY. NY: Morrow, 1943. 1st ed. Almost fine in VG dj. *AARD*. $25

Denny-Brown, D. (ed). SELECTED WRITINGS OF SIR CHAR-LES SHERRINGTON. London, 1939. 1st ed. Dj. Scarce. *FYE*. $250

Dennys, N.B. AN ACCOUNT OF THE CRUISE OF THE ST. GEORGE ON THE NORTH AMERICAN AND WEST INDIAN STATION. London: Saunders, Otley, and Co, 1862. 1st ed. 2 plts. Extrems rubbed. *HUDSON*. $150

Densmore, Frances. CHIPPEWA CUSTOMS. Smithsonian Institution, BAE, Bulletin 86. Washington: GPO, 1929. Cover worn at extrems, o/w VG. *LAURIE*. $30

Densmore, Frances. MANDAN AND HIDATSA MUSIC. Smithsonian Institution, BAE, Bulletin 80. Washington: GPO, 1923. 40 photos. Binding tender, o/w VG. *LAURIE*. $20

Densmore, Frances. PAPAGO MUSIC. Smithsonian Institution, BAE, Bulletin 90. Washington: GPO 1929. VG. *LAURIE*. $17.50

Denson, C.B. AN ADDRESS DELIVERED IN RALEIGH, N.C. ON MEMORIAL DAY 10, 1895...Raleigh, 1895. Undated 2nd ed. 56pp. Fine in wraps. *PRATT*. $20

Dent, C.T. et al. MOUNTAINEERING (BADMINTON LIBRARY). Boston: Little, Brown, and London: Longmans, Green, 1892. 1st US ed. Minor wear to extremities, else VG-NF. *OLD LONDON*. $85

Dent, Lester. DEAD AT THE TAKE-OFF. NY: Doubleday Crime Club, 1946. 1st ed, 1st bk under own name. Fine, sm edgechips to the dj. *ELSE FINE*. $65

Denton, Clara J. NEW YEAR'S TO CHRISTMAS, IN HOLIDAY LAND. Chicago: Albert Whitman & Co., (1928). 1st ed. *KARMIOLE*. $50

Denver Westerners. 1959 BRAND BOOK OF THE DENVER POSSE OF THE WESTERNERS. VOL XV. (Boulder, 1960). One of 500 of the regular ed. Cl. VG in Fine dj. *BOHLING*. $50

Denver Westerners. 1974-1975. BRAND BOOK OF DENVER WESTERNERS, Volume 30-31. Alan Stewart (ed). Denver, (1977). 1st ed, ltd to 525. VF in VF dj. *OREGON*. $45

Denver Westerners. THE 1963 ALL POSSE—CORAL BRAND BOOK OF THE DENVER POSSE OF THE WESTERNERS. Denver, 1964. 1st ed, ltd to 750 numbered (#55). VF in Fine dj. *OREGON*. $60

Denver Westerners. THE DENVER WESTERNERS BRAND BOOK 1968. VOLUME 24. Denver, (1969). Milton W. Callon (ed). One of 700, this unnumbered. VG+. *BOHLING*. $45

Depew, Chauncey M. MY MEMORIES OF EIGHTY YEARS. NY: Charles Scribner's Sons, 1922. Bkpls, few pencil notes. *HUDSON*. $35

Deppe, Ferdinand. TRAVELS IN CALIFORNIA IN 1837. Gustave O. Arlt (trans). LA: Glen Dawson. 1953. Ed ltd to 190. Glassine. Fine. *KARMIOLE*. $50

Derby, George Horatio. PHOENIXIANA, A COLLECTION OF THE BURLESQUES AND SKETCHES OF JOHN PHOENIX, ALIAS JOHN P. SQUIBOB, WHO WAS, IN FACT, LIEUTENANT GEORGE H. DERBY, U.S.A. Ed by Francis Farquhar. SF: Grabhorn Press, 1937. 1/550. 5 plts. VG in Fine dj. *BOHLING*. $150

Dercum, Francis (ed). A TEXT-BOOK ON NERVOUS DISEASES BY AMERICAN AUTHORS. Phila, 1895. 1st ed. Full leather, 1056pp. Hinges cracked. 348 illus. *FYE*. $250

Derleth, August (ed). BEYOND TIME AND SPACE. P & C, 1950. 1st ed. Fine in VG dj. *MADLE*. $40

Derleth, August (ed). DARK MIND, DARK HEART. Arkham House, 1962. 1st ed. VF in dj. *MADLE*. $55

Derleth, August (ed). DARK OF THE MOON. Arkham House, 1947. 1st ed. Ex-lib. VG in Mint 2nd issue dj. *MADLE*. $125

Derleth, August (ed). DARK THINGS. Sauk City: Arkham House, 1971. 1st ed. Fine in dj, pub's $7.50 price sticker affixed. *OTHER WORLDS*. $50

Derleth, August (ed). FAR BOUNDARIES. P & C, 1951. 1st ed. Fine in dj. *MADLE*. $35

Derleth, August (ed). FIRE AND SLEET AND CANDLELIGHT. Arkham House, 1961. 1st ed. NF in Fine dj. *MADLE*. $95

Derleth, August (ed). SLEEP NO MORE. Farrar, 1944. 1st ed. VG *MADLE*. $20

Derleth, August (ed). STRANGE PORTS OF CALL. P & C, 1948. 1st ed. VG in sl frayed, soiled dj. *MADLE*. $30

Derleth, August (ed). THE NIGHT SIDE. NY: Rinehart, (1947). 1st ed. Dj heavily edgeworn, sm chips, tears. *AKA*. $40

Derleth, August (ed). THE NIGHT SIDE. Rinehart, 1947. 1st ed. VG in worn, chipped dj. *MADLE*. $30

Derleth, August (ed). THE OTHER SIDE OF THE MOON. P & C, 1949. 1st ed. NF in dj. *MADLE*. $30

Derleth, August (ed). THE OUTER REACHES P & C, 1951. 1st ed. Fine in dj. *MADLE*. $35

Derleth, August (ed). TIME TO COME. Farrar, 1954. 1st ed. Fine in NF dj. *MADLE*. $35

Derleth, August (ed). WHO KNOCKS. Rinehart, 1946. 1st ed. VG in worn dj. *MADLE*. $30

Derleth, August. A PRAED STREET DOSSIER. Arkham House, 1968. 1st ed. VF in dj. *MADLE*. $55

Derleth, August. ARKHAM HOUSE: THE FIRST TWENTY YEARS. Arkham House, 1959. 1st ed. Fine in wraps. *MADLE*. $200

Derleth, August. BRIGHT JOURNEY. NY: Scribner's, 1940. 1st ed. NF in dj. *BERNARD*. $25

Derleth, August. DWELLERS IN DARKNESS. Sauk City: Arkham House, 1976. 1st ed. Fine in Fine dj. *OTHER WORLDS*. $15

Derleth, August. FELL PURPOSE. Arcadia, (1953). 1st ed. VG in dj with chipping, edgewear, slight soil to rear panel. *BEBBAH.* $28

Derleth, August. FIRE AND SLEET AND CANDLELIGHT. Sauk City: Arkham House, 1961. 1st ed. Fine in NF dj w/some staining to spine. *OTHER WORLDS.* $75

. Derleth, August. HARRIGAN'S FILE. Sauk City: Arkham House, 1975. 1st ed. Fine in dj. *OTHER WORLDS.* $20

Derleth, August. IN RE SHERLOCK HOLMES. Arkham House, 1945. 1st ed. Cvr rubbing, else NF in dj. *MADLE.* $85

Derleth, August. IN RE: SHERLOCK HOLMES. Sauk City: Mycroft & Moran, 1945. 1st ed. NF in price clipped dj w/light edgewear. *OTHER WORLDS.* $75

Derleth, August. IN RE: SHERLOCK HOLMES. THE ADVENTURES OF SOLAR PONS. Sauk City: Mycroft & Moran, 1945. 1st ed, ltd to 3604. Fine in price-clipped dj w/light soiling to rear panel. *ROBBINS.* $125

Derleth, August. LONESOME PLACES. Arkham House, 1962. 1st ed. Fine in dj. *MADLE.* $100

Derleth, August. NOT LONG FOR THIS WORLD. Arkham House, 1948. 1st ed. VG in dj. *MADLE.* $100

Derleth, August. SAC PRAIRIE PEOPLE. Sauk City: Stanton and Lee, 1948. 1st ed. One of 2080 signed. W/Adrian H. Goldstone bkpl. Fine in price clipped dj, spine and corners little rubbed. *POLYANTHOS.* $50

Derleth, August. SAC PRAIRIE PEOPLE. Stanton & Lee, 1948. 1st ed. Fine in dj. Inscribed. *MADLE.* $65

Derleth, August. SOME NOTES ON H.P. LOVECRAFT. Arkham House, 1959. 1st ed. Fine in wraps. *MADLE.* $150

Derleth, August. SOME NOTES ON H.P. LOVECRAFT. Sauk City: Arkham House, 1959. 1st ed. Wrappers. NF. *OTHER WORLDS.* $95

Derleth, August. SOMETHING NEAR. Arkham House, 1945. 1st ed. Fine in dj. *MADLE.* $150

Derleth, August. STILL IS THE SUMMER NIGHT. NY, 1937. 1st ed. Presentation inscription. Bkpl. Fine in dj (little edge rubbed). *POLYANTHOS.* $50

Derleth, August. THE ARKHAM COLLECTOR. Volume 1. Sauk City: Arkham House, 1971. 1st ed. One of 676. As New w/o dj as issued. *ELSE FINE.* $200

Derleth, August. THE CASEBOOK OF SOLAR PONS. Arkham House, 1965. 1st ed. Fine in dj. *MADLE.* $110

Derleth, August. THE CHRONICLES OF SOLAR PONS. Mycroft & Moran, 1973. 1st ed. Fine in Fine dj. *BEBBAH.* $40

Derleth, August. THE CHRONICLES OF SOLAR PONS. Sauk City: Mycroft & Moran, 1973. 1st ed. Fine in dj, browned spine. *OTHER WORLDS.* $18

Derleth, August. THE HOUSE OF MOONLIGHT. IC: Prairie Press, 1953. 1st ed. Signed. Fine, dj darkened at extremities. *ELSE FINE.* $60

Derleth, August. THE MASK OF CTHULHU. Sauk City, WI: Arkham House, (1958). 1st ed, one of 2,000. Fine in lightly worn dj. *AKA.* $100

Derleth, August. THE REMINISCENCES OF SOLAR PONS. Arkham House, 1961. 1st ed. Fine in Mint dj. *MADLE.* $100

Derleth, August. THE SHADOW IN THE GLASS. Duell-Sloan, 1936. 1st ed. Ex-lib. VG in nice dj. *MADLE.* $25

Derleth, August. THE SHIELD OF THE VALIANT. NY: Scribner's, 1945. NF in price-clipped, VG dj. 1st ed. Advance review copy w/publisher's slip laid in. *CHAPEL HILL.* $75

Derleth, August. THE TENT SHOW SUMMER. NY, 1963. 1st ed. Spine sl rubbed, name, dj edge rubbed w/nicks. *POLYANTHOS.* $25

Derleth, August. THE TRAIL OF CTHULHU. Arkham House, 1962. 1st ed. VF in dj. *MADLE.* $75

Derleth, August. THIRTY YEARS OF ARKHAM HOUSE. Arkham House, 1970. 1st ed. VF in dj. *MADLE.* $85

Derleth, August. THREE PROBLEMS FOR SOLAR PONS. Sauk City: Mycroft & Moran, 1952. 1st ed. Sl bow to boards, else NF in browned dj. *OTHER WORLDS.* $225

Derleth, August. VINCENNES: PORTAL TO THE WEST. NJ, 1968. 1st ed. Fine in dj, spine sl sunned, sl edge rubbed. *POLYANTHOS.* $30

Derleth, August. WALDEN WEST. NY, 1961. 1st ed. Woodcuts by Grisha Dotzenko. Signed presentation. Fine in price clipped dj. *POLYANTHOS.* $50

Derleth, August. WILBUR, THE TRUSTING WHIPPOORWILL. Sauk City, WI: Stanton & Lee, 1959. 1st ed. Fine in VG+ price clipped dj (glue mark). *BERNARD.* $35

Derleth, August. WIND OVER WISCONSIN. Scribners, 1938. 1st ed. VG. *MADLE.* $40

Derleth, August. WISCONSIN MURDERS. Sauk City: Mycroft & Moran, (1968). 1st ed. Fine in Fine dj. *OTHER WORLDS.* $45

Dern, Gov. George H. THE COLORADO RIVER. Colo Springs, 1926. Wraps. 20pp. Scarce. Fine. *FIVE QUAIL.* $35

DeRose, Camille. THE CAMILLE DEROSE STORY: THE TRUE STORY OF THE CICERO RACE RIOTS. Chicago: Author, 1953. 1st ed. NF in sl worn, chipped, else VG dj. Scarce. *CONNOLLY & WADE.* $45

Derrick, Charles. MEMOIRS OF THE RISE AND PROGRESS OF THE ROYAL NAVY. London, 1806. 1st ed. (x),309,(1 blank),(19 index, 6 subscribers)pp. Frontis. Later 1/2 morocco, uncut, prelims bit foxed. *LEFKOWICZ.* $350

Desana, Dorothy. WHITE SQUADRON. London: Adventurer's Club, (1961). DJ. *SCHOYER'S.* $16.50

Desault, P.J. A TREATISE ON FRACTURES, LUXATIONS, AND OTHER AFFECTIONS OF THE BONES...Ed. by Xavier Bichat. Phila, 1817. 3rd Amer ed. Leather, 398pp. *FYE.* $250

Deutsch, Albert. THE MENTALLY ILL IN AMERICA: A HISTORY OF THEIR CARE AND TREATMENT FROM COLONIAL TIMES. GC, NY, 1937. 1st ed. Dj. *FYE.* $75

Devere, William. JIM MARSHALL'S NEW PIANNER AND OTHER WESTERN STORIES. M. Witmark & Sons, 1897. 1st ed. Inscribed, signed. Fine. *AUTHORS OF THE WEST.* $30

Devoe, Alan. THE PORTRAIT OF MR. O. W. NY: The Union Square Bk Shop. 1930. Frontis. Ltd to 275 (this copy "out-of-series"). *KARMIOLE.* $75

Devonshire, R.L. RAMBLES IN CAIRO. Cairo, 1931. Fldg map in back pouch. NF. *POLYANTHOS.* $50

Dew, Robb Forman. DALE LOVES SOPHIE TO DEATH. NY: Farrar, Straus & Giroux, (1981). 1st ed, 1st book. NF in dj with one short, internally mended tear on rear panel. *BERNARD.* $20

Dewar, Thomas R. RAMBLE ROUND THE GLOBE. London: Chatto & Windus, 1894. xvi,316pp,32pp pub cat. 12mo. Dec cl, rubbed and discolored, spine cocked, corners bumped. Profusely illus. Ex-lib. *SCHOYER'S.* $60

Dewees, William. A TREATISE ON THE DISEASES OF FEMALES. Phila, 1847. 3rd ed. Full leather, 532pp + 12 fine engrvd plts,some fldg. *FYE.* $125

Dewees, William. AN ESSAY ON THE MEANS OF LESSENING PAIN AND FACILITATING CERTAIN CASES OF DIFFICULT PARTURITION. Phila, 1819. 2nd ed. 156 pp. Orig boards w/paper backstrip. Backstrip cracked and worn, some water stains. Scarce. *FYE.* $300

Dewey, Adelbert M. THE LIFE AND LETTERS OF ADMIRAL DEWEY. Akron: Werner Co., (1899). Pict cl. *SCHOYER'S.* $40

Dewlen, Al. NEXT OF KIN. GC: Doubleday, 1977. 1st ed. Fine in NF dj. *LOPEZ*. $45

Dexter, Colin. SERVICE OF ALL THE DEAD. NY: St. Martin's Press, 1979. 1st Amer ed. Fine in dj. *MORDIDA*. $75

Dexter, Colin. THE DEAD OF JERICHO. NY: St. Martin's Press, 1981. 1st Amer ed. Fine in dj. *MORDIDA*. $45

Dexter, Colin. THE JEWEL THAT WAS OURS. Bristol: Scorpion Press, 1991. 1st ed. One of 150 specially bound numbered, signed by Dexter. Bound in 1/4 leather w/marbled boards. VF in acetate dj. *MORDIDA*. $135

Dexter, Colin. THE JEWEL THAT WAS OURS. London: Macmillan, 1991. 1st ed. Signed. VF in dj. *MORDIDA*. $45

Dexter, Colin. THE JEWEL THAT WAS OURS. London: Macmillan, 1991. 1st ed. Fine in dj. *SILVER DOOR*. $25

Dexter, Colin. THE JEWEL THAT WAS OURS. NY: Crown, 1992. Advance uncorrected proofs. Fine in wraps. *BEASLEY*. $25

Dexter, Colin. THE JEWEL THAT WAS OURS. W/appreciation by H.R.F. Keating. Bristol: Scorpion Press, 1991. 1st ed. 1/150 specially bound numbered, signed. VF in acetate wrapper. *MORDIDA*. $135

Dexter, Colin. THE RIDDLE OF THE THIRD MILE. London: Macmillan, 1983. 1st ed. Fine in dj. *MORDIDA*. $125

Dexter, Colin. THE SECRET OF ANNEXE 3. London: Macmillan, 1986. 1st ed. Signed. VF in dj. *MORDIDA*. $100

Dexter, Colin. THE SECRET OF ANNEXE 3. NY: St. Martin's Press, 1987. 1st Amer ed. Fine in dj, wear top of spine. *MORDIDA*. $25

Dexter, Colin. THE WENCH IS DEAD. London: Macmillan, 1989. 1st ed. Signed. VF in dj. *MORDIDA*. $65

Dexter, Colin. THE WENCH IS DEAD. London: Macmillan, 1989. 1st ed. Fine in dj. *SILVER DOOR*. $25

Dexter, Colin. THE WENCH IS DEAD. NY: St. Martin's Press, 1990. 1st Amer ed. VF in dj. *MORDIDA*. $25

Dexter, Dave Jr. JAZZ CAVALCADE. NY: Criterion, 1946. 1st ed. Fine in lightly chipped dj. *BEASLEY*. $65

Dexter, Pete. BROTHERLY LOVE. Random House, 1991. Uncorrected proof. Fine in wraps. *STAHR*. $35

Dexter, Pete. DEADWOOD. NY: Random, (1986). 1st ed. Light bump top corners, o/w Fine in Fine dj. *AKA*. $40

Dexter, Pete. DEADWOOD. NY: Random House, (1986). 1st ed, 2nd book. Adv rev copy w/publicity release folded & laid in. New in dj. *BERNARD*. $45

Dexter, Pete. DEADWOOD. Random House, 1986. Adv reading copy. About Fine in wraps. Corners lightly bumped. *STAHR*. $35

Dexter, Pete. GOD'S POCKET. NY: Random House, (1983). 1st ed, 1st bk. Fine in price-clipped dj. *CAPTAIN'S BOOKSHELF*. $75

Dexter, Pete. GOD'S POCKET. NY: Random House, (1983). 1st ed. Fine in dj. Signed. *CAPTAIN'S BOOKSHELF*. $125

Dexter, Pete. PARIS TROUT. NY: Random House, (1988). Uncorrected proof. Fine in ptd yellow wrappers. *CAPTAIN'S BOOKSHELF*. $75

Dexter, Pete. PARIS TROUT. NY: Random House, 1988. 1st ed. VF in dj. *MORDIDA*. $25

Dexter, Pete. PARIS TROUT. NY: RH, (1988). 1st ed. Fine in dj. Inscribed. *LOPEZ*. $100

Dexter, Pete. PARIS TROUT. Uncorrected proof. Fine in wraps. *LOPEZ*. $65

Dexter, Walter (ed). THE UNPUBLISHED LETTERS OF CHARLES DICKENS TO MARK LEMON. London: Halton & Truscott, 1927. 1st ltd ed. #119 of 525, partly unopened, vellum spine and tips over purple cloth, teg, covers soiled, quite scarce. VG. *GREAT EXPECTATIONS*. $65

Dexter, Walter. THE LONDON OF DICKENS. London: Cecil Palmer, (1923). 1st ed. 12mo, 269pp, bkpl. Presentation copy. Inscribed, signed, and dated. Light Wear. Good+. *GREAT EXPECTATIONS*. $25

Dhlomo, R.R.R. AN AFRICAN TRAGEDY. Loveday Institution, n.d, n.p., (1928). 1st and only ed. Ptd wraps. Fine. *POLYANTHOS*. $75

Di Donato, Pietro. CHRIST IN CONCRETE. Indianapolis: Bobbs-Merrill, (1939). 1st ed. VG. *SECOND LIFE*. $45

Di Prima, Diane (ed). VARIOUS FABLES FROM VARIOUS PLACES. Illus B. Krigstein. NY: Putnam's, (1960). 1st ed. Pages beginning to brown, else Fine in lightly used dj. *CAPTAIN'S BOOKSHELF*. $35

Dial, Adolph L. and David K. Eliades. THE ONLY LAND I KNOW. SF: Indian Historian Press, (1975). 1st ed. VG in wrappers. *LOPEZ*. $45

Diapea, William. CANNIBAL JACK: THE TRUE AUTOBIOGRAPHY OF A WHITE MAN IN THE SOUTH SEAS. London: Faber & Gwyer, 1928. 1st ed. Smudgy, spotty with small separation bottom of back cvr hinge. Good. Very scarce. *GREAT EPIC*. $55

DIARY IN TURKISH AND GREEK WATERS. (By George W. Howard.) London, 1854. 4th ed. xi,353pp. Bkpl. Uncut. VF. *O'NEILL*. $85

HONEY BEE AND THE ROBBER. London, 1981. Diaz, Lokvig, and Strejan (engs). One tab does not retract all the way, but seems not to be detrimental. *BOOKFINDERS INTL*. $40

Dibdin, Michael. DIRTY TRICKS. London: Faber and Faber, 1991. 1st ed. VF in dj. *MORDIDA*. $45

Dibdin, Michael. RATKING. London: Faber & Faber, 1988. 1st ed. Fine in dj. *MORDIDA*. $35

Dibdin, Thomas F. A BIBLIOGRAPHICAL, ANTIQUARIAN AND PICTURESQUE TOUR IN FRANCE AND GERMANY. London: Jennings and Major, 1829. 2nd ed. 3 vols. Orig red cloth, w/spines renewed and printed labels. Armorial bkpls. Some wear, occas minor foxing, but VG. *HARTFIELD*. $295

Dibdin, Thomas F. A BIBLIOGRAPHICAL ANTIQUARIAN AND PICTURESQUE TOUR IN FRANCE AND GERMANY. London: Robert Jennings, 1829. 2nd ed. 3 vols. Cloth, leather spine labels, light overall wear, scattered foxing. *DAWSON'S*. $200

Dibdin, Thomas. A BIBLIOGRAPHICAL, ANTIQUARIAN AND PICTURESQUE TOUR IN THE NORTHERN COUNTIES OF ENGLAND AND IN SCOTLAND. London: for the author by C. Richards, 1838. 1st ed. 2 vols. xxx,436, (18pp Bohn catalogue bound in); [4], pp 441-1090. Engr frontispieces both vols, 42 plts (incl 2 not called for in list of plts), illus. Full dk brn morocco, gilt, teg, by Zaehnsdorf. Sl offset on title vol II. Extremely Fine. *WREDEN*. $750

Dicey, Edward. SIX MONTHS IN THE FEDERAL STATES. London, 1st ed. 18863. 2 vols in one: (10),310; (6),326 & adv pp. Orig cl (spine expertly repaired). Howes D314. *GINSBERG*. $350

Dicey, Edward. SPECTATOR OF AMERICA. Herbert Mitgang (ed, intro). London: Gollancz, 1972. 1st ed thus. Blue and gilt boards. Fine in VG dj. *CONNOLLY & WADE*. $40

Dicey, Edward. SPECTATOR OF AMERICA. Herbert Mitgang (ed). Chicago, 1971. 1st ed. Dj. Ex-lib. VG+. *PRATT*. $25

Dicey, Edward. STORY OF THE KHEDIVATE. NY: Scribner's, 1902. Somewhat soiled. *SCHOYER'S*. $65

Dick, Everett. THE SOD-HOUSE FRONTIER, 1954-1890. Lincoln: Johnson Pub., (1954). 31 plts. VG. *OREGON*. $35

Dick, Philip K. A HANDFUL OF DARKNESS. Boston: Gregg Press, 1978. 1st US ed. As New, w/o dj as issued. *ELSE FINE*. $175

Dick, Philip K. CLANS OF THE ALPHANE MOON. NY: Ace Books, 1964. 1st ed. Issued in paperback w/paper browning as usual, else VG. *JUVELIS*. $20

Dick, Philip K. DR. BLOODMONEY OR HOW WE GOT ALONG AFTER THE BOMB. NY: Ace, 1965. 1st ed. Issued in paper. VG. *JUVELIS.* $20

Dick, Philip K. DR. FUTURITY. Ace, 1960. 1st ed. Fine in wraps. *MADLE.* $35

Dick, Philip K. EYE IN THE SKY. Ace, 1957. 1st ed. VG in wraps. *MADLE.* $20

Dick, Philip K. EYE IN THE SKY. NY: Ace, 1957. 1st ed. Issued in paper wrappers. VG. *JUVELIS.* $40

Dick, Philip K. GALACTIC POT-HEALER. S.F.B.C., 1969. 1st hb ed. Fine in sl stained dj. *MADLE.* $25

Dick, Philip K. MARTIAN TIME-SLIP. NY: Ballantine, 1964. 1st ed. Issued in paper. VG. *JUVELIS.* $20

Dick, Philip K. SOLAR LOTTERY. Ace Double, n/d. 1st ed. NF in wraps. *MADLE.* $35

Dick, Philip K. THE COSMIC PUPPETS. Ace Double, 1957. 1st ed. VG in wraps. *MADLE.* $25

Dick, Philip K. THE CRACK IN SPACE. Ace, 1966. 1st ed. Fine in wraps. *MADLE.* $35

Dick, Philip K. THE GAME PLAYERS OF TITAN. NY: Ace, 1963. 1st ed. Issued in paper. VG. *JUVELIS.* $20

Dick, Philip K. THE GANYMEDE TAKEOVER. Ace, 1967. 1st ed. NF in wraps. *MADLE.* $25

Dick, Philip K. THE MAN WHO JAPED. Ace, 1956. 1st ed. Fine in wraps. *MADLE.* $45

Dick, Philip K. THE PENULTIMATE TRUTH. Belmont, 1964. 1st ed. Fine in wraps. *MADLE.* $25

Dick, Philip K. THE PENULTIMATE TRUTH. NY: Belmont, 1964. 1st ed. Issued in paper. VG. *JUVELIS.* $20

Dick, Philip K. THE SIMULACRA. NY: Ace, 1964. 1st ed. Issued in paper; browning, else VG. *JUVELIS.* $20

Dick, Philip K. THE TRANSMIGRATION OF TIMOTHY AR-CHER. NY: Timescape, 1982. Review copy. As New in dj. *ELSE FINE.* $40

Dick, Philip K. THE TRANSMIGRATION OF TIMOTHY AR-CHER. NY: Timescape Books, 1982. 1st ed. Fine in dj. *JUVELIS.* $35

Dick, Philip K. THE UNTELEPORTED MAN. Ace, 1966. 1st ed. Fine in wraps. *MADLE.* $30

Dick, Philip K. THE UNTELEPORTED MAN. NY: Ace, 1966. 1st ed. Issued in paper. VG. *JUVELIS.* $20

Dick, Philip K. THE VARIABLE MAN AND OTHER STORIES. NY: Ace, 1957. 1st ed. Issued in paper. VG. *JUVELIS.* $40

Dick, Philip K. THE VARIABLE MAN. Ace, 1957. 1st ed. NF in wraps. *MADLE.* $40

Dick, Philip K. THE WORLD JONES MADE. Ace, 1956. 1st ed. VG in wraps. *MADLE.* $35

Dick, Philip K. THE WORLD JONES MADE: AGENT OF THE UNKNOWN. NY: Ace, 1956. 1st ed. Issued in paper; paper brown-ing, else VG. *JUVELIS.* $20

Dick, Philip K. THE ZAP GUN. Pyramid, 1967. 1st ed. Fine in wraps. *MADLE.* $25

Dick, Philip K. TIME OUT OF JOINT. Belmont, 1965. 1st pb ed. Fine. *MADLE.* $25

Dick, Philip K. WE CAN BUILD YOU. London: Seven House Pub-lishers Ltd, 1988. 1st Eng hc ed. Fine in dj. *JUVELIS.* $60

Dickens, Charles. A CHRISTMAS CAROL. Illus Ronald Searle. Cleveland & NY: World, (1961). 1st Amer ed w/these illus. Orig grn cl. NF in dj. *CHAPEL HILL.* $35

Dickens, Charles. A CHRISTMAS CAROL. Phila, n/d. 147pp. Illus by Rackham, 4 in color. Rebound in buckram, orig title transposed front cover. On heavy paper. *HEINOLDT.* $20

Dickens, Charles. A TALE OF TWO CITIES. London: Chapman and Hall, 1859. 1st ed, 1st issue. 8vo, illus by H.K. Browne, mild foxing to some plts but most images sharp, bound in contemp 1/4 lea with raised spine and lea label over marbled paper covered boards, boards show some shelfwear. Rare. VG+. *GREAT EXPECTATIONS.* $1250

Dickens, Charles. AMERICAN NOTES FOR GENERAL CIR-CULATION. 2 Vols. London: Chapman and Hall, 1842. 1st ed, 1st issue. 8vo, with 2nd page of "Content to Vol 1" numbered XVI, full red morocco by Riviere with gilt spine, inner dentelles, teg, etc., with half-titles and ads bound into vols I and II. Joints sl rubbed. NF. *GREAT EXPECTATIONS.* $875

Dickens, Charles. BARNABY RUDGE. London: Chapman and Hall, 1841. 1st ed. Tall 8vo, illus by George Cattermole and Halbot Browne, 1/4 tan lea over cloth, raised spine with two lea labels, spine mildly rubbed and boards show shelfwear, (A made up vol from chapters appearing in Vols II and III of "Master Humphrey's Clock" with stave marks visible. Unusual in this format.) Good+ *GREAT EXPECTATIONS.* $150

Dickens, Charles. BLEAK HOUSE. London: Bradbury & Evans, 1853. 1st bk ed. 8vo, 624pp. Frontis, engrvd title, 38 full page plts. 19th cent half tan calf and marbled boards w/gilt-tooled spine. Plts oxidized causing browning at edges, 1" crack at top of front outer joint, modest general wear, but VG. *CHAPEL HILL.* $250

Dickens, Charles. BLEAK HOUSE. Phila: Getz & Buck, 1854. Com-plete illus ed. viii,338pp. Benson Lossing (illus). Orig dec bordered blind-stamped black cl w horizontal ribbing. Pict spine gilt. Sl cvr wear, repair. Lacks rear fly. Top of text sl bent. Text foxing, else VG. *DIAMOND.* $125

Dickens, Charles. DOMBEY AND SON. Illus by H.K. Browne. Bos-ton: Bradbury and Guild, 1848. 1st Amer ed. 8vo. 7, 624pp. Orig cloth, a little dull, but quite Good. *M & S.* $375

Dickens, Charles. DOMBEY AND SON. London: Bradbury and Evans, 1848. 1st ed, 1st issue. 8vo, with 12 line errata slip, 1/2 moroc-co by Zaehnsdorf, orig wrapper of issue number 10 bound in, (Extra illustrated by the insertion of the rare set of eight portraits of charac-ters by H.K. Browne published in 1848, and the equally rare set of four plts of Little Paul, Florence, Edith, and Alice by Browne.) NF. *GREAT EXPECTATIONS.* $1350

Dickens, Charles. DRAWN FROM LIFE SKETCHES OF YOUNG LADIES, YOUNG GENTLEMEN AND YOUNG COUPLES. NY: E.J. Hale, 1875. 1st Amer ed. 12mo, 20 illus by Phiz, orig cloth. VG+. *GREAT EXPECTATIONS.* $125

Dickens, Charles. GEORGE SILVERMAN'S EXPLANATION. CA: Santa Susana Press, 1984. 1st ltd ed. Illus by Irving Block. Ed. with intro by Harry Stone. Blue cloth, #163 of 326, signed by Block and Stone. Fine. *GREAT EXPECTATIONS.* $37.50

Dickens, Charles. GREAT EXPECTATIONS. Boston: Gardner A. Fuller, 1862. 30th thousand. 12mo, illus, orig cloth, moderate foxing and top of spine shaved, (As all extant copies of this ed bear the "thirtieth thousand" imprint, and there appears to be no record on an earlier printing by this publisher, this ed is most probably a first thus.) Near VG. *GREAT EXPECTATIONS.* $250

Dickens, Charles. HARD TIMES. London: Bradbury and Evans, 1854. 1st ed. 12mo, full crushed tan morocco, gold rule on covers and 5 raised bands on spine, teg. Fine. *GREAT EXPECTATIONS.* $475

Dickens, Charles. HARD TIMES. NY: LEC, 1966. Tall 8vo, illus by Charles Raymond. 1350 of 1500 signed by the illustrator, half cloth, slipcase. Fine in Fine box. *GREAT EXPECTATIONS.* $75

Dickens, Charles. MASTER HUMPHREY'S CLOCK. London: Chapman & Hall, 1840-41. Lrg 8vo. Orig brown cl. 3 vols. Bkplts, spines lightly faded, slight crease in cl on Vol. III, small repair to top of spine on Vol. I. Still bright, attractive set. 1st ed, 1st issue w/clock hands pointing to vol. numbers (i.e. to 1 on 1st vol, 2 on 2nd, etc.). *CHAPEL HILL.* $1,200

Dickens, Charles. OLIVER TWIST; OR, THE PARISH BOY'S PROGRESS. 3 Vols. London: Richard Bentley, 1838. 1st ed, 1st issue. 8vo, illus by George Cruikshank, full red polished morocco with gilt spines, triple gilt rules on covers, etc. (Fireside plate in Vol. III present, Boz title page, etc.) Fine. *GREAT EXPECTATIONS.* $2500

Dickens, Charles. OUR MUTUAL FRIEND. London, 1865. 1st book ed. 2 vols bound in 1. Contemp 1/2 lea binding, dec spine gilt, leather label. Front hinge started, but firm, bkpl, little edge rubbed. NF. *POLYANTHOS.* $250

Dickens, Charles. OUR MUTUAL FRIEND. London: Chapman and Hall, 1865. 1st ed. 8vo, illus by Marcus Stone, plts foxed, orig straight ribbed green cloth, small stain on front board, gilt spine lettering beginning to wear. VG+. (This ed is actually the 2nd issue of the two vol 1st ed in book form. Very Scarce in the orig cloth.) *GREAT EXPECTATIONS.* $650

Dickens, Charles. OUR MUTUAL FRIEND. NY: Harpers, 1865. 1st Amer ed. 8vo, 350pp, illus, double column format with two vols in one, orig cloth. Fine. *GREAT EXPECTATIONS.* $225

Dickens, Charles. SKETCHES. Leipzig: Bernard Tauchnitz, 1843. Copyright ed. 16mo, 516pp, decorative red cloth, (From the "Collection of British Authors" series, vol number 50. No spine numbers.) VG+. *GREAT EXPECTATIONS.* $35

Dickens, Charles. THE BATTLE OF LIFE. London: Bradbury and Evans, 1846. 1st ed, 4th issue vignette title. 12mo, orig red cloth, bkpl, aeg, wear to outer spine joints and tips. Near VG. *GREAT EXPECTATIONS.* $200

Dickens, Charles. THE CHIMES. London: Bradbury and Evans, 1845. 1st ed, 2nd state vignette title. 12mo, orig red cloth, spine sl cocked and shows light wear, aeg. VG. *GREAT EXPECTATIONS.* $275

Dickens, Charles. THE CRICKET ON THE HEARTH. London: Bradbury and Evans, 1846. 1st ed, 2nd state of ad. 12mo, orig red cloth, light wear and soiling to cloth, aeg. VG. *GREAT EXPECTATIONS.* $250

Dickens, Charles. THE LIFE AND ADVENTURES OF MARTIN CHUZZLEWIT. London, 1844. 1st book ed. Illus by Phiz. Lacks half-title page. Contemp binding, dec spine gilt, extrems professionally repaired, cvrs and edges little rubbed. NF. *POLYANTHOS.* $200

Dickens, Charles. THE LIFE AND ADVENTURES OF NICHOLAS NICKLEBY. London: Chapman and Hall, 1839. 1st ed, 1st issue. 8vo, illus by H.K. Browne, full dec lea stamped in blind and triple gold rules, raised spine, light wear to top of spine, some plts mildly foxed but most exceptionally clean and bright. (Contains all points for first issue in text but lacks pub's catalog at rear. Frontis and plts no. 1, 2, and 4 all contain Chapman and Hall imprint and are first state; plate no. 3 later state.) VG+. *GREAT EXPECTATIONS.* $550

Dickens, Charles. THE LIFE AND ADVENTURES OF NICHOLAS NICKLEBY. With Illustrations by Phiz. London: Chapman & Hall, 1839. 8vo, 624pp. 19th cent half tan calf and marbled boards w/gilt tooled spine and morocco spine label. Enrgvd frontis, 39 plts. Plts heavily foxed, moderate general wear to binding, o/w VG w/bkpl of John Ponsford. 1st ed, evidently bound from parts and containing the following 1st issue points: "visiter" for "sister" on p. 123, line 17, and "Chapman and Hall" on first 4 plts. *CHAPEL HILL.* $200

Dickens, Charles. THE LIFE AND ADVENTURES OF NICHOLAS NICKLEBY. With Numerous Illus by Phiz. Phila: Lea & Blanchard, 1839. Large 8vo. 8,(13)-404pp. Frontis. With the front wrappers for Part 1 and 19/20 bound in. Contemp calf backed cloth, spine repaired. *M & S.* $200

Dickens, Charles. THE LIFE OF OUR LORD. (New York: Simon and Schuster, 1934). 1st Amer ed. Frontis and 1 plt. Cl sl faded at spine and edges, otherwise Excellent. *PIRAGES.* $50

Dickens, Charles. THE MYSTERY OF EDWIN DROOD. Brattleboro: T.P. James, 1873. 1st Amer ed. 488pp. Wear to spine ends & cvr edges but terracotta cloth cvr & interior bright, clean. VG. *BEBBAH.* $150

Dickens, Charles. THE MYSTERY OF EDWIN DROOD. London: Chapman and Hall, 1870. 1st ed. 8vo, 12 illus by S.L. Fildes and a portrait, 1/2 green lea over marbled paper covered boards, marbled endpapers, raised spine, mild sporadic foxing and light rubbing to spine, lacks pub's catalog, orig parts cover tipped in at rear. VG+. *GREAT EXPECTATIONS.* $325

Dickens, Charles. THE OLD CURIOSITY SHOP. London: Chapman and Hall, 1840. 1st ed. Tall 8vo, illus by George Catermole and Hablot Browne, 1/4 tan lea over cloth, raised spine with two lea spine labels, spine mildly rubbed and boards show shelfwear and old stains. (A made up vol, comprising the first 37 chapters from Vol. I and the remainder from Vol. II of "Master Humphrey's Clock." Unusual in this format and actually precedes the first separate issue of the novel, which was not published until 1841.) Good+. *GREAT EXPECTATIONS.* $150

Dickens, Charles. THE PERSONAL HISTORY OF DAVID COPPERFIELD. London: Hodder & Stoughton, (1911). Illus by Frank Reynolds. 1st UK ed. Frontis, 20 tipped in color plts w/ptd tissues. Red cl over boards, dec front cover stamped in gold and black, spine stamped in gold, pict eps. Edges bumped, ink inscrip on recto of frontis, small stains on cvrs. *BOOKMINE.* $200

Dickens, Charles. THE POSTHUMOUS PAPERS OF THE PICKWICK CLUB. 2 Vols. Oxford: Oxford Univ Press of the LEC, 1933. Ltd ed. 4to, illus by John Austen, #634 of 1500 signed by the illustrator, slipcase stained and worn with interior repair at one fold. Fine in Good box. *GREAT EXPECTATIONS.* $125

Dickens, Charles. THE POSTHUMOUS PAPERS OF THE PICKWICK CLUB. Illus in Color by Frank Reynolds. London: Hodder & Stoughton. N.d. (circa 1910). x,534pp+25 mounted color plts, each w/ptd tissue guard. Orig red cl, gilt. *KARMIOLE.* $125

Dickens, Charles. THE POSTHUMOUS PAPERS OF THE PICKWICK CLUB. London: Chapman and Hall, 1837. 1st ed, later issue. 8vo, illus by R. Seymour and Phiz, full morocco, with gilt decorated spine and inner dentelles, aeg. (An extra illus copy. Traces of foxing to plts.) NF. *GREAT EXPECTATIONS.* $750

Dickens, Charles. THE WORKS OF CHARLES DICKENS. (London): Cassell & Co, Ltd, (c1920). "Special Authorised Ed." 20 vols. Orig brn cl, dec gilt spines, cl sl soiled. Good. *KARMIOLE.* $300

Dickens, Mamie (ed). THE LETTERS OF CHARLES DICKENS. 2 Vols. London: Chapman and Hall, 1929. Ltd ed. 8vo, half green lea over marbled boards, spines gilt tooled with three raised bands, teg, joints lightly rubbed. One of 300. NF. *GREAT EXPECTATIONS.* $175

Dickens, Mamie (ed). THE LETTERS OF CHARLES DICKENS. 2 Vols. NY: Scribner's, 1879. 1st Amer ed. 12mo, blue cloth, front hinge Vol. II open. Good+. *GREAT EXPECTATIONS.* $45

Dickens, Mamie (ed). THE LETTERS OF CHARLES DICKENS. 2 Vols. NY: Scribner's, 1879. 1st Amer ed. 12mo, blue cloth. VG. *GREAT EXPECTATIONS.* $60

Dickens, Mamie (ed). THE LETTERS OF CHARLES DICKENS. 3 Vols. London: Chapman and Hall, 1880. 2nd ed. 8vo, red cloth. Vol. III published in 1882 as supplement. Mild dampstaining to spine and roan labels show wear. VG. *GREAT EXPECTATIONS.* $75

Dickens, Mamie. MY FATHER AS I RECALL HIM. NY: Dutton, 1897. 1st Amer ed. 12mo, 147pp, illus, green cloth. Bkpl, spine lettering faded. VG. *GREAT EXPECTATIONS.* $27.50

Dickens, Mamie. MY FATHER AS I RECALL HIM. Westminster: Roxburghe Press, (1897). 1st ed. 12mo, 128pp, blue cloth stamped with image of Dickens and his children in gold. VG. *GREAT EXPECTATIONS*. $35

Dickens. THE WORKS OF CHARLES DICKENS. 40 VOLS. London: Chapman and Hall, 1929. Each vol. illus. by Hablot Knight Browne. Gilt-stamped green buckram. Gilt tops. Ltd. to 150 sets for Great Britain and 150 sets for America. Uncut. Fine. *ARTIS*. $550

Dickerson, Philip J. HISTORY OF THE OSAGE NATION, ITS PEOPLE, RESOURCES AND PROSPECTS...Pawhuska, 1906. 1st ed. 144pp. Orig printed pict wrappers. Howes D321. *GINSBERG*. $150

Dickey, Fannie Porter, Mrs (comp). BLADES O' BLUEGRASS. Louisville: John P. Morton, 1892. 1st ed. (14),331pp. Orig dec grn cl, teg. VG. *CHAPEL HILL*. $75

Dickey, James. A PRIVATE BRINKMANSHIP. Claremont: Pitzer (1963). 1st ed. One of 1000. Signed w/quote. *DORN*. $120

Dickey, James. ALNILAM. GC, NY: Doubleday, 1987. 1st ed. Inscribed. Orig blue cl. Fine in dj. *CHAPEL HILL*. $50

Dickey, James. ALNILAM. GC: Doubleday, 1987. 1st ed. Inscribed. Fine in Fine dj. *LOPEZ*. $65

Dickey, James. BABEL TO BYZANTIUM: POETS & POETRY NOW. NY: FSG (1968). Signed, w/quote. Review copy, slip. NF in dj. *DORN*. $85

Dickey, James. DELIVERANCE. Boston: Houghton Mifflin, 1970. 1st ed, 1st novel. Orig beige cl. Fine in dj. Signed. *CHAPEL HILL*. $75

Dickey, James. DELIVERANCE. Boston: Houghton Mifflin Co., 1970. Uncorrected proof. Spiral-bound in white wrappers. Trifle hand-soiled. Rare. *DERMONT*. $500

Dickey, James. DELIVERANCE. Franklin Center: Franklin Library 1981. Ltd ed. Emb owner stamp else Fine in Franklin leather. *CAPTAIN'S BOOKSHELF*. $60

Dickey, James. DELIVERANCE. Houghton Mifflin, 1970. 1st ed. Fine in dj. *STAHR*. $50

Dickey, James. ENEMY IN EDEN. Lord John Press, 1978. 1/275 numbered/signed. New. *DERMONT*. $35

Dickey, James. JERICHO: THE SOUTH BEHELD. Birmingham, AL: (1974). Stated 1st and ltd ed. Additional laid-in print. Mint in dj. *BOND*. $75

Dickey, James. POEMS 1957-1967. London: Rapp & Carroll, (1967). 1st Eng ed. Signed. Fine in dj. *JUVELIS*. $40

Dickey, James. POEMS 1957-1967. Middletown: Wesleyan Univ Press, (1967). 1st ed. Card signed by author laid in. Fine in dj. *JUVELIS*. $35

Dickey, James. PUELLA. Doubleday, 1982. 1st ed. Fine in dj. Evidence of bkpl removal. *STAHR*. $15

Dickey, James. SELF-INTERVIEWS. Doubleday, 1970. 1st ed. Fine in dj. *STAHR*. $25

Dickey, James. SELF-INTERVIEWS. GC: Doubleday, 1970. 1st ed. Fine in sl used dj. *CAPTAIN'S BOOKSHELF*. $40

Dickey, James. SOUTHERN LIGHT. Birmingham: Oxmoor House (1991). 1st ed. Signed. Fine in dj. *DORN*. $60

Dickey, James. SPINNING THE CRYSTAL BALL. Washington: Library of Congress, 1967. 1st ed. Fine in wraps. Inscribed. *CAPTAIN'S BOOKSHELF*. $25

Dickey, James. SPINNING THE CRYSTAL BALL. Washington: The Library of Congress, 1967. 1st ed. Signed. Fine in dj. *JUVELIS*. $35

Dickey, James. THE EARLY MOTION. Middletown: Wesleyan (1981). 1st ed. Fine in dj. Signed. *CAPTAIN'S BOOKSHELF*. $50

Dickey, James. THE ENEMY FROM EDEN. (Northridge, California: Lord John Press, 1978). 1st ed. One of 275 (of 301 total) signed by Dickey. Mint. *PIRAGES*. $75

Dickey, James. THE ENEMY FROM EDEN. Northridge: Lord John Press, 1978. One of 275 signed. Fine in cl-backed marbled boards. *CAPTAIN'S BOOKSHELF*. $50

Dickey, James. THE EYE-BEATERS, BLOOD, VICTORY, MADNESS, BUCKHEAD, AND MERCY. NY: Doubleday, (1970). 1st Amer ed. Signed. Brief non-authorial inscrip, else NF in dj. *DORN*. $60

Dickey, James. THE STARRY PLACE BETWEEN THE ANTLERS. (Bloomfield Hills, MI and Columbia, SC: Bruccoli Clark, 1981). 1st ed. Orig ptd wraps. Lightly soiled, couple of stickers removed from front wrap, thus VG only. *CHAPEL HILL*. $20

Dickey, James. THE STRENGTH OF FIELDS. Bloomfield Hills and Columbia: Brucolli Clark (1977). 1st ed. One of 350 numbered, signed. Fine in wraps, env. *DORN*. $65

Dickey, James. THE STRENGTH OF FIELDS. GC: Doubleday, 1979. 1st ed. Fine in dj, 2 tears. Inscribed. *CAPTAIN'S BOOKSHELF*. $50

Dickey, James. THE SUSPECT IN POETRY. Madison, MN: The Sixties Press, 1964. 1st ed. Fine in spine-darkened, sl chipped dj. Inscribed. *CAPTAIN'S BOOKSHELF*. $75

Dickey, James. THE SUSPECT IN POETRY. Madison: The Sixties, (1964). Adv rev copy with slips. Inscribed. In dj with small stain bottom corner of front panel, else VG. *DORN*. $95

Dickey, James. THE ZODIAC. GC, NY: Doubleday & Company, Inc, 1976. 1st ed. Inscribed card laid in. Fine in dj. *JUVELIS*. $40

Dickey, James. VARMLAND: POEMS BASED ON POEMS. Palaemon, (1982). 1/150 numbered/signed of which only 45 were for sale. Fine. *DERMONT*. $45

Dickey, Roland F. NEW MEXICO VILLAGE ARTS. Univ of NM, 1949. 1st ed. Fine in chipped dj w/small amount of tape. *VARNER*. $50

Dickinson, Charles. THE WIDOW'S ADVENTURES. Morrow, 1989. 1st Amer ed. VF in dj. Signed. *STAHR*. $45

Dickinson, Clarence E. THE FLYING GUNS. NY: Charles Scribner's Sons. 1942. 1st ed. Fine in dj. *KARMIOLE*. $30

Dickinson, Emily. BOLTS OF MELODY. Mabel Loomis Todd and Millicent Todd Bingham (eds). NY: Harper, 1945. 1st ed. VG. BAL 4695. *SECOND LIFE*. $35

Dickinson, Emily. FURTHER POEMS OF EMILY DICKINSON. Boston, 1929. Martha Dickinson Bianchi and Alfred Leete Hampson eds. Ltd ed, 140/450 (of 465). Teg, uncut, and partly unopened. Fine in box (spine little sunned, top sl chipped, little edge rubbed). *POLYANTHOS*. $200

Dickinson, Emily. LETTERS OF EMILY DICKINSON. Mabel Loomis Todd (ed). Boston: Roberts Brothers, 1894. 1st ed, 1st prtg, 1st binding. 2 vols. Frontispieces. Gilt dec grn cl. Owner sig, bkpls each vol w/faint offsetting to feps, o/w Fine set. *JAFFE*. $500

Dickinson, Emily. POEMS. (Second Series) Boston: Roberts Brothers, 1892. 1st ed. Grn cl w/gold dec and lettering. Teg & edges bevelled. Spine darkened, ends sl worn, owner label pasted to front pastedown, else tight, VG+. BAL 4656. *BERNARD*. $700

Dickinson, Emily. POEMS. Illus by Helen Sewell. Full black leather, slipcase. NY: LEC, 1952. Ltd to 1500 signed by Sewell. Head of spine a bit rubbed, o/w Fine. *JAFFE*. $100

Dickinson, Emily. POEMS. Louis Untermeyer (ed). NY: LEC, 1952. One of 1500 illus, signed by Helen Sewell. Bit of minor rubbing to the spine, else Fine in slipcase. *CAPTAIN'S BOOKSHELF*. $100

Dickinson, Emily. THE POEMS OF EMILY DICKINSON: CENTENARY EDITION. Martha Dickinson Bianchi, Alfred Leete Hampson (eds). Boston: Little, Brown, 1930. 1st ed. Grn cl, teg. Lt fading to edges, else Fine in lightly soiled dj (few sm tears). *CAPTAIN'S BOOKSHELF*. $125

Dickinson, H.W. MATTHEW BOULTON. Cambridge: At the Univ Press. 1937. 1st ed. Fldg plan. Grn cl, gilt. *KARMIOLE*. $75

Dickinson, Peter. SLEEP & HIS BROTHER. NY: Harper, 1971. 1st Amer ed. About Fine in dj with light wear, minor soiling. *SILVER DOOR.* $25

Dickson, Carter (pseud of John Dickson Carr). DEATH IN FIVE BOXES. NY: William Morrow, 1938. 1st ed. Sm label removed from fep o/w Fine in VG dj (1/2" strip residue from removed tape along interior top, bottom edges but does not show through; short closed tears; wear, chips top corner of spine). *MORDIDA.* $300

Dickson, Carter (pseud of John Dickson Carr). SEEING IS BELIEV-ING. NY: William Morrow, 1941. 1st ed. Advance reading copy. VG in wraps bound in the pict dj in custom-made box w/label on spine. *MORDIDA.* $400

Dickson, Carter (pseud of John Dickson Carr). SEEING IS BELIEV-ING. NY: William Morrow, 1941. 1st ed. Eps sl darkened o/w Fine in bright like-new dj. *MORDIDA.* $450

Dickson, Carter (pseud of John Dickson Carr). THE CAVALIER'S CUP. NY: William Morrow, 1953. 1st ed. Fine in dj. *MORDIDA.* $85

Dickson, Gordon. THE TACTICS OF MISTAKE. Doubleday, 1971. 1st ed. VG in dj. *MADLE.* $50

Dickson, H.R.P. THE ARAB OF THE DESERT. London, 1951. 9 fldg maps in pocket. 664pp. 2nd ed. With all maps. *O'NEILL.* $200

Didion, Joan. A BOOK OF COMMON PRAYER. NY: S&S, (1977). Uncorrected proof. Front panel separating from spine near top, sl soiled. VG. *CAPTAIN'S BOOKSHELF.* $50

Didion, Joan. DEMOCRACY. London, 1984. 1st ed. Proof copy in pub printed wraps. Fine. *POLYANTHOS.* $30

Didion, Joan. PLAY IT AS IT LAYS. NY: Farrar, Straus & Giroux, (1970). 1st ed. Fine in dj. *CAPTAIN'S BOOKSHELF.* $60

Didion, Joan. RUN RIVER. Cl, dj. NY: Obolensky, (1963). 1st ed. VF. *JAFFE.* $150

Didion, Joan. RUN RIVER. NY: Ivan Obolensky, (1963). 1st ed, 1st bk. Orig bluegrn cl. Fine in dj, minimal rubbing. *CHAPEL HILL.* $100

Didion, Joan. RUN RIVER. NY: Obolensky, (1963). 1st ed, 1st bk. Fine in dj w/slight rubbing to spinal extremities. *CAPTAIN'S BOOK-SHELF.* $75

Didion, Joan. SALVADOR. NY: Simon & Schuster, (1983). 1st ed. Orig cl-backed boards. Fine in dj. Signed. *CHAPEL HILL.* $50

Didion, Joan. SLOUCHING TOWARDS BETHLEHEM. Farrar, Straus & Giroux, 1968. 1st ed. Fine in dj. *STAHR.* $75

Didion, Joan. SLOUCHING TOWARDS BETHLEHEM. NY: FSG (1968). 1st ed. Sm spot top edge else Fine in NF dj (2 sm edge tears). *DORN.* $70

Didion, Joan. SLOUCHING TOWARDS BETHLEHEM. NY: FSG, (1968). Fine in NF dj. *LOPEZ.* $75

Dietrich, Dr. THE GERMAN EMIGRANTS; OR FREDERICK WOHLGEMUTH'S VOYAGE TO CALIFORNIA. Trans by Leopold Wray. Stanford, CA: James Ladd Delkin, Stanford Univ, 1949. Ed ltd to 1000. 8 hand colored plts. Dj. *KARMIOLE.* $30

Dietz, August. THE CONFEDERATE STATES POST-OFFICE DEPARTMENT. ITS STAMPS AND STATIONERY. Richmond, (1948). 2nd ed. Wrappers. NF. *McGOWAN.* $37.50

Dieulafoy, Jane. AT SUSA: THE ANCIENT CAPITAL OF THE KINGS OF PERSIA. Phila: Gebbie and Co, 1890. (xiii),266pp. Dec cl cvr, bit soiled. Aeg. 121 wood engr, map. *SCHOYER'S.* $150

DiFusco, John et al. TRACERS. NY: Hill & Wang, (1986). Stated 1st ed. Fine in Fine dj. *AKA.* $40

Digby, Bassett. TIGERS, GOLD, AND WITCH-DOCTORS. NY: Harcourt, Brace & Co, (1928). VG. *BLUE DRAGON.* $35

Digby, Sir Kenelm. THE CLOSET OF SIR KENELM DIGBY KNIGHT OPENED. London: Philip Lee Warner, 1910. Anne Mac-

Donell (ed). Frontis, facs title-pg. Brn blind stamped buckram, teg. Fine. *WEBER.* $150

Dillard, Annie. HOLY THE FIRM. NY: Harper, (1977). Uncor-rected proof. Fine in lightly soiled ptd wraps. *CAPTAIN'S BOOKSHELF.* $75

Dillard, Annie. PILGRIM AT TINKER CREEK. London: Cape, 1975. 1st Eng ed. *LOPEZ.* $50

Dillard, Annie. THE LIVING: A NOVEL. Harper Collins, 1992. Ad-vance reading copy. VF in wraps. *STAHR.* $45

Dillenback, H.P. MEDICATED INHALATION IN THE TREAT-MENT OF PULMONARY CONSUMPTION, BRONCHITIS, ASTHMA, CATARRH, AND CLERGYMAN'S SORE THROAT. Boston, 1857. 1st ed. 214pp + plts. Scarce. *FYE.* $100

Diller, Theodore. PIONEER MEDICINE IN WESTERN PEN-NSYLVANIA. NY, 1927. 1st ed. Autographed. *FYE.* $40

Dillon, J.L. THE BLOSSOM CIRCLE OF THE YEAR IN SOUTHERN GARDENS. NY, 1922. Cl, lt scuffing extrems. *SUT-TON.* $35

Dillon, Millicent (ed). OUT IN THE WORLD. SELECTED LET-TERS OF JANE BOWLES 1935-1970. Santa Barbara: Black Spar-row, 1985. 1st ed. 1/200 numbered, signed by ed. Fine. *SMITH.* $35

Dillon, Millicent (ed). OUT IN THE WORLD: SELECTED LET-TERS OF JANE BOWLES 1935-1970. Santa Barbara: Black Spar-row (1985). One of 200 numbered, signed. Fine in acetate. *DORN.* $50

Dillon, R.H. J. ROSS BROWNE: CONFIDENTIAL AGENT IN OLD CALIFORNIA. Univ of OK Press, 1965. 1st ed. Fine in NF dj. *VARNER.* $25

Dillon, Richard (ed). A LONG ROAD TO STONY CREEK, BEING THE NARRATIVES BY RUFUS BURROWS & CYRUS HULL...Ashland: Lewis Osborne, 1971. 1st ed, ltd to 650 numbered. Fine. *OREGON.* $50

Dillon, Richard. BURNT-OUT FIRES, CALIFORNIA'S MODOC INDIAN WAR. Englewood Cliffs, (1973). 1st ed. 371pp. Dj spine faded o/w Fine. *PRATT.* $30

Dillon, Richard. MERIWETHER LEWIS. NY, 1965. 1st ed. Signed. NF in dj. *BAADE.* $45

Dillon, Richard. THE LEGEND OF GRIZZLY ADAMS. NY: Coward McCann, Inc, (1966). Black stamped cl in dj. *DAWSON'S.* $30

DiMaggio, Joe. LUCKY TO BE A YANKEE. Rudolph Field, 1946. 1st ed. Good+ in VG dj. *PLAPINGER.* $75

DiMaggio, Joe. THE DIMAGGIO ALBUMS. NY: Putnam, (1989). 1st ed? 2 vols. New in new slipcase. *AARD.* $50

Dimitrov, Georgi. THE REICHSTAG FIRE TRIAL. London, (1934). 2nd ptg. 21 illus. Spine faded, shelfwear, o/w VG. *DIAMOND.* $35

Dimsdale, Thomas J. THE VIGILANTES OF MONTANA. Univ of OK Press, 1953. 1st ptg. Fine in VG dj. *VARNER.* $15

Dimsdale, Thomas J. THE VIGILANTES OF MONTANA; OR, POPULAR JUSTICE.....Al Noyes (ed). Helena: State Publishing, (n.d.). 5th ed. 1st pub in 1866. Fine. Howes D-345. *LAURIE.* $40

Dinesen, Isak. ANECDOTES OF DESTINY. Michael Joseph, 1958. 1st Eng ed. About Fine in dj (few tears). *STAHR.* $35

Dinesen, Isak. LAST TALES. NY: Random House, 1957. 1st ed. Fine; minor rubbing dj spine top. Name. *ELSE FINE.* $65

Dinesen, Isak. LETTERS FROM AFRICA 1914-1931. Frans Lasson (ed). Chicago: Univ of Chicago Press, (1981). 1st ed. Fine in dj. *CAPTAIN'S BOOKSHELF.* $30

Dinesen, Isak. OUT OF AFRICA. NY, 1938. 1st ed. Name. Fine in like dj. *POLYANTHOS.* $125

Dinesen, Isak. OUT OF AFRICA. NY: Random House, 1938. 1st ed. Fine w/unflaked spine, nicer-than-usual dj w/slight wear at ends of darkened spine. *BEASLEY.* $125

Dinesen, Isak. OUT OF AFRICA. NY: Random House, 1938. 1st ed. Bkpl. Fine; some darkening dj spine. *ELSE FINE.* $125

Dinesen, Isak. SEVEN GOTHIC TALES. Intro by Dorothy Canfield. NY: Harrison Smith & Robert Haas, 1934. 1st ed, 1st bk. Fine in dj. Rare in this condition. *CHAPEL HILL.* $250

Dinesen, Isak. SEVEN GOTHIC TALES. NY: Smith & Haas, 1934. 1st ed. Spine lettering rubbed, else NF. *ELSE FINE.* $30

Dinesen, Isak. SEVEN GOTHIC TALES. Smith & Haas, 1934. 1st ed. VG. *MADLE.* $25

Dinesen, Isak. WINTER'S TALES. Random, 1942. 1st Amer ed. Tiny spot front edge, narrow binding glue stain to hinges else VG in dj with 1/2" closed tear, chips, else VG, bright. *BEBBAH.* $45

Dingle, Edwin J. BORDERLANDS OF ETERNITY. LA: Econolith Press, 1941. Later ptg. Front hinge starting. VG or better. Signed. *STAHR.* $35

Dingwall, E.J. VERY PECULIAR PEOPLE. London: Rider and Co., (1950). 1st ed. Cover scuffed and a bit faded, else internally VG. *WREDEN.* $20

Dinh, Tran Van. NO PASSENGER ON THE RIVER. NY: Vantage, (1965). 1st ed. Sl spine slant. Price clipped, bit of edgewear, lt soil rear panel dj. *AKA.* $75

Dinkins, J. Lester. DUNNELLON—BOOMTOWN OF THE 1890'S. St. Petersburg: Great Outdoors, 1969. 1st ed. Signed. NF. *ARCHER.* $22.50

Dinning, Hector and James McBey. NILE TO ALEPPO. NY, 1920. Some cover stains. 287pp, uncut. *O'NEILL.* $65

Dinning, Hector. NILE TO ALEPPO. NY: Macmillan, 1920. 1st ed. 13 plts. Orig cl, sl rubbed and soiled, slight foxing, o/w VG. *WORLDWIDE.* $75

Dinsmoor, William Bell. THE ARCHONS OF ATHENS. Cambridge: Harvard Univ Press, 1931. 27 tables. Corners lightly bumped, o/w Fine. *ARCHAEOLOGIA.* $550

Diringer, David. THE HAND-PRODUCED BOOK. NY: Philosophical Library, (1953). Dj. *DAWSON'S.* $150

Dirlam, H. Kenneth. JOHN CHAPMAN, BY OCCUPATION A GATHERER AND PLANTER OF APPLESEEDS. Mansfield: Richland County, Ohio SesquiCentennial Committee, 1953. 1st ed. 4pp illus leaflet in rear pocket. Name. NF. *CONNOLLY & WADE.* $40

Dirom, Major. A NARRATIVE OF THE CAMPAIGN IN INDIA. London, 1794. 2nd and best ed. 293pp. Contemp marbled boards, 3/4 calf. *CULLEN.* $500

Disch, Thomas M. GETTING INTO DEATH AND OTHER STORIES. NY, 1976. 1st ed. Signed presentation. Fine in like dj. *POLYANTHOS.* $50

Disch, Thomas M. THE TALE OF DAN DE LION. Minnesota, 1986. 1st ed. Signed presentation w/colored drwg. Mint in like dj. *POLYANTHOS.* $45

Disher, Maurice Wilson. MAD GENIUS. NY: Hutchinson & Co, 1950. 1st ed. Dj repaired. *DRAMATIS.* $25

Disney, Walt. DONALD DUCK. Abbeville, (1978). Folio. 195pp. Color illus Carl Banks. Reprints of 10 of Donald's misadventure of 1940s and '50s. Fine in Fine dj. *BEBBAH.* $25

Disney, Walt. THE ADVENTURES OF MICKEY MOUSE, BOOK NUMBER 2. McKay, (1932). 12mo. Unpaginated. Edgewear, wear to spine ends, bright VG copy. Some page soil. Paper-covered boards w/color pict of Mickey & Pluto on front & Minnie, canary & very happy cat on rear. Very scarce. *BEBBAH.* $350

Disselhoff, Hans and Signald Linne. THE ART OF ANCIENT AMERICA. NY: Greystone Pr, (1966), rev ed. Good in chipped dj. *SILVER.* $20

Distin, William H. and Robert Bishop. THE AMERICAN CLOCK. NY: Dutton, 1976. 1st ed. VG in VG dj. *BACKROOM.* $50

Disturnell, John. PICTURESQUE TOURIST: BEING A GUIDE...NY, 1858. 298pp,ads. 14 full pg illus (lacking #13,), 3 maps (1 folded), gilt titled cl, 16mo. Worn & faded, chipped spine ends, paper darkened, note on ep. *BOHLING.* $45

Disturnell, John. TRIP THROUGH THE LAKES OF NORTH AMERICA; EMBRACING A FULL DESCRIPTION OF THE ST. LAWRENCE RIVER...NY: Disturnell, 1857. 1st ed. 406pp. 14 vignettes, maps, and plts. Orig dec cl. Howes D355. Map folded onto inside rear cover. *GINSBERG.* $300

Ditmars, R.L. A FIELD BOOK OF NORTH AMERICAN SNAKES. NY, 1939. 1st ed. 48 plts. Lt wear. *SUTTON.* $35

Ditmars, R.L. REPTILES OF THE WORLD. NY, (1922). 89 photo plts. Lt browning of eps, edges of dj worn. *SUTTON.* $25

Ditmars, R.L. THE REPTILE BOOK. NY, Mar. 1907. Good. *MIKESH.* $45

Ditmars, R.L. THE REPTILES OF NORTH AMERICA. GC, (1936). Rev. ed. 136 plts (8 colored). Wear, foxing, front hinge cracked, corner of rear ep missing. *SUTTON.* $32

Ditson,George Leighton. THE PARA PAPERS....Paris and NY: Mason, 1858. 1st US ed. Bound in rubbed 3/4 calf, VG. *SECOND LIFE.* $45

Ditzion, Sidney. MARRIAGE, MORALS AND SEX IN AMERICA. NY: Bookman Associates, (1953). 1st ed. Dj. Fine. *WREDEN.* $25

Dixie, Lady Florence. ACROSS PATAGONIA. NY: R. Worthington, 1881. 1st Amer ed. xiii,(iii),251pp,4pp ads. Spine wear, staining. Sm name stamp. Damp-staining, browning some pp, else VG. *DIAMOND.* $50

Dixon, Don. UNIVERSE. Houghton-Mifflin, 1978. 1st ed. Fine in dj. *MADLE.* $35

Dixon, George A. A VOYAGE ROUND THE WORLD; BUT MORE PARTICULARLY TO THE NORTHWEST COAST. London: George Goulding, 1789. 1st ed. Half-title missing, title neatly repaired, occasional light offsetting, later vellum backed boards. 4to, 22 plates and maps (fldg map as frontis). *PARMER.* $1500

Dixon, Olive K. LIFE OF "BILLY" DIXON. Southwest Press, 1927. Rev ed. Fine. *VARNER.* $60

Dixon, Thomas, Jr. THE LEOPARD'S SPOTS. NY: Doubleday, Pg, 1902. 1st ed, 1st bk, in presentation binding. Inscribed. Orig cl-backed boards, teg. Soiled, corners bumped. Owner emb stamp, o/w VG. *CHAPEL HILL.* $95

Dixon, Thomas, Jr. THE LIFE WORTH LIVING. NY: Doubleday, Page, 1905. 1st ed. Inscribed. Orig grn cl. VG+. *CHAPEL HILL.* $65

Dixon, William Hepworth. WHITE CONQUEST. London: Chatto & Windus, 1876. 1st ed. 2 vols. 356, 373pp + publisher's ads. Cl rubbed. Good, sound. *ARTIS.* $75

Dixon, William Scarth. FOX HUNTING IN THE TWENTIETH CENTURY. NY: Dingwall-Rock, 1925. 1st ed. VG-NF. *OLD LONDON.* $45

Dixon, William Scarth. HUNTING IN THE OLDEN DAYS. London: Constable & Co., 1912. 1st ed. Minor edgewear, else VG-NF. *OLD LONDON.* $125

Doane, R.W. et al. FOREST INSECTS...NY, (1936). Some fading, name stamp. *SUTTON.* $35

Dobbs, Caroline. MEN OF CHAMPOEG, A RECORD OF THE LIVES OF THE PIONEERS....Portland, 1932. Prospectus laid in. 1st ed. Fine. *OREGON.* $55

Dobell, Clifford. ANTONY VAN LEEUWENHOEK AND HIS "LITTLE ANIMALS". NY: Harcourt, Brace & Co. 1932. 1st ed. 32 plts (one fldg). Title ptd in red and black. Beige cloth. Fine. *KARMIOLE*. $100

Doberer, K.K. THE GOLDMAKERS. London, 1948. Fine. *POLYANTHOS*. $30

Doberer, K.K. THE GOLDMAKERS: 10,000 YEARS OF ALCHEMY. London: Nicholson & Watson, 1948. VG. *BOOKCELL*. $25

Dobie, J. Frank and Jeff Dykes. 44 & 44. Austin: Encino Press, 1972. Rprt of bibliography 44 RANGE COUNTRY BOOKS by Dobie, orig pub in 1941, supplemented by 44 MORE RANGE COUNTRY BOOKS by Dykes. Bound in paper boards. Fine. *LAURIE*. $75

Dobie, J. Frank. (ed). TONE THE BELL EASY. Austin, TX: The Texas Folklore Society, 1932. 1st ed. Fine in faded dj. *KARMIOLE*. $50

Dobie, J. Frank. A VAQUERO OF THE BRUSH COUNTRY. London: Hammond, Hammond & Co, Ltd, (1949). 1st Eng ed. Cloth in dj w/price clipped and one neat tear. *DAWSON'S*. $50

Dobie, J. Frank. A VAQUERO OF THE BRUSH COUNTRY. NY: Grosset & Dunlap, 1929. Minor discoloration on cover. VG. *BURCHAM*. $30

Dobie, J. Frank. APACHE GOLD & YAQUI SILVER. Little, Brown, 1939. 1st ed. Frontis by Tom Lea. Owner inscrip, else Fine, Nice chipped dj. *AUTHORS OF THE WEST*. $125

Dobie, J. Frank. APACHE GOLD AND YAQUI SILVER. Illus Tom Lea. Boston: Little, Brown, 1953. Fine in Fair dj. *CONNOLLY & WADE*. $32.50

Dobie, J. Frank. APACHE GOLD AND YAQUI SILVER. London: Hammond & Co, (1956). 1st British ed. Illus Tom Lea. Fine in dj. *AUTHORS OF THE WEST*. $85

Dobie, J. Frank. BOB MORE: MAN AND BIRD MAN. Dallas: Encino Press, 1965. William Wittliff (intro, design). One of 550 numbered, this unsigned by Wittliff. Mint in slipcase. *LAURIE*. $200

Dobie, J. Frank. CARL SANDBURG & SAINT PETER AT THE GATE. Austin: Encino Press, 1966. One of 750 numbered, designed by William Wittliff. Bound in 1/4 blue cl and white paper boards. Mint in slipcase. *LAURIE*. $175

Dobie, J. Frank. COW PEOPLE. London: Hammond, Hammond & Co, (1964). 1st British ed. Fine in dj. *AUTHORS OF THE WEST*. $50

Dobie, J. Frank. I'LL TELL YOU A TALE. Boston: Little, Brown, and Co, 1960. 1st ed, signed. NF in dj. *LAURIE*. $90

Dobie, J. Frank. LOST MINES OF THE OLD WEST. London, (1960). 1st Eng ed. Fine in dj. *DIAMOND*. $35

Dobie, J. Frank. LOST MINES OF THE OLD WEST: CORONADO'S CHILDREN. London: Hammond, Hammond & Co, (1960). 1st British ed. Fine in dj. *AUTHORS OF THE WEST*. $50

Dobie, J. Frank. PREFACES. (1975) 1st ed. Fine, clean frayed dj. *AUTHORS OF THE WEST*. $25

Dobie, J. Frank. PREFACES. Little Brown (1975). 1st ed. F in F dj. *OREGON*. $20

Dobie, J. Frank. SOME PART OF MYSELF. Boston: Little, Brown, 1967. 1st ed. Fine in NF dj. *CONNOLLY & WADE*. $60

Dobie, J. Frank. SOME PART OF MYSELF. Little Brown, (1967) 1st ed. VF in VG Dj. *OREGON*. $35

Dobie, J. Frank. TALES OF OLD-TIME TEXAS. Boston: Little, Brown, 1955. Fine in NF dj. *CONNOLLY & WADE*. $22.50

Dobie, J. Frank. THE BEN LILLY LEGEND. London: Hammond, Hammond & Co, 1952. 1st British ed. Fine in VG dj. *BACKMAN*. $62

Dobie, J. Frank. THE FLAVOR OF TEXAS. Dallas, 1936. 1st ed. 287pp. Signed. Bkpl. VG in chipped, backstrip split, but basically complete dj. Very scarce. *BAADE*. $225

Dobie, J. Frank. THE LONGHORNS. Illus Tom Lea. Boston: Little Brown, 1941. 1st trade ed. Some soiling, else NF in price-clipped dj. Inscribed. Additionally, Dobie has drawn several brands. *CAPTAIN'S BOOKSHELF*. $175

Dobie, J. Frank. THE LONGHORNS. London: Nicholson & Watson, (1943). 1st British ed. Illus Tom Lea, frontis. VG+ in dj. *AUTHORS OF THE WEST*. $60

Dobie, J. Frank. THE SEVEN MUSTANGS. Austin: Adams, 1948. 1st ed. Autographed. Orig pict wrappers. NF. *PARMER*. $125

Dobie, J. Frank. THE VOICE OF THE COYOTE. Boston: Little Brown, 1949. 1st ed. Fine in VG dj. *OREGON*. $70

Dobie, J. Frank. THE VOICE OF THE COYOTE. London, (1950). 1st Eng ed. NF in dj. *DIAMOND*. $35

Dobie, J. Frank. TONGUES OF THE MONTE: THE MEXICO I LIKE. London: Hammond, Hammond & Co, (1948). 1st British ed. Fine. *AUTHORS OF THE WEST*. $40

Dobie, J. Frank. THE VOICE OF THE COYOTE. Boston, 1949. Fine in VG+ dj. *MIKESH*. $37.50

Doblin, Alfred. ALEXANDERPLATZ BERLIN. NY: Viking, 1931. 1st US ed. 2 vols. Vol I Fine in dj missing sizable chip at spine crown, sl affecting some text, o/w VG; vol II Fine in NF dj. Together in pub's cardboard slipcase. *LOPEZ*. $250

Dobree, Bonamy. ESSAYS IN BIOGRAPHY 1680-1726. London, OUP, 1925. 1st ed. Bkpl removed. Spine faded w/minor wear at top and bottom. Review slip pasted to title page. *WOOLMER*. $25

Dobree, Bonamy. RESTORATION COMEDY 1660-1720. Oxford: Clarendon Press, 1924. 1st ed. Bkpl removed, else VG. *WOOLMER*. $25

Dobson, Austin et al. AMONG MY BOOKS. NY: Longmans, Green, & Co, 1898. 1st Amer ed. Front hinge cracked, slip removed from ffep, else VG. *WREDEN*. $20

Dobson, Austin. A BOOKMAN'S BUDGET. London...: Oxford Univ Press, 1917. 1st ed. Good. *WREDEN*. $20

Dobson, Austin. OLD KENSINGTON PALACE AND OTHER PAPERS. London: Chatto & Windus, 1910. 1st ed. Slight wear along front spine edge at top, else NF. W/signed presentation inscription, bkpl. *CHAPEL HILL*. $150

Dobson, Austin. ROSALBA'S JOURNAL AND OTHER PAPERS. London: Chatto & Windus, 1915. 1st. NF. *MUELLER*. $20

Dobson, Edward. A RUDIMENTARY TREATISE ON THE MANUFACTURE OF BRICKS AND TILES. London, 1850. Rare. NF. *POLYANTHOS*. $75

Dobyns, Henry F. (ed). HEPAH, CALIFORNIA! THE JOURNAL OF CAVE JOHNSON COUTS FROM MONTEREY...DURING THE YEARS 1848-1849. Tucson: AZ Pioneers' Hist Soc, 1961. 1st ed, ltd to 750. Fine. *BOOK MARKET*. $65

Dockstader, Frederick. INDIAN ART IN MIDDLE AMERICA. CT, NY: Graphic Soc, (1964). 1st ed. 70 tipped-in color plts. Good in chipped dj. *SILVER*. $75

Doctorow, E.L. BIG AS LIFE. NY: Simon & Schuster, (1966). 1st ed. NF in dj with 2" tear bottom front flap fold, o/w VG. *LOPEZ*. $250

Doctorow, E.L. BIG AS LIFE. NY: Simon & Schuster, (1966). 1st ed. Fine in dj. Review w/slip laid in. Signed. *CAPTAIN'S BOOKSHELF*. $350

Doctorow, E.L. BILLY BATHGATE. Cl, slipcase. NY: Random House, (1989). 1st ed. Ltd to 300 signed. Mint. *JAFFE*. $150

Doctorow, E.L. BILLY BATHGATE. NY: Random House, (1989). 1st ed. One of 300 numbered signed. NF in pub's slipcase. *UNGER*. $125

Doctorow, E.L. DRINKS BEFORE DINNER. NY, 1979. Uncorrected proof copy in pub printed wraps. Fine. *POLYANTHOS*. $50

Doctorow, E.L. LIVES OF THE POETS. NY: Random House, (1984). 1st ed. Orig maroon cl. Fine in dj. 1st ed. Signed. *CHAPEL HILL.* $60

Doctorow, E.L. LOON LAKE. NY: Random House, (1980). 1st, ltd issue. One of 350 specially bound, signed. As New in slipcase. *CAPTAIN'S BOOKSHELF.* $125

Doctorow, E.L. LOON LAKE. NY: Random House, (1980). Uncorrected proof. Fine in wraps. *CAPTAIN'S BOOKSHELF.* $75

Doctorow, E.L. RAGTIME. NY: Random House, (1975). 1st ed. #54 of only 150 signed. Orig cream cl. Spine sl sunned, else Fine in slipcase. 1st ed. *CHAPEL HILL.* $200

Doctorow, E.L. THE BOOK OF DANIEL. NY: Random House, (1971). 1st ed. VF in dj. *CAPTAIN'S BOOKSHELF.* $75

Doctorow, E.L. THE BOOK OF DANIEL. NY: Random House, (1971). 1st ed. Orig brn cl. NF in sl soiled dj. Signed. *CHAPEL HILL.* $150

Doctorow, E.L. WELCOME TO HARD TIMES. NY: S&S, (1960). 1st ed 1st bk. Signed on bkpl. Name fep, some discoloring to cl, still VG in dj showing light wear. *UNGER.* $325

Doctorow, E.L. WELCOME TO HARD TIMES. NY: Simon & Schuster, 1960. 1st ed. Pages browning as is usual, else Fine in lightly rubbed dj w/49-cent price stamped on the front flap. Attractive. *CAPTAIN'S BOOKSHELF.* $225

Doctorow, E.L. WELCOME TO HARD TIMES. NY: Simon & Schuster, 1960. 1st ed, 1st bk. Orig cl-backed orange boards. Acidic paper browning as usual, o/w Fine in NF dj. Scarce in such nice condition. *CHAPEL HILL.* $325

Doctorow, E.L. WORLD'S FAIR. NY, 1985. Adv reading copy from uncorrected ms. Signed presentation. Pict wraps. Tiny corner crease. Fine. *POLYANTHOS.* $45

Doctorow, E.L. WORLD'S FAIR. NY: Random House, (1985). 1st ed. Orig blue cl. Fine in dj. Review copy, slip laid in. Signed. *CHAPEL HILL.* $65

Doctorow, E.L. WORLD'S FAIR. Random House, 1985. Advance reading copy. NF. Pict wraps. Edges bumped. *STAHR.* $15

Dodd, Anna Bowman. IN AND OUT OF THREE NORMANDY INNS. Boston: Little, Brown, 1899. Clean white cl stamped in gilt, red and blue, lt blue oil-cl dustcvr. Ffep creased. VG. *SCHOYER'S.* $25

Doderidge, Sir John. THE ENGLISH LAWYER. DESCRIBING A METHOD FOR THE MANAGING OF THE LAWES OF THIS LAND. Ptd by the Assignes of I. More Esq., London, 1631. 1st, and only ed. Title pg; 3 leaves; 271pp. A bit of embrowning, and some pinhole worming in margin; one outer margin torn away, but generally quite Good, crisp and wide-margined. Bound in a later 1/4 calf over early marbled boards, rubbed and somewhat worn, but quite sound. *BOSWELL.* $1,500

Dodge, David. DEATH AND TAXES. NY: Macmillan, 1941. 1st ed. Fine; moderate wear dj extremities. *ELSE FINE.* $60

Dodge, David. HOOLIGAN. NY: Macmillan, 1969. 1st ed. Fine in dj. *MORDIDA.* $25

Dodge, David. IT AIN'T HAY. NY: Dell 270, 1949. 1st prtg of 1st paper ed. NF w/a few corner creases. *BEASLEY.* $25

Dodge, David. IT AIN'T HAY. NY: Simon & Schuster, 1946. 1st ed. Pages darkened o/w Fine in dj w/tiny wear at spine ends and nicks along top edge of front panel. *MORDIDA.* $35

Dodge, David. THE LIGHTS OF SKARO. NY: Random House 1954. 1st ed. Fine in dj w/minor wear at base of spine. *MORDIDA.* $30

Dodge, David. THE LONG ESCAPE. Random, (1948). Stated 1st prtg. Two small on cvr edge but VG+ in Good+ dj with chips, edgewear. *BEBBAH.* $25

Dodge, David. TROUBLESHOOTER. NY: Macmillan, 1971. 1st ed. VF in dj. *MORDIDA.* $30

Dodge, Grenville M. BATTLE OF ATLANTA AND OTHER CAMPAIGN ADDRESSES, ETC. Council Bluffs: Monarch, 1911. 1st ed. Orig cl. Printed presentation slip tipped in. *GINSBERG.* $50

Dodge, Grenville M. BIOGRAPHICAL SKETCH OF JAMES BRIDGER. NY: Unz & Co, 1905. 3 plts, incl view. Wraps. Few words lost pg 6, o/w Fine. Howes D392. *OREGON.* $90

Dodge, Grenville M. PERSONAL RECOLLECTIONS OF ABRAHAM LINCOLN....Council Bluffs, IA: Monarch Printing Co, 1914. 9 plts. Flexible cl. *SCHOYER'S.* $35

Dodge, Grenville M. PERSONAL RECOLLECTIONS OF PRESIDENT ABRAHAM LINCOLN...Council Bluffs, IA, 1914. 1st ed. VG. Author's presentation slip. *DIAMOND.* $35

Dodge, Grenville M. THE BATTLE OF ATLANTA AND OTHER CAMPAIGNS, ADDRESSES, ETC. Council Bluffs, 1911. 183pp. Minor cvr wear o/w Fine. *PRATT.* $45

Dodge, Grenville M. THE BATTLE OF ATLANTA AND OTHER CAMPAIGNS, ADDRESSES, ETC. Council Bluffs, IA: 1911. 1st ed. NF. *DIAMOND.* $35

Dodge, M.E. HANS BRINKER; OR, THE SILVER SKATES. A STORY OF LIFE IN HOLLAND. NY: James O'Keane, 1866. 1st ed. 4 plts by F.O.C. Darley & Thomas Nast. Rubbed, hinges and joint repaired, front edge of eps and flyleaf chipped, scattered foxing, few pp stained. All flyleaves and eps, laid into red and blue cl fldg tray case. Laid in is autographed card. Good. *BLUE MOUNTAIN.* $575

Dodge, Mary Mapes. HANS BRINKER or THE SILVER SKATES. Harper, (1924). 1st ed. Louis Rhead illus. 341pp. Color frontis & pict cvr pastedown. Sl wear to pastedown. VG. *BEBBAH.* $35

Dodge, Richard Irving. OUR WILD INDIANS: THIRTY-THREE YEARS PERSONAL EXPERIENCE....Hartford: A.D. Worthington, 1882. 6 full-pg chromoliths. 1st ed. Front hinge cracked, binding shows some wear. *LAURIE.* $75

Dodge, Richard Irving. OUR WILD INDIANS: THIRTY-THREE YEARS' PERSONAL EXPERIENCE. Hartford, 1882. Illus w/chromoliths, steel-engr. Gilt-pict boards. NF. *POLYANTHOS.* $150

Dodge, Richard Irving. THE HUNTING GROUNDS OF THE GREAT WEST. London: Chatto & Windus, 1877. Fldg map, tables. Front hinge torn. Howes D404. *HUDSON.* $110

Dodsworth, William. HISTORICAL ACCOUNT OF THE EPISCOPAL SEE AND CATHEDRAL CHURCH OF SALISBURY, 1814. 21 engrs. 240pp. Orig marbled boards, eps in 3/4 calf. Raised bands, panels on spine dec in gilt cathedral design. Some rubbing, gilt edges. Fine binding. VG. *CULLEN.* $275

Doe, Janet. A BIBLIOGRAPHY OF THE WORKS OF AMBROISE PARE: PREMIER CHIRURGIEN & CONSEILLER DU ROY. Chicago, 1937. 1st ed. 266pp. Dj. Scarce. *FYE.* $175

Doggett, Carita. DR. ANDREW TURNBULL AND THE NEW SMYRNA COLONY OF FLORIDA. (Florida: The Drew Press. 1919.) 1st ed. Dj sl chipped, soiled. *KARMIOLE.* $45

Doherty, P.C. SATAN IN ST. MARY'S. NY: St. Martin's Press, 1987. 1st Amer ed. Initials on fep, o/w Fine in dj. *MORDIDA.* $30

Doherty, P.C. THE ANGEL OF DEATH. London: Robert Hale, 1989. 1st ed. VF in dj. *MORDIDA.* $45

Doherty, P.C. THE CROWN IN DARKNESS. NY: St. Martin's, 1988. 1st Amer ed. Fine in dj. *SILVER DOOR.* $25

Doherty, P.C. THE MASKED MAN. London: Robert Hale, 1991. 1st ed. Signed. VF in dj. *MORDIDA.* $45

Doherty, P.C. THE SERPENT AMONGST THE LILIES. London: Robert Hale, 1990. 1st ed. VF in dj. *MORDIDA.* $45

Doherty, William and Dagobert Runes. REHABILITATION OF THE WAR INJURED. NY, 1943. *FYE.* $75

Dohrman, H.T. CALIFORNIA CULT. THE STORY OF THE 'MANKIND UNITED.' Boston: Beacon, 1958. 1st ed. NF in NF dj. *CONNOLLY & WADE.* $32.50

Doig, Ivan. DANCING AT THE RASCAL FAIR. Atheneum, 1987. 1st ed. Signed. New in dj. *AUTHORS OF THE WEST.* $35

Doig, Ivan. DANCING AT THE RASCAL FAIR. Atheneum, 1987. Advance reading copy. VF in wraps. *STAHR.* $35

Doig, Ivan. DANCING AT THE RASCAL FAIR. NY: Atheneum, (1987). 1st ed. Adv reading copy. Fine in wraps. *UNGER.* $50

Doig, Ivan. DANCING AT THE RASCAL FAIR. NY: Atheneum, 1987. 1st ed. VF in dj. *ELSE FINE.* $40

Doig, Ivan. RIDE WITH ME, MARIAH MONTANA. Atheneum, 1990. 1st ed. Signed. New in dj. *AUTHORS OF THE WEST.* $35

Doig, Ivan. THE SEA RUNNERS. Atheneum, 1982. Uncorrected proof, softbound. Hand lettering on spine, bottom edge, else Fine. *AUTHORS OF THE WEST.* $30

Doig, Ivan. THE SEA RUNNERS. NY: Atheneum, 1982. 1st ed. Uncorrected proof. Sticker mk, o/w Fine. *LOPEZ.* $40

Doig, Ivan. THIS HOUSE OF SKY: LANDSCAPES OF A WESTERN MIND. NY: Harcourt Brace Jovanovich, (1978). Boards. Signed. Fine in dj. *AUTHORS OF THE WEST.* $60

Doig, Peter, A CONCISE HISTORY OF ASTRONOMY. London: Chapman & Hall, 1950. Good in blue cl. *KNOLLWOOD.* $30

Dolan, J.R. THE YANKEE PEDDLERS OF EARLY AMERICA. NY: Clarkson N. Potter, 1964. 1st ed. VG in Fair dj. *CONNOLLY & WADE.* $35

Dolby, George. CHARLES DICKENS AS I KNEW HIM. THE STORY OF THE READING TOURS IN GREAT BRITAIN AND AMERICA (1866-1870). London: Everett, 1912. 2nd ed. 12mo, 482pp, republished with illus and index, spine dark. VG. *GREAT EXPECTATIONS.* $25

Dole, E.P. HIWA: A TALE OF ANCIENT HAWAII. NY and London, 1900. 1st ed. Very sl soiled. *WEBER.* $75

Dolge, Alfred. PIANOS AND THEIR MAKERS. CA, 1911. Sp sunned. Teg. NF. *POLYANTHOS.* $250

Dollfus, A. (ed.) SURFACES AND INTERIORS OF PLANETS AND SATELLITES. London: Academic Press, 1970. Good ex-lib. *KNOLLWOOD.* $30

Dolph, Jack. HOT TIP. Doubleday, 1951. 1st ed. VG in dj with edgewear, 1" piece missing back panel, skinned patch front panel. *BEBBAH.* $15

Dolph, Jack. MURDER IS MUTUEL. Morrow, 1948. 1st ed. Good with bumps to front edge of cvr in dj with soil, few chips. *BEBBAH.* $15

Domanska, Janina. IF ALL THE SEAS WERE ONE SEA. Macmillan, (1971). 1st ed. Unpaginated. Color etchings by author. Fine in Fine dj. *BEBBAH.* $50

Domanska, Janina. KING KRAKUS AND THE DRAGON. Greenwillow, (1979). 1st ed. Unpaginated. Color illus by author. Fine in Fine dj. *BEBBAH.* $35

Domenech, Emmanuel H. D. MISSIONARY ADVENTURES IN TEXAS AND MEXICO. London, 1858. (16),366,(26)pp. Illus, folded map. Orig cloth, title page mended, no text affected. 1st ed in English. Howes D408. *GINSBERG.* $375

Domestica, Acheta (pseud). EPISODES OF INSECT LIFE, Second Series. NY: J.S. Redfield/ Boston: B.B. Mussey & Co., 1851. VG. *BLUE MOUNTAIN.* $45

Donald, David. CHARLES SUMNER AND THE COMING OF THE CIVIL WAR. NY, 1960. 1st ed. Dj wear and chipping o/w Fine. *PRATT.* $25

DONALD DUCK. London, 1970. Pop-up bk. *BOOKFINDERS INTL.* $35

Donaldson, Lois (comp). ONE HUNDRED FAIRY TALES. Whitman, (1937). 123pp. 8 color plts by Anne Anderson; other illus by Maurieta Wellman. Edgewear to paper-covered illus boards. VG+ in VG dj w/edge tears, chips, wear. *BEBBAH.* $40

Donisthorpe, H. BRITISH ANTS. London, 1927. 2nd ed. 18 plts. Ex-lib. *SUTTON.* $47

Donleavy, J.P. A SINGULAR COUNTRY. NY: Norton, 1988. 1st ed. Fine, pub's promo flyer laid in. *SMITH.* $25

Donleavy, J.P. DONLEAVY'S IRELAND. NY: Viking, 1986. 1st ed. Fine. *SMITH.* $25

Donleavy, J.P. LEILA. NY: Delacorte, 1983. 1st ed. Uncorrected proof. Good in wraps. *SMITH.* $45

Donleavy, J.P. MEET MY MAKER: THE MAD MOLECULE. London, 1965. 1st ed. Fine in like dj (2 tiny tears). *POLYANTHOS.* $30

Donleavy, J.P. THE BEASTLY BEATITUDES OF BALTHAZAR. NY: Delacorte Press, (c1968). In form of uncorrected proof but not so designated. NF in sl soiled pale gray ptd wrappers, sl darkened backstrip. *HELLER.* $50

Donleavy, J.P. THE GINGER MAN. A PLAY. NY, 1961. 1st ed. Fine in Fine dj. *POLYANTHOS.* $25

Donleavy, J.P. THE GINGER MAN. NY: Delacorte, (1971). Review slip. 1st complete and unexpurgated ed. Fine in About Fine dj. *DERMONT.* $25

Donleavy, J.P. THE GINGER MAN. Paris: Olympia, (1958). Traveller's Companion Series. 1st ed. Fine in Fine dj. *POLYANTHOS.* $250

Donleavy, J.P. THE UNEXPURGATED CODE. NY: Delacorte, 1975. 1st ed. Signed. Fine. *SMITH.* $50

Donnelly, Ignatius. ATLANTIS. Appleton, 1882. 1st ed. Good+. *MADLE.* $35

Donnelly, Ignatius. RAGNAROK. Appleton, 1883. Near VG. *MADLE.* $30

Donnelly, Ralph W. THE CONFEDERATE STATES MARINE CORPS. Shippensburg (1989). 1st ed. Fine in dj. *PRATT.* $25

Donoso, Jose. CHARLESTON & OTHER STORIES. Boston: David R. Godine, (1977). No. 24 of deluxe ed. ltd to 200. Signed. New, issued w/out dj, in slipcase. *BERNARD.* $100

Donovan, Robert J. PT 109. NY: McGraw-Hill, (1961). Stated 1st ed. Torn dj. *SCHOYER'S.* $15

Donovan. DRY SONGS & SCRIBBLES. GC: Doubleday, (1971). 1st ed. Bkpl. Lt shelfwear to dj. *AKA.* $35

Dooley, James, Mrs. DEM GOOD OLE TIMES. NY: Doubleday, Pg, 1906. 1st ed. Orig ornately dec pink cl. Fine. *CHAPEL HILL.* $95

Dooner, P. W. LAST DAYS OF THE REPUBLIC. SF: Alta California Pub House, 1880. 258pp + 5 full pg plts. Blind and gold stamped cl, some foxing. *DAWSON'S.* $50

Doran, George H. CHRONICLES OF BARABBAS, 1884-1934. NY: Harcourt, Brace and Co., (1935). 1st ed, 2nd ptg. Spine faded. *OAK KNOLL.* $15

Dorbin, Sanford. A BIBLIOGRAPHY OF CHARLES BUKOWSKI. LA: Black Sparrow, 1969. 1st ed. One of 350 numbered, signed by Dorbin and Buk. Fine. *SMITH.* $150

Doremus, Philip. REMINISCENCES OF MONTCLAIR. Montclair, NJ, 1908. 1st ed. Signed presentation. Some spine wear. *HEINOLDT.* $30

Dorey, Jacques. THREE AND THE MOON. NY: The Junior Literary Guild, 1929. 1st ed. 8 color plts. Dj sl chipped. *KARMIOLE.* $45

Dorfman, Ariel. MASCARA. Viking, 1988. Uncorrected proof. VF in wraps. *STAHR.* $15

Dorgeles, Roland. ON THE MANDARIN ROAD. NY: Century, (1926). 1st ed. VG in VG dj. *AARD.* $30

Dorn, Edward. BY THE SOUND. Santa Rosa: Black Sparrow Press (1991). 1st ed. One of 150 numbered, signed. Fine in acetate. *DORN.* $40

Dorn, Edward. GEOGRAPHY. London: Fulcrum, (1968). 1st British ed. Fine in frayed dj. *AUTHORS OF THE WEST.* $25

Dorn, Edward. THE NORTH ATLANTIC TURBINE. London: Fulcrum, (1967). 1st British ed. Fine in frayed dj. *AUTHORS OF THE WEST.* $25

Dornan, S.S. PYGMIES & BUSHMEN OF THE KALAHARI. London: Seeley, Service & Co. 1925. 1st ed. 318pp. + ads. Index. Fldg map, 37 plates. Orange cloth. *KARMIOLE.* $65

Dornette, William and Verne Brechner. INSTRUMENTATION IN ANESTHESIOLOGY. Phila, 1959. 1st ed. 130 illus. *FYE.* $30

Dorr, John. CYANIDATION AND CONCENTRATION OF GOLD AND SILVER ORES. McGraw-Hill, 1936. 1st ed, 2nd prtg. VG. *OREGON.* $45

Dorr, Julia C. BERMUDA. AN IDYLL OF THE SUMMER ISLANDS. NY: Charles Scribner's Sons. 1884. 1st ed. Fldg map. Extrems bit worn, a few stains front cvr. *KARMIOLE.* $45

Dorris, Michael. A YELLOW RAFT IN BLUE WATER. (London: Hamish Hamilton, 1988). 1st Eng ed. Adv rev copy w/slip laid in. Inscribed. Fine in Fine dj. *LOPEZ.* $85

Dorris, Michael. A YELLOW RAFT IN BLUE WATER. Henry Holt, 1987. Advance reading copy. Fine in dec wraps. *STAHR.* $20

Dorris, Michael. A YELLOW RAFT IN BLUE WATER. Holt, (1987). 1st ed. Fine in Fine dj. *BEBBAH.* $30

Dorris, Michael. A YELLOW RAFT IN BLUE WATER. NY: Henry Holt, (1987). 1st ed. Adv uncorrected proof. Fine in wraps. *UNGER.* $65

Dorris, Michael. THE BROKEN CORD. Harper & Row, 1989. Advance reading copy. VF in wraps. Promo letter laid in. *STAHR.* $35

Dorris, Michael. THE BROKEN CORD. NY: Harper & Row, (1989). 1st ed. Fine in dj. *LOPEZ.* $30

Dorsey, George A. THE ARAPAHO SUN DANCE. Chicago: Field Columbian Museum, 1903. Pub 75. Anthropological Series Vol IV. 137 illus. 3/4 black leather, marbled eps. Exterior scuffed, interior VG. *PARMER.* $250

Dorsey, George A. THE CHEYENNE: II, THE SUN DANCE. Field Columbian Museum, Pub. 103, Anthropological Series vol. IX, no 2. Chicago: Field Columbian Museum, 1905. 51 photos on full-pg plts, 108 in text. Wraps. Spine lightly chipped at head and heel, interior VG. *LAURIE.* $90

Dorsey, George A. TRADITIONS OF THE SKIDI PAWNEE. Boston: Houghton Mifflin, Amer. Folklore Soc. Oct, 1904. 1st ed. Riverside Press. 14 plts. Orig cl. Minor wear. Fine. *CONNOLLY & WADE.* $165

Dorsey, John Syng. ELEMENTS OF SURGERY FOR THE USE OF STUDENTS WITH PLATES. Phila, 1823. 3rd ed. 2 vols. Full leather, 440, 492pp + 28 Fine engrvd plts. Scattered foxing. VG. *FYE.* $450

Dorson, Richard. BLOODSTOPPERS & BEARWALKERS. Cambridge: Harvard Univ Press, 1952. 1st ed. Fine in dj. *ARTIS.* $27.50

Dorys, Georges. PRIVATE LIFE OF THE SULTAN. NY, 1901. xi,277pp. Uncut. *O'NEILL.* $35

Dos Passos, John. 1919. NY: Harcourt, Brace, (1932). 1st ed. Fine in NF dj w/1 closed tear and 1/4" chip across bottom of spine. *CHAPEL HILL.* $300

Dos Passos, John. 1919. NY: Harcourt Brace, 1932. 1st ed. Spine sunned, About Good. Dos Passos signature pasted to title pg. *ARCHER.* $50

Dos Passos, John. ADVENTURES OF A YOUNG MAN. NY: Harcourt, Brace, (1939). 1st ed. Fine in NF dj w/light edgewear and 1" closed tear at head of spine. *CHAPEL HILL.* $55

Dos Passos, John. AIRWAYS, INC. NY: Macauley, (1928). 1st ed. VF, bright in VF dj. Scarce. *BETWEEN COVERS.* $475

Dos Passos, John. FACING THE CHAIR. Boston: Sacco-Vanzetti Defense Committee, 1927. Wraps. Fine, quite scarce in this condition. *BEASLEY.* $175

Dos Passos, John. FACING THE CHAIR. Boston: Sacco-Vanzetti Defence Committee, 1927. 1st ed. Ptd wraps sl faded at backstrip; few lt stains, else Fine. *HELLER.* $125

Dos Passos, John. MOST LIKELY TO SUCCEED. NY: Prentice-Hall, (1954). Copy 827 of 1,000 signed. Fine in VG dj sl worn at spine ends. *BERNARD.* $75

Dos Passos, John. ONE MAN'S INITIATION-1917. London, 1920. 1st ed, 1st state. Spine sunned, extremities little chipped, side spine rear cover edge sunned, and little rubbed. NF. *POLYANTHOS.* $75

Dos Passos, John. THE BIG MONEY. NY, 1936. 1st ed. VG in somewhat worn dj w/some clear tape marks. *PETTLER.* $90

Dos Passos, John. THE FOURTEENTH CHRONICLE. Boston, 1973. Ltd ed, 229/300 (270 for sale). Edited, signed by Townsend Ludington. Fine in like (price clipped) dj. *POLYANTHOS.* $45

Dos Passos, John. THE GARBAGE MAN. NY: Harper, 1926. 1st ed. Name stamp, slight darkening to spine w/small tear to crown, else NF in 1st issue boards. In Fine, bright dj w/negligible wear at crown. Scarce. *BETWEEN COVERS.* $400

Dos Passos, John. U.S.A.: THE 42ND PARALLEL. NINETEEN NINETEEN. THE BIG MONEY. Boston: Houghton Mifflin, 1946. 3 vols. Illus Reginald Marsh, white cl w/leather labels, maroon slipcase w/paper label. 1st illus ed. Ltd to 365 specially bound, signed by Dos Passos & Marsh. Fine set in sl worn slipcase. *JAFFE.* $750

Dostoevsky, Fyodor. A GENTLE SPIRIT. A Fantastic Story. Trans by Constance Garnett. NY: Harrison of Paris. 1931. Mounted India proof frontis and tailpiece. Ltd to 50 numbered copies, on Imperial Japan vellum. Vellum over blue boards, gilt spine. Slipcase. *KARMIOLE.* $250

Dostoevsky, Fyodor. A GENTLE SPIRIT. A FANTASTIC STORY. Trans. from the Russian by Constance Garnett. 1931. 1/495 numbered. Prospectus. As New in like paper slipcase. *DERMONT.* $100

Dostoevsky, Fyodor. A GENTLE SPIRIT: A FANTASTIC STORY. Paris: Harrison of Paris, 1931. 1/495 from total issue of 570. Constance Garnett (trans), Christian Berard (illus). Bound in black silk and housed in grey paper over boards slipcase w/grn paper label on spine. *JUVELIS.* $125

Dostoevsky, Fyodor. A RAW YOUTH. Trans by Constance Garnett. Illus by Fritz Eichenberg. Verona: LEC, 1974. 2 vols. Ed ltd to 2000, ptd at the Stamperia Valdonega by Martino Mardersteig, and signed by artist. Slipcase. *KARMIOLE.* $100

Dostoevsky, Fyodor. AN HONEST THIEF AND OTHER STORIES. Constance Garnett (trans). NY: Macmillan, 1923. 1st US, thus, being Vol XI of The Novels of Fyodor Dostoevsky. Fine in dj (very small chip from front panel). *CAPTAIN'S BOOKSHELF.* $75

Dostoevsky, Fyodor. BURIED ALIVE OR TEN YEARS OF PENAL SERVITUDE IN SIBERIA. Marie von Thilo (trans). NY: Henry Holt and Co, 1881. 1st Amer ed. Pict grn cl dampstained at bottom, bumped, rear eps stained, small tear to front edge of fep & newspaper clipping tipped in at front. VG. *BLUE MOUNTAIN.* $150

Doten, Alfred. THE JOURNALS OF ALFRED DOTEN 1849-1903. Walter Van Tilburg Clark (ed). Reno: Univ of Nevada Press, 1973. 1st ed. 3 vols. New in slipcase. *PARMER.* $125

Doughty, Charles M. TRAVELS IN ARABIA DESERTA. NY, 1923. 3rd ed. All orig maps and plans. 2 vols. Fine. *POLYANTHOS.* $60

Doughty, Charles Montagu. TRAVELS IN ARABIA DESERTA (2 vols). London: Philip Lee Warner, Publisher to the Medici Society and Jonathan Cape. 8vo, xxxv + 623pp + fldg plates and map + fldg end pocket map/xiv + 690pp. Limited 2nd ed. One of 500. Original dark green gilt dec cl. Very minor wear extremes. NF set in new archival slipcase. *GREAT EPIC.* $1500

Douglas, Alan. FOR THE KING. Macrae Smith, 1926. 1st ed. Fine in dj. *MADLE.* $100

Douglas, C.L. and Francis Miller. THE LIFE STORY OF W. LEE O'DANIEL. Dallas: Regional Press, 1938. 1st ed, signed. VG. *GIBBS.* $65

Douglas, C.L. CATTLE KINGS OF TEXAS. C. Baugh, 1939. 2nd ptg. Fine in chipped dj. *VARNER.* $95

Douglas, Ellen (pseud of Josephine Haxton). THE ROCK CRIED OUT. NY & London: Harcourt Brace Jovanovich, (1979). 1st ed. Signed. Orig blue cl-backed boards. Sticker removed from ffep, else Fine in dj. *CHAPEL HILL.* $35

Douglas, Ellen. A FAMILY AFFAIR. Boston: HM, 1962. 1st ed, 1st bk. dj. Inscribed. *CAPTAIN'S BOOKSHELF.* $175

Douglas, Ellen. A LIFETIME BURNING. NY: Random House, (1982). 1st Amer ed. Signed. Fine in dj. *DORN.* $40

Douglas, Ellen. APOSTLES OF LIGHT. Boston: Houghton Mifflin, 1973. 1st ed. Small sticker residue on front pastedown, else Fine in dj. *CAPTAIN'S BOOKSHELF.* $50

Douglas, Ellen. BLACK CLOUD, WHITE CLOUD. Boston: HM, 1963. 1st ed. Fine in sl rubbed dj. Inscribed. *CAPTAIN'S BOOKSHELF.* $50

Douglas, Ellen. THE MAGIC CARPET AND OTHER TALES. Jackson: Univ Press of MS, (1987). 1st ed. As New in dj. Inscribed. *CAPTAIN'S BOOKSHELF.* $60

Douglas, John. BLIND SPRING RAMBLER. NY: St. Martin's Press, 1988. 1st ed. VF in dj. *MORDIDA.* $25

Douglas, Lord Alfred. IN EXCELSIS. London: Martin Secker, 1924. 1 pg carelessly opened, else NF. 1st ed. #13 of only 100 signed by Douglas. *CHAPEL HILL.* $175

Douglas, Lord Alfred. IN EXCELSIS. London: Martin Secker, 1924. 1st ed. One of 100 numbered special copies signed. Front cvr sl stained top corner w/2 small bubbles, front hinge sl cracked. NF. *BLUE MOUNTAIN.* $125

Douglas, Lord Alfred. OSCAR WILDE AND MYSELF. NY: Duffield & Co. 1914. 1st Amer ed. *KARMIOLE.* $35

Douglas, Lord Alfred. THE TRUE HISTORY OF SHAKESPEARE'S SONNETS. London, 1933. 1st ed. Tiny name label, cloth very sl sunned. Fine in dj (spine sunned, tiny nick). *POLYANTHOS.* $45

Douglas, Norman. BIRDS AND BEASTS OF THE GREEK ANTHOLOGY. (London): Chapman and Hall, (1928). 1st trade ed. With errata slip stating book now published by Chatto & Windus. Dj a bit darkened at edges, else Fine. *WOOLMER.* $45

Douglas, Norman. D.H. LAWRENCE AND MAURICE MAGNUS. N.p.: Privately ptd, 1924. Frontis. Brown ptd wrappers. *KARMIOLE.* $45

Douglas, Norman. PANEROS. London: Chatto & Windus, 1931. One of 650 numbered. Fine in sl edgeworn dj w/small tear. *CAPTAIN'S BOOKSHELF.* $60

Douglas, Norman. THE ANGEL OF MANFREDONIA. SF: Windsor Press, 1929. #111/225. 1/4 cl, marbled paper boards. Fine. Issued w/o dj. *HELLER.* $125

Douglas, William Wilberforce. RELIEF OF WASHINGTON, NORTH CAROLINA, BY THE FIFTH RHODE ISLAND

VOLUNTEERS. Providence, 1886. 1st ed. Wrappers. NF. *McGOWAN.* $45

Douthit, Mary Osborn. THE SOUVENIR OF WESTERN WOMEN. Portland: 1905. 1st ed. Grn cl w/scenic paste-on (rebound w/part of orig wrap?). Lt wear, internally clean, sound. *PARMER.* $95

Dove, Rita. THE YELLOW HOUSE ON THE CORNER. Pittsburg: Carnegie Mellon, 1989. 2nd ed, 1st bk. Inscribed. Fine in wrappers. *LOPEZ.* $35

Dow, George Francis, and John Henry Edmonds. THE PIRATES OF THE NEW ENGLAND COAST 1630-1730. Salem, 1923. Pub. 2. Cvr sl soiled. Howes D.437. *LEFKOWICZ.* $100

Dow, George Francis. SLAVE SHIPS AND SLAVING. Salem, 1927. Pub. 15. Fine. Howes D.438. *LEFKOWICZ.* $125

Dow, George Francis. SLAVE SHIPS AND SLAVING. Salem, MA, 1927. 1st ed. Orig cl, sl rubbed, yet VG or better. *McGOWAN.* $165

Dow, George Francis. WHALE SHIPS AND WHALING. A PICTORIAL HISTORY....Salem, 1925. Pub. 10. Spine faded, as usual. Howes D.439. *LEFKOWICZ.* $150

Dow, Lorenzo and Peggy Dow. THE DEALINGS OF GOD, MAN, AND THE DEVIL...THE LIFE...OF LORENZO DOW...NY: Cornish, Lamport & Co, 1850. Orig emb, gilt stamped lea, edgeworn. Good+. Howes 440, 442. *OREGON.* $75

Dow, Sterling T. MAINE POSTAL HISTORY AND POSTMARKS. Portland, ME: Severn-Wylie-Jewett Co. 1943. Maroon cloth, gilt spine. *KARMIOLE.* $40

Dowd, Jerome. THE NEGRO RACES A SOCIOLOGICAL STUDY EAST AND SOUTH AFRICANS, WITH A FULL ACCOUNT OF THE SLAVE TRADE. VOLUME II. NY: Neale Pub. Co, 1914. 1st ed. Orig cl. Ex libris. VG to NF. *McGOWAN.* $250

Dowdey, Clifford. EXPERIMENT IN REBELLION. GC, 1946. 1st ed. Dj wear o/w VG. *PRATT.* $30

Dowdey, Clifford. LEE. NY, 1965. 1st ed. Ex-lib. Sm piece torn from dj; tape residue markings o/w VG. *PRATT.* $32.50

Dowdey, Clifford. LEE'S LAST CAMPAIGN. Boston, (1960). 2nd prtg. Minor dj wear o/w Fine. *PRATT.* $30

Dowdey, Clifford. THE GREAT PLANTATION, A PROFILE OF BERKELEY HUNDRED....NY, 1957. 1st ed. Little dj wear, chipping; o/w Fine. *PRATT.* $27.50

Dowdey, Clifford. THE LAND THEY FOUGHT FOR. GC, (1955). 1st ed. 438pp. Dj worn, chipped; o/w VG. *PRATT.* $35

Dowdey, Clifford. THE SEVEN DAYS, THE EMERGENCE OF ROBERT E. LEE. NY, 1964. 1st ed. Light dj wear o/w Fine. *PRATT.* $30

Downes, P.G. SLEEPING ISLAND. NY: Coward, 1943. VG+. *MIKESH.* $17.50

Downey, Fairfax. INDIAN FIGHTING ARMY. NY: 1941. 1st ed. Orig cl. *GINSBERG.* $75

Downey, Fairfax. INDIAN-FIGHTING ARMY. NY, 1941. 1st ed. Bkpl of Harold Smith on front fly, w/his sig and date. Back of dj carefully affixed to front pastedown, o/w VG. *BAADE.* $60

Downey, Fairfax. SOUND OF THE GUNS. NY, (1956). A little cvr wear o/w VG+ in dj. *PRATT.* $32.50

Downey, Fairfax. THE GUNS AT GETTYSBURG. NY, (1958). 1st ed. Residue of scotch tape repair back of dj o/w VG+. *PRATT.* $50

Downie, Major William. HUNTING FOR GOLD. Palo Alto: American West, 1971. 1st ed thus. Facs of 1893 ed. Gilt dec cl. VF. Howes D448. *CONNOLLY & WADE.* $50

Downie, Ralph Ernest. A PICTORIAL HISTORY OF THE STATE OF WASHINGTON. Seattle: Lowman & Hanford, 1937. 1st ed. Fldg map. Red cl w/gilt. VG. Scarce. *CONNOLLY & WADE.* $50

Downing, A.J. THE FRUITS AND FRUIT TREES OF AMERICA....NY, (1957). 3rd thousand, rev, corrected by Charles Downing. Orig cl worn, soiled; scattered foxing front and back; dampstain rings several pp. *SUTTON.* $125

Downing, Alexander G. DOWNING'S CIVIL WAR DIARY. Des Moines, 1916. 1st ed. Bit shaken, wear to spine ends, else VG. *McGOWAN.* $150

Downing, Antoinette and Vincent J. Scully. THE ARCHITECTURAL HERITAGE OF NEWPORT, RHODE ISLAND. NY: Bramhall House, 1967. 2nd ed. VG in dj. *BACKROOM.* $75

Downing, Fanny Murdaugh. NAMELESS. A Novel. Raleigh, NC: Wm. B. Smith & Co, 1865. 1st ed. 232pp. Orig dark grn cl. Tear in rear flyleaf, slight rippling of cl on rear cover, but VG. *CHAPEL HILL.* $250

Downing, Todd. VULTURES IN THE SKY. GC: Doubleday Crime Club, 1935. Member's ed. VF, minor wear at spine corners of pict dj. *ELSE FINE.* $50

Downs, E. C. FOUR YEARS A SCOUT AND SPY. "GENERAL BUNKER," ONE OF LIEUT. GENERAL GRANT'S MOST DARING AND SUCCESSFUL SCOUTS. BEING A NARRATIVE....Zanesville, OH: Dunne, 1866. 1st ed. (12),404,(1)pp. 10 woodcuts. Contemp half calf. Howes D450. *GINSBERG.* $300

Downs, Frederick. THE KILLING ZONE. NY: Norton, (1978). 1st ed. NF in NF dj. *AKA.* $35

Downs, Harold (ed). THEATRE AND STAGE. An Encyclopaedic Guide...In Two Volumes. London: Sir Isaac Pitman & Sons. (1951). 2 vols. 4to. 594;viii,588pp. 55 plates, 15 in color. *KARMIOLE.* $85

Downs, Joseph. AMERICAN FURNITURE, QUEEN ANNE & CHIPPENDALE. NY: Macmillan Co, 1952. 1st ed. Fine. Leather bound, slipcased later date. *BACKROOM.* $365

Downs, Joseph. AMERICAN FURNITURE. NY: Macmillan Co, 1952. 1st ed. VG. *BACKROOM.* $120

Downs, Joseph. AMERICAN FURNITURE: QUEEN ANNE AND CHIPPENDALE PERIODS. NY: MacMillan, 1952. 1st ed. About Fine in sl chipped dj. *CAPTAIN'S BOOKSHELF.* $150

DOWNWARD PATHS, AN INQUIRY....PROSTITUTE. London: Bell, 1916. 1st ed. VG in cl. *SECOND LIFE.* $75

Doyen, Eugene. SURGICAL THERAPEUTICS AND OPERATIVE TECHNIQUE. London, 1917-1920. 1st Eng trans., 3 vols. 746, 680, 811pp. 1975 illus. Exceptionally Fine. *FYE.* $250

Doyle, A. Conan. RODNEY STONE. London: Smith, Elder, 1896. 1st ed. 8vo, 366pp, (10)pp ads. Orig dk blue cl. Owner's name, corners and spine tips worn, hinges starting, still VG. *CHAPEL HILL.* $150

Doyle, A. Conan. RODNEY STONE. NY, 1896. 1st Amer ed. Fine. *McCLINTOCK.* $25

Doyle, A. Conan. THE ADVENTURES AND MEMOIRS OF SHERLOCK HOLMES. Tokyo: Yushodo, 1986. Facsimile ed. 1/300 of 2 vol set. VF in box w/gold-stamped titles. *MORDIDA.* $450

Doyle, A. Conan. THE ADVENTURES OF SHERLOCK HOLMES. London, 1892. 1st ed. Illus. Rebound 1/2 lea, gilt spine, raised bands, marbled boards. Orig front cvr and spine bound in. Lower edges little rubbed. *POLYANTHOS.* $500

Doyle, A. Conan. THE ADVENTURES OF SHERLOCK HOLMES. London: George Newnes, (1892). THE MEMOIRS OF SHERLOCK HOLMES. London: George Newnes, (1894). Two vols. 1st eds. Rebound in blue lea w/mosaic binding and gilt by Bayntun-Riviere. Backstrip and covers of orig bindings are tipped in. A few flakes in the aging leather, still VG. *UNGER.* $2500

Doyle, A. Conan. THE CROXLEY MASTER. NY: McClure, Philips, and Co, 1907. 1st separate ed. Pict tan cl framed in grn w/black, grn & white illus. Color frontis. Internally bright. NF. *BLUE MOUNTAIN.* $150

Doyle, A. Conan. THE CROXLEY MASTER. Toronto, 1907. 1st ed. Canadian ed. Color frontis. Enameled pict cvr. Sl cvr rub. VG. *McCLINTOCK.* $45

Doyle, A. Conan. THE EDGE OF THE UNKNOWN. London: 1930. 1st ed. Fine in NF dj. *JUVELIS.* $2000

Doyle, A. Conan. THE EDGE OF THE UNKNOWN. London: John Murray, (1930). VG, w/8-page Doyle catalogue laid in. 1st ed. Orig blue cl stamped in gilt. Only 909 ptd, of which some were bound after pub in blue cl stamped in white. Very Scarce. *CHAPEL HILL.* $200

Doyle, A. Conan. THE FIRM OF GIRDLESTONE. NY, Lovell, Coryell Co., (1889). The Belmore Series. Printed wraps. Spine sunned, sides little rubbed, little cocked, edges wraps little sunned. Fine. *POLYANTHOS.* $75

Doyle, A. Conan. THE GREEN FLAG. NY: McClure, Phillips, 1900. 1st US ed. Sl soiled stamped grn cl, front hinge tender, but VG. *SECOND LIFE.* $65

Doyle, A. Conan. THE GULLY OF BLUEMANSDYKE, AND OTHER STORIES. London: Walter Scott, Ltd., (1892). 8vo, 249pp, (6)pp ads. Orig pict yellow wraps. Some dust soiling, wear at edges and extremities of spine, but VG. 1st ed. under this title (previously issued under the title "Mysteries and Adventures"). *CHAPEL HILL.* $150

Doyle, A. Conan. THE LAND OF MIST. Doran, 1926. 1st US ed. Good. *MADLE.* $50

Doyle, A. Conan. THE LOST WORLD. Doran, 1912. 1st US ed. VG (variant in A. L. Burt binding). *MADLE.* $40

Doyle, A. Conan. THE PARASITE. NY, 1895. 1st ed. Simultaneous w/Eng ed. Illus. by Howard Pyle. Fine. *POLYANTHOS.* $60

Doyle, A. Conan. THE SECRET OF GORESTHORPE GRANGE, AND A CASE OF IDENTITY. NY, 1896. 1st thus. Wraps. No. 184 in "Munro's Library of Popular Novels", dated May 6, 1896. Price $.25. No copyright notice credited so probably an American pirate. Cheap paper browned, back wrap gone, light chipping top and bottom of spine, lower edge front cover. Appears uncommon. *McCLINTOCK.* $100

Doyle, A. Conan. THE TRAGEDY OF THE KOROSKO. London: Smith, Elder, 1898. 1st ed. 8vo, 333pp, 6pp ads. Orig red cl. Previous owner's name, dust soiling, hinges starting. VG. 1st ed. Scarce. *CHAPEL HILL.* $100

Doyle, A. Conan. THE TRAGEDY OF THE KOROSKO. London: Smith Elder, 1898. 1st ed. Hinges sl cracked o/w NF in red cvrs w/gold-stamped titles. *MORDIDA.* $200

Doyle, A. Conan. THE WHITE COMPANY. GC, 1943. Frontis. Few scratches to cvr color pict, else NF. *BEBBAH.* $25

Doyle, A. Conan. THE WHITE COMPANY. NY, (1891). 1st authorized Amer ed. One of several variant ad states. 1st illus ed. Pict wrappers. Spine has ptd date of April, 1892. Wraps separated from the sewn signatures; wraps soiled and worn around edges. Last page of ads gone. *McCLINTOCK.* $95

Doyle, A. Conan. THROUGH THE MAGIC DOOR. Gilt-decorated blue cl. NY: McClure, 1908. 1st Amer ed, 1st issue. One of 468. VF. *JAFFE.* $125

Doyle, A. Conan. THROUGH THE MAGIC DOOR. London: Smith, Elder, 1907. 1st ed. Some dust soiling, traces of foxing, else VG. *CHAPEL HILL.* $135

Doyle, Adrian C. and John Dickson Carr. THE EXPLOITS OF SHERLOCK HOLMES. London: Murray, 1954. 1st ed. NF in bit used dj. *BEASLEY.* $65

Doyle, Adrian Conan (ed). SIR ARTHUR CONAN DOYLE CENTENARY 1859-1959. GC, NY: Doubleday & Co. Inc, (1959). 1st trade ed. VG in lightly used dj. Red cl, cream and red jacket. *JUVELIS.* $450

Doyle, Helen MacKnight, M.D. A CHILD WENT FORTH: THE AUTOBIOGRAPHY OF...NY: Gotham House, 1934. Soiled, chipped dj o/w VG. *SCHOYER'S.* $35

DR. SEUSS FROM THEN TO NOW. Random, 1986. 1st ed. 4to. 95pp. Illus. Fine in Fine dj. *BEBBAH.* $45

Drabble, Margaret. A NATURAL CURIOSITY. Cl-backed marbled boards, glassine dj. London: London Limited Editions, 1989. 1st ed. One of 150 signed. Mint. *JAFFE.* $100

Drabble, Margaret. JERUSALEM THE GOLDEN. Morrow, 1967. 1st Amer. ed. Fine in VG+ dj. Corner of ffep clipped. Dj has thumbnail size chip missing at head of spine; small hole on rear panel. *STAHR.* $45

Drabble, Margaret. THE NEEDLE'S EYE. Knopf, 1972. 1st Amer ed. About Fine in dj (lightly rubbed; sm chip rear panel). *STAHR.* $30

Drabble, Margaret. THE RADIANT WAY. Knopf, 1987. 1st Amer ed. VF in dj. *STAHR.* $15

Drabble, Margaret. THE RADIANT WAY. Knopf, 1987. Uncorrected proof of Amer ed. VG or better in orange wraps. 2 lightly soiled spots front cvr; sunned spine. *STAHR.* $25

Drago, Harry S. GREAT AMERICAN CATTLE TRAILS. NY, (1965). 1st ed. Dj. VG+. *PRATT.* $32.50

Drago, Harry S. ROAD AGENTS AND TRAIN ROBBERS. NY, (1973). 1st ed. Dj. Fine. *PRATT.* $25

Drago, Harry S. WILD, WOOLLY & WICKED. NY, 1960. 1st ed. 354pp. Light dj wear, o/w Fine. *PRATT.* $40

Drago, Harry S. WILD, WOOLY & WICKED. THE HISTORY OF THE KANSAS COW TOWNS & THE TEXAS CATTLE TRADE. C.N. Potter, (1960). 1st ed. VG in VG dj. *OREGON.* $25

Drake, David. THE DRAGON LORD. Berkley, 1979. 1st ed. Fine in dj *MADLE.* $22

Drake, Samuel Adams. THE HEART OF THE WHITE MOUNTAINS. NY:Harper and Bros., 1882. 1st ed, probable 2nd prtg. Wear to extremities, still VG. *OLD LONDON.* $225

Drannan, W.F. CAPT. W.F. DRANNAN, CHIEF OF SCOUTS. Chicago: Rhodes & McClure, 1910. 1st ed. Pgs browning, fragile, exterior worn. *CONNOLLY & WADE.* $27.50

Drannan, W.F. THIRTY ONE YEARS ON THE PLAINS AND IN THE MOUNTAINS, THE LAST VOICE FROM THE PLAINS. Chicago, 1899. Pub. date uncertain, probably the 1900 reprint. 586pp & ads. Illus. Cvr wear but VG. *PRATT.* $32.50

Draper, William E. RECOLLECTIONS OF A VARIED CAREER. Boston, 1908. 1st ed. Partially unopened. Minor cover wear o/w Fine. *PRATT.* $40

Dreiser, Theodore. A GALLERY OF WOMEN. Leipzig: B. Tauchnitz, 1930. 2 vols. 1st ed. Pub printed wraps. Names, few small edge tears, small pieces missing lower edges, rear covers. NF. *POLYANTHOS.* $30

Dreiser, Theodore. A GALLERY OF WOMEN. NY: Horace Liveright, 1929. 1st ed. Precedes ltd. ed. 2 vols. Fine in NF djs w/shallow chipping at top of spines and small chip in front panel of Vol. II. Scarce in this condition. *CHAPEL HILL.* $80

Dreiser, Theodore. A HISTORY OF MYSELF. DAWN. New York: Horace Liveright, (1931). 1st ed. #16 of 275 signed, of which 245 are for sale. Orig cl. Few small spots, but very bright. With orig box (sl wear). *M & S.* $325

Dreiser, Theodore. A TRAVELER AT FORTY. NY: The Century Co, 1913. Red cl stamped in gold. 1st ed. Cl very sl rubbed at extrems, NF. *HELLER.* $100

Dreiser, Theodore. AN AMERICAN TRAGEDY. Reginald Marsh (illus). NY: LEC, 1954. One of 1500. Slipcase. VG. *JAFFE.* $85

Dreiser, Theodore. CHAINS. NY: Boni & Liveright, 1927. 1st ed. NF in a VG dj. *LOPEZ.* $65

Dreiser, Theodore. DAWN: A HISTORY OF MYSELF, AN AUTOBIOGRAPHY OF EARLY YOUTH. NY, (1931). 1st ed. Some offsetting one page. Fine in dj (closed tears at folds and edges, edge rubbed, few tiny chips). *POLYANTHOS.* $60

Dreiser, Theodore. HEY RUB-A-DUB-DUB. NY, 1920. 1st ed. Cvrs sl rubbed but lettering fresh, bkpl. NF. *POLYANTHOS.* $75

Dreiser, Theodore. MOODS CADENCED AND DECLAIMED. NY: (Boni and Liveright), 1926. 1st ed. #502 of 550, which the colophon states "are strictly limited, numbered, and signed by the author." Sig not found. 3/4 cl over marbled and gilt sides, w/leather label on spine. *BOOK BLOCK.* $45

Dreiser, Theodore. MOODS, PHILOSOPHIC AND EMOTIONAL, CADENCED AND DECLAIMED. NY, 1935. 1st rev ed. Signed. Faded spine, torn dj. *CULLEN.* $150

Dreiser, Theodore. SISTER CARRIE. NY: B.W. Dodge, 1907. 2nd ed. VG. *LOPEZ.* $200

Dreiser, Theodore. SISTER CARRIE. NY: LEC, 1939. Illus Reginald Marsh. 1/1500. Signed by Marsh. Fine in slipcase, spine sl faded. *JUVELIS.* $350

Dreiser, Theodore. THE "GENIUS." NY: John Lane, Co., 1915. Front hinge starting, as usual w/this thick novel, else VG. 1st ed, 1st issue, bulking 1 3/4" and w/pp 497 numbered. *CHAPEL HILL.* $75

Dreiser, Theodore. THE COLOR OF A GREAT CITY. NY, (1923). 1st ed. Illus by C.B. Falls. Uncut, pict cvrs gilt, ownership initials and number; spine sunned, 2 tiny indentations, rear cvr sl rubbed. *POLYANTHOS.* $75

Dreiser, Theodore. THE HAND OF THE POTTER. NY, 1918. 1st ed, 2nd issue binding. Spine sunned, extremities little rubbed, front cover sl soiled. Fine. *POLYANTHOS.* $30

Dreiser, Theodore. TRAGIC AMERICA. NY: Horace Liveright, (1931). 1st ed. Small bkseller's label, rear cvr a trifle dampstained, else VG in moderately worn, spine-sunned dj. *CHAPEL HILL.* $40

Dreisewerd, Edna. THE CATCHER WAS A LADY. Exposition, 1978. 1st ed. Fine. *PLAPINGER.* $45

Dressler, Albert (ed). CALIFORNIA'S PIONEER CIRCUS....SF: H.S. Crocker, 1926. 1st ed, ltd to 1250, this being #363. A few spots, else Fine. *CONNOLLY & WADE.* $45

Dressler, Albert. CALIFORNIA'S PIONEER CIRCUS. (SF: Albert Dressler, 1926). One of 1250. Gold-stamped dec cl. Bumps top, bottom edges front cvr; lt foxing to prelims. *DAWSON'S.* $40

Drew, Thomas. JOHN BROWN INVASION: AN AUTHENTIC HISTORY....Boston: Campbell, 1860. 1st ed. 112pp. Litho port chipped. Howes D499. *GINSBERG.* $300

Drewry, Carleton. THE SOUNDING SUMMER. NY: Dutton, 1948. 1st ed. Signed. Fine in lightly soiled dj. *CHAPEL HILL.* $25

Dreyfuss, Henry. DESIGNING FOR PEOPLE. NY: Simon & Schuster. 1955. 1st ed. Adv rev copy with slip. Dj. *KARMIOLE.* $60

DRIFTWOOD FLAMES. Nashville: The Poetry Guild, 1923. #6 of 325. Fragile boards rubbed w/chip at spine head. 1st bk appearance of Robert Penn Warren. Donald Davidson's sig. Contributor list laid in. *CAPTAIN'S BOOKSHELF.* $450

Driggs, H.R. WESTWARD AMERICA. Putnam, 1942. Pioneers ed. Signed by author & M.L. Jackson. Fine in sl chipped dj. *VARNER.* $60

Drinker, Cecil. CARBON MONOXIDE ASPHYXIA. NY, 1938. 1st ed. *FYE.* $50

Drinker, Frederick E. HORRORS OF TORNADO, FLOOD AND FIRE...Harrisburg: Minter Co., 1913. Some spotting to cover. *KNOLLWOOD.* $18

Drinkwater, John. COTSWOLD CHARACTERS. New Haven and London: Yale Univ Press, Humphrey Milford, Oxford Univ Press, 1921. Tan speckled paper over boards, paper label w/title on front cvr. Spine repaired, VG. *HELLER.* $95

Driver, Harold E. INDIANS OF NORTH AMERICA. Chicago, 1961. 1st ed. Fldg map in back pocket. Errata slip laid in. Rev copy. NF in partially faded, tear repaired dj. *BAADE.* $50

Driving Hawk Sneve, Virginia. THE CHICHI HOOHOO BOGEYMAN. NY: Holiday House, (1975). 1st ed. NF in dj. *LOPEZ.* $30

Driving Hawk Sneve, Virginia. WHEN THUNDERS SPOKE. NY: Holiday House, (1974). 1st ed. Fine in NF dj. *LOPEZ.* $30

Drucker, P. et al. EXCAVATIONS AT LA VENTA TABASCO, 1955. Smithsonian Bul. #170, GPO, 1959. Fldg maps. Fine. *VARNER.* $20

Druitt, Robert. THE PRINCIPLES AND PRACTICE OF MODERN SURGERY. Phila, 1852. 4th Amer ed. *FYE.* $50

Druitt, Robert. THE PRINCIPLES AND PRACTICE OF MODERN SURGERY. Phila, 1850. 2nd Amer ed. Full leather, 576pp. Burn has affected 1" x 1/2" piece of back board and final 20 leaves of index and ads, contents o/w VG. *FYE.* $30

Drumheller, Uncle Dan. UNCLE DAN DRUMHELLER TELLS THRILLS OF WESTERN TRAILS IN 1854. Spokane: Inland-American, 1925. 1st ed. 1 plt. Signed presentation copy. Fine. Howes D511. *OREGON.* $150

Drummond, Henry. TROPICAL AFRICA. NY: Scribner and Welford, 1889. 1st ed. Spine sunned. Bkpl, else NF. *GREAT EPIC.* $110

Drury, Clifford. DIARIES & LETTERS OF HENRY H. SPALDING AND ASA BOWEN SMITH RELATING TO THE NEZ PERCE MISSION 1838-1842. A.H. Clark, 1958. 1st ed. Frontis, 9 plts. 3 maps (1 fldg). Fine. *OREGON.* $60

Drury, Clifford. MARCUS AND NARCISSA WHITMAN AND THE OPENING OF OLD OREGON. 2 vols. Glendale: The Arthur H. Clark Co, 1973. Frontis each vol. 1st ed. Presentation inscrip in Vol 1, Vol 2 signed. Fine set. *PARMER.* $125

Drury, Clifford. MARCUS WHITMAN, M.D, PIONEER & MARTYR. Caxton, 1937. 1st ed. Frontis. Signed. VG in Good dj. *OREGON.* $85

Drury, Clifford. RUDOLPH JAMES WIG. ENGINEER....Glendale: Arthur H. Clark, 1968. 1st ed. Signed. Fine in VG dj. *CONNOLLY & WADE.* $50

Drury, Clifford. WILLIAM ANDERSON SCOTT, "NO ORDINARY MAN." Glendale, CA: Arthur Clark, 1967. 1st ed. Dj. *HEINOLDT.* $25

Drury, John. OLD CHICAGO HOUSES. Univ of Chicago, (1941). 1st ed. *HEINOLDT.* $35

Du Cane, Florence. THE FLOWERS AND GARDENS OF MADEIRA. London: Adam and Charles Black, 1909. 1st ed. Spine sl soiled, else VG. *WREDEN.* $50

Du Cane, Peter. HIGH-SPEED SMALL CRAFT. Cambridge, Cornell Maritime Press, c. 1951. VG in VG dj. *PARMER.* $45

Du Chaillu, P. IN AFRICAN FOREST AND JUNGLE. Frontis. NY, 1903. Pict cl. *SUTTON.* $35

Du Chaillu, P. THE VIKING AGE. THE EARLY HISTORY...2 vols. NY: Scribner, 1889. 1st ed. xix,591pp; viii,56pp. 8vo. 1 full-pg map. Orig cl, sl rubbed, spine faded, top and bottom of spine sl frayed, o/w VG. *WORLDWIDE.* $45

Du Chaillu, P. WILD LIFE UNDER THE EQUATOR, NARRATED FOR YOUNG PEOPLE. NY, 1868. 231pp,(8 pp ads), orig gilt-dec cl. Spine sl dulled; lt scuffing. *SUTTON.* $65

du Maurier, Daphne. MARY ANNE. London: Victor Gollancz, 1954. 1st ed. VG in dj. *MORDIDA.* $35

du Maurier, George. THE MARTIAN. (New York: Harper & Brothers, 1897). One of 500. Large paper copy. Frontispiece and 49 plts by Du Maurier. Vellum sl smudged, tiny nicks on back cover, o/w unopened, virtually Mint. *PIRAGES.* $125

du Maurier, George. THE MARTIAN. London: Harpers, 1897. 1st ed. Minor bump to bottom edge, else Fine, the dj has one inch piece lacking at the spine head, smaller chips at the corners. *ELSE FINE.* $350

du Maurier, George. TRILBY. Harper, 1894. 1st US ed. Near VG. *MADLE.* $30

du Maurier, George. TRILBY: A NOVEL. NY: Harper & Brothers, 1894. 1st US ed. (1) viii, 464pp, frontis, black and white plts and illus. Presentation binding, half bound in blue green leather, blue green cl over boards, spine and cvrs stamped in gold, marbled eps. Illus by author. Pages trimmed. *BOOKMINE.* $150

Du Ru, Paul. JOURNAL OF PAUL DU RU (FEB 1 TO MAY 8, 1700). MISSIONARY PRIEST TO LOUISIANA. TRANSLATED WITH INTRODUCTION AND NOTES....Chicago: Caxton Club, 1934. 1st ed. Orig cl, paper label on spine and front cover. One of 300. Howes D597. *GINSBERG.* $150

Duberman, Martin. VISIONS OF KEROUAC. Boston: Little Brown, (1977). 1st ed. Fine in sl soiled VG dj. Inscribed. *LOPEZ.* $55

Dubin, Arthur Detmers. SOME CLASSIC TRAINS. (Milwaukee): Kalmbach Pub. Co, (1964). Color frontis, 2 fldg color plts. Fine, jacket lightly rubbed. *BOHLING.* $175

Dubois, Paul. REASON AND SENTIMENT. NY, 1911. 1st Eng trans. *FYE.* $75

DuBois, Theodora. DEATH DINES OUT. Boston: Houghton Mifflin, 1939. 1st ed. Bkpl, sunned spot, o/w Fine in lightly chipped dj. *BEASLEY.* $35

Dubois, W.E.B. THE ORDEAL OF MANSART. NY: Mainstream, 1957. 1st ed. 1st vol in The Black Flame. Signed. Not quite VG in dj. *LAME DUCK.* $500

DuBois, William P. THE THREE POLICEMEN. NY: Viking, 1938. 1st ed. Cl dull, o/w VG. *ARTIS.* $27.50

DuBois, William P. THE TWENTY-ONE BALLOONS. Viking, 1947. 1st ed. 180pp. Wear to cvr edges else VG+ in VG dj w/some chips. *BEBBAH.* $85

DuBois, William P. THE TWENTY-ONE BALLOONS. NY: Viking, 1947. 1st ed. Edgewear. VG. *ACADEMIC LIBRARY.* $40

DuBose, John W. LIFE AND TIMES OF WILLIAM LOWNDES YANCEY....Birmingham, 1892. 1st ed. (17),752pp. Frontis, port, plts. Orig cl, inner hinges mended, upper joint of spine wearing; few tiny holes on lower joint. Howes D524. *GINSBERG.* $150

Dubus, Andre. ADULTERY AND OTHER CHOICES. Boston: Godine, (1977). Uncorrected proof. Fine in wraps. Signed. Uncommon. *CAPTAIN'S BOOKSHELF.* $150

Dubus, Andre. BLESSINGS. Elmwood: Raven Editions, 1987. One of 60 hand-bound in paper over boards and signed. Prospectus laid in. Fine. *CAPTAIN'S BOOKSHELF.* $225

Dubus, Andre. FINDING A GIRL IN AMERICA. Boston: Godine, 1980. 1st ed. Fine in NF dj. *LOPEZ.* $50

Dubus, Andre. THE LAST WORTHLESS EVENING: FOUR NOVELLAS AND TWO STORIES. Boston: Godine, (19861. Uncorrected proof. Fine in wraps. Signed. *CAPTAIN'S BOOKSHELF.* $65

Dubus, Andre. THE LIEUTENANT. NY: Dial, 1967. 1st ed. Name blacked out fep, rubber stamp o/w NF in dj (tape-repaired). *LOPEZ.* $50

Dubus, Andre. THE LIEUTENANT. NY: Dial, 1967. 1st ed. Fine in very lightly soiled example of the white dj. Signed, additionally inscribed in 1990. *CAPTAIN'S BOOKSHELF.* $250

Dubus, Andre. THE TIMES ARE NEVER SO BAD. Boston: Godine, (1983). 1st ed. Fine in price-clipped dj. Inscribed, signed. *CAPTAIN'S BOOKSHELF.* $45

Dubus, Andre. VOICES FROM THE MOON. Boston: Godine, (1984). 1st ed. Fine in dj. Inscribed, signed. *CAPTAIN'S BOOKSHELF.* $35

Dubus, Andre. VOICES FROM THE MOON. Boston: Godine, (1984). Uncorrected proof. Fine in wraps. Signed. *CAPTAIN'S BOOKSHELF.* $50

Dubus, Andre. WE DON'T LIVE HERE ANYMORE. NY: Crown, (1984). Uncorrected proof. Fine in wraps. Signed. *CAPTAIN'S BOOKSHELF.* $75

DuCane, Florence. THE CANARY ISLANDS. A&C Black, 1911. 1st ed. 7s 6d Series. Slight dust spotting on covers, else VG-NF. *OLD LONDON.* $40

DuCane, Florence. THE FLOWERS AND GARDENS OF JAPAN. A&C Black, 1908. 1st ed. 20s Series. VG-NF. *OLD LONDON.* $85

DuCane, Florence. THE FLOWERS AND GARDENS OF MADEIRA. London: Adam & Charles Black. 1909. 1st ed. 23 color plts, each w/ptd tissue guard. *KARMIOLE.* $60

Duchenne, G. B. PHYSIOLOGY OF MOTION DEMONSTRATED BY MEANS OF ELECTRICAL STIMULATION AND CLINICAL OBSERVATION AND APPLIED TO THE STUDY OF PARALYSIS AND DEFORMITIES. Phila, 1949. Ltd ed. 1st Eng trans. 1/4 lea, 612pp. *FYE.* $250

Duckett, Margaret. MARK TWAIN AND BRET HARTE. Norman: Univ of OK Press, 1964. 1st ed. Back cover stained. *BOOKMINE.* $30

Duckworth, Francis. CHESTER. A&C Black, 1910. 1st ed. 7s 6d Series. VG-NF. *OLD LONDON.* $65

Ducroquet, Robert. WALKING AND LIMPING: A STUDY OF NORMAL AND PATHOLOGICAL WALKING. Phila, 1968. 1st Eng trans. *FYE.* $75

Dudding, Earl Ellicott. THE TRAIL OF THE DEAD YEARS. Huntington, 1932. VG. *ARTIS.* $20

Duden, Gottfried. REPORT ON A JOURNEY TO THE WESTERN STATES....Columbia: Univ of Missouri Press, 1980. Fine in dj. *PARMER.* $30

Dudley, Donald R. URBS ROMA: A SOURCE BOOK OF CLASSICAL TEXTS ON THE CITY & ITS MONUMENTS. London: Phaidon, (1967). Dj. Good. *ARCHAEOLOGIA.* $125

Duff, Charles. A HANDBOOK ON HANGING. London: Putnams, 1955. Rev, enl ed. Fine in VG Dj. *MAD DOG.* $25

Duff, E. Gordon. THE PRINTERS, STATIONERS AND BOOKBINDERS OF WESTMINSTER AND LONDON FROM 1476-1535. Cambridge: At the Univ Press, 1906. 1st ed of the 2nd series. Sl scuffed, o/w VG. *WREDEN.* $60

Dufferin, Lord. LETTERS FROM HIGH LATITUDES. London: Oxford Univ Press, (1910). Good+. *BLUE DRAGON.* $37.50

Duffus, Robert Luther. THE SANTA FE TRAIL. NY: Longmans, Green, 1931. NF in Fair dj. *CONNOLLY & WADE.* $45

Duffy, Clinton T. (comp). POCKET DICTIONARY OF PRISON "SLANGUAGE". N.p., 1941. Pict stiff wraps sl soiled, o/w VG. *DIAMOND.* $35

Dufresne, Frank. ALASKA'S ANIMALS AND FISHES. Portland, 1955. 2nd ed. Cloth, dj. *SUTTON.* $25

Dufresne, Frank. NO ROOM FOR BEARS. With drawings. NY, 1965. Cloth dj. *SUTTON.* $24

Dufresne, Frank. ALASKA'S ANIMALS AND FISHES. NY: Barnes & Co, (1946). VG. *BLUE DRAGON.* $35

Dugmore, A. Radclyffe. BIRD HOMES...LAND BIRDS...EASTERN UNITED STATES. NY, 1900. 1st ed. Orig pict cl. Lt scuffing to spine ends. *SUTTON.* $38

Dugmore, A. Radclyffe. CAMERA ADVENTURES IN THE AFRICAN WILD. NY, 1919. VG+. *MIKESH.* $75

Dugmore, A. Radclyffe. CAMERA ADVENTURES IN THE AFRICAN WILD. NY: Doubleday Page, 1910. 1st ed. Minor wear extremes top/bottom of spine else NF. *GREAT EPIC.* $145

Dugmore, A. Radclyffe. IN THE HEART OF THE NORTHERN FORESTS. London: Chatto & Windus, 1930. 64 plts. Spine faded; bkpl, else VG+. *PARMER.* $75

Dugmore, A. Radclyffe. THE ROMANCE OF THE BEAVER, BEING THE HISTORY OF THE BEAVER IN THE WESTERN HEMISPHERE. London, 1914. 1st ed. Gilt-dec cl. Spine dulled; sl crack to front joint; lt foxing. *SUTTON.* $50

Dugmore, A. Radclyffe. THE ROMANCE OF THE BEAVER, BEING THE HISTORY OF THE BEAVER IN THE WESTERN HEMISPHERE. Phila, (c. 1914). 1st Amer ed. Gilt-dec cl. Owner inscrip on pastedown. *SUTTON.* $50

Dugmore, A. Radclyffe. THE WONDERLAND OF BIG GAME. London: Arrowsmith (1925). 1st ed. Good. Bkpl. *AARD.* $45

Dugmore, A. Radclyffe. WILD LIFE AND THE CAMERA. Phila: J.B. Lippincott Co, 1912. 1st ed. Very minor wear extremes else NF. *GREAT EPIC.* $55

Duguid, J. GREEN HELL. NY & London: Century, (1931). Good+. *MIKESH.* $17.50

Duhamel Du Monceau (Henri Louis). A PRACTICAL TREATISE OF HUSBANDRY....London, 1762. 2nd ed. 6 copper plts (4 fldg), fldg chart. Pp xxiv,489,(1),(index-6pp). Contemp full tan calf w/5 raised bands, gilt rules, red leather label. Spine chipped, worn at extrems, outer hinges splitting. Top 1" title pg clipped, flyleaf nearly loose. Bkpl, internally clean. *SUTTON.* $425

Dujardin, Edouard. WE'LL TO THE WOODS NO MORE. Stuart Gilbert, trans. New Directions, 1938. 1st US ed. Spine faded; dj darkened at edges. VG. *WOOLMER.* $35

Duke, Jane Taylor. KENMORE AND THE LEWISES. GC: Doubleday, 1949. Signed. Almost Fine in VG dj. *AARD.* $20

Duke of Beaufort and Morris, Mowbray. HUNTING (BADMINTON LIBRARY). London: Longmans, Green, & Co., 1885. 1st ed. Minor edgewear, else VG-NF. *OLD LONDON.* $75

Duke of Beaufort et al. DRIVING. London and Bombay: Longmans, Green & Co., 1904. Reprint (6th imp). 3/4 levant over orange bds. Minor wear, else VG. *OLD LONDON.* $40

Dulles, Foster Rhea. A HISTORY OF RECREATION. NY: Appleton Century Crofts, (1965, 40). 2nd ed, revised. VG+ in VG, rubbed dj. *AARD.* $20

Dulles, John W. THE RIDE THROUGH PALESTINE. Phila, (1881). 2nd ed. 528 pp. Fldg map. Sl wear spine ends. *O'NEILL.* $75

DULUTH: PAST, PRESENT, AND FUTURE. (Duluth?, np), 1890. (128)pp. Pict wraps, Fine. *SCHOYER'S.* $125

Dumas, Alexandre. A GIL BLAS IN CALIFORNIA. LA: Primavera Press, 1933. Fldg map. Cl w/paper spine label in moderately chipped dj. *DAWSON'S.* $100

Dumas, Alexandre. THE BLACK TULIP. S.J. Adair Fitz-Gerald (trans). Franz Lammers (illus). Full niger morocco, tissue jacket, slipcase. Haarlem: LEC, 1951. One of 1500 ptd by Joh. Enschede En Zonen & signed by him & Lammers. Marginal darkening of cvrs, o/w Fine. *JAFFE.* $150

Dumas, Alexandre. THE THREE MUSKETEERS. Edy Legrand (illus). Blue cl, gilt, cl & foil slipcase. NY: LEC, 1953. Ltd to 1500. VF. *JAFFE.* $45

Dumond, Annie Nelles. THE LIFE OF A BOOK AGENT. St. Louis: Published by the author, 1892. 5th ed, revised. Cl puckering a bit on spine, silverfish nibbling on rear cover, o/w good. *WREDEN.* $60

Dumreicher, Andre Von. TRACKERS & SMUGGLER IN THE DESERTS OF EGYPT. NY, 1931. xii,248pp. *O'NEILL.* $30

Dunant, Henri. THE ORIGINS OF THE RED CROSS. Phila, 1911. 1st Eng trans. *FYE*. $30

Dunbar, Paul Laurence. FOLKS FROM DIXIE. London: James Bowden, (n.d.). 1st Eng ed. Bkpls. Binding bit soiled, front hinge neatly repaired, else VG. Scarce. *BETWEEN COVERS*. $250

Dunbar, Paul Laurence. JOGGIN' ERLONG. NY: Dodd, 1906. 1st ed. Illus. A little spine wear, small chip to label, overall NF. *BEASLEY*. $150

Dunbar, Paul Laurence. LYRICS OF LOVE AND LAUGHTER. NY: Dodd, 1903. 1st ed. Fine but for small dig at bottom of rear spine fold. *BEASLEY*. $150

Dunbar, Paul Laurence. POEMS OF CABIN AND FIELD. NY: Dodd, Mead, 1899. 1st ed. 125pp. Orig dec. grn cl, teg. Spine very sl sunned, owner name. Fine. *CHAPEL HILL*. $150

Dunbar, Paul Laurence. THE UNCALLED. NY: Dodd, 1898. NF but for lightly rubbed spine. *BEASLEY*. $300

Dunbar, Seymour. A HISTORY OF TRAVEL IN AMERICA. Indianapolis: Bobbs-Merrill Company, 1915. 4 vols. 2 maps, 12 color plts. Erasure, Vol 1; owner stamp other vols. Bound w/blue leather spines, marbled paper over boards; modest shelfwear. Overall Attractive set. *PARMER*. $250

Dunbar, Seymour. A HISTORY OF TRAVEL IN AMERICA. NY: Tudor Pub Co, 1937. New ed. 2 maps, 12 colored plts. Bkpl, else VG. *PARMER*. $75

Dunbar, Seymour. A HISTORY OF TRAVEL IN AMERICA... NY: Tudor Publishing, 1937. VG. *LAURIE*. $50

Dunbar, Seymour. A HISTORY OF TRAVEL IN AMERICA....NY, 1937. 51, 1531pp. 400 illus, 2 maps. Frontis. Back end paper torn. *HEINOLDT*. $30

Duncan, Archibald. THE MARINER'S CHRONICLE...NARRATIVES...INCIDENT TO A LIFE OF MARITIME ENTERPRISE...In 2 vols. 2nd ed. London: James Cundee, 1804. (xvi),354; (4),380pp. 20 engr plts, one w/sm piece torn from upper part, affecting sm part of image, one w/pencil marks. Contemp 1/2 calf, cvrs worn, joints cracked, but cords intact. 1st pub the same year; there is a "second edition," 1804-1805, which calls for six vols. This set, however, is complete as pub. *LEFKOWICZ*. $175

Duncan, Bob. BUFFALO COUNTRY. Dutton, 1959. 1st ed. Fine in Fine dj. *OREGON*. $25

Duncan, Bob. BUFFALO COUNTRY. NY, 1959. 1st ed. Dj. VG+. *PRATT*. $20

Duncan, David Douglas. I PROTEST. NY: Signet, (1968). 1st ed. Stiff wraps; issued in wraps only. *AKA*. $35

Duncan, David Douglas. SELF-PORTRAIT: USA. NY: Abrams, (1969). 1st ed. NF in dj. Signed. *CAPTAIN'S BOOKSHELF*. $75

Duncan, David Douglas. WAR WITHOUT HEROES. NY: Harper & Row, (1970). 1st ed. NF in dj (short edgetears, sm pieces rubbed away at corners). *AKA*. $200

Duncan, David Douglas. YANKEE NOMAD. NY: Holt, Rinehart and Winston, 1967. 2nd ed. Red cloth. VG in worn dj. *PARMER*. $75

Duncan, David. BEYOND EDEN. Ballantine, 1955. 1st ed. VG in sl chipped dj, tape repair. *MADLE*. $35

Duncan, Donald. THE NEW LEGIONS. NY: Random House, (1967). 1st ed. Dj. *AKA*. $30

Duncan, Francis. OUR GARRISONS IN THE WEST; OR, SKETCHES IN BRITISH NORTH AMERICA. London: Chapman, 1864. 1st ed. (8),319pp. Fldg map, mended. Orig cl boards, expertly rebacked in calf. *GINSBERG*. $150

Duncan, Harry. POEMS AND TRANSLATIONS. 1st ed. Fine in VG dj (1" closed tear). *DORN*. $60

Duncan, Isadora. MY LIFE. NY: Boni & Liveright. 1927. "Presentation Edition" ltd to 650 numbered. Spine extrems lightly frayed. *KARMIOLE*. $40

Duncan, Louis. MEDICAL MEN IN THE AMERICAN REVOLUTION. NY, 1970. Very Scarce. *FYE*. $100

Duncan, P.M. THE TRANSFORMATIONS (OR METAMORPHOSES) OF INSECTS London, 1882. 6th thousand. 40 engr plts. Full calf. Bkpl. *SUTTON*. $65

Duncan, Robert. A SELECTION OF 65 DRAWINGS FROM ONE DRAWING BOOK 1952-1956. Loose sheets in portfolio, boxed. LA: Black Sparrow Press, 1970. 1st ed. One of 300 signed. Mint. *JAFFE*. $150

Duncan, Robert. AS TESTIMONY: THE POEM & THE SCENE. SF: White Rabbit Press, (1964). 1st ed, 1st impression. One of 350 ptd. Presentation, inscribed. Ptd wraps. Fine. *JAFFE*. $250

Duncan, Robert. BENDING THE BOW. (NY): New Directions, 1968. 1st ed. Fine (os) in price-clipped dj. Signed. *CAPTAIN'S BOOKSHELF*. $45

Duncan, Robert. CAESAR'S GATE. POEMS 1949-1950. (Palma de Mallorca): The Divers Press, 1955. 1st ed, regular issue, One of 200 of total ed of 213. Inside cvrs somewhat foxed, wrappers a trifle rubbed, but VG. Pict wraps. *JAFFE*. $500

Duncan, Robert. DERIVATIONS. London: Fulcrum, (1968). 1st ed. Fine in lightly used price-clipped dj. *CAPTAIN'S BOOKSHELF*. $45

Duncan, Robert. EPILOGOS. (LA: Black Sparrow Press, 1967). 1st ed. One of 100 signed, w/orig pen/ink drwng pg 1. Dec red wraps, sewn. 15 hb in the ed. Fine. *JAFFE*. $275

Duncan, Robert. LETTERS. Highlands: Jargon, 1958. 1/450 issued in wraps and unsigned. This copy signed. Little wear and tiny chip to dj spine. *BEASLEY*. $200

Duncan, Robert. PARIS VISIT. FIVE POEMS. R.B. Kitaj (drwgs). 1/4 red morocco, pict boards, glassine dj. NY: Grenfell Press, (1985). 1st ed. One of 115 (entire ed 130) signed by Duncan & Kitaj. Mint. *JAFFE*. $375

Duncan, Robert. PLAYTIME PSEUDO STEIN. (SF), 1969. 1st ed. Wraps. Initialled by Duncan. Fine. *POLYANTHOS*. $130

Duncan, Robert. RELUCTANT GENERAL, LIFE & TIMES OF ALBERT PIKE. Dutton, (1961). 1st ed. VG in VG dj. *OREGON*. $35

Duncan, Robert. THE CAT AND THE BLACKBIRD. Pictured by Jess. (SF: White Rabbit Press, 1967). One of 500 in spiral bound pict wrappers. Fine. *CAPTAIN'S BOOKSHELF*. $75

Duncan, Robert. THE CAT AND THE BLACKBIRD. Told by Robert Duncan. Pictured by Jess. (SF: White Rabbit Press, 1967). 1st ed. Ltd to 500 (lithographed, plts then destroyed). Bkpl inscribed, dated by both Duncan & Jess. Top loop of plastic spiral binding lacking, o/w VG. *JAFFE*. $250

Duncan, Robert. THE FIVE SONGS. La Jolla, 1981. 1st ed. 1/100 only w/hand-painted design on title page, signed. Wraps. Fine. *POLYANTHOS*. $130

Duncan, Robert. THE SWEETNESS AND GREATNESS OF DANTE'S DIVINE COMEDY. SF, 1965. 1st ed. 1/500. Wraps. Initialled by Duncan. NF. *POLYANTHOS*. $150

Duncan, Robert. THE TRUTH & LIFE OF MYTH. NY: House of Books, 1968. 1st ed. One of 300 signed. Lacking glassine dj, o/w Fine. *JAFFE*. $100

Duncan, Robert. THE YEARS AS CATCHES. 1ST POEMS (1939 1946). Berkeley: Oyez, 1966. 1st ed. One of 200 hb. Promo flyer signed, laid in. Pict boards, dj. VF. *JAFFE*. $225

Duncan, Sara Jeannette. AMERICAN GIRL IN LONDON. NY: Appleton, 1891. 1st Amer ed. Grn cl stamped in black and gilt, sl smudged. *SCHOYER'S*. $25

Duncan, Shirley. TWO WHEELS TO ADVENTURE—THROUGH AUSTRALIA BY BICYCLE. London: Harrap (1957). 1st Eng ed. Signed. VG. *AARD.* $15

Duncan, William Cary. GOLDEN HOOFS. Phila: Lippincott, 1938. 1st ed. VG. *OCTOBER FARM.* $15

Dunglison, Robley. MEDICAL LEXICON. A DICTIONARY OF MEDICAL SCIENCE. Phila, 1874. New ed, rev, enl. *FYE.* $75

Dunglison, Robley. MEDICAL LEXICON. A DICTIONARY OF MEDICAL SCIENCE, CONTAINING A CONCISE ACCOUNT OF THE VARIOUS SUBJECTS AND TERMS—WITH THE FRENCH AND OTHER SYNONYMES—NOTICES OF CLIMATE, AND OF CELEBRATED MINERAL WATERS; FORMULAE FOR VARIOUS OFFICINAL AND EMPIRICAL PREPARATIONS, ETC. Phila, 1845. 5th ed. 771pp. Full lea. *FYE.* $100

Dunham, Curtis. THE GOLDEN GOBLIN, or, The Flying Dutchman, Junior. Indianapolis: The Bobbs-Merrill Co. (1906). 1st ed. Cl a bit rubbed; spine extrems a bit frayed. *KARMIOLE.* $60

Dunham, Wayland A. BLUE ENCHANTMENT: THE STORY OF CRATER LAKE. Caldwell: Caxton Printer, 1942. Cl in lightly chipped dj. *DAWSON'S.* $30

Duniway, Abigail Scott. FROM THE WEST TO THE WEST. A.C. McClurg, 1905. 1st ed. Tinted cvr picture, frontis. VG. *AUTHORS OF THE WEST.* $40

Dunlap, Susan. A DINNER TO DIE FOR. NY: St. Martin's, (1987). 1st ed. Signed. Fine in Fine dj. *UNGER.* $40

Dunlap, Susan. AS A FAVOR. NY: St. Martin's Press, 1984. 1st ed. Inscribed. Fine in dj. *MORDIDA.* $35

Dunlap, Susan. NOT EXACTLY A BRAHMIN. NY: St. Martin's Press, 1985. 1st ed. Inscribed. Fine in dj. *MORDIDA.* $35

Dunlap, Susan. PIOUS DECEPTION. NY: Villiard, (1989). 1st ed. Signed. VF in VF dj. *UNGER.* $40

Dunlap, Susan. THE BOHEMIAN CONNECTION. NY: St. Martin's, 1985. 1st ed. Signed. VF in dj. *SILVER DOOR.* $35

Dunlap, Susan. THE LAST ANNUAL SLUGFEST. NY: St. Martin's Press, 1986. 1st ed. Fine in dj. *MORDIDA.* $25

Dunlap, Susan. TOO CLOSE TO THE EDGE. NY: St. Martin's, (1987). 1st ed. Signed. Review copy w/slip laid in. Fine in Fine dj. *UNGER.* $40

Dunlap, William. A HISTORY OF THE AMERICAN THEATER. NY: Harper, 1832. 1st ed. 420,viiipp,4pp ads. Orig boards w/some staining, sl shaken. Scarce. Good. *CULLEN.* $425

Dunlop, John. HISTORY OF ROMAN LITERATURE...2 vols. Phila: Littell, 1827. 1st Amer ed. Contemp full polished sheep, spine somewhat rubbed; 4pp catalogue for early Phila pub inserted vol 1. *SCHOYER'S.* $65

Dunn, John. VIOLIN PLAYING. NY: Scribners, 1909. 2nd ed. Sl rubbed. VG. *BANCROFT.* $20

Dunn, Katherine. ATTIC. London: Allison & Busby, (1970). 1st UK ed. Trivial foxing to page edges, else Fine in Very NF dj w/very slight surface peel at extremities. Very scarce. *BETWEEN COVERS.* $175

Dunn, Katherine. GEEK LOVE. Knopf, 1989. Review copy. Fine in dj. *STAHR.* $45

Dunn, Katherine. GEEK LOVE. NY: Alfred Knopf, 1989. 1st ed. VF in dj. Signed. *CAPTAIN'S BOOKSHELF.* $50

Dunn, Katherine. THE SLICE: INFORMATION WITH AN AT-TITUDE. Portland: WW Press, (1990). 1st ed. Fine in wraps. Signed. *CAPTAIN'S BOOKSHELF.* $35.

Dunn, Katherine. TRUCK. NY: Harper, (1971). 1st ed. Fine in dj with a few very tiny tears. *BETWEEN COVERS.* $175

Dunn, Oliver and James E. Kelly, Jr. THE DIARIO OF CHRISTOPHER COLUMBUS'S FIRST VOYAGE TO AMERICA 1492-1493. Norman/London: Univ of Oklahoma, 1988. 1st ed. New in dj. *PARMER.* $65

Dunn, Waldo H. THE VANISHED EMPIRE. Cincinnati: Robert Clarke, 1904. 1st ed. Frontis, pict cl. *SCHOYER'S.* $20

Dunne, Finley Peter. MR. DOOLEY IN PEACE AND WAR. Boston: Small, Maynard, 1898. 2nd ed, 1st bk. Orig grn cl, gilt. Fine. *CONNOLLY & WADE.* $35

Dunne, Finley Peter. MR. DOOLEY IN THE HEARTS OF HIS COUNTRYMEN. Boston: Small, Maynard, 1899. 3rd ed. Sl edgewear, else NF. *CONNOLLY & WADE.* $25

Dunne, John Gregory. DUTCH SHEA, JR. Linden, 1982. Uncorrected proof. Fine in wraps. *STAHR.* $30

Dunne, John Gregory. QUINTANA & FRIENDS. Dutton, 1978. 1st ed. Fine in dj. *STAHR.* $15

Dunne, John Gregory. THE RED WHITE AND BLUE. Franklin Center: Franklin Lib, 1987. Leatherbound ltd 1st ed. Signed. Fine. *LOPEZ.* $50

Dunne, John Gregory. THE RED WHITE AND BLUE. Simon and Schuster, 1987. Uncorrected proof. NF in wraps. Rear cover creased. *STAHR.* $15

Dunne, Peter Finley. DISSERTATIONS BY MR. DOOLEY. NY: Harpers, 1906. 1st ed. Lt shelf wear, minor blemish, binding crack, but Nice overall. *AKA.* $35

Dunne, Peter Masten. BLACK ROBES IN LOWER CALIFORNIA. Berkeley: Univ of CA, 1952. 1st ed. Fldg map tipped to rear. Fine. *OREGON.* $50

Dunne, Peter Masten. EARLY JESUIT MISSIONS IN TARAHUMARA. Berkeley and LA: Univ of CA Press. 1948. 1st ed. Fldg map. Dj. *KARMIOLE.* $40

Dunning, H.W. TO-DAY ON THE NILE. NY: James Pott & Company, 1905. 1st ed. Red cl, gilt spine titles, cvr dec. Fldg map. Front hinge cracked, some shelfwear at spine, else VG, bright. *PARMER.* $75

Dunning, John. BOOKED TO DIE. NY: Scribner's, 1992. 1st ed. As New in dj. *ELSE FINE.* $75

Dunning, John. BOOKED TO DIE. NY: Scribner's et al, (1992). 1st ed. (small printing). New in dj. *BERNARD.* $100

Dunning, John. DEADLINE. NY: Fawcett, 1981. 1st ed. Paperback orig. NF in wraps. *ELSE FINE.* $20

Dunning, John. LOOKING FOR GINGER NORTH. NY: Fawcett, 1980. 1st ed. Paperback orig. NF in wraps. *ELSE FINE.* $20

Dunning, John. THE HOLLAND SUGGESTIONS. Indianapolis: Bobbs Merrill, 1974. 1st ed. Name. Fine, minor edgetear at dj flap fold. Scarce 1st mystery. *ELSE FINE.* $175

Dunsany, Lord. A NIGHT AT AN INN. A PLAY IN ONE ACT. NY: The Sunwise Turn, 1916. Neighborhood Playhouse Plays No. 1. Printed wraps w/design in red from a seal cut by author. In beautifully crafted fldg case and 1/2 leather slipcase, title gilt, raised bands. Fine. *POLYANTHOS.* $60

Dunsany, Lord. FIFTY-ONE TALES. London: Elkin Mathews, 1915. 1st ed. Uncut and unopened, cvrs sl edge sunned, corners sl rubbed, spine sl sunned. *POLYANTHOS.* $45

Dunsany, Lord. FIVE PLAYS. NY: Mitchell Kennerley, 1914. 1st ed. Spine sunned, extrems rubbed. NF. *POLYANTHOS.* $25

Dunsany, Lord. THE FOURTH BOOK OF JORKENS. Arkham House, 1948. 1st ed. Fine in dj. *MADLE.* $100

Dunsany, Lord. THE FOURTH BOOK OF JORKENS. Sauk City (WI): Arkham House, 1948. Ltd ed of 3000. Dj. Fine. *WEBER.* $90

Dunsany, Lord. THE FOURTH BOOK OF JORKENS. Sauk City: Arkham House, 1948. 1st ed, ltd to 3118. NF in dj w/some edgewear at head of spine and bottom of rear panel. *ROBBINS.* $60

Dunsany, Lord. THE GODS OF PEGANA. Luce, n.d. 1st US ed. VG. *MADLE.* $25

Dunsany, Lord. THE LAST BOOK OF WONDER. Boston: Luce, (1916). 1st US ed. of TALES OF WONDER. Bkpl. VG. *WOOLMER.* $25

Dunsany, Lord. TIME AND THE GODS. London, 1906. 1st ed. VG. Signed. *MADLE.* $250

Dunshee, Kenneth Holcomb. AS YOU PASS BY. NY: Hastings House, 1952. 1st ed. VG. One of 1000. Slipcase. *BACKROOM.* $75

Dunshee, Kenneth Holcomb. ENJINE!—ENJINE! NY: Home Ins. Co, 1939. 1st ed. VG. Wraps. *BACKROOM.* $70

Dunton, John, ed. ATHENIAN SPORT...London: Brag, 1707. 1st ed. 544pp. Bound w/half title in new 1/2 calf. Very Nice. *SECOND LIFE.* $225

Dupin, Jacques. MIRO: LIFE AND WORK. NY: Abrams, (1962). Dj. Bkpl. VG. *WEBER.* $150

DuPont, Samuel Francis. Ed. by John D. Hayes. SAMUEL FRANCIS DUPONT, A SELECTION FROM HIS CIVIL WAR LETTERS. 3 vols. Ithaca, (1969). 1st ed. Slipcase, plain djs. Fine. *PRATT.* $125

Dupuy, R. Ernest. MEN OF WEST POINT: THE FIRST 150 YEARS OF THE UNITED STATES MILITARY ACADEMY. NY: Wm. Sloane, 1951. 1st ed. Frontis. VG. *CONNOLLY & WADE.* $25

Dupuytren, Guillaume. ON LESIONS OF THE VASCULAR SYSTEM, DISEASES OF THE RECTUM, AND OTHER SURGICAL COMPLAINTS. London, 1854. 1st Eng trans. 378pp. Scarce. *FYE.* $150

Durant, John and Alice. PICTORIAL HISTORY OF THE AMERICAN CIRCUS. NY: Barnes, 1957. 1st ed. Good+. *OCTOBER FARM.* $35

Durant, John. THE YANKEES. Hastings House, 1949 1st ed. Good+ in VG+ dj. *PLAPINGER.* $75

Durbin, John P. OBSERVATIONS IN THE EAST, CHIEFLY IN EGYPT, PALESTINE, SYRIA AND ASIA MINOR. NY, 1847. Fldg maps, one split at fold, without loss. 2 vols. New cl and boards, new eps. xi,347pp; x,298pp. Attractive set. *O'NEILL.* $125

Durham, George as told to Clyde Wantland. TAMING THE NUECES STRIP; THE STORY OF McNELLY'S RANGERS. Austin: Univ of Texas Press, (1962). 1st ed. Fine in dj. *LAURIE.* $40

Durham, Mary E. THROUGH THE LANDS OF THE SERB. London, 1904. Fldg map. xi,345pp. Uncut. Scarce. *O'NEILL.* $45

Durham, Phillip. DOWN THESE MEAN STREETS A MAN MUST GO. Chapel Hill: Univ of NC, (1963). 1st ed. Fine in Fine dj. *UNGER.* $75

Durham, Robert. ENCYCLOPEDIA OF MEDICAL SYNDROMES. NY, 1960. *FYE.* $75

Durham, Walter T. JAMES WINCHESTER TENNESSEE PIONEER. Gallatin, TN, c1979. Signed. Dj. *HUDSON.* $20

Durkee, C.C. WILLIE WHITEWATER. Burton Pub., Kansas City, MO, 1950. 1st ed. Fine. *VARNER.* $20

Durocher, Leo with Ed Linn. NICE GUYS FINISH LAST. Simon & Schuster, 1975. 1st ed. Fine in Fine dj. *PLAPINGER.* $30

Durrell, Gerald. CATCH ME A COLOBUS. Viking, 1972. 1st Amer. ed. Fine in price-clipped dj. *STAHR.* $25

Durrell, Gerald. THE WHISPERING LAND. London: Rupert Hart Davis, 1961. 1st ed. Fine in dj. *JUVELIS.* $50

Durrell, Lawrence (ed). HENRY MILLER READER. NY: New Directions, 1959. 1st ed. NF, few bumps, rubs. *SMITH.* $50

Durrell, Lawrence and Henry Miller. A PRIVATE CORRESPONDENCE. NY, 1963. 1st ed. Extremities, spine minimally rubbed. Fine in dj (few edge nicks). *POLYANTHOS.* $30

Durrell, Lawrence and Henry Miller. A PRIVATE CORRESPONDENCE. George Wickes (ed). NY: Dutton, 1963. Orig brownish red cl. Fine in dj. 1st ed. *CHAPEL HILL.* $40

Durrell, Lawrence. BITTER LEMONS. London: Faber & Faber, (1957). 1st ed. Orig red cl. Bright, VG in dj (few sm closed tears top edge). *CHAPEL HILL.* $150

Durrell, Lawrence. CEFALU. London: Editions Poetry, (1947). 1st ed. Orig red cl. Acidic pp inevitably browned, else Fine in NF pict dj. Quite scarce in this condition. *CHAPEL HILL.* $350

Durrell, Lawrence. CLEA. London: Faber & Faber, (1960). 1st ed. Fine in NF dj. Signed and dated 1985. *CHAPEL HILL.* $300

Durrell, Lawrence. COLLECTED POEMS. London: Faber & Faber, (1960). 1st ed. Fine in NF dj w/large (1" by 2") chip in front panel. *CHAPEL HILL.* $35

Durrell, Lawrence. JUSTINE. London: Faber & Faber, (1957). 1st ed. Orig rose cl. Fine in NF dj; BALTHAZAR. London: Faber & Faber, (1958). 1st ed. Orig blue cl. Fine in NF dj; MOUNTOLIVE. London: Faber & Faber, (1958). 1st ed. Orig tan cl. Fine in NF dj; CLEA. London: Faber & Faber, (1960). 1st ed. Orig red cl. Fine in dj. The set. *CHAPEL HILL.* $1,500

Durrell, Lawrence. JUSTINE. PA, 1980. 1st Franklin Library ed. Signed. Full leather gilt. Fine. *POLYANTHOS.* $75

Durrell, Lawrence. MONSIEUR. Faber, 1974. 1st ed. Fine in dj that is rubbed at spine folds & flyleaf folds; one short tear. *STAHR.* $25

Durrell, Lawrence. MONSIEUR. NY: Viking, 1975. 1st Amer ed. Owner's label under flap, else NF in dj. *CHAPEL HILL.* $35

Durrell, Lawrence. NUNQUAM. Dutton, 1970. 1st Amer. ed. Fine in dj. *STAHR.* $15

Durrell, Lawrence. NUNQUAM. Faber & Faber, 1970. 1st ed. Fine in dj. One small nick on flyleaf fold. *STAHR.* $20

Durrell, Lawrence. NUNQUAM. London: Faber & Faber, (1970). 1st ed. Fine in dj. Signed and dated 1985. *CHAPEL HILL.* $150

Durrell, Lawrence. ON SEEMING TO PRESUME. London: Faber & Faber, (1948). 1st ed. Orig red cl. Lt offsetting to eps, else Fine in dj. 1st ed. *CHAPEL HILL.* $150

Durrell, Lawrence. SICILIAN CAROUSEL. NY, 1977. 1st ed. Fine in dj (tiny edge tear). *POLYANTHOS.* $25

Durrell, Lawrence. THE ALEXANDRIA QUARTET. London: Faber & Faber, (1962). 1st collected ed, #348 of 500 signed. Orig orange buckram w/bevelled edges, teg. Spine a trifle sunned, but NF in rubbed pub's slipcase. *CHAPEL HILL.* $850

Durrell, Lawrence. THE BLACK BOOK. London: Faber & Faber, (1973). 1st British ed. Fine in dj. Signed and dated 1973. *CHAPEL HILL.* $150

Durrell, Lawrence. THE DARK LABYRINTH. London: Faber & Faber, 1959. 1st ed. Fine in dj. *ELSE FINE.* $65

Durrell, Lawrence. THE IKONS AND OTHER POEMS. NY, 1967. 1st ed. Fine. Short edge tear on lower front panel of dj, lower spine little edge rubbed. *POLYANTHOS.* $25

Durrell, Lawrence. TUNC. London: Faber & Faber, (1968). 1st ed. Fine in dj and scarce wrap-around band. Signed and dated 1985. *CHAPEL HILL.* $150

Durrell, Lawrence. TUNC. London: Faber & Faber, (1968). 1st ed. Orig red cl. Fine in dj (sl crease rear panel). *CHAPEL HILL.* $50

Durrenmatt, Friedrich. OEDIPUS. (LEC, 1989). One of 650, signed by author and photographer, Maria Cosindas. Virtually Mint in slipcase. *PIRAGES.* $350

Durrenmatt, Friedrich. OEDIPUS. Photogravures by Marie Cosindas. Trans by Leila Vennewitz. 1/4 morocco & linen box. (NY): LEC, (1989). Ltd to 650 signed by Durrenmatt & Cosindas. New. *JAFFE.* $350

Duruy, Victor. HISTORY OF GREECE, AND OF THE GREEK PEOPLE...Boston: Estes & Lauriat, 1890. 4to. Eight vol. Blue cl. paper spine labels, somewhat rubbed. Ed de Luxe, 184 of 1000, Fldg maps, chromolithos, engrs. *SCHOYER'S.* $300

Dusenbery, B.M. (comp). MONUMENT TO THE MEMORY OF GENERAL ANDREW JACKSON...Phila: Walker & Gillis, 1846. Engr frontis. Scattered foxing. Orig cl. *SCHOYER'S.* $30

Dutton, Clarence E. GEOLOGY OF THE HIGH PLATEAUS OF UTAH. Washington: GPO, 1880. Large 4to, xxxii, 307pp, 11 heliotypes, 2 plts, 2 unnumbered illus. The separate, folio-sized atlas of 8 sheets is not present. This copy is 3/4 lea, gilt lettering and or- namentation, raised bands on spine, all edges marbled, back eps marbled (but same missing at front). Spine sunfaded, corners lightly bumped, and bottom rear cover corner has suffered from dampness. There are a few pages dampstained on corners, not affecting text or images. Overall, very presentable and attractive. *FIVE QUAIL.* $295

Dutton, Clarence E. TERTIARY HISTORY OF THE GRAND CANON DISTRICT. Washington, 1882. USGS Monograph 2, text and atlas. The two-volume Peregrine Press facsimile ed, 1977. Text is 4to. 42 illus. Atlas is folio, 23 double-page plts. Ltd ed of 1500. Mint in orig box. *FIVE QUAIL.* $275

Duval, Mathias. ARTISTIC ANATOMY. London, 1892. 6th ed. 77 Fine woodcut illus. *FYE.* $60

Duveen, Denis and Herbert Klickstein. A BIBLIOGRAPHY OF THE WORKS OF ANTOINE LAURENT LAVOISIER, 1743- 1794. 2 vols. London, 1954-1965. 1st eds. 491, 177pp. *FYE.* $200

Dwiggins, W. A. MILLENIUM I. Knopf, 1945. 1st ed. VG in dj. *MADLE.* $30

Dwiggins, W.A. 22 PRINTERS' MARKS AND SEALS. NY: William Edwin Rudge. 1929. Ed ltd to 350 signed by Dwiggins. *KARMIOLE.* $100

Dwight, Edwin Welles. MEMOIR OF HENRY OBOOKIAH...Rev ed. NY: American Tract Society. N.d. (circa 1840). 12mo. 124pp. Frontis. Brown calf over marbled boards, somewhat worn. Lacking rear ffep. *KARMIOLE.* $75

Dwight, Henry Otis. CONSTANTINOPLE AND ITS PROBLEMS...NY, 1901. 298pp. *O'NEILL.* $45

Dwight, Rev. H.G.O. MEMOIR OF MRS. ELIZABETH B. DWIGHT, INCLUDING AN ACCOUNT OF THE PLAGUE OF 1837. NY, 1840. Cl, worn & shaken. 323pp. *O'NEILL.* $50

Dwight, Sereno Edwards. MEMOIRS OF THE REV. DAVID BRAINERD....New Haven: Converse, 1822. 1st ed. 8vo, Pp. 507. Sl worn, contem calf (chipped at top of spine). VG. Howes B-717. *SECOND LIFE.* $125

Dwight, Theodore F. (ed). CAMPAIGNS IN VIRGINIA 1861-1862. Boston, 1895. 369pp. Fldg maps, errata slip, index. Cvr wear o/w VG+. *PRATT.* $175

Dwight, Thomas. FROZEN SECTIONS OF A CHILD. NY, 1881. 1st ed. 66pp + 15 plts. Ex-lib. *FYE.* $200

Dwight, Thomas. THE INTRACRANIAL CIRCULATION. Cambridge, MA, 1867. 1st ed. Stiff ptd wrappers, 28pp. Scarce. *FYE.* $100

Dwight, Wilder. LIFE AND LETTERS OF....Boston: Ticknor & Fields, 1868. 1st ed. Sl worn pub's cl. Orig tipped in photo frontis. Uncut. *SECOND LIFE.* $75

Dwyer, K.R. (pseud of Dean R. Koontz). DRAGONFLY. NY: Random House 1975. 1st ed. Fine in dj. *MORDIDA.* $125

Dyar, H.G. A LIST OF NORTH AMERICAN LEPIDOPTERA. Washington, 1902. Half calf w/gilt lettering and raised band (light rubbing). *SUTTON.* $65

Dye, Daniel Sheets. A GRAMMAR OF CHINESE LATTICE. Cambridge: Harvard Univ Press, 1949. 2nd prtg, in 1 vol. Dj. *KARMIOLE.* $60

Dye, Eva Emery. MCLOUGHLIN AND THE OLD OREGON. Chicago: McClurg, 1913. Orig pict cl. NF. *CONNOLLY & WADE.* $25

Dye, Eva Emery. THE CONQUEST. Chicago: McClurg, 1902. 1st ed. Orig grey pict cl. VG. *CONNOLLY & WADE.* $25

Dye, Job Francis. RECOLLECTIONS OF A PIONEER 1830-1852. Early CA Travels Series II. LA: Dawson, 1951. 1st ed. Ltd to 200. Frontis. Fine. *OREGON.* $60

Dyer, George. THE LONG DEATH. NY: Charles Scribner's Sons, 1937. 1st ed. Fine in dj (frayed spine ends, wear, closed tears). *MORDIDA.* $45

Dyer, John P. FROM SHILOH TO SAN JUAN, THE LIFE OF "FIGHTING JOE" WHEELER. Baton Rouge, (1941). Rev ed. (1961). 275pp. VG+ in dj. *PRATT.* $65

Dyer, John P. THE GALLANT HOOD. Indianapolis, (1950). 1st ed. 383pp. Dj spine faded with a little wear, o/w VG+. *PRATT.* $50

Dyer, T.F. Thiselton. FOLK-LORE OF WOMEN. London: Stock, 1905. 1st ed. Cvrs sl soiled, hinge tender, paste-down stuck to fly- leaf, o/w VG, uncut. *SECOND LIFE.* $150

Dyer, T.F. Thiselton. GREAT MEN AT PLAY. London: Remington & Co., 1889. 1st ed. 2 vols. Minor edgewear, else VG. *OLD LONDON.* $100

Dyk, Walter. SON OF OLD MAN HAT. NY: Harcourt Brace, (1938). 1st ed. Bkpl, o/w VG in price-clipped dj. *LOPEZ.* $250

Dyke, Samuel E. THE PENNSYLVANIA RIFLE. Lancaster, PA: Lancaster Hist Soc, 1974. VG. Wraps. *BACKROOM.* $10

Dykeman, Wilma. LOOK TO THIS DAY. NY: Holt, (1968). 1st ed. Fine in dj. Review copy, slip laid in. Signed. *CAPTAIN'S BOOKSHELF.* $40

Dykeman, Wilma. PROPHET OF PLENTY. Knoxville: Univ of Ten- nessee Press, (1966). 1st ed. Fine in sl used price-clipped dj. In- scribed. *CAPTAIN'S BOOKSHELF.* $40

Dykeman, Wilma. THE TALL WOMAN. NY: Holt, (1969). 1st ed. Fine in sl used dj. Inscribed. *CAPTAIN'S BOOKSHELF.* $60

Dykes, Jeff. FIFTY GREAT WESTERN ARTISTS, A BIBLIOG- RAPHIC CHECKLIST. Northland Press, (1975). 1st ed. Inscribed. Dj. *HEINOLDT.* $50

Dykes, Jeff. FIFTY GREAT WESTERN ILLUSTRATORS: A BIBLIOGRAPHIC CHECK LIST. Northland, (1975). 1st Collector's Ed of 200 numbered, signed. 96 illus, 10 color. Dk blue pict cvr, black leather shelfback, stamped in silver. Supplemental info bound in back (not in trade ed). New in slipcase. *AUTHORS OF THE WEST.* $100

Dykes, W.R. NOTES ON TULIP SPECIES. E. Katherine Dykes (ed, illus). London, 1930. 54 colored plts. Cloth. Hinges starting. Lt foxing pl versos. 1 pl w/overall smoke film; 1 text pp, 1 pl contain 3" tear; 1 pl w/scuff mark. *SUTTON.* $195

Dykstra, Robert R. THE CATTLE TOWNS. Knopf, 1968. 1st ed. VF in VF dj. *OREGON.* $35

E

E-Yeh-Shure. I AM A PUEBLO INDIAN GIRL. NY: Morrow, 1939. 1st ed. Bkpl, o/w VG in dj. *LOPEZ.* $65

Eadie, R. THE LIFE AND HABITS OF THE PLATYPUS, WITH SIDELIGHTS ON "SPLASH" THE TAME PLATYPUS. Melbourne, 1935. Cl-backed boards. Some staining to lower cover edges. *SUTTON.* $45

Eardley-Wilmot, S. THE LIFE OF A TIGER. London, 1911. Orig gilt-dec cl. Lt wear; sl shaken. *SUTTON.* $60

Earl, George Windsor. THE EASTERN SEAS OR VOYAGES AND ADVENTURES IN THE INDIAN ARCHIPELAGO, IN 1832-33-34, COMPRISING A TOUR OF THE ISLAND OF JAVA-VISITS TO BORNEO, THE MALAY PENINSULA,SIAM, & C.; ALSO AN ACCOUNT OF THE PRESENT STATE OF SINGAPORE WITH OBSERVATIONS ON THE COMMER-CIAL RESOURCES OF THE ARCHIPELAGO. London: Wm. H. Allen, 1837. 1st ed. 8vo, xii, 461pp. Modern half leather, marbled boards and eps. Gilt spine labels. *PARMER.* $800

Earl of Suffolk and Berkshire (ed). THE ENCYCLOPEDIA OF SPORT & GAMES. Phila & London: W. Heinemann, (1911). New & enlg. ed. 4 vols. Ex-lib. VG. *MIKESH.* $150

Earland, Ada. JOHN OPIE AND HIS CIRCLE. London, 1911. 51 illus. Teg. NF *POLYANTHOS.* $60

Earle, Alice M. COLONIAL DAMES AND GOOD WIVES. Boston: Houghton Mifflin, 1896. 1st ed. Spots, o/w VG in chipped dj. *SECOND LIFE.* $65

Earle, Alice M. CURIOUS PUNISHMENTS OF BYGONE DAYS. Chicago: H.S. Stone, 1896. 1st ed. 12mo, 149pp. Cvrs sl stained and shelfworn. Spine soiled. Inner rear hinge reinforced. Some foxing, o/w VG. Contains 1st Stone catalog. *DIAMOND.* $25

Earle, Alice M. SUN-DIALS AND ROSES OF YESTERDAY. NY, 1902. 1st ed. Cl, front hinge cracked. *SUTTON.* $40

Earle, John. MICRO-COSMOGRAPHIE...Ed by Gwendolen Murphy. (London): The Golden Cockerel Press, 1928. Ed ltd to 400 numbered. Dj sl chipped. *KARMIOLE.* $65

Earle, John. MICRO-COSMOGRAPHIE, OR, A PIECE OF THE WORLD DISCOVERED IN ESSAYS AND CHARACTERS. Waltham St. Lawrence, 1928. One of 400. Dj lightly edgeworn. *DAWSON'S.* $100

EARLY CALIFORNIA THEATER. Bk Club of CA, (1974). 1st ed. 11 illus brochures, intro, 10 sketches. Cl, boards folder in slipcase w/leather shelfback, gilt-stamped leather labels. Fine. *AUTHORS OF THE WEST.* $60

Earp, Josephine. I MARRIED WYATT EARP. Collected and ed by Glenn Boyer. Tucson, 1976. 1st ed. Fine in faded dj. *BAADE.* $45

Easby, Elizabeth Kennedy. PRE-COLUMBIAN JADE FROM COSTA RICA. NY: Andre Emmerich, (1968). Map, wraps. Good. *ARCHAEOLOGIA.* $35

EAST OF THE SUN AND WEST OF THE MOON. Doran, (n.d.). 204pp. Mounted color frontis, 24 tipped-in color plates plus illus by Kay Nielsen. Dec endpaper. VG+. *BEBBAH.* $250

Eastlake, Charles L. HINTS ON HOUSEHOLD TASTE IN FURNI-TURE, UPHOLSTERY, AND OTHER DETAILS. Boston, 1874. 2nd Amer ed. Charles C. Perkins, M.A (ed). 8 samples bound in. Lt spine end wear. NF. *McCLINTOCK.* $57.50

Eastlake, William. A CHILD'S GARDEN OF VERSES FOR THE REVOLUTION. NY: Grove, (1970). 1st prtg. VG+ in price-clipped soiled dj. *AKA.* $28

Eastlake, William. THE BRONC PEOPLE. (London): Andre Deutsch, (1963). 1st Eng ed. Fine in sl rubbed dj, few short tears. *HELLER.* $50

Eastman, Charles A. and Elaine Goodale. SMOKY DAY'S WIG-WAM EVENINGS. Boston: Little, Brown, 1912. Later ptg. Spine ends frayed, only Good. *LOPEZ.* $25

Eastman, Charles A. OLD INDIAN DAYS. NY: Doubleday Page, 1910. Later ptg of bk orig pub in 1907. VG. *LOPEZ.* $25

Eastman, Max. KINDS OF LOVE. NY: Scribners, 1931. 1st ed. Fine in NF dj w/tears at folds, small chip. *BEASLEY.* $65

Eastman, Mrs. Mary. DAHCOTAH; OR, LIFE AND LEGENDS OF THE SIOUX AROUND FORT SNELLING. NY: John Wiley, 1849. 1st ed. 2pp pictographs, 3 color lithos. Orig dec blind-stamped cl. Spine & cvr gilt very rubbed. Little cvr wear, staining. Rebacked w/most of orig backstrip. Cvrs reattached. Title-page corner torn, not affecting letterpress. Title-page stained. Much age-staining, foxing, o/w VG. Sig of Wm. Preston Harrison on pastedown. *DIAMOND.* $125

Eastman, Roy. THE MYSTERIES OF BLAIR HOUSE. (Detroit): Conjure House, (1948). Ltd 1st ed, 1st bk. NF in dj. *BERNARD.* $35

Easton, John. AN UNFREQUENTED HIGHWAY, THROUGH SIKKIM AND TIBET TO CHUMOLAORI. London: The Scholar-tis Press. 1928. 16 plts. Ltd to 960. Red cl, spine sl faded. Bkpl. Very nice. *KARMIOLE.* $150

Easton, R. and M. Brown. LORD OF BEASTS, THE SAGA OF BUFFALO JONES. Univ of AZ, 1961. 2nd ptg. Fine in Fine dj. *VARNER.* $20

Easton, Robert and MacKenzie Brown. LORD OF BEASTS. Tucson: Univ of Arizona, 1961. 1st ed. Inscribed. Fine in Good+ dj. *CONNOL-LY & WADE.* $45

Easton, Robert. GUNS, GOLD & CARAVANS. Santa Barbara: Capra, 1978. 1st ed. VG in VG dj. *CONNOLLY & WADE.* $25

Easton, Robert. MAX BRAND. Norman: Univ of OK, (1970). 1st ed. Signed by author. Fine in Fine dj. *UNGER.* $60

Eastwick, Capt. Robert William. A MASTER MARINER, BEING THE LIFE AND ADVENTURES OF CAPTAIN...EASTWICK. London, NY: Macmillan & Co, 1891. Herbert Compton (ed). Fron-tis loose, interior clean. Soiling, shelfwear. Partially unopened. *PARMER.* $45

Eaton, A. MANUAL OF BOTANY, FOR NORTH AMERICA....Al-bany, 1829. 5th ed. 451pp,(1),63,(71). Contemp calf, backstrip near-ly perished, front cvr detached, rear cover missing. Foxed. Ex-lib. *SUTTON.* $75

Eaton, Charles Edward. THE BRIGHT PLAIN. Chapel Hill: Univ. of North Carolina Press, 1942. 1st ed, 1st bk. Orig reddish br cl. Fine in price-clipped dj (sm narrow chip at bottom of spine). *CHAPEL HILL.* $35

Eaton, Clement. A HISTORY OF THE OLD SOUTH. NY, 1949. 1st ed. VG. *PRATT.* $25

Eaton, Clement. JEFFERSON DAVIS. NY, (1977). 1st ed. 334pp, A little dj wear, o/w VG+. *PRATT.* $25

Eaton, E.H. BIRDS OF NEW YORK. 2 vols. Albany, 1910-14. 2nd ed. 106 colored plts. Lt wear. *SUTTON.* $135

Eaton, Leonard. NEW ENGLAND HOSPITALS, 1790-1833. Ann Arbor, 1957. 1st ed. *FYE.* $40

Eaton, W.P. IN BERKSHIRE FIELDS. NY & London: 1920. VG. *MIKESH.* $20

Eaton, Walter P. GREEN TRAILS AND UPLAND PASTURES. Boston, 1925. Rev ed. Fine. *VARNER.* $20

Eaton, Walter Prichard. SKYLINE CAMPS. W. A. Wilde Co., n.p., 1922. 1st ed. Minor wear to extremities, else VG-NF. *OLD LONDON.* $45

Eavenson, Howard. THE FIRST CENTURY AND A QUARTER OF AMERICAN COAL INDUSTRY. Pittsburgh: Privately ptd, 1942. 1st ed. 14 maps. NF. *ARCHER.* $80

Eaves, Charles Dudley and C.A. Hutchinson. POST CITY, TEXAS. Austin: Texas State Hist Assoc, 1952. 1st ed. Presentation from Post's daughter. Dj torn and chipped, o/w VG. *LAURIE.* $30

Ebeling, Walter. HANDBOOK OF INDIAN FOODS AND FIBERS OF ARID AMERICA. Berkeley: Univ of CA Press, 1986. 1st ed. Fine in Fine dj. *BOOK MARKET*. $65

Eberhart, Mignon. FIVE PASSENGERS FROM LISBON. Random, (1946). 1st ed. VG+ in Good+ dj with closed tears, spine chips. *BEBBAH*. $20

Eberhart, Mignon. SPEAK NO EVIL. Random, (1941). Stated 1st prtg. VG+ in VG+ dj with slight edgewear, one 1/4" closed tear. *BEBBAH*. $25

Eberhart, Mignon. WOLF IN MAN'S CLOTHING. NY: Random House,(1942). 1st ed. Fine in little worn and sl soiled dj. *SECOND LIFE*. $65

Eberhart, Perry. TREASURE TALES OF THE ROCKIES. Denver: Sage Press, (1961). Cl, dj. VG. *SCHOYER'S*. $20

Eberhart, Richard. A BRAVERY OF EARTH. NY: Jonathan Cape & Harrison Smith, (1930). Fine in NF dj w/couple of short tears. 1st Amer ed. from Eng sheets w/errata slip tipped in. Signed and dated 1983. *CHAPEL HILL*. $200

Eberhart, Richard. BROTHERHOOD OF MEN. (Pawlet, VT): Banyan Press, (1949). 1st ed. Ltd to 226 signed. Wraps. Fine. *JAFFE*. $250

Eberhart, Richard. COLLECTED POEMS 1930-1960. INCLUDING 51 NEW POEMS. NY: Oxford Univ Press, 1960. 1st Amer ed. Inscribed. Dj sl faded at spine, o/w Fine. *JAFFE*. $150

Eberhart, Richard. COLLECTED VERSE PLAYS. Univ of North Carolina Press, (1962). 1st ed. Fine in dj (extremities little rubbed, tiny chip top). *POLYANTHOS*. $25

Eberhart, Richard. ON POETRY AND POETS. Urbana: Univ of IL Press, (1979). 1st ed. Fine in dj. *CAPTAIN'S BOOKSHELF*. $25

Eberhart, Richard. POEMS TO POETS. Lincoln, (MA): The Penmaen Press, (1975). NF. 1st ed. #143 of 300 signed by Eberhart and Michael McCurdy (pub, illus). *CHAPEL HILL*. $50

Eberhart, Richard. READING THE SPIRIT. NY: Oxford Univ Press, 1937. 1st Amer ed. Cl-backed boards. Dj faded at spine, o/w VG. *JAFFE*. $125

Eberhart, Richard. SELECTED POEMS, 1930-1965. NY: New Directions, (1965). 1st ed. Simultaneous issue in wraps. Signed. NF. *LOPEZ*. $35

Eberhart, Richard. THIRTY ONE SONNETS. NY: Eakins Press, 1967. 1st ed. Fine in like dj (tiny tear). *POLYANTHOS*. $25

Eberlein, H.D. and C.V.D. Hubbard. THE PRACTICAL BOOK OF GARDEN STRUCTURE AND DESIGN. Phila, 1937. Cloth. Chipped dj. *SUTTON*. $80

Ebers. George. UARDA. Coates, n.d. VG. *MADLE*. $35

EBERSTADT CATALOGUE #127. KANSAS AND THE GREAT PLAINS. 1955. VG. *OREGON*. $20

EBERSTADT CATALOGUE #162. TEXAS, BEING A COLLECTION OF RARE & IMPORTANT BOOKS & MANUSCRIPTS RELATING TO THE LONE STAR STATE. 1963. Fine. *OREGON*. $75

Ebert, Frederic Adolphus. A GENERAL BIBLIOGRAPHIC DICTIONARY. Oxford: Univ Press, 1837. 4 vols. Scuffed and sunned, repairs to first pp of each vol, title page lacking vol 1. *DAWSON'S*. $100

Ebert, Justus. THE IWW IN THEORY AND PRACTICE. Chicago: IWW, n.d. 2nd ed. Wraps, lightly worn. *BEASLEY*. $45

Ebin, David (ed). THE DRUG EXPERIENCE. NY: Orion Press, (1961). 1st ed. VG in dj. *LOPEZ*. $35

Ebin, David (ed). THE DRUG EXPERIENCE: FIRST-PERSON ACCOUNTS OF ADDICTS, WRITERS, SCIENTISTS AND OTHERS. NY, 1961. 1st ed. Dj. *FYE*. $50

Eby, Henry H. OBSERVATIONS OF AN ILLINOIS BOY IN BATTLE, CAMP & PRISONS, 1861 TO 1865. Mendota, IL: By the author, 1910. Worn, frayed, spotted, marginal tears. Good. *BOHLING*. $125

Eccles, Audrey. OBSTETRICS AND GYNAECOLOGY IN TUDOR AND STUART ENGLAND. Kent, 1982. 1st ed. Dj. *FYE*. $40

Eccles, John. THE NEUROPHYSIOLOGICAL BASIS OF MIND. Oxford, 1953. *FYE*. $50

Eccles, John. THE PHYSIOLOGY OF NERVE CELLS. Baltimore, 1957. 1st ed. *FYE*. $50

Eccles, John. THE PHYSIOLOGY OF SYNAPSES. Berlin, 1964. 1st ed. Dj. *FYE*. $50

Eckel, John C. THE FIRST EDITIONS OF THE WRITINGS OF CHARLES DICKENS AND THEIR VALUES: A BIBLIOGRAPHY ... London: Chapman & Hall, 1913. Ltd ed of 250, a lg paper copy, signed by compiler and pub. Bkpl. *WEBER*. $400

Eckenhoff, J. ANESTHESIA FROM COLONIAL TIMES: A HISTORY OF ANESTHESIA AT THE UNIVERSITY OF PENNSYLVANIA. Phila, 1966. 1st ed. *FYE*. $40

Ecker, Arthur. NORMAL CEREBRAL ANGIOGRAM. Springfield, 1951. 1st ed. 141 illus. *FYE*. $75

Eckert, Allan W. GATEWAY TO EMPIRE. Boston, (1983). 1st ed. 688pp. Light dj wear, o/w Fine. *PRATT*. $27.50

Eckert, Allan W. THE GREAT AUK. Boston: Little Brown, (1963). 1st ed. Fine in dj. *CAPTAIN'S BOOKSHELF*. $75

Eckhardt, George H. PENNSYLVANIA CLOCKS AND CLOCKMAKERS. NY, 1955. Dj worn, light chipping. NF. *POLYANTHOS*. $35

Eco, Umberto. FOUCAULT'S PENDULUM. London: Secker & Warburg, 1989. 1st ed. Fine. *SMITH*. $45

Eco, Umberto. FOUCAULT'S PENDULUM. NY: Harcourt Brace Jovanovich, 1989. 1st ed. Fine in dj. *ELSE FINE*. $30

Eco, Umberto. POSTSCRIPT TO THE NAME OF THE ROSE. NY: Harcourt Brace Jovanovich, 1984. 1st ed. VF in dj. *ELSE FINE*. $35

Eco, Umberto. THE NAME OF THE ROSE. NY: Harcourt Brace Jovanovich, 1983. 1st ed. VF in dj. *ELSE FINE*. $60

ED. GEER'S EXPERIENCE WITH THE TROTTERS AND PACERS....Buffalo, 1901. 1st ed. VG. *OCTOBER FARM*. $40

Eddings, David. HIGH HUNT. NY: Putnam, 1973. 1st ed. Fine, minor wear to jacket spine ends. *ELSE FINE*. $50

Eddington, A. S. THE INTERNAL CONSTITUTION OF THE STARS. Cambridge Univ Press, 1930 (1926), 2nd ed. Blue cl; front board spotted, rear board bent & wrinkled, fore-edge stained, corners bumped, bkpl, o/w Good clean tight. *KNOLLWOOD*. $85

Eddington, Arthur. RELATIVITY THEORY OF PROTONS AND ELECTRONS. NY: The Macmillan Co. 1936. 1st Am ed. *KARMIOLE*. $100

Eddison, E. R. THE WORM OUROBOROS. Boni, 1926. 1st US ed. VG. *MADLE*. $50

Eddy, Clyde. DOWN THE WORLD'S MOST DANGEROUS RIVER. NY 1929. 1st ed. Yellow cloth, pict cover, 18 illus; xv,293pp. At least VG+ if not NF. *FIVE QUAIL*. $125

Ede, H.S. SAVAGE MESSIAH. London: William Heinemann, 1931. Frontis. Red cl bound, title in gilt on front and spine. Inscribed. Prospectus for Henri Gaudier-Brzeska laid-in. Spine faded, lt scuffing to cvrs, o/w Fine. *HELLER*. $125

Edebohls, George. THE SURGICAL TREATMENT OF BRIGHT'S DISEASE. NY, 1904. 1st ed. *FYE*. $75

Edel, Leon and Dan H. Laurence. A BIBLIOGRAPHY OF HENRY JAMES. London, 1957. 1st ed. NF in NF dj. *POLYANTHOS*. $75

Edes, Rev. Richard S. LETTERS AND JOURNAL OF COL. JOHN MAY (1748-1812) OF BOSTON. Boston, 1873. 16pp. 8vo. Wraps. *ARTIS.* $15

Edgerton, Clyde. KILLER DILLER. Chapel Hill: Algonquin, (1991). 1st Amer ed. Signed. Fine in dj. *DORN.* $35

Edgerton, Clyde. KILLER DILLER. Chapel Hill: Algonquin, 1991. 1st ed. As New in dj. Inscribed. *CAPTAIN'S BOOKSHELF.* $45

Edgerton, Clyde. KILLER DILLER. Chapel Hill: Algonquin Books, 1991. Adv reading copy of 1st ed. Orig red and yellow wraps. Fine. *CHAPEL HILL.* $35

Edgerton, Clyde. RANEY. Chapel Hill: Algonquin, (1985). 1st Amer ed. Signed. Fine in dj. *DORN.* $125

Edgerton, Clyde. THE FLOATPLANE NOTEBOOKS. Algonquin, 1988. 1st ed. Fine in VG dj. *BEBBAH.* $22

Edgerton, Clyde. THE FLOATPLANE NOTEBOOKS. Chapel Hill: Algonquin, (1988). 1st Amer ed. Signed. Fine in dj. *DORN.* $40

Edgerton, Clyde. THE FLOATPLANE NOTEBOOKS. Chapel Hill: Algonquin Books, 1988. Adv reading copy of 1st ed. Signed. Orig blue wraps. Fine. *CHAPEL HILL.* $60

Edgerton, Clyde. WALKING ACROSS EGYPT. Algonquin, 1987. 1st ed. Fine in dj. *STAHR.* $45

Edgerton, Clyde. WALKING ACROSS EGYPT. Chapel Hill: Algonquin, 1987. Adv reading copy. NF, drink ring front panel. Inscribed, signed, dated. *CAPTAIN'S BOOKSHELF.* $50

Edgerton, Clyde. WALKING ACROSS EGYPT. Chapel Hill: Algonquin, 1987. 1st ed. Fine in dj. Presentation inscrip. *CAPTAIN'S BOOK-SHELF.* $50

Edgerton, Clyde. WALKING ACROSS EGYPT. Chapel Hill: Algonquin Books, 1987. 1st ed. Inscribed. Orig black cl. Fine in dj. *CHAPEL HILL.* $65

Edib, Halide. MEMOIRS OF...NY, (1926). vii,472pp. Lib markings, else VG. *O'NEILL.* $35

Edib, Halide. TURKISH ORDEAL, BEING THE FURTHER MEMOIRS... NY, (1928). Fldg map. 407 pp. Fine. *O'NEILL.* $50

Edinger, Ludwig. TWELVE LECTURES ON THE STRUCTURE OF THE CENTRAL NERVOUS SYSTEM. Phila, 1891. 2nd Amer. ed. *FYE.* $65

Edison, Thomas A. THE DIARY OF THOMAS A. EDISON. Old Greenwich, CT, (1970). 1st ed. Hb ed. Mint in dj. *BOND.* $25

Edminster, F.C. AMERICAN GAME BIRDS OF FIELD AND FOREST....NY, 1954. Dj. Some wear. Signed. *SUTTON.* $50

Edmonds, S. Emma. NURSE AND SPY IN THE UNION ARMY: COMPRISING THE ADVENTURES AND EXPERIENCES OF A WOMAN IN HOSPITALS, CAMPS, AND BATTLE-FIELDS. Hartford, 1865. 1st ed. *FYE.* $125

Edmonds, S. Emma. NURSE AND SPY IN THE UNION ARMY...Hartford, CT, 1865. 1st ed. Rebacked w/orig backstrip, little corner wear, little chipping of eps, o/w VG. *DIAMOND.* $45

Edmonds, S. Emma. NURSE AND SPY IN THE UNION ARMY. Hartford: W.S. Williams, 1865. 1st ed. 384pp, brown cloth. Spine sunned, VG. *ARCHER.* $40

Edmonds, Walter D. MOSTLY CANALLERS. Boston: LB, 1934. 1st ed. About Fine (bkpl) in well-worn dj. *CAPTAIN'S BOOKSHELF.* $45

Edmunds, John. A WILLIAMSBURG SONGBOOK. NY: Holt, 1964. Illus. by Fritz Kredel. Bound in linen and marbled. As New. *BANCROFT.* $30

Edmunds, Murrell. BEHOLD, THY BROTHER. NY: Beechhurst Press, (1950). 1st ed. Signed. Dusty in worn dj. *ROBBINS.* $35

Edmunds, R. David. THE OTOE-MISSOURIA PEOPLE. Phoenix: Indian Tribal Series, 1976. #741 of ltd ed of 15,000. Signed by Kenneth E. Black, Chariman, Otoe-Missouria Tribe. Blue cl. VF. *CONNOLLY & WADE.* $35

Edwardes, T. THE LORE OF THE HONEY-BEE. London, (1909). 3rd ed. Gilt dec cl. VG. *MIKESH.* $17.50

Edwards, A. ROCK GARDENS....8 tipped in, colored plts. London, 1929. 1st ed. Cl, some wear at edges, inner hinge cracked, foxing. *SUTTON.* $25

Edwards, Amelia B. A THOUSAND MILES UP THE NILE. NY: H.M. Caldwell Company, c. 1988. 2nd ed. Some shelfwear, else VG. *PARMER.* $35

Edwards, Amelia B. PHARAOHS, FELLAHS AND EXPLORERS. NY: Harper, 1892. Lib cl. VG ex-lib w/number on spine. *WORLDWIDE.* $25

Edwards, Amelia B. PHARAOHS, FELLAHS AND EXPLORERS. NY: Harper & Brothers, 1892. Fairly soiled, traces of labels, bkpl removals. *SCHOYER'S.* $30

Edwards, Charles. PLEASANTRIES ABOUT COURTS AND LAWYERS OF THE STATE OF NEW YORK. NY, 1867. 1st ed. Frontis. Spine tips defective. Bkpl removed, o/w VG. *DIAMOND.* $45

Edwards, Deltus M. THE TOLL OF THE ARCTIC SEAS. NY & London, 1910. 1st ed. Fldg map. Front hinge cracked, else VG. *McCLINTOCK.* $40

Edwards, E.I. THE ENDURING DESERT: A DESCRIPTIVE BIB-LIOGRAPHY. (LA): The Ward Ritchie Press, 1969. Prospectus laid in, signed. Cl, slipcase. *DAWSON'S.* $100

Edwards, Emily. PAINTED WALLS OF MEXICO. Austin: Univ of TX Press, (1966). 1st ed. Chipped dj. *SILVER.* $50

Edwards, Harry Stillwell. SHADOW. A Christmas Story. Macon, GA: The J.W. Burke Co, (1920). 1st ed. Orig ptd wraps. NF. *CHAPEL HILL.* $30

Edwards, Harry Stillwell. SONS AND FATHERS. Atlanta: Brown Pub Co, (1937). 1st ed. #94 of 1000 signed. Orig blue cl. Edges and eps foxed, but VG in dj chipped at spine ends, corners of front panel. *CHAPEL HILL.* $65

Edwards, Oliver. TALKING OF BOOKS. London: Heinemann, (1957). 1st Eng ed. Fine- in VG+ dj. *AARD.* $15

Edwards, Page Jr. THE MULES THAT ANGELS RIDE. Chicago: J. Philip O'Hara, 1972. 1st ed. Fine in Fine dj. *CONNOLLY & WADE.* $25

Edwards, Philip L. CALIFORNIA IN 1837. Published in "Themis" by Authority of the Board of State Library Trustees of the State of Ca. Sacramento: A.J. Johnston & Co. 1890. 48pp. Orig brown cl, rather faded and a bit soiled. Title a bit soiled, sm repaired tear. Howes E66 ("aa"). *KARMIOLE.* $150

Edwards, Ralph and Margaret Jourdain. GEORGIAN CABINET-MAKERS. London: Country Life Ltd. (1946). "Revised Edition." *KARMIOLE.* $45

Edwards, Richard and M. Hopewell. EDWARDS'S GREAT WEST AND HER COMMERCIAL METROPOLIS...AND A COM-PLETE HISTORY OF ST. LOUIS...St. Louis, (1860). 1st ed. 604pp. 116 plts. Orig gold stamped dec cl. Howes E69. *GINSBERG.* $175

Edwards, Ruth Dudley. CORRIDORS OF DEATH. London: Quartet, 1981. 1st ed. NF in dj. *SILVER DOOR.* $25

Edwards, Ruth Dudley. THE SAINT VALENTINE'S DAY MUR-DERS. London: Quartet, 1984. 1st ed. VF in dj. *SILVER DOOR.* $25

Edwards, Samuel E. THE OHIO HUNTER; OR, A BRIEF SKETCH OF THE FRONTIER LIFE OF SAMUEL E. ED-WARDS....Battle Creek, Mi., 1866. 240pp. Frontis, port. Orig cl, spine a little faded. Half morocco slipcase. *GINSBERG.* $750

EDWIN BOOTH IN TWELVE DRAMATIC CHARACTERS. Boston: James R. Osgood, 1872. Large folio, gilt pict cloth; spine ends worn, engr title and plts, tissue guarded, bit shaken, printed within red border. VG. *DRAMATIS PERSONAE.* $50

Edwords, Clarence E. BOHEMIAN SAN FRANCISCO. ITS RESTAURANTS AND THEIR MOST FAMOUS RECIPES. SF: Paul Elder, 1914. 1st ed. Tipped in frontis photo. Untrimmed. Inscription. Fine in fragile, rare dj w/chips. *CONNOLLY & WADE.* $75

Eells, Myron. HYMNS IN THE CHINOOK JARGON LANGUAGE. 2nd ed, rev, enl. Portland, OR: David Steel. 1889. 40pp. Orig pink ptd wraps. *KARMIOLE.* $60

Eells, Myron. MARCUS WHITMAN, PATHFINDER & PATRIOT. Seattle: Harriman, 1909. 1st ed. 20 plts, double-pg map. Blue cl showing wear. Internally Fine. *CONNOLLY & WADE.* $55

Eels, Myron. MARCUS WHITMAN—PATHFINDER AND PATRIOT. Seattle: The Alice Harriman Company, 1909. 1st ed. Shelfwear, esp to spine; overall VG. *PARMER.* $75

Egan, Ferol. FREMONT, EXPLORER FOR A RESTLESS NATION. NY, 1977. 1st ed. 582pp. VG+ in dj. *PRATT.* $30

Egan, Ferol. FREMONT—EXPLORER FOR A RESTLESS NATION. GC: Doubleday & Co, 1977. 1st ed. NF in similar dj. Laid in bk review. *PARMER.* $35

Egan, Pierce. THE LIFE OF AN ACTOR. London: for C.S. Arnold, 1825. 1st ed. Pub's patterned cl; spine gilt; 27 hand-colored aquatint plts (including frontispiece); engr vignettes; wide-margined copy. *DRAMATIS.* $450

Egerton (Thomas and John). EGERTON'S THEATRICAL REMEMBRANCER. London: for T. and J. Egerton, 1788. 1st ed. 12mo; modern quarter cloth; remnant of lea label pasted to spine, small singe hole, not affecting text, else VG. *DRAMATIS PERSONAE.* $175

Eggleston, E.H. AMERICAN SQUAB CULTURE....Frontis. Warrenton, 1921. 2nd ed. *SUTTON.* $37

Eggleston, Edward. THE CIRCUIT RIDER: A TALE OF THE HEROIC AGE. J.B. Ford & Company, 1874. 1st ed, 1st state, w/o the word "Illustrated" on title pg. Frayed at bottom, else Fine. Very Nice. *AUTHORS OF THE WEST.* $75

Eggleston, George T. TAHITI—VOYAGE THROUGH PARADISE. NY: Devin-Adair, 1953. 1st ed. Dj sunned Else Fine+ in NF dj. *GREAT EPIC.* $30

EGYPT. London, 1986. Pop-up bk. *BOOKFINDERS INTL.* $20

EGYPT: PAINTINGS FROM TOMBS AND TEMPLES. Intro by J. Vandier. NYGS, 1954. NF. *POLYANTHOS.* $85

EGYPTIAN SCULPTURE OF THE LATE PERIOD 700 B.C. TO 100 A.D. Brooklyn: Brooklyn Museum, 1960 (1973). 134 plts w/355 illus. *ARCHAEOLOGIA.* $200

Ehle, John. THE JOURNEY OF AUGUST KING. Harper & Row, 1971. 1st ed. Fine in dj. Neat bk plate. *STAHR.* $20

Ehrenburg, Ilya. PEOPLE & LIFE 1891-1921. NY: Knopf, 1962. Stated 1st Amer ed. 453pp. Lightly soiled dj. *AKA.* $32

Ehrenburg, Ilya. POST-WAR YEARS: 1945-1954. Cleveland: World, (1967). 1st ed. 349pp. Fine in Fine dj. *AKA.* $30

Ehrenfest, Hugo. BIRTH INJURIES OF THE CHILD. NY, 1922. 1st ed. *FYE.* $60

Eide, Arthur Hansin. DRUMS OF DIOMEDE: THE TRANSFORMATION OF THE ALASKA ESKIMO. Hollywood: House-Warven, 1952. 1st ed. Inscribed. Grn, lea-like fabricoid. Fine. *CONNOLLY & WADE.* $50

Eidlitz, Walther. ZODIAK. London, 1931. 1st ed. VG. *MADLE.* $75

Eigner, Larry. FROM THE SUSTAINING AIR. (Palma de Mallorca): Divers Press, 1953. 1st ed. One of 250. Spine a trifle split, o/w Fine. Wraps. *JAFFE.* $350

Einstein, Charles. THE BLOODY SPUR. NY: Dell, 1953. 1st ed. Pb orig. Dell 1st ed. No. 5. VF, unread, in wrappers. *MORDIDA.* $30

Einstein, Charles. THE FIRESIDE BOOK OF BASEBALL. Simon & Schuster, 1956. 1st ed. Good in VG dj. *PLAPINGER.* $45

Einstein, Charles. THE SECOND FIRESIDE BOOK OF BASEBALL. Simon & Schuster, 1958. Ltr ptg. Fine in Fine dj. *PLAPINGER.* $45

Einstein, Charles. THE THIRD FIRESIDE BOOK OF BASEBALL. Simon & Schuster, 1968. 1st ed. VG in VG+ dj. The 3rd in the classic series and the hardest to locate. *PLAPINGER.* $85

Eisele, Wilbert E. THE REAL "WILD BILL" HICKOK. FAMOUS SCOUT....LIFE IN THE FAR WEST. Denver: Wm. H. Andre, 1931. 1st ed. "Collector's Edition." Frontis. As New in As New dj. *CONNOLLY & WADE.* $55

Eiseley, Loren. THE BROWN WASPS. Mt. Horeb, WI: Perishable Press, 1969. 1st ed. Ltd to 200. Mint. *JAFFE.* $385

Eiseley, Loren. THE FIRMAMENT OF TIME. London: Gollancz, 1961. 1st Eng ed. Fine in price-clipped dj. *LOPEZ.* $45

Eiseley, Loren. THE IMMENSE JOURNEY. NY: RH, (1957). 1st ed, 1st bk. NF in like dj (rubbing). *CAPTAIN'S BOOKSHELF.* $75

Eisenberg, Deborah. TRANSACTIONS IN A FOREIGN CURRENCY. STORIES. NY: Knopf, 1986. 1st ed. Fine in Fine dj. *ROBBINS.* $25

Eisenschiml, Otto and Ralph Geoffrey Newman. THE AMERICAN ILIAD. Indianapolis, (1947). 1st ed. NF. *McGOWAN.* $45

Eisenschiml, Otto and Ralph Newman. THE AMERICAN ILIAD. Indianapolis, (1947). 1st ed. Dj chipped o/w Fine. *PRATT.* $22.50

Eisenschiml, Otto. THE CELEBRATED CASE OF FITZJOHN PORTER. Indianapolis, (1948). 1st ed. Plain plastic dj. Fine. *PRATT.* $40

Eisenschiml, Otto. WHY WAS LINCOLN MURDERED? Boston, (1937). 1st ed. Minor spine fading o/w VG+. *PRATT.* $40

Eisenstadt, Jill. KISS OUT. NY: Knopf, l991. Uncorrected proof. Fine in ptd wrappers. *CAPTAIN'S BOOKSHELF.* $20

Eitner, Walter H. WALT WHITMAN'S WESTERN JAUNT. Lawrence, (1981). 1st ed. Dj. Fine. *PRATT.* $17.50

Ekvall, Robert B. TIBETAN SKY LINES. NY: Farrar, Straus & Young (1952). 1st ed. Almost Fine in VG dj. *AARD.* $25

EL GRECO. NY, 1938. 13 tipped-in color plts, photogravures. NF. *POLYANTHOS.* $50

El-Baz, Farouk. ASTRONAUT OBSERVATIONS FROM THE APOLLO-SOYUZ MISSION. Washington, DC: Smithsonian Inst Press, 1977. Good in paper wraps; minor spotting fr cvr. *KNOLLWOOD.* $45

Elder, Lonne III. CEREMONIES IN DARK OLD MEN. NY: Farrar, Straus & Giroux, (1969). 1st ed. One bump to bottom edge of front cover o/w Fine in dj. *BERNARD.* $45

Eldredge, Zoeth Skinner. THE BEGINNINGS OF SAN FRANCISCO...SF: Z. S. Eldredge, 1912. 2 vols. Spines sl dulled, o/w VG. *WEBER.* $50

Eldredge, Zoeth Skinner. THE BEGINNINGS OF SAN FRANCISCO...TO THE CITY CHARTER OF APRIL 15, 1850...SF: Zoeth S. Eldredge, 1912. 2 vols. Teg, gilt spine titles. Spines faded, else VG. *PARMER.* $125

Eldridge, George. ELDRIDGE'S COAST PILOT. No. 1. EASTERN SECTION. FROM CHATHAM TO ST. JOHN, N.B. Boston: S. Thaxter and Son, (1880). 1st ed, 1st issue. (7),287,(1 blank), 28 ad pp. Contemp morocco, aeg, extrems rubbed. *LEFKOWICZ.* $150

Eldridge, George. ELDRIDGE'S COAST PILOT. No. 2. SOUTHERN SECTION. FROM CHATHAM TO THE RIO GRANDE. Boston: S. Thaxter and Son, 1883. 1st ed, apparently only ed. (xxxii),536, (2 blank),45 ad pp. Orig sheep cvrs present but loose. *LEFKOWICZ*. $100

ELEVEN YEARS A DRUNKARD, OR THE LIFE OF THOMAS DONER. Sycamore, IL, 1878. 42 pp., crudely illus., wraps. Spine worn, chipped. *NUTMEG*. $50

Elger, T. Gwyn. THE MOON, A FULL DESCRIPTION AND MAP OF ITS PRINCIPAL PHYSICAL FEATURES. London: George Philip & Son, 1895. 1st ed. Rebacked w/orig illus spine laid on; corners bumped & worn; shelf wear. VG. *KNOLLWOOD*. $110

Eliot, George (pseud of Mary Ann Evans). IMPRESSIONS OF THEOPHRASTUS SUCH. NY: Harper, 1879. 1st US ed. Sl rubbing to cl. VG. *SECOND LIFE*. $45

Eliot George (pseud of Mary Ann Evans). DANIEL DERONDA. Edinburgh and London: Blackwood, 1876. 1st ed, 1st issue. 4 Vols. 8vo, contemp 3/4 grn calf and pebbled cloth, all edges rouged. Some rubbing, but generally excellent set of the earliest issue of the 1st ed (indicated by absence of contents leaves). *HARTFIELD*. $495.

Eliot, George (pseud of Mary Ann Evans). SILAS MARNER, THE WEAVER OF RAVELOE. NY: Harper & Bros. 1861. 1st Amer ed. 266pp.+22pp ads. Orig black cloth, gilt spine; edges sl worn. *KARMIOLE*. $100

Eliot, George (pseud of Mary Ann Evans). SILAS MARNER. THE WEAVER OF RAVELOE. Illus by Lynton Lamb. Cl & dec boards, glassine dj. London: LEC, 1953. Ltd to 1500 ptd by The Shenval Press, illus by The Curwen Press, & signed by Lamb. Spine sl spotted, o/w Fine in sl soiled slipcase. *JAFFE*. $75

Eliot, George (pseud of Mary Ann Evans). THE SPANISH GYPSY: A POEM. Boston, 1868. 1st ed. NF. *POLYANTHOS*. $30

Eliot, John. A BIOGRAPHICAL DICTIONARY....Salem: Cushing and Appleton, Boston: Oliver, 1809. 1st ed. 511pp, erratum. Contemp calf, worn, water mk at corner of title pg, some foxing. VG. *SECOND LIFE*. $225

Eliot, T.S. A CHOICE OF KIPLING'S VERSE MADE BY T.S. ELIOT WITH AN ESSAY ON RUDYARD KIPLING. NY: Scribners, 1943. 1st Amer ed. Fine in dj w/light wear to head of spine. *CAPTAIN'S BOOKSHELF*. $50

Eliot, T.S. AFTER STRANGE GODS. NY: Harcourt, 1934. 1st US ed. Fine in NF dj w/light wear at end of darkened spine. *BEASLEY*. $175

Eliot, T.S. ASH WEDNESDAY. NY: The Fountain Press Inc./London: Faber & Faber, Ltd, 1930. 1st ed. Ltd ed of 600 numbered, signed. Blue cloth trifle stained, 3 sm stains on p. 25. Very Nice. *BLUE MOUNTAIN*. $450

Eliot, T.S. BURNT NORTON. London: Faber and Faber, 1941. 1st ed. Wraps, lightly worn. *BEASLEY*. $45

Eliot, T.S. COLLECTED POEMS 1909-1935. NY: HB, 1936. 1st ed. Fine; dj w/small spine chips, a few stains from old internal tape mends. *ELSE FINE*. $85

Eliot, T.S. FOUR QUARTETS. NY: Harcourt, Brace, (1943). Orig black cl. Sl binding defect top front cvr, but NF in VG dj (few sm chips, tears). 1st ed, 1st ptg, w/"first American edition" on copyright pg. One of only 788 thus, this copy stamped "Review Copy" ffep, giving pub date May 11, 1943 and price of $2. Though "first American edition" is stated, this is actually the true first edition, preceding by almost 1 1/2 yrs the London ed pub by Faber & Faber 31 October 1944. Margins incorrectly set in this 1st ptg. *CHAPEL HILL*. $1,250

Eliot, T.S. HOMAGE TO JOHN DRYDEN. THREE ESSAYS....The Hogarth Essays. N.p., n.d. 1st U.S. ed. Printed wraps. Fine. *POLYANTHOS*. $45

Eliot, T.S. OLD POSSUM'S BOOK OF PRACTICAL CATS. NY: Harcourt, Brace, 1939. 1st Amer ed. Grey cl. Fine in Good+ dj. *JUVELIS*. $150

Eliot, T.S. POEMS. NY: Knopf, 1920. 1st US ed. of ARA VOS PREC. Spine loose and reattached w/scotch tape. Newspaper clippings pasted in. Good only. *WOOLMER*. $50

Eliot, T.S. POETRY AND DRAMA. Cl. London: Faber, (1951). 1st Eng ed. Fine in faintly darkened dj w/few short closed tears. *JAFFE*. $45

Eliot, T.S. PRUFROCK AND OTHER OBSERVATIONS. London: The Egoist Limited, 1917. 1st ed, 1st bk. One of 500 ptd. Ptd buff wrappers. Fine linen clamshell box, leather label on spine. *JAFFE*. $5500

Eliot, T.S. SELECTED ESSAYS 1917-1932. London: Faber, (1932). 1st trade ed. One of 3000. Dj sl rubbed spine, corners, o/w VF. *JAFFE*. $450

Eliot, T.S. SWEENEY AGONISTES. London: Faber & Faber, (1932). 1st ed. Orig blue-gray boards. VG in dj (sm chip head of spine). Nice. *CHAPEL HILL*. $175

Eliot, T.S. THE CLASSICS AND THE MAN OF LETTERS. London: Oxford Univ Press, 1942. 1st ed. Pale blue wrappers; spine sunned else VG. *JUVELIS*. $100

Eliot, T.S. THE DARK SIDE OF THE MOON. London: Faber and Faber, (1946). 1st ed. Price clipped dj w/few small chips at top edge. NF in ptd red dj. *BLUE MOUNTAIN*. $35

Eliot, T.S. THE ELDER STATESMAN. A PLAY. NY: Farrar, Straus & Cudahy, (1959). 1st Amer ed. Cl, dj. Fine. *JAFFE*. $65

Eliot, T.S. THE ELDER STATESMAN. NY, 1959. 1st ed. NF in NF dj. *POLYANTHOS*. $25

Eliot, T.S. THE FAMILY REUNION. NY: Harcourt, Brace, (1939). 1st Amer ed. Name, else NF in VG dj w/2 closed tears (1" and 3/4") along top edge. *CHAPEL HILL*. $125

Eliot, T.S. THE WASTE LAND. NY: Boni & Liveright, (1922). 2nd ed. Number 4 of 1,000. Owner's name inside front cover. VG. *WOOLMER*. $175

Elizabeth, C. CHAPTERS ON FLOWERS. London, 1886. New ed. Orig gilt-dec cl (corner wear, 2 soiled spots). *SUTTON*. $35

Elkin, Daniel & Michael DeBakey (eds). SURGERY IN WORLD WAR II. VASCULAR SURGERY. Washington, 1955. 1st ed. Ex-lib. *FYE*. $50

Elkin, Stanley. BOSWELL. NY: Random House, 1964. Wraps. Adv reading copy. A bit worn, soiled w/stain to corner of 1st several prelims. *BEASLEY*. $150

Elkington, E. Way. THE SAVAGE SOUTH SEAS. A&C Black, 1907. 1st ed. 20s Series. In scarce blue cl. Ffep excised, some spine fading, minor foxing, else VG. *OLD LONDON*. $100

Elkins, Aaron & Charlotte. A WICKED SLICE. NY: St. Martin's, (1989). 1st ed. Signed by both authors. *UNGER*. $40

Elkins, Aaron. A DECEPTIVE CLARITY. NY: Walker, 1987. 1st ed. VF in dj. *MORDIDA*. $45

Elkins, Aaron. A DECEPTIVE CLARITY. NY; Walker, (1987). 1st ed. Signed. Fine in Fine dj. *UNGER*. $50

Elkins, Aaron. A GLANCING LIGHT. NY: Scribner's, (1991). 1st ed. Signed. VF in VF dj. *UNGER*. $35

Elkins, Aaron. FELLOWSHIP OF FEAR. NY: Walker, 1982. 1st ed, 1st bk. VF in dj. *ELSE FINE*. $125

Elkins, Aaron. FELLOWSHIP OF FEAR. NY: Walker, 1982. 2nd ed. Fine in dj. *MORDIDA*. $45

Elkins, Aaron. ICY CLUTCHES. NY: Mysterious, (1990). 1st ed. Signed. VF in VF dj. *UNGER*. $35

Elkins, Aaron. OLD BONES. NY: Mysterious Press, 1987. 1st ed. VF in dj. *MORDIDA*. $40

Elkins, Capt. John M. INDIAN FIGHTING ON THE TEXAS FRONTIER. Written for Capt. Elkins by Frank W. McCarty.

Amarillo: Privately ptd, 1929. 1st ed. Frontis. 3 photo plts. Textured pict wraps. Small chips, else Good. Rare. Howes E90. *CONNOLLY & WADE.* $150

Elkins, William M. EDDIE NEWTON'S RIDE, OR THE DIVERTING HISTORY OF A. EDWARD. (NY): Ptd for the friends of A. Edward Newton, Esq, (1934). 1st ed ltd to 300. Signed by Newton, w/an a.n.s. from him tipped in. Orig ptd wrappers. Wrappers a trifle faded, o/w VG. *WREDEN.* $35

Ellenbecker, John G. THE JAYHAWKERS OF DEATH VALLEY. Marysville: John G. Ellenbecker, 1938. Inscription. Fldg sheet of illus, incl 5pp supplement. Ptd wrappers. *DAWSON'S.* $200

Ellenbecker, John G. THE...JAYHAWKERS OF DEATH VALLEY. Marysville, KS: (Privately ptd), 1938. 2nd ed. Orig wraps bound in boards. Photocopy incl (of later-produced supplement, 5p). VG to Fine, fragile. Very scarce. *BOOK MARKET.* $150

Ellet, (Elizabeth F.). PIONEER WOMEN OF THE WEST. NY: Scribner, 1852. 1st ed. Tan cl stamped in blind, faded, stained on front. Expected foxing. Signature pulled, o/w VG. *SCHOYER'S.* $90

Ellet, Mrs. Elizabeth F. THE PIONEER WOMEN OF THE WEST. Phila: Porter & Coates, 1873. 434pp. Cloth, frontis. VG. *GIBBS.* $30

Ellin, Stanley. MYSTERY STORIES. NY: Simon and Schuster, 1956. 1st ed. Pp darkened o/w Fine in dj (short crease-tear front panel). *MORDIDA.* $65

Ellin, Stanley. THE PANAMA PORTRAIT. NY: Random House, 1962. 1st ed. Inscribed. Fine in dj with darkened spine. *MORDIDA.* $50

Ellington, Charles G. THE TRIAL OF U.S. GRANT: THE PACIFIC COAST YEARS, 1852-1854. Glendale: Arthur H. Clark, 1987. 1st collector's ed. Full leather. Fine. *BOOK MARKET.* $85

Ellington, Duke. MUSIC IS MY MISTRESS. GC: Doubleday, 1973. 1st ed. Fine in lightly used dj but for an internally mended tear, small scorch front panel. *BEASLEY.* $75

Elliot, D.G. THE LIFE AND HABITS OF WILD ANIMALS, ILLUSTRATED FROM DESIGNS BY JOSEPH WOLF. NY, 1874. 29 plts. Folio, 122pp, 1/2 leather and marbled boards. Worn; rubbed at edges; dampstaining to lower corner 1st 39 pp, not affecting pl images. *SUTTON.* $95

Elliot, D.G. THE WILD FOWL OF THE UNITED STATES AND BRITISH POSSESSIONS.... NY, 1898. 1st ed. Frontis, 63 plts. Cvrs dirty; pp yellowed, institutional bkpl, sticker on spine. *SUTTON.* $80

Elliot, Daniel Giraud. NORTH AMERICAN SHORE BIRDS. NY: Francis P. Harper, (1895), 1897. 2nd ed. VG. *BACKMAN.* $35

Elliot, W.J. THE SPURS. Spur, Texas: The Texas Spur, 1939. 1st ed, inscribed, signed. 274pp. Tight, Fine, spine faded. Very scarce. *GIBBS.* $175

Elliott, Bob and Ray Goulding. WRITE IF YOU GET WORK. NY: Random House, (1975). 1st ed. Just about Fine in like dj. *CAPTAIN'S BOOKSHELF.* $35

Elliott, F.R. ELLIOTT'S FRUIT BOOK....NY: Saxton, 1855. 2nd ed. 503pp,ads. Nice, tight in spine faded cl. *SECOND LIFE.* $125

Elliott, George P. PARKTILDEN VILLAGE. Boston: Beacon Press, 1958. 1st ed, 1st bk. Fine in close to Fine dj. *BEASLEY.* $50

Elliott, James W. TRANSPORT TO DISASTER. NY, (1962). 1st ed. Light dj wear o/w Fine. *PRATT.* $25

Elliott, Richard Smith. NOTES TAKEN IN SIXTY YEARS. St. Louis, 1883. 1st ed. (8),336pp. Orig cl. Howes E111. *GINSBERG.* $175

Ellis, Bret Easton. LESS THAN ZERO. Simon and Schuster, 1985. Uncorrected proof. VF in gold wraps. *STAHR.* $100

Ellis, G.V. and G.H. Ford. ILLUSTRATIONS OF DISSECTIONS IN A SERIES OF ORIGINAL COLORED PLATES. NY: William Wood, 1882. 2nd ed, 1st ptg, marked Jan. 1882. 2 Vols. 233; 226pp. Blind-stamped black cl cvrs, worn. Internally VG. *SMITHFIELD.* $110

Ellis, George and G.H. Ford. ILLUSTRATIONS OF DISSECTIONS IN A SERIES OF ORIGINAL COLORED PLATES. NY, 1882. 2nd ed. 2 vols. 58 Fine color lithographic plts. *FYE.* $100

Ellis, Havelock. ESSAYS IN WAR-TIME....Boston & NY: Houghton Mifflin, 1917. 1st ed. Good. *SECOND LIFE.* $35

Ellis, Havelock. MORE ESSAYS OF LOVE AND VIRTUE. London: Constable, 1931. 1st ed. Fine. *WREDEN.* $35

Ellis, Havelock. THE DANCE OF LIFE. Boston & NY: Houghton Mifflin, (1923). 6th ed. VG, tight. *SECOND LIFE.* $25

Ellis, J. THE NATURAL HISTORY OF MANY CURIOUS AND UNCOMMON ZOOPHYTES...London, 1786. 63 engr plts. xii, 208 pp. Full calf w/marbled eps and page edges (backstrip mostly missing, front cover detached, unobtrusive emb stamps on plts). Ex-lib. *SUTTON.* $325

Ellis, John. PERSONAL EXPERIENCE OF A PHYSICIAN, WITH AN APPEAL TO THE MEDICAL AND CLERICAL PROFESSIONS. Phila, 1892. 1st ed. Wrappers. *FYE.* $35

Ellis, Thomas T. LEAVES FROM THE DIARY OF AN ARMY SURGEON; OR INCIDENTS OF FIELD CAMP AND HOSPITAL LIFE. NY, 1863. 1st ed. Spine tail repaired, else NF. *McGOWAN.* $225

Ellis, W. THREE VISITS TO MADAGASCAR DURING THE YEARS 1853-1854-1856...WITH NOTICES OF THE NATURAL HISTORY....NY, 1859. 1st Amer ed. Map, double-pg frontis. 514pp (2pp ads). Orig gilt-dec cl. Skillfully rebacked; board edges worn; lt spot front cvr; even lt browning of text; lib stamp; pastedowns renewed. *SUTTON.* $225

Ellis, William. NARRATIVE OF A TOUR THROUGH HAWAII, OR OWYHYEE...HISTORY...OF INHABITANTS OF THE SANDWICH ISLANDS. London: H. Fisher, 1826. 1st ed. 7 plts, 1 fldg map. Orig full morocco. VG. *OREGON.* $325

Ellison, Douglas W. SOLE SURVIVOR: AN EXAMINATION OF THE FRANK FINKEL NARRATIVE. SD: (Privately ptd). 1st ed, ltd to 1,000. Fine. *BOOK MARKET.* $20

Ellison, Emily. FIRST LIGHT. NY: Morrow, (1985). 1st Amer ed. Inscribed. Fine in dj. *DORN.* $40

Ellison, Emily. THE PICTURE MAKERS. NY: Morrow, (1990). 1st Amer ed. Signed. Fine in dj. *DORN.* $35

Ellison, Emily. THE PICTURE MAKERS. NY: Morrow (1991). Uncorrected proof. Fine in wraps. *DORN.* $30

Ellison, Glenn R. "Slim." COWBOYS UNDER THE MOGOLLON RIM. Tucson, 1970, 2nd ptg. NF in VG dj. *FIVE QUAIL.* $45

Ellison, Harlan (ed). DANGEROUS VISIONS: 33 ORIGINAL STORIES. GC: Doubleday, 1967. 1st ed. Typical discoloration (minor) to front and rear endsheets, else Fine in dj (showing lt edgewear spinal extrems). *CAPTAIN'S BOOKSHELF.* $250

Ellison, Harlan. ALONE AGAINST TOMORROW. NY, (1971). 1st ed. Signed. Fine in dj. *McCLINTOCK.* $35

Ellison, Harlan. APPROACHING OBLIVION. Walker, 1971. 1st ed. Fine in dj. Signed. *MADLE.* $50

Ellison, Harlan. LOVE AIN'T NOTHING BUT SEX MISSPELLED. NY: Trident, 1968. 1st ed. Fine but for word "Gift" in corner of one ep, in lightly used dj w/short tears, a few rubs. *BEASLEY.* $150

Ellison, Harlan. STRANGE WINE. Harper, 1978. 1st ed. Fine in dj. *MADLE.* $70

Ellison, Harlan. STRANGE WINE. NY: Harper & Row, (1978). Fine in dj. 1st ed. Signed. *CHAPEL HILL.* $45

Ellison, Harlan. STRANGE WINE. NY: Harper & Row, 1978. 1st ed. VF, minute closed tear to dj. *ELSE FINE.* $60

Ellison, James Whitfield. SUMMER AFTER THE WAR. NY: Dodd Mead, (1972). 1st ed. 216pp. Fine in NF dj, w/price blocked out. *AKA*. $45

Ellison, Ralph. INVISIBLE MAN. NY: Random House, (1952). 1st ed. Inscribed. VG, lacking dj. *LOPEZ*. $650

Ellison, Ralph. SHADOW & ACT. (London: Secker & Warburg, 1967). 1st Eng ed. Inscribed. Fine in Fine dj. *LOPEZ*. $200

Ellison, Ralph. SHADOW & ACT. (NY): NAL, (1966). 1st pb ed. Paper yellowing, o/w VG. Signed. *LOPEZ*. $55

Ellison, Ralph. SHADOW & ACT. Random House, 1964. Ex-lib. 1st ed, VG in dj. Ffep excised, jacket protector residue on pastedowns. Dj missing a large chip foot of spine, few other, smaller chips; also lightly browned and soiled. *STAHR*. $45

Ellison, Robert. FORT BRIDGER WYOMING, A BRIEF HISTORY. COMPRISING...Caspar, WY: Hist. Landmark Comm, 1931. 1st ed. Fldg map. VG. *OREGON*. $50

Ellison, Robert. INDEPENDENCE ROCK...Casper, WY: Natrona County Hist, 1930. 2nd prtg. Fldg map. VG. *OREGON*. $25

Ellison, William. THE LIFE AND ADVENTURES OF GEORGE NIDEVER (1802-1883). Univ of CA, 1937. 1st ed. Frontis, 2 plts. Fine in Fine dj. *OREGON*. $75

Ellmann, Richard. JAMES JOYCE'S TOWER. (Moran Park Dun Laoghaire: Eastern Regional Tourism Organisation, 1969). 1st ed. Spiral bound in ptd grn wrappers. NF. Signed, inscribed. *CAPTAIN'S BOOKSHELF*. $75

Ellmann, Richard. YEATS: THE MAN AND THE MASKS. NY: MacMillan, 1948. 1st ed. Fine in lightly worn dj chipped at spine. Rev copy w/letter, photos laid in. *CAPTAIN'S BOOKSHELF*. $40

Ellroy, James. BLOOD ON THE MOON. Mysterious Press, 1984. 1st ed. Fine in dj. *STAHR*. $25

Ellroy, James. BLOOD ON THE MOON. NY: Mysterious Press, 1984. 1st ed. Signed. VF in dj. *MORDIDA*. $40

Ellroy, James. BROWN'S REQUIEM. London: Allison & Busby, 1984. 1st hb ed. VF in dj. *MORDIDA*. $85

Ellroy, James. BROWN'S REQUIEM. NY: Avon, 1981. 1st ed., 1st novel. Paperback orig. Fine in wrappers. *MORDIDA*. $35

Ellroy, James. L.A. CONFIDENTIAL. NY: Mysterious, (1990). 1st ed. One of 100 numbered, signed. Fine in pub's slipcase. *UNGER*. $125

Ellroy, James. SILENT TERROR. LA: Blood & Guts Press, 1987. 1st hb ed. One of 350 numbered, signed. VF in dj with slipcase. *MORDIDA*. $100

Ellroy, James. SUICIDE HILL. NY: Mysterious Press, 1986. 1st ed. Signed. VF in dj. *SILVER DOOR*. $50

Ellroy, James. THE BIG NOWHERE. Hastings-On-Hudson: Ultramarine Pub, 1988. 1st ed. One of 350 numbered specially bound, signed. As New in slipcase w/o dj as issued. *MORDIDA*. $100

Ellroy, James. THE BIG NOWHERE. NY: Mysterious Press, 1988. 1st ed. Signed. VF in dj. *SILVER DOOR*. $35

Ellroy, James. THE BLACK DAHLIA. NY: Mysterious Press, 1987. 1st ed. Inscribed. VF in dj. *MORDIDA*. $45

Ellsberg, Edward. HELL ON ICE. THE SAGA OF THE "JEANETTE." NY, 1938. 1st ed. VG. *ARTIS*. $8.50

Ellsworth, Henry L. WASHINGTON IRVING ON THE PRAIRIE, OR A NARRATIVE...IN THE YEAR 1832. Stanley Williams & Barbara Simison (eds). NY: American Book Company, 1937. 1st ed. VF in VG dj. *OREGON*. $40

Ellsworth, Henry William. VALLEY OF THE UPPER WABASH, INDIANA, WITH HINTS ON ITS AGRICULTURAL ADVANTAGES NY: Pratt, Robinson & Co, 1838. xii, 175pp. Fldg frontis map (Mitchell's), 3 fldg plts. Orig cl. Backstrip chipped away,

should be rebacked. Map clean & crisp w/slight breaks on main fold. Howes E128. *BOHLING*. $350

Ellsworth, Rodney Sydes. THE GIANT SEQUOIA. Oakland: J.D. Berger, 1924. 1st ed. Signed. 12 photo plts. VG. *CONNOLLY & WADE*. $50

Elmer, Dr. Robert P. ARCHERY. Phila: The Penn Publishing Co., 1926. 1st ed. Minor wear to extremities, else NF. *OLD LONDON*. $50

Elmer, Lucius Q.C. HISTORY OF THE EARLY SETTLEMENT AND PROGRESS OF CUMBERLAND COUNTY, NJ AND THE CURRENCY OF THIS AND ADJOINING COUNTIES. Bridgeton, NJ, 1869, 1st ed. 142pp. Rebound. Contents Fine. *HEINOLDT*. $25

Elmhurst, Captain Pennell. FOXHOUND, FOREST, AND PRAIRIE. Glasgow, Manchester, NY: Routledge, 1892. 1st ed. Some spine soiling, wear to extremities, else VG+. *OLD LONDON*. $50

Elsberg, Charles. DIAGNOSIS AND TREATMENT OF SURGICAL DISEASES OF THE SPINAL CORD AND ITS MEMBRANES. Phila, 1916. 1st ed. Ink underlining on a few pp, o/w VG. *FYE*. $350

Elsberg, Charles. TUMORS OF THE SPINAL CORD AND THE SYMPTOMS OF IRRITATION AND COMPRESSION OF THE SPINAL CORD AND NERVE ROOTS. NY, 1925. 1st ed. Water damage to margins w/many leaves stuck together. *FYE*. $50

Elstob, Peter. THE FLIGHT OF THE SMALL WORLD. Norton, 1959. 1st ed. Fine in VG dj. *MAD DOG*. $15.

Elston, Allan Vaughn and Maurice Beam. MURDER BY MANDATE. Diamond Library, 1945. 1st ed. VG in wraps. *MADLE*. $50

Elston, Roy. THE TRAVELLER'S HANDBOOK FOR EGYPT AND THE SUDAN. London, 1929. Maps and plans. cxxxi,584pp, plus ads. Fldg map in back pocket. *O'NEILL*. $40

Elston, Roy. TRAVELLER'S HANDBOOK FOR NAPLES AND ENVIRONS. London: Simpkin Marshall, Thomas Cook & Son, 1928. Frontis map, 2 fldg maps. *SCHOYER'S*. $30

Elton, Charles I. THE GREAT BOOK-COLLECTORS. London: Kegan Paul, Trench, Trubner & Co., 1893. 1st ed. *OAK KNOLL*. $30

Elworthy, Frederick T. THE EVIL EYE: AN ACCOUNT....London: (John Murray), 1895. 1st ed. Pub's burgundy cl w/gilt dec and titling. 1/4" tear end of spine; some browning to eps. Fresh, sound, attractive. *BOOK BLOCK*. $150

Ely, David. SECONDS. Pantheon, 1963. 1st ed. VG in frayed dj. *MADLE*. $25

Ely, Edward. THE WANDERINGS OF EDWARD ELY. Ed by Anthony & Allison Sirna. NY, (1954). 1st ed. NF in dj. *DIAMOND*. $20

Elytis, Odysseus. SIX AND ONE REMORSES FOR THE SKY. Helsinki, Finland: Eurographica, 1985. 1st of this ed. Ltd to 350 signed. Mint. Wraps. *JAFFE*. $150

Emanuel, Walter. A CONCEITED PUPPY. NY: Dutton, (1905). 1st Amer ed. Ptd in Bavaria. 138 x 108mm. 24 plts by Aldin. Quarter red cl, pict brds. Pp sl browned, o/w VG. Rare. *WEBER*. $200.

Emberley, Barbara. DRUMMER HOFF. Prentice-Hall, 1967. 1st ed. Unpaginated. Ed Emberley (illus). Advance review copy. Fine in Fine dj. *BEBBAH*. $85

Emberley, Ed. GREEN SAYS GO. Little, Brown, (1968). Later ptg. 32pp. Illus & signed. Fine in VG+ dj. *BEBBAH*. $35

Emberley, Michael. MORE DINOSAURS AND OTHER PREHISTORIC BEASTS. Little, Brown, (1983). 1st ed. Illus by author. VG. Signed by Ed Emberley, Michael's father & 1968 Caldecott Medal winner, w/fat smiling dinosaur. *BEBBAH*. $26

Embree, Edwin R. INDIANS OF THE AMERICAS. Boston: Houghton Mifflin, 1939. 1st ed. VG. *LAURIE*. $15

Embry, Carlos B. AMERICA'S CONCENTRATION CAMPS: THE FACTS ABOUT OUR INDIAN RESERVATIONS TODAY. NY: David McKay Co, Inc, 1956. Cl. VG. *BURCHAM.* $30

Emerson, E.W. THE EARLY YEARS OF THE SATURDAY CLUB, 1855-1870. Houghton Mifflin, 1918. VG. *BOOKCELL.* $35

Emerson, Earl W. FAT TUESDAY. NY: William Morrow, 1987. 1st ed. Signed. VF in dj. *MORDIDA.* $30

Emerson, Earl W. THE RAINY CITY. Avon, 1985. 1st ed. Fine to VF in wraps. *STAHR.* $25

Emerson, Earl W. THE RAINY CITY. NY: Avon, 1985. 1st ed. Pb orig. VF, unread, in wrappers. *MORDIDA.* $25

Emerson, James. Count Pecchio & W.H. Humphreys. A PICTURE OF GREECE IN 1825; AS EXHIBITED IN THE PERSONAL NARRATIVES OF...NY, 1826. 2 vols. Cont. calf. 247 and 228pp. Light browning. Contemp lib bkplts front pastedowns. *O'NEILL.* $185

Emerson, James. LETTERS FROM THE AEGEAN. NY, 1829. Cl spine, paper label, rubbed. 248pp, wholly uncut. Signatures of two prev owners. Label. *O'NEILL.* $150

Emerson, Nathaniel B. UNWRITTEN LITERATURE OF HAWAII. Washington: GPO, 1909. 1st ed. 24 plts. *KARMIOLE.* $65

Emerson, Ralph Waldo. ESSAYS (AND) ESSAYS: SECOND SERIES. Boston: James Munroe and Company, 1841-44. 1st ed. 12mo. Bound in full tan morocco with gilt spines, by Riviere. Some staining at inner hinges, but a handsome set in matching bindings. BAL 5189 & 5198. *M & S.* $950

Emerson, Ralph Waldo. LETTERS AND SOCIAL AIMS. Boston: James R. Osgood and Company, 1876. 1st ed, 1st prtg. Orig grayish brown cl, the lightest wear to extremities; small ink name at head of title page, still NF. *JUVELIS.* $100

Emerson, Ralph Waldo. MAY-DAY AND OTHER PIECES. London: George Routledge and Sons, 1867. 1st Eng ed. 16mo. 192pp. Orig printed boards, rubbed; spine very rubbed. Back cover detached. *M & S.* $125

Emerson, Ralph Waldo. THE CONDUCT OF LIFE. Boston, 1860. 288pp. Fep removed. *HEINOLDT.* $20

Emerson, Ralph Waldo. THE ESSAYS OF RALPH WALDO EMERSON. The First and Second Series. SF: LEC, 1934. One of 1500 ptd, signed by John Henry Nash. Fine in sl used slipcase w/faded spine. *CAPTAIN'S BOOKSHELF.* $125

Emerson, W. A SYSTEM OF ASTRONOMY, CONTAINING THE INVESTIGATION AND DEMONSTRATION OF THE ELEMENTS OF THAT SCIENCE. London: J. Nourse, 1769. VG, rebound in modern leather w/marbled eps. *KNOLLWOOD.* $350

Emery, Emma Wilson. AUNT PUSS & OTHERS: OLD DAYS IN THE PINEY WOODS. Austin: Encino Press, 1969. Fine in dj. *LAURIE.* $15

Emery, Walter B. GREAT TOMBS OF THE FIRST DYNASTY II. London: Egypt Exploration Society, 1954. 66 plts. Signature. Good. *ARCHAEOLOGIA.* $150

Emilio, Luis F. BRAVE BLACK REGIMENT, HISTORY OF THE FIFTY-FOURTH REGIMENT OF MASSACHUSETTS INFANTRY. Boston, 1894. 2nd ed., rev and enlarged. 452pp, illus. Fldg map, roster. Cvr worn, o/w VG. Small fading library markings. Frontis of Col. Shaw missing. *PRATT.* $115

Emmel, T.C. BUTTERFLIES. NY, 1975. 1st ed. Inscrip on ep. Dj. *SUTTON.* $48

Emmerson, Joan (ed). CATALOGUE OF THE PYBUS COLLECTION OF MEDICAL BOOKS, LETTERS AND ENGRAVINGS. Manchester, 1981. 1st ed. *FYE.* $75

Emmitt, Robert. THE LAST WAR TRAIL, THE UTES AND THE SETTLEMENT OF COLORADO. Norman, (1954). 1st ed. 333pp. VG in dj. *PRATT.* $30

Emmons, Ebenezer. AGRICULTURE OF NEW YORK. Albany: Van Benthuysen, 1849. Vol II. 343pp+appendix w/colored plts. Blind stamp on edge of each plate. *AMERICAN BOTANIST.* $150

Emmons, Ebenezer. AGRICULTURE OF NEW-YORK....NY, 1846-49-51-54. 5 vols complete. 177 plts (9 tinted, 4 colored and fldg, 133 hand-colored), 3 fldg sections, 2 fldg maps. 1376pp. Orig gilt dec cl (worn at corners, spine ends chipped away). 2 vols w/minor edge splitting of backstrips. Occasional foxing; emb stamps on plts; few plts contain tannish wash background. Ex-lib. *SUTTON.* $575

Emmons, Ebenezer. INSECTS OF NEW YORK. Albany, 1854. 47 hand-colored, 2 plain plts. Pp. viii,272. Orig cl (worn at edges & corners, rebacked, retaining orig backstrip). Emb lib stamps on title, heavy foxing in places. *SUTTON.* $200

Emmons, George F. THE NAVY OF THE UNITED STATES, FROM THE COMMENCEMENT, 1775 TO 1853; WITH A HISTORY....Washington: Gideon & Co., 1853. (8),208pp. Later issue, w/errata slip and terminal (cancel) list of vessels 1850-60. *LEFKOWICZ.* $325

Emmons, Martha. DEEP LIKE RIVERS: STORIES OF MY NEGRO FRIENDS. Austin: Encino Press, 1969. Fine in dj. *LAURIE.* $20

Emory, W.H. LIEUTENANT EMORY REPORTS: A Reprint of Lt. W.H. Emory's NOTES OF A MILITARY RECONNOISSANCE (sic). Intro & notes by Ross Calvin. Albuquerque, 1950 (orig ed 1848). NF in VG dj. *FIVE QUAIL.* $35

Emory, W.H. NOTES OF A MILITARY RECONNAISSANCE FROM FORT LEAVENWORTH...TO SAN DIEGO...MADE IN 1846-7 WITH THE ADVANCE GUARD OF THE "ARMY OF THE WEST." Washington, 1848. Senate Exec. Doc. 7, 30th Congress/1st Session. 416pp. This copy does not include the map, and there was no pocket inside original back cover for such a map. The copy offered here includes 38 plts, and 3 maps or plans. Some foxing throughout and a moderate number of dampstains. Attractively rebound in 3/4 lea with marbled boards and eps. *FIVE QUAIL.* $145

Endicott, William. WRECKED AMONG CANNIBALS IN THE FIJIS....Salem, 1923. Pub. 3. Fine. Worn dj. Prospectus laid in. *LEFKOWICZ.* $120

Endicott, William. WRECKED AMONG CANNIBALS IN THE FIJIS. Salem, Marine Research Society, 1923. 1st ed. Some soiling to boards and eps, overall VG. *PARMER.* $95

Endore, Guy. SLEEPY LAGOON MYSTERY. LA: Sleepy Lagoon Defense Committee, 1944. 1st ed. Wraps. NF w/light chipping, browning. *BEASLEY.* $45

ENDYMION, By the Author of "Lothair". (By Benjamin Disraeli.) London: Longman, 1880. 1st ed. In three vols, 8vo. Victorian binding in 3/4 red polished calf and marbled boards, all edges sprinkled. Nice. Shelf marks and bkpls of Sir Julian Goldschmid. 3 vols. *HARTFIELD.* $245.

Enfield, D.E. L.E.L.: A MYSTERY OF THE THIRTIES. London: Hogarth Press, 1928. 1st ed. Pink silk cl stamped in gilt, somewhat soiled, spine yellowed. *SCHOYER'S.* $50

Enfield, J.E. THE MAN FROM PACKSADDLE. Hollywood: House-Warven, 1951. 1st ed. Fine in Good+ spine faded dj. *OREGON.* $50

Engel, Claire Elaine. A HISTORY OF MOUNTAINEERING IN THE ALPS. London: George Allen & Unwin, Ltd. (1950). 1st ed. *KARMIOLE.* $30

Engel, George. FAINTING: PHYSIOLOGICAL AND PSYCHOLOGICAL CONSIDERATIONS. Springfield, 1950. 1st ed. Dj. *FYE.* $60

Engelhardt, Zephyrin. SAN FERNANDO REY, THE MISSION OF THE VALLEY. Chicago: Franciscan Herald, 1927. 1st ed. Fine. *OREGON.* $45

Engelhardt, Zephyrin. THE FRANCISCANS IN ARIZONA. Harbor Springs, MI: Holy Childhood Indian School, 1899. 236pp, 10pp ads. With scarce map. Postcard pasted on fly. VG. *CULLEN*. $125

Engelhardt, Zephyrin. THE FRANCISCANS IN CALIFORNIA. Harbor Springs, MI, 1897. 1st ed. 516pp. Orig cl. Howes E153. *GINSBERG*. $175

England, George Allan. KEEP OFF THE GRASS. Boston: Small, Maynard, 1919. 1st ed. Fine in NF dj (few short tears). *BEASLEY*. $125

England, George Allan. KEEP OFF THE GRASS. Small-Maynard, 1919. 1st ed. Shelf-wear. VG. *MADLE*. $30

England, George Allan. THE FLYING LEGION. McClurg, 1920. 1st ed. Hinges cracked. Good+. *MADLE*. $45

England, George Allan. THE GOLDEN BLIGHT. Fly, 1916. 1st ed. Near VG. *MADLE*. $125

England, George Allan. THE GOLDEN BLIGHT. NY: H.K. Fly, 1916. 1st ed. A little soiling, but VG+. *BEASLEY*. $150

ENGLISHWOMAN IN RUSSIA: IMPRESSIONS OF THE SOCIETY AND MANNERS OF THE RUSSIANS AT HOME. BY A LADY....NY: Scribner, 1855. Lavender cl stamped in gilt and blind, faded on spine, badly chipped at head. *SCHOYER'S*. $35

Ennemoser, Joseph. THE HISTORY OF MAGIC. William Howitt (trans). London: Henry G. Bohn. 1854. 1st Eng ed. 2 vols. viii,xvi,472; viii,518,(2)pp, 62pp ads. Spine extrems bit frayed, edges chipped, top edges of cvrs gnawed. *KARMIOLE*. $100

Enschede, Charles. TYPEFOUNDRIES IN THE NETHERLANDS FROM THE FIFTEENTH TO THE NINETEENTH CENTURY. Haarlem: Stichtling Museum Enschede, 1878. 1st Eng ed. Ltd ed of 1500. Type specimen collotype facs loosely inserted. 1/4 calf, dec boards. Slipcase. Fine. *WEBER*. $550

Ensko, Stephen. AMERICAN SILVERSMITHS AND THEIR MARKS III. S. Ensko, 1948. 1st ed. VG. Slipcase. *BACKROOM*. $150

Ensko, Stephen. AMERICAN SILVERSMITHS AND THEIR MARKS II. S. Ensko, 1937. 1st ed. VG+. *BACKROOM*. $40

Ensko, Stephen. AMERICAN SILVERSMITHS AND THEIR MARKS. NY, 1927. 1st ed. #261 of 310. Spotting. VG. *BACKROOM*. $260

Ephron, Nora. WALLFLOWER AT THE ORGY. NY: Viking, (1970). 1st ed, 1st bk. Fine in dj. *SCHOYER'S*. $25

Epictetus. THE DISCOURSES OF EPICTETUS. Trans P.E. Matheson, illus Hans Erni. Berne: LEC, 1966. Ed ltd to 1500 signed by Hans Erni. Slipcase bit soiled. *KARMIOLE*. $125

Epstein, Brian. A CELLARFUL OF NOISE. GC: Doubleday, 1964. Stated 1st ed. Owner name, edgewear. Worn dj (sm edge pieces missing at the corners, spine ends). *AKA*. $40

Epstein, Brian. A CELLARFUL OF NOISE. London, 1964. 1st UK ed. Price-clipped dj, photos. VG+. *PETTLER*. $60

Erb, Wilhelm. DISEASES OF THE PERIPHERAL CEREBRO-SPINAL NERVES. NY, 1876. 1st Eng trans. *FYE*. $150

Erb, Wilhelm. HANDBOOK OF ELECTROTHERAPEUTICS. NY, 1883. 1st Eng trans. *FYE*. $125

Erdrich, Louise. BAPTISM OF DESIRE. NY: H & R, (1989). 1st ed. Fine in dj. *LOPEZ*. $35

Erdrich, Louise. LOVE MEDICINE. Holt, 1984. 1st ed. Fine in dj. *STAHR*. $135

Erdrich, Louise. LOVE MEDICINE. NY: Holt Rinehart Winston, (1984). 1st ed. Fine in dj. *LOPEZ*. $150

Erdrich, Louise. LOVE MEDICINE. NY: HRW, (1984). Uncorrected proof. Lt crease on front cvr, o/w Fine in wraps. *LOPEZ*. $375

Erdrich, Louise. THE BEET QUEEN. NY, 1986. 1st ed. Signed w/drawing of a beet. Fine in like dj. *POLYANTHOS*. $45

Erdrich, Louise. THE BEET QUEEN. NY: Henry Holt, 1986. 1st ed. NF. *SMITH*. $30

Erdrich, Louise. THE BEET QUEEN. NY: Holt (1986). Adv uncorrected reading copy. VG+ in wraps. *DORN*. $30

Erdrich, Louise. THE BEET QUEEN. NY: Holt, (1986). Adv rev copy of 2nd novel. Fine in Fine dj, pub's promo sheet laid in. *LOPEZ*. $45

Erdrich, Louise. TRACKS. (London: Hamish Hamilton, 1988). 1st Eng ed. Fine in dj. *LOPEZ*. $45

Erdrich, Louise. TRACKS. Henry Holt, 1988. 1st ed. VF in dj. Signed. *STAHR*. $45

Erdrich, Louise. TRACKS. NY: Holt, (1988). 1st trade ed. Fine in dj w/nick. *LOPEZ*. $25

Erdrich, Louise. TRACKS. NY: Holt (1988). Uncorrected proof. Signed. Fine in wraps. *DORN*. $60

Erichsen, John. OBSERVATIONS ON ANEURISM SELECTED FROM THE WORKS OF THE PRINCIPAL WRITERS ON THAT DISEASE FROM THE EARLIEST PERIODS TO THE CLOSE OF THE LAST CENTURY. London, 1844. 1st ed. 524pp. *FYE*. $200

Erickson, Steve. DAYS BETWEEN STATIONS. NY: Poseidon, (1985). 1st ed. Rmdr mk. Fine in dj. *LOPEZ*. $45

Erickson, Steve. LEAP YEAR. Poseidon Press, 1989. Uncorrected proof. Fine in powder blue wraps. *STAHR*. $35

Erickson, Steve. RUBICON BEACH. NY: Poseidon, (1986). 1st ed. Fine in dj. *LOPEZ*. $45

Erickson, Steve. TOURS OF THE BLACK CLOCK. Poseidon Press, 1989. Advance reading copy. Fine to VF in wraps. *STAHR*. $35

Eriksson, Ruben. ANDREAS VESALIUS' FIRST PUBLIC ANATOMY AT BOLOGNA 1540, AN EYEWITNESS REPORT BY BALDASAR HESELER, MEDICINAE SCOLARIS TOGETHER WITH HIS NOTES ON MATTHEAUS CURTIUS' LECTURES ON ANATOMIA MUNDINI. Stockholm, 1959. 1st ed. 344pp. *FYE*. $300

Erskine, Charles. TWENTY YEARS BEFORE THE MAST...UNDER THE COMMAND OF THE LATE ADMIRAL CHARLES WILKES 1838-1842. Boston: By the Author, 1890. 1st ed. 11 plts. Orig dec cl, spine ends rubbed, lib ink stamps. Quite scarce thus. *LEFKOWICZ*. $150

Erskine, Gladys Smith. BRONCO CHARLIE: A SAGA OF THE SADDLE. NY: Crowell, 1934. Frontis, fldg map. VG. *CONNOLLY & WADE*. $50

Erskine, John. AN INSTITUTE OF THE LAW OF SCOTLAND. In Four Books. 2 vols. Ptd for John Bell, at Addison's Head, Edinburgh, 1773. (1:) Title pg; leaf; (v)-(x), (1)-410pp; (2:) Title pg; (411)-758pp; 15 leaves. Folio. 1st ed. Good, sound set; some lightish foxing and dustiness. Number of marginal tears and defects, never affecting the text, bound in modern, 1/4 crimson morocco over dec boards. *BOSWELL*. $750

Erskine, John. NEW YORK. Chicago: Ziff-Davis, (1945). 1st ed. Acid spotting along outer edge of front cvr cl. Good. *ARTIS*. $75

Erwin, Allen A. THE SOUTHWEST OF JOHN H. SLAUGHTER, 1841-1922, PIONEER CATTLEMAN....Glendale: Arthur H. Clark Co, 1965. 1st ed. Fine in dj. *GIBBS*. $125

Erwin, Carol with Floyd Miller. THE ORDERLY DISORDERLY HOUSE. GC, 1960. 1st Eng ed (1961). 284pp. Dj wear and chipping o/w VG. *PRATT*. $20

Erwitt, Elliot. ELLIOT ERWITT. THE PRIVATE EXPERIENCE. LA: Alskog, 1974. 1st ed. VG. *SMITH*. $25

Eschricht, Reinhardt and Lilljebotg. RECENT MEMOIRS ON THE CETACEA. W. H. Flower (ed). London: Ray Society, 1866. 1st ed.

Ltd to 600 to 750 for subscribers. 6 full-pg lithos. New black cl, sm lib stamp 3pp. Fine. *PARMER.* $500

Esdaile, Arundell. THE BRITISH MUSEUM LIBRARY, A SHORT HISTORY AND SURVEY. London: George Allen & Unwin Ltd., (1946). 1st ed. Spine rubbed along hinges and at extremities. *OAK KNOLL.* $30

Esdaile, James. MESMERISM IN INDIA, AND ITS PRACTICAL APPLICATION IN SURGERY AND MEDICINE. Hartford, 1847. 1st Amer ed. 259pp. Kenneth Keele's copy w/his bkpl. *FYE.* $300

Eshleman, Clayton. THE NAME ENCANYONED RIVER: SELECTED POEMS 1960-1985. Santa Rosa: Black Sparrow (1986). 1st ed. One of 300 numbered, signed. Fine in acetate. *DORN.* $35

Esposito, Vincent J. (ed). THE WEST POINT ATLAS OF AMERICAN WARS—Vol I, 1689—1900; Vol II, 1900—1953. NY, (1959). 5th ptg, 1972. 412 maps. Pict cl. VG+. *PRATT.* $100

Esquemeling, John. THE BUCCANEERS OF AMERICA...NY: E.P. Dutton, n.d. (c. 1930's). Reprint of 2nd impression. VG in worn dj. *PARMER.* $45

Esquirol, Jean Etienne. MENTAL MALADIES. A TREATISE ON INSANITY. TRANSLATED FROM THE FRENCH. WITH ADDITIONS, BY E. K. HUNT, M.D. Phila, 1845. 1st Eng trans. 496pp. Front board detached, rear hinge cracked and board held by cords. Inscription and name stamp on front paste down, scattered foxing, but internally Fine. Rare. *FYE.* $1000

ESSAYS ON THE SUPERSTITIONS OF THE HIGHLANDERS OF SCOTLAND....(By Mrs. Anne Grant of Laggan.) London: Longman, et al. 1811. 1st ed. 2 vols. 304; 365pp. Contemp 3/4 calf. VG set. *SECOND LIFE.* $250

Estergreen, M.M. KIT CARSON: A PORTRAIT IN COURAGE. Univ of OK Press, 1962. 1st ed. Signed. Fine in VG dj. *VARNER.* $40

Estey, Paul. THE WOODCHUCK HUNTER. S.A.T.P. Co, Onslow Co, c. 1936 Aug. 1936 ads. 2nd prtg. VG in Good+ dj. *BACKMAN.* $50

Estleman, Loren D. ACES & EIGHTS. GC: Doubleday, 1981. 1st ed. Fine in price-clipped dj. *MORDIDA.* $40

Estleman, Loren D. ANGEL EYES. Boston: Houghton Mifflin, 1981. 1st ed. Signed. Slight spine slant, else Fine, minor rubs at dj corners. *ELSE FINE.* $60

Estleman, Loren D. ANY MAN'S DEATH. NY: Mysterious Press, 1986. 1st ed. Review copy, signed. Pub's slip laid in. Fine in dj. *SILVER DOOR.* $37.50

Estleman, Loren D. BLOODY SEASON. NY: Bantam, 1988. 1st ed. Signed. VF in dj. *MORDIDA.* $35

Estleman, Loren D. DOWNRIVER. Boston: Houghton Mifflin, 1988. 1st ed. Signed. VF in dj. *MORDIDA.* $30

Estleman, Loren D. DOWNRIVER. Hastings-on-Hudson: Ultramarine, 1988. 1st ed. 1/50 specially bound, numbered, signed. VF w/o dj as issued. *MORDIDA.* $100

Estleman, Loren D. GUN MAN. GC: Doubleday, 1985. 1st ed. Inscribed. VF in dj. *MORDIDA.* $45

Estleman, Loren D. KILL ZONE. NY: Mysterious Press, 1984. 1st ed. Signed. VF in dj. *MORDIDA.* $30

Estleman, Loren D. MISTER ST. JOHN. GC: Doubleday 1983. 1st ed. Signed. VF in dj. *MORDIDA.* $50

Estleman, Loren D. MISTER ST. JOHN. GC: Doubleday, 1983. Signed. 1st ed. Fine. Minor wear to spine ends of dj. *ELSE FINE.* $50

Estleman, Loren D. STAMPING GROUND. GC: Doubleday, 1980. 1st ed. Signed. VF in dj. *MORDIDA.* $65

Estleman, Loren D. SUGARTOWN. Boston: Houghton Mifflin, 1984. 1st ed. Signed. VF in dj. *MORDIDA.* $30

Estleman, Loren D. THE GLASS HIGHWAY. Boston: Houghton Mifflin, 1983. 1st ed. Lower front cover corner bumped o/w Fine in dj w/minor wear, tiny tears. *MORDIDA.* $35

Estleman, Loren D. THE STRANGLERS. GC: Doubleday, 1984. 1st ed. VF in dj. *MORDIDA.* $40

Estleman, Loren D. THE WISTER TRACE. Ottawa, IL: Jameson Books, 1987. 1st ed. VF in dj. *MORDIDA.* $30

Estleman, Loren D. THE WOLFER. London: Robert Hale, 1983. 1st hb ed. Signed. VF in dj. *MORDIDA.* $65

Estleman, Loren D. THE WOLFER. NY: Pocket Books, 1981. Signed. 1st ed. Paperback orig. Fine in wraps. *ELSE FINE.* $30

Estleman, Loren D. THIS OLD BILL. GC: Doubleday, 1984. 1st ed. Signed. VF in dj. *MORDIDA.* $45

Estleman, Loren D. THIS OLD BILL. GC: Doubleday, 1984. 1st ed. Fine in dj. *MORDIDA.* $40

Estleman, Loren. SUGARTOWN. Boston: Houghton Mifflin, 1985. Advance reading copy. Fine in wraps. *BEASLEY.* $35

Estvan, B. WAR PICTURES FROM THE SOUTH. NY, 1963. 1st Amer ed. 352pp. Spine has a half-inch gouge, small portion of the title worn off o/w VG. *PRATT.* $75

Etchison, Dennis. RED DREAMS. Santa Cruz: Scream Press, (1984). 1st ed, trade issue. Bkpl else Almost Fine in Fine dj. *OTHER WORLDS.* $75

Etchison, Dennis. RED DREAMS. Santa Cruz: Scream Press, (1984). 1st ed. One of 250 signed, numbered. Fine in dj, slipcase. *OTHER WORLDS.* $150

Etchison, Dennis. THE DARK COUNTRY. Santa Cruz: Scream Press, (1982). 1st ed. One of 900 trade copies. Bkpl, margins of several pp damaged at fore-edge else VG+ in dj. *OTHER WORLDS.* $75

Etherton, P.T. ACROSS THE ROOF OF THE WORLD. NY: Stokes, n.d. (1911). 1st ed. Minor ex-lib marks, new eps, minor cover wear, but VG+. *OLD LONDON.* $85

Ets, Marie H. THE STORY OF A BABY. Viking, 1939. 1st ed. 4to. 63pp. Illus by author. VG w/edgewear in dj w/chips, tears, large piece missing rear panel. *BEBBAH.* $35

Ettinghausen, Maurice L. RARE BOOKS AND ROYAL COLLECTORS. NY: Simon and Schuster, 1966. 1st ed. Dj. *OAK KNOLL.* $55

Ettinghausen, Maurice L. RARE BOOKS AND ROYAL COLLECTORS. NY: Simon and Schuster, 1966. 1st ed. Presentation from author. Dj spotted. *OAK KNOLL.* $60

Etulain, Richard W. (ed). THE AMERICAN LITERARY WEST. Sunflower Univ Press, 1980. Inscribed, signed. New. *AUTHORS OF THE WEST.* $10

Etulain, Richard W. (ed). WESTERN FILMS: A BRIEF HISTORY. Sunflower Press, 1983. Inscribed, signed. New. *AUTHORS OF THE WEST.* $10

Eustis, Helen. THE FOOL KILLER. GC: Doubleday, 1954. 1st ed. Adv rev copy, slip laid in. VG in dj (nicks, wear). *MORDIDA.* $35

Evans, Barbara. CADUCEUS IN SAIGON. London: Hutchinson, (1968). NF in VG dj. *AKA.* $40

Evans, Billy. UMPIRING FROM THE INSIDE. Self-pub., 1947. 1st ed. Good+. *PLAPINGER.* $100

Evans, C.S. THE SLEEPING BEAUTY. London: Heinemann, 1920. 1st trade ed. Illus by Arthur Rackham. Tipped-in color frontis, 2 doublespread illus in 3 colors. Pict paper-covered board in pink, black and white have edgewear, soil; overall VG+. *BEBBAH.* $95

Evans, C.S. THE SLEEPING BEAUTY. Told by C.S. Evans. Illustrated by Arthur Rackham. London: William Heinemann. (1920). 4to. 110pp. 1 tipped-in color plt. The "Edition Deluxe" ltd to 625 numbered, signed by Rackham. Vellum-like spine over paper boards, gilt; paper boards somewhat darkened. *KARMIOLE.* $600

Evans, Charles. SPINAL ANESTHESIA (SUBARACHNOID RADICULAR CONDUCTION BLOCK) NY, 1929. 1st ed. Includes scarce fldg chart. *FYE.* $75

Evans, Clement A. CONFEDERATE MILITARY HISTORY. Confederate Pub Co, 1899. 12 vols. All vols sl wear. Vol 3 "Virginia" lacks one map, else VG set. *BOOK BROKER.* $275

Evans, David S. et al (eds). HERSCHEL AT THE CAPE, DIARIES AND CORRESPONDENCE...1834-1838. Austin: Univ of TX Press, 1969. Like New in dj. *KNOLLWOOD.* $30

Evans, Eli N. JUDAH B. BENJAMIN, THE JEWISH CONFEDERATE. NY, (1988). 1st ed. 467pp. Fine in dj. *PRATT.* $25

Evans, G.H. ELEPHANTS AND THEIR DISEASES, A TREATISE ON ELEPHANTS. With 36 text-figures. Rangoon, 1961. Cloth w/boards. Lt foxing. *SUTTON.* $75

Evans, George G. ILLUSTRATED HISTORY OF THE UNITED STATES MINT. Phila: George G. Evans, 1886. New rev ed. Spot on rear cvr, some marginal dampstaining, one plt affected. *PARMER.* $65

Evans, George W.B. MEXICAN GOLD TRAIL: THE JOURNAL....Glenn S. Dumke (ed). San Marino: Huntington Lib, 1945. 1st ed. About Fine in Good+ dj. *CONNOLLY & WADE.* $75

Evans, H.M. STING-FISH & SEAFARER. London: Faber, 1943. Illus. Dec cl. Fine in Good+ dj. *MIKESH.* $20

Evans, Humphrey. FALCONRY FOR YOU. London: John Gifford, 1973. 10th imp. NF in dj. *OLD LONDON.* $20

Evans, Humphrey. FALCONRY. NY: Arco, 1974. 1st ed. Dj. NF. *OLD LONDON.* $20

Evans, J.T. THE CHURCH PLATE OF GLOUCESTERSHIRE. Gloucestershire: Privately ptd, 1906. 1st ed. VG. *BACKROOM.* $25

Evans, Joan. A HISTORY OF JEWELLERY, 1100-1870. Boston: Boston Book and Art, Publisher, (1970). 2nd ed. Spine extrems lightly rubbed. Dj. *KARMIOLE.* $75

Evans, Joan. A HISTORY OF JEWELRY, 1100-1870. NY: Pitman Pub Corp. 1953. 1st ed. 186 photogr plts, 10 in color. Grn cl, gilt. Scarce. *KARMIOLE.* $150

Evans, Joan. ART IN MEDIEVAL FRANCE, 987-1498. London: Oxford Univ Press. 1948. 1st ed. Fldg map. Dj chipped. *KARMIOLE.* $100

Evans, John. EZRA TAFT BENSON: PIONEER-STATESMAN-SAINT. Salt Lake, 1947. 1st ed. VG+ in sl worn dj. *BENCHMARK.* $37.50

Evans, John. HALO IN BRASS. Indianapolis: Bobbs-Merrill, 1949. 1st ed. Little soiled, marked, o/w Fine in lightly chipped dj. *BEASLEY.* $125

Evans, Joseph. ACUTE HEAD INJURY. Springfield, 1950. 1st ed. *FYE.* $30

Evans, Mary L. GLIMPSES BY SEA AND LAND, DURING A SIX MONTHS' TRIP TO EUROPE. (Phila: W.H. Pile). 1870. 1st ed. 362pp. Spine extremities, corners sl frayed. *KARMIOLE.* $35

Evans, Max. ONE-EYED SKY. Nash Publishing, (1974). 1st separate ed. New in dj. *AUTHORS OF THE WEST.* $35

Evans, Max. SOUTHWEST WIND. Naylor Co, (1958). 1st ed, 1st bk. Fine in dj. *AUTHORS OF THE WEST.* $75

Evanson, E. ARGUMENTS AGAINST AND FOR THE SABBATICAL OBSERVANCE OF SUNDAY. London: B. Law, 1792. 1st ed. Orig mottled calf. Wear on all edges, but VG. *CONNOLLY & WADE.* $125

EVELINA; OR, THE HISTORY OF A YOUNG LADY'S ENTRANCE INTO THE WORLD. (By Fanny Burney.) A New Edition In Two Vols. London: Printed For The Booksellers, 1794. Contemp tree calf, lea labels and numbering pieces. Wear to hinges and spine edges, armorial bkpl, early sig on front pastedown, but a pleasant set. *HARTFIELD.* $245.

Evelyn, John. MEMOIRS, ILLUSTRATIVE OF THE LIFE AND WRITINGS OF JOHN EVELYN...COMPRISING HIS DIARY, FROM THE YEAR 1641 TO 1705-6, AND A SELECTION OF HIS FAMILIAR LETTERS. London: for Henry Colburn, 1819. 2nd ed. 2 vols. xxviii,671; v,336pp (incl index). Engr frontis portraits, vignette titles, plts, fldg table. Contemp 3/4 calf, marbled boards, leather labels on paneled spines, gilt. Extremities rubbed, hinges reinforced with cl tape, some scattered foxing affecting plts, withal VG. *WREDEN.* $185

Evelyn, John. THE MISCELLANEOUS WRITINGS. Now First Collected, with Occasional Notes by William Upcott. W/4 plts. London: H. Colburn, 1825. 1st ed. Tall, thick quarto, 875pp. Handsome tan morocco spine, raised bands, double lea labels, orig boards. Nice copy of important 1st collected ed. *HARTFIELD.* $395

Evered, Philip. STAGHUNTING WITH THE "DEVON AND SOMERSET" ON EXMOOR. Exeter: James G. Commin and London: Alex'r Denham & Co., 1902. 1st ed. Rebound, orig cover laid down. NF. *OLD LONDON.* $135

Everest, Thomas. A POPULAR VIEW OF HOMOEOPATHY, WITH ANNOTATIONS AND A BRIEF SURVEY OF THE PROGRESS AND HOMOEOPATHIA IN EUROPE BY A. GERALD HULL. NY, 1842. 1st Amer. ed. 243pp. *FYE.* $150

Everett, Alexander Hill. AMERICA. Phila: Carey & Lea, 1827. 1st ed. Contemp marbled boards worn. Rebacked w/new cl, spine label. Marginal damp-staining some pgs, o/w text VG. *DIAMOND.* $150

Everett, Edward. REPORT OF THE SECRETARY OF STATE COMMUNICATING...CORRESPONDENCE RELATING TO THE ENCROACHMENTS OF THE INDIANS OF THE UNITED STATES UPON THE TERRITORIES OF MEXICO. Washington, 1853. 135pp, wraps. 1st pg torn along binding but attached, some cvr wear, internal spotting o/w VG. *PRATT.* $75

Everett, Edward. THE MOUNT VERNON PAPERS. NY, 1860. 1st ed. Slight fray at bottom of spine. Small bump at bottom edge. Good, tight, sound. *ARTIS.* $20

Everett, F. FUN WITH GAME BIRDS. Harrisburg, 1954. Signed. *SUTTON.* $40

Everett, George. CATTLE CAVALCADE IN CENTRAL COLORADO. Denver: Golden Bell, (1966). 1st ed. Fine in VG dj. *OREGON.* $50

Everett, M. THE BIRDS OF PARADISE. NY, 1978. 57 colored plts. *SUTTON.* $30

Everett, Peter. NEGATIVES. NY: Simon & Schuster, 1965. 1st ed. VF in dj. *ELSE FINE.* $45

Everitt, Charles P. THE ADVENTURES OF A TREASURE HUNTER. Boston: Little, Brown and Co., 1951. 1st ed. Dj chipped. *OAK KNOLL.* $30

Evers, John J. and Hugh S. Fullerton. TOUCHING SECOND. Reilly & Britton, 1910. 1st ed. Good+ w/o dj. *PLAPINGER.* $100

Eversdyk-Smulder, Lily. ENIGMATIC TIBET. NY: Vantage Press, (1979). 1st ed. 32 full-pg port paintings. Blue ink mark on fore-edge, else Fine in VG dj. *BLUE DRAGON.* $35

Everson, Bill (William). THESE ARE THE RAVENS. San Leandro, 1935. 1st ed, 1st published work. Self-wrappers. *DAWSON'S.* $250

Everson, William. ARCHETYPE WEST: THE PACIFIC COAST AS A LITERARY REGION. Oyez, 1976. 1st ed. Inscribed, signed. Fine in dj. *AUTHORS OF THE WEST.* $75

Everson, William. MAN-FATE: THE SWAN SONG OF BROTHER ANTONINUS. New Directions, (1974). 1st ed. Fine in dj. *AUTHORS OF THE WEST.* $20

Everson, William. POEMS: MCMXII. (Waldport, OR: Ptd by the author at the Untide Press, 1944-45). 1st ed. One of 500. Errata slip tipped in. Wrappers a bit soiled, small hole in 3 pp not affecting text, 2 small lib stamps (withdrawn), withal Very Nice. Signed. *WREDEN.* $300

Everson, William. POEMS: MCMXLII. (Waldport, OR: Untide Press, 1945). 1st ed. One of 500. Light dampstain (about l"x2") on the lower right hand corner of most pages, else NF in wraps. *CAPTAIN'S BOOKSHELF.* $75

Everson, William. THE BLOWING OF THE SEED. 1/4 calf & batik boards. New Haven: Wenning, 1966. 1st ed. One of 218 ptd at The Banyan Press, signed. VF. *JAFFE.* $150

Everson, William. THE RESIDUAL YEARS. (NY): New Directions, (1948). VG in dj. 1st ed. 1/1000 . *CHAPEL HILL.* $125

Eversz, Robert. THE BOTTOM LINE IS MURDER. NY: Viking, (1988). 1st ed. Signed. Fine in Fine dj. *UNGER.* $35

Eversz, Robert. THE BOTTOM LINE IS MURDER. NY: Viking, 1988. 1st ed., 1st novel. Fine in dj. *MORDIDA.* $25

Everts, L.H. & Co. ILLUSTRATED HISTORICAL ATLAS OF DELAWARE COUNTY, OHIO. Complete in 1 vol. Phila, 1875. 1 double folded map, 1 fldg map laid in. Leather scuffed and torn along spine; smudges, signs of perusal. Average. *BOHLING.* $350

Everts, T.C. THIRTY-SEVEN DAYS OF PERIL. A NARRA-TIVE....SF: Grabhorn Press 1923. While colophon states: One of 375 on handmade paper, this is one of the 500 on machine-made paper. Tan cl w/gilt stamped spine label. Probably one of the un-bound remaindered copies. VG. *OREGON.* $60

Ewan, J. ROCKY MOUNTAIN NATURALISTS. Denver, 1950. Illus. VG+. *MIKESH.* $30

Ewell, R.S. THE MAKING OF A SOLDIER, LETTERS OF GENERAL R.S. EWELL. Ed by Percy Gatling Hamlin. Richmond, 1935. 1st ed. 161pp. Fine in dj. *PRATT.* $50

Ewell, Thomas. PLAIN DISCOVERIES ON THE LAWS OR PROPERTIES OF MATTER: CONTAINING THE ELEMENTS OR PRINCIPLES OF MODERN CHEMISTRY... NY: Brisban and Brannan, 1806. 1st ed. 469pp, cat. 2 plts. Full lea, worn (but tight); backstrip perished; foxing; contents generally bright. *SMITH-FIELD.* $300

Ewers, Hanns. THE SORCERER'S APPRENTICE. Day, 1927. Ltd to 2000. Mahlon Blaine (illus). *MADLE.* $100

Ewers, John C. THE BLACKFEET. Univ of OK, (1958). 1st ed. 3 maps. VG in Fine dj. *OREGON.* $40

Ewing, Elmore Ellis. THE STORY OF THE NINETY-FIRST. Portsmouth, OH, 1868. 1st ed. Wrappers. NF. *McGOWAN.* $45

Ewing, F.A. BIBLE NATURAL HISTORY; OR, A DESCRIPTION OF THE ANIMALS, PLANTS & MINERALS MENTIONED IN THE SACRED SCRIPTURES WITH COPIUS REFERENCES & EXPLANATIONS OF TEXTS. Phila, PA: 1835. 1st ed. Good+. *MIKESH.* $47.50

Ewing, Frederick R. (pseud of Theodore Sturgeon and Jean Shepherd). I, LIBERTINE. London: Michael Joseph, (1957). 1st Eng ed. Slip pasted to ffep indicates Sample Complete Copy Not for Sale. Sl foxing, o/w Fine in rubbed dj, tears top, bottom edge. *HELLER.* $75

Ewing, James. NEOPLASTIC DISEASES. Phila, 1919. 1st ed. 479 illus. *FYE.* $150

EXCURSIONS IN SWITZERLAND. (By James Fenimore Cooper.) London: Richard Bentley, 1836. 1st Eng ed. 2 vols in 1. iv,304; viii,314pp. Red morocco backed red cl; endleaves foxed, corners sl rubbed. BAL 3872. *WEBER.* $175

Exley, Frederick. A FAN'S NOTES. NY: Harper, (1968). Ad-vance reading copy. Top corner of rear panel bent, else Fine in red wraps. Much nicer than usual. *CAPTAIN'S BOOKSHELF.* $125

Exley, Frederick. A FAN'S NOTES. NY: Harper & Row, (c1968). Ptd red wrappers. Adv reading copy of 1st bk. Crease in back wrapper, sm nicks edge of wraps, o/w Fine. *HELLER.* $100

Exley, Frederick. PAGES FROM A COLD ISLAND. NY, 1975. 1st ed. Fine in Fine dj. *POLYANTHOS.* $35

EXPEDITION INTO NEW MEXICO MADE BY ANTONIO DE ESPEJO, 1582-1583; AS REVEALED IN THE JOURNAL OF...A MEMBER OF THE PARTY. LA: Quivira Soc, 1929. 1st ed. Fldg map, plts. Orig boards, spine expertly mended. One of 500 num-bered. *GINSBERG.* $150

EXPERIENCES AND OBSERVATIONS...DURING THE RECENT MEXICAN REVOLUTIONS...WRITTEN BY THE AUTHOR TO HIS DAUGHTER. Chula Vista, CA, 1920. 1st ed. Orig cl. *GINSBERG.* $50

Eycleshymer, Albert & Daniel Schoemaker. A CROSS-SECTION ANATOMY. NY, 1911. 1st ed. *FYE.* $200

Eycleshymer, Albert. ANATOMICAL NAMES ESPECIALLY THE BASLE NOMINA ANATOMICA WITH BIOGRAPHICAL SKETCHES BY ROY LEE MOODIE. NY, 1917. 1st ed. 744pp. Ex-lib. Scattered marginal notations, binding rubbed. Scarce. *FYE.* $200

Eyre, Alice. THE FAMOUS FREMONTS AND THEIR AMERICA. N.p. (Santa Ana): Fine Arts Press, 1948. 1st ed. Signed, inscribed. 24 plts, 6 maps. VF in VF dj. *OREGON.* $125

Eyre, Edward John. AUTOBIOGRAPHICAL NARRATIVE OF RESIDENCE AND EXPLORATION IN AUSTRALIA 1832-1839 BY EDWARD JOHN EYRE. London: Caliban Books, 1984. 1st ed. New in similar dj. *PARMER.* $35

F

Fabes, Gilbert. THE AUTOBIOGRAPHY OF A BOOK. London: Elzevier Press, (1926). 1st ed. Presentation, signed. NF in sl soiled dj. *WREDEN.* $40

Fabian, Monroe. THE PENNSYLVANIA-GERMAN DECORATED CHEST. NY: Universe Books, 1978. 1st ed. NF in NF dj. *BACKROOM.* $425

Fabre, J.H. THE LIFE AND LOVE OF THE INSECT. London: A & C Black, (1918). Illus. Dec cl. VG+. *MIKESH.* $17.50

Fabre, J.H. THE LIFE OF THE SCORPION. NY: Dodd, (1923). VG+ in Good+ dj. *MIKESH.* $25

Fabre, J.H. THE MASON BEES. NY: Dodd, (1914). Full gilt dec lea. Aeg. VG+. *MIKESH.* $25

FACTS AND FANCIES, OR, THREE YEARS' OBSERVATIONS. Watertown, NY: Chas. E. Holbrook, printer, 1878. 200pp, blue cl, gilt spine title, gilt fore edge. VG. *BOHLING.* $30

FAGGOTS FOR THE FIRESIDE; OR, FACT & FANCY, BY PETER PARLEY (Samuel G. Goodrich). NY, 1855. 1st ed. Rebacked w/orig backstrip. Little cvr wear & staining. Some foxing. Bkpl & card pocket removed from pastedowns, o/w VG. *DIAMOND.* $45

Fahey, Herbert. EARLY PRINTING IN CALIFORNIA. SF: The Book Club of CA, 1956. Ltd ed of 400. Signed. Fine, w/prospectus. *WEBER.* $325

Fair, A.A. (pseud of Erle Stanley Gardner). SHILLS CAN'T CASH CHIPS. Morrow, 1961. 1st ed, About Fine in a dj with sunned spine & tear). *STAHR.* $15

Fair, A.A. (pseud of Erle Stanley Gardner). BEWARE THE CUR-VES. Morrow, 1956. 1st ed. About Fine in chipped dj sunned on spine. *STAHR.* $20

Fair, A.A. (pseud of Erle Stanley Gardner). GIVE 'EM THE AX. Morrow, 1944. 1st ed. Wear, corners bumped, 2 book store stamps on ep, just Good. *BEBBAH.* $15

Fair A.A. (pseud of Erle Stanley Gardner). SHILLS CAN'T CASH CHIPS. NY: Morrow, 1965. 1st ed. Fine, minor wear to dj extremities. *ELSE FINE.* $35

Fair, A.A. (pseud of Erle Stanley Gardner). THE COUNT OF NINE. Morrow, 1958. 1st. VG or better in dj (chipped & worn). *STAHR.* $15

Fair, A.A. (pseud of Erle Stanley Gardner). TOP OF THE HEAP. Morrow, 1952. 1st. VG+, dj chipped at edges. *STAHR.* $20

Fair, Ronald L. MANY THOUSAND GONE. NY: Harcourt, 1965. 1st ed. Author's 1st bk. Fine but for inscrip on half-title, in NF dj w/tear rear panel. *BEASLEY.* $50

Fair, Ronald L. WE CAN'T BREATHE. NY: Harper, (1972). 1st ed. Fine in dj. *BETWEEN COVERS.* $45

Fair, Ronald L. WORLD OF NOTHING. NY: Harper, (1970). 1st ed. Fine in Fine dj very sl darkened at extremities. *BETWEEN COVERS.* $60

Fairbairn, Roger (pseud of John Dickson Carr). DEVIL KINSMERE. NY and London: Harper & Brothers Pubs, (1934). 1st Amer ed ptd in Great Britain. Some leaves somewhat roughly opened, else very NF, w/out dj. *HELLER.* $150

Fairbairn, W.E. HANDS OFF! SELF-DEFENSE FOR WOMEN. NY: D. Appleton-Century Co. 1942. 1st ed. Wrappers. Dj. *KARMIOLE.* $30

Fairbank, Alfred. A BOOK OF SCRIPTS. (Harmondsworth, Middlesex): Penguin Books. 1949. 1st ed. Illus boards. Dj. Eps a bit foxed. Inscribed by Fairbank and Jan Tschichold. *KARMIOLE.* $75

Fairbanks, George R. HISTORY OF FLORIDA FROM ITS DISCOVERY BY PONCE DE LEON IN 1512, TO THE CLOSE OF THE FLORIDA WAR, IN 1842. Phila., 1871. 1st ed. 350,(10)pp. Orig cl. Howes F8. *GINSBERG.* $100

Fairchild, D. EXPLORING FOR PLANTS....1925, 1926, AND 1927. NY, 1930. Cl, some cvr spotting, lt spine wear. Eps browned; pencil notes. *SUTTON.* $75

Fairchild, Lucius. CALIFORNIA LETTERS OF LUCIUS FAIRCHILD. Madison: State Hist Soc, 1931. Joseph Schafer (ed). 27 plts. Fine. *LAURIE.* $20

Fairchild, T.B. A HISTORY OF THE TOWN OF CUYAHOGA FALLS, SUMMIT COUNTY, OHIO. Cuyahoga Falls: N.p., 1876. 1st ed. 39pp, stiff wraps. Covers water-stained, internally Fine. *ARCHER.* $70

FAIRFIELD PORTER: REALIST PAINTER IN AN AGE OF ABSTRACTION. Boston: Museum of Fine Arts, (1982). 1st ed. Fine in dj. *CAPTAIN'S BOOKSHELF.* $60

Fairfield, Sumner Lincoln. THE AUTOBIOGRAPHY OF JANE FAIRFIELD....Boston: Bazin and Ellsworth, 1860. 1st ed. Lacks fep. VG. *SECOND LIFE.* $45

Fairholt, F.W. COSTUME IN ENGLAND. A HISTORY....London: Chapman & Hall, 1846. Full pebble grained red morocco. Gilt panels on covers within gilt ruled border, raised bands. Some scuffing, gilt edges. Good. *CULLEN.* $175

Fairholt, F.W. GOG AND MAGOG. THE GIANTS IN GUILDHALL. London: John Camden Hotten, 1859. 1st ed. 12mo, 152pp, (4)pp ads. Orig purple cl w/gilt centerpiece. Colored frontis. Catalogue description taped in at front, some signature separation, but VG. *CHAPEL HILL.* $125

Fairholt, F.W. TOBACCO: ITS HISTORY AND ASSOCIATIONS....London: Chapman & Hall, 1859. vii,332pp. *KARMIOLE.* $75

Fairlie, Gerard. THEY FOUND EACH OTHER. London: Hodder & Stoughton, 1946. 1st ed. VG in dj (minor wear spine ends, corners). Dj. *MORDIDA.* $40

FAIRY TALE THEATRE. London, 1986. A moveable bk. *BOOKFINDERS INTL.* $20

Falconer, William. THE SHIPWRECK, A POEM...With a Life of the Author, by James Stanier Clarke. London: Ptd for William Miller by T(homas) Bensley, 1804. 4th and best ed. 4to, 220pp. Gilt-tooled contemp full diced calf w/sailing ships in spine panels. 3 full-page plts, 5 vignettes. Nearly Fine. Scarce. *CHAPEL HILL.* $400

Falk, Bernard. THOMAS ROWLANDSON: HIS LIFE AND ART. NY: The Beechurst Press. (1952). 1st ed. Dj chipped. Supplement at back, "Rowlandson's Color Plate Books." *KARMIOLE.* $75

Falkner, J. Meade. THE LAST STRADIVARIUS. Appleton, 1896. 1st ed. VG. *MADLE.* $75

Fall, H.C. LIST OF THE COLEOPTERA OF SOUTHERN CALIFORNIA. SF, 1901. Recent clothbacked boards (original wrappers retained), lib stamp on front wrapper. *SUTTON.* $39

Falls, Cyril. WAR BOOKS. A CRITICAL GUIDE. London: Davies, 1930. 1st ed. VG. *JAFFE.* $75

Fanning, Edmund. VOYAGES & DISCOVERIES IN THE SOUTH SEAS 1792-1832. Salem, MA: Marine Research Society, 1924. Light wear to corners, some foxing, generally VG. *PARMER.* $115

Fanning, Edmund. VOYAGES & DISCOVERIES IN THE SOUTH SEAS 1792-1832. Salem, 1924. Pub. 6. Fine in very worn dj; prospectus laid in. Howes F.28. *LEFKOWICZ.* $100

Fanning, Edmund. VOYAGES ROUND THE WORLD. NY: Collins & Hanney, 1833. 499pp. Recent black buckram, ugly but sturdy. 4 (of 5) litho plts, 1 detached at fold, and worn. Light scattered foxing. Howes F27. *SCHOYER'S.* $125

Fante, John. DREAMS FROM BUNKER HILL. Black Sparrow, 1982. 1st ed. Fine in acetate dj, as issued. *STAHR.* $45

Fante, John. FULL OF LIFE. Little, Brown, 1952. 1st ed. Ex libris. VG in trimmed dj w/residue from paper cover on rear panel. Bk has tape on boards, "due slip" on rfep. Nice. *STAHR.* $45

Fante, John. SELECTED LETTERS: 1932 to 1981. Seamus Cooney (ed). Santa Rosa: Black Sparrow (1991). 1st ed. One of 176 numbered, signed by Cooney and Joyce Fante. Fine in acetate. *DORN.* $40

Fante, John. THE BROTHERHOOD OF THE GRAPE. Boston: Houghton Mifflin, 1977. 1st ed. Fine in dj. *ELSE FINE.* $45

Fante, John. THE BROTHERHOOD OF THE GRAPE. Houghton, 1977. 1st ed. Fine in sl rubbed dj. *STAHR.* $45

Faraday, Cornelia Bateman. EUROPEAN AND AMERICAN CARPETS AND RUGS. Grand Rapids: The Dean-Hicks Company/The Decorative Arts Press, 1929. 1st ed. Fine in dec red cl. *CAPTAIN'S BOOKSHELF.* $75

Faraday, Michael. EXPERIMENTAL RESEARCHES IN CHEMISTRY AND PHYSICS. London: Taylor & Francis, 1859. 1st ed. 496pp, 3 plts. Orig grn cl. Backstrip, p.3 coming loose, else VG. *SMITHFIELD.* $245

Farber, James. TEXANS WITH GUNS. San Antonio: Naylor, (1950). VG. *ARTIS.* $16.50

Faris, J.T. OLD GARDENS IN AND ABOUT PHILADELPHIA....Indianapolis, 1932. 1st ed. Cloth. Foxing on eps; worn dj. *SUTTON.* $50

Faris, John T. ROAMING THE ROCKIES. NY, 1930. 1st ed. 332pp. Remains of dj laid in. VG. *FIVE QUAIL.* $27.50

Faris, John T. THE ALASKAN PATHFINDER. NY: Fleming H. Revell, c. 1926. Light wear, VG+. *PARMER.* $45

Farish, Thomas E. HISTORY OF ARIZONA. Phoenix: (Legislature of the State of AZ). 1915. 1st ed. 2 vols. The first two vols of an 8-vol set. (Vols 3-8 were "mug books" of famous Arizonians). Howes F37. Fine. *KARMIOLE.* $40

Farish, Thomas E. HISTORY OF ARIZONA. Phoenix: (Thomas Edwin Farish), 1915. 2 vols. Cloth. *DAWSON'S.* $65

Farish, Thomas E. HISTORY OF ARIZONA...Phoenix, 1915. 2 vols. 1st ed. Orig cl, As New. Howes F37. *GINSBERG.* $35

Farleigh, John. GRAVEN IMAGE: AN AUTOBIOGRAPHICAL TEXTBOOK. London: Macmillan, 1940. Paper board case w/engr matching dj. Bkpl. Fine. *HELLER.* $85

Farley, Walter. THE BLACK STALLION'S FILLY. NY: Random House, 1952. 1st prtg. VG in Good dj. *OCTOBER FARM.* $20

FARM. London, (1950s). 4 double-pg pull down in front. Moveable bk. *BOOKFINDERS INTL.* $70

Farmer, Bernard J. THE GENTLE ART OF BOOK COLLECT-ING. London: Thorsons Publishing Ltd., (1950). 1st ed. Dj sl soiled. *OAK KNOLL.* $30

Farmer, Henry George. HISTORY OF THE ROYAL ARTILLERY BAND, 1762-1953. London: Royal Artillery Inst. (1954). 1st ed. Dj. Fine. *KARMIOLE.* $45

Farmer, John S. (ed). AMERICANISMS—OLD & NEW. A DIC-TIONARY....London: Thomas Poulter. 1889. xx,564pp. Ltd numbered ed, signed by Farmer on the title page. Beige cl spine over blue boards; paper spine label (chipped). Rare. *KARMIOLE.* $85

Farmer, Philip Jose. DAYWORLD. NY, 1985. 1st ed. Signed presentation. Fine in like dj. *POLYANTHOS.* $45

Farmer, Philip Jose. FLESH. Doubleday, 1968. 1st ed. VF in dj. Signed. *MADLE.* $325

Farmer, Philip Jose. FLESH. London: R & W, 1968. 1st ed. Signed. Fine; lightly rubbed dj. *ELSE FINE.* $75

Farmer, Philip Jose. GODS OF RIVERWORLD. NY, 1983. 1st ed. Signed presentation. Fine in dj (sl crease, 1 tiny tear). *POLYANTHOS.* $45

Farmer, Philip Jose. LORD TYGER. Doubleday, 1970 1st ed. NF in dj Signed. *MADLE.* $150

Farmer, Philip Jose. TARZAN ALIVE. GC: Doubleday, 1972. 1st ed. Fine in dj. *ELSE FINE.* $50

Farmer, Philip Jose. THE CELESTIAL BLUEPRINT AND CACHE FROM OUTER SPACE. NY, (1962). Ace Double. 1st ed. Signed, presentation copy. Pict wraps. NF. *POLYANTHOS.* $25

Farmer, Philip Jose. THE DARK DESIGN. NY, (1977). 1st ed. Signed presentation. Fine in like dj. *POLYANTHOS.* $45

Farmer, Philip Jose. THE FABULOUS RIVERBOAT. Putnam, 1971. 1st hb ed. Fine in dj. *MADLE.* $325

Farmer, Philip Jose. THE GATE OF TIME. Belmont, 1966. 1st ed. Fine in wraps. Signed. *MADLE.* $20

Farmer, Philip Jose. THE MAGIC LABYRINTH. Berkley, 1980. 1st ed. Fine in dj. Signed. *MADLE.* $22

Farmer, Philip Jose. THE UNREASONING MASK. NY, 1981. 1st ed. Signed, presentation copy. Fine in Fine dj. *POLYANTHOS.* $45

Farmer, Philip Jose. TO YOUR SCATTERED BODIES GO. Gregg, 1980. 1st ed thus. As New. Signed. *MADLE.* $40

Farnham, Charles H. LIFE OF FRANCIS PARKMAN. Boston: Little Brown, 1901. No 192 of Edition Deluxe. Bkpl. Tissue guard frontis. Minor scuffing to leather spine, else NF, unopened. *PARMER.* $75

Farnham, Eliza W. LIFE IN PRAIRIE LAND. NY: Harper, 1847. 2nd ed, 1st bk. 408pp. Uncut. Nice, tight. *SECOND LIFE.* $165

Farnham, Thomas J. TRAVELS IN CALIFORNIA. Oakland: Biobooks, 1947. One of 750. 1st pub in 1844. Map. Fine. *LAURIE.* $37.50

Farnham, Thomas J. TRAVELS IN THE GREAT WESTERN PRAIRIES, THE ANAHUAC AND ROCKY MOUNTAINS, AND IN THE OREGON TERRITORY. In 2 vols. London, 1843. 297, 315pp. Very nicely rebound in red 1/2 lea and complementary marbled paper over boards. Bkpl inside each front cover. Lacking 1 leaf of advertising at end of Vol 1. Moderate usage to covers, oc-

casional foxing or soiling to pp, o/w VG internally. Near VG condition. Howes F50. *BAADE.* $400

Farnsworth, R.W.C. (ed). A SOUTHERN CALIFORNIA PARADISE, (IN THE SUBURBS OF LOS ANGELES). Pasadena: R.W.C. Farnsworth, 1883. vi,132pp, engr in text. Blind-and-gold stamped cl, fore-edge of boards a bit stained and warped, light stain to fore-edges of leaves not affecting text, bkpl. *DAWSON'S.* $225

Farquhar, Francis P. THE BOOKS OF THE COLORADO RIVER & THE GRAND CANYON. LA: Glen Dawson. 1953. 1st ed. Frontis. Title ptd in red and black. Red linen, paper label. 600 ptd (unstated). *KARMIOLE.* $85

Farquhar, Francis P. YOSEMITE, THE BIG TREES AND THE HIGH SIERRA—A SELECTIVE BIBLIOGRAPHY. Berkeley and LA: Univ of CA Press, 1948. 1st ed. Signed. Title page vignette, gray cl, dj. Fine. *WEBER.* $175

Farrar, J. ELEMENTS OF ALGEBRA BY S.F. LACROIX. 1831, 3rd ed. 298pp. Rebacked, new end leaves, paper label on backstrip. Cvr tip wear, foxing. Good. *BOOKCELL.* $50

Farrell, Henry. WHAT EVER HAPPENED TO BABY JANE? NY: Rinehart, 1960. 1st ed. Pp darkened o/w VG in dj with wear. *MORDIDA.* $45

Farrell, J.G. THE SIEGE OF KRISHNAPUR. London: Weidenfeld & Nicholson, (1973). 1st ed. Fine in price-clipped dj (sl tanned spine). *CAPTAIN'S BOOKSHELF.* $50

Farrell, James T. A NOTE ON LITERARY CRITICISM. NY: Vanguard, 1936. 1st ed. Fine in lightly used dj (few tears; dulled spine). *BEASLEY.* $75

Farrell, James T. CALICO SHOES AND OTHER STORIES. NY, (1934). 1st ed. Fine in Fine dj. *POLYANTHOS.* $200

Farrell, James T. CHILDHOOD IS NOT FOREVER. GC: Doubleday, 1969. 1st ed. Fine in NF dj. Inscribed. *LOPEZ.* $85

Farrell, James T. MY DAYS OF ANGER. NY, (1943). 1st ed. NF in dj (spine sl sunned, little edge rubbed). *POLYANTHOS.* $30

Farrell, James T. MY DAYS OF ANGER. NY: Vanguard, (1943). 1st ed. VG, little worn dj. *SECOND LIFE.* $20

Farrell, James T. REFLECTIONS AT FIFTY. NY, (1954). 1st ed. Signed presentation. Fine in price clipped dj (small tear). *POLYANTHOS.* $50

Farrell, James T. REFLECTIONS AT FIFTY. NY: Vanguard, (1954). 1st ed. NF in lightly darkened dj. Inscribed. *CHAPEL HILL.* $125

Farrell, James T. THE FACE OF TIME. (NY, 1953). 1st ed. Signed presentation. Fine in price clipped dj (few sl tears extremities). *POLYANTHOS.* $50

Farrell, James T. THE ROAD BETWEEN. NY: Vanguard, (1949). 1st ed. Dj edgetears & wear. VG. *AKA.* $20

Farrell, James. MY BASEBALL DIARY. Barnes, 1957. 1st ed. VG. *PLAPINGER.* $35

Farrer, Richard Ridley. A TOUR IN GREECE 1880. Edinburgh, 1883. Fldg map. Newly rebound in dark blue cl, new eps, gold lettered title, author, illustrator and date on spine ornamental borders in gilt head and foot. (xi),216pp. Splendid. *O'NEILL.* $150

Farrere, Claude. BLACK OPIUM. NY: Robert C. Fairberg, 1931. Orange cloth. Privately issued for subscribers. Slipcase edge-chipped, separated into two pieces. *AKA.* $50

Farrington, Oliver C. CATALOGUE OF THE METEORITES OF NORTH AMERICA, TO JANUARY 1, 1909. Memoirs of Nat'l Academy Sciences, Volume XIII, 1915. Good in orig brn cl. 2.5" split front hinge, wear to the extrems, pgs yellowing. *KNOLLWOOD.* $250

Farrington, S. Kip, Jr. FISHING THE PACIFIC. NY, (1953). 1st ed. Fine in dj. *ARTIS.* $40

Farrington, S. Kip, Jr. PACIFIC GAME FISHING. NY: Coward-Mc-Cann, 1942. 1st ed. Minor edgewear, else VG. *OLD LONDON.* $50

Farrington, S. Kip, Jr. THE TRAIL OF THE SHARP CUP. NY, (1974). 1st ed. Signed inscrip. Fine in dj. *ARTIS.* $25

Farrington, S.K. THE DUCKS CAME BACK, THE STORY OF "DUCKS UNLIMITED". NY, 1945. 1st ed. Worn dj. *SUTTON.* $35

Farris, John. KING WINDOM. Trident Press, 1967. 1st ed. Fine. Dj (sl worn along top edge; lightly rubbed front flyleaf fold). *STAHR.* $60

Farris, John. THE FURY. Playboy Press, 1976. 1st ed. Fine. Dj lightly worn at spine ends; small chip missing on rear panel. *STAHR.* $35

Farrow, Edward S. MOUNTAIN SCOUTING: A HANDBOOK FOR OFFICERS AND SOLDIERS ON THE FRON-TIERS....NY: the author, 1881. 1st ed. 248,36,(9 ads)pp. Orig gold stamped pict cl. Signed on flyleaf. Howes F56. *GINSBERG.* $350

Farson, Negley. GOING FISHING. NY: Harcourt, Brace & Co, n.d. Stated 1st Amer ed. VG. *BACKMAN.* $25

Fast, Howard. GENERAL WASHINGTON AND THE WATER WITCH. London: Bodley Head, 1956. 1st ed. Wraps, store stamp, small corner chip on half-title, bit sunned spine, else VG+. Scarce. *BEASLEY.* $75

Fast, Howard. INTELLECTUALS IN THE FIGHT FOR PEACE. NY: New Century, 1949. 1st ed. Wraps. Close to Fine. *BEASLEY.* $35

Fast, Howard. SPARTACUS. NY, 1951. 1st ed. Fine in dj (spine little sunned, extremities little rubbed, 3 small edge tears). *POLYANTHOS.* $45

Fastlicht, Samuel. TOOTH MUTILATIONS AND DENTISTRY IN PRE-COLUMBIAN MEXICO. Berlin, 1976. 1st ed. Dj. *FYE.* $75

Fatout, Paul. AMBROSE BIERCE. THE DEVIL'S LEXICOG-RAPHER. Univ of Oklahoma Press, (1951). 1st ed. Fine in sl chipped dj. *DIAMOND.* $25

Fauchet, Joseph. A SKETCH OF THE PRESENT STATE OF OUR POLITICAL RELATIONS WITH THE UNITED STATES OF NORTH AMERICA. Phila: Bache, 1797. 1st Amer ed. 31pp. Half morocco, last leaf expertly mended on blank part. 1st Eng trans by William Daune. *GINSBERG.* $150

Faulk, Odie B. and Laura E. Faulk. FRANK W. MAYBORN A MAN WHO MADE A DIFFERENCE. N.p.: Univ of Mary Hardin Baylor. 1st ed. VF in dj. *GIBBS.* $20

Faulk, Odie B. DESTINY ROAD. NY, (1973). 1st ed. Dj has light wear and faded spine o/w Fine. Ffep missing. *PRATT.* $20

Faulkner, Henry. ELEPHANT HAUNTS: BEING A SPORTSMAN'S NARRATIVE OF THE SEARCH FOR DOC-TOR LIVINGSTONE...Blantyre, Malawi: Society of Malawi and The Royal Geographical Society, 1984 facsimile reprint of London 1868. Ltd ed #508 of 750. Fine in NF dj. *GREAT EPIC.* $95

Faulkner, William, Benjamin E. Mays and Cecil Sims. THE SEGREGATION DECISIONS PAPERS READ AT A SESSION OF THE TWENTY-FIRST ANNUAL MEETING OF THE SOUTHERN HISTORICAL ASSOCIATION... Atlanta, 1956. 1st ed, 1st prtg. Orig ptd wrappers. NF. Scarce. *McGOWAN.* $250

Faulkner, William. A FABLE. (NY: Random House, (1954). 1st ed. #360 of 1000 signed. Orig greyish blue cl, bevelled edges. NF in edgeworn glassine dj, sl browned pub's slipcase. *CHAPEL HILL.* $650

Faulkner, William. A FABLE. (NY): Random House, (1954). 1st ed. Orig maroon cl. Fine in NF dj (few tiny chips and tears). *CHAPEL HILL.* $95

Faulkner, William. A FABLE. (NY): Random House, (1954). 1st ed. Stain on fep, apparently from bkpl removal, o/w VG in lightly worn dj, internally strengthened along edges. *LOPEZ.* $45

Faulkner, William. A FABLE. NY: Random House, (1954). 1st trade ed. Bumped in dj sl worn at extrems. Owner inscrip. NF. *BLUE MOUN-TAIN.* $35

Faulkner, William. A GREEN BOUGH. NY: Harrison Smith & Robert Haas, 1933. 1st ed. #119 of 360 signed. Lynd Ward. Orig tan cl, mounted cvr illus. Cl sl darkened as usual, but nice, VG. Black lettering intact and unflaked. Maxwell Geismar's copy, few ink marks by him in margins. *CHAPEL HILL.* $750

Faulkner, William. A GREEN BOUGH. NY: Smith and Haas, 1933. One of 360 numbered, signed. Slightest bit of tanning to spine and edges of cl; black lettering intact, unflaked. Fine w/o dj, as issued. *LOPEZ.* $1500

Faulkner, William. AS I LAY DYING. NY, 1930. 1st ed, 2nd issue. Spine sl sunned, top little rubbed, bkpl, traces of removed tape inside cvrs and feps. Dj lined, almost 2/3 of spine missing, remainder of spine sunned and rubbed; front flap rubbed, little soiled, traces of removed scotch tape edges both flaps. *POLYANTHOS.* $150

Faulkner, William. AS I LAY DYING. NY: Jonathan Cape & Harrison Smith, (1930). 1st ed, 1st state, w/lg capital "I" on pg 11 dropped from correct alignment, top edge stained dark brown. 2500 ptd, of which this is finest extant. Very rare. Orig tan cl stamped in brown. Fresh, immaculate in dj w/no wear, faults, or blemishes whatsoever. *CHAPEL HILL.* $5,000

Faulkner, William. DOCTOR MARTINO AND OTHER STORIES. NY: Harrison Smith & Robert Haas, 1934. 1st ed. Orig blue cl. Nick in fore-edge, else Fine in NF dj (lightly sunned spine, couple of tiny nicks). Unusually Nice. *CHAPEL HILL.* $600

Faulkner, William. FLAGS IN THE DUST. Douglas Day (ed, intro). NY: Random House, (1973). 1st ed. Very slight discoloration of eps, else Fine in dj. Engr Random House card of Albert Erksine laid in. *CHAPEL HILL.* $85

Faulkner, William. FLAGS IN THE DUST. Random House, 1973. 1st VG+ in dj. Rmdr stamp. Tears at foot of spine & front flyleaf; scuff on rear panel. *STAHR.* $20

Faulkner, William. GO DOWN MOSES AND OTHER STORIES. NY, 1942. 1st ed, 1st issue binding black cloth. Top edge stained red. Fine in price clipped dj (tiny piece missing top side spine and little rubbed, lower spine tiny nick). *POLYANTHOS.* $300

Faulkner, William. GO DOWN, MOSES. NY: Random House, 1942. 1st ed. NF in price clipped dj w/chip to bottom edge of rear panel. *LAME DUCK.* $850

Faulkner, William. IDYLL IN THE DESERT. NY: Random House, 1931. 1st ed. #241 of 400 signed. Orig red marbled boards, paper label. Tape marks eps, 1" crack top front inner hinge, else VG *CHAPEL HILL.* $550

Faulkner, William. INTRUDER IN THE DUST. Cl. NY: Random House, (1948). 1st ed. Fine in dj (sl rubbed, few tears at top spine). *JAFFE.* $100

Faulkner, William. INTRUDER IN THE DUST. NY, (1948). 1st ed. Lt wear corners of dj. Gilt lettering on spine flaked. Bkpl, o/w Fine. *ARTIS.* $150

Faulkner, William. INTRUDER IN THE DUST. NY: Random House, 1948. 1st ed. Dj (water stains back, sm piece missing top). Front dj art bright. *SMITH.* $125

Faulkner, William. INTRUDER IN THE DUST. NY: Random House, (1948). 1st ed. Fine in price-clipped dj. *UNGER.* $200

Faulkner, William. INTRUDER IN THE DUST. NY: Random House, (1948). 1st ed. Orig black cl. NF in dj. *CHAPEL HILL.* $200

Faulkner, William. INTRUDER IN THE DUST. NY: Random House, 1948. 1st ed. Fine but for owner's name in lightly used dj w/tears at spine folds, flap folds. *BEASLEY.* $90

Faulkner, William. KNIGHT'S GAMBIT. NY: Random House, 1949. 1st ed. VG in almost VG dj. *LAME DUCK.* $45

Faulkner, William. LIGHT IN AUGUST. (NY): Harrison Smith & Robert Haas, (1932). 1st ed. Cl soiled, rear ep just cracking near hinge, thus VG only in soiled dj (faded spine, few tears). *CHAPEL HILL.* $400

Faulkner, William. LIGHT IN AUGUST. (NY): Harrison Smith & Robert Haas, (1932). 1st ed. Orig tan cl stamped in orange and blue. Fine in ptd dj designed by Arthur Hawkins and orig glassine jacket. Dj shows little wear, a few clean tears repaired on verso w/white substance. Glassine dj (few edge chips but in VG condition). Very scarce w/glassine jacket. *CHAPEL HILL.* $900

Faulkner, William. MAYDAY. Univ of Notre Dame, (1978). 1st trade ed. Fine in Fine dj. *POLYANTHOS.* $25

Faulkner, William. MISS ZILPHIA GANT. (Dallas): The Book Club of Texas, 1932. Orig brown cl. Fine. Housed in a handsome custom clamshell box. 1st ed. #128 of 300 . Scarce. *CHAPEL HILL.* $1,200

Faulkner, William. MISS ZILPHIA GANT. (Dallas): The Book Club of Texas, 1932. 1st ed. #245 of 300. Orig br cl. Spine dulled, cvrs stained, last pg carelessly opened. VG. *CHAPEL HILL.* $750

Faulkner, William. MISSISSIPPI POEMS. Oxford, MS: Yoknapatawpha Press, (1979). 1st ed. #60 of 500, promo leaflet laid in. Orig brown cl. Fine in sl soiled pub's slipcase. *CHAPEL HILL.* $150

Faulkner, William. PYLON. NY: Harrison Smith & Robert Haas, 1935. 1st ed. NF in Nice pict dj (few tiny chips at corners). Gilt lettering on spine is notoriously prone to flaking, but intact here. Scarce in such Nice condition. *CHAPEL HILL.* $550

Faulkner, William. PYLON. NY: Harrison Smith and Robert Haas, 1935. 1st ed. NF w/moderately bright spine. Non-authorial presentation on half title. *CAPTAIN'S BOOKSHELF.* $75

Faulkner, William. REQUIEM FOR A NUN. NY: Random House, 1951. 1st ed. Sl less than VG in price clipped dj. *LAME DUCK.* $45

Faulkner, William. REQUIEM FOR A NUN. NY: Random House, (1951). 1st trade ed. Orig black and grn cl. Erasure on fep, very faint tape marks, else NF in dj. *CHAPEL HILL.* $150

Faulkner, William. REQUIEM FOR A NUN. NY: Random House, (1951). 1st ed. #643 of 750 specially bound, signed. Orig half black cl and marbled boards. Touch of shelfwear to bottom edges only but Fine in acetate jacket (sm chip at base of spine). *CHAPEL HILL.* $600

Faulkner, William. REQUIEM FOR A NUN. NY: Random House, 1951. 1st ed. #84 of 750 numbered, signed. Cloth. Fine, issued w/o dj. *UNGER.* $750

Faulkner, William. SALMAGUNDI. (with) A Poem by Ernest Hemingway. Milwaukee: The Casanova Press, 1932. One of 525 numbered. Fine in well-worn slipcase. *CAPTAIN'S BOOKSHELF.* $850

Faulkner, William. SARTORIS. NY: Harcourt, Brace, (1929). 1st ed. Orig black cl stamped in orange. Bright, fresh in red and black dj designed by Arthur Hawkins. Dj has a small spot at the bottom of the rear panel, shallow chip (affecting no lettering) at the head of lightly faded spine. *CHAPEL HILL.* $3,600

Faulkner, William. THE HAMLET. NY: Random House, 1940. 1st ed. #217 of 250 specially bound, signed. Orig half grn cl and paper-covered boards, teg. Fine w/almost imperceptible fading at edges of boards, in orig glassine jacket. Scarce, especially in glassine jacket. *CHAPEL HILL.* $3,200

Faulkner, William. THE HAMLET. NY: Random House, 1940. 1st ed. #115 of 250 signed. Orig half grn cl, boards, teg. Top and fore-edges sl rubbed, browned, else VG or better. Scarce. *CHAPEL HILL.* $2,500

Faulkner, William. THE MANSION. NY, 1959. 1st ed. Fine in dj, spine sl rubbed. *POLYANTHOS.* $40

Faulkner, William. THE MANSION. NY: Random House, (1959). 1st ed. Orig blue cl. NF in dj. 1st ed. *CHAPEL HILL.* $100

Faulkner, William. THE REIVERS. A REMINISCENCE. NY: Random House, (1962). Orig burgundy buckram. Fine in orig acetate dj. 1st ed. #494 of 500 signed. *CHAPEL HILL.* $750

Faulkner, William. THE REIVERS. NY: Random House, (1962). 1st ed. Orig red cl. NF in dj (lt rubbing front panel). *CHAPEL HILL.* $75

Faulkner, William. THE REIVERS. NY: Random House, (1962). 1st ed. Fine in NF, price-clipped dj. *LOPEZ.* $75

Faulkner, William. THE REIVERS. NY: RH, (1962). One of 500 specially-bound, signed. VF, no spine fading. Issued w/o ptd dj or slipcase. *CAPTAIN'S BOOKSHELF.* $750

Faulkner, William. THE SOUND AND THE FURY (Together with) AS I LAY DYING. NY: Modern Library, (1946). 1st ed thus. NF in dj (few tiny chips, long tear on rear panel). *CAPTAIN'S BOOKSHELF.* $50

Faulkner, William. THE SOUND AND THE FURY. NY: Cape, Smith, 1929. 1st ed in presumed 1st issue dj with Humanity Uprooted priced $3.00. VG w/lt wear to spine, spine sl tanned. Dj spine faded with 1/2" deep chip across head of spine and some smaller chips. *LAME DUCK.* $3250

Faulkner, William. THE SOUND AND THE FURY. NY: Cape and Smith, (1929). 1st ed. Scarce and fragile, this has several notable defects: front hinge cracked; dj spine faded, obliterating lettering, brittle and cracked there, affecting some text. Front and rear panels quite bright and fresh, w/sm chip at bottom edge of front panel. In all VG in worn but still Good dj. Custom clamshell box. *LOPEZ.* $2500

Faulkner, William. THE TOWN. NY, 1957. 1st ed, 1st issue. Fine in dj (lower spine minimally rubbed). *POLYANTHOS.* $65

Faulkner, William. THE TOWN. NY: Random House, (1957). 1st ed. Orig red cl. Stray mark on fore-edge, else Fine in dj. *CHAPEL HILL.* $125

Faulkner, William. THE TOWN. NY: Random House, 1957. 1st ed. NF w/owner's name and spine wear in Fine dj but for bit darkened spine. *BEASLEY.* $100

Faulkner, William. THE UNVANQUISHED. NY: Random House, (1938). 1/250 ptd on Arches rag paper and signed. A touch of rubbing at corners, else Fine w/practically none of the habitual gutter browning or spine fading which plague this title. *CAPTAIN'S BOOKSHELF.* $1750

Faulkner, William. THE WILD PALMS. NY: Random House, (1939). 1st ed. Tan cl over boards, gold and grn ptd dj, edges of bk browned, dj sunned and chipped at edges. *JUVELIS.* $200

Faulkner, William. THE WILD PALMS. NY: Random House, (1939). 1st ed. Orig tan cl. Touch of wear at crown of spine, but Fine, clean in dj lightly rubbed at spine ends. Very Nice. *CHAPEL HILL.* $550

Faulkner, William. THESE 13. STORIES. NY: Jonathan Cape & Harrison Smith, (1931). 1st ed. #129 of 299 signed. Orig silver-grey cl with rust cl spine, top edge silver. Edges of cl darkened and spine faded, as is usual, but VG . *CHAPEL HILL.* $950

Faulkner, William. THIS EARTH. NY: Equinox, 1932. 1st ed. Orig ptd lt brn wraps. Fine. 1st ed. Scarce separate ptg of. Albert Heckman (illus). *CHAPEL HILL.* $225

Fauntleroy, A.M. REPORT ON THE MEDICO-MILITARY ASPECTS OF THE EUROPEAN WAR FROM OBSERVATIONS TAKEN BEHIND THE ALLIED ARMIES IN FRANCE. Washington, 1915. 1st ed. 214 photo illus. *FYE.* $150

Faust, Albert B. THE GERMAN ELEMENT IN THE UNITED STATES.... NY, 1927. 2 vols in one. 28, 591; 14, 730pp. Both vols illus. Some discoloration on front cover. *HEINOLDT.* $25

Faust, Irvin. ROAR LION ROAR AND OTHER STORIES. NY: Random House, 1964. 1st ed. Fine; lightly used dj. *ELSE FINE.* $45

Faust, Patricia L. (ed). HISTORICAL TIMES ILLUSTRATED EN-CYCLOPEDIA OF THE CIVIL WAR. NY, (1986). 1st ed. Fine in dj. *PRATT.* $37.50

FAVORITE RECIPES OF THE MOVIE STARS. NY: Tower Books, 1931. Sl worn, o/w VG. *SCHOYER'S.* $20

Fawcett, Clara Hallard. PAPER DOLLS: A GUIDE TO COSTUME. NY: H.L. Lindquist, 1951. 1st ed. Signed. VF. *WREDEN.* $75

Fay, Eliot. LORENZO IN SEARCH OF THE SUN. London, (1955). 1st Eng ed. NF in sl soiled, chipped dj. *DIAMOND.* $25

Fearing, F. REFLEX ACTION: A STUDY IN THE HISTORY OF PHYSIOLOGICAL PSYCHOLOGY. Baltimore, 1930. Inscribed and signed. Spine spotted and dull. *FYE.* $125

Fearing, Kenneth. THE BIG CLOCK. London: Bodley Head/Australasian Pub Co, (1947). Copyright pg states "First Published in Australia, 1947". Text block sl cocked, o/w Fine in sl rubbed dj (2 1" tears front panel). *HELLER.* $75

Fearing, Kenneth. THE BIG CLOCK. NY: Harcourt Brace & Co., (1946). 1st ed. Eps a bit darkened, else About Fine in VG+ dj w/small chips at corners of spine. *BETWEEN COVERS.* $250

Featherstonaugh, G.W. EXCURSION THROUGH THE SLAVE STATES...WITH SKETCHES OF POPULAR MANNERS....NY: Harper, 1844. 1st Amer ed. 188pp. Orig ptd wrappers. Howes F68. *GINSBERG.* $200

Featherstonhaugh, G.W. A CANOE VOYAGE UP THE MINNAY SOTOR. 2 vols. St. Paul: MN Hist Soc, 1970. Facs rpt. Cl. Mint in slipcase. *ARTIS.* $37.50

Feiffer, Jules. PASSIONELLA. NY: McGraw-Hill, 1959. 1st ed. Wraps, mild wear w/marker price corner front wrap. Signed. *BEASLEY.* $45

Feikema, Feike. BOY ALMIGHTY. Itasca Press, 1945. 1st ed. Fine, name. *AUTHORS OF THE WEST.* $25

Feikema, Feike. THE BROTHER. Doubleday & Co, 1950. 1st ed. Fine in chipped dj. *AUTHORS OF THE WEST.* $35

Feikema, Feike. THE CHOKECHERRY TREE. Doubleday, 1948. 1st ed. VG in dj. Ex libris. Bk has tape marks on boards & pastedowns. Dj trimmed & stained from acetate jacket; spine sunned. *STAHR.* $15

Feikema, Feike. THE GIANT. Doubleday & Co, 1951. 1st ed. Fine in chipped dj. *AUTHORS OF THE WEST.* $35

Feikema, Feike. THIS IS THE YEAR. Doubleday, 1947. 1st ed. Ep maps. Fine in clean chipped dj. *AUTHORS OF THE WEST.* $25

Feinberg, Abraham. RABBI FEINBERG'S HANOI DIARY. Don Mills, Ont: Longmans Canada, 1968. NF in VG dj. *AKA.* $75

Feiner, Ruth. CAT ACROSS THE PATH. Phila: Lippincott, (1935). 1st ed. Some dj wear. Fine. *MUELLER.* $25

Feist, Raymond. SILVERTHORN. Doubleday, 1985. 1st ed. Fine in dj. *MADLE.* $35

Feldman, Irving. WORKS AND DAYS AND OTHER POEMS. Boston and Toronto: Little, Brown and Company, (c1961). 1st Amer ed, 1st bk. Fine in sl darkened white dj. *HELLER.* $50

Fell, Edgar Tremlett (comp). HISTORY OF THE SEVENTH DIVISION. UNITED STATES ARMY, 1917-1919. Phila: (Seventh Division Officer's Assoc, 1927). 4 maps in envelope attached to back pastedown ep. *KARMIOLE.* $40

Fellows, Charles. A JOURNAL WRITTEN... DURING AN EX-CURSION IN ASIA MINOR 1838. London, 1839. 21 full-pg plts, fldg map. Boards, new cl spine, lea label. x,347pp. Charles Kingsley's copy, with his sig. *O'NEILL.* $450

Felt, E.P. INSECTS AFFECTING PARK AND WOODLAND TREES. Albany, 1905-06. 70 plts. 2 vols. Ex-lib. *SUTTON.* $100

Feltman, Lieut. William. JOURNAL OF LIEUT. WILLIAM FELTMAN, OF THE FIRST PENNSYLVANIA REGIMENT, 1781-82....Phila: Baird, 1853. 1st ed. 48pp. Orig cl backed boards, paper label on front cover. Howes F75. *GINSBERG.* $150

Felton, R.F. BRITISH FLORAL DECORATION. A&C Black, 1910. 1st ed. 7s 6d Series. Minor tear base of spine, else VG. *OLD LONDON.* $60

Fennell, James. AN APOLOGY FOR THE LIFE OF JAMES FEN-NELL. Phila: Moses Thomas, 1814. 1st ed. Later 1/2 lea, quite rubbed; morocco label; frontis; complete with half-title. VG. *DRAMATIS PERSONAE.* $85

Fenton, E.H. and S. THE ART ALBUM OF NEW ZEALAND FLORA. Vol. I: (All pub) Author's Edition. Wellington: Bock & Cousins, 1889. 1st ed. xviii,180pp. 40+ chromolitho plts. Rebound in 1/2 gilt black calf, over black cl. Rare. *KARMIOLE.* $500

Fenton, Robert W. THE BIG SWINGERS. EDGAR RICE BUR-ROUGHS 1875-1950; TARZAN 1912-. Englewood Cliffs, NJ, (1967). 2nd ptg. Fine, dj. *DIAMOND.* $35

Fenwick, E.P. THE INCONVENIENT CORPSE. Farrar & Rinehart, (1943). 1st ed. VG in Good dj. *BEBBAH.* $20

Ferber, Edna. AMERICAN BEAUTY. NY, 1931. 1st ed. Signed presentation. Spine little sunned, extremities sl rubbed, traces of removed scotch tape inside covers. NF. *POLYANTHOS.* $45

Ferber, Edna. GIANT. Doubleday, 1952. 1st ed. About Fine in price-clipped dj. Owner inscrip. *STAHR.* $60

Ferber, Edna. GIANT. GC, NY: Doubleday, 1952. 1st ed. Bright sl chipped price-clipped dj. *SCHOYER'S.* $35

Ferber, Edna. GIANT. NY, 1952. 1st ed. Traces of removed scotch tape inside covers. Fine in dj (traces of removed scotch tape inside flaps, strengthened internally at edges, extremities, spine sl rubbed, rear panel little soiled). *POLYANTHOS.* $30

Ferguson, Charles D. CALIFORNIA GOLD FIELDS. Oakland: Biobooks, 1948. One of 750. Fine. *LAURIE.* $40

Ferguson, Charles W. ORGANIZING TO BEAT THE DEVIL. GC: Doubleday, 1971. 1st ed. NF in NF dj. *CONNOLLY & WADE.* $42.50

Ferguson, Dugald. VICISSITUDES OF BUSH LIFE IN AUSTRALIA AND NEW ZEALAND. London: Swan Son-nenschein & Co., 1891. Good. *PARMER.* $75

Ferguson, James. ASTRONOMY EXPLAINED UPON SIR ISAAC NEWTON'S PRINCIPLES, AND MADE EASY TO THOSE WHO HAVE NOT STUDIED MATHEMATICS. Phila: Mathew Carey, 1809. 2nd US ed. Rev by Robert Patterson. Orig full leather, worn, w/morocco label. Corners bumped & worn, eps foxed, but Very Nice. *KNOLLWOOD.* $350

Ferguson, Mungo. PRINTED BOOKS IN THE LIBRARY OF THE HUNTERIAN MUSEUM IN THE UNIVERSITY OF GLAS-GOW: A CATALOGUE. Glasgow, 1930. 1st ed. *FYE.* $150

Ferguson, R.S. (ed). OLD CHURCH PLATE IN THE DIOCESE OF CARLISLE. London: George Bell & Sons, 1882. 1st ed. VG. *BACKROOM.* $75

Ferguson, William and John Royce. MAYA RUINS IN CENTRAL AMERICA IN COLOR. Albuquerque: Univ of NM Press, (1984). 1st ed. Good in dj. *SILVER.* $40

Ferguson, William and John Royce. MAYA RUINS OF MEXICO IN COLOR. PALENQUE, UXMAL, KABAH, SAYIL, XLAPAK, LABNA, CHICHEN ITZA, COBA, TULUM. Norman: Univ of OK Press, 1977. 1st ed. VG in dj. *PARMER.* $25

Fergusson, D. LETTER OF THE SECRETARY OF WAR COM-MUNICATING...A COPY OF THE REPORT OF MAJOR D. FERGUSSON ON THE COUNTRY....BETWEEN TUCSON AND LOBOS BAY. Wash., SD1, 1863. 1st ed. 22pp. 3 fldg maps. Half morocco. Howes F87. *GINSBERG.* $300

Fergusson, Erna. MURDER & MYSTERY IN NEW MEXICO. Albuquerque: Merle Armitage Editions, (1948). 1st ed. Frontis. Cl, dj. VG. *SCHOYER'S.* $65

Fergusson, Erna. OUR SOUTHWEST. NY: Knopf, 1946. 2 fldg maps, 1 double-pg map. Pict orange cl faded, else Good. Signed. *CONNOLLY & WADE.* $30

Fergusson, Harvey. FOOTLOOSE McGARNIGAL. Knopf, 1930. 1st ed. Fine, clean dj panels laid in. *AUTHORS OF THE WEST.* $35

Fergusson, Harvey. HOME IN THE WEST: AN INQUIRY INTO MY ORIGINS. Duell, Sloan & Pearce, (1944). 1st ed. Fine, clean dj frayed. *AUTHORS OF THE WEST.* $25

Fergusson, J. TREE AND SERPENT WORSHIP. London: India Museum, 1868. 2nd ed. 45 litho plts w/some edge wear. In cloth portfolio, backstrip split apart, cl ties worn and partially missing, ex-lib. Rare. *SUTTON.* $145

Ferlinghetti, Lawrence. A CONEY ISLAND OF THE MIND. New Directions, (1958). 1st ed, ptd wraps. VG, leaves browned as usual. Scarce. *SECOND LIFE.* $75

Ferlinghetti, Lawrence. LANDSCAPES OF LIVING AND DYING. NY, 1979. 1st ed. Rev copy, w/slip laid in. Signed presentation copy. Fine in Fine dj. *POLYANTHOS.* $30

Ferlinghetti, Lawrence. LITERARY SAN FRANCISCO. SF: City Lights, 1980. 1st ed. NF. *SMITH.* $50

Ferlinghetti, Lawrence. ONE THOUSAND FEARFUL WORDS FOR FIDEL CASTRO. SF: City Lights, 1961. 1st ed. Fldg broadside bearing stamps of Fair Play for Cuba Committee. Fine. *BEASLEY.* $25

Ferlinghetti, Lawrence. THE SECRET MEANING OF THINGS. (NY): New Directions, (1969). One of 150 numbered, signed. Fine in NF pub's slipcase. *LOPEZ.* $100

Fermi, E. COLLECTED PAPERS. 2 vols. Univ of Chicago Press, 1971. Vol. 1, no dj, Vol. 2, dj. Near New. *BOOKCELL.* $60

Fern, Thomas (comp). THE DRAWINGS AND WATERCOLORS OF THOMAS MORAN (1837-1926). Notre Dame, 1976. Stiff cream-colored wraps. Near Mint. *FIVE QUAIL.* $45

Ferrars, E.X. HUNT THE TORTOISE. GC: Doubleday Crime Club, 1950. 1st ed. Fine in dj. *ELSE FINE.* $35

Ferree, B. AMERICAN ESTATES AND GARDENS. NY, (1904). Ornamental gilt dec cl. Some wear at extrems; dampstaining heel of spine, lower section of back cvr (leaving lower marginal stains on eps, lt edge staining last few pp). *SUTTON.* $350

Ferrel, William. A POPULAR TREATISE ON THE WINDS....NY: John Wiley & Sons, 1889 (1889). Ex-lib, bkpl, spine label, sm strip paper glued to cvr, o/w Good in blue cl, gilt titling on spine, corners bumped, extremity wear. *KNOLLWOOD.* $75

Ferrer, Melchor. TITO'S HATS. GC, (1940). Unpaginated. Illus by Jean Charlot. Spotting to ep, edgewear, VG in Fair+ dj separated at spine w/pieces missing, chips. *BEBBAH.* $25

Ferri Pisani (Marcel Victor Paul) Camille. PRINCE NAPOLEON IN AMERICA, 1861. LETTERS....George J. Joyaux (trans). London: Gallery Press, 1960. 1st UK ed. Fine in NF dj. *CONNOLLY & WADE.* $27.50

Ferriar, John. AN ESSAY TOWARDS A THEORY OF APPARITIONS. London: Cadell & Davies. 1813. 1st ed. 140pp. Uncut. Orig drab boards rebacked in later cl; eps lacking. *KARMIOLE.* $125

Ferrier, David. THE FUNCTIONS OF THE BRAIN. NY, 1876. 1st Amer ed. Recent 1/4 leather, 323pp. *FYE.* $500

Ferril, Thomas H. & Helen (eds). THE ROCKY MOUNTAIN HERALD READER. Morrow, 1966. 1st ed. Fine in dj. *AUTHORS OF THE WEST.* $20

Ferris, Benjamin G. UTAH AND THE MORMONS. NY: Harper & Bros, 1854. 1st ed. Orig emb cl w/gilt spine titles. Cl worn, foxing

throughout, offset to eps. Pagination and size conform to Wagner-Camp 238b:1. 25 illus called for are present; in addition there are two "Smith Preaching in the Wilderness" and "Smith Tarred and Feathered" (text illus rather than plts). Excerpt for recruiting poster in this text. Howes F98. *PARMER.* $125

Ferris, Warren Angus. LIFE IN THE ROCKY MOUNTAINS. DIARY OF WANDERINGS ON SOURCES OF RIVERS MISSOURI...Arranged by Herbert Auerbach. Salt Lake City: Rocky Mtn. Bk Shop, (1940). Frontis, 3 plts, fldg map. VG. *OREGON.* $165

Ferris, Warren Angus. LIFE IN THE ROCKY MOUNTAINS. DIARY OF WANDERINGS ON SOURCES OF RIVERS MISSOURI...Paul Phillips (ed). Denver: Old West Pub, 1940. 1st ed. Frontis, 3 facs, 2 maps (1 fldg). VF in VG dj. Howes F100. *OREGON.* $325

Ferris, Warren Angus. LIFE IN THE ROCKY MOUNTAINS: A DIARY OF WANDERINGS...1830-1835. Denver: Old West Publishing, 1983. New rev ed. Fine in orig glassine dj. *BOOK MARKET.* $40

Fetta, Emma Lou. MURDER ON THE FACE OF IT. GC: Doubleday Crime Club, 1940. 1st ed. Fine in dj w/wear, chipping. *MORDIDA.* $35

Feuchtwanger, Franz. THE ART OF ANCIENT MEXICO. London & NY: Thames & Hudson, (1954). 1st ed. 4 color plts, 105 b/w. Good in chipped dj. *SILVER.* $45

Feuchtwanger, Franz. THE ART OF ANCIENT MEXICO. London: Thames and Hudson, (1954). Color frontis, 3 color illus. Good. *ARCHAEOLOGIA.* $35

Fewkes, Jesse Walter. A PREHISTORIC ISLAND CULTURE AREA OF AMERICA. Washington: GPO, 1922. Some wear to olive grn cl. Interior clean, tight. *PARMER.* $55

Fewkes, Jesse Walter. ANTIQUITIES OF MESA VERDE NATIONAL PARK. 1911. Green cloth, 82pp, 35 plts, 4 figures. Fine. *FIVE QUAIL.* $55

Fewkes, Jesse Walter. MESA VERDE NATIONAL PARK. National Park Series, 1919. Pict colored wraps, 16pp. VF. *FIVE QUAIL.* $15

Fewkes, Jesse Walter. PREHISTORIC VILLAGES, CASTLES, AND TOWERS OF SOUTHWESTERN COLORADO. Washington: GPO, 1919. 18 figs, 33 plts. Good. *ARCHAEOLOGIA.* $45

Fewkes, Jesse Walter. PREHISTORIC VILLAGES, CASTLES, AND TOWERS OF SOUTHWESTERN COLORADO. 1919. Green cloth, 79pp, 33 plts, 18 figures. NF. *FIVE QUAIL.* $35

Fewkes, Jesse Walter. PRELIMINARY REPORT ON A VISIT TO THE NAVAHO NATIONAL MONUMENT IN ARIZONA. Smithsonian Institution, BAE, Bulletin 50. Washington: GPO, 1911. NF. *LAURIE.* $25

Fewkes, Jesse Walter. PRELIMINARY REPORT ON A VISIT TO THE NAVAHO NATIONAL MONUMENT, ARIZONA. 1911. Green cloth, 35pp, 22 plts, 3 figures. Fine. *FIVE QUAIL.* $35

Fibbleton, George (pseud of Asa Greene). TRAVELS IN AMERICA. NY: William Pearson and Peter Hill, 1833. 1st ed. Some inner foxing. 66 added plts and views. Howes G376. *HUDSON.* $450

Field, Eugene. LOVE-SONGS OF CHILDHOOD. NY: Scribner's, 1894. 1st ed. Pencilled owner's name, spine a little sunned, but VG. BAL 5761. *CHAPEL HILL.* $40

Field, Eugene. MY BOOK. WITH VIGNETTES BY C.M. SEYPPEL. N.p., 1905. 1st ed. Pict cvr. Vellum spine and rear cvr little soiled. Fine. *POLYANTHOS.* $150

Field, Eugene. POEMS OF CHILDHOOD. NY: Charles Scribner's Sons, 1904. 1st ed. Black cl. 8 color plts by Maxfield Parrish. VG. *BLUE MOUNTAIN.* $125

Field, Eugene. THE HOUSE. AN EPISODE IN THE LIVES OF REUBEN BAKER, ASTRONOMER, AND OF HIS WIFE

ALICE. NY: Scribner's, 1896. 1st ed. NF. BAL 5772. *CHAPEL HILL.* $40

Field, Eugene. THE LOVE AFFAIRS OF A BIBLIOMANIAC. NY: Charles Scribner's Sons, 1896. 1st ed, 1st issue with 8 entries listed on the page opposite the fly-leaf. (BAL 5771). *OAK KNOLL.* $40

Field, Henry M(artyn). GIBRALTER. NY: Scribner, 1888. Some spots, Corners bumped. *SCHOYER'S.* $25

Field, Isobel. THIS LIFE I'VE LIVED. Longmans, 1937. 1st ed. 7 plts. VG in Good+ dj. *OREGON.* $25

Field, Rachel. AVE MARIA. AN INTERPRETATION FROM WALT DISNEY'S "FANTASIA." Random, (1940). Unpaginated. Illus in color, b/w by Disney artists w/scenes made for Fantasia. Initials of Field's new text & Schubert's music set in gilt to accompany illus. Slight wear. VG. *BEBBAH.* $25

Field, Rachel. HITTY, HER FIRST HUNDRED YEARS. Macmillan, 1929. 2nd ptg. Signed. 207pp. Dorothy Lathrop's illus. Edgewear, fading to spine, VG. *BEBBAH.* $60

Field, Rachel. TIME OUT OF MIND. NY: MacMillan, 1935. 1st ed. Some browning to eps, else Fine in NF pict price-clipped dj. Inscribed. *CAPTAIN'S BOOKSHELF.* $50

Field, Richard S. JASPER JOHNS PRINTS 1960-1970. Phila Museum of Art, 1970. White wraps (sl soiled). 80 leaves (2 fldg). *BLUE MOUNTAIN.* $150

Field, Sara Bard. BARABBAS: A DRAMATIC NARRATIVE. Albert & Charles Boni, 1932. 1st ed. Inscribed, signed. Fine in repaired dj. *AUTHORS OF THE WEST.* $50

Field, Saul and Morton Levitt. BLOOMSDAY. Greenwich, CT: NY Graphic Soc, (1972). 1st ed, regular issue. Inscribed by authors. Fine in sl discolored dj (lamination lifted). *JAFFE.* $125

Field, Stephen J. CALIFORNIA ALCALDE. Oakland: Biobooks, 1950. One of 600. Fine. *LAURIE.* $35

Field, Stephen J. PERSONAL REMINISCENCES OF EARLY DAYS IN CALIFORNIA...TO WHICH IS ADDED THE STORY OF HIS ATTEMPTED ASSASSINATION....(Wash), ptd for a few friends. Not published, (1893). (6),472pp. Orig cl. Howes F117. *GINSBERG.* $200

Field, Stephen J. SOME ACCOUNT OF THE WORK OF STEPHEN J. FIELD. np (NY?): S.B. Smith, 1881. Shaken, worn in orig cl. Chauncy Black (ed). *PARMER.* $75

Field, Thomas W. THE BATTLE OF LONG ISLAND WITH PRECEDING AND SUBSEQUENT EVENTS. Brooklyn: Long Island Hist Soc, 1869. Ltd ed, issued in 100 royal 8vo copies and 1000 8vo copies. 5 plts, 2 fldg maps. Owner sig, lt waterstaining. Overall VG. *WEBER.* $100

Fielding, Henry. AN APOLOGY OF THE LIFE OF MRS. SHAMELA ANDREWS. Waltham St. Lawrence: Golden Cockerel Press, 1926. 1st ed. One of 450 numbered. Some marginal worming to final leaves. *MUELLER.* $40

Fielding, Henry. THE HISTORY OF TOM JONES. T. M. Cleland (illus). 2 vols. NY: LEC, 1952. Ltd to 1500 signed by Cleland. Spines sl foxed, o/w a Fine set. Slipcase. *JAFFE.* $100

• Fielding, Henry. THE WORKS. (London: Bickers and Son; H. Sotheran and Co., 1871). 10 vols. Ed by James P. Browne. Cloth sl faded at edges, one hinge cracked, isolated very minor foxing, o/w remarkably well preserved. *PIRAGES.* $250

Fielding, Henry. THE WORKS. With A Life of The Author, In Eight Volumes. London: Strahan, Rivington, etc., 1771. Tall 8vo, frontis port by Hogarth. Full contemp polished calf, gilt rules and dentelles, spines elaborately gilt in panels, double lea labels, marbled eps. Some wear to hinges and edges but still Nice. *HARTFIELD.* $795.

Fields, William and Noreen Lemak. A HISTORY OF STROKE: ITS RECOGNITION AND TREATMENT. NY, 1989. 1st ed. *FYE.* $50

Fierman, Floyd S. SOME EARLY JEWISH SETTLERS ON THE SOUTHWESTERN FRONTIER. El Paso: Texas Western Press, 1960. One of 250. Fine in wraps. *LAURIE.* $125

Fife, Austin and Alta (eds). BALLADS OF THE GREAT WEST. American West Pub Co, (1970). 1st ed. Erratum slip. Fine in clean chipped dj. *AUTHORS OF THE WEST.* $25

Fife, Austin and Alta. SAINTS OF SAGE AND SADDLE. Bloomington: IN Univ, 1956. 1st ed. Fine in VG dj. *CONNOLLY & WADE.* $42.50

Figueroa, Don Jose. THE MANIFESTO TO THE MEXICAN REPUBLIC. Oakland, CA: 1952. Cloth. Ltd to 750. Howes F122. Reprint. *GINSBERG.* $35

FIGURE PAINTING IN WATER COLORS BY CONTEMPORARY BRITISH ARTISTS. London, 1923. 28 tipped-in color plts. NF. *POLYANTHOS.* $50

Figuter, L. REPTILES AND BIRDS. NY, 1870. 306 woodcuts. Lower corners worn, extrems scuffed, hinge cracked, ex-lib. *SUTTON.* $40

Filmer, Henry. THE PAGEANT OF PERSIA...NY, 1936. 422 pp. Dj. Pres. *O'NEILL.* $30

Finch, Christopher. THE ART OF WALT DISNEY—FROM MICKEY MOUSE TO THE MAGIC KINGDOMS. NY: Abrams, (1973). 1st ed. 351 color plts. Fine- in poor dj, badly torn and chipped mylar cvr. *AARD.* $55

Findley, Palmer. PRIESTS OF LUCINA, THE STORY OF OBSTETRICS. Boston, 1939. 1st ed. Backstrip spotted, o/w Fine. *FYE.* $75

Findley, Timothy. THE LAST OF THE CRAZY PEOPLE. London: Macdonald, (1967). 1st Eng ed, 1st bk. Name stamp, o/w Fine in sl soiled largely white dj. *HELLER.* $75

Fine, David (ed). LOS ANGELES IN FICTION: A COLLECTION.... Univ of NM Press, (1984). 1st ed. Softbound. New. *AUTHORS OF THE WEST.* $10

Finely, Martha. ELSIE YACHTING WITH THE RAYMONDS. NY, (1890). 1st ed. Frontis. Emb red cl, gilt stamped. NF. *ARTIS.* $15

Finerty, John. WAR PATH AND BIVOUAC: THE BIG HORN AND YELLOWSTONE EXPEDITION. Chicago: Lakeside Classic, 1955. 1st ed thus. Ed by Milton Quaife. Teg, blue cl. Frontis, 4 maps, 6 plts. Fine. *CONNOLLY & WADE.* $37.50

Fink, Augusta. TIME AND THE TERRACED LAND. Berkeley: Howell-North: 1966. 1st ed. Bkpl. NF. *CONNOLLY & WADE.* $40

Finlay, George. HISTORY OF GREECE UNDER OTHOMAN AND VENETIAN DOMINATION. London, 1856. 367pp. Fine. *O'NEILL.* $85

Finlay, Ian Hamilton. IAN HAMILTON FINLAY (AT THE) SERPENTINE GALLERY. London: Arts Council, 1977. 1st ed. Wraps, Fine. *BEASLEY.* $40

Finlayson, H.H. THE RED CENTRE. Sydney/London: Angus & Robertson, 1943. 5th ed. VG with front hinge started. *PARMER.* $35

Finley, J. B. HISTORY OF THE WYANDOTT MISSION, AT UPPER SANDUSKY, OHIO. Cincinnati, 1840. 1st ed. 432pp. Contemp full calf. Howes F144. *GINSBERG.* $350

Finley, James B. LIFE AMONG THE INDIANS, OR, PERSONAL REMINISCENCES.... D.W. Clark (ed). Cincinnati: Curts & Jennings, (n.d.). VG. Howes F-145. *LAURIE.* $50

Finley, John. A PILGRIM IN PALESTINE...NY, 1919. xiv,251pp. *O'NEILL.* $25

Finney, Charles. THE CIRCUS OF DR. LAO. LEC, 1982. One of 2000 illus, signed by Claire Van Vliet. Fine in slipcase. *CAPTAIN'S BOOKSHELF.* $100

Finney, Humphrey. A STUD FARM DIARY. Berryville: Blue Ridge, 1949. Flexible binding, signed. 1st ed. thus. Good+. *OCTOBER FARM.* $45

Finney, Jack. GOOD NEIGHBOR SAM. Simon & Schuster, 1963, 1st ed. VG. *MADLE.* $65.

Finney, Jack. THE NIGHT PEOPLE. GC: Doubleday, 1977. 1st ed. Fine but for rubbed spine ends, in NF dj w/rubbed spine ends and few short tears. *BEASLEY.* $35

Finney, Jack. TIME AND AGAIN. NY: Simon & Schuster, 1970. 1st ed. Faint stain ep, else Fine in 1st state dj. *ELSE FINE.* $150

Finney, Jack. TIME AND AGAIN. Simon & Schuster, 1970. 1st ed. VG in dj. *MADLE.* $85

Finnie, Richard (text & photos). CANOL. SF: Ryder & Ingram, 1945. 1st ed. Lt water stain on middle fore-edge of first 50pp for about 1/2" in on margins only, else VG. *BLUE DRAGON.* $75

Finnie, Richard. LURE OF THE NORTH. Phila, (1940). VG. *ARTIS.* $30

Finsterbusch, C.A. COCKFIGHTING ALL OVER THE WORLD. Gaffney, SC: Gritt & Steel, 1929. 1st ed. Covers somewhat worn, else VG. *OLD LONDON.* $50

Firbank, Ronald. CONCERNING THE ECCENTRICITIES OF CARDINAL PIRELLI. London, 1926. 1st ed (1000). Frontis. Covers very sl rubbed in a few small areas. Fine. *POLYANTHOS.* $125

Firbank, Ronald. INCLINATIONS. London, 1916. 1st ed (500). 2 dwgs by Albert Rutherston (Rotherstein). Spine little sunned, extremities sl rubbed, tiny crease lower corner front panel. Fine. *POLYANTHOS.* $125

Firbank, Ronald. PRANCING NIGGER. NY, (1924). 1st ed. Fine in lined dj w/chips, pieces missing. *POLYANTHOS.* $75

Firbank, Ronald. SORROW IN SUNLIGHT. London, n.d., (1925). Ltd ed, 798/1000. Fine in lined dj, sunned, chipped, 2 1/4" piece missing lower spine. *POLYANTHOS.* $100

Firbank, Ronald. THE FLOWER BENEATH THE FOOT. NY: Brentano's, 1924. 1st US ed. Fine but for dulling spine, in NF dj w/a few internal mends. *BEASLEY.* $200

Firbank, Ronald. THE PRINCESS ZOUBAROFF. A COMEDY. London, 1920. 1st ed of 513. Colored frontis. Names, cvrs little edge rubbed, front cover sl rubbed. Fine. *POLYANTHOS.* $100

Firbank, Ronald. VALMOUTH. London, 1919. 1st ed. 500 copies. Spine sl rubbed. Fine. *POLYANTHOS.* $100

Firebaugh, Ellen. THE PHYSICIAN'S WIFE AND THE THINGS THAT PERTAIN TO HER LIFE. Phila, 1900. *FYE.* $60

Fireman, Janet R. THE SPANISH ROYAL CORPS OF ENGINEERS IN THE WESTERN BORDERLANDS. A.H. Clark, 1977. 1st ed. Fine. *VARNER.* $30

Fireman, Janet R. THE SPANISH ROYAL CORPS OF ENGINEERS...OF BOURBON REFORM 1764 TO 1815. Glendale, 1977. 1st ed. Orig cl. Spain in the West. Vol. 12. *GINSBERG.* $75

FIRST (AND SECOND) REPORT(S) OF THE COMMISSIONERS FOR INQUIRING INTO THE STATE OF LARGE TOWNS AND POPULOUS DISTRICTS. London, 1844-1845. 1st eds. 351pp,266pp + fldg charts and plans. 2 vols. Orig cl rebacked. Owner inscription. Scarce. *FYE.* $300

FIRST ANNUAL REPORT OF THE UNITED STATES ENTOMOLOGICAL COMMISSION FOR THE YEAR 1877 RELATING TO THE ROCKY MOUNTAIN LOCUST....(By C.V. Riley et al). Washington, 1878. 5 plts. 2 fldg maps. 1/2 morocco. Ex-lib. *SUTTON.* $65

Firth, Walter. THE SACK OF MONTE CARLO. NY: Harper & Brothers, 1898. 1st ed. Some dampstaining on back cover o/w VG in cl covered pict cvrs w/gold stamping. *MORDIDA.* $45

Fischer, Joseph. THE INNER EAR INCLUDING OTONEUROLOGY, OTOSURGERY, AND PROBLEMS IN MODERN WARFARE. NY, 1943. 1st ed. *FYE.* $50

Fish, Donald. AIRLINE DETECTIVE. London: Collins, 1962. 1st ed. VG in lightly used dj. *JUVELIS.* $100

Fish, Robert L. A HANDY DEATH. NY: Simon & Schuster, 1973. 1st ed. Inscribed. Remainder mark on bottom edge o/w Fine in dj. *MORDIDA.* $30

Fish, Robert L. THE XAVIER AFFAIR. NY: Putnam, 1969. 1st ed. Signed. Fine in dj. *SILVER DOOR.* $50

Fishbein, Morris (ed). DOCTORS AT WAR. NY, 1945. 1st ed. *FYE.* $50

Fishbein, Morris. FADS AND QUACKERY IN HEALING, AN ANALYSIS OF THE FOIBLES OF THE HEALING CULTS, WITH ESSAYS ON VARIOUS OTHER PECULIAR NOTIONS IN THE HEALTH FIELD. NY, 1932. 1st ed. *FYE.* $60

Fisher, Alfred Young. THE GHOST IN THE UNDERBLOWS. Ed by Lawrence Clark Powell. LA: Ward Ritchie Press, 1940. 1st ed. Ltd to 300. Spine sl faded; gilt rubbed. Sl staining, o/w VG. *DIAMOND.* $150

Fisher, Clay. THE OLDEST MAIDEN LADY IN NEW MEXICO AND OTHER STORIES. Macmillan, (1962). 1st ed. Fine in dj. *AUTHORS OF THE WEST.* $20

Fisher, George. ARITHMETIC...A NEW EDITION CAREFULLY CORRECTED. Glasgow: A. Duncan, 1770. 312pp. Old calf, rebacked. Occasional text stains. *KARMIOLE.* $125

Fisher, Harry W. ABROAD WITH MARK TWAIN AND EUGENE FIELD....NY, 1922. 1st ed. VG+. *McCLINTOCK.* $15

Fisher, James & R.M. Lockley. SEA-BIRDS. Boston: Houghton Mifflin, 1954. 1st ed. Dj. Spine sunned, o/w VG. *WEBER.* $20

Fisher, M.F.K. A CORDIALL WATER. London: Faber and Faber, 1963. 1st UK ed. Fine but for tape stain on copyright page, in Fine dj but for wear at head of spine. *BEASLEY.* $65

Fisher, M.F.K. HERE LET US FEAST. NY, 1946. 1st ed. Spine sl rubbed, dj extremities sl rubbed. *POLYANTHOS.* $60

Fisher, M.F.K. HERE LET US FEAST. NY: Viking, 1946. 1st ed. VG w/slight spine darkening, yellowing cheap paper. VG dj (few short edge tears, tiny stain). *LOPEZ.* $50

Fisher, M.F.K. NOT NOW BUT NOW. NY: Viking, 1947. 1st ed. Fine but for bkpl, in NF dj (sl wear spine head; lt chipping at foot). *BEASLEY.* $125

Fisher, M.F.K. SPIRITS OF THE VALLEY. (NY): Targ Editions. 1985. Ltd to 250 signed. Glassine dj. Fine. *KARMIOLE.* $100

Fisher, M.F.K. SPIRITS OF THE VALLEY. Cl-backed boards, glassine dj. NY: Targ Editions, 1985. 1st ed. One of 250 signed. Mint. *JAFFE.* $150

Fisher, M.F.K. SPIRITS OF THE VALLEY. NY: Targ Editions, 1985. Signed ed, ltd to 250. *JUVELIS.* $90

Fisher, M.F.K. THE STORY OF WINE IN CALIFORNIA. Berkeley: Univ of CA Press, 1962. 1st ed. Sl spotting o/w VG in dj (few short edge tears, tiny stain). *LOPEZ.* $100

Fisher, Margery and James. SHACKLETON AND THE ANTARCTIC. Boston: Houghton Mifflin, 1958. VG in Good dj. *BLUE DRAGON.* $35

Fisher, Margery and James. SHACKLETON. London: Barrie, 1957. "New Cheap Edition." Dj very worn; bk VG. *PARMER.* $45

Fisher, Raymond H. THE VOYAGE OF SEMEN DEZHNEV IN 1648...WITH SELECTED DOCUMENTS. London: Hakluyt Society, 1981. 1st ed. Fldg map. As New in sl rubbed dj. *PARMER.* $35

Fisher, Steve. GIVEAWAY. NY: Random House, 1954. 1st ed.

VG in worn dj (chipped, soiled, rubbed, short closed tears). *MORDIDA.* $30

Fisher, Steve. IMAGE OF HELL. NY: E.P. Dutton, 1961. 1st ed. Inscribed. Fine in dj (short closed tears; wear). *MORDIDA.* $85

Fisher, Steve. NO HOUSE LIMIT. NY: E.P. Dutton, 1958. 1st ed. Edges lightly spotted o/w Fine in VG dj with wear, spotting. *MORDIDA.* $40

Fisher, Steve. SAXON'S GHOST. LA: Sherbourne Press, 1969. 1st ed. Fine in dj with minor. *MORDIDA.* $37.50

Fisher, Steve. TAKE ALL YOU CAN GET. NY: Random House, 1955. 1st ed. Fine in price-clipped dj with minor wear. *MORDIDA.* $40

Fisher, Steve. THE BIG DREAM. Garden City: Doubleday, 1970. 1st ed. Fine in dj. *MORDIDA.* $45

Fisher, Steve. THE HELL-BLACK NIGHT. LA: Sherbourne, 1970. 1st ed. Fine in dj. *SILVER DOOR.* $37.50

Fisher, Steve. THE HELL-BLACK NIGHT. LA: Sherbourne Press, 1970. 1st ed. Fine in dj. *MORDIDA.* $35

Fisher, Steve. WINTER KILL. NY: Dodd Mead, 1946. 1st ed. VG in dj (chipped, short closed tears, 1" piece missing). *MORDIDA.* $25

Fisher, Vardis. ADAM AND THE SERPENT. Vanguard, (1947). 1st ed. Fine, Nice dj, some straight tears. *AUTHORS OF THE WEST.* $40

Fisher, Vardis. APRIL: A FABLE OF LOVE. Caxton, 1937. 1st ed. Fine, clean chipped dj. *AUTHORS OF THE WEST.* $100

Fisher, Vardis. CHILDREN OF GOD. AN AMERICAN EPIC. NY: Harper, 1939. 1st ed. Good+. *CONNOLLY & WADE.* $25

Fisher, Vardis. CHILDREN OF GOD. AN AMERICAN EPIC. NY: Harper, 1939. 1st ed. About Fine in chipped, though Good dj. *CONNOLLY & WADE.* $45

Fisher, Vardis. CITY OF ILLUSION. Caldwell, ID: The Caxton Printers, Ltd. 1941. De Luxe Ed ltd to 100 numbered, signed. Full black morocco, gilt. *KARMIOLE.* $150

Fisher, Vardis. CITY OF ILLUSION. Caxton, 1941. 1st ltd ed of 1,000, this not numbered. Fine. *AUTHORS OF THE WEST.* $50

Fisher, Vardis. DARKNESS AND THE DEEP. Vanguard, (1943). 1st ed. Fine in dj. *AUTHORS OF THE WEST.* $30

Fisher, Vardis. FORGIVE US OUR VIRTUES: A COMEDY OF EVASIONS. Caxton, 1938. 1st ed. VG, name. *AUTHORS OF THE WEST.* $50

Fisher, Vardis. IN TRAGIC LIFE. Caldwell: Caxton, 1932. 1st ed. VG. *OREGON.* $50

Fisher, Vardis. INTIMATIONS OF EVE. Vanguard, (1946). 1st ed. Fine. *AUTHORS OF THE WEST.* $20

Fisher, Vardis. LOVE AND DEATH: THE COMPLETE STORIES. Doubleday, 1959. 1st ed. Fine in dj. *AUTHORS OF THE WEST.* $40

Fisher, Vardis. NO VILLAIN NEED BE. Caxton, 1936. 1st ed. Fine, clean chipped dj. *AUTHORS OF THE WEST.* $75

Fisher, Vardis. PASSIONS SPIN THE PLOT. Caxton, 1934. 1st ed. Fine in dj. *AUTHORS OF THE WEST.* $75

Fisher, Vardis. PEMMICAN. A NOVEL OF THE HUDSON'S BAY COMPANY. GC: Doubleday, 1956. 1st ed. Fine in lightly chipped dj. *CONNOLLY & WADE.* $30

Fisher, Vardis. TALE OF VALOR. Doubleday, 1958. 1st ed. VG in Good dj with closed tears, edgewear, chips. *BEBBAH.* $55

Fisher, Vardis. THE IDAHO ENCYCLOPEDIA. Caxton, 1938. 1st ed. Fine, Nice dj. *AUTHORS OF THE WEST.* $300

Fisher, Vardis. THE NEUROTIC NIGHTINGALE. Casanova, (1935). 1st ed of 300 numbered, signed. VG+, clean dj chipped, browned at edges. *AUTHORS OF THE WEST.* $150

Fisher, Vardis. THE VALLEY OF VISION: A NOVEL.....Abelard, (1951). 1st ed. Note, else Fine in dj. *AUTHORS OF THE WEST.* $40

Fisher, Vardis. THOMAS WOLFE AS I KNEW HIM AND OTHER ESSAYS. Alan Swallow, (1963). 1st ed. Fine in dj. *AUTHORS OF THE WEST.* $40

Fisher, Vardis. TOILERS OF THE HILLS. Houghton Mifflin, 1928. 1st ed. Fine. *AUTHORS OF THE WEST.* $75

Fishwick, Marshall W. LEE AFTER THE WAR. NY, (1963). 1st ed. Dj wear o/w Fine. *PRATT.* $27.50

Fisk, James Liberty. EXPEDITION FROM FORT ABERCROMBIE TO FORT BENTON. LETTER FROM THE SECRETARY OF WAR...Wash., HED80, 1863. 1st ed. 36pp. Half morocco. Howes F154. *GINSBERG.* $125

Fiske, John. EXCURSIONS OF AN EVOLUTIONIST. Boston: Houghton Mifflin, 1884. 378pp, cat, index. Teg. Blue cl, scattered pencilling o/w contents NF. *SMITHFIELD.* $23

Fiske, John. THE MISSISSIPPI VALLEY IN THE CIVIL WAR. Boston, 1900. 1st ed. 368pp. Minor cvr wear, o/w Fine. *PRATT.* $47.50

Fitch, Michael Hendrick. THE CHATTANOOGA CAMPAIGN. N.p., 1911. 1st ed, ltd to 2,500. 255pp. Spine has minor soiling and/or discoloration, o/w VG+. *PRATT.* $60

Fitch, Samuel Sheldon. SIX LECTURES ON THE USES OF THE LUNGS....NY: Carlisle, 1847. 1st ed. VG. *SECOND LIFE.* $75

Fite, Emerson D. and Archibald Freeman (comp.) A BOOK OF OLD MAPS...Cambridge: Harvard Univ Press. 1926. 1st ed. Frontis map w/ptd tissue guard. Spine extrems lightly frayed. *KARMIOLE.* $150

Fitt, Mary. MURDER MARS THE TOUR. London: Ivor Nicholson & Watson, 1936. 1st ed. Fine (foxing), in lightly used dj. *BEASLEY.* $100

Fitz, Grancel. NORTH AMERICAN HEAD HUNTING. NY: Oxford Univ Press, 1957. 1st ed. VG in Good dj. *BACKMAN.* $25

Fitz, Reginald. ACUTE PANCREATITIS WITH AN ESPECIAL CONSIDERATION OF PANCREATIC HEMORRHAGE, HEMORRHAGIC PANCREATITIS, AND SUBPERITONEAL FAT NECROSIS. NY, 1890. 1st ed. Ex-lib. *FYE.* $50

Fitzgerald, Ed (ed.). THE BOOK OF MAJOR LEAGUE BASEBALL CLUBS. Barnes, 1952. 1st ed. 2-vol set. Each vol Fine in Fine dj in VG+ orig box. *PLAPINGER.* $65

Fitzgerald, Edward. A FITZGERALD FRIENDSHIP BEING HITHERTO UNPUBLISHED LETTERS FROM EDWARD FITZGERALD TO WILLIAM DODHAM DONNE. London: Faber & Faber, 1932. 1st ed, ltd to 750. VG+. *ARCHER.* $45

Fitzgerald, Edward. RUBAIYAT OF OMAR KHAYYAM. Elihu Vedder (illus). Boston: Houghton Mifflin, 1894. 1st ed. French-fold, gilt dec cl. VF in rare dj, (stained, internally & externally mended). *JAFFE.* $125

Fitzgerald, Edward. RUBAIYAT OF OMAR KHAYYAM. NY (1947), complete 1st, 3rd, 4th & 5th eds combined. Intro by Louis Untermeyer. Dec end papers and all borders. 19 full-pg color plts. Dec cloth, boxed. *HEINOLDT.* $15

Fitzgerald, Edward. THE RUBAIYAT OF OMAR KHAYYAM. Elbert Hubbard, ltd 920, signed by Hubbard. Roycroft, East Aurora, NY, 1896. 8, 68pp. Suede soft cover lined w/silk. Corners and top & bottom spine rubbed. *HEINOLDT.* $18

Fitzgerald, F. Scott and Edmund Wilson. THE EVIL EYE. (Cincinnati): John Church Co., 1915. 1st ed. 4to. Cl-backed pict card covers. "Cap and Gown Club" written at top front cover (chipped at corners, several long, closed tears in front & back covers), else Good. Custom linen tray case w/morocco spine label. *CAPTAIN'S BOOKSHELF.* $1100

Fitzgerald, F. Scott and Zelda. BITS OF PARADISE. Scribners, 1973. 1st ed. Fine in NF in price-clipped dj (wrinkled rear panel). *STAHR.* $35

Fitzgerald, F. Scott and Zelda. THE ROMANTIC EGOISTS. Matthew J. Bruccoli, Scotti Fitzgerald Smith and Joan P. Kerr (eds). NY: Scribner's, (1974). 1st ed. One of 500 numbered, signed by Scotti Fitzgerald. Laid in are two repros of Zelda's watercolors. Fine in pub's slipcase. *UNGER*. $225

Fitzgerald, F. Scott. AFTERNOON OF AN AUTHOR, A SELECTION OF UNCOLLECTED STORIES AND ESSAYS. London: Bodley Head, (1958). 1st Eng ed. Fine in dj, sl faded backstrip. *HELLER*. $50

Fitzgerald, F. Scott. ALL THE SAD YOUNG MEN. NY, 1926. 1st ed. Spine sl rubbed, top edges sl rubbed. 125

Fitzgerald, F. Scott. BORROWED TIME: SHORT STORIES. Selected by Alan and Jennifer Ross. (London): Grey Walls Press, (1953). 1st ed, thus. Just About Fine in like price-clipped dj (two tiny chips, few tiny tears). *CAPTAIN'S BOOKSHELF*. $75

Fitzgerald, F. Scott. FIE! FIE! FI-FI! (Cincinnati): John Church Company, 1914. 1st pub ed, preceded only by acting script. Front wrappers worn at outer corners, cl spine pulled away, o/w VG, encl in specially made linen tray case, morocco label on spine. Cl-backed pict card cvrs. *JAFFE*. $1750

Fitzgerald, F. Scott. PREFACE TO THIS SIDE OF PARADISE. John R. Hopkins (ed). Olive cl w/ptd label. Iowa City: Windhover Press & Bruccoli Clark, 1975. 1st ed. Ltd to 150. VF. *JAFFE*. $225

Fitzgerald, F. Scott. PREFACE TO THIS SIDE OF PARADISE. Iowa City: Windhover Press/Buccoli Clark, 1975. One of 150 on Rives Heavy paper, w/tipped in drwg of Fitzgerald. Fine w\o dj as issued. *LOPEZ*. $150

Fitzgerald, F. Scott. TENDER IS THE NIGHT. With the Author's Final Revisions and a Preface by Malcolm Cowley. London: Grey Walls Press, (1953). Offsetting to eps, else Fine in dj. 1st Eng rev. ed. *CHAPEL HILL*. $150

Fitzgerald, F. Scott. THE BEAUTIFUL AND THE DAMNED. NY: Scribner's, 1922. 1st ed, 1st ptg, w/"Printed at the Scribner Press" and no seal on copyright pg, no ads at rear. Orig grn cl. Fine, bright in sl soiled 1st issue dj, w/white lettering outlined in black. Jacket has 1" triangular chip upper right corner front panel (affecting no lettering), and 4" separation along fold between front panel, front flap. Couple minor clean tears. *CHAPEL HILL*. $3,000

Fitzgerald, F. Scott. THE BEAUTIFUL AND THE DAMNED. NY: Scribner's, 1922. 2nd prtg. Fine. *LOPEZ*. $65

Fitzgerald, F. Scott. THE CRACK-UP. NY, New Directions, (1945). Later ptg. Edmund Wilson (ed). Spine lightly sunned. Fine in dj (edge piece missing front panel, spine little sunned, few closed small edge tears, edge rubbed, few small chips). *POLYANTHOS*. $35

Fitzgerald, F. Scott. THE EVIL EYE. (Cincinnati): John Church Company, 1915. 1st ed. "Cap and Gown Club" written top of front cvr (chipped); several long closed tears front & back cvrs, o/w Good, encl in a specially made linen tray case, morocco label on spine. Cl-backed pict card cvrs. *JAFFE*. $1650

Fitzgerald, F. Scott. THE EVIL EYE. Cinn., NY, & London: The John Church Co, 1915. 1st ed. Orig flexible illus boards, orange cl spine as issued. Sm lower corner repair front board, but NF of fragile vol. Scarce, especially in nice condition. *CHAPEL HILL*. $2,200

Fitzgerald, F. Scott. THE GREAT GATSBY. Charles Scribner III (intro). (NY): LEC, (1980). One of 2000 numbered, illus, signed by Fred Meyer. Fine in sl sunned slipcase. *CAPTAIN'S BOOKSHELF*. $125

Fitzgerald, F. Scott. THE GREAT GATSBY. NY: Scribner's, 1925. Bkpl on front pastedown causing faint offsetting to ffep, gilt spine lettering dulled, o/w NF. 1st ed, 1st issue, w/"sick in tired" on p. 205, lines 9-10. *CHAPEL HILL*. $450

Fitzgerald, F. Scott. THE LETTERS OF F. SCOTT FITZGERALD. Andrew Turnbull (ed). NY: Charles Scribner's Sons, (1963). Dj worn, newspaper offsetting at rear. *WEBER*. $25

Fitzgerald, Percy. THE HISTORY OF PICKWICK. London: Chapman and Hall, 1891. 1st ed. 8vo, 375pp, bound without illus, gilt stamped green cloth, bkpl. VG+. *GREAT EXPECTATIONS*. $45

Fitzgerald, Percy. THE HISTORY OF PICKWICK. London: Chapman and Hall, 1891. 1st ed. 8vo, 375pp, plts bound in rear, gilt stamped green cloth, unopened, centenary stamp on frontis. VG+. *GREAT EXPECTATIONS*. $75

Fitzgerald, Percy. THE LIFE OF CHARLES DICKENS AS REVEALED IN HIS WRITINGS. 2 Vols. London: Chatto & Windus, 1905. 1st ed. 8vo, portrait and facs, green cloth, mild rubbing to spine of Vol. I, teg, scarce. VG+. *GREAT EXPECTATIONS*. $60

Fitzgerald, Robert. IN THE ROSE OF TIME: POEMS 1931-1956. (NY): New Directions, (1956). 1st ed. One corner lightly bumped, else Fine in NF dj. Signed. *CAPTAIN'S BOOKSHELF*. $60

Fitzgerald, Zelda. SAVE ME THE WALTZ. London: Grey Walls, (1953). 1st English ed. Name fep, still VG in dj chipped at extremities. *UNGER*. $175

Fitzgerald, Zelda. SAVE ME THE WALTZ. London: Grey Walls, (1953). 1st UK ed, VG in dj. Scarce. *SECOND LIFE*. $95

Fitzgibbon, H.M. THE STORY OF THE FLUTE. London, 1914. Gilt-pict bds. NF. *POLYANTHOS*. $35

Fitzhugh, Bessie Lee. BELLS OVER TEXAS. El Paso: Texas Western Press, 1955. One of 1,250 designed by Carl Hertzog. Presentation signed by Hertzog. Fine in dj. *LAURIE*. $75

Fitzpatrick, P. JOCK OF THE BUSHVELT. London: Longmans, (1949). Color frontis. Gilt dec cl. VG. *MIKESH*. $27.50

Fitzpatrick, T.J. RAFINESQUE A SKETCH OF HIS LIFE WITH BIBLIOGRAPHY. Iowa: Torch, 1911. Rebound in cl, margins waterstained in spots, not affecting text. *AMERICAN BOTANIST*. $150

Fitzsimmons, Cortland, THE MOVING FINGER. NY: Stokes, 1937. 1st ed. Name. Fine; dj has small chips. *ELSE FINE*. $50

Fitzsimmons, Cortland. 70,000 WITNESSES, A FOOTBALL MYSTERY. McBride, 1931. 1st ed. VG+ in dj with chips, wear. *BEBBAH*. $35

Fitzsimmons, Cortland. MYSTERY AT HIDDEN HARBOR. NY: Stokes, 1938. 1st ed. Fine; light edgewear to dj. Inscribed. *ELSE FINE*. $55

Fitzsimmons, Cortland. THE BAINBRIDGE MURDER. NY: McBride, 1930. 1st ed. NF, dj has very small chips. *ELSE FINE*. $40

Fitzsimons, F.W. THE MONKEYFOLK OF SOUTH AFRICA. Portrait frontis. London, 1911. Cloth. Spine faded, scattered foxing. *SUTTON*. $50

Fitzsimons, V.F.M. SNAKES OF SOUTHERN AFRICA. Cape Town, 1962. 74 colored plts, 43 photos, 77 maps (+ 1 fold-out), 106 text figures. Lt soiling and mottling, some ep browning. *SUTTON*. $175

Fitzwilliams, Duncan. ON THE BREAST. London, 1924. 1st ed. Inscribed and signed (in initials). Backstrip faded. *FYE*. $175

Flagg, Fannie. COMING ATTRACTIONS. NY: Wm Morrow & Co, 1981. 1st ed,1st bk. Fine in dj, crease front flap. *BERNARD*. $75

Flaherty, Frances H. ELEPHANT DANCE. John Collier. NY: Charles Scribner's Sons. 1937. 1st ed. Dj. *KARMIOLE*. $50

Flammarion, Camille. THE UNKNOWN. London: Harper, 1900 (France 1900). Good in red cl, deckle edges; Bumped, ffep removed. *KNOLLWOOD*. $35

Flanagan, Hallie. SHIFTING SCENES OF THE MODERN EUROPEAN THEATRE. NY: Coward-McCann, 1928. 1st ed. Fine but for light soiling & fading in Fine dj. *BEASLEY*. $75

Flandrau, Grace. FRONTIER DAYS ALONG THE UPPER MISSOURI. N.p.: Great Northern Railway, n.d. (ca. 1905). Map. Orig wrappers, VG. *CONNOLLY & WADE*. $30

Flandrau, Grace. THEN I SAW THE CONGO. NY: Harcourt Brace & Co. (1929). 1st ed. Black cl, gilt. Dj. *KARMIOLE.* $35

Flanigan, J. Michael. AMERICAN FURNITURE...KAUFMAN COLLECTION. NY: Abrams, 1986. 1st ed. NF in NF dj. *BACKROOM.* $45

Flannagan, Roy. AMBER SATYR. GC: Doubleday, Doran, 1932. 1st ed. Fine in NF dj (sm hole rear spine edge). *CHAPEL HILL.* $50

Flaubert, Gustave. BIBLIOMANIA: A TALE. Evanston: Northwestern, 1929. French wrappers. One of 500 numbered. Fine. *MUELLER.* $35

Flaubert, Gustave. MADAME BOVARY. London: Vizetelly, 1886. 1st ed in Eng. Hinges damaged; catalogue descriptions and picture of Flaubert tipped to front pastedown and verso of ffep; substantial edgewear. VG. *LAME DUCK.* $1000

Flaubert, Gustave. MADAME BOVARY: A STORY OF PROVINCIAL LIFE. London/NY: The Bodley Head Ltd./Dodd Mead and Co, 1928. 1st ed thus. J. Lewis May (intro). John Austen, John Lane (illus). Black cl over boards, gilt title. Sm sig front paste-down, o/w VG. *HELLER.* $60

Flavin, Martin. JOURNEY IN THE DARK. NY: Harper, (1943). 1st ed. Fine in price-clipped dj (some text affected) which has been internally reinforced at edges with tape. *LOPEZ.* $45

Fleming, A.M. THE GUN SIGHT MINE. Boston: Meador, 1929. 1st ed. VG to Fine. *BOOK MARKET.* $250

Fleming, G.H. THE DIZZIEST SEASON. Morrow, 1984. 1st ed. VG in Fine dj. *PLAPINGER.* $30

Fleming, G.H. THE UNFORGETTABLE SEASON. HR & W, 1981. 1st ed. Fine in Fine dj. *PLAPINGER.* $30

Fleming, Howard. NARROW GAUGE RAILWAYS IN AMERICA. Grahame Hardy & Paul Darrell (eds), Brian Thompson (comp). Oakland: G. Hardy, 1949 (orig pub NY, 1875). Orig cl. One of 950 signed by Hardy, Darrell, & Thompson. Fine in dj. *BOHLING.* $100

Fleming, Ian. A JAMES BOND OMNIBUS. London: Jonathan Cape, 1973. Omnibus ed. Edges spotted, o/w Fine in price-clipped dj (short closed tears, creasing, wear). *MORDIDA.* $55

Fleming, Ian. BONDED FLEMING. NY: Viking Press, 1962. Omnibus ed. Fine in dj. *MORDIDA.* $45

Fleming, Ian. CHITTY CHITTY BANG BANG, THE MAGICAL CAR. Random, (1964). Stated 1st ptg. 114pp. Illus. VG+ in dj w/wear, chips, soil. *BEBBAH.* $45

Fleming, Ian. CHITTY CHITTY BANG BANG: THE MAGICAL CAR. London: Cape, 1964. 1st ed. Fine; in NF dj. *ELSE FINE.* $75

Fleming, Ian. DR. NO. London: Cape, 1958. 1st ed. Name. Fine; price clipped dj w/very minor wear at corners. *ELSE FINE.* $350

Fleming, Ian. DR. NO. London: Jonathan Cape, (1958). 1st ed, 1st issue w/outline of girl on dj repeated on cover. NF in dj w/ownership stamp ffep. *JUVELIS.* $300

Fleming, Ian. FOR YOUR EYES ONLY. (London): Jonathan Cape, (1964). 1st UK ed in a later issue dj. VG+ in sl soiled dj. *BERNARD.* $25

Fleming, Ian. FOR YOUR EYES ONLY. London: Jonathan Cape, 1960. 1st ed. Top edge spotted o/w Fine in NF dj (lt stain front panel; crease inner front flap; sm scrape base of spine). *MORDIDA.* $150

Fleming, Ian. FOR YOUR EYES ONLY. NY: Viking, 1960. 1st ed. Fine, minor wear to the dj. *ELSE FINE.* $100

Fleming, Ian. FROM RUSSIA WITH LOVE. London: Jonathan Cape, 1957. 1st ed. VG in dj with darkened spine, wear along folds, chipping at spine ends and at corners, several closed tears and an internal tape mend. *MORDIDA.* $150

Fleming, Ian. GOLDFINGER. London: Jonathan Cape, 1959. 1st ed. Lt spotting on top edge o/w Fine in dj. *MORDIDA.* $250

Fleming, Ian. GOLDFINGER. NY: Macmillan, 1959. 1st Amer ed. Fine in dj with a couple of tiny tears and tiny wear at corners. *MORDIDA.* $150

Fleming, Ian. OCTOPUSSY & THE LIVING DAYLIGHTS. London: Cape, 1966. 1st ed. As New in dj. *ELSE FINE.* $35

Fleming, Ian. OCTOPUSSY AND THE LIVING DAYLIGHTS. London: Jonathan Cape, (1966). 1st UK ed. Fine in price clipped dj. *BERNARD.* $45

Fleming, Ian. OCTOPUSSY AND THE LIVING DAYLIGHTS. London: Cape, (1966). 1st ed. Fine in dj. *JUVELIS.* $30

Fleming, Ian. OCTOPUSSY. NAL, 1965. 1st Amer. ed. About Fine in a price-clipped dj that has two tears and light rubbing. Bkplate on front pastedown. *STAHR.* $15

Fleming, Ian. ON HER MAJESTY'S SECRET SERVICE. London, 1963. 1st ed. Fine in dj. *MADLE.* $110

Fleming, Ian. ON HER MAJESTY'S SECRET SERVICE. London: Jonathan Cape, 1963. 1st ed. Name fep o/w Fine in dj. *MORDIDA.* $50

Fleming, Ian. ON HER MAJESTY'S SECRET SERVICE. NY: NAL, 1963. 1st ed. Fine, price-clipped dj has minor wear at spine ends. *ELSE FINE.* $65

Fleming, Ian. THE DIAMOND SMUGGLERS. NY: Macmillan, 1958. 1st Amer ed. Sm labels removed; spotting on edges o/w VG in dj w/closed tear; wear. *MORDIDA.* $60

Fleming, Ian. THE MAN WITH THE GOLDEN GUN. London: Jonathan Cape, (1965). 1st UK ed. VG in price clipped dj. *BERNARD.* $45

Fleming, Ian. THE MAN WITH THE GOLDEN GUN. London: Jonathan Cape, 1965. 1st ed. Fine in dj. *MORDIDA.* $85

Fleming, Ian. THE MAN WITH THE GOLDEN GUN. London: Jonathan Cape, 1965. 1st ed. Edges spotted o/w VG in Fine dj. *MORDIDA.* $45

Fleming, Ian. THE MAN WITH THE GOLDEN GUN. NAL, (1965). Stated 1st prtg. (1st Amer). NF with slight rubs in Good dj closed edge tears, small wedge missing rear panel. *BEBBAH.* $18

Fleming, Ian. THE MAN WITH THE GOLDEN GUN. NY, 1966. 1st US pb ed. Signet P2735. VG in wrappers. *PETTLER.* $10

Fleming, Ian. THE MAN WITH THE GOLDEN GUN. NY: NAL, 1965. 1st Amer ed. Fine in dj. *MORDIDA.* $65

Fleming, Ian. THE SPY WHO LOVED ME. London: Jonathan Cape, 1962. 1st ed. Uncorrected proof copy. Some tiny lt spotting on edges o/w NF in trade dj. *MORDIDA.* $500

Fleming, Ian. THE SPY WHO LOVED ME. NY: Viking Press, 1962. 1st Amer ed. Fine in dj. *MORDIDA.* $75

Fleming, Ian. THE SPY WHO LOVED ME. NY: Viking, 1962. 1st ed. Fine, light wear to dj extremities. *ELSE FINE.* $40

Fleming, Ian. THRILLING CITIES. NAL, 1964. 1st Amer ed. VG+ in dj price-clipped. Two small tears on cover; wear at head & foot of dj spine. *STAHR.* $20

Fleming, Ian. THUNDERBALL NY: Viking Press, 1961. 1st Amer ed. Erasure fep o/w Fine in dj with minor wear at spine ends and corners. *MORDIDA.* $85

Fleming, Ian. THUNDERBALL. London: Jonathan Cape, 1961. 1st ed. Edges spotted o/w Fine in price-clipped dj. *MORDIDA.* $100

Fleming, Ian. YOU ONLY LIVE TWICE. (London): Jonathan Cape, (1964). 1st ed. Fine in dj. *JUVELIS.* $50

Fleming, Ian. YOU ONLY LIVE TWICE. (NY): NAL, (1964). 1st Amer ed. Fine in dj. *JUVELIS.* $30

Fleming, Ian. YOU ONLY LIVE TWICE. London: Cape, (1964). 1st ed. Minor spotting to edges, else Fine in dj (sm stain on rear panel). *CAPTAIN'S BOOKSHELF.* $50

Fleming, Ian. YOU ONLY LIVE TWICE. London: Jonathan Cape, 1964. 1st ed. NF in very lightly worn dj w/nearly unnoticeable discoloration at head of spine. *BEASLEY.* $45

Fleming, Ian. YOU ONLY LIVE TWICE. NAL, 1964. 1st Amer ed. VG+ in dj (2 sm tears rear panel). *STAHR.* $20

Fleming, Joan. DEATH OF A SARDINE. London: Collins Crime Club, 1963. 1st ed. Fine in dj w/crease-tear on front panel and couple of closed tears. *MORDIDA.* $35

Fleming, Joan. IN THE RED. London: Collins Crime Club, 1961. 1st ed. Edges spotted o/w VG in dj w/staining on back panel and some tiny nicks. *MORDIDA.* $22.50

Fleming, Joan. THE DEEDS OF MR. DEADCERT. London: Hutchinson, 1955. 1st ed. Lt spotting eps, o/w VG in price-clipped dj with wear, spine fading. *MORDIDA.* $40

Fleming, Joan. THE GALLOWS IN MY GARDEN. London: Hutchinson, 1951. 1st ed. Few spots, o/w Fine in VG price-clipped dj (chipped, fraying; few short closed tears; nicks). *MORDIDA.* $45

Fleming, Joan. THE MAN WHO LOOKED BACK. London: Hutchinson, 1951. 1st ed. Name fep, o/w Fine in dj w/minor wear. *MORDIDA.* $45

Fleming, Joan. YOU CAN'T BELIEVE YOUR EYES. London: Collins Crime Club, 1957. 1st ed. Edges spotted o/w Fine in dj. *MORDIDA.* $35

Fleming, Peter. BAYONETS TO LHASA. Harper, 1961. 1st ed. About Fine in price-clipped dj, sl worn and chipped. *STAHR.* $35

Fleming, Peter. BRAZILIAN ADVENTURE. NY: Charles Scribner's Sons, 1934. 1st ed. Original grey buckram cvr. Very minor smudging else NF. *GREAT EPIC.* $25

Fleming, Peter. BRAZILIAN ADVENTURE. Scribner's, 1934. 1st ed. NF. *STAHR.* $15

Fleming, Stephen. THE EXILE OF SERGEANT NEN. Algonquin, 1986. 1st ed. Fine in Fine dj. *BEBBAH.* $20

Fleming, Vivian Minor. CAMPAIGNS OF THE ARMY OF NORTHERN VIRGINIA INCLUDING THE JACKSON VALLEY CAMPAIGN 1861-1865. (Richmond, 1928). 1st ed. 2 fldg maps. Fine. *McGOWAN.* $175

Fleming, Vivian Minor. THE WILDERNESS CAMPAIGN. Richmond, 1922. 1st ed. Wrappers. Fine. *McGOWAN.* $95

Fleming, Walter L. DOCUMENTARY HISTORY OF RECONSTRUCTION....1865 TO THE PRESENT TIME. Cleveland: A. H. Clark, 1906. 2 vols. 1st ed. Orig. cl. Vol 1, Fine; Vol 2 has wear to outer spine and a few tears on rear cover. Howes F182. *GINSBERG.* $200

Flemwell, G. ALPINE FLOWERS AND GARDENS. A&C Black, 1910. 1st ed. 7s 6d Series. VG-NF. *OLD LONDON.* $45

Fletcher, Baylis John. UP THE TRAIL IN '79. Norman, (1968). Ed by Wayne Gard. 1st ed. 118pp. Fine in dj. *PRATT.* $27.50

Fletcher, Colin. THE MAN FROM THE CAVE. NY: Knopf, 1981. 1st ed. Fine in Fine dj. *CONNOLLY & WADE.* $20

Fletcher, Colin. THE MAN WHO WALKED THROUGH TIME. Knopf, 1967. 1st ed. Map. Fine. *AUTHORS OF THE WEST.* $17.50

Fletcher, D.V. GOOD FARM WORKMANSHIP....London: Hodder and Stoughton, (1946). 2nd prtg. Cl. VG. *SECOND LIFE.* $15

Fletcher, Ifan Kyrle. RONALD FIRBANK: A MEMOIR. London, 1930. 1st ed (1500). Extremities little rubbed. NF. *POLYANTHOS.* $45

Fletcher, Inglis. QUEEN'S GIFT. Indianapolis & NY: Bobbs-Merrill, (1952). 1st ed. Constitution ed. Few tape stains, but a Nice in pict dj. *CHAPEL HILL.* $55

Fletcher, J.S. MURDER IN FOUR DEGREES. NY: Alfred A. Knopf, 1931. 1st Amer ed. Fine in dj with tiny wear at corners. *MORDIDA.* $35

Fletcher, L. AN INTRODUCTION TO THE STUDY OF METEORITES. London: British Museum (Natural History), 1914. 11th ed. Card covers. *KNOLLWOOD.* $25

Fletcher, Maurine S. (ed). THE WETHERILLS OF THE MESA VERDE. Dickinson Univ Press, 1977. Mint, signed. *FIVE QUAIL.* $35

Fletcher, Robert H. FREE GRASS TO FENCES. NY, 1960. 1st ed. Fine in Fine dj. *VARNER.* $60

Fletcher, Robert H. FREE GRASS TO FENCES. THE MONTANA CATTLE RANGE STORY. Published for the Montana Stockgrower's Assoc, (1960). 1st ed. Double page map. Fine in VG dj. *OREGON.* $75

Fletcher, William Younger. ENGLISH BOOK COLLECTORS. London: Kegan Paul, Trench, Trubner, 1902. 1st ed. Covers faded w/age darkening along edges. Foxed. *OAK KNOLL.* $55

Flexner, Abraham. MEDICAL EDUCATION: A COMPARATIVE STUDY. NY, 1925. 1st ed. *FYE.* $100

Flexner, Abraham. PROSTITUTION IN EUROPE. NY, 1914. 1st ed. Inscribed. W/scarce advertising leaflet. Ex-lib. *FYE.* $150

Flexner, Abraham. PROSTITUTION IN EUROPE. NY: Century, 1914. 1st ed. Front hinge tender, o/w Good. *SECOND LIFE.* $35

Flickinger, D.K. ETHIOPIA; OR TWENTY YEARS OF MISSIONARY LIFE IN WESTERN AFRICA. Dayton: United Brethren Pub House, 1873. 1st ed. Frontis map, 18 woodcut plts. Extrems rubbed. *KARMIOLE.* $60

FLIM-FLAMS! OR, THE LIFE AND ERRORS OF MY UNCLE AND THE AMOURS OF MY AUNT. (By Isaac Disrailei) London: John Murray, 1805. 1st ed. 3 vols. 12mo. 19th cent 3/4 red morocco by Root. 9 plts. Joints rubbed and a little tender, else VG. *CHAPEL HILL.* $150

Flinn, Frank M. CAMPAIGNING WITH BANKS IN LOUISIANA, '63 AND '64, AND WITH SHERIDAN IN THE SHENANDOAH VALLEY IN '64 AND '65. Lynn, MA, 1887. 1st ed. NF. *McGOWAN.* $125

Flint, C.F. THE CHEMISTRY AND TECHNOLOGY OF RUBBER LATEX. London, 1938. Cl (lt scuffing, spine faded, edge split repaired, hinges reinforced). *SUTTON.* $45

Flint, Charles L. A PRACTICAL TREATISE ON GRASSES AND FORAGE PLANTS. NY: Putnam's, 1857. 1st ed, 1st book. Spine tip repaired, one spine tip defective, little shelfwear, bkpl. Contents Good. *DIAMOND.* $75

Flint, Charles L. GRASSES AND FORAGE PLANTS, A PRACTICAL TREATISE....Boston, 1860. 5th ed. Orig cl; minor dampstaining to 2 blank sheets. *SUTTON.* $85

Flint, Charles L. GRASSES AND FORAGE PLANTS....NY: Putnam and London, 1857. 1st ed. frontis. Faded. VG. *SECOND LIFE.* $65

Flint, Timothy. A CONDENSED GEOGRAPHY...OR THE MISSISSIPPI VALLEY. E.H. Flint: Cincinnati, 1828. 1st ed. Two vols. 592pp;520pp, appendix. Rebacked. Orig boards. VG. *CONNOLLY & WADE.* $425

Flood, Charles B. LEE, THE LAST YEARS. Boston, (1981). 1st ed. Fine in Fine dj. *PRATT.* $25

Flood, Charles B. THE WAR OF THE INNOCENTS. NY: McGraw-Hill, (1970). 1st ed. Fine in NF dj. *AKA.* $30

Florin, Lambert. BOOT HILL. Seattle, (1966). 1st ed. VG in dj. *PRATT.* $30

Florin, Lambert. BOOT HILL. Seattle: Superior, (1966). 1st ed. Fine in Fine dj. *BOOK MARKET.* $35

Florin, Lambert. GHOST TOWN ALBUM. Seattle: Superior, (1962). 1st ed. Fine in Fine dj. *BOOK MARKET.* $35

Florin, Lambert. GHOST TOWN EL DORADO. NY: Bonanza Books, 1968. 1st ed. VG in worn dj. *PARMER.* $35.

Florin, Lambert. GHOST TOWN TREASURES. Seattle: Superior, (1965). 1st ed. Fine in Fine dj. *BOOK MARKET.* $35

Florin, Lambert. GHOST TOWNS OF THE WEST. NY (1970, 1971). Dj. *HEINOLDT.* $20

Florin, Lambert. TALES THE WESTERN TOMBSTONES TELL. Seattle: Superior, (1967). 1st ed. Fine in Fine dj. *BOOK MARKET.* $35

Florin, Lambert. WESTERN GHOST TOWN SHADOWS. Seattle: Superior, (1964). 1st ed. Fine in Fine dj. *BOOK MARKET.* $35

Florin, Lambert. WESTERN GHOST TOWNS. Seattle: Superior, (1961). 1st ed. Fine in Fine dj. *BOOK MARKET.* $35

Flornoy, Bertrand. JIVARO: AMONG THE HEAD-SHRINKERS OF THE AMAZON. NY: Library Pub, 1954. 1st ed. Fine, dj edgeworn. *CONNOLLY & WADE.* $20

Flory, M.A. A BOOK ABOUT FANS: THE HISTORY OF FANS AND FAN-PAINTING...NY: Macmillan, 1895. 1st ed. Cover soiled, else VG. *WREDEN.* $50

Flower, John. MOONLIGHT SERENADE. New Rochelle: Arlington House, 1972. 2nd ptg. Almost As New. *BANCROFT.* $345

Flowers, A.R. DE MOJO BLUES. NY: Dutton, (1986). 1st ed. Fine in Fine dj. *LOPEZ.* $40

Flowers, Charles. IT NEVER RAINS IN LOS ANGELES. NY: Coward-McCann, (1970). 1st ed. VG in dj. *LOPEZ.* $50

Fobes, Harriet Keith. MYSTIC GEMS. Boston: Richard G. Badger, The Gorham Press. (1924). 1st ed. Color frontis, 12 plts. Signed. Boards sl soiled and rubbed. Bkplt. *KARMIOLE.* $65

Fogel, Edwin Miller. BELIEFS AND SUPERSTITIONS OF THE PENNSYLVANIA GERMANS. Phila: American Germanica Press. 1915. 1st ed. Corners sl bumped. *KARMIOLE.* $60

Folger, J.C. & S. Thomson. COMMERCIAL APPLE INDUSTRY OF NORTH AMERICA. NY: Macmillan, 1923. Nearly new. *AMERICAN BOTANIST.* $35

Follett, Ken. THE MAN FROM ST. PETERSBURG. London: H-H, 1982. 1st ed. Fine in dj. *ELSE FINE.* $40

Follett, Ken. THE MAN FROM ST. PETERSBURG. London: Hamish Hamilton, 1982. 1st Eng. ed. Fine in dj. *MORDIDA.* $35

Follett, Ken. TRIPLE. NY: Arbor, 1979. 1st ed. Fine in dj. *ELSE FINE.* $35

Folsom, W.H.. FIFTY YEARS IN THE NORTHWEST. (St. Paul): Pioneer Press Co., 1888. 1st ed. Rebound in full black simulated leather. VG. *LAURIE.* $150

Foner, Philip S. (ed). THE BLACK PANTHERS SPEAK. Phila: Lippincott, (1970). 1st ed. Fine in NF dj. *LOPEZ.* $30

Fonseca, Lew. HOW TO PITCH BASEBALL. Ziff-Davis, 1942. Good+ in VG dj. *PLAPINGER.* $40

Fontana, Lucio. FONTANA. NY: Harry N. Abrams, (1962). 1st ed. Tipped-in color plts. Dj. *KARMIOLE.* $75

Fontenelle, Bernard de. A PLURALITY OF WORLDS. John Glanvill (trans). London: Nonesuch Press, 1929. One of 1400 ptd on hand-made Van Gelder cream laid paper w/Nonesuch watemark. Full ivory vellum w/gilt dec, gilt titling. In pub's slipcase, covered in dec paper (sl worn). Teg. Very nice. *BOOK BLOCK.* $125

Foote, Edward. A TEXT-BOOK OF MINOR SURGERY. NY, 1908. 1st ed. 400+ photo illus. *FYE.* $60

Foote, Horton. HARRISON, TEXAS (8 Television Plays). NY: Harcourt, Brace & Co., (1956). 1st ed. NF in dj which has very tiny chip at top of spine. *BERNARD.* $75

Foote, Horton. THE CHASE. NY: Rinehart, (1956). 1st ed. Pages yellowing, o/w NF in VG dj (mildly spine-faded, bit of wear at extremities). *LOPEZ.* $150

Foote, Mary Hallock. COEUR D'ALENE. Houghton Mifflin, 1894. 1st ed. Inscribed, signed. Fine, bkpl. *AUTHORS OF THE WEST.* $100

Foote, Shelby. LOVE IN A DRY SEASON. NY: Dial, 1951. 1st ed. Fine in dj (lt wear to head of spine; 2 tears). Inscribed. *CAPTAIN'S BOOKSHELF.* $125

Foote, Shelby. SEPTEMBER, SEPTEMBER. NY: RH, (1977). 1st ed. Fine (rmdr mk) in price-clipped dj. Inscribed. *CAPTAIN'S BOOK-SHELF.* $65

Foote, Shelby. SHILOH. NY: Dial, 1952. 1st ed. Fine, owner sig. dj, sl worn, some chipping, fading. Inscribed. *CAPTAIN'S BOOKSHELF.* $200

Footner, Hubert. EASY TO KILL. Harper, 1931. 1st ed. VG with edge soil in dj with some chipping. *BEBBAH.* $15

Footner, Hulbert. THE DOCTOR WHO HELD HANDS. GC: Doubleday Crime Club, 1929. 1st ed. VF. Narrow chip across dj spine top. *ELSE FINE.* $85

Foque, De La Motte. UNDINE. London: William Heinemann, 1920. 6th ed. 15 tipped-in color Rackham illus w/ptd tissue guards. Ptd boards, cloth spine. Tips bumped, spine faded. *DAWSON'S.* $75

Forbes, Alexander. CALIFORNIA: A HISTORY OF UPPER AND LOWER CALIFORNIA. London: Smith, Elder, 1839. 1st ed. 352pp, errata slip. Frontis, fldg map. Orig grn cl w/blind embossed sides; title in gilt on spine. Howes F242. *GINSBERG.* $1200

Forbes, Alexander. CALIFORNIA; A HISTORY OF UPPER AND LOWER CALIFORNIA. SF: John Henry Nash, 1937. One of 650. 9 facs plts, fldg map in rear. Lt wear to dj, cvr lightly rubbed at extrems, o/w NF. *PARMER.* $175

Forbes, Allan and Ralph M. Eastman. YANKEE SHIP SAILING CARDS... Boston: Issued by the State Street Trust Company, 1948-52. 3 vols. Illus. Ptd wrappers. Fine. *WEBER.* $100

Forbes, Allan and Ralph M. Eastman. YANKEE SHIP SAILING CARDS. (And:) OTHER YANKEE SHIP SAILING CARDS. (And:)... VOL. III. Boston: State Street Trust Co., (1948-52). 3 vols. 1st eds. Wrappers. VG. *LEFKOWICZ.* $80

Forbes, Bryan. TRUTH LIES SLEEPING AND OTHER STORIES. London: Methuen & Co. Ltd, (1950). 1st bk. Adv form of bk in dj over plain wrappers. Dj is lettered Rev Copy. VG in badly chipped dj missing piece on backstrip. *HELLER.* $50

Forbes, Colin. THE STOCKHOLM SYNDICATE. London: Collins, 1981. 1st ed. Fine in dj. *SILVER DOOR.* $27.50

Forbes, Eric G., A.J. Meadows and Derek Howse. GREENWICH OBSERVATORY. London: Taylor & Francis, 1975. 3 vols. 1st ed. VG ex-lib. *KNOLLWOOD.* $125

Forbes, Eric G. TOBIAS MAYER'S OPERA INEDITA, THE FIRST TRANSLATION OF THE LICHTENBERG EDITION OF 1775. NY: American Elsevier, 1971. 7 plts. VG in sl torn dj. *KNOLLWOOD.* $37

Forbes, Esther. JOHNNY TREMAIN. Lynd Ward (illus). Boston: Houghton Mifflin, 1943. 1st ed. NF in chipped dj. *CAPTAIN'S BOOK-SHELF.* $50

Forbes, Jack D. WARRIORS OF THE COLORADO. Norman, 1965. 1st ed. 378pp. Fine in NF dj. *FIVE QUAIL.* $40

Forbes, James D. OCCASIONAL PAPERS ON THE THEORY OF GLACIERS...Edinburgh: A & C Black, 1859. Spine faded early 20th-c (?) binding. 10 plts incl frontis. Inscription. Ownership noted. Faint pencil marginal notes, else VG. *PARMER.* $325

Forbes, Robert Bennet. NOTES ON SOME FEW OF THE WRECKS AND RESCUES DURING THE PRESENT CENTURY. Boston, 1889. 1st ed. Orig cl. *LEFKOWICZ.* $110

Forbes, S. Russell. RAMBLES IN ROME. London: Thomas Nelson; Rome: S. Russell Forbes, 1887. 5th ed, rev, enl. Fldg map back pocket. Spine a little rubbed. *SCHOYER'S.* $25

Forbush, E.H. USEFUL BIRDS AND THEIR PROTECTION, BRIEF DESCRIPTIONS. Boston, 1907. 2nd ed. Lt scuffing. *SUTTON.* $35

Forbush, Edward H. BIRDS OF MASSACHUSETTS AND OTHER NEW ENGLAND STATES. MA, 1927-1929. 3 vols. 93 plts. Fine. *POLYANTHOS.* $200

Forche, Carolyn. THE COUNTRY BETWEEN US. Cl-backed boards. (Port Townsend, WA): Copper Canyon Press, (1981). 1st ed. Ltd to 200 signed. VF. *JAFFE.* $200

Ford, Arthur Peronneau and Marion Johnstone. LIFE IN THE CONFEDERATE ARMY BEING PERSONAL EXPERIENCES OF A PRIVATE SOLDIER IN THE CONFEDERATE ARMY BY ARTHUR P. FORD AND SOME EXPERIENCES AND SKETCHES OF SOUTHERN LIFE BY MARION JOHNSTONE FORD. NY & Washington: Neale Publishing Co., 1905. 1st ed. Spine a bit discolored, else VG. *McGOWAN.* $225

Ford, C. WHERE THE SEA BREAKS ITS BACK. Boston & Toronto: Little, Brown, 1966. Fine in VG dj. *MIKESH.* $35

Ford, Charles Henri. THE HALF-THOUGHTS, THE DISTANCES OF PAIN. NY: QVS Press, 1947. 1st ed. One of 400. Presentation, inscribed. Pict wraps. VG. *JAFFE.* $375

Ford, Charles Henri. THE OVERTURNED LAKE. Cincinnati: Little Man Press, 1941. Ltd ed, 400 on blue L'Aiglon. Spine very sl sunned. Fine in dj (spine little sunned). *POLYANTHOS.* $30

Ford, Corey and Alistair MacBain. FROM THE GROUND UP. NY: Scribner, 1943. 1st ed. Fine- in VG dj. *AARD.* $30

Ford, Daniel. INCIDENT AT MUC WA. GC: Doubleday, 1967. 1st ed. VG, sl cocked, minor price marks fep & half-title page; much edgewear to dj. *AKA.* $40

Ford, Ford Madox. A MIRROR TO FRANCE. London: Duckworth, 1926. 1st ed. Fine in lightly used dj w/two small chips, a few tears, and an internal mend. *BEASLEY.* $250

Ford, Ford Madox. FORD MADOX BROWN: A RECORD OF HIS LIFE AND WORKS BY FORD M. HUEFFER. London: Longmans, 1896. 1st ed. 1/1000. NF. *JUVELIS.* $500

Ford, Ford Madox. GREAT TRADE ROUTE, NY: Oxford Univ Press, 1937. 1st ed. No mention of artist on title page. Fine in Fine dj. *DERMONT.* $75

Ford, Ford Madox. NEW YORK ESSAYS. NY: William Rudge, 1927. 1st ed. One of 750 signed. NF in edgeworn dj, sm chip. *CAPTAIN'S BOOKSHELF.* $150

Ford, Ford Madox. NO MORE PARADES. London: Duckworth, (1925). 1st ed. NF lacking dj. *CAPTAIN'S BOOKSHELF.* $100

Ford, Ford Madox. THE MARCH OF LITERATURE. NY: Dial, 1938. 1st ed. Precedes Eng ed. VF in dj, which is chipped at edges. *WOOLMER.* $75

Ford, Ford Madox. THE RASH ACT. NY, 1933. 1st ed. Spine sl sunned, extrems sl rubbed; in spine sunned dj, chipped, little soiled. NF. *POLYANTHOS.* $50

Ford, Gerald R. and John R. Stiles. PORTRAIT OF THE ASSASSIN. NY: Simon and Schuster, (1965). Stated 1st ptg. Dj. Fine. *SCHOYER'S.* $30

Ford, James. FORTY-ODD YEARS IN THE LITERARY SHOP. NY: E.P. Dutton, (1922). Fine, partially unopened. *WREDEN.* $25

Ford, Jesse Hill. THE LIBERATION OF LORD BYRON JONES. Boston: Little, Brown, (1965). 1st ed. Orig black cl. Fine in NF dj. *CHAPEL HILL.* $35

Ford, John M. THE DRAGON WAITING. Timescape, 1983. 1st ed. Sm nick to dj, else Fine. *MADLE.* $65

Ford, Julia Ellsworth. IMAGINA. Arthur Rackham, Lauren Ford (illus). NY: E.P. Dutton (1923). (14),178,(2)pp. 2 full-pg color plts by Rackham. Blue cl, gilt illus front cvr. Color dj. Author's inscrip, orig poem on half title. 2nd ed (1st pub in 1914 by Duffield.) *KARMIOLE.* $175

Ford, Lauren. THE AGELESS STORY. Dodd, Mead, 1939. 146 of 350 numbered. Orig sketch in white, gilt & pencil of a small angel signed. NF in paper-covered slipcase which has soil, tiny split to paper at corners. Owner inscrip. *BEBBAH.* $140

Ford, Lauren. THE LITTLE BOOK ABOUT GOD. Doubleday, Doran, 1934. 1st ed. Pict paper-covered boards have light soil, tiny skinned patches to rear cvr, stain to cl spine, interior VG+. *BEBBAH.* $40

Ford, Leslie. MURDER IN THE OPM. NY: Scribners, 1942. 1st ed. NF, pict dj lightly worn at extremities. *ELSE FINE.* $35

Ford, Leslie. THE BAHAMAS MURDER CASE. NY: Scribners, 1952. 1st ed. VF in dj. *ELSE FINE.* $45

Ford, Leslie. THE DEVIL'S STRONGHOLD. NY: Scribners, 1948. 1st ed. Fine in pict dj. *ELSE FINE.* $35

Ford, Leslie. THE PHILADELPHIA MURDER STORY. NY: Scribners, 1945. 1st ed. Fine; lightly used pict dj. *ELSE FINE.* $35

Ford, Paul Leicester (ed). ESSAYS ON THE CONSTITUTION OF THE UNITED STATES PUBLISHED DURING ITS DISCUSSION BY THE PEOPLE 1787-1788. NY, 1970. Cloth. Howes F251. Reprint. *GINSBERG.* $30

Ford, Paul Leicester (ed). THE JOURNALS OF HUGH GAINE, PRINTER...BIOGRAPHY AND BIBLIOGRAPHY. NY: Dodd, Mead & Co, 1902. 2 vols. 1st ed. Plts (some fldg), NY Water Works note (5.5 x 9 cm) ptd by Gaine in 1775 tipped in. Maroon cl. Fine. *WREDEN.* $110

Ford, Paul Leicester. JANICE MEREDITH. A STORY OF THE AMERICAN REVOLUTION. In 2 vols. NY: Dodd, Mead, 1899. 1st ed. T.e.g., untrimmed; orig cl, gilt on covers and spines. VG. *CONNOLLY & WADE.* $150

Ford, Paul Leicester. THE GREAT K. & A. (TRAIN) ROBBERY. NY: Dodd Mead, 1897. A few ink check marks in margin, else NF. 1st bk ed, 1st prtg, w/the word "Train" omitted from title page, corrected in subsequent printings. BAL 6213. *CHAPEL HILL.* $100

Ford, Richard. A PIECE OF MY HEART. NY: H & R, (1976). 1st ed. NF in a dj (few short tears, tiny stain). Nice w/minor flaws. *LOPEZ.* $175

Ford, Richard. A PIECE OF MY HEART. NY: Harper, (1976). 1st ed. Fine in NF dj. *UNGER.* $185

Ford, Richard. IMES, BIRNEY. JUKE JOINT. PHOTOGRAPHS. U.P. Mississippi, 1990. 1st ed. Specially signed. 60 full color photos. Folio. Mint in like dj. *POLYANTHOS.* $85

Ford, Richard. ROCK SPRINGS: STORIES. Atlantic Monthly Press, 1987. One of 200 signed, numbered. Fine in slipcase as issued. *STAHR.* $150

Ford, Richard. ROCK SPRINGS: STORIES. NY: Atlantic Monthly Press, (1987). Uncorrected proof. Fine in wraps. Photo, publicity sheet laid in. Signed. *CAPTAIN'S BOOKSHELF.* $125

Ford, Richard. THE SPORTSWRITER. London: Collins, 1986. 1st UK ed and 1st ed of hardcover. VF in dj. *CAPTAIN'S BOOKSHELF.* $75

Ford, Richard. THE SPORTSWRITER. NY: Vintage Books, (1986). 1st ed. Wrappers. Signed. Fine. No hb ed. *DERMONT.* $65

Ford, Richard. THE SPORTSWRITER. NY: Vintage Contemporaries, 1986. 1st ed. Wraps. Fine. *BEASLEY.* $40

Ford, Richard. THE ULTIMATE GOOD LUCK. Boston: HM, 1981. 1st ed. Fine in a price-clipped dj (sl tanned on spine). Nice, free of the common binding flaw (wherein rear hinge tends to crack when opened). *LOPEZ.* $275

Ford, Richard. THE ULTIMATE GOOD LUCK. Boston: Houghton Mifflin, 1981. 1st ed. Rear hinge starting as is common w/this title, else Fine in dj w/small scrape. *CAPTAIN'S BOOKSHELF.* $75

Ford, Richard. THE ULTIMATE GOOD LUCK. London, 1989. 1st UK ed. Fine in dj. *PETTLER.* $45

Ford, Richard. WILDLIFE. Cl, slipcase. Boston: Little, Brown, (1990). 1st ed. Ltd to 250 signed. Mint. *JAFFE.* $150

Ford, Richard. WILDLIFE. NY: Atlantic Monthly Press, (1990). 1st ed. Signed. new in dj. *BERNARD.* $45

Ford, Richard. WILDLIFE. NY: Atlantic Monthly Press (1990). 1st ed. As New in dj. Contemp presentation. *CAPTAIN'S BOOKSHELF.* $50

Ford, Richard. WILDLIFE. Ptd wrappers. NY: Atlantic Monthly, (1990). Uncorrected proof. VF. *JAFFE.* $125

Ford, Thomas. A HISTORY OF ILLINOIS...1818 TO 1847...THE RISE, PROGRESS, AND FALL OF MORMONISM... Chicago, 1854. 1st ed. 447pp, ads. Orig tan cl w/sl sunned spine. Names, bkpl, o/w VG. *BENCHMARK.* $125

Forde, Daryll. YAKO STUDIES. London: OUP, 1964. 1st ed. NF in VG+ dj. *ACADEMIC.* $30

Forder, A. VENTURES AMONG THE ARABS IN DESERT, TENT, AND TOWN. NY, 1909. xii,292pp. *O'NEILL.* $55

Fordham, Elias Pym. PERSONAL NARRATIVE OF TRAVEL IN VIRGINIA...AND OF A RESIDENCE IN THE ILLINOIS TERRITORY: 1817-1818. Frederic Austin Ogg (ed). Cleveland: Arthur H. Clark, 1906. 1st ed. Front inner hinge weak, cover worn at extremities, and ex-lib. detractions, still Good reading copy. *LAURIE.* $20

Fordyce, George. FIVE DISSERTATIONS ON FEVER. Boston: T. Bedlington & C. Ewer, 1823. 2nd Amer ed. iv, pp (3)-442 + 2pp. Contemp tree calf covers worn, spine tip defective. Some age staining in text, o/w Good. *DIAMOND.* $75

Forel, August. HYPNOTISM OR SUGGESTION AND PSYCHOTHERAPY. London, 1906. 1st Eng trans. *FYE.* $50

Forel, August. HYPNOTISM OR SUGGESTION AND PSYCHOTHERAPY. Trans from the 5th German Ed by H.W. Armit. Amer Ed, Rev and Corrected. NY: Rebman Co. (1907). 1st Am ed. Binding sl soiled. *KARMIOLE.* $75

Foreman, Carolyn Thomas. THE CROSS TIMBERS. (Muskogee, OK: Star Printery), 1947. Fldg map. Signed. VG+. *BOHLING.* $85

Foreman, Grant. A PATHFINDER IN THE SOUTHWEST: THE ITINERARY OF LIEUTENANT A.W. WHIPPLE...Univ of OK, 1941. 1st ed. 6 plts, fldg map. VG in Good dj. *OREGON.* $60

Foreman, Grant. A PATHFINDER IN THE SOUTHWEST: THE ITINERARY OF LIEUTENANT A.W. WHIPPLE...Norman: Univ of OK Press, (1941). 1st ed. Fine in VG dj. *BOOK MARKET.* $75

Foreman, Grant. A PATHFINDER IN THE SOUTHWEST:THE ITINERARY OF LIEUTENANT A.W. WHIPPLE...Univ of OK Press, 1968. 1st ed, 2nd ptg (1968). Large fldg route map. NF in NF dj. *FIVE QUAIL.* $45

Foreman, Grant. INDIANS & PIONEERS...AMERICAN SOUTHWEST BEFORE 1830. Univ of OK Press, 1967. Rev ed. 2nd ptg. Fine in Fine dj. *VARNER.* $25

Foreman, Grant. INDIANS AND PIONEERS...AMERICAN SOUTHWEST BEFORE 1830. Yale, 1930. 1st ed. 8 plts, 1 fldg map. Fine. Howes F259. *OREGON.* $150

Foreman, Grant. THE ADVENTURES OF JAMES COLLIER. Chicago: Black Cat Press, 1937. 1st ed, ltd. to 250. Dk bl cl, silver. Fine. *CONNOLLY & WADE.* $100

Forester, C.S. ADMIRAL HORNBLOWER IN THE WEST INDIES. Little, Brown, (1958). 1st ed. Advance copy with date stamp on dj flap from NY Times library. VG+ in VG dj with chips, closed tear. *BEBBAH.* $30

Forester, C.S. COMMODORE HORNBLOWER. Little, Brown, 1945. Stated 1st ed. VG in dj with piece missing rear panel, short tear, chips but presentable. *BEBBAH.* $40

Forester, C.S. LIEUTENANT HORNBLOWER. London: Michael Joseph, (1952). 1st ed. NF in lightly rubbed dj. *CAPTAIN'S BOOKSHELF.* $50

Forester, C.S. LONG BEFORE FORTY. Boston: Little-Brown, 1967. 1st ed. Fine in lightly used dj. *ELSE FINE.* $30

Forester, C.S. LORD HORNBLOWER. London: Michael Joseph, 1946. 1st ed. NF, dj soiled, worn at spine corners. *ELSE FINE.* $75

Forester, C.S. RANDALL AND THE RIVER OF TIME. Boston: Little Brown, 1950. 1st ed. VF, short tear to dj. *ELSE FINE.* $35

Forester, C.S. RANDALL AND THE RIVER OF TIME. Little, Brown 1950. 1st ed. VG+ in VG dj with closed edge tears, small discolorations at top. *BEBBAH.* $38

Forester, C.S. THE AGE OF FIGHTING SAIL: THE STORY OF THE NAVAL WAR OF 1812. GC: Doubleday, 1956. 1st ed. Fine. Minor wear dj spine top. *ELSE FINE.* $85

Forester, C.S. THE GOOD SHEPHERD. Boston: Little Brown, 1955. 1st ed. Fine in NF dj. *ELSE FINE.* $35

Forester, C.S. THE GOOD SHEPHERD. London: Michael Joseph, 1955. 1st ed. VF. Minor edgewear to dj. *ELSE FINE.* $60

Forester, C.S. THE SHIP. London: Michael Joseph, 1943. 1st ed. Fine, minor wear to dj extremities. Pub. promo. band present. *ELSE FINE.* $250

Forester, C.S. THE SKY AND THE FOREST. London: Michael Joseph, 1948. 1st ed. Fine. Minor wear to dj spine ends. *ELSE FINE.* $50

Forester, C.S. TO THE INDIES. Boston: Little Brown, 1940. 1st ed. Spine letters flaked, NF, dj worn at corners & spine ends. *ELSE FINE.* $65

Forkert, Otto Maurice. FROM GUTENBERG TO THE CUNEO PRESS. Chicago: Cuneo Press, 1933. Wrappers a trifle soiled, else Fine. *WREDEN.* $25

Forman, H. Chandlee. THE VIRGINIA EASTERN SHORE AND ITS BRITISH ORIGINS. Easton, MD: Eastern Shore Publishers, 1975. 1st ed. #803/1000, signed. Lower corner bumped. Minor tape marks inside dj. VG. *BACKROOM.* $60

Forman, Lionel and E.S. Sachs. THE SOUTH AFRICAN TREASON TRIAL. London: John Calder, (1957). 1st ed. 216pp. Dj price-clipped w/short tear. *AKA.* $33

Forney, John W. LIFE AND MILITARY CAREER OF WINFIELD SCOTT HANCOCK. Phila: Hubbard Bros, et al, (1880). 2 engr ports. Orig purple cl-backed boards. *SCHOYER'S.* $25

Forrest, Earle R. ARIZONA'S DARK & BLOODY GROUND. Caxton, 1952. Rev, enl ed. 5th ptg. Fine in VG dj. Howes F265. *OREGON.* $45

Forrest, Earle R. MISSIONS AND PUEBLOS OF THE OLD SOUTHWEST. Cleveland: Arthur H. Clark, 1929. 1st ed. NF. *PARMER.* $195

Forrest, Earle R. THE SNAKE DANCE OF THE HOPI INDIANS. LA: Westernlore Press, 1961. 1st ed. 172pp. Fine in VG dj. *BOOK MARKET.* $25

Forrest, Felix C. ATOMSK. Duell-Sloan, 1949. 1st ed. NF in dj. *MADLE.* $125

Forrest, Felix C. RIA. Duell-Sloan, 1947. 1st ed, 1st bk. Sl spotting to dj, pp, else Fine. *MADLE.* $100

Forrest, Felix C. RIA. NY: Duell, Sloan, and Pearce, (c1947). 1st ed, 1st bk. Fine in dj. *HELLER.* $75

Forrest, Leon. THE BLOODWORTH ORPHANS. NY: Random House, (1977). 1st ed. Upper corners bumped, faint rmdr mark bottom edge of pages, o/w NF in dj w/sl edgewear. Errata slip laid in. *LOPEZ.* $35

Forrest, Leon. THE BLOODWORTH ORPHANS. NY: Random House, 1977. 1st ed. Signed. Errata slip laid in. Fine but for remainder mark and very slight slant, in Fine dj. *BEASLEY*. $45

Forrest, Leon. THERE IS A TREE MORE ANCIENT THAN EDEN. NY: Random House, (1973). 1st ed, 1st novel. NF in price-clipped dj. *LOPEZ*. $65

FORSTER COLLECTION. A catalogue of the paintings, manuscripts, autograph letters, pamphlets, etc, bequeathed by John Forster...with indexes. London: for her Majesty's Stationery Office, 1893. One of 1000. Spine worn, else VG. *WREDEN*. $75

Forster, E.M. A PASSAGE TO INDIA. London: Arnold, 1924. 1st ed. Signed. Ltd to 200. Drab boards cl spine. Fine in lightly used pub slipcase. *JUVELIS*. $1700

Forster, E.M. ABINGER HARVEST. London: Edward Arnold, (1936). 1st ed. Fine in very lightly spotted dj with short tear. *CAPTAIN'S BOOKSHELF*. $150

Forster, E.M. MARIANNE THORNTON 1797-1887. London: Arnold, (1956). 1st ed. Fine in dj, 2 light creases. *JAFFE*. $45

Forster, E.M. PHAROS AND PHARILLON. Cl backed boards. Richmond: Hogarth Press, 1923. 1st ed, state I of binding. One of 900 . Fine. *JAFFE*. $250

Forster, E.M. PHAROS AND PHARILLON. NY, 1923. 1st ed. Edge rubbed w/2 small chips, spine sl sunned, cvrs sl soiled. *POLYANTHOS*. $60

Forster, E.M. THE ETERNAL MOMENT AND OTHER STORIES. London, 1928. 1st ed. Gilt cvrs; ffep little creased, extrems and sides spine sl rubbed, tips corners touch of rubbing. *POLYANTHOS*. $100

Forster, E.M. THE LIFE TO COME AND OTHER STORIES. Norton, 1972. 1st Amer ed. VF in dj. *STAHR*. $20

Forster, E.M. WHAT I BELIEVE. London: Hogarth, 1939. 1st ed. Number One of the Hogarth Sixpenny Pamphlets. Top corner creased throughout, VG in pale green textured wraps. *LAME DUCK*. $150

Forster, Frank J. COUNTRY HOUSES: THE WORK OF FRANK J. FORSTER. NY: William Helburn, 1931. 1st ed. Lt wear to spinal extrems, else Fine. *CAPTAIN'S BOOKSHELF*. $175

Forster, John. THE LIFE OF CHARLES DICKENS. 2 Vols. London: Chapman and Hall, (1899). 8vo, illus, intro and notes by Andrew Lang. Gadshill Ed, red cloth. VG+. *GREAT EXPECTATIONS*. $42.50

Forster, John. THE LIFE OF CHARLES DICKENS. 3 Vols. Phila, 1872,'73,'74. 1st Amer ed. 8vo, illus, red cloth with gilt motif of Dickens on front board, spines faded uniformly to brown, gilt spine lettering still bright. VG+. *GREAT EXPECTATIONS*. $67.50

Forster, John. THE LIFE OF CHARLES DICKENS. London: Cecil Palmer, 1928. Tall 8vo, 893pp, illus, blue cloth. Ed. and annotated with an intro by J.W.T. Ley. Fine. *GREAT EXPECTATIONS*. $55

Forster, Walter. ZION ON THE MISSISSIPPI. St. Louis: Concordia, 1953. 1st ed. 1 double pp facs map. VF in Good+ dj. *OREGON*. $30

Forsyth, Frederick. NO COMEBACKS AND OTHER STORIES. Helsinki, Finland: Eurographica, 1986. 1st of this ed. Ltd to 350 signed. Ptd wraps. Mint. *JAFFE*. $175

Forsyth, Frederick. NO COMEBACKS. London: Hutchinson, 1982. 1st ed. Fine in dj. *MORDIDA*. $35

Forsyth, Frederick. THE DAY OF THE JACKAL. Taiwan Piracy. 1st ed. VG. *SMITH*. $25

Forsyth, Frederick. THE DOGS OF WAR. NY: Viking Press, 1974. 1st Amer ed. Couple pp roughly opened o/w VF in dj. *MORDIDA*. $35

Forsyth, Frederick. THE FOURTH PROTOCOL. London: Hutchinson, 1984. 1st ed. Fine in dj. *MORDIDA*. $45

Forsyth, William. TREATISE ON THE CULTURE AND MANAGEMENT OF FRUIT TREES. Phila: Morgan, 1802. 259pp., full calf, neatly rebacked, w/13 plts. *AMERICAN BOTANIST*. $125

FORT BRADDOCK LETTERS: OR A TALE OF THE FRENCH AND INDIAN WARS. (By John G.C. Brainard.) Worcester: Dorr & Howland, 1827. 1st ed. 12mo, 98pp. Rubbed and some worn leather backed ptd boards. Hand colored frontis. Reprint of 1824 ed. BAL 1328(B). *SECOND LIFE*. $75

Fort, Charles. LO! London, 1931. 1st British ed. VG. *MADLE*. $40

Fort, Charles. THE BOOKS OF....Holt, 1947. Fine in dj. *MADLE*. $35

FORT PILLOW MASSACRE. (Washington: Reports of the Committee on the Conduct of the War, 1864). Very faint dampstain on fep, some modest fading to spine and patch of front board, else NF. *BETWEEN COVERS*. $125

FORT PILLOW MASSACRE. House Rep., 38th Congress, 1st Session, Report No. 65, May 6, 1864. 128, 34pp; 4pp plts. Recased in buckram by hand binder. *HEINOLDT*. $25

Fossett, Frank. COLORADO ITS GOLD AND SILVER MINES, FARMS AND STOCK RANGES, AND HEALTH AND PLEASURE RESORTS. NY: C.G. Crawford, 1879. 3 fldg maps, 1 fldg view, tables. Howes F281. *HUDSON*. $125

Foster, G. Allen. THE EYES AND EARS OF THE CIVIL WAR. NY, (1963). 1st ed. Light dj wear o/w Fine. *PRATT*. $50

Foster, Genevieve. ABRAHAM LINCOLN'S WORLD. NY: Scribner's, 1944. 1st ptg. Dj. *SCHOYER'S*. $20

Foster, J.W. THE MISSISSIPPI VALLEY: ITS PHYSICAL GEOGRAPHY. Chicago: S.C. Griggs & Co. 1869. Lg. 8vo. xvi,444pp. 3 maps. Orig. grn cloth, gilt spine. *KARMIOLE*. $75

Foster, Samuel T. ONE OF CLEBURNE'S COMMAND. Austin, (1980). Ed by Norman D. Brown. 1st ed. VF in VF dj. *PRATT*. $47.50

Foster, William D. COTTAGES MANOIRS AND MINOR BUILDINGS OF NORMANDY AND BRITTANY. NY: Architectural Bk Pub Co, 1926. 1st ed. Frontis, 84 full-pg plts, ep maps. Wear to bottom corners, sm scrape front pastedown, else Fine. *CAPTAIN'S BOOKSHELF*. $125

Foster, William Z. PAGES FROM A WORKER'S LIFE. NY: International, (1939). 1st ed. Dj tears & chips. *AKA*. $27

Foster-Harris. THE LOOK OF THE OLD WEST. NY: Viking, 1955. 1st ed. Fine. *BOOK MARKET*. $35

Foucault, Michel. THE ARCHAEOLOGY OF KNOWLEDGE AND THE DISCOURSE ON LANGUAGE. NY: Pantheon, (1972). 1st US ed. Fine in dj (tiny tear). *CAPTAIN'S BOOKSHELF*. $30

Fountain, P. THE GREAT MOUNTAINS & FORESTS OF SOUTH AMERICA. London: Longmans, 1902. Plts. Gilt dec cl. VG+. *MIKESH*. $65

Fouque, F.H.C. de la Motte. UNDINE. London: Heinemann, 1909. 1st trade ed. Illus Arthur Rackham. 15 tipped-in color plts. Each pl w/titled slip sheets. Edgewear, 3 small abraded spots to paper-covered pict board. Gilt dec spine. VG. *BEBBAH*. $225

Fowler, Don D. ANTHROPOLOGY OF THE NUMA: JOHN WESLEY POWELL'S MANUSCRIPTS ON THE NUMIC PEOPLES OF WESTERN NORTH AMERICA, 1868-1880. Washington: Smithsonian Contrib to Anthrop No. 14, 1971. Blue stiff wraps. 307pp. Light shelf soil, else VG+. *FIVE QUAIL*. $50

Fowler, Don D. et al. THE GLEN CANYON ARCHEOLOGICAL SURVEY. 3 vols. Salt Lake City, 1959. 1st ed. Univ of UT Anthro. Papers Number 39, Glen Canyon Series No. 6. Heavy wraps. Light surface soil/wear, but all 3 vols at least VG to VG+. *FIVE QUAIL*. $110

Fowler, Gene. TIMBERLINE. NY, 1933. 1st ed. Spine soiled. Little cvr staining. Stain on bottom fore-edge. Thin erasure spots on fly, o/w VG. *DIAMOND*. $25

Fowler, George. A TREATISE ON APPENDICITIS. Phila, 1894. 1st ed. 190pp. *FYE.* $150

Fowler, H.W. THE AMPHIBIANS & REPTILES OF NEW JERSEY (WITH) A SUPPLEMENTARY ACCOUNT OF THE FISHES OF NEW JERSEY. Trenton: State Museum, 1907. NF. *MIKESH.* $75

Fowler, H.W. THE CRUSTACEA OF NEW JERSEY. 150 plts. Trenton, 1912. Ex-lib. *SUTTON.* $45

Fowler, Harlan D. CAMELS TO CALIFORNIA: A CHAPTER IN WESTERN TRANSPORTATION. Stanford: University Press, (1950). 1st ed. Fine in Fine dj. *BOOK MARKET.* $35

Fowler, Jacob. JOURNAL OF...NARRATING AN ADVENTURE FROM ARKANSAS...TO THE SOURCES OF THE RIO GRANDE DEL NORTE, 1821-22. NY, 1898. 1st ed. (24),183,(1)pp. Orig cl. Howes F298. One of 950. *GINSBERG.* $150

Fowler, Jacob. THE JOURNAL OF JACOB FOWLER. NY: Francis P. Harper, 1898. 1st ed, 1/950. Fldg frontis. Pres copy. *HUDSON.* $500

Fowler, Jacob. THE JOURNAL OF...NARRATING AN ADVENTURE FROM ARKANSAS...TO SOURCES OF RIO GRANDE DEL NORTE 1821-22. Harper, 1898. xxiv,183pp, 1pp ad. Fldg frontis. 1st ed, ltd to 950. Rev copy. Howes F298. VG. *OREGON.* $175

Fowler, O.S. and L.N. NEW ILLUSTRATED SELF-INSTRUCTOR IN PHRENOLOGY AND PHYSIOLOGY; WITH OVER 100 ENGRAVINGS. NY, 1868. Signed by O.S. Fowler. *FYE.* $50

Fowler, O.S. and L.N. PHRENOLOGY PROVED, IL-LUSTRATED, AND APPLIED, ACCOMPANIED BY A CHART; EMBRACING AN ANALYSIS OF THE PRIMARY, MENTAL POWERS IN THEIR VARIOUS DEGREES OF DEVELOPMENT, THE PHENOMENA PRODUCED BY THEIR COMBINED ACTIVITY, AND THE LOCATION OF THE PHRENOLOGICAL ORGANS IN THE HEAD. NY, 1838. 3rd ed. *FYE.* $75

Fowler, O.S. and L.N. NEW ILLUSTRATED SELF-INSTRUCTOR IN PHRENOLOGY AND PHYSIOLOGY....NY: Samuel Wells, 1872. 176pp, 2pp ads. Stamped cl. Fine. *SECOND LIFE.* $30

Fowler, O.S. FOWLER'S PRACTICAL PHRENOLOGY: GIVING A CONCISE ELEMENTARY VIEW OF PHRENOLOGY. NY, 1853. 432pp. *FYE.* $50

Fowler, O.S. PHYSIOLOGY, ANIMAL AND MENTAL....NY: Fowler and Wells, 1847. 1st ed. Brn cl (some external wear). Couple of signatures pulled. Good tight. *SECOND LIFE.* $45

Fowler, O.S. PHYSIOLOGY, ANIMAL AND MENTAL: APPLIED TO THE PRESERVATION AND RESTORATION OF HEALTH OF BODY, AND POWER OF MIND. NY, 1847. 312pp. *FYE.* $40

Fowler, Russell. THE OPERATING ROOM AND THE PATIENT. Phila, 1907. 2nd ed. *FYE.* $75

Fowler, W. Warde. THE RELIGIOUS EXPERIENCE OF THE ROMAN PEOPLE FROM EARLIEST TIMES TO AUGUSTUS. London, 1922. NF. *POLYANTHOS.* $30

Fowler, William Chauncey. THE SECTIONAL CONTROVERSY. NY: Scribners, 1862. 1st ed. xii,(1),8-269pp. Orig black emb boards. Corners worn, spine rebound w/orig title piece laid on. Some foxing throughout. *CONNOLLY & WADE.* $250

Fowles, George. LETTERS TO ELIZA FROM A UNION SOL-DIER, 1862-1865. Ed by Margery Greenleaf. Chicago, 1970. 1st ed. 176pp. Light dj wear o/w Fine. *PRATT.* $30

Fowles, John. A MAGGOT. Boston, 1985. 1st ed. Fine in dj (extremities, spine minimally rubbed). Signed. *POLYANTHOS.* $30

Fowles, John. A SHORT HISTORY OF LYME REGIS. Boston: Little, Brown, (1982). 1st US ed. Fine in dj. *BETWEEN COVERS.* $40

Fowles, John. DANIEL MARTIN. Boston: Little, Brown, (1977). 1st ed. Precedes Eng ed. Fine in NF dj. *CHAPEL HILL.* $50

Fowles, John. DANIEL MARTIN. Little, Brown, 1977. 1st, VG+ in dj (3 tears). *STAHR.* $15

Fowles, John. DANIEL MARTIN. London: Cape, (1977). 1st ed. Fine in dj. Signed. *CAPTAIN'S BOOKSHELF.* $75

Fowles, John. DANIEL MARTIN. London: Cape, (1977). 1st English ed. Signed. Fine in Fine dj. *UNGER.* $125

Fowles, John. ISLANDS. London, 1978. 1st ed. Signed, dated. Fine in price clipped dj. *POLYANTHOS.* $35

Fowles, John. ISLANDS. London: Jonathan Cape, (1978). 1st ed. Orig dark brn boards. Fine in dj. Signed. *CHAPEL HILL.* $75

Fowles, John. LAND. Photos Fay Godwin. Boston: Little, Brown, (1985). 1st US ed. 1/150 specially bound, signed by Fowles and Godwin. Fine in slipcase. *CAPTAIN'S BOOKSHELF.* $150

Fowles, John. MANTISSA. Boston, 1982. Special ed. 185/510 signed. Mint in Fine box. *POLYANTHOS.* $125

Fowles, John. MANTISSA. Boston: Little, Brown, (1982). 1st Amer ed. #223 of specially bound ltd ed signed. Mint in dj, orig plastic shrinkwrap. *CHAPEL HILL.* $175

Fowles, John. MANTISSA. Boston: Little Brown, (1982). 1st ed. Fine in very lightly rubbed dj. *UNGER.* $35

Fowles, John. OF MEMOIRS AND MAGPIES. Austin: W. Thomas Taylor, 1983. One of 174 (in ed of 200). Fine in wraps. *CAPTAIN'S BOOKSHELF.* $175

Fowles, John. POOR KOKO. Helsinki: Eurographica, (1988). 1st separate ed. Ltd to 350 signed. Ptd wraps. Mint. *JAFFE.* $275

Fowles, John. THE ARISTOS. Boston: Little, Brown, (1964). 1st US ed. Fine in a moderately rubbed dj. *CAPTAIN'S BOOKSHELF.* $100

Fowles, John. THE ARISTOS. Boston: Little, Brown, 1964. 1st ed. Fine in NF dj. *BEASLEY.* $75

Fowles, John. THE ARISTOS. Boston: Little, Brown and Company, (1964). 1st ed. Precedes Eng ed. Fine in NF dj. *JUVELIS.* $100

Fowles, John. THE COLLECTOR. Boston: LB, (1963). 1st Amer ed, 1st bk. Fine in sl rubbed dj. *CAPTAIN'S BOOKSHELF.* $125

Fowles, John. THE COLLECTOR. Boston: Little, Brown, (1963). 1st Amer ed. Few minor spine defects, dj Fine. *MUELLER.* $85

Fowles, John. THE COLLECTOR. Boston: Little, Brown, and Company, (1963). 1st Amer ed, 1st bk. Fine in VG dj. *JUVELIS.* $100

Fowles, John. THE COLLECTOR. Little, Brown, 1963. 1st Amer. ed. About Fine in a dj. Bkpl; 2 sm stains eps. *STAHR.* $75

Fowles, John. THE COLLECTOR. Pennsylvania, 1982. 1st Franklin Library ed. Ltd ed. privately printed and signed. W/special message to subscribers by author. Aeg, full leather gilt. Fine. *POLYANTHOS.* $75

Fowles, John. THE EBONY TOWER. Boston: Little Brown & Co., (1974). 1st ed. Fine in Fine dj. *UNGER.* $50

Fowles, John. THE ENIGMA OF STONEHENGE. NY: S&S, (1980). 1st US ed. Fine in Fine dj. *UNGER.* $35

Fowles, John. THE ENIGMA OF STONEHENGE. Summit, 1980. 1st Amer ed. Fine in dj. *STAHR.* $17.50

Fowles, John. THE ENIGMA. Helsinki: Eurographica, (1988). 1st separate ed. Ltd to 350 signed. Ptd wraps. Mint. *JAFFE.* $275

Fowles, John. THE FRENCH LIEUTENANT'S WOMAN. London: Cape, (1969). 1st ed. Fine in dj rubbed at corners and head of spine. *CAPTAIN'S BOOKSHELF.* $125

Fowles, John. THE MAGUS. Boston, 1965. 1st US ed, precedes UK ed. VG+ in dj. *PETTLER.* $50

Fowles, John. THE MAGUS. Boston: Little, Brown, (1965). 1st US ed. Just About Fine in like dj. Much better than normal. *CAPTAIN'S BOOKSHELF.* $75

Fowles, John. THE MAGUS. London: Cape, (1966). Uncorrected proof copy of 1st Eng ed. NF. *LOPEZ*. $500

Fowles, John. THE MAGUS. London: Jonathan Cape, (1966). 1st Eng ed. NF in VG dj. *JUVELIS*. $200

Fowles, John. THE TREE. Boston: Little, Brown, (1979). 1st Amer ed. Orig brn cl. Mint in dj, orig plastic shrinkwrap. *CHAPEL HILL*. $40

Fox, Charles J. HISTORY OF THE OLD TOWNSHIP OF DUNSTABLE...Nashua: Charles T. Gill, 1846. Cloth somewhat worn, spine ends and corners frayed, lightly chipped; slight fraying along hinges; orig owner's inscrip ffep. *BOHLING*. $60

Fox, Frances M. NANNETTE. Volland, (1929). 1st ed. 80pp. Illus by Justin C. Gruelle. VG+ w/bright gilt cvr dec on red cl. *BEBBAH*. $40

Fox, Frank. SWITZERLAND. A&C Black, 1914. 1st ed. VG-NF. *OLD LONDON*. $50

Fox, George H. PHOTOGRAPHIC ILLUSTRATIONS OF THE SKIN. NY: E.B. Treat, 1887. 2nd ed. 208pp; 85 hand-colored photos. Newly recased in black cl; 1 index leaf restored. Good+. *SMITHFIELD*. $140

Fox, Gustavus V. CONFIDENTIAL CORRESPONDENCE OF...ASSISTANT SECRETARY OF THE NAVY, 1861-1865. NY: 1918. 1st ed. 2 vols. Orig boards, vellum spines, boxed. One of 1200 numbered sets. *GINSBERG*. $75

Fox, Gustavus V. CONFIDENTIAL CORRESPONDENCE OF...ASSISTANT SECRETARY OF THE NAVY 1861-1865. Ed by Robert Means Thompson & Richard Wainwright. NY: Naval History Soc, 1918-1919. 2 vols. 1/1200 sets. Ptd notice from pub in each vol. Very Nice. *BOHLING*. $150

Fox, Helen M. PATIO GARDENS. NY, 1929. 1 fold out plan. Cl w/some soiling. Name stamp. *SUTTON*. $85

Fox, Helen M. PATIO GARDENS. NY, 1929. 1st ed. NF. *DIAMOND*. $35

Fox, John, Jr. A KNIGHT OF THE CUMBERLAND. NY: Scribner's, 1906. 1st ed. Orig red cl, teg. A bit cocked, bkseller's label, but NF. *CHAPEL HILL*. $35

Fox, John, Jr. A MOUNTAIN EUROPA. NY & London: Harper& Bros, 1899. 1st ed. Orig grn cl. Fine. *CHAPEL HILL*. $45

Fox, John, Jr. THE LITTLE SHEPHERD OF KINGDOM COME. NY: Scribner's, 1903. 1st ed, 1st ptg w/Scribner device on right pg and no list of books by Fox on verso of 2nd leaf. Orig red cl. Couple of nicks at spine ends, else NF. *CHAPEL HILL*. $50

Fox, John, Jr. THE TRAIL OF THE LONESOME PINE. NY, 1908. 1st ed. Fine. *POLYANTHOS*. $35

Fox, John, Jr. THE TRAIL OF THE LONESOME PINE. NY: Scribner's, 1908. Fine and bright. 1st ed, 1st prtg, w/Scribner seal on copyright page. BAL 6256. *CHAPEL HILL*. $60

Fox, Russell, ed. SPORTING SOCIETY OF SPORTING CHAT AND SPORTING MEMORIES. London: Bellairs & Co., 1897. 2 vols. 1st ed. VG-NF. *OLD LONDON*. $90

Fox, William et al. THE MILL. Boston: NY Graphic Society, (1976). 1st US ed. Fine. *BOOK MARKET*. $25

Fox, William F. REGIMENTAL LOSSES IN THE AMERICAN CIVIL WAR 1861-1865. Albany: Albany Pub Co, 1889. 1st ed, comp slip tipped in, orig prospectus laid in. Cl rubbed, bumped, stained, cl of spine wrinkled, front hinge starting, inner edges of front and rear blanks sl damaged. Internally VG. *BLUE MOUNTAIN*. $60

Fox, William Price. DOCTOR GOLF. Phila & NY: J.B. Lippincott & Co., (1963). 1st ed, 2nd book. Fine in VG+ dj which is very sl worn at spine ends. *BERNARD*. $40

Fox, William. NEW YORK AT GETTYSBURG. FINAL REPORT ON THE BATTLEFIELD OF GETTYSBURG. 3 vols. NY Monu-ments Commission. Albany, J.B. Lyon, 1900. 5 fldg maps in pockets. Cl worn & mottled. 1st ed. G+. *OREGON*. $150

Fox-Davies, Arthur Charles. ARMORIAL FAMILIES. A DIRECTORY OF GENTLEMEN OF COAT-ARMOUR. COMPILED AND EDITED BY... London: Hurst & Blackett, 1929-1930. 7th ed. 2 vols. Publisher's brown buckram, teg. Bkplts of Joseph M. Gleason and John Howell. Ex-lib. Fine. *WEBER*. $300

Foxx, Jack (pseud of Bill Pronzini). FREEBOOTY. NY: Bobbs-Merrill, (1976). 1st ed. Signed both as Jack Foxx and Bill Pronzini. Fine in dj with rear panel sl soiled. *UNGER*. $40

Foxx, Jack (pseud of Bill Pronzini). WILDFIRE. Indianapolis: Bobbs-Merrill, 1978. 1st ed. Signed. Fine in dj. *MORDIDA*. $35

Foxx, Red & Norma Miller. THE RED FOXX ENCYCLOPEDIA OF HUMOR. Pasadena: Ward Ritchie Press, (1977). 1st ed. About Fine in dj w/short tear at head of spine. *BETWEEN COVERS*. $50

Foy, Eddie. CLOWNING THROUGH LIFE. NY: Dutton, (1928). 1st ed. Fine. *BOOK MARKET*. $75

Fracastorius, H. CONTAGION, CONTAGIOUS DISEASES AND THEIR TREATMENT. Trans by W. Wright. NY, 1930. 1st Eng trans. *FYE*. $150

Fracastoro, Girolamo. FRACASTOR. SYPHILIS OR THE FRENCH DISEASE. WITH A TRANSLATION, NOTES, AND APPENDIX BY HENEAGE WYNNE-FINCH. London, 1935. *FYE*. $100

Fracastoro, Girolamo. THE SINISTER SHEPHERD: A TRANSLATION OF GIROLAMO FRACASTORO'S SYPHILIDIS SIV DE MORBO GALLICO LIBRI TRES BY WILLIAM VAN WYCK. LA, 1934. 1st ed. *FYE*. $100

Fraenkel, Ernst. MILITARY OCCUPATION AND THE RULE OF LAW. Oxford Univ Press, 1944. 1st ed. NF in sl chipped, repaired dj. *DIAMOND*. $45

Fraenkel, Michael. BASTARD DEATH. THE AUTOBIOGRAPHY OF AN IDEA. Paris: Carrefour, 1946. 1st ed. 2nd ptg. NF in dj. *POLYANTHOS*. $50

Fraenkel, Michael. DEATH IS NOT ENOUGH. London, 1939. 1st ed. Fine in dj, rubbed w/tiny tear. In box. *POLYANTHOS*. $75

Fraenkel, Michael. THE DAY FACE AND THE NIGHT FACE. London: Carrefour, (1947). 1st ed. Ltd ed of 1000. Unopened. Wraps. Fine. *POLYANTHOS*. $45

Frame, Janet. A STATE OF SIEGE. NY, 1966. 1st ed. Extremities spine minimally rubbed. Fine in dj (small piece missing lower spine, 3 small edge tears rear panel, little edge rubbed). *POLYANTHOS*. $35

Frame, Janet. FACES IN THE WATER. NY, 1961. 1st ed. Spine sl sunned, 2 name stamps. Fine in dj (spine little sunned, little edge rubbed). *POLYANTHOS*. $30

Frame, Janet. OWLS DO CRY. NY, 1960. 1st ed. Extremities, spine minimally rubbed. Fine in price clipped dj. *POLYANTHOS*. $45

France, Anatole. THE CRIME OF SYLVESTER BONNARD. Trans by Lafcadio Hearne. NY: Harper, 1890. 1st ed thus. State (ptg ?) 2 of the adv. Brown in olive/brown cl and paper label. Good. BAL 7919. *SECOND LIFE*. $45

France, Anatole. THE REVOLT OF THE ANGELS. Mrs. Wilfred Jackson (trans). Pierre Watrin (illus). NY: LEC, 1953. Ltd to 1500 ptd by The Plantin Press. Fine in sl soiled slipcase. *JAFFE*. $45

France, L.B. MOUNTAIN TRAILS AND PARKS IN COLORADO. Denver: Chain, Hardy & Co, 1888. 2nd ed. Orig grn cl. Extrems sl rubbed. *KARMIOLE*. $40

Frances, John. ANNIVERSARY DISCOURSE BEFORE THE NEW-YORK ACADEMY OF MEDICINE. NY, 1847. 1st ed. Wrappers detached. *FYE*. $50

Franch, Jose Alcina. PRE-COLUMBIAN ART. NY: Harry N. Abrams, 1983. 1st Amer ed. Trans by I. Mark Paris. VF in VF dj. *CONNOLLY & WADE*. $175

Franchere, Gabriel. A VOYAGE TO THE NORTHWEST COAST OF AMERICA. Chicago: Lakeside Classic, 1954. Rprt of the 1854 1st ed. Fine. *PARMER*. $20

Franchere, Gabriel. ADVENTURE AT ASTORIA 1810-1814. Hoyt C. Franchere (trans, ed). Norman: Univ of OK, 1967. 1st ed thus. 16pp plts. Dj. Fine. Howes F310. *CONNOLLY & WADE*. $55

Franchere, Gabriel. ADVENTURE AT ASTORIA, 1810-1814. Norman: Univ of OK Press, (1967). 1st ptg this ed. Extremities bumped. VG+ in dj. *BOHLING*. $30

Francis, Convers. LIFE OF JOHN ELIOT, THE APOSTLE TO THE INDIANS. The Library of American Biography, conducted by Jared Sparks, vol V. NY: Harper & Brothers, 1840. VG. *LAURIE*. $15

Francis, Dick. A JOCKEY'S LIFE: THE BIOGRAPHY OF LESTER PIGGOTT. NY: G.P. Putnam's Sons, 1986. 1st Amer. ed. VF in dj. Illus. *MORDIDA*. $35

Francis, Dick. ACROSS THE BOARD. Harper, 1975. 1st ed. thus. Fine in NF dj (2 sm tears; spine lightly sunned). *STAHR*. $35

Francis, Dick. ACROSS THE BOARD. NY: Harper & Row, 1975. Omnibus ed. VF in dj. Relatively uncommon. *MORDIDA*. $75

Francis, Dick. BANKER. London: Michael Joseph, 1982. 1st ed. VF in dj. *MORDIDA*. $50

Francis, Dick. BANKER. NY: Putnam, 1982. 1st ed. Signed. VF in dj. *ELSE FINE*. $35

Francis, Dick. BANKER. NY: Putnam, 1982. 1st ed. VF in dj. *ELSE FINE*. $30

Francis, Dick. BLOOD SPORT. Harper, 1967. 1st Amer ed. Ex libris. VG or better in sl worn dj w/sunned spine. Lib marks very unobtrusive. *STAHR*. $35

Francis, Dick. BLOOD SPORT. London: Michael Joseph, 1967. 1st ed. NF, light wear to dj extremities. *ELSE FINE*. $250

Francis, Dick. BLOOD SPORT. NY: Harper & Row, 1968. 1st Amer ed. Fine in dj. *MORDIDA*. $100

Francis, Dick. BOLT. London: Michael Joseph, 1986. 1st ed. VF in dj. *MORDIDA*. $40

Francis, Dick. BOLT. NY: Putnam, (1987). 1st Amer ed. Signed. Fine in Fine dj. *AKA*. $35

Francis, Dick. BONECRACK. London, 1971. 1st UK ed. NF in price-clipped dj. *PETTLER*. $55

Francis, Dick. BONECRACK. London: Michael Joseph, 1971. 1st ed. Fine in dj. *MORDIDA*. $90

Francis, Dick. BREAK IN. London: Michael Joseph, 1985. 1st ed. Fine in dj. *MORDIDA*. $35

Francis, Dick. BREAK IN. Putnam, (1986). 1st Amer ed. Fine in Fine dj. *BEBBAH*. $12

Francis, Dick. COMEBACK. London: Michael Joseph, 1991. 1st ed. Signed. VF in dj. *MORDIDA*. $45

Francis, Dick. DEAD CERT. London: Michael Joseph, 1962. 1st ed. Page edges sl darkened and spotted o/w Fine in VG dj w/several closed tears, wear along front flap fold, and slight wrinkling at spine ends. *MORDIDA*. $1,850

Francis, Dick. EDGE. NY: Putnam, (1989). 1st Amer ed. Signed. NF in NF dj. *AKA*. $30

Francis, Dick. ENQUIRY. Harper, 1970. 1st Amer ed. About Fine in dj lightly worn at edges and foxed on verso. *STAHR*. $45

Francis, Dick. ENQUIRY. London: Michael Joseph, 1969. 1st ed. Tiny spotting on top edge o/w Fine in dj w/minor wear at spine ends and at corners. *MORDIDA*. $175

Francis, Dick. FLYING FINISH. Harper, 1966. 1st Amer ed. About Fine in dj chipped at head of spine and lower spine fold. *STAHR*. $60

Francis, Dick. FLYING FINISH. NY: Harper, 1967. 1st ed. Fine in dj. *ELSE FINE*. $125

Francis, Dick. FORFEIT. Harper & Row, 1969. 1st Amer ed. About Fine in dj rubbed and sunned on spine. *STAHR*. $50

Francis, Dick. FORFEIT. NY, 1969. 1st US ed. Fine in VG dj. *PETTLER*. $60

Francis, Dick. HIGH STAKES. London: Michael Joseph, 1975. 1st ed. VF in dj. *MORDIDA*. $75

Francis, Dick. HOT MONEY. London: Michael Joseph, 1987. 1st ed. As New, rub at dj spine heel. *ELSE FINE*. $25

Francis, Dick. HOT MONEY. London: Michael Joseph, 1987. 1st ed. Inscribed. VF in dj. *MORDIDA*. $45

Francis, Dick. HOT MONEY. NY, 1988. Ltd ed, 42/250 only. Signed. Fine in Fine box. No dj as issued. *POLYANTHOS*. $60

Francis, Dick. IN THE FRAME. NY: Harper & Row, 1977. 1st Amer ed. VF in dj. *MORDIDA*. $45

Francis, Dick. KNOCK DOWN. London: Michael Joseph, 1974. 1st ed. Fine in dj. *MORDIDA*. $75

Francis, Dick. KNOCK DOWN. NY, 1974. 1st ed. Fine in dj (short edge tear top front panel). *POLYANTHOS*. $45

Francis, Dick. KNOCK DOWN. NY: Harper & Row, 1974. 1st US ed. Signed. Foxing top edges. Dj bit discolored, spotting, o/w VG+ in Good+ dj. *AKA*. $50

Francis, Dick. LESTER: THE OFFICIAL BIOGRAPHY. London: Michael Joseph, 1986. 1st ed. VF in dj. *MORDIDA*. $45

Francis, Dick. LONGSHOT. London: Joseph, 1990. 1st ed. Signed. VF in dj. *SILVER DOOR*. $47.50

Francis, Dick. ODDS AGAINST. Harper, 1965. 1st Amer ed. NF in dj w/short tear on front (internally mended). *STAHR*. $75

Francis, Dick. ODDS AGAINST. London: Michael Joseph, 1965. 1st ed. Fine in dj. *MORDIDA*. $250

Francis, Dick. ODDS AGAINST. Michael Joseph, 1965. 1st ed. VG or better in dj w/closed bruise, soiled on rear panel. Owner inscrip. *STAHR*. $150

Francis, Dick. ODDS AGAINST. NY: Harper, (1965). 1st Amer ed. Name stamp on half-title, else Fine in Fine, bright dj. Scarce thus. *BETWEEN COVERS*. $150

Francis, Dick. PROOF. London: Michael Joseph, 1984. 1st ed. VF in dj. *MORDIDA*. $40

Francis, Dick. PROOF. London: Michael Joseph, 1984. 1st ed. VF in dj. *ELSE FINE*. $35

Francis, Dick. RAT RACE. London: Michael Joseph, 1970. 1st ed. Fine; minor wear to dj spine head. Inscribed. *ELSE FINE*. $275

Francis, Dick. RAT RACE. London: Michael Joseph, 1970. 1st ed. Fine in sl soiled dj with several closed tears, wear. *MORDIDA*. $125

Francis, Dick. REFLEX. London: Joseph, 1980. 1st ed. Fine in dj. *SILVER DOOR*. $30

Francis, Dick. REFLEX. London: Michael Joseph, 1980. 1st ed. Fine in dj. *MORDIDA*. $35

Francis, Dick. RISK. London: Michael Joseph, 1977. 1st ed. Fine in dj w/crease on inner front flap. *MORDIDA*. $55

Francis, Dick. RISK. NY: Harper, 1978. 1st ed. Fine in dj. *ELSE FINE*. $50

Francis, Dick. SLAY-RIDE. London: Michael Joseph, 1973. 1st ed. Fine in dj. *MORDIDA*. $65

Francis, Dick. SLAY-RIDE. London: Michael Joseph, 1973. 1st ed. Signed. VF in dj. *MORDIDA*. $85

Francis, Dick. SLAYRIDE. Harper & Row, 1974. 1st Amer ed. VG or better in price-clipped dj with light wear. *STAHR.* $20

Francis, Dick. SMOKESCREEN. London: Michael Joseph, 1972. 1st ed. Fine in dj. Inscribed. *ELSE FINE.* $150

Francis, Dick. SMOKESCREEN. London: Michael Joseph, 1972. 1st ed. VF in dj. *MORDIDA.* $85

Francis, Dick. SMOKESCREEN. London: Michael Joseph, 1972. 1st ed. Fine in dj. *ELSE FINE.* $75

Francis, Dick. STRAIGHT. London: Michael Joseph, 1989. 1st ed. VF in dj. *MORDIDA.* $45

Francis, Dick. STRAIGHT. London: Michael Joseph, 1989. 1st ed. Signed. VF in dj. *MORDIDA.* $45

Francis, Dick. STRAIGHT. London: Michael Joseph, 1989. 1st ed. As New in dj. *ELSE FINE.* $25

Francis, Dick. THE DANGER. London: Michael Joseph, 1983. 1st ed. Fine in dj. *MORDIDA.* $40

Francis, Dick. THE DANGER. London: Michael Joseph, 1983. 1st ed. VF in dj. *ELSE FINE.* $25

Francis, Dick. THE EDGE. London: Michael Joseph, 1988. 1st ed. Fine in price-clipped dj. *MORDIDA.* $35

Francis, Dick. THE EDGE. Putnam, 1989. 1st Amer ed. Fine in Fine dj. *BEBBAH.* $12

Francis, Dick. THE SPORT OF QUEENS. NY, 1969. 1st ed, 1st bk. Fine in like dj. *POLYANTHOS.* $150

Francis, Dick. TRIAL RUN. London: Michael Joseph, 1978. 1st ed. Fine in price-clipped dj. *MORDIDA.* $30

Francis, Dick. TRIAL RUN. London: Michael Joseph, 1978. 1st ed. VF in dj. *ELSE FINE.* $50

Francis, Dick. TRIAL RUN. NY: Harper, 1979. 1st ed. VF in dj. *ELSE FINE.* $30

Francis, Dick. TWICE SHY. London: Joseph, 1981. 1st ed. VF in dj. *ELSE FINE.* $45

Francis, Dick. TWICE SHY. London: Michael Joseph, 1981. 1st ed. Fine in dj. *MORDIDA.* $30

Francis, Dick. WHIP HAND. London: Michael Joseph, 1979. 1st ed. Fine in dj. *MORDIDA.* $45

Franciscono, Marcel. WALTER GROPIUS AND THE CREATION OF THE BAUHAUS IN WEIMAR. Urbana: Univ of Illinois, (1971). 1st ed. Fine- in VG+ dj. *AARD.* $30

Francome, John & James MacGregor. EAVESDROPPER. London: Macdonald, 1986. 1st ed. Signed by Francome. VF in dj. *MORDIDA.* $45

Francome, John & James MacGregor. RIDING HIGH. London: Macdonald, 1987. 1st ed. VF in dj. *MORDIDA.* $40

Frank, Johann Peter. A SYSTEM OF COMPLETE MEDICAL POLICE. Baltimore, 1976. 1st Eng trans. Dj. *FYE.* $60

Frankenstein, Alfred V. SYNCOPATING SAXOPHONES. Chicago: Robert O. Ballou, 1925. 1/600. Fine in VG dj. *BEASLEY.* $200

Frankland, Capt. Charles Colville. TRAVELS TO AND FROM CONSTANTINOPLE, IN 1827 AND 1828....London, 1830. 2 vols. 2 hand-colored frontis, 14 aquatint, 11 wood-engr plts (3 fldg), 4 eng maps and plans (2 fldg). Half-titles both vols. Full plum calf, gilt fillet borders on all boards, spines gilt, hinges rubbed, marbled edges. xiv, 373pp; viii,310pp. Fine. *O'NEILL.* $500

Franklin, Benjamin. MEMOIRS. Berkeley, 1949. Orig cl. Parallel text ed. May Farrand (ed). Howes F323. *GINSBERG.* $75

Franklin, Benjamin. POLITICAL, MISCELLANEOUS, AND PHILOSOPHICAL PIECES. London: J. Johnson, 1779. 1st ed. Port, xi, 567, (7)pp + 3 plates and fldg table. Contemp leather, hinges rubbed, wear to top of spine, no blank endleaves, minor con-

temp inkings. The only pub of Franklin's issued in his lifetime. *DAWSON'S.* $1000

Franklin, Benjamin. POOR RICHARD: THE ALMANACKS FOR THE YEARS 1733-1758. Illus Norman Rockwell. 1/4 calf & marbled boards, slipcase. Phila: LEC, 1964. 1st of this ed. Ltd to 1500 ptd by Richard Ellis & signed by Norman Rockwell. Fine. *JAFFE.* $250

Franklin, Benjamin. THE WORKS OF BENJAMIN FRANKLIN. INCLUDING THE PRIVATE AS WELL AS OFFICIAL AND SCIENTIFIC CORRESPONDENCE TOGETHER WITH THE UNMUTILATED AND CORRECT VERSION OF THE AUTOBIOGRAPHY. In 12 vols. Comp by John Bigelow. NY: Putnam, 1904. Federal ed ltd to 1000 signed, numbered sets. This #554. Teg. Fine. *CONNOLLY & WADE.* $300

Franklin, Benjamin. THE WORKS OF THE LATE BENJAMIN FRANKLIN....NY, 1807. 283pp, 2pp. Leather. Front hinge cracked. Contents VG. *HEINOLDT.* $20

Franklin, Benjamin. TWO TRACTS: INFORMATION TO THOSE WHO WOULD REMOVE TO AMERICA, AND REMARKS CONCERNING THE SAVAGES OF NORTH AMERICA. London: Stockdale, 1784. 2nd ed. 38,(1)pp. Howes F333. *GINSBERG.* $600

Franklin County Bank. St. Albans, VT. ST. ALBANS RAID OCTOBER 19, 1864. St. Albans, (1966). Later prtg. Wrappers. VG. *McGOWAN.* $27.50

Franklin, John Hope. A SOUTHERN ODYSSEY. Baton Rouge, (1976). 1977 rprt. Lt dj wear o/w Fine. *PRATT.* $25

Franklin, John Hope. FROM SLAVERY TO FREEDOM. NY, 1947. Rprt of 3rd rev, enl ed (1967). Dj wear o/w Fine. *PRATT.* $30

Franklin, John. NARRATIVE OF A JOURNEY TO THE SHORES OF THE POLAR SEA IN THE YEARS 1819, 20, 21, AND 22 WITH AN APPENDIX ON VARIOUS SUBJECTS RELATING TO SCIENCE AND NATURAL HISTORY. London: John Murray, 1823. 1st ed. 4to, xv, 783pp, 31 plates (11 colored), 5 plates at end instead of 4, 4 fldg maps (linen backed). Quarter bound calf and blue cloth, gilt spine titles. Some offsetting, mild foxing, small mend to title page, some general shelfwear, overall VG. *PARMER.* $950

Franklin, K.J. A MONOGRAPH ON VEINS. Springfield, 1937. 1st ed. *FYE.* $60

Franklin, K.J. DE VENARUM OSTIOLIS 1603 OF HIERONYMUS FABRICIUS OF AQUAPENDENTE. Springfield, 1933. 1st Eng trans. *FYE.* $50

Franklin, Miles and Dymphna Cusack. PIONEERS PARADE. Sydney: Angus & Robertson, (1939). 1st Australian ed. VG- in VG- dj. *AARD.* $25

Franklin, S.R. MEMORIES OF A REAR-ADMIRAL. NY, 1898. 1st ed. Minor cvr silverfishing, soiling, o/w VG. *DIAMOND.* $35

Franklin, Sidney. BULLFIGHTER FROM BROOKLYN. NY: Prentice Hall, 1952. 1st ed. VG. *SMITH.* $25

Franks, David. I TOUCH. N.p.: (Red Wheel Barrow Press, 1965). 1st ed. Fine in wrappers. Inscribed. *CAPTAIN'S BOOKSHELF.* $30

Franks, Lucinda. WAITING OUT A WAR. NY: Coward, McCann & Geoghegan, (1974). Fine in Fine dj. *AKA.* $35

Frantz, Joe B. and J. E. Choate, Jr. THE AMERICAN COWBOY: THE MYTH & THE REALITY. Univ of OK Press, (1955). 1st ed. Inscribed, dated, signed. Fine in dj. *AUTHORS OF THE WEST.* $50

Frantz, Joe B. and J.E. Choate Jr. THE AMERICAN COWBOY....Univ of OK Press, 1955. 1st ed. Fine in Fine dj. *VARNER.* $45

Frantz, Joe B. THE DRISKELL HOTEL. Austin: Encino Press, 1973. Bound in paper boards. Fine. *LAURIE.* $25

Fraprie, Frank (ed). THE AMERICAN ANNUAL OF PHOTOG-RAPHY 1934. Boston, 1933. Vol 48. Cl shelfworn but Good, sound. *ARTIS.* $25

Fraser, Antonia. A HISTORY OF TOYS. N.p.: Delacorte Press, (1966). 1st ed. Dj. Fine. *WREDEN.* $45

Fraser, Edward and John Gibbons (comp). SOLDIER AND SAILOR WORDS AND PHRASES. Dutton, 1925. Lib blind stamp, o/w VG. *MAD DOG.* $25

Fraser, George MacDonald. FLASH FOR FREEDOM. London: Bar-rie & Jenkins, 1971. 1st ed. Fine in dj. *MORDIDA.* $100

Fraser, George MacDonald. FLASHMAN AND THE DRAGON. London: Collins Harvill, 1985. 1st ed. Fine in dj. *MORDIDA.* $65

Fraser, George MacDonald. FLASHMAN AND THE DRAGON. London: Barrie & Jenkins, 1985. 1st ed. VF in dj. *ELSE FINE.* $60

Fraser, George MacDonald. FLASHMAN AND THE REDSKINS. London: Collins, 1982. 1st ed. VF in price-clipped dj. *ELSE FINE.* $65

Fraser, George MacDonald. FLASHMAN AND THE REDSKINS. London: Collins, 1982. 1st ed. Fine in dj. *MORDIDA.* $75

Fraser, George MacDonald. FLASHMAN IN THE GREAT GAME. London: Barrie & Jenkins, 1975. 1st ed. Fine in dj. *MORDIDA.* $85

Fraser, George MacDonald. FLASHMAN. FROM THE FLASH-MAN PAPERS 1839-1842. NY, 1969. 1st ed, 1st bk. Two corners little rubbed. Fine in dj (1 tiny edge nick, flaps little sunned). *POLYANTHOS.* $50

Fraser, George MacDonald. FLASHMAN. London: Jenkins, 1969. 1st ed. NF in dj w/chips. *LAME DUCK.* $125

Fraser, George MacDonald. MCAUSLAN IN THE ROUGH. NY: Knopf, 1974. 1st ed. About Fine in dj. *ELSE FINE.* $45

Fraser, George Macdonald. ROYAL FLASH. Knopf, 1970. 1st Amer ed. About Fine in dj (few short tears, very lt wear). Rmdr mark. *STAHR.* $45

Fraser, George MacDonald. THE PYRATES: Knopf, 1984. 1st Amer. ed. NF in dj (sm tear front panel). *STAHR.* $15

Fraser, George MacDonald. THE SHEIKH AND THE DUSTBIN. London: Collins, 1988. 1st ed. Fine in dj. *BETWEEN COVERS.* $50

Fraser, J(ames) D(uncan). THE GOLD FEVER OR TWO YEARS IN ALASKA. (n.p.) (Honolulu): c. 1923, 1st ed. Lt wear; else VG. *PARMER.* $125

Fraser, James. CATTLE BRANDS IN ARIZONA; A BIBLIOG-RAPHY....Flagstaff: Northland Press, 1968. One of 1,000. Cover sl sunned, else VG. *LAURIE.* $40

Fraser, John A. GOLD DISH AND KAVA BOWL. London: J.M. Dent, 1954. 1st ed. NF in NF dj. *GREAT EPIC.* $35

Fraser, Mrs. Hugh and Hugh. SEVEN YEARS ON THE PACIFIC SLOPE. NY: Dodd, Mead and Co, 1914. 1st ed. Front hinge begin-ning; shelfwear. *PARMER.* $75

Fraser, P.M. RHODIAN FUNERARY MONUMENTS. Oxford, 1977. Fldg map and over 100 plts. xiii,205pp. Dj. *O'NEILL.* $25

Frassanito, William A. GRANT AND LEE, THE VIRGINIA CAM-PAIGNS 1864-1865. NY, (1983). 1st ed. 442pp. Minor dj wear, o/w Fine. *PRATT.* $35

Frassanito. William A. GETTYSBURG. NY, (1975). 1st ed. Dj has a small tear o/w VG+. *PRATT.* $35

Frayn, Michael. THE BOOK OF FUB. London: Collins, 1963. 1st ed. Fine in dj. *LOPEZ.* $65

Frazer, J.G. (ed) PAUSANIA'S DESCRIPTION OF GREECE. Lon-don: Macmillan, 1913-30. 6 vols. 42 plts (1919) + 1 supplementary vol. (58 plts). Orig gilt lettered cl. Some corners bumped, o/w Fine. *ARCHAEOLOGIA.* $650

Frazier, E. Franklin. THE BLACK BOURGEOISIE. Glencoe: Free Press, 1957. 1st ed. Fine (bump/wear at head of spine), in bit rubbed dj w/chip at head of spine. *BEASLEY.* $35

Freas, Kelly. THE ART OF S.F. Donning, 1977. 1st ed. Fine in wraps. *MADLE.* $25

Frederick, J.V. BEN HOLLADAY, THE STAGECOACH KING. A.H. Clark, 1940. 1st ed. Fine. *VARNER.* $150

Frederick, J.V. BEN HOLLADAY, THE STAGECOACH KING. Glendale, CA: The Arthur H. Clark Co. 1940. 1st ed. Frontis, 7 plts, fldg map. Teg. *KARMIOLE.* $150

Frederick, J.V. BEN HOLLADAY. THE STAGECOACH KING. Glendale, 1940. 1st ed. Bkpl. Laid in news clipping. VG, no dj as is-sued. *BAADE.* $140

FREDERICK ROLFE AND "THE TIMES." Edinburgh: Tragara, 1977. 1st ed. Wrappers. One of 175 numbered. Fine. *MUELLER.* $25

Fredericks, Arnold (pseud of Frederic Arnold Kummer). ONE MIL-LION FRANCS. NY: Watt, 1912. 1st ed. VG+, minor rubs to colored cover illus. *ELSE FINE.* $30

Fredericks, Arnold (pseud of Frederic Arnold Kummer). THE MARK OF THE RAT. NY: J.H. Sears, 1929. 1st ed. Fine in VG dj w/faded spine, chipping at corners, several closed tears and short piece missing from back panel. *MORDIDA.* $30

Fredericks, J. Paget. GREEN-PIPES. NY: Macmillan, 1929. 1st ed. Cvrs faded, scratched, sm tears frontis, rear fep torn, else Good. In-scribed, signed. *WREDEN.* $25

Free, George D. HISTORY OF TENNESSEE, FROM ITS EAR-LIEST DISCOVERIES AND SETTLEMENTS TO THE END OF THE YEAR 1894. Church Hill, KY, 1895. Final leaves sl waterstained. *HUDSON.* $35

Freed, Donald. AGONY IN NEW HAVEN. NY: Simon & Schuster, (1973). 1st ed. 347pp. Rem mark bottom edges, small ink initial top edges, o/w Fine in dj w/short edgetear. *AKA.* $35

FreeHand, Julianna. A SEAFARING LEGACY. NY: Random House, 1981. 1st ed. VG in rubbed dj. *PARMER.* $30

Freeling, Nicholas. A CITY SOLITARY. Viking, 1985. 1st Amer ed. Fine in Fine dj. *BEBBAH.* $12

Freeling, Nicholas. STRIKE OUT WHERE NOT APPLICABLE. Harper, (1967). 1st Amer ed. Small stains to back edge, else VG+ in VG+ dj. *BEBBAH.* $12

Freeling, Nicholas. THE NIGHT LORDS. Pantheon, (1978). 1st Amer ed. Fine in Fine dj. *BEBBAH.* $15

Freeling, Nicholas. TSING BOOM. NY: Harper & Row, (1969). Stated 1st US ed. Dj w/chips, tears. *AKA.* $23

Freeling, Nicolas. THE KING OF THE RAINY COUNTRY. NY: Harper & Row, 1966. 1st Amer. ed. Fine in dj. *MORDIDA.* $40

Freeling, Nicolas. THE KITCHEN. Harper & Row, 1970. 1st Amer. ed. NF in dj. White dj lightly rubbed & soiled at folds. *STAHR.* $20

Freeman, Douglas Southall (ed.). LEE'S DISPATCHES. NY, 1915. New ed (1957) with additional dispatches and foreword by Grady McWhiney. Signed by McWhiney. Fldg map. VG+ in dj. *PRATT.* $60

Freeman, Douglas Southall. LEE. NY: 1961. 1st ed this abridged ver-sion. 601pp. VG+. *PRATT.* $30

Freeman, Douglas Southall. LEE'S LIEUTENANTS. 3 vols. NY, (1942-1944). Reprint. Light dj wear o/w Fine. *PRATT.* $105

Freeman, Douglas Southall. R.E. LEE, A BIOGRAPHY. 4 vols. NY, (1943). Vol 1 inscribed; Vols 2,3,4 1st eds. 647; 621; 559; 594pp. Tear top of spine of vol 1; all 4 spines faded; evidence of scotch tape having been removed from lower spines o/w VG+. *PRATT.* $225

Freeman, Douglas Southall. R.E. LEE: A BIOGRAPHY. 4 vols. NY: Scribner's, 1934, (1936). Pulitzer Prize ed. NF in Good bumped slip-case. *ARCHER.* $125

Freeman, Douglas Southall. THE SOUTH TO POSTERITY, AN INTRODUCTION TO THE WRITING OF CONFEDERATE HISTORY. NY, 1939. 1983 reprint. VF in dj. *PRATT.* $30

Freeman, Harry C. A BRIEF HISTORY OF BUTTE, MONTANA....Chicago: Henry O. Shepard, 1900. Frontis, 4 halftone repros. Brn cl, black titles, cvr dec. Spotting on covers. *PARMER.* $95

Freeman, Henry B. THE FREEMAN JOURNAL. San Rafael, (1977). Ed by George A. Schneider. 1st ed, ltd to 1000. Lt dj wear o/w Fine. *PRATT.* $27.50

Freeman, James (ed). PROSE AND POETRY OF THE LIVE STOCK INDUSTRY OF THE UNITED STATES. NY: Antiquarian, 1959. Pict cl. VF in slipcase. Howes P636. *OREGON.* $300

Freeman, Larry. HISTORICAL PRINTS OF AMERICAN CITIES. Watkins Glen, NY: Century House, c1952. *HUDSON.* $65

Freeman, Lewis R. AFLOAT AND AFLIGHT IN THE CARIBBEAN. NY: Dodd, Mead and Company, 1932. Some fading to spine, lt shelfwear, overall VG. *PARMER.* $25

Freeman, Lewis R. DOWN THE GRAND CANYON. London: William Heinemann, 1924. Signed. 30pp photo illus. Gold-stamped cl. *DAWSON'S.* $60

Freeman, Lewis R. DOWN THE GRAND CANYON. NY, 1924. 1st ed. Blue cloth, 371pp. Externally VG, internally NF. *FIVE QUAIL.* $60

Freeman, Lewis R. DOWN THE YELLOWSTONE. Dodd, Mead. 1922. 1st ed. VG. *OREGON.* $45

Freeman, Lewis R. SEA-HOUNDS. NY: Dodd, Mead & Co., 1919. VG. *PARMER.* $45

Freeman, R. Austin. A CERTAIN DR. THORNDYKE. NY: D-M, 1928. 1st ed. Fine, no dj. *ELSE FINE.* $60

Freeman, R. Austin. DR. THORNDYKE INTERVENES. NY: Dodd Mead, 1933. 1st ed. Fore-edge spotted o/w Fine in dj w/crease on spine and crease tear on front panel. *MORDIDA.* $185

Freeman, R. Austin. MR. POTTERMACK'S OVERSIGHT. NY: Dodd Mead, 1930. 1st Amer ed. Edges sl darkened and some internal spotting o/w NF in VF bright Like New price-clipped dj. *MORDIDA.* $350

Freeman, R. Austin. THE STONEWARE MONKEY. London: Hodder and Stoughton, 1938. 1st ed. Fine in dj (minor wear, nicks top of spine; removed, sm internal tape repair lower corner front panel). *MORDIDA.* $275

Freeman, R.B. THE WORKS OF CHARLES DARWIN, AN ANNOTATED BIBLIOGRAPHICAL HANDLIST. London, 1977. 2nd ed. *FYE.* $65

Freeman, Ruth. AMERICAN DOLLS. Watkins Glen, NY: Century House, 1952. 1st ed. Fine. *WREDEN.* $30

Freeman, Sean. FAIR WEATHER FOUL. NY: William Morrow, (1988). 1st ed. Inscribed, signed. Fine in NF dj. *AKA.* $25

Freeman, Walter. NEUROPATHOLOGY: THE ANATOMICAL FOUNDATION OF NERVOUS DISEASES. Phila, 1933. 1st ed. *FYE.* $50

Freemantle, Brian. CHARLIE MUFFIN. London: Jonathan Cape, 1977. 1st ed. Agent's label on fep. Top edge sl darkened o/w Fine in dj. *MORDIDA.* $85

Freemantle, Brian. CHARLIE MUFFIN'S UNCLE SAM. London: Jonathan Cape, 1980. 1st ed. VF in dj. *MORDIDA.* $50

Freemantle, Brian. CLAP HANDS, HERE COMES CHARLIE. London: Jonathan Cape, 1978. 1st ed. Fine in dj. *MORDIDA.* $75

Freemantle, Brian. THE RUN AROUND. London: Century, 1988. 1st ed. Review copy. Pub's slip laid in. Fine in dj. *SILVER DOOR.* $25

Freitag, Ruth S. (comp.) HALLEY'S COMET, A BIBLIOGRAPHY. Library of Congress, USGPO, Washington, DC 1984. VG in blue cl. Frontis. *KNOLLWOOD.* $45

Fremantle, Sir Arthur J.L. and Frank A. Haskell. TWO VIEWS OF GETTYSBURG. Chicago, 1964. 1st ed. Lakeside Classic #62. Fine. *PRATT.* $35

Fremlin, Celia. APPOINTMENT WITH YESTERDAY. London: Victor Gollancz, 1972. 1st ed. Edges sl darkened and spotted o/w Fine in lightly soiled dj. *MORDIDA.* $35

Fremlin, Celia. POSSESSION. London: Victor Gollancz, 1969. 1st ed. Fine in lightly soiled dj. *MORDIDA.* $40

Fremlin, Celia. THE LONG SHADOW. London: Victor Gollancz, 1975. 1st ed. Fine in dj. *MORDIDA.* $35

Fremont, John C. GEOGRAPHICAL MEMOIR UPON UPPER CALIFORNIA IN ILLUSTRATION OF HIS MAP OF OREGON AND CALIFORNIA. SF: Bk Club of CA, 1964. One of 425. Fldg map in rear pocket, pict boards. Rpt of 1848 orig, which incl map, prospectus laid in. *DAWSON'S.* $75

Fremont, John C. MEMOIRS OF MY LIFE. Chicago/NY: Belford, Clarke & Company, 1887. Vol I (all pub). Color fldg maps, full calf worn and crudely rebacked. Lacks frontis fldg map, map facing pp 602, several plts. *HUDSON.* $75

Fremont, John C. NARRATIVE OF THE EXPLORING EXPEDITION OF THE ROCKY MOUNTAINS IN THE YEAR 1842, AND TO OREGON AND NORTH CALIFORNIA IN THE YEAR 1843-44. Washington, DC: Taylor, Wilde, & Co, 1845. 2nd ed, reprinted from official copy. Orig buff printed wrappers, little dogeared and dust soiled. Unusual in wrappered state. *HUDSON.* $200

Fremont, John C. NARRATIVE OF THE EXPLORING EXPEDITION TO THE ROCKY MOUNTAINS IN THE YEAR 1842 AND TO OREGON AND NORTH CALIFORNIA IN THE YEARS 1843-44. Washington: Henry Polkinhorn, 1845. Orig wraps bound into modern gilt-stamped cl. Corner of wraps, first few pp text worn. Good+. Howes F370. *OREGON.* $250

Fremont, John C. NOTES OF TRAVEL IN CALIFORNIA...Dublin: James M'Glashan, 1849. 1st Irish ed. 16mo. 311pp+2pp pub's ads. Small hole in spine. Rear inner hinge cracking, o/w VG. 1849 school prize inscription on ep. Lacks map cited in Cowan, p.4. *DIAMOND.* $125

Fremont, John C. OREGON AND CALIFORNIA. Buffalo and Cleveland: Geo. H. Darby and Co/Smith, Knight & Co, 1850. Later ed. Plts, tables. Orig calf, damped. *HUDSON.* $45

Fremont, John C. OREGON AND CALIFORNIA. THE EXPLORING EXPEDITION TO THE ROCKY MOUNTAINS...Buffalo, NY: Geo. H. Derby, 1851. Later ed. Contemp calf cvrs worn. Rebacked. Names on fly. Much age-staining in text, o/w Good. Recased. *DIAMOND.* $50

Fremont, John C. REPORT OF THE EXPLORING EXPEDITION TO THE ROCKY MOUNTAINS IN THE YEAR 1842, AND TO OREGON AND NORTH CALIFORNIA IN THE YEARS 1843-44. Washington, 1845. 693pp, plus 22 plts, 5 maps, (3 fldg, 1 in rear pocket). Orig cl, scattered foxing. Howes F370. *GINSBERG.* $850

Frenau, Philip. SOME ACCOUNT OF THE CAPTURE OF THE SHIP "AURORA." NY, 1899. 1st ed. 49pp, 3 plts. Unopened. *HEINOLDT.* $35

French, Giles. THE GOLDEN LAND, A HISTORY OF SHERMAN COUNTY, OREGON. Portland: Published by Champoeg Press for Oregon Hist Soc, 1958. 1st ed. Uncut and unopened. VF. *OREGON.* $50

French, Joseph. GREAT GHOST STORIES. Dodd-Mead, 1918. 1st ed. VG. *MADLE.* $40

French, Paul (pseud of Isaac Asimov). LUCKY STARR AND THE MOONS OF JUPITER. Doubleday, 1957. 1st ed. NF in frayed, sl worn dj. *MADLE*. $75

Frenkel, H.S. THE TREATMENT OF TABETIC ATAXIA BY MEANS OF SYSTEMATIC EXERCISE. Phila, 1902. 1st Amer ed. *FYE*. $75

Freud, Anna. INTRODUCTION TO THE TECHNIC OF CHILD ANALYSIS. Authorized trans supervised by L. Pierce Clark. NY & Washington, DC, 1928. 1st ed. Spine tips defective, little corner wear. Lacks fep, a little pencilling in text, o/w Good. *DIAMOND*. $75

Freud, Anna. THE EGO AND MECHANISMS OF DEFENCE. NY, 1954. Dj. *FYE*. $15

Freud, Sigmund and Carl G. Jung. THE FREUD/JUNG LETTERS. William McGuire (ed). Princeton: Univ Press, (1974). Dj. VG. *WEBER*. $30

Freud,, Sigmund and William C. Bullitt. THOMAS WOODROW WILSON...A PSYCHOLOGICAL STUDY. London: Weidenfeld and Nicholson, (1967). 1st ed. Dj. Fine. *WEBER*. $35

Freud, Sigmund. AN AUTOBIOGRAPHICAL STUDY. Trans by James Strachey. London: Leonard and Virginia Woolf at The Hogarth Press, 1935. 1st Eng ed. Internat'l Psychoanalytical Lib, no. 26. Dj worn, torn, generally VG. *WEBER*. $150

Freud, Sigmund. BEYOND THE PLEASURE PRINCIPLE. C.J.M. Hubback (trans). London & Vienna: The International Psycho-Analytical Press, 1922. 1st ed in English. Cl stained, number on spine, owner stamp, sig. VG. *BLUE MOUNTAIN*. $125

Freud, Sigmund. BEYOND THE PLEASURE PRINCIPLE. London, 1922. 1st Eng trans. *FYE*. $100

Freud, Sigmund. CIVILIZATION AND ITS DISCONTENTS. Trans by Joan Riviere. London: The Hogarth Press, 1957. The International Psycho-analytical Library, no. 17. 8th imp. Owner's sig, o/w VG. *WEBER*. $25

Freud, Sigmund. GROUP PSYCHOLOGY AND THE ANALYSIS OF THE EGO. Authorized trans by James Strachey. London & Vienna: International Psycho-analytical Press, 1922. 1st ed. Spine sl soiled, rubbed; few pencil marks some pp, o/w Good. *DIAMOND*. $75

Freud, Sigmund. GROUP PSYCHOLOGY AND THE ANALYSIS OF THE EGO. James Strachey (trans). London & Vienna: The International Psycho-Analytical Press, 1922. 1st ed in English. Cl dampstained; owner number, stamp; ink notations, last 2 leaves dampstained. Owner sig, stamp. *BLUE MOUNTAIN*. $45

Freud, Sigmund. GROUP PSYCHOLOGY AND THE ANALYSIS OF THE EGO. 2nd Eng. ed. Trans by James Strachey. London: Hogarth Press, 1940. Series: The International Psycho-Analytical Library, no. 6. Ownership sig. VG. *WEBER*. $60

Freud, Sigmund. INHIBITIONS, SYMPTOMS AND ANXIETY. Trans by Alix Strachey. London: The Hogarth Press, and the Inst of Psycho-Analysis, 1948. 2nd imp. The International Psycho-Analytical Library, no. 28. VG. *WEBER*. $45

Freud, Sigmund. NEW INTRODUCTORY LECTURES ON PSYCHO-ANALYSIS. W.J.H. Sprott (trans). London: Leonard and Virginia Woolf at The Hogarth Press, 1933. 1st Eng ed. Intern'l Psycho-Analytical Library, no. 24. Scattered pencilling. VG. *WEBER*. $85

Freud, Sigmund. ON APHASIA, A CRITICAL STUDY. NY: International Universities Press, (1953). 1st Amer ed. Dj chipped, o/w VG. *WEBER*. $50

Freud, Sigmund. ON DREAMS. London. 1952. Dj. NF. *POLYANTHOS*. $30

Freud, Sigmund. PSYCHOPATHOLOGY OF EVERYDAY LIFE. Authorized Eng ed. London: T. Fisher Unwin, (1914). 1st Eng ed. Pub's presentation, blindstamp on title. Spine water-speckled, o/w VG. Scarce. *WEBER*. $225

Freud, Sigmund. REFLECTIONS ON WAR AND DEATH. NY, 1918. 1st ed. Spine minimally sunned, extremities and corners sl rubbed, small stain rear cover. Fine. *POLYANTHOS*. $75

Freud, Sigmund. THE EGO AND THE ID...Authorized Translation by Joan Riviere. London: Pub by Leonard and Virginia Woolf at the Hogarth Press,...and the Institute of Psycho-Analysis, 1927. 1st Eng ed. One of 1500 ptd. Sl bumped, rubbed, owner number on spine, signed by Dr. A.N. Foxe w/his stamp on fep. Very Nice, VG. *BLUE MOUNTAIN*. $100

Freud, Sigmund. THE FUTURE OF AN ILLUSION. Robson-Scott, W.D. (trans). London: Hogarth Press, 1928. 1st ed in Eng. Orig grn cl. Owner sig. Lt foxing. 1st ed. NF. *CHAPEL HILL*. $175

Freud, Sigmund. THE FUTURE OF AN ILLUSION. Trans by W.D. Robson-Scott. London: Leonard & Virginia Woolf at The Hogarth Press, 1928. 1st Eng ed. The International Psycho-Analytical Library, no. 15. VG. *WEBER*. $175

Freud, Sigmund. THE FUTURE OF AN ILLUSION....W.D. Robson-Scott (trans). London: Pub by Leonard and Virginia Woolf at the Hogarth Press,...and the Institute of Psycho-Analysis, 1928. 1st ed. Bumped, rubbed, sl spotted, owner number on spine. Signed by Dr. A.N. Foxe w/his stamp of fep. VG. *BLUE MOUNTAIN*. $75

Freud, Sigmund. THE ORIGINS OF PSYCHO-ANALYSIS. LETTERS TO WILHELM FLIESS, DRAFTS AND NOTES: 1887-1902. London, 1954. 1st Eng trans. Dj. *FYE*. $50

Freud, Sigmund. THE ORIGINS OF PSYCHOANALYSIS. LETTERS TO WILHELM FLEISS...1887-1902. Ed by Marie Bonaparte, Anna Freud, Ernst Kris. NY: Basic Books, (1954). 1st Amer ed. Dj. VG. *WEBER*. $27.50

Freud, Sigmund. THE QUESTION OF LAY ANALYSIS. NY, 1950. 1st US ed. NF. *POLYANTHOS*. $30

Freud, Sigmund. THE QUESTION OF LAY ANALYSIS. Trans Nancy Procter-Gregg. London: Imago, (1947). 1st Eng ed. Fine in dj. *WEBER*. $75

Freud, Sigmund. TOTEM AND TABOO. NY: Dodd Mead, n.d. xii,268pp. Brn cl; rubbed, sl shaken, owner sig. *WEBER*. $30

Freud, Sigmund. WIT AND ITS RELATIONS TO THE UNCONSCIOUS. Authorized Eng ed. NY: Moffat, Yard, 1916. 1st Amer ed. Rubbed, sl shaken, spine darkened, top frayed. Bkpl. *WEBER*. $100

Freund, Gisele. THE WORLD IN MY CAMERA. June Guicharnaud (trans). NY: The Dial Press, 1974. Dj. *KARMIOLE*. $50

Freyre, Gilberto. THE GILBERTO FREYRE READER. NY: Knopf, 1974. 1st US ed. 253pp. Rem mark bottom edge. Dj sl soiled, price-clipped. *AKA*. $27

Frick, C. HORNED RUMINANTS OF NORTH AMERICA. NY, 1937. Orig cl. Some spine end wear, 1 corner frayed; ep corner missing, ex-lib, but Good, solid. *SUTTON*. $80

Friedenwald, Harry. THE JEWS AND MEDICINE, ESSAYS. NY, 1967. 2nd ed. 2 vols. *FYE*. $75

Friedman, Bruce Jay. STERN. NY, 1962. 1st ed, 1st bk. Fine in dj, rear panel little scratched. *POLYANTHOS*. $60

Friedman, Kinky. A CASE OF LONE STAR. NY: William Morrow, 1987. 1st ed. Advance review copy, sheet laid in. VF in dj. *MORDIDA*. $25

Friedman, Kinky. GREENWICH KILLING TIME. NY: Morrow, 1986. 1st ed, 1st bk. Fine in dj. *ARCHER*. $22.50

Friedman, Kinky. GREENWICH KILLING TIME. NY: William Morrow, 1986. 1st ed. Signed. VF in dj. *MORDIDA*. $25

Friedman, Kinky. WHEN THE CAT'S AWAY. NY: William Morrow, 1988. 1st ed. VF in dj. *MORDIDA*. $25

Friedman, Myra. BURIED ALIVE: THE BIOGRAPHY OF JANIS JOPLIN. NY: Morrow, (1973). 1st ptg. 12-pp photo inset. VG+ in lightly worn dj. *AKA.* $28

Friedman, Reuben. A HISTORY OF DERMATOLOGY IN PHILADELPHIA. NY, 1955. *FYE.* $65

Friedrich Duke of Wurttemberg, Paul Wilhelm. FIRST JOURNEY TO NORTH AMERICA IN THE YEARS 1822 TO 1824...TRANSLATED FROM THE GERMAN BY DR. WILLIAM G. BEK. Pierre, SD, 1941. 1st Eng ed of 1828 orig. Orig cl. *GINSBERG.* $75

Friel, Arthur O. THE PATHLESS TRAIL. G & D, n.d. VG. *MADLE.* $20

FRIENDS OF FRANCE: THE FIELD SERVICE OF THE AMERICAN AMBULANCE DESCRIBED BY ITS MEMBERS. Boston, 1916. 1st ed. *FYE.* $50

Fries, W.H. THE DOUBLE ELEPHANT FOLIO, THE STORY OF AUDUBON'S BIRDS OF AMERICA. Chicago, 1973. Colored frontis, 35 plts. Simulated leather spine over pict cl. Lt scuffing to extrems; eps clipped off; ex-lib. *SUTTON.* $150

Friesner, Isidore & Alfred Braun. CEREBELLAR ABSCESS. NY, 1916. 1st ed. *FYE.* $75

Frieze, Jacob. A CONCISE HISTORY OF THE EFFORTS TO OBTAIN AN EXTENSION OF SUFFRAGE IN RHODE ISLAND. Providence: Benjamin F. Moore, 1842. 1st ed. 172pp. Spine extrems chipped. *KARMIOLE.* $50

Frimmer, Steve. DEAD MATTER. NY: Holt, Rinehart and Winston, 1982. 1st ed. Fine in dj. *MORDIDA.* $27.50

Frink, M. COW COUNTRY CAVALCADE. Denver, 1954. 1st. Fine in chipped dj. *VARNER.* $40

Frink, M., W.T. Jackson & A.W. Spring. WHEN GRASS WAS KING....Univ of CO, 1956. 1st ed. 1/1500. Fine in Fine dj. *VARNER.* $85

Frisch, Frank (as told to J. Roy Stockton). FRANK FRISCH. Doubleday, 1962. 1st ed. VG+ in VG dj. *PLAPINGER.* $50

Frisch, Max. A WILDERNESS OF MIRRORS. London: Methuen (1965). 1st Eng ed. Lt foxing else Fine in dj. *DORN.* $45

Frisch, Max. A WILDERNESS OF MIRRORS. NY: Random House (1966). 1st Amer ed. Fine in a sl dust soiled dj. *DORN.* $40

Frisch, Max. BLUEBEARD. London: Methuen (1983). 1st Eng ed. Fine in dj. *DORN.* $20

Frisch, Max. HOMO FABER. London: Abelard-Schuman (1959). 1st Eng ed. Bkpl else Fine in dj. *DORN.* $50

Friswell, J. Hain. VARIA: READINGS FROM RARE BOOKS. London: Sampson Low, Son, and Marston, 1866. 1st ed. Cover soiled, else Good. *WREDEN.* $40

Frizzell, Mrs. Lodisa. ACROSS THE PLAINS TO CALIFORNIA IN 1852. JOURNAL OF...NY: NYPL, 1915. 1st ed. Orig ptd wraps. Hutlo Paltsits (ed). *GINSBERG.* $100

Froger, (Francois). A RELATION OF A VOYAGE MADE IN THE YEARS 1695, 1696, 1697 ON THE COASTS OF AFRICA, STREIGHTS OF MAGELLAN...BY A SQUADRON OF FRENCH MEN OF WAR UNDER THE COMMAND OF M. DE GENNES. London, 1698. 1st Eng ed pub same yr as French orig. Contemp calf rebacked. Generally Good w/title pg cropped closely along fore-edge; fold-out portion lacking from pl of the unknown bird (opp p10). Only separate English ed. *BOOK BLOCK.* $460

Froggatt, W.W. SOME USEFUL AUSTRALIAN BIRDS. Sydney, 1921. 61 colored plts. Soiling; white spot front cvr; pp tanned. *SUTTON.* $40

FROM SPHINX TO ORACLE. London: Hurst and Blackett, 1899. 2 fldg maps. Fairly bright, cocked spine, a few signatures pulling, some shelfwear. *SCHOYER'S.* $60

Fromaget, Nicolas. EUNUCHS, ODALISQUES AND LOVE. NY: Privately ptd by the Panurge Press, (1932). 1st ed in Eng. One of 2000. Fine. *WREDEN.* $50

Frome, David (pseud of Leslie Ford). THE STRANGE DEATH OF MARTIN GREEN. GC: Doubleday Crime Club, 1931. 1st ed. Name. NF, pict dj worn at extremities. *ELSE FINE.* $60

Frost, Donald McKay. NOTES ON GENERAL ASHLEY, THE OVERLAND TRAIL AND SOUTH PASS. Worcester Amer Antiq Soc, 1945. 1st ed. Fldg map. Orig wraps bound in grn cl. VG. Howes F392. *OREGON.* $150

Frost, Donald McKay. NOTES ON GENERAL ASHLEY: THE OVERLAND TRAIL AND SOUTH PASS. Worcester: Amer Antiquarian Soc, 1945. 1st ed. 159pp. Orig ptd wrappers bound in cl. Howes F392. *GINSBERG.* $125

Frost, J(ohn). THE MEXICAN WAR AND ITS WARRIORS COMPRISING A COMPLETE HISTORY....New Haven: H. Mansfield, 1848. 1st ed. Hand-colored frontis, 332pp, 11pp w/treaty, 39 plts. 12mo. Black blind-stamped cl w/gilt, foxing throughout, as is usual with this book, edges worn, else tight, clean VG. *CONNOLLY & WADE.* $250

Frost, John. PIONEER MOTHERS OF THE WEST....Boston: Lee and Shepard, 1869. 2nd prtg. Grn cl stamped in gilt, sl worn, shaken. Some foxing. Gutter of ffep stuck to paste-down, o/w VG. *SCHOYER'S.* $35

Frost, John. THRILLING ADVENTURES AMONG THE INDIANS...Phila: J.W. Bradley, 1850. 448pp. Early ed. Dec embossed black sheep sl worn. Rebacked w/orig pict spine gilt, sl defective. Some foxing, o/w VG. *DIAMOND.* $75

Frost, Lawrence. GENERAL CUSTER'S LIBBIE. Seattle, 1976. 1st ed. Light dj wear o/w Fine. *PRATT.* $30

Frost, Lawrence. GENERAL CUSTER'S LIBBIE. Seattle: Superior, (1976). 1st ed. VF in VF dj. *OREGON.* $35

Frost, Lawrence. THE COURT-MARTIAL OF GENERAL GEORGE ARMSTRONG CUSTER. Norman, (1979). 1st ed. 280pp. Light dj wear, o/w Fine. *PRATT.* $40

Frost, Richard I. et al. THE WEST OF BUFFALO BILL. NY, 1974. 1st ed. VG+. *PRATT.* $37.50

Frost, Robert. A MASQUE OF MERCY. NY: Holt, (1947). Fine in Very lightly used publisher's slipcase. 1st ed. #340 of 751 signed. *CHAPEL HILL.* $200

Frost, Robert. A MASQUE OF REASON. NY: Holt, (1945). 1st ed. Tiny pinhole in spine, else NF in VG dj. *CHAPEL HILL.* $40

Frost, Robert. AN UNSTAMPED LETTER IN OUR RURAL LETTER BOX. (NY): Henry Holt, December 1944. Ltd ed by Spiral Press. Title page illus by Thomas W. Nason. Mauve wrappers, ptd cover label. Scarce. Fine. *WEBER.* $125

Frost, Robert. COLLECTED POEMS OF ROBERT FROST. NY: Halcyon House, (1939). 1st Halcyon House ed. NF (owner sig) lacking dj. Signed. *CAPTAIN'S BOOKSHELF.* $125

Frost, Robert. COMPLETE POEMS OF ROBERT FROST 1949. NY: Holt & Company, (1949). 1st ed. Ltd to 500 signed. Fine in slipcase, (sl nicked, bumped at corners). *JAFFE.* $350

Frost, Robert. COMPLETE POEMS OF...1949. NY: Holt, (1949). 1st ed. Nice in little worn dj (soiled on rear, price clipped). One of 7325. *SECOND LIFE.* $75

Frost, Robert. IN THE CLEARING. NY: Holt, (1962). 1st ed. NF in price-clipped dj. *CHAPEL HILL.* $40

Frost, Robert. SELECTED POEMS. NY: Henry Holt & Co, (1937). 3rd ed. Signed presentation. Orig blue gilt cl, sl faded. Good in sl soiled dj. *KARMIOLE.* $175

Frost, Robert. SELECTED POEMS. NY: Holt, 1923. 1st ed. Trace of wear at head of spine and corners, else VF in dj (very shallow chip at head of spine). *CAPTAIN'S BOOKSHELF.* $650

Frost, Robert. THE COMPLETE POEMS OF ROBERT FROST. Thomas Nason (illus). 2 vols. NY: LEC, 1950. 1st ed. Ltd to 1500 signed by Frost & Nason. VF set, in sl worn slipcase. *JAFFE.* $500

Frost, Robert. WEST-RUNNING BROOK. NY, 1928. 1st ed, 2nd state. Top spine minimally rubbed. Fine in dj (spine sunned, extremities sl chipped, 4 small edge tears, very small piece missing top edge front panel). *POLYANTHOS.* $65

Frothingham, Robert (ed). SONGS OF THE SEA & SAILORS' CHANTEYS: AN ANTHOLOGY. Cambridge, (1924). *LEFKOWICZ.* $35

Froude, James Anthony. OCEANA, OR ENGLAND AND HER COLONIES. London: Longmans, Green, 1886. viii,341,ads (1)pp. Engr plts, offsetting to eps. Orig pict boards. Fine. *WEBER.* $150

Fry, Christopher. A PHOENIX TOO FREQUENT. Helsinki: Eurographica, 1985. 1st of this ed. Ltd to 350 signed. Ptd wraps. Mint. *JAFFE.* $150

Fry, Christopher. THE DARK IS LIGHT ENOUGH. NY & London: Oxford Univ Press, 1954. 1st Amer ed. Sticker removed from front pastedown, else NF in dj. *CHAPEL HILL.* $35

Fry, Christopher. THE LADY'S NOT FOR BURNING. Helsinki: Eurographica, 1987. 1st this ed. Ltd to 350 signed. Ptd wraps. Mint. *JAFFE.* $150

Fry, J. Reese and Robert T. Conrad. A LIFE OF GEN. ZACHARY TAYLOR...Phila: Elliot, 1848. 332pp. Port, 22 illus. Orig printed rear wrapper only. *GINSBERG.* $75

Fry, James B. ARMY SACRIFICES; OR, BRIEFS FROM OFFICIAL PIGEON-HOLES...NY, 1879. 1st ed. 254pp. Orig cl, joints lightly wearing, sm chip top of spine. Howes F399. *GINSBERG.* $200

Fry, Roger. LETTERS OF ROGER FRY. Ed, intro Denys Sutton. NY: Random House, (1972). 1st US ed. 2 vols. Fine in dj. *CAPTAIN'S BOOKSHELF.* $40

Fry, Walter & John R. White. BIG TREES. Stanford Univ Press, 1948. Fine in VG dj. *CONNOLLY & WADE.* $30

Fryer, Donald S. SONGS AND SONNETS ATLANTEAN. Sauk City: Arkham House, 1971. 1st ed. Fine in Fine dj. *OTHER WORLDS.* $35

Fryer, Jane E. EASY STEPS IN SEWING FOR BIG AND LITTLE GIRLS or MARY FRANCES AMONG THE THIMBLE PEOPLE. (n.p.): (n.p.), (1913). Illus ptd in black & orange. Pict cvr has rubbing, some soil, some spots of light page soil, ffep missing. Folding sewing patterns for doll clothes, some of which are missing. Full-color frontis. *BEBBAH.* $40

Fryxell, Fritiof. THE TETONS. Berkeley: Univ of CA, 1946. Lrg fldg map at rear. Non-authorial inscript fep. Foxing on few pp. VG. *CONNOLLY & WADE.* $25

Fuchs, Vivian and E. Hilary. THE CROSSING OF ANTARCTICA. Boston, (1958). 1st Amer ed. Fine in dj. *ARTIS.* $17.50

Fuchs, Vivian and E. Hillary. THE CROSSING OF ANTARCTICA. Boston: Little, Brown, 1958. 1st Amer ed. Fine in NF dj. *CONNOLLY & WADE.* $40

Fuchs, Vivian and E. Hillary. THE CROSSING OF ANTARCTICA. London, 1958. Dj. Signed. NF. *POLYANTHOS.* $45

Fuchs, Vivian. OF ICE AND MEN. THE STORY OF THE BRITISH ANTARCTIC SURVEY. 1943-73. Oswestry: Anthony Nelson, 1982. 1st ed. Autographed, slip laid in by publisher. Fine in NF dj. *PARMER.* $65

Fuentes, Carlos. A CHANGE OF SKIN. NY: FSG, (1968). 1st ed. VG in lightly edgeworn dj. *LOPEZ.* $45

Fuentes, Carlos. CHRISTOPHER UNBORN. Alfred MacAdam, author (trans). NY: Farrar Straus Giroux, (1989). 1st ed. One of 150 signed. Cl, slipcase. Mint. *JAFFE.* $125

Fuentes, Carlos. DISTANT RELATIONS. NY: FSG, 1982. 1st ed. VF, sm rumple to rear bottom edge of dj. *ELSE FINE.* $30

Fuentes, Carlos. TERRA NOSTRA. NY: FS&G, (1976). 1st ed. Fine in dj. *CAPTAIN'S BOOKSHELF.* $100

Fuentes, Carlos. TERRA NOSTRA. NY: FSG, 1976. 1st ed. VF in dj. *ELSE FINE.* $65

Fuentes, Carlos. THE DEATH OF ARTEMIO CRUZ. London, 1964. 1st UK ed. Faint splash mark on bottom edges, else Fine in dj (very lightly worn, short internal mend). *CAPTAIN'S BOOKSHELF.* $60

Fuentes, Carlos. THE HYDRA HEAD. Farrar, 1978. 1st Amer. ed. Fine in dj. *STAHR.* $15

Fuentes, Carlos. THE HYDRA HEAD. NY: Farrar Straus & Giroux, (1978). Uncorrected proof of 1st US ed. Spine faded, else Fine. *CAPTAIN'S BOOKSHELF.* $35

Fuentes, Carlos. THE OLD GRINGO. NY: Farrar Straus & Giroux, (1985). Uncorrected proof of 1st US ed. Fine in wraps. *CAPTAIN'S BOOKSHELF.* $40

Fuentes, Carlos. THE OLD GRINGO. NY: Farrar Straus Giroux, 1985. 1st ed. NF. *SMITH.* $35

Fuentes, Carlos. THE OLD GRINGO. NY: FSG, (1985). 1st ed. Fine in Fine dj. *LOPEZ.* $35

Fuentes, Carlos. THE OLD MORALITY AND OTHER STORIES. Helsinki: Eurographica, 1986. 1st of this ed. Ltd to 350 signed. Ptd wraps. Mint. *JAFFE.* $150

Fuentes, Carlos. WHERE THE AIR IS CLEAR. NY, 1960. 1st ed. Extremities, spine sl rubbed, spine and edges little sunned. Fine in dj (lower spine tiny chip, very sl rubbed, few tiny edge nicks). *POLYANTHOS.* $50

Fuentes, Carlos. WHERE THE AIR IS CLEAR. NY: Obolensky, (1960). 1st US ed. Just About Fine in like dj (short tear in rear panel, sl faded spine). *CAPTAIN'S BOOKSHELF.* $65

Fuertes, L.A. and W.H. Osgood. ARTIST AND NATURALIST IN ETHIOPIA. GC, 1936. Gilt-stamped cl. 16 colored plts. Edge rubbing; spotting to cvrs; signs of dampness to lower spine; minor dampstaining in prelim pg gutters, neat penciled name bottom of plate pp. Scarce. *SUTTON.* $135

Fugard, Athol. THE BLOOD KNOT. NY, 1964. 1st US ed, 1st bk. Fine in lightly rubbed dj which shows minor chipping at top edge. *PETTLER.* $90

Fugate, Francis L. FRONTIER COLLEGE: TEXAS WESTERN AT EL PASO, THE FIRST FIFTY YEARS. El Paso: Texas Western Press, 1964. Bound in 1/4 gold cl and paper boards. Mint. *LAURIE.* $50

Fugate, Francis L. THE SPANISH HERITAGE OF THE SOUTHWEST. El Paso: Carl Hertzog and Texas Western Press, 1952. 1st ed, designed by Hertzog. One of 525 numbered deluxe, signed by Hertzog. Fine in sl chipped dj. *LAURIE.* $500

Fuhrer, C. THE MYSTERIES OF MONTREAL, BEING RECOLLECTIONS OF A FEMALE PHYSICIAN. Montreal, 1881. 1st ed. Rare. *FYE.* $200

Fullam, George Townley. THE JOURNAL OF GEORGE TOWNELY FULLAM, BOARDING OFFICER OF THE CONFEDERATE SEA RAIDER ALABAMA. Charles G. Summersell (ed). Univ of AL, (1973). 1st ed. Erratum slip laid in. Lt dj wear o/w Fine. *PRATT.* $35

Fullbright, William J. THE PENTAGON PROPAGANDA MACHINE. NY: Liveright, (1970). 1st ed. VG in VG dj. *AKA.* $30

Fuller, Andrew. FOREST TREE CULTURIST...NY: Woodward, 1866. 188pp. Cloth VG. Contents w/dampstaining to top margin, not in text. *AMERICAN BOTANIST.* $35

Fuller, Andrew. THE NUT CULTURIST, A TREATISE....NY, 1910 (1896). Cl (some worming of gutter feps; pp yellowing), o/w Nice. *SUTTON.* $43

Fuller, Daniel. THE DIARY OF THE REVD. DANIEL FULLER WITH HIS ACCOUNT OF HIS FAMILY AND OTHER MATTERS. WRITTEN AT GLOUCESTER....NY: Devine Press, 1894. 1st ed. 49pp. Orig sm 4to vellum backed boards. One of 100. *GINSBERG.* $125

Fuller, Edwin W. THE ANGEL IN THE CLOUD. (N.p.): Privately ptd, 1907. 5th ed. Orig dec blue cl, teg. Trace of lt foxing, but VG+. *CHAPEL HILL.* $40

Fuller, George (ed). HISTORIC MICHIGAN. 3 vols. National Hist Association, (1924). 1st ed. About 1750pp. VG. *ARTIS.* $95

Fuller, Henry B. BERTRAM COPE'S YEAR. Chicago: Ralph Fletcher Seymour, 1919. Ink name, place, date, o/w VG in sl rubbed, gold stamped grn cl. *HELLER.* $150

Fuller, R. Buckminster. CRITICAL PATH. Adjuvant: Kiyoshi Kuramiya. NY: St. Martins (1981). 1st ed. Signed. Dj. *KARMIOLE.* $75

Fuller, R. Buckminster. HOW LITTLE I KNOW. N.p, October, 1966. 1st ed. Fine w/very light soiling in wraps. *BEASLEY.* $100

Fuller, R. Buckminster. NINE CHAINS TO THE MOON. Phila: Lippincott, (1938). 1st ed, 1st bk. 2 fldg charts. Presentation inscribed, signed. Orig gold cl. Fine in sl chipped dj. *KARMIOLE.* $200

Fuller, R. BUCKMINSTER. NINE CHAINS TO THE MOON. Phila: Lippincott, (1938). 1st ed. Presentation, inscribed. Bkpl, o/w Fine in very sl rubbed dj. *JAFFE.* $350

Fuller, R. Buckminster. SYNERGETICS 2. EXPLORATIONS IN THE GEOMETRY OF THINKING. In Collaboration with E.J. Applewhite. NY: Macmillan Publishing Co. (1979). Dj. Presentation inscrip, sm doodle signed on half-title. *KARMIOLE.* $125

Fuller, R. Buckminster. SYNERGETICS, EXPLORATIONS IN THE GEOMETRY OF THINKING. In Collaboration with E.J. Applewhite. Preface and Contribution by Arthur L. Loeb. NY: Macmillan Publishing Co. (1978). "Third Printing." Dj. Presentation inscrip, sm doodle signed. *KARMIOLE.* $125

Fullmer, Jane. SIR HUMPHRY DAVY'S PUBLISHED WORKS. Cambridge, 1969. 1st ed. Dj. *FYE.* $30

Fulton, J.F. and E.H. Thomson. BENJAMIN SILLIMAN, 1779-1864.... 1947. VG+ in dj. *BOOKCELL.* $28

Fulton, John and A.D. Keller. THE SIGN OF BABINSKI: A STUDY OF THE EVOLUTION OF CORTICAL DOMINANCE IN PRIMATES. Springfield, 1932. 1st ed. Dj. *FYE.* $75

Fulton, John F. HARVEY CUSHING. A BIOGRAPHY. Springfield, IL: C.C. Thomas, 1946. 1st ed. VG in chipped and repaired dj. *DIAMOND.* $45

Fulton, John F. HARVEY CUSHING: A BIOGRAPHY. Springfield, IL: Chas. C. Thomas, 1946. 1st ed. Fine in VG dj. *SMITHFIELD.* $63

Fulton, John. A BIBLIOGRAPHY OF TWO OXFORD PHYSIOLOGISTS: RICHARD LOWER (1631-1691) AND JOHN MAYOW (1643-1679). Oxford, 1935. 1st ed. Wrappers. *FYE.* $75

Fulton, John. HARVEY CUSHING: A BIOGRAPHY. Springfield 1946. 1st ed. *FYE.* $50

Fulton, John. MUSCULAR CONTRACTION AND THE REFLEX CONTROL OF MOVEMENT. Baltimore, 1926. 1st ed. Scarce. *FYE.* $150

Fulton, John. PALESTINE: THE HOLY LAND, AS IT WAS AND AS IT IS. Phila: The John C. Winston Co. (1900). 1st ed. 16 color maps; 29 plts. Dec gilt-stamped red cl. Red linen dj. *KARMIOLE.* $60

Fulton, John. THE GREAT MEDICAL BIBLIOGRAPHERS: A STUDY IN HUMANISM. Phila, 1951. 1st ed. 37 plts. *FYE.* $100

Fulton, Robert Lardin. EPIC OF THE OVERLAND. SF: A.M. Robertson, 1924. 1st ed. Ffep missing, o/w VG. *LAURIE.* $50

FUN AND GAMES POP-UP. London, 1983. Coin toss at back. Pop-up bk. *BOOKFINDERS INTL.* $45

FUNGUS THE BOGEYMAN. London, 1982. Pop-up bk. *BOOKFINDERS INTL.* $35

FUNNY JUNGLELAND MOVING PICTURES. Kellog, 1909. Promo bklet. 3 fold-out pp, plus strips that go back and forth. Sl soiled from age, but overall VG. Moveable. *BOOKFINDERS INTL.* $70

FUR-SEAL FISHERIES OF ALASKA. 17 plts, 4 fold-out maps. Washington, 1889. House of Representatives Report #3883. 1, 415pp. 1/2 morocco. Lt wear, pp tanned, solid ex-lib. *SUTTON.* $45

Furlong, Charles Wellington. LET'ER BUCK. NY & London: G.P. Putnam's Sons, 1921. 1st ed. Laid in 2 pieces ephemera. 2pp ads at end. Inscribed. NF, only slight edgewear. *PARMER.* $65

Furman, Gabriel. ANTIQUITIES OF LONG ISLAND...TO WHICH IS ADDED A BIBLIOGRAPHY OF HENRY ONDERDONK, JR. EDITED BY FRANK MOORE. NY, Bouton, 1874. 1st ed. 478, unopened. Orig cl, a few lt stains on cvrs. Howes F422. *GINSBERG.* $150

Furnas, C.C. and S.M. MAN, BREAD AND DESTINY: THE STORY OF MAN'S FOOD. London, 1938. 1st ed. *FYE.* $45

Furneaux, Patrick & Leo Rosshandler. ARTS OF THE ESKIMO: PRINTS. Barre: Barre Publishers, 1975. VG+ in VG dj. *BLUE DRAGON.* $35

Furtwangler, Adolf. MASTERPIECES OF GREEK SCULPTURE: A SERIES OF ESSAYS ON THE HISTORY OF ART. London: William Heinemann, 1895. 186 figs. Corners heavily bumped. Good. *ARCHAEOLOGIA.* $95

Futrelle, Jacques. MY LADY'S GARTER. Chicago, (1912). 1st ed. Spine faded. Minor cvr staining. Minor stains few pages, o/w VG. *DIAMOND.* $75

Fyfe, Andrew. A SYSTEM OF ANATOMY AND PHYSIOLOGY, WITH THE COMPARATIVE ANATOMY OF ANIMALS. Edinburgh, 1791. 3 vols., full leather, 506, 471, 467pp. Disbound, boards detached or missing from all 3 vols., backstrips intact and contents VG. *FYE.* $100

Fyfe, Thomas Alexander (comp). WHO'S WHO IN DICKENS. London: Hodder & Stoughton, 1912. 1st ed. Tall 8vo, 355pp, red cloth spine over red boards, spine sunned. VG. *GREAT EXPECTATIONS.* $30

Fyfield, Frances. A QUESTION OF GUILT. London: Heinemann, 1988. 1st ed. VF in dj. *MORDIDA.* $45

Fyfield, Frances. SHADOWS ON THE MIRROR. London: Heinemann, 1989. 1st ed. Signed. VF in dj. *MORDIDA.* $45

Fyfield, Frances. TRIAL BY FIRE. London: Heinemann, 1990. 1st ed. VF in dj. *MORDIDA.* $40

G

Gablik, Suzi. MAGRITTE. Greenwich, CT: NY Graphic Soc (1971). Pict dj (top edge damaged). NF in Good dj. *BLUE MOUNTAIN.* $30

Gaboriau, Emile. FILE NO. 113. NY, 1900. Trans from French. 1st ed with 4 plates by W. Glackens. Slight cvr staining. Spine tip defective. Some corner and edge wear. Minor staining on few pages, o/w contents VG. *DIAMOND.* $35

Gabriel, Mabel M. MASTERS OF CAMPANIAN PAINTING. NY: H. Bittner, (1952). 38 plts. Signed presentation. Good. *ARCHAEOLOGIA*. $95

GABRIEL OVER THE WHITE HOUSE. (By Thomas Frederic Tweed). NY: Farrar & Rinehart, (1933). 1st ptg. Lt stain on cvr, few pp. Cl w/torn, soiled dj. *SCHOYER'S*. $35

Gabrielson, I.N. and F.C. Lincoln. BIRDS OF ALASKA. Harrisburg, PA & Wash. DC, 1959. 1st ed. Ex-lib. VG in VG dj. *MIKESH*. $125

Gabrielson, I.N. and S.G. Jewett. BIRDS OF OREGON. Corvallis, OR: OSC, 1940. Map in rear pocket. VG+. *MIKESH*. $65

Gadd, C.J. THE STONES OF ASSYRIA: THE SURVIVING REMAINS OF ASSYRIAN SCULPTURE, THEIR RECOVERY AND THEIR ORIGINAL POSITIONS. London: Chatto and Windus, 1936. 47 plts, 2 plans. Fine in dj. *ARCHAEOLOGIA*. $200

Gaddis, William. JR. NY: Knopf, 1975. 1st ed. 2,000 copies of 2nd book. New in dj. *BERNARD*. $100

Gaddis, William. JR. NY: Knopf, 1975. 1st ed. Orig black cl. Fine in dj. *CHAPEL HILL*. $35

Gaddis, William. THE RECOGNITIONS. London, (1955). 1st ed, 1st bk. Author's sig laid in. Pub cancellation stamp on copyright page has penetrated through title page. Fine in dj (extremities, spine sl rubbed, sl soiled). *POLYANTHOS*. $150

Gaddis, William. THE RECOGNITIONS. NY: Harcourt, Brace & Co., (1955). 1st ed, 1st book. Hinge cracked at title page, spine a bit shaken o/w VG in lightly soiled dj which has one internally mended tear at bottom edge of front panel. *BERNARD*. $175

Gaddis, William. THE RECOGNITIONS. NY: HB, (1955). 1st ed. Spine lettering somewhat rubbed. VG in lightly used price-clipped dj. Signed. *CAPTAIN'S BOOKSHELF*. $400

Gade, John A. THE LIFE AND TIMES OF TYCHO BRAHE. Princeton, NJ: Princeton Univ Press, 1947. Good in tattered dj. *KNOLLWOOD*. $35

Gadea, Hilda. ERNESTO: A MEMOIR OF CHE GUEVARA. GC: Doubleday, 1972. 1st ed. 222pp. Dj, 2 sm pieces missing. *AKA*. $25

Gag, Flavia. TWEETER OF PRAIRIE DOG TOWN. Holt, (1957). 1st ed. 62pp. Illus by author. VG+ in VG dj w/some edgewear, short closed tear rear panel. *BEBBAH*. $40

Gag, Wanda. GONE IS GONE OR THE STORY OF A MAN WHO WANTED TO DO HOUSEWORK. NY: Coward-McCann, (1935). 1st ed. VG. Briefly inscribed. *CAPTAIN'S BOOKSHELF*. $125

Gage, Jack R. WYOMING AFOOT AND HORSEBACK OR HISTORY MOSTLY AIN'T TRUE. Flintlock: Cheyenne, 1966. 1st ed. Inscribed presentation. Fine in VG dj. *CONNOLLY & WADE*. $40

Gaines, Ernest J. A GATHERING OF OLD MEN. NY: Knopf, 1983. 1st ed. VF in dj. *ELSE FINE*. $50

Gaines, Ernest J. OF LOVE & DUST. London: Secker & Warburg, (1968). 1st Eng ed. Fine in NF dj. *LOPEZ*. $45

Gaines, Ernest. THE AUTOBIOGRAPHY OF MISS JANE PITTMAN. NY: Dial, 1971. 1st ed. Fine in Fine dj w/few tiny tears. *BEASLEY*. $75

Gale, John. THE MISSOURI EXPEDITION 1818-1820. THE JOURNAL OF SURGEON JOHN GALE. Univ of OK, (1969). R.L. Nichols (ed). 1st ed. VF in VF dj. *OREGON*. $30

Gale, John. THE MISSOURI EXPEDITION, 1818-1820: THE JOURNAL OF SURGEON JOHN GALE WITH RELATED DOCUMENTS. Norman: Univ of Oklahoma Press, (1969). 1st ed. VG in dj. *LAURIE*. $22.50

Gale, Zona. FRIENDSHIP VILLAGE LOVE STORIES. NY: Macmillan, 1909. 1st ed. VG. *SECOND LIFE*. $35

Galen. ON ANATOMICAL PROCEDURES. TRANSLATION OF THE SURVIVING BOOKS WITH INTRODUCTION AND NOTES BY CHARLES SINGER. London, 1956. 1st Eng trans. *FYE*. $150

GALENA, ILLINOIS. 1937. 1st ed. In wraps. 79pp + portfolio of photos, folding map, other maps. Jerre Mangione states Nelson Algren "wrote most of the Galena Guide, one of the best small-town guidebooks" in the WPA series. VG+. *BEBBAH*. $45

Galileo. DIALOGUES CONCERNING TWO NEW SCIENCES. Chicago: Northwestern Univ, 1946. 4th ptg. Trans by Henry Crew and Alfonso de Salvo. Binding frayed, worn, internally clean. *KNOLLWOOD*. $30

Gallagher, Bertrand. UTAH'S GREATEST MANHUNT—THE TRUE STORY OF THE HUNT FOR LOPEZ. Salt Lake, 1913. 1st ed. Orig red wraps. VG. *BENCHMARK*. $35

Gallagher, Robert E. (ed) BYRON'S JOURNAL OF HIS CIRCUMNAVIGATION, 1764-1766. Hakluyt Society series II, vol. CXXII. Cambridge: Cambridge Univ Press, 1964. Dj chipped at extremities, o/w Fine. *LAURIE*. $40

Gallagher, Tess. AMPLITUDE. NEW AND SELECTED POEMS. St. Paul, MN: Graywolf, 1987. 1st ed. Signed, presentation copy. Fine in Fine dj. *POLYANTHOS*. $30

Gallagher, Tess. INSTRUCTIONS TO THE DOUBLE. Port Townsend: Graywolf, (1976). Ltd ed of 1500. Signed presentation copy. Ptd wraps little soiled. NF. *POLYANTHOS*. $35

Gallagher, Tess. MOON CROSSING BRIDGE. St. Paul: Graywolf (1992). 1st ed. Signed. VF in dj. *DORN*. $40

Gallagher, Tess. THE LOVER OF HORSES; AND OTHER STORIES. NY: Harper & Row (1986). 1st ed. Signed. Fine in dj. *DORN*. $50

Gallagher, Tess. UNDER STARS. Port Townsend, WA: Greywolf, 1978. 1st ed. NF in wraps (lt soiled). Simultaneous cl & paper release. *STAHR*. $15

Gallaher, James. THE WESTERN SKETCH-BOOK. Boston: Crocker and Brewster, 1850. Stained, water soiled. *HUDSON*. $55

Gallant, Mavis. THE OTHER PARIS. (London): Andre Deutsch, (1957). Boards. 1st Eng ed, 1st bk. Fine. Unopened. *HELLER*. $65

Gallant, Mavis. THE OTHER PARIS. Boston: Houghton Mifflin, 1956. 1st ed, 1st bk. Fine in dj. *HELLER*. $85

Gallant, Mavis. THE OTHER PARIS: STORIES. Boston: Houghton Mifflin, 1956. 1st. Fine in very lightly rubbed dj (sm tear). *CAPTAIN'S BOOKSHELF*. $75

Gallatin, A.E. JOHN SLOAN. NY: E.P. Dutton, 1925. 20pp, 4 full-pg plts. Spine ends sl worn, o/w VG. *WEBER*. $75

Gallatin, Albert. THE OREGON QUESTION. NY, 1846. Best ed. 75pp. Orig ptd wrappers. Howes G25. *GINSBERG*. $125

Gallatin, Albert. WRITINGS. NY, 1960. 3 vols. Fldg tables. Orig cl, boxed. Howes G31, reissue. *GINSBERG*. $100

Gallaway, B.P. (ed). THE DARK CORNER OF THE CONFEDERACY. Dubuque, IA: Wm. C. Brown, 1968. 1st ed. VG in wraps. *GIBBS*. $25

GALLEON CUT-OUT STORY BOOK. London, (1960s). About Mint condition. *BOOKFINDERS INTL*. $65

Gallizier, Nathan. UNDER THE WITCHES MOON. Boston: Page, 1917. 1st ed. VG in illus cover. 4 color plts. *ELSE FINE*. $75

Galsworthy, John and Ada Galsworthy. NEW ENGLISH VERSION OF CARMEN: AN OPERA IN FOUR ACTS. London, 1932. Ltd ed. 87/650 signed both authors. Uncut and partly unopened. NF in dj (spine little sunned, top little chipped, short edge tear w/tiny chip top front panel). *POLYANTHOS*. $45

Galsworthy, John. ON FORSYTE 'CHANGE. London: William Heinemann, 1930. 1st ed. Small bkseller's label, else VG in dj w/chip at crown of spine. *CHAPEL HILL*. $60

Galsworthy, John. SOAMES AND THE FLAG. NY: Scribners, 1930. Signed ltd ed, 1/680. VG in pub slipcase. *JUVELIS.* $55

Galsworthy, John. SOAMES AND THE FLAG. London: William Heinemann, 1930. One of 1025, signed. Bound in vellum, title in gilt front cvr, spine, teg. New chemise, slipcase. Fine. *HELLER.* $150

Galsworthy, John. THE WHITE MONKEY. London: William Heinemann Ltd, (1926). Signed ltd ed, 1/265. Fine in NF dj. *JUVELIS.* $75

Galton, Francis and Edgar Schuster. NOTEWORTHY FAMILIES (MODERN SCIENCE)-AN INDEX TO KINSHIPS IN NEAR DEGREES BETWEEN PERSONS WHOSE ACHIEVEMENTS ARE HONOURABLE, AND HAVE BEEN PUBLICLY RECORDED. London, 1906. 1st ed. *FYE.* $50

Galton, Francis. HEREDITARY GENIUS: AN INQUIRY INTO ITS LAWS AND CONSEQUENCES. NY, 1870. 1st Amer ed. Recent buckram,. *FYE.* $200

Galvani, Luigi. COMMENTARY ON THE EFFECTS OF ELECTRICITY ON MUSCULAR MOTION. Norwalk, 1953. 1st Eng trans. Includes a facsimile of the 1st ed., trans. and a bibliography of editions by Fulton and Stanton. *FYE.* $50

Galvin, John (ed). THE FIRST SPANISH ENTRY INTO SAN FRANCISCO BAY 1775: THE ORIGINAL NARRATIVE...BY FR. VINCENTE MARIA....SF: John Howell, 1971. One of 5000. 6 full-color full-pg plts, 4 maps. Fine in dj. *LAURIE.* $75

Galvin, John. THE ETCHINGS OF EDWARD BOREIN. SF: John Howell, 1971. 1st ed. Dj. *KARMIOLE.* $75

Gammons, Rev. John G. THE THIRD MASSACHUSETTS REGIMENT VOLUNTEER MILITIA IN THE WAR OF THE REBELLION, 1861 - 1863. Providence: Snow, 1906. 1st ed. Orig cl, 6 light white numbers on spine; bkpls removed. *GINSBERG.* $100

Gann, Walter. TREAD OF THE LONGHORNS. Naylor, 1949. 1st ed. Fine in VG dj. *VARNER.* $40

Gannett, Henry. 20TH ANNUAL REPORT OF THE U.S. GEOLOGICAL SURVEY. Washington, 1900. Part 5, Forest Reserves. Fldg maps. Fair. *ARTIS.* $45

Ganpat. HIGH SNOW. Doran, 1927. 1st ed. Fine in dj, sm chip. *MADLE.* $50

Gantt, W.H. RUSSIAN MEDICINE. NY, 1947. 1st ed. Small lib bkpl. Head of spine frayed. Contents VG. *FYE.* $60

Garattini, S. and V. Ghetti (eds). PSYCHOTROPIC DRUGS. Amsterdam, 1957. 1st ed. 300+ illus and tables. *FYE.* $100

Garces, Francisco. A RECORD OF TRAVELS IN ARIZONA AND CALIFORNIA 1775-1776. SF: John Howell, 1965. Ltd to 1250. 8 plts, 2 fldg maps. VF. *OREGON.* $50

Garces, Francisco. A RECORD OF TRAVELS IN ARIZONA AND CALIFORNIA 1775-1776. (SF): John Howell, 1965. 1st ed, ltd to 1,250. Fldg map. Fine. *BOOK MARKET.* $85

Garcia Lorca, Federico. THE LIEUTENANT COLONEL AND THE GYPSY. GC: Doubleday, 1971. 1st ed. Gift inscription, else Fine. *BETWEEN COVERS.* $35

Garcia Marques, Gabriel. COLLECTED STORIES. NY: Harper & Row, 1984. 1st ed. Fine. *SMITH.* $45

Garcia Marques, Gabriel. THE GENERAL IN HIS LABYRINTH. NY: Knopf, 1990. 1st ed. One of 350 signed. VF. Leatherbound in slipcase. *SMITH.* $350

Garcia Marquez, Gabriel. CHRONICLE OF A DEATH FORETOLD. Gregory Rabassa (trans). London: Jonathan Cape, (1982). 1st ed in English. Orig blue-grn boards. Fine in pict dj. *CHAPEL HILL.* $50

Garcia Marquez, Gabriel. IN EVIL HOUR. NY: H&R, (1979). 1st U.S. ed. Fine in dj. *LOPEZ.* $50

Garcia Marquez, Gabriel. INNOCENT ERENDIRA AND OTHER STORIES. NY: Harper & Row, (1978). 1st ed. Fine in dj w/several small edge tears. *DERMONT.* $45

Garcia Marquez, Gabriel. INNOCENT ERENDIRA AND OTHER STORIES. Gregory Rabassa (trans). NY: Harper & Row, (1978). 1st ed in English. Orig blue cl. Fine in price-clipped pict dj (smudge rear spine edge). *CHAPEL HILL.* $45

Garcia Marquez, Gabriel. INNOCENT ERENDIRA AND OTHER STORIES. NY: Harper, 1978. 1st ed. VF in dj. *ELSE FINE.* $85

Garcia Marquez, Gabriel. LOVE IN THE TIME OF CHOLERA. Edith Grossman (trans). NY: Knopf, 1988. 1st Amer ed. Orig black cl. Fine in dj. Promo postcard laid in. *CHAPEL HILL.* $40

Garcia Marquez, Gabriel. LOVE IN THE TIME OF CHOLERA. NY, 1988. Ltd ed. 267/350 only, signed. Mint in Mint dec acetate dj in Mint box. *POLYANTHOS.* $450

Garcia Marquez, Gabriel. LOVE IN THE TIME OF CHOLERA. NY: Knopf, 1988. 1st ed. VF in dj, with pub. promo. postcard laid in. *ELSE FINE.* $50

Garcia Marquez, Gabriel. LOVE IN THE TIME OF CHOLERA. Knopf, 1988. Uncorrected proof of 1st Amer ed. VF in white wraps in a black cardboard folder with label. *STAHR.* $100

Garcia Marquez, Gabriel. LOVE IN THE TIME OF CHOLERA. NY, 1988. 1st US ed. VF in dj. *PETTLER.* $35

Garcia Marquez, Gabriel. LOVE IN THE TIME OF CHOLERA. Knopf, 1988. Signed, numbered (350) ed. in slipcase. VF. This copy signed, but lacks a number. *STAHR.* $300

Garcia Marquez, Gabriel. LOVE IN THE TIME OF CHOLERA. Knopf, 1988. 1st Amer ed. VF in dj. Promo postcard laid in. *STAHR.* $45

Garcia Marquez, Gabriel. NO ONE WRITES TO THE COLONEL AND OTHER STORIES. Trans J.S. Bernstein. NY: Harper, (1968). 1st US ed. Beautiful in price-clipped dj. *CAPTAIN'S BOOKSHELF.* $600

Garcia Marquez, Gabriel. NO ONE WRITES TO THE COLONEL AND OTHER STORIES. J.S. Bernstein (trans). NY: Harper & Row, (1968). 1st ed in English. Orig cl-backed mustard boards. Short, nearly invisible clean tear bottom front panel, else Fine in dj. *CHAPEL HILL.* $250

Garcia Marquez, Gabriel. NO ONE WRITES TO THE COLONEL. NY: H&R, (1968). 1st ed. NF in dj. *LOPEZ.* $875

Garcia Marquez, Gabriel. ONE HUNDRED YEARS OF SOLITUDE. Gregory Rabassa (trans), Alastair Reid (intro). (Lunenburg, VT): LEC, (1982). One of 2000 ptd at Stinehour Press, Illus, signed by Rafael Ferrer, Rabassa and Reid. Orig litho by Ferrer laid in. Fine in slipcase. *CAPTAIN'S BOOKSHELF.* $350

Garcia Marquez, Gabriel. ONE HUNDRED YEARS OF SOLITUDE. Gregory Rabassa (trans). NY & Evanston: Harper & Row, (1970). 1st ed in English. Orig grn cl. About Fine in pict dj, few minor nicks. Headbands are green and yellow (priority not determined), 1st paragraph front jacket flap ends in an exclamation point (priority not determined). *CHAPEL HILL.* $500

Garcia Marquez, Gabriel. ONE HUNDRED YEARS OF SOLITUDE. Gregory Rabassa (trans). London: Jonathan Cape, (1970). 1st British ed (preceded by Amer ed). Orig blue boards. Fine in price-clipped pict dj (tiny tape mend verso). *CHAPEL HILL.* $275

Garcia Marquez, Gabriel. ONE HUNDRED YEARS OF SOLITUDE. NY: Harper, 1970. 1st ed. Fine, minor wear at corners, short tear at flap fold of the purported first state of the dj. *ELSE FINE.* $450

Garcia Marquez, Gabriel. ONE HUNDRED YEARS OF SOLITUDE. NY: Harper, (1970). 1st U.S. ed. Covers little bowed, else VG, tight, in little chipped and worn price clipped dj. Scarce 1st US ed. *SECOND LIFE.* $600

Garcia Marquez, Gabriel. THE AUTUMN OF THE PATRIARCH. Harper & Row, (1976). 1st Amer ed. VG in VG dj. *BEBBAH.* $40

Garcia Marquez, Gabriel. THE AUTUMN OF THE PATRIARCH. London: Cape, (1977). 1st Eng ed. Fine in Fine, price-clipped dj. *LOPEZ.* $60

Garcia Marquez, Gabriel. THE GENERAL IN HIS LABYRINTH. Full leatherette, dec slipcase. NY: Knopf, 1990. 1st Amer ed. Ltd to 350 signed. Mint. *JAFFE.* $350

Garcia Marquez, Gabriel. THE GENERAL IN HIS LABYRINTH. NY: Knopf, 1990. 1st ed. VF in dj. *ELSE FINE.* $35

Garcilaso de la Vega, El Inca. THE ROYAL COMMENTARIES OF THE INCAS AND GENERAL HISTORY OF PERU. Harold V. Livermore (trans, ed). Austin: Univ of TX, 1970. In 2 vols. Red cl, dj. Fine to VF. *CONNOLLY & WADE.* $95

Gard, Wayne. CHISHOLM TRAIL. Norman: Univ of OK Press, (1954). 3rd ptg. Corners bumped, dj spine faded, else VG+. *BOHLING.* $24

Gard, Wayne. FABULOUS QUARTER HORSE: STEEL DUST. Duel-Sloane, 1958. 1st ed. Inscribed. Fine in Fine dj. *VARNER.* $35

Gard, Wayne. RAWHIDE TEXAS. Univ of OK, (1965). 1st ed. VF in VF dj. *OREGON.* $35

Gard, Wayne. RAWHIDE TEXAS. Univ of OK Press, 1965. 1st ed. Fine in Fine dj. *VARNER.* $37.50

Gard, Wayne. SAM BASS. Boston: Houghton Mifflin, 1936. 1st ed. VG. *GIBBS.* $47.50

Gard, Wayne. SAM BASS. Boston: Houghton Mifflin, 1936. 1st ed. Good+. *CONNOLLY & WADE.* $50

Gard, Wayne. THE CHISHOLM TRAIL. Norman: Univ of OK, 1954. 1st ed, 2nd prtg. VG in Good dj. *CONNOLLY & WADE.* $35

Gard, Wayne. THE CHISHOLM TRAIL. Univ of OK Press, 1954. 1st ed. Inscribed. Fine in NF dj. *VARNER.* $50

Gardiner, Alan H. EGYPTIAN GRAMMAR; BEING AN INTRODUCTION TO THE STUDY OF HIEROGLYPHS. Oxford: Clarendon Press, 1927. 1st ed. 1 plt. Good. *ARCHAEOLOGIA.* $125

Gardiner, Charles Fox, M.D. DOCTOR AT TIMBERLINE. Caxton: Caldwell, 1939. Fine in VG dj. *CONNOLLY & WADE.* $35

Gardiner, Charles Fox. DOCTOR AT TIMBERLINE. Caldwell, ID, 1946. 5th ptg. NF in dj. *DIAMOND.* $25

Gardiner, Dorothy and Kathrine Sorley Walker (eds). RAYMOND CHANDLER SPEAKING. Boston: Houghton Mifflin Company, 1962. 1st Amer ed. Inscribed by Gardiner. Hinge splitting, else Fine w/pub comp slip laid in. Fine in NF dj. *JUVELIS.* $75

Gardiner, Howard C. IN PURSUIT OF THE GOLDEN DREAM. Ed by Dale L. Morgan. Stoughton, MA: Western Hemisphere, Inc, 1970. 1st ed. 8 plts, 2 fldg maps. *KARMIOLE.* $50

Gardner, Arthur. ENGLISH MEDIEVAL SCULPTURE. Cambridge, 1951. New, enl ed. Gilt-stamped folio. NF. *POLYANTHOS.* $100

Gardner, Arthur. ENGLISH MEDIEVAL SCULPTURE. NY: Hacker, (1973). Rev, enl w/683 photos. *ARTIS.* $30

Gardner, C.A. and H.W. Bennetts. THE TOXIC PLANTS OF WESTERN AUSTRALIA. Perth, 1956. 52 colored, 43 b/w plts; map. Hb, lt wear, corners bumped. *SUTTON.* $75

Gardner, D.P. (ed). THE FARMER'S DICTIONARY: A VOCABULARY....NY: Harper, 1846. 1st ed. 876pp,ads. Foxed, bound in full calf. VG. *SECOND LIFE.* $125

Gardner, Edmund G. THE STORY OF SIENA AND SAN GIMIGNANO. London: J.M. Dent & Sons, 1913. Reprint. *WEBER.* $15

Gardner, Erle Stanley. DRIFTING DOWN THE DELTA. NY: Morrow, 1969. Adv rev copy, slip laid in. Fine in Fine dj. *BEASLEY.* $50

Gardner, Erle Stanley. GYPSY DAYS ON THE DELTA. NY: Morrow, 1967. 1st ed. Dj, NF. Cloth, VF. *CONNOLLY & WADE.* $25

Gardner, Erle Stanley. HOVERING OVER BAJA. NY: William Morrow & Co, 1961. 1st ed. NF in VG dj. *PARMER.* $25

Gardner, Erle Stanley. HOVERING OVER BAJA. NY: William Morrow and Company, 1961. 1st ed. Pict dj. NF. *BLUE MOUNTAIN.* $27.50

Gardner, Erle Stanley. HUNTING THE DESERT WHALE. NY: William Morrow, 1960. 1st ed. Inscribed. Fine in dj, chip corner of upper front panel. *MORDIDA.* $75

Gardner, Erle Stanley. HUNTING THE DESERT WHALE. NY: William Morrow and Company, 1960. 1st ed. Color pict dj sl soiled. NF. *BLUE MOUNTAIN.* $27.50

Gardner, Erle Stanley. MEXICO'S MAGIC SQUARE. NY: William Morrow, 1968. 1st ed. Inscribed. Fine in price-clipped dj. *MORDIDA.* $75

Gardner, Erle Stanley. NEIGHBORHOOD FRONTIERS. NY: Morrow, (1954). 1st ed. Fine in VG dj. *BOOK MARKET.* $40

Gardner, Erle Stanley. OFF THE BEATEN TRACK. NY: William Morrow, 1967. 1st ed. Inscribed. Fine in dj. *MORDIDA.* $75

Gardner, Erle Stanley. THE CASE OF THE ANGRY MOURNER. NY: Morrow, (1951). 1st ed. Fine in little worn dj. *SECOND LIFE.* $30

Gardner, Erle Stanley. THE CASE OF THE BEAUTIFUL BEGGAR. NY: Morrow, 1965. 1st ed. Fine, minor rubs to dj extremities. *ELSE FINE.* $30

Gardner, Erle Stanley. THE CASE OF THE CAUTIOUS COQUETTE. Morrow, (1949). 1st ed. Small stain in front gutter, slight discoloration rear endpaper. VG in Good+ dj with chips, few small closed edge tears. *BEBBAH.* $25

Gardner, Erle Stanley. THE CASE OF THE LAME CANARY. NY: Morrow, 1937. 1st ed. Fine, minor wear at dj corners. *ELSE FINE.* $325

Gardner, Erle Stanley. THE CASE OF THE LUCKY LOSER. NY: Morrow, 1957. 1st ed. Light rubs at spine ends, else Fine, dj edgeworn with sm chips at spine ends. Inscribed yr of pub. *ELSE FINE.* $275

Gardner, Erle Stanley. THE CASE OF THE SCREAMING WOMAN. NY: Morrow, 1957. 1st ed. Fine in Fine dj but for slight rubbing. *BEASLEY.* $25

Gardner, Erle Stanley. THE CASE OF THE TROUBLED TRUSTEE. Morrow, 1965. 1st ed. About Fine in dj rubbed at lower spine fold. *STAHR.* $15

Gardner, Erle Stanley. THE COURT OF LAST RESORT. NY: Sloane, (1952). 1st ed. Inscribed by Gardner to a judge who helped him rescue innocent men from prison. VG in dj chipped at extremities. *UNGER.* $175

Gardner, Erle Stanley. THE D.A. DRAWS A CIRCLE. NY: Morrow, 1939. 1st ed. Fine, dj has lt wear at extremities. *ELSE FINE.* $85

Gardner, Erle Stanley. THE DESERT IS YOURS. NY: William Morrow, 1963. 1st ed. Inscribed. Fine in sl rubbed dj, minor wear spine ends. *MORDIDA.* $75

Gardner, Erle Stanley. THE DESERT IS YOURS: A SPIRITED ACCOUNT....NY: Morrow, 1963. 1st ed. Fine in Fine dj. *BOOK MARKET.* $25

Gardner, Erle Stanley. THE HUMAN ZERO. Morrow, 1981. 1st ed. Fine in dj *MADLE.* $30

Gardner, Ernest A. A HANDBOOK OF GREEK SCULPTURE. London, 1897. 2 vols. xvii,284pp; xv,268pp. *O'NEILL.* $25

Gardner, John & Lewis Dunlap. THE FORMS OF FICTION. NY: Random House, (1962). 1st. Remarkably fresh (owner sig) in cream-colored boards w/o dj, as issued. *CAPTAIN'S BOOKSHELF.* $75.

Gardner, John, and Lennis Dunlap. THE FORMS OF FICTION. NY: Random House, 1962. 1st ed. Fine w/light spine wear; issued w/o dj. *BEASLEY.* $100

Gardner, John. BROKENCLAW. NY: Putnam, 1990. 1st Amer ed. Review copy, signed. Pub's slip laid in. VF in dj. *SILVER DOOR.* $35

Gardner, John. FREDDY'S BOOK. NY, 1980. 1st ed. Signed presentation. Fine in dj, 2 tiny edge nicks. *POLYANTHOS.* $65

Gardner, John. GRENDEL. NY, 1971. 1st ed. Fine in Fine price-clipped dj w/o the usual spine sunning. Very rare in this condition. *PETTLER.* $175

Gardner, John. GRENDEL. NY: Knopf, 1971. 1st ed. Illus. w/14 drawings by Emil Antonucci. Bottom 1/8" of cover very sl faded o/w Fine in dj which is ever so sl faded at spine (much Nicer than usually found). Very attractive copy. *BERNARD.* $200

Gardner, John. GRENDEL. NY: Knopf, 1971. 1st ed. VF in dj. *LOPEZ.* $200

Gardner, John. ICEBREAKER. London: Cape/Hodder & Stoughton, 1983. 1st ed. VF in dj. *MORDIDA.* $40

Gardner, John. IN THE SUICIDE MOUNTAINS. NY, 1977. 1st ed. VF in dj. *PETTLER.* $35

Gardner, John. IN THE SUICIDE MOUNTAINS. NY: Knopf, 1977. 1st ed. Joe Servello (illus). Fine in dj (tiny, unobtrusive abrasion near bottom of front panel). *BERNARD.* $25

Gardner, John. IN THE SUICIDE MOUNTAINS. NY: Knopf, 1977. Uncorrected proof. Fine in wrappers, promo sheet stapled inside front cvr. *LOPEZ.* $150

Gardner, John. JASON AND MEDEIA. NY, 1973. 1st ed. Fine in NF dj. *PETTLER.* $50

Gardner, John. JASON AND MEDEIA. NY: Knopf, 1973. Uncorrected proof. Signed. NF in wrappers. *LOPEZ.* $300

Gardner, John. LICENSE RENEWED. London: Cape/Hodder & Stoughton, 1981. 1st ed. Fine in dj. *MORDIDA.* $40

Gardner, John. NICKEL MOUNTAIN. NY, 1973. 1st ed. Fine in dj. *PETTLER.* $25

Gardner, John. NICKEL MOUNTAIN. NY: Knopf, 1973. 1st ed. Illus. w/etchings by Thomas O'Donohue. New in dj. *BERNARD.* $20

Gardner, John. NICKEL MOUNTAIN. NY: Knopf, 1973. Uncorrected proof. Signed in 1974. Spine a bit sunned, o/w Fine. *LOPEZ.* $250

Gardner, John. NO DEALS MR. BOND. London: Cape/Hodder & Stoughton, 1987. 1st ed. VF in dj. *MORDIDA.* $40

Gardner, John. NOBODY LIVES FOREVER. London: Cape, (1986). 1st ed. Fine in Fine dj. *UNGER.* $45

Gardner, John. OCTOBER LIGHT. NY: Knopf, 1976. 1st ed. Fine in price clipped dj. *BERNARD.* $30

Gardner, John. OCTOBER LIGHT. NY: Knopf, 1976. 1st ed. Fine in dj. Signed. Scarce thus. *CHAPEL HILL.* $100

Gardner, John. ON MORAL FICTION. NY: Basic Books, 1978. Uncorrected proof. *LOPEZ.* $200

Gardner, John. ROLE OF HONOR. London: Cape/Hodder & Stoughton, 1984. 1st ed. VF in dj. *MORDIDA.* $40

Gardner, John. THE COMPLETE WORKS OF GAWAIN POET. Chicago: Univ of Chicago Press, (1965). 1st ed. NF in VG dj. *LOPEZ.* $45

Gardner, John. THE KING'S INDIAN. NY: Knopf, 1974. 1st ed. of 1st collection of stories. Illus. by Herbert L. Fink. New in dj. *BERNARD.* $35

Gardner, John. THE KING'S INDIAN. NY: Knopf, 1974. Uncorrected proof. Signed. *LOPEZ.* $250

Gardner, John. THE RESURRECTION. (NY): NAL, (1966). 1st ed. VG in dj (sl spotted with age, few short edge tears). *LOPEZ.* $475

Gardner, John. THE RESURRECTION. (NY): NAL, (1966). 1st ed. NF in VG price clipped dj which is lightly soiled & internally reinforced with tape at 3 places along top inside edge. *BERNARD.* $450

Gardner, John. THE SUNLIGHT DIALOGUES. NY, 1972. 1st ed. NF in VG dj. *PETTLER.* $40

Gardner, John. THE SUNLIGHT DIALOGUES. NY: Knopf, 1972. Uncorrected proof. Fine. Signed and dated in 1974. *LOPEZ.* $375

Gardner, John. THE WRECKAGE OF AGATHON. NY: Harper & Row, (c1970). 1st ed. Fine in dj. *HELLER.* $125

Gardner, Leonard. FAT CITY. NY: Farrar, Straus and Giroux, (1969). 1st ed, 1st bk. Fine in dj. *HELLER.* $50

Garfield, Brian. DEATH SENTENCE. NY: Evans, (1975). 1st ed. Signed. Fine in NF dj. *UNGER.* $35

Garfield, Brian. HOPSCOTCH. NY: M. Evans, 1975. 1st ed. Signed. VF in dj. *MORDIDA.* $37.50

Garfield, Brian. MANIFEST DESTINY. NY: Penzler, (1989). 1st ed. Signed. Fine in Fine dj. *UNGER.* $35

Garfield, Brian. RELENTLESS. NY: World, 1972. 1st ed. As New in dj. *ELSE FINE.* $45

Garfield, Brian. RELENTLESS. NY: World Publishing, 1972. 1st ed. Fine in dj w/crease on front panel. *MORDIDA.* $25

Garfield, Brian. THE HIT. NY: Macmillan, 1970. 1st ed. Fine in price-clipped dj. *MORDIDA.* $20

Garfield, Brian. THE ROMANOV SUCCESSION. NY: Evans, 1974. 1st ed. As New in dj. *ELSE FINE.* $25

Garfield, Brian. TRAPWIRE. NY: McKay, 1973. 1st ed. As New in dj. *ELSE FINE.* $30

Garland, Hamlin. A DAUGHTER OF THE MIDDLE BORDER. Macmillan, 1922. 1st ed. Fine, name. *AUTHORS OF THE WEST.* $25

Garland, Hamlin. A SON OF THE MIDDLE BORDER. Macmillan, 1917. 1st ed. Back cover foxed, else Fine. *AUTHORS OF THE WEST.* $40

Garland, Hamlin. CRUMBLING IDOLS. Chicago: Stone & Kimball, 1894. 1st ed, 1st binding. Teg, uncut, bkpl, name. *POLYANTHOS.* $45

Garland, Hamlin. CRUMBLING IDOLS: TWELVE ESSAYS ON ART....Stone & Kimball, 1894. 1st ed. Frontis. Teg. Fine, bkpl. *AUTHORS OF THE WEST.* $75

Garland, Hamlin. HAMLIN GARLAND'S DIARIES. Donald Pizer (ed). Huntington Lib, 1968. 1st ed. New in dj. *AUTHORS OF THE WEST.* $20

Garland, Hamlin. HESPER. Harper, 1903. 1st ed. Pict cvr. Fine. *AUTHORS OF THE WEST.* $40

Garland, Hamlin. MAIN-TRAVELLED ROADS. Arena Pub Co, 1892. 1st clothbound ed. Frontis photo. Some foxing, tiny tears on title pg, else VG+. *AUTHORS OF THE WEST.* $90

Garland, Hamlin. MONEY MAGIC. Harper & Bros, 1907. 1st ed. VG+, bkpl, date. *AUTHORS OF THE WEST.* $35

Garland, Hamlin. PRAIRIE FOLKS. Chicago: F.J. Schulte, 1893. 1st ed. 255pp. Orig printed wrappers. Spine chipped, wraps somewhat weary. *M & S.* $150

Garland, Hamlin. PRAIRIE SONGS....Stone & Kimball, 1893. Pict cover in gilt, teg. Straight tear on ep, else Fine. *AUTHORS OF THE WEST.* $90

Garland, Hamlin. THE BOOK OF THE AMERICAN INDIAN. NY: Harper, (1923), "C-B" (1927). Later ed. 2pp ads, 35 plts by Remington. Orig cl & boards w/Remington illus pasted on. Little foxing, o/w VG+ in repaired dj w/Remington color plate pasted on.

In orig sl soiled, chipped & repaired box w/Remington illus label pasted on. Garland ink inscription pasted on fly. *DIAMOND.* $250

Garland, Hamlin. THE EAGLE'S HEART. D. Appleton & Co, 1900. 1st ed. Dec cover. VG+, note, owner stamp. *AUTHORS OF THE WEST.* $75

Garland, Hamlin. THE LIGHT OF THE STAR. Harper, 1904. 1st ed. Frontis, pict cvr. VG; names. *AUTHORS OF THE WEST.* $40

Garland, Hamlin. THE SPIRIT OF SWEETWATER. Curtis Pub Co. and Doubleday & McClure, (1898). Tender hinge, else Fine. *AUTHORS OF THE WEST.* $40

Garland, Hamlin. TRAIL-MAKERS OF THE MIDDLE BORDER. Macmillan, 1926. 1st ed. Pict cover, eps. Fine in chipped dj. *AUTHORS OF THE WEST.* $35

Garland, Hamlin. WAYSIDE COURTSHIPS. D. Appleton & Co, 1897. 1st ed. Fine. *AUTHORS OF THE WEST.* $125

Garner, Bess Adams. MEXICO: NOTES IN THE MARGIN. Boston: Houghton Mifflin Co, 1937. 1st ed. Bkpl. VG in VG dj. *PARMER.* $35

Garner, Bess Adams. WINDOWS IN AN OLD ADOBE. Pomona: Sanders Press, (1939). 1st ed, ltd to 2,000 signed, inscribed. Fine. *BOOK MARKET.* $40

Garner, R.L. APES AND MONKEYS, THEIR LIFE AND LANGUAGE. Port frontis. Boston, 1900. Gilt-stamped, pict cl. Occasional pp smudging, institutional bkpl, # sticker on spine. *SUTTON.* $45

Garner, Thomas and Stratton, Arthur. THE DOMESTIC ARCHITECTURE OF ENGLAND DURING THE TUDOR PERIOD. London: Batsford, (1929). 2nd ed, rev. 2 vols. 210 full-pg plts. Orig w/gilt sl faded. VG-NF. *CHAPEL HILL.* $225

Garnett, David. ASPECTS OF LOVE. NY: Harcourt Brace & Co., (1956). 1st Amer ed. Foxing pp edges, else Fine in dj. *BETWEEN COVERS.* $45

Garnett, David. NEVER BE A BOOKSELLER. NY: Knopf, 1929. 1st ed. Rice paper wraps, paper label. 1/2000 (none for sale). VG. *SECOND LIFE.* $25

Garnett, David. THE GOLDEN ECHO. THE FLOWERS OF THE FOREST. THE FAMILIAR FACES. London: Chatto & Windus, 1953-1962. 1st ed. 3 vols. NF set in djs. *CAPTAIN'S BOOKSHELF.* $100

Garnett, R.S. SOME BOOK-HUNTING ADVENTURES, A DIVERSION. Edinburgh: William Blackwood & Sons, 1931. 1st ed, 2nd imp. Dj chipped, small pieces missing. *OAK KNOLL.* $35

Garnett, Richard. POEMS. London: Elkin Mathews & John Lane, 1893. 8vo, 172, (1)pp, (1), 16pp ads. Orig brown buckram. Small nick at crown of spine, eps foxed, else partially unopened, NF. 1st ed. 1/350 for distribution in Eng, w/tipped-in limitation slip present. *CHAPEL HILL.* $55

Garrard, Lewis. WAH-TO-YAH AND THE TAOS TRAIL...SF: Grabhorn Press, 1936. 1st thus, ltd to 550. Reprint of 1850 ed. Pub's announcement laid in. Map tipped to fep. Fine. Howes G70. *OREGON.* $160

Garratt, Alfred. GUIDE FOR USING MEDICAL BATTERIES. Phila, 1867. 1st ed. 180pp. 129 woodcuts. Scarce. *FYE.* $200

Garretson, Martin. THE AMERICAN BISON. NY, 1938. NF. *POLYANTHOS.* $40

Garretson, Martin. THE AMERICAN BISON. NY: Zoological Soc, (1938) 1st ed. VG in VG dj. *OREGON.* $60

Garrett, Albert. HISTORY OF BRITISH WOOD ENGRAVING. NJ, 1978. NF. *POLYANTHOS.* $75

Garrett, George (ed). THE GIRL IN THE BLACK RAINCOAT. NY: Duel, Sloane, (1966). 1st ed. Fine in dj, tear. Inscribed. *CAPTAIN'S BOOKSHELF.* $50

Garrett, George. AN EVENING PERFORMANCE. GC: Doubleday, 1985. 1st ed. Fine in dj, pub's card laid in. Inscribed. *CAPTAIN'S BOOKSHELF.* $40

Garrett, George. COLD GROUND WAS MY BED LAST NIGHT. Columbia: Univ of MO Press, (1964). 1st ed. Signed. Fine in NF dj. *LOPEZ.* $65

Garrett, George. COLD GROUND WAS MY BED LAST NIGHT. Columbia: Univ of MO Press, (1964). 1st ed. Fine in lightly used dj (sm tear). Signed. *CAPTAIN'S BOOKSHELF.* $50

Garrett, George. DEATH OF THE FOX. GC: Doubleday, 1971. 1st ed. Later ptg. Inscribed. Fine in NF dj. *LOPEZ.* $45

Garrett, George. DEATH OF THE FOX. NY: Doubleday, (1971). 1st Amer ed. Signed. VG in Near VG dj w/edgewear. *DORN.* $50

Garrett, George. DO, LORD, REMEMBER ONE. London: Chapman & Hall, (1965). 1st Eng ed. Signed. Fine in dj. *DORN.* $50

Garrett, George. ENTERED FROM THE SUN. NY: Doubleday (1990). Adv rev copy. Fine in wraps. *DORN.* $25

Garrett, George. ENTERED FROM THE SUN. NY: Doubleday, (1990). 1st Amer ed. Signed. Fine in dj. *DORN.* $40

Garrett, George. IN THE BRIAR PATCH. Austin: Univ of Texas Press, (1961). 1st ed. Fine in VG, price-clipped dj (tears upper edge rear panel). *LOPEZ.* $45

Garrett, George. KING OF THE MOUNTAIN. NY: Charles Scribner's Sons, (1957). 1st Amer ed. Signed. NF in Fine dj. *DORN.* $90

Garrett, George. KING OF THE MOUNTAIN. NY: Scribners, 1957. 1st ed. VF, minor rubs dj spine fold. *ELSE FINE.* $50

Garrett, George. KING OF THE MOUNTAIN. Short Stories. NY: Scribners, (1957). 1st ed, 1st bk. Fine in dj sl darkened spine. Signed. *CAPTAIN'S BOOKSHELF.* $75

Garrett, George. POISON PEN. (Winston Salem): Stuart Wright, (1986). 1st ed. Fine in dj. Signed. *CAPTAIN'S BOOKSHELF.* $50

Garrett, George. SIR SLOB AND THE PRINCESS: A PLAY FOR CHILDREN. NY: French, (1962). 1st Amer ed. Signed. VG with owner's name on cover, some cover soiling. Performance ed in wraps. *DORN.* $40

Garrett, George. THE FINISHED MAN. NY: Scribner's, (1959). 1st Amer ed. Signed. Fine in NF dj. *DORN.* $80

Garrett, George. THE MAGIC STRIPTEASE. NY: Doubleday, (1973). 1st Amer ed. Signed. Fine in dj. *DORN.* $40

Garrett, George. THE SLEEPING GYPSY AND OTHER POEMS. Austin: Univ of Texas Press, 1958. 1st ed. Fine in very lightly used dj. *CAPTAIN'S BOOKSHELF.* $50

Garrett, George. THE SLEEPING GYPSY AND OTHER POEMS. Austin: Univ of TX, (1958). 1st Amer ed. Signed. Fine in dj. *DORN.* $100

Garrett, George. THE SUCCESSION. NY: Doubleday, (1983). 1st Amer ed. Signed. Bottom of spine bumped else Fine in VG dj. *DORN.* $45

Garrett, George. WHICH ONES ARE THE ENEMY?. Boston: LB, (1961). 1st ed. NF in like dj. Inscribed. *CAPTAIN'S BOOKSHELF.* $75

Garrett, George. WHISTLING IN THE DARK. NY: Harcourt Brace Jovanovich, (1992). Uncorrected proof. Fine in wrappers. *LOPEZ.* $35

Garrett, Pat F. THE AUTHENTIC LIFE OF BILLY THE KID. Univ of OK Press, 1954. 2nd ptg. Fine in Fine dj. *VARNER.* $12.50

Garrett, Randall. TOO MANY MAGICIANS. Doubleday, 1967. Exlib in dj. *MADLE.* $45

Garrison, Fielding. AN INTRODUCTION TO THE HISTORY OF MEDICINE. Phila, 1917. 2nd ed. *FYE.* $75

Garrison, Jim. ON THE TAIL OF THE ASSASSINS. NY: Sheridan Square Press, (1988). 1st ed. VG+ in VG+ dj. AKA. $25

Garstang, John. THE BURIAL CUSTOMS OF ANCIENT EGYPT....London: Archibald Constable, 1907. 16 plts (1 color). Teg. Nick at spine. Good. ARCHAEOLOGIA. $650

Garstin, Crosbie. SAMUEL KELLY—AN EIGHTEENTH CENTURY SEAMAN. NY: Frederick A. Stokes Co., 1925. 1st ed. Bkplt. Fine. PARMER. $60

Gartmann, Heinz. THE MEN BEHIND THE SPACE ROCKETS. London: Weidenfeld & Nicolson, 1955. VG in torn dj. KNOLLWOOD. $35

Garton, George. COLT'S S.A.A. POST WAR MODELS. N. Hollywood: Beinfeld Pub. Co, 1979. Stated 1st ed. VG in VG dj. BACKMAN. $32

Garton, Ray. CRUCIFAX AUTUMN. Arlington Heights: Dark Harvest, 1988. 1st ed, trade issue. Bkpl. fore-edge spotting else Fine in dj. OTHER WORLDS. $25

Garve, Andrew. THE CUCKOO LINE AFFAIR. Harper, (1953). 1st Amer ed. VG+ in Good+ dj with chips, closed edge tears. BEBBAH. $14

Garwood, Darrell. CROSSROADS OF AMERICA. THE STORY OF KANSAS CITY. NY, 1948. 1st ed. 331pp. VG. DIAMOND. $12.50

Gascoyne, David. COLLECTED POEMS. London: O.U.P., 1965. 1st ed. Robin Skelton (ed). Fine in price clipped dj (extremities, spine and corners little rubbed). POLYANTHOS. $75

Gash, Jonathan. FIREFLY GADROON. NY: St. Martin's, 1982. 1st ed. VF in dj. ELSE FINE. $40

Gash, Jonathan. MOONSPENDER. London: Collins Crime Club, 1986. 1st ed. Fine in dj w/minor wear. MORDIDA. $35

Gash, Jonathan. MOONSPENDER. NY: St. Martin's, 1987. 1st ed. VF in dj. ELSE FINE. $35

Gash, Jonathan. PEARLHANGER. London: Collins Crime Club, 1985. 1st ed. Signed. Fine in dj w/minor wear. MORDIDA. $65

Gash, Jonathan. PEARLHANGER. NY: St. Martin's, 1985. 1st ed. VF in dj. ELSE FINE. $35

Gash, Jonathan. SPEND GAME. NY: Ticknor & Fields, 1981. 1st ed. VF in dj. ELSE FINE. $60

Gash, Jonathan. THE GONDOLA SCAM. NY: St. Martin's, 1984. 1st ed. VF in dj. ELSE FINE. $35

Gash, Jonathan. THE GREAT CALIFORNIA GAME. London: Century, 1991. 1st ed. VF in dj. MORDIDA. $45

Gash, Jonathan. THE JUDAS PAIR. NY: Harper & Row, 1977. 1st ed, 1st bk. Fine, very minor edgewear, some light rubs to dj extrems. ELSE FINE. $85

Gash, Jonathan. THE SLEEPERS OF ERIN. NY: Dutton, 1983. 1st ed. VF in dj. ELSE FINE. $40

Gash, Jonathan. THE TARTAN RINGERS. London: Collins Crime Club, 1986. 1st ed. Fine in dj. MORDIDA. $45

Gash, Jonathan. THE TARTAN SELL. NY: St. Martin's, 1986. 1st ed. VF in dj. ELSE FINE. $30

Gash, Jonathan. THE VATICAN RIP. NY: Ticknor & Fields, 1981. 1st ed. VF in dj. ELSE FINE. $45

Gash, Jonathan. THE VERY LAST GAMBADO. NY: St. Martin's, 1990. 1st Amer ed. Signed. Promo copy w/sticker on dj. Fine in dj. SILVER DOOR. $37.50

Gaskell, Elizabeth. LIFE OF CHARLOTTE BRONTE. Leipzig: Tauchnitz, 1857. 2 vols. Copyright ed. Leather & cl, sl rubbed. VG. SCHOYER'S. $40

Gaskell, Elizabeth. SYLVIA'S LOVERS. Leipzig: Tauchnitz, 1863. 2 vols in one. Leather & boards, fairly rubbed & worn. Ffep chipped. SCHOYER'S. $20

Gaskell, William. THE INVOLUNTARY NERVOUS SYSTEM. London, 1920. 2nd ed. FYE. $100

Gass, William. IN THE HEART OF THE HEART OF THE COUNTRY AND OTHER STORIES. NY: Harper & Row, (1968). 1st ed. Fine in dj. CAPTAIN'S BOOKSHELF. $100

Gass, William. OMENSETTER'S LUCK. (NY): NAL, (1966). 1st ed, 1st bk. Fine in dj w/trace of wear. CAPTAIN'S BOOKSHELF. $175

Gass, William. ON BEING BLUE. Boston: David Godine, (1975). 1st ed. 1/225 signed. Fine in sl faded slipcase. CAPTAIN'S BOOKSHELF. $100

Gass, William. THE FIRST WINTER OF MY MARRIED LIFE. Northridge: Lord John Press, 1979. One of 275 numbered, signed. Fine, w/o dj, as issued. CAPTAIN'S BOOKSHELF. $75

Gass, William. WILLIE MASTERS' LONESOME WIFE. Evanston: Northwestern, 1968. 1st ed. One of 100 numbered, signed. Fine in orig cl w/pict label w/o dj, as issued. CAPTAIN'S BOOKSHELF. $250

Gastaut, Henri and Roger Broughton. EPILEPTIC SEIZURES: CLINICAL AND ELECTROGRAPHIC FEATURES, DIAGNOSIS AND TREATMENT. Springfield, 1972. 1st ed. Dj. FYE. $40

Gaston, Joseph. PORTLAND, OREGON. ITS HISTORY AND BUILDERS, THE GREAT CITY OF THE PACIFIC. 3 vols. Chicago, 1911. 1st ed. 145 plts. All edges and eps marbled. Some shelfwear, o/w Fine. OREGON. $225

Gaston, Joseph. THE CENTENNIAL HISTORY OF OREGON, 1811-1912. Chicago: S.J. Clarke, 1912. 4 vols. Cl boards w/leather spine and tips. Some wear to spines and tips and spotting to boards. DAWSON'S. $200

Gattinger, Augustin. THE FLORA OF TENNESSEE AND A PHILOSOPHY OF BOTANY. Nashville: Gospel Advocate Publishing Company, 1901. 1st ed. Pres copy. HUDSON. $95

Gatty, Harold. THE RAFT BOOK. NY: George Grady Press, 1943. VG in stiff wraps. Slip-cased. Fldg maps. MAD DOG. $25

Gaul, Harriet A. and Ruby Eiseman, JOHN ALFRED BRASHEAR, SCIENTIST AND HUMANITARIAN, 1840-1920. Phila: Univ of PA Press, 1940. VG in dj; pp edges spotted. KNOLLWOOD. $42

Gault, W.P. OHIO AT VICKSBURG. REPORT....N.p.: n.p, 1906. 1st ed. Frontis, 44 plts. Fldg map at rear. Gilt dec cl. VG. Scarce. CONNOLLY & WADE. $75

Gault, William Campbell. COUNTY KILL. Inner Sanctum, 1962. 1st ed. About Fine in price-clipped dj. STAHR. $30

Gault, William Campbell. DAY OF THE RAM. NY: Random House, (1956). 1st ed. Signed. Autographed letter laid in. Fine in NF dj. UNGER. $75

Gault, William Campbell. DON'T CRY FOR ME. NY: Dutton, 1952. 1st ed. 1st book. Fine but for owner's name, in NF dj. BEASLEY. $65

Gault, William Campbell. THE CONVERTIBLE HEARSE. NY: Random House, 1957. 1st ed. Name on fep o/w Fine in price-clipped dj. MORDIDA. $25

Gault, William Campbell. THE DEAD SEED. NY: Walker, 1985. 1st ed. Signed. Fine in dj. SILVER DOOR. $37.50

Gault, William Campbell. VEIN OF VIOLENCE. NY: S&S, (1961). 1st ed. Signed. Fine in sl soiled dj. UNGER. $45

Gavit, John Palmer. "OPIUM". London: Routledge, 1925. 1st ed. Cloth, spine tip wear, else VG. Ex-libris. DIAMOND. $75

Gay, Carlo. CHALCACINGO. Portland, 1972. 1st Amer ed. 24 color & b/w plts. Good. SILVER. $75

Gay, John. FABLES. By the Late Mr. Gay. London: Ptd for C. Hitch and L. Hawes, (et al.), 1757. Later ed. 2 vols. This ed usually bound in 1 vol. 8vo, 194pp; (195)-334pp. Modern full brown polished calf in simulated period style. NF. CHAPEL HILL. $100

Gay, John. FABLES... In One Volume Complete. London: for J.F. and C. Rivington (and Others), 1792. 12mo; later 3/4 red morocco, corners rubbed; woodcut frontis, 68 text woodcuts by John Bewick; aeg. Fine. *DRAMATIS PERSONAE.* $275

Gay, John. POLLY: AN OPERA. Being The Second Part of "The Beggar's Opera". London: for the Author, 1729. 1st ed. Wide quarto, title-page in red and black, illus w/31pp of engr music. Early full calf, pitted, but nicely rebacked in period style and with the later bkpl of Edward Hale Bierstadt. Good, scarce. *HARTFIELD.* $495

Gay, John. THE BEGGAR'S OPERA. Lithos by Mariette Lydis. Paris: Ptd for the Members of the LEC by G. Govone, 1937. Ed ltd to 1500 numbered, signed by Lydis. Slipcase rubbed and a bit cracked. *KARMIOLE.* $50

Geary, Maj-Gen. John W. A SKETCH OF THE EARLY LIFE AND OF THE CIVIL AND MILITARY SERVICES OF MAJ. GEN. JOHN W. GEARY....Phila. 1866. 1st ed. 32pp. Orig ptd wrappers, a few chips. Howes G90. *GINSBERG.* $150

Gedda, Luigi. TWINS IN HISTORY AND SCIENCE. Springfield, 1961. 1st Eng trans. Ex-lib. *FYE.* $150

Geddie, John. BEYOND THE HIMALAYAS. London: T. Nelson and Sons, 1884. Dec cl. G. *BLUE DRAGON.* $35

Geer, Theodore Thurston. FIFTY YEARS IN OREGON. NY: Neale Pub Co, 1916. 1st ed, 2nd ptg. Fine in NF dj. *McGOWAN.* $150

Geer, Theodore Thurston. FIFTY YEARS IN OREGON. NY: The Neale Publishing Co. 1916 (c. 1912). "Second Printing." *KARMIOLE.* $40

Geer, Theodore. FIFTY YEARS IN OREGON. Neale Pub, 1912. 1st ed. 12 photo plts. Fine. *OREGON.* $45

Geer, Walter. CAMPAIGNS OF THE CIVIL WAR. NY, 1926. 1st ed. 490pp, fldg maps. Minor cvr wear o/w Fine. *PRATT.* $110

Geiger, Maynard J. THE LIFE AND TIMES OF FRAY JUNIPERO SERRA. O.F.M., OR THE MAN WHO NEVER TURNED BACK (1713-1784). A BIBLIOGRAPHY. Washington: Academy of American Franciscan History, (1959). 1st ed. 2 vols. Frontis. Blue cl, lib call numbers on spine. Inscribed. VG. *WEBER.* $50

Geiger, Vincent. TRAIL TO CALIFORNIA. THE OVERLAND JOURNAL OF VINCENT GEIGER AND WAKEMAN BRYARLY. David M. Potter (ed). Yale, 1945. 1st ed. Fldg map. VG. *OREGON.* $40

Geikie, Archibald. ANNALS OF THE ROYAL SOCIETY CLUB. London: Macmillan and Co, 1917. 1st ed. Rear hinge cracked, else VG. *WREDEN.* $35

Geikie, James. MOUNTAINS, THEIR ORIGIN, GROWTH AND DECAY. NY: Van Nostrand, 1914. 1st Amer ed. 80 plts (some fldg); pencil signature of Cleveland Abbe, Jr. on title page. Small stain on spine, o/w Good. *DIAMOND.* $45

Geikie, James. THE GREAT ICE AGE AND ITS RELATION TO THE ANTIQUITY OF MAN. London: W. Isbister & Co., 1874. Fldg charts and maps. Some foxing, wear, hinges weak, overall VG. *PARMER.* $125

Geil, William Edgar. THE ISLE THAT IS CALLED PATMOS. London, (1900). xiv,341pp. *O'NEILL.* $65

Geiser, S.W. NATURALISTS ON THE FRONTIER. Dallas: SMU, 1948. Rev & enlarged. Fine in VG dj. *MIKESH.* $30

Geldzahler, Henry. NEW YORK PAINTING AND SCULPTURE 1940-1970. NY: E.P. Dutton (1969). Pict wraps (soiled, creased). VG. *BLUE MOUNTAIN.* $20

Gelfand, Michael. MEDICINE AND CUSTOM IN AFRICA. Edinburgh 1964. 1st ed. *FYE.* $40

Gell, Sir William. POMPEIANA: THE TOPOGRAPHY, EDIFICES, AND ORNAMENTS OF POMPEII, THE RESULT OF EXCAVATIONS SINCE 1819 (2 vols). London: Lewis A. Lewis, 1835. Modern 3/4 tan calf and marbled boards w/raised bands and gilt lettered black leather labels on spines; marbled

edges, new eps. xxiv,(ii),198pp; (v),207pp. Port, 88 plts on 87 sheets, 13 mounted vignettes on India paper (sm tear to frontis repaired). NF. *BLUE MOUNTAIN.* $375

Gell, Sir William. THE TOPOGRAPHY OF ROME AND ITS VICINITY. New ed, rev and enl by Edward Herbert Bunbury. London: Henry G. Bonn, 1846. Figs, maps, 3/4 calf antique w/5 raised bands. Bkpl, several pp foxed. Good. *ARCHAEOLOGIA.* $250

Geller, Michael. MAJOR LEAGUE MURDER. NY: St. Martin's Press, 1988. 1st ed. VF in dj. *MORDIDA.* $25

GENERAL TAYLOR'S OLD ROUGH AND READY ALMANAC, 1847. Lancaster: Sold by S. & C. Beates, (1846). 6 woodcut illus w/text. *SCHOYER'S.* $85

Genet, Jean. FUNERAL RITES. NY, Grove Press, 1969. 1st ed. Fine in like dj. *POLYANTHOS.* $45

Genet, Jean. OUR LADY OF THE FLOWERS. Bernard Frechtman (trans). Jean-Paul Sartre (intro). NY: Grove Press, (1963). 1st Amer ed, 1st bk. Fine in price-clipped, NF dj. *CHAPEL HILL.* $60

Genet, Jean. THE MAN CONDEMNED TO DEATH/LE CONDAMNE A MORT. NY: Pirated edition (Poets Press), n.d.. Trans by Diane di Prima et al. Wraps, light sunning, o/w Fine. *BEASLEY.* $45

Genet, Jean. THE THIEF'S JOURNAL. NY: Grove, 1964. 1st ed. Fine in VG dj. *POLYANTHOS.* $20

Gentry, T.G. LIFE-HISTORIES OF THE BIRDS OF EASTERN PENNSYLVANIA. 2 vols. (complete). Phila and Salem, 1876-77. Pp xv,(1),399. Orig cl. Corner edge wear; inner hinges cracked in Vol 2. Vol 1 is presentation copy. Vol 2 bears E.A. Samuels' signature. Rare. *SUTTON.* $265

GEOLOGICAL SURVEY OF NJ. Vol III of Final Report. Vermeule, C. C. REPORT ON WATER SUPPLY, WATER POWER, THE FLOW OF STREAMS & ATTENDANT PHENOMENA. Trenton, NJ, 1894. 16,352,96pp; Maps, plans, some fldg. Rebound new buckram, orig spine label transposed. *HEINOLDT.* $20

GEORGE CRUIKSHANK'S OMNIBUS. London, 1942. Illus, aeg, 3/4 lea bdg rubbed, worn along hinges & spine extremities. NF. *POLYANTHOS.* $175

George, David Lloyd. THE WAR MEMOIRS OF DAVID LLOYD GEORGE 1914-1917. 4 vols. Boston: Little Brown, 1933. 1st ed. Fine in sl chipped djs. *ARTIS.* $60

George, Henry. SOCIAL PROBLEMS. N.p.: National Single Tax League, (1883). Owner's mark fep. *AKA.* $40

George, Henry. THE COMPLETE WORKS OF HENRY GEORGE. NY: Doubleday, Page & Co. 1904. 10 vols. Illus. Grn cl, paper spine labels; edges and spine sl faded. *KARMIOLE.* $150

George, N(oah) J. T. A POCKET GEOGRAPHICAL AND STATISTICAL GAZETTEER OF THE STATE OF VERMONT...AND A LARGE NUMBER OF STATISTICAL TABLES OF THE UNITED STATES. Haverhill, NH: Goss, 1823. 1st ed. 264pp. Orig full 16mo calf. Howes G111. *GINSBERG.* $250

George, W. ANIMALS & MAPS. Berkeley: Univ of CA, 1969. Gilt dec cl. VG. *MIKESH.* $25

Gerdts, William H. AMERICAN IMPRESSIONISM. NY: Abbeville Press, (1984). Dj. Fine. *BLUE MOUNTAIN.* $65

Gerhard, Fred. ILLINOIS AS IT IS...Chicago: Keen & Lee; Phila: Desilver, 1857. 2 plts, 3 fldg maps. Faded, spine top frayed, ex-lib w/markings removed, including erasing of rubberstamps, taking portion of some words on 2pp. Maps Nice. *BOHLING.* $85

GERMAN AVIATION MEDICINE, WORLD WAR II. Washington, 1950. 1st ed. 2 vols. Ex-lib. *FYE.* $200

Gernsback, Hugo. RALPH 124c41+. Stratford, 1925. 1st ed. Sl waterstaining, else VG. *MADLE.* $175

Gernsheim, Helmut, & Alison Gernsheim. L.J.M. DAGUERRE (1787-1851). Cleveland and NY: World, (1956). 116 illus on plts. Brn cl, dj. VG. *WEBER*. $100

Gerould, Katherine Fullerton. HAWAII. SCENES AND IMPRESSIONS. NY: Scribner's, 1916. 1st ed. Frontis, map, 28 plts. Sl rubbing and wear, else VG. *CONNOLLY & WADE*. $35

Gerrard, Lewis H. WAH-TO-YAH AND THE TAOS TRAIL. A.H. Clark, 1938. 1st ed. Fine. *VARNER*. $100

Gerstell, Richard. THE STEEL TRAP IN NORTH AMERICA. Harrisburg, (1985). 1st ed. VF in dj. *ARTIS*. $35

Gerstell, Richard. THE STEEL TRAP IN NORTH AMERICA... DESIGN, PRODUCTION, & USE. Stackpole, 1985. 1st ed. VF in Good+ dj. *OREGON*. $45

Gerster, Arpad. THE RULES OF ASEPTIC AND ANTISEPTIC SURGERY. NY, 1890. 3rd ed. Backstrip and corners rubbed, contents Fine. *FYE*. $100

Gertz, Elmer. MOMENT OF MADNESS. Chicago: Follett, (1968). 1st ed. Dj scuffed, chipped, price-clipped. VG. *AKA*. $25

Gervers, Veronika (ed). STUDIES IN TEXTILE HISTORY. Toronto: Royal Ontario Museum, (1977). 1st ed? Fine in Fine- dj. *AARD*. $35

Gesell, Arnold et al., VISION: ITS DEVELOPMENT IN INFANT AND CHILD. NY, 1949. 1st ed. Dj. *FYE*. $35

Gesner, Conrad. THE ADMIRATION OF MOUNTAINS AND DESCRIPTION OF MOUNT PILATUS, Together with ON CONRAD GESNER AND THE MOUNTAINEERING OF THEUERDANK by J. Monroe Thorington. Grabhorn Press, SF, 1937. Ltd to 325. Hans Leonard Schaufelin, illus. Autographed by: Robert Grabhorn (pub); Bill Dock (biogr notes); Francis Farquar; H.B.D.Soule, (trans). Dec boards. Trans for 1st time from Latin to English. *HEINOLDT*. $90

Gessler, Clifford. ROAD MY BODY GOES. NY: John Day, 1937. 1st ed. Orange cl sl sunned else NF. *GREAT EPIC*. $35

Gessler, Clifford. THE LEANING WIND. NY: D. Appleton-Century, 1943. 1st ed. NF in NF dj. *GREAT EPIC*. $35

Gessler, Clifford. THE REASONABLE LIFE. NY: John Day, 1950. 1st ed. NF in sl sunned dj. *GREAT EPIC*. $35

Getchell, F.H. AN ILLUSTRATED ENCYCLOPEDIA OF THE SCIENCE AND PRACTICE OF OBSTETRICS. Phila, 1890. 1st ed, reprinted. Full leather, 276pp + 84 plts. 1 corner of back board water damaged, water stain affecting upper corner of 30 leaves, o/w VF copy. *FYE*. $400

Gettings, Fred. THE BOOK OF THE HAND: AN ILLUSTRATED HISTORY OF PALMISTRY. London, 1967. 1st ed, 2nd ptg. Dj. *FYE*. $50

Gettysburg National Military Park. HISTORIC VIEWS OF AMERICA'S GREATEST BATTLEFIELD GETTYSBURG. Gettysburg, PA, (192?). 1st ed. Wrappers. NF. *McGOWAN*. $37.50

Ghent, W.J. THE EARLY FAR WEST, A NARRATIVE OUTLINE 1540-1850. Longmans, 1931. 1st ed. Frontis, 7 plts. VF in VG dj. *OREGON*. $45

Ghent, W.J. THE ROAD TO OREGON: A CHRONICLE OF THE GREAT EMIGRANT TRAIL. NY: Longmans, Green, 1929. 2nd prtg. VG. *LAURIE*. $22.50

GHOST TOWNS OF COLORADO. NY: Hastings, 1947. American Guide Series. About Fine in VG dj. *CONNOLLY & WADE*. $25

Giandi, Luigi et al. HORSES AND HORSEMANSHIP THROUGH THE AGES. Trans by Iris Brooks. NY: Crown Pubs, Inc. (1968). 1st ed. Dj. *KARMIOLE*. $45

Gibbings, Robert. BLUE ANGELS AND WHALES. NY: Dutton, 1946. 1st ed. Fine in NF dj. *GREAT EPIC*. $30

Gibbings, Robert. THE WOOD ENGRAVINGS OF ROBERT GIBBINGS WITH SOME RECOLLECTIONS BY THE ARTIST. Chicago: Quadrangle Books, (1959). Frontis engr. *DAWSON'S*. $150

Gibbons, Alfred Ringgold. THE RECOLLECTIONS OF AN OLD CONFEDERATE SOLDIER. (Shelbyville, MO: Author, 193-). 1st ed. Wrappers. *McGOWAN*. $37.50

Gibbons, Helen. THE RED RUGS OF TARSUS. NY, 1917. Cl spotted. *O'NEILL*. $45

Gibbons, Kaye. A CURE FOR DREAMS. 1st trade ed. Signed. Fine in dj. *DORN*. $30

Gibbons, Kaye. A CURE FOR DREAMS. Algonquin, 1991. Adv reading copy. About Fine in wraps (corner lightly creased). *STAHR*. $35

Gibbons, Kaye. A CURE FOR DREAMS. Chapel Hill: Algonquin (1991). Adv presentation. Signed. Fine in wraps. *DORN*. $45

Gibbons, Kaye. A VIRTUOUS WOMAN. Chapel Hill: Algonquin, (1989). 1st Amer ed. Signed. Fine in dj. *DORN*. $40

Gibbons, Kaye. A VIRTUOUS WOMAN. Chapel Hill: Algonquin Books, 1989. Orig beige cl. Fine in dj. 1st ed. Signed. *CHAPEL HILL*. $40

Gibbons, Kaye. A VIRTUOUS WOMAN. London: Cape, (1989). 1st ed UK. As New in dj. *CAPTAIN'S BOOKSHELF*. $20

Gibbons, Kaye. ELLEN FOSTER. Chapel Hill: Algonquin, (1987). 1st Amer ed. Signed. Fine in dj. *DORN*. $75

Gibbons, Kaye. ELLEN FOSTER. Chapel Hill: Algonquin, 1987. 1st ed, 1st bk. As New in dj. Signed. *CAPTAIN'S BOOKSHELF*. $100

Gibbons, Kaye. ELLEN FOSTER. London: Cape, (1988). 1st UK ed. As New in dj. *CAPTAIN'S BOOKSHELF*. $35

Gibbons, Kaye. FAMILY LIFE. Rocky Mount: North Carolina Wesleyan College Press, (1990). 1st Amer ed. 1/500 numbered, signed. Fine in wraps. *DORN*. $30

Gibbs, Sharon L. GREEK AND ROMAN SUNDIALS. New Haven & London: Yale Univ Press, 1976. *SCHOYER'S*. $30

Gibson, A.M. THE LIFE AND DEATH OF COLONEL ALBERT JENNINGS FOUNTAIN. Norman: Univ of OK Press, (1965). 1st ed. Cl, dj. Fine. *SCHOYER'S*. $30

Gibson, Arrell M. THE CHICKASAWS. Norman: Univ of Oklahoma Press, (1971). 1st ed. NF in dj. *LAURIE*. $37.50

Gibson, G.A. THE PHYSICIAN'S ART: AN ATTEMPT TO EXPAND JOHN LOCKE'S FRAGMENT DE ARTE MEDICA. Oxford, 1933. 1st ed. *FYE*. $50

Gibson, George Rutledge. JOURNAL OF A SOLDIER UNDER KEARNY AND DONIPHAN, 1846-1847. Glendale: The Arthur H. Clark Co,.1935. Fldg maps, fabricoid. *DAWSON'S*. $125

Gibson, George Rutledge. JOURNAL OF A SOLDIER UNDER KEARNY AND DONIPHAN 1865-1847. Ralph Bieber (ed). A.H. Clark, 1935. 1st ed. 4 plts, fldg map. VG. *OREGON*. $125

Gibson, George Rutledge. THE STOCK EXCHANGE OF LONDON, PARIS AND NEW YORK. NY/London: G.P. Putnam's Sons, 1889. 1st ed. Maroon silk, inner hinge cracked, but VG. *HUDSON*. $75

Gibson, Henry H. AMERICAN FOREST TREES. Chicago: Hardwood Record, 1913. 1st ed. Hu Maxwell (ed). 1/2 leather, raised bands. NF. *CONNOLLY & WADE*. $112.50

Gibson, Miles. DANCING WITH MERMAIDS. London: Heinemann, (1985). 1st ed. Fine in dj. *WOOLMER*. $35

Gibson, Miles. PERMANENT DAMAGE. POEMS. (London), Eyre Methuen, (1973). 1st ed. VF in dj. Signed card loosely inserted. *WOOLMER*. $40

Gibson, Miles. THE SANDMAN. London: Heinemann, (1984). 1st ed. Fine in dj. Signed card loosely inserted. *WOOLMER*. $40

Gibson, Strickland. SOME OXFORD LIBRARIES. London: Oxford Univ Press, 1914. Spine faded, else VG. *WREDEN.* $20

Gibson, Walter B. WITCHCRAFT. London: Arthur Barker Ltd, (1973). 1st UK ed. 2 lines inked out by pub on copyright pg, else Fine in dj. *BERNARD.* $20

Gibson, Wilfred. THE EARLY WHISTLER. London: Faber & Gwyer. Ariel Poems No. 6. Red paper cvrs, drwg, title ptd in black on front cvr. Fine. *HELLER.* $35

Gibson, William and Bruce Sterling. THE DIFFERENCE ENGINE. NY: Bantam, (1991). 1st ed. Signed by both authors. VF in VF dj. *UNGER.* $55

Gibson, William. A SEASON IN HEAVEN. NY, 1974. 1st ed. Spine sl bumped, dj spine little sunned. *POLYANTHOS.* $30

Gibson, William. BURNING CHROME. Arbor House, 1986. 1st ed. VF in dj. Signed. *STAHR.* $45

Gibson, William. COUNT ZERO. Arbor House, 1986. 1st ed. VF in dj. Signed. *STAHR.* $45

Gibson, William. COUNT ZERO. NY: Arbor House, (1986). 1st ptg. As New in dj. *AKA.* $40

Gibson, William. MONA LISA OVERDRIVE. Bantam, 1988. Advance reading copy. About Fine in dec wraps. Rear cover lightly rubbed. *STAHR.* $30

Gibson, William. MONA LISA OVERDRIVE. NY: Bantam, (1988). 1st ed. As New in Fine dj. *AKA.* $30

Gibson, William. YOUNG ENDEAVOUR: CONTRIBUTIONS TO SCIENCE BY MEDICAL STUDENTS OF THE PAST FOUR CENTURIES. Springfield, 1958. 1st ed. Dj. *FYE.* $75

Gichner, Lawrence E. EROTIC ASPECTS OF JAPANESE CULTURE. N.p.: (Privately pub, 1953). Pink boards, stamped in black; bottom of spine and corners chipped. *KARMIOLE.* $35

Giddings, J. Louis. ANCIENT MEN OF THE ARCTIC. NY: Alfred A. Knopf, 1967. 1st ed. Some wear, else VG in worn dj. *PARMER.* $35

Giedion-Welcker, Carola. CONSTANTIN BRANCUSI. NY, 1959. 110 full pg plts. NF. *POLYANTHOS.* $125

Gielgud, John. EARLY STAGES 1921-1936. Revised ed. London, 1974. Signed. Author's compliments card, pub photo laid in. Fine in like dj. *POLYANTHOS.* $45

Giffard, Edward. SHORT VISIT TO THE IONIAN ISLANDS, ATHENS AND THE MOREA. London: John Murray, 1837. 399pp. Badly water-stained grn cl. Dampstains on frontis, early leaves, plts, o/w text is unmarred, largely unopened. Bkpl, w.a.f. *SCHOYER'S.* $100

Giffen, Fannie Reed. OO-MAH-HA TA-WA-THA (OMAHA CITY) 1854-1898. Lincoln: Author pub, 1898. 1st ed. Inscribed. Press of F.B. Festner, Omaha. Frontis, 94pp, 18mo. Pict cl. VG. *CONNOLLY & WADE.* $50

Giffen, Guy J. CALIFORNIA EXPEDITION, STEVENSON'S REGIMENT OF 1ST N.Y. VOLUNTEERS. Oakland: Biobooks, 1951. Ltd to 650. Tipped-in photo. *HEINOLDT.* $25

Giffen, Guy J. CALIFORNIA EXPEDITION. STEVENSON'S REGIMENT....California Relations #26. Biobooks, 1951. 1st thus, ltd to 650. Tipped in port, color plt. VF. *OREGON.* $40

Giffen, Guy J. CALIFORNIA EXPEDITION: STEVENSON'S REGIMENT OF FIRST NEW YORK VOLUNTEERS. Oakland: Biobooks, 1951. VF. *LAURIE.* $35

Giffen, Helen. CASAS & COURTYARDS. HISTORIC ADOBE HOUSES OF CALIFORNIA. Biobooks, 1955. 1st ed. VF. *OREGON.* $45

Gifford, Barry and Lawrence Lee. JACK'S BOOK. NY: St. Martin's, (1978). 1st ed. NF in dj. *LOPEZ.* $30

Gilbert, A.C. with Marshall McClintock. THE MAN WHO LIVES IN PARADISE. NY: Rinehart, (1954). 1st ed. Fine- in VG dj. *AARD.* $75

Gilbert, Bishop of Sarum. AN EXPOSITION OF THE THIRTY-NINE ARTICLES OF THE CHURCH OF ENGLAND. London, 1827. New ed. Full-lea. NF. *POLYANTHOS.* $150

Gilbert, Colleen B. A BIBLIOGRAPHY OF THE WORKS OF DOROTHY L. SAYERS. London: Macmillan, 1979. 1st Eng ed. VF in price-clipped dj. *MORDIDA.* $45

Gilbert, E.W. THE EXPLORATION OF WESTERN AMERICA, 1800-1850....Cambridge Univ, 1933. 1st ed. 6 fldg maps, 4 plts. Fine in Fine dj. *OREGON.* $60

Gilbert, Grove Karl, et al. THE SAN FRANCISCO EARTHQUAKE AND FIRE OF APRIL 18, 1906. Washington, DC: GPO, 1907. 1st ed. 57 plts (3 fldg). Bound in new cl and boards. Orig front wrap bound in. *DIAMOND.* $45

Gilbert, J. Warren. THE BLUE AND THE GRAY, A HISTORY OF THE CONFLICTS DURING LEE'S INVASION AND BATTLE OF GETTYSBURG. (n.p.), (1922). "Peoples Pictorial Edition." Fldg map. Repaired cover wear o/w VG+ in pict wraps. *PRATT.* $27.50

Gilbert, John M. HUNTING AND HUNTING RESERVES IN MEDIEVAL SCOTLAND. Edinburgh: John Donald, 1979. 1st ed. NF in dj. *OLD LONDON.* $40

Gilbert, Melvin Ballou. ROUND DANCING. (Portland, Maine: M. B. Gilbert, 1890). 204,(2)pp. 1st ed. Inscribed, signed by Gilbert on frontis. Morocco-backed cloth boards, front cover with large gilt titled rectangle of differing cloth (apparently taken from the original binding), spine with raised bands, red lea label, gilt titling and dec. Frontis. Spine w/small chips missing, covers somewhat smudged, but tight Inside of spine visible after page 14, a few leaves roughly opened, otherwise excellent internally. *PIRAGES.* $100

Gilbert, Michael. FEAR TO TREAD. London: Hodder & Stoughton, 1953. 1st ed. Edges spotted o/w Fine in price-clipped dj w/several short closed tears and minor wrinkling at spine ends. *MORDIDA.* $50

Gilbert, Michael. GAME WITHOUT RULES. NY: Harper & Row, 1967. 1st ed. Precedes Eng. ed. Fine in dj. *MORDIDA.* $45

Gilbert, Michael. HE DIDN'T MIND DANGER. NY: Harper & Brothers, 1948. 1st Amer ed. VG in dj (sl faded spine; wear; rubbing). *MORDIDA.* $35

Gilbert, Michael. PETRELLA AT Q. London: Hodder & Stoughton, 1977. 1st ed. NF in NF dj. *BEBBAH.* $30

Gilbert, Michael. THE CRACK IN THE TEACUP. NY: Harper, 1966. 1st ed. VF in dj. *ELSE FINE.* $35

Gilbert, Michael. THE EMPTY HOUSE. London: Hodder & Stoughton, 1978. 1st ed. VF in dj. *MORDIDA.* $45

Gilbert, Michael. THE EMPTY HOUSE. NY: Harper, 1979. 1st Amer ed. Fine in dj. *SILVER DOOR.* $22.50

Gilbert, Sarah. DIXIE RIGGS. NY: Warner, (1991). 1st Amer ed. Signed. Fine in dj. *DORN.* $30

Gilbert, W.S. THE STORY OF THE MIKADO. London: Daniel O'-Connor, 1921. 1st ed. 6 color plts. Paper cvrd boards partially split at right spine edge; bkpl some soiling to edges, else VG in chipped dj. *BERNARD.* $125

Gilboy, Bernard. A VOYAGE OF PLEASURE. John Barr Tompkins (ed). Cambridge: Cornell Maritime Press, 1956. 1st ed. Frontis. Folded diagram, folded map. Bkpl. VG in VG dj. *CONNOLLY & WADE.* $30

Gilchrist, Ellen. DRUNK WITH LOVE. Boston: Little, Brown, (1986). 1st ed. Inscribed. Fine in Fine dj. *UNGER.* $50

Gilchrist, Ellen. DRUNK WITH LOVE. London: Faber, (1986). 1st ed Eng ed. Sticker removed, else Fine in dj. Signed. *CAPTAIN'S BOOK-SHELF.* $30

Gilchrist, Ellen. I CANNOT GET CLOSE ENOUGH. Boston: Little, Brown, (1990). 1st Amer ed. Signed. Fine in dj. *DORN.* $30

Gilchrist, Ellen. IN THE LAND OF DREAMY DREAMS. Fayetteville: Univ of Arkansas Press, 1981. 1st ed. Hardcover ed of her first book of fiction. Fine in Fine dj and signed. *LOPEZ.* $850

Gilchrist, Ellen. IN THE LAND OF DREAMY DREAMS. Fayetteville: Univ of Arkansas Press, 1981. 1st ed. One of 1000 in wraps. Orig ptd wraps. Owner blindstamp on half-title and in text, else NF. *CHAPEL HILL.* $125

Gilchrist, Ellen. NET OF JEWELS. Boston: Little, Brown, (1992). 1st ed. Signed. VF in VF dj. *UNGER.* $35

Gilchrist, Ellen. VICTORY OVER JAPAN. Boston: Little, Brown, 1984. Wraps, adv uncorrected proofs, NF. *BEASLEY.* $85

Gilchrist, Ellen. VICTORY OVER JAPAN. Boston: Little, Brown, (1984). 1st ed. Orig cl-backed boards. Fine in dj, minor wear bottom of spine. *CHAPEL HILL.* $40

Gilchrist. Ellen. VICTORY OVER JAPAN. London: Faber, (1985). 1st UK ed. Fine in dj. Signed. *CAPTAIN'S BOOKSHELF.* $45

Giles, Guy Elwyn. 3 DIED VARIOUSLY. NY: Reynal & Hitchcock, 1941. 1st ed. Fine in VG dj (faded spine; chips; Short closed tears). *MORDIDA.* $30

Giles, Laurence. GOAT COTTAGE DREAM POEMS. Illus Warrington Colescott. (Mt. Horeb): Perishable Press, 1978. 1st ed. Ltd to 119. Signed. Wraps. Mint. *JAFFE.* $150

Giles, Rosena A. SHASTA COUNTY, CALIFORNIA: A HISTORY. Oakland: Biobooks, 1949. One of 1000. Map. VG. *LAURIE.* $30

Gill, Bartholomew. MCGARR AND THE LEGACY OF A WOMAN SCORNED. Viking, 1986. 1st Amer ed. Fine in dj. *STAHR.* $35

Gill, Bartholomew. MCGARR AND THE POLITICIAN'S WIFE. Scribner's, 1977. 1st Amer ed. Fine in dj. *STAHR.* $35

Gill, Bartholomew. MCGARR AT THE DUBLIN HORSE SHOW. Scribner's, 1979. 1st Amer ed. Fine in dj. *STAHR.* $35

Gill, Eric. ART & PRUDENCE. Waltham Saint Lawrence: Golden Cockerel Press, 1928. One of 500. Bound in red cl, title in gilt on spine. Spine faded, edges sl soiled, VG. *HELLER.* $365

Gill, Eric. ART-NONSENSE AND OTHER ESSAYS. London: Cassell & Co, Ltd, & Francis Walterson, 1929. Blue buckram, title in gilt on spine. Spine faded, minor shelf wear, VG. *HELLER.* $135

Gill, Eric. SCULPTURE: AN ESSAY ON STONE-CUTTING WITH A PREFACE ABOUT GOD. Ditchling, Sussex: St. Dominic's Press, (1924). Bound in linen over boards, engr, titling in black on front cover. Spine darkened, VG. *HELLER.* $215

Gill, Eric. SONGS WITHOUT CLOTHES. BEING A DISSERTATION ON THE SONG OF SOLOMON....Ditchling, Sussex: St. Dominic's Press, 1921. One of 240. 1/4 canvas, gray paper boards. Minor shelf wear, fading at edges, spine darkened. VG. *HELLER.* $225

Gill, Mrs. SIX MONTHS IN ASCENSION—AN UN-SCIENTIFIC ACCOUNT OF A SCIENTIFIC EXPEDITION. London: John Murray, 1880. 2nd ed. Hinges repaired. *PARMER.* $75

Gillenson, Lewis W. et al (eds). ESQUIRE'S WORLD OF JAZZ. NY: Esquire/Grosset, 1962. 1st ed. Tipped-in color plts. Fine w/owner's name, in NF dj w/short tears. *BEASLEY.* $100

Gillespie, George Cuthbert and Stephen Hockley Walsh. FIRE INSURANCE HOUSE MARKS OF THE UNITED STATES. Phila: Lippincott Co, 1915. 1st ed. #36 of 100 privately ptd. Good+. Spine chipped. Cvrs soiled. *BACKROOM.* $100

Gillespie, Noel. ENDOTRACHEAL ANESTHESIA. Madison, 1941. 1st ed. *FYE.* $50

Gillett, J.B. SIX YEARS WITH THE TEXAS RANGERS. Yale, 1925. 2nd ed. Fine. *VARNER.* $65

Gillette, King C. THE PEOPLE'S CORPORATION. NY: Boni & Liveright, 1924. 237pp. *AKA.* $37

Gillingham, Robert Cameron. THE RANCHO SAN PEDRO. (LA: Ptd by the Cole-Holmquist Press for the Dominguez Estate Co) 1961. 1st ed. Fine in dj. *KARMIOLE.* $85

Gillis, William R. GOLD RUSH DAYS WITH MARK TWAIN. NY: Albert & Charles Boni, 1930. 1st ed. Cl, spine sunned. *SCHOYER'S.* $20

Gillis, William R. MEMORIES OF MARK TWAIN AND STEVE GILLIS. Sonora, CA: The Banner, 1924. Ptd, stapled grn wrappers. Signed. *KARMIOLE.* $40

Gilliss, J.M. ASTRONOMICAL OBSERVATIONS MADE AT THE NAVAL OBSERVATORY...DATED AUGUST 13, 1838. US Senate, Washington, 1846. Full leather, worn & scraped; 1" tear front edge spine, fraying, stamps. Ex-lib? Good. *KNOLLWOOD.* $75

Gilliss, J.M. et al. THE U.S. NAVAL ASTRONOMICAL EXPEDITION TO THE SOUTHERN HEMISPHERE DURING THE YEARS 1849-'50-'51-'52. Washington, 1855. Vols I and II. 15 colored plts, 3 colored plts, 16 plain plts, 13 maps (5 fldg) plus engrs. 1/2 morocco. Extrems scuffed; Vol I w/cvrs nearly detached; scattered foxing; unobtrusive emb stamp on plts; institutional bkpls. *SUTTON.* $350

Gillmor, Frances and Louisa Wade Wetherill. TRADERS TO THE NAVAJOS. Univ of NM, 1952. 265pp. Fine in VG dj. *FIVE QUAIL.* $45

Gillmore, Parker. PRAIRIE AND FOREST...FIELD SPORTS OF NORTH AMERICA. London: Gibbings & Co., 1896. Bkpl removed. VG. *CONNOLLY & WADE.* $35

Gilly Bear. THE ADVENTURES OF PETERKIN. Samuel Gabriel, (1916). 153pp. Illus by Helen Ohrenschall. Slight edgewear to cvr, few scratches, light spot. Cvr dec in orange & gilt on brown cloth. VG. *BEBBAH.* $35

Gilman, Caroline. ORACLES FROM THE POETS. NY & London: Wiley & Putnam, 1845. 2nd ed. 242pp, 22pp ads. Orig ornately gilt-stamped blue cl, aeg. Bkseller's blindstamp, 2" break inside front hinge, but VG. *CHAPEL HILL.* $60

Gilman, Caroline. VERSES OF A LIFE TIME. Boston & Cambridge: James Munroe & Co, 1849. 1st ed. 263pp. Orig cl. Lib bkpl, blindstamp, but Good+. *CHAPEL HILL.* $50

Gilman, D. THE LIFE OF JAMES DWIGHT DANA. Harper, 1899. 409pp. VG. *BOOKCELL.* $50

Gilman, Sander. SEEING THE INSANE: A CULTURAL HISTORY OF MADNESS AND ART IN THE WESTERN WORLD. NY, 1982. 1st ed. Dj. *FYE.* $75

Gilmore, Albert F. YES, 'TIS ROUND THE LOG OF A FAR JOURNEY. Boston: Stratford (1932). 1st ed. Fine in Almost VG dj. *AARD.* $17.50

Gilpatric, Guy. MR. GLENCANNON IGNORES THE WAR. NY: E.P. Dutton, 1944. 1st ed. VG in dj which is soiled on rear panel & sl worn at edges. *BERNARD.* $30

Gilpin, Laura. TEMPLES IN YUCATAN. NY: Hastings House, (1948). 1st ed. Chipped dj. *SILVER.* $65

Gilpin, Laura. TEMPLES IN YUCATAN. NY: Hastings House, 1948. NF in dj (tape repair one corner, portion of spine chipped away). *SCHOYER'S.* $75

Gilpin, Laura. THE RIO GRANDE, RIVER OF DESTINY: AN INTERPRETATION....NY: Duell, (1949). 1st ed. NF in lightly chipped dj. Signed. *CAPTAIN'S BOOKSHELF.* $250

Gilpin, Laura. THE RIO GRANDE: RIVER OF DESTINY; AN IN-TERPRETATION....NY: Duell, Sloan, and Pearce, c. 1949. 2nd ptg. Grn cl, map eps. VG in chipped, worn dj. *PARMER.* $45

Gilpin, William. MISSION OF THE NORTH AMERICAN PEOPLE. GEOGRAPHICAL, SOCIAL AND POLITI-CAL...Phila, 1873. 2nd ed, rev, w/additions, of reprint of Gilpin's "The Central Gold Region (1860). 223pp. 6 fldg maps. Orig cl. Howes G192. *GINSBERG.* $250

Gilpin, William. NOTES ON COLORADO; AND ITS INSCRIP-TION IN THE PHYSICAL GEOGRAPHY OF THE NORTH AMERICAN CONTINENT. Liverpool, (1870). 1st ed. 52pp. Modern marbled boards, ptd paper label front cvr, paper spine. Howes G194. *GINSBERG.* $225

Gilpin, William. THREE ESSAYS ON PICTURESQUE BEAUTY...TRAVEL...TO WHICH IS ADDED A POEM.... London: ptd for R. Blamire in the Strand, 1792. 1st ed. 7 fldg plts (4 hand-tinted). 88,44,iiipp. Nicely bound in orig full tree calf w/gilt dec on spine, cvrs, inner dentelles. Marbled eps. Bkpl. Half title, er-rata. VG. *CULLEN.* $225

Gilson, Etienne. DANTE THE PHILOSOPHER. NY: Sheed & Ward, 1949. 1st US ed. NF in sl chipped dj. *CAPTAIN'S BOOKSHELF.* $30

Ginsberg, Allen. BIXBY CANYON OCEAN PATH WORD BREEZE. NY: Gotham Book Mart, 1972. 1st ed. One of 100 hardbound signed. Illus cl w/pict label. VF. *JAFFE.* $125

Ginsberg, Allen. COLLECTED POEMS 1947-1980. NY, 1984. 1st ed. Signed, dated. Fine in like dj. *POLYANTHOS.* $50

Ginsberg, Allen. HOWL FOR CARL SOLOMON. (SF: Grabhorn Hoyem, 1971). 1st ed of rev version of Howl,The Names, new note. Ltd to 275 ptd on handmade paper, signed. Pict linen. Mint, in orig shipping carton. *JAFFE.* $375

Ginsberg, Allen. HOWL. NY, (1986). Barry Miles (ed). Orig. draft facsimile. Transcript and variant versions. Signed. Fine in like dj. *POLYANTHOS.* $60

Ginsberg, Allen. MANY LOVES. NY, Pequod Press, 1984. Ltd ed, 110/500. Specially signed. Pict wraps. Fine. *POLYANTHOS.* $35

Ginsberg, Allen. MIND BREATHS: POEMS 1972-1977. SF: City Lights, (1977). 1st ed. Fine in lightly rubbed wraps. Review copy, card laid in. *CAPTAIN'S BOOKSHELF.* $50

Ginsberg, Allen. NEW YEAR BLUES. NY: The Phoenix Book Shop, 1972. One of 100 numbered, in wrappers, signed, of 126 total. Fine. *LOPEZ.* $85

Ginsberg, Allen. PLANET NEWS 1961-1967. SF: City Lights, 1968. 1st ed. Specially signed. The Pocket Poets Series. Printed wraps. Spine and 2 rear cover edges little sunned. Fine. *POLYANTHOS.* $25

Ginsberg, Allen. REALITY SANDWICHES. SF: City Lights, (1963). 1st ed. Specially signed. The Pocket Poets Series. Printed wraps. Spine sl sunned. Fine. *POLYANTHOS.* $25

Ginsberg, Allen. THE VISIONS OF THE GREAT REMEM-BERER. (Amherst): Mulch Press, (1974). 1st ed. VG in wrappers. *LOPEZ.* $35

Ginsberg, Allen. WHITE SHROUD. POEMS 1980-1985. NY: Har-per & Row, (1986). 1st ed. Orig red cl. Fine in dj. Signed. *CHAPEL HILL.* $40

Giono, Jean. HARVEST. NY: Viking, 1939. 1st ed. VG in dj (quite worn, internally repaired). *LOPEZ.* $25

Giono, Jean. THE HORSEMAN ON THE ROOF. NY: Knopf (1954). 1st Amer ed. NF in VG dj (lt chipping, sm piece missing front panel). *DORN.* $35

Giovanni, Nikki. THOSE WHO RIDE THE NIGHT WINDS. Poems. NY: Morrow, 1983. 1st ed. Fine in pict wraps. Inscribed. *CAPTAIN'S BOOKSHELF.* $30

Girardeau, Marvin. DRAGONS PENINSULA. NY: Vantage, 1967. 1st ed. Fold-out map. Inscribed. Fine in VG rubbed dj. *ARCHER.* $30

Giraud, J.P. THE BIRDS OF LONG ISLAND. NY, 1844. Pp. xxi,(1),397. 1 plt. Orig cl. Spine ends perished; extrems worn; some foxing. *SUTTON.* $250

Girodias, Maurice. THE BEST OF OLYMPIA. London: Olympia Press/New English Press, 1966. 1st ed. Matte green wraps charac-teristic of Continental Olympia issues (not glossy green wraps as-sociated with NY Olympia Press issues). Traveller's Companion Series No. 107. About Fine. *BEASLEY.* $35

Gironella, Jose Maria. ONE MILLION DEAD. GC: Doubleday, 1963. 1st ed. Dj edgeworn, price-clipped w/internal tape repair. *AKA.* $30

Giroux, E.X. A DEATH FOR A DOCTOR. NY: St. Martin's, 1986. 1st ed. Rev copy with pub slip. VF in dj. *SILVER DOOR.* $22.50

Gish, Robert F. FRONTIER'S END: THE LIFE...OF HARVEY FERGUSSON. Univ of NE Press, (1988). 1st ed. Signed. New List, dj. *AUTHORS OF THE WEST.* $35

Gissing, George. BY THE IONIAN SEA. Portland, ME: Thomas B. Mosher, 1920. One of 700. NF. *SCHOYER'S.* $30

Gissing, George. STRAY LEAVES FROM THE PRIVATE PAPERS OF HENRY RYECROFT. Westport: The Redcoat Press, 1942. Ltd to 175. *OAK KNOLL.* $45

Gissing, George. THE IMMORTAL DICKENS. London: Cecil Pal-mer, (1925). 1st ed. 8vo, 243pp, red cloth. Top of spine sl bumped. VG. *GREAT EXPECTATIONS.* $17.50

Gissing, George. THE PRIVATE PAPERS OF HENRY RYECROFT. Westminster: Constable, 1903. 1st ed (3 ad leaves). Small tears head and foot of spine, corners rubbed. *MUELLER.* $85

Gissing, George. VERANILDA: A ROMANCE. London, 1904. 1st ed. 16 pp ads. Spine little sunned, extremities little rubbed. Fine. *POLYANTHOS.* $60

Gist, Brooks D. THE YEARS BETWEEN. Tulare: (Brooks D. Gist), 1952. 18pp poems, 40pp photo illus. Gold-stamped fabricoid in dj, rear cover sl bowed. *DAWSON'S.* $50

Githens, Thomas. DRUG PLANTS OF AFRICA. Phila, 1948. 1st ed. Wraps. Scarce. *FYE.* $40

Gittinger, Roy. THE FORMATION OF THE STATE OF OK-LAHOMA (1803-1906). Berkeley: Univ of CA, 1917. 1st ed. Fldg frontis map + 4 maps (1 fldg). VG. *OREGON.* $90

Givens, Charles. THE ROSE PETAL MURDERS. Bobbs-Merrill, (1935). 1st ed. VG+ in Good+ dj with chips, separation at fold of front flap. *BEBBAH.* $15

Gizycki, Jerzy. A HISTORY OF CHESS. London: The Abbey Library. (1972). 1st Eng ed. 9 mounted color plts. Dj. *KARMIOLE.* $75

Gladden, Washington. FROM THE HUB TO THE HUDSON....Bos-ton: New England News, 1869. 1st ed. *SECOND LIFE.* $45

Gladstone, W. E. HOMERIC SYNCHRONISM. NY: Harper & Bros, 1876. Former owner's stamps. *SCHOYER'S.* $17.50

Glaisher, James et al. TRAVELS IN THE AIR. London: Richard Bentley. 1871. 1st ed. Cl soiled, spine extrems sl frayed. *KARMIOLE.* $125

Glaisher, James et al. TRAVELS IN THE AIR. London: Richard Bentley, 1871. 1st ed. Orig cl, rebacked, using orig spine, new eps. Emb lib stamp. Sl cocked, rubbed; cvrs smudged. Sm marginal tears neatly mended on 5 leaves; 2 sm tears not repaired; sl yellow cast to text, some foxing on half title, but excellent internally. *PIRAGES.* $275

Glas, George. THE HISTORY OF DISCOVERY AND CON-QUEST OF THE CANARY ISLANDS. London: 1764. 1st ed. Two parts in 1 vol. Map and chart. 3/4 tan calf, black morocco label on spine, marbled paper over boards. Fine in modern binding. *JUVELIS.* $400

Glaser, Lynn. ENGRAVED AMERICA: Iconography of America Through 1800. Phila: Ancient Orb Press. (1970). 222pp. Ed ltd to 1000. Fine. *KARMIOLE.* $250

Glasfurd, A.I.R. RIFLE AND ROMANCE IN THE INDIAN JUNGLE. London: John Lane, The Bodley Head, 1905. 1st ed. Bkpl, "John Lane's File Copy" back pastedown. *BACKMAN.* $165

Glasgow, Ellen. IN THIS OUR LIFE. NY: Harcourt, Brace, (1941). 1st ed. Fine in dj (internally strengthened at edges), o/w NF. *LOPEZ.* $45

Glasgow, Ellen. THE WHEEL OF LIFE. NY: Doubleday, Page, 1906. Couple of tiny nicks at spine ends, front hinge tender, but Fine. 1st ed, w/"Published, January, 1906" on copyright page. *CHAPEL HILL.* $45

Glasgow, Ellen. THEY STOOPED TO FOLLY. GC, NY: Doubleday, Doran, 1929. 1st trade ed. Some soiling, still VG or better in dj (some insect damage, mostly along bottom of rear panel). *CHAPEL HILL.* $45

LECTURES ON NAVAL ARCHITECTURE AND ENGINEERING. WITH CATALOGUE....London and Glasgow: William Collins, Sons, & Co., 1881. viii,245,(1 blank),104 catalog pp. Fldg map. *LEFKOWICZ.* $125

Glass, E.L.N. (ed). THE HISTORY OF THE TENTH CAVALRY 1866-1921. Tucson, Acme, 1921. 1st ed. Orig black keratol w/title in gilt in front cover, ex lib, o/w Fine, clean. *GINSBERG.* $1250

Glasscock, C.B. HERE'S DEATH VALLEY. Bobbs-Merrill, 1940. 1st ed. VG in chipped, waterstained dj. *VARNER.* $20

Glasscock, Carl B. THE BIG BONANZA. THE STORY OF THE COMSTOCK LODE. Indianapolis, (1931). 1st ed. VG. Inscribed. Attached to eps are small glossy photos of Sutro Tunnel, the Sutro Mansion, and Virginia City, 1933. *DIAMOND.* $50

Glasser, Ronald J. 365 DAYS. NY: George Braziller, 1971. 1st ed. Fine in Fine dj. *BEASLEY.* $25

Glassley, Ray. PACIFIC NORTHWEST INDIAN WARS. Binford & Mort, (1953). 1st ed. VG in Good+ dj. *OREGON.* $25

Glatthaar, Joseph T. THE MARCH TO THE SEA AND BEYOND. NY, 1985. 1st ed. Fine in dj. *PRATT.* $30

Glazier, Loss (ed). ALL'S NORMAL HERE: A CHARLES BUKOWSKI PRIMER. Fremont: Ruddy Duck, (1985). 1st ed. VG in wraps. *SMITH.* $45

Glazier, Willard. BATTLES FOR THE UNION. Hartford, 1873. 1883 rpt. VG+. *PRATT.* $40

Glazier, Willard. DOWN THE GREAT RIVER...Phila: Hubbard Bros, 1892. Ffep missing, fldg map taped. Good. *CONNOLLY & WADE.* $35

Glazier, Willard. HEADWATERS OF THE MISSISSIPPI. Chicago/NY: Rand, McNally & Company, 1893. Spine frayed, inner hinges cracked. Ex-lib. Colored maps in text. *HUDSON.* $45

Glazier, Willard. THREE YEARS IN THE FEDERAL CAVALRY. NY, 1870. 1st ed. 339pp. Cover has faded spine and little wear, o/w VG+. *PRATT.* $50

Glazier, Willard. THREE YEARS IN THE FEDERAL CAVALRY. NY: R.H. Ferguson & Co., Publishers. 1873. 1st ed. 348pp. 10 plts, incl engr frontis port. Orig grn cl, black and gilt-stamped; somewhat soiled, rubbed. *KARMIOLE.* $60

Gleason, David King. PLANTATION HOMES OF LOUISIANA AND THE NATCHEZ AREA. Baton Rouge: Louisiana State Univ Press, 1982. VG to NF in VG dj. Signed. *BACKROOM.* $45

Gleason, Duncan. THE ISLANDS AND PORTS OF CALIFORNIA: A GUIDE TO COASTAL CALIFORNIA. NY: Devin-Adair, 1958. 1st ed. Fine in VF dj. *CONNOLLY & WADE.* $37.50

Glenister, A.G. THE BIRDS OF THE MALAY PENINSULA, SINGAPORE AND PENANG. London, 1955 (1951). 8 colored plts. Lt wear. *SUTTON.* $55

Glenn, Thomas Allen. SOME COLONIAL MANSIONS AND THOSE WHO LIVED IN THEM. WITH GENEALOGIES. SECOND SERIES. Phila, 1900. 1st ed. 503pp. Orig cl. Howes G208. *GINSBERG.* $75

Glick, Allen. WINTER'S COMING, WINTER'S GONE. (Austin): (Eakin Press), (1984). 1st ed. Fine in Fine dj. *LOPEZ.* $125

Glisan, Rodney. JOURNAL OF ARMY LIFE...SF: A.L. Bancroft, 1874. 1st ed. 511pp. Orig pict cl. Howes G209. *GINSBERG.* $200

Gloag, John. A SOCIAL HISTORY OF FURNITURE DESIGN FROM B.C. 1300 TO A.D. 1960. NY, 1966. Light wear bottom of spine. NF. *POLYANTHOS.* $45

Gloag, John. MANNA. London: Cassell & Co, (1940). 1st ed. Dj sl worn, chipped. *AKA.* $35

Glotz, Gustave. THE AEGEAN CIVILIZATION. M.R. Dobie and E.M. Riley (trans). NY: Knopf; London: Kegan Paul, Trench, Trubner, 1925. 1st ed. 87 illus, 3 maps, 4 plts. Orig cl, sl rubbed. Ex-lib, o/w VG. *WORLDWIDE.* $65

Glover, Alan (comp). GLORIANA'S GLASS: QUEEN ELIZABETH I REFLECTED IN VERSES....(London): Nonesuch Press, (1953). 1st ed, #1,145 of 1250. Blue & white cl. Joan Hassall engr. *SCHOYER'S.* $35

Gluckman, Arcadi. UNITED STATES MUSKETS, RIFLES AND CARBINES. NY: Otto Ulbrich Co, 1948. 1st ed. VG+ in Good+ dj. *BACKMAN.* $45

Glueck, Nelson. DEITIES AND DOLPHINS (THE STORY OF THE NABATAEANS). NY: Farrar, Straus & Giroux, 1965. 1st ptg. Dj sl worn, o/w NF. *WORLDWIDE.* $45

Goble, Paul. THE GIRL WHO LOVED WILD HORSES. Bradbury, (1978). Later ptg. Unpaginated. Fine in Fine dj. Seal on dj. *BEBBAH.* $30

Goddard, Esther C. and G. Edward Pendray (eds). ROBERT H. GODDARD, ROCKET DEVELOPMENT...RESEARCH 1929-1941. NY: Prentice-Hall, n.d. (circa 1961). Pb. *KNOLLWOOD.* $30

Goddard, Frederick B. WHERE TO EMIGRATE AND WHY. Phila/Cincinnati/Chicago/St. Louis: The People's Publishing Company, 1869. 19 maps (1 fldg). Orig orange pebbled cl. Extra clean. *HUDSON.* $150

Goddard, Ives and K. Bragdon. NATIVE WRITINGS IN MASSACHUSETTS. 2 vols. Phila: Amer Philosophical Soc, 1988. 1st ed. Fine. *ARCHER.* $45

Goddard, Robert H. ROCKETS. NY: Amer Rocket Society. (1946). Dj. *KARMIOLE.* $200

Goddard, T.N. THE HANDBOOK OF SIERRA LEONE. London: Grant Richards Limited, 1925. Very minor rubbing, browning else NF. *GREAT EPIC.* $145

Godden, Rumer. IMPUNITY JANE. Viking, 1954. 1st ed. 48pp. Illus by Adrienne Adams. Tiny bump to back end. VG+ in VG+ dj w/slight wear, small closed edge tear. *BEBBAH.* $42

Godden, Rumer. ST. JEROME AND THE DRAGON. Viking, 1961. 1st ed. Unpaginated. Illus by Jean Primrose. Fine in NF dj. *BEBBAH.* $30

Godden, Rumer. ST. JEROME AND THE LION. Viking, 1961. 1st ed. Unpaginated. Illus by Jean Primrose. NF in NF dj. *BEBBAH.* $26

Godden, Rumer. THE FAIRY DOLL. Viking, 1956. 1st ed. 67pp. Illus by Adrienne Adams. Slight cvr soil, wear, VG. *BEBBAH.* $25

Godey, John. THE MAN IN QUESTION. GC: Doubleday Crime Club, 1951. 1st ed. Fine, minor wear to dj spine ends. *ELSE FINE.* $30

Godfrey, A.S.T. THE CRADLE OF THE NORTH WIND. London: Methuen & Co, 1938. Frontis. Eps foxed, cvrs worn; well used. *PARMER*. $25

Godfrey, E.L.B. HISTORY OF THE MEDICAL PROFESSION OF CAMDEN COUNTY, NJ. Phila, 1896. 1st ed. Ex-lib. *FYE*. $60

Godfrey, E.S. THE DEVELOPMENT OF ENGLISH GLASSMAKING, 1560-1640. North Carolina Press, 1975. New in dj. *BOOKCELL*. $25

Godman, John. RAMBLES OF A NATURALIST. Phila, 1859. 1st ed? Worn cl, ex-lib. Good. *SECOND LIFE*. $15

Godsell, Jean W. I WAS NO LADY. Toronto: The Ryerson Press, 1959. Overall VG. *PARMER*. $20

Godwin, Gail. A MOTHER AND TWO DAUGHTERS. NY: Viking, (1982). 1st ed. Fine in dj. Signed. *CAPTAIN'S BOOKSHELF*. $40

Godwin, Gail. A MOTHER AND TWO DAUGHTERS. NY: Viking, (1982). 1st ed. Inscribed. Fine in lightly used dj w/two closed tears. *ROBBINS*. $40

Godwin, Gail. FATHER MELANCHOLY'S DAUGHTER. Morrow, 1991. Adv reading copy. Fine in dec wraps. *STAHR*. $25

Godwin, Gail. GLASS PEOPLE. NY: Knopf, (1972). 1st Amer ed. Signed. Fine in dj. *DORN*. $75

Godwin, Gail. GLASS PEOPLE. NY: Knopf, 1972. 1st ed. Fine in dj. Signed. *CAPTAIN'S BOOKSHELF*. $75

Godwin, Gail. MR. BEDFORD AND THE MUSES. London: Heinemann, (1984). 1st Eng ed. Signed. Fine in dj. *DORN*. $40

Godwin, Gail. THE FINISHING SCHOOL. London: Heinemann, (1985). 1st UK ed. Fine in dj. *CAPTAIN'S BOOKSHELF*. $25

Godwin, Gail. THE FINISHING SCHOOL. NY: Viking, (1985). 1st Amer ed. Signed. Fine in dj. *DORN*. $40

Godwin, Gail. THE ODD WOMAN. NY: Knopf, 1974. 1st ed. About Fine in like dj. Signed. *CAPTAIN'S BOOKSHELF*. $50

Godwin, Gail. THE PERFECTIONISTS. NY: Harper, (1970). 1st ed. Fine in dj (tiny tear). Signed. *CAPTAIN'S BOOKSHELF*. $125

Godwin, Gail. VIOLET CLAY. NY: Knopf, (1978). 1st Amer ed. Signed. Rem mark else Fine in dj. *DORN*. $50

Godwin, Parke. FIRELORD. Doubleday, 1979. 1st ed. Fine in dj. *MADLE*. $25

Godwin, Parke. WAITING FOR THE GALACTIC BUS. 1988. 1st ed. Fine in dj. Inscribed w/drwg. *MADLE*. $28

Godwin, William. ENQUIRY CONCERNING POLITICAL JUSTICE AND ITS INFLUENCE ON MORALS AND HAPPINESS. London: Robinson, 1796. 2nd ed, corrected. 8vo, xviii;464; x,545pp. Lacks the half titles. Bound in contemp calf, cover of vol 2 separate. VG. 1st issued in 1793. *SECOND LIFE*. $650

Godwin, William. THOUGHTS ON MAN, HIS NATURE, PRODUCTIONS AND DISCOVERIES. London, 1831. NF. *POLYANTHOS*. $150

Godwin, William. THOUGHTS ON MAN....London: Effingham Wilson, 1831. 1st ed. Uncut in orig boards (hinges loose, lacks part of paper on cvr, some of paper label). Nice clean. Incl ads bound in front and rear and Ripon Bk Club reading sign up sheet for 1831, tipped to ep. 9 lending sigs. Scarce. *SECOND LIFE*. $950

Goethe, Johann Wolfgang von. FAUST. Abraham Hayward (trans). Boston: Dana Estes, n.d. (ca 1909). 1st Amer ed, ptd in Eng. 30 full-pg color plts by Willy Pogany. Contemp 3/4 navy blue morocco over bluegrey boards. Fine, bkseller label. *CAPTAIN'S BOOKSHELF*. $250

Goethe, Johann Wolfgang von. FAUST. London: Hutchinson, (n.d., 1912 inscription). Near 4to. 205pp. 30 color plates w/titled slip sheets, initials & tailpiece dec by Willy Pogany. Handsome gilt dec & blind stamped cvr w/tiny spotting at lower edge. VG+, interior Fine. *BEBBAH*. $175

Goethe, Johann Wolfgang von. FAUST. Trans by Abraham Hayward. Illus by Willy Pogany. London: Hutchinson & Co. N.d. (circa 1908). 16 color plts. Red cloth stamped in black and yellow. *KARMIOLE*. $85

Goethe, Johann Wolfgang von. THE STORY OF REYNARD THE FOX. Thomas James Arnold (trans), Fritz Eichenberg (illus). Cl-backed decorated boards, glassine dj, slipcase. NY: LEC, 1954. Ltd to 1500 signed by Eichenberg. VF. *JAFFE*. $65

Goetzinger, Clara Palmer. SMOLDERING FLAMES. Chicago: Zuriel Pub Co, (1928). Tan cl stamped in red, sl soiled. VG. *SCHOYER'S*. $25

Goetzmann, William. ARMY EXPLORATIONS IN THE AMERICAN WEST 1803-1863. Yale, 1959. 1st ed. 5 fldg maps. VG in dj. *OREGON*. $90

Goff and McCaffree. CENTURY IN THE SADDLE. Denver, CO: Cattlemen, (1967). 1st ed. VF in VF dj. *OREGON*. $50

Gogarty, Oliver St. John. MOURNING BECAME MRS. SPENDLOVE. NY: Creative Age, (1948). 1st Amer ed. Dj. Fine. *MUELLER*. $35

Gold, H. L. THE OLD DIE RICH. Crown, 1955. 1st ed. VG in spine-faded dj. Inscribed. *MADLE*. $50

Goldberg, B.Z. THE SACRED FIRE: THE STORY OF SEX AND RELIGION. 1930. 1st ed. *FYE*. $35

Goldberg, Isaac. THE MAN MENCKEN. NY: Simon & Schuster, 1925. 1st ed. VG. *CAPTAIN'S BOOKSHELF*. $30

Golden, Harry. MR. KENNEDY AND THE NEGROES. Cleveland and NY: The World Publishing Co., (1964). 1st ed. Top of spine faded, else About Fine in VG dj. *WREDEN*. $25

Golden, Richard & Charles Roland. SIR WILLIAM OSLER: AN ANNOTATED BIBLIOGRAPHY WITH ILLUSTRATIONS. SF, 1988. 1st ed. Dj. *FYE*. $125

Golder, F.A. BERING'S VOYAGES—AN ACCOUNT OF THE EFFORTS OF THE RUSSIANS TO DETERMINE THE RELATIONS OF ASIA AND AMERICA. (2 VOLUMES). NY: Amer Geographical Soc, 1922. 371 pp + 2 fldg maps/XI + 290 pp + 2 fldg maps + Errata. Rprt of 1922. 2pp of Vol II index unbound and loosely inserted, else both vols VG. *GREAT EPIC*. $95

Golder, F.A. JOHN PAUL JONES IN RUSSIA. NY, 1927. Small piece missing foot of spine. xi,230pp. Uncut. Ltd ed. *O'NEILL*. $30

Golder, F.A. JOHN PAUL JONES IN RUSSIA. NY: 1927. 1st ed. Orig cl, dj. One of 1000 numbered. *GINSBERG*. $75

Golder, F.A. THE MARCH OF THE MORMON BATTALION FROM COUNCIL BLUFFS TO CALIFORNIA. TAKEN FROM THE JOURNAL OF HENRY STANDAGE. NY: Century, 1928. 1st ed. Fine in VG dj. *BOOK MARKET*. $75

Golder, F.A. THE MARCH OF THE MORMON BATTALION FROM COUNCIL BLUFFS...JOURNAL OF HENRY STANDAGE. NY, 1928. 1st ed. Frontis. Sl sunned spine, o/w VG+. *BENCHMARK*. $65

Golding, Amy Thomas. MINIATURE TRAVELERS. Francestown, NH: Marshall Jones, 1956. 1st ed. 18 plts. Isolated, light foxing affecting first two plts. Cloth, gilt. Fine in VG dj. *CONNOLLY & WADE*. $35

Golding, William. FIRE DOWN BELOW. London: Faber, (1989). 1st ed. Signed. Boards, dj. Mint. *JAFFE*. $125

Golding, William. FREE FALL. NY: HB, 1960. 1st ed. VF, minor rubs to dj. *ELSE FINE*. $80

Golding, William. LORD OF THE FLIES. London: Faber & Faber, (1954). 1st ed. Orig red cl. Edges sl sunned, but VG or better in sl used pict dj. Scarce. *CHAPEL HILL*. $1,600

Golding, William. LORD OF THE FLIES. NY: Coward-McCann, (1955). 1st Amer ed. Orig tan cl, grn boards. Almost Fine in pict dj. *CHAPEL HILL*. $350

Golding, William. NOBEL LECTURE. 7 DECEMBER 1983. (Leamington Spa): Sixth Chamber Press, 1983. 1st ed. One of 500. Signed. Wraps. VF. *JAFFE.* $125

Golding, William. PINCHER MARTIN. London: Faber & Faber, (1961), 1st ed. Orig red cl. Eps sl soiled, but just About Fine in dj. *CHAPEL HILL.* $250

Golding, William. THE HOT GATES. NY: HBW, 1966. 1st US ed. Fine in dj. *ARCHER.* $20

Golding, William. THE INHERITORS. Cl, dj. London: Faber, (1955). 1st ed. Spine sl cocked, o/w Fine. *JAFFE.* $275

Golding, William. THE PAPER MEN. London: Faber, (1984). 1st ed. Signed. Boards, dj. Mint. *JAFFE.* $125

Golding, William. THE PAPER MEN. London: Faber & Faber, 1984. 1st ed. As New. *SMITH.* $40

Golding, William. THE PAPER MEN. London: Faber & Faber, 1984. 1st ed. Fine in NF dj. *ARCHER.* $15

Golding, William. THE SPIRE. (London: Faber and Faber, [1964]). 1st ed. Extremely Fine in like dj. *PIRAGES.* $125

Golding. William. THE PYRAMID. (London: Faber and Faber, [1967]). 1st ed. Mint in VF dj. *PIRAGES.* $125

Goldman, Edward A. PLANT RECORDS OF AN EXPEDITION TO LOWER CALIFORNIA. Washington: Smithsonian Institution, 1916. Fldg map, 29 full-pg plts. Cloth. *DAWSON'S.* $35

Goldman, Emma. LIVING MY LIFE. NY, 1931. 1st ed. 2 vols. Illus. Vol I Fine; Vol II NF. Djs. *POLYANTHOS.* $125

Goldman, Emma. THE PLACE OF THE INDIVIDUAL IN SOCIETY. Chicago: Free Society Forum, n.d. Wraps. Fine w/browning pages. *BEASLEY.* $50

Goldman, William and James. BLOOD, SWEAT AND STANLEY POOLE. (NY): Dramatists Play Service, (1962). 1st ed. Fine in wrappers as issued. *BETWEEN COVERS.* $125

Goldman, William. HYPE AND GLORY. NY: Villard, 1990. Uncorrected proof. Fine in wraps. *LOPEZ.* $25

Goldman, William. SOLDIER IN THE RAIN. NY: Atheneum, 1960. Sl foxing pp edges, else NF in lightly rubbed dj. Adv review copy, slip. *BETWEEN COVERS.* $90

Goldman, William. SOLDIER IN THE RAIN. NY: Atheneum, 1960. Advance copy. Fine in wraps, bound in the dj. *ELSE FINE.* $65

Goldman, William. TEMPLE OF GOLD. NY: Knopf, 1957. 1st ed, 1st bk. Fine, minor wear to spine top of dj. *ELSE FINE.* $125

Goldman, William. THE PRINCESS BRIDE. NY: Harcourt Brace Jovanovich, 1973. 1st ed. Fine in dj. *ELSE FINE.* $250

Goldman, William. THE PRINCESS BRIDE. NY: Harcourt, Brace, (1973). 1st ed. Fine in dj (few tiny nicks, tears). *CAPTAIN'S BOOK-SHELF.* $200

Goldman, William. WIGGER. NY, 1974. 1st ed. Fine in dj. *PETTLER.* $45

Goldsborough, Robert. DEATH ON DEADLINE. NY: Bantam, 1987. 1st ed. Signed. VF in dj. *SILVER DOOR.* $35

Goldsby, Thomas. THE INGOLDSBY LEGENDS. London, 1898. 23, 638pp. 12 color plts by Rackham. B/w illus. Dec cover. 1/8" split top spine. *HEINOLDT.* $75

Goldscheider, L. ROMAN PORTRAITS. NY: Oxford/Phaidon, n.d. (ca. 1940). Somewhat shaken. Dj very chipped, torn. *SCHOYER'S.* $40

Goldsmid, Frederic. EASTERN PERSIA. AN ACCOUNT OF THE JOURNEYS OF THE PERSIAN BOUNDARY COMMISSION 1870-71-72. VOL. 1: THE GEOGRAPHY ...VOL. 2: THE ZOOLOGY AND GEOLOGY, BY W.T. BLANFORD. London, 1876. 5 maps and 30 plts. 2 vols. Newly rebound in grn crushed levant in a 3/4 binding, gilt spines. lviii,443pp; viii,516pp. Gilt tops. With all plts. *O'NEILL.* $450

Goldsmith, Margaret. MADAME DE STAEL. London, NY, Toronto: Longmans, Green, (1938). Dj. VG. *WEBER.* $22.50

Goldsmith, Middleton. A REPORT ON HOSPITAL GANGRENE, ERYSIPELAS, AND PYAEMI AS OBSERVED IN THE DEPARTMENTS OF THE OHIO AND THE CUMBERLAND, WITH CASES APPENDED. Louisville, 1863. 1st ed. 95pp. 1" of spine missing, outer hinges cracked, ex-lib. O/w VG. Scarce. *FYE.* $300

Goldsmith, Oliver. SHE STOOPS TO CONQUER. London: Hodder & Stoughton, (n.d.). 198pp. 25 tipped-in color plts; many sketches by Hugh Thomson. Dec cvr, spine in gilt on grey cl. Sl cvr edgewear, bump to rear lower corner, brown to ep. VG+. *BEBBAH.* $175

Goldsmith, Oliver. THE COLLECTED LETTERS OF OLIVER GOLDSMITH. Katherine C. Balderston, (ed). London: Cambridge Univ Press, 1928. 1st ed. Uncut. Nice. *HARTFIELD.* $175

Goldsmith, Oliver. THE DESERTED VILLAGE, A POEM. London: Ptd for W. Griffin, 1770. 1st ed. 4to, 23pp. Modern full morocco. Very Nice, complete w/half-title. *CHAPEL HILL.* $3,300

Goldsmith, Oliver. THE GRECIAN HISTORY, FROM THE EARLIEST STATE TO THE DEATH OF ALEXANDER THE GREAT. NY, 1827. New boards, lea spine, gilt. 316 pp. *O'NEILL.* $25

Goldsmith, Oliver. THE VICAR OF WAKEFIELD. Illus Edmund J. Sullivan. NY: Henry Holt & Co. 1914. 16 color plts (each w/tissue guard). Blue cloth, dec gilt. Teg. *KARMIOLE.* $65

Goldsmith, Oliver. THE VICAR OF WAKEFIELD. London: Adam and Charles Black, 1903. 1st this ed. Large 8vo, 260pp. Frontis, 12 other full-page color illus. Old sig, else VG. *HARTFIELD.* $45

Goldstein, Jonathan. THE LETTERS OF DEMOSTHENES. NY: Columbia Univ Press, 1968. Fine in Fine dj. *OLD LONDON.* $20

Goldstein, Sidney M. PRE-ROMAN AND EARLY ROMAN GLASS IN THE COMING MUSEUM OF GLASS. Corning: Corning Museum of Glass, 1979. 42 plts. Fine in dj. *ARCHAEOLOGIA.* $150

Goldstone, A.H. JOHN STEINBECK. A BIBLIOGRAPHICAL CATALOG OF THE ADRIAN H. GOLDSTONE COLLECTION. Austin: Univ of TX, 1974. 1st ed. One of 1200. Fine. *SMITH.* $200

Goldwater, Barry. PEOPLE AND PLACES. NY, 1967. 1st ed. 88pp. NF in VG+ dj. *FIVE QUAIL.* $30

Golombek, H. & Hubert Phillips. CHESS GAMES. London, 1959. Dj. NF. *POLYANTHOS.* $45

Gombrowicz, Witold. PORNOGRAFIA. NY: Grove (1966). 1st ed. Fine in dj. *DORN.* $45

Gomme, George Laurence. THE LITERATURE OF LOCAL INSTITUTIONS. London: Elliot Stock, 1886. 1st ed. Spine a bit rubbed, else VF on large paper. *WREDEN.* $30

Gompers, Samuel. SEVENTY YEARS OF LIFE & LABOR. NY: Dutton, (1943, 48). 1 vol ed. Front hinge cracked. *AKA.* $25

Goncharov, Ivan. OBLOMOV. London: George Allen & Unwin, 1929. 1st Eng ed. Fine but for sun darkening to edges, in sl used dj w/sl darkened spine. *BEASLEY.* $175

Gonzales, Laurence. JAMBEAUX. NY: HBJ, 1979. 1st ed. VF in dj. *ELSE FINE.* $35

Gonzales, P.C. and C.P. Rees. BIRDS OF THE PHILIPPINES. Manila, 1988. 130 colored plts. Dj. *SUTTON.* $60

GOOD HEALTH: 1870. A POPULAR ANNUAL ON THE LAWS OF CORRECT LIVING, AS DEVELOPED BY MEDICAL SCIENCE, ETC. Boston, 1870. 1st ed. 576pp. *FYE.* $100

Goode, G. Brown. AMERICAN FISHES. A POPULAR TREATISE UPON THE GAME AND FOOD FISHES OF NORTH AMERICA. NY: Standard Book Co. 1888. 1st ed. xvi,496pp. Dec grn cl w/cvr stamped in gold and silver. Very nice. *KARMIOLE.* $125

Goode, George Brown. A MEMORIAL OF GEORGE BROWN GOODE, TOGETHER WITH A SELECTION OF HIS PAPERS ON MUSEUMS AND ON THE HISTORY OF SCIENCE IN AMERICA. Washington, 1901. 1st ed. Ex-lib. *FYE.* $60

Goode, Rev. William H. OUTPOSTS OF ZION; WITH LIMNINGS OF MISSION LIFE. Cincinnati, 1864. 464pp. Orig cl. Howes G236. *GINSBERG.* $150

Goodhart, Arthur L. ESSAYS IN JURISPRUDENCE AND THE COMMON LAW. Cambridge Univ Press, 1931. 1st ed, 1st bk. Spine faded. Sl spine tip wear, o/w VG. *DIAMOND.* $45

Goodis, David. FOUR NOVELS. London: Zomba Books, 1983. Omnibus ed. VF in dj. *MORDIDA.* $30

Goodison, N. ENGLISH BAROMETERS 1680-1860: A HISTORY OF....Potter, 1968. 1st ed. Near New in chipped dj. *BOOKCELL.* $100

Goodland, Roger. A BIBLIOGRAPHY OF SEX RITES AND CUSTOMS. London: George Routledge & Sons, Ltd. 1931. 1st ed. Dj. *KARMIOLE.* $125

Goodlander, Charles W. MEMOIRS AND RECOLLECTIONS OF C.W. GOODLANDER OF THE EARLY DAYS OF FORT SCOTT FROM APRIL 29, 1858, TO JANUARY 1, 1870. Ft. Scott, 1900. 2nd ed, greatly enlarged. VG to NF. Howes G-240. *McGOWAN.* $175

Goodloe, Albert Theodore. SOME REBEL RELICS FROM THE SEAT OF THE WAR. Nashville, 1893. 1st ed. Light wear to spine extremities, else NF. *McGOWAN.* $300

Goodman, David Michael. A WESTERN PANORAMA 1849-1875. A.H. Clark, 1966. 1st ed. Fine. *VARNER.* $47.50

Goodman, David Michael. A WESTERN PANORAMA 1849-1875. Glendale: Arthur H. Clark, 1966. 1st ed. NF. *LAURIE.* $20

Goodman, John B. PERSONAL RECOLLECTIONS OF HARVEY WOOD. Pasadena: Privately ptd, 1955. 1st ed, ltd to 200 signed, numbered. Fine. *BOOK MARKET.* $85

Goodman, Paul. COMMUNITY OF SCHOLARS. NY: Random House, 1962. 1st ed. Sl cocked, name stamp two edges. Dj has edge tears. *AKA.* $20

Goodman, Paul. FIVE YEARS. NY: Brussel & Brussel, 1966. 1st ed. Sunning foot of spine. Dj browned all edges; tears, chip top of spine. *AKA.* $30

Goodrich, Calvin. THE FIRST MICHIGAN FRONTIER. Univ of MI, Ann Arbor, 1940. 1st ed. Ink underlining. Good. *ARTIS.* $25

Goodrich, Caspar F. ROPE YARNS FROM THE OLD NAVY. NY: Naval History Soc, 1931. 1st ed, ltd to 500; this #182. 3 plts, teg. Upper corners sl bumped, else VG. *CONNOLLY & WADE.* $50

Goodrich, Lloyd. REGINALD MARSH. NY: Harry N. Abrams, Inc, (1972). 1st ed. Orig beige cl, gilt. 85 mounted color plts. Good in dj. *KARMIOLE.* $200

Goodrich, Samuel Griswold. A PICTORIAL HISTORY OF THE UNITED STATES. Phila: J.H. Butler & Co, c1865. Spine split w/portion missing. *HUDSON.* $30

Goodwin, C.C. THE WEDGE OF GOLD. Salt Lake City: Tribune Job Printing Co, 1893. 283pp. Black and gold stamped cl, lt wear to extrems, inner hinges weak, lacking a prelim blank or frontis. *DAWSON'S.* $75

Goodwin, Derek. ESTRILDID FINCHES OF THE WORLD. Cornell Univ Press, (1982). 1st ed. Bkpl. Fine in dj. *ARTIS.* $25

Goodwin, John. IN FULL CRY. London: Herbert Jenkins, 1941. 1st ed. Edges spotted o/w Fine in dj, wear at corners. *MORDIDA.* $45

Goodwyn, Frank. LIFE ON THE KING RANCH. NY (1951), 1st ed, dj. *HEINOLDT.* $25

Goody, Jack. DEATH, PROPERTY AND THE ANCESTORS. London: Tavistock, (1962). 1st ed. VG in worn dj. *ACADEMIC.* $38

Gorbatov, A.V. YEARS OFF MY LIFE. NY: Norton, 1965. 1st US ed. 222pp. Dj w/small piece missing, edgetears. *AKA.* $20

Gordimer, Nadine. A GUEST OF HONOR. NY: Viking, 1970. 1st ed. Fine in dj. *ELSE FINE.* $65

Gordimer, Nadine. A GUEST OF HONOR. Viking, 1970. 1st ed. Slight abrasion to one cvr corner. VG+ in VG+ dj with tiny chips. *BEBBAH.* $30

Gordimer, Nadine. A GUEST OF HONOUR. NY: Viking, (1970). Uncorrected proof of 1st Amer ed. Grease-pencil number "40" top right of front cvr, o/w Fine in wraps (lt crease rear cover). Signed. Very Nice. *LOPEZ.* $200

Gordimer, Nadine. A SPORT OF NATURE. London: Cape, (1987). 1st Eng ed. Fine in dj. *LOPEZ.* $45

Gordimer, Nadine. A SPORT OF NATURE. NY: Knopf, 1987. 1st US. Fine in dj. Advance copy, slip laid in. Signed. *CAPTAIN'S BOOKSHELF.* $75

Gordimer, Nadine. A SPORT OF NATURE. NY: Knopf, 1987. 1st ed. Uncorrected proof. Minor corner crease, else Fine in 1st state white wraps. *ELSE FINE.* $75

Gordimer, Nadine. A SPORT OF NATURE. NY: Knopf, 1987. Advance uncorrected proofs. Fine in wraps. *BEASLEY.* $35

Gordimer, Nadine. A WORLD OF STRANGERS. NY, 1958. 1st US ed. NF in price-clipped dj. *PETTLER.* $60

Gordimer, Nadine. BURGER'S DAUGHTER. Jonathan Cape, 1979. Uncorrected proof. About Fine in dk blue wraps. Staple holes front cvr; lt crease front cover. *STAHR.* $45

Gordimer, Nadine. BURGER'S DAUGHTER. NY: Viking, 1979. 1st ed. VF in dj. *ELSE FINE.* $45

Gordimer, Nadine. FACE TO FACE. Johannesburg: Silver Leaf Books, (1949). 1st ed, 1st bk. Fine in sl rubbed dj (sm chip rear panel). Signed. *CAPTAIN'S BOOKSHELF.* $1000

Gordimer, Nadine. FRIDAY'S FOOTPRINT: TWELVE STORIES AND A NOVELLA. NY: Viking, 1960. 1st US ed. Fine in dj (bit soiled at rear fold). *CAPTAIN'S BOOKSHELF.* $60

Gordimer, Nadine. JULY'S PEOPLE. Viking, 1981. 1st Amer ed. Fine in NF dj. *BEBBAH.* $30

Gordimer, Nadine. LIVINGSTONE'S COMPANIONS. NY: Viking, (1971). Uncorrected proof of 1st Amer ed. "Galley #36" on front cvr. Fine in wraps. Signed. *LOPEZ.* $200

Gordimer, Nadine. MY SON'S STORY. NY: FSG, (1990). Uncorrected proof. Fine in wraps. *LOPEZ.* $35

Gordimer, Nadine. OCCASION FOR LOVING. London: Victor Gollancz, 1963. 1st Eng ed. Australian bkst stamp on fep, mild foxing along page edges, o/w VG in price-clipped dj (minor overall soiling). *LOPEZ.* $65

Gordimer, Nadine. SELECTED STORIES. Viking, 1976. 1st Amer ed. NF in NF dj. *BEBBAH.* $35

Gordimer, Nadine. SIX FEET OF THE COUNTRY. London: Gollancz, 1956. 1st ed. Fep overglued at hinge, o/w Fine in lightly soiled and very lightly used dj. *BEASLEY.* $100

Gordimer, Nadine. THE CONSERVATIONIST. London: Cape, 1974. Uncorrected proof. NF in wraps, Amer pub's promo sheet pasted to front cvr. Inscribed. *LOPEZ.* $450

Gordimer, Nadine. THE CONSERVATIONIST. Viking, 1975. 1st Amer ed. Fine in NF dj. *BEBBAH.* $30

Gordimer, Nadine. THE CONSERVATIONIST. Viking, 1975. 1st Amer ed. Fine in dj. *STAHR.* $25

Gordimer, Nadine. THE LATE BOURGEOIS WORLD. NY: Viking (1966). 1st ed. Fine in sl dust soiled NF dj. *DORN.* $50

Gordimer, Nadine. THE SOFT VOICE OF THE SERPENT AND OTHER STORIES. NY: Simon & Schuster, 1952. 1st ed. Orig grey cl. NF in dj, modest soiling. *CHAPEL HILL.* $150

Gordimer, Nadine. THE SOFT VOICE OF THE SERPENT AND OTHER STORIES. NY: Simon & Schuster, 1952. 1st ed. Fine, minor wear to dj. *ELSE FINE.* $100

Gordimer, Nadine. THE SOFT VOICE OF THE SERPENT. NY: Simon & Schuster, 1952. 1st Amer ed. Fine in a sl spine-sunned NF dj. Signed on fep. Pub's "reply card" laid in. *LOPEZ.* $375

Gordin, Morris. UTOPIA IN CHAINS. Boston: Houghton, Mifflin, 1926. 1st ed. DJ missing pieces. *AKA.* $50

Gordinier, H.C. THE GROSS AND MINUTE ANATOMY OF THE CENTRAL NERVOUS SYSTEM. Phila, 1899. 1st ed. 261 illus. *FYE.* $75

Gordon, Armistead Churchill. MEMORIES AND MEMORIALS OF WILLIAM GORDON MCCABE. Richmond, 1925. 2 vols. 1st ed. NF. *McGOWAN.* $125

Gordon, Caroline. GREEN CENTURIES. NY: Scribner's, 1941. 1st ed. Orig grn cl. Very sl cocked, else Fine, bright in pict dj (some minimal edgewear). *CHAPEL HILL.* $125

Gordon, Caroline. HOW TO READ A NOVEL. (NY): Viking, 1957. 1st ed. Orig dark blue cl. NF in dj. *CHAPEL HILL.* $90

Gordon, Caroline. NONE SHALL LOOK BACK. NY: Scribner's, 1937. 1st ed. VF in dj. *JAFFE.* $250

Gordon, Caroline. NONE SHALL LOOK BACK. NY: Scribners, (1937). 1st ed. Fine in dj showing light use only. *DERMONT.* $165

Gordon, Caroline. OLD RED AND OTHER STORIES. NY: Scribners, 1963. 1st ed. Fine in Fine dj. *BEASLEY.* $75

Gordon, Caroline. PENHALLY. NY: Scribner's, 1931. 1st ed. 1st bk. Orig blue cl. VG in dj (sunned spine; rubbed at crown). *CHAPEL HILL.* $750

Gordon, Caroline. THE FOREST OF THE SOUTH. NY: Scribners, 1945. 1st ed. NF, owner sig. dj, lt chipping. *CAPTAIN'S BOOKSHELF.* $225

Gordon, Caroline. THE GARDEN OF ADONIS. NY: Scribners, 1937. 1st ed. NF, lacks dj. *CAPTAIN'S BOOKSHELF.* $40

Gordon, Caroline. THE GLORY OF HERA. GC: Doubleday, 1972. 1st ed. Fine in sl rubbed dj. *CAPTAIN'S BOOKSHELF.* $65

Gordimer, Caroline. THE MALEFACTORS. NY: Harcourt, 1956. 1st ed. Fine in close to Fine dj w/sl wear at ends of bit sunned spine. *BEASLEY.* $65

Gordon, Caroline. THE MALEFACTORS. NY: Harcourt, Brace, (1956). 1st ed. Orig cl-backed boards. Some offsetting to rear fep, else Fine in VG dj (some soiling on rear panel). *CHAPEL HILL.* $75

Gordon, Caroline. THE MALEFACTORS. NY: Harcourt, Brace, (1956). 1st ed. Review copy, pub's slip tipped to front endsheet. Cl-backed boards, dj. VF. *JAFFE.* $125

Gordon, Caroline. THE STRANGE CHILDREN. NY: Scribner's, 1951. 1st ed. Inscribed. Fine in lightly used dj. *BEASLEY.* $200

Gordon, Caroline. THE STRANGE CHILDREN. NY: Scribner's, 1951. 1st ed. Orig grn boards. Just About Fine in dj, some spotting. *CHAPEL HILL.* $85

Gordon, Caroline. THE WOMEN ON THE PORCH. NY: Scribner's, 1944. 1st ed. Orig black cl. About Fine in NF dj. *CHAPEL HILL.* $125

Gordon, Cora and Jan. LUCK OF THIRTEEN. London: Smith, Elder, 1916. Fldg map. Corner bumped. *SCHOYER'S.* $20

Gordon, Cora and Jan. TWO VAGABONDS IN ALBANIA. London: Bodley Head and NY: Dodd, Mead, (1927). *SCHOYER'S.* $20

Gordon, Cora and Jan. TWO VAGABONDS IN THE BALKANS. NY: McBride, 1925. 1st ed. Ex-lib, o/w VG. *WORLDWIDE.* $20

Gordon, Elizabeth. BIRD CHILDREN. Volland, (1912). Later ed. 96pp. Illus by M.T. Ross. 8 leaves have repaired tear, else interior bright, cvrs have edgewear, some soil. VG overall. *BEBBAH.* $30

Gordon, Elizabeth. BUDDY JIM. Wise-Parslow, (1935). 95pp. Illus by John Rae. Fraying to top of spine, one corner. Pict cvr. VG+. *BEBBAH.* $25

Gordon, Elizabeth. REALLY-SO STORIES. Joliet: Volland, (1924). 17th ed. Edgewear, inside NF. *ACADEMIC LIBRARY.* $25

Gordon, Elizabeth. REALLY-SO STORIES. Volland, (1924). 1st ed. 96pp. Illus by John Rae. Corners bumped, edgewear. VG. *BEBBAH.* $35

Gordon, Elizabeth. STORY OF THE LIFE AND WORK OF CORDELIA A. GREENE, M.D. Castile, NY, 1925. Dk blue cl, sl soiled, stamped in gilt, tipped-on photo. Presentation note, sig. VG. *SCHOYER'S.* $30

Gordon, Elizabeth. THE TURNED-INTO'S, JANE ELIZABETH DISCOVERS THE GARDEN FOLK. Wise-Parslow, (1935). 93pp + vocabulary questions. Illus by Janet L. Scott. Slightest edgewear, else NF. *BEBBAH.* $35

Gordon, Elizabeth. THE TURNED-INTO'S. Volland, (1920). Later ed. Unpaginated. Illus by Janet L. Scott. Slight edgewear. VG+. *BEBBAH.* $30

Gordon, H. Laing. SIR JAMES YOUNG SIMPSON AND CHLOROFORM (1811-1870). NY, 1898. 1st ed. *FYE.* $75

Gordon, Harry. THE SIX RIVER MOTOR-BOAT BOYS ON THE COLORADO. NY: Burt, 1913. 3-color cover. 255pp. VG. *FIVE QUAIL.* $25

Gordon, John B. REMINISCENCES OF THE CIVIL WAR. NY, 1903. 1st ed. 2" tear side of upper spine o/w VG. *PRATT.* $115

Gordon, R.G. and M.F. Brown. PARALYSIS IN CHILDREN. Oxford, 1933. 1st ed. 116 illus. Scarce. *FYE.* $50

Gordon, Richard. A QUESTION OF GUILT: THE CURIOUS CASE OF DR. CRIPPEN. NY: Atheneum, 1981. 1st Amer ed. Fine in dj. *MORDIDA.* $30

Gordon, Richard. JACK THE RIPPER. NY: Atheneum, 1980. 1st Amer ed. Fine in dj. *MORDIDA.* $45

Gordon, Roxy. SOME THINGS I DID. Austin: Encino Press, 1971. Fine in dj. *LAURIE.* $15

Gordon, W.J. ROUND ABOUT THE NORTH POLE. London, 1907. 1st ed. *LEFKOWICZ.* $45

Gordon, W.J. ROUND ABOUT THE NORTH POLE. NY: E.P. Dutton and Co, 1907. 1st Amer ed. 67 plts, 6 maps. Cvrs worn, soiled; ffep excised. Good. *PARMER.* $95

Gorer, Edgar and J.F. Blacker. CHINESE PORCELAIN AND HARD STONES ILLUSTRATED BY TWO HUNDRED AND FIFTY-FOUR PAGES OF GEMS OF CHINESE CERAMIC AND GLYPTIC ART... London: Quaritch, 1911. 2 vols. One of 1,000. Bkpl, sig. Inner hinges reinforced. Slipcase w/few stains. *WEBER.* $1,500

Gores, Joe. A TIME OF PREDATORS. Random House, 1969. 1st ed. About Fine in dj w/light wear. Name ffep. Two small scuffed areas on rear panel of dj. *STAHR.* $75

Gores, Joe. INTERFACE. NY: Evans, (1974). 1st ed. Fine in Fine dj. *UNGER.* $50

Gorey, Edward. A LIMERICK. MA: Salt-works, (1973). 1st ed. Fine. *POLYANTHOS.* $25

Gorey, Edward. AMPHIGOREY TOO. NY: Putnam, (1975). 1st ed. Fine in Fine dj. *DERMONT.* $35

Gorey, Edward. DOUBTFUL GUEST. GC: Doubleday, 1957. 1st ed. 1" closed tear to front dj, o/w NF. *SMITH.* $75

Gorey, Edward. DRACULA. A TOY THEATRE. Spiral-bound pict wrappers. NY: Scribner's, 1979. 1st ed. Signed. VF. *JAFFE.* $100

Gorey, Edward. LES PASSEMENTERIES HORRIBLES. NY: Albondocani Press, 1976. 1st ed. One of 300 numbered, signed. Wraps. Fine. *JAFFE.* $100

Gorey, Edward. THE BLUE ASPIC. (NY: Meredith Press, 1968). 1st ed. Fine in dj. *WEBER.* $65

Gorey, Edward. THE DWINDLING PARTY. NY: Random, 1981. A pop-up book. Glazed illus boards. Six pop-ups engineered by Ib Penick. All pop-ups and bk Fine. *ACADEMIC LIBRARY.* $40

Gorey, Edward. THE GREEN BEADS. NY: Albondocani Press, 1978. Ltd. ed. 287/400 (of 426), signed. Pict wraps. Fine. *POLYANTHOS.* $35

Gorey, Edward. THE RAGING TIDE: OR, THE BLACK DOLL'S IMBROGLIO. Beaufort, (1987). 1st Beaufort ed. Oblong 16mo. Unpaginated. Fine in Fine dj. *BEBBAH.* $25

Gorey, Edward. THE UNSTRUNG HARP; OR, MR EARBRASS WRITES A NOVEL. NY: Duell, Sloan and Pearce; Boston: Little, Brown, (1953). 1st ed. Tannish pict boards. Fine in dj. *WEBER.* $300

Gorey, Edward. THE UTTER ZOO. NY: Meredith Press, (1967). 1st ed. White pict boards. Fine in dj. *WEBER.* $45

Gorey, Edward. THE VINEGAR WORKS. THREE VOLUMES OF MORAL INSTRUCTION. NY: Simon and Schuster, 1963. 1st ed. 3 vols. Fine in slipcase. *WEBER.* $125

Gorey, Edward. THE WATER FLOWERS. NY: Congdon & Weed, (1982). 1st ed. Fine in Fine dj. *DERMONT.* $25

Gorey, Edward. THE WILLOWDALE HANDCAR OR THE RETURN OF THE BLACK DOLL. Indianapolis, (1962). 1st ed. Pict wraps. NF. *POLYANTHOS.* $30

Gorki, Maxim. REMINISCENCES OF LEONID ANDREYEV. Mansfield and S.S. Koteliansky (trans). NY: Crosby Gaige, 1928. 1st ed. One of 400. Fine in chipped glassine dj. *CAPTAIN'S BOOKSHELF.* $75

Gorman, Herbert S. JAMES JOYCE, HIS FIRST FORTY YEARS. NY: B.W. Huebsch, Inc, 1924. 1st ed. Fine in sl soiled dj chipped along edges. *HELLER.* $100

Gorman, John A. THE WESTERN HORSE. (Danville, IL: Interstate Printers and Pubs, 1949). 3rd ed. Pict cl. *SCHOYER'S.* $30

Gorman, John. THE WESTERN HORSE, ITS TYPES AND TRAINING. Danville, IL: Interstate Prt, 1949. Rev, enl ed. VG. *OREGON.* $30

Gosch, C.C.A. (ed). DANISH ARCTIC EXPEDITIONS, 1605 TO 1620....I.—THE DANISH EXPEDITIONS...II.—THE EXPEDITION OF CAPTAIN JENS MUNK TO HUDSON'S BAY....London, 1897. Hakluyt Society Series I: 96 & 97. 2 vols. 12 fldg maps. Orig cl, spines faded. *LEFKOWICZ.* $175

Gosling, Paul. THE WYCHFORD MURDERS. London: Macmillan, 1986. 1st ed. VF in dj. *MORDIDA.* $40

Gosling, Paula. A RUNNING DUCK. London: Macmillan, 1978. 1st ed. VF in dj. *MORDIDA.* $65

Gosling, Paula. BACKLASH. London: Macmillan, 1989. 1st ed. VF in dj. *MORDIDA.* $30

Gosling, Paula. HOODWINK. London: Macmillan, 1988. 1st ed. VF in dj. *MORDIDA.* $35

Gosling, Paula. HOODWINK. NY: Doubleday, 1988. 1st Amer ed. Review copy, signed. Pub's slip laid in. Fine in dj. *SILVER DOOR.* $35

Gosnell, Harpur Allen. BEFORE THE MAST IN THE CLIPPERS: COMPOSED IN LARGE PART OF....NY: Derrydale, 1937. #22/950. 19 plts, frontis, 6 fldg maps and diagrams. Fine. *CONNOLLY & WADE.* $175

Gosnell, R.E. THE YEAR BOOK OF BRITISH COLUMBIA AND MANUAL OF PROVINCIAL INFORMATION...Victoria, 1897. 1st ed. Owner inscrip. Front hinge just beginning; sl soil; overall VG. *PARMER.* $195

Goss, Charles. A BRIEF ACCOUNT OF HENRY GRAY, FRS AND HIS ANATOMY, DESCRIPTIVE AND SURGICAL DURING A CENTURY OF ITS PUBLICATION IN AMERICA. Phila, 1959. 1st ed. Wrappers. *FYE.* $45

Goss, Helen Rocca. THE CALIFORNIA WHITE CAP MURDERS....Santa Barbara: Alfred & Lawton Kennedy, 1969. 1st ed. Autographed. Red cl. Near New. *PARMER.* $40

Goss, Helen Rocca. THE LIFE AND DEATH OF A QUICKSILVER MINE. LA, Hist Soc So CA, 1958. 1st ed. VG in chipped dj. *OREGON.* $50

Goss, Warren Lee. JED, A BOY'S ADVENTURE IN THE ARMY OF '61-'65. NY, (1889). 1st ed. 404pp & ads. Illus, pict cl. One illus detached but in place o/w, except for a little cvr wear, Fine. *PRATT.* $27.50

Goss, Warren Lee. RECOLLECTIONS OF A PRIVATE. NY, 1890-1984. Time-Life Collector's Lib of Civil War rprt. Gilt edges, leather. Fine. *PRATT.* $25

Gosse, Edmund (ed). THE LETTERS OF THOMAS LOVELL BEDDOES. London: Elkin Mathews & John Lane, 1894. Bkpl, eps foxed, crown of spine lightly chipped. Still NF. 1st ed. 1/600 for distribution in Eng. *CHAPEL HILL.* $40

Gosse, Edmund. BOOKS ON THE TABLE. London: William Heinemann, (1921). 1st ed. Cvrs a trifle soiled, else VG. *WREDEN.* $30

Gosse, Edmund. SILHOUETTES. NY, (1925). NF. *POLYANTHOS.* $30

Gosse, P.H. EVENINGS AT THE MICROSCOPE...London, 1859. Gilt illus blind stamped purple cl; bottom corner of front board waterstained, corners bumped, o/w Good, clean. *KNOLLWOOD.* $85

Gosse, P.H. NATURAL HISTORY. FISHES. London, 1851. 16mo, 327pp+ads. VG+. *MIKESH.* $95

Gosse, P.H. THE WONDERS OF THE GREAT DEEP. Phila: Quaker City Publishing House, 1874. Burgundy cl, very lightly stained, w/blind rule dec at corners on covers & gilt title above a gilt floral vignette on spine. Frontis foxed. Internally bright. NF. *BLUE MOUNTAIN.* $50

Gosse, Philip. THE HISTORY OF PIRACY. NY: Tudor Publishing, 1946. Reprint. Some fading and wear, else VG in worn dj. *PARMER.* $35

Gothein, M.L. A HISTORY OF GARDEN ART. W.P. Wright (ed) 2 vols. NY, 1928. 2nd ed. Grn cl, gilt lettering. Spine faded, signs of dampstaining at edges, lt soiling. *SUTTON.* $275

GOTHIC ARCHITECTURE, FURNITURE AND ORNAMENT OF ENGLAND. Boston: Polley, (1908). 99 of 100 plts. Loose as issued, laid into cl-backed chemise. *WEBER.* $125

Gottfredson, Peter. HISTORY OF INDIAN DEPREDATIONS IN UTAH. Salt Lake, 1919. 1st ed. VG. Scarce. *BENCHMARK.* $95

Gottschalk, Laura Riding (Laura Riding). THE CLOSE CHAPLET. NY: Adelphi Co, (1926). 1st Amer ed, 1st bk. Orig greyish blue boards, paper label. VG. *CHAPEL HILL.* $450

Goudard, Joseph and Henri Jalabert. LEBANON: THE LAND AND THE LADY. Trans by Eugene P. Burns. Beirut: The Catholic Press; Chicago: Loyola Univ Press. (1966). 1st ed. Dj chipped. *KARMIOLE.* $50

Gould, Emerson W. FIFTY YEARS ON THE MISSISSIPPI; OR GOULD'S HISTORY OF RIVER NAVIGATION. St. Louis: Nixon-Jones Prtg Co, 1889. 1st ed. xv,749pp & errata leaf. Frontis. Gilt stamped maroon cl. VG in VG+ dj. Lt wear. Howes G273. *BOHLING.* $350

Gould, Emerson W. FIFTY YEARS ON THE MISSISSIPPI; OR GOULD'S HISTORY OF RIVER NAVIGATION. Columbus:

Long's College Book Co, 1951. Reprint of 1889 orig. Gilt dec cl. Fine in dj w/plastic wrapper. Howes G273. *BOHLING.* $75

Gould, F. Carruthers. POLITICAL CARICATURES 1904. London: Edward Arnold, 1904. Folio, vellum backed tan boards (stained, vellum split at bottom of joint, corners chipped) titled in black on front cover). 108 leaves, incl 104 plts. Signed, hand numbered. Internally bright. NF. *BLUE MOUNTAIN.* $150

Gould, Frank W. and Thades W. Box. GRASSES OF THE TEXAS COASTAL BEND. College Station: Texas A&M Press, 1965. VG. *BURCHAM.* $30

Gould, George M. CONCERNING LAFCADIO HEARN...Phila: George W. Jacobs & Co, (1908). 1st ed. NF. Scarce. *BLUE MOUNTAIN.* $125

Gould, Mary Earle. ANTIQUE TIN & TOLE WARE....R.W.G. Vail (foreword). Rutland: Tuttle, (1958). 1st ed. Frontis, 255 b/w plts. Fine in dj, slipcase. *CAPTAIN'S BOOKSHELF.* $50

Gould, Mary Earle. EARLY AMERICAN WOODEN WARE & OTHER KITCHEN UTENSILS. Springfield, 1942. Fine. *POLYANTHOS.* $55

Gould, R.T. THE CASE FOR THE SEA-SERPENT. (London): Philip Allan, 1930. 1st ed. Cvrs a bit dust-marked, edges foxed, else VG. *WREDEN.* $35

Gould, Robert Freke. A CONCISE HISTORY OF FREEMASONRY. London: Gale & Polden, 1903. 8 plts. VG. *BLUE DRAGON.* $45

Gould, Roland F. THE LIFE OF GOULD, AN EX-MAN-OF-WAR'S-MAN, WITH INCIDENTS ON SEA AND SHORE, INCLUDING THE THREE-YEAR'S CRUISE...Claremont, NH: Claremont Manufacturing Co., 1867. 1st ed. (v-xii),13-240 pp. Copyright slip tipped in. *LEFKOWICZ.* $275

Gourley, Hugh III. THE NEW ENGLAND SILVERSMITH. Providence, RI: RISD, 1965. Wraps. VG. *BACKROOM.* $20

Gourmont, Remy de. THE NATURAL PHILOSOPHY OF LOVE. NY: Boni and Liveright, (c1922). 1st ptg (14-unit ornament on label, etc). Ezra Pound (trans). Grn cl, ptd label on backstrip. NF w/o dj. *HELLER.* $100

Govan, Gilbert E. and James W. Livingood. THE CHATTANOOGA COUNTRY, 1540-1951: FROM TOMAHAWKS TO TVA. NY: 1952. 1st ed. Orig cl, dj. *GINSBERG.* $35

Govan, Gilbert Eaton. A DIFFERENT VALOR. THE STORY OF GENERAL JOSEPH E. JOHNSTON, C.S.A. Indianapolis, (1956). 1st ed. Fine in VG dj. *McGOWAN.* $65

Gover, Robert. ONE HUNDRED DOLLAR MISUNDERSTANDING. NY: Grove, (1962). 1st ed. NF in price-clipped dj. *UNGER.* $45

Gower, Harry P. 50 YEARS IN DEATH VALLEY—MEMOIRS OF A BORAX MAN. San Bernardino: Inland Printing & Engraving, (1970). 1st ed, ltd to 225, this #2. Autographed. Fine in Fine dj. *BOOK MARKET.* $60

Gowers, W.R. DIAGNOSIS OF DISEASES OF THE BRAIN AND SPINAL CORD. NY, 1885. 1st Amer ed. *FYE.* $175

Gowers, W.R. EPILEPSY AND OTHER CHRONIC CONVULSIVE DISEASES. NY, 1885. 1st Amer ed. 255pp. *FYE.* $175

Gowers, W.R. EPILEPSY AND OTHER CHRONIC CONVULSIVE DISEASES: THEIR CAUSES, SYMPTOMS, AND TREATMENT. London, 1901. 2nd ed. 320pp. *FYE.* $125

Goyen, William. GHOST AND FLESH. NY: Random House, (1952). 1st Amer ed. Signed. Some age discoloration else VG+ in VG dj w/chipping along top edge, wear to extremities. *DORN.* $85

Goyen, William. IN A FARTHER COUNTRY. NY: Random House (1955). 1st ed. NF in VG dj. *DORN.* $35

Goyen, William. NINE POEMS. NY: Albondocani, (1976). 1st Amer ed. 1/200 numbered, signed. VG+ in wraps. *DORN.* $50

Goyen, William. THE COLLECTED STORIES OF WILLIAM GOYEN. NY: Doubleday, (1975). Adv rev copy with slip. Inscribed and signed. Slight edgewear else NF in Fine dj. *DORN.* $150

Goyen, William. THE FACES OF BLOOD KINDRED. NY: Random House, (1960). 1st ed. Fine in Fine dj. *DERMONT.* $45

Goyen, William. THE FACES OF BLOOD KINDRED. NY: Random House, (1960). 1st Amer ed. Inscribed. Light sunning top edges else VG+ in lightly soiled VG dj. *DORN.* $75

Goyen, William. THE HOUSE OF BREATH. NY: Random House (1950). 1st ed. Inscribed, signed. NF in VG dj, wear at extrems. *DORN.* $200

Grabar, Andre. BYZANTINE PAINTING. Switzerland: Skira, (1953). 105 tipped in color plts. Good. *ARCHAEOLOGIA.* $85

Grabar, Andre. CHRISTIAN ICONOGRAPHY. A STUDY OF ITS ORIGINS...Princeton, NJ: Princeton Univ Press, 1980. 1st ed. Bollingen Series, Series XXXV, 10. 341 illus. VG. *WORLDWIDE.* $55

Grady, James. ARCHITECTURE OF NEEL REID IN GEORGIA. Athens: Univ of Georgia, (1973). 1st ed. Fine in dj, sm chip, tears. *CAPTAIN'S BOOKSHELF.* $300

Graf, A.B. EXOTICA, PICTORIAL CYCLOPEDIA OF INDOOR PLANTS. Rutherford, 1957. 1st ed. Cl, lt wear. *SUTTON.* $45

Graf, A.B. TROPICA, COLOR CYCLOPEDIA OF EXOTIC PLANTS AND TREES....East Rutherford, 1978. 1st ed. Cl, torn dj. *SUTTON.* $125

Grafton, C.W. BEYOND A REASONABLE DOUBT. NY: Rinehart, 1950. 1st ed. Signed by Sue Grafton. Edges sl spotted o/w VG in price-clipped dj w/faded spine and wear at top of spine and along folds. *MORDIDA.* $50

Grafton, C.W. THE RAT BEGAN TO GNAW THE ROPE. NY: Farrar & Rinehart, 1943. 1st ed. Signed by daughter Sue Grafton. Fine in dj w/tiny wear at spine ends and corners. *MORDIDA.* $100

Grafton, C.W. THE ROPE BEGAN TO HANG THE BUTCHER. NY: Farrar & Rinehart, 1944. 1st ed. Signed by Sue Grafton. Fine in dj w/chip at top of spine, several closed tears and wear at corners. *MORDIDA.* $85

Grafton, Sue. "A" IS FOR ALIBI. NY: Holt Rinehart Winston, (1982). 1st ed. Fine. Faint sticker removal mark on front pastedown. In Fine dj (production flaw on rear panel, causing a few letters in text to "smear" underneath the lamination). Signed. *LOPEZ.* $950

Grafton, Sue. "C" IS FOR CORPSE. NY: Henry Holt, 1986. 1st ed. Adv rev copy w/slip, flyer and bkpl laid in. VF in dj. *MORDIDA.* $300

Grafton, Sue. "C" IS FOR CORPSE. NY: Henry Holt, 1986. 1st ed. Signed. Advance reading copy. VF in pict wrappers. *MORDIDA.* $100

Grafton, Sue. "C" IS FOR CORPSE. NY: Holt, (1986). 1st ed. Boards. Tiny closed tear dj spine, o/w VF. *JAFFE.* $125

Grafton, Sue. "D" IS FOR DEADBEAT. NY: Henry Holt, 1987. 1st ed. VF in dj. *MORDIDA.* $85

Grafton, Sue. "D" IS FOR DEADBEAT. NY: Holt, 1987. 1st ed. Signed. VF in dj. *SILVER DOOR.* $75

Grafton, Sue. "E" IS FOR EVIDENCE. NY: Henry Holt, 1988. 1st ed. Fine in dj. *MORDIDA.* $75

Grafton, Sue. "E" IS FOR EVIDENCE. NY: Holt, 1988. 1st ed. As New in dj. *ELSE FINE.* $50

Grafton, Sue. "F" IS FOR FUGITIVE. NY: Henry Holt, 1989. 1st ed. Signed. VF in dj. *MORDIDA.* $45

Grafton, Sue. "F" IS FOR FUGITIVE. NY: Holt, (1989). 1st ed. Signed. Fine in Fine dj. *UNGER.* $65

Grafton, Sue. "F" IS FOR FUGITIVE. NY: Holt, (1989). 1st ed. Signed. Fine in Fine dj. *ROBBINS.* $45

Grafton, Sue. "G" IS FOR GUMSHOE. NY: Henry Holt, 1990. 1st ed. Inscribed. VF in dj. *MORDIDA.* $30

Grafton, Sue. "G" IS FOR GUMSHOE. NY: Holt, (1990). 1st ed. Signed. Fine in Fine dj. *ROBBINS*. $45

Grafton, Sue. "H" IS FOR HOMICIDE. NY: Henry Holt, 1991. 1st ed. Signed. VF in dj. *MORDIDA*. $25

Grafton, Sue. "H" IS FOR HOMICIDE. NY: Holt, 1991. 1st ed. Signed. Fine in dj. *ELSE FINE*. $45

Grafton, Sue. "I" IS FOR INNOCENT". NY: Holt, (1992). 1st ed. Signed. Fine in Fine dj. *ROBBINS*. $35

Grafton, Sue. KEZIAH DANE. NY: Macmillan, 1967. 1st ed, 1st bk. VF in dj. *ELSE FINE*. $400

Grafton, Sue. KEZIAH DANE. NY: Macmillan, 1967. 1st ed. Signed. Very faint tiny lettering on top edge o/w Fine in dj. *MORDIDA*. $300

Grafton, Sue. KINSEY AND ME. Santa Barbara: Bench Press, (1991). 1st ed. One of 300 numbered, signed. Fine in burgundy cl slipcase. *UNGER*. $285

Grafton, Sue. KINSEY AND ME. Santa Barbara: Bench Press, 1991. 1st ed. 1/300 numbered, signed. VF in slipcase w/o dj as issued. *MORDIDA*. $250

Grafton, Sue. THE LOLLY-MADONNA WAR. London: Peter Owen, 1969. 1st ed. Fine in VG dj (rubbed front panel; sl spine fading; nicks top of spine, rubbing along folds). *MORDIDA*. $500

Graham, A. and P. Beard. EYELIDS OF MORNING. Greenwich, 1973. 16 colored plts, 220+ photos 165 engrvs, maps. Some wear to edges and spine ends, front cover sltly soiled, fep creased. *SUTTON*. $135

Graham, Caroline. MURDER AT MADINGLEY GRANGE. London: Century/Mysterious Press, 1990. 1st ed. Fine in dj. *SILVER DOOR*. $27.50

Graham, Caroline. THE KILLINGS AT BADGER'S DRIFT. Bethesda, MD: Adler & Adler, 1988. 1st Amer ed. Fine in dj. *MORDIDA*. $50

Graham, Douglas. A PRACTICAL TREATISE ON MASSAGE. NY, 1884. 1st ed. 286pp. Scarce. *FYE*. $100

Graham, Frank. NEW YORK YANKEES. Putnam, 1958. 1st ptg, rev and expanded ed. VG in Fine dj. *PLAPINGER*. $55

Graham, Frank. THE BROOKLYN DODGERS. Putnam, 1945. 2nd prtg. VG in Good+ dj. *PLAPINGER*. $40

Graham, Frank. THE NEW YORK GIANTS. Putnam, 1952. 1st ed. VG. *PLAPINGER*. $45

Graham, Gaunt (pseud of Jonathan Gash). THE INCOMER. GC: Doubleday Crime Club, 1982. 1st Amer ed. Bkpl removed from front pastedown o/w Fine in dj (sl faded spine; short closed tear). *MORDIDA*. $85

Graham, Harry. ACROSS CANADA TO THE KLONDYKE. Toronto: Methuen, 1984. 1st ed. Fine in dj. *PARMER*. $20

Graham, Harvey. ETERNAL EVE....London: Hutchinson, (1960). New rev ed. VG, tight. *SECOND LIFE*. $25

Graham, Harvey. ETERNAL EVE: THE STORY OF GYNECOLOGY. GC, 1951. 1st Amer. ed. *FYE*. $60

Graham, Harvey. THE STORY OF SURGERY. NY, 1939. 1st ed. *FYE*. $50

Graham, James (pseud of Jack Higgins). A GAME FOR HEROES. GC: Doubleday, 1970. 1st ed. NF in dj. *ELSE FINE*. $35

Graham, James D. REPORT OF THE SECRETARY OF WAR, COMMUNICATING...THE REPORT OF LIEUTENANT COLONEL GRAHAM ON THE SUBJECT OF THE BOUNDARY LINE BETWEEN THE UNITED STATES AND MEXICO. Wash., SD121, 1852. 1st ed. 250pp. 2 fldg maps, 1 fldg profile. Orig gold stamped cl. Howes G286. *GINSBERG*. $375

Graham, Peter (ed). LITERATURE IN MEDICINE. VOLUME 4: PSYCHIATRY IN LITERATURE. Baltimore, 1985. 1st ed. *FYE*. $20

Graham, R.B. Cunninghame. See Cunninghame Graham, R.B.

Graham, Robert C. THE CARVED STONES OF ISLAY. Glasgow: James Maclehose, 1895. 117pp. 30 photogr plts. Good. *CULLEN*. $100

Graham, Shirley. PAUL ROBESON. NY: Julian Messner, 1971. 4th ptg. Sl cocked in dj. VG. *AKA*. $20

GRAHAM SUTHERLAND. London. 1950. Ed ltd to 2,000. Dj (1/2" tear top edge spine; nick to back panel). NF. *POLYANTHOS*. $50

Graham, Sylvester. A LECTURE TO YOUNG MEN, ON CHASTITY...Sixth Stereotype Edition. Boston: George W. Light, 1841. 1st ed. 246pp. Orig cloth. Minor chipping to spine. *M & S*. $125

Graham, W.A. LETTER OF...COMMUNICATING THE PROCEEDINGS OF A COURT-MARTIAL ON COMMODORE THOMAS A. CATESBY JONES....Wash., SD45, 1851. 1st ed. 400pp. Cloth. Howes J242. *GINSBERG*. $50

Graham, W.A. THE CUSTER MYTH, A SOURCE BOOK OF CUSTERIANA. Harrisburg, (1953). 1st ed. Dj chipped o/w VG+. *PRATT*. $50

Graham, W.A. THE CUSTER MYTH. A SOURCE BOOK....Harrisburg: Stackpole, 1953. 1st ed. Frontis. NF in About Fine dj. *CONNOLLY & WADE*. $75

Graham, W.A. THE CUSTER MYTH. PA, 1953. Dj scuffed. VG-NF. *POLYANTHOS*. $95

Graham, W.A. THE STORY OF THE LITTLE BIG HORN. Harrisburg: Military Service Publishing, (1952). Rpnt from 1926. Fine in VG dj. *BOOK MARKET*. $32

Graham, W.A. THE STORY OF THE LITTLE BIG HORN. NY, (1926). 1st ed. 174pp. A little cover wear, o/w Fine. *PRATT*. $165

Graham, W.S. THE NIGHTFISHING. NY: Grove, (1955). 1st ed. NF in sl edgeworn, VG dj. *LOPEZ*. $40

Graham, W.S. THE WHITE THRESHOLD. NY: Grove, (1952). 1st ed. NF in sl worn dj. *LOPEZ*. $45

Graham-Mulhall, Sara. OPIUM: THE DEMON FLOWER. NY: Montrose Pub Co, 1926. Black cl stamped in gilt. Soiled chipped dj, o/w VG. *SCHOYER'S*. $20

Grahame, Kenneth. FIRST WHISPER OF "THE WIND IN THE WILLOWS." London: Methuen, (1944). Extremely fragile, the binding is stained and dj shows similar wrinkling. Still, remarkably Nice. *LOPEZ*. $65

Grahame, Kenneth. PAGAN PAPERS. London: Elkin Mathews & John Lane, 1894. 12mo, 165pp, 14, (2)pp ads. Orig grn cl, teg. Owner name, spine and top of front cvr faded, else VG. 1st ed, 1st bk. 1/450 for distribution in Eng, w/tipped-in limitation slip. *CHAPEL HILL*. $200

Grahame, Kenneth. THE GOLDEN AGE. London: John Lane, 1895. 2nd ed. 196pp, 16pp ads. Orig blue cl. VG. W/unsigned presentation inscript dated London, 1896. *CHAPEL HILL*. $200

Grahame, Kenneth. THE GOLDEN AGE. London: John Lane, 1895. 1st ed. 8vo, 196pp, 16pp ads. Orig blue cl. Bombay bkseller's stamp, previous owner's name, else VG. *CHAPEL HILL*. $150

Grahame, Kenneth. THE WIND IN THE WILLOWS. Illus Arthur Rackham. Intro A.A. Milne. Tipped-in color plts, full white calf, glassine dj, cardboard slipcase w/ptd label. London: Methuen, 1951. One Hundredth Anniversary Ed, ltd to 500 ptd on handmade paper. VF. *JAFFE*. $1500

Grainger Thomas. A GUIDE TO THE HISTORY OF BACTERIOLOGY. NY, 1958. *FYE*. $50

Gramatky, Hardie. LITTLE TOOT ON THE MISSISSIPPI. Putnam, (1973). 1st ed. Unpaginated. Illus by author. VG+ in VG dj w/1 closed tear, scrape. *BEBBAH*. $30

Grancsay, Stephen V. AMERICAN ENGRAVED POWDER HORNS. PA: Ray Riling Arms Bks Co, 1965. VG, cvr soiled. *BACKROOM*. $100

Grand, Gordon. COLONEL WEATHERFORD AND HIS FRIENDS. NY: The Derrydale Press, 1933. 1st ed (1450 only). Minor wear to extrems, else VG-NF. *OLD LONDON.* $100

Grande, Francisco and Maurice Visscher. CLAUDE BERNARD AND EXPERIMENTAL MEDICINE. (WITH) THE CAHIER ROUGE OF CLAUDE BERNARD. Hebbell H. Hoff, et al (trans). Cambridge, 1967. 1st ed. *FYE.* $30

Granger, Bill. THE NOVEMBER MAN. NY: Fawcett Gold Medal, 1979. 1st ed. Wraps. NF w/creases. Correct 1st ed of author's 1st bk. *BEASLEY.* $25

Granger, J.T. (comp). BRIEF BIOGRAPHICAL SKETCH OF THE LIFE OF MAJOR-GENERAL GRENVILLE M. DODGE....Ptd for private distribution. NY: Styles & Cash, 1893. 128pp, 3 ports, ptd wraps. Nice, lightly soiled. Howes G302. *BOHLING.* $200

Grant, Anne. MEMOIRS OF AN AMERICAN LADY: WITH SKETCHES...WITH A MEMOIR OF MRS. GRANT BY JAMES GRANT WILSON. Albany, Munsell, 1876. Best Amer ed. 377pp. Engr port. Orig cl, paper label on spine. Howes G303. Biography of Mrs. Grant and engr port, not in 1st ed. *GINSBERG.* $125

Grant, Christina P. THE SYRIAN DESERT...NY, 1938. 16 plts and 4 maps. xv,420pp. *O'NEILL.* $40

Grant, Hugh Duncan. CLOUD AND WEATHER ATLAS. NY: Coward, McCann, 1944, 1st ed. VG in worn, chipped dj. *KNOLLWOOD.* $65

Grant, J.C. Boileau. A METHOD OF ANATOMY: DESCRIPTIVE AND DEDUCTIVE. Baltimore, 1937. 1st ed. *FYE.* $75

Grant, Jonathan (psued of Jonathan Gash). THE SHORES OF SEALANDINGS. London: Century, 1991. 1st ed. VF in dj. *MOR-DIDA.* $45

Grant, Julia Dent. THE PERSONAL MEMOIRS OF JULIA DENT GRANT. NY, (1975). Ed by John Y. Simon. 1st ed. Light dj wear o/w Fine. *PRATT.* $32.50

Grant, M.H. THE MAKERS OF BLACK BASALTES....Edinburgh & London: William Blackwood and Sons, 1910. 1st ed. Presentation. Bkpl. Cvrs rubbed, sm nick in spine, lower edge of front joint cracked, o/w VG. *WREDEN.* $100

Grant, Maxwell. EYES OF THE SHADOW. NY: Street & Smith, 1931. 1st ed. Pict front cover. Pp darkened o/w Fine w/o dj as issued. *MORDIDA.* $135

Grant, Maxwell. THE LIVING SHADOW. NY: Street & Smith, 1931. 1st ed. Pict front cover. Pp darkened o/w Fine w/o dj as issued. *MORDIDA.* $135

Grant, Maxwell. THE SHADOW LAUGHS. NY: Street & Smith, 1931. 1st ed. Pict front cover. Pp darkened o/w Fine w/o dj as issued. *MORDIDA.* $135

Grant, Rev. George M. OCEAN TO OCEAN. Sanford Fleming's Expedition Through Canada in 1872. N.p: M.G. Hurtig (by Tuttle), (1967). Enl, rev ed. Fine in VG dj. *BLUE DRAGON.* $30

Grant, Robert. HISTORY OF PHYSICAL ASTRONOMY FROM THE EARLIEST AGES TO THE MIDDLE OF THE NINETEENTH CENTURY...London: Henry G. Bohn, 1852. Grn cl. Extremities worn, worm hole corner margin of 50pp not affecting contents. Corner torn, hinges tender. *KNOLLWOOD.* $55

Grant, Ulysses S. PERSONAL MEMOIRS OF U.S. GRANT. 2 vols. NY, 1885. 1st ed. Leather. Sl cvr wear o/w Fine. *PRATT.* $125

Grant, Ulysses S. PERSONAL MEMOIRS OF U.S. GRANT. NY: Charles L. Webster & Co. 1885-1886. 2 vols. 584;648pp. Maps, facs (some fldg), other plts. Pub's Deluxe binding of l/2 brown calf; spine sl rubbed. *KARMIOLE.* $60

Grant, Ulysses S. PERSONAL MEMOIRS. NY: Charles L. Webster, 1885-86. 1st ed. 2 vols. 584; 647pp. 2 ports, 2 plts, 2 fldg facs, fldg map. Orig pict grn cl. *SCHOYER'S.* $70

Grass, Gunter. CAT AND MOUSE. Trans by Ralph Manheim. NY: Harcourt, Brace & World, (1963). 1st ed in Eng. NF in lightly foxed, price-clipped dj. *CHAPEL HILL.* $35

Grass, Gunter. THE FLOUNDER. 35 relief etchings by Grass. 3 vols. Natural eelskin & Italian linen slipcase. NY: LEC, 1985. Ltd to 1000 signed. Mint. *JAFFE.* $750

Grass, Gunter. THE TIN DRUM. (London: Secker & Warburg, [1962]). 592pp. 1st ed in English. Signed by Grass. Trans by Ralph Manheim. Corners and spine ends bumped, dj a little smudged, o/w Fine in Fine dj. *PIRAGES.* $300

Grassus, Benevenutus. DE OCULIS EROUMQUE EGRITUDINIBUS ET CURIS. TRANSLATED WITH NOTES AND ILLUSTRATIONS FROM THE FIRST PRINTED EDITION, FERRARA, 1474 A.D. BY CASEY A. WOOD. Stanford, 1929, 1st Eng trans. 101pp. VF in orig slipcase. *FYE.* $300

Gratten, J.H.G. and Charles Singer. ANGLO-SAXON MAGIC AND MEDICINE. London, 1952. 1st ed. *FYE.* $100

Gratz, Simon. A BOOK ABOUT AUTOGRAPHS. Phila: William J. Campbell, 1920. 1st ed. One of 500 numbered. Cvrs a trifle faded, else VG. *WREDEN.* $35

Grau, Shirley Ann. NINE WOMEN. Franklin Center: Franklin Library, 1986. Ltd ed. Signed. Fine in Franklin leather. *CAPTAIN'S BOOKSHELF.* $40

Grau, Shirley Ann. NINE WOMEN. Franklin Center: Franklin Lib, 1986. Leatherbound ltd 1st ed. Fine. Signed. *LOPEZ.* $45

Grau, Shirley Ann. THE CONDOR PASSES. Knopf, 1971. Advance reading copy. Fine in wraps. *STAHR.* $35

Grau, Shirley Ann. THE CONDOR PASSES. NY: Knopf, 1971. 1st ed. Orig grn cl. Name, else Fine in NF dj. *CHAPEL HILL.* $25

Grau, Shirley Ann. THE CONDOR PASSES. NY: Knopf, 1971. 1st ed. Signed. VG in VG dj. *JUVELIS.* $35

Grau, Shirley Ann. THE HARD BLUE SKY. NY: Knopf, 1958. 1st ed. Author's sig card laid in. VG in VG dj. *JUVELIS.* $65

Grau, Shirley Ann. THE HOUSE ON COLISEUM STREET. NY: Knopf, 1961. 1st ed. Signature card laid in. Fine in NF dj. *JUVELIS.* $50

Grau, Shirley Ann. THE HOUSE ON COLISEUM STREET. NY: Knopf, 1961. 1st ed. NF in dj. *CHAPEL HILL.* $40

Grau, Shirley Ann. THE KEEPERS OF THE HOUSE. NY: Knopf, 1964. 1st ed. VG in NF dj. Signed. *CHAPEL HILL.* $75

Grau, Shirley Ann. THE KEEPERS OF THE HOUSE. NY: Knopf, 1964. 1st ed. Card containing quote from bk, signed in ink, "Shirley Ann Grau" laid in. Fine. *JUVELIS.* $50

Grau, Shirley Ann. THE KEEPERS OF THE HOUSE. NY: Knopf, 1964. 1st ed. Complimentary copy, slip, pub's card laid in. Fine in NF dj (sm amount of internal tape strengthening at folds). *LOPEZ.* $35

Grau, Shirley Ann. THE WIND SHIFTING WEST. NY: Knopf, 1973. 1st ed. Crease ffep, else Fine in price-clipped dj. *CAPTAIN'S BOOKSHELF.* $50

Graustein, Jeannette. THOMAS NUTTALL, NATURALIST. EXPLORATIONS IN AMERICA 1808-1841. Harvard, 1967. 1st ed. VF in VG dj. *OREGON.* $50

Graves, Henry Lea. A CONFEDERATE MARINE. Ed by Richard Harwell. Tuscaloosa, AL, 1963. 1st ed. Wrappers. Fine. *McGOWAN.* $150

Graves, J.A. MY SEVENTY YEARS IN CALIFORNIA 1857-1927. LA: Times-Mirror 1927. 1st ed. Rubberstamp on endpapers & half title o/w VG. *OREGON.* $40

Graves, J.A. MY SEVENTY YEARS IN CALIFORNIA. 1857-1927. LA: The Times-Mirror Press, 1927. Worn; offset to eps. *PARMER.* $35

Graves, John. FROM A LIMESTONE EDGE. Knopf, 1980. 1st ed. VG in VG dj. *BEBBAH.* $25

Graves, John. FROM A LIMESTONE LEDGE. NY, 1980. 1st ed. Signed. Fine in price clipped dj. *POLYANTHOS.* $40

Graves, Richard S. OKLAHOMA OUTLAWS: A GRAPHIC HISTORY....Fort Davis, TX: Frontier, 1968. 2nd prtg. Stiff wraps. Light creases, else Fine. *CONNOLLY & WADE.* $30

Graves, Robert. COLLECTED POEMS 1914-1926. GC: Doubleday Doran, 1929. 1st US ed. Fine and bright in NF dj (tiny nicks; sl browned spine). *BEASLEY.* $100

Graves, Robert. COLLECTED SHORT STORIES. Doubleday, 1964. 1st ed. NF. Dj has two small tears on rear panel- spine darkened. Pastedown stamped "A personal reading copy..." *STAHR.* $35

Graves, Robert. GOOD-BYE TO ALL THAT. London: Jonathan Cape, (1929). 1st ed, 1st issue w/Siegfried Sassoon poem pp341-43. Orig pinkish red cl. NF in spine-darkened dj (shallow chip head of spine, not affecting lettering). *CHAPEL HILL.* $950

Graves, Robert. GOOD-BYE TO ALL THAT: AN AUTOBIOGRAPHY. London, 1929. 1st ed. 1st issue contains poem by Siegfried Sassoon which was removed from 2nd issue. Also contains paragraph on p. 290 omitted in 2nd issue. A small number (about 250) survived. Lower spine sl darkened. Fine in dj (spine sunned, top chipped, lower half missing. Spine strengthened internally. Few small edge chips. Small area rear panel near spine missing. Front panel sl soiled but complete). Very scarce. *POLYANTHOS.* $500

Graves, Robert. KING JESUS. NY, (1946). 1st ed. Tiny crease one corner. Fine in spine-sunned dj w/chips, edge tears. *POLYANTHOS.* $50

Graves, Robert. LOVE RESPELT AGAIN. NY, (1969). Ltd ed 637/1000 signed. Dj rear panel 2 tiny tears, tiny area rubbed. Fine. *POLYANTHOS.* $65

Graves, Robert. NEW POEMS. Doubleday, 1962. 1st Amer ed. Fine in dj. *STAHR.* $30

Graves, Robert. ON ENGLISH POETRY. NY, 1922. 1st ed. Top and heel spine few tiny tears, heel spine small area stained; dj professionally repaired and strengthened. 2" piece top spine and 1/2" heel missing, but most of the title present. NF, scarce 1st issue. *POLYANTHOS.* $250

Graves, Robert. POEMS 1926-1930. London: Heinemann, 1931. 1st ed. One of 1000, extra spine label tipped in at rear as issued. Orig dk red cl, white pebbled design and paper labels. VG in faded dj (chipping, sm holes affecting no lettering). Acceptable copy of very scarce dj. 1st ed. *CHAPEL HILL.* $150

Graves, Robert. POEMS 1938-1945. NY: Creative Age, 1946. 1st ed. Fine; dj complete, with a few tears, minor edgewear. Name. *ELSE FINE.* $50

Graves, Robert. POEMS 1968-1970. Doubleday, 1972. 1st Amer ed. Fine in dj. *STAHR.* $35

Graves, Robert. POEMS 1968-1970. GC: Doubleday, 1971. 1st ed. Fine, minor edgewear to price clipped dj. *ELSE FINE.* $25

Graves, Robert. POEMS ABOUT LOVE. Doubleday, 1969. 1st ed. Fine in dj. *STAHR.* $30

Graves, Robert. POEMS ABOUT LOVE. GC: Doubleday, 1969. 1st ed. Fine, dj has a chip out at a rear corner. *ELSE FINE.* $25

Graves, Robert. POEMS. NY: LEC, 1980. Intro by Elaine Kerrigan. Illus by Paul Hogarth. Ltd ed of 2000 numbered, signed by Kerrigan and Hogarth. Fine in Fine matching box. *POLYANTHOS.* $100

Graves, Robert. THE ISLANDS OF UNWISDOM. GC: Doubleday, 1949. 1st US ed. Fine- in Fine- dj. *AARD.* $30

Graves, Robert. THE SHOUT. London: Elkin Mathews & Marrot, 1929. 1st ed. #371 of 530 signed. Orig dec grey boards. Lt offsetting to eps, spine ends sl bumped, else NF in dj (chipping to spine ends, minor edgewear). Pub's subscription slip laid in. *CHAPEL HILL.* $300

Graves, Robert. THE WHITE GODDESS. NY, 1948. 1st ed. Fine in spine sunned dj w/chips. *POLYANTHOS.* $75

Graves, Robert. TO WHOM ELSE? Majorca: The Seizin Press, 1931. 1st ed. 61 of 200 ltd, signed. Sl browning inside cvrs, and blank margins throughout. NF. *POLYANTHOS.* $300

Graves, Robert. WATCH THE NORTHWIND RISE. NY: Creative Age Press, 1949. 1st ed. Fine in VG sl worn dj. *BERNARD.* $45

Graves, Thomas. THE GRAVES PAPERS AND OTHER DOCUMENTS RELATING TO THE NAVAL OPERATIONS OF THE YORKTOWN CAMPAIGN....NY: Naval Hist Soc, 1916. 1st ed. Orig boards, vellum spine. One of 650. *GINSBERG.* $75

Gray, A. SCIENTIFIC PAPERS OF ASA GRAY. Selected by Charles Sargent. 2 vols. Boston & NY, 1889. 1st ed. Orig blue cl w/slight breaking of paper around inner hinges, some lower cover edge rubbing. Sm spine end tears, overall Nice. *SUTTON.* $165

Gray, Asa. DARWINIANA: ESSAYS AND REVIEWS PERTAINING TO DARWINISM. NY, 1876. 1st ed. 396pp. *FYE.* $150

Gray, Charles Glass. OFF AT SUNRISE: THE OVERLAND JOURNAL OF CHARLES GLASS GRAY. San Marino, CA: Huntington Library, 1976. Ed by Thomas D. Clark. VG, dj. *BURCHAM.* $25

Gray, Charles Glass. OFF AT SUNRISE: THE OVERLAND JOURNAL....Huntington Library, (1976). 1st ed. Thomas D. Clark (ed). Fine in dj. *AUTHORS OF THE WEST.* $15

Gray, Edward. WILLIAM GRAY OF SALEM, MERCHANT. Boston: Houghton Mifflin Co. 1914. 1st ed. 8 engr plts. Ltd to 500, numbered. *KARMIOLE.* $40

Gray, Henry. ANATOMY, DESCRIPTIVE AND SURGICAL. Phila, 1862. 2nd Amer ed. Orig full leather. 816pp. *FYE.* $350

Gray, Henry. ANATOMY, DESCRIPTIVE AND SURGICAL. Phila, 1870. New Amer ed. VF. *FYE.* $75

Gray, Henry. ANATOMY, DESCRIPTIVE AND SURGICAL. Phila, 1878. New Amer ed. Full leather. *FYE.* $75

Gray, Henry. ANATOMY, DESCRIPTIVE AND SURGICAL. Phila: Lea Brothers, 1897. New, rev ed from 13th Eng ed. 1249pp. Orig red cl. Front cvr rehinged, paper spine label. Good. *SMITHFIELD.* $35

Gray, J.E. CATALOGUE OF CARNIVOROUS, PACHYDERMATOUS, AND EDENTATE MAMMALIA IN THE BRITISH MUSEUM. 47 woodcuts. London, 1869. vii, 398pp. Orig cl. Worn at corners & spine ends, partial splitting at edges of spine, faded, solid ex-lib. *SUTTON.* $90

Gray, Jane Loring (ed). THE LETTERS OF ASA GRAY. 2 vols. Boston, 1893. 1st ed. Cl worn at extrems. Hinges cracked Vol I; Vol II rebacked, retaining orig backstrip. Lt dampstain prelim pp of Vol II. Ex-lib. *SUTTON.* $125

Gray, Jerome B. ONE HUNDRED YEARS. Phila: Franklin Ins. Co, 1929. 1st ed. VG. *BACKROOM.* $40

Gray, John Alfred. AT THE COURT OF THE AMIR. London, NY: Macmillan, 1901. 2nd ed. Frontis. Orig cl, sl rubbed, spine sl frayed, o/w VG. *WORLDWIDE.* $75

Gray, John Henry. CHINA, A HISTORY OF THE LAWS, MANNERS. AND CUSTOMS OF THE PEOPLE. London: Macmillan, 1878. 2 vols. 397; 374pp. Minor defects. Good. *CULLEN.* $175

Gray, John. GENERAL PARESIS, OR INCOMPLETE PROGRESSIVE PARALYSIS. Albany, 1866. 1st ed. Pamphlet. *FYE.* $40

Gray, Spaulding. IMPOSSIBLE VACATION. NY: Knopf (1992). 1st ed. Signed. VF in dj. *DORN.* $45

Gray, Thomas. ELEGY IN A COUNTRY CHURCHYARD. Newly Created into an Illustrated Book by John Vassos. (NY): E.P. Dutton & Co. (1931). 1st ed. 18 plts. Signed on fep. Lightly soiled. Dj rather chipped. *KARMIOLE*. $150

Gray, Thomas. ELEGY WRITTEN IN A COUNTRY CHURCH-YARD. Intro. by Sir Hugh Walpole (intro). Agnes Miller Parker (illus). Dec cl, tissue dj, slipcase. London: LEC, 1938. Ltd to 1500 signed by Parker. VF. *JAFFE*. $150

Gray, Thomas. ODES by Mr. Gray. Strawberry Hill: For R. and J. Dodsley. 1757. 4to. 21,(1)pp. Complete with the half title. Engraved vignette on the title page. Speckled calf (late l9th century), skillfully rebacked, backstrip ornately gilt with a red morocco label; outer corners bit worn, o/w Very Nice. 1st book of the Strawberry Hill Press; 1st issue with the reading 'Ilissus' on p. 8 and no comma after 'swarm' on p. 16. Hazen #1. Rothschild 1067. *KARMIOLE*. $1,000

Gray, Thomas. POEMS AND LETTERS BY THOMAS GRAY. London: Chiswick Press, 1874. xvi,415pp. 4 plts of actual albumen photos. Contemp full morocco w/5 raised bands, marbled eps, richly gilt spine, inner dentelle, expertly rebacked. Top of spine chipped, sl foxing; 1st, last few leaves w/edge-fraying, o/w VG; aeg. *WORLDWIDE*. $75

Gray, William F. FROM VIRGINIA TO TEXAS, 1835. DIARY OF COL. WM. F. GRAY...Houston: Fletcher Young, 1965. Reprint of 1909 1st ed. Fine. *OREGON*. $50

Grayson, William John. SELECTED POEMS BY WILLIAM J. GRAYSON. Selected and Compiled by Mrs. William H. Armstrong (His Daughter). NY & Washington: Neale, 1907. 1st ed. Orig cl, teg. Some spotting on cover, but VG. *CHAPEL HILL*. $40

Greard, Valery C.O. MEISSONIER HIS LIFE AND HIS ART. Lady Mary Loyd, Miss Florence Simmonds (trans). NY: A.C. Armstrong and Son, 1897. 34 plts. Bumped and rubbed, head and tail of spine chipped w/short tears, hinges cracked, frontis loose, eps foxed. VG. *BLUE MOUNTAIN*. $135

GREAT WESTERN INDIAN FIGHTS. 1960. 1st ed. Fine in VG dj. *VARNER*. $20

GREATER AMERICA. ESSAYS IN HONOR OF HERBERT EUGENE BOLTON. Berkeley: Univ of CA, 1945. 1st ed. Frontis, 12 fldg maps tipped in. NF in somewhat worn, Good dj. *CONNOLLY & WADE*. $75

Greaves, Richard P. (pseud of George Barr McCutcheon.) BREWSTER'S MILLIONS. Chicago: Herbert S. Stone, 1903. 1st ed. Dec cvrs, gilt, teg, uncut; name stamps, spine sl sunned. Fine. *POLYANTHOS*. $60

GREECE (Guide Bleue). Paris: Hachette, 1955. Text in Eng. Dj. *SCHOYER'S*. $15

Greeley, Horace. HINTS TOWARD REFORMS, IN LECTURES, ADDRESSES, AND OTHER WRITINGS. NY: Harper, 1850. 1st ed. 400pp. Cl, sl foxing, wear at spine ends, Good, tight. *ARTIS*. $35

Greeley, Horace. RECOLLECTIONS OF A BUSY LIFE: INCLUDING REMINISCENCES...FROM THE OPENING OF THE MISSOURI CONTEST TO THE DOWNFALL OF SLAVERY. NY, 1868. 1st ed. Orig cl. NF. *McGOWAN*. $85

Greely, Adolphus W. THE POLAR REGIONS IN THE TWENTIETH CENTURY. Boston: Little, Brown, and Company, 1928. 1st ed. Fldg map. Dj poor; some flaking to white titles on spine, tear on fold line of map repaired. *PARMER*. $85

Greely, Adolphus W. THE POLAR REGIONS IN THE TWENTIETH CENTURY. Boston, 1928. Fold-out color map taped. Tattered dj, o/w VG. *ARTIS*. $40

Greely, Adolphus W. THREE YEARS OF ARCTIC SERVICE. AN ACCOUNT OF THE LADY FRANKLIN BAY EXPEDITION OF 1881-84...NY: 1st ed, Charles Scribner's Sons, 1886. 2 vols. 1st ed. Shelfwear, lt foxing. Bkpl; pg from "Who's Who" tipped in. VG+. *PARMER*. $295

Greely, Adolphus W. THREE YEARS OF ARCTIC SERVICE. NY: Charles Scribner's Sons, 1886. 2 vols. 1st ed. VG. *WEBER*. $120

Green, Anna Katharine. HAND AND RING. NY, 1883. 1st ed. Cvrs sl edge rubbed. NF. *POLYANTHOS*. $200

Green, Anna Katharine. THE CIRCULAR STUDY. NY, 1900. 1st ed, 1st bdg. Dec grn cl gilt, spine minimally rubbed, name. Fine. *POLYANTHOS*. $75

Green, Anna Katharine. THE CIRCULAR STUDY. NY: McClure-Phillips, 1900. 1st ed. Fine in 1st state binding, grn ribbed cl, emb in gilt & black. *ELSE FINE*. $75

Green, Anna Katharine. THE FILIGREE BALL. Indianapolis, March, (1903). 1st ed, 1st issue w/printer's slug printed in red. Fine. *POLYANTHOS*. $75

Green, Anna Katharine. THE FILIGREE BALL. Indianapolis: Bobbs, Merrill, (1903). 1st ed, March on copyright pg. Bright, NF in grn cl stamped in red and gilt. *CAPTAIN'S BOOKSHELF*. $50

Green, Anna Katharine. THE FILIGREE BALL. Indianapolis: Bobbs-Merrill, 1903. 1st ed. Inscribed. Fine w/owner's neat label on front pastedown. *BEASLEY*. $175

Green, Anna Katharine. THE GOLDEN SLIPPER & OTHER PROBLEMS FOR VIOLET STRANGE. NY: Putnam, 1915. 1st ed. VF in dec cvr. Pict dj has lg chip at spine top, moderate edgewear. *ELSE FINE*. $65

Green, Anna Katharine. THE MAYOR'S WIFE. Indianapolis, (1907). 1st ed. Illus, pict cl gilt, spine sl rubbed. Fine. *POLYANTHOS*. $40

Green, Anna Katharine. THE MILLIONAIRE BABY. Indianapolis, 1905. 1st ed. Illus by Arthur I. Keller. Owner's inscrip, extremities little rubbed. VG. *POLYANTHOS*. $50

Green, Anna Katharine. THE WOMAN IN THE ALCOVE. Indianapolis: Bobbs-Merrill, 1906. 1st ed. Inscribed. Fine. *BEASLEY*. $175

Green, Ben A. BIOGRAPHY OF THE TENNESSEE WALKING HORSE. Nashville, 1960. 1st ed. VG. *OCTOBER FARM*. $65

Green, Ben A. BIOGRAPHY OF THE TENNESSEE WALKING HORSE. Nashville, TN, 1960. 1st ed. Fine. *BOND*. $65

Green, Ben A. BIOGRAPHY OF THE TENNESSEE WALKING HORSE. Nashville: The Parthenon Press, (1960). Orig grn cl. 1st ed. Signed presentation. Fine. *CHAPEL HILL*. $150

Green, Ben K. A THOUSAND MILES OF MUSTANGIN'. Flagstaff, 1972. 1st ed. Fine in pict dj. *BAADE*. $150

Green, Ben K. THE VILLAGE HORSE DOCTOR. WEST OF THE PECOS. NY: Knopf, 1971. Signed presentation. 1st ed. VG in VG dj. *OCTOBER FARM*. $65

Green, Bill. THE DANCING WAS LIVELY. FORT CONCHO, TEXAS....Privately ptd, 1974. 1st ed, ltd to 1000. Inscribed presentation. Letter from Green incl. Fine in VG dj. *CONNOLLY & WADE*. $50

Green, Dana Saintsbury. MASKS & PUPPETS. London: The Studio, n.d. (1942). 1st ed. Large 8vo, cloth sunned; numerous line and photo. illus, some tipped in. VG. *DRAMATIS PERSONAE*. $30

Green, Henry. LIVING. NY: Dutton, 1929. Grn cl stamped in black on backstrip. Owner name, address ink-stamped, o/w VG w/o dj. *HELLER*. $100

Green, Henry. NOTHING. NY: Viking, 1950. 1st ed. Fine, minor wear to dj. *ELSE FINE*. $45

Green, Horace. A TREATISE ON THE DISEASES OF THE AIR PASSAGES. NY, 1855. 3rd ed. 305pp + 7 fine colored plts. *FYE*. $150

Green, Horace. A TREATISE ON THE DISEASES OF THE AIR PASSAGES. NY, 1846. 1st ed. 276pp + 7 plts. Wear to head and tail of spine, corners bumped, scattered foxing. This copy distinguished in that it once was in the lib of the US Patent Office. *FYE.* $500

Green, John. BIRDS OF BRITAIN. NY: Macmillan, 1967. 1st US ed. Fine- in VG+ (1" tear). *AARD.* $25

Green, N.B. and T.K. Pauley. AMPHIBIANS AND REPTILES IN WEST VIRGINIA. Pittsburgh, 1987. 85 colored photos, maps. Signed. *SUTTON.* $35

Green, Paul. DRAMATIC HERITAGE. NY: Samuel French, (1953). 1st ed. Virtually as New in dj. *CHAPEL HILL.* $25

Green, Paul. SONG IN THE WILDERNESS. Poem by Paul Green. Music by Charles Vardell. Chapel Hill: Univ. of NC Press, 1947. 1st ed. #119 of 600 signed by Green and Vardell. NF in dj. *CHAPEL HILL.* $125

Green, Paul. THE FIELD GOD AND IN ABRAHAM'S BOSOM. NY: McBride, 1927. 1st ed. Fine in dj chipped at spine ends (affecting no lettering). Scarce in this condition. *CHAPEL HILL.* $125

Green, Paul. THE NO 'COUNT BOY. PLAY IN ONE ACT. NY: Samuel French, (1928). 1st separate ed. Fine. Orig grn wraps. Signed. *CHAPEL HILL.* $120

Green, Paul. WIDE FIELDS. NY: Robert M. McBride & Co, 1928. 1st ed. Orig cl-backed dec boards w/paper spine label. Owner sig, else NF in pict dj. *CHAPEL HILL.* $150

Green, Thomas M. SPANISH CONSPIRACY...CONTAINING PROOFS OF THE INTRIGUES OF JAMES WILKINSON...Cincinnati, 1891. 1st ed. 406,(2)pp. Orig cl. Howes G374. Scarce. *GINSBERG.* $350

Greenaway, Kate. KATE GREENAWAY PICTURES FROM ORIGINALS PRESENTED BY HER TO JOHN RUSKIN AND OTHER PERSONAL FRIENDS (HITHERTO UN-PUBLISHED). London: Warne, 1921. 1st ed. 20 color illus each on a handmade sheet preceded by titled slipsheet. Frontis port. Uncut forward end & back end. Cream buckram spine, grn buckram over boards, lettering in black & gilt. NF. *BEBBAH.* $295

Greenaway, Kate. KATE GREENAWAY PICTURES. H.M. Cundall (appreciation). London: Frederick Warne and Co, 1921. Frontis. 20 plts w/titled slipsheets. Color illus tipped in on each pg. 1/4 cream buckram and grn buckram over boards, titling in black and gilt on cvr, grn on spine. Minor fading of cvrs. Fine. *HELLER.* $245

Greenaway, Kate. KATE GREENAWAY PICTURES. London: Frederick Warne, 1921. 1st ed. Tissue-guarded colored plts mounted on hand-made paper. Fine. *DERMONT.* $300

Greenaway, Kate. KATE GREENAWAY'S ALMANACK FOR 1888. (London): George Routledge & Sons, (1888). 1st ed. (24)pp. Full-pg color frontis. Covers sl foxed. Fine. *BLUE MOUNTAIN.* $125

Greenaway, Kate. MOTHER GOOSE, OR THE OLD NURSERY RHYMES. London and NY: George Routledge and Sons, n.d. 12mo, 16.9 cm. 48pp. 1st ed. Illus Kate Greenaway. Engr, ptd by Edmund Evans. Color frontis, pict titles. Orig white cl w/title "Mother Goose" ptd in brn on front cover surrounded by olive green latticework design. Cvrs foxed, head of spine worn, hinges cracked, last signature loose, inside margins of 4ff crudely reinforced w/tape not affecting text, stain not affecting text. Fair. *WREDEN.* $55

Greenaway, Kate. UNDER THE WINDOW. PICTURES & RHYMES....London: Frederick Warne & Co, n.d. 55,(1)pp. Color frontis, pict title. Orig black cl, gold glazed pict boards. Cvrs sl soiled, sm nicks rear cover, corners worn, sm dampstain not affecting text. Withal Very Nice. *WREDEN.* $80

Greenberg, D.B. RAISING GAME BIRDS IN CAPTIVITY. NY, 1949. *SUTTON.* $35

Greenberg, D.B. RAISING GAME BIRDS IN CAPTIVITY. Princeton, NJ, 1949. 1st ed. Fine in NF dj. *MIKESH.* $25

Greenberg, Martin H. (ed). AFTER THE KING: STORIES IN HONOR OF J.R.R. TOLKIEN. Tor, 1992. Uncorrected proof. VG or better in yellow wraps. Cover lightly soiled. *STAHR.* $35

Greenbie, Sidney and Marjorie Barstow. ANNA ELLA CARROLL AND ABRAHAM LINCOLN: A BIOGRAPHY. Manchester: Univ of Tampa and Falmouth, 1952. 1st trade ed. Frontis, 7 plts. Fine in NF dj. *CONNOLLY & WADE.* $55

Greenbie, Sydney. FURS TO FURROWS, AN EPIC....Caxton Press, 1939. 1st ed. Frontis, 29 plts. Fine. *OREGON.* $50

Greenburg, D.B. RAISING GAME BIRDS IN CAPTIVITY. NY, 1949. Cl. *SUTTON.* $35

Greene, Charles W. SKETCH OF KINGSTON AND ITS SUR-ROUNDINGS. THE MINING CENTER OF THE FAMOUS PERCHA DISTRICT, NEW MEXICO. ITS RESOUR-CES...Kingston, 1883. 1st ed. 48pp. Orig ptd wrappers. Howes G379. *GINSBERG.* $750

Greene, Francis Vinton. THE REVOLUTIONARY WAR AND THE MILITARY POLICY OF THE UNITED STATES. NY: Scribner's, 1911. 1st ed. 46 plts of colored maps. NF. *CONNOLLY & WADE.* $60

Greene, Frederick D. THE ARMENIAN CRISIS IN TURKEY. THE MASSACRES OF 1894....NY, 1895. Cvr soil; much rubbing. *O'NEILL.* $45

Greene, Frederick Davis. ARMENIAN MASSACRES OF THE SWORD OF MOHAMMED....Henry Davenport Northrop (ed). Wash, DC, 1896. Fine. *O'NEILL.* $45

Greene, Graham. 19 STORIES. London: Heinemann, (1947). 1st ed. NF in somewhat soiled dj (few tiny chips). Inscribed. *CAPTAIN'S BOOK-SHELF.* $750

Greene, Graham. 19 STORIES. NY: Viking, 1949. 1st ed. Name. Fine. Minor rubbing spine corners of dj. *ELSE FINE.* $175

Greene, Graham. A BURNT-OUT CASE. Viking, 1961. 1st Amer ed. Fine in price-clipped dj. *STAHR.* $25

Greene, Graham. A SORT OF LIFE. London: Bodley Head, (1971). 1st ed. Fine in price-clipped, NF dj. *CHAPEL HILL.* $50

Greene, Graham. A SORT OF LIFE. London: Bodley Head, 1971. 1st ed. Fine, sm sticker pull, minor wear at extremities of dj. *ELSE FINE.* $45

Greene, Graham. ANOTHER MEXICO. NY: Viking, 1939. 1st ed. Chipped dj. *SILVER.* $45

Greene, Graham. BRIGHTON ROCK. NY: Viking, 1938. 1st ed, w/"Published in June, 1938" on copyright pg. Precedes British ed. Orig rose and black cl. Owner sig, else NF in VG pict dj, couple of holes in spine panel ("G" in "Greene" is missing). Quite presentable. *CHAPEL HILL.* $300

Greene, Graham. DOCTOR FISCHER OF GENEVA, OR THE BOMB PARTY. London: The Bodley Head, (1980). 1st ed. Fine in dj. *CHAPEL HILL.* $35

Greene, Graham. DOCTOR FISCHER OF GENEVA, OR THE BOMB PARTY. NY: Simon & Schuster, 1980. 1st ed. Rm. As New in dj. *ELSE FINE.* $20

Greene, Graham. GETTING TO KNOW THE GENERAL. (N.p) (Toronto): Lester & Orpen Dennys, 1984. 1st Canadian ed. 224pp. NF in dj. *AKA.* $20

Greene, Graham. GRAHAM GREENE COUNTRY. With Paul Hogarth. London: Pavillion/Michael Joseph, 1986. 1st ed. RM. Large quarto. VF, short edgetears to dj. *ELSE FINE.* $75

Greene, Graham. IN SEARCH OF A CHARACTER. NY: Viking, 1961. 1st US ed. Fine in Fine dj. *BEASLEY.* $35

Greene, Graham. IN SEARCH OF A CHARACTER. TWO AFRICAN JOURNALS. NY, (1962). 1st ed. 1/600 adv copies specially designed for friends. Fine in orig glassine dj. *POLYANTHOS.* $150

Greene, Graham. IN SEARCH OF A CHARACTER. TWO AFRICAN JOURNALS. NY: Viking, (1962). 1st ed. Fine in sl used dj. *DERMONT*. $20

Greene, Graham. LORD ROCHESTER'S MONKEY. NY: Viking Studio Book, (1974). 1st ed. VF in Fine dj. *BOND*. $30

Greene, Graham. MAY WE BORROW YOUR HUSBAND? & OTHER COMEDIES OF THE SEXUAL LIFE. NY: Viking, 1967. 1st ed. Fine in dj. *ELSE FINE*. $40

Greene, Graham. MAY WE BORROW YOUR HUSBAND? AND OTHER COMEDIES OF THE SEXUAL LIFE. London: Bodley Head, (1967). 1st ed. Fore-edge foxed, but NF in bright dj w/1" closed tear in rear panel. *CHAPEL HILL*. $50

Greene, Graham. ORIENT EXPRESS. Doubleday Doran, 1933. 1st Amer ed. VG. Binding loose, rental lib stamps; boards soiled. *STAHR*. $60

Greene, Graham. OUR MAN IN HAVANA. London: Heinemann, 1958. 1st ed. Fine in dj. *ELSE FINE*. $125

Greene, Graham. OUR MAN IN HAVANA. NY, 1958. 1st Amer ed. VG in sl stained pict dj. Ink name. *DIAMOND*. $25

Greene, Graham. REFLECTIONS ON TRAVELS WITH MY AUNT. NY, 1989. Ltd ed, 250 numbered only. Signed. Frontis. Pub 4pp publicity brochure laid in. Mint. *POLYANTHOS*. $175

Greene, Graham. REFLECTIONS. London: Reinhardt, (1991). 1st Eng ed. Amer pub's promo sheet attached to front of dj. Fine in dj. *LOPEZ*. $45

Greene, Graham. STAMBOUL TRAIN. London, (1932). 1st ed. Orig. black cloth with small gilt vignette on spine. Slight cvr staining. Little foxing on fore-edges & pages at end. Inner hinges straining, o/w VG. *DIAMOND*. $150

Greene, Graham. THE CAPTAIN AND THE ENEMY. NY: Viking, (1988). Uncorrected proof. Fine in ptd wrappers. *DERMONT*. $35

Greene, Graham. THE COMEDIANS. London: Bodley Head, (1966). Nearly Fine in dj. 1st ed. *CHAPEL HILL*. $65

Greene, Graham. THE COMEDIANS. London: Bodley Head, 1966. 1st ed. Brief inscription. Fine in dj. *ELSE FINE*. $75

Greene, Graham. THE COMEDIANS. NY, (1966). Ltd 1st ed, 1/500 specially bound for presentation in adv of pub. Fine. *POLYANTHOS*. $120

Greene, Graham. THE COMPLAISANT LOVER. NY: Viking, 1961. 1st US ed. Fine in Fine dj (barely sunned spine). *BEASLEY*. $50

Greene, Graham. THE COMPLAISANT LOVER: A COMEDY. NY: Viking, 1961. 1st ed. Fine. Dj lightly edgeworn. *ELSE FINE*. $45

Greene, Graham. THE COMPLAISANT LOVER: A PLAY. London: Heinemann, 1959. 1st ed. Fine in dj. *ELSE FINE*. $125

Greene, Graham. THE END OF THE AFFAIR. London: Heinemann, (1951). 1st ed. Fine in price-clipped dj. Scarce in this condition. *CHAPEL HILL*. $125

Greene, Graham. THE HEART OF THE MATTER. NY: Viking, (1948). 1st US ed. NF in VG dj. *UNGER*. $85

Greene, Graham. THE HEART OF THE MATTER. NY: Viking, 1948. 1st US ed. Fine in NF dj (few tiny tears). *BEASLEY*. $40

Greene, Graham. THE HONORARY CONSUL. Bodley Head, 1973. 1st ed. Fine in a NF in dj (sm closed tear; lightly rubbed). *STAHR*. $27.50

Greene, Graham. THE HONORARY CONSUL. London: Bodley Head, 1973. 1st ed. VF in dj. *ELSE FINE*. $60

Greene, Graham. THE HUMAN FACTOR. London: Bodley Head, (1978). 1st ed. Fine in dj. *CHAPEL HILL*. $35

Greene, Graham. THE LABYRINTHINE WAYS. NY: Viking, 1940. 1st US ed, rare 1st state w/pp 165 and 256 transposed. Fine in Fine dj w/bit darkened spine. *BEASLEY*. $750

Greene, Graham. THE LITTLE HORSE BUS. Doubleday, (1974). 1st Amer ed. Illus by Edward Ardizzone. VG in VG dj w/minor edge wrinkles. *BEBBAH*. $30

Greene, Graham. THE LITTLE STEAMROLLER. NY: Doubleday, (1974). 1st Amer ed. Dj has several folds, shows wear. NF. *ACADEMIC LIBRARY*. $35

Greene, Graham. THE LOST CHILDHOOD. London: E & S, 1951. 1st ed. Lightly bumped spine heel, else Fine, minor rubs at dj spine corners. *ELSE FINE*. $185

Greene, Graham. THE MAN WITHIN. GC: Doubleday-Doran, 1929. 1st ed, 1st novel. Name. Fine, dj has lt wear at corners, sm spots on front panel. *ELSE FINE*. $600

Greene, Graham. THE NAME OF ACTION. NY, 1931. 1st ed. Spine sunned, extremities little rubbed. NF. *POLYANTHOS*. $100

Greene, Graham. THE POTTING SHED: A PLAY. NY: Viking, 1957. 1st ed, precedes British ed. by 1 yr. Review copy, slip laid in. Fine, dj spine has a few light spots, age darkening. *ELSE FINE*. $90

Greene, Graham. THE MONSTER OF CAPRI. Helsinki: Eurographica, (1985). 1st ed. Ltd to 500 signed. Facs, linen, dj. Mint. *JAFFE*. $450

Greene, Graham. THE QUIET AMERICAN. London: Heinemann, (1955). 1st ed. Very sl cocked, o/w VF in Fine dj, w/pub's wraparound band. *LOPEZ*. $200

Greene, Graham. THE QUIET AMERICAN. NY: Viking, 1956. 1st ed. Fine in NF dj (shallow spine chips). *BEASLEY*. $45

Greene, Graham. THE THIRD MAN. NY: Viking, 1950. 1st ed, preceding Eng ed. Fine in very lightly rubbed price-clipped dj w/short tear. *CAPTAIN'S BOOKSHELF*. $150

Greene, Graham. THE THIRD MAN. NY: Viking, 1950. Fine in faintly spine-sunned dj. 1st ed. Scarce. *CHAPEL HILL*. $175

Greene, Graham. THE THIRD MAN. Helsinki: Eurographica, (1988). 1st this ed. Ltd to 500 signed. Linen, dj. Mint. *JAFFE*. $450

Greene, Graham. TRAVELS WITH MY AUNT. Taiwan piracy. (1970). Fine in NF dj. *POLYANTHOS*. $25

Greene, Graham. TRAVELS WITH MY AUNT. Viking, 1970. 1st Amer ed. About Fine in dj. *STAHR*. $20

Greene, Graham. WAYS OF ESCAPE. London: Bodley Head, (1980). 1st ed. Fine in Fine dj. *UNGER*. $40

Greene, Graham. YES AND NO. A PLAY IN ONE ACT. Helsinki: Eurographica, 1984. 1st of this ed. Ltd to 350 signed. Facs of orig ms, ptd wraps. Mint. *JAFFE*. $250

Greene, Harlan. WHAT THE DEAD REMEMBER. NY: Dutton (1991). Uncorrected proof. NF in wraps. *DORN*. $40

Greene, Homer. A LINCOLN CONSCRIPT. Boston, (1909). 1st ed. 283pp. VG+. *PRATT*. $15

Greene, Jonathan. THE RECKONING. Annandale-on-Hudson: Matter, 1966. 1st ed. Fine. *BEASLEY*. $45

Greene, Josiah. MADMEN DIE ALONE. NY: William Morrow, 1938. 1st ed. Fine in dj w/minor rubbing. *MORDIDA*. $35

Greene, Max. THE KANZAS REGION...DESCRIPTIONS OF...INTERSPERSED WITH INCIDENTS OF TRAVEL...NY, 1856. 1st ed. 192,(4),(4)pp. Map. Orig cl. Nice. Howes G383. *GINSBERG*. $500

Greene, Melissa Fay. PRAYING FOR SHEETROCK. Reading: Addison Wesley, (1991). 1st Amer ed. Signed. Fine in dj. *DORN*. $35

Greene, Merle, et al. MAYA SCULPTURE FROM THE SOUTHERN LOWLANDS, HIGHLANDS AND PACIFIC PIEDMONT....Berkeley: Lederer, Street, & Zeus, 1972. 1st ed. Fine in VG dj. *CONNOLLY & WADE*. $75

Greene, Merle et al. MAYA SCULPTURE. Berkeley: Lederer, (1972). 1st ed. 201 full pg photos. Good in dj. *SILVER*. $50

Greener, W.W. MODERN BREECH-LOADERS: SPORTING AND MILITARY. London: Cassell, Petter and Galpin, n.d. (c. 1870's). Page between fly and title page missing. Cloth, ads. VG. *GIBBS.* $25

Greenewalt, C.H. HUMMINGBIRDS. GC, 1960. 1st ed. 69 colored plts (tipped-in). Dj, sm tears. *SUTTON.* $285

Greenewalt, C.H. HUMMINGBIRDS. GC, NY: Amer. Mus. of Nat. History, 1960. 1st ed. Fine in VG+ dj. *MIKESH.* $235

Greenewalt, C.H. HUMMINGBIRDS. GC, NY: Amer. Mus. of Nat. History, 1960. 1st ed. Fine. *MIKESH.* $175

Greenewalt, C.H. HUMMINGBIRDS. GC: Doubleday, 1960. Pub for the Amer Museum of Natural Hist. 250pp. Tipped-in plts. Gray cl. VG. *SMITHFIELD.* $115

Greenfield, J. Godwin and E.A. Carmichael. THE CEREBRO-SPINAL FLUID IN CLINICAL DIAGNOSIS. London, 1925. 1st ed. *FYE.* $100

Greenhood, David and Helen Gentry. CHRONOLOGY OF BOOKS & PRINTING. NY: The Macmillan Co., 1936. Revised ed. Spine age darkened. *OAK KNOLL.* $45

Greenhow, Robert. THE HISTORY OF OREGON AND CALIFORNIA, AND THE OTHER TERRITORIES OF THE NORTHWEST COAST OF NORTH AMERICA...Boston. 1844. 1st ed. 482pp. Fldg map (mended). Contemp half morocco. Emb lib stamp. Howes G389. *GINSBERG.* $300

Greening, C.E. THE GREENING PICTORIAL SYSTEM OF LANDSCAPE GARDENING....Monroe, (1910). 1/2 morocco, corners and spine ends perished. Lt dampstaining pp edges, margins, not affecting text or photos; some pp smudging. *SUTTON.* $185

Greenleaf, Stephen. GRAVE ERROR. NY: Dial Press, 1979. 1st ed. Fine in dj. *MORDIDA.* $35

Greenspan, Sophie. WESTWARD WITH FREMONT, THE STORY OF SOLOMON CARVALHO. Phila: Jewish Public Soc of Amer, 1969. 1st ed. VF in VF dj. *OREGON.* $40

GREENWICH HOSPITAL, A SERIES OF NAVAL SKETCHES...By an old sailor. (By M.H. Barker.) Illus George Cruikshank. London: James Robins and Co, 1826. 1st ed. (iv),200pp. 12 color plts. Later 3/4 morocco, gilt, a.e.g, binding a little rubbed and faded, lt offsetting and lt toning opposite plts, but VG. Bkpl. Scarce. *LEFKOWICZ.* $900

Greenwood, Annie Pike. WE SAGEBRUSH FOLKS. NY: Appleton-Century, 1934. 30 photos on 16 plts. Cl, dj. *SCHOYER'S.* $30

Greenwood, Ernest. PROMETHEUS U.S.A. NY: Harper, 1929. 1st ed. Fine- in VG dj. *AARD.* $30

Greenwood, Grace. NEW LIFE IN NEW LANDS: NOTES OF TRAVEL. NY: J.B. Ford, 1873. 1st ed. Brick red cl stamped in gilt and black, rubbed edges, sl soiled, o/w VG. *SCHOYER'S.* $60

Greenwood, Major. SOME BRITISH PIONEERS OF SOCIAL MEDICINE. London, 1948. 1st ed. *FYE.* $50

Greenwood, Thomas. EDWARD EDWARDS, THE CHIEF PIONEER OF MUNICIPAL LIBRARIES. London: Scott, Greenwood and Co, 1902. 1st ed. Some fading, else internally VG. *WREDEN.* $35

Greenwood, William. SCOPOLAMINE-MORPHINE, SEMI-NARCOSIS DURING LABOUR. London, 1918. 1st ed. Scarce. *FYE.* $40

Greer, Germaine. THE OBSTACLE RACE....NY: Farrar Straus Giroux, 1979. 1st ed. Fine. *SMITH.* $40

Greer, William Royal. GEMS OF AMERICAN ARCHITECTURE. St. Paul: Brown & Bigelow, c1935. Wraps. *HUDSON.* $45

Greger, Debora. CARTOGRAPHY. POEMS. Lisbon, Iowa: Penumbra Press, 1980. 1st ed. One of "approximately" 225 ptd, signed by printer, Bonnie O'Connell & Greger. 6-color title-pg print, dec cl, dj. Mint. *JAFFE.* $150

Greger, Debora. MOVABLE ISLANDS. POEMS. Princeton: Princeton Univ Press, (1980). 1st ed. Cl, dj. VF. *JAFFE.* $35

Gregg, Cecil Freeman. INSPECTOR HIGGINS SEES IT THROUGH. NY: D. Appleton-Century, 1934. 1st Amer ed. Fine in dj w/light chipping at spine ends, small chip on front panel and chipped corners. *MORDIDA.* $35

Gregg, Frank M. THE FOUNDING OF A NATION. Cleveland: Arthur Clark, 1915. 1st ed. Almost Fine. *AARD.* $60

Gregg, Frank. THE FOUNDING OF A NATION....A.H. Clark, 1915. 2 vols. 1st ed. 9 plts (3 color maps). VG. *OREGON.* $75

Gregg, Josiah. COMMERCE OF THE PRAIRIES...Lakeside Classic, 1926. Frontis, fldg map. VG. *OREGON.* $30

Gregg, Josiah. COMMERCE OF THE PRAIRIES: OR THE JOURNAL OF A SANTA FE TRADER DURING EIGHT EXPEDITIONS....AND A RESIDENCE OF NEARLY NINE YEARS IN NORTHERN MEXICO. NY: J. & G.H. Langley, 1845 & 1844. 2 vols. 320pp, frontis, 2 plts; 318pp, frontis, 2 plts, 1 map. Mixed set: vol 1, 1845 2nd ed; vol 2, 1st Eng ed. Bindings nearly identical being emb, lettered alike but vol 2 is sl more brown. Spine ends, edges worn on vol 1, lacks ffep in vol 1, rfep in vol 2. VG. Howes G401. *OREGON.* $500

Gregg, Josiah. COMMERCE OF THE PRAIRIES: OR, THE JOURNAL OF A SANTA FE TRADER....NY, 1844. 1st ed, 1st issue. 2 vols. 6 plts, 2 maps. 1 fldg map. Orig black cl, blind embossed borders on sides, gilt vignettes on front covers, title in gilt on backstrip. Professionally rebacked w/orig spine, overall Fine, clean. *GINSBERG.* $2000

Gregg, Josiah. DIARY & LETTERS OF JOSIAH GREGG. EXCURSIONS IN MEXICO AND CALIFORNIA, 1847-1850. Univ of OK, 1944. 1st ed. Fine in VG dj. *OREGON.* $75

Gregg, Josiah. DIARY & LETTERS OF JOSIAH GREGG. SOUTHWESTERN ENTERPRISES, 1840-1847. Maurice Fulton (ed). Univ of OK, 1941. 1st ed. Frontis, 10 plts, 2 fldg maps. Sm chip dj. Fine in dj. *OREGON.* $70

Gregg, Kate. THE ROAD TO SANTA FE. JOURNAL AND DIARIES OF GEORGE CHAMPLIN SIBLEY...1825-1827. Univ of NM, (1952). 1st ed. Frontis. Fine in VG dj. *OREGON.* $40

Gregg, Thomas. THE PROPHET OF PALMYRA. NY, 1890. 1st ed., 552pp, plates, ports, cover sl worn, brown paper tape on end-sheets, title page, 2 pp in text, and on rear hinges; light foxing and pencilled notes. Good. *BENCHMARK.* $100

Gregorovius, Ferdinand. CORSICA: PICTURESQUE, HISTORICAL AND SOCIAL...Phila: Parry & M'Millan, 1855. 1st Amer ed. 522pp, 6pp ads. Backstrip repaired. Spine rubbed, sl cocked. Frontis. *SCHOYER'S.* $45

Gregory, Dick. DICK GREGORY'S POLITICAL PRIMER. NY: H&R, (1972). 1st ed. Fine in NF, price-clipped dj. *LOPEZ.* $45

Gregory, Dick. DICK GREGORY'S POLITICAL PRIMER. NY: Harper, 1972. 1st ed. Fine but for slight sunning and very minor stain foot of spine, in like dj. *BEASLEY.* $25

Gregory, Dick. FROM THE BACK OF THE BUS. NY: Dutton, 1962. 1st ed, 1st book. Only issued in wrappers. VG. *LOPEZ.* $35

Gregory, Dick. NIGGER. NY: Dutton, 1964. 1st ed. Mildly foxed, VG in dj. *LOPEZ.* $50

Gregory, Dick. UP FROM NIGGER. NY: Stein and Day, (1976). Uncorrected proof. NF in wrappers. *LOPEZ.* $75

Gregory, Dick. WHAT'S HAPPENING? NY: Dutton, 1965. 1st ed. NF in wrappers. *LOPEZ.* $30

Gregory, Herbert E. and Raymond C. Moore. THE KAIPAROWITS REGION; A GEOGRAPHIC AND GEOLOGIC RECONNAISSANCE OF PARTS OF UTAH AND ARIZONA. 1931. USGS Prof Paper 164. 161pp. VG+. *FIVE QUAIL.* $100

Gregory, Herbert E. GEOLOGY AND GEOGRAPHY OF THE ZION PARK REGION, UTAH AND ARIZONA. USGS Prof Paper 220. vi, 200pp, 5 fldg pocket plts, 133 figures, including photos. Scarce. Original paper, including covers, recased in black cloth. Ex-lib, o/w NF. *FIVE QUAIL*. $125

Gregory, J.C. A SHORT HISTORY OF ATOMISM. London: Black, 1931. VG+ in dj. *BOOKCELL*. $50

Gregory, J.W. THE NATURE AND ORIGIN OF FIORDS. London: John Murray, 1913. Edges foxed; cvr spotted, shelfwear. *PARMER*. $75

Gregory, Lady (Augusta). IRISH FOLK-HISTORY PLAYS, FIRST SERIES. NY: Putnam, 1912. 1st US ed. Cl backed boards, some stained, VG. *SECOND LIFE*. $40

Greiner, T. HOW TO MAKE THE GARDEN PAY. Phila: Maule, 1890. 272pp. Cloth stained, worn; contents VG. *AMERICAN BOTANIST*. $22

Greiner, T. THE NEW ONION CULTURE. NY: Orange Judd, 1918. Cloth lightly worn, else VG. *AMERICAN BOTANIST*. $25

Grenfell, Wilfred T. FORTY YEARS FOR LABRADOR. Boston: Houghton Mifflin, 1932. 1st thus. Cvrs soiled and worn, interior lightly foxed. *PARMER*. $30

Gresham, William Lindsay. NIGHTMARE ALLEY. NY: Rinehart, 1946. 1st ed. Fine in Fine dj but for few tiny tears, shallow chipping. Author's 1st book. *BEASLEY*. $45

Gresham, William Lindsay. NIGHTMARE ALLEY. Rinehart, 1946. 1st ed. VG or better in dj (chipped at spine ends, short tears, rubbed spots). *STAHR*. $30

Gress, Edmund G. THE AMERICAN MANUAL OF TYPOGRAPHY...New York: Oswald Publishing Company, 1905. Quarter lea. 2nd ed. *OAK KNOLL*. $125

Grew, J.C. SPORT AND TRAVEL IN THE FAR EAST. Boston/NY: Houghton Mifflin, 1910. Grn dec cl, gilt titles. Some foxing to edges, prelims, else VG. *PARMER*. $100

Grey, Edward. FLY FISHING. London: Dent, 1899. 2nd ed. Plts, b/w decs by Rackham, orig. dec cl. Extrems sl rubbed, o/w Fine. *JAFFE*. $65

Grey Owl. PILGRIMS OF THE WILD. NY: Scribner, 1935. 1st ed. VG in worn dj, missing several significant chunks. *LOPEZ*. $40

Grey Owl. PILGRIMS OF THE WILD. Toronto, 1934. Photos, drawings. NF. *MIKESH*. $27.50

Grey Owl. SAJO AND THE BEAVER PEOPLE. NY: Scribner, 1936. 1st ed. VG, lacking dj. *LOPEZ*. $30

Grey, Zane. 30,000 ON THE HOOF. NY: Harper, (1940). 1st ed. VG in VG dj. *UNGER*. $185

Grey, Zane. ARIZONA AMES. London, (1931). 1st ed. Fine in dj (very small edge tear lower front panel, few tiny edge nicks). *POLYANTHOS*. $75

Grey, Zane. CAPTIVES OF THE DESERT. London: Hodder & Stoughton, (1953). 1st British ed. Fine. *AUTHORS OF THE WEST*. $20

Grey, Zane. CODE OF THE WEST. London, 1934. 1st ed. Lower spine minimally rubbed. Fine in like dj. *POLYANTHOS*. $75

Grey, Zane. DESERT GOLD: A ROMANCE OF THE BORDER. Harper & Brothers, 1913. 1st, with C-N. Cvr picture in color. Spine corners sl frayed, else VG+. *AUTHORS OF THE WEST*. $50

Grey, Zane. MAJESTY'S RANCHO. NY: Harper, 1942. 1st ed. Fine in very nice dj. (sl chipped at extrems and sl soiled). *SECOND LIFE*. $135

Grey, Zane. ROPING LIONS IN THE GRAND CANYON. Grosset & Dunlap, (c. 1930). Fine in chipped dj. *VARNER*. $30

Grey, Zane. STAIRS OF SAND. NY: Harper, 1943. 1st ed. Fine in very nice dj (some minor chipping at extrems and soiling to rear panel). *SECOND LIFE*. $150

Grey, Zane. TALES OF LONELY TRAILS. NY: Harper & Bros. (1922). 1st ed. Frontis port, 72 photos. Grn cl stamped in grn and gold, w/mounted photo on front cover. *KARMIOLE*. $150

Grey, Zane. THE CALL OF THE CANYON. Harpers, (1924). 1st ed. Pict cl, soiled. Good+. *OREGON*. $20

Grey, Zane. THE CALL OF THE CANYON. Toronto: Musson, (1924). 1st Canadian ed. Pict cvr. Fine in chipped dj. *AUTHORS OF THE WEST*. $40

Grey, Zane. THE DESERT OF WHEAT. NY/London: Harper & Bros, 1919. 1st ed. Bit cocked, spine sunned, VG. *ARCHER*. $25

Grey, Zane. THE FUGITIVE TRAIL. London: Hodder & Stoughton, (1958). 1st British ed. Fine. *AUTHORS OF THE WEST*. $25

Grey, Zane. THE LIGHT OF THE WESTERN STARS. NY, 1914. 1st ed. Colored frontis. Pict cl, gilt. Fine. *POLYANTHOS*. $75

Grey, Zane. THE MAVERICK QUEEN. NY, 1950. 1st ed. Spine sunned, some waterstaining to covers; contents Fine. Dj chipped, small piece missing lower edge front panel. *POLYANTHOS*. $45

Grey, Zane. THE MYSTERIOUS RIDER. NY: Harper & Bros, 1921. 1st ed. Cloth. Fine. *GIBBS*. $20

Grey, Zane. THE RAINBOW TRAIL. Harper, (1915). 1st ed. Frontis in color, pict cover. VG, name & date. *AUTHORS OF THE WEST*. $50

Grey, Zane. THE REEF GIRL. 1st ed. NY: Harper, 1977. Fine in Fine dj. *BEASLEY*. $65

Grey, Zane. THE REEF GIRL. Harper, (1977). 1st ed. Fine in dj. *AUTHORS OF THE WEST*. $35

Grey, Zane. THE SHEPHERD OF GUADELOUPE. NY, 1930. 1st ed. Spine faded. Sl cvr staining. Short crayon line top fore-edge. Minor damp-wrinkling top fore-edges of 8pp, o/w VG. *DIAMOND*. $25

Grey, Zane. THE THUNDERING HERD. NY: Harper, 1925. 1st ed. Sl chipped cl in VG dj. *SECOND LIFE*. $125

Grey, Zane. WANDERER OF THE WASTELAND. Harper & Brothers, 1923. 1st ed. Lt wear foot of spine, o/w clean, bright. *STAHR*. $25

Grey, Zane. WANDERER OF THE WASTELAND. NY: Harper, (1923). 1st ed. Illus by W. Herbert Dunton. From the Zane Grey Library with Grey's blind-stamp. Fine in a NF, lightly rubbed dj. *UNGER*. $400

Grey, Zane. WANDERER OF THE WASTELAND. NY: Harper, (1923). 1st ed. 419pp. Fine in Fine dj & hand-made slipcase. *BOOK MARKET*. $225

Grey, Zane. WILD HORSE MESA. Harper, 1928. 1st ed. Fine. *AUTHORS OF THE WEST*. $30

Grey, Zane. ZANE GREY: THE MAN AND HIS WORK. NY: Harper, (1928). 1st ed. Issued for friends of the family in a small printing and never offered for sale. Small 8vo lea. VF. *UNGER*. $175

Gribble, Francis H. LAUSANNE. A&C Black, 1909. 1st ed. 7s 6d Series. Minor wear, minor foxing on fore edge, else VG-NF. *OLD LONDON*. $75

Gribble, Francis H. MONTREUX. A&C Black, 1908. 1st ed. 7s 6d Series. VG-NF. *OLD LONDON*. $45

Gribble, Francis. GENEVA. A&C Black, 1908. 1st ed. 7s 6d Series. VG-NF. *OLD LONDON*. $75

Gribble, Leonard R. FAMOUS FEATS OF DETECTION AND DEDUCTION. Doubleday Doran, 1934. 1st ed. VG- in VG- dj. *AARD*. $15

Gribble, Leonard. THE SECRET OF TANGLES. Phila: J.B. Lippincott, 1934. 1st Amer ed. VG in dj (short closed tears, sl soiled back panel). *MORDIDA*. $35

Gribble, Leonard. THE SERPENTINE MURDER. NY: Dodd Mead, 1932. 1st Amer ed. Pub. in Eng as Is This Revenge? Fine in dj w/minor wear at spine ends and at corners. *MORDIDA.* $37.50

Grierson, Benjamin H. ANNUAL REPORT OF COLONEL B. H. GRIERSON...COMMANDING DEPARTMENT OF ARIZONA, 1889. Np, 1889. 1st ed. (i-ii), (1)-32,(33 blank),(34)pp. 9 blue print maps, 8 of which are listed. Orig ptd stiff wrappers. Howes G417. *GINSBERG.* $1250

Grierson, Francis. THE VALLEY OF SHADOWS. Boston: Houghton Mifflin, 1948. 1st ed thus. Bkpl. NF in Good dj. *CONNOLLY & WADE.* $35

Grierson, H.J. (ed). THE POEMS OF JOHN DONNE. Oxford, 1912. 2 vols. Spine labels rubbed. NF. *POLYANTHOS.* $75

Grierson, John. CHALLENGE TO THE POLES. London: Foulis, (1964). 1st prtg. VG VG dj. *BLUE DRAGON.* $45

Griesinger, Wilhelm. MENTAL PATHOLOGY AND THERAPEUTICS. NY, 1882, 375pp. *FYE.* $100

Grifalconi, Ann. THE VILLAGE OF ROUND AND SQUARE HOUSES. Boston: Little, Brown, (1986). 1st ed. Paper over boards. Signed. Fine in Fine dj. *ACADEMIC LIBRARY.* $30

Griffin, Appleton P. C. BIBLIOGRAPHY OF AMERICAN HISTORICAL SOCIETIES. (House Documents, 59th Congress, 1st Session, Vol II). Annual Report Amer Hist Assn for 1905. Washington GPO, 1907. New buckram. *HEINOLDT.* $25

Griffin, Charles (ed). LATIN AMERICA. Austin, (1971). 1st ed. Good in dj. *SILVER.* $50

Griffin, Howard. CRY CADENCE. NY, 1947. 1st ed, 1st bk. Spine sunned, lower spine little stained. NF. *POLYANTHOS.* $30

Griffin, John Howard. BLACK LIKE ME. Boston: Houghton Mifflin Co., 1961. 1st ed. W/signed presentation inscrip. Fine in lightly used dj. *DERMONT.* $300

Griffin, John Howard. THE DEVIL RIDES OUTSIDE. London: Collins, 1953. 1st Eng ed, 1st bk. NF in dj, few tears. *HELLER.* $50

Griffin, Solomon Bulkley. MEXICO OF TO-DAY. NY: Harper & Brothers, 1886. 1st ed. Double pg color map. Cloth sl rubbed. VG. Scarce. *BLUE MOUNTAIN.* $95

Griffith, A.K. MICKEY FREE, MANHUNTER. Caxton, 1969. 1st ptg. Fine in Fine dj. *VARNER.* $35

Griffith, Albert. PETER TAYLOR. NY: Twayne, (1970). 1st ed. Fine in sl used dj. Signed. *CAPTAIN'S BOOKSHELF.* $40

Griffith, Albert. THE OLD FOREST AND OTHER STORIES. NY: Dial, 1985. 1st ed. Fine in dj. Signed by Peter Taylor. *CAPTAIN'S BOOKSHELF.* $75

Griffith, G.W. MY 96 YEARS IN THE GREAT WEST. LA, For the Author, 1929. 4 ports. *SCHOYER'S.* $40

Griffith, George. THE OUTLAWS OF THE AIR. London, 1897. Illus bds. NF. *POLYANTHOS.* $125

Griffith, John William. A PRACTICAL MANUAL, CONTAINING A DESCRIPTION, GENERAL, CHEMICAL, AND MICROSCOPICAL CHARACTERS OF THE BLOOD, AND SECRETIONS OF THE BODY, with G. Owen Rees, ON THE ANALYSIS OF THE BLOOD AND URINE, IN HEALTH AND DISEASE; AND ON THE TREATMENT OF URINARY DISEASES, with Alfred Markwick, A GUIDE TO THE EXAMINATION OF THE URINE IN HEALTH AND DISEASE. Phila, 1848. 1st ed. 3 vols. in 1. 182, 165, 113pp. VF. *FYE.* $75

Griffith, John. A JOURNAL OF THE LIFE, TRAVELS, AND LABOURS IN THE WORK OF THE MINISTRY...Phila: Joseph Crukshank. 1780. 2 parts in one. (2),iv,426,(8),112pp. Contemp calf, extrems bit rubbed. *KARMIOLE.* $200

Griffith, R. Eglesfeld. MEDICAL BOTANY: OR DESCRIPTIONS OF THE MOST IMPORTANT PLANTS USED IN MEDICINE,

WITH THEIR HISTORY, PROPERTIES, AND MODE OF ADMINISTRATION. Phila, 1847. 1st ed. 704pp. Recent lib buckram w/new eps. Contents VG. Scarce. *FYE.* $225

Griffiths, J. TRAVELS IN EUROPE, ASIA MINOR, AND ARABIA. London, 1805. Frontis, fldg map, 3 (of 4) plts. Lacking pl of St. Sophia at p. 70. New 1/4 calf marbled boards. xx,396pp. Uncut. *O'NEILL.* $450

Griffiths, William H. THE STORY OF THE AMERICAN BANK NOTE COMPANY. (NY: American Bank Note Company, 1959). 92pp. *OAK KNOLL.* $100

Grifi, E. SAUNTERINGS IN FLORENCE. 2nd ed, rev, enl. Florence: Bemporad & Fiuglio, 1899. Somewhat spotted, lacks ffep. 2 fldg maps back pocket. *SCHOYER'S.* $20

Griggs, Robert F. THE VALLEY OF TEN THOUSAND SMOKES. Washington DC: Nat. Geo. Soc., 1922. 1st ed. Good+. *MIKESH.* $37.50

Griggs, Robert F. THE VALLEY OF TEN THOUSAND SMOKES. Wash: Nat'l Geographic Soc, 1922. 1st ed. Bumping, minor wear. Interior clean; fldg maps, panorama excellent cond. *PARMER.* $75

Grigson, G. THE ENGLISHMAN'S FLORA. London, 1955. Cloth. Lt spotting, spine faded, leather spine label worn. *SUTTON.* $75

Grigson, Geoffrey (ed). THE MINT: A MISCELLANY OF LITERATURE ART AND CRITICISM. (London): Routledge, (1946). 1st ed. Ffep browned, else Fine in dj. Signed by Taylor at his entry. *CAPTAIN'S BOOKSHELF.* $75

Grigson, Geoffrey. WILD FLOWERS IN BRITAIN. London: William Collins, 1944. 1st ed. Dj. Fine. *WREDEN.* $15

Grimes, Absalom. ABSALOM GRIMES, CONFEDERATE MAIL RUNNER. M.M. Quaife (ed). New Haven, 1926. 1st ed. Minor cvr spotting o/w VG+. *PRATT.* $55

Grimes, Absalom. ABSALOM GRIMES. CONFEDERATE MAIL RUNNER. Ed by M.M. Quaife. New Haven: Yale Univ Press. 1926. 1st ed. *KARMIOLE.* $30

Grimes, J. Stanley. ETHEROLOGY, AND THE PHRENO-PHILOSOPHY OF MESMERISM AND MAGIC ELOQUENCE. Boston, 1850. Rev. ed. 251, 121pp. Ex-lib. *FYE.* $75

Grimes, Martha. THE ANODYNE NECKLACE. Boston & Toronto: Little, Brown, (1983). 1st ed. Fine in VG+ dj. *BERNARD.* $60

Grimes, Martha. THE ANODYNE NECKLACE. Boston: Little Brown, 1983. 1st ed. VF in dj. *ELSE FINE.* $100

Grimes, Martha. THE DEER LEAP. Boston, Toronto: Little, Brown, (1985). 1st ed. Signed. New in dj. *BERNARD.* $50

Grimes, Martha. THE DEER LEAP. Boston: Little Brown, 1985. 1st ed. Fine in dj. *MORDIDA.* $35

Grimes, Martha. THE DIRTY DUCK. Boston: Little Brown, 1984. 1st ed. Fine in dj. *MORDIDA.* $35

Grimes, Martha. THE DIRTY DUCK. Little, Brown, (1984). 1st Amer ed. NF in NF dj with tiny closed edge tear. *BEBBAH.* $20

Grimes, Martha. THE DIRTY DUCK. Little, Brown, 1984. 1st ed. About Fine in dj (2 tiny rubbed spots). *STAHR.* $60

Grimes, Martha. THE FIVE BELLS AND BLADEBONE. London: O'Mara, 1988. 1st English ed. Patch of soil to front cvr, owner's name inked out on endpaper. VG+ in NF dj. *BEBBAH.* $20

Grimes, Martha. THE MAN WITH A LOAD OF MISCHIEF. Boston: Little Brown, 1981. 1st ed, 1st bk. Fine in dj. *ELSE FINE.* $150

Grimes, Martha. THE MAN WITH A LOAD OF MISCHIEF. Boston: Little Brown, 1981. 1st ed. Fine in dj w/closed tear and slight wrinkle at base of spine, couple of short closed tears, and small chip at lower corner. *MORDIDA.* $125

Grimes, Martha. THE OLD FOX DECEIV'D. Boston: Little Brown, 1982. 1st ed. VF in dj. *ELSE FINE.* $125

Grimes, Martha. THE OLD FOX DECEIV'D. Boston: Little Brown, 1982. 1st ed. Fine in price-clipped dj. *MORDIDA*. $85

Grimm, Claus. THE BOOK OF PICTURE FRAMES. NY: Abaris Books, 1981. 1st ed. VG. *BACKROOM*. $50

Grimm, Herbert L. and Paul L. Ray. HUMAN INTEREST STORIES OF THE THREE DAY'S BATTLES AT GETTYSBURG. Gettysburg, 1927. 63pp. Wraps. VG. *PRATT*. $30

Grimm, Hermann. THE LIFE OF MICHAEL ANGELO. 2 VOLS. Boston: Little Brown, 1903. New ed. Gilt cl. Gilt tips. Cloth djs. VF. *ARTIS*. $27.50

Grimm, Jacob and Wilhelm Grimm (Grimm Brothers). GRIMM'S FAIRY TALES. Walter Crane, E.H. Wehnert (illus). To Which is Added Grimm's Goblins, with Colored Pictures by George Cruikshank. NY: R. Worthington. 1883. Frontis, 7 color plts. Orig grn cl over illus boards, edges worn. *KARMIOLE*. $100

Grimm, Jacob and Wilheim Grimm (Grimm Brothers). HANSEL AND GRETEL AND OTHER STORIES. Doran, (n.d. but 1925). 4to. 310pp. 22 mounted color illus by Kay Nielsen, other b/w illus & dec initials. Edgewear, chips, scratches to gilt, black, red pict pastedown. 1 leaf has short closed edge tear. Title page has faint library stamp, copyright page has faint stamp, small accession & date stamp, 1 other library mark. VG. *BEBBAH*. $200

Grimm, Jacob and Wilheim Grimm (Grimm Brothers). HANSEL AND GRETEL. Reilly & Britton, (1908). 12mo. 58pp. Illus by John R. Neill. Ad for OZ books lists titles through Emerald City. Interior VG+, cvr wear, dec cvr w/circular pict pastedown. Overall VG. *BEBBAH*. $40

Grimm, Jacob and Wilhelm Grimm (Grimm Brothers). THE JUNIPER TREE AND OTHER TALES FROM GRIMM. Selected by Lore Segal, Maurice Sendak. Trans Lore Segal. Four Tales Translated by Randall Jarrell. Pictures by Maurice Sendak. NY: Farrar, Straus & Giroux. (1973). 1st ed. 2 vols. Djs. Slipcase. Inscribed by Sendak. *KARMIOLE*. $75

Grimm, Jacob and Wilhelm Grimm (Grimm Brothers). THE JUNIPER TREE AND OTHER TALES FROM GRIMM. Selected by Lore Segal and Maurice Sendak. Trans by Lore Segal w/Four Tales trans by Randall Jarrell. NY: Farrar Straus & Giroux, (1973). 1st trade ed. 2 vols. Illus Maurice Sendak. Fine in djs w/sl darkened spines and pict slipcase. Bkpl signed by Sendak tipped onto front pastedown of Vol 1. *CAPTAIN'S BOOKSHELF*. $100

Grimm, Wilhelm. DEAR MILI. FSG, 1988. 1st ed. Illus by Maurice Sendak. Fine in Fine dj. *BEBBAH*. $25

Grimwade, A.G. THE QUEEN'S SILVER. London: The Connoisseur, 1953. 1st ed. VG in dj torn at head. *BACKROOM*. $40

Grimwood, Ken. REPLAY. Arbor House, 1986. 1st ed. Fine in dj. *MADLE*. $35

Grimwood, Ken. REPLAY. NY: Arbor House, (1986). 1st ed. NF in dj. *OTHER WORLDS*. $25

Grimwood, V.R. AMERICAN SHIP MODELS AND HOW TO BUILD THEM. NY: W.W. Norton & Company, Inc., 1942. Fldg plates. Spine darkened, scuffed; covers soiled; interior VG. *PARMER*. $35

Grinker, Roy and John Spiegel. WAR NEUROSES IN NORTH AFRICA, THE TUNISIAN CAMPAIGN. NY, 1943. 1st ed. Rare. *FYE*. $75

Grinnell, George Bird. BEYOND THE OLD FRONTIER. Scribner's, 1913. 1st ed. 15 plts, 1 map. Rear cvr, corner 1st few pp dampstained. Good+. *OREGON*. $50

Grinnell, George Bird. THE FIGHTING CHEYENNES. NY, 1915. 1st ed. 431pp. A little cover wear and soiling but VG. *PRATT*. $125

Grinnell, George Bird. THE FIGHTING CHEYENNES. Univ of OK, (1971). Fine in VG dj. *OREGON*. $30

Grinnell, George Bird. THE FIGHTING CHEYENNES. Norman: Univ of Oklahoma Press, (1956). 15 photos, 11 maps. NF in dj. *LAURIE*. $50

Grinnell, George Bird. THE FIGHTING CHEYENNES. Univ of OK Press, 1956. NF in Good dj. *VARNER*. $30

Grinnell, George Bird. TRAILS OF THE PATHFINDERS. Toronto: William Briggs, 1911. 1st Canadian ed. Map. Pict tinted cvr. Fine, bkpl. *AUTHORS OF THE WEST*. $50

Grinnell, J. and T.I. Storer. ANIMAL LIFE IN THE YOSEMITE, AN ACCOUNT OF THE MAMMALS, BIRDS, REPTILES & AMPHIBIANS IN A CROSS-SECTION OF THE SIERRA NEVADA. Berkeley: Univ of CA, 1924. 1st ed. VG. *MIKESH*. $135

Grinnell, J. and T.I. Storer. ANIMAL LIFE IN THE YOSEMITE, ETC. Berkeley, Univ of CA, 1924. 1st ed. Ex-lib. Good+. *MIKESH*. $75

Grinnell, Joseph. GOLD HUNTING IN ALASKA. Elgin, IL, (1901). Double columns, photos. Pict wraps worn at hinge. *ARTIS*. $45

Grinnell, Joseph. GOLD HUNTING IN ALASKA. Elizabeth Grinnell (ed). Chicago: David C. Cook, (1901). 1/2 cl and marble paper boards, worn at extremities, else VG. *LAURIE*. $50

Griscom, L. et al. THE WARBLERS OF AMERICA, A POPULAR ACCOUNT...WESTERN HEMISPHERE. NY, 1957. 35 six-color offset plts. Dj w/edge tears. *SUTTON*. $65

Grisham, Noel. TAME THE RESTLESS WIND. Austin: San Felipe, 1968. 1st ed. Fine in Fine dj. *CONNOLLY & WADE*. $30

Griswold, P.R. COLORADO'S LONELIEST RAILROAD, THE SAN LUIS SOUTHERN. Pruett, 1980. 1st ed. Fine in VG dj. *VARNER*. $27.50

Griswold, Sandy G.V. THE MADMAN OF THE COLORADO. Cleveland, 1908. Beadle's Frontier Series No. 21. 12mo, softcover, 97pp plus ads, multi-colored cover. Light chipping to covers, else VG. *FIVE QUAIL*. $20

Griswold, Wayne. KANSAS HER RESOURCES AND DEVELOPMENTS. Cincinnati, 1871. 1st ed. 95pp. Orig ptd wrappers, minor x-l. Howes G439. *GINSBERG*. $225

Grivas, Theodore. MILITARY GOVERNMENT IN CALIFORNIA 1845-1851. Glendale, 1963. 1st ed. Fine. *PRATT*. $37.50

Grivas, Theodore. MILITARY GOVERNMENTS IN CALIFORNIA 1846-1850....Glendale: Clark, 1963. 1st ed. *GINSBERG*. $25

Groddeck, Georg. EXPLORING THE UNCONSCIOUS. London, 1933. Dj. NF. *POLYANTHOS*. $45

Groddeck, Georg. THE WORLD OF MAN AS REFLECTED IN ART, WORDS AND DISEASE. London, 1934. Dj. NF. *POLYANTHOS*. $45

Grogan, Emmett. RINGOLEVIO. Boston: Little, Brown, 1972. 1st ed. Fine in lightly used dj w/tiny chips at spine head. *BEASLEY*. $35

Grogan, Ewart S. and Arthur H. Sharp. FROM THE CAPE TO CAIRO: THE FIRST TRAVERSE OF AFRICA FROM SOUTH TO NORTH. London: Hurst and Blackett, 1902. Rev ed. Frontis, 2 color fldg maps. Owner sig. Blue cl, a bit rubbed. VG. *WEBER*. $100

Groh, George W. GOLD FEVER. NY: Morrow, 1966. 1st ed. Fine in NF dj. *CONNOLLY & WADE*. $40

Grohmann, Will. PAUL KLEE DRAWINGS. NY: Abrams (1960). White cl backed b/w pict white boards (joints rubbed; spine sl darkened). Tipped-in frontis. NF. *BLUE MOUNTAIN*. $125

Grooch, William Stephen. SKYWAY TO ASIA. NY: Longmans, Green & Co. 1936. 1st ed. Dj. Fine. *KARMIOLE*. $35

Gross, Milton. YANKEE DOODLES. House of Kent, 1948. 1st ed. Good+ in Good+ dj. *PLAPINGER*. $35

Gross, Miriam. THE WORLD OF RAYMOND CHANDLER. NY: A&W, 1978. 1st Amer ed. Fine in dj. *SILVER DOOR*. $25

Gross, Samuel D. A SYSTEM OF SURGERY...Illustrated by Nine Hundred and Thirty-Six Engravings. Phila: Blanchard & Lea, 1859. 1st ed. 2 vols. Contemp full sheep, leather labels on spines. Early owner's sig on titles & bkplts inside front covers. Remarkably Fine. *M & S.* $2000

Gross, Samuel D. A SYSTEM OF SURGERY; PATHOLOGICAL, DIAGNOSTIC THERAPEUTIC, AND OPERATIVE. Phila, 1882. 6th ed. Full leather, 2 vols. 1194, 1174pp. 1600+ woodcuts. *FYE.* $300

Gross, Samuel D. ELEMENTS OF PATHOLOGICAL ANATOMY. Phila, 1845. 2nd ed. Full leather. 250 illus, Fine hand-colored engrvd plts. Ex-lib. Logan Clendening's copy with his bkpl. *FYE.* $400

Gross, Samuel D. ELEMENTS OF PATHOLOGICAL ANATOMY. Phila, 1857. 3rd ed. Full leather, 770pp. 342 Fine woodcut illus. *FYE.* $250

Grosser, Morton. THE DISCOVERY OF NEPTUNE. Cambridge, MA: Harvard Univ Press, 1962. VG in dj. *KNOLLWOOD.* $35

Grossman, M.L. and J. Hamlet. BIRDS OF PREY OF THE WORLD. NY, 1964. 1st ed. VG+. *MIKESH.* $37.50

Grosz, George. ECCE HOMO. NY, (1966). 2nd ptg. Henry Miller intro. 16 color, 84 b/w plts. 4 extra color plts for framing laid in. Dj sl worn, o/w Fine. *ARTIS.* $25

Grosz, George. LITTLE YES AND A BIG NO. Trans Lola Sachs Dorin. NY: The Dial Press, 1946. 1st ed. Dj sl chipped. *KARMIOLE.* $75

Grote, Mrs. MEMOIR OF THE LIFE OF ARY SCHEFFER. London: John Murray, 1860. 1st ed. 166pp. Bound in full calf w/raised bands, gilt, etc. Rubbed along spine. Issued w/orig tipped in photo frontis. *SECOND LIFE.* $150

Groth, John. STUDIO: EUROPE. NY: Vanguard Press, 1945. 1st ed. Illus. by Groth. Intro. by Ernest Hemingway. Bookplate o/w VG+. *BERNARD.* $35

Grout, Roy A. (ed). THE HIVE AND THE HONEYBEE. Hamilton, IL, 1946. 1st ed. thus. VG. *ARTIS.* $15

Grove, Frederick Philip. THE TURN OF THE YEAR. Toronto: Mc-Clelland & Stewart, (1923). 1st Canadian ed. VG+. *AUTHORS OF THE WEST.* $40

Grove, Lee Edmonds. OF BROOKS & BOOKS. Minneapolis: Univ of MN Press, (1945). Ed ltd to 1500 numbered. Dj. *KARMIOLE.* $30

Grove, Lee Edmonds. OF BROOKS & BOOKS. Minneapolis: Univ of MN Press, (1945). 1st ed. One of 1500. Fine in VG dj. *WREDEN.* $45

Grover, David. DIAMONDFIELD JACK. A STUDY IN FRONTIER JUSTICE. Univ Nevada, 1968. 1st ed. VF in F dj. *OREGON.* $30

Grover, Eulalie Osgood (ed). MOTHER GOOSE. Volland, (1915). 1st ed. 4to. Unpaginated. Illus by Frederick Richardson. Some page soil, cvr wear, intricate pict pastedown inset into cvr has one chip. VG+. *BEBBAH.* $50

Groves, Colin P. HORSES, ASSES, AND ZEBRAS IN THE WILD. Hollywood, FL: Ralph Curtis, 1947. 1st ed. Good+. *OCTOBER FARM.* $22

GROVES DICTIONARY OF MUSIC AND MUSICIANS. NY: Macmillan, 1911. 5 vols. 2nd ed. Sl shelfwear. VG. *BANCROFT.* $75

GROVES DICTIONARY OF MUSIC AND MUSICIANS. NY: Macmillan, 1946. 5 vols. 3rd ed. VG. *BANCROFT.* $95

Groves, G.I. FAMOUS AMERICAN INDIANS. Chicago: Private, 1944. 1st ptg. Fine in Fine dj. *VARNER.* $47.50

GROWTH AND MANUFACTURE OF SILK, LETTER FROM THE SECRETARY OF THE TREASURY...MAY 11, 1826. (By R. Rush.) Washington, 1828. 220pp. 54 engr plts (1 fldg), fold-out table. 1/4 leather w/some edge scuffing, corners worn; 1" tear, lib no. on title; foxed. *SUTTON.* $165

Grubb, Davis. THE WATCHMAN. NY: Scribners, 1961. 1st ed. As New, tiny rub at dj spine corner. *ELSE FINE.* $35

Grubb, Davis. TWELVE STORIES OF SUSPENSE AND THE SUPERNATURAL. Scribners 1964. 1st ed. NF in sl rubbed VG dj. *MADLE.* $125

Grubb, E. and W. Guilford. THE POTATO. NY: Doubleday, 1912. Cloth lightly soiled, else VG. *AMERICAN BOTANIST.* $25

Grubb, N.H. CHERRIES. London, 1949. 28 plts (12 colored). Cl (ink inscrip ep, foxing), worn dj. *SUTTON.* $38

Gruber, Frank. BUFFALO GRASS. NY & Toronto, (1956). 1st ed. VG in dj. *McCLINTOCK.* $17.50

Gruber, Frank. BUGLES WEST. NY & Toronto, (1954). 1st ed. Fine in NF dj (light edgewear). *McCLINTOCK.* $17.50

Gruber, Frank. LONESOME RIVER. NY: Rinehart, (1957). 1st ed. Review copy. Fine in NF dj. *UNGER.* $60

Gruber, Frank. THE MIGHTY BLOCKHEAD. NY: Farrar & Rinehart, 1942. 1st ed. Fine in dj w/minor wear at spine ends and at corners. *MORDIDA.* $85

Gruber, Ruth. I WENT TO THE SOVIET ARCTIC. NY: Simon & Schuster, 1939. 1st ed. Signed. Fading, wear to extremities. *PARMER.* $40

Gruelle, Johnny. RAGGEDY ANDY STORIES. Donohue, (1920). Unpaginated. Gruelle illus in color. Edgewear, repaired split at spine, tape-repaired tears to title page, dedication page. Good+ in dj w/chips, spine wear, 2" x 2.25" piece missing. *BEBBAH.* $30

Gruelle, Johnny. RAGGEDY ANN AND ANDY AND THE CAMEL WITH THE WRINKLED KNEES. Chicago: Donohue, (1924). 1st ed. Cover, full-color illus by author. Corners a bit worn, owner sig on title pg, else Fine. *CAPTAIN'S BOOKSHELF.* $60

Gruelle, Johnny. RAGGEDY ANN STORIES. Volland, (1918). 1st ed. Unpaginated. Gruelle color illus. Some page edge tears, first few pp. have partial separation at gutter, crease to cvr w/edgewear. Good+. *BEBBAH.* $45

Gruening, Ernest (ed). AN ALASKAN READER 1867-1967. NY: Meredith Press, (1966). 1st ed. Inscribed. NF in VG- dj. *BLUE DRAGON.* $30

Grund, Francis. ARISTOCRACY IN AMERICA: FROM THE SKETCHBOOK OF A GERMAN NOBLEMAN. London: Richard Bentley, 1839. 1st ed. 2 vols. (12),319pp; (8),331pp. 4 ports. VG. *CONNOLLY & WADE.* $195

Grundy, W.M. THE SKETCH BOOK OF SHIPPING AND CRAFT. London: Charles Tilt, n.d. (probably between 1838 and 1840). Only ed. (4)pp, 24 litho plts. Orig dec cl, front cover gilt, lt foxing, but VG. Rare. *LEFKOWICZ.* $900

Gruner, O. Cameron. A TREATISE ON THE CANON OF MEDICINE OF AVICENNA INCORPORATING A TRANSLATION OF THE FIRST BOOK. London, 1930. 1st ed. Rare. *FYE.* $200

GT-99. TWENTY YEARS A LABOR SPY. Indianapolis: Bobbs-Merrill, (1937). 1st ed. Bright in worn dj. *AKA.* $30

Guenon, F. A TREATISE ON MILCH COWS....N.P. Trist (trans), John S. Skinner (intro). NY: Judd, (1856). 63rd thousand. 88pp. Worn cl. VG. *SECOND LIFE.* $45

Guenon, F. A TREATISE ON MILCH COWS....NY, 1856. 63rd thousand. Orig cl. Corners worn, spine ends perished. Corners of 4pp missing (some text loss), scattered lt foxing. Ex-lib. *SUTTON.* $25

Guenther, K. A NATURALIST IN BRAZIL....Boston & NY, 1931. 32 plts. Cl, some spotting on cvrs. *SUTTON.* $50

Guernsey, C.A. WYOMING COWBOY DAYS. NY, 1936. 1st ed. VG; sl rubbed. *VARNER.* $50

Guernsey, Orrin and Josiah F. Willard. HISTORY OF ROCK COUNTY, AND TRANSACTIONS OF THE ROCKY COUNTY AGRICULTURAL SOCIETY...Janesville, WI, 1856. 1st ed. (12),350pp. 5 plts. Orig cl, paper label on lower spine, bkpl removed. Howes G454. *GINSBERG.* $175

Guerra, Francisco. AMERICAN MEDICAL BIBLIOGRAPHY, 1639-1783. NY: Lathrop C. Harper, 1962. Cloth, cloth spine label, lower paper edges shelf soiled. *DAWSON'S.* $125

Guest, Barbara. POEMS. THE LOCATION OF THINGS....GC: Doubleday, 1962. 1st ed. Fine in price-clipped dj. *JAFFE.* $85

Guggenheim, Peggy. OUT OF THIS CENTURY. NY: Dial, 1946. 1st ed. Plates. Cheap paper has darkened, else Fine. Dj w/several tears at edges, but complete. *WOOLMER.* $75

Guggisberg, C.A.W. WILD CATS OF THE WORLD. NY: Taplinger, 1975. Illus. Fine in VG dj. *MIKESH.* $35

GUIDE TO DEPOSITORIES OF MANUSCRIPT COLLECTIONS IN THE UNITED STATES: CALIFORNIA. Prepared by The Northern and Southern CA Hist Records Survey Projects Div of Community Service Programs Works Projects Admin. LA: The Southern CA Hist Records Survey Project. 1941. Mimeographed text. Ptd stiff wraps w/black cl tape spine. *KARMIOLE.* $35

GUIDE TO GREECE, THE ARCHIPELAGO, CONSTAN-TINOPLE, THE COASTS OF ASIA MINOR, CRETE AND CYPRUS. London: Macmillan & Co, 1908. 3rd ed. Sl rubbed, owner markings. Fldg maps, plans. Lacks fldg map of Greece. *SCHOYER'S.* $20

GUIDEBOOK OF THE WESTERN U. S. IN 4 VOLUMES. U.S. GEOLOGICAL SURVEY, WASHINGTON: BULLETIN 611, Part A—THE NORTHERN PACIFIC ROUTE WITH A SIDE TRIP TO YELLOWSTONE PARK by Marius R. Campbell, et al, 1915, 212pp, 27 fldg map routes, 23 plts, 38 figures. BULLETIN 612, PART B - THE OVERLAND ROUTE WITH A SIDE TRIP TO YELLOWSTONE PART by Willis T. Lee et al. 1915. 244pp, 25 route maps, 49 plts, 20 figures. BULLETIN 613, PART C - THE SANTA FE ROUTE WITH A SIDE TRIP TO THE GRAND CANYON OF THE COLORADO by N. H. Darton et al. 1916. 24 route maps, 42 plts, 40 figures. 200pp. BULLETIN 614, PART D - THE SHASTA ROUTE AND COASTLINE BY J. S. Diller et al, 1915, 142pp. 19 fldg route maps, 33 plts, 15 figures. Rebound in new buckram. *HEINOLDT.* $75

Guillame, Paul and Thomas Munro. PRIMITIVE NEGRO SCULP-TURE. NY, 1926. VG-NF. *POLYANTHOS.* $75

Guille, Peter. STERLING AND FRANCINE CLARK ART IN-STITUTE EXHIBIT 14 OLD SILVER TEA POTS. Williamstown, MA, 1960. 1st ed. VG. Wraps. *BACKROOM.* $20

Guille, Peter. STERLING AND FRANCINE CLARK ART IN-STITUTE EXHIBIT 18 OLD SILVER TEA ACCESSORIES. Wil-liamstown, MA, 1962. 1st ed. VG. Wraps. *BACKROOM.* $25

Guillem de Poitou. HIS ELEVEN EXTANT POEMS TRANS. BY PAUL BLACKBURN. George Economou (ed). Mt. Horeb: Perish-able Press, (1976). One of 165 (the entire ed). 1/4 morocco and marbled boards. Title-pg illus by Roland Ginzel. VF w/prospectus. *CAPTAIN'S BOOKSHELF.* $250

Guillemin, A. THE HEAVENS, AN ILLUSTRATED HAND-BOOK....London: Bentley, 1868. 3rd ed. Tight, clean. *BOOKCELL.* $60

Guillemin, Amadee. THE SUN. London: Richard Bentley, 1870. Trans T.L. Phipson. Good in illus red cl; corner bumped, worn, ex-tremities worn, bkpl removed, tear to margin p23. *KNOLLWOOD.* $75

Guimaraes Rosa, Joao. THE DEVIL TO PAY IN THE BACK-LANDS. Trans Taylor & de Onis. NY: Knopf, 1963. 1st US ed. Fine in price-clipped dj lightly worn. *CAPTAIN'S BOOKSHELF.* $75

Gulick, Bill. CHIEF JOSEPH COUNTRY, LAND OF THE NEZ PERCE. Caldwell, 1981. 1st ed. Inscribed. Fine in dj. *PRATT.* $35

Gunn, John C. GUNN'S DOMESTIC MEDICINE, OR POOR MAN'S FRIEND, IN THE HOURS OF AFFLICTION, PAIN, AND SICKNESS. NY, 1842. 893pp. Lea. *FYE.* $200

Gunn, John C. GUNN'S NEW DOMESTIC PHYSICIAN: OR, HOME BOOK OF HEALTH. A COMPLETE GUIDE FOR FAMILIES...Cincinnati, 1864. 1129pp. Full lea. *FYE.* $200

Gunn, Lewis C. and Elizabeth Le Breton Gunn. RECORDS OF A CALIFORNIA FAMILY. JOURNALS AND LETTERS OF LEWIS C. GUNN AND ELIZABETH LE BRETON GUNN...San Diego, 1928. Anna Lee Marston (ed). 1st ed. Orig 1/2 morocco. 2pp ALS from Marston. One of 300 numbered. Howes M324. Inscribed presentation. *GINSBERG.* $300

Gunn, Thom. A GEOGRAPHY. Iowa City: Stone Wall Press, 1966. 1st ed. Ltd to 220 signed. Frontis, red wrappers. Fine. *JAFFE.* $375

Gunn, Thom. AT THE BARRIERS (DORE ALLEY FAIR). (NY): Nadja, (1989). 1st ed. Dec wraps. Mint. *JAFFE.* $125

Gunn, Thom. JACK STRAW'S CASTLE; AND OTHER POEMS. NY: FSG (1976). 1st ed. Fine in dj. *DORN.* $25

Gunn, Thom. THE SENSE OF MOVEMENT. Chicago: Univ of Chicago Press (1959). 1st ed. Stamp. Fine in About VG dj. *DORN.* $125

Gunnison, J.W. THE MORMONS; OR, LATTER DAY SAINTS, IN THE VALLEY OF THE GREAT SALT LAKE: A HIS-TORY....Phila, 1852. 1st ed. 168,(27 ads)pp. Frontis. Orig cl, lt dis-coloration upper spine; emb lib stamps, bkpl w/presentation in-script. Howes G463. *GINSBERG.* $200

Gunst, F. THE MARTYRS OF THE SPANISH INQUISITION. H.C. Kloppenburg (trans). SF: Privately ptd, 1870. 1st ed. Orig peb-bled cl, gilt. VG. Rare. *CONNOLLY & WADE.* $100

Gunther, A. THE REPTILES OF BRITISH INDIA. London: Ray Society, 1864. Tall folio, 452pp+plts. 26 full page b & w litho plts. Full contem reptile lea. NF. *MIKESH.* $550

Gurdjieff, G.I. MEETINGS WITH REMARKABLE MEN. NY: Dut-ton, 1963. 1st Amer ed. Stained, mostly on rear cvr and rear panel of dj, thus only Good. *LOPEZ.* $25

Gurganus, Allan. BLESSED ASSURANCE. Rocky Mount, NC: NC Wesleyan College Press, 1990. 1st ed. One of 2000 signed. Mint. *JAFFE.* $35

Gurganus, Allan. GOOD HELP, BEING A CHAPTER....Rocky Mount, NC: NC Wesleyan College Press, 1988. 1st ed. One of 1000 signed. Wraps. Mint. *JAFFE.* $45

Gurganus, Allan. OLDEST LIVING CONFEDERATE WIDOW TELLS ALL. NY: Knopf, 1989. 1st ed. Fine in dj. Inscribed. *CAPTAIN'S BOOKSHELF.* $60

Gurganus, Allan. OLDEST LIVING CONFEDERATE WIDOW TELLS ALL. A NOVEL. NY: Knopf, 1989. Uncorrected (1st) proof. Pub's marks, front wrapper, ffep, dating on spine. Ptd wraps. VF. *JAFFE.* $150

Gurganus, Allan. OLDEST LIVING CONFEDERATE WIDOW TELLS ALL. NY: Knopf, (1989). 1st ed. Signed. Fine in Fine dj. *UNGER.* $75

Gurganus, Allan. WHITE PEOPLE. STORIES. Ptd yellow wrappers. NY: Knopf, 1991. Uncorrected proof. Mint. *JAFFE.* $75

Gurganus, Allan. WHITE PEOPLE: STORIES AND NOVELLAS. NY: Knopf, 1991. Fine in dj. Signed. *CAPTAIN'S BOOKSHELF.* $50

Gurney, Joseph John. A WINTER IN THE WEST INDIES, DESCRIBED IN FAMILIAR LETTERS TO HENRY CLAY OF KENTUCKY. London: John Murray, 1840. VG in faded edgeworn boards. *PARMER.* $175

Gurney, Joseph John. FAMILIAR LETTERS TO HENRY CLAY OF KENTUCKY, DESCRIBING A WINTER IN THE WEST IN-DIES. NY: Press of Mahlon Day & Co. 1840. 1st Amer ed. 204pp.

Orig. blue cl, blind-stamped, gilt spine; spine extrems bit chipped, some text foxing. *KARMIOLE.* $85

Gustorf, Frederick Julius. THE UNCORRUPTED HEART: JOURNAL AND LETTERS OF FREDERICK JULIUS GUSTORF 1800-1845. Columbia: Univ of Missouri Press, 1969. Fine. *LAURIE.* $25

Guthrie, A.B., Jr. ARFIVE. Houghton Mifflin, 1971. Fine in dj. *AUTHORS OF THE WEST.* $30

Guthrie, A.B., Jr. BIG SKY, FAIR LAND: THE ENVIRONMENTAL ESSAYS. Northland, (1988). 1st ed. David Petersen (ed). Inscribed, signed. New in dj. *AUTHORS OF THE WEST.* $50

Guthrie, A.B., Jr. FAIR LAND, FAIR LAND. Boston: Houghton Mifflin, (1982). 1st ed. Signed. Fine in Fine dj. *UNGER.* $75

Guthrie, A.B., Jr. FAIR LAND, FAIR LAND. Houghton Mifflin, 1982. 1st ed. Ep maps. Boards. Signed. New in dj. *AUTHORS OF THE WEST.* $50

Guthrie, A.B., Jr. MURDER IN THE COTSWOLDS. Houghton Mifflin, 1989. 1st ed. Boards. New in dj. *AUTHORS OF THE WEST.* $20

Guthrie, A.B., Jr. ONCE UPON A POND. Mountain Press Pub, 1973. 1st ed. Boards. Signed. Fine in dj. *AUTHORS OF THE WEST.* $60

Guthrie, A.B., Jr. PLAYING CATCH-UP. Boston: Houghton Mifflin, 1985. 1st ed. Inscribed. VF in dj. *ELSE FINE.* $45

Guthrie, A.B., Jr. PLAYING CATCH-UP. Boston: Houghton Mifflin, (1985). 1st ed. Signed. Fine in Fine dj. *UNGER.* $65

Guthrie, A.B., Jr. THE BIG IT AND OTHER STORIES. Houghton Mifflin, 1960. 1st ed. Fine in dj. *AUTHORS OF THE WEST.* $40

Guthrie, A.B., Jr. THE BIG SKY. NY: Sloane, 1947. 1st ptg. VG in torn dj. *BURCHAM.* $100

Guthrie, A.B., Jr. THE BIG SKY. William Sloane, (1947). 1st ed. Sl browned rectangle on ep, else Fine in Fine dj. *AUTHORS OF THE WEST.* $65

Guthrie, A.B., Jr. THE BLUE HEN'S CHICK. McGraw-Hill, (1965). 1st ed. Fine in dj. *AUTHORS OF THE WEST.* $50

Guthrie, A.B., Jr. THE LAST VALLEY. Houghton Mifflin, 1975. 1st ed. Boards. Fine in dj. *AUTHORS OF THE WEST.* $40

Guthrie, A.B., Jr. THE WAY WEST. NY: Sloane, (1949). 1st ed. Fine in dj (sm tear). Uncommon in this condition. *CAPTAIN'S BOOKSHELF.* $75

Guthrie, A.B., Jr. THE WAY WEST. William Sloane Associates, (1949). 1st, (not the common false "first edition" Bk of the Month Club printing). Fine in fine dj. *AUTHORS OF THE WEST.* $125

Guthrie, A.B., Jr. THESE THOUSAND HILLS. Boston: Houghton Mifflin, 1956. 1st ed. Fine, lt wear to dj extremities. *ELSE FINE.* $35

Guthrie, A.B., Jr. THESE THOUSAND HILLS. Boston: Houghton Mifflin, (1956). 1st ed. Signed. Fine in VG dj w/edge creases. *UNGER.* $100

Guthrie, A.B., Jr. WILD PITCH. Houghton Mifflin, 1973. 1st ed. Fine in dj. *AUTHORS OF THE WEST.* $40

Guthrie, C.C. BLOOD VESSEL SURGERY AND ITS APPLICATIONS (WITH) THE CONTRIBUTIONS OF DR. C.C. GUTHRIE TQ VASCULAR SURGERY by SAMUEL HARBISON AND BERNARD FISHER. Pittsburgh, 1959. 1st ed. thus. Dj. Scarce. *FYE.* $100

Guthrie, Douglas. A HISTORY OF MEDICINE. Phila, 1946. 1st ed. *FYE.* $50

Guthrie, George. COMMENTARIES ON THE SURGERY OF THE WAR IN PORTUGAL, SPAIN, FRANCE, AND THE NETHERLANDS, FROM THE BATTLE OF ROLICA, IN 1808, TO THAT OF WATERLOO, IN 1815...REVISED TO OCTOBER 1855. Phila, 1862. 1st Amer ed. 614pp. Fine. *FYE.* $350

Guthrie, George. ON DISEASES AND INJURIES OF ARTERIES, WITH THE OPERATIONS REQUIRED FOR THEIR CURE. London, 1830. 1st ed. 416pp. Cloth-backed boards. Lib stamp on title, o/w VG. Quite rare. *FYE.* $750

Guthrie, Leonard. FUNCTIONAL NERVOUS DISORDERS IN CHILDHOOD. London, 1907. 1st ed. *FYE.* $75

Guthrie, Lord. 'CUMMY' THE NURSE OF ROBERT LOUIS STEVENSON. Edinburgh, Otto Schulze & C. 1913. 1st ed. In original shipping box (box is broken). VG. *OREGON.* $45

Guthrie, W. (trans). QUINTILLIAN'S INSTITUTES OF ELOQUENCE. London: Dutton et al, 1805. 2 vols. 3/4 lea over brwn cl bds. Bindings bruised, but firm. *OLD LONDON.* $225

Gutkind, Lee. THE BEST SEAT IN BASEBALL, BUT YOU HAVE TO STAND. Dial, 1975. 1st ed. VG+ in Fine dj. *PLAPINGER.* $40

Guttmann, O. BLASTING: A HANDBOOK FOR THE USE OF ENGINEERS....London: Griffin, 1906. 2nd ed. Newly rebound, new marbled end leaves, paper label. Good+. *BOOKCELL.* $35

GUY RIVERS. (By William Gilmore Simms.) NY: Harper & Bros, 1834. 2 vols, 1st ed. 278; 321,(2)pp. Orig cl w/paper spine labels. Some lt rubbing, spotting, and foxing, cl separating at bottom of hinges, else untrimmed, VG set. Apparently a made-up set, with vol I sl taller than vol II. *CHAPEL HILL.* $375

Guzman, German. CAMILO TORRES. NY: Sheed & Ward, (1969). Trans John D. Ring. Dj chipped, torn. *AKA.* $25

Guzman, Martin Luis. MEMOIRS OF PANCHO VILLA. Austin: Univ. of Texas Press, 1965. 1st ed. Virginia H. Taylor (trans). Grey cl. Black/orange spine titles. Some soiling, else VG in VG dj. *PARMER.* $45

Gwin, Laura (McClanahan), Mrs. MISCELLANEOUS POEMS. (Greenville, SC: G.E. Elford, printer, 1860). 1st ed. 218pp. Contemp 1/2 calf w/raised bands. Lib bkpl, blindstamp, front flyleaf lacking, but Good. *CHAPEL HILL.* $175

Gysin, Brion. THE PROCESS. GC: Doubleday, 1969. 1st ed. NF in dj (lightly spine-faded; mild edgewear but still About VG). *LOPEZ.* $100

H

H(oskyns), C(handos) W(ren). TALPA....Buffalo: Danforth, Hawley, 1854. 1st US ed. VG. *SECOND LIFE.* $35

Haagensen, C.D. DISEASES OF THE BREAST. Phila, 1956. 1st ed. 400+ figures. *FYE.* $100

Haardt, Georges-Mari and Audouin-Dubreuil, Louis. THE BLACK JOURNEY. NY: Cosmopolitan, 1927. 1st ed. NF in NF dj. *GREAT EPIC.* $110

Haas, Ernst. THE GRAND CANYON. NY: Time Life, 1972. 1st ed. VG w/o dj. *SMITH.* $40

Haas, Irvin. CITADELS, RAMPARTS & STOCKADES, AMERICA'S HISTORIC FORTS. NY, (1979). 1st ed. 211pp. VG+ in dj. *PRATT.* $17.50

Haber, Heinz. MAN IN SPACE. Bobbs-Merrill, Indianapolis, 1953, 1st ed. VG in worn, chipped dj. *KNOLLWOOD.* $25

Haberly, Loyd. PURSUIT OF THE HORIZON. NY, 1948. 1st ed. Parts of dj attached to front pastedown, fly & blank part of title-page. VG. *DIAMOND.* $25

Haberly, Loyd. PURSUIT OF THE HORIZON: A LIFE OF GEORGE CATLIN....NY: Macmillan, 1948. 1st ed. 17 full-pg plts. NF in sl worn dj. *LAURIE.* $50

Haberly, Loyd. THE FOURTH OF JULY: OR, AN OREGON ORATOR. (St. Louis: The Haberly Press, 1942). Ltd to 350. Presentation copy. Spine extrems bit rubbed. *KARMIOLE*. $125

Habersham, Alexander Wylly. THE NORTH PACIFIC SURVEYING AND EXPLORING EXPEDITION; OR, MY LAST CRUISE.... Phila: Lippincott, 1857. 1st ed. Frontis, engr title, 507,(1 blank, 4 ad)pp. 28 plts. Modern cl, orig front, back cvrs preserved and laid down, 1st few leaves w/dark stain. *LEFKOWICZ*. $175

Hachisuka, M. THE DODO AND KINDRED BIRDS, OR THE EXTINCT BIRDS OF THE MASCARENE ISLANDS. London, 1953. 22 plts (11 colored). Ltd to 485 numbered. Dj, some spotting, chipping. *SUTTON*. $550

Hackenbroch, Yvonne. CHELSEA AND OTHER ENGLISH PORCELAIN...IRWIN UNTERMYER COLLECTION. MA: Harvard Univ Press, 1957. VG in dj. *BACKROOM*. $125

Hackett, L.W. MALARIA IN EUROPE, AN ECOLOGICAL STUDY. Oxford, 1937. *FYE*. $40

Hader, Berta & Elmer. BILLY BUTTER. Macmillan, 1936. 1st ed. 91pp. Illus. Cvr has light soil. VG. *BEBBAH*. $35

Hadfield, M., R. Harling and L. Highton. BRITISH GARDENERS, A BIOGRAPHICAL DICTIONARY. London, 1980. *SUTTON*. $35

Hadlock, Adah. MY LIFE IN THE SOUTHWEST: THE MEMOIR OF ADAH HADLOCK. El Paso: Texas Western Press, 1969. Fine in dj. *LAURIE*. $30

Haeger, Knut. THE ILLUSTRATED HISTORY OF SURGERY. NY, 1988. 200 illus. Dj. *FYE*. $30

Hafen, LeRoy and W.J. Ghent. BROKEN HAND. THE LIFE OF THOMAS FITZPATRICK....Denver: Old West Pub, 1931. 1st ed. Frontis, 8 plts. Fine. Howes H10. *OREGON*. $350

Hafen, LeRoy R. BROKEN HAND. THE LIFE OF THOMAS FITZPATRICK: MOUNTAIN MAN, GUIDE AND INDIAN AGENT. Denver: Old West Publishing Co, (1973). One of 200 numbered of deluxe ed, specially bound and signed. Fine in slipcase. *LAURIE*. $200

Hafen, Leroy and Francis M. Young. FORT LARAMIE AND THE PAGEANT OF THE WEST, 1834-1890. Glendale: The Arthur C. Clark Co, 1938. Blue cl. Inscrip by Young. Wear to spine. *PARMER*. $195

Hafen, LeRoy and Francis Young. FORT LARAMIE AND THE PAGEANT OF THE WEST, 1834-1890. A.H. Clark Co, 1938. 1st ed. Frontis, 12 plts, fldg map. Rear board bent o/w Fine. Uncut, unopened. *OREGON*. $100

Hafen, LeRoy and R. Ann W. (eds). POWDER RIVER CAMPAIGNS AND SAWYERS EXPEDITION OF 1865: A DOCUMENTARY ACCOUNT...."The Far West and the Rockies Historical Series: 1820-1875," volume XII. Glendale: Arthur H. Clark, 1961. 1st ed. NF. *LAURIE*. $50

Hafen, LeRoy (ed). RUXTON OF THE ROCKIES. Univ of OK Press, 1950. 1st ed. Fine in Fine dj. *VARNER*. $30

Hafen, LeRoy (ed). RUXTON OF THE ROCKIES. Univ of OK, (1950). 1st ed. Fine in Fine dj. *OREGON*. $45

Hafen, LeRoy. THE OVERLAND MAIL 1849-1869. A.H. Clark, 1926. 1st ed. Ex-lib, spine marking, pocket removed back fly leaf. No other markings. NF. *VARNER*. $145

Hafendorfer, Kenneth A. PERRYVILLE, BATTLE FOR KENTUCKY. Louisville, (1981). 1st ed. Fine in dj. *PRATT*. $50

Hagedorn, H. ROOSEVELT IN THE BADLANDS. Boston & NY: Houghton Mifflin, 1921. Photos, plts. Dec cl. VG. *MIKESH*. $27.50

Hagedorn, Herman. ROOSEVELT IN THE BADLANDS. Boston/NY for the Roosevelt Memorial Assoc: Houghton Mifflin Co, 1921. 1st ed. The true 1st ed w/gold medallion on the front. May be an ex-lib (stain on spine heel). No interior marks (residue mark, tear to back blank page). Scarce w/map eps and index. Light wear to edges. VG. *BACKMAN*. $25

Hagedorn, Hermann. ROOSEVELT IN THE BADLANDS. Houghton Mifflin, 1921. 1st ed. 52 photos on 31 plts. Spine lightly faded. VG. *OREGON*. $45

Hagel, Bob. GAME LOADS AND PRACTICAL BALLISTICS FOR THE AMERICAN HUNTER. NY: Knopf, 1978. Stated 1st ed. Fine in Fine dj. *BACKMAN*. $25

Hagenbeck, Carl. BEASTS AND MEN. London: Longmans, Green and Co., 1912. Dec cloth, gilt; light soiling and wear, inked stamp to one leaf; text VG; illus. *DRAMATIS PERSONAE*. $75

Hager, Anna Marie and Everett. THE HISTORICAL SOCIETY OF SOUTHERN CALIFORNIA BIBLIOGRAPHY OF ALL PUBLISHED WORKS 1884-1957. 1958. 1st ed. Signed by Everett. Fine in Fine dj. *BOOK MARKET*. $35

Hagerbaumer, D. and S. Lehman. SELECTED AMERICAN GAME BIRDS. Caldwell, 1972. 26 colored plts. *SUTTON*. $85

Haggard, H. Rider. ALLAN AND THE ICE GODS. Doubleday, 1927. 1st US ed. VG. *MADLE*. $75

Haggard, H. Rider. ALLAN QUATERMAIN. Chicago, (1897). Reprint. Yellow wrappers. Cheap paper browned, spine ends shallowly chipped, light cover soil. VG. *McCLINTOCK*. $30

Haggard, H. Rider. ALLAN QUATERMAINE. London: Longman's, Green, 1887. 1st ed. Minor wear, faded spine. VG. *LAME DUCK*. $450

Haggard, H. Rider. AYESHA, THE RETURN OF SHE. London: Ward, Lock, & Co, 1905. 1st UK ed. 32 b/w plts. Eps browned; sl foxing pp margins. VG+. *BERNARD*. $150

Haggard, H. Rider. BEATRICE. London: Longmans, Green & Co, 1890. 1st UK ed. Bkpl, blue cl faded to grn; spine sl worn, browned, corner tips sl bent, else VG. *BERNARD*. $75

Haggard, H. Rider. BELSHAZAR. Doubleday, 1930. 1st US ed. Near VG. *MADLE*. $25

Haggard, H. Rider. CLEOPATRA. London, 1889. VG. *MADLE*. $95

Haggard, H. Rider. FINISHED. Longman's, 1917. 1st US ed. Good+. *MADLE*. $45

Haggard, H. Rider. FINISHED. MacDonald, 1962. Fine in dj. *MADLE*. $20

Haggard, H. Rider. HEU-HEU. Doubleday, 1924. 1st US ed. VG. *MADLE*. $30

Haggard, H. Rider. KING SOLOMON'S MINES. Imprint Society, 1970. One of 1950 numbered, boxed. Fine. *MADLE*. $20

Haggard, H. Rider. MARY OF MARION'S ISLE. London, 1929. VG. *MADLE*. $40

Haggard, H. Rider. MIAWA'S REVENGE. Chicago & NY, n.d. Reprint. White wraps featuring a color painting on front cover. Possible pirate copy. Cheap paper browned, spine ends shallowly chipped in wraps. Close to Fine. *McCLINTOCK*. $35

Haggard, H. Rider. NADA THE LILY. London, 1897. 1st ed. VG. *MADLE*. $100

Haggard, H. Rider. PEARL MAIDEN. Longman's, 1903. VG. *MADLE*. $30

Haggard, H. Rider. QUEEN OF THE DAWN. Doubleday, 1925. 1st US ed. VG. *MADLE*. $75

Haggard, H. Rider. QUEEN OF THE DAWN: A LOVE TALE OF OLD EGYPT. GC: Doubleday Page, 1925. 1st Amer ed. Binding cracked, name else Good to VG. *OTHER WORLDS*. $20

Haggard, H. Rider. SHE (A HISTORY OF ADVENTURE). London: Longmans, Green & Co, 1887. 1st UK ed. Repaired nicks top spine edge, VG+. *BERNARD*. $225

Haggard, H. Rider. SHE. London: Longman's, Green, 1887. 1st ed. Joints sl shaken, minor wear to spine. VG. *LAME DUCK*. $600

Haggard, H. Rider. THE HOLY FLOWER. London, n.d. NF in chipped dj *MADLE.* $50

Haggard, H. Rider. THE SPIRIT OF BAMBATSE. Longman's, 1906. 1st ed. Near VG. *MADLE.* $50

Haggard, H. Rider. THE WITCH'S HEAD. NY: Lovell, (1887). Lovell's Library No. 876. Pict wrappers. Spine heel flaking, tiny edge tear to rear, else VG+. *OTHER WORLDS.* $75

Haggard, H. Rider. THE WIZARD. Longman's, 1896, 1st US ed. VG. *MADLE.* $100

Haggard, H. Rider. THE YELLOW GOD. Cupples & Leon, 1908. 1st US ed. Near VG. *MADLE.* $75

Haggard, H. Rider. WISDOM'S DAUGHTER. Doubleday, 1923. 1st US ed. VG. *MADLE.* $75

Haggard, H. Rider. WORLD'S DESIRE. London, 1890. Spine worn, else VG. *MADLE.* $35

Haggard, Howard. THE DOCTOR IN HISTORY. New Haven, 1934. *FYE.* $50

Hague, Eleanor. LATIN AMERICAN MUSIC. Santa Ana: The Fine Arts Press, 1934. Hand-colored frontis. Presentation. Red cl. Scarce. Only 400 ptd. *KARMIOLE.* $150

Hague, Harlan. THE ROAD TO CALIFORNIA. THE SEARCH FOR A SOUTHERN OVERLAND ROUTE, 1540-1848. A.H. Clark, 1978. 1st ed. VF. *OREGON.* $50

Haig-Brown, Roderick L. ALISON'S FISHING BIRDS. Vancouver, BC: Colophon, 1980. Ltd ed. #343/500. Fine. *MIKESH.* $200

Haig-Brown, Roderick L. FISHERMAN'S FALL. William Morrow, 1964. 1st ed. Boards. Small scuff. VG+ in dj. *AUTHORS OF THE WEST.* $50

Haig-Brown, Roderick L. FISHERMAN'S SPRING. NY, (1975). New ed. Mint in dj. *ARTIS.* $25

Haig-Brown, Roderick L. FISHERMAN'S SUMMER. NY, (1975). New ed. Mint in dj. *ARTIS.* $25

Haig-Brown, Roderick L. FISHERMAN'S SUMMER. William Morrow, 1959. 1st ed. Dec cover. Fine in dj. *AUTHORS OF THE WEST.* $60

Haig-Brown, Roderick L. MEASURE OF THE YEAR. William Morrow, 1950. 1st ed. Dec cvr. Feps browned. Fine in dj. *AUTHORS OF THE WEST.* $60

Haig-Brown, Roderick L. PANTHER. London: Collins, (1946). Illus. NF in Good dj. *MIKESH.* $17.50

Haig-Brown, Roderick L. POOL AND RAPID: THE STORY OF A RIVER. London: Jonathan Cape, (1936). 1st JC printing. Signed. VG+. *AUTHORS OF THE WEST.* $35

Haig-Brown, Roderick L. RETURN TO THE RIVER: A STORY OF THE CHINOOK RUN. Morrow, 1941. 1st ed. Review copy, letter laid in. Fine in dj. *AUTHORS OF THE WEST.* $75

Haight, Anne Lyon (ed). PORTRAIT OF LATIN AMERICA AS SEEN BY HER PRINT MAKERS. NY: Hastings House, (1946). 1st ed. Good in chipped dj. *SILVER.* $30

Hail, Marshall. KNIGHT IN THE SUN: HARPER B. LEE....Boston: Little, Brown, 1962. 1st ed. Fine in About Fine dj. *CONNOLLY & WADE.* $35

Haile, Berard. BEAUTYWAY: A Navaho Ceremonial...Ed by Leland C. Wyman. "Bollingen Series LIII." (NY): Pantheon Press. (1957). 1st ed. xii,218pp. 16 plates. Booklet in rear pocket. Dj. *KARMIOLE.* $150

Haines, Anna. HEALTH WORK IN SOVIET RUSSIA. NY, 1928. 1st ed. Scarce. *FYE.* $40

Haines, Francis (ed). THE SNAKE COUNTRY EXPEDITION OF 1830-1831....Univ of OK Press, 1971. 1st ed. Fine in Fine dj. *VARNER.* $25

Haines, Francis. APPALOOSA: THE SPOTTED HORSE IN ART AND HISTORY. Univ of Texas, 1963. 1st ed. Signed. Fine in Fine dj. *VARNER.* $60

Haines, Francis. THE NEZ PERCES, TRIBESMEN....Univ of OK, (1955). 1st ed. 16 plts. VG in Good+ dj. *OREGON.* $60

Haines, John & Stafford. NORTH BY WEST: A COLLECTION OF POETRY. Spring Rain Press, (1975). 1st ed. Pict cvr. Softbound. Fine. *AUTHORS OF THE WEST.* $25

Haining, Peter (ed). THE FANTASTIC PULPS. London: Gollancz, 1975. 1st ed. NF in dj w/spot staining to rear edge. *OTHER WORLDS.* $30

Haining, Peter. MOVABLE BOOKS. AN ILLUSTRATED HISTORY. New English Library, 1979. VG in VG dj. Pop-up bk. *BOOKFINDERS INTL.* $100

Haining, Peter. THE SHERLOCK HOLMES SCRAPBOOK. NY: Potter, 1974. 1st Amer ed. Fine in NF dj. *SILVER DOOR.* $30

Haj, Fareed. DISABILITY IN ANTIQUITY. NY, 1970. 1st ed. Dj. *FYE.* $45

Hakewell, James. A PICTURESQUE TOUR OF ITALY...1816—1817. London: Murray, 1820. 1st ed. 63 full-pg engr views and plans. Some foxed. VG, bound in early 3/4 lea calf and marble boards. *SECOND LIFE.* $600

Hakola, John (ed). FRONTIER OMNIBUS. MT State Univ, (1962). 1st ed. VF. *OREGON.* $45

Halberstam, David. THE NOBLEST ROMAN. Boston, 1961. 1st ed, 1st bk. Dj sl chipped at spine, light name/address stamp, else VG+. *PETTLER.* $25

Haldane, Charlotte. I BRING NOT PEACE. London: Chatto & Windus, 1932. 1st ed. 313pp. Blue cl, dj. Mint. Rare. *WEBER.* $250

Haldane, J.B.S. THE PHILOSOPHY OF A BIOLOGIST. Oxford, 1935. 1st ed. *FYE.* $35

Haldane, James. TREKKING AMONG MOROCCAN TRIBES. London: Pickering & Inglis Ltd., 1948. 1st ed. Fine in NF dj. *GREAT EPIC.* $35

Haldeman, Joe W. WAR YEAR. NY: Holt Rinehart Winston, (1972). Stated 1st ed. Bottom corner of front flap clipped. Signed. Fine in NF dj. *AKA.* $150

Haldeman, Joe. MINDBRIDGE. St Martins, 1976. 1st ed. Fine in dj. Signed. *MADLE.* $50

Haldeman, Joe. THE FOREVER WAR. St Martins, 1974. 1st ed. Fine in dj. Signed. *MADLE.* $75

Hale, Annie. THESE CULTS: AN ANALYSIS OF THE FOIBLES OF DR. MORRIS FISHBEIN'S "MEDICAL FOLLIES" AND AN INDICTMENT OF MEDICAL PRACTICE IN GENERAL. NY, 1926. 1st ed. *FYE.* $75

Hale, Edward E. KANSAS AND NEBRASKA: THE HISTORY, GEOGRAPHICAL AND PHYSICAL CHARACTERISTICS, AND POLITICAL POSITION OF THOSE TERRITORIES; AN ACCOUNT.... Boston: Phillips, Sampson, 1854. 1st ed. Map missing, photocopy laid in. Wear at extremities, some foxing, still Good. *LAURIE.* $150

Hale, Edward Everett. HISTORY OF THE UNITED STATES, WRITTEN FOR THE CHAUTAQUA READING CIRCLES. NY: Chautaqua, 1887. 1st ed. Tipped-in US map frontis. VG. *CONNOLLY & WADE.* $35

Hale, Edward Everett. MEMORIES OF A HUNDRED YEARS. Macmillan, 1902. 2 vols. 1st ed. Fine. *OREGON.* $60

Hale, Edward Everett. THE MAN WITHOUT A COUNTRY. Boston: J. Stilman Smith & Co., 1896. 8vo, 45pp, (7)pp ads. Later ed. Orig white cl w/Amer flag ptd in red and blue on front cvr. Gift inscript, faintest of soiling, but Fine. Signed. *CHAPEL HILL.* $95

Hale, Edward Everett. THE MAN WITHOUT A COUNTRY. Boston: Little, Brown, 1903. Orig pict cl. NF. CONNOLLY & WADE. $30

Hale, Edward Everett. THE MAN WITHOUT A COUNTRY. Intro Carl Van Doren, illus Edward A. Wilson. NY: LEC, 1936. 1/1500, signed by Wilson. Bound in calf, w/illus stenciled by hand. In box. SECOND LIFE. $35

Hale, Lucretia Peabody. FAGOTS FOR THE FIRESIDE. Boston: Ticknor and Co, 1889. 1st ed. Spine faded. VG. SECOND LIFE. $35

Hale, Mrs. Sarah J. NORTHWOOD; A TALE OF NEW ENGLAND. Boston: Bowles & Dearborn, 1827. 1st ed. 258,242pp. Leather backed marble boards, hinges loose, lt water stain. Good, tight. BAL 6776. SECOND LIFE. $325

Hale, P.M. THE WOODS AND TIMBERS OF NORTH CAROLINA. Raleigh, 1883. Fold-out map. Orig gilt-stamped cl, spine ends frayed. Ex-lib. SUTTON. $55

Hale, Rev. E.E. and Susan Hale. A FLIGHT THROUGH MEXICO. Boston: Lothrop, (1886). 1st ed. Pict cl w/gilt lettering. Edges rubbed, front hinge broken; contents VG. SILVER. $35

Hale, S.J. FLORA'S INTERPRETER....Boston, 1842. 11th ed. 2 hand-colored plts. 262pp,(2). Orig gilt dec cl, some wear at extrems; foxed, sm ink spot edges few pp. SUTTON. $55

Hale, Will (pseud of William Hale Stone). TWENTY-FOUR YEARS A COWBOY & RANCHMAN IN SOUTHERN TEXAS & OLD MEXICO. Norman: Univ of OK Press, (1959). 1st ptg of new ed. Fine in plastic dj. BOHLING. $35

Hales, John G. SURVEY OF BOSTON AND ITS VICINITY. Boston: Ezra Lincoln, 1821. Fldg map, orig boards w/ptd label. Spine chipped, front cover detached, nice interior w/foxing; mostly un-opened. BOHLING. $50

Hales, Philip. THE MADONNA. Boston: Bates and Guild, 1908. 1st ed. 20 plts. VG+. AARD. $25

Haley, Alex. ROOTS. GC, 1976. 1st ed. VG in dj. PETTLER. $45

Haley, Alex. ROOTS. GC: Doubleday, (1976). 1st ed. One of 500 numbered, signed. Fine in full lea in pub's slipcase. UNGER. $300

Haley, Alex. ROOTS. GC: Doubleday, 1976. 1st ed. NF in dj. LOPEZ. $150

Haley, J. Evetts et al. SOME SOUTHWESTERN TRAILS. El Paso: Carl Hertzog, 1948. Bound in full cl. Some chipping to paper label on spine of box, o/w NF in slipcase. LAURIE. $250

Haley, J. Evetts et al. SOME SOUTHWESTERN TRAILS. El Paso: Carl Hertzog, 1948. (30)pp. Frontis, illus, Harold D. Bugbee. Beige and br pict cl w/slight fading on spine. Slipcase with slight wear only at corners. Scarce. CONNOLLY & WADE. $375

Haley, J. Evetts. CHARLES GOODNIGHT, COWMAN AND PLAINSMAN. Boston: Houghton Mifflin Co, 1936. 1st ed. Tan cl. Illus. H.D. Bugbee, map. Spine mottled, worn, text clean. Howes H36. PARMER. $200

Haley, J. Evetts. EARL VANDALE ON THE TRAIL OF TEXAS BOOKS. Canyon, TX, 1965. Ptd by Carl Hertzog. Ltd to 500. VF. GIBBS. $150

Haley, J. Evetts. EARL VANDALE ON THE TRAIL OF TEXAS BOOKS. Canyon: Palo Duro Press, 1965. One of 500. Designed by Carl Hertzog, w/presentation signed by him. Bound in dusty red cl, stamped in gilt. Fine. LAURIE. $200

Haley, J. Evetts. ERLE P. HALLIBURTON, GENIUS WITH CE-MENT. Duncan: (Halliburton Oil Well Cementing Co.), 1959. Designed by Carl Hertzog, w/presentation signed by him. One of 2,000 bound in grey pict cl. Fine. LAURIE. $50

Haley, J. Evetts. ERLE P. HALLIBURTON, GENIUS WITH CE-MENT. Duncan, (Halliburton Oil Well Cementing Co.), 1959. Designed by Carl Hertzog. One of 8,000 bound in pict wraps. VG. LAURIE. $25

Haley, J. Evetts. F. REAUGH: MAN AND ARTIST. El Paso: Carl Hertzog, 1960. 7 full-color plts. Designed by Carl Hertzog w/dedica-tion signed by him. VG in wraps. LAURIE. $40

Haley, J. Evetts. FOCUS ON THE FRONTIER. Amarillo: Shamrock Oil and Gas Corp., 1957. Fine. LAURIE. $40

Haley, J. Evetts. LIFE ON THE TEXAS RANGE. Univ of Texas, 1952. 1st ed. Fine in NF slipcase. VARNER. $150

Haley, J. Evetts. SOME SOUTHWESTERN TRAILS. San Angelo, TX: San Angelo Standard-Times, 1948. Illus Harold Bugbee. Designed and ptd by Carl Hertzog. Inscribed, signed twice. VG. GIBBS. $175

Haley, J. Evetts. THE HERALDRY OF THE RANGE: SOME SOUTHWESTERN BRANDS. Canyon: Panhandle Plains Hist Soc, 1949. Fine in dj. LAURIE. $500

Haley, J. Evetts. THE XIT RANCH OF TEXAS, AND THE EARLY DAYS OF THE LLANO ESTACADO. Chicago: The Lakeside Press, 1929. 261 pp. 1st ed. Dec cl, teg. Fldg map. Fine. Howes H39 GIBBS. $475

Haley, J. Evetts. THE XIT RANCH OF TEXAS. Univ of Oklahoma Press, 1953. New ed. 1st ptg. Fine in Fine dj. VARNER. $40

Haley, John W. THE REBEL YELL AND YANKEE HURRAH, THE CIVIL WAR JOURNAL OF A MAINE VOLUNTEER. Camden, Maine, (1985). Ed by Ruth L. Silliker. 1st ed. Light dj wear o/w Fine. PRATT. $22.50

HALEY'S COMET. London, 1985. Patrick Moore and Heather Couper. Pop-up bk. BOOKFINDERS INTL. $30

HALF-HOURS WITH THE CHILDREN. Phila and Baltimore: Fisher & Brother, n.d. (ca. 1850). 3" high. 192pp. Gilt-stamped purple cl. Lacks ffep. SCHOYER'S. $30

Hall, Adam. THE SCORPION SIGNAL. GC: Doubleday, 1980. 1st Amer ed. Fine in dj. MORDIDA. $20

Hall, Adelaide S. TWO WOMEN ABROAD. Chicago and Phila: Monarch Book Co, 1897. Grey cl stamped in gilt and black, some-what soiled. Faintly foxed. SCHOYER'S. $45

Hall, Ansel F. (ed, comp). HANDBOOK OF YOSEMITE NATION-AL PARK. NY: Putnam, 1921. 1st ed. 26 full-pg b/w photo plts, fldg map of Yosemite Valley. Grn pict cl. VF. CONNOLLY & WADE. $75

Hall, Basil. FRAGMENTS OF VOYAGES & TRAVELS. Edin-burgh: Robert Cadell/London: Whittaker, Treacher, & Co, 1831. 1st ed of 1st series. 3 vols. 3/4 grn leather & marbled boards, sl rubbed. Newly rebacked w/new grn leather spines, titled & ruled in gilt, marbled edges and eps. Edges of 1st 10 pgs of vol 1 stained; minor flaws. Engr title pg each vol. NF. BLUE MOUNTAIN. $250

Hall, Bert L. ROUND-UP YEARS. OLD MUDDY TO BLACK HILLS. Pierre, 1954. 1st ed. Signed. Fine; 1884 round-up article laid in as issued. VARNER. $175

Hall, Carroll D. DONNER MISCELLANY. SF: The Bk Club of CA. 1947. Ed ltd to 350. KARMIOLE. $250

Hall, Charles F. NARRATIVE OF THE SECOND ARCTIC EX-PEDITION MADE BY CHARLES F. HALL. Washington, DC: GPO, 1879. 5,1,644pp. Frontis, 7 plates, 20 maps (8 fldg; 1 Circum-polar Map w/explorers' name in back pocket). Orig pict gilt dec grn cl w\some shelf wear and rubbing. Good. BLUE DRAGON. $135

Hall, Charles Francis. ARCTIC RESEARCHES AND LIFE AMONG THE ESQUIMAUX, BEING THE NARRATIVE OF AN EXPEDITION IN SEARCH OF SIR JOHN FRANKLIN, IN THE YEARS 1860, 1861, AND 1862. NY: Harper & Bros., 1865. 1st Amer ed. Fldg map. Wear to corners, spine. Bkpls, spine faded, map repaired. PARMER. $295

Hall, D.G. THE BLOWFLIES OF NORTH AMERICA. N.p., 1948. 51 plts. Inscribed, signed. SUTTON. $40

Hall, David and Abner Levin. THE DISC BOOK. NY: Long Player Publications, (1955). 446pp + addenda, index, + ads. Dj scuffed at extremities with tear, chips. *AKA.* $30

Hall, Donald. SEASONS AT EAGLE POND. NY: Ticknor & Fields, 1987. Advance review w/promo folder, photo laid in. Signed. Fine in slipcase, as issued. *LOPEZ.* $60

Hall, Donald. THE ONE DAY: A POEM IN THREE PARTS. NY: Ticknor & Fields (1988). Uncorrected proof. Fine in wraps. *DORN.* $30

Hall, Gertrude. ALLEGRETTO. Roberts Brothers, 1894. 12mo. 111pp. Illus by Oliver Herford. Sunning of spine. W/dec cvrs. VG+. *BEBBAH.* $50

Hall, H.R. A SEASON'S WORK AT UR AL'UBAID, ABU SHAHRAIN (ERIDU), AND ELSEWHERE. London: Methuen, (1930). Frontis, 276 illus and maps. Fine. *ARCHAEOLOGIA.* $125

Hall, Henry and James Hall. CAYUGA IN THE FIELD. Auburn, NY, 1873. 1st ed. Fine. Rare. *McGOWAN.* $450

Hall, Henry Marion. THE RUFFED GROUSE. NY: Oxford Univ Press, 1946. 1st ed. VG. *BACKMAN.* $25

Hall, Henry Marion. WOODCOCK WAYS. NY: Oxford Univ Press, 1946. 1st ed. VG in worn dj. *BACKMAN.* $35.50

Hall, Henry Marion. WOODCOCK WAYS. NY, 1946. 8 colored plts. Dj. *SUTTON.* $30

Hall, J.K. (ed). ONE HUNDRED YEARS OF AMERICAN PSYCHIATRY. NY, 1944. 1st ed. *FYE.* $125

Hall, J.K. (ed). ONE HUNDRED YEARS OF AMERICAN PSYCHIATRY. NY, 1947. 1st ed. Ex-lib. *FYE.* $75

Hall, James and J.D. Whitney. REPORT ON THE GEOLOGICAL SURVEY OF THE STATE OF IOWA: EMBRACING THE RESULTS OF INVESTIGATIONS MADE DURING PORTIONS OF THE YEARS 1855, 56 & 57. Vol. I, Part I: Geology. 3 fldg maps (1 color, 2 repaired). Rebacked w/orig backstrip; bkpl removed, o/w Good. *DIAMOND.* $75

Hall, James Norman and Nordhoff, Charles Bernard. FAERY LANDS OF THE SOUTH SEAS. GC: Garden City Pub Co, 1926. NF in VG dj. *GREAT EPIC.* $35

Hall, James Norman. DOCTOR DOGBODY'S LEG. Two-toned cl w/ptd label. (NY): Redbook Magazine, 1939. 1st ed. Ltd to 1500. VG. *JAFFE.* $35

Hall, James W. BONES OF CORAL. NY: Alfred A. Knopf, 1991. 1st ed. Advance reading copy. VF in pict wrappers. *MORDIDA.* $30

Hall, James W. BONES OF CORAL. NY: Alfred A. Knopf, 1991. 1st ed. Signed. VF in dj. *MORDIDA.* $27.50

Hall, James W. TROPICAL FREEZE. NY: W.W. Norton, 1989. 1st ed. VF in dj. *MORDIDA.* $30

Hall, James W. UNDER COVER OF DAYLIGHT. NY: Norton, (1987). 1st ed. Fine in Fine dj. *UNGER.* $35

Hall, James. STATISTICS OF THE WEST, AT THE CLOSE OF THE YEAR 1836. Cincinnati: J.A. James, 1836. 1st ed. Cover wear, tears at head and heel of spine, front hinge weak. Howes H-79. *LAURIE.* $60

Hall, Joseph. THE DISCOVERY OF A NEW WORLD (MUNDUS ALTER ET IDEM). Cambridge: Harvard Univ Press, 1937. Huntington Brown (ed). Frontis, map, 9 plts. Lightly sunned spine, else VG. *BLUE DRAGON.* $40

Hall, Marshall. LECTURES ON THE NERVOUS SYSTEM AND ITS DISEASES. Phila, 1836. 1st Amer ed. 240pp. Recent 1/4 leather, new eps. Scattered foxing as usual. *FYE.* $200

Hall, Oakley. THE CORPUS OF JOE BAILEY. NY: Viking, 1953. 1st ed. Bkpl. VG+ in dj. *LAME DUCK.* $100

Halle, Fannina. WOMEN IN THE SOVIET EAST. NY: Dutton, 1938. 1st US ed. M. Green (trans). Fine- in VG dj. *AARD.* $35

Halle, Louis. RIVER OF RUINS. NY: Henry Holt, (1941). 1st ed. 16 b/w plts. Good in dj. *SILVER.* $25

Hallenbeck, Cleve. LAND OF THE CONQUISTADORES. Caldwell: Caxton, 1950. Fldg map. 1st ed. VG in VG dj. *OREGON.* $60

Hallenbeck, Cleve. THE JOURNEY OF FRAY MARCOS DE NIZA. Dallas: Univ Press, 1949. One of 1,065. Dj chipped and worn at extremities, bk Fine. Uncut. *LAURIE.* $200

Haller, John and Robin. THE PHYSICIAN AND SEXUALITY IN VICTORIAN AMERICA. Chicago, 1974. 1st ed. Dj. *FYE.* $35

Halliburton, Richard. NEW WORLDS TO CONQUER. Indianapolis: Bobbs-Merrill, (1929). 1st ed. Inscribed. Little cover marking, o/w VG in chipped and repaired dj. *DIAMOND.* $25

Halliburton, Richard. RICHARD HALLIBURTON'S COMPLETE BOOK OF MARVELS. Indianapolis, 1941. 1st ed thus. Practically as new, in Good dj. *BOND.* $37.50

Halliday, Brett. DIE LIKE A DOG. NY: Torquil, 1959. 1st ed. Inscribed. Stains on bottom edge o/w VG in dj w/minor wear. *MORDIDA.* $30

Hallock, Charles. CAMP LIFE IN FLORIDA; A HANDBOOK FOR SPORTSMEN AND SETTLERS. NY: Forest and Stream Publishing Company, 1876. *HUDSON.* $85

Hallock, Charles. THE SPORTSMAN'S GAZETTEER AND GENERAL GUIDE. NY: Forest and Stream Publishing Company, Orange Judd Company, 1879. 5th ed. 2 fldg maps (lacks map from pocket). *HUDSON.* $95

Halper, Albert. FOUNDRY. NY: Viking, 1934. 3rd prtg. Dj w/pieces missing, o/w clean. *AKA.* $18

Halsey, Mina Deane. A TENDERFOOT IN SOUTHERN CALIFORNIA. NY: Ptd for the author, 1990. 6th ed. VG. *BOOK MARKET.* $15

Halstead, B.W. POISONOUS AND VENOMOUS MARINE ANIMALS OF THE WORLD. 3 vols. Washington, 1965-67-70. 1st ed. Some corners bumped. *SUTTON.* $425

Halstead, Murat. FIRE THE SALUTE! ABE LINCOLN IS NOMINATED! Kingsport, TN, 1960. Centennial Edition ltd to 1,250. Plastic dj, slipcase. Case worn and two small tears on dj o/w Fine. *PRATT.* $35

Halsted, Byron. BARN PLANS AND OUTBUILDINGS. NY: Orange Judd, 1907. 1st pub 1881. As New. *AMERICAN BOTANIST.* $75

Halsted, William. THE EMPLOYMENT OF FINE SILK IN PREFERENCE TO CAT-GUT. Boston, 1939. 1st ed. in book form. Vellum, 34pp. *FYE.* $100

Hamady, Walter. HUNKERING IN WISCONSIN. ANOTHER INTERMINABLE GAGGERBLABB. Illus Jack Beal. (Mt. Horeb): Perishable Press, (1975). 1st ed. Ltd to 125. Wraps. VF. *JAFFE.* $350

Hamady, Walter. IN SIGHT OF BLUE MOUNDS. Illus Ellen Lanyon, loose sheets in portfolio, cl slipcase. Mt. Horeb: Perishable Press, 1972. 1st ed. Ltd to 125. Signed. Mint. *JAFFE.* $275

Hamady, Walter. PAPERMAKING BY HAND. (Perry Township, WI: Perishable Press. 1982.) Sm 4to. (12),42,(4)pp. 4 sheets of handmade paper at rear of text, 1 w/enclosure. Ed ltd to 200. Fine. *KARMIOLE.* $350

Hamady, Walter. PAPERMAKING BY HAND: A BOOK OF SUSPICIONS. (Mt. Horeb): The Perishable Press, (1982). 1st ed. One of 200. Full linen. Fine. *CAPTAIN'S BOOKSHELF.* $550

Hamady, Walter. THUMBNAILING THE HILEX. ANOTHER (3) INTERMINABLE GABBERJABB. Illus Jack Beal. (Mt. Horeb): Perishable Press, 1974. 1st ed. One of 125. Wraps. VF. *JAFFE.* $275

Hamady, Walter. TWO DECADES OF HAMADY AND THE PERISHABLE PRESS LIMITED...ANNOTATED CHECK LIST. St. Louis: Univ of MO, 1984. 1st ed. Mint. *JAFFE.* $45

Hambleton, Chaikley J. A. A GOLD HUNTER'S EXPERIENCE. Chicago: ptd for private circulation, 1898. 1st ed. 116pp. Orig grn cl w/title in gilt on front cover. Presentation copy from author. *GINSBERG.* $500

Hamby, W.B. THE CASE REPORTS AND AUTOPSY RECORDS OF AMBROISE PARE. Springfield, 1960. 1st Eng trans. Dj. *FYE.* $100

Hamby, Wallace. INTRACRANIAL ANEURYSMS. Springfield, 1952. 1st ed. 104 illus. *FYE.* $50

Hamer, Malcolm. SUDDEN DEATH. London: Headline, 1991. 1st ed. VF in dj. *MORDIDA.* $45

Hamil, Harold. COLORADO WITHOUT MOUNTAINS. Kansas City, MO: Lowell, 1976. 1st ed. VF in NF dj. Signed. *CONNOLLY & WADE.* $25

Hamilton, Adrian. THE INFAMOUS ESSAY ON WOMAN, OR, JOHN WILKES SEATED BETWEEN VICE AND VIRTUE. London: Andre Deutsch, (1972). One of 2000 numbered. Accompanied by a reading copy, also limited to 2000, to form a set of 2 vols. Extremities of reading copy a bit rubbed, else VG in orig box. *WREDEN.* $100

Hamilton, Allan. A MANUAL OF MEDICAL JURISPRUDENCE, WITH SPECIAL REFERENCE TO DISEASES AND INJURIES OF THE NERVOUS SYSTEM. NY, 1883. 1st ed. *FYE.* $75

Hamilton, Allan. RAILWAY AND OTHER ACCIDENTS WITH RELATION TO INJURY AND DISEASE OF THE NERVOUS SYSTEM. NY, 1904. 1st ed. Photo plts. Ex-lib. *FYE.* $75

Hamilton, Allan. TYPES OF INSANITY, AN ILLUSTRATED GUIDE IN THE PHYSICAL DIAGNOSIS OF MENTAL DISEASE with G. Fielding Blanfurd INSANITY AND ITS TREATMENT. NY, 1886. 379pp. Fine plts. *FYE.* $125

Hamilton, Charles W. EARLY DAY OIL TALES OF MEXICO. Houston: Gulf Pub Co, 1966. Some lt wear, overall VG in dj. *PARMER.* $30

Hamilton, Chas. F. (ed). OUR HIAWATHA LAND. Chicago, 1940. 1st ed. Cl. VG. *ARTIS.* $27.50

Hamilton, D. H. HISTORY OF COMPANY M: FIRST TEXAS VOLUNTEER INFANTRY; HOOD'S BRIGADE....Waco, 1962. Cloth. One of 250. Facsimile reprint of rare 1935 orig ed. *GINSBERG.* $50

Hamilton, Edwin T. HANDICRAFT FOR GIRLS. NY: The Junior Literary Guild and Harcourt, Brace and Co., 1932. 1st ed. Spine faded, cvrs dust-marked, else internally Fine. *WREDEN.* $35

Hamilton, Genesta. PRINCES OF ZINJ-THE RULERS OF ZANZIBAR. London: Hutchinson, 1957. 1st ed. Minor edge foxing else Fine in Fine dj. *GREAT EPIC.* $95

Hamilton, H. W. RURAL SKETCHES OF MINNESOTA, THE EL DORADO OF THE NORTHWEST; CONTAINING FULL DESCRIPTIONS...WITH A TABLE OF DISTANCES. Milan, Ohio, 1850. 1st ed. 40pp. Orig ptd wraps. Howes H127. Rare. *GINSBERG.* $1250

Hamilton, Holman. ZACHARY TAYLOR. Indianapolis: Bobbs-Merrill, (1951). Stated 1st ed. 13 plts. Cl w/color facs of orig dj. *SCHOYER'S.* $25

Hamilton, James. OBSERVATIONS ON THE UTILITY AND ADMINISTRATION OF PURGATIVE MEDICINES IN SEVERAL DISEASES. Phila: James Webster, 1818. From the 5th Edinburgh ed. xix, 122+168pp. Contemp tree calf covers sl worn, o/w Good. *DIAMOND.* $75

Hamilton, James. THE BATTLE OF FORT DONELSON. NY, (1968). 1st ed. 378pp. Ffep neatly removed. A little dj chipping, o/w VG+. *PRATT.* $55

Hamilton, Patrick. HANGOVER SQUARE, OR THE MAN WITH TWO MINDS. NY: Random House, 1942. 1st ed. NF in lightly used dj w/chip at foot of spine. *BEASLEY.* $30

Hamilton, Virginia. THE GATHERING. NY: Greenwillow, (1981). 1st ed. Fine in dj. *BETWEEN COVERS.* $35

Hamilton, W.R. THE YUKON STORY. Vancouver, 1964. 1st ed. Fine in worn dj. *VARNER.* $20

Hamilton, W.T. MY SIXTY YEARS ON THE PLAINS....E.T. Sieber (ed). Illus C.M. Russell. NY: Forest & Stream, 1905. 1st ed. 6 full-pg illus, 2 full-pg photos. Good+. *OREGON.* $135

Hamilton, Walter. FRENCH BOOK-PLATES....London: George Bell & Sons, 1892. 1st ed. Ltd to 500. Orig grn cl. Spine covering missing. *OAK KNOLL.* $30

Hamlin, C.E. RESULTS OF AN EXAMINATION OF SYRIAN MOLLUSCAN FOSSILS....Cambridge, 1884. 6 plts. Contemp half morocco. Nice ex-lib. *SUTTON.* $47

Hammerstein, Oscar. CARMEN JONES. NY: Knopf, 1945. 1st ed. NF in dj. *BLUE MOUNTAIN.* $100

Hammett, Dashiell. *ELSE FINE.* $106,000 BLOOD MONEY. NY: Spivak, 1943. Pb orig. 1st ed. Fine in wraps. *ELSE FINE.* $125

Hammett, Dashiell. A MAN CALLED SPADE. NY: Dell Pub, (1945). Pb ed. Dell mapback #90. Scrape top of spine, wear, short crease, o/w VG. *MORDIDA.* $35

Hammett, Dashiell. A MAN NAMED THIN. Intro. by Ellery Queen. NY: Joseph W. Ferman, 1962. 1st ed. VF in wrappers. *MORDIDA.* $150

Hammett, Dashiell. BLOOD MONEY. NY: Dell Pub, (1944). Pb ed. Dell mapback #53. Pp darkened; rubbing along spine edge, o/w NF in wrappers. *MORDIDA.* $45

Hammett, Dashiell. DEAD YELLOW WOMEN. Intro. by Ellery Queen. NY: Lawrence E. Spivak, 1947. 1st ed, Pb orig. Pp darkened, o/w Fine in pict wraps w/tiny wear base of spine. *MORDIDA.* $125

Hammett, Dashiell. THE BATTLE OF THE ALEUTIANS, A GRAPHIC HISTORY 1942-1943. Adak, AK, 1943 (ptd 1944). Unpaginated oblong brochure in wraps. Illus., maps, 2 colors. Text written by Cpl. Dashiell Hammett & captions by Cpl. Robert Colodny. Fine. *BEBBAH.* $225

Hammett, Dashiell. THE BIG KNOCKOVER. Ed by Lillian Hellman. NY: Random House, (1966). 1st ed. Fine in dj w/trace of edgewear. *CAPTAIN'S BOOKSHELF.* $75

Hammett, Dashiell. THE CONTINENTAL OP. NY: Dell Pub, (1946). Pb ed. Dell mapback #129. Wear, o/w VG in wrappers. *MORDIDA.* $30

Hammett, Dashiell. THE DAIN CURSE. NY: Grosset & Dunlap, n.d. Rprt ed. Pp darkened o/w VG in dj (tiny tears, minor wear). While the dj is orange in color similar to the 1st ed, the pict front panel is entirely different. *MORDIDA.* $75

Hammett, Dashiell. THE DASHIELL HAMMETT OMNIBUS. London: Cassell, 1950. Omnibus ed. Fine in VG dj (sl faded spine; closed tears; staining back panel, 1" piece missing front panel). *MORDIDA.* $200

Hammett, Dashiell. THE GLASS KEY. NY: Grosset & Dunlap, 1931. Rprt ed. Sm label removed from fep, o/w Fine in dj (couple short tears, minor wear). Pict portion of dj is same as 1st ed. except the highlights are red in color, not grn. While the sheets are from the Alfred A. Knopf 5th ptg 1931 plts, the dj is about 1935 or later in date. *MORDIDA.* $75

Hammett, Dashiell. THE MALTESE FALCON. NY: Grosset & Dunlap, n.d. Rprt ed. Pp darkened, o/w VG in Fine dj. Pict portion of dj same as 1st ed. *MORDIDA.* $75

Hammett, Dashiell. THE THIN MAN. In 6 Redbook Novels. NY: McCall, 1934. Rprt ed. VG w/o dj as issued. *MORDIDA.* $85

Hammett, Dashiell. THE THIN MAN. NY: Alfred A. Knopf, 1934. 1st ed. Spotting on fore-edge; cvrs mottled as usual o/w VG in grn-highlighted dj (sl faded spine; chipping top of spine, at corners; closed tears; internal tape mends, rubbing front panel. *MORDIDA.* $500

Hammett, Dashiell. THE THIN MAN. NY: Grosset & Dunlap, 1934. Alfred A. Knopf 5th ed w/Grosset & Dunlap dj. Bkpl on fep and covers mottled, o/w VG in dj (wear, closed tears, scratches). Pict portion of dj same as 1st ed and has grn highlights. *MORDIDA.* $75

Hammett, Dashiell. WOMAN IN THE DARK. London: Headline, 1988. 1st British ed. Fine in dj. *SILVER DOOR.* $25

Hammond, George (ed.) DIGGING FOR GOLD WITHOUT A SHOVEL. THE LETTERS OF DANIEL WADSWORTH COIT...Denver: Old West, (1967). 1st ed, ltd to 1250. VF. *OREGON.* $35

Hammond, George P. and Agapito Rey. OBREGON'S HISTORY OF 16TH CENTURY EXPLORATIONS...ENTITLED "CHRONICLES...MEXICO, 1584. LA: Wetzel, 1928. (34),351pp. Facs leaf from orig ms, fldg map. Orig cl, a few white numbers on spine. Eng trans of 1924 1st ptg of ms. Howes O5. *GINSBERG.* $125

Hammond, George P. and Dale L. Morgan. CAPTAIN CHARLES M. WEBER: PIONEER OF....Berkeley: Friends of the Bancroft Library, 1966. 1st ed. Ltd to 700. VF. *CONNOLLY & WADE.* $90

Hammond, George. ADVENTURES OF ALEXANDER BARCLAY....MEMORANDUM DIARY 1845 TO 1850. Denver: Old West, 1976. 1st ed. Frontis, 3 fldg maps in pocket. VF in VF dj. *OREGON.* $40

Hammond, Isaac B. REMINISCENCES OF FRONTIER LIFE. Portland, OR, 1904. Orig grey ptd wraps. Privately ptd. Inscribed. Howes H142. *GINSBERG.* $250

Hammond, N.H. ANTHOLOGY OF PATTERN. NY, 1949. Illus. *POLYANTHOS.* $100

Hammond, O.G. (ed.) THE UTAH EXPEDITION 1857-1858. LETTERS OF CAPT. JESSE A. GOVE....NH Hist Soc Collections Vol 12. Concord, 1928. 1st ptg. Fine. *VARNER.* $85

Hammond, S. H. HUNTING ADVENTURES IN THE NORTHERN WILDS. Phila: Potter, 1863. Probable 1st Amer ed. Wear to extremities, some interior spotting, else G+. *OLD LONDON.* $50

Hammond, William. A TREATISE ON INSANITY IN ITS MEDICAL RELATIONS. NY, 1883. 1st ed. 767pp. Rare. *FYE.* $300

Hammond, William. INSANITY IN ITS MEDICO-LEGAL RELATIONS. OPINION RELATIVE TO THE TESTAMENTARY CAPACITY OF THE LATE JAMES C. JOHNSTON. NY, 1866. 1st ed. 72pp. Heavy ink marginal notations on 2 leaves w/ink underlining on several other leaves. Water stain affecting margins of title page and several other leaves. Very scarce. *FYE.* $100

Hammond, William. SEXUAL IMPOTENCE IN THE MALE AND FEMALE. Detroit, 1887. 1st ed. 305pp. *FYE.* $250

Hamod, Sam. AFTER THE FUNERAL OF ASSAM HAMADY. Mt. Horeb: Perishable Press, 1971. 1st ed. Ltd to 120. Presentation to the Hamadys, inscribed. Signed by Walter Hamady. Wraps. Mint. *JAFFE.* $350

Hampl, Patricia. A ROMANTIC EDUCATION. Houghton Mifflin, 1981. 1st ed. VF in dj. Signed & inscribed. *STAHR.* $20

Hampton, Isabel Adams. NURSING: ITS PRINCIPLES AND PRACTICE FOR HOSPITAL AND PRIVATE USE. Cleveland, 1903. 2nd ed. Inner hinges cracked, shaken. *FYE.* $100

Hancock, H. Irving. MAKING THE LAST STAND FOR OLD GLORY. Altemus, 1916, 1st ed. VG in sl chipped dj. *MADLE.* $100

Hancock, Mrs. W.S. REMINISCENCES OF WINFIELD SCOTT HANCOCK BY HIS WIFE. NY, 1887. 1st ed. 340pp. Gilt edges, leather. Minor cvr wear o/w Fine. *PRATT.* $85

Hancock, Ralph and Weston, Julian A. THE LOST TREASURE OF COCO'S ISLAND. NY: Thomas Nelson, 1960. 325 pp. 1st ed. NF in NF dj. *GREAT EPIC.* $30

Hancock, Ralph. FABULOUS BOULEVARD. NY: Funk & Wagnalls, (1949). Pict boards in dj. *DAWSON'S.* $25

Hancock, Samuel. THE NARRATIVE OF SAMUEL HANCOCK, 1845-1860. NY: McBride, 1927. 1st trade ed. VG in VG dj. *OREGON.* $40

Hand, William. THE HOUSE SURGEON AND PHYSICIAN; DESIGNED TO ASSIST HEADS OF FAMILIES, TRAVELERS, AND SEA-FARING PEOPLE. New Haven, 1820. 2nd ed. Rebound in cloth-backed boards w/paper label. *FYE.* $100

Handcock, H. Irving. PHYSICAL TRAINING FOR WOMEN BY JAPANESE METHODS. NY & London: (G.P. Putnam's), 1904. Pub's yellow cl. Nice, some occasional signs of handling; 1 badly opened pg (an ad) at rear. *BOOK BLOCK.* $75

Handke, Peter. A SORROW BEYOND DREAMS. NY: Farrar, Straus, & Giroux, (1975). 1st US ed. New in dj. *BERNARD.* $20

Handler, Hans. THE SPANISH RIDING SCHOOL. Trans by Russell Stockman. NY: McGraw-Hill Book Co. (1972). 1st ed. Dj. *KARMIOLE.* $60

Handley, C.O. and C.P. Patton. WILD MAMMALS OF VIRGINIA. Richmond, 1947. Cloth. Lt spotting to cvrs. Signed by John Wendell Bailey. *SUTTON.* $55

Handlin, Oscar (ed.) CHILDREN OF THE UPROOTED. NY: George Braziller, (1966). 1st ed. 551pp. Dj w/some edgetear. *AKA.* $28

Hanes, Bailey C. BILL DOOLIN: OUTLAW. Norman, (1968). 1st ed. 207pp. Fine in dj. *PRATT.* $27.50

Hanks, O.T. HISTORY OF CAPTAIN B.F. BENTON'S COMPANY, HOOD'S TEXAS BRIGADE, 1861-1865. (Austin, TX, 1984). 1st ed, ltd to 300. Wrappers. Fine. *McGOWAN.* $37.50

Hanna, Phil Townsend. LIBROS CALIFORNIANOS. Rev, enl by Laurence Clark Powell. LA: Zeitlin & Ver Brugge, 1958. Ltd to 1000. Signed. Paper label on spine, front cvr. VG. *CONNOLLY & WADE.* $45

Hanna, Warren L. THE LIFE AND TIMES OF JAMES WILLARD SCHULTZ. Norman: Univ of OK Press, (1986). 1st ed. Fine in Fine dj. *BOOK MARKET.* $25

Hannah, Barry. AIRSHIPS. Knopf, 1978. 1st ed., inscribed. Fine with remainder mark back edge in VG dj with 2 tiny chips. *BEBBAH.* $75

Hannah, Barry. AIRSHIPS. NY: Knopf (1978). 1st ed. Fine in dj. *DORN.* $50

Hannah, Barry. BOOMERANG. Boston: Houghton Mifflin Co., (1989). 1st Amer ed. Signed. Fine in dj. *DORN.* $30

Hannah, Barry. GERONIMO REX. NY: Viking, (1972). 1st Amer ed. Signed. Some age spotting on extremities else VG+ w/very small stain base of spine. *DORN.* $120

Hannah, Barry. HAY JACK. NY: Dutton, (1987). 1st Amer ed. Signed. Fine in dj. *DORN.* $30

Hannah, Barry. NEVER DIE. Boston: Houghton Mifflin, 1991. Uncorrected proof. Fine in wraps. *CAPTAIN'S BOOKSHELF.* $50

Hannah, Barry. NEVER DIE. Boston: Houghton Mifflin, 1991. Uncorrected proof of 1st ed. Orig ptd grn wraps. Fine. *CHAPEL HILL.* $40

Hannah, Barry. NIGHTWATCHMEN. NY, 1973. 1st ed. Sig laid in. NF in Fine dj. *POLYANTHOS.* $60

Hannah, Barry. NIGHTWATCHMEN. NY: Viking, (1973). 1st ed. Orig blue-grey cl. Fine in dj. Scarce. *CHAPEL HILL*. $150

Hannah, Barry. RAY. NY: Knopf, (1980). 1st Amer ed. Signed. Fine in dj. *DORN*. $50

Hannah, Barry. RAY. NY: Knopf, 1980. 1st ed. Fine in dj. Signed. *CAPTAIN'S BOOKSHELF*. $50

Hannan, Thomas. FAMOUS SCOTTISH HOUSES: THE LOWLANDS. London: A & C Black, 1928. 1st ed. Just About Fine in like, severely price-clipped dj. *CAPTAIN'S BOOKSHELF*. $100

Hanniball, P(eter) M. THRICE A PIONEER. A STORY OF FORESTS, PLAINS, AND MOUNTAINS. Blair: Danish Lutheran Publishing, (1901). 1st ed. Tear in cloth at heel of spine, still Good. Howes H-165. *LAURIE*. $75

Hannum, Alberta. PAINT THE WIND. London: Michael Joseph, (1959). 1st Eng ed. Fine in NF dj. *LOPEZ*. $35

Hannum, Alberta. SPIN A SILVER DOLLAR. NY: Viking, 1945. Bkpl, o/w Fine in NF dj. *LOPEZ*. $45

HANSEL AND GRETEL. American Crayon, (1943) folio. Un-paginated. 6 full-page color plates by Fern Bisel Peat + decs. VG w/edgewear, chips top, bottom of spine. A Mary Perks book. *BEB-BAH*. $45

Hansen, Joseph. EARLY GRAVES. Mysterious Press, 1987. 1st ed. VF in dj. *STAHR*. $25

Hansen, Joseph. FADEOUT. Harper, 1970. 1st ed. Fine in dj w/lightly sunned spine, some browning to front flyleaf fold. *STAHR*. $45

Hansen, Joseph. FADEOUT. NY: Harper & Row, 1970. 1st ed. Fine in dj (minor wear base of spine; sl fading spine, front panel). *MOR-DIDA*. $85

Hansen, Joseph. GRAVEDIGGER. NY: Holt, (1982). 1st ed. Signed. Fine in Fine dj. *UNGER*. $40

Hansen, Joseph. THE MAN EVERYBODY WAS AFRAID OF. NY: Holt, (1978). 1st ed. Signed. Fine in Fine dj. *UNGER*. $40

Hansen, L. Taylor. HE WALKED THE AMERICAS. London: Neville Spearman, 1963. 1st ed. Fine in VG dj. *CONNOLLY & WADE*. $35

Hansen, Ron. THE ASSASSINATION OF JESSE JAMES BY THE COWARD ROBERT FORD. NY: Knopf, 1983. 1st ed. Fine in dj. Signed. *BETWEEN COVERS*. $50

Hansen, Ron. THE ASSASSINATION OF JESSE JAMES BY THE COWARD ROBERT FORD. London: Souvenir, 1984. 1st Eng ed. *LOPEZ*. $30

Hansen, Thorkild. NORTH WEST TO HUDSON BAY. London: Collins, 1970. 1st ed. James McFarlane & John Lynch (trans). Fine in VG dj. *CONNOLLY & WADE*. $30

Hansen, Thorkild. NORTH WEST TO HUDSON BAY: THE LIFE AND TIMES OF JENS MUNK. London: Collins, 1970. VG in lightly worn dj. *PARMER*. $35

Hanshew, T.W. THE WORLD'S FINGER, A LONDON MYSTERY. Ogilvie, (1901). 283pp. VG+. *BEBBAH*. $18

Hanson, H.C. and R.H. Smith. CANADA GEESE OF THE MISSIS-SIPPI FLYWAY WITH SPECIAL REFERENCE TO AN IL-LINOIS FLOCK. Urbana, 1950. Wraps. Spine & edges faded. *SUT-TON*. $23

Hanson, James. METAL WEAPONS, TOOLS AND ORNAMENTS OF THE TETON DAKOTA INDIANS. Univ of NE, (1975). 1st ed. VF in VF dj. *OREGON*. $45

Hanson, Joseph Mills. BULL RUN REMEMBERS. Manassas, 1957. 2nd ed. VG in dj. *PRATT*. $20

Hanson, Joseph Mills. FRONTIER BALLADS. Chicago: A.C. Mc-Clurg. 1910. 1st ed. Illus by Maynard Dixon. Orig limp suede, gilt. This copy signed by Hanson. In pub's orig box. Fine. *KARMIOLE*. $85

Hanzlicek, C.G. LIVING IN IT. Iowa City: Stone Wall Press, (1971). 1st ed. Ltd to 240. Cl, matching slipcase. Fine. *JAFFE*. $85

Hapgood, Hutchins. THE AUTOBIOGRAPHY OF A THIEF. NY: Fox, Duffield, 1903. 1st ed. VG+ w/sl soiling. *BEASLEY*. $65

HAPPENINGS HERE AND THERE ALONG THE TRAIL (by Will Bradley). Pasadena: (The Typophiles), 1949. 1st ed. Ltd to 500. Stiff paper wraps. *OAK KNOLL*. $45

HAPPY FAMILIES AND THEIR TALES. London: Nister. #264. (1880s) 5 pull-down movables w/multi-dimensional scenes. Couple tabs re-glued. Lt wear extrems, reinforcing tape between 2pp—not affecting movables. Sm piece missing top of one goat's head. Move-able bk. *BOOKFINDERS INTL*. $600

Harcourt, Helen. FLORIDA FRUITS AND HOW TO RAISE THEM....Louisville, KY: Morton, 1886. Rev, enl, index. 347pp. VG. Scarce. *SECOND LIFE*. $65

Hardacre, V. WOODLAND NUGGETS OF GOLD....NY, 1968. 1st ed. 3 maps. Hb. Chipped dj. *SUTTON*. $35

Hardaway, W.A. ESSENTIALS OF VACCINATION, A COMPILA-TION OF FACTS RELATING TO VACCINE INOCULATION AND ITS INFLUENCE IN THE PREVENTION OF SMALL-POX. St. Louis, 1886. 1st ed. Scarce. *FYE*. $75

Hardeman, Nicholas Perkins. WILDERNESS CALLING: THE HARDEMAN FAMILY...1750-1900. Knoxville: Univ of TN, 1977. 1st ed. Fine in Fine dj. *CONNOLLY & WADE*. $30

Harden, Donald B. ROMAN GLASS FROM KARANIS FOUND BY THE UNIVERSITY OF MICHIGAN ARCHAEOLOGICAL EXPEDITION IN EGYPT, 1924-29. Ann Arbor: Univ of MI Press, 1936. 4 figs, 22 plts. Good. *ARCHAEOLOGIA*. $450

Harding, A.R. GINSENG AND OTHER MEDICINAL PLANTS....Columbus, (1908). Cl, corners bumped. *SUTTON*. $36

Harding, Addie Clark, as told by Garnett Laidlaw Eskew. AMERICA RIDES THE LINERS. NY (1956), 1st ed. Illus, dj. *HEINOLDT*. $15

Harding, George C. THE MISCELLANEOUS WRITINGS OF...In-dianapolis, 1882. 1st ed. 358pp. Orig cl. *GINSBERG*. $75

Hardoy, Jorge E. PRE-COLUMBIAN CITIES. Judith Thorne (trans). NY: Walker, 1973. 1st Amer ed. Fine in NF dj. *CONNOLLY & WADE*. $50

Hardoy, Jorge. PRE-COLUMBIAN CITIES. NY: Walker & Co, (1973). 1st Amer ed. Good in dj. *SILVER*. $35

Hardwick, Elizabeth. THE GHOSTLY LOVER. NY: Harcourt, (1945). 1st ed, 1st book. NF in dj w/minimal edgewear. *ROBBINS*. $175

Hardwick, Elizabeth. THE GHOSTLY LOVER. NY: Harcourt, Brace, (1945). 1st ed. Dj sl rubbed, o/w unusually Fine. *JAFFE*. $275

Hardwick, Michael & Mollie. THE MAN WHO WAS SHERLOCK HOLMES. London: John Murray, 1964. 1st ed. Fine in dj w/wear at spine ends, at corners and along edges. *MORDIDA*. $50

Hardwick, Michael. SHERLOCK HOLMES—MY LIFE & CRIMES. London: Harvill, 1984. 1st ed. Fine in dj. *SILVER DOOR*. $25

Hardwick, Mollie. THE DREAMING DAMOZEL. London: Cen-tury, 1990. 1st ed. VF in dj. *MORDIDA*. $30

Hardwicke, Sir Charles. A VICTORIAN IN ORBIT. NY, 1961. Dj rubbed at extreme edges. Signed. NF. *POLYANTHOS*. $35

Hardy, Alister. GREAT WATERS. London: Collins, 1967. VG in VG- dj. *BLUE DRAGON*. $25

Hardy, Alister. GREAT WATERS. NY: Harper & Row, (1967). 1st US ed. VG in VG dj. *BLUE DRAGON*. $25

Hardy, James D., Harold Wolff & Helen Godell. PAIN SENSA-TIONS AND REACTIONS. Baltimore, 1952. Dj. *FYE*. $50

Hardy, Phil. THE WESTERN. William Morrow, 1983. 1st ed. Fine, VG dj. *AUTHORS OF THE WEST*. $25

Hardy, R.W.H. TRAVELS IN THE INTERIOR OF MEXICO; IN BAJA....Glorieta, NM: Rio Grande, 1977. 1st ed thus. (1829). Fldg map. As New. *CONNOLLY & WADE.* $42.50

Hardy, Ronald. THE IRON SNAKE. NY: Putnam, (1965). 1st US ed. VG+ in VG dj. *AARD.* $25

Hardy, Thomas. 'DEAREST EMMIE.'...London: Macmillan, 1963. Carl J. Weber (ed). 1st Eng ed. VG in dj. *WEBER.* $20

Hardy, Thomas. A GROUP OF NOBLE DAMES. NY, 1891. 1st ed. Illus. Dec cvrs gilt. Fine. *POLYANTHOS.* $75

Hardy, Thomas. AN INDISCRETION IN THE LIFE OF AN HEIRESS. Baltimore: Johns Hopkins Press, 1935. 1st US ed. Carl J. Weber (ed). Uncut, Fine in sl soiled dj. *SECOND LIFE.* $75

Hardy, Thomas. HUMAN SHOWS FAR PHANTASIES. NY: Macmillan, 1925. Cl. Dj. *WEBER.* $40

Hardy, Thomas. MAUMBURY RING. BY THE HISTORIAN OF WESSEX. Waterville, Maine: Colby College Lib, 1942. Ltd ed of 100. (16)pp. White paper backed gray boards. Fine. *WEBER.* $100

Hardy, Thomas. TESS OF THE D'URBERVILLES. London: Macmillan, 1926. 1st illus ed. One of 325 large paper copies signed by Hardy. Vellum stamped spine and marbled boards. Corners a bit rubbed, some moderate soiling to spine, else VG in repaired slipcase. *BETWEEN COVERS.* $1250

Hardy, Thomas. TESS OF THE D'URBERVILLES. NY: Harper & Bros., 1892. 1st US ed. (6),455pp. Frontis, 10 plates. Rust cloth over boards, dec cover, spine stamped in gold and black. Back cover minor stains; sl foxing top edge and rear endpapers. NF. *BOOKMINE.* $350

Hardy, Thomas. THE MAYOR OF CASTERBRIDGE. NY: LEC, 1964. One of 1500. Illus, signed by Agnes Miller Parker. Fine in slipcase. *CAPTAIN'S BOOKSHELF.* $125

Hardy, Thomas. THE OLD CLOCK. Portland, Maine: The Southworth-Anthoensen Press, 1946. Ltd ed of 245. Subsequently this pamphlet was shown to be not by Hardy at all. Pamphlet; spine joint beginning to split, o/w VG. Owner's inked name. *WEBER.* $30

Hardy, Thomas. THE THREE WAYFARERS. Dorset: 1935. 1st ed, 1/250. Buff wrappers, edges brown, else Fine. *JUVELIS.* $75

Hardy, Thomas. THE WRITINGS OF THOMAS HARDY IN PROSE AND VERSE. WITH PREFACES AND NOTES. NY & London: (Harper & Bros.), n.d. (1920). 21 vols. Pub's red cl w/blind dec front cvr, gilt titling on spine, teg, others untrimmed. Nice set in Quite Good condition. *BOOK BLOCK.* $475

Hardy, Thomas. UNDER THE GREENWOOD TREE OR THE MELLSTOCK QUIRE: A RURAL PAINTING....London: Macmillan, 1940. Clare Leighton (illus). Grn cl boards, title in gilt on spine within black frame. Edges of cvrs soiled, Fine in dj. *HELLER.* $195

Hardy, Thomas. WESSEX POEMS AND OTHER VERSES. (London: Harper, 1898). 1st ed, regular issue. Dec grn cl, teg. 3 previous owner's sigs, else Fine. *CAPTAIN'S BOOKSHELF.* $150

Hardy, Thomas. WINTER WORDS. NY, 1928. Ltd ed, 261/500. Vellum spine gilt lettering, spine little sunned and rubbed. In box, edge sunned and rubbed. *POLYANTHOS.* $75

Hare, Cyril. BEST DETECTIVE STORIES OF CYRIL HARE. NY: Walker, 1961. 1st Amer ed. Fine in dj. *MORDIDA.* $25

Hare, Cyril. HE SHOULD HAVE DIED HEREAFTER. London: Faber & Faber, 1958. 1st ed. VF in jaggedly price-clipped dj. *MORDIDA.* $40

Hare, Cyril. UNTIMELY DEATH. Macmillan, 1957. 1st Amer ed. About Fine in dj (lightly sunned on spine, one small chip foot of spine). *STAHR.* $25

Hare, Cyril. WHEN THE WIND BLOWS. London: Faber and Faber, 1949. 1st ed. Small bkseller's label on front pastedown. Some spotting on edges o/w VG in dj w/crease along base of front and back panel, chipping at corners, and wear at top of spine. *MORDIDA.* $35

Hare, Kenneth. ROADS AND VAGABONDS. Cecil Aldin (illus). NY: Scribner's, (n.d.). 1st US ed. VG in Fair dj. *OCTOBER FARM.* $135

Hargrave, Carrie Guerphan. AMERICAN PRIMITIVE LIFE AS I SAW IT IN SIERRA LEONE BRITISH WEST AFRICA. Privately ptd. (Wilmington, NC, 1944). 1st ed. Orig cl, bkpl removed, else NF. Scarce. *McGOWAN.* $150

Hargrave, Catherine Perry. A HISTORY OF PLAYING CARDS AND A BIBLIOGRAPHY OF CARDS AND GAMING. Boston: Houghton Mifflin Co. 1930. 1st ed. Red cl. Dj. Fine in pub's slipcase. *KARMIOLE.* $450

Hargraves, Michael. HARRY CREWS: A FIRST BIBLIOGRAPHY. SF, 1981. Ltd ed, 109/200 only. Name, printed wraps. Fine. *POLYANTHOS.* $35

Hargreaves, Reginald. THE ENEMY AT THE GATES. Harrisburg, PA: Military Service Publ., 1948. 1st US ed. VG+ in Good+ dj. *AARD.* $20

Hargreaves, William. ALCOHOL AND SCIENCE, OR ALCOHOL: WHAT IT IS, AND WHAT IT DOES. NY, 1882. 1st ed. *FYE.* $50

Hargrett, Lester (ed). THE GILCREASE-HARGRETT CATALOGUE OF IMPRINTS. Norman: Univ of Oklahoma Press, (1972). 1st ed. Fine. *LAURIE.* $27.50

Harington, Donald. THE CHOIRING OF THE TREES. San Diego: Harcourt, Brace & Jovanovich, (1991). 1st Amer ed. Signed. Fine in dj. *DORN.* $35

Harkey, Dee. MEAN AS HELL. Univ of NM, 1948. 1st ed. 2nd state. Fine. *OREGON.* $40

Harkey, Dee. MEAN AS HELL. Univ of NM, 1948. 1st ed, 2nd state. Fine in VG dj. *VARNER.* $80

Harlan, R. FAUNA AMERICANA: BEING A DESCRIPTION OF THE MAMMIFEROUS ANIMALS INHABITING NORTH AMERICA. Phila, 1825. 318pp,(1),errata. Contemp calf, rebacked w/later calf. Worn, front cover nearly detached, rear hinge tender, partial foxing, institutional bkpl. Rare. *SUTTON.* $285

Harlan, Richard. FAUNA AMERICANA....Phila: Finley, 1825. 1st ed. ii,318pp. Bound in contemp calf (cvr separate). Lt foxing. VG. *SECOND LIFE.* $350

Harley, George Davies. AN AUTHENTIC BIOGRAPHICAL SKETCH OF THE LIFE, EDUCATION, AND PERSONAL CHARACTER, OF WILLIAM HENRY WEST BETTY, THE CELEBRATED YOUNG ROSCIUS. 2nd ed. London: for Richard Phillips, 1804. Modern wraps; engr frontis; reinforced at inner margin of blank recto; fore-edges raggedly trimmed. *DRAMATIS PERSONAE.* $200

Harlow, Alvin. THE SERENE CINCINNATIANS. NY: Dutton, 1950. 1st ed. NF in Good dj chipped at head & tail of spine. *ARCHER.* $25

Harlow, Francis H. MODERN PUEBLO POTTERY 1880-1960. Flagstaff: Northland, 1977. 1st ed. Fine in VG dj. *CONNOLLY & WADE.* $37.50

Harmon, Daniel W. A JOURNAL OF VOYAGES AND TRAVELS IN THE INTERIOUR OF NORTH AMERICA, BETWEEN THE 47TH AND 58TH DEGREES OF NORTH LATITUDE...INCLUDING AN ACCOUNT OF THE PRINCIPAL OCCURRENCES....Andover, 1820. 1st ed. Daniel Haskell (ed). 432pp, errata slip at end. Fldg map (in facsimile), port. Orig full calf, leather label on spine. Howes H205. *GINSBERG.* $750

Harmon, Daniel. A JOURNAL OF VOYAGES & TRAVELS...BETWEEN 47TH & 58TH DEGREES N. LAT....Andover, VT: Flagg & Gould, 1820. 1st ed. 432pp, frontis. Fldg map missing western half. Orig full tree calf & morocco spine label. Foxed, lacks rfep. Good+. Howes D205. *OREGON*. $300

Harmon, Maurice. THE POETRY OF THOMAS KINSELLA. (Dublin): Wolfhound Press, (1974). 1st ed. Fine in dj. *CAPTAIN'S BOOKSHELF*. $25

Harmon, R.W. & C.B. Pollard. BIBLIOGRAPHY OF ANIMAL VENOMS. Gainesville, 1943. *FYE*. $30

Harnsberger, Carolina Thomas (compiler). THE LINCOLN TREASURY. Chicago, (1950). 1st ed. VG+. *PRATT*. $20

Harpel, Oscar H. HARPEL'S TYPOGRAPH OR BOOK OF SPECIMENS. Cincinati: Ptd and pub by author, 1870. 252 pages + full-pg (some fldg), illus, 14 page Advertisers Addenda. Gold-stamped cloth, scuffed and stained, rebacked w/orig spine laid down. Most complete, missing none of the extra material. Less than 3000 ptd. *DAWSON'S*. $700

Harpending, Asbury. THE GREAT DIAMOND HOAX AND OTHER STIRRING....James H. Wilkins (ed). SF: James H. Barry, 1913. True 1st ed w/dated title pg. Frontis, 285pp. Lt blue cl, gilt dec & letters. Gilt partially worn on spine, else Fine. *CONNOLLY & WADE*. $95

Harpending, Asbury. THE GREAT DIAMOND HOAX AND OTHER STIRRING INCIDENTS IN THE LIFE OF ASBURY HARPENDING. Ed James Wilkins. SF: J.H. Barry Co. 1913. 1st ed. Edgeworn. G+. *OREGON*. $55

Harper, C.C. WESSEX. A&C Black, 1911. 1st ed (this series). W/o dj. Fair only. *OLD LONDON*. $10

Harper, F. THE BARREN GROUND CARIBOU OF KEEWATIN. Lawrence, 1955. Stiff wraps. *SUTTON*. $23

Harper, L. PRELIMINARY REPORT ON THE GEOLOGY AND AGRICULTURE OF THE STATE OF MISSISSIPPI. Jackson: E. Barksdale, 1857. Fldg color frontis, 9 plts and maps. Spine faded, scattered foxing. VG. *BOHLING*. $150

Harper, Michael S. HISTORY IS YOUR OWN HEARTBEAT. Urbana: Univ of Illinois Press, (1971). 1st ed. Fine in Fine dj, very sl spine faded. Signed. Ownership stamp of novelist Barry Beckham. *BETWEEN COVERS*. $100

Harper, Michael S. IMAGES OF KIN. Urbana: Univ of Illinois Press, (1977). 1st ed. Fine in lightly soiled NF dj w/single short tear. Signed. *BETWEEN COVERS*. $85

Harper, Michael S. PHOTOGRAPHS: NEGATIVES: HISTORY AS APPLE TREE. SF: Scarab Press, 1972. 1st ed. Fine in dj a bit tanned at spine and extremities. Inscribed. *BETWEEN COVERS*. $100

Harper, Robert H. LINCOLN AND THE PRESS. NY, (1951). 1st ed. Dj. VG. *PRATT*. $25

HARPER'S PICTORIAL HISTORY OF WAR WITH SPAIN. NY: Harper, 1899. 33 color plts. Rebound w/orig front cover, emblem from back cvr, label from spine transposed. *HEINOLDT*. $100

HARRIMAN ALASKA EXPEDITION, Vol 13, LAND AND FRESH WATER MOLLUSKS by W. H. Dall; HYDROIDS by C.C. Nutting. NY, 1905. 15 plts. Light wear. *SUTTON*. $135

HARRIMAN ALASKA EXPEDITIONS. Washington, 1904. Vol. IX, Insects. Part 2, by W.H. Ashmead et al. Frontis, 3 plts. In worn slipcase. Has Smithsonian Instit 1910 title page. *SUTTON*. $125

Harrington, Alan. THE REVELATIONS OF DR. MODESTO. (London): Andre Deutsch, (1957). 1st Eng ed, 1st bk. Fine in NF dj sl chipped head, foot of backstrip. *HELLER*. $60

Harrington, Alan. THE SECRET SWINGER. NY: Knopf, (1966). 1st ed. Fine in little worn dj. Scarce. *SECOND LIFE*. $75

Harrington, F.H. HANGING JUDGE. Caxton, 1951. 1st ed. Fine in sl faded dj. *VARNER*. $35

Harrington, Jessie. SILVERSMITHS OF DELAWARE. DE: Colonial Dames of America, 1939. 1st ed. VG. *BACKROOM*. $175

Harrington, William. WHICH THE JUSTICE, WHICH THE THIEF. Indianapolis: Bobbs Merrill, (1963). 1st ed, 1st bk. Signed. Fine in dj sl rubbed head, foot of backstrip. *HELLER*. $60

Harris, A.C. ALASKA AND THE KLONDIKE GOLD FIELDS. New Haven: Butler & Alger, (1897). 566pp. Illus, fldg map (half gone). Orig brown dec cloth. Good+. *BLUE DRAGON*. $45

Harris, Benjamin. THE GILA TRAIL: THE TEXAS ARGONAUTS AND THE CALIFORNIA GOLD RUSH. Norman: Univ of OK, (1960). Richard Dillon (ed). 1st ed. Signed by Dillon. Fine in Fine dj. *BOOK MARKET*. $38

Harris, Beth Coombs. IN THE GRIP OF THE DRUIDS. London, (1930s). VG. *MADLE*. $50

Harris, Burton. JOHN COLTER, HIS YEARS IN THE ROCKIES. Scribner's, 1952. 1st ed. Signatures, "Get Well" presentation o/w Fine in chipped dj. *OREGON*. $85

Harris, C.R.S. THE HEART AND VASCULAR SYSTEM IN ANCIENT GREEK MEDICINE FROM ALCMAEON TO GALEN. Oxford: Clarendon Press, 1973. 5 figs. Good in faded dj. *ARCHAEOLOGIA*. $125

Harris, David. BRITAIN AND THE BULGARIAN HORRORS OF 1876. Chicago, 1939. vii,437pp. *O'NEILL*. $35

Harris, Frank and Lord Alfred Douglas. NEW PREFACE TO "THE LIFE AND CONFESSIONS OF OSCAR WILDE." London: Fortune Press, (1925). 1st ed. One of 225 numbered. Signed by Douglas. Fine. *MUELLER*. $85

Harris, Frank. BERNARD SHAW. AN UNAUTHORIZED BIOGRAPHY BASED ON FIRST HAND INFORMATION WITH A POSTSCRIPT BY MR. SHAW. London: Gollancz, 1931. 1st ed. Clippings pasted in, else VG. *WOOLMER*. $35

Harris, Frank. MY REMINISCENCES AS A COWBOY. Boni, 1930. 1st ed. Pb. Good. *VARNER*. $12.50

Harris, Helena J, Mrs. SOUTHERN SKETCHES. New Orleans: Crescent Job Print, 1866. 1st ed. 20pp. Orig ptd wraps. Lt soiling of wraps, else NF. *CHAPEL HILL*. $225

Harris, Hyde (pseud of Timothy Harris). KYD FOR HIRE. London: Victor Gollancz, 1977. 1st ed. Fine in dj. *MORDIDA*. $40

Harris, Hyde (pseud of Timothy Harris). KYD FOR HIRE. London: Gollancz, (1977). 1st ed. Signed. Fine in Fine dj. *UNGER*. $45

Harris, James E. and Edward F. Wente (eds). AN X-RAY ATLAS OF THE ROYAL MUMMIES. Chicago and London: Univ of Chicago Press, (1980). 5 microfiches in back pocket. Signature. Good in dj. *ARCHAEOLOGIA*. $75

Harris, Joel Chandler. A LITTLE UNION SCOUT. NY: McClure, Phillips & Co, 1904. 1st ed. Orig dec grn cl. Owner sig, name stamp, marginal tear in front fly, else bright, NF. *CHAPEL HILL*. $75

Harris, Joel Chandler. AARON IN THE WILDWOODS. Boston & NY: Houghton, Mifflin, 1897. 1st ed. 270pp. Orig pict yellow cl. Owner sig, lt soiling, but Nice, VG. *CHAPEL HILL*. $125

Harris, Joel Chandler. BALAAM AND HIS MASTER And Other Sketches and Stories. Boston & NY: Houghton, Mifflin, 1891. 1st ed, 1st binding, w/dots in spine imprint. 293pp. Orig mottled tan cl. Cl sl soiled, else NF. *CHAPEL HILL*. $150

Harris, Joel Chandler. DADDY JAKE THE RUNAWAY AND SHORT STORIES TOLD AFTER DARK. NY: The Century Co., (1889). 1st ed. 4to, 145pp. Orig glazed pict boards. Some scratches and abrasions to cvrs, spine ends worn, but VG of fragile volume. Scarce. BAL 7117. *CHAPEL HILL*. $400

Harris, Joel Chandler. FREE JOE AND OTHER GEORGIAN SKETCHES. NY: Scribner's, 1887. 1st ed. 236pp, (12)pp ads. Orig dec brn cl. NF. *CHAPEL HILL*. $175

Harris, Joel Chandler. GABRIEL TOLLIVER. NY: McClure, Phillips & Co, 1902. 1st ed. Orig dec red cl. Sm dampstain at upper corner of front, rear cvrs, else Fine, bright in orig ptd dj, missing most of the spine portion, but w/front, rear panels, flaps intact. *CHAPEL HILL.* $300

Harris, Joel Chandler. GABRIEL TOLLIVER: A STORY OF RECONSTRUCTION. NY: McClure & Phillips, 1902. 1st ed. Red cl, tooled in blind. Tiny nick at head of spine, rear outer joint, else bright, Fine. *CAPTAIN'S BOOKSHELF.* $75

Harris, Joel Chandler. MINGO AND OTHER SKETCHES IN BLACK AND WHITE. Boston: James R. Osgood & Co, 1884. 1st ed. 273pp. Orig dec mustard cl. Variant binding not noted by BAL 7112, which lists only grey and grn cl. VG. *CHAPEL HILL.* $175

Harris, Joel Chandler. MR. RABBIT AT HOME, A SEQUEL TO LITTLE MR. THIMBLEFINGER & HIS QUEER COUNTRY. Houghton Mifflin, 1896. 304pp. Illus by Oliver Herford. Good+. Dec cvr in brown, gilt & grn on yellow cloth. *BEBBAH.* $25

Harris, Joel Chandler. NIGHTS WITH UNCLE REMUS. Houghton Mifflin, (1917). 339pp. Illus by Milo Winter. VG+ w/some soil to few leaves. *BEBBAH.* $75

Harris, Joel Chandler. ON THE WING OF OCCASIONS.... NY: Doubleday, Pg, 1900. 1st ed. 310pp. Orig grn cl. Lt soiling of prelims, spine ends and corners rubbed, still VG or better. Frontis. *CHAPEL HILL.* $65

Harris, Joel Chandler. SISTER JANE, HER FRIENDS AND AC-QUAINTANCES. Boston & NY: Houghton, Mifflin, 1896. 1st ed, 2nd ptg. 363pp. Orig smooth grn cl. Owner name, else VG. *CHAPEL HILL.* $60

Harris, Joel Chandler. SISTER JANE, HER FRIENDS AND AC-QUAINTANCES. Boston & NY: Houghton, Mifflin, 1897. 2nd ed. 363pp. Orig rough grn cl. Owner sig, faint offsetting to eps, else NF. *CHAPEL HILL.* $50

Harris, Joel Chandler. SISTER JANE, HER FRIENDS AND AC-QUAINTANCES. Boston & NY: Houghton, Mifflin, 1896. 1st ed. 363pp. Orig grn cl. Lib bkpl, blindstamp, else VG+. *CHAPEL HILL.* $75

Harris, Joel Chandler. TALES OF THE HOME FOLKS IN PEACE AND WAR. Boston & NY: Houghton, Mifflin, 1898. 1st ed. 8vo, 417pp. Orig dec dk grn cl. Spine sl dulled, else NF. BAL 7141. *CHAPEL HILL.* $80

Harris, Joel Chandler. TALES OF THE HOME FOLKS IN PEACE AND WAR. Boston & NY: Houghton, Mifflin, 1898. 1st ed. 417pp. Orig dec lt grn cl. Fine. *CHAPEL HILL.* $125

Harris, Joel Chandler. THE CHRONICLES OF AUNT MINERVY ANN. NY: Scribner's, 1899. 1st ed, 1st binding state, w/edges trimmed. 210pp. Orig pict brn cl, teg. Rear hinge cracked, front hinge starting, else VG. *CHAPEL HILL.* $75

Harris, Joel Chandler. THE MAKING OF A STATESMAN AND OTHER STORIES. NY: McClure, Phillips, 1902. 1st ed. Tan cl, tooled in blind. NF. *CAPTAIN'S BOOKSHELF.* $75

Harris, Joel Chandler. THE MAKING OF A STATESMAN AND OTHER STORIES. NY: McClure, Phillips & Co, 1902. 1st ed. Orig lt brn cl. Bkpl, else Fine. *CHAPEL HILL.* $75

Harris, Joel Chandler. UNCLE REMUS AND HIS FRIENDS. Boston: Houghton Mifflin, 1914. 1st ed. Spine, rear panel a touch faded, else beautiful in pict cl. *CAPTAIN'S BOOKSHELF.* $75

Harris, Joel Chandler. UNCLE REMUS. HIS SONGS AND HIS SAYINGS. THE FOLK-LORE OF THE OLD PLANTATION. NY, 1881. 1st ed. Illus by Frederick S. Church and James H. Moser. Aeg; bound by Bennett, NY, in full red calf, raised bands gilt, inlaid small rabbit, white and gilt, on front cvr. Orig pict cl of cvrs and spine bound in. *POLYANTHOS.* $650

Harris, Joel Chandler. UNCLE REMUS. Illus by A.B. Frost. New/revised ed. Appleton Century Crofts, 1921. Spine sunned, o/w VG. *MAD DOG.* $15

Harris, Joel Chandler. UNCLE REMUS....Seong Moy (illus). NY: LEC, 1957. Ed ltd to 1500 numbered, signed by Seong Moy. Slip-case. *KARMIOLE.* $75

Harris, Joel Chandler. WALLY WANDEROON AND HIS STORY-TELLING MACHINE. NY: McClure, Phillips & Co, 1903. 1st ed, prob. 1st state, w/8 pgs ads. Orig pict tan cl. Hinges cracked and repaired, small ink markings on rear pastedown. Near VG. *CHAPEL HILL.* $100

Harris, John. THE ARTIST AND THE COUNTRY HOUSE. London: Sotheby Parke Bernet, (1979). 1st ed. Dj. Fine. *WEBER.* $55

Harris, Joseph. HARRIS ON THE PIG. NY: Orange Judd, 1911. VG. *AMERICAN BOTANIST.* $30

Harris, Mark. BANG THE DRUM SLOWLY. NY: Knopf, 1956. 1st ed. Fine in dj sl sunned at spine. *CAPTAIN'S BOOKSHELF.* $100

Harris, Mark. BANG THE DRUM SLOWLY. NY: Knopf, 1956. 1st ed. Signed: "Mark Harris, Oakland, 4-2-56" on flyleaf. Some foxing to spine & endpapers o/w VG in dj which is worn to edges. *BERNARD.* $125

Harris, Mark. IT LOOKED LIKE FOREVER. NY, (1979). 1st ed. Signed presentation. Fine in like dj. *POLYANTHOS.* $40

Harris, Mark. MARK THE GLOVE BOY. Macmillan, 1964. 1st ed. Fine in dj with stain at front flyleaf fold. *STAHR.* $25

Harris, Mark. THE SOUTHPAW. NY, 1953. 1st ed. VG in dj (few spine chips, spine little sunned). *POLYANTHOS.* $75

Harris, Sarah H. UNWRITTEN CHAPTER OF SALT LAKE 1851-1901. (NY, privately ptd 1901). 1st ed. Ptd in ltd ed. 89pp. Orig grn cl w/title stamped in gilt on front cover. Fine. Howes H231. Very scarce in bright condition. *GINSBERG.* $500

Harris, Sheldon. BLUES WHO'S WHO. New Rochelle: Arlington House, 1979. 1st ed. Fine in NF dj w/chips. *BEASLEY.* $85

Harris, Stanley. BASEBALL—HOW TO PLAY IT. Stokes, 1925. 1st ed. Signed by sports writer Bill Bryson. VG w/o dj. *PLAPINGER.* $100

Harris, Thaddeus Mason. BIOGRAPHICAL MEMORIALS OF JAMES OGLETHORPE FOUNDER OF THE COLONY OF GEORGIA, IN NORTH AMERICA. Boston, ptd for the author, 1841. 1st ed. (22),424pp. Fldg map, 3 plts. Orig cl, leather label on spine, light discoloration at lower spine. Howes H232. George Marshall's copy, w/his plt. *GINSBERG.* $250

Harris, Thomas. BLACK SUNDAY. NY: G.P. Putnam's Sons, 1975. 1st ed. Fine in VG dj (sl darkened spine; scrape front panel; short internal tape mend that has bled through at top of front panel; tears). *MORDIDA.* $75

Harris, Thomas. BLACK SUNDAY. NY: Putnam, 1975. 1st ed. Fine; minor foxing at dj flap fold. *ELSE FINE.* $85

Harris, Thomas. RED DRAGON. NY: G.P. Putnam's Sons, 1981. 1st ed. Fine in dj. *MORDIDA.* $65

Harris, Thomas. RED DRAGON. NY: Putnam, (1981). 1st ed. Fine-in Fine- dj. *AARD.* $40

Harris, Thomas. RED DRAGON. NY: Putnam, 1981. 1st ed. Fine in dj. *ELSE FINE.* $65

Harris, Thomas. THE SILENCE OF THE LAMBS. NY, 1988. 1st ed. Adv reading copy. Fine in pict wrappers. *MORDIDA.* $50

Harris, Thomas. THE SILENCE OF THE LAMBS. NY, 1988. 1st ed. VF in dj. *MORDIDA.* $45

Harris, Timothy. GOOD NIGHT AND GOOD-BYE. NY: Delacorte Press, 1979. 1st ed. Advance review copy, slip, photo laid in. Fine in dj. *MORDIDA.* $40

Harris, Wilfred. NEURITIS AND NEURALGIA. London, 1926. 1st ed. 418pp. Geoffrey Jefferson's copy, w/his bkpl. Scarce. *FYE.* $125

Harrison, B.S. FORTUNE FAVORS THE BRAVE. Ward-Richie, 1953. 1st ptg. Fine in chipped dj. *VARNER.* $30

Harrison, Carter H. A SUMMER'S OUTING, AND THE OLD MAN'S STORY. Chicago: Dibble, 1891. 1st ed. Wrappers worn at extremities, o/w VG. *LAURIE.* $40

Harrison, J.E. and D.S. MacColl. GREEK VASE PAINTINGS. London: T. Fisher Unwin, 1894. 43 plts. Bkpl. Good. *ARCHAEOLOGIA.* $150

Harrison, James. PLAIN SONG. NY: Norton, (1965). 1st ed, 1st bk. Orig ptd wraps. VG. Signed. *CHAPEL HILL.* $175

Harrison, James. PLAIN SONG. NY: Norton, (1965). 1st ed, 1st bk. Orig olive grn cl. Gilt spine lettering sl dulled, else Fine in price-clipped dj (sm tear rear panel). Signed. *CHAPEL HILL.* $225

Harrison, Jim. A GOOD DAY TO DIE. NY: Simon & Schuster, (1973). 1st ed. NF in dj w/traces of edgewear. *ROBBINS.* $225

Harrison, Jim. A GOOD DAY TO DIE. NY: Simon & Schuster, (1973). 1st ed. Remainder line bottom edge of pages, o/w Fine in dj. *LOPEZ.* $275

Harrison, Jim. A GOOD DAY TO DIE. NY: Simon & Schuster, 1973. 1st ed. VF in price clipped dj. Inscribed w/self portrait in caricature. *CAPTAIN'S BOOKSHELF.* $300

Harrison, Jim. FARMER. NY, 1976. 1st ed. Fine in dj. *PETTLER.* $75

Harrison, Jim. FARMER. NY: Viking, (1976). 1st ed. Fine in Fine dj. *LOPEZ.* $50

Harrison, Jim. JUST BEFORE DARK. Livingston: Clark City Press, (1991). One of 250 specially-bound, numbered, signed. VF in slipcase. *CAPTAIN'S BOOKSHELF.* $150

Harrison, Jim. LEGENDS OF THE FALL. London: Collins, 1980. 1st Eng. Fine in dj. *STAHR.* $35.

Harrison, Jim. LEGENDS OF THE FALL. NY: Delacorte, (1979). Uncorrected proof. NF in ptd red wraps. *CAPTAIN'S BOOKSHELF.* $150

Harrison, Jim. LETTERS TO YESENIN. Fremont, MI: Sumac Press, (1973). 1st ed, wrappered issue. NF in pict wraps. *CAPTAIN'S BOOKSHELF.* $60

Harrison, Jim. LETTERS TO YESNIN AND RETURNING TO EARTH. LA: Center Publications, 1979. 1st ed. Fine in wraps. *ELSE FINE.* $45

Harrison, Jim. LOCATIONS. NY: Norton, (1968). 1st ed. 1,250 copies. Fine in dj. *BERNARD.* $125

Harrison, Jim. LOCATIONS. NY: Norton, 1968. 1st ed. Fine; minor wear spine top of dj. *ELSE FINE.* $150

Harrison, Jim. OUTLYER AND GHAZALS. NY: Simon & Schuster, (1971). 1st ed. Sm rmdr mk bottom pg edges, else Fine in VG+ dj (creased). *BERNARD.* $300

Harrison, Jim. PLAIN SONG. NY: Norton, 1965. 1st ed. Fine in dj. Signed. *ELSE FINE.* $300

Harrison, Jim. RETURNING TO EARTH. (Berkeley): Ithaca House, (1977). 1st ed. Fine in ptd wraps. *CAPTAIN'S BOOKSHELF.* $225

Harrison, Jim. SUNDOG. NY: Dutton/Lawrence, (1984). 1st ed. Fine in NF dj w/trace of edgewear lower back panel. *ROBBINS.* $30

Harrison, Jim. THE THEORY AND PRACTICE OF RIVERS AND NEW POEMS. Livingston: Clark City Press, (1989). 1st ed thus. New in dj. Signed. *CAPTAIN'S BOOKSHELF.* $50

Harrison, Jim. THE WOMAN LIT BY FIREFLIES. Boston: Houghton Mifflin, 1990. 1st ed. Orig cl-backed boards. Fine in dj. Signed. *CHAPEL HILL.* $50

Harrison, Jim. THE WOMAN LIT BY FIREFLIES. Boston: Houghton, 1990. 1st ed. New in dj. Signed. *CAPTAIN'S BOOKSHELF.* $45

Harrison, Jim. WARLOCK. NY, 1981. One of 250 signed, numbered. Gold edged pp. VF in NF slipcase. *PETTLER.* $100

Harrison, Jim. WARLOCK. NY: Delacorte, 1981. 1st ed. VF in dj. *ELSE FINE.* $60

Harrison, Jim. WOLF. NY: Simon & Schuster, 1971. 1st ed. Author's 1st novel. Fine in dj. *LAME DUCK.* $225

Harrison, Juanita. MY GREAT WIDE BEAUTIFUL WORLD. NY: Macmillan, 1936. 1st ed. Fine but for light wear to spine ends, in lightly used dj. *BEASLEY.* $40

Harrison, Lt. THE THRILLING STARTLING AND WONDERFUL NARRATIVE OF....Cincinnati: by author, 1848 (i.e., New Haven: Frederick Beinecke, 1957) orig wraps. Sl worn. 1/300 issued. *SECOND LIFE.* $45

Harrison, Michael. BEYOND BAKER STREET. Indianapolis: Bobbs-Merrill, 1976. 1st Amer ed. Fine in dj (tiny tear, wear). *MORDIDA.* $45

Harrison, Michael. CLARENCE: WAS HE JACK THE RIPPER? NY: Drake Pubs, 1972. 1st Amer ed. Fine in dj w/minor wear at spine ends and along top edge. *MORDIDA.* $35

Harrison, Michael. I, SHERLOCK HOLMES. NY: E.P. Dutton, 1977. 1st Amer ed. Fine in dj w/crease on inner front flap. *MORDIDA.* $30

Harrison, Michael. THE EXPLOITS OF CHEVALIER DUPIN. Arkham House, 1968. 1st ed. VF in dj. *MADLE.* $65

Harrison, Michael. THE EXPLOITS OF THE CHEVALIER DUPIN. Ellery Queen intro. Sauk City: Mycroft & Moran, 1968. 1st ed. Fine in dj. *MORDIDA.* $60

Harrison, Michael. THE LONDON OF SHERLOCK HOLMES. NY: Drake Pubs, 1972. 1st Amer ed. Fine in dj (scrapes spine edge, base of spine; sm sticker removed). *MORDIDA.* $45

Harrison, Michael. THE WORLD OF SHERLOCK HOLMES. NY: E P. Dutton, 1975. 1st Amer ed. Fine in dj. *MORDIDA.* $35

Harrison, Robert. THE DUBLIN DISSECTOR, OR MANUAL OF ANATOMY TOGETHER WITH THE ELEMENTS OF PATHOLOGY. NY, 1840. 1st Amer ed. Recent red buckram w/white lettering. Ex-lib. *FYE.* $25

Harrison, Shelby M. SOCIAL CONDITIONS IN AN AMERICAN CITY. NY, 1920. Minor shelfwear. *ARTIS.* $17.50

Harrison, William. THE THEOLOGIAN. NY: Harper & Row, (c1965). 1st ed, 1st bk. Fine in dj. *HELLER.* $50

Harriss, Will. THE BAY PSALM BOOK MURDER. NY: Walker, 1983. 1st ed. VF, minor rubs to dj corners. *ELSE FINE.* $85

Harriss, Will. TIMOR MORTIS. NY: Walker, 1986. 1st ed. Fine in dj. *ELSE FINE.* $35

Harrod, Howard. MISSION AMONG THE BLACKFEET. 1st ed. VF in F dj. *OREGON.* $35

Harshberger, John W. THE BOTANISTS OF PHILADELPHIA AND THEIR WORK. Phila: Author, 1899. 457pp. Cloth margins rubbed, contents VG. Lib mark on spine but nothing internal. *AMERICAN BOTANIST.* $175

Harston, J.E. COMANCHE LAND. Naylor, 1963. 1st ptg. Fine in clipped o/w Fine dj. *VARNER.* $30

Hart, Fred H. THE SAZERAC LYING CLUB. SF, 1878. NF. *POLYANTHOS.* $60

Hart, Fred H. THE SAZERAC LYING CLUB. SF: Henry Keller, 1878. 1st ed. 240pp. Frontis. Worn pub's cl, lacks ffep. Good tight. *SECOND LIFE.* $125

Hart, Henry. A RELEVANT MEMOIR, THE STORY OF THE EQUINOX COOPERATIVE PRESS. Three Mountains, 1977. 111pp. Illus. Fine in Fine dj. *BEBBAH.* $30

Hart, Herbert M. OLD FORTS OF THE FAR WEST. NY: Bonanza Books, c1965. Dj. *HUDSON.* $45

Hart, Herbert M. OLD FORTS OF THE NORTHWEST. Seattle: Superior, (1963). Lower spine corner bumped. VG in dj. *ARTIS.* $16.50

Hart, Herbert M. OLD FORTS OF THE SOUTHWEST. Seattle, (1964). 1st ed. A little dj wear o/w Fine. *PRATT.* $22.50

Hart, I.B. THE MECHANICAL INVESTIGATIONS OF LEONARDO DA VINCI. London: Chapman & Hall, 1925. VG. *BOOKCELL.* $40

Hart, I.R.G. TORTURE ISLAND. NY: Simon & Schuster, 1928. 1st ed, 1st bk. VF, sm chip at spine head of pict dj. *ELSE FINE.* $35

Hart, James D. THE PRIVATE PRESS VENTURES OF SAMUEL LLOYD OSBORNE AND R.L.S. SF: Bk Club of CA, 1966. 1/500. Facs pamphlets in pocket at end, 2pp photo illus. Black-stamped cl. *DAWSON'S.* $50

Hart, Katherine (ed). PEASE PORRIDGE HOT....& HOME REMEDIES OF THE PEASE FAMILY. (Austin): Encino Press, 1967. Mint. *LAURIE.* $20

Hart, Roy. A FOX IN THE NIGHT. London: Macmillan, 1988. 1st ed. VF in dj. *MORDIDA.* $40

Hart, Roy. A PRETTY PLACE FOR A MURDER. London: Macmillan, 1987. 1st ed. VF in dj. *MORDIDA.* $45

Hart, Roy. SEASCAPE WITH DEAD FIGURES. London: Macmillan, 1987. 1st ed. Signed. VF in dj. *MORDIDA.* $60

Hart, Scott. THE MOON IS WANING. NY: Derrydale Press, (1939). 1st ed. #926/950. Orig cl. F. *McGOWAN.* $125

Hart, William S. and Mary Hart. PINTO BEN AND OTHER STORIES. NY, (1919). 1st ed. Orig flexible calf printed in gilt. NF. Inscribed. *DIAMOND.* $75

Hart, William S. A LIGHTER OF FLAMES. NY, (1923). 1st ed. 4 color plts. Sl soiled, o/w VG. 1/1000 signed, inscribed by Hart. *DIAMOND.* $75

Hart, William S. HOOFBEATS. NY, 1933. 1st ed. Cvrs sl stained & soiled, o/w VG. Inscribed. *DIAMOND.* $75

Hart, William S. MY LIFE EAST AND WEST. Boston, 1929. 1st ed. Inscribed. Former owner's sig and date verso of front fly, moderate foxing on title page, light elsewhere, backstrip chipped. Thus, Good. *BAADE.* $75

Hart, William S. TOLD UNDER A WHITE OAK TREE....Boston, (1922). 1st ed. Spine sl faded, o/w VG. Inscribed. *DIAMOND.* $75

Harte, Bret and Mark Twain. SKETCHES OF THE SIXTIES. SF, 1926. Ltd ed, 2000. Uncut. Traces of removed scotch tape inside covers and feps. Fine in dj (spine little sunned, tiny edge nick, sl soiled, traces of removed scotch tape flap folds). *POLYANTHOS.* $35

Harte, Bret. BRET HARTE'S COMPLETE POEMS. London: Chatto & Windus, 1887. Author's copyright ed. Cloth, beveled boards. 324pp. Teg, deckle edges. VG. *CONNOLLY & WADE.* $45

Harte, Bret. BY SHORE AND SEDGE. Houghton Mifflin, 1885. 1st ed. Blue cl. Fine. *AUTHORS OF THE WEST.* $25

Harte, Bret. CLARENCE. Boston: Houghton Mifflin, 1895. 1st Amer ed. Front inner hinge cracked. *MUELLER.* $20

Harte, Bret. ECHOES OF THE FOOT-HILLS. James R. Osgood & Co, 1875. 1st ed. Fine, bkpl. *AUTHORS OF THE WEST.* $50

Harte, Bret. OPENINGS ON THE OLD TRAIL. Boston, 1902. 1st ed. *HEINOLDT.* $25

Harte, Bret. POEMS. Boston: J.R. Osgood, 1871. 3rd ptg. Sig. Spine tips worn. Little corner wear. Spine sunned, o/w VG. BAL 7253. *DIAMOND.* $35

Harte, Bret. SALOMY JANE. Boston: Houghton Mifflin, 1910. Illus by Harrison Fisher and Arthur I. Keller. Dec page borders, dec cl, rather loose in binding, some wear to binding. *DAWSON'S.* $30

Harte, Bret. SAN FRANCISCO IN 1866. Bk Club of CA, 1951. 1st ltd ed of 400 ptd by the Grabhorn Press. George R. Stewart, Edwin S. Russell (eds). Foldout plt. Club brochure laid in. Fine in plain dj. *AUTHORS OF THE WEST.* $125

Harte, Bret. THANKFUL BLOSSOM: A ROMANCE OF THE JERSEYS 1779. James R. Osgood & Co, 1877. 1st ed. Sl rubbing to spine, but Fine. *AUTHORS OF THE WEST.* $75

Harte, Bret. THE QUEEN OF THE PIRATE ISLE. London: Chatto and Windus, (n.d.). Ins. 1886. Kate Greenaway (illus). Dec cl. Aeg. Covers somewhat darkened, else NF. *ACADEMIC LIBRARY.* $175

Harte, Geoffrey Bret (ed). THE LETTERS OF BRET HARTE. Houghton Mifflin, 1926. 1st ed. Fine. *AUTHORS OF THE WEST.* $25

Harte, Glynn Boyd. TEMPLES OF POWER. (London): The Cygnet Press, (1979). 1st ed. Gavin Stamp (intro), John Betjeman (foreword). 16 orig colored lithos, 1/4 calf, dec boards, dj. One of 250 signed by Harte & Stamp. VF. *JAFFE.* $350

Harting, J.E. BIBLIOTHECA ACCIPITRARIA. London: The Holland Press, 1977. 2nd imp. NF. *OLD LONDON.* $50

Hartje, Robert G. VON DORN, THE LIFE AND TIMES OF A CONFEDERATE GENERAL. Charlotte, (1967). 1st ed. Light dj wear o/w Fine. *PRATT.* $40

Hartley, B. Cecil. LIFE OF DANIEL BOONE. Phila: John E. Potter & Company, n.d. VG. *GIBBS.* $25

Hartley, L.P. THE HIRELING. NY, 1958. 1st ed. Fine in VG dj. *POLYANTHOS.* $25

Hartley, L.P. THE TRAVELING GRAVE AND OTHER STORIES. Sauk City: Arkham House, 1948. 1st ed, ltd to 2047. Fine in dj with some traces of rubbing to edges. *ROBBINS.* $100

Hartley, L.P. THE TRAVELING GRAVE. Arkham House, 1948. 1st ed. NF in sl soiled dj. *MADLE.* $100

Hartley, Marsden. TWENTY-FIVE POEMS. (Paris: Contact, 1923). 1st ed. Total prtg around 300. Ptd wrappers. Virtually New, unopened, in orig glassine sleeve. Signed. *DERMONT.* $1000

Hartman, C.G. POSSUMS. Austin: Univ of TX, 1952. Photos, drawings. NF in VG dj. *MIKESH.* $27.50

Hartwig, Dr. G. HEROES OF THE POLAR WORLD. London/NY: Longmans, Green, and Co., 1892. VG. *PARMER.* $40

Harvester, Simon. CAT'S CRADLE. London: Jarrolds, 1952. 1st ed. VG in VG dj with light soil. *BEBBAH.* $20

Harvester, Simon. LUCIFER AT SUNSET. London: Jarrolds, 1953. 1st ed. Fine in VG dj with light soil, edgewear. *BEBBAH.* $25

Harvester, Simon. TIGER IN THE NORTH. London: Jarrolds, 1955. 1st ed. VG in VG dj. *BEBBAH.* $20

Harvey, A.G. DOUGLAS OF THE FIR, A BIOGRAPHY. Cambridge, 1947. Cl, dj (some wear). *SUTTON.* $37

HARVEY CUSHING'S SEVENTIETH BIRTHDAY PARTY. APRIL 8,1939. Springfield, 1939. 1st ed. *FYE.* $100

Harvey, John. EARLY GARDENING CATALOGUES. London: Phillimore, 1972. As New in dj. *AMERICAN BOTANIST.* $25

Harvey, John. ROUGH TREATMENT. NY: Holt, 1990. 1st Amer ed. Review copy, signed. Pub's slip laid in. VF in dj. *SILVER DOOR.* $35

Harvey, Samuel. THE HISTORY OF HEMOSTASIS. NY, 1929. 1st ed. *FYE.* $50

Harvey, William. CHURCH OF THE HOLY SEPULCHRE JERUSALEM. STRUCTURAL SURVEY. FINAL REPORT. Oxford, 1935. 5 fldg plts. *O'NEILL.* $60

Harvey, William. DE MOTU LOCALI ANIMALIUM, 1627. Cambridge, 1959. Ltd ed. Dj. *FYE.* $100

Harvey, William. MOVEMENT OF THE HEART AND BLOOD IN ANIMALS. Trans K.J. Franklin. Springfield, 1957. Ltd ed. Dj. *FYE.* $60

Harvey, William. STRUCTURAL SURVEY OF THE CHURCH OF THE NATIVITY BETHLEHEM. Oxford, 1935. 6 fldg plans. *O'NEILL.* $60

Harvey, William. THE ANATOMICAL EXERCISES OF DR. WILLIAM HARVEY: DE MOTU CORDIS 1628: DE CIRCULATIONE SANGUINIS 1649: THE FIRST ENGLISH TEXT OF 1653 NOW NEWLY EDITED BY GEOFFREY KEYNES. London, 1928. Ed of 1450 ptd at Nonesuch Press. *FYE.* $325

Harwell, Richard B. (ed.) SONGS OF THE CONFEDERACY. NY, (1951). 1st ed. Signed. VG in VG dj. *McGOWAN.* $125

Harwell, Richard B. (ed.) THE CONFEDERATE READER. NY, 1957. 1st ed. VG. *PRATT.* $27.50

Harwell, Richard B. (ed). THE UNION READER. AS THE NORTH SAW THE WAR. NY, (1958). 1st ed. Dj. VG. *PRATT.* $30

Harwell, Richard B. THE UNION READER. NY: Longmans, Green, 1958. 1st ed. Fine in Good dj. *CONNOLLY & WADE.* $37.50

Haskell, Frank Aretas. THE BATTLE OF GETTYSBURG. Bruce Catton (ed). Boston: Houghton Mifflin/Cambridge: Riverside Press, 1958. 1st ed. Fine in edgeworn dj. *CONNOLLY & WADE.* $30

Haskell, William B. TWO YEARS IN THE KLONDIKE AND ALASKAN GOLD FIELDS; A THRILLING NARRATIVE. Hartford: Hartford Publishing Company, 1898. 1st ed. Frontis loose, else VG. *LAURIE.* $150

Haskin, Frederic J. THE PANAMA CANAL. GC: Doubleday, Page, 1913. 1st ed. 1 color fldg plt. Staining, plt repaired, o/w Good. *DIAMOND.* $15

Haskin, L.L. WILD FLOWERS OF THE PACIFIC COAST, ETC. Portland, OR, 1934. 1st ed. VG. *MIKESH.* $25

Haskins, C.P. OF ANTS AND MEN. NY, (1939). *SUTTON.* $35

Haslam, Gerald W. and James D. Houston (eds). CALIFORNIA HEARTLAND: WRITING FROM THE GREAT CENTRAL VALLEY. Capra Press, (1978). 1st ed. New in dj. *AUTHORS OF THE WEST.* $15

Haspels, C.H. Emilie. THE HIGHLANDS OF PHRYGIA: SITES AND MONUMENTS. 2 vols. Princeton: Princeton Univ Press, 1971. 7 figs. Dj. Good. *ARCHAEOLOGIA.* $150

Hassanein, A.M. THE LOST OASES. BEING A NARRATIVE ACCOUNT OF THE AUTHOR'S EXPLORATIONS INTO THE MORE REMOTE PARTS OF THE LIBYAN DESERT AND HIS REDISCOVERY OF TWO LOST OASES. NY: Century, 1925. 1st ed. Minor foxing few pages. NF in NF dj. *GREAT EPIC.* $135

Hassin, George. HISTOPATHOLOGY OF THE PERIPHERAL AND CENTRAL NERVOUS SYSTEMS. Baltimore, 1933. 1st ed. *FYE.* $40

Hassler, Jon. STAGGERFORD. NY: Atheneum, 1977. 1st ed. Author's 1st bk. Rev copy w/slip and pub card laid in. Sl cocked, tasteful bkpl. Fine in NF dj. *LAME DUCK.* $165

Hassler, Jon. THE LOVE HUNTER. Morrow, 1981. Advance reading copy. Fine in pict wrappers. *STAHR.* $25

Hassler, Warren W., Jr. COMMANDERS OF THE ARMY OF THE POTOMAC. Baton Rouge, (1962). 1st ed. VG+ in dj. *PRATT.* $35

Hassler, Warren W., Jr. GENERAL GEORGE B. MCCLELLAN, SHIELD OF THE UNION. Baton Rouge, (1957). 1st ed. VG+. *PRATT.* $37.50

Hassler, Warren W., Jr. GENERAL GEORGE B. MCCLELLAN. Baton Rouge, 1957. 1st ed. *GINSBERG.* $25

Hassler, William Woods. COLONEL JOHN PELHAM, LEE'S BOY ARTILLERIST. Chapel Hill, (1960). 1st ed. 185pp. VG+ in dj. *PRATT.* $37.50

Hassrick, Peter H. FREDERIC REMINGTON. Pub by Harry Abrams, Inc w/Amon Carter Museum of Western Art. 1973. 94 plts, (59 in color). Some are fldg. *HEINOLDT.* $25

Hassrick, Peter. FREDERICK REMINGTON. NY: Abrams, (1973). 1st ed. Fine in Fine dj. *AARD.* $60

Hastings, Frank. A RANCHMAN'S RECOLLECTIONS. Breeder's Gazette, 1921. 1st ed. 13 plts. Very small tear at upper spine edges. VG. Howes H287. *OREGON.* $200

Hastings, John. THE PRACTICE OF SURGERY: EMBRACING MINOR SURGERY AND THE APPLICATION OF DRESSINGS. Phila, 1850. 1st ed. 479pp. Scattered foxing. VF. *FYE.* $300

Hatch, John Davis. THE HISTORIC CHURCH SILVER....Norfolk, VA: Norfolk Mus of Arts & Sci, 1953, NF. Wraps. *BACKROOM.* $20

Hatcher, Harlan. LAKE ERIE. Indianapolis: Bobbs Merrill, 1945. 1st ed. NF in Good dj. Signed. *CONNOLLY & WADE.* $45

Hatcher, Robert and Martin Wilbert. THE PHARMACOPOEIA AND THE PHYSICIAN: A SERIES OF ARTICLES WHICH ORIGINALLY APPEARED IN THE JOURNAL OF THE AMERICAN MEDICAL ASSOCIATION...Chicago 1908. 2nd ed. *FYE.* $100

Hatlem, John. THE WAR AGAINST GERMANY AND ITALY: MEDITERRANEAN AND ADJACENT AREAS. Washington: Dept. of the Army/USGPO, 1951. 1st ed. Spine a trifle sunned, o/w VG+. *ARCHER.* $30

Hattaway, Herman and Archer Jones. HOW THE NORTH WON, A MILITARY HISTORY....Urbana, (1983). 1st ed. VG+ in dj. *PRATT.* $37.50

Haughton, Percy D. FOOTBALL & HOW TO WATCH IT. Boston: Marshall Jones Co, 1922. 1st ed. Fine in soiled, edgeworn dj. *CAPTAIN'S BOOKSHELF.* $75

Hauk, Z. William. THE STONE SLOOPS OF CHEBEAGUE...2nd ed, rev. Boston, 1953. *LEFKOWICZ.* $85

Hausman, L.A. BIRDS OF PREY OF NORTHEASTERN NORTH AMERICA. New Brunswick, 1948. 1/2 cl (lt edge wear), dj, sm tears. *SUTTON.* $38

Haven, E. O. RHETORIC: A TEXT-BOOK. NY: Harper & Brothers, 1869. 1st ed. Minor wear, else VG. *OLD LONDON.* $45

Havighurst, Walter. VEIN OF IRON. Cleveland, (1958). 1st ed. VG. *ARTIS.* $17.50

Haviland, Maud D. A SUMMER ON THE YENESEI (1914) London: Edward Arnold, 1915. 1st ed. Small tear top of spine, else Near VG. *BLUE DRAGON.* $50

Hawes, Mrs. Joel. MEMOIRS OF MRS. MARY VAN LENNEP... WIFE OF THE REV. HENRY VAN LENNEP... MISSIONARY IN TURKEY, BY HER MOTHER... Hartford, 1848. 382 pp. *O'NEILL.* $45

Hawgood, John A. AMERICA'S WESTERN FRONTIERS....TRANS-MISSISSIPPI WEST. NY, 1967. 1st Amer ed. Fine in VG dj. *CONNOLLY & WADE.* $40

Hawk, John. THE HOUSE OF SUDDEN SLEEP. NY: Mystery League, 1930. 1st ed. Fine in pict Art Deco dj. *ELSE FINE.* $35

Hawken, Paul. THE MAGIC OF FINDHORN. NY: Holt & Rinehart, (1975). 1st ed. Fine in NF dj. *LOPEZ.* $35

Hawkes, John. DEATH, SLEEP & THE TRAVELER. NY: New Directions, 1974. 1st ed. VF in dj. *ELSE FINE.* $30

Hawkes, John. DEATH, SLEEP & THE TRAVELER. NY: New Directions, 1974. 1st ed. Fine dj. *JUVELIS.* $25

Hawkes, John. INNOCENCE IN EXTREMIS. 1/4 morocco & boards. NY: Grenfell Press, 1985. 1st ed. One of 85 (entire ed of 118) signed by Hawkes & Solein. Mint. *JAFFE.* $275

Hawkes, John. LUNAR LANDSCAPES. NY: New Directions, 1963. 1st ed. Fine in dj. *BEASLEY.* $50

Hawkes, John. LUNAR LANDSCAPES: STORIES AND NOVELS 1949-1963. (NY): New Directions, (1969). One of 150 specially bound, signed. Fine in slipcase. *CAPTAIN'S BOOKSHELF.* $125.

Hawkes, John. SECOND SKIN. Norfolk: New Directions (1964). 1st ed. Bkpl front pastedown else Fine in spine sunned VG dj. *DORN.* $35

Hawkes, John. THE BEETLE LEG. NY: New Directions (1951). 1st issue binding in orange cl. Fine in a NF dj. *DORN.* $200

Hawkes, John. THE BEETLE LEG. NY: New Directions, 1951. 1st ed. 1st state orange binding. Some text underlining, else Fine in dj. *ELSE FINE.* $125

Hawkes, John. THE BLOOD ORANGES. NY: New Directions, (1971). 1st ed. VF in dj. *ELSE FINE.* $65

Hawkes, John. THE CANNIBAL. Norfolk: New Directions (1949). 1st state binding in gray cl. VG+ in dust soiled VG dj. *DORN.* $200

Hawkes, John. THE CANNIBAL. Norfolk: New Directions, 1949. 1st ed. NF, minor edgewear, tiny chips at dj corners. 1st state gray binding. *ELSE FINE.* $175

Hawkes, John. THE CANNIBAL. Norfolk: New Directions, 1949. 1st ed. Inscribed. Fine in the correct gray binding, in Nice dj but for sm chip on front panel and another on back. *BEASLEY.* $225

Hawkes, John. THE GOOSE ON THE GRAVE. NY: New Directions, 1954. 1st ed. Inscribed. Fine in Fine dj. *BEASLEY.* $225

Hawkes, John. THE INNOCENT PARTY. NY: New Directions, 1966. Fine in Fine dj. *BEASLEY.* $50

Hawkes, N. EARLY SCIENTIFIC INSTRUMENTS. Abbeville Press, 1981. *BOOKCELL.* $100

Hawkins, Evelyn. VIETNAM NURSE. (NY): Zebra, (1984). 384pp. Pb orig. Fine. *AKA.* $25

Hawkins, Sir John. A GENERAL HISTORY OF THE SCIENCE & PRACTICE OF MUSIC. NY: Dover, 1963. 2 vols. VG in dj. *BANCROFT.* $46

Hawkins, Wallace. THE CASE OF JOHN C. WATROUS...A POLITICAL STORY OF HIGH CRIMES AND MIS-DEMEANORS. Dallas: Univ Press in Dallas, 1950. 1st ed. One of 1,200. Fine in dj. *LAURIE.* $50

Hawksley, Enid Dickens (comp). CHARLES DICKENS BIRTHDAY BOOK. London: Faber & Faber, (1948). 1st ed. 8vo, pict cloth, signed and dated Feb. 1949. Illus by Edward Ardizzone. NF. *GREAT EXPECTATIONS.* $35

Hawley, Walter A. ORIENTAL RUGS ANTIQUE AND MODERN. NY: Tudor,1937. 11 color plts, fldg frontis reinforced. Slipcase. *WEBER.* $150

Hawley, Walter A. ORIENTAL RUGS: ANTIQUE & MODERN. NY: Tudor Pub Co, 1937. VG in VG chipped dj. *BACKROOM.* $100

Hawthorne, Hildegarde. CALIFORNIA'S MISSIONS. NY: Appleton Century, 1942. 1st ed. Almost Fine in VG dj. *AARD.* $30

Hawthorne, Nathaniel. A WONDER BOOK FOR BOYS AND GIRLS. Boston, NY, and Cambridge, (1884). 6th ed. 1st illus ed. Pict red, gold cl. Beveled edges, aeg. NF. *McCLINTOCK.* $45

Hawthorne, Nathaniel. LIFE OF FRANKLIN PIERCE. Boston: Ticknor, Reed, and Fields, 1852. 4pp pub's cat,144 pp. Engr frontis. Orig blind-stamped brn cl, stained; dampstain last 14 leaves. Cl reback w/orig backstrip. Bkpls. Cl slipcase. *SCHOYER'S.* $100

Hawthorne, Nathaniel. OUR OLD HOME: A SERIES OF ENGLISH SKETCHES. Boston: Ticknor & Fields, 1863. 398pp, (1)p ads. Orig blindstamped brown cl. Small abrasion and early bkseller's blindstamp on ffep, else VG. 1st ed, 1st issue, w/ads on page (399). 1863 ownership sig in ink on title page and in pencil on half-title and front fly. *CHAPEL HILL.* $175

Hawthorne, Nathaniel. PASSAGES FROM THE AMERICAN NOTE-BOOKS OF NATHANIEL HAWTHORNE. Boston: Ticknor and Fields, 1868. 1st ed. 2 vols. Orig green cl, cvrs blindstamped, spine ornamented and lettered in gilt. Both vols in 1st binding state. Sl dampstaining to lower center margins vol I. Extrems sl rubbed, Fine. BAL 7632. *POLYANTHOS.* $350

Hawthorne, Nathaniel. SEPTIMIUS FELTON: OR THE ELIXIR OF LIFE. (Una Hawthorne, Robert Browning, eds). Boston, 1872. 1st ed. 229pp. Eps a little dusty, else Nice in orig brown stamped cl, nick to top of spine. BAL 7638, in the primary binding of terra-cotta cl. Pub posthumously. *SECOND LIFE.* $75

Hawthorne, Nathaniel. THE HOUSE OF SEVEN GABLES. Introduction by Van Wyck Brooks. NY: LEC, 1935. One of 1/1500 illus, signed by Valenti Angelo. Fine in silver slipcase (rubbed at extrems). *CAPTAIN'S BOOKSHELF.* $100

Hawthorne, Nathaniel. THE HOUSE OF THE SEVEN GABLES, A ROMANCE. Boston: Ticknor, Reed, and Fields, 1851. 1st ed. 12mo. 344pp. Orig cloth, ends of spine chipped. Better than average copy with the March 1851 ads. Text with some foxing, but very clean & sound. BAL 7604, binding B with the March 1851 catalogue, printing A. *M & S.* $500

Hawthorne, Nathaniel. THE MARBLE FAUN: OR, THE ROMANCE OF MONTE BENI. Boston: Ticknor & Fields, 1860. 2 vols. 1st Amer ed, 3rd ptg. 238pp, 16pp ads; 284pp. Orig blindstamped brown cl. Early bkseller's blindstamp, owner's sig, but handsome w/spine extremities a tad frayed and corners lightly rubbed. VG or better. BAL 7621. *CHAPEL HILL.* $200

Hawthorne, Nathaniel. THE SNOW IMAGE. 1930. 1st ed w/these illustrations. 16mo 69pp. Double-spread color plate, illus by Dorothy Lathrop. VG+. Chips, small closed edge tears but VG. *BEBBAH.* $70

Hawthorne, Nathaniel. THE WORKS OF NATHANIEL HAW-THORNE. Boston: Houghton Mifflin Co, (c1900). 15 vol set. Vols 1 and 11 have one cvr that has damp mottling, o/w all vols VG to NF. *AARD.* $65

Hawthorne, Nathaniel. TWICE-TOLD TALES. NY: LEC, 1966. 1/1500 illus and signed by Valenti Angelo. Fine sl used slipcase. *CAPTAIN'S BOOKSHELF.* $100

Hay, James Jr. THE BELLAMY CASE. NY: Dodd-Mead, 1925. 1st ed. VF, lt wear to extremities of pict dj. *ELSE FINE.* $35

Hay, John. CASTILIAN DAYS. Boston & NY: Houghton, Mifflin, 1903. 1st prtg. Minor rubbing, bumped corners. *SCHOYER'S.* $30

Hay, John. CASTILIAN DAYS. London, 1903. 1st Eng ed. 111 plts. Sl cover fading, contents Good. *DIAMOND.* $25

Hay, John. JIM BLUDSO OF THE PRAIRIE BELLE, AND LIT-TLE BREECHES. Illus S. Eytinge, Jr. Boston: James R. Osgood & Co. 1871. 8 full-pg illus. Orig ptd orange wrappers bound in l9th century 1/2 grn morocco over marbled boards, gilt; spine edges a bit worn. 2-page A.L. signed by Hay tipped in to fep. Bkpl. *KARMIOLE.* $150

Hay, John. LETTERS OF JOHN HAY AND EXTRACTS FROM DIARY. NY, 1969. 3 vols. Orig cl. Reprint from rare 1908 ed which was ptd but not pub. Howes H335. *GINSBERG.* $50

Hay, John. PIKE COUNTY BALLADS AND OTHER PIECES. James R. Osgood & Co, 1871. 1st ed. Fine. *AUTHORS OF THE WEST.* $35

Hay, Sara Henderson. THIS, MY LETTER. NY: Knopf, 1939. Presentation inscrip ffep. #812 of 1,000. Chipped dj, o/w VG. *SCHOYER'S.* $25

Hay, T.R. & M.R. Werner. THE ADMIRABLE TRUMPETER. Doubleday, 1941. 1st ed. Fine in Good dj. *VARNER.* $17.50

Haycox, Ernest. DEEP WEST. Little Brown & Co, 1937. VG+. *AUTHORS OF THE WEST.* $30

Haycox, Ernest. LONG STORM. Little, Brown & Co, 1946. 1st ed. Inscribed, signed. Fine, bkpl. *AUTHORS OF THE WEST.* $35

Haycox, Ernest. OUTLAW. Little, Brown & Co, (1939). 1st ed. Fine, eps foxed some. *AUTHORS OF THE WEST.* $30

Haycox, Ernest. THE BORDER TRUMPET. NY: Council on Books in Wartime, n.d. Armed Services Edition F-164. Unusual, clean in wraps. *LAURIE.* $25

Haycroft, Howard (ed). THE ART OF THE MYSTERY STORY; A COLLECTION OF CRITICAL ESSAYS. NY: Simon & Schuster, 1946. 1st ed. NF lacking dj. *CAPTAIN'S BOOKSHELF.* $45

Hayden, A.S. EARLY HISTORY OF THE DISCIPLES IN THE WESTERN RESERVE, OHIO. Cincinnati: Chase and Hall, 1876. 476pp,4pp ads. Cloth, some wear to binding, bkpls removed. *DAWSON'S.* $50

Hayden, Julian D. EXCAVATIONS, 1940, AT UNIVERSITY IN-DIAN RUIN—TUCSON, ARIZONA. Gila Pueblo, Globe Arizona: Univ. of AZ, 1957. 1st ed. Ptd red wrappers. Fine in sl worn wraps. *PARMER.* $35

Hayden, Robert (ed). KALEIDOSCOPE: POEMS BY AMERICAN NEGRO POETS. NY: Harcourt, Brace, & World, (c1967). 1st ed. Fine in black dj, few sm tears. *HELLER.* $50

Hayden, Robert. ANGLE OF ASCENT. NY: Liveright, (1975). 1st ed. Fine in dj. *BETWEEN COVERS.* $50

Hayden, Robert. SELECTED POEMS. NY: October House, (1966). 1st ed. Fine in Fine dj w/negligible edge wear. Inscribed. *BETWEEN COVERS.* $100

Hayden, Robert. WORDS IN THE MOURNING TIME. NY: Oc-tober House, (1970). 1st ed. Fine in dj w/tiny tear rear panel. In-scribed. *BETWEEN COVERS.* $100

Hayens, Herbert. PLAY UP, GREYS! London: Collins' Clear-Type Press, n.d. 1st ed. Blue illus cl over bds. *OLD LONDON.* $40

Hayes, A. A., Jr. NEW COLORADO AND THE SANTA FE TRAIL. NY, 1880. 1st ed. Orig cl, rebacked w/orig backstrip. Eps chipped. 1/4" of inner pastedown paper defective, o/w VG. Erasure, small stamp on copyright page (no lib stamps). *DIAMOND.* $75

Hayes, Albert. DISEASES OF THE NERVOUS SYSTEM; OR, PATHOLOGY OF THE NERVES AND NERVOUS MALADIES. Boston, 1875. *FYE.* $50

Hayes, Daniel. A LONG JOURNEY. THE STORY OF DANIEL HAYES. Portland, ME, 1876. 1st ed. 76pp. Orig gold stamped vel-lum. One of 100. Howes H344. *GINSBERG.* $225

Hayes, Isaac Israel. THE LAND OF DESOLATION: BEING A PERSONAL NARRATIVE...IN GREENLAND. NY: Harper & Bros, 1872. Brn cl w/gilt spine titles, cvr dec. Some wear, soiling, hin-ges beginning. *PARMER.* $95

Hayes, Jess G. APACHE VENGEANCE. Albuquerque: Univ of NM, 1954. 1st ed. Inscribed, signed, dated ffep. Also signed on half title. Fine in VG dj. *CONNOLLY & WADE.* $95

Hayes, Rutherford B. IN MEMORIAM BREVET MAJOR GENERAL RUTHERFORD B. HAYES, U.S. VOLUNTEERS. N.p., n.d. circa 1893. VG+ to NF. *BEASLEY.* $60

Haymaker, Webb and Barnes Woodhall. PERIPHERAL NERVE IN-JURIES, PRINCIPLES OF DIAGNOSIS. Phila, 1953. 2nd ed. 272 illus. *FYE.* $100

Hayne, Coe. VANGUARD OF THE CARAVANS, A LIFE-STORY OF JOHN MASON PECK. Phila: Judson Press, (1931). 13 plts. Nice in chipped, worn dj. *BOHLING.* $35

Haystead, Ladd. IF THE PROSPECT PLEASES....Norman: Univ of OK Press, 1945. Stated 1st ed. Cl, dj. *SCHOYER'S.* $20

Hayward, Arthur. COLONIAL LIGHTING. Boston: B.J. Brimmer Co, 1923. 1st ed. VG. *BACKROOM.* $80

Hayward, Arthur. COLONIAL LIGHTING. Boston: B.J. Brimmer, (1923). One of 206 ptd on Normandy vellum and bound in 3/4 French Levant morocco. Howes H-352 (aa). *CULLEN.* $250

Hayward, George. SURGICAL REPORTS, AND MISCEL-LANEOUS PAPERS ON MEDICAL SUBJECTS. Boston, 1855. 1st ed. 452pp. VF. Rare. *FYE.* $225

Hayward, Helena. WORLD FURNITURE. NY: McGraw-Hill Co, 1965. 1st ed. VG (soiled, chipped dj). *BACKROOM.* $75

Hayward, J. THE SCIENCE OF HORTICULTURE, INCLUDING A PRACTICAL SYSTEM....London, 1818. 12 fldg engr plts w/some edge chipping, foxed. Pp xiv,(2),249. Contemp 1/2 calf, marbled boards very scuffed and worn. Professionally rebacked. Lt foxing in text. *SUTTON.* $250

Hayward, J.F. HUGUENOT SILVER IN ENGLAND, 1688-1727. London: Faber & Faber. (1959). 1st ed. 96 plts, color frontis. Dj. *KARMIOLE.* $35

Hayward, J.F. VIENNESE PORCELAIN OF THE DU PAQUIER PERIOD. London: Rockliff Publishing Corp. (1952). 1st ed. Dj. *KARMIOLE.* $85

Hayward, Walter B. THE LAST CONTINENT OF ADVENTURE. NY: Dodd, Mead & Co., 1930. 1st ed. Lightly soiled and faded, else VG. *PARMER.* $30

Haywood, Gar Anthony. FEAR OF THE DARK. NY: St. Martin's, (1988). 1st ed. Signed. VF in VF dj. *UNGER.* $40

Hazard, Thomas R. THE JOHNNY-CAKE PAPERS OF "SHEPHERD TOM" TOGETHER WITH REMINISCEN-CES....Boston, 1915. 1st ed. Map, 6 plts. Orig cl backed boards, lightly soiled and faded. One of 600 ptd by the Merrymount Press. Howes H367. *GINSBERG.* $85

Hazel, Paul. UNDERSEA: VOLUME II OF THE FINNBRANCH. Boston: Atlantic/Little, Brown, (1982). 1st ed. Fine in Fine dj. *OTHER WORLDS.* $25

Hazel, Paul. YEARWOOD. Boston: Atlantic/Little, Brown, (1980). 1st ed. Almost Fine in dj, closed tears. *OTHER WORLDS.* $25

Hazelton, Jno M. A HISTORY OF LINEBRED ANXIETY 4TH HEREFORDS OF STRAIGHT GUDGELL & SIMPSON BREEDING. Kansas City, 1939. 1st ed. Shelfworn, still VG. *OC-TOBER FARM.* $95

Hazelton, Jno M. HISTORY AND HANDBOOK OF HEREFORD CATTLE AND HEREFORD BULL INDEX. 3rd ed. Kansas City: Walker, 1935. Shelfworn, still VG. *OCTOBER FARM.* $85

Hazen, Allen T. A CATALOGUE OF HORACE WALPOLE'S LIBRARY. ...WITH HORACE WALPOLE'S LIBRARY BY WILMARTH SHELDON LEWIS. New Haven and London: Yale Univ Press, 1969. 1st ed. 3 vols. Cl, ptd djs. Fine. *WEBER.* $185

Hazlitt, W. Carew. OLD COOKERY BOOKS AND ANCIENT CUISINE. London: Elliot Stock, 1902. Popular ed. Series: The Book-Lover's Library. Index, grn cl. VG. *WEBER.* $45

Hazlitt, W. Carew. SCHOOLS, SCHOOL-BOOKS AND SCHOOL-MASTERS. London: J.W. Jarvis & Son, 1888. 1st ed. 4 (ads for works or editions by Hazlitt), iv,300pp (incl index). Orig blind ruled cl. Front cover a trifle rubbed, else VG. *WREDEN.* $40

Hazlitt, W. Carew. STUDIES IN JOCULAR LITERATURE. Lon-don: Elliot Stock, 1890. 1st ed. Orig 1/4 blue buckram over blue cl. Cvrs rubbed, bottom of spine bumped. *OAK KNOLL.* $50

Hazlitt, W. Carew. STUDIES IN JOCULAR LITERATURE. Lon-don: Elliot Stock, 1890. 1st ed. VG on large paper. Bkpl. *WREDEN.* $32

Hazlitt, W. Carew. THE BOOK-COLLECTOR, A GENERAL SUR-VEY OF THE PURSUIT AND OF THOSE WHO HAVE ENGAGED IN IT AT HOME AND ABROAD ...London: George Redway, 1904. 1st ed. Bkpl; inside hinges cracked. *OAK KNOLL.* $45

Hazlitt, William. A VIEW OF THE ENGLISH STAGE. London: for Robert Stodart.. Anderson and Chase, 1818. 1st ed. Later half morocco, edges rubbed; bound without half title or advertisement leaf; spine gilt to compartments; aeg. *DRAMATIS.* $200

Hazlitt, William. A VIEW OF THE ENGLISH STAGE...London, 1818. Aeg; 3/4 lea. NF *POLYANTHOS.* $200

Hazlitt, William. LECTURES ON THE ENGLISH COMIC WRITERS. London: for Taylor and Hessey, 1819. 1st ed. Later 1/2 calf, rebacked w/orig spine retained; ends and hinges rubbed; morocco labels; first two leaves remargined at gutter; lacking the ads. VG in cloth slipcase. *DRAMATIS PERSONAE.* $100

Hazlitt, William. LECTURES ON THE ENGLISH COMIC WRITERS. London: Taylor & Hessey, 1819. 1st ed. (4), 344pp. Bound in 1/2 red morocco (c. 1900), gilt spine. *KARMIOLE.* $150

Hazzard, Shirley. CLIFFS OF FALL AND OTHER STORIES. Knopf, 1963. 1st Amer ed. VG or better in price-clipped dj (missing piece foot of spine and chipped along top edge). *STAHR.* $25

Head, Henry. STUDIES IN NEUROLOGY. London, 1920. 1st ed. 2 vols. 862pp. Spine of vol. 1 sl darkened. *FYE.* $250

Headlam. Cecil. INNS OF COURT. A&C Black, 1909. 1st ed. 7s 6d Series. NF. *OLD LONDON.* $50

Headland, Isaac Taylor. COURT LIFE IN CHINA. NY et al: Revell, (1909). 2nd ed. Yellow cl dec in black and teal. Slight wear and soil. *SCHOYER'S.* $40

Headley, J.T. SACRED MOUNTAINS. NY: Baker & Scribner. 1848. Eng title page (dated 1847). 9 engr. Lacks ffep. Foxed. *SCHOYER'S.* $50

Headley, J.T. THE ACHIEVEMENTS OF STANLEY AND OTHER AFRICAN EXPLORERS. 1 fld map (missing). Phila, 1878. 605pp. Orig gilt-dec cl. Scuffed at extrems; lt flecking on cvrs; front hinge starting; 2pp w/sm gutter tear, 1p creased; smudging, sl shaken. *SUTTON.* $100

Headley, J.T. THE SACRED MOUNTAINS. Buffalo: Wanzer, McKim & Co., 1856. 240pp. 3 (probably of 5) tinted plts. Good. *WORLDWIDE.* $25

Heald, C.B. INJURIES AND SPORT. London, 1931. 1st ed. 543pp. 300 illus. *FYE.* $250

Healy, Capt. M.A. REPORT OF THE CRUISE OF THE REVENUE MARINE STEAMER CORWIN....1885. Wash: GPO, 1887. 1st ed. Professionally rebound in cl. *PARMER.* $100

Healy, Jeremiah. BLUNT DARTS. London: Macmillan, 1986. 1st Eng. ed. VF in dj. *MORDIDA.* $65

Healy, Jeremiah. SWAN DIVE. NY: Harper, (1988). 1st ed. Signed. VF in VF dj. *UNGER.* $35

Healy, Laurin Hall and Kutner, Luis. THE ADMIRAL. Chicago: Ziff Davis (1944). 1st ed. VG in Good dj. *AARD.* $20

Healy, M.A. REPORT OF THE CRUISE OF THE REVENUE STEAMER CORWIN...1884. Wash: GPO, 1889. Rebound in later cl. VG+. *PARMER.* $95

Heaney, Seamus. AFTER SUMMER. Old Deerfield & Dublin: 1978. Co-pub by Deerfield Press and Gallery Press. 1st ed, one of 250 numbered, signed. Additionally signed by Heaney. Fine in Fine dj. *BEASLEY.* $250

Heaney, Seamus. AFTER SUMMER. Old Deerfield, MA: Deerfield Press & Dublin: Gallery Press, (1978). One of 250 signed. Fine in dj. *CAPTAIN'S BOOKSHELF.* $200

Heaney, Seamus. AMONG SCHOOLCHILDREN. Belfast: John Malone Memorial Committee, 1983. Signed and dated in 1987. Fine in stapled wrappers. Scarce. *LOPEZ.* $125

Heaney, Seamus. BOG POEMS. (London): The Rainbow Press, 1975. 1st ed. One of 150 (entire ed) signed. Maroon morocco, gilt-stamped marbled boards, cl slipcase. VF. *JAFFE.* $1000

Heaney, Seamus. DEATH OF A NATURALIST. NY: Oxford Univ Press, 1966. 1st Amer ed. Signed, inscribed. NF in VG dj (some wear at extremities of spine). *LOPEZ.* $350

Heaney, Seamus. DOOR INTO THE DARK. London: Faber & Faber, (1969). 1st ed. Orig black cl. Fine in price-clipped dj. *CHAPEL HILL.* $225

Heaney, Seamus. DOOR INTO THE DARK. NY: Oxford, 1969. 1st ed. Fine but for price stamp fep, owner's inscrip on blank; in Fine dj but for two short tears, tiny chip rear panel. *BEASLEY.* $150

Heaney, Seamus. HEDGE SCHOOL. Claire Van Vliet (illus). Newark, VT: Janus Press, 1979. 1st ed. One of 285 signed by Heaney & Van Vliet. Wraps. Mint. *JAFFE.* $450

Heaney, Seamus. NEW SELECTED POEMS 1966-1987. London: Faber, (1990). 1st ed. Boards, dj. Mint. *JAFFE.* $45

Heaney, Seamus. NORTH. London: Faber & Faber, (1975). 1st ed, paper issue. Light rubbing of top wrapper, else Fine. Signed. *WOOLMER.* $75

Heaney, Seamus. POEMS 1965-1975. NY: Farrar Straus Giroux, (1980). Uncorrected proof. Fine in wrappers. *DERMONT.* $125

Heaney, Seamus. POEMS AND A MEMOIR. Henry Pearson (illus), Thomas Flanagan (intro), Seamus Heaney (preface). Full emb calf, slipcase. (NY): LEC, (1982). 1st ed. Ltd to 2000 signed by Heaney, Pearson & Flanagan. Mint. *JAFFE.* $250

Heaney, Seamus. POEMS AND A MEMOIR. NY: LEC, 1982. Henry Pearson illus. Thomas Flanagan (intro). Ltd ed, 2000 numbered, signed by author, Pearson, and Flanagan. Teg, full calf. Fine in Fine box. *POLYANTHOS.* $250

Heaney, Seamus. PREOCCUPATIONS. SELECTED PROSE 1968-1978. London: Faber & Faber, (1980). 1st ed. Fine in dj. Signed. *WOOLMER.* $125

Heaney, Seamus. SELECTED POEMS 1966-1987. NY: Farrar Straus & Giroux, (1990). 1st US ed. VF in dj. Signed. *CAPTAIN'S BOOKSHELF.* $45

Heaney, Seamus. SELECTED POEMS 1966-1987. NY: Farrar, Straus & Giroux, (1990). 1st Amer ed. Ltd to 200 signed. Cl, slipcase. Mint. *JAFFE.* $75

Heaney, Seamus. STATION ISLAND. NY, 1985. 1st ed. Signed, dated presentation. Fine in like dj. *POLYANTHOS.* $75

Heaney, Seamus. SWEENEY ASTRAY. A VERSION FROM THE IRISH. Derry: A Field Day Publication, 1983. 1st ed. As New in like dj. *DERMONT.* $100

Heaney, Seamus. SWEENEY ASTRAY. NY, 1984. Special ed. 314/350 only. Signed. Mint. No dj as issued, in Mint box. In pub mailing box. *POLYANTHOS.* $75

Heaney, Seamus. SWEENEY ASTRAY: A VERSION OF THE IRISH. NY: Farrar Straus & Giroux, (1984). 1st US ed. One of 350 specially bound, signed. Fine in slipcase. *CAPTAIN'S BOOKSHELF.* $85

Heaney, Seamus. THE REDRESS OF POETRY. Oxford, 1990. 1st ed. Signed, dated. Pict wraps. Mint. *POLYANTHOS.* $45

Heaney, Seamus. WINTERING OUT. NY: Oxford, 1973. 1st US ed. Fine but for owner's name, in Fine dj w/tiny tear. *BEASLEY.* $150

Heap, Gwinn H. CENTRAL ROUTE TO THE PACIFIC, FROM THE VALLEY OF THE MISSISSIPPI TO CALIFORNIA: JOURNAL OF THE EXPEDITION OF E. F. BEALE...AND GWINN HARRIS HEAP, FROM MISSOURI TO CALIFORNIA, IN 1853...Phila., 1854. 1st ed. 136pp. 13 tinted litho plts, fldg map at rear, linen backed. Orig black cl, new eps, "Athenaeum" stamped in gold on front cover, rubber stamped on title page and blank margins of plts and map. Howes H378. *GINSBERG.* $1250

Heard, H.F. A TASTE FOR HONEY. NY: Vanguard Press, 1941. 1st ed. VG in dj (3/4" piece missing corner of top of spine; chipped corners; short closed tears). *MORDIDA.* $150

Heard, H.F. MURDER BY REFLECTION. NY: Vanguard, 1942. 1st ed. Fine, minor rubs to extremities of pict dj. *ELSE FINE.* $45

Heard, H.F. THE NOTCHED HAIRPIN. NY: Vanguard Press, 1949. 1st ed. Fine in dj. *MORDIDA.* $65

Heard, J.E. REVOKED VENGEANCE. A Novel. Baltimore: Press of John Cox's Sons, 1886. 1st ed. Presentation, dated. Orig cl-backed boards. Hinges a bit weak, else Fine. *CHAPEL HILL.* $75

Hearn, Lafcadio. A HISTORY OF ENGLISH LITERATURE. Kanda, Tokyo: The Hokuseido Press. 1927. 1st ed. 2 vols.

(8),iv,478,xii; (8),iv,479-914,xiipp. Indices. Frontis in both vols. Maroon cl, gilt; spines faded, upper spine extremity vol I lightly frayed. Teg. BAL 7998. *KARMIOLE.* $150

Hearn, Lafcadio. A JAPANESE MISCELLANY. Boston, 1901. 1st ed, 1st issue. 6 plts, illus, teg, uncut, pict cvrs gilt, bkpl. Name, spine sl sunned, extrems little rubbed. Ex-libris. Fine. *POLYANTHOS.* $150

Hearn, Lafcadio. CHIN CHIN KOBAKAMA. (Tokyo: T. Hasegawa, 1903). 1st ed, colophon A. (20)pp. French fold, silk sewn wrappers. BAL 7939. *DAWSON'S.* $150

Hearn, Lafcadio. EXOTICS AND RETROSPECTIVES. Boston: Little Brown, 1899. 1st ed. (10) 299pp. Emb floral cl, gilt stamped. Gilt tips. 1/2" x 1" stain on back, o/w NF. *ARTIS.* $85

Hearn, Lafcadio. FANTASTICS AND OTHER FANCIES. Boston: Houghton Mifflin Co, (1914). 1st ed. Chas. W. Hutson (ed). 1/4 cl, paper boards. VG. *ARTIS.* $65

Hearn, Lafcadio. GLIMPSES OF UNFAMILIAR JAPAN (FIRST SERIES). Leipzig: (Bernard Tauchnitz), 1907. Copyright ed. Pub's buff wrappers. Owner inscrip; contemp poem (1911), written on blank inner wrapper. *BOOK BLOCK.* $35

Hearn, Lafcadio. IN GHOSTLY JAPAN. Boston, 1899. 1st ed. Teg, uncut. Pict covers. Spine little sunned, extremities minimally rubbed. Name. Fine. *POLYANTHOS.* $75

Hearn, Lafcadio. KOTTO. BEING JAPANESE CURIOS, WITH SUNDRY COBWEBS. NY: Macmillan, 1902. 1st ed. Orig dec olive brown cl. Bright and NF. Scarce in this condition. BAL 7938. *CHAPEL HILL.* $85

Hearn, Lafcadio. KWAIDAN. Boston: Houghton Mifflin Co, (1904). 1st state bluegreen pict cloth. Only slight edge wear else Outstanding. *DORN.* $200

Hearn, Lafcadio. KWAIDAN: STORIES AND STUDIES OF STRANGE THINGS. Tokyo, 1932. Oscar Lewis (intro). Printed for the Members of LEC. Ltd ed, 1348/1500. Color plts by Yasumasa Fujita and signed by him. Printed silk binding, orig glassine dj small tear. In silk wraparound case, sides spine rubbed, one corner skillfully repaired. Fine. *POLYANTHOS.* $100

Hearn, Lafcadio. LETTERS FROM THE RAVEN: BEING THE CORRESPONDENCE OF LAFCADIO HEARN AND HENRY WATKIN. NY: Brentano's, 1907. 1st ed. Old bkseller's sticker, else Fine. Inscribed 1908. *CAPTAIN'S BOOKSHELF.* $125

Hearn, Lafcadio. THE GOBLIN SPIDER. (Tokyo: T. Hasegawa, 1899). 2nd crepe paper ed. (18)pp. 6" x 4". French fold, silk-sewn wrappers. BAL 7932. Later enlarged. *DAWSON'S.* $75

Hearn, Lafcadio. THE OLD WOMAN WHO LOST HER DUMPLING. Tokyo: T. Hasegawa (1902). 1st ed, colophon B. (20)pp. French fold, silk- sewn wrappers. BAL 7937. *DAWSON'S.* $150

Hearn, Lafcadio. TWO YEARS IN THE FRENCH WEST INDIES. NY: Harper, 1890. 1st ed. 431pp. Slight cover wear, o/w VG. BAL 7920 *DIAMOND.* $60

Hearn, Lafcadio. TWO YEARS IN THE FRENCH WEST INDIES. NY: Harper, 1900. 2nd ed. *DIAMOND.* $25

Heat Moon, William Least. BLUE HIGHWAYS. Boston, 1982. 1st ed. Inscribed. Upper corners sl bumped, o/w Fine in moderately worn dj. *BAADE.* $37.50

Heat Moon, William Least. BLUE HIGHWAYS. Boston, 1982. 1st ed, 1st bk. Fine in dj. *PETTLER.* $75

Heat Moon, William Least. BLUE HIGHWAYS. Boston: Little Brown, (1982). 3rd prtg. Inscribed. Fine in NF dj. *LOPEZ.* $25

Heat Moon, William Least. BLUE HIGHWAYS: A JOURNEY INTO AMERICA. Boston: Little, Brown, (1982). 1st ed. Just About Fine in like dj. *CAPTAIN'S BOOKSHELF.* $50

Heat Moon, William Least. PRAIRYERTH. Boston: Houghton Mifflin, 1919. Adv reading copy in ptd wraps. Fine. *LOPEZ.* $45

Heath, Frank M. FORTY MILLION HOOFBEATS. NY: Tured, 1941. Signed. 1st ed. Good in Fair dj. *OCTOBER FARM.* $58

Heath, Thomas. THE TWENTIETH CENTURY ATLAS OF POPULAR ASTRONOMY...Edinburgh: W. & A.K. Johnston, 1922. 3rd ed. Extremities worn, foxing to endpapers, o/w Good. *KNOLLWOOD.* $150

HEATH'S INFALLIBLE COUNTERFEIT DETECTOR AT SIGHT. (By Laban Heath.) Boston: Laban Heath, (1864). 12mo, brown cl (bumped & rubbed, sl stained, slight wear to cl at spine). 32pp text, 10 plts (2 fldg). Printer's vignette on copyright page (minor foxing). VG. *BLUE MOUNTAIN.* $350

Heathcote, J.M. et al. SKATING/FIGURESKATING...(BADMINTON LIBRARY). Boston: Little, Brown, and London: Longmans, Green, 1892. 1st Amer ed. Minor edgewear, some foxing, else VG-NF. *OLD LONDON.* $75

Heathcote, J.M. et al. TENNIS, LAWN TENNIS, RACKETS, FIVES (BADMINTON LIBRARY). Boston: Little, Brown, and London: Longmans, Green, 1890. 1st Amer ed. Minor wear to extremities, foxing, else VG-NF. *OLD LONDON.* $90

Heber, A. Reeve and Kathleen M. Heber. IN HIMALAYAN TIBET. Phila: J.B. Lippincott. 1926. 1st ed. Fldg map. Bright orange cloth, gilt. *KARMIOLE.* $75

Heber, Reginald. NARRATIVE OF A JOURNEY THROUGH THE UPPER PROVINCES OF INDIA...1824-1825. (With Notes Upon Ceylon). Phila: Carey, Lea, & Carey. 1828. 2 vols. 1st Amer ed. 508; 396pp + pub's ads front of each vol. Fldg map vol I. Orig cl over boards, paper spine labels; spines faded and cvrs soiled. Uncut. Some text foxing. *KARMIOLE.* $150

Heberden, M.V. MURDER MAKES A RACKET. Garden City: Doubleday Crime Club, 1942. 1st ed. Fine in dj (crease-tear; wear). *MORDIDA.* $35

Heberden, William. AN INTRODUCTION TO THE STUDY PHYSIC (NOW FOR THE FIRST TIME PUBLISHED) WITH A PREFATORY ESSAY BY L. CRUMMER WITH A REPRINT OF HEBERDEN'S SOME ACCOUNT OF A DISORDER OF THE BREAST. NY, 1929. Ltd ed. Signed. Backstrip soiled with small tear at tail of spine. *FYE.* $200

Hebert, Walter H. FIGHTING JOE HOOKER. Indianapolis, (1944). 1st ed. 366pp. Dj worn w/small pieces missing, o/w VG+. *PRATT.* $65

Hecht, Anthony. AESOPIC. TWENTY FOUR COUPLETS TO ACCOMPANY THE THOMAS BEWICK WOOD ENGRAVINGS FOR SELECT FABLES. Northampton, MA: Gehenna Press, (1967). 1st ed. One of 500 on Arches. Boards w/ptd label, tissue dj. VF. *JAFFE.* $225

Hecht, Anthony. THE SEVEN DEADLY SINS. Northhampton: Gehenna Press, 1958. Leonard Baskin (illus). Blue wraps, paper label, small stain. Ltd to 300. Signed by Baskin and Hecht. Rare. VG. *CULLEN.* $250

Hecht, Ben and Maxwell Bodenheim. CUTIE: A WARM MAMMA. Chicago: The Hectshaw Press, privately printed, 1924. Ltd ed, 200. Extremities, spine and edge little rubbed. NF. *POLYANTHOS.* $35

Hecht, Ben. A BOOK OF MIRACLES. NY, 1939. 1st ed. In brown wraps. Proof copy? Wraps. Few tiny edge chips, sl soiled. Fine. *POLYANTHOS.* $75

Hecht, Ben. TALES OF CHICAGO STREETS. Little Blue Book No. 698. Girard: Haldeman-Julius, n.d. 1st ed. 57pp. Cvrs Good only. Contents VG. *CONNOLLY & WADE.* $22.50

Hecht, Ben. THE KINGDOM OF EVIL. Chicago: Covici, 1924. 1/2000. Illus by Anthony Angarola. VG+ in dj. *LAME DUCK.* $75

Hecht, Ben. THE KINGDOM OF EVIL. Chicago: Pascal Covici, 1924. 1st ed. Illus Anthony Angarola. One of 2,000, this unnumbered. Fine and bright in Fine dj w/very slight wear at spine head. *BEASLEY.* $200

Hecker, J.F.C. THE EPIDEMICS OF THE MIDDLE AGES. Trans by B.G. Babington. London, 1846. 1st Eng trans. 380pp. *FYE.* $150

Heckewelder, John. A NARRATIVE OF THE MISSION OF THE UNITED BRETHREN AMONG THE DELAWARE AND MOHEGAN INDIANS, FROM ITS COMMENCEMENT, IN THE YEAR 1740, TO THE CLOSE OF THE YEAR 1808....Phila.: McCarty, 1820. 1st ed. (12),17-430pp, errata leaf. Port. Orig full calf. Howes H392. *GINSBERG.* $375

Heckscher, Morrison H. AMERICAN FURNITURE IN THE METROPOLITAN MUSEUM OF ART. NY: MMA, 1985. 1st ed. NF. *BACKROOM.* $45

Heckscher, William. REMBRANDT'S ANATOMY OF DR. NICOLAAS TULP, AN ICONOLOGICAL STUDY. NY, 1958. 1st ed. 48 plts. *FYE.* $150

Heden, Karl E. DIRECTORY OF SHIPWRECKS OF THE GREAT LAKES. Boston, (1966). Back cvr dented, o/w VG. *ARTIS.* $20

Hedley, F.Y. MARCHING THROUGH GEORGIA. Chicago, 1890. 490pp. Illus. Pict cloth. A little cvr wear o/w VG+. *PRATT.* $45

Hedley, W.S. THERAPEUTIC ELECTRICITY AND PRACTICAL MUSCLE TESTING. London, 1899. 1st ed. 278pp. Photo illus. *FYE.* $100

Hedrick, U.P. GRAPES AND WINE FROM HOME GARDENS. NY: Oxford Univ Press, 1945. 1st ed. 326pp. 24 half tones, 37 diagrams. VG in worn dj. Inscribed. *SECOND LIFE.* $75

Hedrick, U.P. MANUAL OF AMERICAN GRAPE-GROWING. NY: Macmillan, 1919. 1st ed. 458pp. VG. *SECOND LIFE.* $65

Hedrick, U.P. MANUAL OF AMERICAN GRAPE-GROWING. NY: Macmillan, 1924. Revised. Cloth worn, bumped; contents VG. *AMERICAN BOTANIST.* $30

Hedrick, U.P. VEGETABLES OF NY: BEANS. Albany: Lyon, 1931. Stiff paper, in original mailer. As New. *AMERICAN BOTANIST.* $40

Heermans, Forbes. THIRTEEN STORIES OF THE FAR WEST. Syracuse, NY: C.W. Bardeen, 1887. 1st ed. Cvrs sl stained, shelfworn, & nicked. Small hole in spine. Spine tip & corner wear. Recased w/new eps, o/w VG. *DIAMOND.* $125

Heggen, Thomas. MISTER ROBERTS: A PLAY. NY: Random House, 1948. 1st ed. NF, light wear dj extremities. *ELSE FINE.* $45

Heib, Louis. TONY HILLERMAN: A BIBLIOGRAPHY....Tucson: Press of the Gigantic Hound, 1990. 1st ed, ltd to 1,000. Fine. *BOOK MARKET.* $30

Heigh, A. E. THE ATTIC THEATRE. Oxford: Clarendon Press, 1889. 1st ed. Grn lea over bds. Pres bkpl. Minor wear, else Fine. *OLD LONDON.* $100

Heighway, Osborn W. Trenery. LEILA ADA, THE JEWISH CONVERT AN AUTHENTIC MEMOIR. Phila: Presbyterian Board of Publication (1853) 1st US ed. 230pp. Pub's cl, VG. *SECOND LIFE.* $85

Heilbron, B.L. (ed). WITH PEN AND PENCIL OF THE FRONTIER IN 1851....MN Hist Soc, 1932. 1st ptg. Fine in Fine clear dj. *VARNER.* $50

Heilner, Van Campen and Frank Stick. THE CALL OF THE SURF. GC: Doubleday, Page & Co, (1920). Later ptg. VG. *BACKMAN.* $50

Heilner, Van Campen. A BOOK ON DUCK SHOOTING. Phila: Penn. Pub. Co, (1939). 4th ptg, Nov 1940. VG+. *BACKMAN.* $65

Heilner, Van Campen. OUR AMERICAN GAME BIRDS. Garden City: Doubleday & Co, Inc, (1941). VG in Good dj. *BACKMAN.* $41

Heilner, Van Campen. OUR AMERICAN GAME BIRDS. GC, 1947 (1941). 19 colored plts. Front joint cracked. *SUTTON.* $48

Heilprin, Angelo. THE ERUPTION OF PELEE. Geog Soc of Phila, 1908. 1st ed. VG. *ARTIS.* $60

Hein, O.L. MEMORIES OF LONG AGO. NY: Putnam, 1925. 1st ed. Orig cl. *GINSBERG.* $125

Heine, Heinrich. POEMS AND BALLADS. NY, 1881. Teg. NF. *POLYANTHOS.* $35

Heinemann, Katherine Arnstein. BRANDINGS. Cl. West Branch, IA: Cummington Press, 1968. 1st ed. Ltd to 236. Lower edge of front cvr dust-soiled, o/w VG frayed glassine ed. *JAFFE.* $75

Heinemann, Larry. CLOSE QUARTERS. NY: Farrar Straus & Giroux, (1977). 1st ed. Fine in dj (three tiny edge tears). *CAPTAIN'S BOOKSHELF.* $100

Heinemann, Larry. PACO'S STORY. NY: Farrar, Straus and Giroux, (1986). 1st ed. Fine in Fine dj. *AKA.* $35

Heinemann, Larry. PACO'S STORY. NY: FSG, (1986). 1st ed. Fine in dj. *ROBBINS.* $25

Heinlein, Robert A. I WILL FEAR NO EVIL. NY, (1970). 1st ed. Fine in sl spine rubbed dj. *POLYANTHOS.* $75

Heinlein, Robert A. METHUSELEH'S CHILDREN. Gnome Press, 1960. 1st ed. Fine in dj. Signed. *MADLE.* $600

Heinlein, Robert A. REQUIEM: NEW COLLECTED WORKS BY AND TRIBUTES TO THE GRAND MASTER. Tor, 1992. Uncorrected proof. VF in white wraps with image of dj on front cover. *STAHR.* $60

Heinlein, Robert A. SIXTH COLUMN. Gnome Press, 1949. 1st ed. Fine in Mint dj. *MADLE.* $325

Heinlein, Robert A. THE GREEN HILLS OF EARTH. Chicago: Shasta, 1951. 1st ed. Fine in NF dj w/minor wear to head of spine. *BEASLEY.* $150

Heinlein, Robert A. THE GREEN HILLS OF EARTH. Chicago: Shasta, (1951). 1st ed. Fine in sl rubbed dj. *DERMONT.* $200

Heinlein, Robert A. UNIVERSE. Dell Book 36. 10 cents. NY (1951). complete and unabridged; pict wraps. Fine. *POLYANTHOS.* $65

Heinlein, Robert. BETWEEN PLANETS. NY: Scribner, 1951. 1st ed. NF in like dj w/wear at spinal extremities, short tear. *CAPTAIN'S BOOKSHELF.* $150

Heinlein, Robert. BEYOND THIS HORIZON. G & D, n.d. VG in dj. *MADLE.* $50

Heinlein, Robert. HAVE SPACE SUIT—WILL TRAVEL. Scribners, 1958. 1st ed. Ex-lib. Good. *MADLE.* $15

Heinlein, Robert. HAVE SPACE SUIT—WILL TRAVEL. Scribners, 1958. 1st ed. Sl fraying to rear of dj, else Fine. *MADLE.* $425

Heinlein, Robert. ORPHANS OF THE SKY. Putnam, 1964. 1st ed. Fine, sl edge-rubbed dj. *MADLE.* $350

Heinlein, Robert. ROCKET SHIP GALILEO. Scribners, 1947. 1st ed. Fine in Fine price-clipped dj. *MADLE.* $750

Heinlein, Robert. SPACE CADET. Scribners, 1949. VG in worn dj. *MADLE.* $75

Heinlein, Robert. STARMAN JONES. NY: Scribner, (1953). 1st ed. VG in like dj. *CAPTAIN'S BOOKSHELF.* $150

Heinlein, Robert. THE PAST THROUGH TOMORROW. NY: Putnam, (1967). 1st ed. A little foxing to eps, some faint dampstaining to top edge, else NF in NF dj very sl faded on spine, w/touch of rubbing. Inscribed, signed. *BETWEEN COVERS.* $600

Heinlein, Robert. THE ROLLING STONES. NY: Scribner, (1952). 1st ed. VG in chipped, NF dj. *CAPTAIN'S BOOKSHELF.* $150

Heinlein, Robert. THE STAR BEAST. NY: Scribner, (1954). 1st ed. NF dj w/two chips. *CAPTAIN'S BOOKSHELF.* $150

Heinlein, Robert. TIME FOR THE STARS. NY: Scribner, (1956). 1st ed. VG in dj. *CAPTAIN'S BOOKSHELF.* $150

Heinlein, Robert. TUNNEL IN THE SKY. Scribners, 1955. 1st ed. Fine in sl frayed, chipped dj. *MADLE.* $250

Heinlein, Robert. UNIVERSE. Dell, 1951. 1st ed. Near VG in wraps. *MADLE.* $50

Heinlein, Robert. UNIVERSE. Dell Book 36. NY, (1951). 1st ed. Complete and unabridged. Pict wraps. Fine. *POLYANTHOS.* $65

Heins, Rev Hardy. EDGAR RICE BURROUGHS BIBLIOG-RAPHY. Donald Grant, 1964. NF in soiled dj. *MADLE.* $400

Heins, Rev Henry Hardy. THE GOLDEN ANNIVERSARY BIBLI-OGRAPHY OF E R B. Grant, 1964. 1st ed. Fine in dj. *MADLE.* $450

Heise, Jack. HOW TO WRITE AND SELL FACT DETECTIVE STORIES. Seattle, 1943. 1st ed. Wraps. *DIAMOND.* $25

Heisenberg, Werner. THE PHYSICAL PRINCIPLES OF THE QUANTUM THEORY. Univ of Chicago Press, 1930. VG ex-lib. *KNOLLWOOD.* $60

Heitman, Francis B. HISTORICAL REGISTER AND DICTION-ARY OF THE UNITED STATES ARMY...SEPTEMBER 19, 1789 TO MARCH 2, 1903. Wash: GPO, 1903. 2 vols. Orig cl. *GINSBERG.* $150

Heizer, R.F. and M.A. Whipple (eds). THE CALIFORNIA IN-DIANS. Berkeley: Univ of CA, 1973. Rev, enl 2nd ed. Fine in NF dj. *CONNOLLY & WADE.* $35

Heizer, Robert F. (ed). HANDBOOK OF NORTH AMERICAN IN-DIANS. Vol 8 (only). Washington: Smithsonian, 1978. *AR-CHAEOLOGIA.* $85

Heizer, Robert F. and Albert B. Elsasser (eds). ORIGINAL AC-COUNTS OF THE LONE WOMAN OF SAN NICOLAS IS-LAND. Berkeley: Univ of CA Archaelogical Survey, 1961. Ptd wrap-pers, newspaper stain to inside front wrapper. *DAWSON'S.* $35

Heizer, Robert F. and Martin A. Baumhoff. PREHISTORIC ROCK ART OF NEVADA AND EASTERN CALIFORNIA. Berkeley, LA: Univ of CA Press, 1962. Wrappers. *DAWSON'S.* $50

Heizer, Robert F. THEY WERE ONLY DIGGERS. Ramona: Bal-lena Press, 1974. NF in orig ptd wraps. *PARMER.* $30

Held, John, Jr. and Frank B. Gilbreth, Jr. HELD'S ANGELS. NY: Thomas Y. Crowell Co. (1952). 1st ed. Dj. *KARMIOLE.* $35

Held, John Jr. THE SAGA OF FRANKIE AND JOHNNY. NY: Wal-ter V. McKee, 1930. 1st ed, ltd to 1,050.Red cl over red velour. Fine in worn slipcase. *CONNOLLY & WADE.* $65

Hell, Xavier Hommaire de. TRAVELS IN THE STEPPES OF THE CASPIAN SEA, THE CRIMEA, THE CAUCASUS...London, 1847. Trace of shelf-mark. viii,436pp. NF. *O'NEILL.* $135

Heller, Joseph and Speed Vogel. NO LAUGHING MATTER. NY: Putnam, (1986). Uncorrected proof. VG. *LOPEZ.* $25

Heller, Joseph. CATCH-22. NY, 1961. 1st ed, 1st book. Extrems sl rubbed. Fine in dj w/a few small chips. *POLYANTHOS.* $400

Heller, Joseph. CATCH-22. NY: Simon & Schuster, 1961. 1st ed, 1st bk. Fine, bright dj has lt edgewear, short tear in the bottom edge, sm chip at lower spine corner, a few rubs. *ELSE FINE.* $450

Heller, Joseph. CATCH-22. NY: Simon & Schuster, 1961. 1st ed. Fine in sl rubbed dj, 1/2" closed tear. *JAFFE.* $450

Heller, Joseph. CATCH-22. NY: Simon & Schuster, 1961. 1st ed, 1st bk. Orig blue cl. Fine in NF dj (crease rear panel). *CHAPEL HILL.* $650

Heller, Joseph. SOMETHING HAPPENED. NY: Knopf, (1974). 1st ed. Fully inscribed. Fine in NF dj, a trifle rubbed. *UNGER.* $50

Heller, Keith. MAN'S ILLEGAL LIFE. London: Collins, 1984. 1st ed. Signed. VF in dj. *SILVER DOOR.* $35

Heller, Lorenz. MURDER IN MAKE-UP. NY: Julian Messner, 1937. 1st ed. VG in dj w/wear. *MORDIDA.* $25

Heller, Michael. FIGURES OF SPEAKING. Fldg title pg, wrappers. Mt. Horeb: Perishable Press, 1977. 1st ed. Ltd to 155. Signed by Walter Hamady. Mint. *JAFFE.* $100

Helliwell, Robert A. WHISTLERS AND RELATED IONOS-PHERIC PHENOMENA. Stanford Univ Press, 1965. VG in sl worn, chipped dj. *KNOLLWOOD.* $25

Hellman, Lillian. AN UNFINISHED WOMAN. Boston: Little, Brown, 1969. 1st ed. One of special ed reserved for friends. No dj as issued. Red cl. Fine. *SMITH.* $50

Hellman, Lillian. ANOTHER PART OF THE FOREST. NY, 1947. Spine very lightly sunned. Fine in dj (very sl sunned, sl edge rubbed). *POLYANTHOS.* $35

Hellman, Lillian. PENTIMENTO. Boston: Little, Brown, (1973). 1st ed, special issue reserved for friends. Signed. 2-toned cl, acetate dj. Fine. *JAFFE.* $150

Hellman, Lillian. SCOUNDREL TIME. Boston: Little, Brown, (1976). 1st ed, special issue reserved for friends. Signed. Cl-backed boards, acetate dj. Fine. *JAFFE.* $150

Hellman, Lillian. THE CHILDREN'S HOUR. NY: Knopf, 1934. 1st ed, 1st bk. Spine, edges of boards darkened, else VG in dj, 2 chips. *CAPTAIN'S BOOKSHELF.* $350

Hellman, Lillian. THE SEARCHING WIND. NY: Viking, 1944. 1st ed. Fine in fine dj w/traces of wear at top edge. *BEASLEY.* $65

Helm, H.T. AMERICAN ROADSTERS AND TROTTING HOR-SES. Chicago: Rand McNally & Co, 1878. 1st ed. Small 4to, 552pp. Brown cl rubbed, bumped & soiled, Title, vignettes in gilt on spine. Tear to corner of one page and front edge of 2 others. 15 plts, incl 13 photographic (darkened). VG. *BLUE MOUNTAIN.* $250

Helm, Katherine. THE TRUE STORY OF MARY, WIFE OF LIN-COLN. NY, 1928. 1st ed. Some cvr wear o/w Fine. *PRATT.* $35

Helm, Mrs. Mary S. SCRAPS FROM TEXAS HISTORY. Austin: Ptd for the author at the office of B.R. Warner & Co, 1884. 1st ed. 198pp, cl. Cover faded and stained, but gold lettering on front cover clear and bright. Internally tight, w/o usual foxing. Very scarce. *GIBBS.* $475

Helmholtz, Hermann von. ON THE SENSATIONS OF TONE AS A PHYSIOLOGICAL BASIS FOR THE THEORY OF MUSIC. London, 1885. 2nd ed. 576pp. Fine. *FYE.* $150

Helms, Anthony Zachariah. TRAVELS FROM BUENOS AYRES, BY POTOSI, TO LIMA. WITH NOTES...CONTAINING TOPOGRAPHICAL DESCRIPTIONS OF THE SPANISH POS-SESSIONS IN SOUTH AMERICA....London: Richard Phillips, 1807. 2nd ed of Eng trans of 1806. viii,9-92pp. 1/2 lea, marbled boards. NF. *PARMER.* $250

Helprin, Mark (adaptation). SWAN LAKE. Chris Van Allsburg (illus). Boston: Houghton, 1989. 1st ed. Cl w/pict inset. 13 color plts. Signed by Van Allsburg. Fine. No dj as issued. *ACADEMIC LIBRARY.* $40

Helprin, Mark. A DOVE OF THE EAST AND OTHER STORIES. NY: Knopf, 1975. 1st ed, 1st bk. Fine in dj. Inscribed. *CAPTAIN'S BOOKSHELF.* $125

Helprin, Mark. A SOLDIER OF THE GREAT WAR. NY: Har-court, (1991). 1st ed. As New in dj. Contemp presentation inscrip. *CAPTAIN'S BOOKSHELF.* $45

Hemans, Mrs. Felicia (Browne). THE LEGEND OF THE ALPS, THE SIEGE OF VALENCIA...AND OTHER POEMS. Boston: Hilliard, Gray, Little and Wilkins, 1826. 1st US ed. 480pp. Bound in contemp full calf (rubbed), marble eps. Good, tight. *SECOND LIFE.* $150

Hemingway, Ernest. A DIVINE GESTURE. NY: Aloe Editions, 1974. This ed printed at the Oliphant Press. Ltd ed, 57/250 only. Printed wraps. Fine. *POLYANTHOS.* $85

Hemingway, Ernest. A FAREWELL TO ARMS. NY, 1929. 1st ed, 2nd state. Name erased fep, extrems sl rubbed. NF. *POLYANTHOS.* $50

Hemingway, Ernest. A FAREWELL TO ARMS. NY: Scribner's, 1929. 1st trade ed, 1st ptg, w/o disclaimer which was added in 2nd ptg. Orig black cl w/gold paper labels. Fine in VG pict dj. *CHAPEL HILL.* $800

Hemingway, Ernest. A FAREWELL TO ARMS. NY: Scribners, 1929. 1st ed, 1st issue. Fine in dj (few tiny nicks, white strip at heel of spine sl discolored). Very nice. *CAPTAIN'S BOOKSHELF.* $1500

Hemingway, Ernest. A MOVEABLE FEAST. London, 1964. 1st ed. Fine in price clipped dj. *POLYANTHOS.* $60

Hemingway, Ernest. A MOVEABLE FEAST. NY, 1964. 1st ed. NF in price-clipped dj (sm chip). *PETTLER.* $30

Hemingway, Ernest. A MOVEABLE FEAST. NY: Scribner's, (1964). 1st ed. Fine, dj. *JAFFE.* $75

Hemingway, Ernest. A MOVEABLE FEAST. NY: Scribner's, (1964). 1st ed. Fine in NF dj. *UNGER.* $75

Hemingway, Ernest. A MOVEABLE FEAST. NY: Scribners, 1964. 1st ed. Fine but for owner's name, in NF dj (few short tears; lt soiling rear panel). *BEASLEY.* $60

Hemingway, Ernest. ACROSS THE RIVER AND INTO THE TREES. NY: Scribner's, 1950. Owner's name, else Fine in 1st issue dj w/spine lettered in yellow. Dj bright, shows only light edgewear. 1st Amer ed. *CHAPEL HILL.* $100

Hemingway, Ernest. ACROSS THE RIVER AND INTO THE TREES. NY: Scribner's, 1950. VG in 1st issue dj (yellow lettering on spine) w/browned and worn edges, light soiling, couple of minor closed tears. 1st Amer ed. *CHAPEL HILL.* $85

Hemingway, Ernest. ACROSS THE RIVER AND INTO THE TREES. NY: Scribner's, 1950. 1st ed. Cl, dj. NF. *JAFFE.* $65

Hemingway, Ernest. COLLECTED POEMS. SF, 1960. Pirated ed. Orig pub in Paris. Printed wraps. Front wrap edge crease. NF. *POLYANTHOS.* $25

Hemingway, Ernest. FOR WHOM THE BELL TOLLS. NY, 1940. 1st ed, 2nd issue dj w/small piece missing spine and top corner front panel; small tears, edge rubbed. Panels bright, price clipped unevenly. *POLYANTHOS.* $125

Hemingway, Ernest. FOR WHOM THE BELL TOLLS. NY: Scribner's, 1940. VG in dj. 1st ed, 1st issue dj, w/o photographer's name credited on rear panel. *CHAPEL HILL.* $250

Hemingway, Ernest. FOR WHOM THE BELL TOLLS. NY: Scribner's, 1940. Inner gutters browned, but VG in price-clipped dj w/some soiling and edgewear. 1st ed, 1st issue dj, w/o photographer's name credited on rear panel. *CHAPEL HILL.* $175

Hemingway, Ernest. FOR WHOM THE BELL TOLLS. NY: Scribner's, 1940. 1st ed. VG+ in spine faded, 1st state dj. *LAME DUCK.* $200

Hemingway, Ernest. FOR WHOM THE BELL TOLLS. NY: Scribners, 1940. 1st ed. Fine but for owner's inscrip in NF 1st state dj w/wear at head of spine. *BEASLEY.* $285

Hemingway, Ernest. GREEN HILLS OF AFRICA. NY & London: Scribner's, 1935. 1st ed. Some fading of spine, in VG dj which is sl chipped at spine ends & moderately worn at edges. *BERNARD.* $700

Hemingway, Ernest. IN OUR TIME. NY: Boni & Liveright, 1925. 1st Amer ed. Recently rebound in full black morocco w/orig cover design duplicated in gilt on front panel. Marbled eps. Fine. *CAPTAIN'S BOOKSHELF.* $450

Hemingway, Ernest. ISLANDS IN THE STREAM. NY, 1970. 1st ed. Map eps. Fine in dj. *PETTLER.* $40

Hemingway Ernest. ISLANDS IN THE STREAM. NY: Scribner, (1970). 1st ed. Light spotting to top and fore-edges, else Fine in dj. Rev copy, slip laid in. *CAPTAIN'S BOOKSHELF.* $100

Hemingway, Ernest. ISLANDS IN THE STREAM. NY: Scribner's, (1970). 1st ed. VF, dj. *JAFFE.* $45

Hemingway, Ernest. ISLANDS IN THE STREAM. NY: Scribners, 1970. 1st ed. VF in dj. *ELSE FINE.* $50

Hemingway, Ernest. MEN WITHOUT WOMEN. Stories. London: Jonathan Cape, (1928). Bkpl, small Parisian bkseller's label on front

pastedown, but VG in dj (rubbed at spine, shallow chipping at spine ends affecting no lettering). 1st Eng ed. Rare, esp in dj. *CHAPEL HILL.* $900

Hemingway, Ernest. SELECTED LETTERS 1917-1961. Carlos Baker (ed). Two-toned cl, glassine dj, slipcase. NY: Scribner's, (1981). 1st ed. Ltd to 500 signed by Baker. VF. *JAFFE.* $150

Hemingway, Ernest. THE GARDEN OF EDEN. NY: Scribner's, 1986. As New in dj. 1st ed. *CHAPEL HILL.* $40

Hemingway, Ernest. THE NICK ADAMS STORIES. NY: Scribners, 1972. 1st ed. Fine; minor tear rear spine fold of dj. *ELSE FINE.* $75

Hemingway, Ernest. THE OLD MAN AND THE SEA. London: Jonathan Cape (1952). 1st UK ed. Fine in NF dj. Bkpl. *SECOND LIFE.* $75

Hemingway, Ernest. THE OLD MAN AND THE SEA. NY: Scribner, 1952. 1st ed. Fine in NF 1st issue dj w/trace of sunning. *LOPEZ.* $450

Hemingway, Ernest. THE OLD MAN AND THE SEA. NY: Scribner's, 1952. 1st ed. Orig lt blue cl. Fine in dj. Unusually Nice. *CHAPEL HILL.* $500

Hemingway, Ernest. THE OLD MAN AND THE SEA. NY: Scribner's, 1952. 1st ed. Previous owner's name, o/w Fine in NF dj with a few short tears. Nice. *LOPEZ.* $350

Hemingway, Ernest. THE OLD MAN AND THE SEA. NY: Scribner, 1952. 1st ed. Sm stain on dj, owner sig, o/w NF. *SMITH.* $250

Hemingway, Ernest. THE SUN ALSO RISES. (NY): Grosset & Dunlap, n.d. (1930). 1st G & D ed (an early reprint). VG in dj which is chipped at spine ends & with a few internally mended edge-tears & edge-wear. *BERNARD.* $40

Hemingway, Ernest. TO HAVE AND HAVE NOT. NY, 1937. 1st ed. Top spine very sl rubbed. Fine in dj (top spine sl chipped, few tiny edge tears, top edges little rubbed). Very attractive. *POLYANTHOS.* $500

Hemingway, Ernest. TO HAVE AND HAVE NOT. NY: Scribner's, 1937. 1st ed. Orig black cl. Very bright, fine in price-clipped dj, minimal rubbing. Scarce in this condition. *CHAPEL HILL.* $750

Hemingway, Ernest. TO HAVE AND HAVE NOT. NY: Scribner's, (1937). 1st ed. VG+ in VG dj, creased at spine ends. *UNGER.* $600

Hemingway, Ernest. TODAY IS FRIDAY. Englewood, NJ: The As Stable Publications, 1926. 1st ed, #137 of 300 ptd (only 260 for sale). Orig wraps illus w/drawing by Jean Cocteau. Some separation along spine, but NF in orig env. Excellent. *CHAPEL HILL.* $1,000

Hemingway, Ernest. WINNER TAKE NOTHING. NY & London: Charles Scribner's Sons, 1933. 1st ed in 1st issue dj (w/Lawrence Stallings quote). Owner's name; one page corner creased. Fine in Very Nice dj. *BLUE MOUNTAIN.* $675

Hemingway, Ernest. WINNER TAKE NOTHING. NY: Scribners, 1933. 1st ed. Small hole in front joint, else VF; bright dj has small chips at extremities. *ELSE FINE.* $650

Hemingway, Ernest. WINNER TAKE NOTHING. NY, 1933. 1st ed. Bkpl, spine little sunned, extrems sl rubbed. *POLYANTHOS.* $100

Hempel, Amy. REASONS TO LIVE. NY: Knopf, 1985. 1st ed, 1st bk. Fine in Fine dj. *BEASLEY.* $35

Hempel, Charles J. ORGANON OF SPECIFIC HOMOEOPATHY. Phila: Rademacher & Sheek, 1854. 1st ed. 216, 8pp ads. Modern rebacking, paper boards. VG. *SECOND LIFE.* $165

Hemsley, W.B. HANDBOOK OF HARDY TREES, SHRUBS AND HERBACEOUS PLANTS....Boston: Estes & Lauriat, 1873. 1st ed. 687pp. Ptd in UK. Front hinge tender, some minor foxing. VG. *SECOND LIFE.* $75

Henderson, Alice Palmer. THE RAINBOW'S END; ALASKA. NY: H.S. Stone & Co, 1898. Frontis, plts. Gilt dec blue cl. VG. *PARMER.* $125

Henderson, Charles. HENDERSON'S PICTURESQUE GAR-DENS. NY: Peter Henderson, 1901. Cloth worn and stained, contents VG. *AMERICAN BOTANIST*. $45

Henderson, Daniel. FROM THE VOLGA TO THE YUKON...NY: Hastings House, 1945. 2nd prtg. NF in VG+ dj. *GREAT EPIC*. $35

Henderson, Daniel. THE HIDDEN COAST. NY (1953). 1st ed. Some dj wear o/w VG+. *PRATT*. $25

Henderson, Ebenezer. ICELAND; or The Journal of....The Second Edition. Edinburgh: Printed for Waugh and Innes, and T. Hamilton, J. Hatchard, and L.B. Seeley. 1819. xiv,(2),576pp. Index. 16 plts, incl fldg map. 19th century brown calf over textured brown cl, leather spine label; spine extremities rubbed. Bkplts. *KARMIOLE*. $200

Henderson, G.F.R. THE CIVIL WAR, A SOLDIER'S VIEW. Chicago, (1958). Ed by Jay Luvaas. 1st ed. Dj wear and soiling o/w VG. *PRATT*. $42.50

Henderson, G.C. THE DISCOVERERS OF THE FIJI ISLANDS. London: John Murray. (1933). 1st ed. 3 fldg maps, fldg map in rear pocket). Purple cl, gilt spine. Dj a bit soiled and chipped. *KARMIOLE*. $100

Henderson, John B. THE CRUISE OF THE TOMAS BARRERA. NY/London: G.P. Putnam's, 1916. Fldg map. Fine. *PARMER*. $50

Henderson, John. LETTERS AND POEMS... Dublin: for Byrne, Lewis, Jones and Moore, 1786. 1st Irish ed. 12mo; contemp calf, extremities worn, spine ends chipped; morocco label; paper label to spine; old lib stamp; occas light foxing; complete w/half-title. VG. *DRAMATIS PERSONAE*. $75

Henderson, John. THE WEST INDIES. A&C Black, 1905. 1st ed. 20s Series. W/o dedication to Sir Alfred Jones. Spine fading, minor cover spotting, else VG. *OLD LONDON*. $125

Henderson, John. THE WORLD OF THE ANCIENT MAYA. Ithaca: Cornell Univ, (1981). 1st ed. Chipped dj. *SILVER*. $30

Henderson, P. HENDERSON'S HANDBOOK OF PLANTS. NY, 1881. 1st ed. Orig cl (corners, spine ends worn, hinges starting). Ex-lib. *SUTTON*. $35

Henderson, Randall. SUN, SAND AND SOLITUDE: VIGNETTES....LA: Westernlore, 1968. 1st ed. Signed, dated presentation. 12 full-color photo plts. Fine in NF dj. *CONNOLLY & WADE*. $60

Henderson, Robert W. BALL, BAT, AND BISHOP. Rockport Press, 1947. 1st ed. VG+ in Good+ dj. *PLAPINGER*. $85

Hendrick, Burton J. LINCOLN'S WAR CABINET. Boston, 1946. 1st ed. Dj worn and chipped o/w VG+. *PRATT*. $27.50

Hendrick, Burton J. LINCOLN'S WAR CABINET. Boston: Little, Brown, 1946. 1st ed. VG. *ARCHER*. $17.50

Hendrick, Burton J. THE LEES OF VIRGINIA. Boston, 1935. 1st ed. 455pp. VG. *PRATT*. $55

Hendricks, Robert J. BETHEL AND AURORA, AN EXPERIMENT IN COMMUNISM AS PRACTICAL CHRISTIANITY. Press of Pioneers, 1933. 1st ed. 11 photo plts. VF in VG dj. *OREGON*. $75

Henie, Sonja. WINGS ON MY FEET. NY: Prentice Hall, 1940. 1st ed. VG+ in VG dj. *AARD*. $75

Heninger, S.K. Jr. THE COSMOGRAPHICAL GLASS, RENAISSANCE DIAGRAMS OF THE UNIVERSE. San Marino, CA: The Huntington Library, 1977. VG in grn cl. *KNOLLWOOD*. $40

Hennen, John. PRINCIPLES OF MILITARY SURGERY, COMPRISING OBSERVATIONS ON THE ARRANGEMENT, POLICE, AND PRACTICE OF HOSPITALS, AND ON THE HISTORY TREATMENT, AND ANOMALIES OF VARIOLA AND SYPHILIS. London, 1829. 3rd ed. 583pp. Recently rebound w/new eps. *FYE*. $250

Hennepin, Father Louis. A NEW DISCOVERY OF A VAST COUNTRY IN AMERICA...Chicago, 1903. 2 vols. Orig cl, backed boards. Reprint from 2nd London issue of 1698, w/facsimiles of orig title-pages, maps, illus, and addition of intro, notes and index. Howes H416. *GINSBERG*. $250

Henri, Adrian, and Nell Dunn. I WANT. London: Jonathan Cape, 1972. 1st ed. Fine in Fine dj. *BEASLEY*. $50

Henry, Alexander. TRAVELS & ADVENTURES IN CANADA AND THE INDIAN TERRITORIES BETWEEN THE YEARS 1760 AND 1776. NY, 1969. Orig cl. Reprint of 1901 ed. Howes H420. *GINSBERG*. $30

Henry, Arthur. NICHOLAS BLOOD, CANDIDATE. NY: Oliver Dodd, Publisher, (c1890). 1st bk. 1/4 cl, paper boards. Cl sl rubbed, o/w VG. *HELLER*. $150

Henry, Frederick. CAPTAIN HENRY OF GEAUGA. Cleveland: Gates Press, 1942. 1st ed. NF. *ARCHER*. $65

Henry, J. T. THE EARLY AND LATER HISTORY OF PETROLEUM...ITS DEVELOPMENT IN WESTERN PENNSYLVANIA...Phila., 1873. 1st ed. 607pp. 5 plts, 28 orig photo ports. Howes H421. *GINSBERG*. $1750

Henry, John F. THE HISTORY OF THE HENRY FAMILY...TO THE PRESENT TIME. LA: Wetzel, 1946. 1st ed. Orig cl. *GINSBERG*. $50

Henry, Marguerite. BRIGHTY OF THE GRAND CANYON. Chicago: Rand McNally, 1953. 1st ed. Good+ in Fair dj. *OCTOBER FARM*. $12

Henry, Marguerite. BRIGHTY OF THE GRAND CANYON. Illus by Wesley Dennis. Chicago/NY, 1953. Light rubbing edges, else VG. *FIVE QUAIL*. $15.

Henry, Marguerite. GAUDENZIA, PRIDE OF THE PALIO. Rand McNally, 1960. 1st ed. Illus by Lynd Ward. Slight edgewear, VG+. *BEBBAH*. $35

Henry, Michael. MURDER IN THE OLD JAIL. London: Hamilton, 1938. 1st ed. Fine, minor wear to pict dj. *ELSE FINE*. $45

Henry, O. (pseud of William Sydney Porter). THE GENTLE GRAFTER. NY: The McClure Co, 1908. 1st ed, 2nd prtg. Orig red cl. Owner sig, sm bkseller's stamp, else bright, VG to NF. Binding B, w/Doubleday Pg & Co. spine imprint. *CHAPEL HILL*. $35

Henry, O. (pseud of William Sidney Porter). HEART OF THE WEST. McClure, 1907. 1st ed. Pict cvr. VG+, spine faded. *AUTHORS OF THE WEST*. $60

Henry, O. (pseud of William Sidney Porter). THE STORIES OF HENRY O. LEC, 1965. 1st ed. Fancy dec cl w/leather spine label stamped, gilt. Fine in slipcase. *AUTHORS OF THE WEST*. $75

Henry, O. (pseud of William Sidney Porter). THE VOICE OF THE CITY. NY: LEC, 1935. One of 1500. Illus, signed by George Grosz. Fine in slipcase. *CAPTAIN'S BOOKSHELF*. $300

Henry, Robert Selph. TRAINS. NY, Indianapolis: Bobbs-Merrill, (1954). Dj. Fine. *WEBER*. $20

Henry, Stuart. CONQUERING OUR GREAT AMERICAN PLAINS: A HISTORICAL DEVELOPMENT. NY: E.P. Dutton, (1930). 1st ed. VG. *LAURIE*. $25

Henry, Sue. DOUBLE WHAMMY. NY: G.P. Putnam's Sons, 1987. 1st ed. VF in dj. *MORDIDA*. $40

Henry, Sue. MURDER ON THE IDITAROD TRAIL. NY: Atlantic Monthly Press, 1991. 1st ed. VF in dj. *MORDIDA*. $25

Henry Vaughan. SILUREST. POEMS...AN ESSAY...TWO LETTERS. London: Nonesuch Press, 1924. One of 850 ptd on Wolvercote Mill cream wove rag paper. Bound in black, gold-speckled paper-covered boards w/paper spine label. In orig black, gilt-lettered dw (worn, torn). Binding worn at extrems. *BOOK BLOCK*. $35

Henry, Will. ALIAS BUTCH CASSIDY. Random House, (1967). 1st ed. VF in VF dj. *OREGON.* $35

Henry, Will. I, TOM HORN. Phila, (1975). 1st ed. 339pp. VG+ in dj. *PRATT.* $25

Henry, Will. SAN JUAN HILL. Random House, (1962). 1st ed. Boards. Fine in dj. *AUTHORS OF THE WEST.* $17.50

Henry, Will. THE DAY FORT LARKING FELL. Phila.: Chilton, (1969). 1st ed. Fine in Fine dj. *UNGER.* $65

Henry, Will. THE GATES OF THE MOUNTAINS. Random House, (1963). 1st ed. Fine in chipped dj. *AUTHORS OF THE WEST.* $20

Henshaw, J.W. MOUNTAIN WILD FLOWERS OF CANADA. Toronto, 1906. Cloth (lt wear corners, spine ends; sm split upper spine end; rear hinge starting). *SUTTON.* $350

Henshaw, J.W. WILD FLOWERS OF THE NORTH AMERICAN MOUNTAINS. NY, (1915). 16 colored, 64 plain plts. Orig dec cl. Lt staining of half-title, blank sheet. *SUTTON.* $65

Henty, G.A. IN THE HEART OF THE ROCKIES. 8 full-page illus by G.A. Hindley. NY: Scribner's, 1905. Red cloth w/designs. 353pp plus 16pp adverts. 1st US ed, predating 1st British. Moderate cover wear, hinges tender. About Good+. *FIVE QUAIL.* $30

Hepworth, Barbara. A PICTORIAL AUTOBIOGRAPHY. NY: Praeger Pubs. (1970). 1st ed. Dj. *KARMIOLE.* $30

Hepworth, George H. THROUGH ARMENIA ON HORSEBACK. NY, 1898. Fldg map. ix,355pp. Sl rubbing of spine ends, else Fine. *O'NEILL.* $150

Herbert, Charles. A RELIC OF THE REVOLUTION, CONTAINING A FULL AND PARTICULAR ACCOUNT...OF ALL THE AMERICAN PRISONERS CAPTURED ON THE HIGH SEAS, AND CARRIED INTO PLYMOUTH, ENGLAND, DURING THE REVOLUTION OF 1776...Boston: Charles H. Pierce, 1847. 1st ed. Frontis, half title w/woodcut vignette, (2), 258 pp. Some foxing, lacking a flyleaf. Howes H.434. *LEFKOWICZ.* $150

Herbert, Frank. DRAGON IN THE SEA. Doubleday, 1956. 1st ed, 1st bk. Ex-lib. VG in dj. *MADLE.* $75

Herbert, Frank. DUNE MESSIAH. Putnam, 1969. 1st ed. VG in wrinkled dj. *MADLE.* $100

Herbert, Frank. THE WHITE FLOWER. Putnam, 1982. One of 500 numbered, signed. VG in slipcase. *MADLE.* $150

Herbert, William V. THE DEFENCE OF PLEVNA 1877. WRITTEN BY ONE WHO TOOK PART IN IT. London, 1895. 8 fldg maps. xvii,488pp. Uncut. 1st ed. Unusually Nice. *O'NEILL.* $225

Hereford, Elizabeth J. REBEL RHYMES AND OTHER POEMS. NY & London: Putnam's, 1888. 1st ed. 78pp. Orig cl, teg. Crown of spine lightly rubbed, sm bump bottom edge, else VG+. *CHAPEL HILL.* $35

Hergesheimer, Joseph. BERLIN. NY: Knopf, 1932. 1st ed. Cl-backed boards. One of 125 numbered. Signed. Spine evenly sunned. *MUELLER.* $45

Hergesheimer, Joseph. FROM AN OLD HOUSE. NY: Knopf, 1925. 1st ed. One of 1050 numbered. Signed. Fine. *MUELLER.* $35

Hergesheimer, Joseph. JAVA HEAD. NY: Knopf, 1919. 1/100 of the "large paper edition," numbered, signed by author. Fine w/extra spine label. *BEASLEY.* $100

Hergesheimer, Joseph. QUIET CITIES. NY: Knopf, 1928. 1st ed. Dj. Fine. *MUELLER.* $30

Hergesheimer, Joseph. TAMPICO. NY: Knopf, 1926. 1st ed. Dj. Fine. *MUELLER.* $25

Hergesheimer, Joseph. THE THREE BLACK PENNYS. NY, 1917. 1st ed., 1st state. With medallion on half-title about 2" from the bottom of the page. Spine title faded, still VG, NF copy. *BOND.* $30

Heriot, George. TRAVELS THROUGH THE CANADAS....TO WHICH IS SUBJOINED A COMPARATIVE VIEW OF THE MANNERS AND CUSTOMS OF SEVERAL OF THE INDIAN NATIONS OF NORTH AND SOUTH AMERICA....London: for Richard Phillips, 1807. 1st ed. xii,602pp. Fldg frontis, 26 plts (5 fldg), fldg colored map. 1/2 calf, marbled boards. Frontis, fldg map rehinged, sl dampstaining inside of upper margin throughout affecting frontis but not text; foxing, offsetting. Withal VG, tight. *WREDEN.* $1500

Herlihy, James Leo. MIDNIGHT COWBOY. Simon and Schuster, 1965. 1st ed. NF in dj (lt wear). *STAHR.* $25

Herlihy, James Leo. THE SLEEP OF BABY FILBERTSON. NY: Dutton, 1959. 1st ed. Fine in dj. *ELSE FINE.* $60

Herman, I., C.S.A. MEMOIRS OF A VETERAN. Atlanta, 1911. 1974 ltd ed rprt. VG+ in dj. *PRATT.* $35

Herman, Zvi. PEOPLES, SEAS AND SHIPS. London: Phoenix House, (1966). 10 color plts. Signature. Dj. Good. *ARCHAEOLOGIA.* $95

Hermann, Binger. THE LOUISIANA PURCHASE AND OUR TITLE WEST OF THE ROCKY MOUNTAINS. GPO, Washington, DC. 1900, 87pp. Illus. Fldg maps, some tinted. Cover and spine spotted. *HEINOLDT.* $25

Hermann, Charles H. RECOLLECTIONS OF LIFE AND DOINGS IN CHICAGO....BY AN OLD TIMER. Chicago: Normandie, 1945. Dj slight chipping, else bright, clean, VG. Wine cl, gilt dec on spine, cover. Fine. *CONNOLLY & WADE.* $35

Herms, W.B. and H.F. Gray. MOSQUITO CONTROL. NY, (1944). 2nd ed. Fldg chart. *SUTTON.* $25

Herndon, Sarah Raymond. DAYS ON THE ROAD...1865. NY: Burr Printing House, 1902. 1st ed. 270pp. Frontis. Eps, half-title very browned, o/w VG, tight. Howes H439. *SECOND LIFE.* $265

Herndon, William H. and Jesse William Weik. HERNDON'S LINCOLN, THE TRUE STORY OF A GREAT LIFE. 3 vols. Chicago, 1889. The Herndon's Lincoln Publishing Company Edition. 638pp. Minor cover wear, 2 vols have small spots on cover, o/w Fine. *PRATT.* $100

Herndon, William Lewis and Lardner Gibbon. EXPLORATION OF THE VALLEY OF THE AMAZON. Washington: House of Representatives, 1854. Fading; board separated from one of atlas vols. Maps generally Fair w/foxing, tears. Cloth. 2 vols w/atlases of maps. Tinted plts. Good, foxing. *PARMER.* $390

Herndon, William Lewis and Lardner Gibbon. EXPLORATION OF THE VALLEY OF THE AMAZON....Washington: Nicholson, 1854. 2 vols. Senate Doc no 36. pp. 414; 339pp. Foxed, lt water staining vol 1. Binding wear. Good set. 52 plts, 2 fldg maps. *SECOND LIFE.* $125

Herndon, William Lewis and Lardner Gibbon. EXPLORATION OF THE VALLEY OF THE AMAZON...PART 1 AND 2. Washington, 1854. House of Representatives, 33rd Congress, 1st Session, Executive No. 53. 2 vols. 417pp; 339pp. Orig blind-stamped purple cl faded vol 2. Spines chipped, scattered foxing, lt water stain some plts, text. 16 plts vol 1; 36 plts (lacks 1) vol 2. *SILVER.* $100

Herne, Peregrine. PERILS AND PLEASURES OF A HUNTER'S LIFE. Phila: Potter, n.d. (18-?). Appears to be a cheap reprint. Good only. *OLD LONDON.* $20

Herner, Charles. THE ARIZONA ROUGH RIDERS. Tucson, (1970). 1st ed. 275pp. VG+ in dj. *PRATT.* $45

Hernton, Calvin. SCARECROW. GC: Doubleday, 1974. 1st ed. Remainder spray, o/w Fine in dj. *LOPEZ.* $35

Herodotus. THE HISTORIES OF HERODOTUS OF HALICARNASSUS. Haarlem: LEC, 1958. One of 1500 illus, signed by Edward Bawden. Fine, owner sig in slipcase. *CAPTAIN'S BOOKSHELF.* $225

Herondas. THE MIMIAMBS OF HERONDAS. Trans by Jack Lindsay. (London): Fanfrolico Press. (1926). Ed ltd to 375. *KARMIOLE*. $185

Herr, Michael. DISPATCHES. NY, 1977. 1st ed, 1st bk. Couple lt spots front board, else NF in Fine dj. *PETTLER*. $65

Herr, Michael. DISPATCHES. NY: Knopf, 1977. 1st ed. Fine in dj, sunning to spine. *CAPTAIN'S BOOKSHELF*. $100

Herr, Michael. DISPATCHES. NY: Knopf, 1977. 1st ed. Fine in Fine dj. *HELLER*. $100

Herr, Pamela. JESSIE BENTON FREMONT: AMERICAN WOMAN OF THE 19TH CENTURY. NY: Franklin Watts, (1987). 1st ed. Fine in Fine dj. *BOOK MARKET*. $27

Herrick, F.H. NATURAL HISTORY OF THE AMERICAN LOBSTER. Washington, 1911. 20 plts. Orig wrappers (lib stamp on title, backstrip tears repaired). *SUTTON*. $75

Herrick, James. A SHORT HISTORY OF CARDIOLOGY. Springfield, 1942. 1st ed. *FYE*. $125

Herrigel, Eugen. ZEN IN THE ART OF ARCHERY. NY: Pantheon Books, 1959. 4th prtg. NF in dj. *OLD LONDON*. $15

Herrlinger, Robert. HISTORY OF MEDICAL ILLUSTRATION FROM ANTIQUITY TO 1600. NY, 1970. 1st Eng trans. Slipcase. *FYE*. $150

Herrmann, Dieter B.. THE HISTORY OF ASTRONOMY FROM HERSCHEL TO HERTZSPRUNG. Cambridge Univ Press, 1984 (Germany 1973). 1st Eng ed. Trans & rev by Kevin Krisciunas. VG in dj. *KNOLLWOOD*. $30

Herschel, John F.W. ESSAYS FROM THE EDINBURGH AND QUARTERLY REVIEW....London: Longman, Brown, Green, Longman & Roberts, 1857, Ist, only ed. Ex-lib. Half black leather, maroon cl (chipping, wear, bkpl, stamps, lt foxing. Internally Good. *KNOLLWOOD*. $200

Herschel, Sir John F.W. A TREATISE ON ASTRONOMY. London: Longman, Rees, et al, 1834 (1833). New ed. Good ex-lib. *KNOLLWOOD*. $80

Hersey, John. HIROSHIMA. Jacob Lawrence (illus-orig silk-screen prints). W/new poem by Robert Penn Warren. Folio, full black calf, cl slipcase. NY: LEC, 1984. 1st of this ed. Ltd to 1500 signed by Hersey, Lawrence & Warren. *JAFFE*. $750

Hersey, John. THE WAR LOVER. NY: Knopf, 1959. 1st ed. VF in dj. *ELSE FINE*. $45

Hersey, John. UNDER THE EYE OF THE STORM. NY: Knopf, 1967. 1st ed. NF. *SMITH*. $25

Hertwig, Oscar. TEXT-BOOK OF THE EMBRYOLOGY OF MAN AND MAMMALS. London, 1892. 1st Eng trans. 339 figures. Ex-lib in rubbed lib buckram. *FYE*. $50

Hertzler, Arthur E. THE HORSE AND BUGGY DOCTOR. NY: Harper & Bros., 1938. 1st ed. 7 plts. Fine in Good+ dj. *CONNOLLY & WADE*. $25

Hertzler, Arthur E. THE HORSE AND BUGGY DOCTOR. NY: Harper, 1938. 1st ed. Fine in Fine dj. *BOOK MARKET*. $37

Hertzler, Arthur. A TREATISE ON TUMORS. Phila, 1912. 1st ed. Photo illus. *FYE*. $100

Hertzog, Peter. LITTLE KNOWN FACTS ABOUT BILLY THE KID. Santa Fe: The Press of the Territorian, 1963. 1st ed. Ptd wrappers. VG. *CONNOLLY & WADE*. $25

Hervey, John. THE AMERICAN TROTTER. A HISTORY OF THE STANDARD-BRED HORSE. NY: Coward McCann, 1947. 1st ed. VG in Good dj. *OCTOBER FARM*. $125

Hervey, John. THE AMERICAN TROTTER. NY, 1947. NF in sl chipped dj. *DIAMOND*. $50

Herzl, Theodore, THE COMPLETE DIARIES OF ... NY & London. 1960. 5 vols. Boxed. Fine. *POLYANTHOS*. $100.

Heseltine, Nigel. MADAGASCAR. NY: Praeger, (1971). 1st US ed. Fine in VG dj. *AARD*. $20

Heslop, Harold. THE GATE OF A STRANGE FIELD. London: Brentano's, 1929. 1st ed. Fine but for a little pale blotching, in Fine dj. *BEASLEY*. $75

Hess, Joan. MADNESS IN MAGGODY. NY: St. Martin's (1991). 1st ed. Signed. Fine in dj. *DORN*. $35

Hess, Joan. MALICE IN MAGGODY. NY: St. Martin's, (1987). 1st ed. VF in VF dj. *UNGER*. $35

Hesse, Hermann. GOLDMUND. London: Peter Owen, (1959). 1st Eng ed. NF in VG dj. *DORN*. $75

Hewett, E.L. CAMPFIRE & TRAIL. Albuquerque, NM, 1943. 1st ed. NF. *MIKESH*. $25

Hewett, Edgar L. ANCIENT ANDEAN LIFE. Indianapolis, 1939. Pull-out map. NF. *POLYANTHOS*. $45

Hewett, Edgar L. ANCIENT ANDEAN LIFE. Indianapolis: Bobbs-Merrill Co, c. 1939. 1st ed. Blue cl. Gilt cover, spine titles. Fldg map. Some wear, else VG+. *PARMER*. $60

Hewett, Edgar L. ANCIENT LIFE IN MEXICO AND CENTRAL AMERICA. Indianapolis, 1936. Spine lightly sunned. NF. *POLYANTHOS*. $45

Hewett, Edgar L. ANCIENT LIFE IN THE AMERICAN SOUTH-WEST. NY: Tudor, 1943. Later ed. Grn-stamped cl in dj w/head of spine and top corners chipped. *DAWSON'S*. $35

Hewett, Edgar L. ANCIENT LIFE IN THE AMERICAN SOUTH-WEST. Indianapolis: Bobbs-Merrill, 1930. 1st ed. Frontis. 30 plts. Blue cl, red lettering. Fine. *CONNOLLY & WADE*. $40

Hewitt, Edward Ringwood. TELLING ON THE TROUT. NY: Charles Scribner's Sons, (1926). 1930, new and rev ed. Name, old price on 1st blank pg. VG. *BACKMAN*. $25

Hewitt, Frederic. ANAESTHETICS AND THEIR ADMINISTRATION. London, 1901. 2nd ed. Head and tail of spine chipped, eps missing. Contents VG. *FYE*. $150

Hewitt, Girart. MINNESOTA: ITS ADVANTAGES TO SETTLERS. BEING A BRIEF SYNOPSIS....St. Paul, 1867. 1st ed. 36,(8)pp. Orig ptd wrappers. Howes H455. *GINSBERG*. $150

Hewitt, Girart. MINNESOTA: ITS ADVANTAGES TO SETTLERS. St. Paul, 1867. 5th ed. Front wrap says "4th ed." Spine reinforced. Nice. *BOHLING*. $90

Hewitt, John Michael. THE ALASKA VAGABOND, DR. SKOOKUM. NY, (1953). Fine in dj. *ARTIS*. $12.50

Hewitt, R.H. NOTES BY THE WAY. Seattle: Frank McCaffrey Pubs, 1955. Red cl, spine stamped in blue. Reprint of rare 1863 ed. *KARMIOLE*. $30

Hewitt, Robert. COFFEE: ITS HISTORY, CULTIVATION, AND USES....NY: D. Appleton, 1872. 1st ed. 102pp. Chromolitho frontis, hand-colored S-section fldg map. Orig dec orange cl, gilt; spine sunned. Presentation, signed by "the author." *KARMIOLE*. $200

Hey, William. PRACTICAL OBSERVATIONS IN SURGERY, ILLUSTRATED WITH CASES AND PLATES. Phila, 1805. 1st Amer ed. 332pp. *FYE*. $300

Heydemarck, Haupt. WAR FLYING IN MACEDONIA. London, (1920). Fldg map. 196pp. *O'NEILL*. $40

Heydenryck, Henry. THE ART AND HISTORY OF FRAMES. NY: James H. Heineman, 1963. Fine in slipcase. *BLUE MOUNTAIN*. $150

Heyer, Georgette. BLACK SHEEP. London: Bodley Head, 1966. 1st ed. Fine, slight mottling to dj spine. *ELSE FINE*. $45

Heyer, Georgette. COTILLION. NY: Putnam, 1953. 1st ed. Fine, light edgewear, chip to top edge of dj. *ELSE FINE*. $35

Heyer, Georgette. FALSE COLOURS. NY: Dutton, 1964. 1st ed. Fine, dj minor wear. *ELSE FINE.* $30

Heyer, Georgette. MY LORD JOHN. NY: Dutton, 1975. 1st ed. Fine in dj. *ELSE FINE.* $30

Heyer, Georgette. THE NONESUCH. NY: Dutton, 1963. 1st ed. Fine, dj minor wear. *ELSE FINE.* $35

Heyerdahl, Thor. AKU-AKU. THE SECRET OF EASTER IS-LAND. London: George Allen & Unwin, 1958. First UK ed. Fine in NF dj. *GREAT EPIC.* $25

Heyerdahl, Thor. AMERICAN INDIANS IN THE PACIFIC....Oslo, (1952). 1st ed. Chipped dj. 8 color plts, 90 b/w. 11 maps. Hinges loose, contents VG. *SILVER.* $65

Heyerdahl, Thor. FATU-HIVA. BACK TO NATURE. GC: Doubleday & Co, Inc, 1975. 1st Amer ed. VG in similar dj. *PARMER.* $30

Heyerdahl, Thor. FATU-HIVA. BACK TO NATURE. GC: Doubleday, 1974. 2nd ptg. Fine in Fine dj. *GREAT EPIC.* $20

Heyerdahl, Thor. KON-TIKI. Rand-McNally, (1960). 1st ed, thus. Special ed for young people. Signed. 4to. 165pp. Illus by William Neese. Signed. NF in NF dj. *BEBBAH.* $30

Heyerdahl, Thor. THE ART OF EASTER ISLAND. GC: Doubleday & Co, Inc, 1975. Front hinge beginning, else NF in VG dj. *PARMER.* $135

Heyman, Max L. PRUDENT SOLDIER, A BIOGRAPHY OF MAJOR GENERAL E.R.S. CANDBY. Glendale, 1959. 1st ed. Minor shelf wear o/w Fine. *PRATT.* $110

Heyman, Max L. PRUDENT SOLDIER. Glendale, CA: The Arthur H. Clark Co. 1959. 1st ed. Fldg map. *KARMIOLE.* $40

Heyman, Max. PRUDENT SOLDIER, BIOGRAPHY OF MAJOR GENERAL E.R.S. CANBY 1817-1873...Glendale: A.H. Clark, 1959. 1st ed. Fldg map. Fine. *OREGON.* $80

Heyward, Dorothy and DuBose Heyward. PORGY: A PLAY IN FOUR ACTS. The Theatre Guild Acting Version. GC: Doubleday, Page & Co., 1927. 1st ed. Orange paper over stiff boards. Spine faded, edges chipped; sl soiled.) Internally Fine. *BLUE MOUNTAIN.* $150

Heyward, DuBose and Herbert Ravenel Sass. FORT SUMTER. NY, (1938). 1st ed, thus. VG. *McGOWAN.* $27.50

Heyward, DuBose and Hervey Allen. CAROLINA CHANSONS: LEGENDS OF THE LOW COUNTRY. NY: Macmillan, 1922. 1st ed, 1st book. Corners bumped, a bit soiled. *ARCHER.* $45

Heyward, DuBose. BRASS ANKLE. NY, 1931. 1st trade ed. NF in lightly chipped bright orange dj. *PETTLER.* $45

Heyward, DuBose. PORGY. NY: Doran, (1925). 1st ed, 1st issue binding. Orig black cl stamped in gold. VG in dj (2" chip top of spine: title, author's name missing; 3.5" closed tear front panel). *CHAPEL HILL.* $125

Heyward, DuBose. SKYLINES AND HORIZONS. NY: Macmillan, 1924. 1st ed. Orig blue cl w/paper cover label. Sm bkseller's ticket, owner name, else Fine. *CHAPEL HILL.* $125

Heyward, DuBose. THE HALF PINT FLASK. NY, 1928. 1st trade ed. 1" chip at the top and bottom of dj spine, else VG. *PETTLER.* $40

Heyward, DuBose. THE HALF PINT FLASK. NY: Farrar & Rinehart, 1929. 1st ed. One of 175 numbered lg paper copies, signed by Heyward and illus Joseph Sandford. Fine. *MUELLER.* $50

Hiaasen, Carl and William D. Montalbano. POWDER BURN. NY: Atheneum, 1981. 1st ed. Signed by Montalbano. Edges spotted, o/w Fine in dj. *MORDIDA.* $100

Hiaasen, Carl with William D. Montalbano. POWDER BURN. NY: Atheneum, 1981. 1st ed. VF in dj. *ELSE FINE.* $65.

Hiaasen, Carl. DOUBLE WHAMMY. NY: G.P. Putnam's Sons, 1987. 1st ed. Signed. VF in dj. *MORDIDA.* $40

HIAWATHA. NY, (c. 1916). Willy Pogany illus. Story by Edith Elias. Lt wear extrems, but overall VG. *BOOKFINDERS INTL.* $180

Hibben, Frank C. TREASURE IN THE DUST. London: Cleaver-Hume, (1953). 16 plts. Inscription. Good in tattered dj. *ARCHAEOLOGIA.* $25

Hibberd, Shirley. THE AMATEUR'S FLOWER GARDEN....London: Groombridge, 1871. 1st ed. 6 hand-colored plts. 284pp. Soiled grn cl, aeg; hinges tender. Good. *SECOND LIFE.* $75

Hichens, Robert. THE NEAR EAST. DALMATIA, GREECE AND CONSTANTINOPLE. NY: Century, 1913. 1st ed. 50 plts, 11 color. Orig cl sl rubbed. Ex-lib. VG. *WORLDWIDE.* $45

Hicken, Victor. ILLINOIS IN THE CIVIL WAR. Urbana, (1960). 1st ed. Light dj wear o/w Fine. *PRATT.* $45

Hickey, J.J. A GUIDE TO BIRD WATCHING. NY, 1943. Pp yellowed. *SUTTON.* $27

Hickman, John. THE ENCHANTED ISLANDS—THE GALAPAGOS DISCOVERED. Shropshire: Anthony Nelson, 1985. 1st ed. New in similar dj. *PARMER.* $25

Hicks, Dave (ed). 1971 BRAND BOOK. THE DENVER WESTERNERS. Boulder, CO: Johnson Publishing Co, 1972. #358/750. VG. *BURCHAM.* $50

Hicks, John Edward. ADVENTURES OF A TRAMP PRINTER, 1880-1890 Kansas City: Midamericana, (1950). 1st ed. Dj chipped. Prospectus inserted. *OAK KNOLL.* $25.

Hicks, John Edward. ADVENTURES OF A TRAMP PRINTER 1880-1890. Kansas City, MO: Midamerican Press, 1950. 1st ed. VG. *CONNOLLY & WADE.* $37.50

HIDE AND SEEK RIDDLE BOOK. NY, 1943. Gadgets, illus Carlyle Leech. Spiral binding, a little past its prime, has near VG dj. Moveable bk. *BOOKFINDERS INTL.* $50

Hieb, Louis A. FIFTY FOREIGN FIRSTS: A TONY HILLERMAN CHECKLIST. Santa Fe: Parker Books of the West, 1991. 1st ed. 1/50 numbered, signed by Hillerman and Hieb. Handsewn in French-fold wraps w/15 pages and 5 colored plts. VF. *MORDIDA.* $50

Hieb, Louis A. TONY HILLERMAN: A BIBLIOGRAPHY. Tucson: Press of the Gigantic Hound, 1990. 1st ed. Pub. in an ed. of 1,000. Signed. VF w/o dj as issued. *MORDIDA.* $35

Hielscher, Kurt. PICTURESQUE SPAIN. ARCHITECTURE, LANDSCAPE, LIFE OF THE PEOPLE. NY: Brentano, n.d. (c. 1920). 1st ed. Corners rubbed, spine faded, o/w VG. *WORLDWIDE.* $25

Higbe, Kirby and Martin Quigley. THE HIGH HARD ONE. Viking, 1967. 1st ed. VG in Fine dj. *PLAPINGER.* $75

Higbe, Kirby and Martin Quigley. THE HIGH HARD ONE. Viking, 1967. 1st ed. VG in Good+ dj. *PLAPINGER.* $55

Higgins, Anthony. NEW CASTLE DELAWARE: 1651-1939. Boston: Houghton Mifflin Co., 1939. 1st ed. #437 of 765 (750 signed, and for sale). VG. *BACKROOM.* $125

Higgins, C.A. TO CALIFORNIA OVER THE SANTA FE TRAIL. Chicago, 1905. 208pp. VG+. *FIVE QUAIL.* $20

Higgins, F.R. ISLAND BLOOD. London: John Lane, (1925). 1st ed. Name stamp ffep, else VG. *WOOLMER.* $25

Higgins, George V. THE FRIENDS OF EDDIE COYLE. NY, 1972. 1st ed, 1st bk. NF in dj. *PETTLER.* $20

Higgins, Jack. CONFESSIONAL. NY: Stein & Day, 1985. 1st ed. VF in dj. *ELSE FINE.* $30

Higgins, Jack. DAY OF JUDGMENT. London: Collins, 1978. 1st ed. Fine in price-clipped dj. *MORDIDA.* $45

Higgins, Jack. DILLINGER. As Patterson. NY: Stein & Day, 1983. 1st ed. VF in dj. *ELSE FINE.* $40

Higgins, Jack. EXOCET. NY: Stein & Day, 1983. 1st ed. VF in dj. *ELSE FINE.* $35

Higgins, Jack. LUCIANO'S LUCK. NY: Stein & Day, 1981. 1st ed. VF in dj. *ELSE FINE.* $35

Higgins, Jack. SOLO. NY: S & D, 1980. 1st ed. VF in dj. *ELSE FINE.* $40

Higgins, Jack. STORM WARNING. NY: Holt, Rinehart and Winston, 1976. 1st Amer ed. Pp darkened, o/w Fine in dj. *MORDIDA.* $25

Higgins, Jack. TO CATCH A KING. As Patterson. NY: S & D, 1979. 1st ed. VF in dj. *ELSE FINE.* $45

Higgins, Jack. TOUCH THE DEVIL. NY: Stein & Day, 1982. 1st ed. VF in dj. *ELSE FINE.* $35

Higginson, A. and Julian Chamberlain. THE HUNTS OF THE UNITED STATES AND CANADA. Boston: Wiles, 1908. 1st ed, ltd to 500, signed by both authors. Good+. *OCTOBER FARM.* $125

Higginson, A. Henry, ed. AS HOUNDS RAN. NY: Huntington Press, 1930. 1st ed. Ltd to 990. Cover dusty, minor spotting, else VG. *OLD LONDON.* $45

Higginson, A. Henry. BRITISH AND AMERICAN SPORTING AUTHORS. London: Hutchingson, 1951. 1st Eng ed. VG. *OCTOBER FARM.* $125

Higginson, Ella. ALASKA. THE GREAT COUNTRY. NY: Macmillan, 1926. New ed w/new matter. Fine in VG dj. *BLUE DRAGON.* $30

Higginson, Mary Thatcher. THOMAS WENTWORTH HIGGINSON. Boston, 1914. 1st ed. Spine faded o/w VG+. *PRATT.* $30

Highsmith, Patricia. DEEP WATER. NY: Harper & Brothers, 1967. 1st ed. Top edge lightly spotted o/w Fine in dj w/minor wear. *MORDIDA.* $45

Highsmith, Patricia. LITTLE TALES OF MISOGYNY. NY: Penzler Book, 1986. 1st Amer. ed. One of 250 numbered, signed. VF in slipcase w/o dj as issued. *MORDIDA.* $45

Highsmith, Patricia. PEOPLE WHO KNOCK ON THE DOOR. NY: Penzler Book, 1985. 1st Amer ed. One of 250 numbered, signed. VF in slipcase w/o dj as issued. *MORDIDA.* $45

Highsmith, Patricia. SLOWLY SLOWLY IN THE WIND. NY: Penzler Book, 1985. 1st Amer ed. One of 250 numbered, signed. VF in dj w/slipcase. *MORDIDA.* $45

Highsmith, Patricia. STRANGERS ON A TRAIN. NY: Harper & Bros, (1950). 1st ed, 1st bk. VG in dj (sl chipped, faded; short, internally mended tears). *BERNARD.* $275

Highsmith, Patricia. THE ANIMAL-LOVER'S BOOK OF BEASTLY MURDER. NY: Penzler Book, 1986. 1st Amer ed. One of 250 numbered, signed. VF in slipcase w/o dj as issued. *MORDIDA.* $45

Highsmith, Patricia. THE ANIMAL-LOVER'S BOOK OF BEASTLY MURDERS. Penzler, 1986. Uncorrected page proofs of 1st U.S. ed. Touch of soil to white wraps else Fine. *BEBBAH.* $20

Highsmith, Patricia. THE BLACK HOUSE. NY: Penzler Books, 1988. 1st Amer ed. One of 250 numbered, signed. VF in slipcase w/o dj as issued. *MORDIDA.* $45

Highsmith, Patricia. THE BLUNDERER. NY: Coward-McCann, (1954). 1st ed. Bottom corner tips sl worn, else VG in dj (chipped; internally mended tears). *BERNARD.* $150

Highsmith, Patricia. THE GLASS CELL. London: Heinemann, 1965. 1st UK ed. Fine in NF dj. *BEASLEY.* $45

Highsmith, Patricia. THE MAN WHO WROTE BOOKS IN HIS HEAD AND OTHER STORIES. Helsinki: Eurographica, 1986. 1st of this ed. Ltd to 350 signed. Ptd wraps. Mint. *JAFFE.* $175

Highsmith, Patricia. THE STORY-TELLER. GC: Doubleday, 1965. 1st ed. Fine in lightly used dj w/spine wear. *BEASLEY.* $50

Highsmith, Patricia. THE TREMOR OF FORGERY. London: Heinemann, 1969. 1st Eng ed. Fine in dj. *MORDIDA.* $45

Highwater, Jamake. ARTS OF THE INDIAN AMERICAS. NY: H&R (1983). 1st ed. Fine in dj. *LOPEZ.* $60

Highwater, Jamake. ARTS OF THE INDIAN AMERICAS. NY: Harper & Row, 1983. 1st ed. Cl, silver dec. Fine in Fine dj. *CONNOLLY & WADE.* $45

Highwater, Jamake. FODOR'S INDIAN AMERICA. NY: McKay, 1975. 1st ed. Note in pen to top of title page, NF in dj. *LAME DUCK.* $45

Highwater, Jamake. I WEAR THE MORNING STAR. NY: H&R, (1986). 1st ed. Fine in price-clipped dj. *LOPEZ.* $35

Highwater, Jamake. JOURNEY TO THE SKY. NY: Crowell, (1978). 1st ed. Fine in dj. *LOPEZ.* $35

Highwater, Jamake. LEGEND DAYS. NY: H&R, (1984). 1st ed. Fine in price-clipped dj. *LOPEZ.* $45

Highwater, Jamake. MANY SMOKES, MANY MOONS. Phila: Lippincott, (1978). Fine in NF dj. *LOPEZ.* $65

Highwater, Jamake. NATIVE LAND. Boston: Little Brown, (1986). 1st ed. NF in dj. *LOPEZ.* $35

Highwater, Jamake. SHADOW SHOW. NY: Alfred van der Marck, (1986). 1st ed. Fine in Fine dj. *LOPEZ.* $25

Highwater, Jamake. SONG FROM THE EARTH. Boston: NY Graphic Soc, (1976). 1st ed. Hb issue (there was a simultaneous issue in wraps). Fine in NF dj. *LOPEZ.* $125

Highwater, Jamake. THE CEREMONY OF INNOCENCE. (NY): H&R, (1985). 1st ed. Fine in price-clipped dj. *LOPEZ.* $35

Highwater, Jamake. THE PRIMAL MIND. NY: H&R, (1981). 1st ed. Fine in price-clipped dj. *LOPEZ.* $25

Highwater, Jamake. THE SWEET GRASS LIVES ON. NY: Lippincott & Crowell, (1980). 1st ed. Fine in NF dj. *LOPEZ.* $85

Hijuelos, Oscar. OUR HOUSE IN THE LAST WORLD. NY: Persea (1983). 1st ed. Fine in a NF dj (1/4" edge tear). *DORN.* $75

Hijuelos, Oscar. THE MAMBO KINGS PLAY SONGS OF LOVE. NY: Farrar Straus Giroux, (1989). 1st ed. Fine in dj. *LOPEZ.* $45

Hijuelos, Oscar. THE MAMBO KINGS PLAY SONGS OF LOVE. NY: FSG, 1989. 1st ed. VF in dj. *ELSE FINE.* $65

Hijuelos, Oscar. THE MAMBO KINGS PLAY SONGS OF LOVE. NY: FS&G, (1989). 1st ed. As New in dj. *CAPTAIN'S BOOKSHELF.* $45

Hijuelos, Oscar. THE MAMBO KINGS PLAY SONGS OF LOVE. NY: FSG, (1989). 1st ed. Fine in Fine dj. *UNGER.* $60

Hilder, Brett. THE VOYAGE OF TORRES. THE DISCOVERY OF THE SOUTHERN COASTLINE BY CAPTAIN LUIS BAEZ DE TORRES IN 1606. St. Lucia: Univ of Queensland, 1980. As New in similar dj. *PARMER.* $40

Hill, Alfred J. HISTORY OF COMPANY E OF THE SIXTH MINNESOTA REGIMENT OF VOLUNTEER INFANTRY. St. Paul: Pub by Prof. T.H. Lewis at the Pioneer Press Co., 1899. Appendix by Capt. Charles J. Stees. Fine in wraps. *LAURIE.* $150

Hill, Alfred T. VOYAGES. TALES FROM THE GREAT AGE OF SAIL INCLUDING "VOYAGE TO CALCUTTA ABOARD THE CHARLES COOPER." NY: David McKay Company, Inc., 1977. 1st ed. VG in rubbed and worn dj. *PARMER.* $20

Hill, Alice Polk. TALES OF THE COLORADO PIONEERS. Denver: Pierson & Gardner, 1884. Spine ends worn, cloth lightly coated maybe varnish o/w VG. 1st ed. *OREGON.* $80

Hill, Dennis and Geoffrey Parr (eds). ELECTROENCEPHALOGRAPHY, A SYMPOSIUM ON ITS VARIOUS ASPECTS. London, 1950. 1st ed. Dj. *FYE.* $50

Hill, Geoffrey. COLLECTED POEMS. 1/4 navy calf & marbled boards, slipcase. (London): Deutsch, (1986). 1st ed. One of 100 signed. Mint. *JAFFE.* $250

Hill, Geoffrey. SOMEWHERE IS SUCH A KINGDOM. POEMS 1952-1971. Boston: Houghton Mifflin, 1975. 1st ed. Although the copyright page states "1st Amer ed", there was no equivalent English ed. Cl, dj. VF. *JAFFE.* $125

Hill, Geoffrey. THE MYSTERY OF THE CHARITY OF CHARLES PEGUY. (London): Agenda Editions; Andre Deutsch, (1983). 1st ed. One of 100, signed. Cl, acetate dj. VF. *JAFFE.* $175

Hill, Henry. RECOLLECTIONS OF AN OCTOGENARIAN. Boston: D. Lothrop & Co, (1884). 1st, only ed. Orig cl, paper browned, title loose, still Good. *LEFKOWICZ.* $75

Hill, Howard G. RIDING THE LIMITEDS' LOCOMOTIVES. Superior, 1972. 1st ed. Fine in Fine dj. *VARNER.* $30

Hill, J.L. THE END OF THE CATTLE TRAIL. Long Beach, CA: Geo. W. Moyle, n.d. (c. 1930). 1st ed. Orig ptd wrappers. *KARMIOLE.* $50

Hill, J.L. THE END OF THE CATTLE TRAIL. Long Beach, CA: Geo. W. Moyle, n.d. (ca. 1905-1910). 1st ed. Orig ptd wraps. Bit chipped at spine ends, o/w About Fine. Quite scarce. *CONNOLLY & WADE.* $75

Hill, Joe and Ola Davis Hill. IN LITTLE AMERICA WITH BYRD. Boston: Ginn & Co, 1937. Athenaeum Press. 1st ed. Frontis, double-pg map. Pict cl w/gilt stamped words "complimentary professional copy" on front cover. About Fine. Scarce. *CONNOLLY & WADE.* $45

Hill, Judith P. A HISTORY OF HENRY COUNTY, VIRGINIA WITH BIOGRAPHICAL SKETCHES...AND GENEALOGICAL HISTORIES...Martinsville, Va, 1925. 1st ed. Orig cl, sm paper label on spine, bkpl removed. *GINSBERG.* $125

Hill, N.P. THE BIRDS OF CAPE COD, MASSACHUSETTS. NY, 1965. Scuffed dj. *SUTTON.* $28

Hill, Norman Newell. HISTORY OF KNOX COUNTY, OHIO. Mt. Vernon, Ohio: A.A. Graham & Co., 1881. 6 plts. Recased, retaining orig boards, new backstrip; sturdy, repair to title page, w/lib blindstamp 4 leaves. *BOHLING.* $150

Hill, Reginald. A PINCH OF SNUFF. NY: Harper, 1978. 1st ed. VF in dj. Signed. *ELSE FINE.* $35

Hill, Reginald. CHILD'S PLAY. London: Collins Crime Club, 1987. 1st ed. Signed. VF in dj. *MORDIDA.* $45

Hill, Reginald. PASCOE'S GHOST. London: Collins Crime Club, 1979. 1st ed. VF in price-clipped dj. *MORDIDA.* $75

Hill, Reginald. THERE ARE NO GHOSTS IN THE SOVIET UNION. London: Collins Crime Club, 1987. 1st ed. Fine in dj. *MORDIDA.* $35

Hill, Reginald. UNDER WORLD. London: Collins, 1988. 1st ed. VF in dj. *SILVER DOOR.* $25

Hill, Reginald. UNDER WORLD. London: Collins Crime Club, 1988. 1st ed. Signed. VF in dj. *MORDIDA.* $45

Hill, Russell. LUCY BOOMER. NY: Ballantine (1992). Uncorrected proof. Fine in wraps. *DORN.* $25

Hill, Ruth Beebe. HANTA YO. GC: Doubleday & Co, 1979. 1st ed. VG in worn dj. *PARMER.* $19.50

Hill, Sarah Jane Full. MRS. HILL'S JOURNAL, CIVIL WAR REMINISCENCES. Ed by Mark M. Krug. Chicago, 1980. 1st ed. Lakeside Classics #78. Fine. *PRATT.* $37.50

Hill, Sir George. A HISTORY OF CYPRUS. Vol 1. Cambridge, 1949. Fldg map. *O'NEILL.* $95

Hillard, Katharine. MY MOTHER'S JOURNAL. A YOUNG LADY'S DIARY OF FIVE YEARS SPENT IN MANILA, MACAO, AND THE CAPE OF GOOD HOPE. Boston: George H. Ellis, 1900. Cl. Frontis. Cvrs worn, faded, else VG. *PARMER.* $150

Hiller, L. SURGERY THROUGH THE AGES: A PICTORIAL CHRONICLE. NY, 1944. *FYE.* $75

Hillerman, Tony and Ernie Bulow. TALKING MYSTERIES. Albuquerque: Univ of New Mexico, (1991). 1st ed. One of an unspecified number w/an orig drawing by Ernest Franklin. Signed by Hillerman, Bulow and Franklin. Fine in Fine dj. *UNGER.* $125

Hillerman, Tony and Robert Reynolds. RIO GRANDE. (Portland): (Belding), (1975). 1st ed. Foxing to top page edges. VG in dj that is creased on the flaps but o/w VG. *LOPEZ.* $200

Hillerman, Tony. A THIEF OF TIME. Harper & Row, (1988). 1st ed. New in dj. *AUTHORS OF THE WEST.* $25

Hillerman, Tony. A THIEF OF TIME. Harper & Row, 1988. Advance reading copy. Fine in dec wraps. *STAHR.* $45

Hillerman, Tony. A THIEF OF TIME. NY: Harper & Row, 1988. 1st ed. Signed. This copy contains a full-page colored, pen-and-ink frontis illus by Ernest Franklin. VF in dj w/slipcase. *MORDIDA.* $350

Hillerman, Tony. A THIEF OF TIME. NY: Harper & Row, 1988. 1st ed. Adv rev copy w/slip, photo and flyer laid in. VF in dj. *MORDIDA.* $50

Hillerman, Tony. A THIEF OF TIME. NY: Harper & Row, 1988. 1st ed. One of 250 specially bound, numbered, signed. As New in slipcase. *MORDIDA.* $200

Hillerman, Tony. COYOTE WAITS. Harper & Row, (1990). 1st ed. Boards. New in dj. *AUTHORS OF THE WEST.* $30

Hillerman, Tony. COYOTE WAITS. NY: Harper & Row, 1990. 1st ed. One of 500 specially bound, numbered, signed. VF in slipcase w/o dj as issued. *MORDIDA.* $100

Hillerman, Tony. COYOTE WAITS. NY: Harper & Row, 1990. 1st ed. Signed. 2 colored, pen-and-ink illus by Ernest Franklin. VF dj w/slipcase. *MORDIDA.* $375

Hillerman, Tony. DANCE HALL OF THE DEAD. London: Pluto Press, 1985. 1st Eng. ed. Signed. VF in dj. *MORDIDA.* $125

Hillerman, Tony. HILLERMAN COUNTRY. With photos by Barney Hillerman. NY: Harper Collins, 1991. 1st ed. Signed. VF in dj. *MORDIDA.* $70

Hillerman, Tony. INDIAN COUNTRY. With photos by Bela Kalman. Flagstaff: Northland Press, 1987. 1st ed. VF in dj. *MORDIDA.* $150

Hillerman, Tony. LISTENING WOMAN. NY: Harper & Row, 1978. 1st ed. VF in dj. *MORDIDA.* $300

Hillerman, Tony. RIO GRANDE. Portland: Charles H. Belding, 1975. 1st ed. VF in dj. *MORDIDA.* $200

Hillerman, Tony. SKINWALKERS. Harper & Row, (1986). 1st ed. Boards. Fine in dj. *AUTHORS OF THE WEST.* $35

Hillerman, Tony. SKINWALKERS. Harper & Row, 1986. Adv reading copy. About Fine in dec wraps. Corners bumped. *STAHR.* $40

Hillerman, Tony. SKINWALKERS. London: Joseph, (1988). 1st Eng ed. Fine in dj. *LOPEZ.* $45

Hillerman, Tony. SKINWALKERS. London: Michael Joseph, 1988. 1st Eng ed. Signed. VF in dj. *MORDIDA.* $50

Hillerman, Tony. SKINWALKERS. NY: Harper & Row, 1986. 1st ed. Signed. This copy contains two colored pen-and-ink illus by Navajo artist, Ernest Franklin. VF in dj w/slipcase. *MORDIDA.* $450

Hillerman, Tony. TALKING GOD. Harper & Row, (1989). 1st ed. Boards. New in dj. *AUTHORS OF THE WEST.* $25

Hillerman, Tony. TALKING GOD. London: Michael Joseph, 1990. 1st Eng ed. VF in dj. *MORDIDA.* $45

Hillerman, Tony. TALKING GOD. NY: Harper & Row, 1989. 1st ed. One of 300 specially bound numbered, signed. As New in slipcase w/o dj as issued. *MORDIDA.* $150

Hillerman, Tony. TALKING GOD. NY: Harper & Row, 1989. 1st ed. Inscribed. VF in dj. *MORDIDA*. $45

Hillerman, Tony. TALKING GOD. NY: Harper & Row, 1989. 1st ed. Signed. 2 colored, pen-and-ink illus by Ernest Franklin. VF in dj with slipcase. *MORDIDA*. $450

Hillerman, Tony. TALKING GOD. NY: Harper & Row, 1989. 1st ed. Signed. Fully illus w/20 orig pen-and-ink, water colored drwgs by Ernest Franklin. VF in dj w/slipcase. *MORDIDA*. $1600

Hillerman, Tony. THE BLESSING WAY. Evanston, London, NY: Harper & Row, (1970). 1st ed, 1st bk. NF in unevenly faded dj. *BERNARD*. $700

Hillerman, Tony. THE BLESSING WAY. NY: Harper, 1970. 1st ed. Author's 1st book. Ex-lib w/these marks: pocket and label traces on rear eps and front pastedown, stamps on prelims, grease spots on early pages; dj lightly worn w/signs of label removal at lower spine. No library marks on boards. *BEASLEY*. $275

Hillerman, Tony. THE BLESSING WAY. London: Macmillan, 1970. 1st Eng ed. Signed. Tiny spotting on edges o/w Fine in lightly soiled dj. *MORDIDA*. $250

Hillerman, Tony. THE BLESSING WAY. NY: Armchair Detective Library, 1990. Reprint ed. One of 250 specially bound. This copy contains 2 orig pen and ink colored illus by Ernest Franklin. VF in custom slipcase w/o dj as issued. *MORDIDA*. $300

Hillerman, Tony. THE DARK WIND. London: Victor Gollancz, 1983. 1st Eng ed. Signed. VF in dj. *MORDIDA*. $45

Hillerman, Tony. THE DARK WIND. NY: Harper & Row, 1982. 1st ed. VF in dj. *MORDIDA*. $100

Hillerman, Tony. THE GHOSTWAY. London: Gollancz, 1985. 1st Eng. ed. Signed. VF in dj. *MORDIDA*. $45

Hillerman, Tony. THE GHOSTWAY. NY: Harper & Row, 1985. 1st trade ed. Fine in dj w/short closed tear and couple of tiny nicks. *MORDIDA*. $100

Hillerman, Tony. THE GREAT TAOS BANK ROBBERY. Albuquerque: Univ of New Mexico Press, (1973). 1st ed. Fine in just About Fine, price-clipped dj w/very slight stain front panel. Scarce. *BETWEEN COVERS*. $650

Hillerman, Tony. THE GREAT TAOS BANK ROBBERY. Albuquerque: Univ of NM Press, 1973. 1st ed. Fine in dj (short closed crease-tear front panel; has has 2 illus back panel). *MORDIDA*. $350

Hillerman, Tony. THE JIM CHEE MYSTERIES. NY: Harper Collins, 1990. 1st ed. VF in dj. *MORDIDA*. $35

Hillerman, Tony. THE JIM CHEE MYSTERIES. NY: Harper Collins, 1990. Omnibus ed. Signed. 4 colored, pen-and-ink illus by Ernest Franklin. VF in dj w/slipcase. *MORDIDA*. $450

Hillerman, Tony. THE JOE LEAPHORN MYSTERIES. NY: Harper & Row, 1989. Omnibus ed. Signed. Illus by Ernest Franklin w/4 colored pen-and-ink drwgs. VF in dj w/slipcase. *MORDIDA*. $450

Hillerman, Tony. WORDS, WEATHER AND WOLFMEN. Ernest Franklin (illus). Gallup: The Southwesterner/Books, 1989. 1st ed. This copy was a prototype, which eventually was not selected, for the 26 specially bound lettered copies. Signed by Hillerman, Franklin, and Ernie Bulow and instead of a letter or copy #, it has sm pen-and-ink drwg by Franklin on signature pg. Also incl is separate orig pen-and-ink water colored drwg by Franklin. VF in leather bound boards stamped in gold in slipcase w/o dj as issued. *MORDIDA*. $600

Hillerman, Tony. WORDS, WEATHER AND WOLFMEN. Gallup: Southwestern, (1989). 1st ed. One of 272 numbered and signed by Hillerman and the illus, Ernest Franklin. Fine in Fine dj. *UNGER*. $125

Hillerman, Tony. WORDS, WEATHER AND WOLFMEN. With art by Ernest Franklin. Gallup: The Southwesterner/Books, 1989. 1st

ed. 1/350 signed by Hillerman, Franklin and Ernie Bulow. As New in dj. *MORDIDA*. $125

Hilles, M.W. THE POCKET ANATOMIST: BEING A COMPLETE DESCRIPTION OF THE ANATOMY OF THE HUMAN BODY. Phila, 1860. 1st Amer ed. *FYE*. $40

Hillier, J. JAPANESE MASTERS OF THE COLOUR PRINT. London, 1954. Tipped-in color plts. NF. *POLYANTHOS*. $75

Hilton, James. GOOD-BYE, MR. CHIPS. Illus H. M. Brock. (Boston): Little, Brown, 1935. 1st illus ed. Ltd to 600 numbered signed by Hilton & Brock. Parchment-backed boards. Slipcase lightly soiled, o/w Fine. *JAFFE*. $250

Hilton, James. GOODBYE, MR. CHIPS. (London): Hodder & Stoughton, 1934. 1st ed. Foxed throughout text, thus only VG in NF dj w/some very slight wear at extremities, two small tears on rear panel. Uncommon. *BETWEEN COVERS*. $275

Hilton, James. GOODBYE, MR. CHIPS. Boston: Little, Brown & Co, 1934. 1st ed. Inscribed. Fine in dj (complete, split at hinge and front fold). *JUVELIS*. $250

Hilton, James. LOST HORIZON. London: Macmillan, (1933). 1st ed. Laid in is a card informing members of the British Service Club of the death of Hilton in 1954. NF/Fine in an illustrated dj with minimal chipping at spine ends. *UNGER*. $1450

Hilton, James. SO WELL REMEMBERED. Boston: Atlantic-Little, Brown, 1945. 1st ed. Owner's inscrip on half title, o/w Fine in NF dj. *BEASLEY*. $30

Hilton, John. ON REST AND PAIN. NY, 1879. 2nd Amer ed. *FYE*. $50

Hilton, Richard. THE INDIAN MUTINY: A CENTENARY HISTORY. London: Hollis & Carter, (1957). 1st ed. Lg piece rear dj panel missing. *AKA*. $17

Hilton, William Hayes. SKETCHES IN THE SOUTHWEST AND MEXICO 1858-1877. 1st ed. LA: Dawson's, 1963. 1st ed. Fine. *BOOK MARKET*. $50

Himes, Chester. A CASE OF RAPE. NY: Targ Editions, 1980. 1st ed. Signed, ltd to 350. As issued in beige cl and dj. *JUVELIS*. $40

Himes, Chester. A RAGE IN HARLEM. London: Allison & Busby, 1985. 1st hardcover ed. Pub in US as For Love of Amabelle. Remainder mark on bottom edge o/w Fine in dj. *MORDIDA*. $30

Himes, Chester. ALL SHOT UP. NY: Avon, 1960. 1st ed. Pb orig. Stamp on inner front cover o/w VG in wrappers. *MORDIDA*. $20

Himes, Chester. BLACK ON BLACK. GC: Doubleday, 1973. 1st ed. Fine in NF dj. *LOPEZ*. $85

Himes, Chester. CAST THE FIRST STONE. NY, 1952. 1st ed. NF in NF dj (tiny light chipping at spine base). *PETTLER*. $125

Himes, Chester. PINKTOES. NY: Putnam, (1965). 1st ed. Very sl cocked, else NF in VG dj w/usual spine fading, short tear at crown. Ownership stamp of novelist Barry Beckham. *BETWEEN COVERS*. $75

Himes, Chester. THE CRAZY KILL. NY: Avon, (1959). 1st ed. Pb orig. Spine chipped at heel. VG in wrappers. *LOPEZ*. $25

Himes, Chester. THE HEAT'S ON. NY: Putnam, (1966). 1st ed. Cvrs sl bowed, o/w NF in dj. *LOPEZ*. $150

Himes, Chester. THE QUALITY OF HURT. GC: Doubleday, 1972. 1st ed. Fine in dj. Ownership stamp of Barry Beckham. *BETWEEN COVERS*. $85

Himes, Chester. THE QUALITY OF HURT. GC: Doubleday, 1972. 1st ed. Glue stain on fep and one faint tape shadow on each board, in close to Fine dj. *BEASLEY*. $65

Himes, Chester. THE REAL COOL KILLERS. London: Allison & Busby, 1985. 1st hardcover ed. VF in dj. *MORDIDA*. $30

Himes, Chester. THE REAL COOL KILLERS. NY: Avon, (1959). Pb orig. Fine in wraps. Signed. *LOPEZ*. $200

Himes, Chester. THE REAL COOL KILLERS. NY: Avon, 1959. 1st ed. Pb orig. Pp darkened o/w Fine, unread, in wrappers. *MORDIDA.* $40

Himmelheber, Georg. BIEDERMEIER FURNITURE. London: Faber & Faber, (1974). Trans and ed by Simon Jervis. 1st ed. Dj. *KARMIOLE.* $45

Hind, Arthur M. INTRODUCTION TO A HISTORY OF WOOD-CUT: DETAILED SURVEY OF WORK DONE IN THE 15TH CENTURY. Boston, 1935. 2 vols. NF. *POLYANTHOS.* $150

Hind, Henry Youle. NORTH-WEST TERRITORY REPORTS OF PROGRESS; TOGETHER WITH....Toronto: John Lovell, 1859. 1st ed. 202pp. 8 partially colored fldg maps, some tears w/no loss. Same collation as called for in Wagner-Camp, 330:1, except there is an additional full-pg woodcut facing p. 86. "Punk Island Exposure on Deer Island, etc." which is also not noted on Content page. Edgeworn, w/some stains, orig cl w/early rebacking. Orig paper label on cover. Folio. Faint damp line on page edge, not affecting text. Good, sound. Scarce. *CONNOLLY & WADE.* $950

Hindle, Brooke. THE PURSUIT OF SCIENCE IN REVOLUTIONARY AMERICA 1735-1789. Chapel Hill: Pub for The Institute of Early American Hist and Culture, Williamsburg, VA by The Univ of NC Press, 1956. VG in sl chipped dj. *KNOLLWOOD.* $38

Hinman, Royal R. A HISTORICAL COLLECTION...OF THE PART SUSTAINED BY CONNECTICUT DURING THE WAR OF THE REVOLUTION. WITH AN APPENDIX....Hartford: Gleason, 1842. 1st ed. 643,(1)pp. 2 port. Orig cl. Howes H509. *GINSBERG.* $175

Hinton, Richard J. THE HAND-BOOK TO ARIZONA: ITS RESOURCES, HISTORY, TOWNS, MINES, RUINS AND SCENERY. SF: Payot, Upham, & Co, 1878. 2 fldg maps, plts, tables, 44pp ads (1 in color). Spine faded, early bkseller's label pasted to title obscuring imprint date. Howes H513. *HUDSON.* $250

Hinton, S.E. THE OUTSIDERS. NY: Viking, 1967. 1st ed. Few light stains to top edge, else Fine in price clipped, spine faded dj. Wrap around band present but detached from point at which it had been tipped onto spine. Scarce. *LAME DUCK.* $250

Hipkiss, Edwin J. EIGHTEENTH CENTURY AMERICAN ARTS: THE M & M KAROLIK COLLECTION, Boston: MFA, 1941. 1st ed, 1st ptg. Rubbing top of spine. Water spots back cover. VG. *BACKROOM.* $375

Hipkiss, Edwin J. THE PHILIP LEFFINGWELL SPALDING COLLECTION OF EARLY AMERICAN SILVER. Cambridge, MA: Harvard Univ Press. 1943. 1st ed. *KARMIOLE.* $45

Hippocrates. ON INTERCOURSE AND PREGNANCY. AN ENGLISH TRANSLATION ON SEMEN AND ON THE DEVELOPMENT OF THE CHILD BY TAGE ELLINGER. NY, 1952. 1st Eng trans. Dj. *FYE.* $100

Hippocrates. THE GENUINE WORKS OF HIPPOCRATES TRANSLATED FROM THE GREEK WITH A PRELIMINARY DISCOURSE AND ANNOTATIONS BY FRANCIS ADAMS. London, 1849. 1st ed. 2 vols. 874pp + plts. Head and tail of spine chipped as usual, o/w Fine. *FYE.* $300

Hirschfeld, Magnus. THE SEXUAL HISTORY OF THE WORLD WAR...NY: Falstaff Press, (1937). VG. *WREDEN.* $45

Hirschfield, Magnus. SEXUAL PATHOLOGY, A STUDY. NY: Emerson Books, 1940. Jerome Gibbs (trans). Rev ed. VG in worn dj w/flap separate. *SECOND LIFE.* $35

Hirschman, Jack. A CORRESPONDENCE OF AMERICANS. Bloomington: IN Univ Press. 1960. 1st ed. Lightly chipped glassine. *KARMIOLE.* $45

Hirshberg, Al. THE BRAVES, THE PICK, AND THE SHOVEL. Waverly House, 1948. 1st ed. Good+ in VG dj. *PLAPINGER.* $45

Hirshberg, Al. THE RED SOX, THE BEAN AND THE COD. Waverly House, 1947. 1st ed. VG. Scarce. *PLAPINGER.* $65

Hislop, Herbert R. AN ENGLISHMAN'S ARIZONA: THE RANCHING LETTERS...1876-1878. Tucson: Overland Press, 1965. Bernard L. Fontana (intro). One of 510 signed by the Fontanas. Fine. *LAURIE.* $90

HISTORICAL ACCOUNT OF THE CIRCUMNAVIGATION OF THE GLOBE....TO THE DEATH OF CAPTAIN COOK. London: Thomas Nelson, 1849. Engr frontis. 423pp. Fldg facs. Engr by Wright from the orig. Facs has a short, closed tear and lt foxing. Tissue guards on all eng plts. All edges gilt. 12mo. Lacks ffep. Orig red cl, emb, dec in gilt. Two short splits on backstrip edge. Some edgewear. VG. *CONNOLLY & WADE.* $75

HISTORICAL AND BIOGRAPHICAL RECORD OF THE CATTLE INDUSTRY....Antiquarian Press, 1959. Ltd to 550. Cl, leather reprint of orig 1894 set. 2 vols. Ex-lib. Binding rubbed, usual markings, but clean, tight set. *VARNER.* $175

HISTORICAL ANECDOTES OF THE LIFE OF ROBIN HOOD. London: Prntd for the Booksellers. 1846. 256pp. Woodcut frontis and title page vignette. l9th century blue calf over marbled boards, edges rubbed. *KARMIOLE.* $85

HISTORICAL MEMOIRS OF STEHANIE LOUISE DE BOURBON CONTI. Newbern, (NC), 1801. 1st Amer ed. 12mo. Early 20th century half red morocco w/raised bands. Lib bkpl, blindstamp, corners lightly bumped, old catalogue descrip tipped in, but VG. *CHAPEL HILL.* $650

HISTORICAL MEMORANDA RELATIVE TO THE DISCOVERY OF ETHERIZATION, AND TO THE CONNECTION WITH IT OF THE LATE DR. WILLIAM T. G. MORTON. Boston, 1871. 1st ed. 16pp. Wrappers soiled. Scarce. *FYE.* $150

HISTORIES OF GAME STRAINS. Gaffney: DeCamp, 1955. Good. *OCTOBER FARM.* $95

HISTORY OF CINCINNATI AND HAMILTON COUNTY, OHIO; THEIR PAST AND PRESENT. Cincinnati: S.B. Nelson & Co., 1894. Double color map. Rebound in buckram. VG. *BOHLING.* $135

HISTORY OF CONTRA COSTA COUNTY, CALIFORNIA. SF: Slocum, 1882. 1st ed. 710pp. Orig full calf, lea labels on spine, front hinge mended, sm paper label on lower spine, bkpl removed. Howes C718 (b). *GINSBERG.* $475

HISTORY OF DAVIESS COUNTY, KENTUCKY, TOGETHER WITH SKETCHES...PORTRAITS OF PROMINENT PERSONS. Chicago, Inter-state, 1st ed. 1883. 870pp. 28 ports, fldg map. Contemp thick half morocco, sm paper label on lower spine, bkpl removed. *GINSBERG.* $250

HISTORY OF DEARBORN & OHIO COUNTIES, INDIANA. Chicago: Weakley & Co, 1885. Tight, lea worn, cloth peeling at corners. *BOHLING.* $150

HISTORY OF GIBRALTER AND ITS SIEGES. WITH PHOTOGRAPHIC ILLUSTRATIONS BY J. H. MANN. London: Provost & Co., 1870. (By Frederic George Stephen.) Lib ed. Rebacked, somewhat rubbed, faded. Some foxing. Owner marks half-title. 1 engr map, 4 mounted photos. *SCHOYER'S.* $100

HISTORY OF HENNEPIN COUNTY & THE CITY OF MINNEAPOLIS. (By George E. Warner.) Minneapolis: North Star Pub Co., 1881. Rebound in cloth. Nice. *BOHLING.* $135

HISTORY OF JONES COUNTY, IOWA, CONTAINING A HISTORY OF THE COUNTY. Chicago: Western Historical Co., 1879. Double map. Rebound in buckram. Stamp on title page; lacks frontis map. Sturdy. *BOHLING.* $125

HISTORY OF MADISON COUNTY, ILLINOIS. Edwardsville, IL: W.R. Brink & Co., 1882. 34 plts. Rebound in buckram. Some wear. Good, solid. *BOHLING.* $250

HISTORY OF MARIN COUNTY, CALIFORNIA...AND BIOGRAPHICAL SKETCHES...ALSO AN HISTORICAL SKETCH...THE RAISING OF THE BEAR FLAG. (By J. P. Munro-Fraser.) SF: Alley, 1880. 516pp. 1st ed. Engr ports. Orig full calf w/leather labels, paper label on lower spine; bkpl removed. Howes M896. *GINSBERG.* $750

HISTORY OF MCDONOUGH COUNTY, ILLINOIS. Springfield, IL: Continental Historical Co., 1885. Some scuffing, light wear. VG. *BOHLING.* $150

HISTORY OF MCLEAN COUNTY, ILLINOIS. Chicago: Wm. Le Baron, Jr., 1879. Double color map. Somewhat worn, scuffed; cloth on upper rear corner peeling away from leathers. *BOHLING.* $135

HISTORY OF MEDICINE AND SURGERY AND PHYSICIANS AND SURGEONS OF CHICAGO. Chicago, 1922. 1st ed. 928pp. Scarce. *FYE.* $250

HISTORY OF MUSCATINE COUNTY, IOWA. Chicago: Western Historical Society, 1879. Some scuffing, light wear. Good, solid. *BOHLING.* $150

HISTORY OF PIKE AND DUBOIS COUNTIES, INDIANA. Chicago: Goodspeed Bros, 1885. 23 plts. Somewhat worn, scuffed; pencil notes rear ep. *BOHLING.* $135

HISTORY OF SANTA CLARA COUNTY, CALIFORNIA. SF: Alley, Bowen & Co, 1881. Scuffed, starting to split along upper hinges, bkpl removed, paper label on spine, no other lib markings, owner inscrip reverse of frontis has bled through in places. Howes S101. *BOHLING.* $650

HISTORY OF STEVENS COUNTY, KANSAS. Privately ptd, 1967. 1st ed. Autographed. Fine in Fine dj. *VARNER.* $75

HISTORY OF THE AMERICAN PHYSIOLOGICAL SOCIETY SEMICENTENNIAL, 1887-1937. Baltimore, 1938. 1st ed. *FYE.* $60

HISTORY OF THE CITY OF DENVER, ARAPAHOE COUNTY AND COLORADO. Chicago, 1880. 1st ed. 652pp. Orig half morocco. Howes D262. *GINSBERG.* $300

HISTORY OF THE TRIAL OF GEORGE VANDERPOOL. Detroit, 1870. 1st ed. 2 plts. Orig defective wraps mounted on new wraps. Lacks frontis. Tears, staining. Fair. *DIAMOND.* $25

HISTORY OF THE UNITED STATES OF AMERICA BY A CITIZEN OF MASSACHUSETTS. NH: Keane, 1823. 276pp, frontis. Front hinge broken, lt foxing. Laid in specially designed box. *HEINOLDT.* $25

HISTORY OF TRANSPORTATION IN THE OHIO VALLEY. Westport, CT (1970). *HEINOLDT.* $18

HISTORY OF TRUMBELL & MAHONING COUNTIES. Cleveland; H.Z. Williams, 1882. 2 vols. Some scuffing; usual wear. *BOHLING.* $175

HISTORY OF WORCESTER COUNTY, MASSACHUSETTS. Boston: Jewett 1879. 1st ed. 2 vols. Hinges loose, x-lib. VG. *SECOND LIFE.* $75

Hitchcock, Champion I. THE DEAD MEN'S SONG & RECOLLECTIONS BY YOUNG EWING ALLISON. KY, 1914. Inscrib & signed. NF. *POLYANTHOS.* $75

Hitchcock, E. REPORT ON THE GEOLOGY, MINERALOGY...OF MASSACHUSETTS. Adams, 1833. 692pp. Rebound, w/o pl atlas. VG. *BOOKCELL.* $90

Hitchcock, E. REPORT ON THE GEOLOGY OF VERMONT. Vol 1. Claremont, 1861. 558pp. Rebacked, new paper label on new backstrip. VG. *BOOKCELL.* $75

Hitchcock, H.R. AN ENGLISH-HAWAIIAN DICTIONARY. SF: The Bancroft Co. 1887. 1st ed. 256pp. Orig black cl, gilt. Scarce. *KARMIOLE.* $125

Hitchcock, Mary E. TWO WOMEN IN THE KLONDIKE. NY: G.P. Putnam's Sons. 1899. 1st ed. xiv,(2),486pp+(2)pp ads. Fldg map in rear pocket. Bright. *KARMIOLE.* $150

Hitchins, P.E. PRODUCTION OF TOMATOES UNDER GLASS. London: GBC, 1952. Dj worn out; cl & contents VG. *AMERICAN BOTANIST.* $20

Hitchman, Janet. SUCH A STRANGE LADY: A BIOGRAPHY OF DOROTHY L. SAYERS. NY: Harper & Row, 1975. 1st ed. VF in dj. *MORDIDA.* $35

Hitschmann. Dr. E. FREUD'S THEORIES OF THE NEUROSES. London, 1921. 1st Eng ed. NF. *POLYANTHOS.* $40

Hittell, John S. HITTELL'S HAND-BOOK OF PACIFIC COAST TRAVEL. SF: The Bancroft Company, 1887. 2 fldg maps, tables. *HUDSON.* $125

Hoag, E.B. CRIME, ABNORMAL MINDS AND THE LAW. Indianapolis, 1923. 1st ed. Cvrs sl stained, o/w VG. *DIAMOND.* $35

Hoban, Russell. KLEINZEIT. NY, 1974. 1st US ed. NF in dj. *PETTLER.* $35

Hoban, Russell. RIDDLEY WALKER. NY: Summit, 1980. 1st ed. Fine in Fine dj. *BEASLEY.* $35

Hoban, Russell. TURTLE DIARY. NY: Random House, 1975. 1st ed. Fine but for owner's name in Fine dj. *BEASLEY.* $45

Hobart, Admiral (Augustus Charles) Pasha. SKETCHES FROM MY LIFE. London: Longmans Green, 1886. Good with some wear to corners. Hinges cracked but holding. *PARMER.* $95

Hobbs, A.S. & J.I. Whalley. BEATRIX POTTER, THE V&A COLLECTION. London: Victoria & Albert Museum & Warne, 1985. 1st ed. 240pp. Illus in color & b/w. *BEBBAH.* $50

Hobbs, J.B. MY CRICKET MEMORIES. William Heinemann, 1924. 1st ed. Minor soil. VG. *OLD LONDON.* $25

Hobbs, James. WILD LIFE IN THE FAR WEST. PERSONAL ADVENTURES....SERVICES UNDER DONIPHAN IN WAR WITH MEXICO. Hartford: Wiley, Waterman, Eaton, 1872. 1st ed. 488pp, frontis, 20 plts. Full lea, rebacked. Dampstain lower portion 1st few pp, corners worn. Good+. Howes H550. *OREGON.* $275

Hobbs, William Herbert. AN EXPLORER-SCIENTIST'S PILGRIMAGE. AN AUTOBIOGRAPHY OF WILLIAM HERBERT HOBBS. Ann Arbor: J.W. Edwards, Inc., 1952. Bkpl. VG. *PARMER.* $45

Hobbs, William Herbert. EXPLORING ABOUT THE NORTH POLE OF THE WINDS. NY: G.P. Putnam's, 1930. 1st ed. Bumped. NF in VG dj. *PARMER.* $65

Hobhouse, J.C. A JOURNEY THROUGH ALBANIA, AND OTHER PROVINCES OF TURKEY IN EUROPE AND ASIA, TO CONSTANTINOPLE. DURING THE YEARS 1809 AND 1910. London, 1813. 2nd ed. 6 costume plts in color, 9 landscape plts in color (of 10), 6 fldg, 1 fldg map, 1 uncolored pl, 2pp music, 2pp facs letters. 2 vols. Orig mottled calf, rubbed, corners bumped, some scattered internal spotting. *O'NEILL.* $800

Hobhouse, John Cam. RECOLLECTIONS OF A LONG LIFE. NY, 1909. 2 vols. Uncut. *O'NEILL.* $85

Hobsbawm, Eric and George Rude. CAPTAIN SWING: A SOCIAL HISTORY OF THE GREAT ENGLISH AGRICULTURAL UPRISING OF 1830. NY: Pantheon, (1968). 1st US ed. 382pp. Dj price-clipped. *AKA.* $30

Hobson, Anne. IN OLD ALABAMA, BEING THE CHRONICLES OF MISS MOUSE, THE LITTLE BLACK MERCHANT. NY, 1903. 1st ed. Orig dec cl, lightly soiled, contemp inscription. VG. *McGOWAN.* $85

Hobson, Elizabeth Christophers (Kimball). RECOLLECTIONS OF A HAPPY LIFE. NY, 1914. 1st ed. Ltd to 250 privately ptd. Orig boards, corners lightly bumped, slight rubbed spot on rear board, else VG, untrimmed. *McGOWAN.* $125

Hobson, R. CHARLES WATERTON: HIS HOME, HABITS & HANDIWORK. London & Leeds: Whittaker, 1866. 12mo, 319pp. Gilt dec cl. Illus. VG. *MIKESH.* $85

Hoch, Edward D. THE JUDGES OF HADES AND OTHER SIMON ARK STORIES. North Hollywood: Leisure Books, 1971. 1st ed. Pb orig. Fine, unread, in wrappers. *MORDIDA.* $20

Hocken, Edward. A TREATISE ON AMAUROSIS. Phila, 1842. 1st Amer ed. Full leather, 201pp. Rare. *FYE.* $150

Hocking, Joseph. THE MAN WHO FOUND OUT. London: Ward-Locke, 1933. 1st ed. Fine, sm chips at spine corners of pict dj. *ELSE FINE.* $45

Hodel, Michael P. and Sean M. Wright (eds). ENTER THE LION: A POSTHUMOUS MEMOIR OF MYCROFT HOLMES. NY: Hawthorne Books, 1979. 1st ed. VF in dj. *MORDIDA.* $40

Hodge, Edwin T. MOUNT MULTNOMAH: ANCIENT ANCESTOR OF THE THREE SISTERS. Eugene: Univ of OR, 1925. Fldg map in rear pocket. Ptd wrappers, rear wrapper creased. *DAWSON'S.* $30

Hodge, Frederick W. HANDBOOK OF AMERICAN INDIANS NORTH OF MEXICO. BAE Bulletin 30. In 2 vols. 1907 & 1912. 1st ptg vol 1, 2nd ptg vol 2. Fldg map. VG. Howes H556. *OREGON.* $100

Hodges, Elizabeth Jamison. FREE AS A FROG. (Reading, MA): Addison-Wesley, (1969). 1st ed. Fine in NF dj w/couple short tears. *BETWEEN COVERS.* $60

Hodges, Margaret. SAINT GEORGE AND THE DRAGON. Little, Brown, (1984). 1st ed. Unpaginated. Illus by Trina Hyman. VG+ in VG+ dj w/2 short closed tears. *BEBBAH.* $55

Hodges, Richard. ON THE NATURE, PATHOLOGY AND TREATMENT OF PUERPERAL CONVULSIONS. London, 1864. 1st ed. 96pp. Backstrip missing, boards detached, ex-lib. Contents VF. *FYE.* $200

Hodges, Richard. PRACTICAL DISSECTIONS. Phila, 1867. 2nd ed. Backstrip missing, ex-lib. Contents Fine. *FYE.* $50

Hodgkin, R.H. SIX CENTURIES OF AN OXFORD COLLEGE. Oxford: Basil Blackwell, 1949. 1st ed. Pencil underlining, bkpl. VG. *WEBER.* $20

Hodgkins, William Henry. THE BATTLE OF FORT STEDMAN (PETERSBURG, VA) MARCH 25, 1865. (Boston: Privately ptd, 1889). 1st ed. Fldg map. Wrappers bound in marbled boards w/cloth spine. NF. *McGOWAN.* $75

Hodgkinson, Frank. SEPIK DIARY. Northbridge: Reid Books, 1984. Fine in similar dj. *PARMER.* $65

Hodgson, William Hope. CARNACKI THE GHOST FINDER. Arkham House, 1947. 1st ed. NF in Fine dj. *MADLE.* $110

Hodgson, William Hope. CARNACKI: THE GHOST-FINDER. Sauk City: Mycroft & Moran, 1947. 1st Amer. ed. Head of spine badly bumped, name, date else VG+/NF in dj (spine browned, ends worn, sl chipped, closed tears). *OTHER WORLDS.* $60

Hodgson, William Hope. DEEP WATERS. Arkham House, 1967. 1st ed. VF in dj. *MADLE.* $110

Hodgson, William Hope. DEEP WATERS. Sauk City: Arkham House, 1967. 1st ed. Name, date else NF in dj; browning, worn (effaced) spots to spine. *OTHER WORLDS.* $75

Hodgson, William Hope. POEMS OF THE SEA. London: Ferret Fantasy, 1977. 1/500. Fine in Fine dj. *BEASLEY.* $50

Hodgson, William Hope. THE HOUSE ON THE BORDERLAND AND OTHER NOVELS. Sauk City: Arkham House, 1946. 1st ed thus. NF in as New dj. *OTHER WORLDS.* $350

Hodgson, William Hope. THE HOUSE ON THE BORDERLAND AND OTHER NOVELS. Sauk City: Arkham House, 1946. 1st ed. NF. Bkpl, sm private lib # on copyright pg in like dj, sl darkened at spine. *CAPTAIN'S BOOKSHELF.* $300

Hodgson, William Hope. THE HOUSE ON THE BORDERLAND. Arkham House, 1946. 1st ed. Fine in Mint dj. *MADLE.* $400

Hodgson, William Hope. THE HOUSE ON THE BORDERLAND. Sauk City: Arkham House, 1946. 1st ed. Fine in fine dj. *DERMONT.* $350

Hodier, Andre. TOWARD JAZZ. NY: Grove, 1962. 1st ed. Fine in Fine dj. *BEASLEY.* $35

Hoefler, Paul L. AFRICA SPEAKS—A STORY OF ADVENTURE. Chicago: Winston, 1931. 1st ed. NF in VG, scarce dj. *GREAT EPIC.* $85

Hoehling, A.A. LAST TRAIN FROM ATLANTA. NY, (1958). 1st ed. VG+ in dj. *PRATT.* $30

Hoehling, A.A. THE GREAT EPIDEMIC. Boston, 1961. 1st ed. *FYE.* $27.50

Hoenshel, Elmer U. MY THREE DAYS IN GILEAD. Dayton, VA, 1909. 85pp. *O'NEILL.* $35

Hofberg, Herman. SWEDISH FAIRY TALES. Chicago: Conkey, 1903. 225pp. Color litho frontis and cover. Paper-covered boards and cl. Sl edgewear. VG. *ARTIS.* $19.50

Hofer, Ernst. ARCTIC RIVIERA. Berne: Kummerly & Frey, (1957). VG in VG- dj. *BLUE DRAGON.* $35

Hofer, Tamas and Edit Fel. HUNGARIAN FOLK ART. Oxford: Oxford Univ Press. 1979. 1st ed. Dj. *KARMIOLE.* $65

Hoff, Ebbe C. & John Fulton. A BIBLIOGRAPHY OF AVIATION MEDICINE. Springfield, 1942. 1st ed. Dj. *FYE.* $50

Hoff, Ebbe C. A BIBLIOGRAPHICAL SOURCEBOOK OF COMPRESSED AIR, DIVING AND SUBMARINE MEDICINE. Washington, 1948. 1st ed. *FYE.* $60

Hoff, Ernie (ed). PIONEER LEAGUE RECORD BOOK. Pioneer Lg. 1949-53. 1st ed. VG+ without dj as issued. *PLAPINGER.* $150

Hoffman, Abbie. SQUARE DANCING IN THE ICE AGE: UNDERGROUND WRITINGS. NY: Putnam, 1982. 1st ed. Rem stamp top edge. 2 short edgetears front panel dj. VG. *AKA.* $25

Hoffman, Alice. ANGEL LANDING. NY: Putnam, (1980). 1st ed. Fine in dj. *CAPTAIN'S BOOKSHELF.* $35

Hoffman, Alice. PROPERTY OF. Farrar, Straus and Giroux, 1977. 1st ed. NF in dj w/price cut front flyleaf; sm stain on top, front cvr. *STAHR.* $45

Hoffman, Alice. PROPERTY OF. NY: FSG, (1977). 1st ed, 1st book. Fine in price-clipped dj w/traces of edgewear. *ROBBINS.* $45

Hoffman, E.T.A. NUTCRACKER. London: Bodley Head, 1984. 1st British ed in US dj as issued. Illus by Maurice Sendak. Fine in Fine dj. *BEBBAH.* $55

Hoffman, E.T.W. WEIRD TALES. London, 1885. 2 vols. VG. *MADLE.* $65

Hoffman, Frederick J. THE LITTLE MAGAZINE. A HISTORY AND A BIBLIOGRAPHY. Princeton: Princeton Univ Press, 1946. 1st ed. NF in lightly used dj. *BEASLEY.* $60

Hoffman, John. ANDY PAFKO—THE SOLID MAN. Barnes, 1951. 1st ed. Good+. *PLAPINGER.* $40

Hoffman, Sylvan (ed). NEWS OF THE NATION. GC: Garden City Pub, (c. 1942). Plastic spiral binding. VG+. *AARD.* $25

Hoffman, Wilbur. SAGAS OF OLD EASTERN TRAVEL & TRANSPORT. San Diego: Howell-North, 1980. 1st ed. VG in Good+ dj. *OCTOBER FARM.* $35

Hofling, Charles K. CUSTER AND THE LITTLE BIG HORN, A PSYCHOBIOGRAPHICAL INQUIRY. Detroit, 1981. 1st ed. 118pp. VG+. in dj. *PRATT.* $20

Hofsinde, Robert. THE INDIAN'S SECRET WORLD. NY: Morrow, 1955. 1st ed. VG, lacking dj. *LOPEZ.* $45

Hogaboam, James J. THE BEAN CREEK VALLEY...Hudson, MI: Jas. M. Scarritt, 1876. Lightly soiled, chipped. VG. *BOHLING.* $65

Hogan, Jane & Bill. TALES FROM THE MANCHACA HILLS. Hauser, 1960. 1st ed. Fine in Good dj. *VARNER.* $22.50

Hogan, John Joseph. ON THE MISSION IN MISSOURI 1857-1868. Kansas City, MO, 1892. 1st ed. 221 pp. Orig cl. Howes H573. *GINSBERG.* $50

Hogan, William Ransom. THE TEXAS REPUBLIC. A SOCIAL AND ECONOMIC HISTORY. Norman: Univ of OK Press, 1946. 1st ed. VF in dj. *GIBBS.* $65

Hogarth, David G. THE LIFE OF CHARLES M. DOUGHTY. Oxford, 1928. Fldg map. xi,216pp. Uncut. Spine sunned, else Fine. *O'NEILL.* $85

Hogarth, David G. WANDERING SCHOLAR. Oxford, 1925. Cvr stains. 274 pp. *O'NEILL.* $35

Hogarth, David George. THE PENETRATION OF ARABIA. London: Lawrence & Bullens, 1904. 1st ed. 52 plts, 2 fldg maps. Orig cl, sl rubbed and soiled. Ex-lib, o/w VG. *WORLDWIDE.* $125

Hogarth, Paul. ARTISTS ON HORSEBACK. NY: Watson-Guptill in cooperation with Riveredge Foundation, Calgary, Canada, 1972. 1st ed. 2-pg plt. Fine in sl chipped, else VG dj. *CONNOLLY & WADE.* $40

Hogarth, William. THE GENUINE WORKS OF WILLIAM HOGARTH....by John Nichols and the late George Stevens. London: (Longman et al), 1808-1810. 2 vols. Contemp diapered calf, rebacked. Very nice. Some foxing; many of orig tissues in place. *BOOK BLOCK.* $350

Hogg, James. THE PILGRIMS OF THE SUN; A POEM. London: Murray, Edinburgh: Blackwood, 1815. 1st ed. 148pp. Uncut in orig paper backed boards w/remnant of paper label, hinges loose (front almost separate). *SECOND LIFE.* $125

Hogg, Thomas Jefferson. TWO HUNDRED AND NINE DAYS. NY, 1827. 2 vols. NF. *POLYANTHOS.* $75

Hogner, Dorothy Childs. BIRDS OF PREY. NY: Crowell, 1969. 1st ed. Dj sl frayed, minor wear, else VG. *OLD LONDON.* $15

Hogrogian, Nonny. ONE FINE DAY. Macmillan, (1971). 1st ptg. Illus, inscribed by author. Fine in VG+ dj. *BEBBAH.* $85

Hohman, Elmo P. THE AMERICAN WHALEMAN....London, (1972). Facs reprint of orig ed of 1928. *LEFKOWICZ.* $50

Hohman, Elmo Paul. THE AMERICAN WHALEMAN; A STUDY OF LIFE AND LABOR IN THE WHALING INDUSTRY. NY, 1928. 1st ed. NF. *LEFKOWICZ.* $100

Hoig, Stan. THE BATTLE OF WASHITA, THE SHERIDAN-CUSTER INDIAN CAMPAIGN OF 1867-69. GC, 1976. 1st ed. Light dj wear o/w Fine. *PRATT.* $37.50

Hoig, Stan. THE WESTERN ODYSSEY OF JOHN SIMPSON SMITH, FRONTIERSMAN, TRAPPER, TRADER AND INTERPRETER. Glendale, 1974. 1st ed. 254pp. Minor shelf wear o/w Fine. *PRATT.* $40

Hoig, Stan. WESTERN ODYSSEY OF JOHN SIMPSON SMITH, FRONTIERSMAN. Glendale: Clark, 1974. 1st ed. *HEINOLDT.* $25

HOLBEIN'S DANCE OF DEATH AND BIBLE WOODCUTS. NY, 1947. Ltd ed, ptd by Sylvan Press. *FYE.* $75

Holbrook, James. TEN YEARS AMONG THE MAIL BAGS...Phila: H. Cowperthwait, 1855. 1st ed. Cvrs sl worn. Lacks ffep. Staining & foxing some pages, o/w VG. *DIAMOND.* $75

Holbrook, Stewart. AMERICA'S ETHAN ALLEN. Houghton Mifflin, 1949. 1st ed. 96pp. Illus by Lynd Ward. Some cvr soil, edgewear. Signed by Holbrook. VG. *BEBBAH.* $30

Holbrook, Stewart. MURDER OUT YONDER. NY: Macmillan, 1941. 1st ed. VG in dj. *CONNOLLY & WADE.* $47.50

Holbrook, Stewart. PROMISED LAND. Whittlesey House, (1945). 1st ed. Fine in chipped dj. *AUTHORS OF THE WEST.* $15

Holbrook, Stewart. ROCKY MOUNTAIN REVOLUTION. NY: Henry Holt, (1956). Stated 1st. 318pp. Owner's name. Dj w/light edgewear. *AKA.* $25

Holbrook, Stewart. THE COLUMBIA. Rinehart, (1956). 1st ed. Signed by author. Inscribed, signed by Ernest Richardson (illus). Fine in dj. *AUTHORS OF THE WEST.* $50

Holbrook, Stewart. THE COLUMBIA. NY: Rinehart, 1956. 1st ed. Special Lewis and Clark Ed of 50th Vol in Rivers of America series, ltd to 2,500 signed, 2,300 for sale. This copy No. A440. Fine. *CONNOLLY & WADE.* $35

Holbrook, Stewart. YANKEE LOGGERS. NY, 1961. 123pp, 4to. Pb. Fine. *VARNER.* $20

Holden, Edward S. LIST OF RECORDED EARTHQUAKES IN CALIFORNIA...AND WASHINGTON TERRITORY. Sacramento: Univ of CA, 1887. Wraps. *KNOLLWOOD.* $26

Holden, W.C. ALKALI TRAILS. Southwest Press, 1930. 1st ed. Inscribed. *VARNER.* $200

Holden, W.C. ROLLIE BURNS....Southwest Press, 1932. Inscribed. 1st ed, 2nd state. Fine (few pp browned). *VARNER.* $175

Holden, William C. THE SPUR RANCH. Boston: Christopher, (1934). 1st ed. Signed. VG. Howes H583. *OREGON.* $275

Holden, William Curry. A RANCHING SAGA....San Antonio, 1976. 1st ed. 2 vols. Slipcased, signed. VF, now scarce. *GIBBS.* $125

Holden, William Curry. ALTON HUTSON. REMINISCENCES OF A SOUTH PLAINS YOUTH. San Antonio: Trinity Univ Press, 1975. 1st ed. Fine. *GIBBS.* $25

Holder, C.F. BIG GAME AT SEA. NY: Outing, 1908. Illus. Dec cl. VG. *MIKESH.* $37.50

Holder, Charles Frederick. RECREATIONS OF A SPORTSMAN ON THE PACIFIC COAST. NY: G.P.Putnam's Sons, 1910. 1st ed. Name on 1st blank pg, wear to spine edges. Good+. *BACKMAN.* $75

Holder, Heidi. CROWS, AN OLD RHYME. FSG, 1987. 1st ed. 4to. Unpaginated. Illus & signed. Fine in Fine dj. *BEBBAH.* $30

Holding, Elisabeth Sanxay. THE UNLIT LAMP: A STUDY OF INTER-ACTIONS. NY: Dutton, (1922). 1st. Dj. Fine. *MUELLER.* $30

Hole, Christina. WITCHCRAFT IN ENGLAND. Scribner's, 1947. 1st US ed. 168pp. Illus by Mervyn Peake. VG in VG dj. *BEBBAH.* $55

Hole, Hugh Marshall. THE JAMESON RAID. London: Philip Allan, 1930. 1st ed. Minor wear extremes. Front internal hinge starting else VG. *GREAT EPIC.* $95

Hole, S.R. A BOOK ABOUT ROSES, HOW TO GROW AND SHOW THEM. Edinburgh, 1870. 3rd ed. Orig dec cl soiled and stained, wear at extrems; corner of flyleaf missing, some pp soiling. *SUTTON.* $35

Holland, Clive. FROM THE NORTH FORELAND TO PENZANCE. NY & London, 1908. NF. *POLYANTHOS.* $45

Holland, Clive. WARWICKSHIRE. A&C Black, 1922. 2nd ed, rev. W/o dj, else VG. *OLD LONDON.* $20

Holland, Clive. WESSEX. A&C Black, 1906. 1st ed. 20s Series. Minor wear at edges, slight rippled cl front edge, else VG-NF. *OLD LONDON.* $65

Holland, H. RECOLLECTIONS OF PAST LIFE. London, 1868. Inscrib, signed, dated. 1/2 lea. Fine. *POLYANTHOS.* $200

Holland, Henry. ESSAYS ON SCIENTIFIC AND OTHER SUBJECTS. London, 1862. 1st ed. 499pp. *FYE.* $60

Holland, Josiah Gilbert. HISTORY OF WESTERN MASSACHUSETTS. Springfield: S. Bowles, 1855. 2 vols. Fldg frontis. Spines faded, vol 2 spine top chipped, paper bit darkened; clean and tight. VG+. *BOHLING.* $165

Holland, J(oshia) G. THE LIFE OF ABRAHAM LINCOLN. Springfield, MA: Gurdon Bill, 1866. 544pp. 4 engr plts. *SCHOYER'S.* $40

Holland, Ray P. BIRD DOGS. NY: A.S. Barnes & Co, 1948. 1st ed. VG. *BACKMAN.* $30

Holland, Rubert. YANKEE SHIPS IN PIRATE WATERS. GC, 1940s ptg. 317pp. Illus by Frank Schoonover. Faint smudge to back end, else VG+. *BEBBAH.* $25

Holland, Vyvan. HAND COLORED FASHION PLATES 1770 TO 1899. Boston: Boston Bk and Art Shop. (1955). 1st ed. 200pp. 5 color plts. Dj. *KARMIOLE.* $50

Holland, W.I. THE BUTTERFLY BOOK. GC, 1947 (1931). 2nd ed. 77 plts. Extremities scuffed, some cover soiling, name stamp. *SUTTON.* $35

Holland, W.J. TO THE RIVER PLATE AND BACK...NY, 1913. Some scuffing corners & spine ends. *SUTTON.* $50

Hollander, John. REFLECTIONS ON ESPIONAGE. THE QUESTION OF CUPCAKE. Cl. NY: Atheneum, 1976. 1st ed. Signed. Fine in dj, tiny nick head of spine. *JAFFE.* $45

Hollenback, Frank and William Russell, Jr. PIKES PEAK BY RAIL. Denver: Sage Books, 1962. #54 of ltd ed, signed by both authors. Fine in dj. *BOHLING.* $125

Holley, Frances Chamberlain. ONCE THEIR HOME. Chicago: Donohue and Henneberry, 1890. 405pp,28 full-pg illus. Black and gold stamped cl. Light wear to joints and tips. *DAWSON'S.* $100

Holley, George W. NIAGARA: ITS HISTORY AND GEOLOGY....NY: Sheldon, Buffalo and Toronto: Sheldon, 1872. 1st ed. Grn cl, fldg map in rear. Lacks the fep. *SECOND LIFE.* $75

Holley, Mary Austin. TEXAS: OBSERVATIONS HISTORICAL, GEOGRAPHICAL AND DESCRIPTIVE IN A SERIES OF LETTERS. Austin: Overland, 1981. Map. 3/4 leather. One of 325. Numbered and signed by the printer and author of the foreword, Tom Whitridge and Ron Tyler. Howes H593. *GINSBERG.* $240

Holliday, C.W. THE VALLEY OF YOUTH. Caxton, 1948. 1st ed. Fine. *OREGON.* $30

Holliday, J.S. THE WORLD RUSHED IN: THE CALIFORNIA GOLD RUSH EXPERIENCE. London: Victor Gollancz, 1983. 1st British ed. Fine in dj. *AUTHORS OF THE WEST.* $20

Holling, Holling C. THE BOOK OF COWBOYS. NY: Platt & Munk, (1936). 1st ed. VG. *DIAMOND.* $25

Hollister, Ovando J. COLORADO VOLUNTEERS IN NEW MEXICO 1862. Denver, 1863. 1962 rprt ed by Richard Harwell. Lakeside Classics #60. Pict cl. Fine. *PRATT.* $40

Hollitscher, Walter. SIGMUND FREUD, AN INTRODUCTION. NY: Oxford Univ Press, 1947. 1st ed. Spine sl faded, else Fine. *WEBER.* $25

Hollon, W.E. BEYOND THE CROSS TIMBERS....Univ of Ok Press, 1955. 1st ed. Fine in Fine dj. *VARNER.* $40

Hollow, John. AGAINST THE NIGHT, THE STARS. Fine in dj w/review slip. *MADLE.* $25

Holm, Donald. THE CIRCUMNAVIGATORS—SMALL BOAT VOYAGES OF MODERN TIMES. Englewood Cliffs: Prentice Hall, 1974. 1st ed. VG+ in similar dj. *PARMER.* $35

Holm, James (ed). PORTAGE HERITAGE. N.p.: Portage Co. Hist. Soc., 1957. 1st ed. Red leatherette. Fine. *ARCHER.* $30

Holman, A. M. and Contant R. Marks. PIONEERING IN THE NORTHWEST. NIOBRARA-VIRGINIA CITY WAGON ROAD. Sioux City, 1924. 1st ed. Orig printed wrappers. *GINSBERG.* $75

Holman, Dennis. MASSACRE OF THE ELEPHANTS. NY: Holt Rinehart, 1967. 1st Amer ed. NF in NF dj. *GREAT EPIC.* $55

Holman, Emile. NEW CONCEPTS IN SURGERY OF THE VASCULAR SYSTEM. Springfield, 1955. 1st ed. *FYE.* $45

Holman, John. SOUABBLE AND OTHER STORIES. Ticknor & Fields, 1990. Uncorrected proof. Fine in orange wraps. *STAHR.* $20

Holme, Geoffrey (ed). DESIGN IN THE THEATRE. (London): The Studio, 1927. Orig wraps bound in; 120 plts, many full page, some color. VG. *DRAMATIS PERSONAE.* $40

Holmes, Alice A. LOST VISION. NY: De Vinne Press, 1888. 1st ed. 94pp. Orig cl, Front hinge tender. *SECOND LIFE.* $35

Holmes, Anne Middleton. ALGERON SYDNEY SULLIVAN. Concord, 1929. 1st ed. Fine in pristine dj. *McGOWAN.* $45

Holmes, Bayard. THE SURGERY OF THE HEAD. NY, 1903. 1st ed. *FYE.* $150

Holmes, F. Ratcliffe. THE SECRET PEOPLE. London, n.d. 1st ed. VG. *MADLE.* $35

Holmes, Harold C. SOME RANDOM REMINISCENCES OF AN ANTIQUARIAN BOOKSELLER. Oakland: The Holmes Book Co., 1967. 1st ed. Dj. *OAK KNOLL.* $40

Holmes, John Clellon. GET HOME FREE. NY: Dutton, 1964. 1st ed. Name, address stamp else VG+ in dj. *BERNARD.* $45

Holmes, John Clellon. NOTHING MORE TO DECLARE. (London): Deutsch, (1968). 1st Eng ed. Fine in NF dj. *LOPEZ.* $35

Holmes, John Clellon. THE BOWLING GREEN POEMS. PA, 1977. Ltd ed, 250 only, signed. Pict wraps. Fine. *POLYANTHOS.* $35

Holmes, Louis A. FORT MCPHERSON, NEBRASKA...GUARDIAN OF THE TRACKS AND TRIALS. Lincoln, NE, (1963). 1st ed. Number X of limited ed. "Printers Copy For the Hagars, Lawton Kennedy." Orig cl boards. *GINSBERG.* $100

Holmes, Mary C. BETWEEN THE LINES IN ASIA MINOR. NY, (1923). *O'NEILL.* $45

Holmes, Oliver W. A DISSERTATION ON ACUTE PERICARDITIS. Boston, 1937. 1st ed. Full vellum. *FYE.* $60

Holmes, Oliver W. BORDER LINES OF KNOWLEDGE IN SOME PROVINCES OF MEDICAL SCIENCE. Boston, 1862. 1st ed. 80pp. Ex-lib. *FYE.* $150

Holmes, Oliver W. BOYLSTON PRIZE DISSERTATIONS FOR THE YEARS 1836 AND 1837. Boston, 1838. 1st ed. Recent cloth, 371pp. Lib perforation stamp on title, o/w VG. Scarce. *FYE.* $250

Holmes, Oliver W. CURRENTS AND COUNTER-CURRENTS IN MEDICAL SCIENCE WITH OTHER ADDRESSES AND ESSAYS. Boston, 1861. 1st ed. 406pp. Spine rubbed, head and tail of spine chipped, o/w VG. *FYE.* $175

Holmes, Oliver W. RALPH WALDO EMERSON. Boston: Houghton, Mifflin, (1885). Full tree calf, red leather label on paneled spine, gilt, inside gilt dentelles, aeg. NF. *WREDEN.* $35

Holmes, Oliver W. SONGS IN MANY KEYS. Boston, 1862. 1st ed. 308pp. Fine. Scarce. *FYE.* $100

Holmes, Oliver W. THE AUTOCRAT OF THE BREAKFAST TABLE EVERY MAN HIS OWN BOSWELL. Boston, 1858. 1st ed. 373pp. Backstrip and corners worn. *FYE.* $150

Holmes, Oliver W. THE CLAIMS OF DENTISTRY. Boston: Ptd by Rand, Avery, & Co., 1872. 35pp. Orig ptd tan wraps. Embossed lib stamp on front wrap, some wear along spine edges, but VG. 1st ed. Back wrapper unptd; priority undetermined. *CHAPEL HILL.* $200

Holmes, Oliver W. THE COMMON LAW. Boston: Little, Brown, and Co, 1881. 1st ed. xci,422pp. Orig brn cl (bumped, quite rubbed; head, tail of spine chipped). Bkpl, small chip to top edge of front blank, hinges starting. VG. *BLUE MOUNTAIN.* $375

Holmes, Oliver W. THE COMMON LAW. Little, Brown, and Company, Boston, 1881. A working copy, bearing the John Wilson and Son imprint, bound in orig maroon pebbled cl. Ex-lib, crudely rebacked in cl w/portion of orig spine laid down. 2 blanks at beginning, 1 at the end. Owner inscrip. A copy for someone who wishes a 1st ed which may be read and handled with ease, but which is a long way from being an attractive copy. *BOSWELL.* $200

Holmes, Oliver W. THE NEW CENTURY AND THE BUILDING OF THE HARVARD MEDICAL SCHOOL. 1783-1883. Cambridge, 1884. 1st ed. 55pp. *FYE.* $100

Holmes, Oliver W. THE POET AT THE BREAKFAST-TABLE. Boston, 1872. 1st ed. *FYE.* $100

Holmes, Oliver W. THE PROFESSOR AT THE BREAKFAST-TABLE; WITH THE STORY OF IRIS. Boston, 1860. 1st ed, reprinted. 410pp. VF. *FYE.* $125

Holmes, Oliver W. THE PROFESSOR AT THE BREAKFAST-TABLE; WITH THE STORY OF IRIS. Boston: Ticknor & Fields, 1860. 1st ed, 1st issue. Slight foxing on feps only, orig embossed cl. VG. *CONNOLLY & WADE.* $200

Holmes, Oliver W. THE WRITINGS OF OLIVER WENDELL HOLMES. Boston, 1891. Large paper ltd. ed. of 275 sets. 14 vols. Vellum backstrips, paper labels soiled and rubbed, o/w Fine. Incl scarce 14th vol. *FYE.* $550

Holmes, Richard. WINDSOR. A&C Black, 1908. 1st ed. 7s 6d Series. VG-NF. *OLD LONDON.* $55

Holmes, Thomas et al., THE NOSE: AN EXPERIMENTAL STUDY OF REACTIONS WITHIN THE NOSE AND HUMAN SUBJECTS DURING VARYING LIFE EXPERIENCES. Springfield, 1950. 1st ed. *FYE.* $30

Holmes, Timothy. A SYSTEM OF SURGERY, THEORETICAL AND PRACTICAL, IN TREATISES BY VARIOUS AUTHORS. Phila, 1882. 1st Amer ed. 3 vols. 1007, 1063pp. *FYE.* $300

Holmes, Tommy. DODGER DAZE AND KNIGHTS. McKay, 1953. 1st ed. VG+ without dj. *PLAPINGER.* $50

Holmes, William D. SAFARI R.S.V.P. NY: Coward McCann, 1960. 1st ed. Name. VG+ in VG dj w/small amount of chipping to dj spine edge. *BACKMAN.* $30

Holmstedt, B. and G. Liljestrand (eds). READINGS IN PHARMACOLOGY. NY, 1963. *FYE.* $75

Holroyd, James Edward. BAKER STREET BY-WAYS. London: George Allen & Unwin, 1959. 1st ed. Fine in dj (sl spine fading; rubbing along spine folds). *MORDIDA.* $85

Holt, Gavin. THE GOLDEN WITCH. London: Hodder and Stoughton, 1933. 1st ed. Edges spotted o/w VG in dj (darkened spine; wear at corners). *MORDIDA.* $35

Holt, R. GEORGE WASHINGTON CARVER, AN AMERICAN BIOGRAPHY. GC, 1943. 1st ed. Cl. *SUTTON.* $40

Holtby, Winifred. LETTERS TO A FRIEND. Ed by Alice Holtby and Jean McWilliams. NY: Macmillan, 1938. 1st US ed. Fine in little worn dj. *SECOND LIFE.* $35

Holton, Isaac. NEW GRENADA. Carbondale: Southern Illinois Univ Press, 1967. 1st ed. Fine in NF dj. *CONNOLLY & WADE.* $25

Holton, Leonard. A PROBLEM IN ANGELS. NY: Dodd Mead, 1970. 1st ed. Fine in dj. *MORDIDA.* $25

Holton, Leonard. A TOUCH OF JONAH. NY: Dodd Mead, 1968. 1st ed. Fine in dj. *MORDIDA.* $25

Holway, John. VOICES FROM THE GREAT BLACK BASEBALL LEAGUES. Dodd Mead, 1975. 1st ed. Fine in Fine dj. *PLAPINGER.* $100

Holzworth, J.M. THE TWIN GRIZZLIES OF ADMIRALTY ISLAND. 16 photos. Phila, (1932). Cloth, chipped dj. *SUTTON.* $44

Holzworth, J.M. THE TWIN GRIZZLIES OF ADMIRALTY ISLAND. Phila & London, (1932). Signed presentation. VG. *MIKESH.* $37.50

Holzworth, J.M. THE WILD GRIZZLIES OF ALASKA. NY & London, 1930. VG+. *MIKESH.* $60

Holzworth, John M. THE WILD GRIZZLIES OF ALASKA. NY: Putnam's, 1930. Stated 1st ed. VG (owner inscrip). *BACKMAN.* $90

HOMAGE TO HENRI MATISSE. NY, 1970. Bright dj w/chip on bottomfront panel, chipping extreme top of spine. NF. *POLYANTHOS.* $75

Homans, J. Smith and J. Smith Homans, Jr. CYCLOPEDIA OF COMMERCE AND COMMERCIAL NAVIGATION. London, (1974). 2 vols, Facs reprint of orig ed, NY, 1858. *LEFKOWICZ.* $90

Homans, J. Smith, Jr. HISTORICAL AND STATISTICAL ACCOUNT OF THE FOREIGN COMMERCE OF THE UNITED STATES....London, (1974). Facs reprint of orig ed, pub NY, 1857. *LEFKOWICZ.* $45

Homans, John. THREE HUNDRED AND EIGHTY-FOUR LAPAROTOMIES FOR VARIOUS DISEASES. Boston, 1887. 1st ed. 56pp +26 fold out tables. Scarce. *FYE.* $150

HOME AS FOUND. (By James Fenimore Cooper.) Phila: Lea & Blanchard, 1838. 1st ed. BAL 3884, 2nd ptg. 12mo. 2 vols. Orig cloth, faded. Orig printed labels, rubbed. *M & S.* $250

HOME AS FOUND. Phila: Lea & Blanchard, 1838. 2 vols. 239; 253pp. 1st ed, w/o notice regarding the quality of paper on which the bk is ptd. Purple muslin cl, paper spine labels; worn. Lib marks front cvr, front & back flyleaves in ink & pencil. Owner stamp. Vol 2 with 1/5 of flyleaf torn away. Foxed, a few signatures loose. Red cl slipcase, red leather spine label. BAL 3884. *WEBER.* $300

Home, Everard. PRACTICAL OBSERVATIONS ON THE TREATMENT OF STRICTURES IN THE URETHRA, AND THE ESOPHAGUS. London, 1805-1821. Set made of different eds., as issued. Vol. 1 is 3rd ed., Vol. 2 is 2nd ed., Vol. 3 is 1st ed. Orig paper backed boards, 1 board detached. Fine engrvd plts. *FYE.* $150

Home, Everard. PRACTICAL OBSERVATIONS ON THE TREATMENT OF ULCERS OF THE LEGS, CONSIDERED AS A BRANCH OF MILITARY SURGERY. Phila, 1811. 1st Amer ed. Full leather, 297pp. Backstrip chipped, front board and prelim leaves detached. Contents Fine. *FYE.* $150

Home, Gordon. THE ROMANCE OF LONDON. A&C Black. 1924 reprint. Only fair. *OLD LONDON.* $10

Home. Gordon. YORKSHIRE: VALES AND WOLDS. A&C Black, 1908. 1st ed. 7s 6d Series. Minor foxing to bottom edge, else VG-NF. *OLD LONDON.* $45

Homer. THE ILIAD. (WITH:) THE ODYSSEY. Trans by Alexander Pope. 2 vols. Full niger morocco, marbled slipcases. (London): Nonesuch Press, 1931. Ltd to 1450 & 1300 respectively. Ptd by Joh. Enschede en Zonen in the Greek type of J. van Krimpen. Spines darkened, cvrs of the first vols. a bit spotted, o/w a VG set in edgeworn slipcases. *JAFFE.* $1000

Homer. THE ILIAD. Robert Fitzgerald (trans). GC: Anchor Press, 1974. 1st ed. One corner sl bumped, else Fine in lightly used dj. *CAPTAIN'S BOOKSHELF.* $45.

Homer. THE WHOLE WORKS OF HOMER...N HIS ILIADS, AND ODYSSES. George Chapman (trans). Oxford: Shakespeare Head Press, 1930. 5 vols. Ltd to 450 ptd on handmade paper. Illus 1/4 calf, cl. Fine set, the soft calf showing little trace of usual rubbing. *JAFFE.* $850

HOMES OF CALIFORNIA AUTHORS. Bk Club of CA, (1967). 1st ed. 12 folders w/photos, text. Cl folder in slipcase, gilt-stamped leather labels on spine. Fine. *AUTHORS OF THE WEST.* $100

Hone, Joseph. THE PARIS TRAP. London: Secker & Warburg, 1977. 1st ed. Fine in dj. *MORDIDA.* $45

Hone, Philip. THE DIARY OF...1828-1851. NY, 1927. Best ed. 2 vols. Orig cl. Allan Nevins (ed, intro). Howes H620. *GINSBERG.* $50

Honey, William Bowyer. EUROPEAN CERAMIC ART. FROM THE END OF THE MIDDLE AGES TO ABOUT 1815. NY: D. Van Nostrand. 1949. 1st ed. DJ chipped, bit soiled. *KARMIOLE.* $60

Honig, Donald. THE NEW YORK YANKEES. Crown, 1981. 1st ed. VG+ in Fine dj. *PLAPINGER.* $30

Honig, Louis. THE PATHFINDER OF THE WEST, JAMES BRIDGER. Kansas City: Lowell Pr, 1951. 1st ed. Deluxe subscriber's ed ltd to 525 numbered, signed. VG. *OREGON.* $95

Hood, Graham. AMERICAN SILVER...1650-1900. NY: Praeger, (1971) 1st. Fine in dj. *CAPTAIN'S BOOKSHELF.* $35

Hood, Mary. AND VENUS IS BLUE. Ticknor & Fields, 1986. 1st ed. VF. *STAHR.* $20

Hooker, John. SOME REMINISCENCES OF A LONG LIFE. Hartford: Belknap & Warfield, 1899. 1st ed. Pub's cl. VG. *SECOND LIFE.* $125

Hooker, Joseph Dalton and John Ball. JOURNAL OF A TOUR IN MAROCCO AND THE GREAT ATLAS. London: Macmillan, 1878. 1st ed. xvi,489pp. 9 plts (2 fldg), 13 engrs in text, 1 fldg map. Orig cl, edges rubbed, spine frayed, tears in spine. Ex-lib, o/w Good. *WORLDWIDE.* $120

Hooper, E.J. HOOPER'S WESTERN FRUIT BOOK: A COMPENDIOUS COLLECTION OF FACTS...Cincinnati: Moore, Wilstach, Keys & Co., 1857. 1st ed. 4 leaves; 433,(3)pp. Litho frontis, 4 colored lithos of fruit. Spine faded & rubbed. *M & S.* $250

Hooper, Robert. LEXICON MEDICUM; OR MEDICAL DICTIONARY. NY, 1835. 4th Amer ed. 2 vols in 1. Full lea. *FYE.* $100

Hoover, Herbert. THE MEMOIRS OF HERBERT HOOVER: 1929-1941. THE GREAT DEPRESSION. NY: Macmillan, 1952. 1st ed. Slight bump to edge of spine and dj, else NF in dj. Inscribed. *BETWEEN COVERS.* $200

Hoover, J. Edgar. A STUDY OF COMMUNISM. NY: Holt, Rinehart & Winston, Inc, (1962). 1st ed. Laid in is signed ptd card. Dj. *KARMIOLE.* $65

Hopkins, Edward J. and Edward F. Rimbault. THE ORGAN, ITS HISTORY AND CONSTRUCTION. London: Robert Cocks & Co, 1877. 3rd ed. xxxi(i),160pp & 636pp. Front hinge starting. Burgundy cl bumped, sl rubbed. Gilt vignette within dec blind frame on front cover & gilt title on spine. Fldg plt. Very Nice. *BLUE MOUNTAIN.* $245

Hopkins, Esek. THE CORRESPONDENCE OF....Providence, 1933. 1st ed. Orig cl. *GINSBERG.* $35

Hopkins, Esek. THE LETTER-BOOK OF...1775-1777. Providence, 1932. 1st ed. Orig cl. *GINSBERG.* $45

Hopkins, Gerard Manley. POEMS: SECOND EDITION, WITH ADDITIONAL POEMS. Charles Williams (ed). Oxford: Oxford Univ Press, 1930. 1st this ed. Fine in sl rubbed dj. *JAFFE.* $150

Hopkins, Owen Johnston. UNDER THE FLAG OF THE NATION. Otto F. Bond (ed). Columbus, (1961). 1st ed. Some dj wear o/w Fine. *PRATT.* $30

Hopkins, Samuel. THE YOUTH OF THE OLD DOMINION. Boston: 1856. 1st ed. (8), 473pp. Orig cl, lax front flyleaf. *GINSBERG.* $75

Hopkins, Samuel. THE YOUTH OF THE OLD DOMINION. John P. Jewett, 1856. 1st ed. 473pp. *BOOK BROKER.* $35

Hopley, George (pseud of Cornell Woolrich). NIGHT HAS A THOUSAND EYES. NY, Toronto: Farrar & Rinehart, (1945). 1st

ed. Name inked out on flyleaf, else VG+ in dj (chipped). *BERNARD.* $200

Hoppe, E.O. IN GIPSY CAMP AND ROYAL PALACE. NY: Charles Scribner's Sons. 1924. 1st ed. Fine in sl chipped dj. *KARMIOLE.* $85

Hoppe, E.O. ROMANTIC AMERICA. NY: B. Westermann Co, Inc. (1927). 304 full-pg rotogravure photos and map. Cream cl stamped in 3 colors. In orig slipcase (rubbed) w/ptd paper label. Scarce in this condition. *KARMIOLE.* $125

Hoppin, James Mason. LIFE OF ANDREW HULL FOOTE, REAR-ADMIRAL UNITED STATES NAVY. NY, 1874. 1st ed. 411pp & ads. A little cvr wear o/w Fine. *PRATT.* $70

Hoppin, Joseph Clark. A HANDBOOK OF ATTIC RED-FIGURED VASES SIGNED BY OR ATTRIBUTED TO THE VARIOUS MASTERS OF THE SIXTH AND FIFTH CENTURIES B.C. 2 vols (complete). Cambridge: Harvard Univ Press, 1919. Teg. Foxing to few pp. *ARCHAEOLOGIA.* $300

HORACE WELLS, DENTIST, FATHER OF SURGICAL ANESTHESIA. PROCEEDINGS OF CENTENARY COMMEMORATIONS OF WELLS' DISCOVERY IN 1844 AND LISTS OF WELLS MEMORABILIA INCLUDING BIBLIOGRAPHIES, MEMORIALS AND TESTIMONIALS. Hartford, 1948. 1st ed. 415pp. Ex-lib. *FYE.* $125

Horan, James D. (ed). MCKENNEY-HALL PORTRAIT GALLERY OF AMERICAN INDIANS. Crown, NY (1972). De Luxe Ltd, #59 of 259. Presentation copy. One-half leather, boxed. *HEINOLDT.* $175

Horan, James D. ACROSS THE CIMARRON. NY: Crown, 1956. 1st ed. Fine in dj. *CONNOLLY & WADE.* $35

Horan, James D. CONFEDERATE AGENT. A DISCOVERY IN HISTORY. NY: Crown, 1954. 1st ed. Fine in Good+ dj. *CONNOLLY & WADE.* $40

Horan, James D. CONFEDERATE AGENT, A DISCOVERY IN HISTORY. NY, (1954). 1st ed. 326pp, illus, endpaper maps. Light dj wear, o/w Fine. *PRATT.* $30

Horan, James D. DESPERATE MEN. NY: Putnam, 1949. 1st ed. VG. *CONNOLLY & WADE.* $35

Horan, James D. DESPERATE MEN; REVELATIONS....Putnam, 1951. 3rd ptg. Inscribed. Fine in Fine dj. *VARNER.* $25

Horan, James D. DESPERATE WOMEN. NY, (1952). 1st ed. 336pp. Light dj wear o/w Fine. *PRATT.* $35

Horan, James D. DESPERATE WOMEN. Putnam, 1952. 1st ed. Inscribed. Fine in Fine dj. *VARNER.* $35

Horan, James D. THE GREAT AMERICAN WEST. NY, (1959). 1st ed. 288pp. A little dj wear, o/w Fine. *PRATT.* $50

Horan, James D. THE MCKENNY-HALL PORTRAIT GALLERY OF AMERICAN INDIANS. NY: Crown Publishers, (1972). One of 249 numbered of deluxe ed, signed. 238 full-pg repros. Bound in 1/2 leather. Box. Fine. *LAURIE.* $200

Horan, James D. THE PINKERTONS: THE DETECTIVE DYNASTY THAT MADE HISTORY. NY: Crown, 1967. 1st ed. Fine in Good dj. *CONNOLLY & WADE.* $45

Horgan, Paul. A DISTANT TRUMPET. Farrar, Straus & Cudahy, (1960). 1st ed. Fine in dj. *AUTHORS OF THE WEST.* $35

Horgan, Paul. EVERYTHING TO LIVE FOR. Farrar, Straus & Giroux, (1968). 1st ed. Fine in dj. *AUTHORS OF THE WEST.* $20

Horgan, Paul. GIVE ME POSSESSION. NY: FS & C, 1957. 1st ed. NF in dj. *ELSE FINE.* $40

Horgan, Paul. GREAT RIVER, RIO GRANDE IN NORTH AMERICAN HISTORY. 1954. 1st ed. 2 vols. Boxed. *HEINOLDT.* $25

Horgan, Paul. GREAT RIVER. Rinehart, 1954. 1st ed. 2 vols boxed. VG in Good+ slipcase. *OREGON.* $50

Horgan, Paul. GREAT RIVER. THE RIO GRANDE IN NORTH AMERICAN HISTORY. NY, 1954. 1st ed. 2 vols. NF in sl edge rubbed box. *POLYANTHOS.* $60

Horgan, Paul. LAMY OF SANTA FE. NY, 1975. 1st prtg. NF in sl worn dj. *BAADE.* $37.50

Horgan, Paul. LAMY OF SANTA FE: A BIOGRAPHY. NY: Farrar, Straus & Giroux, 1975. 1st ed. Signed. VG in VG dj. *CONNOLLY & WADE.* $65

Horgan, Paul. LAMY OF SANTA FE: HIS LIFE AND TIMES. NY: Farrar, Straus & Giroux, 1975. 1st ed. Signed. VG. *BURCHAM.* $70

Horgan, Paul. LAMY OF SANTA FE: HIS LIFE AND TIMES. NY: Farrar, Straus & Giroux, 1975. 1st ed. *BURCHAM.* $40

Horgan, Paul. MAIN LINE WEST. NY: Harpers, 1936. 1st ed. Bkpl and gift inscrip front pastedown, VG+ in dj w/some staining and tape repair to verso. *LAME DUCK.* $75

Horgan, Paul. MOUNTAIN STANDARD TIME....London: Macmillan & Co, 1962. 1st British ed. Very Nice dj. Fine in dj. *AUTHORS OF THE WEST.* $25

Horgan, Paul. THE CENTURIES OF SANTA FE. Dutton, 1956. 1st ed. Fine in dj. *AUTHORS OF THE WEST.* $25

Horgan, Paul. THE HEROIC TRIAD: ESSAYS.... NY: Holt, Rinehart and Winston, (1970). 1st ed. VG in dj. *LAURIE.* $25

Horgan, Paul. THE HEROIC TRIAD: ESSAYS....London: Heinemann, (1971). 1st British ed. Fine in dj. *AUTHORS OF THE WEST.* $20

Horgan, Paul. THE PEACH STONE. Farrar, Straus & Giroux, (1967). 1st ed. Bkpl. Signed. Fine in dj. *AUTHORS OF THE WEST.* $25

Horgan, Paul. THE PEACH STONE: STORIES FROM FOUR DECADES. NY: FSG, 1967. 1st ed. Inscribed. VG in torn, sunned Near Good dj. *ARCHER.* $22.50

Horgan, Paul. THE RETURN OF THE WEED. Northland Press, 1980. 1st Northland ed. Frontis. New in dj. *AUTHORS OF THE WEST.* $25

Horgan, Paul. THE THIN MOUNTAIN AIR. Farrar, Straus & Giroux, (1977). 1st ed. Signed. Fine in dj. *AUTHORS OF THE WEST.* $35

Horgan, Paul. WHITEWATER. NY: Farrar, Straus & Giroux, 1970. 1st ed. Fine in VG dj. *CONNOLLY & WADE.* $25

Horgan, Thomas P. OLD IRONSIDES: THE STORY OF THE U.S.S. CONSTITUTION. Boston: Burdette, 1963. 1st ed. Fine in NF dj. *CONNOLLY & WADE.* $55

Horn, Calvin. NEW MEXICO'S TROUBLED YEARS...EARLY TERRITORIAL GOVERNORS. Albuquerque: Horn & Wallace, (1963). Foreword by John F. Kennedy. 1st ed. Fine in dj. *LAURIE.* $35

Horn, Madeline D. FARM ON THE HILL. Scribner's, 1936. 1st ed. 78pp. 8 color plates by Grant Wood. Endpaper. Small red spot to top edge of cvr. VG. *BEBBAH.* $65

Horn, Stanley (ed). THE ROBERT E. LEE READER. NY, (1949). 1st ed. Dj wear o/w VG+. *PRATT.* $42.50

Horn, Stanley Fitzgerald. INVISIBLE EMPIRE THE STORY OF THE KU KLUX KLAN 1866-1871. Boston, 1939. 1st ed. Orig cl. VG. *McGOWAN.* $60

Horn, Tom. LIFE OF TOM HORN, GOVERNMENT SCOUT AND INTERPRETER. WRITTEN BY HIMSELF....Denver, 1904. 1987 rprt. Doyce B. Nunis, Jr (ed). Lakeside Classic #85. Plastic dj. Fine. *PRATT.* $35

Hornaday, W.T. CAMP-FIRES IN THE CANADIAN ROCKIES. NY, 1906. 1st ed. Very light edgewear. VG. Scarce. *BAADE.* $150

Hornaday, W.T. CAMP-FIRES IN THE CANADIAN ROCKIES. NY, (1909). VG. *MIKESH.* $45

Hornaday, W.T. THE EXTERMINATION OF THE AMERICAN BISON, WITH A SKETCH OF ITS DISCOVERY AND LIFE

HISTORY. 20 plts, 1 lg colored fldg map. Washington, 1887. Pp (367-) 548. Later cl-backed boards. Some browning of cvrs, pp yellowed w/marginal dampstaining lower edges several pp. Ex-lib. Scarce. *SUTTON.* $125

Hornby, Sir Edmund. SIR EDMUND HORNBY. AN AUTOBIOGRAPHY. Boston & NY: Houghton Mifflin, 1928. Dj torn. VG. *WORLDWIDE.* $22

Horne, John. MANY DAYS IN MOROCCO. NY, 1927. NF *POLYANTHOS.* $60

Horner, Harlan Hoyt. LINCOLN AND GREELEY. Univ of Illinois, 1953. 1st ed. VG in chipped, worn dj. *CONNOLLY & WADE.* $45

Horner, William. A TREATISE ON SPECIAL AND GENERAL ANATOMY. Phila, 1830. 2nd ed. 2 vols. Orig leather. 535, 528pp. Front boards of both vols detached, labels missing, eps of Vol. 2 missing, contents VG. *FYE.* $100

Hornsby, Rogers and Bill Surface. MY WAR WITH BASEBALL. Coward McCann, 1953. Good+ in VG dj. *PLAPINGER.* $45

Hornsby, Rogers. MY KIND OF BASEBALL. McKay, 1953. 1st ed. Good+ in VG dj. *PLAPINGER.* $45

Hornung, E.W. FATHERS OF MEN. London: Smith Elder, 1912. 1st ed. Edges foxed o/w VG w/o dj. *MORDIDA.* $50

Horowitz, David. THE FIRST FRONTIER, THE INDIAN WARS AND AMERICA'S ORIGINS: 1607-1776. NY, (1978). 1st ed. A little dj wear o/w Fine. *PRATT.* $20

Horracks, James. MY DEAR PARENTS, THE CIVIL WAR AS SEEN BY AN ENGLISH UNION SOLDIER. NY, (1982). 1st Amer ed. Fine in dj. *PRATT.* $25

Horridge, G.A. (ed). THE COMPOUND EYE AND VISION OF INSECTS. Cloth. Oxford, 1975. *SUTTON.* $65

Horsley, J. Shelton. SURGERY OF THE BLOOD VESSELS. St. Louis, 1915. 1st ed. 89 illus. *FYE.* $300

Horsley, J. Shelton. SURGERY OF THE STOMACH AND SMALL INTESTINE. NY, 1926. 1st ed. *FYE.* $75

Horton, George. HOME OF NYMPHA AND VAMPIRES. THE ISLES OF GREECE. Indianapolis, 1929. 319 pp. Dj. 1st ed. Fine. *O'NEILL.* $35

Horton, George. IN ARGOLIS. Chicago, 1902. Frontis, 15 plts. xiii,226pp. Uncut. Clipped photo of author pasted to ep. Presentation. *O'NEILL.* $45

Horton, George. IN ARGOLIS. Chicago: A.C. McClurg, 1902. Spine faded. Largely unopened. *SCHOYER'S.* $35.

Horwood, Murray. PUBLIC HEALTH SURVEYS: WHAT THEY ARE, HOW TO MAKE THEM, HOW TO USE THEM. NY, 1921. 1st ed. Autographed. *FYE.* $100

Hoskin, Beryl. A HISTORY OF THE SANTA CLARA MISSION LIBRARY. Oakland: Biobooks, 1961. 1st ed, ltd to 500. Damp mark on front cvr. Affects nothing. NF. *CONNOLLY & WADE.* $45

Hosmer, William. SLAVERY AND THE CHURCH. Auburn: William J. Moses. 1853. 1st ed. 200pp. Orig brn cloth, gilt spine; cl somewhat soiled, some internal soiling. *KARMIOLE.* $60

Hotchkiss, Bill. AMMAHABAS. W.W. Norton, (1983). 1st ed. Signed. New in dj. *AUTHORS OF THE WEST.* $25

Hotchkiss, Bill. THE MEDICINE CALF. Norton, (1981). 1st ed. Frontis. Boards. Signed. New in dj. *AUTHORS OF THE WEST.* $25

Hotchner, A.E. PAPA HEMINGWAY. NY: Random House, (1966). 1st ed. VG+ in Fine dj. *BERNARD.* $25

Hott, James W. JOURNEYINGS IN THE OLD WORLD...Dayton, OH: United Brethren Pub House, 1884. Little rubbed. *SCHOYER'S.* $35

Hott, James W. JOURNEYINGS IN THE OLD WORLD; or, EUROPE PALESTINE, AND EGYPT....Dayton, OH, 1884. *O'NEILL.* $65

Hotten, John Camden (ed). ABYSSINIA AND ITS PEOPLE, OR LIFE IN THE LAND OF PRESTER JOHN. London, 1868. 1st ed. Fldg map. Ex-lib, only two marks. Professionally rebound in half chocolate leather, raised bands, gold stamping. NF. *McCLINTOCK.* $85

Hotton, John Camden (ed). THE ORIGINAL LISTS OF PERSONS OF QUALITY...TO THE AMERICAN PLANTATIONS, 1600-1700....A. Barker, 1931. Binding sl weak. VG. *BOOK BROKER.* $65

Houck, Louis. A HISTORY OF MISSOURI FROM THE EARLIEST EXPLORATIONS AND SETTLEMENTS. Chicago, Donnelley, 1908. 1st ed. 3 vols. Orig grn cl w/black morocco spine label. Fine. Howes H671. *GINSBERG.* $350

Houck, Louis. HISTORY OF MISSOURI FROM THE EARLIEST EXPLORATIONS...UNTIL THE ADMISSION OF THE STATE INTO THE UNION. Chicago: R.R. Donnelly, 1908. 1st ed. 3 vols. Feps, 1 rear ep stuck together, lea spine labels scuffed. Good+. Howes H671. *OREGON.* $160

Houdini, Harry. MIRACLE MONGERS AND THEIR METHODS. NY: Dutton, (1920). 1st ed. Tan cl bumped and sl rubbed, title in black. Frontis, 12 plts, 3 facs. VG. *BLUE MOUNTAIN.* $125

Hough, Alfred Lacey. SOLDIER IN THE WEST, THE CIVIL WAR LETTERS OF ALFRED LACEY HOUGH. Phila, 1957. Ed by Robert G. Athearn. 1st ed. Small piece torn from top of dj spine o/w VG. *PRATT.* $30

Hough, Emerson. MOTHER OF GOLD. D. Appleton & Co, 1924. 1st ed. Frontis. VG. *AUTHORS OF THE WEST.* $25

Hough, Emerson. THE MAGNIFICENT ADVENTURE:...THE WORLD'S GREATEST EXPLORATION...ROMANCE OF A VERY GALLANT GENTLEMAN. D. Appleton & Co, 1916. 1st ed. Pict cvr. Fine in campNice dj. *AUTHORS OF THE WEST.* $150

Hough, Emerson. THE WAY TO THE WEST...BOONE-CROCKETT-CARSON, (1903). 1st ed. Illus Frederick Remington. Dec cvr. Top edge scuffed, else Fine. *AUTHORS OF THE WEST.* $100

Hough, Horatio Gates. DIVING, OR AN ATTEMPT TO DESCRIBE UPON HYDRAULIC AND HYDROSTATIC PRINCIPLES, A METHOD OF SUPPLYING THE DIVER WITH AIR UNDERWATER. Hartford, CT: John Russell, Jr, 1813. 1st ed. 8pp, incl title; uncut and unopened; diagram last leaf. Faint stains, owner ink handstamp, short tear first text leaf. VG. *SMITHFIELD.* $170

Houghton, Eliza P. Donner. THE EXPEDITION OF THE DONNER PARTY, AND ITS TRAGIC FATE. LA: Grafton Pub Corp. 1920. 1st ed. Sm worm hole on spine. *KARMIOLE.* $50

Houghton, W. GLEANINGS FROM THE NATURAL HISTORY OF THE ANCIENTS. London, (1879). Pp (3),252. Orig ornate cl. Lt wear, institutional bkpl, # sticker; tears to lower edges few pp; pp tanned. *SUTTON.* $36

Hougthon, Claude. THE TAVERN OF DREAMS: A VOLUME OF VERSE. London: Richards, 1919. 1st. Dj. Signed. One page roughly opened, else VF. *MUELLER.* $40

House, Boyce. OIL BOOM. THE STORY OF SPINDLETOP. Caldwell, ID: The Caxton Printers, 1941. 1st ed. VG, white paint flecks on cover. *GIBBS.* $30

House, H.D. WILD FLOWERS OF NEW YORK. Albany: NYS Univ, 1923. 2nd ptg. 264 color photo plts. 362pp & plts. 2 vols. VG+. *MIKESH.* $60

House, Humphrey. THE DICKENS WORLD. London: Oxford Univ Press, 1941. Dj. *WEBER.* $20

Houseman, A.E. A SHROPSHIRE LAD and LAST POEMS. (Chipping Camden, The Alcuin Press, 1929.) Boards, cloth backs. 2 vols in slipcase. One of 325 sets, printed in red and black. Label of 1st

vol has a stain and some wear that doesn't affect the type. Attractive. *WOOLMER.* $225

Houseman, Clemence. THE WERE-WOLF. London, 1896. 1st ed. Top of spine chipped; cvr sl soiled, else Near VG. *MADLE.* $175

Housman, Clemence. THE WERE-WOLF. London, 1896. 1st ed. 6 illus by Laurence Housman. Uncut. Extremities, spine sl bumped, covers little soiled. Fine. *POLYANTHOS.* $200

Housman, Clemence. THE WERE-WOLF. London: John Lane. Chicago: Way & Williams, 1896. 1st ed, 2nd binding. Frontis, 5 plts inserted. Brn cl stamped in black. Nicks, minor foxing, else Fine. *SECOND LIFE.* $200

Housman, Clemence. THE WERE-WOLF. With Six Illustrations by Laurence Housman. London: John Lane, 1896. 123,(1)pp,16pp ads. Orig brown (remainder?) cl (very minor soiling, fading). Else NF. 1st ed. One of 1000. *CHAPEL HILL.* $225

Housman, Laurence. CYNTHIA. (London): Sidgwick & Jackson, (1947). VG in dj (few chips, tears). Extra spine label tipped in at rear as issued. 1st ed. One of 500 signed. *CHAPEL HILL.* $65

Housman, Lawrence. PRINCESS BADOURA. Illus Edmund Dulac. London: Hodder & Stoughton, n.d. 1st trade ed. Dec white cl tooled in grn and gilt. 10 tipped-in color plts. Extrems sl dust soiled, else Fine. *CAPTAIN'S BOOKSHELF.* $175

Houston, Mrs. (Matilda C.). TEXAS AND THE GULF OF MEXICO; OR, YACHTING IN THE NEW WORLD. Phila: G.B. Zieber & Co, 1845. 1st Amer ed. 288pp, orig cl. Corners and spine worn at top & bottom. Front ep gone. *GIBBS.* $295

Houston, Mrs. (Matilda C.). TEXAS AND THE GULF OF MEXICO; or, Yachting in the New World. Phila: G.B. Zieber & Co. 1845. 1st Amer ed. 288pp. Frontis litho, several text woodcuts. Orig blind-stamped brown cl, spine faded; eps a bit soiled, some text foxing, but overall nice. Howes H693. *KARMIOLE.* $300

Hover, John C. et al (eds). MEMOIRS OF THE MIAMI VALLEY. Chicago: R.O. Law Company, 1919-20. 3 vols. 11 plts; 15 plts; 64 plts. Vols 1 & 2 Very Nice. Vol 3 used, soiled, w/chipped spine ends. *BOHLING.* $175

Hover, John C. et al (eds). MEMOIRS OF THE MIAMI VALLEY. Chicago, 1919-1920. 1st ed. 3 vols. Orig half morocco. *GINSBERG.* $175

Hovey, Tamara. JOHN REED: WITNESS TO REVOLUTION. NY: Crown, (1975). 1st ed. 227pp. Fine in lightly worn dj. *AKA.* $25

HOW TO GET A FARM AND WHERE TO FIND ONE....(By James Miller.) NY: James Miller, 1864. 1st ed. 345pp, ads. Worn pub's cl. VG. *SECOND LIFE.* $125

HOW TO PLAY BASEBALL. Crowell, 1913. Reprint of 1912 orig. VG+. *PLAPINGER.* $90

Howard, David and John Ayers. MASTERPIECES OF CHINESE EXPORT PORCELAIN...MOTTAHEDEH COLLECTION...NY: Sotheby Parke Bernet, 1981. 1st ed. NF. *BACKROOM.* $22.50

Howard, Fred. WILBUR AND ORVILLE: A BIOGRAPHY....NY: Knopf, 1987. 1st ed. Fine in Fine dj. *BOOK MARKET.* $35

Howard James L. SETH HARDING, MARINER. New Haven: Yale Univ Press. 1930. 1st ed. Blue cl, dj. *KARMIOLE.* $35

Howard, John. SCRIPTURE HISTORY FOR THE YOUNG. VOL. 1. NY: Virtue & Yorston (n.d., owner inscrip dated 1871). Aeg. Blind-stamped leather binding has wear. 320pp. Fldg frontis of Adam naming the creation. Color chromolithed title pg. *BEBBAH.* $25

Howard, Joseph Kinsey. STRANGE EMPIRE: A NARRATIVE OF THE NORTHWEST. NY: Morrow, 1952. 1st ed. NF in chipped, worn dj. *CONNOLLY & WADE.* $35

Howard, L.O. FIGHTING THE INSECTS. NY, 1933. Spine faded. *SUTTON.* $45

Howard, L.O. THE HOUSE FLY. NY, 1911. Spine faded. *SUTTON.* $27

Howard, L.O. THE INSECT BOOK. NY: 1901. 1st ed. Light scuffing to extremities, name on pastedowns & occasionally in text). *SUTTON.* $48

Howard, Louise and Hearnden, Beryl. WHAT COUNTRY WOMEN USE. London: Allen Unwin, (1939). 1st ed. Worn dj. *SECOND LIFE.* $30

Howard, Maureen. EXPENSIVE HABITS. Summit, 1986. Uncorrected proof. Fine in wraps. *STAHR.* $20

Howard, Oliver Otis. GENERAL TAYLOR. NY: D. Appleton, (1892). (xiii),386pp. 2 ports, 5 maps (2 fldg). Lg Paper Ed, #92/1000. Teg. *SCHOYER'S.* $50

Howard, Robert E. and Tevis Clyde Smith. RED BLADES OF BLACK CATHAY. West Kingston: Grant, 1971. 1st ed. Name, date else Fine in perfect as New dj. *OTHER WORLDS.* $60

Howard, Robert E. ALMURIC. West Kingston: Grant, 1975. 1st thus. Bkpl else Almost Fine in dj nicked at head of spine. *OTHER WORLDS.* $25

Howard, Robert E. ALWAYS COMES EVENING. Arkham House, 1957. 1st ed. VF in dj. *MADLE.* $500

Howard, Robert E. CONAN THE BARBARIAN. NY: Gnome Press, (1954). 1st ed. NF in dj sl chipped at spine ends & front corner tips. *BERNARD.* $100

Howard, Robert E. ETCHINGS IN IVORY: POEMS IN PROSE. Pasadena: Lord, 1968. 1st ed. 1/268. Fine in ptd wrappers. *OTHER WORLDS.* $250

Howard, Robert E. LORD OF THE DEAD. West Kingston, RI: Donald M. Grant, 1981. 1st ed. Illus. Fine in dj. *BERNARD.* $25

Howard, Robert E. RED NAILS. West Kingston: Grant, 1975. 1st ed. Fine in dj. *OTHER WORLDS.* $40

Howard, Robert E. RED SHADOWS. Donald Grant, 1968. 1st ed. Fine in sl dusty dj. *MADLE.* $125

Howard, Robert E. SINGERS IN THE SHADOWS. West Kingston: Grant, 1970. 1st ed. NF in perfect as New dj. *OTHER WORLDS.* $150

Howard, Robert E. SKULL-FACE AND OTHERS. Arkham House, 1946. 1st ed. VG in sl frayed dj. *MADLE.* $475

Howard, Robert E. THE COMING OF CONAN. NY: Gnome Press, (1953). 1st ed. NF in dj which is sl worn at edges. *BERNARD.* $100

Howard, Robert E. THE DARK MAN AND OTHERS. Arkham House, 1963. 1st ed. VF in dj. *MADLE.* $200

Howard, Robert E. THE DARK MAN AND OTHERS. Sauk City: Arkham House, 1963. 1st ed, ltd to 2029. Fine in dj with light soiling to rear panel. *ROBBINS.* $175

Howard, Robert E. THE GARDEN OF FEAR AND OTHER STORIES....LA: Crawford Publication, (1945). Wraps. *CULLEN.* $20

Howard, Robert E. THE GARDEN OF FEAR AND OTHER STORIES OF THE BIZARRE AND FANTASTIC. LA: Crawford, (1945). 1st ed. NF in wrappers. *ROBBINS.* $35

Howard, Robert E. THE PEOPLE OF THE BLACK CIRCLE. West Kingston, RI: Donald M. Grant, 1974. 1st ed. 3,000 copies. Illus. with 4 color plates & 8 b&w drawings by David Ireland. Fine in dj. *BERNARD.* $35

Howard, Robert E. THE PEOPLE OF THE BLACK CIRCLE. West Kingston: Grant, 1974. 1st ed thus. NF in dj w/two short tears. *OTHER WORLDS.* $30

Howard, Robert E. THE ROAD OF AZRAEL. West Kingston: Grant, 1979. 1st ed thus. 1/310 signed (Roy G. Krenkel). Fine in dj, slipcase. *OTHER WORLDS.* $90

Howard, Robert E. TIGERS OF THE SEA. West Kingston, RI: Donald M. Grant, 1974. 1st ed. Illus. Fine in dj. *BERNARD.* $25

Howard, Robert E. TIGERS OF THE SEA. West Kingston: Grant, 1974. 1st ed. Spine cocked, name, date else NF in dj, short tears. *OTHER WORLDS.* $25

Howard, Robert E. WORMS OF THE EARTH. West Kington: Grant, 1974. 1st ed. Name, date else Almost Fine in NF dj, some creasing to rear flap corner. *OTHER WORLDS.* $25

Howard, Robert W. (ed). THIS IS THE WEST. NY: NAL, 1957. 1st ptg. Lacks front fly, o/w VG. *DIAMOND.* $15

Howard, Robert West. THUNDERGATE. THE FORTS OF NIAGARA. Englewood Cliffs, NJ (1968), 1st ed. Dec eps. *HEINOLDT.* $15

Howard, Sanford. SEVENTH ANNUAL REPORT OF STATE BOARD AGRICULTURE STATE OF MICHIGAN. Lansing: Kerr, 1868. 490pp. Cloth lightly worn, else VG. *AMERICAN BOTANIST.* $30

Howard, Wiley Chandler. SKETCH OF COBB LEGION CAVALRY AND SOME INCIDENTS AND SCENES REMEMBERED. (Marietta, GA, 1949). 2nd prtg. Wrappers. NF. *McGOWAN.* $65

Howay, F. W. THE DIXON-MEARES CONTROVERSY....Toronto: Ryerson, (1929). 1st ed. Orig cl. One of 450 numbered. Howes H714. *GINSBERG.* $125

Howe, E.W. A MAN STORY. Ticknor & Co, 1889. 1st ed. VG+. *AUTHORS OF THE WEST.* $40

Howe, E.W. THE STORY OF A COUNTRY TOWN. Dodd, Mead, 1932. Inscribed, signed. VG. *AUTHORS OF THE WEST.* $35

Howe, Edgar F. and Wilbur J. Hall. THE STORY OF THE FIRST DECADE IN IMPERIAL VALLEY, CALIFORNIA. Imperial: Edgar F. Howe & Sons, 1910. Gold-stamped buckram w/morocco spine and tips, shaken, bit scuffed w/chip to tail of spine. *DAWSON'S.* $100

Howe, Ellic. THE MAGICIANS OF THE GOLDEN DAWN. London: Routledge & Kegan Paul, (1972). 1st ed. Fine in VG dj. *BLUE DRAGON.* $50

Howe, H. MEMOIRS OF THE MOST EMINENT AMERICAN MECHANICS...EUROPEAN MECHANICS. Harper, 1847. Good. *BOOKCELL.* $50

Howe, James Virgil. THE MODERN GUNSMITH. In Two Volumes. NY: Funk & Wagnalls Co. 1934. 1st ed. Presentation, inscribed. Djs. Slipcase. *KARMIOLE.* $75

Howe, Joseph. EXCESSIVE VENERY, MASTURBATION AND CONTINENCE. THE ETIOLOGY, PATHOLOGY AND TREATMENT OF THE DISEASES RESULTING FROM VENEREAL EXCESSES, MASTURBATION AND CONTINENCE. NY, 1883. 1st ed. *FYE.* $80

Howe, Julia Ward. FROM THE OAK TO THE OLIVE. Boston: Lea & Shepard, 1868. Maroon cl stamped in gilt and blind, worn, soiled, o/w VG. *SCHOYER'S.* $45

Howe, Julia Ward. FROM THE OAK TO THE OLIVE. Boston, 1868. vi,304pp. *O'NEILL.* $35

Howe, Maud. ROMA BEATA—LETTERS FROM THE ETERNAL CITY. Boston: Little, Brown, 1905. Red cl w/gilt titles, cvr dec. Bumped, shelfwear. VG. *PARMER.* $20

Howe, Octavius T. and Frederick C. Matthews. AMERICAN CLIPPER SHIPS 1833-1858. Volume I (-II) Salem, 1927-27. Pub. 13. 2 vols. Fine set. *LEFKOWICZ.* $300

Howe, R.H. and E. Sturtevant. THE BIRDS OF RHODE ISLAND. N.p., 1899. 6 plts. 111pp, cl. Ex-lib. *SUTTON.* $45

Howell, A.B. SPEED IN ANIMALS, THEIR SPECIALIZATION FOR RUNNING & LEAPING. Chicago: Univ of Chicago, 1944. 1st ed. VG+. *MIKESH.* $25

Howell, A.H. BIRDS OF ARKANSAS. Washington, 1911. Fldg map, 6 b/w plts. Binder's buckram. Soiling to cvrs; ex-lib. *SUTTON.* $30

Howell, Hamilton Grady, Jr. GOING TO MEET THE YANKEES. Jackson, MS, (1981). 1st ed. Fine in Fine dj. *McGOWAN*. $75

Howells, John Mead. THE ARCHITECTURAL HERITAGE OF THE PISCATAQUA. NY: Architectural Book Pub, 1937. 1st ed. VG, dj sl worn. *BACKROOM*. $120

Howells, V. A NATURALIST IN PALESTINE. London, 1956. Dj chipped. *SUTTON*. $28

Howells, William Dean. A LITTLE GIRL AMONG THE OLD MASTERS. Boston: Osgood, 1884. 1st ed. Blanck's state C (for identification only) w/title page and letter press ptd on laid paper throughout. 54 plts. Worn blue/grey cl. BAL 9612. Good. *SECOND LIFE*. $25

Howells, William Dean. MY MARK TWAIN. REMINISCENCES AND CRITICISMS. NY: Harper & Bros., 1910. 1st ed. Double-pg frontis w/tissue guard. 6 plts. Teg. Orig cl w/ornate gilt and red lettering. Fine. *CONNOLLY & WADE*. $45

Howells, William Dean. QUESTIONABLE SHARES. Harper, 1903. 1st ed. VG. *MADLE*. $35

Howells, William Dean. ROMAN HOLIDAYS AND OTHERS. NY: Harper, 1908. 1st trade ed. Attractive blue-grn cl stamped in gilt and red. BAL 9791. *SCHOYER'S*. $25

Howells, William Dean. THE LADY OF THE AROOSTOOK. Boston, 1879. 1st ed. Pict cl gilt. Spine and corners sl rubbed, spine little cocked, NF. BAL 9584. *POLYANTHOS*. $50

Howells, William Dean. THE RISE OF SILAS LAPHAM. Boston: Ticknor & Co., 1885. 515pp. Lightest of shelfwear, else bright, NF. 1st ed, 1st ptg, w/boxed ad at front headed "Mr. Howells's Latest Works," and w/"sojourner" perfectly ptd in last line of p. 176. BAL 9619. *CHAPEL HILL*. $275

Howells, William Dean. VENETIAN LIFE. Boston: Houghton Mifflin, 1892. 1st trade ed thus, w/color illus. 2 vols. White cl gilt, teg. Some lt spotting, else Fine set in orig unptd oilcloth djs. *CAPTAIN'S BOOKSHELF*. $75

Howie, Adda. MODERN FAIRY LORE. Milwaukee, 1890. Near 4to. 113pp. Illus. Cvrs have wear, few chips but VG+. *BEBBAH*. $25

Howitt, William (ed). THE BOY'S COUNTRY BOOK. London: Longman, Orme, Brown, Green and Longmans, 1839. 1st ed. 12mo; full contemp green calf; gilt panels, spine dec gilt to compartments, gilt dentelles, marbled edges; morocco label; engr vignettes throughout. Fine. *DRAMATIS PERSONAE*. $100

Howitt, William. HISTORY OF PRIESTCRAFT IN ALL AGES AND NATIONS.....London: Effingham Wilson, NY: for the bksellers, 1833. 1st US ed. Uncut. Orig faded cl, paper label. VG. *SECOND LIFE*. $75

Howland, Arthur (ed). MATERIALS TOWARD A HISTORY OF WITCHCRAFT COLLECTED BY HENRY CHARLES LEA. Phila, 1939. 1st ed. 3 vols. VF. *FYE*. $200

Howship, John. PRACTICAL OBSERVATIONS ON THE SYMPTOMS, DISCRIMINATION AND TREATMENT, OF SOME OF THE MOST IMPORTANT DISEASES OF THE LOWER INTESTINES AND ANUS. London, 1821. 2nd ed. Full leather, 240pp. VF. *FYE*. $200

Hoyle, Fred and N. C. Wickramasinghe. DISEASES FROM SPACE. J.M. Dent, London, 1979. Fine in Fine dj. *KNOLLWOOD*. $18

Hoyne, Thomas Temple. INTRIGUE ON THE UPPER LEVEL. Chicago: Reilly & Lee, 1934. 1st ed. Bkpl else VG+ in worn, trimmed dj completely backed w/brown paper. *OTHER WORLDS*. $40

Hoyne, Thomas. INTRIGUE ON THE UPPER LEVEL. Reilly & Lee, 1934. 1st ed. VG. *MADLE*. $35

Hoyt, Henry F. A FRONTIER DOCTOR. Chicago: The Lakeside Press, Christmas, 1979. Ed by Doyce B. Nunis, Jr. Rpt of 1929 1st ed. VG. *OUTPOST*. $25

Hoyt, Richard. 30 FOR A HARRY. NY: M. Evans, 1981. 1st ed. VF in dj. *MORDIDA*. $35

Hoyt, Richard. DECOYS. NY: M. Evans, 1980. 1st ed. VF in dj. *MORDIDA*. $35

Hrdlicka, Ales. ALASKA DIARY 1926-1931. Lancaster, PA, 1943. Spine faded. Worn dj. *ARTIS*. $40

Hrdlicka, Ales. ALASKA DIARY. Lancaster, PA: Jacques Cattell Press, 1943. Cl, dj. VG. *SCHOYER'S*. $60

Hrdlicka, Ales. ALASKA DIARY—1926-1931. Lancaster, PA: The Jacques Cattel Press, 1943. 1st ed. Minor wear bottom of spine, very minor sunning top of spine. NF in VG+ dj. *GREAT EPIC*. $75

Hrdlicka, Ales. PHYSIOLOGICAL AND MEDICAL OBSERVATIONS AMONG THE INDIANS OF SOUTHWESTERN UNITED STATES AND NORTHERN MEXICO. Washington, 1908. 1st ed. *FYE*. $100

Hrdlicka, Ales. SKELETAL REMAINS SUGGESTING OR ATTRIBUTED TO EARLY MAN IN NORTH AMERICA. BAE Bull 33. Washington: GPO, 1907. 1st ed. 21 plt, 16 figures. Unopened, untrimmed. NF in ptd wrappers. *CONNOLLY & WADE*. $85

Hrebelianovich, Princess Lazarovich. PLEASURES AND PALACES. NY: Century Co., 1915. 1st ed. Fine-. *AARD*. $30

Hubbard, Bernard R. MUSH, YOU MALAMUTES! NY, 1932. 1st ed. VG in dj. *ARTIS*. $18.50

Hubbard, Bert. IMPRESSIONS, BEING SHORT SKETCHES AND INTIMACIES CONCERNING ELBERT HUBBARD...(N.p.: The Roycrofters, 1921). 129pp. Inscribed. *OAK KNOLL*. $35

Hubbard, Elbert. LITTLE JOURNEYS TO THE HOMES OF FAMOUS WOMEN NY: The Roycrofters, 1908. Ltd ed. 1/4 suede, dk gray boards; hinges broken. *WEBER*. $35

Hubbard, John N. SKETCHES OF BORDER ADVENTURES IN THE LIFE AND TIMES OF MAJOR MOSES VAN CAMPEN....Bath, NY: Underhill, 1842. Early ed. 310pp. Orig cl, spine mended. Howes H752. *GINSBERG*. $200

Hubbard, L. Ron. DIANETICS. Hermitage, 1950. 1st ed. Notes in text, else VG in sl chipped dj. *MADLE*. $225

Hubbard, L. Ron. FINAL BLACKOUT. Hadley, 1948. 1st ed. Dj spine sl frayed, else Fine. *MADLE*. $300

Hubbard, L. Ron. RETURN TO TOMORROW. NY: Ace, (1954). 1st ed. Ace S-66. NF in wrappers. *OTHER WORLDS*. $45

Hubbard, L. Ron. THE KINGSLAYER. LA: Fantasy Publishing Co., 1949. 1st ed. VG in dj sl chipped & worn at edges, rear panel soiled. *BERNARD*. $100

Hubbard, L. Ron. TRITON AND BATTLE OF WIZARDS. LA: Fantasy Publishing Co., 1949. 1st ed, 1st binding. Bookplate on front pastedown o/w VG in Good dj which is moderately chipped at spine ends & corner tips, edges worn & rear panel soiled. *BERNARD*. $100

Hubbard, L. Ron. TYPEWRITER IN THE SKY (AND) FEAR. Gnome Press, 1951. 1st ed. NF in sl frayed dj. *MADLE*. $275

Hubbard, L. Ron. TYPEWRITER IN THE SKY (AND) FEAR. NY: Gnome, 1951. 1st ed. Fine in NF dj but for two small internal mends, and one short mend at top of front panel. *BEASLEY*. $150

Hubbard, P.M. KILL CLAUDIO. London: Macmillan, 1979. 1st ed. Fine in dj. *MORDIDA*. $45

Hubermont, Pierre. THIRTEEN MEN IN THE MINE. NY: Macmillan, 1931. 1st ed. Trans by L.H. Titterton. Light edgewear. *AKA*. $25

Hubert, Cam (Anne Cameron). DREAMSPEAKER. Toronto: Clarke Irwin, (1978). 1st ed. VG in dj. Uncommon. *LOPEZ*. $75

Huc, M. A JOURNEY THROUGH THE CHINESE EMPIRE. NY: Harper, 1855. 2 vols. 421, 422pp. Fldg map. Bound in 1/2 calf, lea labels, raised bands, marbled edges. *CULLEN*. $100

Hudson, Frederic. AN ACCOUNT OF THE MASSACRE AT LEXINGTON GREEN AND THE FIGHT AT CONCORD BRIDGE. Ashland: Oregon Book Society, 1976. Ltd to 350. VF. *OREGON*. $35

Hudson, Joshua Hilary. SKETCHES AND REMINISCENCES. Columbia, SC, 1903. 1st ed. Orig cl, flecked, a little worn. Howes H764. *GINSBERG*. $400

Hudson, Maxim. REMINISCENCES AND COMMENTS, AS REPORTED BY CLIFTON JOHNSON. GC, NY: Doubleday, Page & Co, 1924. 1st ed. Cvrs sl faded, front hinge cracked, else VG in worn dj, repaired. *WREDEN*. $40

Hudson, Tom. THREE PATHS ALONG A RIVER. Palm Desert: Desert-Southwest, (1964). 1st ed. Fine in VG dj. *BOOK MARKET*. $45

Hudson, W.H. A LITTLE BOY LOST. A.D. McCormick (illus). London: Duckworth, 1905. 1st ed. Lt foxing, spine darkened, but VG, bkpl. Pict cl, teg. *CAPTAIN'S BOOKSHELF*. $100

Hudson, W.H. and R.B. Cunningham Graham. GAUCHOS OF THE PAMPAS AND THEIR HORSES. Hanover, NH: Westholm, 1963. 1st ed. One of 400. Fine in dj w/short tear. Nice. *CAPTAIN'S BOOKSHELF*. $40

Hudson, W.H. DEAD MAN'S PLACK AND AN OLD THORN. London & Toronto: Dent, 1920. Bkpl, tiny bkseller's stamp, else NF. 1st ed. *CHAPEL HILL*. $45

Hudson, W.H. FAR AWAY AND LONG AGO. Illus by Raul Rosarivo. Buenos Aires: Ptd for LEC by Guillermo Kraft. 1943. Ltd to 1500 numbered, signed by Alberto Kraft (designer) and Rosarivo. Sl soiled, but decent. No slipcase. *KARMIOLE*. $125

Hudson, W.H. GREEN MANSIONS. London: Duckworth, 1904. Lightly soiled, eps foxed, hinges worn and tender, but VG. Custom grn cl chemise and quarter morocco slipcase. 1st ed, 1st issue, w/o blindstamped publisher's device on rear cvr. *CHAPEL HILL*. $350

Hudson, W.H. THE PURPLE LAND. London: Duckworth, (1911). 3rd imp. Fine. Inscribed from John Galsworthy to Ellen Glasgow w/Glasgow's bkpl. *CAPTAIN'S BOOKSHELF*. $375

Hueffer, Ford Madox. BETWEEN ST. DENNIS AND ST. GEORGE. A SKETCH OF THREE CIVILISATIONS. London: Hodder and Stoughton, 1915. Adv reading copy in printed gray wraps, NF but for wear and small chips to lower spine, tears to wallet edges of wraps. *BEASLEY*. $1000

Hueffer, Ford Madox. THE HEART OF THE COUNTRY. London, 1906. 1st ed. Teg, uncut, bkpl, scattered foxing, spine sl sunned, extrems sl rubbed. *POLYANTHOS*. $75

Hueffer, Oliver Madox. SOME OF THE ENGLISH. NY: Appleton, 1930. 1st Amer ed. Grn cl. VG in like dj. *DERMONT*. $35

Hufeland, Otto. WESTCHESTER COUNTY DURING THE AMERICAN REVOLUTION, 1775-1783. (NY: Knickbocker) privately printed, 1926. 1st ed. Errata laid in. Orig cl. One of 250 numbered. *GINSBERG*. $150

Huggins, Sir William and Lady. AN ATLAS OF REPRESENTATIVE STELLAR SPECTRA FROM 4870 TO 3300...PRECEDED BY A SHORT HISTORY OF THE OBSERVATORY AND ITS WORK. London: William Wesley, 1899. Laid in sheet with authors' address and "Presented by the authors, London, 1900." Later presented by W.G. Adams to King's College Library. Brown cloth. Hinges cracked, spine darkened & torn, corners bumped, stamps & lib markings. *KNOLLWOOD*. $420

Hugh Cowan. REPORT OF THE TRIAL OF JOHN THOMSON ALIAS PETER WALKER...FOR THE MURDER OF AGNES MONTGOMERY BY PRUSSIC ACID (ETC.). Thomas Constable and Co, Edinburgh, 1858. Title pg;leaf;(5)-103pp. Quite nice, in modern marbled wraps, and ptd paper label. *BOSWELL*. $225

HUGH JOHNSON'S POP-UP WINE BOOK. London, 1989. Ron Van der Meer. Pop-up bk. *BOOKFINDERS INTL*. $20

Hughes, Dorothy B. FALLEN SPARROW. NY: Duell, Sloan & Pearce, (1942). 1st ed. Front hinge split, some spots on binding. *SCHOYER'S*. $50

Hughes, Dorothy B. JOHNNIE. London: Nicolson & Watson, 1946. 1st British ed. Signed. Sl spine crease, minor wear o/w VG in sl worn dj. *SILVER DOOR*. $35

Hughes, Dorothy B. RIDE THE PINK HORSE. NY: DS&P, 1946. 1st ed. Page browning, else Fine; dj w/small chip. *ELSE FINE*. $45

Hughes, Dorothy B. RIDE THE PINK HORSE. NY: Duell, Sloan and Pearce, 1946. 1st ed. Pp darkened as usual o/w Fine in bright unfaded dj w/short closed tears, tiny wear at base of spine and spotting on inner back flap. *MORDIDA*. $75

Hughes, Dorothy B. THE BLACKBIRDER. NY: Duell, Sloan & Pearce, (1943). 1st ed. Chipped, creased dj, o/w VG. *SCHOYER'S*. $50

Hughes, Dorothy B. THE BLACKBIRDER. NY: Duell, Sloan and Pearce, 1943. 1st ed. VG in dj (wear spine ends, corners; several short closed tears). *MORDIDA*. $60

Hughes, Dorothy B. THE DELICATE APE. NY: Duell, Sloan and Pearce, 1944. 1st ed. VG in dj (minor wear spine ends, corners). *MORDIDA*. $45

Hughes, Dorothy B. THE SO BLUE MARBLE. NY: Duell, Sloane, & Pearce, 1940. 1st ed. Signed. Fine; minor wear to rear panel, 2 small chips front lower corners of dj. Owner's name, address. *ELSE FINE*. $400

Hughes, Elizabeth. CALIFORNIA OF THE PADRES; OR, THE FOOTPRINTS OF ANCIENT COMMUNISM. SF: I.N. Coynskl, 1875. Spine ends chipped. VG. *BOHLING*. $45

Hughes, John T. DONIPHAN'S EXPEDITION...Cincinnati: J.A. & U.P. James, 1848. 2nd ed. Plts. Newly bound. Map mentioned in title does not seem to ever have been present. Ex-lib. Howes H769. *HUDSON*. $150

Hughes, Katherine. FATHER LACOMBE. THE BLACK-ROBE VOYAGEUR. NY: Moffat, Yard and Company, 1911. 1st ed. General wear, inscribed in pencil ffep "from the authoress" (sic). *PARMER*. $50

Hughes, Langston (ed). NEW NEGRO POETS: USA. Bloomington: Indiana Univ Press, (1964). NF in dj. Inscribed May, 1964. *LOPEZ*. $350

Hughes, Langston. ASK YOUR MAMA: 12 MOODS FOR JAZZ. NY: Alfred A. Knopf, 1961. 1st ed. VG+ in dj w/chip at spine bottom & sl worn at edges. *BERNARD*. $125

Hughes, Langston. BLACK MISERY. NY, 1969. 1st ed. Illus by Arouni. Dj sl sunned, tiny nick top edge rear panel, price clipped. *POLYANTHOS*. $60

Hughes, Langston. FREEDOM'S PLOW. NY: Musette, 1943. 1st ed. NF in wrappers. Signed. *LOPEZ*. $375

Hughes, Langston. NOT WITHOUT LAUGHTER. NY: Knopf, 1941. Cheaply made Knopf "Alblabooks" reprint ed. Cl chipped at spine extrems, text sound. Good. *LOPEZ*. $20

Hughes, Langston. SELECTED POEMS. NY: Knopf, 1959. 1st ed. Fine in NF dj, light wear. *BEASLEY*. $125

Hughes, Langston. SHAKESPEARE IN HARLEM. NY: Knopf, 1942. 1st ed. Fine but for pencilling to one section and soiling to foot of spine. No dj. *BEASLEY*. $50

Hughes, Langston. SIMPLE SPEAKS HIS MIND. (NY): Simon & Schuster, (1950). 1st ed. Simultaneous softcover issue of this "Simple" novel. Cheap paper yellowing, o/w Fine in dj. *LOPEZ*. $40

Hughes, Langston. TAMBOURINES TO GLORY. NY: John Day Co., (1958). 1st ed. Orig black cl. VG to NF in bright dj, 2 1/2" tear (from which tape has been removed on recto) between spine, rear panel. *CHAPEL HILL*. $85

Hughes, Langston. THE BACKLASH BLUES. Detroit: Broadside, 1967. 1st ed. *BEASLEY.* $65

Hughes, Langston. THE LANGSTON HUGHES READER. Cl-backed boards, dj. NY: Braziller, 1958. 1st ed. Top edge spotted, o/w Fine. *JAFFE.* $65

Hughes, Langston. THE LANGSTON HUGHES READER....NY: George Braziller, 1958. 1st ed. Fine in dj (sm tears, lt wear). *CAPTAIN'S BOOKSHELF.* $60

Hughes, Langston. THE NEGRO MOTHER...(NY): The Golden Stair Press, (1931). 1st ed. Yellow pict wraps sl soiled w/sm edge tears, sm chip from bottom front corner. Signed. Owner annotations. *CAPTAIN'S BOOKSHELF.* $1750

Hughes, Langston. THE SWEET FLYPAPER OF LIFE. NY: Simon & Schuster, 1955. 1st ed. Issued in wrappers. Spine rubbed, affecting text, o/w VG. *LOPEZ.* $35

Hughes, Langston. THE SWEET FLYPAPER OF LIFE. NY: S&S, 1955. 1st ed. Hb issue, one of 2920 ptd. Fine in sl chipped dj. *CAPTAIN'S BOOKSHELF.* $175

Hughes, Mrs. Elizabeth. THE CALIFORNIA OF THE PADRES....SF: Choynski, 1875. 1st ed. 41pp. Ptd wraps. Interior back cvr has ad for Choynski 'Antiquarian Book Store.'Extrems sl browned, minor external wear. VG. *SECOND LIFE.* $125

Hughes, Richard. A HIGH WIND IN JAMAICA. London: Chatto & Windus, 1929. 1/150 numbered/signed. Fine, partially unopened. *DERMONT.* $300

Hughes, Ted. CROW. NY: Harper & Row, (1971). Dj in clear protective sleeve neatly taped to book, else Fine in dj. 1st Amer ed, later prtg. Inscribed. *CHAPEL HILL.* $40

Hughes, Ted. LUPERCAL. NY, (1960). 1st ed. Name. Fine in dj (spine little sunned, also top edge front panel, tiny edge nick rear panel). *POLYANTHOS.* $35

Hughes, Ted. THE EARTH-OWL AND OTHER MOON-PEOPLE. London, 1963. 1st ed. Illus R.A. Brandt. Fine in dj (tiny edge nick rear panel). *POLYANTHOS.* $60

Hughes, Ted. THE HAWK IN THE RAIN. NY: Harper (1957). 1st Amer ed. NF in dj. *DORN.* $120

Hughes, W.E. THE JOURNAL OF A GRANDFATHER. (St. Louis, privately ptd, 1912). 1st ed. 15 plts. Orig cl boards, spine faded. Full-pg presentation inscript. Probably less than 100 ptd. Howes C856. *GINSBERG.* $1500

Hughes, W.J. REBELLIOUS RANGER: RIP FORD AND THE OLD SOUTHWEST. Univ of Ok Press, 1964. 1st ed. Fine in NF sunned spine dj. *VARNER.* $75

Hugo, Richard. DEATH AND THE GOOD LIFE. NY: St. Martin's Press, 1981. 1st ed. VF in dj. *MORDIDA.* $50

Hugo, Richard. DEATH AND THE GOOD LIFE. NY: St. Martin's Press, 1981. 1st ed. Fine in dj w(short crease front panel). *MORDIDA.* $35

Hugo, Richard. ROAD ENDS AT TAHOLA. Pittsburg: Slow Loris Press, (1978). 1st ed. One of 64 numbered (ed of 1000) signed. Fine in ptd wraps. *CAPTAIN'S BOOKSHELF.* $75

Hugo, Victor. HISTORY OF A CRIME (DEPOSITION OF A WITNESS). NY, 1888. 1st US ed. 2 vols bound in one. NF. *POLYANTHOS.* $45

Hugo, Victor. NOTRE-DAME DE PARIS. Illus by Bernard Lamotte. Dec cl, glassine dj, slipcase. NY: LEC, 1955. Ltd to 1500 signed by Lamotte. VF. *JAFFE.* $85

Hugo, Victor. NOTRE-DAME DE PARIS. Jessie Haynes (trans), Justin O'Brien (intro). NY: LEC, 1950. One of 1500 illus, signed by Bernard LaMotte. Fine in a lightly worn slipcase. *CAPTAIN'S BOOKSHELF.* $85

Hugo, Victor. NOTRE-DAME OF PARIS. Paris: LEC, 1930. Illus by Frans Masereel. Ed ltd to 1500, signed by Masereel. Orig ptd wrappers. Housed in a folder and paper-covered slipcase (both somewhat cracked, as is very common with this set). The 2 vols Fine. *KARMIOLE.* $175

Hugo, Victor. TOILERS OF THE SEA. Verona: Printed at the Officina Bodoni for LEC, 1960. One of 1500 signed by Tranquillo Marangoni (illus), Giovanni Mardersteig (ptr). Fine in dj, slipcase. dj, sunned spine. *CAPTAIN'S BOOKSHELF.* $150

Huie, William Bradford. THE EXECUTION OF PRIVATE SLOVIK. Duell Sloan and Pierce, 1954. Advance reading copy. VG+ in wraps. Light rubbing to spine; partial glass stain on front panel. *STAHR.* $75

Huie, William Bradford. THE KLANSMAN. NY: Delacorte Press, (1967). Adv reading copy of 1st ed. Orig ptd grey wraps. Fine. *CHAPEL HILL.* $30

Huish, Marcus B. HAPPY ENGLAND. A&C Black, 1904. Reprint. VG-NF. *OLD LONDON.* $65

Hulaniski, F.J. (ed). THE HISTORY OF CONTRA COSTA COUNTY CALIFORNIA. In One Volume. Berkeley: The Elms Pub Co, Inc. 1917. Orig 1/2 calf over black cl, spine rebacked w/old calf laid down. *KARMIOLE.* $175

Hulbert, Archer Butler. FORTY-NINERS. THE CHRONICLE OF....Boston: Little, Brown, 1931. 1st ed. Grn cl over boards, gilt spine titles. NF. *PARMER.* $50

Hulbert, Archer Butler. FORTY-NINERS: THE CHRONICLE OF THE CALIFORNIA TRAIL. Boston: Little, Brown, 1931. 1st ed. VG. *LAURIE.* $20

Hulbert, Archer Butler. PATHS OF THE MOUND-BUILDING INDIANS AND GREAT GAME ANIMALS. Cleveland: Arthur H. Clark, 1902. 1st ed. 4 plts. VG. *SCHOYER'S.* $40

Hulbert, Archer. SOUTHWEST ON THE TURQUOISE TRAIL, THE FIRST DIARIES ON THE ROAD TO SANTA FE. Denver: Stewart Commission, (1933). 1st ed. Sm white stain on spine o/w VG. *OREGON.* $95

Hull, Denison Bingham. HOUNDS AND HUNTING IN ANCIENT GREECE. Chicago: Univ of Chicago, 1964. 1st ed. Some smudges to dj, else NF. *OLD LONDON.* $30

Hull, Edward. A TREATISE ON THE BUILDING AND ORNAMENTAL STONES OF GREAT BRITAIN AND FOREIGN COUNTRIES....London: Macmillan, 1872. 1st ed. 333pp. 2 tipped-in photos. Cl, worn at spine, corners, lib bkpls, stamps. *SECOND LIFE.* $150

Hulme, F.E. FAMILIAR WILD FLOWERS. London, c. 1875. 1st ed. 5 vols. 200 colored plts. Grn dec cl, lt wear to spine ends; emb stamp on plts, white numbers upper corner cvrs. Ex-lib. *SUTTON.* $115

Hulton, Ann. LETTERS OF A LOYALIST LADY: BEING THE LETTERS OF ANN HULTON....Boston: 1767-1776. Cambridge, Harvard, 1927. 1st ed. Orig cl spine over marbled boards. One of 750. *GINSBERG.* $50

Humbert, Claude (comp). LABEL DESIGN. NY: Watson-Guptill, (1972). 1st ed. Upper front cover bumped. Dj. *KARMIOLE.* $65

Hume, A. (comp). THE LEARNED SOCIETIES AND PRINTING CLUBS OF THE UNITED KINGDOM. London: Longman, Brown, Green, and Longmans, 1847. 1st ed. xxxii,307 (incl index), 32pp (publisher's list dated April 1847). Front joint cracked, else VG. *WREDEN.* $50

Hume, David. THE JAIL GATES ARE OPEN. NY: D. Appleton-Century, 1935. 1st Amer ed. Pub in Eng as The Gaol Gates Are Open. Fep and 1st 2pp have insect holes o/w VG in dj w/chipped spine ends and corners. *MORDIDA.* $25

Hume, David. THEY CALLED HIM DEATH. NY: D. Appleton-Century, 1935. 1st Amer ed. Fine in dj w/minor wear at spine ends and at corners and a couple of short closed tears. *MORDIDA*. $45

Hume, Ivor Noel. HISTORICAL ARCHAEOLOGY. NY: Knopf, 1969. 1st ed. Fine in Fine dj. *CONNOLLY & WADE*. $25

Humphrey, William. HOME FROM THE HILL. NY: Knopf, 1958. 1st ed. VF in dj. *ELSE FINE*. $85

Humphrey, William. THE ORDWAYS. Knopf, 1965. 1st. About Fine in dj. Spine of dj lightly sunned; two small chips at flyleaf folds. *STAHR*. $45

Humphrey, William. THE ORDWAYS. NY: Knopf, 1965. 1st ed. Orig red cl. Fine in NF dj (couple of clean tears, 2 1/4", 1/2", front panel. *CHAPEL HILL*. $30

Humphrey, William. THE ORDWAYS. NY: Knopf, 1965. 1st ed. VF in dj. *ELSE FINE*. $45

Humphrey, William. THE SPAWNING RUN. NY, 1970. 1st ed. Fine in price-clipped dj. *PETTLER*. $25

Humphreys, A(ndrew) A(tkinson) and H.L. Abbot. REPORT UPON THE PHYSICS & HYDRAULICS OF THE MISSISSIPPI RIVER. Phila, 1861. Fldg plts, maps, charts. Rebound in sturdy brn buckram, folio. Unopened, rubberstamp on title page & contents leaf. Nice. *BOHLING*. $350

Humphreys, Andrew A. THE VIRGINIA CAMPAIGN OF '64 AND '65, THE ARMY OF THE POTOMAC AND THE ARMY OF THE JAMES. NY, 1883. 1st ed. Fldg map. Minor cover wear o/w Fine. *PRATT*. $42.50

Humphreys, Charles A. FIELD, CAMP, HOSPITAL AND PRISON IN THE CIVIL WAR, 1861-1865. Boston, 1918. 1st ed. Shelfwear o/w Fine. *PRATT*. $85.

Humphreys, F.M.D. HUMPHREY'S HOMEOPATHIC MENTOR OR FAMILY ADVISER....NY: Humphrey's Homeo. Med. Co, 1915. 1st ed. Some wear to corners. Inner hinges carefully strengthened. Good+. *CONNOLLY & WADE*. $25

Humphreys, Josephine. DREAMS OF SLEEP. NY: Viking, (1984). 1st ed. Fine in dj. Signed. *CAPTAIN'S BOOKSHELF*. $75

Humphreys, Josephine. DREAMS OF SLEEP. NY: Viking, (1984). 1st ed. 1st bk. Signed. Orig blue, grn boards. Fine in dj (couple of tiny closed tears). *CHAPEL HILL*. $50

Humphreys, Josephine. DREAMS OF SLEEP. NY: Viking, (1984). 1st ed, 1st book. Signed. Fine in Fine dj. *ROBBINS*. $60

Humphreys, Josephine. RICH IN LOVE. NY, (1987). 1st ed. Fine in dj. Signed. *CAPTAIN'S BOOKSHELF*. $45

Humphreys, Josephine. RICH IN LOVE. NY: Viking, (1987). 1st ed. Signed. Fine in Fine dj. *ROBBINS*. $35

Humphreys, Josephine. RICH IN LOVE. Viking, 1987. Uncorrected proof. Fine in wraps. *STAHR*. $25

Humphreys, Josephine. THE FIREMAN'S FAIR. NY: Viking, (1991). 1st ed. Fine in dj. Inscribed. *CAPTAIN'S BOOKSHELF*. $30

Humphreys, Josephine. THE FIREMAN'S FAIR. NY: Viking, (1991). 1st Amer ed. Signed. Fine in dj. *DORN*. $35

Humphries, Jefferson. CONVERSATIONS WITH REYNOLDS PRICE. Jackson: Univ Press of Mississippi, (1991). 1st ed. As New in dj. Signed. *CAPTAIN'S BOOKSHELF*. $35

Humphries, W. J. RAIN MAKING AND OTHER WEATHER VAGARIES. Baltimore: Williams & Wilkins, 1926. VG in crisp maroon cl, bright gilt spine titling. *KNOLLWOOD*. $32

Hun, Henry. AN ATLAS OF THE DIFFERENTIAL DIAGNOSIS OF THE DISEASES OF THE NERVOUS SYSTEM. NY, 1914. 2nd ed. *FYE*. $40

Huncke, Herbert. GUILTY OF EVERYTHING. NY: Paragon, 1990. 1st ed. Review copy. Fine. *SMITH*. $30

Hungerford, Edward. LOCOMOTIVES ON PARADE. NY (1940), 1st ed, dj. *HEINOLDT*. $22

Hungerford, Edward. THE STORY OF THE WALDORF-ASTORIA. NY: Putnam's, 1925. 1st ed. Gilt cl, VG. *ARTIS*. $20

Hungerford, Edward. WELLS FARGO, ADVANCING THE AMERICAN FRONTIER. NY, (1949). 1st ed. 274pp. Dj wear o/w VG+. *PRATT*. $37.50

Hungerford, Edward. WELLS FARGO: ADVANCING THE AMERICAN FRONTIER. NY: Random House, (1941). 1st ed. Some small nicks and minor etchings in dj. VG in dj. *BOHLING*. $35

Hungry Wolf, Adolf. THE BLOOD PEOPLE. NY: H&R, (1977). 1st ed. Fine in NF dj. *LOPEZ*. $30

Hunnicutt, John L. RECONSTRUCTION IN WEST ALABAMA. Tuscaloosa, AL, 1959. 1st ed, ltd to 450. Wrappers, margins sunned, else NF. *McGOWAN*. $75

Hunphreys, H. Noel. A HISTORY OF THE ART OF PRINTING FROM ITS INVENTION TO ITS WIDE-SPREAD DEVELOPMENT IN THE MIDDLE OF THE SIXTEENTH CENTURY. London: Bernard Quaritch, 1868. Later quarter leather, top edge gilt. xvi,216pp. 100 photolitho facs. 2nd issue with section on references at end of book in the first issue suppressed because of errors. Ex-lib w/number on spine, perforated lib stamp on title page. *OAK KNOLL*. $200

Hunt, Aurora. KIRBY BENEDICT, FRONTIER FEDERAL JUDGE. A.H. Clark, 1961. 1st ed. Fldg map. Uncut and unopened. VF. *OREGON*. $27.50

Hunt, Aurora. MAJOR GENERAL JAMES HENRY CARLETON 1814-1873, WESTERN FRONTIER DRAGOON. Glendale, A.H. Clark, 1958. Fldg map.1st ed. VF. *OREGON*. $65

Hunt, Aurora. THE ARMY OF THE PACIFIC. ITS OPERATIONS IN CALIFORNIA, TEXAS, ARIZONA, NEW MEXICO, UTAH, NEVADA, OREGON, WASHINGTON, PLAINS REGION, MEXICO, ETC. 1860-1866. Glendale, A.H. clark, 1951. 1st ed. Fldg map. 1st ed. VF. *OREGON*. $150

Hunt, Aurora. THE ARMY OF THE PACIFIC: ITS OPERATIONS IN CALIFORNIA, TEXAS....MEXICO, ETC. 1860-1866. Glendale: Arthur H. Clark Co, 1951. 1st ed. VG. *BOOK MARKET*. $160

Hunt, Cornelius E. THE SHENANDOAH; OR, THE LAST CONFEDERATE CRUISER. NY, 1867. 1st ed. 270pp. Orig cl. Howes H799. *GINSBERG*. $125

Hunt, Elvid. HISTORY OF FORT LEAVENWORTH. Fort Leavenworth, KS, 1926. 2nd ed, (1937) updated by Walter E. Lorance. 301pp. Minor cover wear, o/w VG+. *PRATT*. $75

Hunt, Frazier. THE TRAGIC DAYS OF BILLY THE KID. NY: Hastings House Pubs, (1956). 1st ed. Maps. VG in dj. *OUTPOST*. $35

Hunt, J.H. Leigh. THE OLD COURT SUBURB. Phila & London, (1902). 2 vols. Teg. Gilt-pict bds. NF. *POLYANTHOS*. $75

Hunt, Rockwell. PERSONAL SKETCHES OF CALIFORNIA PIONEERS I HAVE KNOWN. Univ of Pacific, 1962. Ltd to 500. 1st ed. Fine. *OREGON*. $50

Hunt, Wilson Price. THE OVERLAND DIARY OF WILSON PRICE HUNT. Hoyt C. Franchere (trans, ed). Ashland: OR Book Soc, 1973. Ltd to 600 numbered. 1st thus. Fine. *OREGON*. $65

Hunter, Alan. GENTLY COLOURED. London: Cassell, 1969. 1st ed. Fine in dj. *SILVER DOOR*. $30

Hunter, Dard. MY LIFE WITH PAPER. NY: Knopf, 1958. 1st ed. Orig brownish red cl. NF in dj. Complete w/paper samples tipped in at p105 and p145. *CHAPEL HILL*. $125

Hunter, Dard. PAPERMAKING IN PIONEER AMERICA. Phila: Univ of PA Press. 1952. 1st ed. Fine. *KARMIOLE*. $125

Hunter, Dard. PAPERMAKING THROUGH EIGHTEEN CENTURIES. NY: William Edwin Rudge, 1930. 1st ed. Fldg frontis. Dj (thin mark on front). *DAWSON'S*. $200

Hunter, Dard. PAPERMAKING. THE HISTORY AND TECHNIQUE OF AN ANCIENT CRAFT. 2nd ed, rev, enl. London: Pleiades Books. 1947. Fldg diagram, fldg map. Blue cl, gilt spine. Dj (lg chip missing base of spine, top of spine). *KARMIOLE*. $125

Hunter, Donald. THE DISEASES OF OCCUPATIONS. Boston, 1959. 2nd ed. *FYE*. $75

Hunter, Evan. LAST SUMMER. GC: Doubleday, 1968. 1st ed. Review stamp. VF in Fine dj. *AARD*. $25

Hunter, J. Marvin (comp and ed). THE TRAIL DRIVERS OF TEXAS...Pub under the direction of George W. Saunders. Nashville: Cokesbury, 1925. 2nd ed rev, 2 vols in 1. xvi,1044pp. Port frontis. Dark blue cl over boards, front cover and spine lettered in gold. Sl foxing to eps, some edgewear. *BOOKMINE*. $250

Hunter, J. Marvin. THE TRAIL DRIVERS OF TEXAS. N.p., 1920. 1st ed. Vol 1 only. 498pp. Fine. *OREGON*. $175

Hunter, J. Marvin. THE TRAIL DRIVERS OF TEXAS. N.p., 1920 & 1923. 1st eds. 2 vols. 498, 496pp. Vol. 1 Fine, Vol. 2 Good+. Howes H816. *OREGON*. $395

Hunter, J.A. HUNTER. NY: Harper & Brothers, 1952. 1st ed. Fine in NF dj. *GREAT EPIC*. $65

Hunter, J.A. HUNTER'S TRACKS. NY: Appleton-Century-Crofts, 1957. 1st ed. Fine in VG dj. *GREAT EPIC*. $55

Hunter, John. A TREATISE ON THE BLOOD, INFLAMMATION, AND GUN-SHOT WOUNDS. Phila, 1840. 1/2 lea, 611pp. *FYE*. $200

Hunter, John. A TREATISE ON THE BLOOD, INFLAMMATION, AND GUN-SHOT WOUNDS. Phila, 1817. 2nd Amer ed. Full lea, 514pp + 8 engrvd plts. Spine label missing, signature of orig owner marked through on title page. Contents VG. *FYE*. $500

Hunter, John. ESSAYS AND OBSERVATIONS ON NATURAL HISTORY, ANATOMY PHYSIOLOGY, PSYCHOLOGY, AND GEOLOGY, BEING THE POSTHUMOUS PAPERS ON THOSE SUBJECTS. Arranged and rev. by Richard Owen. London, 1861. 1st ed. 2 vols. 403pp, 507pp. Orig cloth, skillfully recased. Geoffrey Jefferson's copy w/his bkpl. *FYE*. $300

Hunter, John. LECTURES ON THE PRINCIPLES OF SURGERY. Phila, 1839. 404pp. Bound with THE LIFE OF JOHN HUNTER BY Drewry Ottley, 139pp. *FYE*. $150

Hunter, John. OBSERVATIONS ON CERTAIN PARTS OF THE ANIMAL OECONOMY. Phila, 1840. Recent buckram, 479pp. *FYE*. $75

Hunter, John. WORKS OF JOHN HUNTER. FOUR VOLUMES. Phila, 1839. 1st Amer ed. 1/2 leather, various paginations. Bindings rubbed, some boards detached. Contents foxed, but o/w VG. *FYE*. $250

Hunter, Kenneth (ed). THE WAR AGAINST GERMANY: EUROPE AND ADJACENT AREAS. Washington: Dept of the Army/USGPO, 1951. 1st ed. Near VG. *ARCHER*. $25

Hunter, Robert Jr. QUEBEC TO CAROLINA IN 1785-1786. Louis B. Wright, Marion Tinling (eds). San Marino, CA: The Huntington Lib, 1943. 1st ed. Dj. *KARMIOLE*. $35

Huntford, Roland. SHACKLETON. NY: Antheneum, 1986. 1st Amer ed. Fine in Fine dj. *BLUE DRAGON*. $40

Huntington, A.O. STUDIES OF TREES IN WINTER....Boston, 1902 (1901). 12 colored plts. Cl, lt wear, spine end frayed. *SUTTON*. $35

Huntington, Bill. BILL HUNTINGTON'S GOOD MEN AND SALTY CUSSES. Billings, (1952). 1st ed. Signed. VG in tape repaired dj. Does not have limitation colophon pasted to rear flyleaf. *OREGON*. $45

Huntington, D.W. OUR BIG GAME. 16 photos. NY, 1904. Pict cl. Lt edge wear; scattered, emb lib stamps; 4 pp w/sm stain on margin. *SUTTON*. $37

Huntington, Ellsworth. THE CLIMATIC FACTOR AS ILLUSTRATED IN ARID AMERICA. Washington D.C.: Carnegie Institution, 1914. 90 figs, 12 plts, 2 maps. Good. *ARCHAEOLOGIA*. $150

Huntington, Gale. SONGS THE WHALEMEN SANG. Barre Pubs, 1964. 1st ed. VF in Fine dj. *OREGON*. $45

Hurd, C.W. BENTS STOCKADE, HIDDEN IN THE HILLS. Las Animas. 1st ed. VG. *OREGON*. $30

Hurd, Edith & Clement Hurd. THE BLUE HERON TREE. Viking, 1968. 1st ed. 66pp. Illus Clement Hurd and signed by both. VG+ in dj w/edgewear, one short tear. *BEBBAH*. $30

Hurd-Mead, Kate Campbell. A HISTORY OF WOMEN IN MEDICINE FROM THE EARLIEST TIMES TO THE BEGINNING OF THE NINETEENTH CENTURY. Haddam, 1938. 1st ed. Ex-lib. *FYE*. $225

Hurley, P.J. IN SEARCH OF AUSTRALIA. Sidney: Dymocks Book Arcade, 1943. Paper very age-darkened; small marginal dampstain. Dj chipped. *PARMER*. $25

HURRAY WE'RE MOVING! London, (1950). Band that was around (?) bk, now stuck inside front cover, explaining the bk. 7 illus story pp, 7pp into which cut-outs have been inserted (and can be removed). Fine, all pieces intact. Cut-out bk. *BOOKFINDERS INTL*. $150

Hurston, Zora Neale. I LOVE MYSELF WHEN I AM LAUGHING. Ed by Alice Walker. (Old Westbury): Feminist Press, (1979). 1st ed. The issue in wrappers. VG. Uncommon in any ed. *LOPEZ*. $85

Hurston, Zora Neale. JONAH'S GOURD VINE. London: Duckworth, (1934). 1st Eng ed. NF lacking dj. *CAPTAIN'S BOOKSHELF*. $300

Hurston, Zora Neale. JONAH'S GOURD VINE. Phila: Lippincott, 1971. 1st ed. 2 corners sl bumped, else Fine in dj, sm tears. *CAPTAIN'S BOOKSHELF*. $100.

Hurston, Zora Neale. JONAH'S GOURD VINE. Phila: Lippincott 1934. Exceedingly scarce 1st bk. VG w/o dj. *LOPEZ*. $1,000

Hurston, Zora Neale. MULES AND MEN. Phila: Lippincott, 1935. 1st ed. VG lacking dj. *CAPTAIN'S BOOKSHELF*. $250

Hurston, Zora Neale. TELL MY HORSE. Phila: Lippincott, (1938). 1st ed. Lt wear head of spine, corners, else NF lacking dj. *CAPTAIN'S BOOKSHELF*. $250

Hurston, Zora Neale. THE MAN OF THE MOUNTAIN. London: Dent, (1941). 1st Eng ed. About Fine in edgeworn dj (several sm chips; tear front panel). *CAPTAIN'S BOOKSHELF*. $750

Hurston, Zora Neale. VOODOO GODS....London: Dent, (1939). 1st UK ed. NF, owner sig, lacking dj. *CAPTAIN'S BOOKSHELF*. $175.

Hurter, Albert. HE DREW AS HE PLEASED. NY: Simon & Schuster, (1948). 1st ed. Spine ends frayed. Good, sound. *ARTIS*. $40

Husmann, G. AMERICAN GRAPE GROWING AND WINE MAKING....1890 (1883). 2nd ed. Orig gilt dec cl (worn, front cover scuffed); 2 joints cracked, shaken; ex-lib. *SUTTON*. $35

Hussey, C. ENGLISH GARDENS AND LANDSCAPES, 1700-1750. NY, 1967. Cl, dj. *SUTTON*. $150

Hutchings, J.M. IN THE HEART OF THE SIERRAS: THE YOSEMITE VALLEY....Oakland: Pacific Press, 1886. 1st ed. Mint. *BOOK MARKET*. $600

Hutchings, J.M. SCENES OF WONDER AND CURIOSITY IN CALIFORNIA. NY: A. Roman and Co, 1872. 292pp + 4pp ads. Gold stamped cl, spine sl sunned, lt wear. *DAWSON'S*. $100

Hutchings, J.M. SCENES OF WONDER AND CURIOSITY IN CALIFORNIA. SF: Hutchings & Rosenfield (1860) 1st ed. 236pp. 92 engr. Bound in full calf binding stamped in gold, worn at extrems of spine. Owner presentation. Foxing, soiling. Good. Couple of signatures pulled, Good in presentation binding. *SECOND LIFE*. $350

Hutchinson, Isobel Wylie. NORTH TO THE RIME-RINGED SUN...London: Blackie & Son, 1935. 262pp + ads, fldg map. 2nd ed. Inscrip, signed. Review tipped-in. NF in VG+ dj. *GREAT EPIC.* $45

Hutchinson, Isobel Wylie. STEPPING STONES FROM ALASKA TO ASIA. London: Blackie & Son, 1937. 246pp. 1st ed. Autographed note signed by author tipped-in. Minor foxing prelims and fore-edge. NF in VG+ dj. *GREAT EPIC.* $95

Hutchinson, W.H. A BAR CROSS MAN. Norman: Univ of OK Press, (1956). Cloth in dj. 2 maps, 1st ed. Signed. *DAWSON'S.* $50

Hutchinson, W.H. A NOTEBOOK OF THE OLD WEST. Designed, ptd at Chico, CA By Bob Hurst for author. 1947. 1st ed. H.D. Bugbee (illus). Pict wrappers. About Fine. Scarce. *CONNOLLY & WADE.* $85

Hutchinson, W.H. ANOTHER NOTEBOOK OF THE OLD WEST. Chico, CA: Hurst & Yount, (1954). 1st ed. Stapled wraps. VG. *OREGON.* $40

Hutchinson, W.H. THE WORLD, THE WORK AND THE WEST OF W. H. D. KOERNER. U of Okla (1978), 1st ed, dj. *HEINOLDT.* $50

Hutchinson, Woods. THE DOCTOR IN WAR. Boston, 1918. 1st ed. Scarce. *FYE.* $100

Hutt, Allen. POST-WAR HISTORY OF THE BRITISH WORKING CLASS. NY: Coward-McCann, 1938. 1st ed. VG. *AKA.* $25

Hutton, Edward. GLIMPSES OF GREECE. London: Medici Society, 1928. Spine faded. Fldg map. *SCHOYER'S.* $35

Hutton, Edward. IN UNKNOWN TUSCANY. London, 1909. 3/4 lea, teg. Rubbing front hinge. *POLYANTHOS.* $50

Hutton, Edward. IN UNKNOWN TUSCANY. London: Methuen (1909). 1st ed. Almost Fine. *AARD.* $30

Hutton, H. VIGILANTE DAYS....Sage Books, 1978. 1st ed. Fine in Fine dj. *VARNER.* $25

Hutton, Harold. DOC MIDDLETON, LIFE AND LEGENDS OF THE NOTORIOUS PLAINS OUTLAW. Chicago, (1974). 1st ed. 290pp. VG+ in dj. *PRATT.* $25

Huxley, Aldous. ALONG THE ROAD. NOTES AND ESSAYS OF A TOURIST. London: Chatto & Windus, 1925. 1st ed. Spine faded, bkpl removed, lacks dj. *WOOLMER.* $20

Huxley, Aldous. ARABIA INFELIX, AND OTHER POEMS. NY: Fountain Press, London: Chatto & Windus, 1929. One of 692, signed. This copy noted "Out of series." Uncut, cl backed boards. Nice. *SECOND LIFE.* $125

Huxley, Aldous. BEYOND THE MEXIQUE BAY. NY: Harper, (1936). 1st ed. 30pp b/w plts. Lt cvr wear; contents VG. *SILVER.* $25

Huxley, Aldous. BRAVE NEW WORLD. (Avon, CT): LEC, 1974. One of 1500 illus, signed by Mary McAfee. Fine in slipcase. *CAPTAIN'S BOOKSHELF.* $125

Huxley, Aldous. BRAVE NEW WORLD. London: Chatto & Windus, 1932. 1st ed, trade issue. Spine sl cocked, o/w Fine in dj (sl wear at the head of spine, short closed tear at top of front panel of dj). *JAFFE.* $875

Huxley, Aldous. BRAVE NEW WORLD. London: Chatto & Windus, 1932. 1st ed. #211 of 324 specially bound lg paper, signed. Orig yellow buckram, bevelled edges, leather spine label, teg. Bkpl, but Fine, untrimmed, unopened. Custom brn cl clamshell box w/leather spine label. *CHAPEL HILL.* $3,500

Huxley, Aldous. BRAVE NEW WORLD. London: Chatto & Windus, 1932. 1st trade ed. Orig blue cl. NF in nice, VG dj expertly repaired along fold between front panel, spine. *CHAPEL HILL.* $500

Huxley, Aldous. BRIEF CANDLES. London: Chatto & Windus, 1930. 1st ed. Cl, dj. Fine. *JAFFE.* $125

Huxley, Aldous. BRIEF CANDLES. NY: Fountain Press, 1930. 1/800 numbered/signed. VF in orig torn glassine dj. *DERMONT.* $200

Huxley, Aldous. COLLECTED ESSAYS. NY, (1959). 1st ed. Fine in dj (spine sl sunned, extremities, spine sl rubbed). *POLYANTHOS.* $25

Huxley, Aldous. DO WHAT YOU WILL. London: Chatto & Windus, 1929. 1st ed. Fine. Lacks dj. *WOOLMER.* $25

Huxley, Aldous. DO WHAT YOU WILL. London: Chatto & Windus, 1929. 1st trade ed. NF in lightly used dj w/darkened spine. *JUVELIS.* $150

Huxley, Aldous. DO WHAT YOU WILL. London: Chatto & Windus, 1929. 1st ed. Fine in dj sl darkened at spine. *JAFFE.* $125

Huxley, Aldous. ENDS AND MEANS. AN ENQUIRY....NY.: Chatto & Windus, 1937. 1st ed. Cl, dj. Fine. *JAFFE.* $100

Huxley, Aldous. EYELESS IN GAZA. London: Chatto & Windus, 1936. 1st trade ed. Fine in dj. *JUVELIS.* $275

Huxley, Aldous. HEAVEN & HELL. London: Chatto & Windus, 1956. 1st ed. VG in mildly spine-sunned, edgeworn dj. *LOPEZ.* $45

Huxley, Aldous. ISLAND. London: Chatto & Windus, 1962. 1st ed. Fine in price-clipped dj (2 tears, darkened spine). *CAPTAIN'S BOOKSHELF.* $75

Huxley, Aldous. LEDA. Engrs by Eric Gill. GC, NY: Doubleday, Doran & Co, Inc, 1929. Ltd to 361 numbered, signed. Few minor stains. Slipcase sl soiled. *KARMIOLE.* $200

Huxley, Aldous. LEDA. London: Chatto & Windus, 1920. 1st ed, ltd to 160 signed. Orig boards, linen backstrip. Lt wear. *CULLEN.* $150

Huxley, Aldous. LITTLE MEXICAN & OTHER STORIES. London: Chatto & Windus, 1924. 1st ed, w/top edge stained crimson. Orig red cl, paper spine label. Fine in dj. *CHAPEL HILL.* $200

Huxley, Aldous. MORTAL COILS. London: Chatto, (1922). 1st ed. VG+ in VG dj lightly chipped at spine ends. *UNGER.* $125

Huxley, Aldous. MUSIC AT NIGHT AND OTHER ESSAYS, NY: Fountain Press, 1931. 1/800 numbered/signed. VF in torn orig glassine. *DERMONT.* $200

Huxley, Aldous. MUSIC AT NIGHT AND OTHER ESSAYS. London, 1931. 1st ed. Cvrs sl edge sunned. Dj spine sunned; little rubbed, sl chipped. *POLYANTHOS.* $60

Huxley, Aldous. POINT COUNTER POINT. London: Chatto & Windus, 1928. 1st ed. Spine little faded; name inked out. Lacks dj. *WOOLMER.* $25

Huxley, Aldous. THE CICADAS AND OTHER POEMS. GC: Doubleday, 1931. 1st US ed. Spine faded; some wear to dj. *WOOLMER.* $25

Huxley, Aldous. THE CICADAS AND OTHER POEMS. London, 1931. 1st ed. Spine little sunned. NF. *POLYANTHOS.* $30

Huxley, Aldous. THE CICADAS AND OTHER POEMS. NY, 1931. 1st ed. Sl offsetting front and rear eps. Fine in dj (spine little sunned, top tiny chip). *POLYANTHOS.* $100

Huxley, Aldous. THE DEVILS OF LOUDUN. Harper & Brothers, 1952. 1st Amer. ed. NF in VG+ dj (chipped head, foot of spine). *STAHR.* $25

Huxley, Aldous. THE DEVILS OF LOUDUN. London, 1952. 1st ed. NF. *McCLINTOCK.* $15

Huxley, Aldous. THE GENIUS AND THE GODDESS. Harper, 1955. 1st Amer ed. NF in worn & soiled dj. *STAHR.* $20

Huxley, Aldous. THE WORLD OF LIGHT. London, 1931. 1st ed. Sl offsetting ffep. Dj spine sl sunned. *POLYANTHOS.* $75

Huxley, Aldous. THE WORLD OF LIGHT. London: Chatto & Windus, 1931. 1st ed. Fine in dj that is darkened and w/minor chipping at head of spine. *WOOLMER.* $35

Huxley, Aldous. TWO OR THREE GRACES AND OTHER STORIES. London: Chatto & Windus, 1926. 1st ed. Fine in dj faintly darkened at spine. *JAFFE.* $125

Huxley, Aldous. WHAT ARE YOU GOING TO DO ABOUT IT? THE CASE FOR CONSTRUCTIVE PEACE. London: Chatto & Windus, 1936. 1st ed. Stapled wrappers, light overall soiling, staples rusted. *DAWSON'S.* $75

Huxley, Aldous. WORDS AND THEIR MEANINGS. LA: The Ward Ritchie Press. 1940. 1st ed. Title pg ptd in black and peach. Gray boards stamped in blue and peach. Dj. Tls laid in signed by Ritchie discussing ed size (1100). *KARMIOLE.* $50

Huxley, Elspeth. NEW EARTH: AN EXPERIMENT IN COLONIALISM. London: Chatto & Windus, (1960). Chipped torn dj, o/w VG. *SCHOYER'S.* $20

Huxley, Elspeth. THEIR SHINING ELDORADO. A JOURNEY THROUGH AUSTRALIA. NY: William Morrow & Co Inc, 1967. Good+, very worn dj. *PARMER.* $35

Huxley, L. LIFE & LETTERS OF THOMAS HENRY HUXLEY. 2 vols. London: Macmillan, 1900. 1st Eng ed. Cvrs darkened, sm tear, new end leaves. Good+. *BOOKCELL.* $40

Huxley, T.H. AN INTRODUCTION TO THE CLASSIFICATION OF ANIMALS. 47 text-figures. London, 1869. 1st separate ed. Pp (5),147, (40 pp catalog dated Jan. 1872). Orig cl. Worn; some backstrip splitting; front joint very open; shaken. *SUTTON.* $75

Huxley, T.H. AN INTRODUCTION TO THE CLASSIFICATION OF ANIMALS. London: Churchill, 1869. 147pp, 1st ed. Rebacked with old backstrip label, new end leaves. Good. *BOOKCELL.* $50

Huxley, T.H. ESSAYS UPON SOME CONTROVERTED QUESTIONS. London: Macmillan, 1892. 1st ed. 625pp. Good. *BOOKCELL.* $65

Huxley, T.H. EVIDENCE AS TO MAN'S PLACE IN NATURE. Appleton, 1863. 1st Amer ed. Paper label on backstrip almost illegible, cvrs worn, most leaves dampstained, not affecting text. Good. *BOOKCELL.* $40

Huxley, Thomas. THE SCIENTIFIC MEMOIRS OF THOMAS HENRY HUXLEY. Ed. by Michael Foster and E. Ray Lankester. London, 1898-1902. 1st ed. 5 vols. 2529pp, more than 100 plts (many fldg). Ex-lib. *FYE.* $400

Hyams, Edward. GREAT BOTANICAL GARDENS OF THE WORLD. (London): Nelson, (1969). 1st ed. Dj. Fine. *WREDEN.* $50

Hyams, Edward. MELONS UNDER CLOCHES. London: Faber, 1952. As New in dj. *AMERICAN BOTANIST.* $28

Hyde, George. INDIANS OF THE HIGH PLAINS...TO THE COMING OF THE EUROPEANS. Univ of OK, (1959). 1st ed. VF in VF dj. *OREGON.* $35

Hyde, H. Montgomery. PRINCESS LIEVEN. Boston: Little, Brown, 1938. 1st ed. VG in VG dj. Name, bkpl. *AARD.* $20

Hyde, H. Montgomery. SOLITARY IN THE RANKS. NY: Atheneum 1978. 288 pp. 1st US ed. Fine in Fine dj. *GREAT EPIC.* $45

Hyde, Philip. DRYLANDS: THE DESERTS OF NORTH AMERICA. San Diego: Yolla Bolly Press, (1987). 1st ed.. Fine in Fine dj. *BOOK MARKET.* $100

Hyde, Walter W. ANCIENT GREEK MARINERS. Oxford, 1947. Dj. *O'NEILL.* $25

Hyer, Helen Von Kolnitz. SANTEE SONGS. Columbia, SC: The State Company, 1923. 1st ed. Frontis. Orig cl-backed boards w/paper label. NF in browned and edgeworn dj chipped at spine ends. *CHAPEL HILL.* $75

Hyer, Julien. THE LAND OF BEGINNING AGAIN: THE ROMANCE OF THE BRAZOS. Atlanta: Tupper & Love, (1952). 24 full-pg illus. Pict cl in lightly chipped dj. *DAWSON'S.* $35

Hylander, Charles J. CRUISERS OF THE AIR....NY: Macmillan, 1931. 1st ed. Orig pict cl, a few black numbers on spine, bkpl removed, sm emb lib stamp. *GINSBERG.* $100

Hyman, L.H. THE INVERTEBRATES: ECHINODERMATA, THE COELOMATE BILATERIA. NY, 1955. Bkplt. *SUTTON.* $45

Hyman, L.H. THE INVERTEBRATES: PROTOZOA THROUGH CTENOPHORA. NY, (1940). *SUTTON.* $65

Hynd, Alan. ARRIVAL 12:30. THE BALTIMORE PLOT AGAINST LINCOLN. NJ: Nelson, 1967. 1st ed. Fine in NF dj. *CONNOLLY & WADE.* $20

Hynes, Michael J. THE MISSION OF RINUCCINI, NUNCIO EXTRAORDINARY TO IRELAND 1645-1649. Dublin: Browne & Nolan Ltd. 1932. Frontis, color map. Grn cl, gilt. *KARMIOLE.* $35

Hyslop, James. ENIGMAS OF PSYCHICAL RESEARCH. Boston, 1906. 1st ed. *FYE.* $75

I

Ibn Arabshah, Ahmed. TAMERLANE OR TIMUR THE GREAT AMIR. London: Luzac & Co, 1936. Trans J.H. Sanders. Blue cl stamped in gilt, fairly faded. Some foxing. Frontis illus, 2pp line map. *SCHOYER'S.* $35

Ibn Haukal. THE ORIENTAL GEOGRAPHY OF EBN HAUKAL, AN ARABIAN TRAVELLER OF THE TENTH CENTURY. Trans from a Manuscript in His Own Possession, Collated with One Preserved in the Library of Eton College, by Sir William Ouseley. London: Ptd at the Oriental Press for T. Cadell, Jun. and W. Davies. 1800. 1st ed in English. 4to. xxxvi,328pp. Index. Fldg map frontis. Contemp vellum over boards, uncut, largely unopened. In custom-made vellum backed fldg box. *KARMIOLE.* $1,250

Ibsen, Henrik. THE WORKS OF HENRIK IBSEN. The Viking Edition. NY: Scribner's, 1911-12. 13 vols. Gilt-lettered cloth; spines sunned; gravure frontispieces, photo plts; teg. About Fine. *DRAMATIS PERSONAE.* $225

IDAHO. NY, 1950. American Guide Series. WPA guide. 2nd ed. W/dj. Fine. *SCHOYER'S.* $35

Idriess, Ion L. FLYNN OF THE INLAND. Sydney: Angus & Robertson, 1934. Some cvr wear, offset to ep, overall VG. *PARMER.* $30

Ignatow, David. THE GENTLE WEIGHT LIFTER. (N.p.): Morris Gallery (1955). 1st ed. Less than 650 bound. Fine in NF dj (1/4" chip missing front panel). *DORN.* $300

Ii, John Papa. FRAGMENTS OF HAWAIIAN HISTORY. Bishop Mus.: n.p, 1953. 1st ed. Mary Kawena Pukui (trans), D.B. Barrere (ed). Stiff wraps. Front corners of spine worn, else VG. *CONNOLLY & WADE.* $35

Ikbal Ali Shah, Sirdar. THE GOLDEN EAST. London: Long, 1931. 1st ed. 32 plts. Ffep clipped. Ex-lib, o/w VG. *WORLDWIDE.* $25

Iliff, Flora Gregg. PEOPLE OF THE BLUE WATER. NY: Harper, 1954. VG, dj. *BURCHAM.* $25

Illingworth, Frank. FALCONS AND FALCONRY. London: Blandford Press, n.d. Probable 1st ed. Dj only fair, else VG. *OLD LONDON.* $20

Imes, Birney. JUKE JOINT. Jackson: Univ Press of Mississippi, (1990). 1st ed. Ltd to 100 numbered signed. Dj, slipcase. Mint. *JAFFE.* $225

Imhof, T.A. ALABAMA BIRDS. University, 1962. 43 plts. Bkpl; minor pg sticking. *SUTTON.* $45

Imison, John. ELEMENTS OF SCIENCE AND ART; BEING A FAMILIAR INTRODUCTION TO NATURAL PHILOSOPHY

AND CHEMISTRY, TOGETHER WITH THEIR APPLICA-
TION TO A VARIETY OF ELEGANT AND USEFUL ARTS. 2
vols. London: Cadell & Davies, 1808. New ed, enl, adapted by
Thomas Webster. Vol I has 25 plts (2 are numbered IV, 10 are
fldg); Vol II has 7 plts. VG, rebound in 1/4 cl & marbled boards
w/new eps; page edges browned. *KNOLLWOOD.* $250

IMPERIAL FRESNO: RESOURCES, INDUSTRIES AND
SCENERY ILLUSTRATED AND DESCRIBED. Fresno: Fresno
Republican, 1897. 144,(4)pp, photo illus in text. Dec boards
w/leather spine, boards and spine stamped in mock-crocodile pattern. Light wear to extremities, some soiling to boards and title pg,
one leaf a bit loose. *DAWSON'S.* $100

IN MEMORIAM. ERASTUS BLAKESLEE, 1838-1908. (N.p.), pub
for private distribution, (1908). 1st ed. 34pp. Orig printed wrappers.
GINSBERG. $75

Inchbold, A.C. UNDER THE SYRIAN SUN. THE LEBANON,
BAALBEC, GALILEE AND JUDEA. London, 1906. 40 full-pg
plts. 2 vols. viii,262pp; viii,266pp. Very Nice. *O'NEILL.* $85

INCIDENTS OF A TRIP THROUGH THE GREAT PLATTE
VALLEY...IN THE FALL OF 1866. (By Silas Seymour). NY,
1867. 1st ed. 129pp. Orig brown cl, gilt stamp on front cover. Inscribed, signed. Nice. Howes S315. *BOHLING.* $350

INCIDENTS OF TRAVEL IN EGYPT, ARABIA, PETRAEA,
AND THE HOLY LAND. By an American. NY, 1842. (By John
Lloyd Stephens). 10th ed. 2 vols. 240 and 286 pp. VF. *O'NEILL.* $125

Inderwick, Surgeon James. CRUISE OF THE U.S. BRIG ARGUS
IN 1813. JOURNAL OF SURGEON JAMES INDERWICK. NY:
NY Public Lib, 1917. Ptd wraps somewhat chipped and age-
darkened, overall VG. *PARMER.* $45

INDIAN PAINTING: THE LIGHTS OF CANOPUS. NY & Lon-
don, (ca 1930). 36 tipped-in full-color miniatures. Teg. NF. *POLYAN-
THOS.* $75

INDIANA AT CHICKAMAUGA, 1863. Indianapolis, 1900. 1st ed.
Separate map missing. Fine. *PRATT.* $30

Ingalls, Raymond. TUMORS OF THE ORBIT AND ALLIED
PSEUDO TUMORS, AN ANALYSIS OF 216 CASE HIS-
TORIES. Springfield, 1953. 1st ed. 140 illus. Dj. *FYE.* $50

Ingersoll, Charles (Jared, Jr.). FEARS FOR DEMOCRACY
REGARDED FROM THE AMERICAN POINT OF VIEW.
Phila: Lippincott, 1875. 1st ed. Bevelled cl sl rubbed, stained. Spine
sl faded. Spine tip wear. Foxing, pencilling in text, o/w VG. *DIAMOND.*
$50

Ingersoll, Chester. OVERLAND TO CALIFORNIA IN 1847.
Chicago: Black Cat Press. 1937. 1st ed. Ed ltd to 350. Spine sl
soiled. *KARMIOLE.* $50

Ingersoll, E. (ed). ALASKAN BIRD LIFE. NY, 1914. 1st ed. Good+
to VG+. *MIKESH.* $27.50

Ingersoll, Ernest. THE CREST OF THE CONTINENT. Chicago,
1885. 1st ed. Good, sound. *ARTIS.* $17.50

Ingham, George T. DIGGING GOLD AMONG THE ROCK-
IES...Phila: Hubbard Bros, 1888. Edgewood Ed. 2nd reprinting.
Some cvr staining. Spine & cvr gilt dull. Small marginal tears on
4pp, o/w VG. *DIAMOND.* $45

Ingles, Lloyd Glenn. MAMMALS OF CALIFORNIA. Stanford Univ,
1947. 1st ed. Adv rev copy, slip laid in. Fine in VG dj. *CONNOLLY &
WADE.* $50

Ingold, Ernest. TALES OF A PEDDLER. SF: Wallace Kibbee, 1942.
1st ed. Gold dec cl. VG. Quite scarce. *CONNOLLY & WADE.* $35

Ingram, John H. EDGAR ALLAN POE. HIS LIFE, LETTERS,
AND OPINIONS. London: New Edition, 1886. Bevelled cloth sl silverfished. Spine sl faded, o/w VG. *DIAMOND.* $25

Ingram, Sir Bruce (ed). THE ILLUSTRATED LONDON NEWS
CORONATION NUMBER. QUEEN ELIZABETH II. London,
1953. 16 color plts. Stiff wraps. VG. *ARTIS.* $30

Ingrams, Harold. ARABIA AND THE ISLES. London, 1942. 2 fldg
maps. xvi,354pp. Uncut. *O'NEILL.* $35

Ingrham, Franc and Donald Matson. NEUROSURGERY OF IN-
FANCY AND CHILDHOOD. Springfield, 1954. 381 illus. Spine
dull, o/w VG. *FYE.* $75

Ingstad, Helge. NUNAMIUT—AMONG ALASKA'S INLAND ES-
KIMOS. NY: W. W. Norton, 1954. 303pp + fldg map. 1st Eng language ed. NF in NF dj. *GREAT EPIC.* $35

Inman, Henry (ed). BUFFALO JONES' FORTY YEARS OF AD-
VENTURE. Topeka: Crane Publishers, 1899. 1st ed. 469pp. Fine.
BOOK MARKET. $100

Inman, Henry and W.F. Cody. THE GREAT SALT LAKE TRAIL.
Ross & Haines, 1966. Ltd to 1500. Fine in Fine dj. *VARNER.* $30

Inman, Henry and W.F. Cody. THE GREAT SALT LAKE TRAIL.
NY: Macmillan, 1898. Frontis, 7 plts, fldg map. Ex-lib. Orig brown
pict cl, clean, Good. *SCHOYER'S.* $60

Inman, Henry and W.F. Cody. THE GREAT SALT LAKE TRAIL.
NY: Macmillan, 1898. xiii,529pp, fldg map, 9 full-pg illus. Pict cl.
DAWSON'S. $100

Inman, Henry. THE OLD SANTA FE TRAIL. NY: Macmillan, 1897.
1st ed, 2nd ptg. xvi,493pp+3pp ads. Frontis, 8 plts, fldg map. Ex-lib
in orig pict cl. Clean. *SCHOYER'S.* $50

Inman, Henry. THE OLD SANTA FE TRAIL. Topeka, 1916. 3rd ed.
Grn pict cl. Fine. *VARNER.* $75

Inman, Henry. THE OLD SANTA FE TRAIL. Topeka: Crane, 1912.
8 plts, 1 fldg map. Fine. Howes I57. *OREGON.* $50

Innes, Hammond. CAMPBELL'S KINGDOM. London: Collins,
1952. 1st ed. Fine in dj. *ELSE FINE.* $35

Innes, Hammond. THE DOOMED OASIS. London: Collins, 1960.
1st ed. Fine in dj. *ELSE FINE.* $40

Innes, Hammond. THE LAND GOD GAVE TO CAIN. London: Collins, 1958. 1st ed. Fine in dj. *ELSE FINE.* $40

Innes, Hammond. THE LAST VOYAGE. CAPTAIN COOK'S
LOST DIARY. NY: Alfred A. Knopf, 1979. 1st ed. Fine in VG dj.
PARMER. $25

Innes, Hammond. THE STRANGE LAND. London: Collins, 1954.
1st ed. Fine; dj has minor rubs at spine ends. *ELSE FINE.* $35

Innes, Michael. A NIGHT OF ERRORS. London: Gollancz, 1948.
1st ed. Stain on back cover and smudge on fore-edge o/w VG in dj
(sl darkened spine; sm stain back panel). *MORDIDA.* $45

Innes, Michael. A PRIVATE VIEW. London: Gollancz, 1952. 1st ed.
VG in price-clipped dj w/darkened spine, chip at base of spine, and
wear at top of spine. *MORDIDA.* $30

Innes, Michael. APPLEBY'S ANSWER. London: Gollancz, 1973. 1st
ed. Name on fep o/w Fine in dj. *MORDIDA.* $30

Innes, Michael. CHRISTMAS AT CANDLESHOE. London: Gol-
lanz, 1953. 1st ed. Edges darkened o/w VG in dj w/light ring-stain on
front panel, nicks at spine ends and at corners and sl darkened spine
and front panel. *MORDIDA.* $35

Innes, Michael. FROM LONDON FAR. London: Gollancz, 1946. 1st
ed. VG in dj sl darkened spine. *MORDIDA.* $45

Innes, Michael. HARE SITTING UP. London: Gollancz, 1959. 1st ed.
Fine in VG dj w/internal tape mends, scrape on front panel and nick
at base of spine. *MORDIDA.* $35

Innes, Michael. HONEYBATH'S HAVEN. London: Gollancz, 1977.
1st ed. Fine in dj. *MORDIDA.* $30

Innes, Michael. SHEIKS AND ADDERS. London: Gollancz, 1982.
1st ed. Fine in dj w/small dampstain base front panel. *MORDIDA.* $30

Innes, Michael. SHEIKS AND ADDERS. NY: Dodd Mead, 1982. 1st Amer ed. VF in dj. *MORDIDA*. $25

Innes, Michael. THE AMPERSAND PAPERS. London: Gollancz, 1978. 1st ed. Fine in dj. *MORDIDA*. $30

Innes, Michael. THE AMPERSAND PAPERS. New York: Dodd, Mead, (1978). 1st US ed. *OAK KNOLL*. $25

Innes, Michael. THE APPLEBY FILE. London: Gollancz, 1975. 1st ed. Fine in dj. *MORDIDA*. $30

Innes, Michael. THE MYSTERIOUS COMMISSION. NY: Dodd Mead, 1975. 1st Amer ed. Fine in dj. *MORDIDA*. $30

Innes, Michael. THE WEIGHT OF THE EVIDENCE. NY: Dodd Mead, 1948. 1st Amer ed. Name, stamps o/w VG in Fine price-clipped dj. *MORDIDA*. $40

Innes, W.T. GOLDFISH VARIETIES AND WATER GARDENS. Phila, 1947. 1st ed. Cloth. Spine label partially perished; lt spotting mostly at lower corners, pencil mark 3pp. *SUTTON*. $65

Inshta Theamba (Bright Eyes). PLOUGHED UNDER: THE STORY OF AN INDIAN CHIEF, TOLD BY HIMSELF... NY: Fords, Howards, & Hulbert, 1881. 1st ed. Some wear at extremities, else VG. *LAURIE*. $75

Institoris, Henricus Kramer (called). MALLEUS MALEFICARUM. (Bungay): John Rodker, 1928. 1st ed in English. One of 1275. Orig buckram, (vellum-like) paper spine, leaves untrimmed at fore and tail edges. Frontis. Excellent, only minor defects. *PIRAGES*. $400

INSTRUCTION FOR HEAVY ARTILLERY; PREPARED BY A BOARD OF OFFICERS....Washington: GPO, 1863. 39 plts. Cl rubbed, stained and chipped. Top edge dampstained, front hinge cracked, lacks feps and blanks. Fair. *BLUE MOUNTAIN*. $90

INTERNATIONAL CIRCUS. London, 1983. Adaptation of antique pop-up by Lother Meggendorfer. Orig pub 1887. Pop-up bk. *BOOK-FINDERS INTL*. $55

International Committee for Political Prisoners. THE FASCIST DICTATORSHIP. NY: The Committee, 1926. 1st ed. Owner stamp. Cover detached. Wraps. *AKA*. $45

INTO SPACE FIFTH ACE BRAVE. London, (c.1969). 4 pop-ups. Pop-up bk. *BOOKFINDERS INTL*. $40

INVENTORY OF FEDERAL ARCHIVES IN THE STATES: SERIES IX: THE DEPARTMENT OF AGRICULTURE; NO. 12: ILLINOIS, VOL. B. Chicago, 1938. Lightly soiled. VG. *BOHLING*. $25

INVENTORY OF THE COUNTY ARCHIVES OF ILLINOIS: CUMBERLAND COUNTY (TOLEDO). No. 18. Chicago, 1938. VG. *BOHLING*. $30

INVENTORY OF THE COUNTY ARCHIVES OF OKLAHOMA. MCINTOSH COUNTY ARCHIVES. Oklahoma City: Hist Records Survey (WPA), 1938. 1st ed. VG in wraps. *GIBBS*. $25

INVESTIGATION OF INDIAN FRAUDS, MAR. 3, 1873. Bound in new buckram. *HEINOLDT*. $30

Ionesco, Eugene. JOURNEYS AMONG THE DEAD. (LEC, 1987). One of 1,000, signed by the author. Mint in slipcase. *PIRAGES*. $350

Ionesco, Eugene. JOURNEYS AMONG THE DEAD. Barbara Wright (trans). Stiff parchment cvrs in matching slipcase. (NY): LEC, (1987). Ltd to 1000 signed by Ionesco. Mint. *JAFFE*. $175

IOWA. NY, 1941. American Guide Series. WPA guide. 2nd ptg. Fldg map, dj. *SCHOYER'S*. $35

Iredale, T. BIRDS OF PARADISE AND BOWER BIRDS. Melbourne, 1950. 33 colored plts; fldg map. 1/2 morocco. Spine ends chipped; leather rubbed & somewhat brittle; pp yellowed. *SUTTON*. $200

Ireland, John B. WALL-STREET TO CASHMERE. NY: Rollo, 1859. 1st ed. xviii,531pp. Over 70 plts. Orig cl, a little rubbed and soiled, top of spine frayed. Ex-lib, o/w VG. *WORLDWIDE*. $95

Ireland, John. HOGARTH ILLUSTRATED. London: George Routledge, 1884. 2nd ed. 20th-c. 3/4 morocco & cl w/raised bands, teg. Sl discoloration top edge. NF. *CHAPEL HILL*. $200

Ireland, M.W. (ed). THE MEDICAL DEPARTMENT OF THE U.S. ARMY IN THE WORLD WAR. 17 vols. Washington, 1921-1929. Only ed. Ex-lib. Fine w/minimal markings. *FYE*. $750

Ireland, Tom. THE GREAT LAKES—ST. LAWRENCE DEEP WATERWAY TO THE SEA. NY: Putnam's, 1934. 1st ed. Fine in dj w/small tear else Fine. *ARCHER*. $25

Ireland, William. THE BLOT UPON THE BRAIN: STUDIES IN HISTORY AND PSYCHOLOGY. NY, 1886. 1st Amer ed. Front hinge cracked, backstrip loose. *FYE*. $50

Iremonger, Valentine (ed). IRISH SHORT STORIES. London: Faber & Faber, (1960). 1st ed. Fine in price-clipped dj. *CAPTAIN'S BOOKSHELF*. $35

Irish, William (pseud of Cornell Woolrich). BORROWED CRIME. NY: Avon, 1946. 1st ed. Pb orig. Murder Mystery Monthly no. 42. Fine in wrappers. *MORDIDA*. $100

Irish, William (pseud of Cornell Woolrich). DEAD MAN BLUES. Phila: J.B. Lippincott, 1948. 1st ed. Fine in dj w/tiny wear at spine ends and closed tear along back fold. *MORDIDA*. $250

Irish, William (pseud of Cornell Woolrich). EYES THAT WATCH YOU. NY: Rinehart, (1952). 1st ed. Tiny hole in front hinge, Fine in NF dj w/two small stains on flaps and shadow from sticker. *BETWEEN COVERS*. $285

Irish, William (pseud of Cornell Woolrich). EYES THAT WATCH YOU. NY: Rinehart, 1952. 1st ed. Store stamp bottom edge, dates rear pastedown, o/w NF in NF dj w/internal mend. *BEASLEY*. $125

Irish, William (pseud of Cornell Woolrich). IF I SHOULD DIE BEFORE I WAKE. Avon #104. 1st ed. 228pp. Edgewear to wraps, creases to one cvr corner, slight soil but VG. *BEBBAH*. $25

Irish, William (pseud of Cornell Woolrich). THE BLUE RIBBON. Phila: J.B. Lippincott, 1949. 1st ed. Fine in dj (sl darkened spine; nicks top of spine; minor wear at corners). *MORDIDA*. $200

Irish, William (pseud of Cornell Woolrich). WALTZ INTO DARKNESS. Phila, NY: Lippincott, 1947. 1st ed. One corner tip sl bumped, else VG in dj (3/4" chip, few internally mended tears). *BERNARD*. $95

Irish, William (pseud of Cornell Woolrich). WALTZ INTO DARKNESS. Phila: Lippincott, 1947. 1st ed. NF, light edgewear, small chips at corners of dj. *ELSE FINE*. $95

Ironside, Robin. PRE-RAPHAELITE PAINTERS. WITH A DESCRIPTIVE CATALOGUE BY JOHN GERE. NY: Phaidon. 94 plts. Dj. Fine. *WEBER*. $100

Irvine, Keith. THE RISE OF THE COLORED RACES. NY: Norton, 1970. 1st ed. Fine in Fine dj. *CONNOLLY & WADE*. $35

Irving, John Treat Jr. INDIAN SKETCHES, TAKEN DURING AN EXPEDITION TO THE PAWNEE TRIBES (1833). American Exploration and Travel Series, vol 18. John Francis McDermott (ed). Norman: Univ of Oklahoma Press, (1955). 1st ed. NF in dj. *LAURIE*. $60

Irving, John Treat, Jr. INDIAN SKETCHES...1833. Univ of Ok Press, 1955. 1st ptg. Fine in chipped dj. *VARNER*. $27.50

Irving, John. A PRAYER FOR OWEN MEANY. Morrow, 1989. 1st ed. VF in dj. Signed. *STAHR*. $60

Irving, John. A PRAYER FOR OWEN MEANY. NY: Morrow, (1989). One of 250 specially bound, signed. Fine in slipcase. *CAPTAIN'S BOOKSHELF*. $125

Irving, John. A PRAYER FOR OWEN MEANY. NY: Morrow, 1989. Uncorrected proof. Date, else NF in ptd wraps. *CAPTAIN'S BOOKSHELF*. $75

Irving, John. THE 158-POUND MARRIAGE. NY: Random House, (1974). 1st ed. Orig cl-backed boards. Fine in dj. Signed. *CHAPEL HILL.* $200

Irving, John. THE 158-POUND MARRIAGE. NY: RH, (1974). 1st ed. Fine in Fine dj. *LOPEZ.* $85

Irving, John. THE CIDER HOUSE RULES. Morrow, 1985. 1st ed. VF in dj. Signed. *STAHR.* $60

Irving, John. THE CIDER HOUSE RULES. Morrow, 1985. Signed presentation. One of 750 not for sale. Fine in glassine dj. *STAHR.* $45

Irving, John. THE CIDER HOUSE RULES. NY: Morrow, (1985). 1st ed. One of 795 specially-bound, signed. Sticker removed, else Fine in slipcase. *CAPTAIN'S BOOKSHELF.* $100

Irving, John. THE WORLD ACCORDING TO GARP. NY, 1978. 1st ed. VF in dj. *PETTLER.* $60

Irving, John. THE WORLD ACCORDING TO GARP. NY: Dutton, 1978. 1st ed. Adv reading copy. Orig ptd wraps. Spine sl faded, soiled, else NF. Signed by Irving on the half-title. *CHAPEL HILL.* $150

Irving, John. THE WORLD ACCORDING TO GARP. NY: E.P. Dutton, (1978). Prepublication copy of 1st ed. Wrappers. Mint. *WREDEN.* $125

Irving, Washington. A TOUR ON THE PRAIRIES....Phila: Carey, Lea, Blanchard, 1835. 1st Amer ed. 274pp, 24pp ads. Orig grn cl; only residue of spine label remains. Some foxing, o/w VG. Howes I86. *OREGON.* $175

Irving, Washington. ADVENTURES OF CAPTAIN BON-NEVILLE....London: Richard Bentley. 1837. 3 vols. 1st Eng ed. (4),304; (4),292; (4),302pp. 20th-c l/2 burnt orange calf over marbled boards, blue gilt lea spine labels. Nice set, w/the half-title. BAL 10150; pub in America the same yr under the title ROCKY MOUNTAINS.... *KARMIOLE.* $175

Irving, Washington. JOURNAL, 1803. Stanley T. Williams (ed). NY: Oxford, 1934. 1st ed. Cl-backed marbled boards, paper label. Fine in somewhat rubbed slipcase. *CAPTAIN'S BOOKSHELF.* $50

Irving, Washington. THE ADVENTURES OF CAPTAIN BON-NEVILLE...AND FAR WEST. Univ of OK, 1961. 1st annotated ed, 1st OK ptg. Fine in Fine dj. *OREGON.* $30

Irving, Washington. THE LIFE AND VOYAGES OF CHRIS-TOPHER COLUMBUS. London: John Murray, 1837. (1831). The Family Library. No. XI. Abridged by author. Frontis, pict title page. xi,354pp. 2 plts, 2 fldg maps, 1 in text, 1 at rear. 16mo. Backstrip sl darkened, sm chip at head. Light foxing on pgs near plts and tissue guards. Short split on rear map, expertly repaired. Orig cl. VG. An early ptg. *CONNOLLY & WADE.* $125

Irving, Washington. THE ROCKY MOUNTAINS, OR SCENES...DIGESTED FROM THE JOURNAL OF CAPTAIN B.L.E. BONNEVILLE. In 2 vols. Phila: Carey, Lea, Blanchard, 1837. 1st Amer ed. 248,248pp, 2 fldg maps (tissue repaired tears). Orig cl w/paper spine labels. Lt foxing. Spine labels scuffed, chipped. VG. Howes I85. *OREGON.* $400

Irving, Washington. THE SKETCH BOOK (OF GEOFFREY CRAYON, GENT.). NY: Heritage Press. Fine in worn slipcase. *BOOK MARKET.* $20

Irving, Washington. THE WESTERN JOURNALS OF WASHINGTON IRVING. Annotated by John McDermott. Univ of OK, 1944. 1st ed. 8 plts, fldg map. VG. *OREGON.* $35

Irwin, Inez Haynes. THE CALIFORNIACS. SF: A.M. Robertson, 1916. 1st ed, 2nd prtg. Ptd at Philopolis Press. Tipped-in color frontis. Cl over pict boards stamped in gilt. Fine in Good+ dj. *CONNOLLY & WADE.* $35

Irwin, Richard B. HISTORY OF THE NINETEENTH ARMY CORPS. NY, 1892. 1st ed. 528pp. Minor cover wear and fading, o/w VG+. *PRATT.* $150

Isaacs, Edith J.R. THE NEGRO IN THE AMERICAN THEATRE. NY: Theatre Arts, Inc, 1947. 1st ed. Fine in sl chipped dj. *BANCROFT.* $22

Isaiah. THE BOOK OF THE PROPHET ISAIAH IN THE KING JAMES VERSION. Franklin Littell (intro). (NY): LEC, 1979. One of 2000 illus, signed by Chaim Gross. Fine (wear to top of slipcase). *CAPTAIN'S BOOKSHELF.* $200

Iseley, Bliss. BLAZING THE WAY WEST. NY: Scribner's, 1939. 1st ed. VG in dj. *LAURIE.* $30

Isham, Norman and Albert Brown. EARLY CONNECTICUT HOUSES. Providence, RI: Preston Rounds Company, 1900. 1st ed. VG. *BACKROOM.* $125

Isherwood, Christopher. ALL THE CONSPIRATORS. NY: New Directions (1958). 1st ed. Fine in dj. *DORN.* $35

Isherwood, Christopher. CHRISTOPHER AND HIS KIND 1929-1939. Farrar Straus Giroux, 1976. 1st ed. VF in dj. Signed. *STAHR.* $75

Isherwood, Christopher. LIONS AND SHADOWS. London: Hogarth Press, 1938. 1st ed, 1st binding. One of 3580 ptd. Faint darkening to dj, o/w Fine. Cl, dj. *JAFFE.* $750

Isherwood, Christopher. MY GURU AND HIS DISCIPLE. NY: Farrar Straus Giroux, (1980). Uncorrected proof. Inscribed. Ptd wraps. Fine. *JAFFE.* $175

Isherwood, Christopher. PEOPLE ONE OUGHT TO KNOW. Doubleday, 1982. 1st ed. VF in dj. *STAHR.* $25

Isherwood, Christopher. THE BERLIN STORIES. New Directions, 1945. 1st thus. VG or better in dj worn and reinforced at spine ends and flyleaf folds. *STAHR.* $150

Isherwood, Christopher. THE BERLIN STORIES. NY: New Directions (1945). 1st ed. VG in dust soiled dj, edge chipping. *DORN.* $75

Isherwood, Christopher. THE CONDOR AND THE COWS. NY: Random House, (1949). 1st ed. *SILVER.* $25

Isherwood, Christopher. THE MEMORIAL. A PORTRAIT OF A FAMILY. London: Hogarth Press, 1932. 1st ed, 1st binding. One of 1222 ptd. Cl, dj. Fine. Scarce. *JAFFE.* $850

Isherwood, Christopher. THE WORLD IN THE EVENING. NY: Random House, 1954. 1st US ed. Back cover stained, o/w Fine in lightly worn, clipped dj. *ARCHER.* $27.50

Ishiguro, Kazuo. AN ARTIST OF THE FLOATING WORLD. London: Faber & Faber, (1986). 1st ed. Fine in dj. *CAPTAIN'S BOOKSHELF.* $175

Ishiguro, Kazuo. AN ARTIST OF THE FLOATING WORLD. NY, 1986. 1st US ed. Fine in NF dj. *PETTLER.* $35

Ishiguro, Kazuo. THE REMAINS OF THE DAY. London: Faber & Faber, (1989). 1st ed. Fine in Fine dj. *LOPEZ.* $75

Ishiguro, Kazuo. THE REMAINS OF THE DAY. NY: Knopf, 1989. 1st US ed. Fine in dj. Signed. *CAPTAIN'S BOOKSHELF.* $100

Ishiguro, Kazuo. THE REMAINS OF THE DAY. NY: Knopf, 1989. Uncorrected proof of 1st Amer ed. Ptd wraps. Mint. *JAFFE.* $75

Isley, Bliss. BLAZING THE WAY WEST. Scribner's, 1939. 1st ed. Fine in chipped dj. *VARNER.* $20

Issler, Anne. HAPPIER FOR HIS PRESENCE: SAN FRANCISCO AND ROBERT LOUIS STEVENSON. Stanford Univ Press, (1949). 1st ed. Fine, chipped dj. *AUTHORS OF THE WEST.* $25

Issler, Anne. OUR MOUNTAIN HERMITAGE. Stanford, (1950). 1st ed. Fine in Good+ dj. *OREGON.* $40

ITALY: WITH SKETCHES OF SPAIN AND PORTUGAL. By the Author of "Vathek." (By William Beckford.) Two vols. Phila: Key & Biddle, 1834. 255; 257 (misnumbered as 357) pp. 1st Amer ed. Orig violet cl, faded, especially on spine. Vol I lacks feps. Some foxing. *SCHOYER'S.* $125

Izzi, Eugene. BAD GUYS. NY: St. Martin's, (1988). 1st ed. Signed. VF in VF dj. *UNGER.* $45

Izzi, Eugene. THE BOOSTER. NY: St. Martin's Press, 1989. 1st ed. VF in dj. *MORDIDA.* $25

Izzi, Eugene. THE TAKE. NY: St. Martin's, (1987). 1st ed. Signed. VF in VF dj. *UNGER.* $45

Izzi, Eugene. THE TAKE. St. Martin's Press, 1987. 1st ed. About Fine in dj. *STAHR.* $35

J

Jackman, W.J. and T.H. Russell. FLYING MACHINES: CONSTRUCTION AND OPERATION. Chicago: Chas. C. Thompson, 1910. 1st ed. Gilt-lettered red cl (worn); hinges neatly taped; contents VG. *SMITHFIELD.* $150

Jackson, A.V.W. FROM CONSTANTINOPLE TO THE HOME OF OMAR KHAYYAM...NY, 1911. Color frontis, lacks a map. Pict cl. Uncut. *O'NEILL.* $55

Jackson, Andrew. MESSAGE FROM THE PRESIDENT... CONCERNING THE FUR TRADE AND INLAND TRADE TO MEXICO. 22nd Congress Senate Dec. 90, 1832. 1st ed. 86pp. Modern cl w/older gilt stamped leather spine label. VG. *OREGON.* $275

Jackson, Andrew. REPORTS OF THE FUR TRADE AND INLAND TRADE TO MEXICO 1831. Missouri Hist Glimpses of the Past, Vol 9. #1 & 2. St. Louis, 1942. VG. *OREGON.* $45

Jackson, Blyden. OPERATION BURNING CANDLE. NY: The Third Press, (1973). 1st ed. Fine in NF dj. *LOPEZ.* $125

Jackson, Charles James. HISTORY OF ENGLISH PLATE. England, 1911. 1st ed. 2 vol set. 1/4 bound in grn leather. VG. *BACKROOM.* $350

Jackson, Christopher. MANUEL. NY: Knopf, 1964. 1st ed. Bound in 1/4 blue cl and paper boards. NF in dj. *LAURIE.* $15

Jackson, Clarence S. and Lawrence W. Marshall. Univ of Denver Press (1952). QUEST OF THE SNOWY CROSS. (Denver). Dj worn at extremities, o/w VG. *LAURIE.* $30

Jackson, Donald and Mary Spence. THE EXPEDITIONS OF JOHN CHARLES FREMONT. 3 vols. Univ of IL, 1970. 1st eds. VF in VF djs. *OREGON.* $150

Jackson, Donald Dale. GOLD DUST. NY, 1980. 1st ed. 361pp. Fine in dj. *PRATT.* $30

Jackson, Donald. LETTERS OF THE LEWIS & CLARK EXPEDITION, WITH RELATED DOCUMENTS 1783-1854. Univ of IL, 1962. 1st ed. Fine. *OREGON.* $60

Jackson, F. Hamilton. THE SHORES OF THE ADRIATIC. THE AUSTRIAN SIDE: THE KUSTENLANDE, ISTRIA, AND DALMATIA. NY: Dutton, 1908. 1st ed. Plts. Orig cl, rubbed, spine frayed, eps very sl foxed, o/w VG, teg. *WORLDWIDE.* $95

Jackson, Grace. CYNTHIA ANN PARKER. San Antonio, (1959). 1st ed. 138pp. VG in dj. *PRATT.* $32.50

Jackson, Helen. CAT STORIES. Boston: Roberts Brothers, 1889. 156pp + ads. Gold-stamped cl. Some wear spine extrems and tips; owner sig. *DAWSON'S.* $100

Jackson, Helen. GLIMPSES OF THREE COASTS. Boston, 1886. 1st ed. Covers sl silverfished o/w VG. BAL 10462. *DIAMOND.* $45

Jackson, Helen. GLIMPSES OF THREE COASTS. Roberts Brothers, 1886. 1st ed. Sharp gilt printing on spine. VG, name. *AUTHORS OF THE WEST.* $40

Jackson, Helen. RAMONA. A STORY. 2 vols. Monterey Ed. Boston, 1900. 1st ed w/these illus. Few pp carelessly opened, o/w NF in Fine cl djs. *DIAMOND.* $75

Jackson, Helen. RAMONA: A STORY. Little, Brown, 1900. 1st Monterey ed. 2 vols. Susan Coolidge (intro). Tinted frontis. 3/4 leather bound, marbled boards, eps. Title ptd in red & black. Teg. Gilt-stamped leather spines. Fine. *AUTHORS OF THE WEST.* $150

Jackson, Helen. RAMONA: A STORY. Roberts Brothers, 1884. 1st ed. Gilt dec cl. Fine, stamp; tears, chips not affecting type on 6pp. *AUTHORS OF THE WEST.* $500

Jackson, Helen. ZEPH: A POSTHUMOUS STORY. Roberts Brothers, 1885. 1st ed. Dec cvr. VG+. *AUTHORS OF THE WEST.* $40

Jackson, Herbert J. EUROPEAN HAND FIREARMS OF THE SIXTEENTH, SEVENTEENTH & EIGHTEENTH CENTURIES. London: Holland Press. (1959). 2nd ed. Ltd to 750. Blue gilt cl, dj sl chipped. *KARMIOLE.* $75

Jackson, Holbrook. THE ANATOMY OF BIBLIOMANIA. NY: Farrar, (1950). 2nd ptg. Dj darkening along spine, edge chips. *AKA.* $35

Jackson, Holbrook. THE EIGHTEEN NINETIES. A REVIEW OF ART AND IDEAS AT THE CLOSE OF THE NINETEENTH CENTURY. NY: Knopf, 1923. 1st US ed. Plates. Spine darkened; edges rubbed. *WOOLMER.* $25

Jackson, James et al. A REPORT ON SPASMODIC CHOLERA. Boston, 1832. 1st ed. 190pp. Fldg map. Orig cl backed boards. Ex-lib. *FYE.* $150

Jackson, James. A MEMOIR OF JAMES JACKSON, JR, M.D. Boston: I.R. Butts, 1835. 1st ed. Inscribed presentation copy from Jackson. 8vo. 444pp. Orig cloth. Cvr nearly loose, stained. *M & S.* $175

Jackson, James. A MEMOIR OF JAMES JACKSON, JR, MD. Boston: I.R. Butts, 1835. 1st ed. 444 pp. Orig cl, worn; backstrip reattached; lt foxing, o/w VG. Paper spine label. Inscribed. *SMITHFIELD.* $120

Jackson, James. LETTERS TO A YOUNG PHYSICIAN JUST ENTERING UPON PRACTICE. Boston, 1855. 1st ed. 344pp. *FYE.* $100

Jackson, Jon A. DIEHARD. NY: Random House, 1977. 1st ed. Edges darkened o/w Fine in dj. *MORDIDA.* $35

Jackson, Joseph H. ANYBODY'S GOLD. NY, 1941. 1st ed. Cvrs sl spotted. Spine sl faded. Spine & cvr gilt dull. 1pp margin sl wrinkled, o/w VG. *DIAMOND.* $25

Jackson, Joseph H. THE CHRISTMAS FLOWER. Harcourt, Brace, (1951). 1st ed. 31pp. Illus by Tom Lea. VG+ in VG+ dj w/2 tiny closed edge tears. *BEBBAH.* $35

Jackson, Joseph Henry. BAD COMPANY. NY: Harcourt, Brace, (1940). 1st ed. 14pp section of illus. Cl, dj. *SCHOYER'S.* $30

Jackson, Shirley. HANGSAMAN. (NY: Farrar, Straus & Young, (1951). Fine in price-clipped, VG dj (some rubbing, edgewear, a few handwritten numerals). 1st ed. *CHAPEL HILL.* $65

Jackson, Shirley. LIFE AMONG THE SAVAGES. NY: Farrar, Straus & Young, (1953). Bkpl, stamp, else NF in pict dj w/slight edgewear. 1st ed. *CHAPEL HILL.* $55

Jackson, Shirley. THE BAD CHILDREN: A MUSICAL IN ONE ACT FOR BAD CHILDREN. Chicago: Dramatic Publishing Company, (1959). Fine in wrappers as issued. Scarce. *BETWEEN COVERS.* $225

Jackson, Shirley. THE BIRD'S NEST. NY: Farrar, Straus, & Young, (1954). 1st ed. Dj sl soiled on rear panel. NF. *BERNARD.* $95

Jackson, Shirley. THE LOTTERY: THE ADVENTURES OF JAMES HARRIS. 1st ed. Page edges sl soiled, else NF in Good dj, worn at spine and w/small chips and tears. *BETWEEN COVERS.* $175

Jackson, Shirley. THE ROAD THROUGH THE WALL. NY: Farrar, 1948. 1st ed. Fine in Fine dj w/few short tears. Author's 1st book. *BEASLEY.* $125

Jackson, Shirley. THE SUNDIAL. Farrar, Straus, & Cudahy, (1958). 1st ed. Fine in NF dj. *BERNARD.* $75

Jackson, Shirley. THE SUNDIAL. NY: FSG, 1958. 1st ed. VF in dj. *ELSE FINE.* $165

Jackson, T.G. DALMATIA, THE QUARNERO AND ISTRIA WITH CETTIGNE IN MONTENEGRO AND THE ISLAND OF GRADO. Oxford, 1887. 3 vols. Cl, parchment spines, lea labels, chipped and cover soil. 418, 397, and 453pp. *O'NEILL.* $65

Jackson, Thomas Graham. HOLIDAY IN UMBRIA. London: John Murray, 1916. Foxed. Partially unopened. Color frontis. *SCHOYER'S.* $30

Jackson, William H. TIME EXPOSURE. NY, 1940. 1st ed. Rebound w/gilt lettering and decs, w/label from orig cover ("TIME EXPOSURE W.H.J.") neatly laid on. Title page w/small, inoffensive embossed lib stamp; no other lib markings. Clean, tight. *FIVE QUAIL.* $45.

Jacob, Naomi and James C. Robertson. OPERA IN ITALY. London: Hutchinson & Co, 1948. VG in sl chipped dj. *BANCROFT.* $22

Jacobi, Carl. PORTRAITS IN MOONLIGHT. Arkham House, 1964. 1st ed. VF in dj. *MADLE.* $75

Jacobi, Carl. REVELATIONS IN BLACK. Arkham House, 1947. 1st ed. Fine in dj. *MADLE.* $115

Jacobs, Carl. GUIDE TO AMERICAN PEWTER. NY: The McBride Co, 1957. VG in dj. *BACKROOM.* $30

Jacobs, Harvey. THE EGG OF THE GLAK. NY: Harper & Row, (1969). 1st ed. Inscribed. Fine in NF dj. *LOPEZ.* $25

Jacobs, James R. TARNISHED WARRIOR, THE STORY OF MAJOR-GENERAL JAMES WILKINSON. NY, 1938. 1st ed. 380pp. A little dj wear o/w VG+. *PRATT.* $35

Jacobs, M. NOTES ON THE REBEL INVASION OF MARYLAND AND PENNSYLVANIA AND THE BATTLE OF GETTYSBURG, July 1st, 2d and 3d, 1863. Accompanied by an Explanatory Map. Phila: J.B. Lippincott & Co. 1864. 48pp. Fldg color map (w/repaired tear). Orig purple cl, gilt; spine extrems bit rubbed, cl faded. Some foxing. *KARMIOLE.* $85

Jacobs, W.R. DIPLOMACY AND INDIAN GIFTS. Stanford U, CA (1950), 1st ed, dj. *HEINOLDT.* $18

Jacobs, W.R. LETTERS OF FRANCIS PARKMAN. Univ of Ok Press, 1960. 1st ed. 2 vols. Fine in VG slipcase. *VARNER.* $75

Jacobsen, Thorkild and Seton Lloyd. SENNACHERIB'S AQUEDUCT AT JERWAN. Chicago: Univ of Chicago Press, (1935). 12 figs, 36 plts. Torn dj. Good. *ARCHAEOLOGIA.* $125

Jacobsthal, Paul. GREEK PINS AND THEIR CONNEXIONS WITH EUROPE AND ASIA. Oxford: Clarendon Press, 1956. 86 plts containing 650 figs. Fine in dj. *ARCHAEOLOGIA.* $650

Jacquemart, Albert. HISTORY OF FURNITURE. London, (n.d). Teg. Gilt-pict cover. Spine lightly sunned. NF. *POLYANTHOS.* $75

Jacques, Futrelle. MY LADY'S GARTER. Rand McNally, (1912). 1st ed. VG with dec cvr bright. *BEBBAH.* $30

Jaeger, B. THE LIFE OF NORTH AMERICAN INSECTS. NY: 1959. Spine ends & corners worn, eps dampstained, name on title page. *SUTTON.* $45

Jaeger, Doris. THE FACULTY OF THE COLLEGE OF PHYSICIANS & SURGEONS COLUMBIA UNIVERSITY IN THE CITY OF NEW YORK: TWENTY-FOUR PORTRAITS. NY, 1919. 1st ed. Folio (26 1/2 cms x 39 1/2 cms). VF. *FYE.* $450

Jahn, Michael. DEATH GAMES. NY: W.W. Norton, 1987. 1st ed. VF in dj. *MORDIDA.* $25

Jahn, Michael. KILLER ON THE HEIGHTS. NY: Fawcett Gold Medal, 1977. 1st ed. Pb orig. Faint crease on front cover o/w Fine in wrappers. *MORDIDA.* $25

Jahn, Michael. NIGHT RITUALS. NY: W.W. Norton, 1982. 1st ed. Adv rev copy w/slip laid in. VF in dj. *MORDIDA.* $30

Jahn, Michael. THE OLYMPIAN STRAIN. NY: Fawcett Gold Medal, 1980. 1st ed. Pb orig. Fine, unread in wrappers. *MORDIDA.* $25

Jahn, Michael. THE QUARK MANEUVER. NY: Ballantine Books, 1977. 1st ed. Pb orig. Faint reading crease on front cover and stamp on page one of text o/w VG in wrappers. *MORDIDA.* $25

Jahn, Michael. THE SCENE. NY: Bernard Geis Associates, 1970. 1st ed. Edges lightly spotted o/w Fine in dj. *MORDIDA.* $25

Jakes, John. JOHNNY HAVOC MEETS ZELDA. NY: Belmont Books, 1962. 1st ed. Pb orig. VF, unread, in wrappers. *MORDIDA.* $45

Jakob, Christfried. ATLAS OF THE NERVOUS SYSTEM. Phila, 1901. 84 Fine chromo-lithograph plts, several engrvs w/fldg flaps. *FYE.* $100

James, Arthur E. CHESTER COUNTY CLOCKS AND THEIR MAKERS. Exton, PA: Schiffer Pub Ltd., 1976. Signed, numbered. NF. *BACKROOM.* $20

James, Arthur E. THE POTTERS AND POTTERIES OF CHESTER COUNTY, PENNSYLVANIA. (West Chester): Pub (by) the Chester County Hist Soc, 1945. 1st ed. 1/600 (actually 738) ptd. NF. *CAPTAIN'S BOOKSHELF.* $75

James, Bushrod W. ALASKANA, OR, ALASKA IN DESCRIPTIVE AND LEGENDARY POEMS. Phila, 1894. 3rd ed. Ex-lib. Inscribed. *DIAMOND.* $45

James, Edith Coulson. BOLOGNA ITS HISTORY, ANTIQUITIES, AND ART. London: Henry Frowde, 1909. 1st ed. VG. *AARD.* $30

James, George Wharton. A LITTLE JOURNEY TO SOME STRANGE PLACES AND PEOPLES IN OUR SOUTHWESTERN LAND (NEW MEXICO AND ARIZONA). Chicago: A. Flanagan Co, (1911). 2pp ads. Dec cl, nicks to margins of 4 leaves, small hole at top of spine. Color frontis. *DAWSON'S.* $40

James, George Wharton. ARIZONA THE WONDERLAND. Boston, 1917. 1st ed. Map, 60 plts. Light cover wear, bumps, hinges tender, else VG. *FIVE QUAIL.* $45

James, George Wharton. B.R. BAUMGARDT & CO.'S TOURISTS' GUIDE BOOK TO SOUTH CALIFORNIA. LA: B.R. Baumgardt & Co, 1895. 458pp, fldg map, 16pp ads. Dec ptd wraps, top corners of first leaves sl bent. *DAWSON'S.* $125

James, George Wharton. HEROES OF CALIFORNIA. Boston: Little, Brown & Company, 1910. 1st ed. Pict cl, teg, spotting to rear cover, light wear to extremities, foxing to first few leaves. *DAWSON'S.* $60

James, George Wharton. IN AND AROUND THE GRAND CANYON. Pasadena Edition. Boston, 1900. 1st ed. Orig 3/4 morocco, rebacked w/new cl. Sl cvr wear. Cvr cl foxed. Contents VG. Ltd to 500 signed (#83). *DIAMOND.* $100

James, George Wharton. IN AND AROUND THE GRAND CANYON. Boston, 1913. Blue-green cloth, pict cover. Very clean w/only minor cover flaws, internally VG+ to NF. *FIVE QUAIL.* $35

James, George Wharton. INDIAN BASKETRY AND HOW TO MAKE INDIAN AND OTHER BASKETS. 2 vols in 1. 3rd ed. Pasadena, CA, 1903, 1904. Minor shelfwear, o/w NF. *DIAMOND.* $75

James, George Wharton. INDIAN BLANKETS AND THEIR MAKERS. Chicago, A.C. McClurg, 1934. 72 plts. 2nd ed. Fine. *OREGON.* $175

James, George Wharton. PRACTICAL BASKET MAKING. (New ed, enl, rev; new illus). Boston: J.L. Hammett Co. N.d. (circa 1915). 4 illus pasted to fep. Black cl, gilt; spine extrems rubbed. Imprint on this copy is ptd on a slip cancel. *KARMIOLE.* $40

James, George Wharton. THE GRAND CANYON OF ARIZONA. Boston: Little, Brown, 1910. 1st ed. 2 fldg maps, frontis. Old ex-lib, yet very clean. *HUDSON.* $55

James, George Wharton. THE WONDERS OF THE COLORADO DESERT. Boston, 1906. 1st ed. 2 vols. xliv, 270; xiv,271-547pp. NF. *FIVE QUAIL.* $150

James, George Wharton. TRAVELER'S HANDBOOK TO SOUTHERN CALIFORNIA. Pasadena: George Wharton James, 1904. Gold-stamped cl, newspaper stain to fep. *DAWSON'S.* $50

James, H.K. DESTRUCTION OF MEPHISTO'S GREATEST WEB, OR, ALL GRAFTS LAID BARE...COMPLETE EXPOSURE OF ALL GAMBLING, GRAFT, & CONFIDENCE GAMES. Salt Lake City, 1914. 1st ed. 313pp, 21 illus. Cloth gilt. NF. *DIAMOND.* $45

James, H.K. THE DESTRUCTION OF MEPHISTO'S GREATEST WEB OR, ALL GRAFTS LAID BARE. BEING A COMPLETE EXPOSURE....Salt Lake City: Raleigh, 1914. 1st ed. Fldg frontis, 20 plts. Fine. Scarce. *CONNOLLY & WADE.* $100

James, Harry C. THE CAHUILLA INDIANS. (LA): Westernlore Press, (1960). 1st ed, ltd to 1,250. Signed. Fine in Fine dj. *BOOK MARKET.* $85

James, Henry et al. THE GREAT STREETS OF THE WORLD. NY: Scribner's, 1892. 1st ed. 93 illus. Spine ends & corner tips sl worn, tear in flyleaf Near top of inner hinge o/w VG navy & gold binding with teg. *BERNARD.* $75

James, Henry. A THIN GHOST. London, 1925. 1st ed. VG. *MADLE.* $60

James, Henry. CONFIDENCE. Boston, 1880. 1st ed. Extremities spine and edges little rubbed. Fine. *POLYANTHOS.* $150

James, Henry. CONFIDENCE. Boston: Houghton, Osgood & Co, 1880. 1st Amer ed. Binding w/"Houghton Osgood" on spine; grn cl; wear to edges and top and bottom of spine, sl cocked, else VG. *JUVELIS.* $300

James, Henry. DAISY MILLER: A STUDY. Cambridge: LEC, 1969. One of 1500 bound in full red leather; illus, signed by Gustave Nebel. Fine in slipcase. *CAPTAIN'S BOOKSHELF.* $125

James, Henry. ESSAYS IN LONDON & ELSEWHERE. NY: Harpers, 1893. 1st ed. VG or better. *DERMONT.* $50

James, Henry. FOREIGN PARTS. Leipzig: Bernhard Tauchnitz, 1883. Cvrs sl soiled, spine darkened, feps repaired, but VG. 1st Continental ed, rev from Boston ed pub in 1875 as Transatlantic Sketches. 18 sepia photos. BAL 10559. *CHAPEL HILL.* $150

James, Henry. HAWTHORNE. NY: Harper & Brothers, 1880. 1st Amer ed. Cl cvrs sl marked. Internally Fine. Overall NF. *HELLER.* $150

James, Henry. IN THE CAGE. Chicago: H.S. Stone, 1898. 1st ed. Teg, dec cvrs and spine, gilt, NF. *POLYANTHOS.* $125

James, Henry. NOTES AND REVIEWS. Cambridge, MA: Dunster House, 1921. Dk blue cl, lt blue paper boards. Fine. Unopened. *HELLER.* $100

James, Henry. PARTIAL PORTRAITS. London: Macmillan, 1888. 1st ed. VG or better. *DERMONT.* $65

James, Henry. TERMINATIONS. NY, 1895. 1st ed. Dec cvrs gilt, spine sunned, extrems sl rubbed. Cvrs little soiled. Fine. *POLYANTHOS.* $60

James, Henry. THE AMBASSADORS. NY & London: Harper & Brothers, 1903. 1st Amer ed. Orig blue boards rubbed & bumped. Title in gilt, within gilt rules, on spine. Teg. NF. BAL 10656. *BLUE MOUNTAIN.* $150

James, Henry. THE AMBASSADORS. NY: Harper, 1903. 1st Amer ed, 1st issue. One of 4000 ptd. Orig blue boards, cl, dj. Flawless copy of fragile bk, virtually As New. *JAFFE.* $750

James, Henry. THE AWKWARD AGE. NY/London: Harper & Brothers, 1899. 1st Amer ed. 1000 ptd. Brn cl stamped in gold. Bkpl. Fine. *HELLER.* $150

James, Henry. THE DIARY OF A MAN OF FIFTY AND A BUNDLE OF LETTERS. NY, 1880. 1st ed. Harper's Half-Hour Series. Prtd wraps, corners chipped, extremities, spine chipped. Fine in Fine cl backed, marbled box, printed title label. *POLYANTHOS.* $100

James, Henry. THE MIDDLE YEARS. London: W. Collins Sons & Co, Ltd, (1917). Rev copy, so stamped (blind). Blue cl; soiling to back cover, spine sl sunned, bkpl removed, else Good. *JUVELIS.* $100

James, Henry. THE OTHER HOUSE. NY: Macmillan, 1896. Owner's sig, bkpl. Moderately heavy foxing throughout, else VG. 1st Amer ed. *CHAPEL HILL.* $150

James, Henry. THE OUTCRY. NY, 1911. 1st ed. Teg, uncut, spine and top edges sl sunned, Fine. *POLYANTHOS.* $75

James, Henry. THE PRIVATE LIFE, LORD BEAUPRE, THE VISITS. NY: Harper, 1893. 1st US ed. One of the early bindings (blue gray cloth stamped in gold and silver, priority undetermined) and not a remainder binding. Close to Fine. *BEASLEY.* $100

James, Henry. THE QUESTION OF OUR SPEECH. THE LESSON OF BALZAC....Boston: Riverside Press, 1905. Teg, partly unopened, extremities sl rubbed. Fine. *POLYANTHOS.* $30

James, Henry. THE QUESTION OF OUR SPEECH/THE LESSON OF BALZAC. Boston, NY: Houghton Mifflin and Co, The Riverside Press, 1905. 1st ed, 1/2000. Blue cl; wear to edges, else VG. *JUVELIS.* $100

James, Henry. THE TRAGIC MUSE. Boston, 1890. 1st ed. 2 vols. Gilt cvrs and spines. Extrems and corners sl rubbed, edge front cvr sl damp stained, Fine. *POLYANTHOS.* $400

James, Henry. VIEWS AND REVIEWS. Boston: The Ball Publishing Co., 1908. 1st ed. VG or better. *DERMONT.* $50

James, Lionel. WITH THE CONQUERED TURK. THE STORY OF A LATTER-DAY ADVENTURER. London, (1915). 370 pp. *O'NEILL.* $25

James, Marquis and Bessie R. BIOGRAPHY OF A BANK. NY: Harper, 1954. 1st ed. About Fine in Good+ dj. *CONNOLLY & WADE.* $35

James, Marquis. THE TEXACO STORY: THE FIRST FIFTY YEARS, 1902-1952. N.p.: Texas Co, 1953. 1st ed. VF. *CONNOLLY & WADE.* $35

James, Mary Ann, ELITES IN CONFLICT....New Brunswick, NJ: Rutgers Univ Press, 1987. Fine in Fine dj (stamp rear fep). *KNOLLWOOD.* $30

James, P.D. A TASTE FOR DEATH. Faber & Faber, 1986. 1st ed. Fine in dj. *STAHR.* $35

James, P.D. AN UNSUITABLE JOB FOR A WOMAN. NY: Scribners, 1972. 1st ed. Small erasure on fep, else Fine in dj. *ELSE FINE.* $95

James, P.D. COVER HER FACE. NY: Scribner, (1962). 1st US. Fine (owner sig) in dj (tiny rub). *CAPTAIN'S BOOKSHELF.* $150

James, P.D. DEATH OF AN EXPERT WITNESS. London: Faber and Faber, 1977. 1st ed. Spotting on top edge; sl darkening to eps o/w Fine in dj w/sl spine fading. *MORDIDA.* $65

James, P.D. DEATH OF AN EXPERT WITNESS. London: Faber, 1977. 1st ed. Fine; small sticker peel to dj. *ELSE FINE.* $70

James, P.D. DEATH OF AN EXPERT WITNESS. London: Faber & Faber, 1977. 1st ed. Fine in dj. *MORDIDA.* $90

James, P.D. DEVICES AND DESIRES. London: Faber, 1989. 1st ed. As New in dj. *ELSE FINE.* $40

James, P.D. DEVICES AND DESIRES. NY: Knopf, (1989). 1st US ed. Signed. VF in VF dj. *UNGER.* $50

James, P.D. DEVICES AND DESIRES. NY: Knopf, 1990. 1st ed. Signed. Fine in Fine dj, 2 scratches. *BEASLEY.* $45

James, P.D. DEVICES AND DESIRES. Knopf, 1990. 1st Amer ed. VF in dj. Signed. *STAHR.* $35

James, P.D. INNOCENT BLOOD. London: Faber & Faber, 1980. 1st ed. Fine in dj. *MORDIDA.* $60

James, P.D. INNOCENT BLOOD. London: Faber, 1980. 1st ed. Fine, small rub on dj. *ELSE FINE.* $40

James, P.D. INNOCENT BLOOD. London: Faber, 1980. 1st ed. Signed. Slight browning outer edges, o/w VG in dj. *SILVER DOOR.* $40

James, P.D. THE BLACK TOWER. London: Faber & Faber, 1975. 1st ed. Fine in dj w/wear at spine ends, at corners and along folds. *MORDIDA.* $165

James, P.D. THE BLACK TOWER. NY: Charles Scribner's Sons, 1975. 1st Amer ed. Fine in dj. *MORDIDA.* $75

James, P.D. THE BLACK TOWER. NY: Scribner's, 1975. 1st ed. Fine in dj. *ELSE FINE.* $65

James, P.D. THE SKULL BENEATH THE SKIN. NY, 1982. 1st US ed. Signed. Fine in dj. *PETTLER.* $50

James, P.D. THE SKULL BENEATH THE SKIN. NY: Scribner's, (1982). 1st Amer ed. Fine in dj. Signed. *LOPEZ.* $50

James, P.D. UNNATURAL CAUSES. NY: Charles Scribner's Sons, 1967. 1st Amer ed. Fine in dj. *MORDIDA.* $85

James, P.D. and T.A. Critchley. THE MAUL AND THE PEAR TREE. NY, 1986. 1st ed. Inscribed by James. Fine in like dj. *POLYANTHOS.* $45

James, Thomas. THREE YEARS AMONG THE INDIANS AND MEXICANS. Waterloo, IL, 1846. Lakeside Classic #51 (1953) ed. Fine. *PRATT.* $27.50

James, Thomas. THREE YEARS AMONG THE MEXICANS AND THE INDIANS. Milo Milton Quaife (ed). Lakeside Classic, 1953. *OREGON.* $35

James, Thomas. THREE YEARS AMONG THE MEXICANS AND THE INDIANS. Walter B. Douglas (ed). St. Louis: Missouri Hist Soc, 1916. 2nd ed. Ltd to 365 numbered. Frontis, 11 port plts, map. Fine. Howes J49. *OREGON.* $250

James, Thomas. THREE YEARS AMONG THE MEXICANS AND THE INDIANS. Reprints 1846 ed. Lippincott, (1962). Fine in VG dj. *OREGON.* $20

James, Will. BIG-ENOUGH. Charles Scribner's Sons, 1931. 1st ed. Frontis photo. Signed. Dec cvr. VG. *AUTHORS OF THE WEST.* $75

James, Will. BIG-ENOUGH. NY: Scribner's, (1931). 1st ed. VG+ in a VG+ dj with a few edge nicks. *UNGER.* $225

James, Will. COW COUNTRY. Charles Scribner's Sons, 1927. 1st ed. Dec cvr. Fine, name. *AUTHORS OF THE WEST.* $75

James, Will. LONE COWBOY, MY LIFE STORY. NY: Scribner's, 1930. 1st ed. Spine faded, o/w VG. *OREGON.* $35

James, Will. LONE COWBOY. NY: Scribner's, (1930). 1st ed. VG+ in VG dj with mild wear at spine ends. *UNGER.* $150

James, Will. LONE COWBOY: MY LIFE STORY. Charles Scribner's Sons, 1930. 1st ed. Frontis photo. Pict cvr. VG, sm nick. *AUTHORS OF THE WEST.* $40

James, Will. SCORPION. A GOOD BAD HORSE. NY: Scribner's, 1936. 1st ed. Good+. *OCTOBER FARM.* $58

James, Will. SCORPION: A GOOD BAD HORSE. Charles Scribner's Sons, 1936. 1st ed. Frontis. Fine. *AUTHORS OF THE WEST.* $50

James, Will. SMOKY THE COW HORSE. NY: Scribner's, 1929. 1st Illus Classics Ed (color). Full color frontis, 14 plts. Bl cl w/color illus on front cvr. NF. *CONNOLLY & WADE.* $57.50

James, Will. THE THREE MUSTANGEERS. Charles Scribner's Sons, 1933. 1st ed. Pict cvr. VG. *AUTHORS OF THE WEST.* $40

James, Will. THE THREE MUSTANGERS. NY: Scribner's, (1933). 1st ed. NF in a bright dj w/some rubbed spots to spine. *UNGER.* $225

James, Will. UNCLE BILL A TALE OF TWO KIDS AND A COWBOY. NY: Scribner's, 1932. 1st ed. Good+. *OCTOBER FARM.* $58

James, William. THE NAVAL HISTORY OF GREAT BRITAIN, FROM THE DECLARATION OF WAR BY FRANCE IN 1793, TO THE ACCESSION OF GEORGE IV.... New ed, with additions, notes, account of Burmese War and Battle of Navarino, by Captain Chamier, R.N. London: Richard Bentley, 1837. 6 vols. I: xii,xxxii,404 pp. 3 plts, 4 fldg tables; II: (viii),396 pp. 3 plts, 3 fldg tables; III: viii,376 pp. 3 plts,6 fldg tables; IV: (vii),(376)pp. 3 plts, 2 fldg tables; V: (viii),404pp. 3 plts, 4 fldg tables; VI: viii,(568)pp. 4 plts, 9 fldg tables. Contemp half polished calf, one joint tender, but VG, clean set. 1st pub in 1822-24. *LEFKOWICZ.* $500

Jamieson, Alexander. A GRAMMAR OF RHETORIC AND POLITE LITERATURE NY: Kiggins, & Kellogg, 1818. Early ed. Good+. *OLD LONDON.* $30

Jamieson, Tulitas. TULITAS OF TORREON: REMINISCENCES OF LIFE IN MEXICO. El Paso: Texas Western Press, 1969. 1st ed. Fine in dj. *LAURIE.* $25

Jamieson, Tulitas. TULITAS OF TORREON: REMINISCENCES OF LIFE IN MEXICO. El Paso, TX: Texas Western Pr, 1969. 1st ed. As New in Fine dj. *CONNOLLY & WADE.* $35

Jane, Cecil (trans). A SPANISH VOYAGE TO VANCOUVER AND THE NORTH-WEST COAST OF AMERICA. London: Argonaut Press, 1930. One of 525. 2 fldg maps. Bkpl. Some darkening to vellum, sl soiling to cvrs. *PARMER.* $500

Janet, Pierre. THE MAJOR SYMPTOMS OF HYSTERIA. NY, 1907. 1st Eng trans. *FYE.* $100

Janowitz, Tama. AMERICAN DAD. NY: Putnam's, (1981). 1st ed, 1st bk. VG+ in dj, sm spot. *BERNARD.* $35

Janson, Charles William. THE STRANGER IN AMERICA: CONTAINING OBSERVATIONS....OF THE PEOPLE OF THE UNITED STATES...AND THE SLAVE TRADE. London: Cundee, 1807. 1st ed. (13),(1),499pp. 9 tinted plts, 1 plan, 1 vignette, extra-engr title pg. Modern red half morocco, raised bands. Aquatint ed, tinted by hand w/sepia wash. Howes J59. *GINSBERG.* $1250

Janssens, Agustin (Victor Eugene August). THE LIFE AND ADVENTURES IN CALIFORNIA OF DON AGUSTIN JANSSENS, 1834-1856. Francis Price (trans), William H. Ellison and Francis Price (eds). San Marino: Huntington Library, 1953. 1st ed. Dj worn at extremities, else VG. *LAURIE.* $20

Janvier, Thomas. LEGENDS OF THE CITY OF MEXICO. NY: Harper & Brothers, 1910. 1st ed. *SILVER.* $35

Jaques, F.P. AS FAR AS THE YUKON. NY: Harper, 1951. Fine in Good+ dj. *MIKESH.* $25

Jaques, F.P. CANADIAN SPRING. NY & London: Harper, 1947. VG+ in Fair dj. *MIKESH.* $25

Jaques, F.P. FRANCIS LEE JAQUES, ARTIST OF THE WILDERNESS WORLD. GC, 1973. Spine sl sunned. Slipcase, 1 bumped corner. Scarce. *SUTTON.* $265

Jaques, F.P. SNOWSHOE COUNTRY. Minn: Univ of MN, (1945). Dec cl. NF. *MIKESH.* $17.50

Jaramillo-Arango, Jaime. THE CONQUEST OF MALARIA. London, 1950. 1st ed. *FYE.* $65

Jardine, D.R. CRICKET. London: Dent, 1946. Rev ed. NF in Good dj. *OLD LONDON.* $20

Jarratt, Rie. GUTIERREZ DE LARA: MEXICAN-TEXAN, THE STORY OF A CREOLE HERO. Austin: Creole Texana, 1949. Uncut. Fine. *LAURIE.* $125

Jarrell, Randall (trans). THE RABBIT CATCHER AND OTHER FAIRY TALES OF LUDWIG BECHSTEIN. Illus by Ugo Fontana. NY: Macmillan, 1962. 1st ed. Fine copy in sl used dj. *DERMONT.* $150

Jarrell, Randall. A SAD HEART AT THE SUPERMARKET. Essays & Fables. NY: Atheneum, 1962. 1st ed. Inscribed. Orig greyish blue cl. Spine a little flecked, thus VG in NF dj. *CHAPEL HILL.* $250

Jarrell, Randall. A SAD HEART AT THE SUPERMARKET. NY: Atheneum, 1962. 1st ed. Fine in lightly used dj. *DERMONT.* $45

Jarrell, Randall. BLOOD FOR A STRANGER. (New York: Harcourt, Brace, [1942]). 1st ed. Author's first book. Dj w/sl faded spine, sl tears or fraying at spine ends, bottom of front panel o/w VF. *PIRAGES.* $550

Jarrell, Randall. BLOOD FOR A STRANGER. Cl. NY: Harcourt, Brace, (1942). 1st ed. Fine in a trifle rubbed dj. *JAFFE.* $350

Jarrell, Randall. FLY BY NIGHT. Pictures by Maurice Sendak. NY: Farrar Straus & Giroux, (1976). 1st ed. Fine in dj. *CAPTAIN'S BOOK-SHELF.* $25

Jarrell, Randall. LITTLE FRIEND, LITTLE FRIEND. NY: Dial, 1945. 1st ed. VF in dj. Rev copy w/slip inserted. *WOOLMER.* $275

Jarrell, Randall. LITTLE FRIEND, LITTLE FRIEND. NY: Dial Press, 1945. 1st ed. Orig dark blue cl. VG in price-clipped dj (some chipping top edge front panel). *CHAPEL HILL.* $95

Jarrell, Randall. LOSSES. Poems. NY: Harcourt, (1948). 1st ed. Fine in sl rubbed dj. Signed. *CAPTAIN'S BOOKSHELF.* $300

Jarrell, Randall. PICTURES FROM AN INSTITUTION. NY: Knopf, 1954. 1st ed. Inscribed. Orig grn cl. NF in VG dj. *CHAPEL HILL.* $250

Jarrell, Randall. PICTURES FROM AN INSTITUTION. NY: Knopf, 1954. 1st ed. Inscribed. Ownership notation, bkpl. VG in dj. *LOPEZ.* $450

Jarrell, Randall. PICTURES FROM AN INSTITUTION. NY: Knopf, 1954. Adv reading copy. Very Nice in very sl spine-faded blue wrappers. *CAPTAIN'S BOOKSHELF.* $175

Jarrell, Randall. PICTURES FROM AN INSTITUTION. NY: Knopf, 1954. 1st ed, 1st novel. Fine, light edgewear and spine fading to dj. *ELSE FINE.* $100

Jarrell, Randall. RANDALL JARRELL'S LETTERS. Mary Jarrell (ed). Boston: HM, 1985. 1st ed. Fine in dj. Signed by Mary Jarrell. *CAPTAIN'S BOOKSHELF.* $40

Jarrell, Randall. THE ANIMAL FAMILY. Decorations by Maurice Sendak. (NY): Pantheon, (1965). 1st ed. Fine in dj. *CAPTAIN'S BOOK-SHELF.* $40

Jarrell, Randall. THE BAT POET. Pictures by Maurice Sendak. NY: MacMillan, (1964). 1st ed. Fine in dj with sl darkened spine. *CAPTAIN'S BOOKSHELF.* $40

Jarrell, Randall. THE COMPLETE POEMS. NY: Farrar, Straus & Giroux, (1969). 1st ed. Orig grn cl. Fine in dj, couple of unnoticeable clean tears. *CHAPEL HILL.* $50

Jarrell, Randall. THE SEVEN-LEAGUE CRUTCHES. Cl. NY: Harcourt, Brace, (1951). 1st ed. VF in price-clipped dj. *JAFFE.* $125

Jarves, James J. HISTORY OF THE HAWAIIAN OR SANDWICH ISLANDS, EMBRACING THEIR ANTIQUITIES, MYTHOLOGY, LEGENDS, DISCOVERY BY EUROPEANS IN THE SIXTEENTH CENTURY, RE-DISCOVERY BY COOK, WITH THEIR CIVIL, RELIGIOUS AND POLITICAL HISTORY. FROM THE EARLIEST TRADITIONARY PERIOD TO THE PRESENT TIME. Boston: Tappan and Dennet, 1843. 1st ed. 8vo, orig brown embossed cloth, gilt titles. xx, (map), 407pp. 25 illus (incl 5 full-page plates and fldg map). 7 appendices. Fine. Expertly rehinged, showing some wear to lower edges and corners. *PARMER.* $1500

Jarvis, Charles E. VISIONS OF KEROUAC. Lowell: Ithaca Press, (1974). 1st ed. VG in wrappers. Inscribed. *LOPEZ.* $45

Jarvis, H. Wood. PHARAOH TO FAROUK. NY: Macmillan, 1955. 1st US ed. Dj. NF. *WORLDWIDE.* $35

Jay, Charlotte. A HANK OF HAIR. Harper, (1964). 1st Amer ed. 135pp. NF in VG+ dj. *BEBBAH.* $18

Jay, Charlotte. ARMS FOR ADONIS. London: Collins Crime Club, 1960. 1st ed. Edges sl darkened o/w Fine in dj. *MORDIDA.* $45

Jay, Charlotte. THE FUGITIVE EYE. Harper, (1953). 1st Amer ed. 212pp. VG+ in VG dj with light chips. *BEBBAH.* $18

Jay, William. LIFE OF JOHN JAY; WITH SELECTIONS...NY: Harper, 1833. 2 vols. 1st ed. (8),520; (4),502pp. Port. Contemp half morocco. Howes J71. *GINSBERG.* $150

Jean, Marcel. THE HISTORY OF SURREALIST PAINTING. NY, 1967. 2nd prtg. Dj. Fine. *POLYANTHOS.* $65

Jeannes, William. GUNTER'S MODERN CONFECTIONER. London: Dean & Son, (1861). 3rd ed. xvi,246,ads,(2)pp. Frontis. Grn cl, rubbed. Good. *WEBER.* $40

Jeans, James. ASTRONOMY AND COSMOGONY. Cambridge Univ Press, 1929 (1928). 2nd ed. Good ex-lib. *KNOLLWOOD.* $70

Jeans, James. THE DYNAMICAL THEORY OF GASES. Cambridge Univ Press, 1916 (1904), 2nd ed. Good in blue cl w/beveled edges (sl fading, fraying; bumped, worn). Typed obit notice laid in, pencil marks, notes. *KNOLLWOOD.* $75

Jearey, B.F. PRIDE OF LIONS. London: Longmans, (Sept 1936). VG+. *MIKESH.* $20

Jebb, R.C. THE ATTIC ORATORS. London: MacMillan and Co., 1876. 1st ed. 2 vols. Minor foxing, wear, soil. *OLD LONDON.* $125

Jefferies, Richard. AN ENGLISH VILLAGE. Boston: LB, 1903. 1st ed, thus. Lt foxing, else Fine in pict cl, teg. *CAPTAIN'S BOOKSHELF.* $60

Jefferies, Richard. FIELD & HEDGEROW, BEING THE LAST ESSAYS. NY & London: Longmans, (1904). Frontis gravure. Ex private libris. VG. *MIKESH.* $30

Jefferies, Richard. HODGE AND HIS MASTERS. London: Smith, Elder & Co. 1880. 1st ed. 2 vols. vii,(3),360; (6),312pp. + (4)pp. of ads. Half-titles present. Bound in l/2 grn morocco over marbled boards, gilt spine. Teg. Fine. *KARMIOLE.* $150

Jefferies, Richard. THE GAMEKEEPER AT HOME. London: Smith, Elder, 1880. Illus by Charles Whymper. 1st illus ed. Some foxing, else NF. *OLD LONDON.* $135

Jefferies, Richard. THE OPEN AIR. London: Chatto & Windus. 1885. 1st ed. (8),270,(2)pp. + 32pp. of ads. Half-title present. Bound in l/2 grn morocco over marbled boards, gilt spine. Teg. Fine. *KARMIOLE.* $85

Jefferies, Richard. THE SCARLET SHAWL. London: Tinsley Bros. 1874. 1st ed. (6),310pp. Half-title present. Bound in l/2 grn morocco over marbled boards, gilt spine. Teg. Fine. *KARMIOLE.* $150

Jeffers, H. Paul. MURDER MOST IRREGULAR. NY: St. Martin's, (1983). 1st ed. Inscribed. Fine in Fine dj. *UNGER.* $75

Jeffers, H. Paul. THE ADVENTURE OF THE STALWART COMPANIONS. NY: Harper & Row, 1978. 1st ed. Rmdr mk bottom edge o/w Fine in dj. *MORDIDA.* $35

Jeffers, Robinson. BE ANGRY AT THE SUN. NY: Random House, (1941). Fine in price-clipped, VG dj w/couple of chips at top of front panel. 1st trade ed. *CHAPEL HILL.* $75

Jeffers, Robinson. BE ANGRY AT THE SUN. NY: Random House, 1941. 1st ed. Piece missing from dj top spine and jacket darkened, o/w VG+. *SMITH.* $90

Jeffers, Robinson. BE ANGRY AT THE SUN. Random House, (1941). 1st ed. VG+, name. *AUTHORS OF THE WEST.* $35

Jeffers, Robinson. CAWDOR AND OTHER POEMS. NY, 1928. Ltd ed, 213/350. Signed. Uncut and partly unopened. Spine sl sunned. Fine in Fine glassine dj. Box edge sunned and edge rubbed. *POLYANTHOS.* $300

Jeffers, Robinson. GIVE YOUR HEART TO THE HAWKS. NY: Random House, 1933. Ltd ed of 200, signed. 1/4 tan calf, marbled boards, black slipcase; spine sl darkened, ends rubbed, o/w Fine; slipcase with 1" tear at top, corner bumped, open edge worn. Generally VG. *WEBER*. $200

Jeffers, Robinson. HUNGERFIELD AND OTHER POEMS. NY: Random House, (1954). Fine in dj. 1st ed. Inscribed. *CHAPEL HILL*. $300

Jeffers, Robinson. HUNGERFIELD AND OTHER POEMS. NY: Random House, (1954). Fine in dj w/almost unnoticeable closed tear. 1st ed. *CHAPEL HILL*. $75

Jeffers, Robinson. MEDEA. NY: Random House, 1946. 1st ed. "Least" present on page 99. Sm chip missing from dj and some browning, o/w NF. *SMITH*. $100

Jeffers, Robinson. NOT MAN APART. SF: Sierra Club, (1965). 1st ed. Orig red cl. Fine in dj. *CHAPEL HILL*. $50

Jeffers, Robinson. RETURN. SF: (Ptd by The Grabhorn Press for Gelber, Lilienthal, Inc.), 1934. 1st ed. #60 of 250. Orig lt orange paper-covered boards. Some splitting along fragile paper spine, but easily VG. Very scarce. *CHAPEL HILL*. $250

Jeffers, Robinson. RHYTHM AND RHYME. (Monterey, CA: Peters Gate Press, 1966). 1st ed. #450 of 500. Fine in matching env and orig mailing env addressed from the press. Brief ALS from the pub laid in. *CHAPEL HILL*. $45

Jeffers, Robinson. SOLSTICE AND OTHER POEMS. NY: Random House, 1935. Ltd ed of 320. Some offsetting to eps, o/w Fine. *WEBER*. $250

Jeffers, Robinson. THE ALPINE CHRIST & Other Poems. Commentary, Notes by William Everson. (Monterey, CA): Cayucos Books, 1973. Fine. 1st ed. #233 of 250 signed by Everson. *CHAPEL HILL*. $225

Jeffers, Robinson. THE BEGINNING & THE END & OTHER POEMS: THE LAST WORKS. NY: Random House, (1963). 1st ed. Fine in NF dj. *AKA*. $45

Jeffers, Robinson. THE DOUBLE AXE AND OTHER POEMS. NY: Random House, (1948). 1st ed. Fine w/light wear. *AKA*. $30

Jeffers, Robinson. THE DOUBLE AXE AND OTHER POEMS. NY, 1948. 1st ed. NF in VG dj. *POLYANTHOS*. $30

Jeffers, Robinson. THEMES IN MY POEMS. SF: The Bk Club of CA, 1956. Ltd ed of 350. Signed. Fine. *WEBER*. $200

Jeffers, Susan. THREE JOVIAL HUNTSMEN. Bradbury, (1973). 1st ed. 4to. Unpaginated. Illus by author. Fine in VG+ dj. *BEBBAH*. $70

Jeffers, Una. VISITS TO IRELAND. LA: The Ward Ritchie Press, 1954. Ltd ed of 300. Spine evenly sun faded. Slipcase. *WEBER*. $250

Jeffers, Una. VISITS TO IRELAND. LA: Ward Ritchie, 1954. Forward by Robinson Jeffers. Boards, cl. VG slipcase. One of 300. Fine. *SMITH*. $300

Jefferson, Beatrice. SMALL TOWN MURDER. NY: E.P. Dutton, 1941. 1st ed. Inscribed. Bkseller's sm label. VG in dj with wear. *MORDIDA*. $30

JEFFERSON COUNTY REMINISCENCES. Portland: Binford & Mort (1957). 1st ed. VF in VG dj. *OREGON*. $45

Jefferson, Joseph. THE AUTOBIOGRAPHY OF JOSEPH JEFFERSON. NY: The Century Company, c1890. Binding soiled. *HUDSON*. $50

Jefferson, Thomas. CORRESPONDENCE BETWEEN...AND PIERRE SAMUEL DU PONT DE NEMOURS 1798-1817. Boston: Houghton Mifflin, 1930. 1st ed. VG, ex-lib. *BOOK BROKER*. $45

Jefferson, Thomas. DOCUMENTS RELATING TO PURCHASE & EXPLOR. OF LOUISIANA. I: LIMITS & BOUNDS OF LOUISIANA. II: EXPLORATION OF RED, BLACK &

WASHITA RIVERS. Boston: Houghton Mifflin, 1904. 1st ed, 1st ptg, ltd to 550 numbered. Paper spine label, 2 plts, fldg map. Uncut & unopened. VG. *OREGON*. $135

Jefferson, Thomas. MEMOIRS OF THE HON. THOMAS JEFFERSON. 2 vols. (NY): Ptd for Purchasers, 1809. 1st, only ed. vi,404; (ii),434pp. Names; ink note 3pp vol 1. Newly rebound in cl, boards. Foxing. Howes C-164. *SCHOYER'S*. $185

Jefferson, Thomas. THE WRITINGS. Saul K. Padover (ed). Lunenburg, VT: LEC, 1967. One of 1500 ptd at Stinehour Press, illus, signed by Lynd Ward. Fine in slipcase. *CAPTAIN'S BOOKSHELF*. $100

Jeffery, George. A BRIEF DESCRIPTION OF THE HOLY SEPULCHRE, JERUSALEM AND OTHER CHRISTIAN CHURCHES IN THE HOLY CITY. Cambridge, 1919. xii,233pp. Uncut. *O'NEILL*. $55

Jeffrey, John Mason. ADOBE AND IRON....La Jolla, CA: Prospect Ave., 1969. 1st ed. VG, wraps. *CONNOLLY & WADE*. $20

Jeffries, Ewel. A SHORT BIOGRAPHY OF JOHN LEETH WITH AN ACCOUNT OF HIS LIFE AMONG THE INDIANS. Cleveland: Burrows, 1904. 70pp. Orig cl. One of 167 numbered. Howes J86. *GINSBERG*. $125

Jekyll, Gertrude and E. Mawley. ROSES FOR ENGLISH GARDENS. NY, 1902. 1st Amer ed. Orig cl w/gilt lettering. Spine faded, lt edge rubbing, some brn spotting to prelim pp. *SUTTON*. $95

Jekyll, Gertrude and Lawrence Weaver. GARDENS FOR SMALL COUNTRY HOUSES. London, 1913. Rev expanded ed. Teg. NF. *POLYANTHOS*. $75

Jellison, Charles A. FESSENDEN OF MAINE, CIVIL WAR SENATOR. Syracuse, (1962). 1st ed. VG+ in dj. *PRATT*. $30

JEMIMA PUDDLE-DUCK. London, 1985. From Beatrix Potter by Colin Twinn. David Rosendale (eng). Pop-up bk. *BOOKFINDERS INTL*. $25

Jen, Gish. TYPICAL AMERICAN. Boston: Houghton Mifflin, 1990. Uncorrected proof. Fine in ptd wraps. *CAPTAIN'S BOOKSHELF*. $45

Jenkins, Ferguson (as told to George Vass). LIKE NOBODY ELSE. Regnery, 1973. Signed. 1st ed. Fine in VG dj. *PLAPINGER*. $65

Jenkins, John H. AUDUBON AND OTHER CAPERS, CONFESSIONS OF A TEXAS BOOKMAKER. Austin: The Pemberton Press, 1976. 1st ed. Dj. *OAK KNOLL*. $45

Jenkins, Paul B. THE BOOK OF LAKE GENEVA, (ILLINOIS). Pub for the Chicago Hist Soc Chicago: The Univ of Chicago Press. (1922). 1st ed. Presentation copy. Dj bit chipped. *KARMIOLE*. $45

Jenkins, Peter and Barbara. THE WALK WEST. WALK ACROSS AMERICA 2. Morrow, 1981. 1st ed, special ltd ed of 750 signed, numbered. Full gilt stamped lea, in lea covered slipcase. VF in VF slipcase. *OREGON*. $35

Jenkins, Will. THE MURDER OF THE USA. Crown, 1946. 1st ed. Fine in dj, chip. *MADLE*. $35

Jenks, Robert W. THE BRACHIAL TELEGRAPH. NY: Sanders, 1852. 1st ed. 56,(1)pp. Orig cl, fep lacking. *GINSBERG*. $250

Jenks, Tudor. GALOPOFF THE TALKING PONY. Phila: Altemus, 1901. 1st ed. VG. *OCTOBER FARM*. $15

Jenner, Edward. AN INQUIRY INTO THE CAUSES AND EFFECTS OF VARIOLAE VACCINAE. Milan, 1923. Facs of the 1798 ed. Paper covered boards, rebacked. Colored engrs. Ex-lib. *FYE*. $60

Jenness, John S. NOTES ON THE FIRST PLANTING OF NEW HAMPSHIRE AND ON THE PISCATAOUA PATENTS. Portsmouth, NH: Brewster, privately ptd, 1878. 1st ed. 91 pp. 2 maps. Orig stiff wrappers,chipped, mended at spine, piece of rear wrapper gone. Howes J98. *GINSBERG*. $125

Jenness, John S. THE ISLES OF SHOALS. NY: Hurd & Houghton, 1873. 1st ed. 4 fldg maps. Light wear. *BOHLING*. $65

Jennett, Sean. JOURNAL OF A YOUNGER BROTHER: THE LIFE OF THOMAS PLATTER AS A MEDICAL STUDENT IN MONTPELLIER AT THE CLOSE OF THE SIXTEENTH CENTURY. London, 1963. 1st Eng trans. Dj. *FYE.* $27.50

Jennett, Sean. PIONEERS IN PRINTING. London: Routledge & Kegan Paul, (1958). 1st ed. Dj. *OAK KNOLL.* $35

Jennings, Gary. THE TREASURE OF THE SUPERSTITION MOUNTAINS. NY: Norton, 1973. 1st ed. Fine in NF dj. *CONNOLLY & WADE.* $25

Jennings, George Henry. ANECDOTAL HISTORY OF THE BRITISH PARLIAMENT...TO THE PRESENT TIME... NY: Appleton, 1881. Cvrs sl stained, worn. Sml hole in cvr, through p.xv, affecting few letters only, o/w VG. *DIAMOND.* $45

Jennings, John. THEATRICAL AND CIRCUS LIFE. St. Louis: Sun Publishing, 1882. 1st ed. Thick 8vo; orig gilt pict cloth; pict spine dulled; extremities frayed, first sig pulling; chromolitho frontis, 8 chromolitho plts and other illus. to text; clean. VG. *DRAMATIS PERSONAE.* $300

Jennings, O.E. WILD FLOWERS OF WESTERN PENNSYLVANIA AND THE UPPER OHIO BASIN. 2 vols. Pittsburgh, 1953. 200 colored plts. Cl, djs. VF. *SUTTON.* $450

Jepson, Edgar and Maurice LeBlanc. ARSENE LUPIN. NY: Doubleday, 1909. 1st ed. Green cloth stamped in black w/paper dec front board. Fine but for traces of wear to spine ends. *BEASLEY.* $65

Jerningham, Hubert. TO AND FROM CONSTANTINOPLE. 1st ed. Hurst & Blackett, 1873, x,365 pp. Engr frontis, title-pg. Orig cl, edges rubbed, spine frayed, sl shaken, sl smudged, o/w Good. Ex-lib. *WORLDWIDE.* $95.

Jerome, Jerome K. THREE MEN IN A BOAT. (UK): Bristol, 1889. 1st ed, later issue. Illus by A. Frederics. Offsetting feps, spine sl rubbed, spine and front cover bubbled, sl cocked. *POLYANTHOS.* $65

Jervis, Henry. HISTORY OF THE ISLAND OF CORFU, AND OF THE REPUBLIC OF THE IONIAN ISLANDS. London, 1852. 4 full-pg plts. Orig dec cl, rebacked in brown morocco, gilt. vii,323pp. *O'NEILL.* $160

Jesse, E. GLEANINGS IN NATURAL HISTORY, ETC. London: J. Murray, (1832); 1834; 1835. 3 vols. 1st, 2nd, & 3rd Series. NF. *MIKESH.* $375

JESSE JAMES: THE LIFE AND DARING ADVENTURES OF THIS BOLD HIGHWAYMAN AND...FRANK JAMES. TOGETHER WITH THE THRILLING EXPLOITS...WRITTEN BY (ONE WHO DARE NOT NOW DISCLOSE HIS IDENTITY)....Phila., ca 1882. 1st ed. 19-96pp. Orig ptd front wrapper, a few Scotch Tape repairs, p.95/96 has lower corner lacking affecting several letters of text. Howes J47. *GINSBERG.* $750

Jessup, Richard. THE CINCINNATI KID. Boston: LB, (1963). 1st ed, 1st bk. Fine in sl rubbed dj, sm tears. *CAPTAIN'S BOOKSHELF.* $75

Jewett, Sarah Orne. A MARSH ISLAND. Boston: Houghton, Mifflin and Company, 1885. 1st ed, 1st prtg, with A MARSH ISLAND listed as "In Press" in the ads. Two-tone grn cl. VG w/minimal wear to spine and minor foxing to eps. *JUVELIS.* $125

Jewett, Sarah Orne. THE COUNTRY OF THE POINTED FIRS. Boston & NY: Houghton Mifflin, 1896. . Early owner's name, rear endpaper foxed, else VG. Gilt-dec front cvr bright and attractive. 1st ed, 1st ptg w/title and dedication leaves as inserted conjugates. BAL 10910. *CHAPEL HILL.* $185

Jewett, Sarah Orne. THE QUEEN'S TWIN AND OTHER STORIES. Boston, 1899. Pub in ed of 3020, in Nov, 1899. 1st ed. 232pp. Blue/Grn cl. Closed tear to top of fep, contemp inscrip. Nice. BAL 10913. *SECOND LIFE.* $75

Jewett, Sarah Orne. THE TORY LOVER. Boston: Houghton, Mifflin, 1901. 1st ed, 1st ptg, w/p reading "Lackynge," and p 154 w/34 lines of text. Stamped red cl. VG. BAL 10914 *SECOND LIFE.* $85

Jewett, Taylor, Shaw and Aldrich. BIRDS OF WASHINGTON STATE. Seattle: Univ of WA, 1953. 1st ed. NF in VG dj. *MIKESH.* $75

Jhabvala, Ruth Prawer. IN SEARCH OF LOVE AND BEAUTY. Morrow, 1983. 1st Amer ed. Fine in dj. *STAHR.* $15

Jhabvala, Ruth Prawer. THREE CONTINENTS. Morrow, 1987. Uncorrected proof. VF in wraps. *STAHR.* $15

Jihei, Kunisaki. KAMISUKI CHOHOKI. A HANDY GUIDE TO PAPERMAKING. Charles E. Hamilton (trans). Berkeley: The Bk Arts Club, Univ of CA, 1948. 1st ed. Ed ltd to 1000. *KARMIOLE.* $85

Joan, Natalie. AMELIARANNE IN TOWN. London: Harrap, 1937. Illus by Susan Pearse. Some cvr edgewear, soil but VG. *BEBBAH.* $25

Job, Thomas. GIANTS IN THE EARTH. NY: Harper, 1929. 1st ed. Fine but for dulled, sunned spine, in NF dj w/wear to spine and edges. *BEASLEY.* $50

Jobson, Hamilton. JUDGE ME TOMORROW. London: Collins Crime Club 1978. 1st ed. Fine in dj. *MORDIDA.* $25

Jobson, Hamilton. THE EVIDENCE YOU WILL HEAR. London: Collins Crime Club, 1975. 1st ed. Fine in dj, bumped top corners, wear. *MORDIDA.* $25

Jobson, Richard. THE GOLDEN TRADE; OR A DISCOVERY OF THE RIVER GAMBRA...NOW REPRINTED FOR THE FIRST TIME. Charles G. Kingsley (ed). Teignmouth, Devonshire: Speight & Walpole, 1904. 1st ed. 127 of ed ltd to 300. Orig boards w/cl spine, very sl rubbed, corners sl dented, eps sl soiled, o/w VG. *WORLDWIDE.* $125

Joesting, Edward. THE ISLANDS OF HAWAII. N.p.: (Bishop National Bank of Hawaii, 1958). 1st ed. 132 repros Ansel Adams photos. White ptd wrappers sl soiled at spine and extremities, else NF lacking dj. *CAPTAIN'S BOOKSHELF.* $100

Johansen, Hjalmar. WITH NANSEN IN THE NORTH. NY/London: New Amsterdam Bk Company/Ward, Lock and Co, (n.d.). H. L. Braekstad (trans). Ex-lib. Hinges reinforced; and eps. Quite acceptable. *PARMER.* $200

John, Evan. ATLANTIC IMPACT 1862. London, (1952). 1st ed. VG+ in dj. *PRATT.* $25

John, Evan. TIME AFTER EARTHQUAKE. London, 1954. xix,140pp. Dj. *O'NEILL.* $25

John, Francis A. THE BIBLIOGRAPHY OF ARTHUR WALEY. New Brunswick: (Rutgers Univ Press), 1968. Orig pub's grn cl w/silver stamping. *BOOK BLOCK.* $30

John, W.D. and Warren Baker. OLD ENGLISH LUSTRE POTTERY. Newport, England: The Ceramic Bk Co, 1962. Ltd to 1000. 2nd ed. VG. *BACKROOM.* $165

JOHNS HOPKINS UNIVERSITY CELEBRATION OF THE TWENTY-FIFTH ANNIVERSARY OF THE FOUNDING OF THE UNIVERSITY AND INAUGURATION OF IRA REMSEN. Baltimore, 1902. 1st ed. Orig boards rebacked and inner hinges strengthened w/paper tape. Scarce. *FYE.* $50

Johns, Jane Martin. PERSONAL RECOLLECTIONS OF EARLY DECATUR...AND THE CIVIL WAR. Richard C. Schaub (ed). Decatur, IL, 1912. 1st ed. VG. *PRATT.* $35

Johnsgard, P.A. THE GROUSE OF THE WORLD. Lincoln, NE & London, Univ of Nebraska, 1983. Fine in NF dj. *MIKESH.* $50

Johnsgard, P.A. WATERFOWL OF NORTH AMERICA. Bloomington, 1975. *SUTTON.* $50

Johnson, A.F. FRENCH SIXTEENTH CENTURY PRINTING. London: Ernest Benn, 1928. 1st ed. 50pp. Dj. *OAK KNOLL.* $65

Johnson, Abner Morse. RURAL RHYMES. Milwaukee: Advocate Publishing, 1926. 1st ed. Signed. VG. *LAURIE.* $45

Johnson, Adam Rankin. THE PARTISAN RANGERS OF THE CONFEDERATE STATES ARMY. Louisville, 1904. 1st ed. Bit of discoloration on rear board, else NF. *McGOWAN.* $450

Johnson, Alfred (ed, trans). SHIPS AND SHIPPING: A COLLECTION OF PICTURES...Salem, 1925. Pub. 9. 9 plts. Fine. 1st ed of all but intro text, which had been pub in a small ed in France in 1883. *LEFKOWICZ.* $130

Johnson, Amandus. JOURNAL AND BIBLIOGRAPHY OF NICHOLAS COLLIN, 1746-1831. NJ Soc. of PA, 1936. 1st ed. *HEINOLDT.* $35

Johnson, Amandus. SWEDISH CONTRIBUTIONS TO AMERICAN FREEDOM, 1776-1783. Phila: Swedish Colonial Foundation, 1953-57. 1st ed. 2 thick vols. Orig gold stamped cl. Inscribed presentation. *GINSBERG.* $150

Johnson, Amandus. SWEDISH SETTLEMENTS OF THE DELAWARE....NY, 1970. 2 vols. Cloth. Reprint of 1911 ed. Howes J124. *GINSBERG.* $40

Johnson and Newkirk. THE CERAMIC ARTS. NY: Macmillan, 1942. 1st ed. VG in worn dj. *ARTIS.* $20

Johnson, Charles R. BLACK HUMOR. Chicago: Johnson Pub Co, 1970. 1st ed. As New in wrappers. Scarce. *BETWEEN COVERS.* $100

Johnson, Charles R. BLACK HUMOR. Chicago: Johnson Pub Co, 1970. 1st ed. Wraps. Author's 1st bk. *BEASLEY.* $100

Johnson, Charles R. BLACK HUMOR. Chicago: Johnson Pub Co,(1970). 1st ed. Only issued in wraps. Fine. *LOPEZ.* $85

Johnson, Charles R. FAITH AND THE GOOD THING. NY: Viking, (1974). 1st ed. Paperclip indentation first few pp, else Fine in dj. Scarce. *BETWEEN COVERS.* $150

Johnson, Charles R. FAITH AND THE GOOD THING. NY: Viking, (1974). 1st ed. NF in dj. *LOPEZ.* $150

Johnson, Charles. MIDDLE PASSAGE. NY: Atheneum, 1990. 1st ed. Inscribed. Fine in About Fine dj. *BEASLEY.* $150

Johnson, Charles. OXHERDING TALE. Bloomington, IN: (1982). 1st ed. Fine in dj. *LOPEZ.* $65

Johnson, Charles. THE SORCERER'S APPRENTICE, TALES AND CONJURATIONS. NY: Atheneum, 1986. 1st ed. Signed. Fine in Fine dj. *BEASLEY.* $125

Johnson, Clifton. OLD-TIME SCHOOLS AND SCHOOL-BOOKS. NY: Macmillan, 1904. 1st ed. Silverfish nibbling on cvrs, o/w Fine. *WREDEN.* $30

Johnson, Denis. FISKADORO. NY: Knopf, (1985). 1st ed. Fine in Fine dj. *UNGER.* $35

Johnson, Diane. DASHIELL HAMMETT—A LIFE. NY: Random, 1983. 1st ed. Fine in dj. *SILVER DOOR.* $35

Johnson, Dorothy M. ALL THE BUFFALO RETURNING. Dodd, Mead & Co, (1979). 1st ed. Fine in dj. *AUTHORS OF THE WEST.* $25

Johnson, Dorothy M. THE BLOODY BOZEMAN. NY, (1971). 1st ed. 366pp. VG. *PRATT.* $25

Johnson, Dorothy M. THE BLOODY BOZEMAN....McGraw Hill, (1971). 1st ed. Fine in dj. *AUTHORS OF THE WEST.* $35

Johnson, Dorothy M. THE BLOODY BOZEMAN: THE PERILOUS TRAIL....NY; McGraw-Hill, (1971). 1st ed. Fine in Fine dj. *BOOK MARKET.* $18

Johnson, Dorothy M. THE HANGING TREE. NY: Ballantine, (1957). 1st ed. Fine in lightly rubbed dj. *UNGER.* $50

Johnson, E. Pauline (Tekahionwake). LEGENDS OF VANCOUVER. Toronto: McClelland, Goodchild, & St, (1911). New ed. 7 plts. 1 pl retipped. VG in VG dj. *AARD.* $30

Johnson, E. Pauline. LEGENDS OF VANCOUVER. Toronto: McClelland, Goodchild & Stewart, (1911). 2nd ed, illus. VG, lacking dj. *LOPEZ.* $85

Johnson, E.C. ON THE TRACK OF THE CRESCENT. London, 1885. Fldg map. xvi,322pp. *O'NEILL.* $75

Johnson, F.H. GUIDE TO NIAGARA FALLS AND ITS SCENERY....Phila: George W. Childs. 1864. 1st ed. 72pp, incl 6pp ads. Orig pebbled red cl, gilt. *KARMIOLE.* $50

Johnson, Frederick. THE TUMBLEWEEDS SOMERSAULTING UP AND OUT OF THE CITY STREETS. NY: Harper, (1977). 1st ed. Fine in Fine dj. *BOOK MARKET.* $18

Johnson, George W. (ed).THE GARDENERS' DICTIONARY....London: Bell, 1877. Grn cl, ex-lib. VG. *SECOND LIFE.* $45

Johnson, George W. THE COTTAGE GARDENER....2 vols. London, 1849. Contemp calf worn at extrems, scuffed. Label removed from front cvr vol 2, o/w Nice set. *SUTTON.* $200

Johnson, Gerald. THE SECESSION OF THE SOUTHERN STATES. NY: Putnam's, 1933. 1st ed. Pencil notes ffep. Fine in VG+ dj. *ARCHER.* $30

Johnson, Greg. A FRIENDLY DECEIT. Baltimore: Johns Hopkins (1992). Uncorrected proof. Fine in wraps. *DORN.* $30

Johnson, Guion Griffis. A SOCIAL HISTORY OF THE SEA ISLANDS. Chapel Hill: Univ of NC Press, 1930. 1st ed. Close to Fine. *BEASLEY.* $60

Johnson, Harold "Speed". WHO'S WHO IN MAJOR LEAGUE BASE BALL. Buxton, 1933. 1st ed. VG, Hinges ripped, some cover edge wear, without dj. *PLAPINGER.* $400

Johnson, Harold "Speed". WHO'S WHO IN MAJOR LEAGUE BASEBALL. Buxton, 1933. 1st ed. VG. *PLAPINGER.* $450

Johnson, Harrison. JOHNSON'S HISTORY OF NEBRASKA. Omaha: Henry Gibson, 1880. Map missing, o/w Good. *LAURIE.* $100

Johnson, James Weldon. ALONG THIS WAY. NY: Viking Press, 1933. 1st ed. Frontis. Orig red cl. NF in sl edgeworn dj w/sl darkened spine. Excellent. *CHAPEL HILL.* $400

Johnson, James Weldon. SAINT PETER RELATES AN INCIDENT. SELECTED POEMS. NY: Viking, 1935. 1st ed. Orig black cl. Some foxing, thus VG in dj w/a few tiny nicks and holes. *CHAPEL HILL.* $250

Johnson, James Weldon. THE BOOK OF AMERICAN NEGRO SPIRITUALS. NY: Viking, 1925. 1st ed. NF. *BEASLEY.* $75

Johnson, John Lipscomb. AUTOBIOGRAPHICAL NOTES. (Boulder?, CO), 1958. 1st ed, ltd to 500. NF. *McGOWAN.* $75

Johnson, John. TYPOGRAPHIA, OR THE PRINTER'S INSTRUCTOR; INCLUDING AN ACCOUNT OF THE ORIGIN OF PRINTING...Two volumes. London: Longman, Hurst, Rees, Orme, Brown & Green, 1824. 1st ed.. Vol I is of the l2mo ptg and vol II is of the 8vo edition. Two leaves in facs in vol II and 4 pages missing altogether. A working copy priced accordingly. *OAK KNOLL.* $85

Johnson, John. TYPOGRAPHIA, OR THE PRINTERS' INSTRUCTOR. London: Longman, Hurst, Rees, Orme, & Green, 1824. 1st ed. 2 vols. xii,610(10)pp; iv,663,(16)pp. Engr frontis. 1/4 grn cl and boards, orig paper spine labels. Bkpl. VG. *WEBER.* $300

Johnson, Josephine. NOW IN NOVEMBER. NY: Simon & Schuster, (1934). 1st ed. Fine in very sl spine-faded but still Fine dj. *LOPEZ.* $50

Johnson, Kenneth M. THE NEW ALMADEN QUICKSILVER MINE WITH AN ACCOUNT OF THE LAND CLAIMS INVOLVING THE MINE AND ITS ROLE IN CALIFORNIA HISTORY. Georgetown: Talisman Press, 1963. Fldg map, 2 ephemeral items in rear pocket. #24/75 signed. Light wear. VG. *BOHLING.* $65

Johnson, Laurence. OVER THE COUNTER AND ON THE SHELF: COUNTRY STOREKEEPING IN AMERICA, 1620-1920. Tuttle, (1961). 1st ed. Fine in Fine dj. *BOOK MARKET.* $50

Johnson, Leroy and Jean. ESCAPE FROM DEATH VALLEY AS TOLD BY WILLIAM L. MANLY AND OTHER '49ERS. Reno: Univ of NV Press, 1987. 1st ed, ltd to 500 hb copies. Fine in Fine dj. *BOOK MARKET.* $50

Johnson, M. CONGORILLA, ADVENTURES WITH PYGMIES AND GORILLAS IN AFRICA. 41 photos. NY, 1932 (1931). Cloth. Sm tear heel of spine. Signed. *SUTTON.* $28

Johnson, Margaret. WHAT DID THE BLACK CAT DO? GUESS! Illus by the Author. Boston: Dana Estes & Co. (1898). 82pp. Frontis. Orig dec grn cl; extremities a bit worn, bottom of spine frayed. Dec cl binding signed by Blanche McManus. *KARMIOLE.* $75

Johnson, Martin. OVER AFRICAN JUNGLES. NY: Harcourt, Brace, 1946. Dampstain bottom back cvr and dj. VG in VG scarce dj. *GREAT EPIC.* $35

Johnson, Merle. A BIBLIOGRAPHY OF THE WORKS OF MARK TWAIN. NY, 1935. Rev and enlrgd. 1st ed. Traces of removed scotch tape inside covers. Fine in dj (spine sunned, few edge chips). Edge strengthened internally, traces of scotch tape flap folds. *POLYANTHOS.* $100

Johnson, Merle. AMERICAN FIRST EDITIONS; BIBLIOG-RAPHIC CHECK LISTS OF THE WORKS OF ONE HUNDRED AND FIVE AMERICAN AUTHORS. NY: Bowker, 1929. vii,242pp. 1st ed ltd to 1000. Unopened. *BOOKMINE.* $75

Johnson, Michael P. TOWARD A PATRIARCHAL REPUBLIC. Baton Rouge, (1977). 1st ed. Inscribed by author. VG+ in dj. *PRATT.* $30

Johnson, Olga. FLATHEAD & KOOTENAY. THE RIVERS...THE REGION'S TRADERS. A.H. Clark, 1969. 1st ed. Frontis, fldg map. VF. *OREGON.* $60

Johnson, Oliver. WM LLOYD GARRISON AND HIS TIMES. Boston 1880. 432pp. *HEINOLDT.* $15

Johnson, Osa. I MARRIED ADVENTURE. Phila, etc., 1940. Signed ltd ed. #119/520. Fine. *MIKESH.* $65

Johnson, Osa. TARNISH, THE TRUE STORY OF A LION CUB. Wilcox & Follett, (1944). 59pp. Illus Arthur Jansson. Edgewear. VG in VG dj w/edgewear. *BEBBAH.* $25

Johnson, Overton and William H. Winter. ROUTE ACROSS THE ROCKY MOUNTAINS. Princeton, 1932. Facsim title pg of 1846 1st ed. VG. Howes J142. *OREGON.* $35

Johnson, Paul E. A SHOPKEEPER'S MILLENNIUM...IN ROCHESTER, NEW YORK, 1815-1837. NY: Hill and Wang, 1978. 1st ed. Grey cl, silver spine titles. NF in VG dj. *PARMER.* $25

Johnson, Robert. A COMPLETE TREATISE ON THE ART OF RETOUCHING PHOTOGRAPHIC NEGATIVES. London: Marion & Co. 1886. 1st ed. (4),88pp, 16pp ads. 8 litho plts. 1/2 maroon calf over maroon cl, dec gilt spine, grn leather spine label; spine faded. *KARMIOLE.* $125

Johnson, Ronald. THE AFICIONADO'S SOUTHWESTERN COOKING. N.p.: Univ of New Mexico Press, (1968). 1st ed. Fine in very lightly used dj. *CAPTAIN'S BOOKSHELF.* $100

Johnson, Ronald. THE AFICIONADO'S SOUTHWESTERN COOKING. Univ of NM Press, (1968). 1st ed. VF in dj (1 sm chip top of back panel). *JAFFE.* $150

Johnson, Rossiter. THE FIGHT FOR THE REPUBLIC: A NARRA-TIVE....NY: Putnam, 1917. 1st ed. Frontis, 5pp adv, 3 full-pg photo plts, 28 maps, 13 are fldg. Grey-blue cl w/gilt. Spine faded, edges worn, contents; overall VG. *CONNOLLY & WADE.* $45

Johnson, Samuel D. THE FIREMAN. NY: Samuel French, 1856. 1st ed. orig printed wraps, sewn. Fine. *DRAMATIS PERSONAE.* $22

Johnson, Samuel. A DICTIONARY OF THE ENGLISH LAN-GUAGE: IN WHICH THE WORDS ARE DEDUCED FROM THEIR ORIGINALS, ETC....London: Ptd by W. Strahan, for J. and P. Knapton; T. and T. Longman; C. Hitch and L. Hawes; A. Mil-lar; and R. and J. Dodsley. 1st ed. Folio. 2 vols. Titles ptd in red and black. Titles in both vols skillfully repaired at inner margin and in vol I along a tear from the top near the inner margin down 1/3 of page. Rebound in handsome modern quarter morocco over linen.

Scattered light foxing, occasional old ink notations, but overall VG. *CAPTAIN'S BOOKSHELF.* $7500

Johnson, Samuel. LETTERS OF SAMUEL JOHNSON. George Birkbeck Hill (ed). 2 vols. NY: Harper & Bros. 1892. 1st ed. Fldg facs letter. *KARMIOLE.* $40

Johnson, Samuel. LONDON: A POEM AND THE VANITY OF HUMAN WISHES. T.S. Eliot (intro). London: Frederick Etchells & Hugh Macdonald, 1930. Total ed of 450 ptd, this one of 150 num-bered on Kentish rag paper, signed by Eliot. Bumped, rubbed top of front cvr, spine darkened. Internally Fine. *BLUE MOUNTAIN.* $475

Johnson, Samuel. ORIENTAL RELIGIONS AND THEIR RELA-TION TO UNIVERSAL RELIGIONS: PERSIA. Boston, 1885. 782 pp. VF. *O'NEILL.* $45

Johnson, Swafford. HISTORY OF THE U.S. CAVALRY. Green-wich, (1985). 1st ed. 192pp. Fine in dj. *PRATT.* $25

Johnson, Virgin S. MILLVILLE GLASS, THE EARLY DAYS. Millville, NJ: Delaware Bay Trading Co., 1971. 1st ed. Faded spot on cvr. *HEINOLDT.* $25

Johnson, Virginia W. THE UNREGIMENTED GENERAL: A BIOGRAPHY....Boston: Houghton Mifflin, 1962. 1st ed. 8k plts, 6 maps. Fine in Good dj. *CONNOLLY & WADE.* $40

Johnson, W. Fletcher. LIFE OF SITTING BULL...INDIAN WARS OF 1890-91. Edgewood, 1891. 1st ed. Good. Sl rubbing on cvrs, rear hinge cracked, o/w interior Fine. *VARNER.* $35

Johnson, William Henry. AUTOBIOGRAPHY. Albany: The Argus Co, 1900. 1st ed. Dampstaining to top edge and last few pp, spotting to boards, few tears to cloth, not quite VG. Very scarce. *BETWEEN COVERS.* $175

Johnson, William Weber. KELLY BLUE. GC: Doubleday, 1960. 1st ed. Inscribed. Fine in Fine dj. *CONNOLLY & WADE.* $35

Johnston, Annie Fellows. THE LITTLE COLONEL AT BOARD-ING-SCHOOL. L.C. Page, 1939. VG in dj edgewear, few scratches but VG. *BEBBAH.* $30

Johnston, Carol. THOMAS WOLFE: A DESCRIPTIVE BIBLIOG-RAPHY. Univ of Pittsburgh Press, 1987. 1st ed. Orig blue cl. Fine. *CHAPEL HILL.* $45

Johnston, Charles. NARRATIVE OF THE INCIDENTS ATTEND-ING CAPTURE, DETENTION, AND RANSOM...NY, 1827. 1st ed. 264pp. Full contemp calf, mended. Howes J158. *GINSBERG.* $200

Johnston, Gerald W. ANDREW JACKSON, AN EPIC IN HOMESPUN. NY: Minton, Balch, 1927. 1st ed. Plates. Top of spine label chipped, else VG. *WOOLMER.* $35

Johnston, Grace. THE COTTON TOTS. Chicago, (1926). 14pp. 16mo. in color wraps. Illus. Small piece missing rear wrap, few small edge tears but VG for such a fragile piece. *BEBBAH.* $30

Johnston, H.V. MY HOME ON THE RANGE....Saint Paul, 1942. 1st ed. (?). NF; sm spot on cover. Scarce. *VARNER.* $45

Johnston, Harry. GEORGE GRENFELL AND THE CONGO. A history and description of the Congo Independent State...London: Hutchinson & Co., 1908. (Two Vols). 1st ed. Orig Very Rare ptd dj. NF in VG dj. *GREAT EPIC.* $1250

Johnston, Harry. THE NILE QUEST A RECORD OF THE EX-PLORATION OF THE NILE AND ITS BASIN. NY: Stokes (1903). 1st US ed. Fine. *AARD.* $85

Johnston, Henry. THE YORKTOWN CAMPAIGN AND THE SUR-RENDER OF CORNWALLIS: 1781. NY, 1881, 1881. 1st ed. Fine. *BOND.* $22.50

Johnston, I.N. FOUR MONTHS IN LIBBY, AND THE CAM-PAIGN AGAINST ATLANTA. Cincinnati: Methodist Book Con-cern, 1864. 1st ed. 191pp, wraps, paper jacket stitched around cover. VG+. *ARCHER.* $100

Johnston, M.F. CORONATION OF A KING, or, THE CEREMONIES, PAGEANTS....London, 1902. Spine faded. Spine lettering almost rubbed. Silverfishing front cvr, o/w VG. *DIAMOND.* $45

Johnston, Mary. CEASE FIRING. Boston, 1912. 1st ed. Pict cl. Cvr wear o/w VG. *PRATT.* $25

Johnston, Mary. SIR MORTIMER. NY & London: Harper & Bros., 1904. Pencilled owner's sig, else bright, About Fine. 1st ed w/"Published March, 1904" on copyright page. *CHAPEL HILL.* $45

Johnston, Mary. THE LONG ROLL. Boston, 1911. 1st ed. Sl cvr staining, minor bumping of few pp of text, o/w VG. *DIAMOND.* $45

Johnston, Mary. THE LONG ROLL. Boston, 1911. 1st ed. Pict cl. VG+. *PRATT.* $32.50

Johnston, Mary. THE WITCH. Boston & NY: Houghton Mifflin, 1914. 1st ed. Orig brn cl. Corners bumped, gilt lettering on spine dulled, else VG. *CHAPEL HILL.* $35

Johnston, Mary. TO HAVE AND TO HOLD. Boston & NY: Houghton, Mifflin, 1900. 1st ed. Orig dec tan cl. Front hinge a little weak, tiny bkseller's handstamp, but Nice, VG. *CHAPEL HILL.* $40

Johnston, S. Paul. FLYING SQUADRONS. NY: Duell, Sloan & Pearce, (1942). 1st ed. Dj. *KARMIOLE.* $40

Johnston, Tony. YONDER. Dial, (1988). 1st ed. Unpaginated. Signed. Fine in Fine dj. *BEBBAH.* $25

Johnston, William G. OVERLAND TO CALIFORNIA. Oakland, CA, 1948. Fldg blue map. Cloth. Reissue of 1892 ed. Howes J173. *GINSBERG.* $50

Johnston, William G. OVERLAND TO CALIFORNIA. Oakland: Biobooks, 1948. Foreword by Joseph A. Sullivan. One of 1,000. 1st pub in 1892 as EXPERIENCES OF A FORTY-NINER. Fldg map at back. Fine. Howes J-173. *LAURIE.* $40

Johnston, William Preston. MY GARDEN WALK. New Orleans: F.F. Hansell & Bro, 1894. 1st ed. Slip laid in. 183pp. Orig purple cl. Lt spotting on cover, couple of pgs pulled, but VG. *CHAPEL HILL.* $45

Jolas, Eugene (ed). TRANSITION WORKSHOP. NY: Vanguard, (1949). 1st ed. Dj internally tape-reinforced, couple short edgetears, price-clipped, o/w clean, bright. VG. *AKA.* $35

Jolley, Elizabeth. FOXYBABY. (NY): Viking, (1985). 1st Amer ed. Inscribed. Fine in dj. *LOPEZ.* $45

JOLLY JUMP-UPS, A CHILD'S GARDEN OF VERSES. McLoughlin, (1946). Measures 8.25" x 10.75" closed. 6 pop-ups. Illus Geraldine Clyne. Cvr edgewear, scratches, small scrape. VG, interior and pop-ups NF. *BEBBAH.* $60

JOLLY JUMP-UPS AND THEIR NEW HOUSE. McLoughlin, 1934. Written by Geraldine Clyne. Six jump-ups. Thick boards. Sm repair 1st pg. Pop-up bk. *BOOKFINDERS INTL.* $70

JOLLY JUMP-UPS ON THE FARM. McLoughlin, (1960). Measures 7.5" x 10.5" closed. 6 color pop-ups w/text by Geraldine Clyne. Some cvr edgewear. VG+, interior and pop-ups VG+. *BEBBAH.* $45

Jolly, Rudolf. ATLAS OF MICROSCOPIC DIAGNOSIS AND GYNECOLOGY. NY, 1911. 1st Eng trans. 52 mounted colored lithographs. *FYE.* $75

Jones, A.H.M. THE GREEK CITY FROM ALEXANDER TO JUSTINIAN. Oxford: Clarendon Press, 1940. Signature. Good. *ARCHAEOLOGIA.* $125

Jones, Berenice Nelson. A KISS ON MY FINGER. Albuquerque: Calvin Horn, 1974. 1st ed. Fine in VG dj. *CONNOLLY & WADE.* $20

Jones, Bernard (ed). THE POEMS OF WILLIAM BARNES. Southern IL Univ Press, 1962. 2 vols. NF. *POLYANTHOS.* $45

Jones, Bessie Zaban and Lyle Gifford Boyd. THE HARVARD COLLEGE OBSERVATORY, THE FIRST FOUR DIRECTORS, 1839-1919. Cambridge, MA: Belknap Press of Harvard Univ Press, 1971. VG in faded dj. *KNOLLWOOD.* $50

Jones, Billy. HOLOCAUST AT MARY SMOKES. Australia: Hale & Iremonger, 1983. 1st ed. One of a few w/orig illus by Jones. VF. *SMITH.* $25

Jones, C.W. IN PRISON AT POINT LOOKOUT. (Martinsville, VA), n.d. 1st ed. Orig self wraps. NF. *McGOWAN.* $45

Jones, Charles H. AFRICA—THE HISTORY OF EXPLORATION AND ADVENTURE. NY: Henry Holt, 1875. 1st ed. Worn extremes else VG. *GREAT EPIC.* $175

Jones, Craig. FATAL ATTRACTION. Crown, 1983. 1st ed. Fine in dj. *MADLE.* $25

Jones, Douglas C. ARREST SITTING BULL, A NOVEL. NY, (1977). 1st ed. 249pp. Fine in dj. *PRATT.* $15

Jones, E. Alfred. OLD SILVER OF EUROPE AND AMERICA. Phila: Lippincott, 1928. 1st ed. VG in VG dj, tape repairs. *BACKROOM.* $75

Jones, E. Alfred. THE OLD CHURCH PLATE OF THE ISLE OF MAN. London: Bemrose & Sons, 1907. 1st ed. VG. 31pp. *BACKROOM.* $95

Jones, E. Lester. REPORT OF ALASKA INVESTIGATIONS IN 1914. Bureau of Fisheries, 1915. 1st ed. VG. *OREGON.* $50

Jones, E.H. ROAD TO EN-DOR. London & NY: John Lane, n.d. (c. 1925). 6th ed. Fairly worn and faded maroon cl. *SCHOYER'S.* $20

Jones, Evan. CITADEL IN THE WILDERNESS. NY, 1966. 1st ed. Light dj wear with one small piece torn off, o/w Fine. *PRATT.* $25

Jones, Fernando. I WAS THERE WHEN THE BLUES WAS RED HOT. Chicago: the author, 1989. 1st ed. Signed. Fine in Fine dj. *BEASLEY.* $40

Jones, G. Wayman. ALIAS MR. DEATH. NY: Fiction League, 1932. 1st ed. Fine in dj. *MORDIDA.* $40

Jones, Gayl. CORREGIDORA. NY: Random House, (1975). 1st ed, 1st book. Fine in price clipped dj. *BERNARD.* $45

Jones, Gayl. EVA'S MAN. NY: Random House, (1976). 1st ed, 2nd book. New in dj. *BERNARD.* $35

Jones, Gayl. EVA'S MAN. NY: Random House, (1976). 1st ed. Fine in Fine dj. *LOPEZ.* $45

Jones, Gayl. WHITE RAT. NY: Random House, 1977. 1st ed. Fine in Fine dj. *BEASLEY.* $40

Jones, Handfield and Edward Sieveking. A MANUAL OF PATHOLOGICAL ANATOMY. Phila, 1854. 1st Amer ed. 37 Fine woodcut illus. *FYE.* $75

Jones, Hannah Maria. THE GIPSY MOTHER. London: Virtue, Tallis (1833). 1st ed. 858pp. Engr half title, 9 engr plts. Bound in full straight grained morocco, hinges rubbed. VG. *SECOND LIFE.* $250

Jones, Holway R. JOHN MUIR AND THE SIERRA CLUB. THE BATTLE FOR YOSEMITE. SF: Sierra Club, (1965). 1st ed. Fine in Fine dj. *BOOK MARKET.* $100

Jones, Isaac. EQUILIBRIUM AND VERTIGO. Phila, 1918. 1st ed. 130 illus. *FYE.* $100

Jones, J. William. ARMY OF NORTHERN VIRGINIA, MEMORIAL VOLUME. Richmond, 1880. 1976 rprt. Fine. *PRATT.* $25

Jones, J. William. PERSONAL REMINISCENCES, ANECDOTES AND LETTERS OF GEN. ROBERT E. LEE. NY, 1875. 509pp & ad. Pict cloth. Three plates missing. VG. *PRATT.* $75

Jones, J.F.D. A TREATISE ON THE PROCESS EMPLOYED BY NATURE IN SUPPRESSING THE HEMORRHAGE FROM DIVIDED AND PUNCTURED ARTERIES, AND ON THE USE OF THE LIGATURE; CONCLUDING WITH OBSERVATIONS ON SECONDARY HEMORRHAGE. Phila, 1811. 1st

Amer ed. Full leather, 236pp. 15 plts. Bottom margin of boards chewed, hinges cracked, scattered foxing. Scarce. *FYE.* $400

Jones, James. FROM HERE TO ETERNITY. NY: Charles Scribner's Sons, 1951. 1st ed. NF in NF dj. *JUVELIS.* $150

Jones, James. FROM HERE TO ETERNITY. NY: Scribner's, 1951. 1st ed, 1st bk. NF in dj. *ELSE FINE.* $175

Jones, James. SOME CAME RUNNING. NY: Scribner's, 1957. 1st ed. VG+ in dj. *ELSE FINE.* $35

Jones, James. VIET JOURNAL. NY: Delacorte, (1974). 1st ed. Signed. Owner name under front dj flap, o/w Fine in Fine dj. *LOPEZ.* $150

Jones, Jenkins Lloyd. AN ARTILLERYMAN'S DIARY. N.p., 1914. 1st ed ltd to 2500. Ex-lib. Spine discolored where external lib markings removed o/w VG. *PRATT.* $95

Jones, John Paul. LETTERS OF JOHN PAUL JONES...IN MR. W. K. BIXBY'S COLLECTION....Boston: Bibliophile Soc, (1905). 1st ed. Orig blue vellum backed boards, boxed. Small ed for members only. *GINSBERG.* $75

Jones, John Paul. LIFE AND CORRESPONDENCE OF JOHN PAUL JONES, INCLUDING HIS NARRATIVE. NY, 1830. Frontis portrait. Expertly rebacked. Some dampstains ffep and first few pp. *PARMER.* $125

Jones, Joseph. MAN, MORAL AND PHYSICAL: OR THE INFLUENCE OF HEALTH AND DISEASE ON RELIGIOUS EXPERIENCE. Phila, 1861. 324pp. *FYE.* $75

Jones, Katharine M. (ed). NEW CONFEDERATE SHORT STORIES. Columbia, 1954. 1st ed. Some dj wear o/w Fine. *PRATT.* $37.50

Jones, Katharine M. THE PLANTATION SOUTH. Indianapolis, (1957). 1st ed. A little dj wear, sm piece torn from back o/w Fine. *PRATT.* $25

Jones, L. and F.I. Scard. THE MANUFACTURE OF CANE SUGAR. London, 1909. Cl, some soiling. *SUTTON.* $95

Jones, Laurence C. PINEY WOODS AND ITS STORY. NY and Chicago, (1922). 1st ed, presentation. Orig cl, minor dampstain at lower corner, else NF. *McGOWAN.* $45

Jones, LeRoi (Imamu Akiri Bakara). THE SYSTEM OF DANTE'S HELL. London: M & K, 1966. 1st ed. Fine, lt wear at dj extremities, sm rub on front panel. *ELSE FINE.* $35

Jones, LeRoi. A POEM FOR BLACK HEARTS. Detroit: Broadside, 1967. 1st ed. Fine. *BEASLEY.* $30

Jones, LeRoi. HOME: SOCIAL ESSAYS. NY: Morrow, 1966. 1st ed. Very NF in VG, price-clipped dj w/bit of rubbing. *BETWEEN COVERS.* $50

Jones, LeRoi. PREFACE TO A TWENTY VOLUME SUICIDE NOTE....NY: Totem Press, (1961). 1st ed. 47pp, wraps. Browning along spine, else NF. *AKA.* $35

Jones, LeRoi. THE SYSTEM OF DANTE'S HELL. NY: Grove, (1965). 1st ed. NF in dj. *LOPEZ.* $35

Jones, Louis Thomas. THE QUAKERS OF IOWA. Iowa City: State Hist Soc of Iowa, 1914. 1st ed. VG. *LAURIE.* $50

Jones, M. DR. KANE—THE ARCTIC HERO. London: T. Nelson, 1866. VG. *PARMER.* $65

Jones, Madison. AN EXILE. NY: Viking, (1967). 2nd prtg. Inscribed. NF in dj. *LOPEZ.* $25

Jones, Madison. LAST THINGS. Baton Rouge: LSU Press, 1989. 1st ed. As New in dj. Inscribed. *CAPTAIN'S BOOKSHELF.* $35

Jones, Madison. SEASON OF THE STRANGLER. GC: DD, 1982. 1st ed. Fine in sl rubbed dj, sm hole. *CAPTAIN'S BOOKSHELF.* $40

Jones, Mat E. and M.E. Jones. FIDDLEFOOTED. Sage, 1966. 1st ptg. Fine in VG dj. *VARNER.* $25

Jones, Max and John Chilton. LOUIS. Boston: Little, Brown, (1971). 1st ed. VG in dj. *LOPEZ.* $25

Jones, Mother. THE AUTOBIOGRAPHY OF MOTHER JONES. Chicago: Kerr, 1925. 1st ed. Front ep missing, o/w Fine. *BEASLEY.* $25

Jones, Nettie. FISH TALES. NY: Random House, (1983). 1st ed. Fine in dj. *LOPEZ.* $25

Jones, Oakah L., Jr. PUEBLO WARRIORS & SPANISH CONQUEST. Norman, (1966). 1st ed. 225pp. VG+ in dj. *PRATT.* $30

Jones, Owen. THE SPORT OF SHOOTING. London: Edward Arnold, 1928. 2nd ed. VG+. *OLD LONDON.* $45

Jones, Paul A. CORONADO AND QUIVIRA. Lyons, KS, (1937). Cl dusty. VG. *ARTIS.* $30

Jones, Peter. HISTORY OF THE OJEBWAY INDIANS...London, 1861. 1st ed. 6,2,278,2,24pp. 16 litho plts. Orig cl, spine rebacked. Howes J238. *GINSBERG.* $275

Jones, Ralph F. LONGHORNS NORTH OF THE ARKANSAS. Naylor, 1969. 1st ptg. Signed. Fine in Fine dj. *VARNER.* $35

Jones, Raymond F. PLANET OF LIGHT. Phila: Winston, 1953. 1st ed. Fine, pict dj has sm chips at the spine corners. *ELSE FINE.* $45

Jones, Raymond F. PLANET OF LIGHT. Winston, 1953. 1st ed. VG in chipped dj. *MADLE.* $35

Jones, Raymond F. RENAISSANCE. NY: Gnome Press, (1951). 1st ed. VG in dj. *McCLINTOCK.* $20

Jones, Raymond F. RENAISSANCE. NY: Gnome Press, 1951. 1st ed. Fine, minor edgewear to dj, internal tape at spine top. *ELSE FINE.* $30

Jones, T.E. LEAVES FROM AN ARGONAUTS NOTE BOOK. SF: Whitaker & Ray, 1905. 1st ed. 6 plts. Minor cvr spotting, o/w Fine. Howes J240. *OREGON.* $140

Jones, Terry L. LEE'S TIGERS, THE LOUISIANA INFANTRY IN THE ARMY OF NORTHERN VIRGINIA. Baton Rouge, (1987). 1st ed. 274pp. VG+ in dj. *PRATT.* $35

Jones, Tristan. ICE. Kansas City: Sheed Andrews and McMeel, 1978. 1st ed. NF in VG dj. *PARMER.* $30

Jones, Virgil Carrington. GRAY GHOSTS AND REBEL RAIDERS. NY, (1956). 1st ed. VG+. *PRATT.* $45

Jones, Virgil Carrington. RANGER MOSBY. Chapel Hill, (1944). 4th ptg. VG+. *PRATT.* $40

Jones, W.F. THE EXPERIENCES OF A DEPUTY U.S. MARSHALL OF THE INDIAN TERRITORY. (n.p.), (1937). 40pp, illus; wraps. VG+. *PRATT.* $35

Jones, W.H.S. MALARIA AND GREEK HISTORY TO WHICH IS ADDED THE HISTORY OF GREEK THERAPEUTICS AND THE MALARIA THEORY. Manchester, 1909. 1st ed. Ex-lib. Head of spine torn. *FYE.* $75

Jones, Wilbur Devereux. THE CONFEDERATE RAMS AT BIRKENHEAD. Tuscaloosa, AL, 1961. 1st ed, ltd to 450. Wrappers, front margin little sunned, else NF. *McGOWAN.* $75

Jones, William. FINGER-RING LORE. HISTORICAL, LEGENDARY, ANECDOTAL. London: Chatto and Windus, 1877. 1st ed. Quarter-bound in gilt-stamped brown lea; bit rubbed. VG+. *BEASLEY.* $50

Jong, Erica. ANY WOMAN'S BLUES. NY: Harper, 1990. 1st ed. Uncorrected proof. NF in wraps, few pen notes on cvr. *SMITH.* $25

Jong, Erica. FRUITS AND VEGETABLES. NY: Holt 1971. 1st ed, 1st bk. Fine. *SMITH.* $50

Jong, Erica. HOW TO SAVE YOUR OWN LIFE. NY: HRW, (1977). 1st ed. Inscribed. Few marginal markings in text; VG in dj. *LOPEZ.* $35

Jong, Erica. HOW TO SAVE YOUR OWN LIFE. NY: Holt, (1977). 1st ed. Fine in price-clipped dj. Inscribed. *CAPTAIN'S BOOKSHELF.* $50

Jong, Erica. LOVERROOT. NY: Holt, 1975. 1st ed. Inscribed. NF. *SMITH.* $35

Jong, Erica. SERENISSIMA. Boston: HM, 1987. 1st ed. Fine in dj. Inscribed. *CAPTAIN'S BOOKSHELF.* $40

Jonson, Ben. VOLPONE OR THE FOX. Illus by Rene Ben Sussan. Dec cl, dj, slipcase. Oxford: LEC, 1952. One of 1500 designed by Francis Meynell, signed by Ben Sussan. VF. *JAFFE.* $150

Jordan, D.S. REPORTS ON CONDITION OF SEAL LIFE ON THE PRIBILOF ISLANDS, ETC. FROM 1868 TO 1895. Washington, DC: GPO, 1898. Fldg map, photo. Vol 1 of 4. VG+ *MIKESH.* $45

Jordan, David M. WINFIELD SCOTT HANCOCK. Bloomington, (1958). 1st ed. Lt dj wear o/w Fine. *PRATT.* $30

Jordan, David Starr and Barton Warren Evermann. AMERICAN FOOD AND GAME FISHES. NY: Doubleday, 1903. Chromoliths, photos. Soiled. *HUDSON.* $125

Jordan, Joe. THE BLUEGRASS HORSE COUNTRY. Lexington: Transylvania, 1940. Signed. 1st trade ed. VG. *OCTOBER FARM.* $65

Jordan, Pat. CHEAT. Villard, 1984. 1st. About Fine in dj (sm chip rear of dj). *STAHR.* $25

Jordan, Weymouth T. REBELS IN THE MAKING. Tuscaloosa, AL, 1958. 1st ed, ltd to 450. Wrappers, front margin little sunned, else NF. *McGOWAN.* $75

JORROCK'S JAUNTS AND JOLLITIES. London, 1924. New ed. 15 colored illus by Henry Alken. Spine faded, contents Fine. *HEINOLDT.* $20

Joscelyn, Archie. THE GOLDEN BOWL. Cleveland: International Fiction Library, 1931. 1st ed. Edges sl darkened o/w Fine in dj. *MORDIDA.* $45

Joseph, Alice et al. THE DESERT PEOPLE. Chicago: Univ of Chicago Press, 1949. Fldg plan. Dj. Lightly foxed. *HUDSON.* $45

Joseph, Alice. THE DESERT PEOPLE. U of Chicago Press (1949), 1st ed, dj. *HEINOLDT.* $18

Josephson, Matthew. THE ROBBER BARONS: THE GREAT AMERICAN CAPITALISTS 1861-1901. NY: Harcourt-Brace, 1934. 1st ed. VG in Fair dj. *CONNOLLY & WADE.* $35

Josephy, Alvin. THE NEZ PERCE INDIANS AND THE OPENING OF THE NORTHWEST. Yale, 1965. 1st ed. Preferred grn buckram binding. VF in VG dj. *OREGON.* $65

Josephy, Helen and McBride, Mary Margaret. PARIS IS A WOMAN'S TOWN. NY: Coward-McCann, 1929. 1st ed. Fine in chipped, worn dj. *SECOND LIFE.* $35

Joshi, S.T. H.P. LOVECRAFT: AN ANNOTATED BIBLIOGRAPHY. Kent State Univ Press, 1981. 1st ed. As New. *MADLE.* $35

Joslin, Sesyle. SENIOR BABY ELEPHANT THE PIRATE. London: Collins, (1965). NF in VG dj. *ACADEMIC LIBRARY.* $25

Joslynn, Major Jep (pseud of John E.P. Doyle). TAR-HEEL TALES IN VERNACULAR VERSE. NY: M. Doolady, 1873. 1st ed. 12mo, 69pp,(3)pp ads. Orig red cl. Lib bkpl, blindstamp, old catalogue descrip on front pastedown, else VG. *CHAPEL HILL.* $60

Josselyn, John. AN ACCOUNT OF TWO VOYAGES TO NEW ENGLAND, MADE DURING THE YEARS 1638, 1663. Boston: William Veazie, 1865. One of 250. (viii),211pp. Orig cl, spine rubbed. *LEFKOWICZ.* $150

Jourdain, Margaret and F. Rose. ENGLISH FURNITURE: THE GEORGIAN PERIOD 1750-1830. London: B.T. Batsford Ltd, 1953. 1st ed. VG. *BACKROOM.* $110

Jourdain, Margaret. ENGLISH INTERIOR DECORATION, 1500 TO 1830. London: B.T. Batsford, Ltd. (1950). 1st ed. Corners bit bumped. *KARMIOLE.* $85

JOURNAL OF MODERN LITERATURE. John Fowles Special Number. Vol 8, No 2, 1980/1981. (Phila: Temple Univ, 1981). 1st ptg. Signed on front wrap. Orig ptd wraps, photo of Fowles front wrap. NF. *CHAPEL HILL.* $40

JOURNAL OF THE TWENTIETH ANNUAL SESSION OF THE NATIONAL ENCAMPMENT GRAND ARMY OF THE REPUBLIC, SAN FRANCISCO, CALIFORNIA, AUGUST 4TH, 5TH AND 6TH, 1886. Washington, 1886. Cvr wear, o/w VG+. *PRATT.* $30

JOURNEY TO JAPAN. London, 1986. UNICEF bk. Pop-up bk. *BOOKFINDERS INTL.* $20

Jowett, William. CHRISTIAN RESEARCHES IN SYRIA AND THE HOLY LAND, IN 1823 & 1824. Boston, 1826. Contemp calf, rubbed. 364pp. Fldg map; lacking frontis map. *O'NEILL.* $85

Joyce, James. A FIRST DRAFT VERSION OF FINNEGAN'S WAKE. David Hayman, ed. Austin: Univ of Texas Press, 1963. 1st ed. *OLD LONDON.* $35

Joyce, James. A PORTRAIT OF THE ARTIST AS A YOUNG MAN. London: The Egoist, Ltd., London, 1916. 1st Eng ed. Rebound in 3/4 morocco. 750 only. Rare, thus. Minor smudge bottom edge. NF. *OLD LONDON.* $485

Joyce, James. A PORTRAIT OF THE ARTIST AS A YOUNG MAN. A Facsimilie of the Final Holograph Manuscript (Prefaced and arranged by Hans Walter Gabler). NY and London: Garland Pub, Inc, 1977. 1st ed. 2 vols. Minor wear to bottom edges only. W/o djs, as issued. NF. *OLD LONDON.* $175

Joyce, James. A PORTRAIT OF THE ARTIST AS A YOUNG MAN. NY: Huebsch, 1922. 5th Amer ed. Spine darkened; bkpl, bibliogr note pasted in. Lacks dj. *WOOLMER.* $45

Joyce, James. A SHORTER FINNEGAN'S WAKE. Ed Anthony Burgess. London: Faber & Faber, (1966). 1st ed. Fine in dj. *CAPTAIN'S BOOKSHELF.* $125

Joyce, James. ANNA LIVIA PLURABELLE. Criterion Miscellany #15. London: Faber and Faber, 1930. 1st Eng ed, 2nd imp, with recording announcement laid in. Tiny tear at base of cover, else Fine in wraps. *OLD LONDON.* $100

Joyce, James. CHAMBER MUSIC. Boston: The Cornhill Company, n.d. (1918). 1st Amer ed, unauthorized. W/o orig protective tissue wrapper. Scarce. Minor spotting, else NF. *OLD LONDON.* $300

Joyce, James. CHAMBER MUSIC. London: Elkin Mathews, n.d. 1st ed, third issue (509 only) Rare, thus. Sans dj, as issued. NF. Slocum-Cahoon A3. *OLD LONDON.* $1200

Joyce, James. CHAMBER MUSIC. William York Tindall (ed). NY: Columbia Univ. Press, 1954. 1st ed, w/new material. VF in dj w/rare wraparound band. *JAFFE.* $150

Joyce, James. COLLECTED POEMS OF JAMES JOYCE. NY: The Black Sun Press, 1936. 1st ed (ltd to 800 of which this is number 379). NF with marker ribbon intact, in clear wraparound plastic protector. Quite scarce. *OLD LONDON.* $650

Joyce, James. COLLECTED POEMS. Frontis by Augustus John, dec parchment boards, orig tissue dj. NY: Black Sun Press, 1936. 1st ed. One of 750 numbered. VF in lightly worn tissue. *JAFFE.* $750

Joyce, James. COLLECTED POEMS. NY: Viking, 1937. 1st US ed. Fine. Dj is chipped at top edge and has several scratches. *WOOLMER.* $125

Joyce, James. EXILES—A PLAY IN THREE ACTS. London: Grant Richards, 1918. 1st ed, Half grn cl over boards, issued w/o dj. cl worn at top and base of spine, spine paper label darkened. Scarce. *OLD LONDON.* $450

Joyce, James. FINNEGAN'S WAKE. (Corrections of Misprints in...). London: Faber and Faber, 1945. Only ed. The scarce pamphlet distributed to purchasers of the later reprint. Fine in wraps. *OLD LONDON.* $75

Joyce, James. FINNEGAN'S WAKE. London: Faber & Faber, (1939). 1st ed. Bit of foxing first couple of pages, o/w Fine in a Fine dj with one short tear. *LOPEZ*. $2,250

Joyce, James. FINNEGAN'S WAKE. London: Faber & Faber; NY: Viking, 1939. 1st ed. #374 of 425, signed. Orig red buckram, teg. Fine in moderately soiled pub's yellow cl slipcase. *CHAPEL HILL*. $5000

Joyce, James. FINNEGAN'S WAKE. London: Faber and Faber, 1939. 1st ed (i.e., 1st Eng ed, regular). Slight wear to top and base of spine, unobtrusive owners plt front fep, top edge dust-darkened, else VG w/o dj. *OLD LONDON*. $600

Joyce, James. FINNEGAN'S WAKE. London: Faber & Faber, (1939). 1st ed. Fine (some offsetting to first, last pages of text) in dj (internally strengthened at edges, folds w/tape which has bled slightly). In custom slipcase. *LOPEZ*. $1,250

Joyce, James. FINNEGAN'S WAKE. NY: The Viking Press, 1939. 1st US trade ed. Minor chipping dj extremities, else Fine in NF dj. *OLD LONDON*. $450

Joyce, James. FINNEGAN'S WAKE. NY: Viking, 1939. 1st US trade ed. Clippings pasted in, else Fine. Dj not present. The "corrections of misprints" pamphlet is loosely inserted. *WOOLMER*. $125

Joyce, James. GIACOMO JOYCE. London: Faber & Faber, (1968). 1st Eng ed. Fine in dj. *WOOLMER*. $35

Joyce, James. GIACOMO JOYCE. NY: The Viking Press, 1st and only prtg. In slipcase, w/o dj (as issued). Fine. *OLD LONDON*. $45

Joyce, James. HAVETH CHILDERS EVERYWHERE. Paris: Babou and Kahane, and NY: The Fountain Press, 1930. Ltd to 600 (this being #328/600), in the rare slipcase. Bottom edge of case needs repair, else F/VG. *OLD LONDON*. $800

Joyce, James. HAVETH CHILDERS EVERYWHERE. Paris: Henry Babou & Jack Kahane, 1930. 1st ed. #302 of 500 (numbered 101-600) on Vidalon paper. Orig ptd wraps. Virtually Fine in orig glassine dj, somewhat worn pub's slipcase split along couple of edges. *CHAPEL HILL*. $900

Joyce, James. INTRODUCING JAMES JOYCE. London: Faber and Faber, 1942. 1st ed. Intro by T.S. Eliot. Some soiling to book and dj spine, else VG in VG dj. *OLD LONDON*. $50

Joyce, James. LETTERS. NY: Viking Press, 1966. 3 vols in boxed set, complete as issued (Vol I, 2nd prtg; Vols II and III, 1st prtgs. NF in NF djs. *OLD LONDON*. $100

Joyce, James. LETTERS. NY: Viking, 1957. Stuart Gilbert, ed. 1st ed. Fine. Dj a touch darkened and with half-inch hole in spine. *WOOLMER*. $50

Joyce, James. LETTERS—JAMES JOYCE. NY: Viking Press, 1957. Stuart Gilbert, ed. 1st ed. NF in NF dj. *OLD LONDON*. $40

Joyce, James. POMES PENYEACH. Paris: Shakespeare and Company, 1927. 1st ed, with errata slip tipped in. W/o dj, as issued. NF with only slight soil spotting and discoloration. *OLD LONDON*. $300

Joyce, James. TALES TOLD OF SHEM AND SHAUN. Paris: The Black Sun Press, 1929. 1st ed. #97 of 500 on Holland Van Gelder Zonen. Orig ptd wraps. Fine in orig glassine jacket. Brancusi port. *CHAPEL HILL*. $800

Joyce, James. THE CAT AND THE DEVIL. London: Faber and Faber, 1965. Illus by Gerald Rose. 1st ed thus. Fine in Fine dj. *OLD LONDON*. $45

Joyce, James. THE CRITICAL WRITINGS OF JAMES JOYCE. London: Faber and Faber, 1959. 1st ed. Fine in Fine dj. *OLD LONDON*. $35

Joyce, James. THE CRITICAL WRITINGS OF JAMES JOYCE. The Viking Press, 1959. 1st ed. Fine in VG dj. *OLD LONDON*. $30

Joyce, James. THE MIME OF MICK, NICK AND THE MAGGIES. The Hague: The Servire Press, and London: Faber and Faber, 1934.

1st ed in the scarce box (needs repair). NF with orig protective tissue covering wraps. Ltd to 1000. *OLD LONDON*. $450

Joyce, James. ULYSSES. Illus Henri Matisse. NY: LEC, 1935. 1st illus ed. One of 1500 signed by Matisse. Fine in gilt-dec cl, sl faded and soiled slipcase. *CAPTAIN'S BOOKSHELF*. $3000

Joyce, James. ULYSSES. London: Egoist Press, 1922. 1st Eng ed (published in France). Ltd to 2000, a large number of which were reportedly destroyed. Rebound in 3/4 grn morocco, errata slip laid in. NF. *OLD LONDON*. $2,200.

Joyce, James. ULYSSES. NY: Random House, 1934. 1st US ed containing the Morris Ernst foreword, the US District Court decision to lift the ban on Ulysses, and Joyce's 1932 letter to Bennett Cerf. Head of spine sl frayed, w/very light spotting to the spine, else Fine in dj (very lightly chipped). *CAPTAIN'S BOOKSHELF*. $250

Joyce, James. ULYSSES. Paris: Shakespeare and Company, 1926. 8th ed. Blue ptd wraps, chipped at head, foot of backstrip; sl rubbed along edges. *HELLER*. $350

Joyce, James. ULYSSES—A FACSIMILIE OF THE MANUSCRIPT. London: Faber and Faber, and Phila: Rosenbach Foundation, 1975. 1st ed. 3 vols. Fine w/o djs as issued in Fine case. *OLD LONDON*. $175

Joyce, James. STEPHEN HERO, A PART OF THE 1st DRAFT OF THE PORTRAIT OF THE ARTIST AS A YOUNG MAN. Binghampton: New Directions, 1944. 1st US ed. Slight fading, wear. VG. *OLD LONDON*. $80

Joyce, Mary H. PIONEER DAYS IN THE WYOMING VALLEY. Author, 1928. 20 plts. *HEINOLDT*. $15

Joyce, Stanislaus. MY BROTHER'S KEEPER. NY: Viking, 1958. 1st ed. Richard Ellmann (ed). VG in dj. *BERNARD*. $25

Joyce, Thomas. SOUTH AMERICAN ARCHAEOLOGY. NY: Putnam, 1912. 1st ed. Fldg map, color frontis. 25 b/w plts. Spine faded, contents VG+. *SILVER*. $50

Judd, Cyril. GUNNER CADE. Simon & Schuster, 1952. 1st ed. Fine in tape-stained dj. *MADLE*. $25

Judd, Laura Fish. HONOLULU. SKETCHES OF LIFE...IN THE HAWAIIAN ISLANDS FROM 1828 TO 1861. NY: Anson D.F. Randolph & Co, c. 1880. Brn cl w/gilt titles, spine dec. Some wear to cvrs. Overall VG. *PARMER*. $200

Judd, Neil M. THE DISCOVERY OF RAINBOW BRIDGE. Cummings Publ Council, Tucson, 1959. Bulletin No. 1. NF. *FIVE QUAIL*. $25

Judson, Katharine Berry (ed). MYTHS AND LEGENDS OF CALIFORNIA AND THE OLD SOUTHWEST. Chicago: A.C. McClurg, 1912. 1st ed. Water stained corner, o/w clean and tight. *LAURIE*. $30

Judson, L. Carroll. SAGES AND HEROES OF THE AMERICAN REVOLUTION. Phila: Pub by author, 1851. 1st ed. 480pp engr portrait, foxed. Recased black buckram. Contents clean. *HEINOLDT*. $25

Judson, Phoebe. A PIONEER'S SEARCH FOR AN IDEAL HOME. Bellingham, WA: Union Printing, 1925. 1st ed. 309pp. VG. *BOOK MARKET*. $90

Juffe, Mel. FLASH. NY: Viking, (1974). 1st ed. Inscribed. Fine in NF dj. *LOPEZ*. $25

Juhl (pseud of Julius J. Fleming). THE JUHL LETTERS TO THE CHARLESTON COURIER. John Hammond Moore (ed). Athens (1974). 1st ed. Tear, lt wear on dj o/w Fine. *PRATT*. $25

Jung, Carl G. FLYING SAUCERS: A MODERN MYTH OF THINGS SEEN IN THE SKY. R.F.C. Hull (trans). NY: Harcourt, (1959). 1st US ed. Fine in lightly rubbed price-clipped dj. *CAPTAIN'S BOOKSHELF*. $65

Jungman, Beatrix. HOLLAND. A&C Black, 1904. 1st ed. 20s Series. Slight wear extremities, else VG. *OLD LONDON.* $65

Just, Ward. TO WHAT END: REPORT FROM VIET NAM. Boston, 1968. 1st ed, 1st bk. VG in bit worn dj. *PETTLER.* $30

Justice, Donald. DEPARTURES. Iowa City: Penumbra Press/The Stone Wall Press, 1973. 1st ed. Ltd to 275 signed. Fine, w/erratum. Cl, ptd label on spine. *JAFFE.* $375

Justice, Donald. NIGHT LIGHT. Middletown: Wesleyan, (1967). 1st ed. Fine in dj. Review copy, slip laid in. Inscribed, initialled. *CAPTAIN'S BOOKSHELF.* $90

Justice, Donald. THE SUMMER ANNIVERSARIES. Middletown, CT: Wesleyan Univ Press, (1960). 1st ed. Fine, in later issue dj (new price front flap, old prices deleted from back flap). *JAFFE.* $125

K

Kadare, Iismail. THE GENERAL OF THE DEAD ARMY. NY, 1972. Dj. *O'NEILL.* $20

Kaese, Harold. THE BOSTON BRAVES. Putnam, 1948. 1st ed. VG in Fine dj. *PLAPINGER.* $65

Kafka, Franz. A FRANZ KAFKA MISCELLANY. NY: Twice a Year Press, (1940). 1st ed. NF in like dj. *DERMONT.* $60

Kafka, Franz. IN THE PENAL COLONY. (LEC, 1987). One of 800 signed by the artist, Michael Hafftka. Mint in folding box. *PIRAGES.* $350

Kagan, Solomon. CONTRIBUTIONS OF EARLY JEWS TO AMERICAN MEDICINE. Boston, 1934. 1st ed. *FYE.* $50

Kahn, Fritz. MAN IN STRUCTURE AND FUNCTION. NY: Knopf, 1943. George Rosen (trans). 1st US ed. 2 vols. VF in F djs in VG+ slipcase. *AARD.* $60

Kahn, Gordon. HOLLYWOOD ON TRIAL. THE STORY OF THE 10 WHO WERE INDICTED. NY, (1948). 1st ed. Signed by Albert Maltz, one of the 10. Extrems sl chipped. Dj spine sunned, edge chipped, few edge tears. *POLYANTHOS.* $30

Kahn, James. THE UMPIRE'S STORY. Putnam, 1953. 1st ed. VG+ without dj. *PLAPINGER.* $40

Kahn, Roger. THE BOYS OF SUMMER. H & R, 1972. VG in Good+ dj. *PLAPINGER.* $27.50

Kahrl, William L. et al. THE CALIFORNIA WATER ATLAS. CA: State of CA, (1979). 1st ed. Fine. *BOOK MARKET.* $200

Kaiser, Georg. GAS. London: Chapman & Dodd, 1924. 1st Eng ed. VG in dj. *LAME DUCK.* $150

Kakonis, Tom. MICHIGAN ROLL. NY: St. Martin's Press, 1988. 1st ed, 1st novel. VF in dj. *MORDIDA.* $35

Kalish, Max. LABOR SCULPTURE. NY: (Max Kalish). 1938. 43 photogr plts. Ltd to 500. Inscribed by Alice Kalish, artist's wife. Beige cl, a bit soiled. Dj. *KARMIOLE.* $65

Kamal, Ahmad. LAND WITHOUT LAUGHTER. NY: Scribner, 1940. 1st ed. Almost VG in Almost VG dj. *AARD.* $20

Kaminsky, Stuart M. BLACK KNIGHT IN RED SQUARE. Charter, 1984. 1st ed. VF, wraps. *STAHR.* $30

Kaminsky, Stuart. A COLD RED SUNRISE. NY: Charles Scribner's Sons, 1988. 1st ed. VF in dj. *MORDIDA.* $35

Kaminsky, Stuart. BULLET FOR A STAR. London: Severn House, 1981. 1st Eng ed. Fine in dj. *MORDIDA.* $25

Kaminsky, Stuart. BULLET FOR A STAR. NY: St. Martin's Press, 1977. 1st ed. Fine in dj. *MORDIDA.* $150

Kaminsky, Stuart. BURIED CAESARS. NY: Mysterious Press, 1989. 1st ed. VF in dj. *MORDIDA.* $25

Kaminsky, Stuart. HE DONE HER WRONG. NY: St. Martin's Press, 1983. 1st ed. VF in dj. *SILVER DOOR.* $25

Kaminsky, Stuart. THE HOWARD HUGHES AFFAIR. NY: St. Martins, 1979. 1st ed. Fine in Fine dj (traces of wear spine ends). *BEASLEY.* $45

Kane, Elisha K. and Margaret Fox. THE LOVE-LIFE OF DR. KANE; CONTAINING THE CORRESPONDENCE...SECRET MARRIAGE BETWEEN ELISHA K. KANE AND MARGARET FOX. NY: Carleton, Publisher, 1866. Frontis. Blue cl. Spine faded, shelfwear, else VG+. *PARMER.* $125

Kane, Elisha Kent. ARCTIC EXPLORATIONS: THE SECOND GRINNELL EXPEDITION IN SEARCH OF SIR JOHN FRANKLIN, 1853, '54, '55. Phila: Childs & Peterson, 1856. 1st ed. 2 vols. 464,467pp. Internal foxing. Good+ set. *BLUE DRAGON.* $95

Kane, Elisha Kent. ARCTIC EXPLORATIONS: THE SECOND GRINNELL EXPEDITION...1853, '54, '55. London, 1873. Later, 1 vol ed. Pict cl, fldg map. 1st signature pulling, chip top of spine. Good. *McCLINTOCK.* $40

Kane, Elisha Kent. ARCTIC EXPLORATIONS; THE SECOND GRINNELL EXPEDITION IN SEARCH OF SIR JOHN FRANKLIN, 1853, '54, '55. Phila: Childs & Peterson, 1856. 1st ed. 2 vols. 2 fldg maps. Some foxing to frontis and engr titles. Spine ends showing light wear, o/w VG set. *LEFKOWICZ.* $150

Kane, Elisha Kent. ARCTIC EXPLORATIONS; THE SECOND GRINNELL EXPEDITION. Phila: Childs & Peterson, 1856. 1st ed. 2 vols. Serious wear, text clean, tight. Fair. *PARMER.* $125

Kane, Elisha Kent. THE U.S. GRINNELL EXPEDITION IN SEARCH OF SIR JOHN FRANKLIN. NY: Harper & Brothers, 1854. 1st ed. 13 litho plts, fldg map. Foxing. VG. *WEBER.* $175

Kane, Elisha Kent. THE U.S. GRINNELL EXPEDITION IN SEARCH OF SIR JOHN FRANKLIN.... NY: Harper & Brothers, 1854. 552 pp. 1 fldg map. 14 plts. Some spine tears. Reprint of rare 1st ed, pub in previous yr. *LEFKOWICZ.* $150

Kane, Frank. TRIGGER MORTIS. Rinehart, 1958. 1st ed. NF, dj. Light wear head & foot dj spine. *STAHR.* $25

Kane, Harnett T. QUEEN NEW ORLEANS; CITY BY THE RIVER. NY, 1949. 1st ed. Inscribed. Fine in NF dj. *VARNER.* $25

Kane, Harnett T. SPIES FOR THE BLUE AND GRAY. GC, (1954). 1st ed. VG in dj. *PRATT.* $35

Kane, Harnett T. THE GALLANT MRS. STONEWALL. GC, 1957. 320pp. Dj wear repaired o/w VG. *PRATT.* $17.50

Kane, Harnett T. THE GALLANT MRS. STONEWALL. GC: Doubleday, 1957. 1st ed. Inscribed. VG in Good dj. *BOOK BROKER.* $15

Kane, Harnett T. THE GOLDEN COAST. Doubleday, 1959. 1st ed. VG. Inscribed. *CONNOLLY & WADE.* $25

Kane, Patricia E. 300 YEARS OF AMERICAN SEATING FURNITURE. MA: NY Graphic Soc, 1976. 1st ed. VG. *BACKROOM.* $85

Kane, Thomas. THE MORMONS: A DISCOURSE DELIVERED BEFORE THE HISTORICAL SOCIETY OF PENNSYLVANIA, MARCH 26, 1850. Phila, 1850. 2nd ed. Rebound in modern burgundy lib cl, ex-lib. Owner stamp, emb lib stamp, o/w VG. *BENCHMARK.* $500

Kanin, Garson. REMEMBERING MR. MAUGHAM. NY: Atheneum, 1966. 1st ed. NF in dj. *ELSE FINE.* $25

Kanner, Leo. FOLKLORE OF THE TEETH. NY, 1936. *FYE.* $45

KANSAS. NY, 1939. American Guide Series. WPA guide. 1st ptg, w/fldg map and dj. *SCHOYER'S.* $50

Kant, Candace C. ZANE GREY'S ARIZONA. Northland, (1984). 1st ed. Signed. New in dj. *AUTHORS OF THE WEST.* $25

Kantor, MacKinlay and Tim Kantor. HAMILTON COUNTY. NY: Macmillan, (1970). Stated 1st ed. 289pp. Dj price-clipped w/small piece missing, closed tear. AKA. $27

Kantor, MacKinlay. ANDERSONVILLE. Cleveland, (1955). 1st ed. 598pp. Dj wear and little spotting on cover, o/w VG. PRATT. $35

Kantor, MacKinlay. ANDERSONVILLE. Cleveland: World, 1955. 1st ed. Fine in VG dj. CONNOLLY & WADE. $37.50

Kantor, Mackinlay. DIVERSEY. NY: Coward-McCann, 1928. 1st ed, 1st bk. Red cl, beige ptd dj (torn and chipped, top half of back missing). JUVELIS. $150

Kany, Charles. LIFE AND MANNERS IN MADRID, 1750-1800. Berkeley: Univ of CA Press, 1932. 1st ed. Very slight silverfish nibbling on cvrs, else Fine. WREDEN. $35

Kapp, Friedrich. IMMIGRATION AND THE COMMISSIONERS OF EMIGRATION OF THE STATE OF NEW YORK. NY, 1820, 240pp. 6 engr. Rebound. HEINOLDT. $40

Karalus, Karl E. and Allan W. Eckert. THE OWLS OF NORTH AMERICA. (NORTH OF MEXICO). GC, NY: 1974. 60 color plts (one mounted). Special ed ltd to 250 numbered, signed by Karalus and Eckert. Full grn morocco, gilt, aeg. Slipcase. Fine. KARMIOLE. $250

Karlgren, Bernhard. A CATALOGUE OF THE CHINESE BRONZES IN THE ALFRED F PILLSBURY COLLECTION. Minneapolis: Univ of MN Press for the Minneapolis Inst of Arts, (1952). Glassine wrapper. Fine. WEBER. $200

Karolevitz, Robert. DOCTORS OF THE OLD WEST, A PICTORIAL HISTORY OF MEDICINE ON THE FRONTIER. NY, 1967. FYE. $40

Karouzou, Semni. THE AMASIS PAINTER. Oxford: Clarendon Press, 1956. 44 plts. Fine in dj. ARCHAEOLOGIA. $300

Karpinski, Louis C. THE HISTORY OF ARITHMETIC. Chicago, 1925. VG-NF. POLYANTHOS. $65

Karsner, David. DEBS. HIS AUTHORIZED LIFE AND LETTERS. NY: Boni, 1919. 1st ed. Fine in worn dj w/chips. BEASLEY. $75

Kart, Lawrence. THAT OLD BALL GAME. Ed by David Phillips. Regnery, 1975. 1st ed. VG in Fine dj. PLAPINGER. $50

Kates, George N. CHINESE HOUSEHOLD FURNITURE. NY: Harper & Bros. (1948). 1st ed. KARMIOLE. $45

Katz, Michael J. LAST DANCE IN REDONDO BEACH. NY: Putnam, 1989. 1st ed. Review copy, signed. Pub's slip laid in. Fine in dj. SILVER DOOR. $35

Katzenbach, John. DAY OF RECKONING. NY: G.P. Putnam's Sons, 1989. 1st ed. VF in dj. MORDIDA. $20

Katzenbach, John. IN THE HEAT OF THE SUMMER. NY: Atheneum, 1982. 1st ed. Fine in dj. MORDIDA. $25

Katzenbach, John. IN THE HEAT OF THE SUMMER. NY: Atheneum, (1982). 1st ed. Fine in Fine dj. UNGER. $40

Katzenbach, John. THE TRAVELER. NY: G.P. Putnam's Sons, 1987. 1st ed. VF in dj. MORDIDA. $20

Katzenbach, John. THE TRAVELER. NY: Putnam, (1987). 1st ed. Inscribed by author to John Ball. Fine in Fine dj. UNGER. $40

Kauffman, Henry J. AMERICAN AXES. Brattleboro, VT: Stephen Greene Press, 1972. VG to NF in VG dj. BACKROOM. $65

Kauffman, Henry J. AMERICAN COPPER & BRASS. (Camden, NJ): Thomas Nelson & Sons. (1968). 1st ed. KARMIOLE. $40

Kauffman, Henry J. EARLY AMERICAN IRONWARE CAST AND WROUGHT. NY: Weathervane Books, 1966. 1st ed. VG. BACKROOM. $40

Kauffman, Henry J. PENNSYLVANIA DUTCH FOLK ART. NY: American Studio, 1946. 1st ed. VG in Good+ dj. Some foxing, minor spotting. BACKROOM. $55

Kauffman, Henry J. THE COLONIAL SILVERSMITH. NY (1969). Dj. HEINOLDT. $16

Kauffman, Henry J. THE COLONIAL SILVERSMITH. NY: Galahad Books, 1969. 1st ed. VG in dj. BACKROOM. $25

Kauffman, Janet. PLACES IN THE WORLD A WOMAN COULD WALK. NY: Knopf, 1983. 1st ed. Sm remainder mk, o/w Fine in Fine dj. Signed. LOPEZ. $35

Kauffman, Reginald Wright. THE SENTENCE OF SILENCE. NY: Moffat, Yard, 1912. 1st ed. NF w/light soiling to spine. BEASLEY. $125

Kaufman, George S. and Hart, Moss THE MAN WHO CAME TO DINNER. NY: Random House, (1939). Fine in NF dj. 1st ed. CHAPEL HILL. $85

Kaufman, Lewis et al. MOE BERG—ATHLETE, SCHOLAR, SPY. Little Brown, 1974. Ltr ptg. VG+ in Fine dj. PLAPINGER. $40

Kaufmann, Edgar (ed). FRANK LLOYD WRIGHT. NY, 1955. Dj rubbed, chipped. NF. POLYANTHOS. $75

Kaufmann, John and Heinz Meng. FALCONS RETURN. NY: Morrow, 1975. 2nd prtg. NF in dj. OLD LONDON. $20

Kavanagh, Dan (pseud of Julian Barnes). DUFFY. London: Jonathan Cape, 1980. 1st ed. VF in dj with clipped inner front flap and price sticker. MORDIDA. $75

Kavanagh, Dan (pseud of Julian Barnes). FIDDLE CITY. London: Cape, (1981) 1st ed. VF in dj. JAFFE. $125

Kavanagh, Dan (pseud of Julian Barnes). GOING TO THE DOGS. London: Viking, 1987. 1st ed. VF in dj. MORDIDA. $45

Kavanagh, Dan (pseud of Julian Barnes). PUTTING THE BOOT IN. London: Jonathan Cape, 1985. 1st ed. Fine in dj. BEASLEY. $65

Kavanagh, Martin. LA VERENDRYE. HIS LIFE AND TIMES. Brandon: Martin Kavanagh, 1968. 2nd ed. 7 foldouts. Rubber stamp, else VG in worn dj. PARMER. $35

Kavanaugh, Ethel. WILDERNESS HOMESTEADERS. Caldwell: Caxton, 1950. 1st ed. VG in VG- dj. BLUE DRAGON. $25

Kawabata, Yasunari. BEAUTY AND SADNESS. NY: Knopf (1975). 1st Amer ed. Fine in dj. DORN. $25

Kawabata, Yasunari. THE SOUND OF THE MOUNTAIN. NY: Knopf (1970). 1st Amer ed. Fine in Fine dj. DORN. $35

Kawakita, Michiaki. CONTEMPORARY JAPANESE PRINTS. John Bester (trans). Tokyo: Kodansha, (1970). 3rd ptg. 47 tipped-on color plts. Fine in acetate dj w/wraparound band intact. CAPTAIN'S BOOKSHELF. $125

Kay, Terry. AFTER ELI. Boston: Houghton Mifflin Co., (1981). 1st Amer ed. Signed. Fine in price-clipped VG+ dj. DORN. $45

Kay, Terry. DARK THIRTY. NY: Poseidon Press, (1984). 1st Amer ed. Signed. Rem stamp bottom edge else Fine in VG+ dj. DORN. $40

Kay, Terry. THE YEAR THE LIGHTS CAME ON. Boston: Houghton Mifflin Co., (1976). 1st Amer ed. Signed. Rem dot bottom edge else VG in dj. DORN. $70

Kay, Terry. TO DANCE WITH THE WHITE DOG. Atlanta: Peachtree Publishers, (1990). 1st Amer ed. Signed. Fine in dj. DORN. $45

Kazantzakis, Nikos. ENGLAND: A TRAVEL JOURNAL. NY: Simon & Schuster, (1965). 1st US ed. Fine in price-clipped dj (sl darkened spine). CAPTAIN'S BOOKSHELF. $25

Kazantzakis, Nikos. JAPAN CHINA: A JOURNAL OF TWO VOYAGES TO THE EAST: 1935 AND 1957. NY: Simon & Schuster, (1963). 1st US ed. Fine in a lightly used price-clipped dj. CAPTAIN'S BOOKSHELF. $25

Kazantzakis, Nikos. ZORBA THE GREEK. NY: Simon & Schuster, (1953). 1st ed. Fine in VG dj. LOPEZ. $200

Kazin, Alfred. AN AMERICAN PROCESSION. NY: Knopf, (1984). 1st ed. Signed. Fine in dj with a small crease to the back panel. *UNGER.* $50

Keane, John. MORE IRISH SHORT STORIES. Dublin & Cork: The Mercier Press, (1981). Fine. 1st ed. Inscribed. *CHAPEL HILL.* $35

Kearney, Thomas H. and Robert H. Pebbles. FLOWERING PLANTS AND FERNS OF ARIZONA. U.S.D.A Misc Pub #423. Washington: G.P.O, 1942. 1st ed. Frontis, 29 plts. Map. Grn buckram, gilt. NF. *CONNOLLY & WADE.* $115

Kearton, C. THE LION'S ROAR. London, 1934. Photos. VG+. *MIKESH.* $20

Keating, H.R.F. CRIME & MYSTERY—THE 100 BEST BOOKS. London: Xanadu, 1987. 1st ed. Promo material laid in. VF in dj. *SILVER DOOR.* $35

Keating, William H. NARRATIVE OF AN EXPEDITION TO THE SOURCE OF ST. PETER'S RIVER, LAKE WINNEPEEK, LAKE OF THE WOODS &C. PERFORMED IN THE YEAR 1823. 2 vols. London: Geo. B. Whitaker, 1825. 1st Eng ed, pub after 1st Amer ed of 1824. Rebound in blue cl. VG. Howes K-20. *LAURIE.* $250

Keats, John. LIFE, LETTERS, AND LITERARY REMAINS OF JOHN KEATS. Ed by Richard Monckton Milnes (Baron Houghton). Complete In One Volume. NY: Geo. P. Putman, 1848. 1st Amer ed. 8vo, 393pp. Port frontis, tissue guard. Orig stamped cloth, dec in blind. Signed Holograph Note From Monckton Milnes laid in. Nice, scarce. *HARTFIELD.* $295

Keats, John. THE POETICAL WORKS AND OTHER WRITINGS. H. Buxton Forman (ed). Maurice Buxton Forman (revision), John Masefield (intro). 8 vols. NY: Scribner's, 1938. The Hampstead Edition. Ltd to 1050 sets signed by Masefield & Forman. Fine set. Cl, leather labels, slipcases. *JAFFE.* $750

Keays, F.L. OLD ROSES. NY, 1935. 1st ed. Cl, dj. *SUTTON.* $50

Keefe, Charles S. (ed). THE AMERICAN HOUSE. NY: U.P.C. Book Co., 1922. 1st ed. Bumped and rubbed. VG. *BLUE MOUNTAIN.* $150

Keeler, Harry S. and Hazel Goodwin Keeler. THE STRANGE WILL. London: Ward Lock, 1949. 1st ed. Inscribed, signed by both Keelers. VG in dj w/chipping at top of spine and at corners and wear along folds. Laid in are 2 newspaper articles by Vincent Starrett. *MORDIDA.* $85

Keeler, Harry S. BY THIRD DEGREE. London: Ward Lock, 1948. 1st Eng ed. Pub in US as The Sharkskin Book. Inscribed. VG in dj w/wear at top of spine and at corners. *MORDIDA.* $60

Keeler, Harry S. FINE ACTOR HART. London: Ward Locke, 1939. 1st ed. Some staining on top edge o/w VG in price-clipped dj w/stains, short tears, wear. *MORDIDA.* $45

Keeler, Harry S. THE BOX FROM JAPAN. NY: E.P. Dutton, 1932. 1st ed. Eps darkened o/w VG in price-clipped dj w/internal tape mends and chipping at top of spine and at corners. *MORDIDA.* $85

Keeler, Harry S. THE CASE OF THE LAVENDER GRIPSACK. NY: Phoenix, 1944. 1st ed. NF in NF dj (lt wear spine ends). *BEASLEY.* $45

Keeler, Harry S. THE FIVE SILVER BUDDHAS. London: Ward Locke, 1935. 1st Eng ed. Inscribed. Fine in dj w/minor wear spine ends. *MORDIDA.* $85

Keeler, Harry S. THE GREEN JADE HAND. London: Ward Locke, 1930. 1st Eng ed. Inscribed. Fine in dj (minor wear spine ends; sl faded spine, short closed tears). *MORDIDA.* $85

Keeler, Harry S. THE IRON RING. London: Ward Lock, 1944. 1st ed. Pub in US as The Case of the Mysterious Moll. Bkseller's small label on front pastedown. Edges spotted o/w VG in dj w/wear at corners and along folds. *MORDIDA.* $65

Keeler, Harry S. THE MATILDA HUNTER MURDER. NY: E.P. Dutton, 1931. 1st ed. VG in dj w/wraparound intact and internal tape mends, light chipping at spine ends and corners and lightwear along top edge of front panel. *MORDIDA.* $85

Keeler, Harry S. THE MONOCLED MONSTER. London: Ward Lock, 1947. 1st ed. Edges and front cover spotted o/w VG in dj (sl faded spine; wear spine ends, corners; tears). *MORDIDA.* $45

Keeler, Harry S. THE SPECTACLES OF MR. CAGLIOSTRO. NY: E.P. Dutton, 1929. 1st Amer ed (?). There may have been an earlier US ed as the copyright pg states "...copyrighted, 1926, by Complete Novel Corporation, under the title The Blue Spectacles". Names, o/w VG in dj (faded spine; internal and external tape mends; chipping). *MORDIDA.* $35

Keeler, James E. PHOTOGRAPHS OF NEBULAE AND CLUSTERS MADE WITH THE CROSSLEY REFLECTOR. Pubs of Lick Observatory, Vol VIII, Sacramento, 1908. 2 tears spine, o/w Good in orig cl. 70 plts w/tissue guards. *KNOLLWOOD.* $400

Keen, A.M. SEA SHELLS OF TROPICAL WEST AMERICA. Stanford, 1958. *SUTTON.* $35

Keen, Alan and Roger Lubbock. THE ANNOTATOR. NY: Macmillan, 1954. 1st ed. Fine- in VG- price-clipped dj. *AARD.* $15

Keen, W.W. SELECTED PAPERS AND ADDRESSES. Phila, 1923. 1st ed. Scarce. *FYE.* $50

Keen, W.W. THE TREATMENT OF WAR WOUNDS. Phila, 1917. 1st ed. *FYE.* $100

Keen, William and J. William White (eds). AN AMERICAN TEXT-BOOK OF SURGERY. Phila, 1892. 1st ed. Full leather, 1209pp. Photo plts and nearly 500 woodcuts. *FYE.* $200

Keene, Day. PASSAGE TO SAMOA. Gold Medal (823), 1958. 1st ed. Almost Fine in pb. Lightest wear at spine; bkstore stamp inside cover. *STAHR.* $25

Kees, Weldon. POEMS: 1947-1954. Cl-backed boards w/wide ptd wraparound band quoting Malcolm Cowley & Allen Tate. SF: Adrian Wilson, 1954. 1st ed. One of 500. Review copy, pub's slip laid in. VF. *JAFFE.* $375

Kees, Weldon. THE CEREMONY AND OTHER STORIES. Dana Gioia (ed). Omaha, NE: Abattoir Editions, 1983. 1st ed. Ltd to 295. Cl, ptd label. Mint. *JAFFE.* $50

Kees, Weldon. THE COLLECTED POEMS OF WELDON KEES. 1/4 black morocco & Japanese paper over boards. Iowa City: The Stone Wall Press, 1960. 1st ed, regular issue. One of 180 numbered ptd on Rives Light. Delicate Japanese paper on front cvr is faded, o/w Fine. *JAFFE.* $750

Kees, Weldon. THE FALL OF THE MAGICIANS. POEMS. NY: Reynal & Hitchcock, (1947). 1st ed. Fine in sl rubbed, faded dj. *JAFFE.* $100

Kehr, Hans. INTRODUCTION TO THE DIFFERENTIAL DIAGNOSIS OF THE SEPARATE FORMS OF GALLSTONE DISEASE...433 LAPAROTOMIES FOR GALLSTONES. Phila, 1901. 1st Eng trans. Inscribed by trans. *FYE.* $100

Keifetz, Norman. THE SENSATION. Atheneum, 1975. 1st ed. Fine in dj. *STAHR.* $35

Keiley, A.M. IN VINCULIS OR THE PRISONER OF WAR BEING THE EXPERIENCE OF A REBEL IN TWO FEDERAL PENS. NY: Blelock & Co, 1866. 216pp. Rev of 1st ed. Good. *CULLEN.* $75

Keill, John. AN INTRODUCTION TO THE TRUE ASTRONOMY; OR, ASTRONOMICAL LECTURES....ptd for Bernard Lintot, London, 1730, 2nd ed. Ex-lib, full hand-tooled leather, raised bands, red spine label; hinges broken, front board nearly detached, 2 corners worn to boards, some spotting, browning of pgs. Emb stamp, number. 26 fldg plts (numbered I to 27 but no. 18 not called for), 2 fldg lunar plates. 396 pp. *KNOLLWOOD.* $450

Keillor, Garrison. LAKE WOBEGON DAYS. NY: Viking, (1985). 1st ed. Fine in dj. Inscribed. *CAPTAIN'S BOOKSHELF.* $50

Keillor, Garrison. LEAVING HOME. (NY): Viking, (1987). Signed, ltd ed. 1/1500. Fine w/o dj, in slipcase, as issued. *LOPEZ.* $75

Keith, E.C. GUN FOR COMPANY. London: Country Life Ltd, 1937. 1st ed. Fine in VG dj w/owner inscript. *BACKMAN.* $40

Keith, Elmer. BIG GAME RIFLES AND CARTRIDGES. Plantersville: S.A.T.P. Co, (c1936), 1946 ads, 161pp + ads. Frontis. Grn cl w/gilt lettering. Owner's stamp feps. VG+ in Good dj. *BACKMAN.* $125

Keith, Elmer. KEITH'S RIFLES FOR LARGE GAME. Huntington: Standard Publications, Inc, 1946. 1st ed. VG w/light shelf wear to edges. *BACKMAN.* $650

Keithahn, Edward L. IGLOO TALES. (Lawrence, KS): United States Indian Service. (1950). Blue cl, spiral-bound text. Dj. Sketch of a polar bear, signed and dated, on title page. *KARMIOLE.* $100

Keithahn, Edward L. MONUMENTS IN CEDAR. Ketchikan: Roy Anderson, 1944. 1st ed. Autographed. VG. *BLUE DRAGON.* $37.50

Keithahn, Edward L. MONUMENTS IN CEDAR. Ketchikan: Roy Anderson, 1945. 1st ed. Folded map. Inscribed. Very nice. *PARMER.* $95

Keleher, William A. THE FABULOUS FRONTIER: TWELVE NEW MEXICO ITEMS. Santa Fe: Rydal, (1945). 1st ed. Ep maps, plts. Orig cl. One of 500. Howes K37. *GINSBERG.* $125

Keleher, William A. VIOLENCE IN LINCOLN COUNTY 1869-1881. Univ of NM, 1957. 1st ed. Signed. Fine in Fine dj. *VARNER.* $100

Keleman, Pal. MEDIEVAL AMERICAN ART. NY: Macmillan, 1946. 2 vols. 3rd ptg. Red cl, spines sl faded, contents VG+. *SILVER.* $100

Keleman, Pal. MEDIEVAL AMERICAN ART. NY: Macmillan, 1956. 1st 1 vol ed. 308 b/w plts. Good in chipped dj. *SILVER.* $50

Kelemen, Pal. MEDIEVAL AMERICAN ART. NY 1943. 2 vols. Djs. VG-NF. *POLYANTHOS.* $200

Kelemen, Pal. MEDIEVAL AMERICAN ART. NY: Macmillan, 1944. 2nd ptg. 2 vols, 306 b/w plts in vol 2. Good. *SILVER.* $100

Keller, Allan. MORGAN'S RAID. Indianapolis, (1961). 1st ed. VG+. *PRATT.* $37.50

Keller, David H. TALES FROM UNDERWOOD. Arkham House, 1952. 1st ed. VF in dj. *MADLE.* $125

Keller, David H. TALES FROM UNDERWOOD. Spearman, 1974. Fine in dj. *MADLE.* $35

Keller, David H. THE DEVIL AND THE DOCTOR. Simon & Schuster, 1940. 1st ed. Cvrs waterstained. Near VG in frayed, rubbed dj. *MADLE.* $75

Keller, David H. THE SOLITARY HUNTERS AND THE ABYSS....Phila: New Era, 1948. 1st ed. Inscribed. Bkpl, name, date else VG+/NF in sl chipped, edgeworn dj. *OTHER WORLDS.* $30

Keller, David H. THE THOUGHT PROJECTOR. Stellar Pubs, 1929. 1st ed. Soiled, else VG in wraps. *MADLE.* $75

Keller, Helen. OUR DUTIES TO THE BLIND...JANUARY 5, 1904. Perkins Hall. Boston: (Ptd by Thomas Todd). Orig burgundy wraps w/lettering on cover. Fine. Privately ptd. *BOOK BLOCK.* $50

Keller, Helen. OUR DUTIES TO THE BLIND...JANUARY FIFTH, 1904, Perkins Hall, Boston. Boston: Thomas Todd. (1904). Purple ptd wrappers. Fine. *KARMIOLE.* $25

Kellerman, Faye. THE RITUAL BATH. NY: Arbor, 1986. 1st ed. Signed. Fine in dj. *SILVER DOOR.* $37.50

Kellerman, Faye. THE RITUAL BATH. NY: Arbor House, 1986. 1st ed. VF in dj. *MORDIDA.* $30

Kellerman, Jonathan. BLOOD TEST. Atheneum, 1986. 1st ed. Fine in price-clipped dj. Signed. *STAHR.* $40

Kellerman, Jonathan. BLOOD TEST. NY: Atheneum, 1986. 1st ed. Inscribed. Fine in NF dj. *LOPEZ.* $50

Kellerman, Jonathan. OVER THE EDGE. NY: Antheneum, (1987). 1st ed. This copy has the wrap-around band by Stephen King and is signed by Kellerman. Fine in Fine dj. *UNGER.* $50

Kellerman, Jonathan. OVER THE EDGE. NY: Atheneum, 1987. Uncorrected proof copy. Inscribed. VG in wrappers. *LOPEZ.* $50

Kellerman, Jonathan. OVER THE EDGE. NY: Atheneum, 1987. 1st ed. Signed. Fine in dj. *SILVER DOOR.* $35

Kellerman, Jonathan. PRIVATE EYES. Bantam, 1992. 1st ed. VF in dj. Signed. *STAHR.* $35

Kellerman, Jonathan. WHEN THE BOUGH BREAKS. Atheneum, 1985. 1st ed. Fine in dj (two tears at head of spine, rubbed at corners). *STAHR.* $45

Kellerman, Jonathan. WHEN THE BOUGH BREAKS. NY: Atheneum, 1985. 1st ed. Fine in dj. *MORDIDA.* $85

Kelley, Donald G. Jack W. Edgemond and Drew W. Chick. THREE SCOUT NATURALISTS IN THE NATIONAL PARKS. NY: Brewer, Warren & Putnam, 1931. 1st ed. About VG. *CONNOLLY & WADE.* $30

Kelley, Hall J. A GENERAL CIRCULAR TO ALL PERSONS...WHO WISH TO EMIGRATE TO THE OREGON TERRITORY...Tarrytown, NY: Abbatt, 1918. Orig ptd wrappers, boxed. Howes K43. *GINSBERG.* $75

Kelley, Hall J. A GEOGRAPHICAL SKETCH OF THAT PART OF NORTH AMERICA, CALLED OREGON...Tarrytown, NY: Abbatt, 1919. Orig ed. 88pp. Fldg map. Orig ptd wrappers. Howes K44. *GINSBERG.* $100

Kelley, J.D. Jerrold. AMERICAN YACHTS THEIR CLUBS AND RACES. NY: (Scribners), 1884. Contemp 3/4 black morocco over marbled boards; front cvr joint broken, rear joint rubbed. Teg. *BOOK BLOCK.* $75

Kelley, William Melvin. A DIFFERENT DRUMMER. GC: Doubleday, 1962. 1st ed, 1st book. Fine in Fine dj but for 2 tiny tears. *BEASLEY.* $100

Kelley, William Melvin. DANCERS ON THE SHORE. GC: Doubleday & Co, 1964. 1st ed. NF in VG price clipped, bit rubbed dj. *BERNARD.* $60

Kelley, William Melvin. DUNFORDS TRAVELS EVERYWHERES. GC: Doubleday, 1970. Fine in VG dj sl darkened at spine. *BETWEEN COVERS.* $45

Kellogg, George Albert. A HISTORY OF WHIDBEY'S ISLAND. State of Washington. 1934. (Oak Harbor, WA: George B. Astel). 1934. Ed ltd to 250 numbered. Presentation copy. Brown stiff wrappers, gilt. *KARMIOLE.* $75

Kellogg, John Harvey. A HOUSEHOLD MANUAL OF HYGIENE, FOOD AND DIET, COMMON DISEASES, ACCIDENTS AND EMERGENCIES, AND USEFUL HINTS AND RECIPES. Battle Creek, MI: Office of the Health Reformer, 1877. 1st ed. Covers sl worn, owner's names ffep, pencil marks on few pp, o/w Good. *DIAMOND.* $45

Kellogg, John Harvey. SUNBEAMS OF HEALTH AND TEMPERANCE. Battle Creek, MI: Good Health Pub Co, 1889. (c. 1887) Extremities lightly rubbed. *KARMIOLE.* $40

Kellogg, Jonathan. BENEATH THE STONE. NY: Neale, 1918. 1st ed. Orig dk red cl. Owner sig, lt foxing of fore-edge, but VG. *CHAPEL HILL.* $40

Kellogg, Louise P. THE BRITISH REGIME IN WISCONSIN AND THE NORTHWEST. Madison, 1925. 1st ed. Fldg maps, plts. Orig cl. Howes K50. *GINSBERG.* $75

Kellogg, Marjorie. TELL ME THAT YOU LOVE ME, JUNIE MOON. NY: Farrar, Straus & Giroux, (1968). 1st ed, 1st book. NF in dj. *BERNARD.* $30

Kellogg, Steven. PECOS BILL. Morrow, (1986). 1st ed. Unpaginated. Color illus by Kellogg. Signed by Kellogg w/drawing of longhorn in love. Fine in Fine dj. *BEBBAH.* $30

Kellogg, V.L. AMERICAN INSECTS. NY, 1908. 2nd ed. Front hinge cracked *SUTTON.* $40

Kelly, Charles. MILES GOODYEAR, FIRST CITIZEN OF UTAH...CALIF. PIONEER. Salt Lake City: Privately ptd, 1937. 1st ed, ltd to 350 numbered. Bkpl, name, address. Ink title dj spine, few lines underlined on bk ads dj back o/w Fine in Fine dj. Howes K56. *OREGON.* $200

Kelly, Charles. OLD GREENWOOD, THE STORY OF CALEB GREENWOOD. Salt Lake City: Privately ptd, 1936. 1st ed, ltd to 350 numbered. Bkpl, name, address on fep. VG in chipped, torn dj. Howes K57. *OREGON.* $200

Kelly, Charles. OLD GREENWOOD, THE STORY OF CALEB GREENWOOD. Kelly & Morgan. Georgetown: Talisman, 1965. Ltd to 750. Rev, enl, 1st thus. Fldg map. VF in VF dj. *OREGON.* $80

Kelly, Charles. SALT DESERT TRAILS—A HISTORY OF THE HASTINGS CUTOFF. Salt Lake, 1930. 1st ed. Frontis, photos, map, ports. Orig dec textured boards, w/minor stains, o/w NF. *BENCHMARK.* $150

Kelly, Eric P. THE TRUMPETER OF KRAKOW. NY: Macmillan, (1928). 1929 rprt. Color frontis. Fine in Fine dj. *ACADEMIC LIBRARY.* $35

Kelly, Francis M. and Randolph Schwabe. A SHORT HISTORY OF COSTUME & ARMOUR CHIEFLY IN ENGLAND, 1066-1800. London: B.T. Batsford, Ltd. (1931). 1st ed. 2 vols in one. Dj. *KAR-MIOLE.* $100

Kelly, Fred C. ONE THING LEADS TO ANOTHER. THE GROWTH OF AN INDUSTRY. (Photos by Margaret Bourke--White). Boston: Houghton Mifflin Co. 1936. 1st ed. Dj sl chipped. *KARMIOLE.* $45

Kelly, Fred C. THE WRIGHT BROTHERS. NY: Harcourt Brace, (1943). 1st ed. Fine- in VG dj. *AARD.* $25

Kelly, Howard and Charles Noble. GYNECOLOGY AND AB-DOMINAL SURGERY. Phila, 1908. 1st ed. 2 vols. *FYE.* $150

Kelly, Howard and Elizabeth Hurdon. THE VERMIFORM APPEN-DIX AND ITS DISEASES. Phila, 1905. 1st ed. 827pp. Fine. *FYE.* $400

Kelly, Howard. OPERATIVE GYNECOLOGY. NY, 1898. 2 vols.. 1st ed. Ex-lib, shaken, top of one backstrip torn. *FYE.* $150

Kelly, J. Frederick. EARLY CONNECTICUT ARCHITECTURE: SECOND SERIES. NY: William Helburn, Inc, 1931. 1st ed. 20 plts. Good+. *BACKROOM.* $100

Kelly, LeRoy Victor. THE RANGE MEN: THE STORY OF THE RANCHERS AND INDIANS OF ALBERTA. Toronto, 1913. 1st ed. 468pp. Orig pict cl. Howes K66. *GINSBERG.* $850

Kelly, Luther. YELLOWSTONE KELLY, MEMOIRS OF LUTHER S. KELLY. M.M. Quaife (ed). Yale, 1926. 1st ed. Fron-tis, 16 plts. Fine. *OREGON.* $70

Kelly, R. Talbot. BURMA. A&C Black, 1933. 2nd ed, rev. W/o dj, else VG. *OLD LONDON.* $20

Kelly, R. Talbot. EGYPT. A&C Black, 1923. 1st ed (this series). W/o dj, else VG indeed. *OLD LONDON.* $30

Kelly, Robert. KILL THE MESSENGER. Santa Barbara: Black Spar-row (1979). 1st ed. One of 250 numbered, signed. Fine in acetate. *DORN.* $40

Kelly, Robert. NOT THIS ISLAND MUSIC SANTA BARBARA: Black Sparrow (1987). 1st ed. One of 150 numbered, signed. Fine in acetate. *DORN.* $40

Kelly, Susan. THE GEMINI MAN. Walker, 1985. 1st ed, 1st bk. Fine in dj. *STAHR.* $25

Kelly, Walt. SONG OF THE POGO. Simon & Schuster, 1956. 1st ptg. Illus in color by Kelly. Some cvr edgewear, couple tiny spots to rear cvr. VG+. *BEBBAH.* $50

Kelly, Walt. THE INCOMPLEAT POGO. NY, (1954). 1st ed. Pict wraps, spine sl sunned, gift inscribed. *POLYANTHOS.* $25

Kelly, Walt. UNCLE POGO. SO-SO STORIES. NY, 1953. 1st ed. Pict wraps. Front wrap sl creased. NF. *POLYANTHOS.* $25

Kelly, William. A STROLL THROUGH THE DIGGINGS IN CALIFORNIA. with Paintings by Charles Nahl. Biobooks, 1950. 2 plts. Ltd to 750. *OREGON.* $50

Kelly, William. A STROLL THROUGH THE DIGGINGS OF CALIFORNIA. Oakland: Biobooks, 1950. One of 750. Reprinted from the 1852 ed. Fine. Howes K-68. *LAURIE.* $40

Kelly, William. AN EXCURSION TO CALIFORNIA OVER THE PRAIRIE, ROCKY MOUNTAINS, AND GREAT SIERRA NEVADA. London, 1851. 2 vols. 1st ed. Orig grn cl, embossed design on sides, title stamped in gilt on backstrip, slight fading to spine but normal for this work. Howes K68. *GINSBERG.* $600

Kelman, Rev. John. THE HOLY LAND. A&C Black, 1902. 1st ed. 20s Series. Ffep excised, else NF. *OLD LONDON.* $75

Kelsey, Charles. DISEASES OF THE RECTUM AND ANUS. NY, 1882. 1st ed. *FYE.* $100

Kelsey, Henry. THE KELSEY PAPERS. Ottawa: F.A. Acland, Printer..,1929. 1st ed. Frontis, fldg map. Orig ptd stiff wrappers. As New, unopened. *WREDEN.* $110

Kelton, Elmer. THE GOOD OLD BOYS. GC: Doubleday, (1978). 1st ed. Fine in sl rubbed dj. *UNGER.* $45

Kemble, John Haskell. SAN FRANCISCO BAY. Cambridge: Cornell Maritime Press, 1957. NF in VG dj. *PARMER.* $45

Kemelman, Harry. SATURDAY THE RABBI WENT HUNGRY. NY: Crown Pubs, 1966. 1st ed. Fine in price-clipped dj. *MORDIDA.* $30

Kemelman, Harry. SUNDAY THE RABBI STAYED HOME. NY: G.P. Putnam's Sons, 1969. 1st ed. Fine in dj w/wear. *MORDIDA.* $25

Kemelman, Harry. THE NINE MILE WALK. NY: G.P. Putnam's Sons 1967. 1st ed. Fine in dj w/minor wea, lt rubbing, couple short closed tears. *MORDIDA.* $50

Kemp, B.W. and J.C. Dykes. COW DUST AND SADDLE LEATHER. Univ of OK Press, 1968. 1st ed. Fine in Fine dj. *VARNER.* $50

Kendall, George W. NARRATIVE OF AN EXPEDITION ACROSS THE GREAT SOUTHWESTERN PRAIRIES, FROM TEXAS TO SANTA FE....London: Bogue, 1845. 1st Eng ed. 2 vols. Fldg map, 2 plts. Orig 12mo cl. Nice set. Howes K75. *GINSBERG.* $400

Kendall, George W. NARRATIVE OF THE TEXAN SANTA FE EXPEDITION, COMPRISING A DESCRIPTION....NY, 1844. 1st ed, 1st issue. 2 vols. 5 plts, fldg map. Orig cl, small nick in spine of vol 1. Howes K75. *GINSBERG.* $750

Kendall, George W. NARRATIVE OF THE TEXAN SANTA FE EXPEDITION. NY: Harper & Brothers. Early, not 1st ed. Ed and dates obliterated from title. 2 vols bound in 1. Old tan paper lib case binding, map repaired, removed and encapsulated. Frontis plt miss-ing, foxed. *HUDSON.* $400

Kendall, George W. NARRATIVE OF THE TEXAN SANTA FE EXPEDITION. In 2 vols. NY: Harper and Brothers, 1844. 1st ed. 5 engrvd plts, lacks map. Spine chips, but above average. *HUDSON.* $125

Kendall, Henry and Florence. MUSCLES: TESTING AND FUNC-
TION. Baltimore, 1949. 1st ed. 150+ photo plts. *FYE.* $50

Kendall, Oswald. THE VOYAGE OF THE MARTIN CONNOR.
Houghton Mifflin, 1931. 1st illus Riverside ed. Illus by Donald
Teague. VG w/bright color pict pastedown. *BEBBAH.* $25

Kendricken, Paul H. MEMOIRS OF PAUL HENRY. Boston:
privately printed, 1910. 1st ed. Orig dec cl. *GINSBERG.* $125

Keneally, Thomas. BRING LARKS & HEROES. NY: Viking, 1967.
1st ed. As New in dj. *ELSE FINE.* $40

Keneally, Thomas. BRING LARKS AND HEROES. NY: Viking
Press, (1968). 1st ed. Signed. Fine in price clipped dj. *BERNARD.* $60

Keneally, Thomas. GOSSIP FROM THE FOREST. NY: HBJ, 1975.
1st ed. As New in dj. *ELSE FINE.* $30

Keneally, Thomas. TO ASMARA. NY: Warner, (1989). 1st ed.
Signed. VF in VF dj. *UNGER.* $45

Kenealy, A.J. YACHTING WRINKLES: A PRACTICAL AND HIS-
TORICAL HANDBOOK....NY & London, (1899). At head of title:
"Outing Library of Sport." *LEFKOWICZ.* $85

Kennard, Joseph Spencer. MASKS AND MARIONETTES. NY: The
Macmillan Co, 1935. 1st ed. *KARMIOLE.* $35

Kennard, Joseph Spencer. SOME EARLY PRINTERS AND THEIR
COLOPHONS. Phila: George W. Jacobs and Company, 1902. 1st
ed ltd to 450 numbered. Presentation from publishers on ffep.
Minor cover soiling. *OAK KNOLL.* $95

Kennedy, Alexander. PETRA ITS HISTORY AND MONUMENTS.
London: Country Life, 1925. 4 plts, 4 maps. Dj. Splendid. Scarce.
O'NEILL. $200

Kennedy, Elijah R. THE CONTEST FOR CALIFORNIA IN 1861,
HOW COLONEL E.D. BAKER SAVED THE PACIFIC STATES
TO THE UNION. Boston, 1912. 1st ed. 361pp. Inscribed. VG+ in
dj. *PRATT.* $75

Kennedy, John F. WHY ENGLAND SLEPT. NY: Wilfred Funk,
1940. 1st ed. Orig red cl. Owner sig, some pencilled underlining, still
VG in sl soiled dj chipped at head of spine (affecting no lettering).
CHAPEL HILL. $350

Kennedy, John. IN THE SHADOW OF THE CHEKA. Macaulay,
(1935). 1st ed. VG in VG dj with closed tear, chips. *BEBBAH.* $20

Kennedy, Michael. COWBOYS AND CATTLEMEN. Hastings
House, (1964). 1st ed. VG in VG dj. *OREGON.* $45

Kennedy, P.G. et al. THE BIRDS OF IRELAND, AN ACCOUNT.
Edinburgh, 1954. 11 b/w plts. Chipped, worn dj. *SUTTON.* $135

Kennedy, Philip P. THE BLACKWATER CHRONICLE...AN EX-
PEDITION...IN RANDOLPH COUNTY, VIRGINIA...NY, 1853.
1st ed. (2),223,(16ads)pp. Strother (illus). Frontis, engr title pg.
Orig cl, slight chipping, light water staining. Howes K90. *GINSBERG.*
$150

Kennedy, Rankin. PHOTOGRAPHIC AND OPTICAL ELECTRIC
LAMPS. London: H. Alabaster. 1895. 60pp. Index. 59 text woodcut
figures. 1/2 brown calf over brown cl, gilt spine; spine faded. Orig.
maroon gilt cl covers bound in at back. *KARMIOLE.* $125

Kennedy, William. BILLY PHELAN'S GREATEST GAME. NY:
Viking, (1978). 1st ed. Boards, dj. VF. *JAFFE.* $125

Kennedy, William. BILLY PHELAN'S GREATEST GAME. Viking,
1978. 1st ed. Fine in NF dj with light wear head of spine; rubbed at
rear flyleaf fold. *STAHR.* $60

Kennedy, William. CHARLIE MALARKEY AND THE BELLY-
BUTTON MACHINE. With Brendan Kennedy. Boston: Atlantic
Monthly Press, 1986. 1st ed. As New in dj. *ELSE FINE.* $25

Kennedy, William. CHARLIE MALARKEY AND THE BELLY-
BUTTON MACHINE. Illus by Glen Baxter. Boston: Atlantic
Monthly Press, (1986). 1st ed. Fine in Fine dj. *DERMONT.* $20

Kennedy, William. IRONWEED. NY, 1983. 1st ed. Fine in like dj.
POLYANTHOS. $50

Kennedy, William. IRONWEED. NY: Viking, (1983). 1st ed. VF in
dj, promo material laid in. *CAPTAIN'S BOOKSHELF.* $150

Kennedy, William. LEGS. NY, 1975. 1st ed. Fine in dj which has one
small skinned spot. Rare 2nd bk. *PETTLER.* $150

Kennedy, William. LEGS. NY: CMG, 1975. 1st ed., 2nd book. Fine in
dj. *ELSE FINE.* $150

Kennedy, William. LEGS. NY: Coward, 1975. 1st ed. Signed. Fine
w/store stamp, in lightly used dj w/short tears. *BEASLEY.* $85

Kennedy, William. O ALBANY! NY: Viking, (1983). 1st ed. Orig cl-
backed slate boards. 11 maps. As New in dj. Signed. *CHAPEL HILL.*
$100

Kennedy, William. QUINN'S BOOK. (NY): Viking, (1988). Adv rev
copy w/slip and promo sheet laid in. Signed. Fine in Fine dj. *LOPEZ.*
$75

Kennedy, William. THE INK TRUCK. NY: Dial Press, 1969. 1st ed,
1st bk. VF, bright, unfaded dj has Very minor rubs, one inch
creased tear. *ELSE FINE.* $225

Kenner, Charles. HISTORY OF NEW MEXICAN-PLAINS IN-
DIAN RELATIONS. Univ of OK, (1969). 1st trade ed. VG in VG
dj. *OREGON.* $35

Kenner, Hugh. THE POUND ERA. Berkeley: Univ of CA, 1971. 1st
ed. Fine in dj. *CAPTAIN'S BOOKSHELF.* $60

Kenner, Hugh. WYNDHAM LEWIS. Norfolk: New Directions
(1954). 1st ed. Fine in price-clipped VG dj. *DORN.* $40

Kennerly, David Hume. SHOOTER. NY: Newsweek Books, (1979).
1st ed. NF in lightly worn dj. *AKA.* $50

Kenneth R., and Owen Gingerich (eds). A SOURCE BOOK IN
ASTRONOMY AND ASTROPHYSICS, 1900-1975. Harvard Univ
Press, 1979. Good in chipped, torn dj; some shelf wear. *KNOLLWOOD.*
$55

KENNEY'S: TWENTY POEMS FOR A LOST TAVERN. William
Murray (foreword). Iowa City: Windover Press, (1970). 1st ed. One
of 250. Excised paragraph band present. Fine. *CAPTAIN'S BOOKSHELF.*
$75

Kenny, Charles J. (pseud of Erle Stanley Gardner). THIS IS MUR-
DER. NY: Morrow, 1935. 1st ed. VG+, no dj. Scarce. *ELSE FINE.* $75

Kenny, Maurice. DANCING BACK STRONG THE NATION. Marvin: Blue Cloud Quarterly Press, (1979). Inscribed. Fine in wrappers. *LOPEZ.* $30

Kenrick, Tony. 81ST SITE. NY: NAL, 1980. 1st Amer ed. Fine in dj.
MORDIDA. $25

Kenrick, Tony. CHINA WHITE. Boston: Little Brown, 1986. 1st
Amer ed. Fine in dj. *MORDIDA.* $25

Kenrick, Tony. FARADAY'S FLOWERS. GC: Doubleday, 1985. 1st
Amer ed. VF in dj. *MORDIDA.* $25

Kenrick, Tony. THE NIGHTTIME GUY. NY: William Morrow,
1979. 1st Amer ed. Fine in dj. *MORDIDA.* $25

Kenrick, Tony. THE ONLY GOOD BODY'S A DEAD ONE. NY:
Simon & Schuster, 1970. 1st Amer ed, 1st novel. Fine in dj w/tiny
wear at top of spine and at corners. *MORDIDA.* $45

Kenrick, Tony. TWO FOR THE PRICE OF ONE. London: Michael
Joseph, 1974. 1st ed. Fine in dj. *MORDIDA.* $35

Kenrick, Tony. TWO FOR THE PRICE OF ONE. London: Joseph,
1974. 1st ed. Fine in dj. *SILVER DOOR.* $27.50

Kent, Alexander. COMMAND A KING'S SHIP. NY: Putnam, 1974.
1st ed. Fine, minor wear at dj corners. *ELSE FINE.* $25

Kent, Alexander. IN GALLANT COMPANY. London: Hutchinson,
(1977). 1st ed. Fine in Fine dj. *UNGER.* $60

Kent, Alexander. THE FLAG CAPTAIN. London: Hutchinson, 1971. 1st ed. NF in dj. *ELSE FINE*. $45

Kent, Charles. CHARLES DICKENS AS A READER. NY: Lippincott, 1872. 1st Amer ed. Orig bevelled cl. Sl spine tip, corner wear. Text VG. *DIAMOND*. $45

Kent, Rockwell. AFTER LONG YEARS. Cl-backed marbled boards, tissue dj. Ausable Forks, NY: Asgaard Press, 1968. 1st ed. Ltd to 250 signed. VF. *JAFFE*. $150

Kent, Rockwell. GREENLAND JOURNAL. NY: Obolensky, (1962). 1st ed. Ltd to 1000 w/separate suite of 6 lithos, 1 signed. Inscribed by Kent's widow. Fine. Cl, slipcase. *JAFFE*. $250

Kent, Rockwell. N BY E. NY: Brewer & Warren, 1930. 1st ed. Illus. Fine in repaired dj. Bkpl. *SECOND LIFE*. $35

Kent, Rockwell. OF MEN AND MOUNTAINS. Ausable Forks, NY: Asgaard Press, 1959. 1st ed. Ltd to 250 signed. Cl backed marbled boards. Fine (lacking tissue dj). *JAFFE*. $125

Kent, Rockwell. WILDERNESS. A JOURNAL OF QUIET ADVENTURE IN ALASKA....LA: Wilderness Press, 1970. Ltd ed. VF in slipcase. Signed. *PARMER*. $135

Kent, S.H. WITHIN THE ARCTIC CIRCLE—EXPERIENCES OF TRAVEL THROUGH NORWAY, TO THE NORTH CAPE, SWEDEN, AND LAPLAND. London: Richard Bentley and Son, 1877. 2 vols in one. 4 tipped in "Woodburytype" photo illus. Dec red cl, aeg. Spine faded, hinges weak, cvr spotted. *PARMER*. $250

Kenyon, Frederic G. ANCIENT BOOKS AND MODERN DISCOVERIES. Chicago: The Caxton Club. 1927. 30 collotype plts. Ed ltd to 350. *KARMIOLE*. $450

Keppel, Major, the Hon. George. PERSONAL NARRATIVE OF A JOURNEY FROM INDIA TO ENGLAND....London, 1834. Fldg map, 3 colored plts (of 4). 2 vols. Orig cl, chipped and worn, internally Very Nice. xii,338pp; vii,351pp. Uncut. *O'NEILL*. $150

Keppel, Major, the Hon. George. PERSONAL NARRATIVE OF TRAVELS IN BABYLONIA, ASSYRIA, MEDIA AND SCYTHIA, IN THE YEAR 1824. London, 1827. Fldg map, 4 hand-colored plts. 2 vols in 1. Contemp 1/2 calf, rebacked. xii,338pp; vii,351pp. Some internal soiling. *O'NEILL*. $275

Keppler, Victor. THE EIGHTH ART. NY, 1938. 31 full color photos. Signed. NF. *POLYANTHOS*. $75

Kerensky, Alexander. THE CRUCIFIXION OF LIBERTY. NY, 1934. NF. *POLYANTHOS*. $45

Kerenyi, Charles. ASKLEPIOS: ARCHETYPAL IMAGE OF THE PHYSICIAN'S EXISTENCE. London, 1960. 1st Eng trans. *FYE*. $125

Kerfoot, J.B. AMERICAN PEWTER. Boston: Houghton Mifflin, 1924. 1st ed. VG in scarce dj (damp stained base of spine, lt spotting, soiling). *BACKROOM*. $125

Kerlin, Robert T. THE VOICE OF THE NEGRO 1919. NY: Dutton, 1920. 1st ed. VG w/sl dampstain to one corner of 1st few pages. *BEASLEY*. $85

Kern, G.M. PRACTICAL LANDSCAPE GARDENING, WITH REFERENCE TO THE IMPROVEMENT OF RURAL RESIDENCES....Cincinnati, 1855. 3rd ed. 5 tinted litho plts. Orig blind stamped gilt cl faded. Lt soiling, spine ends frayed, scattered foxing. *SUTTON*. $300

Kerouac, Jack. BIG SUR. London: Deutsch, 1963. 1st UK ed. NF in price-clipped dj sl spine-faded. *LOPEZ*. $125

Kerouac, Jack. BIG SUR. NY, 1962. 1st ed. Extremities, spine minimally rubbed. Fine in dj (spine minimally sunned). *POLYANTHOS*. $150

Kerouac, Jack. BIG SUR. NY: Bantam, (1963). 1st pb ed. About Fine w/light spine crease. *AKA*. $25

Kerouac, Jack. BIG SUR. NY: Farrar, Straus and Cudahy, (1962). Review copy. Fine in dj. *LOPEZ*. $300

Kerouac, Jack. BIG SUR. NY: Farrar, Strauss and Cudahy, (1962). 1st ed. *WEBER*. $125

Kerouac, Jack. BOOK OF DREAMS. (SF): City Lights, (1961). 1st ed, ptd wraps. Very Nice. 5000 issued. *SECOND LIFE*. $95

Kerouac, Jack. BOOK OF DREAMS. (SF): City Lights, (1961). 1st ptg, wrappers; there was no hb ed. Sm owner name, date o/w NF. *LOPEZ*. $125

Kerouac, Jack. DEAR CAROLYN. (California, PA: n.p., 1983). One of 1000. NF. *LOPEZ*. $35

Kerouac, Jack. DESOLATION ANGELS. London: Deutsch, 1966. 1st Eng ed. NF in dj. *LOPEZ*. $125

Kerouac, Jack. DESOLATION ANGELS. NY: Coward-McCann, (1965). 1st ed. NF in VG dj, much less spine-faded than usual. *LOPEZ*. $200

Kerouac, Jack. DOCTOR SAX. London: Deutsch, 1977. 1st Eng hb ed. Fine in price-clipped dj. *LOPEZ*. $100

Kerouac, Jack. DOCTOR SAX. NY: Grove, (1959). 1st ed. Scarce hb issue. VG in dj chipped at extrems of spine, along top of front panel affecting lettering of the title slightly. *LOPEZ*. $500

Kerouac, Jack. DOCTOR SAX. NY: Grove Press, (1959). 1st ed, 1st issue. Corner wrinkles, creases, in wraps. VG. *AKA*. $40

Kerouac, Jack. DOCTOR SAX. NY: Grove Press, (1959). 1st ed. Grey cl in a sl chipped, little worn orig dj. Very Nice. *SECOND LIFE*. $700

Kerouac, Jack. EXCERPTS FROM VISIONS OF CODY. (NY: New Directions, 1959). One of 750 numbered, signed. Fine in pub's orig acetate dj (chipped) w/prospectus laid in. *LOPEZ*. $750

Kerouac, Jack. EXCERPTS FROM VISIONS OF CODY. Cl-backed boards, acetate dj. (NY: New Directions, 1959). 1st ed. Ltd to 750 signed. Sl abrasions on front endsheet, o/w a Fine w/orig prospectus laid in. *JAFFE*. $650

Kerouac, Jack. HYMN. Portland: Yes! Press, 1971. 3rd ed. Fine but for sm dimple at colophon. *BEASLEY*. $25

Kerouac, Jack. LAST WORDS & OTHER WRITINGS. (n.p.): Zeta Press, (1985). Fine in stapled wrappers. *LOPEZ*. $40

Kerouac, Jack. LONESOME TRAVELER. London: Deutsch, 1962. 1st Eng ed. Fine in NF dj. *LOPEZ*. $125

Kerouac, Jack. LONESOME TRAVELER. NY: McGraw-Hill, (1960). 1st ed. NF in VG, price-clipped dj, chipped at heel. *LOPEZ*. $150

Kerouac, Jack. MAGGIE CASSIDY. London: Deutsch, 1974. 1st British hb ed. Fine in price-clipped dj. *LOPEZ*. $85

Kerouac, Jack. MAGGIE CASSIDY. NY: Avon, (1959). Pb orig, the correct 1st ed w/2pp title page spread. Slight stain at bottom of pgs, light overall wear. Good. *LOPEZ*. $30

Kerouac, Jack. MAGGIE CASSIDY. NY: Avon, 1959. 1st ed. NF in wraps. *ARCHER*. $40

Kerouac, Jack. OLD ANGEL MIDNIGHT. Wales: Unicorn Bookshop, (1976). 1st ed. Pict stiff wraps. Fine. *POLYANTHOS*. $25

Kerouac, Jack. ON THE ROAD. NY: Viking, 1957. 1st ed. Offsetting to fep and tape shadows there; some black edge staining on the front and rear eps. Dj lightly rubbed, two creases. *LOPEZ*. $375

Kerouac, Jack. ON THE ROAD. NY: Viking, 1957. 1st ed. Fine in dj (very lightly rubbed, two creases). *LOPEZ*. $1,000

Kerouac, Jack. PIC. NY: Grove, (1971). Pb orig, no hb ptg in this country. Front cover creased at bottom. VG. *LOPEZ*. $30

Kerouac, Jack. PULL MY DAISY. NY: Grove, 1959. 1st ed. VG (a few creases). Not issued in cloth. *BEASLEY*. $85

Kerouac, Jack. SAN FRANCISCO BLUES. (n.p.): Beat Books, (1983). 1st complete ed. Fine in stapled wrappers. *LOPEZ*. $45

Kerouac, Jack. SARTORI IN PARIS. NY: Grove, (1966). 1st ed. Fine in dj. *CAPTAIN'S BOOKSHELF.* $100

Kerouac, Jack. SATORI IN PARIS. NY: Grove, (1966). 1st ed, hb issue. Contemp newspaper review pasted to fep, couple of underlinings on 1st few pgs) o/w Fine in Fine dj. *LOPEZ.* $60

Kerouac, Jack. SCATTERED POEMS. (SF): City Lights, (1971). 1st ed. Only issued in wrappers. Spine sl age-darkened, o/w NF. *LOPEZ.* $45

Kerouac, Jack. THE DHARMA BUMS. London: Deutsch, 1950 (sic). 1st Eng ed. NF in edgeworn dj, internally strengthened w/tape. *LOPEZ.* $75

Kerouac, Jack. THE DHARMA BUMS. NY: Viking, 1958. 1st ed. Lt offsetting eps, owner's sig, else Fine in sl rubbed dj. *CAPTAIN'S BOOKSHELF.* $125

Kerouac, Jack. THE DHARMA BUMS. NY: Viking, 1958. 1st ed. Fine in lightly rubbed dj w/no other signs of wear. *BEASLEY.* $200

Kerouac, Jack. THE DHARMA BUMS. NY: Viking, 1958. 1st ed. Fine in NF dj. *LOPEZ.* $200

Kerouac, Jack. THE GREAT WESTERN BUS RIDE. A Pacific Red Car Publication, 1984. One of 100. Wraps. Fine. *WOOLMER.* $55

Kerouac, Jack. THE SCRIPTURE OF THE GOLDEN ETERNITY. NY: Totem Press/Corinth Books, (1960). 1st ptg w/cvr ptd in purple. Sm owner name, date; paper darkening a bit w/age. VG in stapled wrappers. *LOPEZ.* $100

Kerouac, Jack. THE SUBTERRANEANS AND PIC. (London): Deutsch, (1973). 1st British ed thus, and 1st hb ed of PIC. Part of the Uniform Edition of Kerouac's writings. Fine in dj. *LOPEZ.* $85

Kerouac, Jack. THE SUBTERRANEANS. (London): Andre Deutsch, (1960). 1st UK ed. 5,000 copies. Dj illus. NF in dj which is sl worn at spine edges. *BERNARD.* $100

Kerouac, Jack. THE SUBTERRANEANS. London: Deutsch, 1960. 1st Eng ed, 1st issue, in red paper-covered boards. NF in VG dj, lightly edgeworn and rubbed on spine. *LOPEZ.* $100

Kerouac, Jack. THE SUBTERRANEANS. NY: Grove, (1958). Trade hb ed. Bound in beige linen stamped in brown. Lacking rare dj. Bkpl front pastedown, spine sl sunned. VG. *LOPEZ.* $200

Kerouac, Jack. THE SUBTERRANEANS. NY: Grove, 1958. 1st ed. Fine in wraps. Issued simultaneously w/cloth ed. *BEASLEY.* $45

Kerouac, Jack. THE SUBTERRANEANS. NY: Grove Press, (1958). 1st ed. Sl soiled tan cl. VG. *SECOND LIFE.* $300

Kerouac, Jack. THE SUBTERRANEANS. NY: Grove Press, (1958). Wraps. VG. The simultaneous paper ed. 1st ed. *SECOND LIFE.* $65

Kerouac, Jack. THE VISION OF THE HOODED WHITE ANGELS. (n.p.): Pacific Red Car, 1985. One of 100 only. Fine in stapled wrappers. *LOPEZ.* $45

Kerouac, Jack. TRISTESSA. London: World, 1963. 1st Eng ed. Pb orig (incorrectly indicating an earlier British pub on copyright pg). Spine sl darkened but NF. *LOPEZ.* $65

Kerouac, Jack. TRISTESSA. NY: Avon, (1960). Pb orig. Light crease front cover. VG. *LOPEZ.* $50

Kerouac, Jack. TRISTESSA. NY: Avon, 1960. Wraps. 1st ed. NF w/a few small creases. *BEASLEY.* $50

Kerouac, Jack. TWO STORIES. (n.p.: Pacific Red Car, 1984). One of 100 in stapled wrappers. *LOPEZ.* $45

Kerouac, Jack. VANITY OF DULUOZ. London: Deutsch, 1969. 1st Eng ed. Fine in dj. *LOPEZ.* $100

Kerouac, Jack. VANITY OF DULUOZ. NY: Coward-McCann, (1967). 1st ed. Ex-lib, markings erased. Good in sl worn dj. *SECOND LIFE.* $75

Kerouac, Jack. VANITY OF DULUOZ. NY: Coward-McCann, (1968). 1st ed. Covers sl bowed, spine gilt faded as is usual. VG in dj. *LOPEZ.* $100

Kerouac, Jack. VISIONS OF CODY. NY, 1972. Allen Ginsberg (intro). 1st ed. Price-clipped dj, NF. *PETTLER.* $65

Kerouac, Jack. VISIONS OF CODY. NY: McGraw-Hill, (1972). 1st ed. Fine in NF dj. *LOPEZ.* $75

Kerouac, Jack. VISIONS OF GERARD. London: Deutsch, 1964. 1st Eng ed. Bound together w/1st British hb of TRISTESSA (1st hb appearance in Eng). VG in dj (lg piece torn from front panel but still present). *LOPEZ.* $75

Kerouac, Jack. VISIONS OF GERARD. NY: Farrar, Straus, (1963). Advance review copy w/slip laid in. Corners sl bumped. VG in dj. *LOPEZ.* $225

Kerouac, Jan. TRAINSONG. NY: Holt, (1988). Uncorrected proof. Fine in wraps. *LOPEZ.* $30

Kerouac, John (Jack). THE TOWN AND THE CITY. NY: Harcourt, (1950). 1st ed, 1st bk. Top corner sl bumped, else Fine, owner sig. Dj (internally mended, price-clipped). *CAPTAIN'S BOOKSHELF.* $175

Kerouac, John (Jack). THE TOWN AND THE CITY. NY: Harcourt, Brace, (1950). 1st ed. VF in dj (lt edgewear but still Fine or Very NF). *LOPEZ.* $500

Kerr, Orpheus C. THE ORPHEUS C. KERR PAPERS. 3 vols. NY, 1865. Uniform ed. Gilt-stamped cl. Nice set. *ARTIS.* $35

Kerr, Winfield S. JOHN SHERMAN HIS LIFE AND PUBLIC SERVICES. 2 vols. Mansfield, OH, 1907. 1st ed. 456,425pp. 2 ports. Gilt cl. Good, sound. *ARTIS.* $25

Kerry, John and Vietnam Veterans against the War. THE NEW SOLDIER. NY: Macmillan, (1971). Ed by David Thorne & George Butler. Stated 1st ed. 174pp. Fine in NF dj. *AKA.* $65

Kersey, Ralph T. BUFFALO JONES. 1958. 1st ed. Signed. Fine in NF dj. *VARNER.* $30

Kersting, Rudolf. THE WHITE WORLD. NY: Lewis, Scribner & Co, 1902. Inscribed by contributor Henry Biederbick. Near VG. *BLUE DRAGON.* $75

Kesey, Ken. KESEY'S GARAGE SALE. NY: Viking Press, (1973). 1st ed. Signed on special printed label pasted to flyleaf. VG in dj. *BERNARD.* $150

Kesey, Ken. SOMETIMES A GREAT NOTION. NY: Viking, (1964). Fine in Nearly Fine dj (few small closed tears). 1st ed, 1st issue w/publisher's Viking ship logo on half-title. *CHAPEL HILL.* $200

Ketchum, Hiram. GENERAL MCCLELLAN'S PENINSULA CAMPAIGN. (NY), 1864. 1st ed, thus. Orig self-wraps, minor wear about edges, else VG. *McGOWAN.* $75

Ketchum, Milo S. DESIGN OF WALLS, BINS & GRAIN ELEVATORS. NY: Engineering News, 1907. As New. *AMERICAN BOTANIST.* $65

Ketchum, Philip. THE GREAT AXE BRETWALDA. Little-Brown, 1955. 1st ed. VG in chipped dj. *MADLE.* $25

Ketchum, William. AUTHENTIC & COMPREHENSIVE HISTORY OF BUFFALO. Buffalo, 1864-5. 2 vols. 2 fldg maps. Spine faded, lightly frayed, w/foxing. VG. Howes K110. *BOHLING.* $110

Ketham, Johannes De. FASCICULUS MEDICINAE. Facsimile of the 1st ed. of 1491 With English trans by Luke Demaitre. Birmingham, 1988. *FYE.* $90

Kettell, Russell Hawes. PINE FURNITURE OF EARLY NEW ENGLAND. GC: Doubleday, 1929. 1st ed. Sl soiling o/w VG. *BACKROOM.* $185

Ketterer, David. IMPRISONED IN A TESSERACT. Kent State Univ Press, 1987. 1st ed. As New. *MADLE.* $35

Key, Della Tyler. IN THE CATTLE COUNTRY: HISTORY OF POTTER COUNTY, 1887-1966. Quanah, TX: Nortex, 1972. 2nd ed, signed. Fine in dj w/ring stain. *GIBBS.* $30

Keyes, E.D. FROM WEST POINT TO CALIFORNIA. Oakland: Biobooks, (1950). Fine. *LAURIE.* $27.50

Keyes, Edward L. LEWIS ATTERBURY STIMSON, M.D. NY, 1918. 1st ed. VG. *McGOWAN.* $85

Keyes, Frances Parkinson. THE OLD GRAY HOMESTEAD. Boston & NY: Houghton Mifflin, 1919. 1st ed of 1st bk. A couple of tiny nicks at crown of spine, but Nearly Fine. *CHAPEL HILL.* $150

Keyes, Leonhard A. LINEAGE OF THE NINTH REGIMENT OF THE STATE OF NEW YORK. NY, 1953. 1st ed. Fldg map. VG+. *PRATT.* $45

Keynes, Geoffrey (ed). THE LETTERS OF WILLIAM BLAKE. NY: Macmillan, 1956. Blue cl over boards. Owner sig, date. Good in dj chipped at spine. *HELLER.* $95

Keynes, Geoffrey. A BIBLIOGRAPHY OF SIR THOMAS BROWNE. Oxford, 1968. Dj. *FYE.* $200

Keynes, Geoffrey. BIBLIOTHECA BIBLIOGRAPHICI. A CATALOGUE...FORMED BY GEOFFREY KEYNES. London: Trianon Press, 1964. 1st ed. Ltd to 500. Fine. *JAFFE.* $350

Keynes, Geoffrey. WILLIAM BLAKE. POET, PRINTER, PROPHET. NY: Orion Press, 1964. (Ptd by Trianon Press.) Dj w/tears & chips to top spine extremity. NF. *POLYANTHOS.* $150

Keynes, John Maynard. THE ECONOMIC CONSEQUENCES OF PEACE. NY: Harcourt Brace & Howe, 1920. 1st Amer ed. Blue cl; minor wear to tips, else VG. *JUVELIS.* $150

Keynes, John Maynard. THE END OF LAISSEZ-FAIRE. London: Pub by Leonard & Virginia Woolf at the Hogarth Press, 1926. 1st ed. Boards bumped and stained, paper label chipped from spine. Internally bright, Fine. *BLUE MOUNTAIN.* $95

Keys, Thomas. THE HISTORY OF SURGICAL ANAESTHESIA. NY, 1945. 1st ed. Ex-lib. *FYE.* $75

Khanikoff, M. BOKHARA: ITS AMIR AND ITS PEOPLE, TRANSLATED FROM THE RUSSIAN OF...BY THE BARON CLEMENT A DE BODE. London, 1845. Fldg map, strengthened in one fold. xxix,316pp. Minor repair to external hinges, internally Fine. *O'NEILL.* $350

Kherdian, David. HOMAGE TO ADANA. Illus Robert Totten. Blue cl w/red morocco tips. Mt. Horeb: Perishable Press, (1970). 1st ed. Ltd to 120. Signed by Walter Hamady. VF. *JAFFE.* $225

Kherdian, David. SIX POETS OF THE SAN FRANCISCO RENAISSANCE. Giligia Press, (1967). 1st ed. Signed. New in dj. *AUTHORS OF THE WEST.* $40

Kidder, D.P. and J.C. Fletcher. BRAZIL AND THE BRAZILIANS. Phila: Childs & Peterson, 1857. 1st ed. 630pp,ads. 2 maps, 2 color bird plts, 150 text engr. Orig cl. Edges, spine rubbed to boards; tissue guard on frontis partially missing; foxing. Contents VG. *SILVER.* $100

Kidder, Daniel P. SKETCHES OF RESIDENCE AND TRAVELS IN BRAZIL, EMBRACING HISTORICAL....Phila/London: Sorin & Ball/Wiley & Putnam, 1845. Spine fading, some wear, spotting. Frontis vol II supplied in facs. Both vols internally clean, tight. Emb cl. Gilt spine titles, cvr decs. xv,(17)-369pp; viii(9)-404pp. *PARMER.* $295

Kidder, Tracy. AMONG SCHOOLCHILDREN. Boston: Houghton Mifflin, 1989. 1st ed. Signed. Fine in dj. *LOPEZ.* $40

Kidder, Tracy. AMONG SCHOOLCHILDREN. Franklin Center: Franklin Library, 1989. 1st ed. One of an unspecified number signed. Fine in full lea. *BETWEEN COVERS.* $50

Kidder, Tracy. THE SOUL OF A NEW MACHINE. Boston: Little Brown, (1981). Uncorrected proof. A little bit of spotting along the page edges, o/w Fine in wrappers, laid into a proof dj. *LOPEZ.* $175

Kiefer, Warren. OUTLAW. NY: Donald I. Fine, 1989. 1st ed. Advance review copy; slip, photo, flyer laid in. VF in dj. *MORDIDA.* $25

Kiefer, Warren. THE KIDNAPPERS. NY: Harper & Row, 1977. 1st ed. Advance review copy, slip laid in. Fine in dj. *MORDIDA.* $25

Kiefer, Warren. THE PONTIUS PILATE PAPERS. NY: Harper & Row, 1976. 1st ed. Fine in dj. *MORDIDA.* $25

Kilbourne, D. W. STRICTURES OF DR. I. GALLAND'S PAMPHLET, ENTITLED, "VILLAINY EXPOSED," WITH SOME ACCOUNT...Fort Madison, 1850. 1st ed. Uncut. 24pp. Sewn as issued. Howes K131. *GINSBERG.* $300

Killanin, Lord. SIR GODFREY KNELLER AND HIS TIMES 1646-1723. London B.T. Batsford Ltd. (1948). 1st ed. 4 color plates. *KARMIOLE.* $30

Killebrew, J(oseph)B(uckner). SPECIAL REPORT ON THE COALFIELD OF LITTLE SEQUATCHEE....Nashville: Tavel, Eastman & Howell, 1876. 40pp. Wraps w/fold-out map. Nice. *SECOND LIFE.* $95

Killens, John Oliver. AND THEN WE HEARD THE THUNDER. NY: Knopf, 1963. 1st ed. Fine but for a few specks on eps, in NF dj w/a few specks. *BEASLEY.* $85

Killens, John Oliver. THE COTILLION; OR ONE GOOD BULL IS HALF THE HERD. NY: Trident, (1971). 1st ed. Nearly invisible spot on fore-edge, else Fine in Very NF dj w/touch of shelfwear. Adv review copy w/slip. *BETWEEN COVERS.* $75

Kilpatrick, Jack Frederick and Anna Gritts. WALK IN YOUR SOUL: LOVE INCANTATIONS....Dallas: Southern Methodist Univ Press, (1965). Fine in dj. *LAURIE.* $20

Kimball, Horace. THE NAVAL TEMPLE; CONTAINING A COMPLETE HISTORY....Boston: 1816. 1st ed. 258pp. 7 plts, incl engr title pp, some lightly tinted. Full contemp calf. *GINSBERG.* $150

Kimes, William and Maymie (comps). JOHN MUIR: A READING BIBLIOGRAPHY. Palo Alto: William P. Wreden, 1977. 1st ed. ltd. to 300. Dj. Signed by compilers and printer. Prospectus laid in. As New. *WREDEN.* $200

Kimmel, Stanley. THE MAD BOOTHS OF MARYLAND. Indianapolis: Bobbs-Merrill, 1940. 1st ed. 7 plts. Fine. *CONNOLLY & WADE.* $50

Kincaid, Jamaica. ANNIE, GWEN, LILLY, PAM AND TULIP. Cl-backed boards, pict card slipcase. NY: Knopf, 1989. 1st trade ed, after ltd ed pub by The Whitney Museum. New. *JAFFE.* $45

Kincaid, Jamaica. AT THE BOTTOM OF THE RIVER. NY: Farrar Straus & Giroux, (1983). 1st ed. Review copy, slip, photo laid in. Fine in dj. *CAPTAIN'S BOOKSHELF.* $100

Kincaid, Jamaica. AT THE BOTTOM OF THE RIVER. NY: Farrar Straus Giroux, (1983). 1st ed. Fine in Fine dj. *LOPEZ.* $55

Kincaid-Smith, Priscilla. THE KIDNEY, A CLINICO-PATHOLOGICAL STUDY. Oxford, 1975. 1st ed. 200+ illus. *FYE.* $75

Kindera, Milan. THE FAREWELL PARTY. Trans by Peter Kussi. NY: Knopf, (1976). 1st Amer ed. Fine in lightly dust soiled dj. *DORN.* $50

King, Alvy L. LOUIS T. WIGFALL, SOUTHERN FIRE-EATER. Baton Rouge, (1970). 1st ed. 259pp. Fine in dj. *PRATT.* $27.50

King, Ben. BEN KING'S SOUTHLAND MELODIES. Chicago: Forbes & Co, 1911. 1st ed. Orig dec grn cl. Fine. *CHAPEL HILL.* $125

King, Blanche Busey. UNDER YOUR FEET. NY: Dodd, Mead, 1939. 1st ed. Frontis. 21 plts. Cl, gilt. NF. *CONNOLLY & WADE.* $35

King, C.W. THE NATURAL HISTORY OF PRECIOUS STONES & OF THE PRECIOUS METALS. London, 1870. 1st ed. VG+. *MIKESH.* $45

King, Charles. A DAUGHTER OF THE SIOUX. NY (1903), 1st ed. Illus by Remington & Edwin W. Deming. Writing on pg listing illus. *HEINOLDT.* $15

King, Charles. A DAUGHTER OF THE SIOUX....Hobart, 1903. 1st ed. Illus Frederic Remington, Edwin Willard Deming. Full length color port on cvr. Teg. One corner rubbed, sm snag, spine, else Fine. *AUTHORS OF THE WEST.* $60

King, Charles. A TAME SURRENDER: A STORY OF THE CHICAGO STRIKE. Phila: Lippincott, 1896. 1st ed. Lacks ffep. Fine. *MUELLER.* $37.50

King, Charles. A WAR-TIME WOOING. NY, (1888). 1st ed. 195pp. Wear at spine extrems o/w VG+. *PRATT.* $20

King, Charles. AN APACHE PRINCESS. NY, 1903. 1st ed. 8 plts. Orig cl gilt w/photo pasted on. Few stains, silverfish marks on cvr, o/w VG. *DIAMOND.* $125

King County Hist Soc (ed). KING COUNTY WINDMILLS & BARBED WIRE. Quanah, TX: Nortex Press, 1976. 1st ed. VF. *GIBBS.* $35

King, F.H. FARMERS OF FORTY CENTURIES....Madison, WI: Mrs. F.H. King, 1911. 1st US ed. VG. *SECOND LIFE.* $75

King, Florence. SOUTHERN LADIES AND GENTLEMEN. NY: Stein & Day, (1975). 1st ed. NF in like dj. Signed by King. *CAPTAIN'S BOOKSHELF.* $75

King, Frank M. LONGHORN TRAIL DRIVERS. N.p. (LA): Private-ly ptd, 1940. 1st ed. Ptd in ed of only 400. Signed. VG. Howes K150. *OREGON.* $150

King, Frank M. PIONEER WESTERN EMPIRE BUILDERS: A TRUE STORY....Pasadena: Trail's End, 1946. "Privately published by the author for his friends." 1st ed. Frontis. Red cl, gilt dec. Sl fade on spine, else Fine. Scarce. *CONNOLLY & WADE.* $75

King, Frank. PIONEER WESTERN EMPIRE BUILDERS. Pasadena, 1946. 1st ed. Bkpl. Occasional printing press wrinkle, sl faded backstrip, o/w VG. *BAADE.* $50

King, Frank. SKEEZIK AND PAL. Reilly & Lee, (1925). 1st ed. 105pp. Illus by author. Inner hinges cracked, names, watercolor smear on ffep. Pict cvr has wear but Good+. *BEBBAH.* $30

King, Grace. MEMORIES OF A SOUTHERN WOMAN OF LET-TERS. NY, 1932. 1st ed. Minor cvr wear o/w Fine. *PRATT.* $50

King, Helen H. WILLY. GC: Doubleday, (1971). 1st ed. Faint erasure to coated paper on front fly, else Fine in NF dj w/couple very short tears, faint stain. *BETWEEN COVERS.* $85

King, James. LOCAL ANESTHESIA IN OTOLARYNGOLOGY AND RHINOLOGY. NY, 1926. 1st ed. Fldg chart. *FYE.* $75

King, John Anthony. TWENTY FOUR YEARS IN THE ARGEN-TINE REPUBLIC. NY: Appleton, 1846. 324pp + ads. Orig em-bossed covers sl worn. Text foxed. Several signatures loose, o/w Good. *DIAMOND.* $45

King, John. HEADACHES AND THE CONCOMITANT SYMPTOMS. Chicago, 1879. 1st ed. Scarce. *FYE.* $30

King, Joseph L. HISTORY OF THE SAN FRANCISCO STOCK AND EXCHANGE BOARD. SF: Jos. L. King. 1910. 1st ed. xxvi,374pp. Gray cl w/pasted-down repro of stock certificate on front cvr. *KARMIOLE.* $75

King, Larry L. OF OUTLAWS, CONMEN, WHORES. NY: Viking, 1980. 1st ed. Fine. *SMITH.* $25

King, Larry L. THAT TERRIBLE NIGHT SANTA GOT LOST IN THE WOODS. (Austin): Encino Press, (1981). Fine. *LAURIE.* $30

King, Leonard W. A HISTORY OF BABYLON FROM THE FOUNDATION OF THE MONARCHY TO THE PERSIAN CONQUEST. London: Chatto & Windus, 1915. Frontis, 72 figs, 31 plts, 13 maps and plans, teg. Torn at spine, corners bumped, rubbed at extremities. Good. *ARCHAEOLOGIA.* $55

King, Lester. THE MEDICAL WORLD OF THE EIGHTEENTH CENTURY. Chicago, 1958. Dj. *FYE.* $40

King, Lester. THE PHILOSOPHY OF MEDICINE: THE EARLY EIGHTEENTH CENTURY. Cambridge, 1978. 1st ed. Dj. *FYE.* $40

King, Louis M. THE WARDEN OF THE MARCHES. Houghton Mifflin, 1938. 1st Amer ed. VG in Good dj with chips, wear. *BEBBAH.* $18

King, Martin Luther, Jr. STRIDE TOWARD FREEDOM: THE MONTGOMERY STORY. NY, (1958). 1st ed. Orig cl, a bit of neat ink underlining and note on rear pastedown, else F in NF dj. *McGOWAN.* $150

King, Martin Luther, Jr. WHERE DO WE GO FROM HERE: CHAOS OR COMMUNITY? NY: Harper & Row, 1967. 1st ed. Name, o/w NF in sl used dj. *AKA.* $40

King, Moses. KING'S HANDBOOK OF THE UNITED STATES. Buffalo: Moses King Corporation, 1892. 51 color maps. *HUDSON.* $55

King, Mrs. E.L. HUNTING BIG GAME IN AFRICA. 1926, Winona, Minnesota, n.p. 1st ed. Very minor wear extremes else NF. *GREAT EPIC.* $95

King, Rufus. DESIGN IN EVIL. Garden City: Doubleday Crime Club, 1942. 1st ed. VG in dj (internal tape mends; crease; wear, short closed tears; chipped spine ends). *MORDIDA.* $35

King, Rufus. LETHAL LADY. Garden City: Doubleday Crime Club, 1947. 1st ed. Pp darkened o/w VG in dj with minor wear, crease-tear. *MORDIDA.* $30

King, Rufus. MALICE IN WONDERLAND. Garden City: Doubleday Crime Club 1958. 1st ed. VG in dj (scrapes front panel; short closed tear). *MORDIDA.* $50

King, Rufus. MURDER BY LATITUDE. GC: Doubleday Crime Club, 1930. 1st ed. Fine; minor edgewear to dj. *ELSE FINE.* $75

KING, Rufus. MURDER BY THE CLOCK. Garden City: Doubleday Crime Club, 1929. 1st ed. Fine in dj with a couple of closed tears and wraparound intact. *MORDIDA.* $250

King, Rufus. MURDER MASKS MIAMI. GC: Doubleday Crime Club, 1939. 1st ed. Fine; dj w/minor rubs. *ELSE FINE.* $50

King, Rufus. PROFILE OF A MURDER. NY: Harcourt Brace, 1935. 1st ed. VG in chipped and torn dj. *MORDIDA.* $35

King, Rufus. THE DEADLY DOVE. Garden City: Doubleday Crime Club, 1945. 1st ed. Fine in dj (chipping, short closed tears). *MOR-DIDA.* $35

King, Rufus. THE FACES OF DANGER. Garden City: Doubleday Crime Club, 1964. 1st ed. Fine in dj. *MORDIDA.* $40

King, Spencer B. DARIEN. Macon, (1981). 1st ed. Dj. Fine. *PRATT.* $25

King, Stephen. See also Bachman, Richard.

King, Stephen and f-stop Fitzgerald. NIGHTMARES IN THE SKY. (NY): Viking, (1988). 1st ed. Fine in dj. *OTHER WORLDS.* $25

King, Stephen and Peter Straub. THE TALISMAN. Boston: Donald Grant, 1984. 1/1200 signed, numbered. 2 vols. Fine in box. *POLYAN-THOS.* $250

King, Stephen and Peter Straub. THE TALISMAN. Grant, 1984. 2 vols in slipcase w/color plts. As New. *MADLE.* $125

King, Stephen and Peter Straub. THE TALISMAN. Viking, 1984. 1st ed. As New. *MADLE.* $25

King, Stephen. CARRIE. Doubleday, 1974. 1st ed. Near VG in taped-down dj. *MADLE.* $200

King, Stephen. CHRISTINE. Grant, 1983. One of 1000 numbered, signed in slipcase. Fine. *MADLE.* $400

King, Stephen. CHRISTINE. NY: Viking, 1983. 1st ed. Fine, rubs at dj corners. *ELSE FINE.* $30

King, Stephen. CUJO. NY: Viking, 1981. 1st ed. Fine in dj. *ELSE FINE.* $35

King, Stephen. CUJO. Viking, 1981. 1st ed. Fine in dj. *MADLE.* $23

King, Stephen. CYCLE OF THE WEREWOLF. (Westland): Land of Enchantment, (1983). 1st ed. 1/350 signed, numbered, this being one of 250 Deluxe Edition copies. Fine in dj in slipcase. *OTHER WORLDS.* $600

King, Stephen. CYCLE OF THE WEREWOLF. Land of Enchantment, 1983. Signed ltd ed, 1/350. Fine in like dj in box. *POLYANTHOS.* $350

King, Stephen. DANSE MACABRE. Everest House, 1981. 1st ed. Fine in dj. *MADLE.* $75

King, Stephen. DANSE MACABRE. NY: Everest House, (1981). 1st trade ptg. Sl crimp to spine else VG+ in edgeworn dj. *OTHER WORLDS.* $45

King, Stephen. DANSE MACABRE. NY: Everest House, 1981. 1st ed. Fine in lightly used dj. *BEASLEY.* $45

King, Stephen. DIFFERENT SEASONS. NY: Viking, (1982). 1st ed. Spine badly cocked else VG+ in lightly stained dj. *OTHER WORLDS.* $25

King, Stephen. DIFFERENT SEASONS. Viking, 1982. 1st ed. Fine in dj. *MADLE.* $60

King, Stephen. DOLAN'S CADILLAC. California: Lord John Press, 1989. 1st ed. Adv proof. Fine in wraps. *POLYANTHOS.* $150

King, Stephen. DOLAN'S CADILLAC. Northridge: Lord John Press, 1989. 1st ed. 1/250 signed, numbered deluxe copies. One of 4 bound in leather. Fine w/o dj as issued. *OTHER WORLDS.* $500

King, Stephen. DOLORES CLAIBORNE. NY: Viking, 1992. 1st ed. Wraps. Advance uncorrected proof. Fine. *BEASLEY.* $125

King, Stephen. EYES OF THE DRAGON. Maine: Philtrum Press, 1984. Signed ltd ed, 1/1000. Fine in box. *POLYANTHOS.* $600

King, Stephen. EYES OF THE DRAGON. NY, 1987. 1st ed. Signed presentation. Fine. *POLYANTHOS.* $85

King, Stephen. FIRESTARTER. NY: Viking, 1980. 1st ed. Fine in dj. *ELSE FINE.* $65

King, Stephen. FIRESTARTER. NY: Viking, (1980). 1st trade ed. Good to VG in VG dj. *OTHER WORLDS.* $25

King, Stephen. FIRESTARTER. Viking, 1980. 1st trade ed. Fine in dj. *MADLE.* $50

King, Stephen. FIRESTARTER. Viking, 1980. Bk club ed. Fine in dj. *MADLE.* $15

King, Stephen. FOUR PAST MIDNIGHT. NY: Viking, 1990. Advance uncorrected proofs. Fine in wraps. *BEASLEY.* $150

King, Stephen. GERALD'S GAME. NY: Viking, 1992. One of an unspecified number specially bound for attendees of the 1992 ABM convention. Fine in Fine printed cardboard slipcase. *BEASLEY.* $150

King, Stephen. IT. NY: Viking, 1986. 1st ed. Fine in dj. *ELSE FINE.* $25

King, Stephen. IT. Viking, 1986. 1st ed. Fine in dj. *MADLE.* $25

King, Stephen. MISERY. (NY: Viking, (1987). Fine in pict dj. 1st trade ed. *CHAPEL HILL.* $40

King, Stephen. MISERY. London: Hodder & Stoughton, (1987). 1st UK ed. NF in dj. *OTHER WORLDS.* $40

King, Stephen. MISERY. Ptd wraps. NY: Viking, (1987). Uncorrected proof. Mint. *JAFFE.* $250

King, Stephen. MISERY. Viking, 1987. 1st ed. As New. *MADLE.* $19

King, Stephen. MY PRETTY PONY. Knopf, 1989. 1st ed. Fine in slipcase. *MADLE.* $75

King, Stephen. MY PRETTY PONY. Pict boards, board slipcase. (NY: Knopf, 1989). 1st trade ed. Mint. *JAFFE.* $75

King, Stephen. NEEDFUL THINGS. NY, 1991. 1st ed. Rev copy w/promo material. Fine in Fine dj. *POLYANTHOS.* $50

King, Stephen. NIGHT SHIFT. Doubleday, 1978. 1st ed. Fine in Mint dj. *MADLE.* $675

King, Stephen. PET SEMATARY. Doubleday, 1983. 1st ed. NF in dj. *MADLE.* $25

King, Stephen. PET SEMATARY. London: Hodder & Stoughton, (1983). 1st UK ed. Spine somewhat cocked else NF in dj. *OTHER WORLDS.* $50

King, Stephen. PET SEMATARY. Proof in wraps. Cvrs creased. Near VG. *MADLE.* $75

King, Stephen. PRIME EVIL. NY, 1988. 1st ed. Signed. Fine in like dj. *POLYANTHOS.* $100

King, Stephen. RAGE. (NY): Signet/NAL, (1977). 1st ed. Pict wrappers. Average, spine roll and creasing but tight, clean. *OTHER WORLDS.* $60

King, Stephen. ROADWORK: A NOVEL OF THE FIRST ENERGY CRISIS. (NY): Signet/NAL, (1981). 1st ed. Pict wrappers. VG+ to NF, flat uncreased spine. *OTHER WORLDS.* $85

King, Stephen. SALEM'S LOT. GC: Doubleday, 1975. 1st ed. VG+ to NF in $7.95/"Cody" dj (edgewear, several short closed tears). *OTHER WORLDS.* $600

King, Stephen. SALEM'S LOT. GC: Doubleday, 1975. 1st ed. Spine quite concave, 2 corners bumped, store name ffep else decent in worn, torn, and chipped dj w/price cut out. *OTHER WORLDS.* $165

King, Stephen. SILVER BULLET. Signet, 1985. 1st ed. Fine in wraps. *MADLE.* $15

King, Stephen. SKELETON CREW. California: Scream Press, 1985. 1st ed. 1/1000 signed, numbered. Fine in box. *POLYANTHOS.* $250

King, Stephen. SKELETON CREW. NY: Putnam's, 1985. Owner's sig, else Fine in price-clipped dj. 1st trade ed. *CHAPEL HILL.* $40

King, Stephen. SKELETON CREW. Putnam, 1985. 1st trade ed. As New. *MADLE.* $19

King, Stephen. SKELETON CREW. Scream Press, 1985. One of 1000 numbered, signed. As New in slipcase. *MADLE.* $300

King, Stephen. THE BACHMAN BOOKS. NAL, 1985. 1st ed. Fine in dj. *MADLE.* $40

King, Stephen. THE DARK HALF. Viking, 1989. 1st ed. Fine in dj. *MADLE.* $25

King, Stephen. THE DARK TOWER II: THE DRAWING OF THE THREE. Grant, 1987. 1st ed. As New. *MADLE.* $60

King, Stephen. THE DARK TOWER II: THE DRAWING OF THE THREE. Grant, 1987. One of 850 numbered, signed in slipcase. As New. *MADLE.* $425

King, Stephen. THE DARK TOWER III: THE WASTE LANDS. Hampton Falls: Grant, 1991. 1/1,200 signed, numbered. Fine in dj, slipcase. *OTHER WORLDS.* $400

King, Stephen. THE DARK TOWER III: THE WASTE LANDS. Hampton Falls: Grant, (1991). 1st ed. Adv rev copy in white ptd wrappers. As New (not illus as issued) plus a set of separate illus in plain env. *OTHER WORLDS.* $600

King, Stephen. THE DARK TOWER III: THE WASTELANDS. Grant, 1991. One of 1250 numbered, signed in slipcase. As New. *MADLE.* $375

King, Stephen. THE DARK TOWER III: THE WASTELANDS. Grant, 1991. 1st ed. As New. *MADLE.* $38

King, Stephen. THE DARK TOWER: THE GUNSLINGER. Grant, 1982, 1st ed. Fine in dj. *MADLE.* $575

King, Stephen. THE DARK TOWER: THE GUNSLINGER. Grant, 1982, 1st ed. Fine in dj. Inscribed. *MADLE.* $750

King, Stephen. THE DARK TOWER: THE GUNSLINGER. Rhode Island: Donald Grant, 1982. 1st ed. Fine in like dj. *POLYANTHOS*. $600

King, Stephen. THE DARK TOWER: THE GUNSLINGER. West Kingston: Grant, 1982. 1st ed. One of 500 signed, numbered. Fine in dj, slipcase. *OTHER WORLDS*. $1,350

King, Stephen. THE DARK TOWER: THE GUNSLINGER. West Kingston: Grant, 1982. 1st ed. Fine in Fine dj. *OTHER WORLDS*. $550

King, Stephen. THE DARK TOWER: THE GUNSLINGER. West Kingston: Grant, 1982. 1st ed. VG+ (spine cocked) in NF dj, short closed tear. *OTHER WORLDS*. $300

King, Stephen. THE DARK TOWER: THE GUNSLINGER. West Kingston: Grant, 1982. 1st ed. One of 500 signed, numbered. Owner blindstamp to contents pg, else Fine in Fine dj. Lacking slipcase. *OTHER WORLDS*. $750

King, Stephen. THE DEAD ZONE. Viking, 1979. 1st ed. Fine in dj. *MADLE*. $75

King, Stephen. THE EYES OF THE DRAGON. Philtrum Press, 1984. One of 1000 numbered in black, signed. As New in slipcase. *MADLE*. $625

King, Stephen. THE EYES OF THE DRAGON. Viking, 1987. 1st trade ed. As New. *MADLE*. $20

King, Stephen. THE LONG WALK. Signet, 1979. 1st ed. NF in wraps. *MADLE*. $40

King, Stephen. THE MIST IN DARK FORCES. NY, 1980. 1st ed. Fine in like dj. *POLYANTHOS*. $40

King, Stephen. THE SHINING. Doubleday, 1977. 1st ed. Fine in sl frayed dj. *MADLE*. $175

King, Stephen. THE SHINING. Doubleday, 1977. 1st ed. Tape stains eps, else VG in dj. *MADLE*. $100

King, Stephen. THE SHINING. GC: Doubleday, 1977. 1st ed. Fine in lightly worn dj. *ELSE FINE*. $165

King, Stephen. THE SHINING. NAL, 1978. 1st pb ed. VG. *MADLE*. $10

King, Stephen. THE STAND. Doubleday, 1978. 1st ed. Fine in Mint dj. *MADLE*. $250

King, Stephen. THE STAND. Doubleday, 1978. 1st issue w/price of $12.95 on flap. Fine in Nearly Fine dj. *DERMONT*. $200

King, Stephen. THE STAND. Doubleday, 1990. Ltd ed. Signed & numbered. VF in box as issued. *STAHR*. $1200

King, Stephen. THE STAND. Fine in Mint dj. Inscribed. *MADLE*. $325

King, Stephen. THE STAND. London, 1990. 1st British ed of complete text. As New. *MADLE*. $50

King, Stephen. THE STAND. NY, 1978. 1st ed. Fine in dj (small piece missing top spine, few tiny tears). *POLYANTHOS*. $150

King, Stephen. THE TOMMYKNOCKERS. NY: Putnam's, (1987). Fine in dj w/author's name in gold lettering on front panel. 1st ed, 1st state w/"Permissions to Come" as last line on copyright page. *CHAPEL HILL*. $45

King, Stephen. THE TOMMYKNOCKERS. Putnam, 1987. 1st ed. As New. *MADLE*. $22

Kinglake, Alexander W. EOTHEN. NY, 1864. New ed. NF. *POLYANTHOS*. $40

Kinglake, Alexander W. THE INVASION OF THE CRIMEA. NY, 1888. 6 vols. 20 fldg maps, plans. Traces of lib markings; else stout, clean. *O'NEILL*. $150

Kingman, Lee. PIERRE PIDGEON. Houghton Mifflin, (1943). 4to. Unpaginated. Illus and signed by Arnold E. Bare. VG w/front inner hinge barely starting. Dj VG with a touch of soil. *BEBBAH*. $60

KINGS AND QUEENS OF ANCIENT EGYPT. NY: Charles Scribner's Sons. 1926. 1st ed. Extrems lightly rubbed. Bkpl. *KARMIOLE*. $100

Kingsley, Charles Jr. THE SAINT'S TRAGEDY; OR, THE TRUE STORY OF ELIZABETH OF HUNGARY. London, 1848. 1st ed, 1st bk. Covers little rubbed. NF. *POLYANTHOS*. $175

Kingsley, Charles. AT LAST: A CHRISTMAS IN THE WEST IN-DIES. NY: Harper, 1871. 1st Amer ed. VG with edgewear. *PARMER*. $85

Kingsley, Charles. GLAUCUS; OR, THE WONDERS OF THE SHORE. (Cambridge: Macmillan & Co., 1855). 1st ed. 3 p.l. (bound without the half title), 165 pp, (1) leaf, 16 pp (ads). Orig green cloth. Frontis. Extremely Fine. *PIRAGES*. $75

Kingsley, Charles. LECTURES DELIVERED IN AMERICA IN 1874. London: Longmans, Green, 1875. 1st ed. 149pp. Uncut and some unopened. Bound in 3/4 morocco w/raised bands and gold stamping by Root and Son. Teg. Nice. *SECOND LIFE*. $35

Kingsley, Charles. MISCELLANIES....London: Parker, 1859. 1st ed. 2 vols. 407; 389pp. Teg. Nice set bound in clean 3/4 morocco w/gold stamped spine. *SECOND LIFE*. $45

Kingsley, Charles. THE WATER BABIES. Winston, (1930). 282pp. Illus by Ethel Everett. Slight wear to spine ends, VG+. *BEBBAH*. $45

Kingston, Maxine Hong. CHINA MEN. NY: Alfred A. Knopf, 1980. 1st ed, 2nd book. New in dj. *BERNARD*. $25

Kingston, Maxine Hong. CHINA MEN. NY: Knopf, 1980. Signed. Fine in dj. *LOPEZ*. $75

Kingston, Maxine Hong. CHINA MEN. Ptd wraps. NY: Knopf, 1980. Uncorrected proof, pub's info sheet stapled inside front wrapper. Fine. *JAFFE*. $100

Kingston, Maxine Hong. THE WOMAN WARRIOR: MEMOIRS OF A GIRLHOOD AMONG GHOSTS. London: Allen Lane, (1977). 1st UK ed. Fine in dj. *CAPTAIN'S BOOKSHELF*. $45

Kingston, Maxine Hong. TRIPMASTER MONKEY. NY: Knopf, 1989. Signed. Fine in Fine 1st issue dj (quoting "James" Leonard on flap). *LOPEZ*. $50

Kinietz, W.V. CHIPPEWA VILLAGE; THE STORY OF KATIKITEGON. Cranbrook Institute Bulletin No. 25, 1947. 1st ed. Fine in Fine dj. Scarce. *VARNER*. $50

Kinnaird, Lawrence. SPAIN IN THE MISSISSIPPI VALLEY, 1765-1794. 3 vols. Annual report of Amer Hist Assoc for 1945. 1st ed. Fine. *OREGON*. $85

Kinnell, Galway. BLACK LIGHT. London: Rupert Hart-Davis (1967). 1st Eng ed. Signed. Fine in dj. *DORN*. $50

Kinnell, Galway. BLACK LIGHT. SF: North Point (1980). Rev ed. Signed. Fine in wraps. *DORN*. $25

Kinnell, Galway. BODY RAGS. Boards, dj. London: Rapp & Whiting, 1969. 1st Eng ed. One of 100 signed. VF. *JAFFE*. $150

Kinnell, Galway. BODY RAGS: POEMS. Boston: Houghton Mifflin, 1968. 1st ed. Fine in dj. Review copy, slip laid in. Signed. *CAPTAIN'S BOOKSHELF*. $125

Kinnell, Galway. FERGUS FALLING. Hand-colored litho by Claire Van Vliet. Cl-backed dec boards. Newark, VT: Janus Press, 1979. 1st ed. Ltd to 120 signed by Kinnell & Van Vliet. Mint. *JAFFE*. $125

Kinnell, Galway. FIRST POEMS 1946-1954. 1/4 green morocco & marbled boards. Mt. Horeb, WI: Perishable Press, 1970. 1st ed. One of 150 ptd. Signed. Spine a bit faded, o/w Fine. *JAFFE*. $275

Kinnell, Galway. FIRST POEMS 1946-1954. Mt. Horeb: Perishable Press, 1970. One of 150 in 1/4 leather over marbled boards signed by Kinnell. Fine. *CAPTAIN'S BOOKSHELF*. $275

Kinnell, Galway. SAINT FRANCIS AND THE SOW. Evanston: No Mountains Broadsides, 1976. 1st ed. One of 150 numbered, signed. NF. *BEASLEY*. $100

Kinnell, Galway. THE BOOK OF NIGHTMARES. Boston: Houghton Mifflin, 1971. 1st ed. Cl, dj. VF. *JAFFE*. $65

Kinnell, Galway. THE BOOK OF NIGHTMARES. Boston: Houghton Mifflin, 1971. 1st ed. Fine in dj. Signed. *CAPTAIN'S BOOKSHELF.* $100

Kinnell, Galway. THE HEN FLOWER. Frensham, Farnham, Surrey: Sceptre Press, (1969). 1st ed. One of 100. Wraps. Fine. *JAFFE.* $100

Kinnell, Galway. THE LAST HIDING PLACES OF SNOW. Frontis by Barry Moser, cl-backed boards. (NY): Red Ozier Press, 1980. 1st ed. Ltd to 150 signed by Kinnell & Moser. Mint. *JAFFE.* $150

Kinnell, Galway. THREE POEMS. NY: Phoenix Book Shop, 1976. 1st ed. Ltd to 126, this marked hors commerce & numbered "iv." Signed. Wraps. VF. *JAFFE.* $125

Kinnell, Galway. WHAT A KINGDOM IT WAS. Boston: Houghton Mifflin, 1960. 1st ed. Orig cl-backed boards. NF in sl soiled dj, minor wear spine ends. Signed; his ink correction on last pg of text. *CHAPEL HILL.* $200

Kinnell, Galway. WHAT A KINGDOM IT WAS. Cl-backed boards, dj. Boston: Houghton Mifflin, 1960. 1st ed. Inscribed. VF. *JAFFE.* $175

Kinnell, Galway. WHEN ONE HAS LIVED A LONG TIME ALONE. Ptd wraps. NY: Knopf, (1990). Uncorrected proof. Mint. *JAFFE.* $45

Kinsella, Thomas. A SELECTED LIFE. (Dublin): Peppercanister 2, (1972). 1st ed. One of 150 special copies signed. 1/2 calf and cl. Fine in acetate dj. *CAPTAIN'S BOOKSHELF.* $175

Kinsella, Thomas. ANOTHER SEPTEMBER. Dublin: Dolmen Press, 1958. 1st ed. One of 50 specially ptd, bound, signed. Fine in 1/4 vellum and marbled boards w/cloth and board slipcase. *CAPTAIN'S BOOKSHELF.* $450

Kinsella, Thomas. FIFTEEN DEAD (with) ONE AND OTHER POEMS. (Dublin): Dolmen Press/Peppercanister, 1979. 1st ed. 2 vols. One of 125 in parchment-backed boards. Signed. Fine in slipcase. *CAPTAIN'S BOOKSHELF.* $200

Kinsella, Thomas. FINISTERE. (Dublin: Dolmen, 1972). 1st ed. 1/250 signed. Bound in 1/4 leather and cl. Fine in acetate dj. *CAPTAIN'S BOOKSHELF.* $175

Kinsella, Thomas. MORALITIES. (Dublin): Dolmen, (1960). One of 500. Wrappers a bit darkened, but VG. *WOOLMER.* $20

Kinsella, Thomas. NEW POEMS 1973. (Dublin): Dolmen Press, (1973). 1st ed. Fine in dj. Inscribed. *CAPTAIN'S BOOKSHELF.* $75

Kinsella, Thomas. NIGHTWALKER AND OTHER POEMS. (Dublin): Dolmen Press, (1967). 1st ed. Top of spine sl bumped, else Fine in dj w/tiny tear. *CAPTAIN'S BOOKSHELF.* $60

Kinsella, Thomas. NIGHTWALKER AND OTHER POEMS. (Dublin): Dolmen Press, (1967). 1st ed. 1/100 signed. Fine in orig glassine dj. *CAPTAIN'S BOOKSHELF.* $250

Kinsella, Thomas. NOTES FROM THE LAND OF THE DEAD. Poems. Dublin: Cuala Press, 1972. 1st ed. 1/500 in Holland-backed boards w/paper label. Signed (not called for). Fine in unprinted dj. *CAPTAIN'S BOOKSHELF.* $125

Kinsella, Thomas. NOTES FROM THE LAND OF THE DEAD. Poems. Dublin: Cuala Press, 1972. 1st ed. 1/500 in Holland-backed boards, paper label. Fine in unptd dj. *CAPTAIN'S BOOKSHELF.* $75

Kinsella, Thomas. ONE. Drawings by Anne Yeats. (Dublin): Peppercanister 5, (1974). 1st ed. 1/124 signed by Kinsella and Yeats. Fine in 1/4 calf and boards, acetate dj. *CAPTAIN'S BOOKSHELF.* $225

Kinsella, Thomas. POEMS & TRANSLATIONS. NY: Atheneum, 1961. 1st ed. Fine in dj. *CAPTAIN'S BOOKSHELF.* $75

Kinsella, Thomas. SELECTED POEMS 1956-1968. (Dublin): Dolmen Press, (1973). 1st ed. Fine in price-clipped dj. Inscribed. *CAPTAIN'S BOOKSHELF.* $75

Kinsella, Thomas. SELECTED POEMS 1962-1989. Helsinki: Eurographica, (1989). 1st ed. Ltd to 350 signed by Kinsella. Ptd wraps. Mint. *JAFFE.* $150

Kinsella, Thomas. THE GOOD FIGHT, A POEM FOR THE TENTH ANNIVERSARY OF THE DEATH OF JOHN F. KENNEDY. (Dublin): Peppercanister 4, (1973). 1st ed. One of 125 signed. Fine in 1/4 calf and boards and unptd dj. *CAPTAIN'S BOOKSHELF.* $175

Kinsella, Thomas. THE MESSENGER. (Dublin): Peppercanister 8, (1978). 1st ed. 1/50 bound in full vellum, ptd on handmade paper and signed w/additional holograph poem. Fine in slipcase. *CAPTAIN'S BOOKSHELF.* $275

Kinsella, Thomas. VERTICAL MAN: A SEQUEL TO A SELECTED LIFE. (Dublin): Peppercanister 3, (1972). 1st ed. 1/100 bound in 1/2 calf and cl and signed. Fine in acetate dj. *CAPTAIN'S BOOKSHELF.* $175

Kinsella, Thomas. WORMWOOD. (Dublin): Dolmen Press, (1966). 1st ed. 1/350 signed. Fine in glassine dj. *CAPTAIN'S BOOKSHELF.* $225

Kinsella, W.P. and Ann Knight. RAINBOW WAREHOUSE. Lawrencetown Beach: Pottersfield Press, (1989). 1st ed. Signed by both authors. Fine. *LOPEZ.* $75

Kinsella, W.P. BORN INDIAN. (Canada): (Oberon), (1981). 1st ed. Issue in wrappers. NF and signed. *LOPEZ.* $100

Kinsella, W.P. CHAPTER ONE OF A WORK IN PROGRESS. One of 300 numbered, signed, issued in wrappers. *LOPEZ.* $85

Kinsella, W.P. DANCE ME OUTSIDE. (Canada): (Oberon), (1977). 1st ed. His first book. Issue in wrappers. NF. *LOPEZ.* $150

Kinsella, W.P. DANCE ME OUTSIDE. Boston: Godine, (1986). 1st Amer ed. Signed. Fine in Fine dj. *LOPEZ.* $75

Kinsella, W.P. DANCE ME OUTSIDE. Boston: Godine, 1986. 1st Amer ed. Advance review ed. with promo material laid in. Fine in Fine dj. *LOPEZ.* $55

Kinsella, W.P. FIVE STORIES. (Vancouver): (Hoffer/Tanks), (1986). One of 100 numbered, signed. Fine w/o dj, as issued. *LOPEZ.* $200

Kinsella, W.P. FIVE STORIES. Vancouver: Hoffer/Tanks, (1986). 1/150. Illus wrappers. Fine. *DERMONT.* $40

Kinsella, W.P. RED WOLF, RED WOLF. Toronto: Collins, (1987). 1st ed. Signed. Fine in dj. *LOPEZ.* $75

Kinsella, W.P. SCARS. (Canada): (Oberon), (1978). 1st ed. Uncommon hardcover issue, reportedly ptd in edition of only a couple of hundred copies. Signed. Fine in Fine dj. *LOPEZ.* $350

Kinsella, W.P. SHOELESS JOE JACKSON COMES TO IOWA. (Canada): (Oberon), (1980). 1st ed. Scarce hb ed. Fine in dj with very sl rubbing at edges. Signed with "Best Wishes" on fep. *LOPEZ.* $450

Kinsella, W.P. SHOELESS JOE. (London): WH Allen, (1988). 1st Eng ed. Fine in dj. *LOPEZ.* $75

Kinsella, W.P. SHOELESS JOE. Boston: Houghton Mifflin, 1982. Uncorrected proof. Ptd wraps. Mint. *JAFFE.* $375

Kinsella, W.P. SHOELESS JOE. Boston: Houghton Mifflin, 1982. Signed. Fine in Fine dj. *LOPEZ.* $275

Kinsella, W.P. SHOELESS JOE. Boston: Houghton Mifflin, 1982. 1st ed. Orig beige cl, grey boards. Fine in dj. Signed "Bill Kinsella." *CHAPEL HILL.* $150

Kinsella, W.P. SHOELESS JOE. Houghton Mifflin, 1982. 1st ed. Fine in VG+ dj. *PLAPINGER.* $130

Kinsella, W.P. THE ALLIGATOR REPORT. Minneapolis: Coffee House, 1985. 1st ed. Orig wrappers, not issued in hb. Fine. *LOPEZ.* $35

Kinsella, W.P. THE BALLAD OF THE PUBLIC TRUSTEE. (Vancouver): Standard Editions, 1982. One of 300 numbered in wrappers, of 326 total, signed. Fine. *LOPEZ.* $85

Kinsella, W.P. THE FENCEPOST CHRONICLES. (Boston): (Houghton Mifflin), (1987). 1st Amer ed. Signed. Lower corners bumped o/w Fine in NF dj. *LOPEZ.* $85

Kinsella, W.P. THE FENCEPOST CHRONICLES. (Ontario): Totem, (1986). Paperback orig. This being the true 1st ed. Fine in wrappers. *LOPEZ.* $75

Kinsella, W.P. THE FURTHER ADVENTURES OF SLUGGER MCBATT. Toronto: Collins, (1988). True 1st ed. Signed. Fine in Fine dj. *LOPEZ.* $125

Kinsella, W.P. THE FURTHER ADVENTURES OF SLUGGER MCBATT. (Boston): (Houghton Mifflin), (1988). 1st Amer ed. Fine in NF dj. *LOPEZ.* $25

Kinsella, W.P. THE IOWA BASEBALL CONFEDERACY. (Boston): (Houghton Mifflin), (1986). 1st Amer ed. Fine in dj. *LOPEZ.* $30

Kinsella, W.P. THE IOWA BASEBALL CONFEDERACY. Boston: Houghton Mifflin, 1986. Wraps. Advance uncorrected proof, bit worn w/lt cover creases. *BEASLEY.* $65

Kinsella, W.P. THE IOWA BASEBALL CONFEDERACY. Toronto: Collins, 1986. 1st ed. Correct 1st ed. Signed. Fine in Fine dj. *LOPEZ.* $150

Kinsella, W.P. THE MOCCASIN TELEGRAPH. (n.p.): Penguin, (1983). Paperback orig. Cheap paper browning, o/w Fine in wrappers. Signed by author. *LOPEZ.* $175

Kinsella, W.P. THE MOCCASIN TELEGRAPH. Boston: Godine, (1984). 1st Amer ed. Signed. Fine in dj. *LOPEZ.* $75

Kinsella, W.P. THE THRILL OF THE GRASS. (Vancouver): Hoffer, 1984. One of 26 lettered, signed, the entire hb ed. Fine w/o dj as issued. *LOPEZ.* $350

Kinsella, W.P. THE THRILL OF THE GRASS. Vancouver: New Play Centre, (1988). Issued as a ltd ed. Stapled wrappers. Fine. Signed. *LOPEZ.* $100

Kinsella, W.P. THE THRILL OF THE GRASS. William Hoffer, 1984. 1/300 numbered/signed. Sewn grn wrappers. Fine. *DERMONT.* $75

Kinzie, Mrs. John H. (Juliette A. McGill). WAU-BUN: THE EARLY DAYS IN THE NORTHWEST. Eleanor Kinzie Gordon (ed). Chicago: Rand, McNally, (1901). Some exterior wear, still Good. Howes K171. *LAURIE.* $25

Kip, Lawrence. ARMY LIFE ON THE PACIFIC. JOURNAL OF EXPEDITION AGAINST NORTHERN INDIANS...IN SUMMER OF 1858. NY: Redfield, 1859. 1st ed. Orig cl, spine ends worn, o/w Fine. Howes K172. *OREGON.* $275

Kip, Lawrence. ARMY LIFE ON THE PACIFIC; A JOURNAL OF THE EXPEDITION AGAINST THE NORTHERN INDIANS...IN THE SUMMER OF 1858. NY, Redfield, 1859. 144pp. 1st ed. Orig cl (sl crinkled, sm chip crown of spine). Howes K172. *GINSBERG.* $325

Kipling, Rudyard. BRAZILIAN SKETCHES. NY: Doubleday, 1940. 1st ed. Some discoloration fep. Contents VG. Chipped dj. *SILVER.* $35

Kipling, Rudyard. CAPTAINS COURAGEOUS. London: Macmillan, 1897. Scattered light foxing, still VG or better. 1st ed. *CHAPEL HILL.* $250

Kipling, Rudyard. CAPTAINS COURAGEOUS: A STORY OF THE GRAND BANKS. NY: The Century Co., 1897. 1st US ed. Pict grn cl in gilt and red. Attractive, NF (owner sig). *CAPTAIN'S BOOKSHELF.* $125

Kipling, Rudyard. COLLECTED DOG STORIES. GC: Doubleday, Doran, 1934. Illus by Marguerite Kirmse. 1st ltd Amer ed. One of 450 numbered, signed and w/drwg by Kirmse. Owner bkpl w/presentation. *WREDEN.* $195

Kipling, Rudyard. COLLECTED DOG STORIES. London: Macmillan, 1934. Illus G.L. Stampa. Full grn leather w/inlaid pict title, t.e.g, ptd buff cardboard box. 1st ed, Eng deluxe issue. VF in sl rubbed box. *JAFFE.* $250

Kipling, Rudyard. COLLECTED VERSE OF RUDYARD KIPLING. NY: Doubleday, Page, 1907. 1st ed, 1st issue w/o index at rear. Few spots fore-edge, else Fine in red ribbed cl, teg. *CAPTAIN'S BOOKSHELF.* $75

Kipling, Rudyard. FROM SEA TO SEA: LETTERS OF TRAVEL. NY: Doubleday, McClure, 1899. 2 vols. 1st ed, 1st state w/errors on p90 and p153 of vol II. Orig emb sea-grn cl. Name, bkpl. NF. *CONNOLLY & WADE.* $125

Kipling, Rudyard. IN BLACK AND WHITE. Allahabad: Wheeler & Co. n.d. 1st ed. Indian Railway Library No. 3. Pict wraps. Spine frayed and rubbed, but nice, firm. *POLYANTHOS.* $150

Kipling, Rudyard. LIMITS AND RENEWALS. London, 1932. 1st ed. Teg Bkpl, spine minimally sunned. Fine in dj (spine little sunned). *POLYANTHOS.* $65

Kipling, Rudyard. OUT OF INDIA: THINGS I SAW AND FAILED TO SEE IN CERTAIN DAYS AND NIGHTS AT JEYPORE AND ELSEWHERE. NY: Dillingham, 1896. Pirated Amer pub. 8vo; pp vi, 340 (4, List of Dillingham publications for 1899). Orig beige pict cl. Sl wear spine ends, else Fine. *HARTFIELD.* $85.

Kipling, Rudyard. PUCK OF POOK'S HILL. London, 1906. 1st ed. Teg; bkpl, spine sl sunned, covers sl edge soiled. NF. *POLYANTHOS.* $150

Kipling, Rudyard. STALKY & CO. NY: Doubleday & McClure, 1899. 1st US ed. Dec grn cl, teg. NF (owner sig). *CAPTAIN'S BOOKSHELF.* $50

Kipling, Rudyard. THE DEAD KING. London: Hodder & Stoughton, 1910. 1st ed (also issued in cl). Orig violet paper covered wraps (corner chipped, some spine lacking) w/silver port vignette, title in purple. VG. *BLUE MOUNTAIN.* $50

Kipling, Rudyard. THE LIGHT THAT FAILED. London: Macmillan, 1891. Eps foxed, gift inscription dated 1891, else VG. 1st Eng ed. *CHAPEL HILL.* $125

Kipling, Rudyard. THE SECOND JUNGLE BOOK. NY, (1895). 1st Amer. ed. Small head and tailpiece decs. Spine rubbed w/light wear. VG. *McCLINTOCK.* $20

Kipling, Rudyard. THEY. London: MacMillan, 1905. 1st ed, 1st issue. NF in white cl. *CAPTAIN'S BOOKSHELF.* $125

Kipling, Rudyard. WITH THE NIGHT MAIL: A STORY OF 2000 A.D. NY: Page, 1909. Frank X. Leyendecker, H. Reuterdahl (illus). 1st ed, 1st issue. Illus blue cl, pict eps. Hinges cracked but tight, else NF. *CAPTAIN'S BOOKSHELF.* $125

Kipping, Robert. RUDIMENTARY TREATISE ON MASTING, MAST-MAKING, AND RIGGING OF SHIPS. ALSO TABLES.... 22nd impression. London: Crosby Lockwood and Son, 1921. *LEFKOWICZ.* $50

Kirby, W.E. BUTTERFLIES & MOTHS OF THE UNITED KINGDOM. London, 1912. 70 colored plts. Cover crinkled, wear at extremities, sl shaken, back cover dampstained. *SUTTON.* $37

Kirby, W.F. A HAND-BOOK TO THE ORDER LEPIDOPTERA. London, 1896-97. 2nd issue. 156 colored and 2 plain plts. 5 vols. Unobtrusive, emb name stamps on plts. Ex-lib. *SUTTON.* $165

Kircher, Henry Adolph. A GERMAN IN THE YANKEE FATHERLAND. (Kent, 1983). 1st ed. Fine in dj. *McGOWAN.* $30

Kirk, John T. AMERICAN CHAIRS. NY: Knopf. 1st ed. VG in dj. *BACKROOM.* $275

Kirk, Russell. THE PRINCESS OF ALL LANDS. Sauk City: Arkham House, (1979). 1st ed. NF in dj, sl sunned spine. *OTHER WORLDS.* $37.50

Kirk, Russell. THE SURLY SULLEN BELL. Fleet, 1962. 1st ed. VG in dj. *MADLE.* $75

Kirk, William. RIGHT OFF THE BAT. Dillingham, 1911. 1st ed. VG, dj not issued. *PLAPINGER.* $130

Kirke, Edmund (pseud of James Robert Gilmore). AMONG THE PINES OR SOUTH IN SECESSION-TIME. NY, 1862. 1st ed. 310pp. Minor internal spotting o/w VG. *PRATT.* $30

Kirke, Edmund (pseud of James Roberts Gilmore). AMONG THE PINES. OR, SOUTH IN SECESSION-TIME. NY: Carleton, 1864. 40th thousand. Spine defective, staining on some pp, o/w VG. *DIAMOND.* $25

Kirke, Edmund (pseud of James Roberts Gilmore). DOWN IN TENNESSEE AND BACK BY WAY OF RICHMOND. NY: Carleton, 1864. 1st ed. 282pp + ads. Orig cl. Lt shelfwear, but VG+. *CHAPEL HILL.* $60

Kirke, Edmund (pseud of James Roberts Gilmore). MY SOUTHERN FRIENDS. NY: Carleton, 1863. 1st ed. 308pp + ads. Orig cl. Fine. *CHAPEL HILL.* $40

Kirker, James. CAPTAIN DON SANTIAGO KIRKER. Reprinted from Santa Fe Republican. LA: Privately ptd, 1948. 1st ed, ltd to 200. Fine. *OREGON.* $50

Kirkham, Stanton Davis. MEXICAN TRAILS. NY: G.P. Putnam's Sons. 1909. 1st ed. Staining to rear cvr. *KARMIOLE.* $35

Kirkland, Caroline M. WESTERN CLEARING. NY, 1848. 2nd ed. (8) 238pp. Pub's ads. Good, sound. *ARTIS.* $65

Kirkwood, James. HIT ME WITH A RAINBOW. NY: Delacorte, (1980). 1st ed. W/lengthy inscrip by the author. Fine in dj. *LOPEZ.* $30

Kirkwood, James. SOME KIND OF HERO. NY: Thomas Y. Crowell, (1975). 1st ed. Signed. NF in price-clipped dj. *LOPEZ.* $40

Kirsch, Robert. IN THE WRONG RAIN. Boston: Little Brown, 1959. 1st ed, 1st bk. Signed. VG. *SMITH.* $100

Kirwan, Albert D. JOHN J. CRITTENDEN. Lexington, (1962). 1st ed. Some dj wear o/w VG+. *PRATT.* $25

Kisch, E.H. THE SEXUAL LIFE OF WOMAN IN ITS PHYSIOLOGICAL, PATHOLOGICAL AND HYGIENIC ASPECTS. NY, 1910. 1st Eng trans. 97 woodcut illus. *FYE.* $30

Kitchell, Joseph. THE EARL OF HELL. Century, 1924. 1st ed. Fine in dj. *MADLE.* $85

Kitchiner, William. THE COOK'S ORACLE AND HOUSEKEEPER'S MANUAL. (NY): Harper, 1831. Stereotype ed. 432pp. Lt foxing, bound in contemp calf. Good, tight. *SECOND LIFE.* $125

Kite, Elizabeth S. BRIGADIER-GENERAL LOUIS LEBEQUE DUPORTAIL. Baltimore, 1933. 1st ed. Orig boards w/cl backstrip. *GINSBERG.* $35

Kite, Elizabeth S. L'ENFANT AND WASHINGTON 1791-1792. Baltimore: J. Hopkins/Inst. Francais DC, 1929. 1st ed. Bkpl. VG. *AARD.* $25

Kitto, John. THE PICTORIAL HISTORY OF PALESTINE AND THE HOLY LAND. London, 1844. 2 vols. Fine. *O'NEILL.* $85

Kitton, Frederic G. (comp). DICKENSIANA: A BIBLIOGRAPHY OF THE LITERATURE RELATING TO CHARLES DICKENS AND HIS WRITINGS. London: George Redway, 1886. 1st ed. 8vo, 510pp, ltd to 500; news article relating to the sale of Kitton's Dickens collection tipped in, green cloth with light smudge rear board. NF. *GREAT EXPECTATIONS.* $75

Kitton, Frederic G. THE MINOR WRITINGS OF CHARLES DICKENS: A BIBLIOGRAPHY AND SKETCH. London: Elliot Stock, 1900. 1st ed. 260pp, green cloth, bkpl. VG+. *GREAT EXPECTATIONS.* $45

Kizer, Carolyn. THE UNGRATEFUL GARDEN. Bloomington: Indiana Univ Press, (1961). Inscribed. Fine in VG spine-faded dj. *LOPEZ.* $225

Klaas, Joe. AMELIA EARHART LIVES. NY: McGraw-Hill, (1970). 1st ed. 272pp. Dj. Signed. *AKA.* $27

Klah, Hasteen. NAVAJO CREATION MYTH. Recorded by Mary C. Wheelwright. Santa Fe, NM: Museum of Navajo Ceremonial Art. 1942. Ed ltd to 1000. Dj. Fine. *KARMIOLE.* $150

Klaus, M. and O. Mayr. THE CLOCKWORK UNIVERSE: GERMAN CLOCKS & AUTOMATA 1550-1650. Smithsonian Inst. & Neale Watson, 1980. New in dj. *BOOKCELL.* $100

Klavan, Andrew. DON'T SAY A WORD. NY: S&S, (1991). 1st ed. VF in VF dj. *UNGER.* $35

Kleberg, Robert J., Jr. THE SANTA GERTRUDIS BREED OF BEEF CATTLE. Kingsville: King Ranch, (1954). VG in wraps. *LAURIE.* $15

Klee, Paul. PAUL KLEE ON MODERN ART. London, 1948. NF. *POLYANTHOS.* $45

Klee, Paul. PEDAGOGICAL SKETCH BOOK. NY: Nierendorf Gallery, 1944. 1st Eng trans. Fine in orig acetate dj. *POLYANTHOS.* $100

Klein, A.M. THE ROCKING CHAIR AND OTHER POEMS. Toronto: Ryerson, (1948). 1st ed. Lacking dj. *WOOLMER.* $35

Klein, Frederic Shriver (ed). JUST SOUTH OF GETTYSBURG, CARROLL COUNTY, MARYLAND IN THE CIVIL WAR. Westminster, MD, 1963. 1st ed. 247pp. Inscribed. Dj wear and chipping, o/w VG. *PRATT.* $50

Klein, Henry H. MY LAST FIFTY YEARS. NY, 1935. Inscr & signed. NF. *POLYANTHOS.* $35

Klein, Maury. EDWARD PORTER ALEXANDER. Athens, (1971). 1st ed. Fine in dj. *PRATT.* $37.50

Klein, William. ROME: THE CITY AND ITS PEOPLE. NY: Viking, (1959). 1st ed. NF in like dj. *CAPTAIN'S BOOKSHELF.* $275

Kleinberg, Samuel. SCOLIOSIS: PATHOLOGY, ETIOLOGY, AND TREATMENT. Baltimore, 1951. 1st ed. Dj. 163 illus. *FYE.* $75

Klickstein, Herbert. WILHELM KONRAD ROENTGEN ON A NEW KIND OF RAYS, A BIBLIOGRAPHICAL STUDY. 1966. 1st ed. Wrappers. *FYE.* $50

Kline, Otis A. CALL OF THE SAVAGE. Clode, 1937. 1st ed. Sm chip to rear panel of dj; sl fading to spine, else Fine. *MADLE.* $350

Klippart, John. 20TH ANNUAL REPORT OHIO STATE BOARD OF AGRICULTURE. Columbus: Nevins, 1866. 376pp+78pp. Nearly New. *AMERICAN BOTANIST.* $32

Klippart, John. THE WHEAT PLANT ITS ORIGIN, CULTURE, VARIETIES, ETC. A FEW REMARKS ON INDIAN CORN, ITS CULTURE, ETC. Cincinnati: Moore, 1860. 760pp. Lea spine taped to boards, contents w/minor foxing, plts present. Acceptable working copy of scarce title. *AMERICAN BOTANIST.* $55

Klippart, John. THE WHEAT PLANT: ITS ORIGIN....Cincinnati, 1860. 8 plts. Orig cl faded, soiled, stained. Ink inscrip, staining, pp yellowed. *SUTTON.* $115

Klose, Kevin and Philip McCombs. TYPHOON SHIPMENTS. NY: Norton, (1974). 1st ed. Very light bumping, o/w NF in dj (corner of front flap clipped; lt damp stain). *AKA.* $35

Kluckhohn, Clyde. TO THE FOOT OF THE RAINBOW. NY, 1927. The 1967 Rio Grande Press reprint of 1927 orig text. Spine lettering a bit dull, else VG+. *FIVE QUAIL.* $30

Kluger, Steve. CHANGING PITCHES. St. Martin's 1984. 1st ed. Fine. Dj lightly worn at spine ends. *STAHR.* $20

Klute, J. WOODLAND PORTRAITS. Boston, 1954. 50 colored plts. Cloth. Upper corner of front cvr bumped; lt scuffing back cvr; lt foxing last pp. *SUTTON*. $95

Knapp, H.S. HISTORY OF THE MAUMEE VALLEY...Toledo, 1877. 1st ed. Cl, VG. *ARTIS*. $85

Knapp, Samuel L. A MEMOIR OF THE LIFE OF DANIEL WEBSTER. Boston: Stimson & Clapp, 1831. 1st ed. Linen covered boards, paper label. Frontis (worn). VG. *SECOND LIFE*. $45

Knibbs, Henry Herbert. SUNDOWN SLIM. Boston: Houghton Mifflin, 1915. 1st ed. Gold-stamped cl, owner inscription on fep. Laid in is illus advert/order form. *DAWSON'S*. $50

Knibbs, Henry Herbert. THE SUNGAZERS. Houghton Mifflin, 1926. 1st ed. Advance review copy, slip tipped in. Fine, name. *AUTHORS OF THE WEST*. $25

Knibbs, Henry Herbert. WILD HORSES. Houghton Mifflin, 1924. 1st ed. Fine, stamp. *AUTHORS OF THE WEST*. $20

Knight, Allanna. R.L.S. IN THE SOUTH SEAS, AN INTIMATE PHOTOGRAPHIC RECORD. Edinburgh: Mainstream Publishing, 1986. As New in dj. *PARMER*. $30

Knight, Charles. PASSAGES OF A WORKING LIFE, DURING HALF A CENTURY WITH A PRELUDE OF EARLY REMINISCENCES. Two Volumes. Shannon: Irish Univ Press, (1971). Rprt of 1864 ed. *OAK KNOLL*. $45

Knight, Damon (ed). NEBULA AWARD STORIES 1965. Doubleday, 1966. 1st ed. Fine in dj. *MADLE*. $150

Knight, Damon (ed). THE CLARION AWARDS. Doubleday, 1984. 1st ed. Fine in dj. *MADLE*. $25

Knight, E.F. WHERE THREE EMPIRES MEET. A NARRATIVE OF RECENT TRAVEL IN KASHMIR....London, 1897. xv,528pp. *O'NEILL*. $45

Knight, E.H. KNIGHT'S AMERICAN MECHANICAL DICTIONARY: A DESCRIPTION...HISTORY OF INVENTIONS. 3 vols. Houghton Mifflin, 1884. 7000 engrs. Leather covers. VG. *BOOKCELL*. $275

Knight, Francis A. THE RAMBLES OF A DOMINIE. London: Wells Gardner, Darton & Co, 1891. Dec cl. VG. *BURCHAM*. $85

Knight, J. A. OL' BILL AND OTHER STORIES. NY: Charles Scribner's Sons, 1942. 1st trade ed. VG+ in Good dj. *BACKMAN*. $42

Knight, J.A. WOODCOCK. NY. 1944. 5 colored plts. *SUTTON*. $30

Knight, Kathryn Laskey. TRACE ELEMENTS. NY: W.W. Norton, 1986. 1st ed. VF in dj. *MORDIDA*. $25

Knight, Lucian L. GEORGIA'S LANDMARKS, MEMORIALS AND LEGENDS. Atlanta, 1913-1914. 1st ed. 2 vols. 54 plts. Orig half morocco, light crack on each spine above a small paper label; bkpls, embossed lib stamps. Howes K215. *GINSBERG*. $175

Knight, Oliver. FOLLOWING THE INDIAN WARS. Norman, (1960). 1st ed. 348pp. VG+ in dj. *PRATT*. $37.50

Knight, Wm. H. (ed). HAND-BOOK ALMANAC FOR THE PACIFIC STATES. SF: H.H. Bancroft and Company, 1862. 5pp ads. Blind-and-gold stamped cl, spotting to upper cover, 1 gathering sprung. *DAWSON'S*. $150

Knittle, Rhea Mansfield. EARLY OHIO SILVERSMITHS AND PEWTERERS 1787-1847. Np: The author, (1943). 1st ed. NF in ptd wraps. *CAPTAIN'S BOOKSHELF*. $35

Knittle, Rhea Mansfield. EARLY OHIO TAVERNS, TAVERN-SIGN, BARGE, BANNER, CHAIR, AND SETTEE PAINTERS. Ashland, OH, 1937. Ptd wraps. #219 of unstated limitation. VG. *BOHLING*. $20

Knobel, E. BEETLES OF NEW ENGLAND AND THEIR KIND. Boston, 1895. Ex-lib. Covers dingy, orig wraps retained. *SUTTON*. $23

Knopf, S.A. PULMONARY TUBERCULOSIS. ITS MODERN PROPHYLAXIS AND THE TREATMENT IN SPECIAL INSTITUTIONS AND AT HOME. Phila, 1899. 343pp. Inner hinges cracked. Scarce. *FYE*. $100

KNOWING THE THUNDER BAY REGION. State of MI, nd (c1940). WPA guide. 1st ed. Wraps worn at edges. *ARTIS*. $45

Knox, Bill. DEAD MAN'S MOORING. London: Century, 1987. 1st ed. VF in dj. *SILVER DOOR*. $25

Knox, Bill. STORMTIDE. Garden City: Doubleday Crime Club, 1973. 1st Amer. ed. Fine in dj. *MORDIDA*. $25

Knox, Dudley W. THE NAVAL GENIUS OF GEORGE WASHINGTON. Boston: Houghton, 1932. 1st ed. 15 plts. Orig boards, muslin spine, paper labels on front cover and backstrip. One of 550 numbered. *GINSBERG*. $85

Knox, Hugh. THE QUEEN OF SNAKES. A POEM. Omaha: Abattoir Editions, Univ of NE, 1978. Ed ltd to 208 numbered. *KARMIOLE*. $35

Knox, Thomas W. ADVENTURES OF TWO YOUTHS IN A JOURNEY TO EGYPT AND THE HOLY LAND. NY: Harper & Brothers, 1883. 438pp, 4pp pub ads. Somewhat soiled, spine rubbed. Chromolitho frontis. *SCHOYER'S*. $40

Knox, Thomas W. BOY'S LIFE OF GENERAL GRANT. Akron: Werner Company, 1899. 420pp, 7pp ads. Frontis, 8 plts. Pict cl. *SCHOYER'S*. $12.50

Knox, Thomas W. THE BOY TRAVELLERS IN THE LEVANT. NY, 1895. xvi,494pp. *O'NEILL*. $40

Knox, Thomas W. THE BOY TRAVELLERS ON THE CONGO. Harper, 1988. 463pp. Illus. Pict cvr, spine in gilt, brown, red on grn cloth, faint cvr edgewear. *BEBBAH*. $30

Knox, Thomas. HORSE STORIES AND STORIES OF OTHER ANIMALS. NY: Cassell, 1890. VG. *OCTOBER FARM*. $25

Knox, Thomas. THE YOUNG NIMRODS IN NORTH AMERICA. Harper, (1881). 299pp. Sl edgewear. Dec cvr in gilt, brown on grn cl. *BEBBAH*. $40

Kobbe, Gustau. THE NEW JERSEY COAST AND PINES, AN ILLUSTRATED GUIDE BOOK WITH ROAD MAPS. Short Hills, NJ: Pub by author, 1889. 108pp. *HEINOLDT*. $40

Kober, George and William Hanson (eds). DISEASES OF OCCUPATION AND VOCATIONAL HYGIENE. Phila, 1916. 1st ed. Inscribed. Scarce. *FYE*. $100

Koch, Frederick H. (ed). CAROLINA FOLK-PLAYS. NY: Holt, (1924). 1st ed, 2nd prtg. Orig tan cl. Owner sig, spine sl darkened, but VG. *CHAPEL HILL*. $25

Koch, Kenneth. POEMS. Prints (by) Nell Blaine. NY: Tibor de Nagy Gallery, 1953. 1st ed. One of 300 ptd, with Blaine's silkscreens ptd from the orig blocks. Short tear to top of back wrapper, else VG. Inscribed. *CAPTAIN'S BOOKSHELF*. $600

Koch, Theodore Wesley (trans). MORE TALES FOR BIBLIOPHILES. Chicago: At the Sign of the Gargoyle, (1945). 1st ed, printed in a limited number. Small 8vo, 51pp, printed French fold. *OAK KNOLL*. $35

Kocher, Theodor. OPERATIVE SURGERY. NY, 1894. 1st Eng trans. 279pp. Ex-lib. Orig owner's name on title page. *FYE*. $150

Kocher, Theodor. TEXT-BOOK OF OPERATIVE SURGERY. London, 1911. 3rd Eng ed. 723 pp. 425 Fine illus. *FYE*. $200

Kocher, Theodor. TEXT-BOOK OF OPERATIVE SURGERY. NY, 1911. 3rd Eng ed. 415 Fine illus. *FYE*. $150

Kochno, Boris. DIAGHILEV AND THE BALLETS RUSSE. NY, 1970. Dj w/closed tears bottom edge. NF. *POLYANTHOS*. $75

Kocke, James. HYPNOTISM. HOW IT IS DONE; ITS USES AND DANGERS. Boston, 1894. 1st ed., 7th thousand. Ex-lib. *FYE*. $50

Koebel, H. SOUTH AMERICA. A&C Black, n.d. (1912). 1st ed. 20s Series. VG-NF. *OLD LONDON.* $60

Koebel, W.H. ARGENTINA PAST AND PRESENT. A&C Black, 1914. 2nd ed. 20s Series. VG-NF. Scarce. *OLD LONDON.* $35

Koehn, Alfred. THE ART OF JAPANESE FLOWER ARRANGEMENT (IKEBANA)...A HANDBOOK FOR BEGINNERS. Japan: J.L. Thompson & Co, (1933). A bit shaky, small stain front cover, o/w VG. *WREDEN.* $35

Koenig, George. DEATH VALLEY TAILINGS RARELY TOLD TALES OF OLD DEATH VALLEY. Morongo Valley: Sagebrush, 1986. 1st ed, ltd to 275 hb copies. 125pp. Fine in Fine dj. *BOOK MARKET.* $18

Koestler, Arthur. GHOST IN THE MACHINE. London: Hutchinson, 1967. Uncorrected proof. Light shelfwear. *AKA.* $50

Koestler, Arthur. REFLECTIONS ON HANGING. NY, 1957. Dj. VG. *POLYANTHOS.* $35

Koestler, Arthur. SPANISH TESTAMENT. London: Gollancz/Left Book Club, 1937. Orange linen wraps, the correct 1st ed. Sl worn. *BEASLEY.* $75

Koestler, Arthur. THE SLEEPWALKERS. NY: Macmillan, 1959. 1st prtg. Good in worn dj. *KNOLLWOOD.* $28

Kohl, Edith Eudora. DENVER'S HISTORIC MANSIONS. Denver: Sage Books. (1957). 1st ed. 268pp. Dj sl chipped. *KARMIOLE.* $30

Kohr, Herbert O. AROUND THE WORLD WITH UNCLE SAM. Akron, OH: Commercial Ptg Co. 1907. Grn cl. Extrems sl rubbed. *KARMIOLE.* $75

Kolb, E.L. THROUGH THE GRAND CANYON FROM WYOMING TO MEXICO. Macmillan, 1914. 1st ed. 72 photos, cvr photo, frontis. Inscribed, signed. Teg. Rear hinge tender, else Fine. *AUTHORS OF THE WEST.* $60

Koldewey, Captain. THE GERMAN ARCTIC EXPEDITION OF 1869-70, AND ...WRECK OF 'HANSA' IN THE ICE. Rev. L. Mercier (trans), H.W. Bates (ed). London: Sampson Low, Marston, Low, & Searle, 1874. Cl rubbed; hinges strengthened; repair to spine; some pgs roughly opened. *PARMER.* $550

Koningsberger, Hans. THE FUTURE OF CHE GUEVARA. GC: Doubleday, (1971). 1st ed. Name. Touch of wear at extrems, o/w NF in sl worn dj. *AKA.* $30

Koontz, Dean R. BEASTCHILD. NY: Lancer Books, 1970. 1st ed. Pb orig. Crease front cvr o/w VG in wrappers. *MORDIDA.* $25

Koontz, Dean R. COLD FIRE. NY: G.P. Putnam's Sons, 1991. 1st ed. One of 750 numbered, specially bound. As New in dj w/slipcase. *MORDIDA.* $250

Koontz, Dean R. COLD FIRE. Putnam, 1990. One of 750 numbered, signed. As New in slipcase. *MADLE.* $150

Koontz, Dean R. LIGHTNING. (n.p.): Ultramarine Publishing, 1988. 1/200 numbered, signed. Quarter-bound in leather and marbled paper boards. Fine. *LOPEZ.* $150

Koontz, Dean R. LIGHTNING. NY: G.P. Putnam's Sons, 1988. 1st ed. Fine in dj. *MORDIDA.* $30

Koontz, Dean R. MIDNIGHT. Putnam, 1989. 1st ed. Fine in frayed dj. *MADLE.* $25

Koontz, Dean R. NIGHT CHILLS. NY: Atheneum, 1976. 1st ed. Fine in dj. *MORDIDA.* $150

Koontz, Dean R. NIGHTMARE JOURNEY. NY: Berkley-Putnam, 197. 1st ed. Fine in dj. *ELSE FINE.* $225

Koontz, Dean R. PHANTOMS. Berkley, 1983. 1st ed. Near VG. *MADLE.* $50

Koontz, Dean R. PHANTOMS. NY: Putnam, 1983. 1st ed. VF in dj. *ELSE FINE.* $250

Koontz, Dean R. SHADOWFIRES. NY: Avon, 1987. Book club and 1st hb ed. Fine in dj (crease-tear; chip; couple short closed tears). *MORDIDA.* $30

Koontz, Dean R. STRANGERS. NY: G.P. Putnam's Sons, 1986. 1st ed. VF in dj. *MORDIDA.* $35

Koontz, Dean R. STRANGERS. NY: Putnam, (1986). 1st ed. Fine in Fine dj. *OTHER WORLDS.* $40

Koontz, Dean R. STRANGERS. NY: Putnam, 1986. 1st ed. As New in dj. *ELSE FINE.* $40

Koontz, Dean R. THE BAD PLACE. NY: Putnam, (1990). 1st ed. One of 250 numbered, signed. Fine in pub's slipcase. *UNGER.* $175

Koontz, Dean R. THE VISION. NY: G.P. Putnam's Sons, 1977. 1st ed. Fine in dj w/closed tear, few nicks. *MORDIDA.* $125

Koontz, Dean R. WATCHERS. Putnam, (1987). 1st ed. NF with endpaper inscrip in VG+ dj with 2 closed edge tears. *BEBBAH.* $18

Koontz, Dean R. WATCHERS. Putnam, 1987. 1st ed. Fine in dj. *MADLE.* $25

Koontz, Dean R. WHISPERS. NY: Putnam, 1980. 1st ed. VF in dj. *ELSE FINE.* $375

Koontz, Dean R. WRITING POPULAR FICTION. Cincinnati: Writer's Digest, 1972. 1st ed. Fine in dj. *MORDIDA.* $125

Kopal, Zdenek. A NEW PHOTOGRAPHIC ATLAS OF THE MOON. London: Robert Hale, 1971. VG. *KNOLLWOOD.* $35

Kopal, Zdenek. A NEW PHOTOGRAPHIC ATLAS OF THE MOON. NY: Taplinger, 1971. VG in sl tattered dj. *KNOLLWOOD.* $50

Koppett, Leonard. THE NEW YORK METS. Macmillan, 1970. Fine in VG dj. *PLAPINGER.* $45

Korn, Bertram W. AMERICAN JEWRY AND THE CIVIL WAR. Phila, (1951). 1st ed. VG in dj. *PRATT.* $45

Kornbluh, Jesse (ed). NOTES FROM THE NEW UNDERGROUND. NY: Viking, (1968). 1st ed. NF in NF price-clipped dj. *AKA.* $35

Korngold, Ralph. THADDEUS STEVENS, A BEING DARKLY WISE AND RUDELY GREAT. NY, (1955). 1st ed. Dj has tear and light wear o/w Fine. *PRATT.* $35

Korngold, Ralph. TWO FRIENDS OF MAN. Boston, (1950). 1st ed. Some dj wear o/w Fine. *PRATT.* $30

Korstian, C.F. and W. Maughan. THE DUKE FOREST, A DEMONSTRATION AND RESEARCH LABORATORY. Durham, 1935. 4 fldg maps (3 colored). Wrappers, hinges reinforced. *SUTTON.* $65

Kosinski, Jerzy. BEING THERE. London: Bodley Head (1971). 1st Eng ed. Fine in dj. *DORN.* $50

Kosinski, Jerzy. BLIND DATE. Boston: Houghton Mifflin, 1977. Inscribed. Kosinski has drawn one of his self-caricatures as well. Fine in dj. *LOPEZ.* $65

Kosinski, Jerzy. THE PAINTED BIRD. Boston: Houghton Mifflin, 1965. 1st ed, 1st state of p.270 w/extraneous line at top. Fine in sl soiled white dj, few sm chips. *HELLER.* $125

Kosinski, Jerzy. THE PAINTED BIRD. Boston: Houghton Mifflin, 1965. NF in dj (short closed tear in front panel). 1st ed, 1st state of text w/spurious line at top of p. 270. *CHAPEL HILL.* $175

Koster, R.M. THE PRINCE. NY: Morrow, 1972. Owner gift inscrip. Signed. VG in price-clipped dj. *LOPEZ.* $75

Koster, R.M. THE PRINCE. NY: William Morrow, 1972. 1st ed, 1st bk. Fine in dj (few tiny marks). *CAPTAIN'S BOOKSHELF.* $50

Kotker, Norman. MISS RHODE ISLAND. NY: Farrar Straus Giroux, (1978). 1st ed. Inscribed. VG in dj. *LOPEZ.* $30

Kotker, Zane. A CERTAIN MAN. NY: Knopf, 1976. 1st ed. Signed. Fine in NF dj. *LOPEZ.* $30

Kotlowitz, Robert. THE BOARDWALK. NY: Knopf, 1977. 1st ed. Rev copy. Signed. Fine in Fine dj. *LOPEZ*. $25

Kotzwinkle, William. GREAT WORLD CIRCUS. NY: Putnam's, (1983). 1st ed. NF in lightly used dj w/tiny tear. *AKA*. $25

Kotzwinkle, William. JACK IN THE BOX. NY: Putnam's, (1980). 1st ed. Fine in NF dj. *AKA*. $25

Kotzwinkle, William. THE MIDNIGHT EXAMINER. Houghton Mifflin, 1989. 1st ed. VF, dj. Signed & dated (4/12/89). *STAHR*. $35

Kotzwinkle, William. TROUBLES IN BUGLAND: A COLLECTION OF INSPECTOR MANTIS MYSTERIES. Illus Joe Servello. Boston: David R. Godine, 1983. 1st ed. VF in dj. *MORDIDA*. $65

Kovacs, Ernie. HOW TO TALK AT GIN. GC: Doubleday, 1962. 1st ed. Offsetting to eps, else NF in VG dj w/spine fading, bit of soiling. *BETWEEN COVERS*. $45

Kovacs, Ernie. HOW TO TALK AT GIN. GC: Doubleday, 1962. Stated 1st ed. Dj price clipped, lt edge soil, tiny tear. *AKA*. $40

Kovacs, Ernie. HOW TO TALK AT GIN. NY: Doubleday, (1962). 1st ed. Fine in NF price clipped dj. *DORN*. $30

Kovic, Ron. BORN ON THE FOURTH OF JULY. NY: McGraw-Hill, (1976). 1st prtg. VG in somewhat worn dj. Inscribed. *LOPEZ*. $125

Kozloff, E.N. PLANTS & ANIMALS OF THE PACIFIC NORTHWEST, AN ILLUSTRATED GUIDE...WESTERN OREGON, WASHINGTON & BRITISH COLUMBIA. Seattle & London: Univ of WA, 1976. 1st ed. VG. *MIKESH*. $32.50

Kraay, Colin M. GREEK COINS. London: Thames and Hudson, (1966). 20 color plts, 4 maps. Fine in dj. *ARCHAEOLOGIA*. $650

Krafft-Ebbing, R. von. TEXT-BOOK OF INSANITY BASED ON CLINICAL OBSERVATIONS. Phila, 1904. 1st Eng trans. *FYE*. $100

Kraft, Stephanie. NO CASTLES ON MAIN STREET. Chicago: Rand McNally, (1979). 1st ed. Fine in dj. *CAPTAIN'S BOOKSHELF*. $25

Krakel, Dean. ADVENTURES IN WESTERN ART. Lowell, 1977. 1st ed. Inscribed. Fine in Fine dj. *VARNER*. $40

Kramer, Jane. ALLEN GINSBERG IN AMERICA. NY: Random House, (1969). 1st ed. VG in dj. *LOPEZ*. $40

Kramer, Jane. THE LAST COWBOY. Harper, (1977). 1st ed. Boards. Fine in dj. *AUTHORS OF THE WEST*. $17.50

Kramrisch, Stella. THE ART OF INDIA. London, 1954. NF. *POLYANTHOS*. $60

Kransheninnikov, Stepan Petrovich. EXPLORATIONS OF KAMCHATKA: NORTH PACIFIC SCIMITAR. Portland: Oregon Hist Soc, 1972. VG. *BLUE DRAGON*. $50

Krarup-Nielson, A. HELL BEYOND THE SEAS. London: John Lane The Bodley Head, 1935. 1st Eng ed. NF in VG+ dj. *GREAT EPIC*. $45

Kraus, George. HIGH ROAD TO PROMONTORY: BUILDING....Palo Alto: American West, 1969. 1st ed. Fine in worn dj. *CONNOLLY & WADE*. $45

Kraus, Herbert. NEIGHBOR BOY. Midland House, 1939. 1st ed. Fine. *AUTHORS OF THE WEST*. $40

Kraus, Herbert. THE OXCART TRAIL. Bobbs-Merrill, (1954). 1st ed. Ltd Minnesota ed, signed. Also inscribed. Brochure, order blank laid in. Fine in dj. *AUTHORS OF THE WEST*. $60

Kraus, Herbert. WIND WITHOUT RAIN. Bobbs-Merrill, (1939). 1st ed, 1st novel. Inscribed, signed. VG+ in dj. *AUTHORS OF THE WEST*. $75

Kraus, Theodor. POMPEII AND HERCULANEUM: THE LIVING CITIES OF THE DEAD. NY: Harry N. Abrams, (1975). Dj. Good. *ARCHAEOLOGIA*. $95

Krause, Herbert and Gary D. Olson. PRELUDE TO GLORY: A NEWSPAPER ACCOUNTING....Brevet Press, (1974). 1st ed. New in dj. *AUTHORS OF THE WEST*. $25

Kreisel, Henry. THE ALMOST MEETING. Edmonton: NeWest Press, (1981). 1st Canadian ed. Fine in dj. *AUTHORS OF THE WEST*. $20

Kreisel, Henry. THE BETRAYAL. Toronto: McClelland & Stewart, (1964). 1st ed. Canadian ed. Signed. Fine in dj. *AUTHORS OF THE WEST*. $30

Kremers, Edward and George Urdang. A HISTORY OF PHARMACY. Phila: Lippincott, (1940). 1st ed. Blue cl. VG. Signed by both authors. *SMITHFIELD*. $70

Kremers, Edward and George Urdang. A HISTORY OF PHARMACY. Phila: Lippincott, (1940). 1st ed. Blue cl. VG. *SMITHFIELD*. $63

Krey, Laura. ON THE LONG TIDE. Boston: Houghton Mifflin, 1940. 1st. Dj. Fine. *MUELLER*. $25

Kreymborg, Alfred et al (eds). AMERICAN CARAVAN IV....NY: Macauley, 1931. 1st ed. Light wear, generally Nice. *AKA*. $30

Kreymborg, Alfred. THE PAMPHLET POETS. NY: Simon and Schuster, 1928. 1st ed. Wraps, close to Fine w/tiny chip on rear corner. *BEASLEY*. $45

Kreymborg, Alfred. THE PLANETS. NY: Farrar & Rinehart, (1938). Offsetting to pastedowns from binder's glue, spine tips chipped, else VG. Later ptg. Inscribed. *CHAPEL HILL*. $35

Kreymborg, Alfred. TROUBADOUR: AN AUTOBIOGRAPHY. NY: Liveright, (1925). 1st ed. *AKA*. $30

Krim, Seymour. SHAKE IT FOR THE WORLD, SMARTASS. NY: Dial, 1970. 1st ed. Minor stain bottom fore-edge, o/w VG+ in price-clipped dj with wear. *AKA*. $25

Krinov, E. L. GIANT METEORITES. London: Pergamon, 1966. 1st Eng lang ed. Trans by J.S. Romankiewicz. Fine in gold cl. *KNOLLWOOD*. $45

Krinov, E.L. PRINCIPLES OF METEORITICS. NY: Pergamon Press, 1960. Trans Irene Vidziunas. VG. *KNOLLWOOD*. $48

Kroeber, Theodora and Robert F. Heizer. ALMOST ANCESTORS. THE FIRST CALIFORNIANS. SF: Sierra Club, 1968. 1st ed. VF in Fine dj. *CONNOLLY & WADE*. $35

Krug, Mark M. LYMAN TRUMBULL, CONSERVATIVE RADICAL. NY, (1965). 1st ed. Dj wear o/w VG+. *PRATT*. $20

Krug, Merton E. DUBAY, SON-IN-LAW OF OSHKOSH. Appleton, Wis (1946), 1st ed. dj. *HEINOLDT*. $15

Krussman, G. and N. Raban (trans). ROSES. London, 1982. Cl, dj. *SUTTON*. $45

Krussmann, G. and N. Raban (trans). THE COMPLETE BOOK OF ROSES. Portland, 1981. Cl, scuffed dj. *SUTTON*. $45

Kuhlman, Charles. DID CUSTER DISOBEY ORDERS....? Harrisburg: Stackpole, 1957. 1st ed. Stiff pict wraps. Fine. *CONNOLLY & WADE*. $25

Kull, Irving S. (ed). NEW JERSEY, A HISTORY. NY: American Hist Soc, 1930-32. 5 vols. Vols. 1-4 VG+, Vol. 5 w/dampstaining base of spine and front cover. *BOHLING*. $110

Kultermann, Udo. TROVA. NY: Abrams, (1978). 1st ed. 176 plts, 48 in color. Fine in dj. Signed. *CAPTAIN'S BOOKSHELF*. $250

Kulturmann, Udo (ed). KENZO TANGE, 1946-1969—ARCHITECTURE AND URBAN DESIGN. NY: Praeger, (1970). 1st US ed. VF in Fine slipcase. *AARD*. $75

Kumin, Maxine and Anne Sexton. JOEY AND THE BIRTHDAY PRESENT. NY: McGraw-Hill, (1971). Signed. Fine in Fine dj. *LOPEZ*. $20

Kumin, Maxine. IN DEEP: COUNTRY ESSAYS. NY: Viking (1987). Uncorrected proof. NF in wraps. *CAPTAIN'S BOOKSHELF*. $20

Kumin, Maxine. UP COUNTRY. Poems of New England, New and Selected. NY: Harper & Row, (1972). Fine in dj w/small round price sticker on front flap. 1st ed. Signed. *CHAPEL HILL.* $40

Kummer, Frederic Arnold. A LOST PARADISE. NY: Watt, 1914. 1st ed. Fine. *ELSE FINE.* $30

Kummer, Frederic Arnold. A SONG OF SIXPENCE. NY: Watt, 1913. 1st ed. Fine; bright copy. Illus. *ELSE FINE.* $35

Kummer, Frederic Arnold. THE SCARECROW MURDERS. NY: Dodd Mead, 1938. 1st ed. VF, minor wear at dj spine ends. *ELSE FINE.* $75

Kundera, Milan. LIFE IS ELSEWHERE. NY: Knopf, (1974). 1st Amer ed. Fine in NF dj. *DORN.* $100

Kundera, Milan. THE FAREWELL PARTY. NY: Knopf (1976). 1st Amer ed. Fine in sl dust soiled dj. *DORN.* $50

Kundera, Milan. THE FAREWELL PARTY. NY: Knopf, 1976. 1st US ed. Fine in dj. *CAPTAIN'S BOOKSHELF.* $75

Kundera, Milan. THE JOKE. David Hamblyn, Oliver Stallybrass (eds). NY: Coward-McCann (1969). 1st Amer ed. Fine in a NF dj, chips. *DORN.* $95

Kundera, Milan. THE JOKE. NY, 1969. 1st ed, 1st bk. Fine in dj (top spine tiny nick). *POLYANTHOS.* $95

Kundera, Milan. THE JOKE. NY, 1969. 1st US ed, 1st bk. Owner inscription else Fine in NF dj. *PETTLER.* $80

Kundera, Milan. THE UNBEARABLE LIGHTNESS OF BEING. Harper & Row, 1984. 1st ed. Fine in dj (closed tear on front panel, shows lightest of wear). *STAHR.* $25

Kunitz, Stanley. THE COAT WITHOUT A SEAM. SIXTY POEMS 1930-1972. Port by Leonard Baskin, 1/4 vellum & blue boards. Gehenna Press: 1974. 1st ed. Ltd to 250 signed by Kunitz. VF. *JAFFE.* $275

Kunstler, William M. DEEP IN MY HEART. NY: Morrow, 1966. 1st ed. Tear rear panel dj, o/w Fine in Fine dj. *AKA.* $35

Kuntz, R.E. SNAKES OF TAIWAN. Taipei, 1963. Some cover bowing. *SUTTON.* $40

Kunz, G.F. SHAKESPEARE AND PRECIOUS STONES. Phila & London, 1916. Illus, teg. Inscrib & signed. VG-NF. *POLYANTHOS.* $125

Kunz, George Frederick. NATAL STONES. 18th ed. NY: Tiffany, (1909?). Orig quarter navy blue morocco, marbled sides, morocco corners, teg. Inscribed. *WEBER.* $50

Kupferberg, Tuli. THE BOOK OF THE BODY. NY: Birth, 1966. 1st ed. Wraps, some creasing and folding, else Nice. *BEASLEY.* $30

Kurten, B. (ed). TEETH: FORM, FUNCTION, AND EVOLUTION. NY, 1982. Cloth, dj. *SUTTON.* $66

Kurtx, Donna Carol. ATHENIAN WHITE LEKYTHOI. Oxford: Clarendon Press, 1975. 34 figs, 72 plts (1 color). Good in torn dj. *ARCHAEOLOGIA.* $200

Kurz, Rudolph F. JOURNAL OF RUDOLPH FRIEDERICH KURZ: AN ACCOUNT OF HIS EXPERIENCES....1846 TO 1852. Wash., 1937. 1st ed. Orig ptd wrappers. Howes K281. *GINSBERG.* $150

Kurz, Rudolph Friedreich. JOURNAL OF... EXPERIENCES AMONG FUR TRADERS & AMERICAN INDIANS...1846-1852. 1937 BAE Bulletin #115. 1st ed. VG in wraps. *OREGON.* $85

Kurzweil, Allen. A CASE OF CURIOSITIES. NY: HBC, (1992). 1st ed. Signed. VF in VF dj. *UNGER.* $40

Kushner, Ervan F. ALFRED G. PACKER, CANNIBAL VICTIM? Colorado, 1980, ltd, inscribed. Bonded leather, half binding. *HEINOLDT.* $40

Kussmaul, Adolf. DISTURBANCES OF SPEECH. AN ATTEMPT IN THE PATHOLOGY OF SPEECH. NY, 1877. 1st Eng trans. Recent 1/4 leather, 312pp. *FYE.* $200

Kussmaul, Adolf. MEMOIRS OF AN OLD PHYSICIAN. Washington, 1981. 1st ed. Ex-lib. Dj. *FYE.* $30

Kuttner, Henry. AHEAD OF TIME. Ballantine, 1953. 1st ed. VG. *MADLE.* $30

Kuttner, Henry. FURY. G & D, 1950. 1st ed. NF in sl shelf-worn dj. *MADLE.* $35

Kuttner, Henry. MUTANT. London, 1954. 1st British ed. Fine in dj. Inscribed to Julius Schwartz. *MADLE.* $350

Kuttner, Henry. THE DARK WORLD. NY: Ace, 1965. 1st ed. Fine in wraps. *BEASLEY.* $25

Kuttner, Henry. THE MURDER OF ELEANOR POPE. Permabooks, 1956. 1st ed. Fine in wraps. Inscribed to Julius Schwartz. *MADLE.* $200

Kutumbiah, P. ANCIENT INDIAN MEDICINE. Bombay, 1962. Dj. *FYE.* $65

Kyle, R.A. and M.A. Shampo. MEDICINE AND STAMPS. Chicago, 1970. 1st ed. Dj. *FYE.* $40

Kyne, Peter B. NEVER THE TWAIN SHALL MEET. Cosmopolitan, 1923. 1st ed. VG+. *AUTHORS OF THE WEST.* $17.50

Kyne, Peter B. THE PARSON OF PANAMINT AND OTHER STORIES. Cosmopolitan, 1929. 1st ed. Fine. *AUTHORS OF THE WEST.* $25

Kyne, Peter B. THE PRIDE OF PALOMAR. Cosmopolitan, 1921. 1st ed. Centerfold double pg. Inscribed, signed. VG, Nice bright dj. *AUTHORS OF THE WEST.* $75

Kyne, Peter B. THE THREE GODFATHERS. NY, (1913). 4 plts. Author's 1st bk. Stain on rear cvr. Spine soiled. Little shelfwear. Little staining on few pp. Erasure on pastedown, o/w VG. Inscribed. *DIAMOND.* $75

Kyne, Peter B. TIDE OF EMPIRE. Cosmopolitan, 1928. 1st ed. Fine in dj. *AUTHORS OF THE WEST.* $50

L

L'Amour, Louis. CROSSFIRE TRAIL. Boston: Gregg Press, 1980 (1954). 1st hb ed. VF in dj. *ELSE FINE.* $25

L'Amour, Louis. DARK CANYON. Bantam, (1983). 1st ed. Leather bound; aeg. Inscribed, signed. Deluxe ed. Fine. *AUTHORS OF THE WEST.* $125

L'Amour, Louis. FAIR BLOWS THE WIND. NY: E.P. Dutton, (1978). 1st ed. Fine in dj. *LAURIE.* $50

L'Amour, Louis. FRONTIER. Photos by David Muench. Bantam, (1984) 216pp. 1st ed. F in F dj. *OREGON.* $40

L'Amour, Louis. HELLER WITH A GUN. Boston: Gregg Press, 1981 (1955). 1st hb ed. VF in dj. *ELSE FINE.* $35

L'Amour, Louis. KILKENNY. Boston: Gregg Press, 1980 (1954). 1st hb ed. VF in dj. *ELSE FINE.* $25

L'Amour, Louis. LAST STAND AT PAPAGO WELLS. Boston: Gregg Press, 1981 (1957). 1st hb ed. VF in dj. *ELSE FINE.* $35

L'Amour, Louis. OVER ON THE DRY SIDE. NY: Saturday Review Press/E.P. Dutton, (1975). 1st ed. Bound in 1/4 cl and paper boards. Fine in dj. *LAURIE.* $50

L'Amour, Louis. RADIGAN. NY: Bantam, 1958. 1st ed. Pb orig. NF in wraps. *ELSE FINE.* $15

L'Amour, Louis. SACKETT'S LAND. E.P. Dutton & Co, 1974. 1st ed. Fine in dj. *AUTHORS OF THE WEST.* $100

L'Amour, Louis. SACKETT'S LAND. NY: Saturday Review Press/E.P. Dutton, 1974. 1st ed. Fine in dj. *LAURIE.* $50

L'Amour, Louis. SHOWDOWN AT YELLOW BUTTE. Boston: Gregg Press, 1980 (1953). 1st hb ed. VF in dj. *ELSE FINE.* $30

L'Amour, Louis. SMOKE FROM THIS ALTAR. Lusk Pub Co, (1939). 1st ed. Fine, bright, names. *AUTHORS OF THE WEST.* $600

L'Amour, Louis. THE CHEROKEE TRAIL. Toronto: Bantam Books, (1982). 1st ed. Bound in 1/4 cl and paper boards. Fine in dj. *LAURIE.* $50

L'Amour, Louis. THE TALL STRANGER. Boston: Gregg Press, 1981 (1957). 1st hb ed. VF in dj. *ELSE FINE.* $35

L'Amour, Louis. TO TAME A LAND. Boston: Gregg Press, 1981 (1954). 1st hb ed. VF in dj. *ELSE FINE.* $25

L'Amour, Louis. UTAH BLAINE. Boston: Gregg Press, 1980 (1954). 1st hb ed. VF in dj. *ELSE FINE.* $25

L'Anson Fausett, Hugh. WALT WHITMAN: POET OF DEMOCRACY. London: Jonathan Cape, (1932). VG. *WEBER.* $20

L'Engle, Madeleine. A SEVERED WASP. NY: Farrar Straus Giroux, (1982). 1st ed. Fine in dj. *BETWEEN COVERS.* $35

L'Engle, Madeleine. A WIND IN THE DOOR. NY: Farrar Straus & Giroux, (1973). 1st ed. Very slight stain on front board, else Fine in Very NF dj w/very slight rubbing. *BETWEEN COVERS.* $200

L'Engle, Madeleine. A WRINKLE IN TIME. NY: Farrar Straus Giroux, (1987). 1/500 numbered, signed. Twenty-Fifth Anniversary ed. Attractive cl binding, Fine w/o dj as issued, in pub's slipcase. *LOPEZ.* $65

L'Engle, Madeleine. A WRINKLE IN TIME. Red cl, slipcase. N. Y: Farrar Straus Giroux, (1987). 25th Anniversary Collector's Ed. Ltd to 500 signed. Mint. *JAFFE.* $75

L'Engle, Madeleine. AN ACCEPTABLE TIME. NY: Farrar Straus Giroux, (1989). 1st ed. Signed. Fine in dj. *LOPEZ.* $45

L'Engle, Madeleine. DRAGONS IN THE WATERS. NY: Farrar Straus & Giroux, (1976). 1st ed. Fine in very sl soiled dj. *BETWEEN COVERS.* $50

L'Engle, Madeleine. LADDER OF ANGELS: SCENES FROM THE BIBLE ILLUSTRATED BY THE CHILDREN OF THE WORLD. NY: Seabury, (1979). 1st ed. Fine in NF dj (1 1/2" tear edge front panel). *BETWEEN COVERS.* $45

L'Engle, Madeleine. LINES SCRIBBLED ON AN ENVELOPE. NY: Farrar Straus & Giroux, (1969). 1st ed. Fine in very sl rubbed dj. *BETWEEN COVERS.* $65

L'Engle, Madeleine. MEET THE AUSTINS. NY: Vanguard, (1960). 1st ed. Fine in Very NF dj w/slight tear. Inscribed. *BETWEEN COVERS.* $175

L'Engle, Madeleine. THE ARM OF THE STARFISH. (NY): Farrar Straus Giroux, (1965). 1st ed. Fine in dj. *BETWEEN COVERS.* $100

L'Engle, Madeleine. THE IRRATIONAL SEASON. NY: Seabury, (1977). 1st ed. Fine in NF dj rubbed at extremities. *BETWEEN COVERS.* $45

L'Engle, Madeleine. THE MOON BY NIGHT. NY: Ariel, (1963). 1st ed. Small scrape on front board, else Fine in dj w/slightest of rubbing at extremities. *BETWEEN COVERS.* $125

L'Engle, Madeleine. THE SPHINX AT DAWN. NY: Seabury, (1982). 1st ed. Fine in dj. *BETWEEN COVERS.* $45

L'Engle, Madeleine. THE TWENTY-FOUR DAYS BEFORE CHRISTMAS. NY: Ariel, (1964). 1st ed. Fine in dj. Very uncommon. *BETWEEN COVERS.* $175

La Farge, John. A REPORT ON THE AMERICAN JESUITS BY JOHN LA FARGE, S.J. NY: FS&C, (1956). 1st ed. Photos by Margaret Bourke-White. Church owner stamps, else NF in edgeworn, price-clipped dj. *CAPTAIN'S BOOKSHELF.* $45

La Farge, John. A REPORT ON THE AMERICAN JESUITS. Photographs by Margaret Bourke-White. NY: Farrar, Straus & Cudahy. (1956). 1st ed. Dj. Endpapers sl soiled. *KARMIOLE.* $45

La Farge, Oliver (ed). THE CHANGING INDIAN. Univ of OK Press, (1942). 1st ed. VG+, dampstain on rear cvr, top of spine. *AUTHORS OF THE WEST.* $20

La Farge, Oliver and Douglas Byers. THE YEAR BEARER'S PEOPLE. New Orleans: Tulane Univ, M.A.R.I. Pub. No. 3, 1931. 2 color plts. Ex-lib. *SILVER.* $75

La Farge, Oliver. A PICTORIAL HISTORY OF THE AMERICAN INDIAN. NY: Crown, 1956. 1st ed. Fine in repaired Good dj. *CONNOLLY & WADE.* $35

La Farge, Oliver. ALL THE YOUNG MEN. Houghton Mifflin, 1935. 1st ed. Fine in Nice dj. *AUTHORS OF THE WEST.* $60

La Farge, Oliver. AS LONG AS THE GRASS SHALL GROW. Alliance Bk Corp, (1940). 1st ed. Inscribed, signed. VG+, bkpl, eps foxed. *AUTHORS OF THE WEST.* $50

La Farge, Oliver. LAUGHING BOY. Boston: HM, 1929. 1st ed, 1st issue, 1st bk. VG in sl chipped dj (1.5" tear). *CAPTAIN'S BOOKSHELF.* $175

La Farge, Oliver. RAW MATERIAL. Boston: Houghton-Mifflin, 1945. Cl. VG. *BURCHAM.* $45

La Farge, Oliver. SPARKS FLY UPWARD. Houghton Mifflin, 1931. 1st ed. VG+ in dj. *AUTHORS OF THE WEST.* $30

La Farge, Oliver. THE DOOR IN THE WALL: STORIES. Houghton Mifflin, 1965. 1st ed. Fine in dj. *AUTHORS OF THE WEST.* $25

La Farge, Oliver. THE MAN WITH THE CALABASH PIPE: SOME OBSERVATIONS. W.T. Scott (ed). 1st ed. Review copy, slip laid in. La Farge signature laid in. Fine in dj. *AUTHORS OF THE WEST.* $35

La Flesche, Francis. A DICTIONARY OF THE OSAGE LANGUAGE. W. David Baird (ed). Smithsonian Institution, BAE, Bulletin 109. Phoenix: Indian Tribal Press, 1975. One of 1,000 numbered, also signed by Sylvester J. Tinker, Osage Tribal Leader. Mint in dj. *LAURIE.* $75

La Flesche, Francis. A DICTIONARY OF THE OSAGE LANGUAGE. Edited by W. David Baird. Smithsonian Institution, BAE, Bulletin 109. Washington: GPO, 1932. VG in wraps. *LAURIE.* $20

La Grange, Helen and Jacques. CLIPPER SHIPS OF AMERICA GREAT BRITAIN 1833-1869. NY: G.P. Putnam's, 1936. #177/300 numbered. Fine w/lt wear to edges. Bkplt. Signed by author and illus. 37 tipped-in color plts. *PARMER.* $275

La Perouse, John Francis Galaup de. THE VOYAGE OF LA PEROUSE ROUND THE WORLD, IN THE YEARS 1785, 1786, 1787, AND 1788, WITH THE NAUTICAL TABLES. ARRANGED BY M.L.A. MILET MUREAU...London: Ptd for John Stockdale, 1798. 2 vols. 8vo, (xx), cxc (sic), 290pp; viii,442,64,119 (1)pp. 51 plts and maps. (Note that there is another London ed of the same year which is 3 vols. + atlas). Modern rebacking with spine labels; boards in somewhat worn early calf. Marbled edges have faded. Some offsetting and light foxing, small separation at center fold of one chart. Very Nice set. *PARMER.* $950

La Pierre, Janet. CHILDREN'S GAMES. NY: Scribner, 1989. 1st ed. Review copy, signed. Pub's slip laid in. Fine in dj. *SILVER DOOR.* $35

La Spina, Greye. INVADERS FROM THE DARK. Arkham House, 1960. 1st ed. Fine in dj. *MADLE.* $110

La Verendrye, Pierre Gaultier de Varennes. JOURNALS AND LETTERS OF...TOUCHING THE SEARCH FOR THE WESTERN SEA. Toronto, 1927. Ltd ed of 550 numbered. Lawrence J. Burpee (ed), William Dawson LeSeur (trans). 7 fldg maps. Orig cl (faded and lightly darkened). Howes L149. Very scarce. *GINSBERG.* $400

Labat, Gaston. REGIONAL ANESTHESIA. Phila, 1922. 1st ed. *FYE.* $200

Lachtman, Howard. SHERLOCK SLEPT HERE. Santa Barbara: Capra Press, 1985. 1st ed. Fine in stiff pict paper wrappers. *MORDIDA*. $25

Lackington, James. THE CONFESSIONS OF J. LACKINGTON. NY: John Wilson and Daniel Hitt, for the Methodist Connection. 1808. 12mo. 189,(3)pp. + 2pp ads. 2nd Amer ed of Lackington's rev memoirs. Very pretty copy in contemp calf. *KARMIOLE*. $150

LaCour, Tage and Harald Mogensen. THE MURDER BOOK. NY: Herder and Herder, 1971. 1st ed. Fine in NF dj w/a few short tears. *BEASLEY*. $40

Lacroix, Paul. FRANCE IN THE EIGHTEENTH CENTURY. NY, (1963). Reprint of 1876 ed. Cloth. NF in sl chipped & repaired dj. *DIAMOND*. $25

Lacroix, Paul. MANNERS, CUSTOMS, AND DRESS DURING THE MIDDLE AGES, AND DURING THE RENAISSANCE PERIOD. Fourth Thousand. London: Bickers & Son. N.d. (circa 1875). 15 chromolithos, incl frontis. 437 text engr. Bound in 1/2 purple morocco over marbled boards, dec gilt spine; spine faded, edges rubbed. Teg. Lib bkpl. *KARMIOLE*. $150

Lacroix, Paul. MILITARY AND RELIGIOUS LIFE IN THE MIDDLE AGES AND AT THE PERIOD OF THE RENAISSANCE. Fourth Thousand. London: Bickers & Son. N.d. (circa 1875). 14 chromolithos, incl frontis. 408 text engr. 1/2 purple morocco over marbled boards, dec gilt spine; spine faded, edges rubbed. Teg. Lib bkpl. *KARMIOLE*. $150

Lacroix, Paul. SCIENCE AND LITERATURE IN THE MIDDLE AGES. London: Bickers & Son. 1878. 13 chromolithos, 418 text engr. 1/2 purple morocco over marbled boards, dec gilt spine; spine faded, edges rubbed. Teg. Lib bkpl. *KARMIOLE*. $150

Lacy, Ed. THE HOTEL DWELLERS. NY: Harper & Row, 1966. 1st ed. Fine in dj. *MORDIDA*. $35

Lacy, Leslie Alexander. THE RISE AND FALL OF A PROPER NEGRO. NY: Macmillan, (1970). 1st ed. Fine in NF dj. *LOPEZ*. $25

LADIES' REPOSITORY FOR 1868. Vol. 28. Fine. *VARNER*. $80

LADIES' REPOSITORY FOR 1871. Vol. 31. Fine. *VARNER*. $80

Ladner, Mildred. D. O. C. SELTZER, PAINTER OF THE OLD WEST. U of Okla (1980), 2nd ptg, dj. *HEINOLDT*. $50

Ladner, Mildred. WILLIAM DE LA MONTAGNE CARY. Univ of OK & Gilcrease Institute, (1984). 1st ed. Frontis. VF in VF dj. *OREGON*. $40

Laennec, R.T.H. A TREATISE ON THE DISEASES OF THE CHEST AND ON MEDIATE AUSCULTION. John Forbes, M.D. (trans). London: Longman, Rees, Orme, Brown, Green, and Longman, 1834. 4th ed. 2 plts. Orig grn cl bumped, rubbed at extrems, top corner of rear board cracked; title, frontis worn at inner edge, sm tears to front edge of frontis, 1 sm tear front of title. VG, sound. Scarce. *BLUE MOUNTAIN*. $375

Lafferty, R.A. DOES ANYONE ELSE HAVE SOMETHING FURTHER TO ADD? Scribners, 1974. 1st ed. Fine in dj. *MADLE*. $27

Lafferty, R.A. NOT TO MENTION CAMELS. Bobbs-Merrill, 1976. 1st ed. Fine in dj. *MADLE*. $27

Lagerkvist, Par. PILGRIM AT SEA. NY: Random House (1964). 1st Amer ed. Fine in VG dj. *DORN*. $30

Lagerkvist, Par. THE MARRIAGE FEAST; AND OTHER STORIES. London: Chatto & Windus (1955). 1st Eng ed. Lt foxing top edge else NF in VG dj. *DORN*. $35

Lagerkvist, Par. THE SIBYL. London: Chatto & Windus (1958). 1st Eng ed. Fine in dj. *DORN*. $45

Lagrange, Francis with William Murray. FLAG ON DEVIL'S ISLAND. Doubleday, 1961. 1st ed. About Fine in dj rubbed and worn at the spine ends. Signed by Murray. *STAHR*. $45

Laidler, Percy and Michael Gelfand. SOUTH AFRICA, ITS MEDICAL HISTORY 1652-1898. A MEDICAL AND SOCIAL STUDY. Cape Town, 1971. 1st ed. *FYE*. $100

Laiken, Deidre S. DEATH AMONG STRANGERS. NY: Macmillan, 1987. 1st ed. VF in dj. *MORDIDA*. $30

Laing, Alexander. THE CADAVER OF GIDEON WYCK. Farrar, 1934. VG in sl chipped dj. *MADLE*. $50

Laing, Graham A. TOWARDS TECHNOCRACY. LA: Angelus Press, 1933. 1st ed. NF in NF dj. *CONNOLLY & WADE*. $55

Laird, Carobeth. ENCOUNTER WITH AN ANGRY GOD. Banning, CA: Malki Museum, 1975. 1st ed. Fine in Fine dj. Signed. *CONNOLLY & WADE*. $35

Laird, Carobeth. ENCOUNTER WITH AN ANGRY GOD. Banning: Malki Museum Press, 1975. VG in dj. *LOPEZ*. $35

Lait, Jack. ZION NATIONAL MONUMENT. National Park Series, 1919. Pict colored wraps, 16pp. Fine. *FIVE QUAIL*. $15

Lake, Carolyn. UNDER COVER FOR WELLS FARGO. Houghton Mifflin, 1969. 1st ed. VG in VG dj. *OREGON*. $25

Lake, Stuart. WYATT EARP, FRONTIER MARSHALL. Houghton Mifflin, (1931). 1st ed., 1st issue, w/ellby for belly on line 18, pp 54. 15 plts. VG. Howes L27. *OREGON*. $60

Lalic, Ivan V. FIRE GARDENS. SELECTED POEMS 1956-1969. NY: New Rivers, 1970. Simic, Charles and C.W. Truesdale, (trans). 1st ed. Fine in lightly soiled wrappers. *CAPTAIN'S BOOKSHELF*. $20

Lally, Michael. DUES. (Iowa City): Stone Wall Press, (1975). 1st ed. Ltd to 235. Eps foxed, o/w VG. Cl, w/ptd label. *JAFFE*. $50

LAMARCK'S GENERA OF SHELLS, WITH A CATALOGUE OF SPECIES. Boston: Allen and Ticknor, 1833. 1st ed. Augustus A. Gould, M.D. (trans). New burgundy morocco titled in gilt on spine, new eps. xiii(iii),100pp. Scattered foxing. Frontis foxed and darkened. *BLUE MOUNTAIN*. $175

Lamb, Charles and Mary. TALES FROM SHAKESPEARE. McKay, 1922. 377pp. Illus by Elizabeth S.G. Elliott. Cvr wear, small scrape to rear cvr, cvr, spine dec in gilt w/color pict pastedown that has few tiny scrapes. VG+. *BEBBAH*. $70

Lamb, Charles and Mary. THE COMPLETE LETTERS OF CHARLES AND MARY LAMB. London, 1935. Lucas, E.V. (ed). 1st complete ed. 3 vols. 2 short edge tears on vols 1 and 3. Fine. *POLYANTHOS*. $150

Lamb, Charles. A TALE OF ROSAMUND GRAY AND THE OLD BLIND MARGARET. London: Golden Cockerel Press for Frank Hollings, 1928. 1st ed thus. One of 500 numbered. Fine. *MUELLER*. $50

Lamb, Charles. THE LETTERS OF CHARLES LAMB. London: Grey Walls Press, 1950. 1st ed. Sl cocked o/w Fine in VG price-clipped dj. *ARCHER*. $20

Lamb, D. with J. Cleveland. ENCHANTED VAGABONDS. NY & London: Harper, (1938). 6th ed. Signed by author and wife. VG+. *MIKESH*. $30

Lamb, G.F. FRANKLIN: HAPPY VOYAGER. London: Ernest Benn, 1956. VG in similar dj. *PARMER*. $25

Lamb, Winifred. GREEK AND ROMAN BRONZES. London: Methuen, (1929). 37 illus, 96 plts. Bkpl. Good. *ARCHAEOLOGIA*. $65

Lambert, Gavin. THE DANGEROUS EDGE. London: Barrie, 1975. 1st ed. NF in dj. *SILVER DOOR*. $25

Lambert, Mercedes. DOGTOWN. NY: Viking, 1991. 1st ed. VF in dj. *MORDIDA*. $25

Lambert, Rose. HADJIN, AND THE ARMENIAN MASSACRES. NY, (1911). Cover soil. *O'NEILL*. $55

Lambert, S. et al. THREE VESALIAN ESSAYS TO ACCOMPANY THE ICONES ANATOMICAE OF 1934. NY, 1952. 1st ed. Dj. *FYE.* $50

Lamborn, R.H. (ed). DRAGONFLIES VS. MOSQUITOS. NY, 1890. Hand-colored frontis, 9 plts. Lib numbers on spine, unobtrusive emb stamps. *SUTTON.* $45

Lambuth, Letcher. THE ANGLER'S WORKSHOP. Ed, intro Steve Raymond. Intro Roderick Haig-Brown. (Portland, OR): Champoeg Press. 1979. Photogr frontis portrait, title page illus. Ltd to 1250 numbered. Blue gilt cl. *KARMIOLE.* $75

Lamott, K. WHO KILLED MR. CRITTENDEN? NY, 1963. 305pp. Spine sl faded, o/w NF. *DIAMOND.* $12.50

Lampell, Millard. THE LONG WAY HOME. NY: Messner, 1946. 1st ed. Fine in Fine dj. *BEASLEY.* $45

Lamport, Felicia. LIGHT METRES. Edward Gorey (illus). NY: Everest House, (1982). One of 350 specially-bound, signed by Gorey and Lamport. Fine in slipcase. *CAPTAIN'S BOOKSHELF.* $75

LAMPS ON THE PRAIRIE: A HISTORY OF NURSING IN KANSAS. Comp by Writer's Program of the W.P.A. Emporia Gazette Press, 1942. 1st ed. Fep corner clipped. Fine in chipped dj. Very scarce. *CONNOLLY & WADE.* $45

Lancaster, Clay. NEW YORK'S FIRST SUBURB, OLD BROOKLYN HEIGHTS, INCLUDING DETAILED ANALYSES OF 619 CENTURY-OLD HOUSES. Rutland, (1961). 1st ed. *HEINOLDT.* $25

Lancaster, Samuel C. THE COLUMBIA. Portland, 1916. 2nd ed. 3pp color fold-out. Pict cl dusty. Good, sound. *ARTIS.* $20

Lance, Phillip C. QUEENDOM OF THE HONEY BEES. Stackpole Telegraph Press, 1938. Fine in VG Dj. *MAD DOG.* $25

Lancisi, G.M. ANEURYSMS: THE LATIN TEXT OF ROME, 1745. Trans and ed by W.C. Wright. NY, 1952. 1st Eng trans. *FYE.* $50

Land, Myrick. THE FINE ART OF LITERARY MAYHEM. NY: Holt, (1963). 1st ed. Fine in dj (bkpl under flap, tiny edge tears). *CAPTAIN'S BOOKSHELF.* $40

Lander, Frederick West. ADDITIONAL ESTIMATE FOR FORT KEARNEY, SOUTH PASS, AND HONEY LAKE WAGON ROAD....Wash., HD63, 1861. 1st ed. 27pp. Sewn and uncut as issued. Howes L57. *GINSBERG.* $100

Landesman, Jay (ed). NEUROTICA. London: Landesman, 1981. Inscribed. Fine in dj. *LOPEZ.* $85

Landon, Herman. THE VOICE IN THE CLOSET. NY: Horace Liveright, 1930. 1st ed. VG in price-clipped dj (faded spine; couple closed tears; lightly soiled back panel). *MORDIDA.* $30

Landor, A. Henry Savage. IN THE FORBIDDEN LAND: 2 vols. NY & London: Harper, 1899. (xvi),307; (xii)(250)pp. Grn dec cl. Teg. Frontis, 8 chromoliths. Lacks fldg map. Shaken, some signatures pulled. Hinges repaired. *SCHOYER'S.* $75

Landor, A. Henry Savage. TIBET AND NEPAL. A&C Black, 1905. 1st ed. One of a small number from the 1st prtg bound in 3/4 lea over marbled boards with marbled eps. Binding Fair to Good with very minor loss at base of spine and hinge starting. *OLD LONDON.* $160

Landor, Walter Savage. EPICURUS, LEONTION AND TERNISSA. Ptd at the Ballantyne Press (for Vale Press, 1896). One of 200 for sale (of 210 total). Orig paper boards, paper label on spine and front cvr, edges untrimmed. Spine sl darkened, bit worn; paper sl soiled, rear joint beginning to crack, but binding sound. VF internally. *PIRAGES.* $150

Lane, Levi. THE SURGERY OF THE HEAD AND NECK. Phila, 1898. 2nd ed. 1180pp. *FYE.* $200

Lane, M. LIFE WITH IONIDES. London, 1963. Dj. *SUTTON.* $30

Lanes, S.G. THE ART OF MAURICE SENDAK. Abrams, (1980). 1st ed. Thick oblong 4to. 278pp. 261 illus including 94 color plates and pop-up. In ptd mylar dj as issued. Fine in Fine dj. *BEBBAH.* $85

Lang, Andrew. LETTERS ON LITERATURE. London: Longmans, Green, 1889. Some soiling, bkpl and owner's sig, o/w NF. 1st ed. *CHAPEL HILL.* $75

Lang, Andrew. OXFORD...NOTES. London: Seeley; NY: Macmillan, 1890. 1st ed. Inner hinges cracked, o/w VG. *WEBER.* $20

Lang, Jean. A BOOK OF MYTHS. NY: Putnam's, (1915). 20 orig dwgs. VG. *BLUE DRAGON.* $55

Lang, John D. and Samuel Taylor. REPORT OF A VISIT TO SOME OF THE TRIBES OF INDIANS LOCATED WEST OF THE MISSISSIPPI RIVER. NY: Day, 1843. 1st ed. 34pp. Orig ptd wrappers. Howes L72. *GINSBERG.* $175

Lang, William. HISTORY OF SENECA COUNTY, FROM THE CLOSE OF THE REVOLUTIONARY WAR TO JULY, 1880. Springfield, OH, 1880. 13 plts. Spine little faded, scattered foxing. VG. *BOHLING.* $150

Lange, A. IN THE AMAZON JUNGLE, ADVENTURES IN REMOTE PARTS OF THE UPPER AMAZON RIVER, INCLUDING A SOJOURN AMONG CANNIBAL INDIANS. NY & London, 1912. 1st ed. VG. *MIKESH.* $37.50

Lange, J. CRIME AND DESTINY. NY, 1930. 250pp. Stiff wraps rubbed, o/w VG. *DIAMOND.* $15

Langfield, William and Philip Blackburn. A BIBLIOGRAPHY COMPILED BY WILLIAM LANGFELD AND PHILIP BLACKBURN. (Washington Irving). NY: Public Library, 1933. 1st ed, ltd to 450. Signed, corrections made by Blackburn. Fine. *BOOK MARKET.* $100

Langford, John Alfred. PRISON BOOKS AND THEIR AUTHORS. London: William Tegg, 1861. 1st ed. 357pp. Covers faded. *OAK KNOLL.* $15

Langford, Nathaniel Pitt. VIGILANTE DAYS AND WAYS. NY: D.D. Merrill Co. 1893. 2 vols. xxvi,426;xiv,(2),486pp. Both vols. inscribed by Langford in 1905. T.e.g. Sm labels removed from spines, o/w Fine. Howes L78. 1st rpt ed after orig 1890 ed. *KARMIOLE.* $275

Langford, Nathaniel Pitt. VIGILANTE DAYS AND WAYS... 2 vols. NY: D.D. Merrill, 1893. 2nd ed. Ffeps missing in both vols, o/w VG. *LAURIE.* $60

Langford, Nathaniel. DIARY OF THE WASHBURN EXPEDITION TO THE YELLOWSTONE & FIREHOLE RIVERS, IN THE YEAR 1870. n.p., 1905. xxxii,122pp,frontis,21 plts. Illus pict cl, teg. 1st ed. Fine. *OREGON.* $120

Langford, T. PLAIN AND FULL INSTRUCTIONS TO RAISE ALL SORTS OF FRUIT-TREES THAT PROSPER IN ENGLAND...REVISED AND ENLARGED...ADDITION OF TWO ENTIRE CHAPTERS OF GREENS AND GREENHOUSES. London: Chiswell, 1696. 2nd ed. xxix,1-220,vipp. Bound in modern 3/4 calf w/raised bands, lea label, new eps. Marginal paper repair, sl foxing, staining. 2 plts. *SECOND LIFE.* $650

Langhorne, G. MAMMY'S LETTERS. Macon, GA: J.W. Burke Co, 1922. 1st ed. 12mo. Orig ptd wraps. Owner name, Very small stain on front wrap, else NF. *CHAPEL HILL.* $25

Langley, H.D. TO UTAH WITH THE DRAGOONS....Univ of Utah, 1974. 1st ptg. Fine in Fine dj. *VARNER.* $25

Langley, Harold. TO UTAH WITH THE DRAGOONS...Salt Lake City: Univ Utah, (1974). 1st ed. VF in VF dj. *OREGON.* $35

Langley, Henry G. THE SAN FRANCISCO DIRECTORY FOR THE YEAR COMMENCING MARCH, 1877. SF, 1877. Binding worn, chipped, splitting along rear hinge, 2pp w/wrinkle, closed tear; lacking map. *BOHLING.* $225

Langley, S. P. with C. G. Abbot. THE 1900 SOLAR ECLIPSE EXPEDITION. Washington: USGPO, 1904. Recently rebound, blue cl, new eps. VG. 22 full-pg plts. *KNOLLWOOD.* $100

Langley, Samuel P. RESEARCHES ON SOLAR HEAT, AND ITS ABSORPTION BY THE EARTH'S ATMOSPHERE. Washington, DC: GPO, 1884. 1st ed, 1st book. Plts (some fldg). Orig cl rebacked. *DIAMOND.* $150

Langley, Samuel P. THE NEW ASTRONOMY. Boston: Houghton Mifflin, 1889. Rebound w/orig gilt illus grn cl laid over new boards & spine, new eps, deckle edges, teg. *KNOLLWOOD.* $50

Langlotz, Ernst. THE ART OF MAGNA GRAECIA: GREEK ART IN SOUTHERN ITALY AND SICILY. London: Thames and Hudson, (1965). 10 figs, 188 plts (20 color). Good in dj. *ARCHAEOLOGIA.* $125

Langone, John. LIFE AT THE BOTTOM—THE PEOPLE OF ANTARCTICA. Boston: Little, Brown, 1977. 1st ed, 2nd prtg. Lib stamps pastedowns, dj chipped, o/w VG. *PARMER.* $25

Langsdorff, G. H. Von. VOYAGES AND TRAVELS IN VARIOUS PARTS OF THE WORLD DURING THE YEARS 1803, 1804, 1805, 1806 AND 1807. Carlisle, PA: 1817. 617,(17)pp. Fldg plate, stained, mended with part of borders lacking. Howes L81. Very scarce. *GINSBERG.* $650

Langston, N. and B. THE CAT IN ANCIENT EGYPT. Cambridge: Cambridge Univ Press, 1940. Frontis, 19 plts. Inscription, lightly rubbed. Good. *ARCHAEOLOGIA.* $375

Langton, Robert. THE CHILDHOOD AND YOUTH OF CHARLES DICKENS WITH RETROSPECTIVE NOTES, AND ELUCIDATIONS, FROM HIS BOOKS AND LETTERS. London: Hutchinson, 1891. 1st ltd ed. 260pp, illus. Ed de luxe ltd to 300 numbered, this being #58. Gilt stamped bevelled boards, top of spine sl frayed, teg. VG+. *GREAT EXPECTATIONS.* $65

Langwell, W.H. THE CONSERVATION OF BOOKS A DOCUMENTS. London: Pitman, (1957). 1st ed. *OAK KNOLL.* $55

Langworthy, Franklin. SCENERY OF THE PLAINS, MOUNTAINS AND MINES; OR, A DIARY KEPT UPON THE OVERLAND ROUTE TO CALIFORNIA...1850, '51, '52 AND '53...Ogdensburg: Sprague, 1855. 1st ed. 324pp. Orig cl, spine faded; wear to extremities. Howes L359. *GINSBERG.* $450

Lanham, Edwin. ONE MURDER TWO MANY. NY: Harcourt, 1952. 1st ed. Store stamp bottom edge, dates rear pastedown, o/w NF in lightly worn dj. *BEASLEY.* $40

Lania, Leo. THE DARKEST HOUR. Boston: Houghton Mifflin Co. 1941. 1st ed. Dj. Signed. Fine. *KARMIOLE.* $35

Lanier, Richard Nunn. THE ANGEL OF MARYE'S HEIGHTS. Fredericksburg, VA, 1961. 1st ed. Wrappers. NF. *McGOWAN.* $37.50

Lanier, Sidney. HYMNS OF THE MARSHES. NY: Scribner, 1907. Illus. 1st ed. Grn cl, teg. Spine somewhat dull, else NF. *CAPTAIN'S BOOKSHELF.* $50

Lanier, Sidney. POEM OUTLINES. NY: Scribner's, 1908. 1st ed. Orig grn cl, teg. Fine. *CHAPEL HILL.* $55

Lanier, Sidney. POEMS OF SIDNEY LANIER. Edited by His Wife. NY: Scribner, 1884. 1st ed. Grey bevelled cl, teg. Scattered lt foxing, spine a bit sunned, but VG. Uncommon. Errata slip called for, not present. *CAPTAIN'S BOOKSHELF.* $125

Lanier, Sidney. SELECTED POEMS OF SIDNEY LANIER. (Selected and) With a Preface by Stark Young. NY: Scribner's, 1947. 1st ed. Adv rev copy, slip laid in. Orig grey cl. Fine in VG dj. *CHAPEL HILL.* $65

Lanier, Sidney. THE SCIENCE OF ENGLISH VERSE. NY: Scribner, 1880. 1st ed. Bright, NF. Inscribed in May, 1880. *CAPTAIN'S BOOKSHELF.* $500

Lanks, Herbert C. HIGHWAY TO ALASKA. NY, (1944). 1st ed. Fine in dj. *ARTIS.* $17.50

Lansdale, Joe R. ACT OF LOVE. London: Kinnell, 1989. 1st hb ed. Signed. VF in dj. *MORDIDA.* $45

Lansdale, Joe R. COLD IN JULY. Shingletown, CA: Mark V. Ziesing, 1990. 1st hb ed. Signed. VF in dj. *MORDIDA.* $40

Lansdale, Joe R. DEAD IN THE WEST. London: Kinnell, 1990. 1st hb ed. VF in dj. *MORDIDA.* $45

Lansdale, Joe R. THE DRIVE-IN. London: Kinnell, 1989. 1st hb ed. Signed. VF in dj. *MORDIDA.* $45

Lansdale, Joe R. THE NIGHTRUNNERS. Intro Dean R. Koontz; illus Gregory Manchess. Arlington Heights: Dark Harvest, 1987. 1st ed. One of 300 numbered, signed by Lansdale, Koontz and Manchess. VF in dj w/slipcase. *MORDIDA.* $200

Lapierre, Janet. UNQUIET GRAVE. NY: St. Martin's Press, 1987. 1st ed. Fine in dj w/tiny wear at base of spine. *MORDIDA.* $25

LaPlace, Pierre Simon de, Marquis. MECANIQUE CELESTE.... Nathaniel Bowditch (trans). Boston: Hilliard, Gray, Little, and Wilkins, 1829-1839. 4 vols. 1st and best ed in English. 29.8 cm. xxiv,746,(1 errata); xviii,990,(1, errata); (xx),910,(unpaginated tables); 168,xxxvi,1018 pp. 3 engr ports. Orig cl, uncut, orig paper labels. Fine set, preserved in clamshell boxes. *LEFKOWICZ.* $2750

Lapointe, Frank. THE SIOUX TODAY. NY: Crowell-Collier, (1972). 1st ed. Fine in dj. *LOPEZ.* $45

Laporte, Laurent. SAILING ON THE NILE. Boston: Roberts Brothers, 1872. Signature, worn at extremities, tears and chipping at spine. Ex-lib. Good. *ARCHAEOLOGIA.* $25

Lardner, Ring W. BIB BALLADS. Chicago: Vollard & Co, (1915). Illus. by Fontaine Fox. 1st ed, 1st bk. 1/500. In rare pub's box stamped w/design on cover of bk. Box missing one edge, else VG. Book Fine. *JUVELIS.* $600

Lardner, Ring W. ROUND UP. London: Williams & Norgate, (1935). Spine faded, but nice, NF. 1st Eng ed. *CHAPEL HILL.* $35

Lardner, Ring W. ROUND UP: THE STORIES OF RING W. LARDNER. NY, 1929. 1st ed. Fine. *POLYANTHOS.* $60

Lardner, Ring W. THE BIG TOWN. NY, 1925. 1st ed. Spine little sunned, extrems sl rubbed. NF. *POLYANTHOS.* $30

Lardner, Ring W. THE STORY OF A WONDER MAN. NY, 1927. 1st ed. Illus. Spine little sunned, extrems sl rubbed. NF. *POLYANTHOS.* $50

Laren, A.J. van. SUCCULENTS OTHER THAN CACTI. LA, (1934). Trans E.J. Labarre. 155 tipped-in color illus. 1 edge a bit bumped. One of 1000. *DAWSON'S.* $250

Lariar, Lawrence. YOU'VE GOT ME IN STITCHES. NY, 1954. 1st ed. Dj. *FYE.* $50

Larkin, David (ed). THE UNKNOWN PAINTINGS OF KAY NIELSEN. Bantam, (1977). Stated 1st ed. 42 color plates in wraps. NF. *BEBBAH.* $25

Larkin, Paschal. PROPERTY IN THE EIGHTEENTH CENTURY...Dublin: Cork Univ Press, Longmans, Green, 1930. 1st ed. 252pp. VG. *HARTFIELD.* $65

Larkin, Philip. HIGH WINDOWS. Cl, dj. London: Faber, (1974). 1st ed. VF. *JAFFE.* $125

Larkin, Thomas Oliver. CHAPTERS IN THE EARLY LIFE OF THOMAS OLIVER LARKIN. Ed by Robert J. Parker. Special Publication 16, SF: CA Hist Soc, 1939. *KARMIOLE.* $40

Larmoth, Jeannie. MURDER ON THE MENU. NY: Charles Scribner's Sons, 1972. 1st ed. Edges sl darkened, eps stained; rmdr streak bottom edge, o/w VG in dj. *MORDIDA.* $35

Larpenteur, Charles. FORTY YEARS A FUR TRADER ON THE UPPER MISSOURI. PERSONAL NARRATIVE...1833-1872. Elliott Coues (ed). Harper, 1898. 1st ed. 2 vols. xxvii,236; ix,237-473pp. 2 frontis, 16 plts (incl 6 maps, 2 fldg). VG. Howes C800. *OREGON.* $350

LARRY THE LAMB IN TOYTOWN. London, 1972. Pop-up bk. *BOOKFINDERS INTL.* $30

Larsell, O. THE DOCTOR IN OREGON: A MEDICAL HISTORY. Portland, 1947. *FYE.* $45

LaRue, E.C. COLORADO RIVER AND ITS UTILIZATION. 1916. 231pp. Seven foldouts in separate map pocket. Stiff cover wrap laid on, spine restructured, else VG. *FIVE QUAIL.* $50

Lasater, Laurence M. THE LASATER PHILOSOPHY OF CATTLE RAISING. Texas Western Press, 1972. VG in Fine dj. *BOHLING.* $35

Lasky, Jesse L., Jr. NAKED IN A CACTUS GARDEN. Indianapolis: Bobbs-Merrill, (1961). 1st ed. Boards, cl spine in dj. *DAWSON'S.* $40

Lass, William. A HISTORY OF STEAMBOATING ON THE UPPER MISSOURI RIVER. Univ of NV, (1962). 1st ed. VF in VG dj. *OREGON.* $30

Lassek, Arthur. THE UNIQUE LEGACY OF DR. HUGHLINGS JACKSON. Springfield, 1970. 1st ed. Dj. *FYE.* $75

LATER BOOKPLATES & MARKS OF ROCKWELL KENT. NY: Pynson Printers, 1937. Dj. 83+(1)pp. Ltd ed of 1250 numbered, signed by Kent. VF w/prospectus inserted. *OAK KNOLL.* $250

Latham, Aaron. CRAZY SUNDAYS: F. SCOTT FITZGERALD IN HOLLYWOOD. Viking, 1971. 1st ed. About Fine in dj. *STAHR.* $30

Latham, Francis S. TRAVELS IN THE REPUBLIC OF TEXAS, 1842. "Narratives of the American West," Vol II. Gerald S. Pierce (ed). Austin: Encino Press, 1971. Fine. *LAURIE.* $20

Latham, Henry. BLACK AND WHITE. A JOURNAL OF A THREE MONTHS' TOUR IN THE UNITED STATES. London, 1867. 1st ed. Minor cover spotting, else VG. Inscribed. Howes L-117. *McGOWAN.* $350

Latham, Hiram. TRANS-MISSOURI STOCK RAISING; THE PASTURE LANDS OF NORTH AMERICA: WINTER GRAZING. Denver, 1962. 1/999 ptd by Carl Hertzog. Fine. *BOHLING.* $35

Latham, Hiram. TRANS-MISSOURI STOCK RAISING: THE PASTURE LANDS OF NORTH AMERICA: WINTER GRAZING. Denver, 1962. E. M. Schiwetz (illus). Orig cl, dj. Jeff Dykes (intro). Facsimile, ltd to 999. Howes L118. *GINSBERG.* $30

Latham, Peter M. THE COLLECTED WORKS OF DR. P.M. LATHAM, WITH MEMOIR BY SIR THOMAS WATSON. 2 vols. London, 1876-1878. 1st ed. 480pp, 575pp. *FYE.* $225

Latham, Philip. FIVE AGAINST VENUS. John C. Winston, 1952. 1st ed. VG. Ex libris; broken hinge. Dj rubbed. *STAHR.* $15

Latham, Philip. MISSING MEN OF SATURN. Winston, 1953. 1st ed. NF in frayed dj. *MADLE.* $45

Lathan, Emma. PICK UP STICKS. Inner Sanctum, 1970. 1st ed. About Fine in dj. Foxing to inside of dj. *STAHR.* $22.50

Lathrop, Dorothy. THE HAPPY FLUTE. Stokes, 1939. 1st ed. 54pp. Lathrop illus. VG in dj w/pieces missing, holes at forward edge but color illus undamaged. *BEBBAH.* $30

Lathrop, Elise. HISTORIC HOUSES OF EARLY AMERICA. NY: Tudor, 1946. *HUDSON.* $25

Lathrop, Elsie. HISTORIC HOUSES OF EARLY AMERICA. NY: Tudor, 1927. First Tudor ed. Just About Fine in sl used dj and orig box. *CAPTAIN'S BOOKSHELF.* $100

Latimer, Jonathan. BLACK IS THE FASHION FOR DYING. NY: Random House, 1959. 1st ed. VG in sl soiled dj (couple closed tears; sl wrinkled back panel). *MORDIDA.* $30

Latimer, Jonathan. DARK MEMORY. GC: Doubleday Crime Club, 1937. 1st ed. VG+, lacking dj. *ELSE FINE.* $35

Latimer, Jonathan. HEADED FOR A HEARSE. GC: Doubleday Crime Club, 1935. 1st ed. Name. Fine, no dj. Member's ed. *ELSE FINE.* $45

Latimer, Jonathan. RED GARDENIAS. GC: Doubleday Crime Club, 1939. 1st ed. Fine, minor wear to dj spine ends. *ELSE FINE.* $275

Latimer, Jonathan. SINNERS AND SHROUDS. NY: Simon and Schuster, 1955. 1st ed. Fine in lightly soiled dj, wear, sm tears. *MORDIDA.* $50

Latimer, Jonathan. SOLOMON'S VINEYARD. London: Methuen, 1941. 1st ed. The complete unexpurgated ed, which precedes Amer pub by 41 yrs. VG w/o dj. *MORDIDA.* $45

Latimer, Jonathan. SOLOMON'S VINEYARD. Santa Barbara: Neville, 1982. 1st Amer ed. 1st hb ed and 1st unexpurgated text to be pub in US. Incl is a previously unpub interview. One of 300 numbered, signed. VF in acetate wrapper. *MORDIDA.* $75

Latimer, Jonathan. THE LADY IN THE MORGUE. GC: Doubleday Crime Club, 1936. 1st ed. Name. NF, dj worn at folds, spine ends. *ELSE FINE.* $250

Latimore, Sarah Briggs and Grace Clark Haskell. ARTHUR RACKHAM: A BIBLIOGRAPHY. LA: Sutton House, 1936. 1st ed. 1/550 numbered. Slipcase. Spine dull, else Fine. *CAPTAIN'S BOOKSHELF.* $175

Latrobe, Benjamin Henry B. IMPRESSIONS RESPECTING NEW ORLEANS. DIARY & SKETCHES 1818-1820. Samuel Wilson, Jr (ed). NY: Columbia Univ, 1951. 1st ed. Some edgewear. Good+ w/Fine contents. *CONNOLLY & WADE.* $55

Latta, Brevet Lieut. Colonel James W. WAS SECESSION TAUGHT AT WEST POINT? N.p., 1909. Wraps. VG. *PRATT.* $30

Lattimore, Ralston B. (ed). THE STORY OF ROBERT E. LEE. Washington, 1964. 1st ed. VG in dj. *PRATT.* $30

Laubin, Reginald and Gladys. AMERICAN INDIAN ARCHERY. Norman: Univ of OK Press, 1981. 1st ed. 2nd prtg. NF in dj. *OLD LONDON.* $30

Laufe, Abe (ed). AN ARMY DOCTOR'S WIFE ON THE FRONTIER. Univ of Pittsburgh Press, 1962. 1st ed. Fine in dj. *ARTIS.* $25

Laughlin, James. SOME NATURAL THINGS. Connecticut: New Directions, (1945). 1st ed. Prtd at the Prairie Press. NF in dj (few small edge tears, little dust soiled). *POLYANTHOS.* $50

Laughlin, Ledlie. PEWTER IN AMERICA. Boston: Houghton Mifflin, 1940. 1st ed. VG. Slipcase. *BACKROOM.* $225

Laumer, Keith. NINE BY LAUMER. Doubleday, 1967. 1st ed. Fine in sl soiled dj. *MADLE.* $50

Laumer, Keith. ONCE THERE WAS A GIANT. Doubleday, 1975. 1st ed. Fine in dusty dj. *MADLE.* $35

Laumer, Keith. RETIEF TO THE RESCUE. Timescape, 1983. 1st ed. Fine in dj, review slip. *MADLE.* $25

Laumer, Keith. THE ULTIMAX MAN. St Martins, 1978. 1st ed. Fine in rubbed dj. *MADLE.* $22

Laurens, Henry. THE PHYSIOLOGICAL EFFECTS OF RADIANT ENERGY. NY, 193. 1st ed. *FYE.* $100

Laurgaard, Rachel Kelley. PATTY REED'S DOLL. Caldwell, ID: Caxton Press, (1956). 1965. Signed. Fine in Fine dj. *ACADEMIC LIBRARY.* $35

Lauridsen, Peter. VITUS BERING: THE DISCOVERER OF BERING STRAIT. Chicago: S.C. Griggs & Company, 1889. Covers spotted, one of the fldg charts supplied in facsimile. *PARMER.* $125

Laut, Agnes C. THE FUR TRADE OF AMERICA. NY: Macmillan, 1921. 31pp photo illus. Cl, light wear and spotting to binding, tips bumped. *DAWSON'S.* $50

Laut, Agnes C. THE FUR TRADE OF AMERICA. NY: The Macmillan Co. 1921. 1st ed. Cl sl soiled. *KARMIOLE.* $40

Laut, Agnes. THE FUR TRADE OF AMERICA. Macmillan, 1921. 1st ed. Frontis. VG. *OREGON.* $50

Lauterbach, Ann. LATER THAT EVENING. Wrappers w/ptd wraparound label. (NY: Jordan Davies, 1981). 1st ed. Ltd to 210 signed. Mint. *JAFFE*. $45

Lauterbach, Ann. SACRED WEATHER. Frontis by Louisa Chase, dec boards. (NY: The Grenfell Press, (1984). 1st ed. One of 115 signed by Lauterbach & Chase. Mint. *JAFFE*. $75

Lautreamont, Maldoror. Alexis Lykiard (trans). NY: Crowell, (1970). 1st US ed, thus. Fine in dj. *CAPTAIN'S BOOKSHELF*. $30

Laval, Pierre. THE UNPUBLISHED DIARY OF...London, 1948. Dj. NF. *POLYANTHOS*. $30

Lavater, J.C. ESSAYS ON PHYSIOGNOMY...TRANSLATED INTO ENGLISH BY THOMAS HOLCROFT, ILLUSTRATED BY THREE HUNDRED AND SIXTY ENGRAVINGS. 3 vols. London, 1789. 1st Eng trans. 241, 324, 314pp. Full-page engrvd plts. Full lea, hinges broken, boards detached, one board missing with feps to that volume. Contents Fine. Rather scarce. *FYE*. $500

Lavender, David. ANDY CLAYBOURNE. GC: Doubleday, 1946. 1st ed. Cl in moderately chipped dj, newspaper reviews pasted to rear ep, staining from the clippings. *DAWSON'S*. $35

Lavender, David. CLIMAX AT BUENA VISTA. Phila: J.B. Lippincott Co, (1966). 1st ed. Inscription. Cloth in dj. *DAWSON'S*. $40

Lavender, David. GOLDEN TREK. Phila: Westminster Press, (1948). Red-stamped cl in dj. Inscription. *DAWSON'S*. $45

Lavender, David. LAND OF GIANTS. Doubleday, 1958. VG in VG dj. *OREGON*. $30

Lavender, David. LAND OF GIANTS. THE DRIVE TO THE PACIFIC NORTHWEST. NY, 1958. NF. *DIAMOND*. $15

Lavender, David. LAND OF GIANTS: THE DRIVE TO THE PACIFIC NORTHWEST 1750-1950. NY: Doubleday, 1958. VG in VG dj. *CONNOLLY & WADE*. $25

Lavender, David. MIKE MARONEY: RAIDER. Phila: Westminster Press, (1945). 2 full-pg line drawings, red-stamped cl in moderately chipped dj, sl cocked, tips a bit bumped. *DAWSON'S*. $35

Lavender, David. NOTHING SEEMED IMPOSSIBLE. Palo Alto: American West, 1975. 1st ed. Fine (sl chipped dj). *CONNOLLY & WADE*. $45

Lavender, David. ONE MAN'S WEST. GC: Doubleday, 1956. 2nd ed. Cloth in lightly chipped dj. Inscribed. *DAWSON'S*. $35

Lavender, David. ONE MAN'S WEST. GC: Doubleday, Doran, 1943. 1st ed. Cl in moderately chipped dj, sl cocked, bkpl. *DAWSON'S*. $45

Lavender, David. RED MOUNTAIN. GC: Doubleday & Co, 1963. 1st ed. Cl, somewhat cocked. *DAWSON'S*. $30

Lavender, David. THE BIG DIVIDE. Doubleday, 1948. 1st ed. VG in Good+ dj. *OREGON*. $25

Lavender, David. THE FIST IN THE WILDERNESS. Doubleday 1964. 1st ed. 2 fldg plts. Fine in Fine dj. *OREGON*. $35

Lavender, David. THE ROCKIES. Harper & Row, (1968). 1st ed. VF in VG dj. *OREGON*. $25

Lavender, David. THE ROCKIES. NY: Harper & Row, 1968. 1st ed. 2 fldg maps. Fine in Fine dj. *CONNOLLY & WADE*. $35

Lavender, David. THE STORY OF CYPRUS MINES CORPORA-TION. San Marino: Huntington Library, 1962. 24 pp photo illus. Cl in dj. Inscription. *DAWSON'S*. $30

Lavender, David. THE STORY OF THE CYPRUS MINES COR-PORATION. San Marino: Huntington Library, 1962. 1st ed. Fine in NF dj. *CONNOLLY & WADE*. $35

Lavender, David. TROUBLE AT TAMARACK. Phila: Westminster Press, 1943. Cl in moderately chipped dj, tips bumped, pencil nota-tions on rear ep and a few in the text. Inscription. *DAWSON'S*. $50

Lavender, David. WESTWARD VISION. NY: McGraw-Hill, (1963). 1st ed. Inscription. Cl in dj. *DAWSON'S*. $35

Laver, James. LOVE'S PROGRESS: OR, THE EDUCATION OF ARAMINTA. London: Nonesuch Press, 1929. One of 1525 ptd on Arches mould-made cream paper. Cased in semi-stiff boards loosely covered w/marbled paper; ptd cvr title-label. Issued w/glassine dw, (present but torn). Fine. *BOOK BLOCK*. $40

Laver, James. THE AGE OF OPTIMISM. London: Weidenfeld and Nicolson, (1966). Fine in Good dj w/2 small tears. *WREDEN*. $30

Lavin, Mary. TALES FROM BECTIVE BRIDGE. London: Joseph, (1943). 1st Eng ed. Cl, dj. Fine. *JAFFE*. $250

Law, James D. HERE AND THERE IN TWO HEMISPHERES. Lancaster, Pa, 1903. Orig pict cl. *GINSBERG*. $75

Law, John. THE COLONIAL HISTORY OF VINCENNES...Vincen-nes, 1858. 156pp. Orig cl. Howes L152. Presentation, unsigned. *GINSBERG*. $100

LaWall, Charles. THE CURIOUS LORE OF DRUGS AND MEDICINES (FOUR THOUSAND YEARS OF PHARMACY). GC, 1927. 1st ed, rptd. *FYE*. $60

Lawrence, Charles. HISTORY OF THE PHILADELPHIA ALMSHOUSES AND HOSPITALS FROM THE BEGINNING OF THE EIGHTEENTH TO THE ENDING OF THE NINETEENTH CENTURIES...(Phila), 1905. 1st ed. Very scarce. *FYE*. $150

Lawrence, D.H. A PROPOS OF LADY CHATTERLEY'S LOVER. London: Mandrake Press, 1930. 1st ed. NF in sl soiled, chipped dj. *BLUE MOUNTAIN*. $150

Lawrence, D.H. AMORES. NY: Heubsch, 1916. 1st ed. NF. *ELSE FINE*. $60

Lawrence, D.H. ENGLAND, MY ENGLAND. London: Martin Seck-er, 1924. 1st Eng ed. NF in NF dj. *JUVELIS*. $220

Lawrence, D.H. KANGAROO. London: Martin Secker, (1923). 1st ed. VG in lightly used dj (split at front hinge but complete). *JUVELIS*. $250

Lawrence, D.H. KANGAROO. NY: T. Seltzer, 1923. 1st US ed. About VG, spine rubbed. *ARCHER*. $75

Lawrence, D.H. LADY CHATTERLEY'S LOVER. London: Martin Secker, (1932). 1st authorized Eng ed. (1st pub Florence, Italy in 1928, ed of 1000 signed). Orig brn cl. Hinges cracking, prelims sl foxed, thus VG only. *CHAPEL HILL*. $50

Lawrence, D.H. LADY CHATTERLEY'S LOVER. Orig dec boards w/paper label on spine, plain cream dj. (Florence): Privately Ptd, 1928. 1st ed. Ltd to 1000 signed. Some foxing on rear inside flap of dj. Mint. *JAFFE*. $3500

Lawrence, D.H. MORNINGS IN MEXICO. London: Martin Secker, 1927. 1st ed. Fine, lacking dj. *CAPTAIN'S BOOKSHELF*. $175

Lawrence, D.H. MY SKIRMISH WITH JOLLY ROGER. Boards w/ptd label. NY: Random House, 1929. 1st ed. Ltd to 600. Bkpl, o/w Fine in a 1/2 morocco slipcase. *JAFFE*. $125

Lawrence, D.H. PANSIES. (London: Privately ptd for subscribers only by P.R. Stephensen), June, 1929. 1st definitive complete ed (another ltd ed appeared earlier the same yr). #344 of 500 signed. Orig ptd wraps. Fine in orig glassine jacket, pub's slipcase. Lovely. *CHAPEL HILL*. $750

Lawrence, D.H. PANSIES. (London): Privately Ptd, June 1929. Signed. Ltd ed, 1/500. Stiff white wrappers ptd in red and black. VF in glassine dj. *JUVELIS*. $400

Lawrence, D.H. PORNOGRAPHY AND OBSCENITY. London, 1929. 1st ed. Criterion Miscellany No. 5. Sl edge rubbed. NF. Of 5000 prtd, some were bound in boards. Boards sl edge soiled. Fine. *POLYANTHOS*. $50

Lawrence, D.H. REFLECTIONS ON THE DEATH OF A POR-CUPINE AND OTHER ESSAYS. Phila: The Centaur Press, 1925.

1st ed. Uncut, partly unopened. Spine lightly sunned, corners minimally rubbed. Fine. *POLYANTHOS.* $100

Lawrence, D.H. SONS AND LOVERS, A FACSIMILE OF THE MANUSCRIPT. Berkeley and LA: Univ of California Press, 1977. Dj. *OAK KNOLL.* $75

Lawrence, D.H. SONS AND LOVERS. Avon, CT: LEC, 1975. One of 1500 illus, signed by Sheila Robinson. Fine in slipcase. *CAPTAIN'S BOOKSHELF.* $100

Lawrence, D.H. STUDIES IN CLASSIC AMERICAN LITERATURE. NY: Thomas Seltzer, 1923. 1st ed. NF in a lightly sunned dj (some minor chipping at spinal extremities, few closed tears). *CAPTAIN'S BOOKSHELF.* $650

Lawrence, D.H. THE CAPTAIN'S DOLL. NY: Seltzer, 1923. 1st Amer ed of The Ladybird. Owner pencilled sig, date. Fine in scarce dj, which is sl nicked & dust-soiled. *JAFFE.* $450

Lawrence, D.H. THE MAN WHO DIED. (London: Martin Secker, 1931). 1st Brit ed. Orig green gilt stamped buckram. Except for some browning to end papers, virtually Mint in VF dj (just sl wrinkled along top edge). *PIRAGES.* $175

Lawrence, D.H. THE VIRGIN AND THE GIPSY. Florence: Orioli, 1930. 1st ed. 1/810 ptd for Orioli by The Tipografia Giuntina. White boards w/Lawrence phoenix in red, label on spine, grn ptd dj. VF in lightly sunned dj. *JUVELIS.* $325

Lawrence, D.H. THE VIRGIN AND THE GIPSY. London: Martin Secker, (1930). 1st Eng ed. 1/5800, preceded only by a ltd ed of 810 pub in Florence. Brown cl stamped in gilt on spine, tan dj ptd in red (only minor traces of use and one small tape reinforcement on interior). Discreet ex-libris. Bk fresh and gilt stamping As New. *JUVELIS.* $250

Lawrence, D.H. THE VIRGIN AND THE GIPSY. London: Martin Secker, 1930. 1st ed. Name. Fine, dj has light wear, small chips at spine ends. *ELSE FINE.* $150

Lawrence, D.H. TORTOISES. NY: T. Seltzer, 1921. 1st ed. Name, extremities spine and corners chipped, edge rubbed. Fine. *POLYANTHOS.* $100

Lawrence, D.H. TWILIGHT IN ITALY. London: Duckworth, (1916). 1st ed, scarce 1st bk. Blue cl, spine dulled, else Fine. *JUVELIS.* $350

Lawrence, D.H. WOMEN IN LOVE. NY: (Privately ptd for subscribers only), 1920. 1st ed, pub 9 November 1920 at $15; the 1st ptg consisting of 1250 copies. This is copy #641 numbered in red ink on the justification pg which is on the verso of the half title. Pub's blue buckram, stamped in gilt on spine. There were "16 or 18 copies" of this ed which Lawrence is said to have signed. Inner hinges strengthened. Rather heavy for its size, hinges are very vulnerable. Very nice. *BOOK BLOCK.* $450

Lawrence, Hilda. A TIME TO DIE. NY: Simon and Schuster, 1945. 1st ed. Name, o/w Fine in dj w/sm chips, tears. *MORDIDA.* $25

Lawrence, Hilda. BLOOD UPON THE SNOW. NY: Simon & Schuster, 1944. 1st ed. Fine; minor wear dj spine corners. *ELSE FINE.* $45

Lawrence, Hilda. THE PAVILION. NY: Simon and Schuster, 1946. 1st ed. Nice in dj. *SECOND LIFE.* $25

Lawrence, Lars. OLD FATHER ANTIC. NY: International, 1961. 1st ed. Fine in NF dj. *BEASLEY.* $40

Lawrence, Margery. NUMBER SEVEN QUEER STREET. Arkham House, 1969. VF in dj. *MADLE.* $95

Lawrence, T.E. and C. Leonard Woolley. THE WILDERNESS OF ZIN. Jonathan Cape, 1935. 1st ed. Chapter on Greek Inscriptions by M.N. Tod. Double cr 8vo. 1 lrg fldg plan; 40 half-tone plts. Hammered pale brownish orange wrappers, cut flush, printed outside in black; made up w/o eps. Wrappers faded, stained, creased, and sl chipped; half-title spotted, and frayed and chipped at corners; very

light foxing of several early leaves; numerous small corners turned. In general, Near Nice. Uncorrected proof, w/legend 'Duplicate Proof Retention: Does not contain Proof Reader's marks' on front wrapper. *POLYANTHOS.* $450

Lawrence, T.E. MINORITIES. Wilson, J.M. (ed). Lewis, Cecil Day, The Poet Laureate of England (Pref.) London, Bertram Rota & Jonathan Cape, 1971. 8vo, 272pp, 1st ed. Limited #49 of 110 for sale. Signed by Day Lewis. Only copy additionally signed by J.M. Wilson. Original yellow morocco backed grey bevelled cl, gilt titles on brown morocco spine label in glassine dj. Top edge gilt. Cream colored ribbon place marker. Fine in new custom fitted archival slipcase. *GREAT EPIC.* $1300

Lawrence, T.E. REVOLT IN THE DESERT. NY: Doran, 1927. 1st US trade ed. Just About Fine in dj (some shallow chipping, few short tears). Dj is uncommon. *CAPTAIN'S BOOKSHELF.* $300

Lawrence, T.E. REVOLT IN THE DESERT. NY: Doran, 1927. 1st US ed. Frontis, title pg bit foxed, else Fine in VG, scarce dj (sm chips at extrems effecting a couple of letters in title). *BETWEEN COVERS.* $400

Lawrence, T.E. SEVEN PILLARS OF WISDOM. GC: Doubleday Doran, 1935. 1st Amer ed. Sl spine darkened, lacking dj. VG. *LOPEZ.* $85

Lawrence, T.E. SEVEN PILLARS OF WISDOM. NY: Doubleday, Doran, 1935. 1st US ptg. Sl rubbed, front eps w/tear, o/w VG. Bkpl. *WORLDWIDE.* $22

Lawrence, T.E. THE HOME LETTERS OF T. E. LAWRENCE AND HIS BROTHERS. NY: Macmillan, 1954. 1st ed, Amer issue. Fine in dj (1" closed tear). *JAFFE.* $175

Lawrence, T.E. THE LETTERS OF T. E. LAWRENCE. David Garnett (ed). London: Cape, (1938). 1st ed, 1st state of text. Immaculate, New in dj. *JAFFE.* $225

Lawrence, T.E. THE ODYSSEY OF HOMER. (London): (Privately ptd), 1932. 1st Eng ed of Lawrence's trans, one of 530 bound in full black Niger morocco. Teg, ptd on grey handmade paper. VF in orig black cardboard slipcase, which shows some rubbing and wear but is still good. *LOPEZ.* $3,250

Lawrence, William. LIFE OF AMOS A. LAWRENCE WITH EXTRACTS FROM HIS DIARY AND CORRESPONDENCE. Boston & NY, 1888. 1st ed. Orig cl. VG to NF. *McGOWAN.* $45

Lawrence, William. THE LIFE OF AMOS A. LAWRENCE. Boston & NY: Houghton, Mifflin and Company, 1888. 1st ed. 5 plts. Cl rubbed, sl stained, eps foxed. Contents bright, NF. *BLUE MOUNTAIN.* $25

Lawrie, W.H. ENGLISH TROUT FLIES—A REFERENCE BOOK. NY: A.S. Barnes & Co, 1969. 1st Amer ed. VG+ in Good+ dj. *BACKMAN.* $25

LAWS OF WISCONSIN TERRITORY, PASSED BY THE LEGISLATIVE ASSEMBLY, AT THE SESSION THEREOF COMMENCED IN FEBRUARY, A.D. 1848. Madison: H.A. Tenney, 1848. Paper wrappers w/considerable wear at extremities. Largely intact but fragile. *LAURIE.* $200

Lawson, Robert. COUNTRY COLIC, THE WEEDER'S DIGEST. Little, Brown, 1944. 1st ed. 69pp. Lawson illus. Slightest soil. VG+ in VG dj w/soil in 2 tiny edge tears, edgewear. *BEBBAH.* $60

Lawson, Robert. RABBIT HILL. Viking, 1960 ptg. 128pp. Robert Lawson illus. VG+ in VG+ dj w/light wear. *BEBBAH.* $30

Lawson, Robert. THE TOUGH WINTER. Viking, 1954. 1st ed. Signed by author/illus. 128pp. Edgewear, VG+ in VG+ dj w/closed tear. *BEBBAH.* $60

Lawton, Eba Anderson (ed). HISTORY OF THE SOLDIER'S HOME WASHINGTON, D.C. NY: Putnam, 1914. 1st ed. VG. *CONNOLLY & WADE.* $45

Layard, Austen H. DISCOVERIES AMONG THE RUINS OF NINEVEH AND BABYLON; WITH TRAVELS...Putnam, 1853. 1st US ed. xiv,686pp. 8 tinted plts, 7 fldg plans, maps. 1/2 morocco, very worn, spinal strip missing, a few maps torn, but no loss, portion of 1 fldg plan missing, supplied in facs, o/w Good. *WORLDWIDE.* $95

Layard, Austen H. NINEVEH AND ITS REMAINS...NY: George P. Putnam, 1849. 1/4 black morocco, dk brn cl, gilt, aeg; spine repaired, preserving orig, new endleaves; generally VG. *WEBER.* $90

Layard, George Somes. SUPPRESSED PLATES, WOOD ENGRAVINGS &C., TOGETHER WITH OTHER CURIOSITIES GERMANE THERETO BEING AN ACCOUNT OF CERTAIN MATTERS PECULIARLY ALLURING TO THE COLLECTOR. London: Adam and Charles Black, 1907. 1st ed. Bkpl, eps foxed. *OAK KNOLL.* $85

Laymon, Richard. THE CELLAR. Warner, 1980. 1st ed. Uncorrected proof. Fine. *MADLE.* $75

Layne, J. Gregg. WESTERN WAYFARING. Intro Phil Townsend Hanna. LA: Automobile Club of Southern CA, 1954. Dec boards. *DAWSON'S.* $35

Lazarovich-Hrebvelianovich. Prince (Stephan Lazar Eugene) and Eleanor I (Calhoun) Lazarovich-Hrebvelianovich. SERVIAN PEOPLE...2 vols. NY: Scribner's, 1910. Somewhat rubbed, heads of spines chipped. Largely unopened. *SCHOYER'S.* $50

Lazarus, Edward. BLACK HILLS, WHITE JUSTICE. (NY): Harper Collins, (1991). Uncorrected proof. Fine in wrappers. *LOPEZ.* $45

Le Blond, Mrs. Aubrey. MOUNTAINEERING IN THE LAND OF THE MIDNIGHT SUN. Phila: Lippincott, and London: T. Fisher Unwin, 1908. 1st ed. Minor shelfwear, else VG-NF. *OLD LONDON.* $125

Le Blond, Mrs. Aubrey. THE OLD GARDENS OF ITALY, HOW TO VISIT THEM. London & NY, 1912. Cl, spine darkened, some cvr fading. *SUTTON.* $35

le Carre, John (pseud of David John Moore Cornwell). A MURDER OF QUALITY. NY: Walker, 1963. 1st US ed. Sl cocked, former owner's sig, VG in dj w/shallow chipping to extrems and several abrasions to front panel. *LAME DUCK.* $550

le Carre, John. A MURDER OF QUALITY. NY: Walker, (1963). 1st Amer ed. Spine bit rolled and yellow cloth very sl soiled, still Very NF in like dj w/one small scuff at head of spine, little fading on spine, single short pen stroke along front spine edge. Exceptionally scarce. *BETWEEN COVERS.* $950

le Carre, John. A PERFECT SPY. Knopf, 1986. 1st Amer ed. VF in dj. *STAHR.* $20

le Carre, John. A PERFECT SPY. Knopf, 1986. Uncorrected proof of 1st Amer ed. VF in wraps. *STAHR.* $75

le Carre, John. A PERFECT SPY. London, (1986). 1st ed. Signed. Fine in like dj. *POLYANTHOS.* $45

le Carre, John. A PERFECT SPY. London: Hodder & Stoughton, 1986. 1st ed. Signed. VF in dj. *MORDIDA.* $175

le Carre, John. A PERFECT SPY. NY: Alfred A. Knopf, 1986. 1st Amer ed. Adv rev copy, slip and flyer laid in. VF in dj. *MORDIDA.* $50

le Carre, John. A SMALL TOWN IN GERMANY. Coward-McCann, 1968. 1st Amer ed. NF in dj (bumped foot of spine; lightly faded). *STAHR.* $25

le Carre, John. A SMALL TOWN IN GERMANY. London: Heinemann, 1968. 1st ed. Signed. Erasure on fep, o/w Fine in dj. *MORDIDA.* $185

le Carre, John. A SMALL TOWN IN GERMANY. NY: Coward-Mc-Cann, 1968. 1st Amer ed. Date fep o/w Fine in price clipped dj. *MORDIDA.* $30

le Carre, John. A SMALL TOWN IN GERMANY. NY: Coward-Mc-Cann, 1968. 1st ed. One of 500 numbered presentation, signed. VF in tissue dj. *MORDIDA.* $375

le Carre, John. SMILEY'S PEOPLE. Hodder & Stoughton, 1980. 1st ed. NF in a dj worn at edges & chipped at head of spine. *STAHR.* $20

le Carre, John. SMILEY'S PEOPLE. Knopf, 1980. 1st trade. Fine in dj. Rmdr stamp. *STAHR.* $15

le Carre, John. SMILEY'S PEOPLE. London: Hodder and Stoughton, 1979. 1st ed. Fine in price-clipped dj. *MORDIDA.* $35

le Carre, John. SMILEY'S PEOPLE. NY: Alfred A. Knopf, 1980. 1st Amer trade ed. Fine in dj. *MORDIDA.* $30

le Carre, John. THE CLANDESTINE MUSE. Portland, OR: Seluzicki, (1986). 1st ed. Ltd to 250 ptd at Janus Press, signed. Marbled wraps. Mint. *JAFFE.* $175

le Carre, John. THE HONOURABLE SCHOOLBOY. Franklin Center, PA: Franklin Library, 1977. 1st Amer ed. Bound in full leather with gold stamping and titles. Pages gold gilt-edged. VF w/o dj as issued. *MORDIDA.* $75

le Carre, John. THE HONOURABLE SCHOOLBOY. NY: Alfred A. Knopf, 1977. 1st Amer trade ed. Fine in dj. *MORDIDA.* $30

le Carre, John. THE LITTLE DRUMMER GIRL. Frontis, cl, acetate dj, slipcase. NY: Knopf, 1983. 1st Amer ed. One of 1048 numbered, specially ptd, bound for BMOC, signed. VF. Scarce issue. *JAFFE.* $250

le Carre, John. THE LITTLE DRUMMER GIRL. London: Hodder and Stoughton, 1983. 1st Eng ed. VF in dj. *MORDIDA.* $60

le Carre, John. THE LITTLE DRUMMER GIRL. NY: Alfred A. Knopf, 1983. 1st ed. One of unknown # of copies w/addt'l sheet tipped-in and signed. VF in dj. *MORDIDA.* $165

le Carre, John. THE LITTLE DRUMMER GIRL. NY: Alfred A. Knopf 1983. Ltd ed. One of 1048 specially bound, numbered, signed by Le Carre and for sale exclusively to members of BMOC. VF in acetate dj w/slipcase. *MORDIDA.* $375

le Carre, John. THE LOOKING-GLASS WAR. London: Heinemann, (1965). 1st ed. Fine in Fine dj without the usual sunning to spine. *UNGER.* $100

le Carre, John. THE LOOKING-GLASS WAR. London: Heinemann, 1965. 1st ed. VF in dj. *MORDIDA.* $85

le Carre, John. THE NAIVE AND SENTIMENTAL LOVER. Knopf, 1972. 1st Amer ed. NF in dj (lt wear to edges). *STAHR.* $15

le Carre, John. THE NAIVE AND SENTIMENTAL LOVER. London: Hodder & Stoughton, 1971. 1st ed. VF in price-clipped dj. *MORDIDA.* $100

le Carre, John. THE NAIVE AND SENTIMENTAL LOVER. NY: Alfred A. Knopf, 1972. 1st Amer ed. Fine in dj w/wear, closed tear. *MORDIDA.* $30

le Carre, John. THE RUSSIA HOUSE. (London): London Limited Editions, (1989). 1/250 numbered, signed. Quarterbound in grn cl and marbled paper boards, w/unptd glassine dj. *LOPEZ.* $200

le Carre, John. THE RUSSIA HOUSE. Cl-backed boards, dj. NY: Knopf, 1989. 1st Amer ed. Signed. Mint. *JAFFE.* $125

le Carre, John. THE RUSSIA HOUSE. Cl-backed dec boards, glassine dj. London: London Limited Editions, 1989. 1st ed. One of 250 signed. Mint. *JAFFE.* $250

le Carre, John. THE RUSSIA HOUSE. Full leather, slipcase. London: Hodder & Stoughton, 1989. 1st ed. Collector's Ed, Ltd to 500. VF. *JAFFE.* $250

le Carre, John. THE RUSSIA HOUSE. Knopf, 1989. Uncorrected proof. VF in tan wraps; slip of paper. Signed, laid in. Precedes English ed. *STAHR.* $110 le Carre, John. THE RUSSIA HOUSE. Knopf, 1989. Uncorrected proof of Amer ed. Fine in buff wraps. Small chip at head of spine. Pub 3 wks before British ed. *STAHR*. $75

le Carre, John. THE RUSSIA HOUSE. London: Hodder, (1989). 1st ed. Signed. VF in VF dj. *UNGER*. $100

le Carre, John. THE RUSSIA HOUSE. London: Hodder & Stoughton, 1989. "Presentation Book Proof", letter from pub laid in. Dec wraps. Fine. *JAFFE*. $175

le Carre, John. THE RUSSIA HOUSE. NY: Knopf, 1989. 1st Amer ed. Signed on tipped-in leaf. Fine in dj. *LOPEZ*. $125

le Carre, John. THE SECRET PILGRIM. (London: Hodder & Stoughton, 1991). 1st UK ed. Signed. Fine in Fine dj. *LOPEZ*. $100

le Carre, John. THE SECRET PILGRIM. Knopf, 1991. Uncorrected proof. VF in slate blue wraps. Precedes the English ed. *STAHR*. $75

le Carre, John. THE SECRET PILGRIM. London: Hodder & Stoughton, 1991. 1st ed. Uncorrected proof. Fine in ptd wrappers w/proof dj w/wrinkled back panel. *MORDIDA*. $125

le Carre, John. THE SECRET PILGRIM. NY: Knopf, 1991. 1st Amer ed. Signed on tipped-in leaf. Fine in dj. *LOPEZ*. $100

le Carre, John. THE SECRET PILGRIM. NY: Knopf, 1991. Uncorrected proof of 1st Amer ed. Fine in wraps. *CAPTAIN'S BOOKSHELF*. $60

le Carre, John. TINKER, TAILOR, SOLDIER, SPY. London: Hodder, (1974). 1st ed. Fine in dj with a couple Very minor nicks. *UNGER*. $75

le Carre, John. TINKER TAILOR SOLDIER SPY. London: Hodder & Stoughton, 1974. 1st ed. Uncorrected proof. VG in wrappers w/dj. *MORDIDA*. $200

Le Conte, Emma. WHEN THE WORLD ENDED. NY, 1957. Ed by Earl Schench Miers. 1st ed. Dj. Fine. *PRATT*. $37.50

Le Conte, Joseph. 'WARE SHERMAN. A JOURNAL...LAST DAYS OF THE CONFEDERACY. Berkeley: Univ of CA, 1937. 1st ed. Frontis. Grey dec cl. NF. *CONNOLLY & WADE*. $75

Le Conte, Joseph. 'WARE SHERMAN. Berkeley, 1937. 2nd ed. (1938). Spine of dj faded o/w fine .*PRATT*. $37.50

Le Fanu, J. Sheridan. ALL IN THE DARK. 2 vols. London: Richard Bentley, 1866. 1st UK ed. Rebound into one volume in 3/4 leather & marbelized boards. Bookplate on front pastedown, many pages spotted due to acid content of paper o/w VG. *BERNARD*. $400

Le Fanu, J. Sheridan. GREEN TEA. Arkham House, 1945. 1st ed. NF in dj. *MADLE*. $185

Le Fanu, J. Sheridan. THE EVIL GUEST. London: Downey & Co., n.d. (1895). 1st UK ed. 30 illus. Dark green & gold dec. cloth with March 1895 ads in rear. Top edge gilt. Lower left spine corner chipped, but o/w the binding is extremely bright & attractive. *BERNARD*. $600

Le Fanu, J. Sheridan. THE WATCHER & OTHER WEIRD STORIES. London: Downey & Co., n.d., (1894). 1st UK ed. 21 illus. Top edge of flyleaf a bit ragged & with one mended tear o/w VG+ in bright, attractive grey, silver & black pict binding. *BERNARD*. $700

Le Fanu, J. Sheridan. UNCLE SILAS. London, 1947. Fine in dj. *MADLE*. $40

Le Fanu, J. Sheridan. WYLDER'S HAND. London: Chapman & Hall, 1876. 3rd ed. Binding a bit dull & sl worn at edges o/w Good+. *BERNARD*. $60

Le Fanu, William. A BIO-BIBLIOGRAPHY OF EDWARD JENNER 1749-1823. London, 1951. 1st ed. *FYE*. $60

Le Fanu, William. A LIST OF THE ORIGINAL WRITINGS OF JOSEPH LORD LISTER. Edinburgh, 1965. 1st ed. Wrappers. *FYE*. $35

Le Fanu, William. ENGLISH BOOKS PRINTED BEFORE 1701 IN THE LIBRARY OF THE ROYAL COLLEGE OF SURGEONS OF ENGLAND. Edinburgh, 1963. 1st ed. *FYE*. $30

Le Gallienne, Richard. PROSE FANCIES (Second Series). London: John Lane; Chicago: H.S. Stone & Co, 1896. Spine sl sunned, else NF. 1st ed. *CHAPEL HILL*. $45

Le Gallienne, Richard. THE BOOK-BILLS OF NARCISSUS...NY: G.P.Putnam's, 1895. 3rd ed. Bkpl. *OAK KNOLL*. $30

Le Gallienne, Richard. THE RELIGION OF A LITERARY MAN (Religio Scriptoris). London: Elkin Mathews & John Lane, 1893. Feps tanned, but generally Fine. 1st ed. Ads dated November 1893 and September 1893. *CHAPEL HILL*. $65

Le Gallienne, Richard. THE RELIGION OF A LITERARY MAN (RELIGION SCRIPTORIS). London: (Elkin Mathews & John Lane); NY: (G.P. Putnam's), 1893. One of 250 lg paper copies, ptd in black and red on deckle-edge, hand-made paper. Pub's cl, designed to resemble an 18th century calf binding. 2 separate sections of ads at end, both dated 1893. The trade ed was bound in blue, vertical-ribbed cloth. Flawless. *BOOK BLOCK*. $135

Le Gallienne, Richard. THE WORSHIPPER OF THE IMAGE. London & NY: John Lane, The Bodley Head, 1900. NF. 1st ed. *CHAPEL HILL*. $55

Le Grand, Julia. THE JOURNAL OF...NEW ORLEANS, 1862-1863. Richmond, 1911. 1st ed. Orig cl. Kate Mason Rowland, Mrs. Morris Croxall (eds). *GINSBERG*. $100

Le Guin, Ursula. CITY OF ILLUSIONS. Harper & Row, 1978. 1st thus. Fine in dj. *STAHR*. $35

Le Guin, Ursula. CITY OF ILLUSIONS. NY: Ace, 1967. 1st ed. Close to Fine in wraps. *BEASLEY*. $20

Le Guin, Ursula. ROCANNON'S WORLD, PLANET OF EXILE & CITY OF ILLUSIONS. Ace, 1966. 1st eds. NF set in wraps. *MADLE*. $40

Le Guin, Ursula. SOLOMON LEVIATHAN'S NINE HUNDRED AND THIRTY-FIRST TRIP AROUND THE WORLD. NY: Philomel, (1983). 1st ed. Fine in dj. *BETWEEN COVERS*. $50

Le Guin, Ursula. THE DISPOSSESSED. Harper, 1974. 1st ed. VG in dj. *MADLE*. $65

Le Guin, Ursula. THE EYE OF THE HERON. Harper & Row, 1983. 1st Amer ed. NF in dj w/2 small tears. *STAHR*. $25

Le Guin, Ursula. THE FARTHEST SHORE. NY, 1972. 1st ed. Fine in NF dj (small touches of shelfwear to edge of dj). *McCLINTOCK*. $150

Le Guin, Ursula. THE WORD FOR WORLD IS FOREST. Berkley, 1972. 1st ed. Couple pp wrinkled, else VG in Fine dj. *MADLE*. $40

Le Guin, Ursula. WIND'S TWELVE QUARTERS. Harper, 1975. 1st ed. Fine in dj. *MADLE*. $37

Le Queux, William. THE RAT TRAP. NY: Macaulay, 1930. 1st ed. Fine, minor wear at extremities of bright pict dj. *ELSE FINE*. $45

Le Roy, Virginia. THREE MONTHS IN EUROPE. Streator, IL: Le Roy Printing House, 1896. Grn cl stamped in black and gilt, sl shaken. Corners bumped. Frontis. VG. *SCHOYER'S*. $30

Le Sage, (Alain Rene). THE BACHELOR OF SALAMANCA.... Trans by Mr. (John) Lockman. Dublin: Ptd by George Faulkner Bookseller, 1737-40. 2 vols. Engr frontis, 2 plts in Vol 1. Gutter margins of first and last few leaves stained (not affecting text), joints cracking but sound. VG set, w/engr bkpl and initials on title page of Vol 1. 1st Dublin ed. *CHAPEL HILL*. $150

Le Souef, A.S. and H. Burrell. THE WILD ANIMALS OF AUSTRALASIA EMBRACING THE MAMMALS OF NEW GUINEA AND THE NEARER PACIFIC ISLANDS...105 photos and 8 drawings. London, 1926. Cloth. Some edge wear, spine ends chipped; 2 pp tears repaired w/tape; some foxing, spine faded. *SUTTON*. $75

Le Vert, Octavia Walton, Madame. SOUVENIRS OF TRAVEL. Mobile: S.H. Goetzel & Co., 1857. 1st ed. 2 vols. Emb covers, gilt-dec spines. Owner sig. Bright. VG-NF set. *CHAPEL HILL.* $200

Lea, Henry C. SUPERSTITION AND FORCE. Henry C. Lea, Phila, 1866. Title pg;leaf;(13)-407pp. 1st ed. 8vo. Bound in orig, grn pebbled cl, gilt. Worn, the spine dulled; very lightish embrowning, and a little pencilling; the binding the sl bit strained. *BOSWELL.* $225

Lea, Henry. AN HISTORICAL SKETCH OF SACERDOTAL CELIBACY IN THE CHRISTIAN CHURCH. Phila: J.B. Lippincott, 1867. 1st ed. Cover soiled and faded, else Good. *WREDEN.* $35

Lea, Tom. BULLFIGHT MANUAL FOR SPECTATORS. San Carlos: Nourse, 1949. 1st Amer ed. Pict overhanging wraps. Fine. *CONNOLLY & WADE.* $40

Lea, Tom. OLD MOUNT FRANKLIN. (El Paso): (Carl Hertzog), (1968). One of 150 numbered of the Sand and Rock ed, this one out of series and marked "x", "printer's sample." Total ed of 450. Designed by Hertzog and signed by him. Bound in buckram. Fine. *LAURIE.* $125

Lea, Tom. THE HANDS OF CANTU. Boston: Little, Brown, 1964. 1st ed. Signed. About VG in dj. *CONNOLLY & WADE.* $75

Lea, Tom. THE HANDS OF CANTU. Little Brown, (1964). 1st ed. 8 double pp illus. Signed. Inscription, o/w Fine in VG dj. *OREGON.* $75

Lea, Tom. THE HANDS OF CANTU. Little Brown, (1964). 1st ed. VF in Fine dj. *OREGON.* $50

Lea, Tom. THE KING RANCH. 2 vols. Researched by Holland McCombs. Annotated by Francis L. Fugate. Kingsville: Ptd for the King Ranch, 1957. 43 full-pg drwgs by author, many in color. 7 maps, and 11 documentary facsimiles. One of 3,000 of private ed, none sold, all were given to friends and relatives. Ptd on all rag paper watermarked w/the Running W brand. Bound in heavy crash linen resembling the King Ranch saddle blanket. Linen covered slipcase w/leather label. VG. *LAURIE.* $2,000

Lea, Tom. THE KING RANCH. 2 vols. Researched by Holland McCombs. Annotated by Francis L. Fugate. Boston: Little, Brown, & Co, (1957). 1st ed, 1st state. (p. 507 begins "Alice," later corrected to "For Alice"). Bound in full grey and coral red cl. Slipcase. Spine on vol one sl soiled, o/w Fine. *LAURIE.* $150

Lea, Tom. THE KING RANCH. Boston: Little, Brown & Co. (1957). 2 vols. 1st ed. Pres copy inscribed by Lea. Beige and red cloth. *KARMIOLE.* $200

Lea, Tom. THE KING RANCH. Kingsville, TX: The King Ranch, 1957. 2 vols. Dec (Indian-blanket pattern) coarse cl in matching slipcase w/leather label. Ptd on rag paper w/"running W" watermark. Private ed, not for sale. *DAWSON'S.* $750

Lea, Tom. THE PRIMAL YOKE. Little, Brown, (1960). 1st ed. Frontis. Fine in dj. *AUTHORS OF THE WEST.* $35

Lea, Tom. THE WONDERFUL COUNTRY. Boston: Little, Brown, 1952. 1st ed. Fine in dj. *GIBBS.* $25

Lea, Tom. THE WONDERFUL COUNTRY. Boston: Little, Brown, 1952. 1st ed, special presentation copy signed on leaf inserted after copyright page. 50 to 150 of these estimated. Dj spine is sunned and wrinkled w/small tears. *GIBBS.* $95

Lea, Tom. THE WONDERFUL COUNTRY. Boston: Little, Brown, 1952. 1st ed. Fine in Good+ dj. *CONNOLLY & WADE.* $30

Lea, Tom. THE WONDERFUL COUNTRY. Little, Brown, (1952). 1st ed. Signed. Fir? in nice dj browned some at spine. *AUTHORS OF THE WEST.* $100

Lea, Tom. WESTERN BEEF CATTLE: A SERIES OF ELEVEN PAINTINGS....THE WESTERN RANGE ANIMAL. (Austin): Encino Press, (1967). Color title page illus, 11 b/w plts. One of 850 numbered. Bound in brown buckram. Fine in slipcase. *LAURIE.* $200

Leach, A.J. EARLY DAY STORIES: THE OVERLAND TRAIL, ANIMALS AND BIRDS THAT LIVED HERE, HUNTING STORIES, LOOKING BACKWARD. (Norfolk): (Huse), (1916). 1st ed. VG. Howes L-162A. *LAURIE.* $125

Leach, Joseph. THE TYPICAL TEXAN: BIOGRAPHY OF AN AMERICAN MYTH. Dallas: Southern Methodist Univ Press, 1952. Frontis. Signed. Fine in dj. *LAURIE.* $45

Leacock, Stephen. FURTHER FOOLISHNESS. NY: John Lane, London, and Toronto, 1916. 1st ed. VG in chipped dj. *SECOND LIFE.* $35

Leacock, Stephen. MY DISCOVERY OF ENGLAND. NY: Dodd, Mead, 1922. 1st ed. VG in red cl. *SECOND LIFE.* $25

Leacock, Stephen. THE BOY I LEFT BEHIND ME. NY: Doubleday, 1946. 1st ed. VG. *SMITH.* $40

Leaf, Munro. WEE GILLIS. Viking, 1938. 1st ed. Unpaginated. Illus Robert Lawson. Touch of soil to few pp; edgewear, corner chips pict paper-covered boards but VG+. *BEBBAH.* $70

Leake, William. RESEARCHES IN GREECE. London, 1814. Engr pl showing facs of Suliot song. Full contemp calf, rebacked, chip at top of spine. xiv,472pp. 1st ed. Scarce. *O'NEILL.* $1,100

Leakey, John. THE WEST THAT WAS. SMU, 1958. 1st ed. Fine in sl rubbed dj. *VARNER.* $40

Lear, Edward. LETTERS TO CHICHESTER FORTESCUE, LORD CARLINGFORD; AND FRANCES, COUNTESS WALDEGRAVE. Ed by Lady Strachey. NY: Duffield, n.d. (circa 1910). 1st Amer ed. 328pp, appendix list of paintings, index. Grn cloth, gilt on black title, gilt, top edge gilt, uncut; 20 plts. VG. *HARTFIELD.* $95.

Lear, Edward. THE JUMBLIES. NY: Young Scott, 1968. 1st ed. Ink stain dj spine o/w NF. *SMITH.* $35

Lear, John. KEPLER'S DREAM, WITH THE FULL TEXT AND NOTES OF SOMNIUM, SIVE ASTRONOMIA LUNARIS, JOANNIS KEPLERI. Berkeley: Univ of CA Press, 1965. Trans by Patricia Frueh Kirkwood. VG in sl chipped dj with 1/2" tear, owner's name. *KNOLLWOOD.* $45

Lear, Peter (pseud of Peter Lovesey). GOLDENGIRL. London: Cassell, 1977. 1st ed. Fine in dj. *MORDIDA.* $45

Lear, Peter (pseud of Peter Lovesey). SPIDER GIRL. London: Cassell, 1980. 1st ed. VF in dj. *SILVER DOOR.* $30

Leary, Timothy et al. THE PSYCHEDELIC EXPERIENCE. New Hyde Park: University Books, (1964). Scarce 1st ptg. Cvrs sl bowed but NF w/o dj, as issued. *LOPEZ.* $125

Leary, Timothy. CONFESSIONS OF A HOPE FIEND. NY: Bantam, (1973). Adv reading copy of pb orig. NF. *LOPEZ.* $100

Leavitt, David. FAMILY DANCING. NY: Weidenfeld & Nicholson, (1989). Adv rev copy. Signed. Fine in dj. *LOPEZ.* $45

Leblanc, Maurice. THE TREMENDOUS EVENT. Macaulay, 1922. 1st ed. VG. *MADLE.* $27

Leckenby, Charles H. THE TREAD OF PIONEERS: SOME HIGHLIGHTS IN THE DRAMATIC & COLORFUL HISTORY OF NORTHWESTERN COLORADO. Steamboat Springs, CO, (1945). 2nd ed. Signed. Spine lettering dull, bkpl. VG. *BOHLING.* $150

Leckenby, Charles H. THE TREAD OF PIONEERS: SOME HIGHLIGHTS....Steamboat Springs, CO: Pilot Press, 1945. Private, small ptg. 1st ed. Signed. Fldg brochure on Dinosaur National Monument w/photos, map laid in. Grn cl, gilt. VF. Quite scarce. *CONNOLLY & WADE.* $175

Leckie, William H. and Shirley A. UNLIKELY WARRIORS, GENERAL BENJAMIN GRIERSON AND HIS FAMILY. Norman, 1984. 1st ed. 368pp. Fine in dj. *PRATT.* $27.50

LeClerq, Chrestien. NEW RELATION OF GASPESIA. WITH THE CUSTOMS AND RELIGION....Toronto: Champlain Soc, 1910. Orig cl. Ltd to 520 numbered. William F. Ganong (trans, ed w/reprint of orig). *GINSBERG.* $300

Lederer, William and Eugene Burdick. SARKHAN. NY: McGraw-Hill, (1965). Stated 1st ed. Edge rubbing, o/w NF in NF dj. *AKA.* $45

LeDuc, William G. RECOLLECTIONS OF A CIVIL WAR QUARTERMASTER. St. Paul, (1963). 1st ed. 167pp. VG+ in dj. *PRATT.* $25

Ledwidge, Francis. LAST SONGS. London: Jenkins, 1918. 1st ed. Front panel of dj laid in. *WOOLMER.* $35

Ledyard, Bill. A WINTER IN FLORIDA; OR, OBSERVATIONS OF THE SOIL, CLIMATE, AND PRODUCTS OF OUR SEMI-TROPICAL STATE... NY: Wood & Holbrook, 1869. 2nd ed. 222pp + ads. Frontis, 3 plts, map. Orig grn cl, gilt. *KARMIOLE.* $75

Lee, "Powder River" Jack H. THE STAMPEDE, AND OTHER TALES OF THE FAR WEST. Author pub, privately ptd, n.d. Frontisport, pl. Some edgewear, else VG. *CONNOLLY & WADE.* $65

Lee, Andrea. SARAH PHILLIPS. NY: Random House, (1984). 1st ed. Fine in dj. *LOPEZ.* $25

Lee, Arthur S. Gould. THE ROYAL HOUSE OF GREECE. London, 1948. 296pp. *O'NEILL.* $35

Lee, Dougal. FLYING THE SKY CLIPPER WITH WINSIE ATKINS. Racine, WI, (1936). 1st ed. Big Little Book #1108. VG. *McCLINTOCK.* $20

Lee, Frances. NEW JERSEY AS A COLONY AND STATE. 4 vols. Pub. Soc of NJ (1902) 1st ed. 422; 402; 400; 456pp. Large paper. Tear on spine of Vols I and 4. Spines discolored. *HEINOLDT.* $45

Lee, Fred J. CASEY JONES: EPIC OF THE AMERICAN RAILROAD. Kingsport, TN: Southern Pub., 1939. 1st ed. A bit rubbed, o/w VG. *ARCHER.* $40

Lee, Gypsy Rose. MOTHER FINDS A BODY. NY: Simon and Schuster, 1942. 1st ed. Name, address o/w Fine in dj w/closed tear, minor wear. *MORDIDA.* $65

Lee, Gypsy Rose. THE G-STRING MURDERS. Simon & Schuster, 1941. 1st ed. VG+. *BEBBAH.* $20

Lee, H. SEA FABLES EXPLAINED (WITH) SEA MONSTERS UNMASKED. London: W. Clowes, 1883. 2 vols in 1. 8vo, 122; 103pp. 66 engrs. VG+. *MIKESH.* $37.50

Lee, H(enry) Jr. OBSERVATIONS ON THE WRITINGS OF THOMAS JEFFERSON WITH PARTICULAR REFERENCE TO THE ATTACK THEY CONTAIN ON THE MEMORY OF THE LATE GEN. HENRY LEE. NY: Charles De Behr, 1832. 1st ed. 237pp & ad leaf. Cl spine torn at top, paper over boards, front hinge tear. Ex-lib. Good+. Howes L.205. *BOOK BROKER.* $125

Lee, Harper. TO KILL A MOCKINGBIRD. London, Melbourne, Toronto: Heinemann, (1960). 1st Eng ed, 1st bk. NF in sl rubbed dj, few sm tears. *HELLER.* $100

Lee, Harper. TO KILL A MOCKINGBIRD. London: Heinemann, (1960). 1st English ed. Fine in NF dj, a trifle edge rubbed. Harper Lee photo rear panel. *UNGER.* $200

Lee, Harper. TO KILL A MOCKINGBIRD. London: Heinemann, (1960). 1st UK ed. Fine in dj w/touch of rubbing at the corners. *CAPTAIN'S BOOKSHELF.* $250

Lee, Harper. TO KILL A MOCKINGBIRD. Phila: Lippincott, (1960). 1st ed. Owner inscription, o/w NF in dj (internally strengthened, carefully retouched where the color had rubbed). *LOPEZ.* $1250

Lee, Harper. TO KILL A MOCKINGBIRD. Phila: Lippincott, (1960). 1st ed. VG-NF in like dj, rubbed along the joints and extremities w/tiny chips from the corners. *CAPTAIN'S BOOKSHELF.* $900

Lee, Henry. THE WHITE WHALE. (Wrapper title.) London: R. K. Burt & Co., (1878). 16 pp. Orig ptd wrappers (a little soiled). Scarce. *LEFKOWICZ.* $100

Lee, James Kendall. THE VOLUNTEER'S HAND BOOK...Richmond: West & Johnston, No. 145 Main Street, 1861. Bound in 1/2 leather. VG. *McGOWAN.* $350

Lee, John D. A MORMON CHRONICLE: THE DIARIES OF JOHN D. LEE, 1848-1876. Ed, annotated by Robert Glass Cleland and Juanita Brooks. San Marino, CA: The Huntington Library. 1955. 1st ed. 2 vols. Djs. Scarce. *KARMIOLE.* $125

Lee, John S. NATURE AND ART IN THE OLD WORLD...Cincinnati, 1871. Sl rubbing. 441pp. *O'NEILL.* $45

Lee, John. HAND-BOOK FOR CORONERS. Phila, 1881. 1st ed. *FYE.* $100

Lee, L.P. (ed). HISTORY OF THE SPIRIT LAKE MASSACRE! 8TH MARCH, 1857, AND OF MISS ABIGAIL GARDNER'S THREE MONTHS CAPTIVITY AMONG THE INDIANS ACCORDING TO HER OWN ACCOUNT. New Britain, CT, 1857. 1st ed. 48pp. Illus. Pict. wraps. Minor staining o/w Fine. *PRATT.* $185

Lee, P. GIANT: THE PICTORIAL HISTORY OF THE HUMAN COLOSSUS. NY, 1970. *FYE.* $60

Lee, Richard Henry. LIFE OF ARTHUR LEE, LL.D....CORRESPONDENCE AND HIS PAPERS. Boston: 1829. 1st ed. 2 vols. Orig cl backed boards w/paper label, sm rubber lib stamp, bkpls. Howes L214. *GINSBERG.* $125

Lee, Robert E. THE WARTIME PAPERS OF R.E. LEE. NY, (1961). Ed by Clifford Dowdey and Louis H. Manarin. 994pp. Dj. Fine. *PRATT.* $40

Lee, Ronald A. THE KNIBB FAMILY: CLOCKMAKERS...(Liverpool: The Manor House Press, 1964). Ltd ed of 500. 187pp, 190 plts. Dj. Navy blue buckram. Fine. *WEBER.* $500

Lee, W. Storrs. THE ISLANDS. NY: Holt, (1966). 1st ed. Review slip laid in. Fine in Fine dj. *BOOK MARKET.* $30

Lee, Wayne C. SCOTTY PHILIP, THE MAN WHO SAVED THE BUFFALO. Caldwell: The Caxton Printers, 1975. xvii,334p. Black ptd cl in dj. *DAWSON'S.* $35

Lee, Wayne C. SCOTTY PHILIP, THE MAN WHO SAVED THE BUFFALO. Caxton: Caldwell, 1975. 1st ed. As New in dj. *CONNOLLY & WADE.* $35

Lee, Weston and Jeanne. TORRENT IN THE DESERT. Flagstaff, 1962. 1st ed. Fine in edgeworn, lightly worn dj. *BAADE.* $65

Lee, Weston and Jeanne. TORRENT IN THE DESERT. Flagstaff: Northland Press, 1962. 1st ed. Fine in Fine dj. *BOOK MARKET.* $45

Lee, Weston and Jeanne. TORRENT IN THE DESERT. Flagstaff: Northland, 1962. 1st ed. NF in Good+ dj. *CONNOLLY & WADE.* $60

Leech, Harry Harewood. LETTERS OF A SENTIMENTAL IDLER, FROM GREECE, TURKEY, EGYPT, NUBIA, AND THE HOLY LAND. NY, 1869. x,463pp. *O'NEILL.* $60

Leeper, David Rohrer. THE ARGONAUTS OF FORTY NINE. South Bend, IN: J.B. Stoll & Co., 1894. 1st ed. Spine wear, o/w Fine. Howes L226. *OREGON.* $145

Leeper, David. THE ARGONAUTS OF 'FORTY-NINE: SOME RECOLLECTIONS. South Bend, IN, 1894. 1st ed. 145,xvipp. Orig cl. Howes L226. Inscribed presentation. *GINSBERG.* $175

Leeper, Sir Reginald. WHEN GREEK MEETS GREEK. London, 1950. xxii,244pp. *O'NEILL.* $35

Leffingwell, Albert. VIVISECTION. NY, 1889. 1st ed. Wrappers detached, paper browned and brittle. *FYE.* $30

LeFors, Joe. WYOMING PEACE OFFICER, AN AUTOBIOGRAPHY. Laramie, WY: Laramie Printing Co, 1953. 1st ed. Fine in dj w/several small pieces gone. Scarce. *GIBBS.* $175

LeFors, Joe. WYOMING PEACE OFFICER. Laramie, 1953. 1st ed. Fine in Fine dj. *VARNER.* $100

Legallois, Julien. EXPERIMENTS ON THE PRINCIPLE OF LIFE, AND PARTICULARLY ON THE PRINCIPLE OF THE MOTIONS OF THE HEART, AND ON THE SEAT OF THIS PRINCIPLE. Phila, 1813. 1st Eng trans. 328pp. Full leather, rebacked w/new eps. Inner margins of plate and title page repaired. Scarce. *FYE.* $500

Legendre, Sidney J. OKOVANGO—DESERT RIVER. NY: Julian Messner, Inc, 1939. 1st ed. VG+ in VG dj. *BACKMAN.* $40

LEGENDS OF THE MIGHTY SIOUX. South Dakota Writers' Project, WPA. Chicago: Whitman, 1941. 1st ed. VG in VG dj w/modest edgewear, sl faded spine. Scarce. *LOPEZ.* $150

Legman, G. LOVE & DEATH: A STUDY IN CENSORSHIP. NY, 1949. 1st ed. Orig red stiff wraps ptd in black. NF. *DIAMOND.* $45

Legman, G. THE HORN BOOK. NY, 1964. Dj. NF. *POLYANTHOS.* $45

Lehmann, Rosamond. DUSTY ANSWER. NY, 1927. 1st US ed. Fine in dj. *SECOND LIFE.* $45

Lehmann, Rosamond. THE WEATHER IN THE STREETS. London: Collins, 1936. 1st ed. Spine cocked & dull, o/w VG in lightly dust-soiled dj. *JAFFE.* $65

Lehmann, V.W. FORGOTTEN LEGIONS: SHEEP IN THE RIO GRANDE PLAIN OF TEXAS. El Paso: Texas Western, Univ of TX, 1969. 1st ed after ltd ed of 300. Ltd to 2,000. Map. Pict hopsacking. Fine in Fine dj. *CONNOLLY & WADE.* $50

Lehmann-Haupt, Hellmut. THE LIFE OF THE BOOK. London and NY: Abelard-Schuman, (1957). 1st ed. Dj. *OAK KNOLL.* $35

Leiber, Fritz. A SPECTER IS HAUNTING TEXAS. Walker, 1968. 1st ed. Fine in dj. Signed. *MADLE.* $75

Leiber, Fritz. ERVOOL. Roanoke: Cheap Street, 1980. 1st ed. One of 200 numbered, signed. Fine in env. *BEASLEY.* $45

Leiber, Fritz. GATHER DARKNESS. G & D, n.d. Fine in dj. *MADLE.* $25

Leiber, Fritz. GATHER, DARKNESS! NY: Grosset & Dunlap, 1950. Dj faded. Fine. *WEBER.* $15

Leiber, Fritz. NIGHT'S BLACK AGENTS. Arkham House, 1947. 1st ed. VF in dj. *MADLE.* $200

Leiber, Fritz. NIGHT'S BLACK AGENTS. Sauk City: Arkham House, 1947. 1st ed. Inscribed. VG+ in dj, worn at spine ends, 2 short closed tears. *OTHER WORLDS.* $125

Leiber, Fritz. SHIP OF SHADOWS. London, 1979. 500 numbered, signed. Fine in dj. *MADLE.* $75

Leiber, Fritz. THE BIG TIME AND THE MIND SPIDER AND OTHER STORIES. NY: Ace Double, 1961. 1st ed. VF in wraps. *BEASLEY.* $25

Leiber, Fritz. THE BIG TIME. London, 1976. 1st British ed. Fine in sl frayed dj. Signed. *MADLE.* $50

Leiber, Fritz. THE GREEN MILLENIUM. London, 1977. Fine in dj. Signed. *MADLE.* $50

Leiber, Fritz. THE WANDERER. London, 1967. 1st Brit & 1st hb ed. VG in dj. Signed. *MADLE.* $100

Leiber, Fritz. TWO SOUGHT ADVENTURE. Gnome Press, 1957. 1st ed. Fine in Mint dj. Signed. *MADLE.* $175

Leibowitz, J. THE HISTORY OF CORONARY HEART DISEASE. London, 1970. 1st ed. *FYE.* $75

Leidy, J. FRESH-WATER RHIZOPODS OF NORTH AMERICA. Washington, 1879. Lt wear, some spotting, foxing, lib stamp ep. *SUTTON.* $145

Leighton, Ann. AMERICAN GARDENS IN THE EIGHTEENTH CENTURY. Boston: Houghton Mifflin, 1976. VG in dj. *AMERICAN BOTANIST.* $25

Leighton, Ann. EARLY AMERICAN GARDENS. Boston: Houghton Mifflin, 1970. VG in worn dj. *AMERICAN BOTANIST.* $25

Leighton, Clare. WOOD-ENGRAVING AND WOODCUTS. London: Studio, 1932. 11 tipped-in duotone illus, full-pg wood engr. Dec boards, cloth spine a bit rumpled w/short tear to top. *DAWSON'S.* $65

Leighton, Dorothea and Clyde Kluckhorn. CHILDREN OF THE PEOPLE. THE NAVAHO INDIVIDUAL AND HIS DEVELOPMENT. Cambridge: Harvard Univ, 1947. 1st ed. NF in chipped, worn dj. *CONNOLLY & WADE.* $47.50

Leinster, Murray (pseud of Will F. Jenkins). SIDEWISE IN TIME: AND OTHER SCIENTIFIC ADVENTURES. Chicago: Shasta, 1950. 1st ed. Subscriber's copy, signed as both Leinster and Will F. Jenkins. Bkpl, name, date else NF in edgeworn dj, browned spine. *OTHER WORLDS.* $100

Leinster, Murray. THE LAST SPACESHIP. Fell, 1949. Fine in dj. *MADLE.* $65

Leipnik, F.L. HISTORY OF FRENCH ETCHING FROM THE 16TH CENTURY TO PRESENT. London, 1924. Light rubbing to spine. NF. *POLYANTHOS.* $100

Leitch, Adelaide. THE BLUE ROAN. NY: Walck, 1971. 1st U.S. ed. VG in VG dj. *OCTOBER FARM.* $12

Leitch, Mary and Margaret W. SEVEN YEARS IN CEYLON: Stories of Mission Life. NY: American Tract Society, (1890). viii,172pp. Cl and ptd bds, rubbed on edges. Front hinge cracking. *SCHOYER'S.* $40

Leland, Effie Williams. CROSSIN' OVER. Columbia: State Company, (1937). 1st ed. VG in dj. *LOPEZ.* $25

Lem, Stanislaw. CHAIN OF CHANCE. NY: Harcourt, Brace, Jovanovich, (1978). 1st US ed. Dj beginning to darken, soil rear panel, o/w Fine in Fine dj. *AKA.* $25

Lemaitre, Georges. BEAUMARCHAIS—A BIOGRAPHY. NY: Knopf, 1949. 1st ed. Name stamp. Fine- in Fine- dj. *AARD.* $25

Lemarchand, Elizabeth. CYANIDE WITH COMPLIMENTS. London: MacGibbon, 1972. 1st ed. NF in dj. *SILVER DOOR.* $25

LeMay, Alan. OLD FATHER OF WATERS. Doubleday, Doran & Co, 1928. 1st ed. VG. *AUTHORS OF THE WEST.* $35

LeMay, Alan. SUMMER OF THE GUN. NY: Lippincott, (1978). 1st ed. Fine in Fine dj. *UNGER.* $40

LeMay, Alan. THE SEARCHERS. Harper & Brothers, (1954). 1st signed, ltd ed of 800. Fine in dj. *AUTHORS OF THE WEST.* $125

LeMay, Alan. THE SMOKY YEARS. Farrar & Rinehart, (1935). 1st ed. Spine faded some, else Fine. *AUTHORS OF THE WEST.* $35

Lemos, Pedro J. GUATEMALA ART CRAFTS. Worcester, MA: The Davis Press. (1950). Rev, enl ed. Dj. *KARMIOLE.* $35

Lennon, John. IN HIS OWN WRITE. NY, 1964. 1st ed. Illus. Name, small sticker removed front cvr, extrems minimally rubbed. NF. *POLYANTHOS.* $25

Lennon, John. SKYWRITING BY WORD OF MOUTH. NY: Harper & Row, (1986). 1st ed. Fine in price-clipped dj. *LOPEZ.* $30

Lenski, Lois. STRAWBERRY GIRL. Lippincott, (1945). 1st ed. 194pp. Illus by Lenski plus head & tailpieces. VG+ and chips, 2 closed tears, insect nibbles to rear panel. Good+. *BEBBAH.* $40

Lent, William Bement. HOLY LAND FROM LANDAU, SADDLE AND PALANQUIN. NY: Bonnell, Silver & Co., 1899. Spine rubbed, a few corrections in text. Author's pres inscrip. *SCHOYER'S.* $30

Lenygon, Francis. THE DECORATION AND FURNITURE OF ENGLISH MANSIONS DURING THE SEVENTEENTH & EIGHTEENTH CENTURIES. London: T. Werner Laurie, Clifford's Inn, 1909. Folio, grn cl (rubbed). 28 tipped in photo illus. VG. *BLUE MOUNTAIN.* $75

Leodhas, Sorche. ALWAYS ROOM FOR ONE MORE. HRW, (1965). 1st ed. Illus by Nonny Hogrogian. Fine in VG+ dj. *BEBBAH.* $65

Leonard, Elizabeth Jane and Julia Cody Goodman. BUFFALO BILL: KING OF THE OLD WEST. NY: Library Publications, 1955. 1st ed. Fine in VG dj. *AARD.* $25

Leonard, Elmore. BANDITS. NY: Arbor House, (1987). 1st ed. Inscribed. NF in dj. *LOPEZ.* $60

Leonard, Elmore. CAT CHASER. NY: Arbor House, 1982. 1st ed. Fine in NF dj. *BEASLEY.* $30

Leonard, Elmore. CITY PRIMEVAL. Arbor House, 1980. 1st ed. NF. Light rubbing on dj. *STAHR.* $20

Leonard, Elmore. CITY PRIMEVAL. NY: Arbor House, 1980. 1st ed. Signed. VF in dj. *MORDIDA.* $35

Leonard, Elmore. CITY PRIMEVAL. NY: Arbor, 1980. 1st ed. Fine, minor rubs to dj corners. *ELSE FINE.* $35

Leonard, Elmore. DUTCH TREAT. Arbor House, (1987). 1st ed. & review copy with publisher's slip laid in. NF in NF dj. *BEBBAH.* $20

Leonard, Elmore. DUTCH TREAT. NY: Mysterious Press, n.d. 1/350 specially bound, dec w/tipped-on portrait of author. Numbered and signed on tipped-in leaf. Fine in Fine slipcase. *BEASLEY.* $75

Leonard, Elmore. FIFTY-TWO PICK UP. NY: Delacorte, 1974. 1st ed. Sl shaken, sunned edges, o/w Nice in sl worn dj (few short tape repairs). *BEASLEY.* $150

Leonard, Elmore. FIFTY-TWO PICKUP. London, 1974. 1st UK ed. VF in dj. *PETTLER.* $100

Leonard, Elmore. FIFTY-TWO PICKUP. NY: Delacorte Press, 1974. 1st ed. Fine in dj. *MORDIDA.* $225

Leonard, Elmore. FORTY LASHES LESS ONE. Bantam, 1972. 1st ed. VG+, wraps. Reading crease; cover rubbed. *STAHR.* $15

Leonard, Elmore. GET SHORTY. Delacorte, 1990. 1st ed. Fine in Fine dj, signed. *BEBBAH.* $28

Leonard, Elmore. GLITZ. NY: Arbor House, 1985. advance reading copy. Fine in wraps. *ARCHER.* $30

Leonard, Elmore. GOLD COAST. Bantam, 1980. 1st ed. NF in wraps. Light reading crease on spine; 2" crease on front cover. *STAHR.* $15

Leonard, Elmore. GUNSIGHTS. Bantam, 1979. 1st ed. VG+ in wraps. Reading crease; usual wear. *STAHR.* $15

Leonard, Elmore. HOMBRE. NY: Armchair Detective Library, 1989. 1st Amer hb ed. One of 100 numbered, signed. VF in slipcase w/o dj as issued. *MORDIDA.* $75

Leonard, Elmore. HOMBRE. NY: Armchair Library, (1989). 1st hardcover ed. One of 100 numbered and signed. In custom slipcase. *UNGER.* $125

Leonard, Elmore. MR. MAJESTYK. NY: Dell Publishing, 1974. 1st ed. Pb orig. Signed. VF, unread, in wrappers. *MORDIDA.* $65

Leonard, Elmore. MR. MAKESTYK. Dell, 1974. 1st ed. About Fine in pb. Lt rubbing to front cvr. *STAHR.* $25

Leonard, Elmore. NOTEBOOKS. Northridge: Lord John Press, 1991. 1st ed. 1/300 numbered, signed. VF w/o dj as issued. *MORDIDA.* $50

Leonard, Elmore. SPLIT IMAGES. NY: Arbor House, 1981. 1st ed. Signed. Fine in dj. *MORDIDA.* $35

Leonard, Elmore. STICK. NY: Arbor, (1983). 1st ed. Signed. Fine in NF dj. *UNGER.* $45

Leonard, Elmore. STICK. NY: Arbor, 1983. 1st ed. Signed. VF in dj. *SILVER DOOR.* $40

Leonard, Elmore. SWAG. Delacorte, 1976. 1st ed. About Fine in pb. Lt rubbing to front cvr. *STAHR.* $25

Leonard, Elmore. SWAG. NY: Delacorte Press, 1976. 1st ed. Signed. VF in dj. *MORDIDA.* $85

Leonard, Elmore. THE BIG BOUNCE. Fawcett (R2079), 1969. 1st ed. NF in pb. Spine lightly cocked, creased. *STAHR.* $45

Leonard, Elmore. THE BIG BOUNCE. NY: Mysterious Press, 1989. 1st Amer hardcover ed. 1/26 lettered, signed. VF in slipcase w/o dj as issued. *MORDIDA.* $150

Leonard, Elmore. THE MOONSHINE WAR. GC: Doubleday, 1969. 1st ed. Signed. Name, spine sl cocked, rear ep replaced (excellent color match) o/w VG in NF price clipped dj. *BERNARD.* $250

Leonard, Elmore. THE SWITCH. NY: Bantam Books, 1978. 1st ed. Pb orig. Signed. VF, unread in wrappers. *MORDIDA.* $50

Leonard, Elmore. UNKNOWN MAN NO. 89. London, 1977. 1st UK ed. Fine in dj. *PETTLER.* $100

Leonard, Elmore. UNKNOWN MAN NO. 89. London: Secker & Warburg, (1977). 1st UK ed. Eps lightly foxed o/w VG+ in price clipped dj. *BERNARD.* $125

Leonard, Elmore. UNKNOWN MAN NO. 89. NY: Delacorte Press, 1977. 1st ed. Inscribed. VF in dj. *MORDIDA.* $350

Leonard, John. PRIVATE LIVES IN THE IMPERIAL CITY. NY: Knopf, 1979. 1st ed. Inscribed. Fine in Fine dj. *BEASLEY.* $35

Leonard, William Ellery. GILGAMESH. Avon: LEC, 1974. #564/2000 ltd. Signed by illus, Irving Amen. 98 color illus. Slipcase. Good. *ARCHAEOLOGIA.* $150

Leonard, Zenas. ADVENTURES OF ZENAS LEONARD, FUR TRADER. John Ewers (ed). Univ of OK, (1959). 1st OK ed. VF in VG dj. Howes L264. *OREGON.* $40

LEONARDO DA VINCI. London & NY, 1984. John Strejan (paper eng). Illus A. & M. Provensen. Pop-up bk. *BOOKFINDERS INTL.* $30

LEONARDO DA VINCI. NY: Reynal & Co, (1956). 1st U.S. ed. 12 color plts. Fine- in VG+ dj (1" tear). *AARD.* $75

Leopold, Aldo. A SAND COUNTY ALMANAC AND SKETCHES HERE AND THERE. NY: Oxford Univ Press, 1949. 1st ed. VG+ in VG dj. *BACKMAN.* $60

LePlongeon, Augustus. SACRED MYSTERIES AMONG THE MAYAS AND THE QUICHES. NY, 1886. 1st ed. xvi,163pp. Pict blind-stamped cl. Defective spine tip. Penciling; p. margin torn, else VG. *DIAMOND.* $75

Lepsius, Richard. DISCOVERIES IN EGYPT, ETHIOPIA, AND THE PENINSULA OF SINAI. London: Richard Bentley, 1853. Color frontis, 1 map. Expertly rebacked w/leather label, 1 corner bumped, signature. Good. *ARCHAEOLOGIA.* $150

Lepsius, Richard. LETTERS FROM EGYPT, ETHIOPIA....London: Bohn, 1853. 1st ed. Leonora and Joanna B. Horner (trans). Frontis, 2 fldg maps. Orig cl, sl rubbed, o/w VG, uncut, unopened. Bkpl. *WORLDWIDE.* $125

Leroux, Gaston. NOMADS OF THE NIGHT. NY: Macaulay, 1925. 1st Amer ed. Pub in Eng as The Dancing Girl. Fine in lightly soiled dj w/couple of short closed tears. *MORDIDA.* $80

Leroux, Gaston. NOMADS OF THE NIGHT. NY: Macauley, 1925. 1st US ed. 312pp. Pict boards, spine sunned. VG. *ARCHER.* $20

Leroux, Gaston. THE KISS THAT KILLED. Macaulay, 1934. 1st US ed. VG. *MADLE.* $35

Lesky, Erna. THE VIENNA MEDICAL SCHOOL OF THE 19TH CENTURY. Baltimore, 1979. 1st Eng trans. *FYE.* $75

Lesley, Lewis Burt. UNCLE SAM'S CAMELS. Harvard, 1929. 1st ed. 298pp, fldg map. Largely unopened, NF. *FIVE QUAIL.* $100

Leslie, A.S. (ed). THE GROUSE IN HEALTH AND IN DISEASE. London: Smith, Elder, 1912. Popular Ed. Shelfworn, Good only. Scarce. *OLD LONDON.* $35

Lesser, Mary. THE ART OF LEARNING MEDICINE. NY, 1974. 1st ed. *FYE.* $75

Lesser, Milton. THE STAR SEEKERS. Winston, 1953. 1st ed. VG in chipped, soiled dj. *MADLE.* $40

Lessing, Doris. A MAN AND TWO WOMEN. NY: Simon and Schuster, 1963. 1st ed. Fine in sl worn dj. *SECOND LIFE.* $35

Lessing, Doris. A MAN AND TWO WOMEN. STORIES. NY, 1963. Fine in NF dj. *POLYANTHOS.* $30

Lessing, Doris. BRIEFING FOR A DESCENT INTO HELL. Knopf, 1971. 1st ed. Fine in dj. *STAHR.* $15

Lessing, Doris. CANOPUS IN ARGOS. Knopf, 1979-1983. 5 vols. 1st eds. VG—Fine set in djs. *MADLE.* $95

Lessing, Doris. MARTHA QUEST. A PROPER MARRIAGE. NY: Simon & Schuster, 1964. 1st ed thus. Sl chipped dj, o/w VG. *SCHOYER'S.* $25

Lessing, Doris. MARTHA QUEST. London: Michael Joseph, (1952). VG in lightly worn dj. *LOPEZ.* $150

Lessing, Doris. PARTICULARLY CATS. Simon and Schuster, 1967. 1st Amer ed. VG+. Lt spotting lower front panel of price-clipped dj; sm tear rear panel. *STAHR.* $20

Lessing, Doris. RETREAT TO INNOCENCE. London, 1956. 1st ed. Name. Fine in dj (extremities, spine and top corners little rubbed, tiny edge chip). *POLYANTHOS.* $60

Lessing, Doris. RIPPLE FROM THE STORM. LANDLOCKED. NY: Simon & Schuster, 1966. 1st ed thus. Fresh in sl faded dj. *SCHOYER'S.* $25

Lessing, Doris. THE GRASS IS SINGING. NY, 1950. 1st US ed, rare 1st bk. 2 letter stamps & small ink name/date on ep, else NF in VG dj. *PETTLER.* $65

Lessing, Doris. THE GRASS IS SINGING. NY: Crowell, 1950. 1st US ed. Author's 1st bk. Sl foxing to fore edge, spine sl spotted, else NF in dj w/small red stain to lower portion of spine panel. *LAME DUCK.* $50

Lessing, Doris. THE HABIT OF LOVING. NY, (1957). 1st ed. Extremities spine minimally rubbed. Fine in dj (top spine little chipped, few edge nicks, little rubbed). *POLYANTHOS.* $40

Lessing, Doris. THE SUMMER BEFORE THE DARK. Jonathan Cape, 1973. 1st ed. Fine in NF dj (2 corners bumped; lt rubbing). *STAHR.* $25

Lessing, Doris. THE SUMMER BEFORE THE DARK. Jonathan Cape, 1973. 1st ed. Fine in NF dj (2 corners bumped; lt rubbing). *STAHR.* $25

Lessing, Doris. THE SUMMER BEFORE THE DARK. London: Cape, (1973). 1st ed. Fine in dj. *SECOND LIFE.* $35

Lester, J.A. (ed). A CENTURY OF PHILADELPHIA CRICKET. Phila: Univ of PA Press, 1951. 1st ed. VG in Near VG dj. *OLD LONDON.* $35

Lester, John Erastus. THE ATLANTIC TO THE PACIFIC. London, 1873. 1st ed. Fldg map, errata slip. Cl cvrs sl worn, pp badly opened, o/w VG. *DIAMOND.* $45

Lester, John Erastus. THE YOSEMITE: ITS HISTORY. Providence, 1873. VG in fragile wraps. *BOOK MARKET.* $100

Lester, Julius. TWO LOVE STORIES. NY: Dial, (1972). 1st ed. Fine in NF dj. *LOPEZ.* $30

Lester, Katherine Morris and Bess Viola Oerke. ACCESSORIES OF DRESS. Peoria, IL: The Manual Arts Press, (1940). 69 plts. Dj. VG. *WEBER.* $100

Lester, Richard I. CONFEDERATE FINANCE AND PURCHASING IN GREAT BRITAIN. Charlottesville, VA, (1975). 1st ed. NF. *McGOWAN.* $35

LeSueur, Meridel. NORTH STAR COUNTRY. Duell, Sloan & Pearce, (1945). 1st ed. Ep map. Fine in clean dj quite chipped. *AUTHORS OF THE WEST.* $17.50

LeSueur, Meridel. RIPENING: SELECTED WORK, 1927-1980. Feminist Press, (1982). Uncorrected proofs, softbound. Fine. *AUTHORS OF THE WEST.* $25

LeSueur, Meridel. SPARROW HAWK. NY: Knopf, 1950. 1st ed. Fine in lightly used & chipped dj. *BEASLEY.* $50

Lesure, Thomas B. ADVENTURES IN ARIZONA: AN INFORMAL GUIDE.... San Antonio: Naylor, 1956. 1st ed. Faint damp mark on lower edge of pgs affecting nothing, o/w VG in Good+ dj. *CONNOLLY & WADE.* $25

LET'S TAKE A TRIP AROUND THE HARBOUR. London, 1988. Illus Borge Svensson. Pop-up bk. *BOOKFINDERS INTL.* $15

LETTERS FROM PALESTINE, DESCRIPTIVE OF A TOUR THROUGH GALILEE AND JUDEA...(By Thomas R. Joliffe.) London, 1820. 2nd ed. Orig 1/2 calf, marbled boards. viii,377pp. *O'NEILL.* $225

LETTERS OF ALGERNON SYDNEY...BY AN EMINENT CITIZEN OF VIRGINIA, AND FIRST PUBLISHED...IN 1818-19...THE REMARKS OF MR. RITCHIE...(By Benjamin W. Leigh.) Richmond, 1830. 1st ed. (8),65pp. Half morocco. Howes L238. *GINSBERG.* $300

LETTERS OF J. DOWNING. NY: Harper, 1834. xi,271,(4)pp. 2 frontispieces, 6 plts. Later 3/4 leather w/marbled boards. Teg; other edges untrimmed. Engr bkpl. BAL 4496. *SCHOYER'S.* $85

LETTERS TO SQUIRE PEDANT, IN THE EAST, BY LORENZO ALTISONANT, AN EMIGRANT TO THE WEST. (By Samuel Klinefetter Hoshour.) Indianapolis, 1870. 4th ed, enl, improved. New cl w/gilt stamped morocco spine label. Nice. *BOHLING.* $85

Leupp, Francis E. IN RED MAN'S LAND; A STUDY OF THE AMERICAN INDIAN. NY: Fleming H. Revell, (1914). 1st ed. Fine in dj. *LAURIE.* $60

Leupp, Francis E(llington). IN RED MAN'S LAND. A STUDY OF THE AMERICAN INDIAN. NY: Revell, 1914. 1st ed. Frontis, 8 plts, ptd red wraps. Worn, sm chip backstrip, else Fine. *CONNOLLY & WADE.* $55

Levasseur, A. LAFAYETTE IN AMERICA, IN 1824 AND 1825, OR, JOURNAL....NY: 1829. 2 vols. 227,284pp. Orig boards, spines expertly mended, w/paper labels preserved, but faded. Howes L301. *GINSBERG.* $150

Levertov, Denise. A MARIGOLD FROM NORTH VIET NAM. (NY): (Ampersand Books and Albondocani Press, 1968). 1/300 issued as Christmas greeting. Inscribed by pub. Fine in wrappers and well-used orig env. *CAPTAIN'S BOOKSHELF.* $45

Levertov, Denise. A TREE TELLING OF ORPHEUS. Drawings by author. LA: Black Sparrow Press, 1968. 1st ed, wrappered issue, 1/250 signed. Fine. *CAPTAIN'S BOOKSHELF.* $40

Levertov, Denise. CHEKHOV ON THE WEST HEATH. Andes, NY: Woolmer/Brotherson, 1977. 1st ed. 1/200 numbered, signed. Fine in marbled wrappers w/paper label. *CAPTAIN'S BOOKSHELF.* $45

Levertov, Denise. EL SALVADOR: REQUIEM AND INVOCATION. Music W.N. Hendricks. Stage set Michael Mazur. Larry Hill, conductor. (Boston): Back Bay Chorale, 1983. 1st ed. 1/100 specially bound, signed by author, composer, designer, and conductor. Fine in wrappers. *CAPTAIN'S BOOKSHELF.* $150

Levertov, Denise. EL SALVADOR: REQUIEM AND INVOCATION. N.p, (1984). 1st revised ed. Fine in wrappers. *CAPTAIN'S BOOKSHELF.* $20

Levertov, Denise. EMBROIDERIES. Cl-backed boards, acetate dj. LA: Black Sparrow Press, 1969. 1st ed. One of 150 hb signed. VF. *JAFFE.* $150

Levertov, Denise. EMBROIDERIES. LA: Black Sparrow Press, 1969. 1st ed. 1/150 hardbound, signed. Fine. *CAPTAIN'S BOOKSHELF.* $75

Levertov, Denise. FOOTPRINTS. (NY): New Directions, (1972). 1st ed. Fine in dj. *CAPTAIN'S BOOKSHELF.* $35

Levertov, Denise. FOOTPRINTS. Cl-backed boards, dj. (NY): New Directions, (1972). 1st ed. Signed. VF. *JAFFE.* $45

Levertov, Denise. IN THE NIGHT. A STORY. NY: Albondocani Press, 1968. 1st ed. 1/150 numbered, signed. Fine in marbled wrappers w/paper label. *CAPTAIN'S BOOKSHELF.* $100

Levertov, Denise. O TASTE AND SEE. Cl-backed boards, dj. (Norfolk, CT): New Directions, (1964). 1st ed. Signed. VF. *JAFFE.* $100

Levertov, Denise. O TASTE AND SEE: NEW POEMS. (NY): New Directions, (1964). 1st ed. Fine in dj. *CAPTAIN'S BOOKSHELF.* $60

Levertov, Denise. OVERLAND TO THE ISLANDS. Japanese paper wrappers. Highlands: Jonathan Williams, 1958. 1st ed. Ltd to 450. Fine. *JAFFE.* $250

Levertov, Denise. SUMMER POEMS/1969. Berkeley: Oyez, (1970). 1st ed. 1/300. Fine in wrappers. *CAPTAIN'S BOOKSHELF.* $40

Levertov, Denise. THE COLD SPRING AND OTHER POEMS. (Norfolk, CT): New Directions, (1968). 1st ed. 1/100 ptd by Carol Hammer and signed by Levertov. Fine in dj. *CAPTAIN'S BOOKSHELF.* $500

Levertov, Denise. THE DOUBLE IMAGE. London: Cresset Press, 1946. 1st ed, dj. VF. *JAFFE.* $150

Levertov, Denise. THE FREEING OF THE DUST. (NY): New Directions, (1975). 1st ed. Fine in dj. *CAPTAIN'S BOOKSHELF.* $35

Levertov, Denise. THE POET IN THE WORLD. Cl backed boards, dj. (NY): New Directions, (1973). 1st ed. Signed. VF. *JAFFE.* $45

Levertov, Denise. THREE POEMS. Mt Horeb, WI: Perishable Press, 1968. 1st ed. One of 250. Wraps. Fine. *JAFFE.* $175

Levertov, Denise. THREE POEMS. Mt. Horeb, WI: Perishable Press, 1968. 1st ed. 1/250. Fine in wrappers. *CAPTAIN'S BOOKSHELF.* $125

Levertov, Denise. TO STAY ALIVE. (NY): New Directions, (1971). 1st ed. Fine in dj. *CAPTAIN'S BOOKSHELF.* $35

Levertov, Denise. WITH EYES AT THE BACK OF OUR HEADS. (Norfolk, CT): New Directions, (1959). 1st ed, dj. Signed. VF. *JAFFE.* $150

Levey, Martin. THE MEDICAL FORMULARY OF AL-SAMARQANDI AND THE RELATION OF EARLY ARABIC SIMPLES TO THOSE FOUND IN THE INDIGENOUS MEDICINE OF THE NEAR EAST AND INDIA. Phila, 1967. 1st ed. Dj. *FYE.* $40

Levi, Primo. THE REAWAKENING. Boston: A/LB, 1965. 1st US ed. NF in price clipped dj. Uncommon. *LAME DUCK.* $45

Levi, Primo. THE REAWAKENING. Boston: LB, (1965). 1st ed. Prev owner's rubber-stamp on front and rear eps, o/w Fine in Fine dj. *LOPEZ.* $45

Levi, W.M. THE PIGEON. Columbia, 1945. 2nd ed. 2 colored plts. Staining; ep, prelim pg foxing; pp yellowed; bkpl. Inscribed. *SUTTON.* $65

Levi-Strauss, C. A WORLD ON THE WANE. NY: Criterion Books, (1961). 1st Amer ed. *SILVER.* $25

Levin, Harry. JAMES JOYCE. A CRITICAL INTRODUCTION. New Directions, (1941). 1st ed. Dj darkened, else Fine. *WOOLMER.* $50

Levin, Ira. A KISS BEFORE DYING. NY: Simon and Schuster, 1953. 1st ed. Pp darkened, lt cvr spotting o/w VG in dj (wear, tears, sm scrapes). *MORDIDA.* $35

Levin, Martin (ed). FIVE BOYHOODS. GC: Doubleday, 1962. 1st ed. VG in like dj. *CAPTAIN'S BOOKSHELF.* $30

Levine, Philip. 1933: POEMS. NY: Atheneum, 1974. 1st ed. Fine in wraps. Signed. *CAPTAIN'S BOOKSHELF.* $45

Levine, Philip. 7 YEARS FROM SOMEWHERE. NY: Atheneum, 1979. Fine in wraps, as issued. Inscribed. *CAPTAIN'S BOOKSHELF.* $45

Levine, Philip. A WALK WITH TOM JEFFERSON. NY: Knopf, 1988. 1st ed. Signed on tipped-in leaf. Dj. VF. *JAFFE.* $85

Levine, Philip. ASHES: POEMS NEW AND OLD. NY: Atheneum, 1979. 1st Atheneum ed, pb orig. Fine in wraps. Presentation inscrip. *CAPTAIN'S BOOKSHELF.* $45

Levine, Philip. ON THE EDGE. (Iowa City): The Second Press, 1964. 2nd ed. Fine in wraps. Inscribed. *CAPTAIN'S BOOKSHELF.* $40

Levine, Philip. ON THE EDGE. Iowa City: Stone Wall Press, (1963). 1st ed. One of 225 signed by Levine. Spine sl darkened, else a NF, issued w/o dj. Fellow poet C.K. Williams' owner sig on ffep. *CAPTAIN'S BOOKSHELF.* $1350

Levine, Philip. RED DUST. (Santa Cruz: Kayak, 1971). 1st ed. One of 1200. Fine in wraps. Henry Carlile's owner stamp. *CAPTAIN'S BOOKSHELF.* $60

Levine, Philip. THEY FEED THEY LION: POEMS. NY: Atheneum, 1972. Uncorrected proof. About Fine in ptd wraps. Inscribed. *CAPTAIN'S BOOKSHELF.* $75

Levinrew, Will. DEATH POINTS A FINGER. Mystery League, 1933. 1st ed. Wear bottom of spine, VG in Good+ dj. *BEBBAH.* $20

Levison, J.J. THE HOME BOOK OF TREES AND SHRUBS....NY: 1940. 1st ed. Fine. *SECOND LIFE.* $25

Levitt, Stan. THE CRACKERBARREL PAPERS. Chicago, (1977). 1st ed. VG+ in dj. *PRATT.* $15

Levy, Charles. SPOILS OF WAR. Boston: Houghton Mifflin, 1974. 1st ptg. Minor edgewear w/wrinkle front panel of dj. *AKA.* $40

Lewes, George Henry. ON ACTORS AND THE ART OF ACTING. NY: Henry Holt, 1878. 1st Amer ed. Fine. *DRAMATIS.* $45

Lewin, Michael Z. OUT OF SEASON. Morrow, 1984. 1st ed. VF in dj. *STAHR.* $25

Lewins Robert. LIFE AND MIND ON THE BASIS OF MODERN MEDICINE (MATERIALISM). London, 1877. 1st ed. *FYE.* $75

Lewis, Alfred H. APACHES OF NEW YORK. NY, 1912. 1st ed. Spine faded. VG. *DIAMOND.* $25

Lewis, Alfred Henry. THE BLACK LION INN. NY, 1903. 1st ed. Lt cvr soil, else Fine. *McCLINTOCK.* $35

Lewis, Alfred Henry. WOLFVILLE DAYS. Stokee, (1902). 1st ed. Corners and spine ends worn, o/w VG. *OREGON.* $75

Lewis, C.S. CHRISTIAN REFLECTIONS. London: G. Bles, 1967. 1st ed. Fine in VG torn and chipped dj. *ARCHER.* $30

Lewis, C.S. PERELANDRA. MacMillan, 1944. 1st ed. VG in frayed, soiled dj. *MADLE.* $85

Lewis, C.S. THE PROBLEM OF PAIN. London: Centenary Press, 1940. 1st ed. Fine in NF dj (trifle rubbing). *ARCHER.* $35

Lewis, C.S. TRILOGY OF OUT OF THE SILENT PLANET, PERELANDRA, AND THAT HIDEOUS STRENGTH. NY: MacMillan, 1943-1946. 1st Amer eds. Set is mildly spotted on bindings and page edges and has slight edgewear to dj. Overall VG in VG dj's. *LOPEZ.* $375

Lewis, Cecil. THE TRUMPET IS MINE. London: Peter Davies, 1938. 1st ed. Minor fore-edge foxing. Dj has minor smudging and foxing else NF in NF dj. *GREAT EPIC.* $55

Lewis, Charles L. MATTHEW FONTAINE MAURY, PATHFINDER OF THE SEAS. Annapolis, MD: United States Naval Institute, 1927. Presentation. Blind stamped blue cl. *KNOLLWOOD.* $60

Lewis, Dio. OUR DIGESTION. Phila and Boston: Maclean, 1872. 1st ed. NF in orig grn cl. *SECOND LIFE.* $65

Lewis, Edith. WILLA CATHER LIVING, A PERSONAL RECORD. NY: Knopf, 1953. 1st ed. VG in worn dj. Lacks fep. *SECOND LIFE*. $25

Lewis, Elizabeth F. YOUNG FU OF THE UPPER YANGTZE. Winston, (1932). 1st ed. 265pp. Illus by Kurt Wiese. Announcement of Newberry award, dj flaps pasted to endpaper, pastedown remains reverse of color frontis, cvr wear, corner bumps but Good+. *BEB-BAH*. $40

Lewis, Franklin. THE CLEVELAND INDIANS. Putnam, 1949. 1st ed. Good+ in VG+ dj. *PLAPINGER*. $45

Lewis, H.L. BUTTERFLIES OF THE WORLD. Chicago, 1973. 1st ed. Corrigenda sheet laid in. Dj. *SUTTON*. $55

Lewis, Harry. PULSARS. THREE STATES OF A SINGLE POEM. Orig silk-screen print by Sam Gilliam. Mt. Horeb: Perishable Press, (1974). 1st ed. Ltd to 150. Signed by Walter Hamady. VF. *JAFFE*. $250

Lewis, Henry. THE VALLEY OF THE MISSISSIPPI IL-LUSTRATED. St. Paul: MN Hist Soc, (1967). Bertha Heilbron (ed). 1st complete ed in Eng, ltd to 2000. 78 color plts. Fine in Fine dj. Howes L312. *OREGON*. $50

Lewis, Henry. THE VALLEY OF THE MISSISSIPPI IL-LUSTRATED. St Paul: Minnesota Hist Soc Press, (1967). 1st ed. 78 full-pg color plts. Bertha Heilbron (ed). #1656 of 2000. VF in dj. *ARTIS*. $45

Lewis, Lloyd. CAPTAIN SAM GRANT. Boston, (1950). 1st ed. 512pp, Dj wear and chipping o/w VG+. *PRATT*. $27.50

Lewis, Lloyd. CAPTAIN SAM GRANT. Little Brown, 1950. 1st ed. 1st ed. F in F dj. *OREGON*. $30

Lewis, Meriwether and William Clark. HISTORY OF THE EXPEDI-TION. Prepared for the Press by Paul Allen. In Two Volumes. Phila: Bradford & Inskeep. 1814. 1st ed (less than 2,000 ptd). xxviii, 470; x, 522pp. 5 engr charts. The frontis map, not issued with all copies, is not present in this set. Mid-19th century 1/2 black calf over marbled boards. Title page of vol 1 soiled, occasional stains and text foxing, but overall a pretty decent set. Howes L317. *KARMIOLE*. $3,000

Lewis, Meriwether and William Clark. THE JOURNALS OF THE EXPEDITION UNDER THE COMMAND OF CAPTAINS LEWIS AND CLARK. 2 vols. Nicholas Biddle (ed). NY: LEC, 1962. John Bakeless (intro). 2 fldg maps. One of 1,500 numbered. Bound in full natural buckram. Fine in slipcase. *LAURIE*. $300

Lewis, Oscar (ed). CALIFORNIA IN 1846. DESCRIBED IN LET-TERS FROM THOMAS O. LARKIN. SF: Grabhorn Press, 1934. 1st ed. 9 plts. VG. *OREGON*. $125

Lewis, Oscar and Carroll D. Hall. BONANZA INN: AMERICA'S FIRST LUXURY HOTEL. NY: Knopf, 1939. 1st ed. VG in sl chipped dj. Signed. *CONNOLLY & WADE*. $50

Lewis, Oscar. CALIFORNIA HERITAGE. Crowell, NY, 1949. 1st ed. Review copy. Fine in sl chipped dj. *VARNER*. $35

Lewis, Oscar. HIGH SIERRA COUNTRY. Duell, Sloan, Pearce (1955). 1st ed. Signed. VG in VG dj. *OREGON*. $35

Lewis, Oscar. SAN FRANCISCO, MISSION TO METROPOLIS. Berkeley, Howell-North, 1966. Christmas presentation on halftitle o/w fine. 1st ed. VG. *OREGON*. $15

Lewis, Oscar. SEA ROUTES TO THE GOLD FIELDS. NY: Knopf, 1949. Fldg map. Facs of 1850 map. Orange lea spine. Marbled boards. Fine. *CONNOLLY & WADE*. $35

Lewis, Oscar. SILVER KINGS. NY: Knopf, 1947. 1st ed. VG in Fine dj. Bkpl. *BOHLING*. $37

Lewis, Oscar. SILVER KINGS. NY: Knopf, 1947. 1st ed. VG in Good+ dj. Signed. *CONNOLLY & WADE*. $45

Lewis, Oscar. THE BIG FOUR: THE STORY OF....NY: Knopf, 1938. 1st ed, 3rd prtg. Headband strengthened. NF. *CONNOLLY & WADE*. $35

Lewis, Oscar. THE TOWN THAT DIED LAUGHING. Boston: Lit-tle, Brown, 1955. 1st ed. VG in chipped, Fair dj. *CONNOLLY & WADE*. $30

Lewis, R.W.B. EDITH WHARTON A BIOGRAPHY. NY: Harper & Row, (1975). 1st ed. Fine in dj. *JUVELIS*. $40

Lewis, Roy Harley. WHERE AGENTS FEAR TO TREAD. London: Hale and NY: St. Martin's, 1984. 1st ed. VF in dj. *SILVER DOOR*. $27.50

Lewis, Sinclair. DODSWORTH. Foreword by Clifton Fadiman. NY: Modern Library, (1947). 1st ML edition. Fine in a lightly used dj with a small chip from the head of the spine. *CAPTAIN'S BOOKSHELF*. $20

Lewis, Sinclair. ELMER GANTRY. NY: HB, (1927). 1st, 1st issue with the "G" appearing as a "C". Fine in lightly edgeworn and dusty dj. *CAPTAIN'S BOOKSHELF*. $250

Lewis, Sinclair. MAIN STREET. NY, 1920. 1st ed. Little foxing inside covers and front and rear ep. Fine. *POLYANTHOS*. $150

Lewis, Sinclair. MAIN STREET. NY: Harcourt, Brace & Howe, 1920. Spine ends frayed, front hinge cracked at half-title, but Good. 1st ed, 2nd state, w/battered page-numeral on p. 54. *CHAPEL HILL*. $30

Lewis, Sinclair. THE PRODIGAL PARENTS. GC, NY: Doubleday, Doran & Co., 1938. Orig red cl. Inkstamp on front pastedown, else NF in dj. 1st ed. *CHAPEL HILL*. $45

Lewis, Thomas A. THE GUNS OF CEDAR CREEK. NY, (1988). 1st ed. Fine in dj. *PRATT*. $27.50

Lewis, W.H. LEVANTINE ADVENTURER. THE TRAVELS AND MISSIONS OF THE CHEVALIER D'ARVIEUX 1653-1697. NY, 1963. 232pp. Dj. *O'NEILL*. $25

Lewis, W.J. THE LANGUAGE OF CRICKET. London: Oxford Univ Press, 1934. 1st ed. VG in VG dj. *OLD LONDON*. $45

Lewis, W.M. THE PEOPLE'S PRACTICAL POULTRY BOOK....NY, 1871. 2nd ed. Orig cl. Extrems worn; spine nearly perished; front hinge repaired; bkpl. *SUTTON*. $35

Lewis, Wilmarth. COLLECTOR'S PROGRESS. NY, 1951. 1st ed. Fine in dj w/short tear top spine, little edge rubbed. *POLYANTHOS*. $30

Lewis, Wilmarth. COLLECTOR'S PROGRESS. NY: Alfred Knopf, 1951. 1st ed. Jake Zeitlin's copy w/his sig. Dj. *DAWSON'S*. $40

Lewis, Wyndham. COUNT YOUR DEAD: THEY ARE ALIVE! OR A NEW WAR IN THE MAKING. Cl. London: Lovat Dickson, (1937). 1st ed. One of 1500 ptg. Dj lightly worn, dust soiled. VG. *JAFFE*. $150

Lewis, Wyndham. PALEFACE; THE PHILOSOPHY OF THE MELTING POT. London: Chatto & Windus, (1929). 1st Eng ed. NF. *DORN*. $150

Lewis, Wyndham. REVENGE FOR LOVE. Chicago: Regnery (1952). 1st Amer ed. Name, else VG in dj, sm pieces missing from extrems. *DORN*. $35

Lewis, Wyndham. ROTTING HILL. Chicago: Regnery (1952). 1st Amer ed. VG+ in dj, chips. *DORN*. $40

Lewis, Wyndham. THE APES OF GOD. London: The Arthur Press, 1930. 1st ed. Ltd to 750 signed. Orig cl, dj. Fine. *JAFFE*. $1250

Lewis, Wyndham. THE CHILDERMASS. NY, 1928. 1st Amer ed. Titled Part I, with the promise that Part II would appear the following spring, but it never did. Almost as New. *BOND*. $135

Lewis, Wyndham. THE OLD GANG AND THE NEW GANG. Lon-don: Harmsworth, 1933. 1st ed, 1st binding. Spine darkened, o/w VG in sl worn, darkened dj. *JAFFE*. $125

Lewis, Wyndham. WYNDHAM LEWIS THE ARTIST FROM "BLAST" TO BURLINGTON HOUSE. London: Laidlaw (1939). 1st ed. 3 color plts, 6 half tones. Name, else Fine. *DORN*. $95

Ley, Willy. DRAGONS IN AMBER. Sidgwick & Jackson, 1951. Good. *KNOLLWOOD*. $25

Ley, Willy. ROCKETS AND SPACE TRAVEL, THE FUTURE OF FLIGHT....NY: Viking, 1947. 1st ed. Front board stained, hinge weak. *KNOLLWOOD*. $35

Ley, Willy. ROCKETS, MISSILES, & SPACE TRAVEL. NY: Viking, June 1951. 1st ptg of this title (ROCKETS 1944). Fldg chart laid in. Few spots of wear to extremities. Good. *KNOLLWOOD*. $28

Ley, Willy. THE LUNGFISH, THE DODO & THE UNICORN. Viking, 1948. 1st ed. VG in sl chipped dj. *MADLE*. $25

Leydet, Francois. TIME AND THE RIVER FLOWING: GRAND CANYON. Ed by David Brower. SF, 1964. 1st ed. NF in repaired dj. *FIVE QUAIL*. $40

Leymarie, Jean. THE JERUSALEM WINDOWS. NY: Braziller, (1962). 1st ed. 212pp. 2 Fine full-pg orig lithos. Owner's sig. on front and rear pastedowns as well as the top and fore-edge. Title page somewhat wrinkled, else NF in like dj. *CAPTAIN'S BOOKSHELF*. $900

Li, H.L. THE GARDEN FLOWERS OF CHINA. 18 plts. NY, 1959. Cl, dj. *SUTTON*. $45

Licht, Hans. SEXUAL LIFE IN ANCIENT GREECE. NY, 1953. 1st ed. *FYE*. $40

Licht, Sidney. MUSIC IN MEDICINE. Boston, 1946. 1st ed. Scarce. *FYE*. $50

Lichtenstein, Roy. DRAWINGS AND PRINTS. NY, 1969. 1st ed. Fine. Lacking slipcase. Erratum slip present. *POLYANTHOS*. $350

Lida. POMPOM...THE LITTLE RED SQUIRREL. NY: Harper, 1936. 1st Amer ed. Georges Duplaix (trans). Pict paper-covered boards and cl. Corners sl worn, o/w VG. *ARTIS*. $22.50

Liddell Hart, B.H. HISTORY OF THE SECOND WORLD WAR. NY: Putnam's, 1970. 1st ed. VG+. *ARCHER*. $25

Liddell, Henry George and Robert Scott. GREEK-ENGLISH LEXICON. NY et al: Amer Bk Co. (1882). 8th ed. Full lea. Little rubbed, but sturdy. *SCHOYER'S*. $125

Liddell, Robert. AEGEAN GREECE. London: Jonathan Cape (1954). Dj sl stained. *SCHOYER'S*. $30

Lieb, Fred and Stan Baumgartner. THE PHILADELPHIA PHILLIES. Putnam, 1953. 1st ed. VG. *PLAPINGER*. $110

Lieb, Fred. THE BOSTON RED SOX. Putnam, 1947. 1st ed. VG without dj. *PLAPINGER*. $40

Lieb, Fred. THE BOSTON RED SOX. Putnam, 1947. 2nd ptg. VG. *PLAPINGER*. $40

Lieb, Fred. THE DETROIT TIGERS. Putnam, 1946. 1st ed. VG without dj. *PLAPINGER*. $40

Lieb, Fred. THE DETROIT TIGERS. Putnam, 1946. 1st ed. VG in VG dj. Ffep removed. *PLAPINGER*. $50

Lieb, Fred. THE PITTSBURGH PIRATES. Putnam, 1948. 1st ed. Good without dj. *PLAPINGER*. $45

Lieb, Fred. THE ST. LOUIS CARDINALS. Putnam, 1946. 5th ptg. Good+ in VG dj. *PLAPINGER*. $50

Lieb, Frederick. CONNIE MACK. Putnam, 1945. 1st ed. VG+. *PLAPINGER*. $40

Liebig, C.A. and George Rohe. PRACTICAL ELECTRICITY IN MEDICINE AND SURGERY. Phila, 1890. 1st ed. 383pp. 250 woodcut illus. Scarce. *FYE*. $150

Liebling, A.J. BACK WHERE I CAME FROM. NY: Sheridan House, (1938). 1st ed, 1st book. VG+ in VG dj which is sl chipped at spine ends. *BERNARD*. $275

Liebling, A.J. THE REPUBLIC OF SILENCE. NY: Harcourt, Brace (1947). 1st ed. Fine in price-clipped dj (uniformly spine-darkened with a small spot mid-spine, thus VG. *LOPEZ*. $75

Liebling, A.J. THE WAYWARD PRESSMAN. GC: Doubleday, 1947. 1st ed. VG in dj which has one chip at top edge of front panel, very sl chipping at top spine edge & one hole in center of dj spine. *BERNARD*. $50

Liebow, Averill. ENCOUNTER WITH DISASTER: A MEDICAL DIARY OF HIROSHIMA, 1945. NY, 1970. 1st ed. Dj. *FYE*. $75

Liebowitz, Annie. PHOTOGRAPHS, 1970-1990. NY: Harper Collins, 1991. 1st ed. Signed. As New. *SMITH*. $100

Lienhard, Heinrich. FROM ST. LOUIS TO SUTTER'S FORT, 1846. Trans & ed by Erwin & Elisabeth Gudde. Univ of OK, (1961). 1st ed. VF in F dj. *OREGON*. $35

Liesmann, Frederick J. WHITE BUFFALO. St. Louis: Concordia, 1918. 1st ed. 74pp. Red cl, black. NF. Rare. *CONNOLLY & WADE*. $50

Lieutaud, Joseph. SYNOPSIS OF THE UNIVERSAL PRACTICE OF MEDICINE. EXHIBITING A CONCISE VIEW OF ALL DISEASES, BOTH INTERNAL AND EXTERNAL. Phila, 1816. 1st Eng trans. Full leather, 642pp. Hinges cracked, backstrip rubbed. *FYE*. $200

LIFE AND CHARACTER OF THE HON. JOHN C. CALHOUN, WITH ILLUSTRATIONS. J. Winchester, 1843. 24pp. Acidic pamphlet covers detached. Ex-lib. Good. *BOOK BROKER*. $45

LIFE AND EXPLOITS OF S. GLENN YOUNG. Herrin, IL: Mrs. S. Glenn Young, (c1924). Photos. *SCHOYER'S*. $115

LIFE AND REMINISCENCES OF JEFFERSON DAVIS BY DISTINGUISHED MEN OF HIS TIME. Baltimore, 1890. 1st ed. Contemp lib calf cvrs sl worn, and stained. Rebacked, recased, o/w VG. *DIAMOND*. $45

LIFE AND REMINISCENCES OF JEFFERSON DAVIS BY DISTINGUISHED MEN OF HIS TIME. Baltimore, 1890. 1st ed. 490pp. Shelf wear and chipping at spine extremities, o/w Fine. *PRATT*. $90

LIFE IN AN ANT HILL. Chicago: Albert Whitman, 1940. 1st ed. Good to VG. *BEASLEY*. $30

LIFE OF JEFFERSON DAVIS WITH AN AUTHENTIC ACCOUNT...TOGETHER WITH THE LIFE OF "STONEWALL" JACKSON (By Addey Markenfield.) NY: (1890). 1st ed, thus. 197, 300pp. VG. *McGOWAN*. $45

LIFE, TRAVELS AND OPINIONS OF BENJAMIN LUNDY. INCLUDING HIS JOURNEYS TO TEXAS AND MEXICO. (By Thomas Earle.) Phila., 1847. 1st ed. 316pp. Port, fldg map. Orig cl. Howes E10, listed under compiler Thomas Earle. *GINSBERG*. $1000

Lighthall, William Douw (ed). SONGS OF THE GREAT DOMINION: VOICES FROM THE FORESTS AND WATERS...CANADA. London: Walter Scott, 1889. 1st ed. Pict blue cl bumped, front hinge starting. NF, bright. BAL #2604. *BLUE MOUNTAIN*. $45

Lightwood, James T. CHARLES DICKENS AND MUSIC. London: Charles H. Kelly, (1912). 1st ed. 12mo, 177pp, blue cloth stamped in gold, bkpl. Fine. *GREAT EXPECTATIONS*. $27.50

Lightwood, James T. THE ROMANCE OF THE CYCLISTS' TOURING CLUB. London, 1928. 1st ed. Minor wear to extremities, else VG. *OLD LONDON*. $100

Lilford (Lord). NOTES ON THE BIRDS OF NORTHAMPTONSHIRE AND NEIGHBOURHOOD. London, 1895. Frontis, 23 plts, 44 wood-engr, fldg map. 2 vols. Pp xvi,352; viii,(1),315. Orig cl. Lt rubbing; some foxing prelim pp Vol 1. *SUTTON*. $275

Liliencrantz, O.A. THE THRALL OF LEIF THE LUCKY, A STORY OF VIKING DAYS. McClurg, 1902. 1st ed. 354pp. Illus by Troy & Margaret Kinney. Some cvr wear but pict cvr bright. VG+. *BEBBAH*. $25

Lilienthal, Howard. THORACIC SURGERY: THE SURGICAL TREATMENT OF THORACIC DISEASE. Phila, 1925. 1st ed. 2 vols. 694, 600pp. *FYE.* $250

Lillywhite, Bryant. LONDON SIGNS. London: George Allen & Unwin Ltd. (1972). 1st ed. 25 plts (5 in color). Grn cl, gilt spine. Dj. Cardboard slipcase. *KARMIOLE.* $50

Lin-Le (pseud of Augustus F. Lindley). TI-PING TIEN-KWOH: THE HISTORY OF THE TI-PING REVOLUTION INCLUDING A NARRATIVE....London: Day & Son, 1866. 2 vols, (xx),424; (viii), pp425-842. Tall 8vo. 3/4 leather, spines badly rubbed and chipped. and quite weak on joints. Tear in dedication page repaired. Fldg frontis, 2 fldg color maps, 18 chromolithos. *SCHOYER'S.* $300

Lincoln, Abraham and Stephen A. Douglas. POLITICAL DEBATES BETWEEN HON. ABRAHAM LINCOLN AND HON. STEPHEN A. DOUGLAS IN THE CELEBRATED CAMPAIGN OF 1858, IN ILLINOIS. (Columbus: Follett, Foster and Company, et al., 1860). 1st ed, later issue. Orig pebble grain cloth. Howes L-338. Occas light foxing, spine ends somewhat frayed, corners a little worn, covers sl spotted, but generally very pleasing. *PIRAGES.* $175

Lincoln, Abraham and Stephen A. Douglas. POLITICAL DEBATES BETWEEN...IN THE CELEBRATED CAMPAIGN OF 1858. Columbus: (Follett, Foster), 1860. 1st ed, later issue (rule above the imprint on copyright pg; no press figure at the bottom of p.17). Orig brn cl w/blind dec on cvrs, gilt titling. Very nice (lt spotting). *BOOK BLOCK.* $225

Lincoln, Abraham. NEW LETTERS AND PAPERS OF LINCOLN. Comp by Paul M. Angle. Boston and NY: Houghton Mifflin, 1930. 1st ed. Bkpl. VG. *WEBER.* $30

Lincoln, Abraham. THE COLLECTED WORKS OF ABRAHAM LINCOLN. New Brunswick: Rutgers Univ Press. c1953. 8 vols. Roy P. Basler, ed. Gray cl over boards, gilt and clue lettered spine. History Book Club ed. *BOOKMINE.* $125

Lincoln, C. Eric. THE AVENUE, CLAYTON CITY. NY: Morrow, (1988). 1st ed, 1st novel. Orig cl-backed boards. Fine in dj. *CHAPEL HILL.* $25

LINCOLN CENTENNIAL ASSOCIATION PAPERS. Springfield: The Association, 1928. 92pp. Cl, pict boards. *SCHOYER'S.* $15

Lincoln, Charles H. CORRESPONDENCE OF WILLIAM SHIRLEY, GOVERNOR OF MASSACHUSETTS....NY: 1912. 1st ed. 2 vols. Orig cl, sm emb lib stamp on title pp, a few white numbers on lower spines. *GINSBERG.* $75

Lincoln, F.C. THE MIGRATION OF AMERICAN BIRDS. NY, 1939. 12 colored plts. Chipped dj. *SUTTON.* $35

Lincoln, Joseph C. GALUSHA, THE MAGNIFICENT. NY: Appleton, 1921. 1st ed. 3 minor tears at top of spine, else VG. *BURCHAM.* $75

Lincoln, Joseph C. THE BRADSHAWS OF HARNISS. NY: Appleton, 1943. 1st ed. VG in chipped dj. *SECOND LIFE.* $25

Lincoln, William S. ALTON TRIALS: OF WINTHROP S. GILMAN, WHO WAS INDICTED....NY, 1838. 1st ed. 158,111pp. Frontis. Contemp half morocco, embossed lib stamp and paper label. Howes L348. *GINSBERG.* $125

Lind, L.R. STUDIES IN PRE-VESALIAN ANATOMY. Phila, 1975. 1st ed. *FYE.* $75

Lindbergh, Anne Morrow. CHRISTMAS IN MEXICO, 1927. Harcourt Brace Jovanovich, (1971). 1st ltd ed, pub as New Yr's greeting to friends. Slip laid in. Red boards, gilt-stamped white shelfback. Fine in Nice glassine dj. *AUTHORS OF THE WEST.* $35

Lindbergh, Charles. "WE." NY: (Putnam), 1927. 1st ed. Pub's bright blue cl w/gilt stamping. Dj (few minor chips top, bottom of spine; sl sunned). In pub's dec board slipcase (sl rubbed). Frontis port has repaired short tear; contemp newspaper clipping laid in (left offsetting mark). *BOOK BLOCK.* $225

Lindbergh, Charles. "WE." NY: Putnam, 1927. 1st trade ed. Almost Fine in Almost VG dj. *AARD.* $30

Lindeboom, G.A. DUTCH MEDICAL BIOGRAPHY: A BIOGRAPHICAL DICTIONARY OF DUTCH PHYSICIANS AND SURGEONS, 1475-1975. Amsterdam, 1984. 1st ed. Dj. *FYE.* $125

Lindemann, Jack (ed). THE CONFLICT OF CONVICTIONS. Phila, (1968). 1st ed. Lt dj wear o/w Fine. *PRATT.* $25

Linderman, Frank B. RECOLLECTIONS OF CHARLEY RUSSELL. Univ of OK Press, 1963. 1st ed. Fine in sl chipped dj. *VARNER.* $50

Lindig, Otto. 100 YEARS HISTORICAL RECOLLECTIONS OF GILLESPIE COUNTY, 1870-1970. Stonewall, TX: Otto Lindig, 1970. 1st ed. Fine. *GIBBS.* $35

Lindley, J. THE THEORY OF HORTICULTURE. London, 1840. 1st ed. Pp xvi,387,(32pp-ads). Orig cl worn, soiled, skillfully rebacked. Lt soiling, creasing in text, few brn spots. Hand stamp, eps renewed. *SUTTON.* $87

Lindquist, A.S. JESS SWEETON, TEXAS LAWMAN. Naylor, 1961. 1st ptg. Inscribed. Fine in Good dj, sm waterstain. *VARNER.* $25

Lindquist, G.E.E. et al. THE RED MAN IN THE UNITED STATES: AN INTIMATE STUDY. NY: George H. Doran, (1923). 1st ed. VG. *LAURIE.* $30

Lindsay, David Moore. CAMP FIRE REMINISCENCES, OR, TALES OF HUNTING AND FISHING IN CANADA AND THE WEST. Boston: Dana Estes & Co., (1912). 1st ed. 37 plts. Uncut, unopened. VF. *OREGON.* $100

Lindsay, David T. THE NINTH PLAGUE. London, n.d. VG. *MADLE.* $25

Lindsay, David. A VOYAGE TO ARCTURUS. NY: Macmillan, 1963. 1st Amer ed. Ownership stamp front and rear eps, o/w VF in dj. *LOPEZ.* $75

Lindsay, J. Seymour. IRON AND BRASS IMPLEMENTS OF THE ENGLISH HOUSE. London: Alec Tiranti. 1970. 1st ed. Dj. *KARMIOLE.* $45

Lindsay, Jack. BYZANTIUM INTO EUROPE. London, 1952. 485pp. 1st ed. Lib name perforated on title, else Fine. *O'NEILL.* $37.50

Lindsay, Jack. DIONYSOS. Nietzsche Contra Nietzsche. London: The Fanfrolico Press. (1928). Ed ltd to 500. *KARMIOLE.* $175

Lindsay, Jack. LEISURE AND PLEASURE IN ROMAN EGYPT. (NY) Barnes & Noble (1966). *SCHOYER'S.* $25

Lindsay, Jack. STORM AT SEA. London: Golden Cockerel Press, 1935. One of 250 signed. 1/4 blue morocco, ptd cl over boards; title in gilt on spine; teg. Spine faded, cvrs shelf worn. VG. *HELLER.* $225

Lindsay, Vachel. COLLECTED POEMS. Cl-backed boards with paper labels. NY: Macmillan, 1923. 1st ed. One of 400 signed. Front inner hinge weak, corners bumped, spine label tanned, o/w VG. *JAFFE.* $125

Lindsay, Vachel. COLLECTED POEMS. Macmillan, 1923. 1st ed. VG+, tiny nick, fep. *AUTHORS OF THE WEST.* $30

Lindsay, Vachel. EVERY SOUL IS A CIRCUS. MacMillan, 1929. 1st ed. Fine. *AUTHORS OF THE WEST.* $40

Lindsay, Vachel. THE GOLDEN WHALES OF CALIFORNIA AND OTHER RHYMES....Macmillan, 1920. 1st ed. Dec cvr. Fine, clippings tipped in. *AUTHORS OF THE WEST.* $30

Lindsay, Vachel. THE GOLDEN WHALES OF CALIFORNIA. NY, 1920. 1st ed. Spine little sunned, extremities sl rubbed, eps little foxed. NF. *POLYANTHOS.* $30

Lindsay, Vachel. THE GOLDEN WHALES OF CALIFORNIA....NY, 1920. 1st ed. Pict cl. Spine sl darkened, o/w VG. *DIAMOND.* $45

Lindsay, Vachel. THE LITANY OF WASHINGTON STREET. NY: The Macmillan Co, 1929. 1st ed. Boards rubbed and sl faded top, front edge, color pict dj darkened and chipped at edges. Inscribed. Internally bright, NF. *BLUE MOUNTAIN.* $75

Lindsey, David L. A COLD MIND. NY: Harper & Row, 1983. 1st ed. Fine in dj. *MORDIDA.* $40

Lindsey, David L. HEAT FROM ANOTHER SUN. NY: Harper & Row, 1984. 1st ed. VF in dj. *MORDIDA.* $35

Lindsey, David L. IN THE LAKE OF THE MOON. NY: Athenaeum, 1988. 1st ed. VF in dj. *MORDIDA.* $30

Lindsey, David L. SPIRAL. NY: Athenaeum, 1986. 1st ed. Fine in dj. *MORDIDA.* $30

Lindsley, A. L. SKETCHES OF AN EXCURSION TO SOUTHERN ALASKA. (Portland, OR, 1881). 1st ed. Privately ptd. 73pp. Orig ptd wrappers, rebacked. Howes L357. Rare. Inscribed. Withdrawn stamp. *GINSBERG.* $200

Lingenfelter, Richard E. (ed). DEATH VALLEY LORE CLASSIC TALES....Reno: Univ of NV, (1988). 1st ed. Fine in Fine dj. *BOOK MARKET.* $25

Lingenfelter, Richard E. PRESSES OF THE PACIFIC ISLANDS, 1817-1867. LA: The Plantin Press, 1967. Ed ltd to 500. Fldg map, 6 plts (1 fldg), 5 woodcuts. Owner inscrip ffep. *KARMIOLE.* $75

Lingenfelter, Richard E. STEAMBOATS ON THE COLORADO RIVER, 1852-1916. Tucson, 1978. VF in Fine dj. *FIVE QUAIL.* $45

Link, Mae and Hubert Coleman. MEDICAL SUPPORT OF THE ARMY AIR FORCES IN WORLD WAR II. Washington, 1955. 1st ed. *FYE.* $100

Linklater, E. THE VOYAGE OF THE CHALLENGER. GC, 1972. Dj chipped. *SUTTON.* $40

Linklater, Eric. THE CRUSADER'S KEY. NY: Knopf, 1933. 1st US ed. Fine- in Fine- dj. *AARD.* $35

Linscott, Eloise Hubbard. FOLK SONGS OF OLD NEW ENGLAND. NY: Macmillan, 1939. 1st ed. Dj (sm pieces missing & wrinkles), else fairly bright. *AKA.* $43

Linsley, John S. M.D. JERSEY CATTLE IN AMERICA. NY: Burr, 1885. 1st ed. 744pp. Worn cl (front spine loose, rear cl soiled). Scattered foxing. Very nice. *SECOND LIFE.* $200

Linssen, E.F. (ed). MEDICAL PHOTOGRAPHY IN PRACTICE. London, 1961. 1st ed. *FYE.* $100

LIONEL LINCOLN; OR, THE LEAGUER OF BOSTON. (By James Fenimore Cooper.) NY: Charles Wiley, 1825, 1824. 1st ed. 2 vols. xii,263; 270pp. Orig brn calf-backed marbled boards, red lea spine label. Bkpl. Pp. 77-8 corner torn off (no loss). *WEBER.* $275

Lipman, Jean et al. YOUNG AMERICA: A FOLK-ART HISTORY. NY: Hudson Hills Press, 1986. NF in NF dj. *BACKROOM.* $40

Lipman, Jean. AMERICAN FOLK ART IN WOOD, METAL AND STONE. N.p: Pantheon, 1948. 1st ed. Fine. *CONNOLLY & WADE.* $75

Lipman, Jean. RUFUS PORTER. YANKEE PIONEER. NY: Potter, 1968. 1st ed, 1st ptg. VG in VG dj. *BACKROOM.* $70

Lipman, Jean. RUFUS PORTER. YANKEE PIONEER. NY: Clarkson N. Potter, 1968. 1st ed. 22 plts in full color, 102 in black & white. VF in Fine dj. *CONNOLLY & WADE.* $45

Lippincott, Horace M. EARLY PHILADELPHIA AND ITS PEOPLE, LIFE AND PROGRESS. Phila, 1917. 1st, ltd ed. Rebacked, bright orig front cover. Spot corner back cover. Contents Fine. *HEINOLDT.* $25

Lippmann, Friedrich. THE ART OF WOOD-ENGRAVING IN ITALY IN THE FIFTEENTH CENTURY. London: Bernard Quaritch, 1888. 4to. Orig leather-backed pebbled cloth, top edge gilt, others uncut. xxii, 179 pages. 1st ed in English. Spine rubbed, worn at head. *OAK KNOLL.* $150

Lipsner, Captain Benjamin. THE AIRMAIL—JENNIES TO JETS. Chicago: Wilcox & Follett, 1951. 1st ed. NF in scarce Good+ dj. *GREAT EPIC.* $25

Lish, Gordon. DEAR MR. CAPOTE. NY: HRW., (1983). 1st ed. Inscribed. Fine in NF dj. *LOPEZ.* $60

Liss, Howard. THE MICKEY MANTLE ALBUM. Hawthorn, 1966. 1st ed. Good+ in VG+ dj. *PLAPINGER.* $75

Liss, Howard. THE WILLIE MAYS ALBUM. Hawthorn, 1966. 1st ed. Good+ in VG+ dj. *PLAPINGER.* $75

LISTER & THE LISTER WARD IN THE ROYAL INFIRMARY OF GLASGOW: A CENTENARY CONTRIBUTION. Glasgow, 1927. 1st ed. 132pp + 28 plts, some fldg. *FYE.* $60

LISTER AND THE LIGATURE. A LANDMARK IN THE HISTORY OF MODERN SURGERY. New Brunswick, NJ, 1925. 1st ed. Wrappers. *FYE.* $35

Lister, Joseph. SIX PAPERS BY JOSEPH LISTER WITH A SHORT BIOGRAPHY AND EXPLANATORY NOTES BY SIR RICKMAN GODLEE. London, 1921. *FYE.* $50

Lister, Joseph. THE THIRD HUXLEY LECTURE. London, 1907. 1st ed. *FYE.* $80

Lister, Raymond. HAMMER AND HAND. AN ESSAY. Cambridge: Ptd for his friends by the University Printer. Christmas, 1969. Ltd to 500. *KARMIOLE.* $75

Lister, Robert and Florence (eds). IN SEARCH OF MAYA GLYPHS. Santa Fe: Museum of NM Press, (1970). 1st ed. Good in chipped dj. *SILVER.* $30

Liston, Robert. ELEMENTS OF SURGERY. Phila, 1837. 1st Amer ed. 540pp. *FYE.* $200

LITCHFIELD COUNTY CENTENNIAL CELEBRATION HELD AT LITCHFIELD, CT. 13TH & 14TH AUG 1851. 1st ed. 212pp. Wraps in cloth bound folder and slipcase specially made for it. Leather label. Light stains. *HEINOLDT.* $25

Litchfield, Jack. THE CANADIAN JAZZ DISCOGRAPHY 1916-1980. Toronto: Univ of Toronto Press, 1982. 1st ed. Issued w/o dj. Like new. *BEASLEY.* $35

Lithgow, William. TRAVELS & VOYAGES THROUGH EUROPE, ASIA, AND AFRICA, FOR NINETEEN YEARS. Leith, 1814. 12th ed. Contemp half calf, viii,412pp. Attractive. *O'NEILL.* $175

Littauer, Capt. Vladimir S. BE A BETTER HORSEMAN. NY: The Derrydale Press, (1941). One of 1,500. Bottom corner bumped. *WEBER.* $75

LITTLE CAPTAIN TAR. London, (1950). Story Verrent. Devised by David White. Moveable bk. *BOOKFINDERS INTL.* $30

Little, Constance and Gwyneth. THE BLACK CURL. GC: Doubleday, 1953. 1st ed. Store stamp bottom edge, dates stamped rear pastedown, little soiled. VG+ in NF dj. *BEASLEY.* $30

Little, Constance and Gwyneth. THE BLACK DREAM. GC: Doubleday, 1952. 1st ed. Store stamp bottom edge, dates rear pastedown, o/w NF in NF dj. *BEASLEY.* $30

Little, Nina Fletcher. THE ABBY ALDRICH ROCKEFELLER FOLK ART COLLECTION. Hutchinson of London, 1957. 1st ed. VG in sl worn slipcase. *BACKROOM.* $165

LITTLE ORPHAN ANNIE. Chicago: Pleasure Books, 1935. 3 double-pg pop-ups. Illus bds. Sl scuffling edges, internally excellent condition. Scarce. Pop-up bk. *BOOKFINDERS INTL.* $210

LITTLE RED RIDING HOOD. NY: McLoughlin Brothers, n.d. One of "Aunt Friendly's Colored Picture Books." Pict linen, dec wraps. Wrappers somewhat worn at spine & corners. VG. *JAFFE.* $150

Little, Richard Henry. BETTER ANGELS. NY, 1928. 1st ed. 43pp. VG+. *PRATT.* $20

Littlefield, Bill. PROSPECT. Boston: Houghton Mifflin, 1989. 1st ed, 1st bk. Fine in dj. *CAPTAIN'S BOOKSHELF*. $35

Littlefield, Lyman. REMINSCENCES OF LATTER-DAY SAINTS....Logan, 1888. 1st ed. 208pp. Orig. brn dec cl, frontis, sl exterior wear, owner stamps, o/w VG. *BENCHMARK*. $100

Littlefield, Lyman. THE MARTYRS. Salt Lake, 1882. 1st ed, 120 pp, orig blue cloth, writing ffep, lacks 2 ports, o/w VG+. *BENCHMARK*. $25

Littleton, William G. THE BATTLE BETWEEN ALABAMA AND THE KEARSARGE, OFF CHERBOURG, FRANCE, SUNDAY, JUNE 19, 1864. (Phila, 1933). 1st ed. Wrappers. NF. *McGOWAN*. $37.50

Littleton, William G. THE CUMBERLAND, THE MONITOR AND THE VIRGINIA (POPULARLY CALLED THE MERRIMAC). (Phila: Privately ptd, 1933). 1st ed. Wrappers. NF. *McGOWAN*. $37.50

Livermore, Mary. MY STORY OF THE WAR: A WOMAN'S NARRATIVE OF FOUR YEARS PERSONAL EXPERIENCE AS A NURSE...Hartford, 1889. 700pp. Faded spine o/w VG. *PRATT*. $45

Livermore, Mary. MY STORY OF THE WAR: A WOMAN'S NARRATIVE OF FOUR YEARS PERSONAL EXPERIENCE AS A NURSE IN THE UNION ARMY. Hartford, 1890. 700pp. 1st ed. *FYE*. $150

Livermore, Mary. THE STORY OF MY LIFE...WITH HITHERTO UNRECORDED INCIDENTS AND RECOLLECTIONS OF THREE YEARS' EXPERIENCE AS AN ARMY NURSE IN THE GREAT CIVIL WAR. Hartford, 1898. 730pp. 1st ed. *FYE*. $75

LIVES AND SPEECHES OF ABRAHAM LINCOLN AND HANNIBAL HAMLIN. NY: W.A. Townsend & Co; Columbus: Follett, Foster & Co, 1860. 406pp. 2 heavily foxed ports; wood-cut pl. Yellow eps. Orig cl, spine sunned. *SCHOYER'S*. $65

Livingston, Edward M. A CLINICAL STUDY OF THE ABDOMINAL CAVITY & PERITONEUM. NY, 1932. 1st ed. *FYE*. $50

Livingston, Flora V. (ed). CHARLES DICKENS'S LETTERS TO CHARLES LEVER. Cambridge: Harvard Univ Press, 1933. 1st ed. 12mo, 65pp, brown cloth, bkpl. VG+ in Good+ dj. *GREAT EXPECTATIONS*. $40

Livingston, Robert B., MD, ed. NARCOTIC DRUG ADDICTION PROBLEMS. Bethesda: DHEW/NIH/NIMH, 1959. 1st ed. Fine, issued w/o dj. *BEASLEY*. $45

Livingston, Samuel. THE DIAGNOSIS AND TREATMENT OF CONVULSIVE DISORDERS IN CHILDREN. Springfield, 1954. 1st ed. Dj. *FYE*. $50

Livingstone, David. MISSIONARY TRAVELS AND RESEARCHES IN SOUTH AFRICA; INCLUDING A SKETCH OF SIXTEEN YEARS' RESIDENCE IN THE INTERIOR OF AFRICA. NY, 1858. 1st Amer ed. 732pp + fldg maps and plts. *FYE*. $150

Livingstone, David. THE LAST JOURNALS OF DAVID LIVINGSTONE IN CENTRAL AFRICA. NY: Harper, 1875. Horace Waller (ed). 1st ed. (ii),541pp. Fldg map. Sl rubbed, spine sl frayed, o/w VG ex-lib. *WORLDWIDE*. $45

Livy. THE HISTORY OF EARLY ROME. Aubrey de Selincourt (trans). Verona: LEC, 1970. One of 1500 ptd, signed by Giovanni Mardesteig; illus, signed by Raffaele Scorzelli. Fine in slipcase. *CAPTAIN'S BOOKSHELF*. $125

Llewellyn, Richard. HOW GREEN WAS MY VALLEY. NY: Macmillan, 1940. 1st Amer ed. Bumped head of spine, else VG in About VG dj chipped 3/4" deep at crown and part of front panel. Adv rev copy w/slip. *BETWEEN COVERS*. $100

Llosa, Mario Vargas. See Vargas Llosa, Mario.

Lloyd, Everett. LAW WEST OF THE PECOS....Naylor, 1936. 5th ptg. Fine. *VARNER*. $30

Lloyd, J.U. and C.G. DRUGS AND MEDICINES OF NORTH AMERICA. VOLUME I—RANUNCULACEAE. Cincinnati, 1885. 1st ed. 304pp. Exceptionally Fine. *FYE*. $150

Lloyd, James T. LLOYD'S STEAMBOAT DIRECTORY, AND DISASTERS ON THE WESTERN WATERS. Cincinnati: James T. Lloyd & Co, 1856. 1st ed. 46 maps, 100 engrvs. Howes L406. *HUDSON*. $475

Lloyd, John Uri. ETIDORPHA. Dodd-Mead, 1901. VG. *MADLE*. $35

Lloyd, John Uri. OUR WILLIE. Cincinnati: John G. Kidd & Son, 1934. 1st ed. Orig grn cl. Sm bkseller's handstamp, but Fine, bright in NF dj. *CHAPEL HILL*. $30

Lloyd, John Uri. RED-HEAD. NY: Dodd, Mead, 1903. 1st ed. Frontis. 9 plts. Teg. Untrimmed. VF. *CONNOLLY & WADE*. $67.50

Lloyd, John Uri. STRINGTOWN ON THE PIKE. NY: Dodd, Mead, 1900. 1st ed. Orig tan cl w/mounted cover photo. Fine in NF dj. *CHAPEL HILL*. $75

Lloyd, John Uri. STRINGTOWN ON THE PIKE. NY: Dodd, Mead, 1901. NF. *CONNOLLY & WADE*. $25

Lloyd, John Uri. WARWICK OF THE KNOBS. NY: Dodd, Mead, 1901. 1st ed. Orig tan cl w/mounted cover port. Fine, bright in VG dj. *CHAPEL HILL*. $75

Lloyd, John Uri. WARWICK OF THE KNOBS. NY: Dodd, Mead, 1901. 1st ed. NF. *CONNOLLY & WADE*. $42.50

Lloyd's Register of Shipping. LLOYD'S REGISTER OF AMERICAN YACHTS: A LIST....1910. NY, 1910. 48 color plts. Inner hinges strengthened, cvrs rubbed. *LEFKOWICZ*. $125

Lobb, Theophilus. A TREATISE ON DISSOLVENTS OF THE STONE, AND ON CURING THE STONE AND GOUT BY ALIMENT. London, 1739. 1st ed. Full leather, 450pp. Ex-lib, leather scuffed, hinges cracked. Contents VG. Scarce. *FYE*. $300

Lobel, Anita. POTATOES, POTATOES. Harper & Row, (1967). Unpaginated. Inscribed. VG+ w/bkpl in VG dj w/chips. *BEBBAH*. $35

Lobel, Arnold. ON MARKET STREET. Greenwillow, (1981). 1st ed. Unpaginated. Illus by Anita Lobel. Fine in VG dj w/closed tear, touch of soil. Inscribed, w/drwg of apple. *BEBBAH*. $25

LOCAL LAWS OF THE STATE OF INDIANA, PASSED AT THE THIRTIETH SESSION OF THE GENERAL ASSEMBLY, BEGUN ON THE FIRST MONDAY IN DECEMBER, 1845. Indianapolis: J.P. Chapman, 1846. Newly bound in cl w/gilt-stamped lea spine label. Ptd wrap edgeworn. Nice. *BOHLING*. $75

Locher, A. WITH STAR AND CRESCENT. Phila, 1889. 634pp. *O'NEILL*. $35

Locher, A. WITH STAR AND CRESCENT. Phila: Aetna Pub Co, 1891. 634pp. Dark grn dec cl stamped in gilt and black, a little shaken. Aeg. *SCHOYER'S*. $45

Lochte, Dick. SLEEPING DOG. NY: Arbor, (1985). 1st ed. Signed. Fine in Fine dj. *UNGER*. $35

Locke, A. THE TIGERS OF TRENGGANU. NY: Scribner, (1954). 1st US ed. Photos, maps. NF in Good+ dj. *MIKESH*. $30

Locke, E.W. THREE YEARS IN CAMP AND HOSPITAL. Boston, 1870. 1st ed. 408pp. Title page soiled and spotted. Scarce. *FYE*. $225

Locke, Edwin. TUBERCULOSIS IN MASSACHUSETTS. Boston, 1908. 1st ed. *FYE*. $75

Locke, John. AN ESSAY CONCERNING HUMAN UNDERSTANDING: with THOUGHTS ON THE CONDUCT OF UNDERSTANDING. To which is prefixed The Life of the Author. In 3 vols. London: Allen and West, 1795. Large 12mo. xv,271pp; xv,264pp; and xiv,308pp. Contemp full polished calf, morocco labels and numerals. Some wear to hinges, early name on title, but attractive. *HARTFIELD*. $385

Locker, Thomas. THE YOUNG ARTIST. Dial, (1989). 1st ed. Signed. Fine in Fine dj. *BEBBAH*. $30

Locker-Lampson, Frederick. MY CONFIDENCES, AN AUTOBIOGRAPHICAL SKETCH ADDRESSED TO MY DESCENDANTS. NY: Charles Scribner's Sons, 1896. 1st US ed. Rubbed along hinges; back cover spotted. *OAK KNOLL*. $55

Lockley, R.M. THE CHARM OF THE CHANNEL ISLANDS. London: Evans Brothers, (1950). 1st ed. A bit faded, bumped, else VG. *WREDEN*. $22

Lockridge, Ross, Jr. RAINTREE COUNTY. Boston: Houghton Mifflin, 1948. NF in price-clipped, VG pict dj (few chips). 1st ed. *CHAPEL HILL*. $65

Lockwood, Charles and Adamson, H.C. TRAGEDY AT HONDA. Phila: Chilton (1960). VG in VG dj. *AARD*. $30

Lockwood, Frank and Donald Page. TUCSON—THE OLD PUEBLO. Phoenix: Manuf. Stationers, n.d. 1st ed. 15 plts. Hinges reinforced. Signed. *OREGON*. $90

Lockwood, Frank C. WITH PADRE KINO ON THE TRAIL. Univ of AZ Bulletin, Vol. 5, #2, Feb. 15, 1934. 1st ptg. Fold-out map. VG. *VARNER*. $80

Lockwood, George Browning. THE NEW HARMONY COMMUNITIES. Marion, IN: Chronicle Company, 1902. 24 plts. Ex-lib. Good. *BOHLING*. $35

Lockwood, Luke Vincent. COLONIAL FURNITURE IN AMERICA NY: Scribners, 1926. 3rd ed, 1st ptg. VG. *BACKROOM*. $175

Lodge, David. SMALL WORLD. Macmillan, 1984. 1st Amer ed. Fine in dj. *STAHR*. $25

Lodge, Henry Cabot. LIFE AND LETTERS OF GEORGE CABOT. Boston, 1877. 1st ed. (11),615pp. Orig cl. Howes L421. *GINSBERG*. $125

Lodge, R.B. BIRD HUNTING THROUGH WILD EUROPE. NY: Appleton, 1909. 125 photos. Dec cl, teg. Ex libris. VG+. *MIKESH*. $37.50

Loeb, Jacques. COMPARATIVE PHYSIOLOGY OF THE BRAIN AND COMPARATIVE PSYCHOLOGY. NY, 1900. 1st ed. *FYE*. $50

Loeb, Jacques. FORCED MOVEMENTS, TROPISMS, AND ANIMAL CONDUCT. Phila, 1918. 1st ed. *FYE*. $60

Loeb, Leo. THE BIOLOGICAL BASIS OF INDIVIDUALITY. Springfield, 1945. 1st ed. *FYE*. $45

Loechel, William. MEDICAL ILLUSTRATION: A GUIDE FOR THE DOCTOR-AUTHOR AND EXHIBITOR. Springfield, 1964. 1st ed. 273 illus. Inscribed and signed. Dj. *FYE*. $100

Loening, Grover C. MONOPLANES AND BIPLANES. NY: Munn, 1911. 1st ed. Orig pict cl, bkpl removed, sm embossed lib stamp, a few black numbers on spine. *GINSBERG*. $100

Loesser, Arthur. MEN, WOMEN & PIANOS: A SOCIAL HISTORY. NY: Simon & Schuster, 1954. 1st ptg. Fine in dj. *BANCROFT*. $20

Lofland, John. THE POETICAL AND PROSE WRITINGS OF JOHN LOFLAND, M.D. Baltimore: John Murphy; Pittsburgh: George Quigley, 1846. 1st ed. 332pp. Orig cl w/gilt-stamped spine. Flyleaves wanting, spine ends and corners lightly rubbed, traces of light foxing, else VG. *CHAPEL HILL*. $75

Loft, Abram. VIOLIN AND KEYBOARD: THE DUO REPERTOIRE. NY: Grossman, 1973. 2 vols. VG in dj. *BANCROFT*. $25

Loftie, Rev. W.J. PICTURESQUE SCOTTISH SCENERY. NY and London, 1875. T.L. Rowbotham (illus). Elaborate gilt stamped beveled boards. Worn corners, gilt edges. VG. *CULLEN*. $120

Lofting, Hugh. DOCTOR DOLITTLE AND THE SECRET LAKE. Lippincott, (1948). Stated 1st ed. 366pp. Drwgs by author; frontis;

cvr pastedown. Sl edgewear, faint round mark to cvr pict VG in dj w/chips, creases, piece missing top of spine. Good. *BEBBAH*. $45

Lofting, Hugh. DOCTOR DOLITTLE IN THE MOON. Stokes, (1928). 1st Amer ed. 307pp. Illus by author. VG+. *BEBBAH*. $55

Lofting, Hugh. THE STORY OF DOCTOR DOLITTLE. Stokes, 1920. 1st Amer ed. 180pp. Illus by author, color frontis, cvr pastedown. Cvr wear, soil, faint number on spine, but VG. *BEBBAH*. $60

Logan, H.C. BUCKSKIN AND SATIN. Stackpole, 1954. 1st ed. Fine in Fine dj. *VARNER*. $30

Logan, Herschel C. BUCKSKIN AND SATIN: THE LIFE OF TEXAS JACK (J.B. OMOHUNDRO). Harrisburg: Stackpole, 1954. 1st ed. Fine in NF dj. *CONNOLLY & WADE*. $35

Logan, Herschel. BUCKSKIN AND SATIN. Harrisburg: Stackpole, (1954). Dec boards in dj. *DAWSON'S*. $50

Logan, Jeffrey (ed). THE COMPLETE BOOK OF OUTER SPACE. The Gnome Press, 1953. Fine in dj. *MADLE*. $150

Logan, John A. THE GREAT CONSPIRACY: ITS ORIGIN AND HISTORY. NY, 1886. 1st ed. A little cover wear o/w VG+. *PRATT*. $45

Loines, Elma. THE CHINA TRADE POST-BAG OF THE SETH LOW FAMILY OF SALEM AND NY 1829-1873. Manchester, ME: Falmouth Pub House, 1953. 1st ed. Dj. VG. *WEBER*. $35

Lom, Herbert. ENTER A SPY: THE DOUBLE LIFE OF CHRISTOPHER MARLOWE. London: Merlin Press, 1978. 1st ed. Fine in sl rubbed dj. *MORDIDA*. $35

Lomax, Alan. THE FOLK SONGS OF NORTH AMERICA. GC: Doubleday, (1960). 12th ptg. Fine- in VG- dj. *AARD*. $25

Lomax, Alfred. PIONEER WOOLEN MILLS IN OREGON. Binfords & Mort, (1941). 1st ed. 8 plts. Ltd ed binding of morocco and wool w/few moth-eaten areas in wool. Uncut, unopened. VG. *OREGON*. $55

Lomax, John A. ADVENTURES OF A BALLAD HUNTER. NY: Macmillan, 1947. Adv rev copy w/slip and promo material. Fine in lightly used dj. *BEASLEY*. $751

Lomax, John A. and Alan. AMERICAN BALLADS AND FOLK SONGS. NY: Macmillan, 1934. 1st ed. One of 500 signed by the Lomaxes. Front inner hinge strained, cream spine tanned, o/w VG. *JAFFE*. $125

London, Charmian. THE BOOK OF JACK LONDON. NY: The Century Co. 1921. 1st Amer ed. 2 vols. Grn cl, gilt spines; spine lightly faded. *KARMIOLE*. $125

London, Charmian. THE LOG OF THE SNARK. NY: Macmillan, 1916. 2nd impression. Orig gilt dec lt blue cl. Very minor wear extremes. Sm unobtrusive stain top edge rear pg. VG+. *GREAT EPIC*. $45

London, Jack. ADVENTURE. NY, 1911. 1st ed. Spine ends rubbed, front hinge weak. Good. *McCLINTOCK*. $45

London, Jack. BEFORE ADAM. MacMillan, 1907. 1st ed. Almost VG. *MADLE*. $50

London, Jack. BEFORE ADAM. NY, 1907. "Published February 1907." 1st ed. Illus Charles Livingston Bull. Uncut. Spine minimally sunned, extremities minimally rubbed, tiny stain top edge. Fine. *POLYANTHOS*. $95

London, Jack. CHILDREN OF THE FROST. NY, (1913). Regent Press rpt. VG. *McCLINTOCK*. $15

London, Jack. DUTCH COURAGE AND OTHER STORIES. NY, 1922. 1st ed. "Published September 1922." Ink marks on Table of Contents pp, owner's inscrip, traces of removed scotch tape inside covers and feps, covers little soiled. NF. *POLYANTHOS*. $120

London, Jack. HEARTS OF THREE. NY, 1920. 1st ed. "Published September 1920." Sl edge rubbed, traces of removed scotch tape inside covers and feps. Fine. *POLYANTHOS*. $100

London, Jack. JOHN BARLEYCORN. The Century Co, 1913. 1st ed. VG+. *AUTHORS OF THE WEST.* $125

London, Jack. LOST FACE. NY, (1913). Regent Press rpt. VG. *McCLINTOCK.* $15

London, Jack. LOVE OF LIFE AND OTHER STORIES. NY, 1907. 1st ed. "Published September 1907." Spine little cocked, little edge rubbed, faint traces of removed scotch tape inside covers and feps, front hinge repaired. NF. *POLYANTHOS.* $100

London, Jack. MICHAEL BROTHER OF JERRY. NY, 1917. 1st ed. "Published November 1917." Spine sunned, traces of removed scotch tape inside covers and feps. Fine. *POLYANTHOS.* $60

London, Jack. MICHAEL BROTHER OF JERRY. NY, 1917. 1st ed. Fine. *McCLINTOCK.* $145

London, Jack. MOON-FACE AND OTHER STORIES. NY, 1906. 1st ed. "Published September 1906." Spine little soiled, little edge rubbed, traces of removed scotch tape inside covers and feps. NF. *POLYANTHOS.* $100

London, Jack. MOON-FACE AND OTHER STORIES. NY: Macmillan, 1906. 1st ed. Dec blue cl gilt, teg. Spine sl darkened. Little cvr rubbing. Gilt top edge sl silverfished. Ink name on pastedown, o/w VG. BAL 11895. *DIAMOND.* $95

London, Jack. REVOLUTION AND OTHER ESSAYS. NY, 1910. 1st ed. "Published March, 1910." 1st issue binding. Spine sunned, extremities rubbed, traces of removed scotch tape inside covers and feps. VG. Scarce. *POLYANTHOS.* $150

London, Jack. STORIES OF HAWAII. NY: Appleton, Century, 1965. Advance rev copy, slip. Fine in lightly used dj. *BEASLEY.* $50

London, Jack. TALES OF THE FISH PATROL. NY, 1905. 1st ed. "Published September 1905." Illus George Varian. Spine little sunned, extremities little rubbed, traces of removed scotch tape inside covers and feps. NF. *POLYANTHOS.* $100

London, Jack. THE ABYSMAL BRUTE. NY: Century, 1913. 1st ed. Smooth grn cl stamped in dark grn and yellow, tape marks on front and back pastedowns and fly-leaves, some wear to tips, spine sl sunned. Generally VG. *JUVELIS.* $150

London, Jack. THE ABYSMAL BRUTE. NY: Century, 1913. 1st ed. Light grn cl stamped in black & yellow. Very minor wear. Nice. BAL 11945. *SECOND LIFE.* $225

London, Jack. THE CALL OF THE WILD. Franklin Library, 1977. 1st Franklin "ltd edition". Bound in full leather, silk eps, bkmk; aeg. Fine. *AUTHORS OF THE WEST.* $40

London, Jack. THE CALL OF THE WILD. Illus by Henry Varnum Poor. LA: LEC, 1960. Ltd to 1500 numbered, signed by Poor. Slipcase. *KARMIOLE.* $150

London, Jack. THE CALL OF THE WILD. NY: Macmillan, 1903. 1st ed. Sl stain to copyright and contents pages, else VG+ in heavily tape-repaired and reinforced jacket, some pieces missing. *LAME DUCK.* $1500

London, Jack. THE CRUISE OF THE SNARK. NY, 1911. 1st ed. "Published June 1911." Teg. Spine sunned, extremities little rubbed, traces of removed scotch tape inside covers and feps. NF. *POLYANTHOS.* $200

London, Jack. THE FAITH OF MEN AND OTHER STORIES. NY, (1904). Regent Press rpt. Good. *McCLINTOCK.* $15

London, Jack. THE GAME. London: Wm. Heinemann, 1905. 1st Eng ed. Pict dark blue cl illus in red & white. Gilt lettering. Spine darkened. Spine gilt dull. Cvr gilt rubbed. Little cvr rubbing. One page repaired. Small name stamp on ep, o/w VG. BAL 11886. *DIAMOND.* $75

London, Jack. THE GAME. NY, 1905. 1st ed, 1st issue. "Published June 1905." Henry Hutt, T.C. Lawrence (illus, decs). Spine little sunned, extremities rubbed, traces of removed scotch tape inside covers and feps. NF. *POLYANTHOS.* $125

London, Jack. THE GAME. NY: Macmillan, 1905. 1st ed, w/rubber stamp A. 182,(6)pp (ads). Color frontis, pict title in black and brown, plts (incl in pagination), illus. Pict cl, teg. A few stains on cvrs, else VG. *WREDEN.* $85

London, Jack. THE HOUSE OF PRIDE AND OTHER TALES OF HAWAII. NY, 1914. Regent Press rpt. VG. *McCLINTOCK.* $15

London, Jack. THE HUMAN DRIFT. NY, 1917. 1st ed. "Published February 1917." Extremities, spine minimally rubbed, traces of removed scotch tape inside covers and feps. Fine. *POLYANTHOS.* $200

London, Jack. THE IRON HEEL. NY & London, 1908. 1st ed. VG. *McCLINTOCK.* $95

London, Jack. THE LITTLE LADY OF THE BIG HOUSE. Macmillan, 1916. 1st ed. Pict cvr, frontis. Cl rippled some, but bright, VG. *AUTHORS OF THE WEST.* $75

London, Jack. THE MUTINY OF THE ELSINORE. NY, 1914. 1st ed. "Published September 1914." Colored frontis, spine little sunned, extremities sl rubbed, rear cover very sl soiled. Fine. *POLYANTHOS.* $175

London, Jack. THE PEOPLE OF THE ABYSS. NY: Macmillan, 1903. 1st ed. 3982 ptd. Spine bit dulled, rubbed; front board quite bright. *BEASLEY.* $350

London, Jack. THE SCARLET PLAGUE. NY, 1915. 1st ed. "Published May 1915." Illus Gordon Grant. Faint traces of removed scotch tape inside covers and feps, lower spine little rubbed, tiny area rubbed rear cover. Fine. *POLYANTHOS.* $125

London, Jack. THE SEA-WOLF. NY: Macmillan, 1904. 1st ed, mixed issue. Blue pict cl, teg. Some cvr wear. Spine lettering rubbed off. Inner hinges rehinged. Erasures on fly. Foxing & sl staining on some pp. Some page margins sl stained. Gilt top edge dull & rubbed, o/w text VG. BAL 11882. Title page not a cancel. Copyright notices dated 1903 & 1904. BAL's "B" binding (no priority assigned), w/lettering on spine in white. *DIAMOND.* $45

London, Jack. THE SON OF THE WOLF. Boston & NY, 1900. 1st ed, according to Sissons and Martens bibliography 2nd ptg and Woodbridge's 2nd state of pub's imprint at bottom of spine. Fine. *McCLINTOCK.* $500

London, Jack. WHITE FANG. NY: Macmillan, 1906. 1st ed. Blue-gray pict cl. 8 color plts. Cvrs sl rubbed. Front pict ep folded. Inner front hinge starting, o/w VG. BAL 11896. Cancel title-page on laid paper. *DIAMOND.* $100

Long, A.W. IRISH SPORT OF YESTERDAY. Boston and NY: Houghton Mifflin Co., 1923. 1st US ed. Minor wear to extremities, else VG-NF. *OLD LONDON.* $35

Long, Amelia Reynolds. 4 FEET IN THE GRAVE. Bart House, 1945. 1st ed. Fine in wraps. *MADLE.* $35

Long, E.B. THE SAINTS AND THE UNION, UTAH TERRITORY DURING THE CIVIL WAR. Urbana, (1981). 1st ed. 310pp. VG+ in dj. *PRATT.* $25

Long, E.B. with Barbara Long. THE CIVIL WAR DAY BY DAY. NY, 1971. Contemp rprt. VG+. *PRATT.* $30

Long, Elias A. THE HOME FLORIST. Springfield, OH: Chas. Reeser, 1886. 2nd ed, rev, enl. Fine. *SECOND LIFE.* $65

Long, Frank Belknap. THE HORROR FROM THE HILLS. Sauk City: Arkham House, 1963. 1st ed. Variant w/Arkham cancel on copyright pg. Fine in NF dj. *OTHER WORLDS.* $85

Long, Frank Belknap. THE HOUNDS OF TINDALOS. Arkham House, 1946. 1st ed. Fine in dj. *MADLE.* $210

Long, Frank Belknap. THE RIM OF THE UNKNOWN. Sauk City: Arkham House, 1972. 1st ed. Traces of browning else Fine in dj. *OTHER WORLDS.* $30

Long, George. ATLAS OF CLASSICAL GEOGRAPHY. NY, (1856), 76pp; 52 tinted maps, 26 plts. Rebound, part of orig front cover transposed. *HEINOLDT.* $35

Long, Haniel. PITTSBURGH MEMORANDA. Santa Fe: Writers' Editions. (1935). Ed ltd to 1000 numbered, signed, this w/addt'l signed inscrip. Dj. *KARMIOLE.* $125

Long, Huey P. EVERY MAN A KING: THE AUTOBIOGRAPHY OF HUEY P. LONG. New Orleans: National Book Co., (1933). 343pp. Dj price-clipped, w/chips, small piece missing. *AKA.* $50

Long, James T. GETTYSBURG...THE ORIGINAL STORY....N.p.: n.p., (Gettysburg) n.d. (circa 1900). Frontis. Illus pink wraps sl darkened around edges. Sm chip on top at spine. 1st pg browned, else Fine. *CONNOLLY & WADE.* $45

Long, James Thomas. GETTYSBURG. HOW THE BATTLE WAS FOUGHT. Harrisburg, PA, 1891. 2nd ed. Wrappers, minor chipping at top of backstrip, else VG. *McGOWAN.* $45

Long, John. JOHN LONG'S VOYAGES AND TRAVELS IN THE YEARS 1768-1788. London, 1791. 1922 reprint. Lakeside Classic. Ed by Milo Milton Quaife. Fldg map. VG+. *PRATT.* $45

Long Lance, Chief Buffalo Child. LONG LANCE. NY: Cosmopolitan, 1928. 1st ed. Owner name, date front pastedown, o/w VG in dj missing 1 1/2" at base of spine, few other edge chips. *LOPEZ.* $85

Long, Margaret. THE SHADOW OF THE ARROW. DEATH VALLEY 1849-1949. Caxton: Caldwell, 1950. 2nd, rev, enl ed. Dj has closed tears but is complete. Fine in Good dj. *CONNOLLY & WADE.* $47.50

Long, Stephen H. THE NORTHERN EXPEDITIONS OF. THE JOURNALS OF, 1817 & 1823. Minnesota Hist Soc, 1978. 1st ed. VF in dj. *ARTIS.* $25

Long, Stephen H. VOYAGE IN A SIX-OARED SKIFF TO THE FALLS OF SAINT ANTHONY IN 1817. Phila: H. Ashmead, 1860. 87(1)pp, map. Ptd wraps, lt stain & waviness of lower portion throughout, spine chipped, else VG. Howes L445 *BOHLING.* $200

Long, W.J. FOLLOWING THE DEER. Boston, 1903. 1st ed. VG+. *MIKESH.* $37.50

Longacre, J.J. (ed). CRANIOFACIAL ANOMALIES: PATHOGENESIS AND REPAIR. Phila, 1968. 1st ed. 200+ photos. *FYE.* $100

Longacres, Edward G. THE MAN BEHIND THE GUNS, A BIOGRAPHY OF GENERAL HENRY J. HUNT. NY, (1977). 1st ed. Light dj wear o/w Fine. *PRATT.* $25

Longfellow, Henry Wadsworth. COPLAS DE DON JORGE MANRIQUE, Translated from the Spanish, with an Introductory Essay on the Moral and Devotional Poetry of Spain by Henry W. Longfellow. Boston: Allen & Ticknoe, 1833. 1st ed. Binding A, BAL 12054. Short tear in ffep, else VG in sl spine-faded boards with paper spine label being somewhat soiled. *CAPTAIN'S BOOKSHELF.* $150

Longfellow, Henry Wadsworth. TALES OF A WAYSIDE INN. Boston: Ticknor & Fields, 1863. 1st Amer ed, 1st ptg, 1/1863 on title pg (changed to 1864 in 2nd ptg). Orig purple cl, teg. Spine faded, sl foxing to vignette title, signature separation couple of places, else VG. Custom maroon cl chemise, leather spine label, matching slipcase. Printing A of pub's catalog, w/Tales of a Wayside Inn unpriced, described as "Nearly ready" on p11. BAL 12136. *CHAPEL HILL.* $300

Longfellow, Henry Wadsworth. THE COURTSHIP OF MILES STANDISH, AND OTHER POEMS. Boston: Ticknor & Fields, 1858. Spine tips and upper corners lightly rubbed, else NF w/early New Orleans bkseller's ticket. 1st Amer ed, 1st ptg, w/title page dated MDCCCLVIII and w/"treacherous wine" on p. 124, line 3. BAL 12122. *CHAPEL HILL.* $195

Longfellow, Henry Wadsworth. THE COURTSHIP OF MILES STANDISH. Indianapolis: Bobbs-Merrill Co, c1903. 1st ed thus. Illus by Howard Chandler Christy. Fine. *BOOKMINE.* $85

Longfellow, Henry Wadsworth. THE DIVINE TRAGEDY. Boston: James R. Osgood & Co., 1871. Spine faded, early (1872) gift inscript and trace of card or bkpl removal on front fly, else a VG 1st ed, probable 1st issue. BAL 12157. *CHAPEL HILL.* $45

Longfellow, Henry Wadsworth. THE MASQUE OF PANDORA AND OTHER POEMS. Boston: Osgood, 1875. 1st ed. 12mo, 146pp. Prev owner's name, name stamp. Fine-. *AARD.* $50

Longfellow, Henry Wadsworth. THE SONG OF HIAWATHA. Boston, NY, & Cambridge, 1891. 1st ed. Suede binding state. Rebacked w/matching buckram keeping most of orig spine, covers intact. Teg. Owner blind stamp, else interior Fine. *McCLINTOCK.* $47.50

Longfellow, Henry Wadsworth. THE SONG OF HIAWATHA. Boston: Ticknor and Fields, 1855. 1st Amer ed. Blind stamped brown cl. VG to NF. *JUVELIS.* $350

Longfellow. Henry Wadsworth. THE SONG OF HIAWATHA. Boston: Ticknor and Fields, 1855. 1st Amer ed, 1st ptg. (iv),316pp. Brn cl bumped and rubbed, chipped at head & tail of spine. Title in gilt w/blind rules on spine. VG. *BLUE MOUNTAIN.* $150

Longhurst, John E. (trans). ALFONSO DE VALDES AND THE SACK OF ROME. Univ of NM Press, 1952. 1st ed. VG+. *MAD DOG.* $15

Longley, John Lewis. ROBERT PENN WARREN: A COLLECTION OF CRITICAL ESSAYS. NY: NY Univ Press, 1965. 1st ed. Fine in price clipped dj w/sm tears. *CAPTAIN'S BOOKSHELF.* $20

Longman, C.J. and Walrond, Col. H. ARCHERY (BADMINTON LIBRARY). London: Longmans, Green, and Co., 1894. 1st ed. Some wear to extremities, else VG. *OLD LONDON.* $65

Longman, C.J. and Walrond, Col. H. ARCHERY (BADMINTON LIBRARY). London and Boston: Longmans, Green, and Co., 1894. 1st Amer ed. Minor foxing, else VG-NF. *OLD LONDON.* $65

Longman, C.J. and Walrond, Col. H. ARCHERY (BADMINTON LIBRARY). London and Bombay: Longmans, Green, and Co., 1901. Reissue. Minor bump, minor wear to extremities, else VG-NF. *OLD LONDON.* $45

Longmore, Thomas. A TREATISE ON GUNSHOT WOUNDS. Phila, 1862. 1st separate ed. 132pp. VF. *FYE.* $400

Longstreet, Augustus B. GEORGIA SCENES, CHARACTERS, INCIDENTS, ETC...BY A NATIVE GEORGIAN. NY: Harper, 1851. 2nd ed. 214pp. 12 plts. Orig cl. Howes L448. *GINSBERG.* $100

Longstreet, Helen D. LEE AND LONGSTREET AT HIGH TIDE: GETTYSBURG IN THE LIGHT OF THE OFFICIAL RECORDS. Gainesville, GA, author, 1905. 2nd ed. Orig cl, spine faded and browned. Howes L450. *GINSBERG.* $75

Longstreet, Stephen. WAR CRIES ON HORSEBACK. GC, (1970). 1st ed. 335pp. Dj wear, o/w VG+. *PRATT.* $25

Longworth, Alice Roosevelt. CROWDED HOURS. NY: Scribner, 1933. 1st ed. VG in Almost VG dj. *AARD.* $25

Longworth, Alice Roosevelt. CROWDED HOURS. NY: Charles Scribner's Sons, 1933. 1st ed. Bkpl. Burgundy cl, gilt spine, titles. VG. *PARMER.* $35

Longyear, John M. ARCHAEOLOGICAL INVESTIGATIONS IN EL SALVADOR. Cambridge: Peabody Museum, Memoirs, Vol 9, No. 2, 1944. 15 plts. VG+. *SILVER.* $100

Lonn, Ella. RECONSTRUCTION IN LOUISIANA AFTER 1868. NY, 1918. 1st ed. Presentation copy. NF. *McGOWAN.* $150

Looker, S.J. THE NATURE DIARIES & NOTE BOOKS OF RICHARD JEFFERIES, ETC. Essex, UK: Grey Walls, 1941. NF. *MIKESH.* $47.50

Loomis, Alfred F. YACHTS UNDER SAIL. NY: William Morrow & Company, 1933. Age-darkened, lightly soiled. Interior VG. *PARMER.* $30

Loomis and Nasatir. PEDRO VIAL AND THE ROADS TO SANTA FE. Univ of OK, (1967). 1st ed. VF in Fine dj. *OREGON.* $50

Loomis, C. Grant. WHITE MAGIC. Cambridge, 1948. NF. *POLYANTHOS.* $30

Loomis, Eben J. AN ECLIPSE PARTY IN AFRICA, CHASING SUMMER ACROSS THE EQUATOR IN THE U.S.S. PENSACOLA. Boston: Roberts Bros, 1896. Gilt illus grey cl, teg, deckle edges, wear to corners & extremities, o/w Nice. *KNOLLWOOD.* $165

Loomis, Edward. END OF A WAR. London: Heinemann, (1958). 1st Eng ed, 1st bk. Fine in dj. *HELLER.* $50

Loomis, Noel. THE TEXAN-SANTA FE PIONEERS. Univ of OK, (1958). 1st ed. Fldg map. VF in Fine dj. *OREGON.* $50

Loornis, Elias, A TREATISE ON ASTRONOMY. NY: Harper, 1879 (1865). Rebound, blue cl, gilt titling on spine, new eps; marbled edges. Foxing on frontis tissue, o/w clean, bright. 8 plts. *KNOLLWOOD.* $70

Loos, Anita. A MOUSE IS BORN. NY: Doubleday, 1951. 1st ed. Fine; dj w/minor edgewear, usual spine fade. *ELSE FINE.* $25

Loos, Anita. BUT GENTLEMEN MARRY BRUNETTES. NY: Boni & Liveright, 1928. 1st ed. Fine; dj w/lt edgewear. *ELSE FINE.* $95

Lopez, Barry. ARCTIC DREAMS. NY: Scribner's, (1986). 1st ed. Signed. Fine in dj. *AUTHORS OF THE WEST.* $50

Lopez, Barry. ARCTIC DREAMS. London: Macmillan, (1986). 1st British ed. Signed. Fine in dj. *AUTHORS OF THE WEST.* $40

Lopez, Barry. CROSSING OPEN GROUND. Charles Scribner's Sons, (1987). 1st ed. Signed. Fine in dj. *AUTHORS OF THE WEST.* $25

Lopez, Barry. CROSSING OPEN GROUND. NY: Scribner's, (1988). 1st ed. Fine in dj. Signed. *LOPEZ.* $65

Lopez, Barry. CROW & WEASEL. SF: North Point, 1990. 1st ed, 1st issue with gold stamping on cover. Fine in NF dj. *ROBBINS.* $45

Lopez, Barry. CROW AND WEASEL. SF: North Point Press, 1990. 1st ed. Fine (of the second issue, without gold stamping on the front cover) in Fine dj and signed. *LOPEZ.* $125

Lopez, Barry. CROW AND WEASEL. SF: North Point Press, 1990. 1st issue w/gold stamping on front cover which was removed before the 1st ptg was complete and does not appear on later ptgs. Fine in Fine dj. *LOPEZ.* $85

Lopez, Barry. DESERT NOTES. Kansas City: Sheed, Andrews, McMeel, (1976). 1st ed. VG in VG dj. *OREGON.* $35

Lopez, Barry. GIVING BIRTH TO THUNDER, SLEEPING WITH HIS DAUGHTER. Kansas City: Sheed Andrews and McMeel, (1977). Fine in dj (lightly rubbed at extremities of spine, as is usual—the dj stock is a glossy but unlaminated paper). *LOPEZ.* $150

Lopez, Barry. OF WOLVES AND MEN. Charles Scribner's Sons, (1978). 1st ed. Signed. Bkpl, Fine in dj. *AUTHORS OF THE WEST.* $60

Lopez, Barry. OF WOLVES AND MEN. NY: Scribner's, (1978). 2nd prtg. Name whited out; signed. NF in dj. *LOPEZ.* $40

Lopez, Barry. OF WOLVES AND MEN. NY: Scribner's, (1978). 1st ed. Owner name, address. NF in dj. *LOPEZ.* $100

Lopez, Barry. RIVER NOTES. Kansas City: Andrews & McMeel, (1979). 1st ed. Fine in NF price-clipped dj (short tear upper edge rear panel). Signed. *LOPEZ.* $150

Lopez, Barry. RIVER NOTES. Kansas City: Andrews & McMeel, (1981). 1st ed. Fine in Fine dj. *UNGER.* $75

Lopez, Barry. THE DISCOVERY OF NORTH AMERICA. Univ Press of KY, (1990). 1st ed. Signed. New in dj. *AUTHORS OF THE WEST.* $30

Lopez, Barry. THE REDISCOVERY OF NORTH AMERICA. (Lexington): Univ Press of Kentucky, (1991). 1st ed. Fine in Fine dj and signed. *LOPEZ.* $75

Lopez, Barry. THE REDISCOVERY OF NORTH AMERICA. (Lexington): Univ Press of Kentucky, (1990). 1st ptg. *LOPEZ.* $35

Lopez, Barry. WINTER COUNT. NY: Scribner's, (1981). 1st ed. Signed. Fine in Fine dj. *UNGER.* $100

Lorac, E.C.R. DISHONOUR AMONG THIEVES. London: Collins Crime Club, 1959. 1st ed. Name on fep o/w Fine in dj. *MORDIDA.* $60

Lorac, E.C.R. MURDER BY MATCHLIGHT. London: Collins Crime Club, 1945. 1st ed. Name on front pastedown o/w VG in dj w/couple of closed tears and tiny nicks. *MORDIDA.* $90

Lorant, Stefan. THE NEW WORLD. NY (1946), 1st ed. 292pp. Boxed, de luxe. *HEINOLDT.* $35

Lorant, Stefan. THE NEW WORLD: THE FIRST PICTURES OF AMERICA MADE BY JOHN WHITE AND JACQUES LE MOYNE AND ENGRAVED BY THEODORE DE BRY...AND THE VIRGINIA COLONY 1585-1590. NY: Duell, Sloan, Pearce, 1946. 1st ed. Fine in VG dj. *CONNOLLY & WADE.* $85

Lorca, Frederico Garcia. See Garcia Lorca, Frederico.

Lord Cohen of Birkenhead. SHERRINGTON: PHYSIOLOGIST, PHILOSOPHER AND POET. Springfield, 1958. 1st Amer ed. *FYE.* $45

Lord, Eliot. COMSTOCK MINING AND MINERS. Berkeley: Howell-North, 1959. 1st ed thus. Fldg map in text, fldg diagram, fldg map in rear pocket. NF in Good+ dj. *CONNOLLY & WADE.* $55

Lord, John. FRONTIER DUST. Hartford, 1926. 1st ed. Ltd to 1000. VG; spine label chipped. *VARNER.* $45

Lord, Joseph and Henry. A DEFENSE OF DR. CHARLES T. JACKSON'S CLAIMS TO THE DISCOVERY OF ETHER. Boston, 1848. 1st separate ed. 37pp. Water stained, rear wrapper detached. Ex-lib. *FYE.* $350

Lord, Priscilla Sawyer and Daniel S. Foley. THE FOLK ARTS AND CRAFTS OF NEW ENGLAND. NY: Chilton Books, 1965. 1st ed. VG to NF. *BACKROOM.* $75

Lord, Theodore A. A SUMMARY OF THE CASE OF GENERAL FITZ-JOHN PORTER. SF: 1883. 2nd ed. Wrappers, front wrap starting to split along joint, else NF. *McGOWAN.* $45

Lord, Walter. A TIME TO STAND. NY, 1961. 1st ed. Light dj wear o/w Fine. *PRATT.* $30

Lorde, Audre. FROM A LAND WHERE OTHER PEOPLE LIVE. Detroit: Broadside Press, (1973). 1st ed. Fine in wrappers. Adv rev copy w/pub's mimeographed info. Scarce. *BETWEEN COVERS.* $100

Lore, John M. Jr. AN ATLAS OF HEAD AND NECK SURGERY. Phila, 1973. 2nd ed. 2 vols. Ex-lib. *FYE.* $50

Lorentz, Pare (ed). THE ROOSEVELT YEAR: A PHOTOGRAPHIC RECORD. NY: Funk & Wagnalls, 1934. Stated 1st ptg. Dj. *SCHOYER'S.* $50

Lorenz, D. E. NEW MEDITERRANEAN TRAVELLER. NY: Revell (1929). 16th (1930) ed. Fldg maps. *SCHOYER'S.* $20

Lorimer Norma. BY THE WATERS OF CARTHAGE. NY: James Pott. London: Hutchinson, 1906. *SCHOYER'S.* $35

Loring, George B. A VINDICATION OF GENERAL SAMUEL HOLDEN PARSONS...TREASONABLE CORRESPONDENCE DURING THE REVOLUTIONARY WAR. Salem, Ma, 1888, 1st ed. 38pp. Orig printed wrappers, spine chipped. *GINSBERG.* $50

Lorraine, M.J. THE COLUMBIA UNVEILED. LA: Times-Mirror Press, 1924. Fldg map. Pict cl. Inscribed. VG. *SCHOYER'S.* $65

Lorton, William. OVER THE SALT LAKE TRAIL IN THE FALL OF '49. LA: Privately ptd, 1957. 1st ed, ltd to 150. Fine. *BOOK MARKET.* $100

LOS ANGELES GUIDE. NY, 1941. American Guide Series. WPA guide. 1st ptg, no dj. *SCHOYER'S.* $30

LOSS OF HIS MAJESTY'S SHIP CENTAUR OF SEVENTY-FOUR GUNS, THE 23RD OF SEPTEMBER, 1782; AND MIRACULOUS PRESERVATION OF THE PINNACE....London: Ptd for Thomas Tegg, n.d. 18cm. Frontis. Modern 1/2 lea, marbled paper over boards. Split (approx 1") on frontis, else VG. *PARMER.* $85

Lossing, Benson J. A BIOGRAPHY OF JAMES A GARFIELD. NY, Henry Goodspeed (1882) 840pp. Cl worn & soiled. Fair. *OREGON.* $40

Lossing, Benson J. A HISTORY OF THE CIVIL WAR 1861-65. 16 parts. NY, (1912). 9 x 12 inches, 512pp. Frontis portraits in color, wraps. VG. *PRATT.* $90

Lossing, Benson J. A HISTORY OF THE CIVIL WAR, 1861-65. War Mem Assn, NY, 1912. Rebound by hand in new buckram, orig front cover & spine transposed. *HEINOLDT.* $50

Lossing, Benson J. HARPERS POPULAR CYCLOPEDIA OF U. S. HISTORY. 2 vols. NY 1892. 1631pp. Over 1000 engr. Rebacked, new eps. *HEINOLDT.* $25

Lossing, Benson J. THE PICTORIAL FIELD-BOOK OF THE REVOLUTION; OR, ILLUSTRATIONS.....NY: Harper & Brothers, 1851-52. 2 vols. 1st ed in bk form. Color frontis. Contemp 3/4 calf, buckram. Extrems a bit scuffed, front hinges cracking, else generally VG. *WREDEN.* $95

Losson, Christopher. TENNESSEE'S FORGOTTEN WARRIORS, FRANK CHEATHAM AND HIS CONFEDERATE DIVISION. Knoxville, (1989). 1st ed. 352pp. Stain on front cover, apparently a printing defect, o/w Fine in dj. *PRATT.* $22.50

Lothrop, Eleanor. THROW ME A BONE. NY: Whittlesey House, (1948). Signature; spine and top board faded. Good. *ARCHAEOLOGIA.* $35

Lothrop, S.K. TREASURES OF ANCIENT AMERICA. NY: Skira/Crown, 1972. New ed. Rose/burgundy cl w/gilt spine and cover titles. Tipped in color illus. NF. *PARMER.* $125

Lothrup, S.K. et al. ROBERT WOODS BLISS COLLECTION PRE-COLUMBIAN ART. NY: Phaidon Pub, (1959). 2nd ed, rev. 162 color and b/w plts, maps. 3 lib perforation stamps. Cl front cvr sl faded 1" bottom. Contents VG+. *SILVER.* $150

Lothrup, S.K. TREASURES OF ANCIENT AMERICA. NY: Skira/Crown, 1972. New ed. Tipped-in color illus. NF. *PARMER.* $125

Lothrup, S.K. TREASURES OF ANCIENT AMERICA. Geneva: Skira, (1964). 1st ed. 85 tipped-in color plts. Lt wear, contents VG. No dj. *SILVER.* $75

Loti, Pierre. AN ICELAND FISHERMAN. Guy Endore (trans), Yngue Berg (illus). Stockholm: Ptd for the LEC by Norstedt & Soner, 1931. First thus. Fine in box. Signed by Berg. Ptd on handmade linen rag paper by Van Gelder Zonen. *SECOND LIFE.* $50

Loti, Pierre. LIVES OF TWO CATS. Trans by M.B. Richards. Illus. by C.E. Allen. Boston: (Richards), 1900. 1st ed. Pict grn cl, teg. Fine. *CAPTAIN'S BOOKSHELF.* $50

Loud, Gordon. THE MEGIDDO IVORIES. Chicago: Univ Chicago Press, 1939. 8 figs, 63 plts. Vol. LII of the Oriental Institute Publications. Good. *ARCHAEOLOGIA.* $650

Loudon, J.C. AN ENCYCLOPAEDIA OF AGRICULTURE. London, 1826 (1825). Pp xvi,1226. Contemp 1/2 leather worn at extrems; edges very scuffed, early bkpls. *SUTTON.* $250

Loudon, J.C. AN ENCYCLOPAEDIA OF GARDENING. London, 1878. New ed. Mrs. Louden (ed). Orig cl (some foxing, minor joint cracking). Very solid. *SUTTON.* $195

Loudon, J.C. AN ENCYCLOPAEDIA OF TREES AND SHRUBS....London, 1869 (1842). Recent buckram. Name. *SUTTON.* $135

Loughridge, R.M. ENGLISH AND MUSKOKEE DICTIONARY. St. Louis, 1890. Orig cloth w/gilt title. Used, worn, frayed; paper darkened and somewhat brittle, 1st few leaves cracked at hinge, hinges strengthened, sabbath lib markings. *BOHLING.* $150

LOUIS AGASSIZ FUERTES AND THE SINGULAR BEAUTY OF BIRDS. F.G. Marcham (ed). 60 colored plts. NY, 1971. Dj. *SUTTON.* $95

LOUISE NEVELSON: ATMOSPHERES AND ENVIRONMENTS. Intro Edward Albee. NY: Clarkson Potter/Whitney Museum, (1980). 1st ed. Fine in dj. *CAPTAIN'S BOOKSHELF.* $50

Louys, Pierre. THE TWILIGHT OF THE NYMPHS. London: Fortune Press, (1928). 1st ed thus. One of 1200 numbered. Dj. Fine. *MUELLER.* $75

Louys, Pierre. THE TWILIGHT OF THE NYMPHS. N.p.: Pierre Louys Society. 1927. 28 color plts, each w/a tissue guard. Ed ltd to 1,250. *KARMIOLE.* $45

Love, Frank. MINING CAMPS AND GHOST TOWNS. LA: Westernlore, 1974. 1st ed. VF in VF dj. *OREGON.* $35

Lovecraft, H.P. and August Derleth. THE LURKER AT THE THRESHOLD. Arkham House, 1945. 1st ed. Fine in dj. *MADLE.* $100

Lovecraft, H.P. and August Derleth. THE SURVIVOR AND OTHERS. Sauk City: Arkham House, 1957. 1st ed. NF in browned dj. *OTHER WORLDS.* $100

Lovecraft, H.P. and August Derleth. THE SURVIVOR AND OTHERS. Arkham House, 1957. 1st ed. Fine in dj. *MADLE.* $100

Lovecraft, H.P. and August Derleth. THE WATCHERS OUT OF TIME AND OTHERS. Sauk City: Arkham House, 1974. 1st ed. NF in Almost Fine dj. *OTHER WORLDS.* $40

Lovecraft, H.P. and Divers Hands. THE DARK BROTHERHOOD AND OTHER PIECES. Sauk City: Arkham House, 1966. 1st ed. Fine in NF dj w/dust soiling to rear. *OTHER WORLDS.* $100

Lovecraft, H.P. and Divers Hands. THE DARK BROTHERHOOD AND OTHER PIECES. Sauk City: Arkham House, 1966. 1st ed. Fine in dj. *OTHER WORLDS.* $125

Lovecraft, H.P. and Others. TALES OF THE CTHULHU MYTHOS. Arkham House, 1969. 1st ed. Fine in NF dj. *MADLE.* $95

Lovecraft, H.P. AT THE MOUNTAINS OF MADNESS. Arkham House, 1964. 1st ed. VF in dj. *MADLE.* $75

Lovecraft, H.P. AT THE MOUNTAINS OF MADNESS. London: Gollancz, 1966. 1st Eng ed. Bkpl, else Fine in NF dj. *LOPEZ.* $65

Lovecraft, H.P. BEST SUPERNATURAL STORIES OF H.P. LOVECRAFT. Cleveland and NY, (1945). 1st ed. Tower Books ed. Cheap paper browned, bk finer than usual, in VG dj. *McCLINTOCK.* $20

Lovecraft, H.P. BEYOND THE WALL OF SLEEP. Arkham House, 1943. 1st ed. NF in VG dj (lt chipping). *MADLE.* $1500

Lovecraft, H.P. COLLECTED POEMS. Arkham House, 1963. 1st ed. VF in dj. *MADLE.* $150

Lovecraft, H.P. COLLECTED POEMS. Sauk City: Arkham House, 1963. 1st ed. Fine in Fine dj. *OTHER WORLDS.* $150

Lovecraft, H.P. DAGON AND OTHER MACABRE TALES. Sauk City, WI, 1965. 2nd ptg. Fine and bright in dj. *McCLINTOCK.* $30

Lovecraft, H.P. DAGON. Arkham House, 1965. 1st ed. VF in dj. *MADLE.* $75

Lovecraft, H.P. DREAMS AND FANCIES. Arkham House, 1962. 1st ed. VF in dj. *MADLE.* $175

Lovecraft, H.P. DREAMS AND FANCIES. Sauk City: Arkham House, 1962. 1st ed, ltd. to 2030. Fine in NF dj with light soiling to rear panel. *ROBBINS.* $95

Lovecraft, H.P. MARGINALIA. Arkham House, 1944. 1st ed. NF in NF dj. *MADLE.* $300

Lovecraft, H.P. MARGINALIA. Sauk City: Arkham House, 1944. 1st ed. VG+ (upper corners bumped) in VG dj. *OTHER WORLDS.* $250

Lovecraft, H.P. SELECTED LETTERS (III) 1929-1931. Sauk City: Arkham House, 1971. 1st ed. NF in dj. *OTHER WORLDS.* $90

Lovecraft, H.P. SELECTED LETTERS VOLUME III. Arkham House, 1971, 1st ed. Fine in dj. *MADLE.* $125

Lovecraft, H.P. SOMETHING ABOUT CATS AND OTHER PIECES. Collected by August Derleth. Sauk City, WI: Arkham House, 1949. 1st ed. Sl bumped in VG pict dj chipped at corners and edges. Internally Fine, bright. *BLUE MOUNTAIN.* $125

Lovecraft, H.P. SOMETHING ABOUT CATS AND OTHER PIECES. Sauk City: Arkham House, 1949. 1st ed. VG to VG+ in dj. *OTHER WORLDS.* $90

Lovecraft, H.P. SOMETHING ABOUT CATS AND OTHER PIECES. Sauk City: Arkham House, 1949. 1st ed. Name, date else NF in VG+ dj. *OTHER WORLDS.* $125

Lovecraft, H.P. SOMETHING ABOUT CATS. Arkham House, 1949. 1st ed. VF in dj. *MADLE.* $275

Lovecraft, H.P. THE DARK BROTHERHOOD. Arkham House, 1966. 1st ed. Fine in dj. *MADLE.* $125

Lovecraft, H.P. THE DUNWICH HORROR. Arkham House, 1963. 1st ed. VF in dj. *MADLE.* $70

Lovecraft, H.P. THE HORROR IN THE MUSEUM AND OTHER REVISIONS. Sauk City: Arkham House, 1970. 1st ed. Fine in dj. *OTHER WORLDS.* $45

Lovecraft, H.P. THE HORROR IN THE MUSEUM. Arkham House, 1970. 1st ed. VF in dj. *MADLE.* $65

Lovecraft, H.P. THE LURKING FEAR AND OTHER STORIES. NY: Avon, (1947). 1st ed. Pict wraps little edge rubbed. Fine. *POLYANTHOS.* $50

Lovecraft, H.P. THE SHADOW OUT OF TIME. London: Gollancz, 1968. 1st Eng ed. Bkpl, o/w Fine in Fine dj. *LOPEZ.* $65

Lovecraft, H.P. THE SHUTTERED ROOM. Arkham House, 1959. 1st ed. VF in dj. *MADLE.* $250

Lovecraft, H.P. THE WEIRD SHADOW OVER INNSMOUTH AND OTHER STORIES OF THE SUPERNATURAL. NY: Bart House Books, (1944). 1st ed. Pict wraps. Little edge rubbed. Fine. *POLYANTHOS.* $50

Lovecraft, H.P. THREE TALES OF HORROR. Arkham House, 1967. 1st ed. VF in dj (illus Lee Browne Coye). *MADLE.* $200

Lovejoy, Esther Pohl. CERTAIN SAMARITANS. NY: Macmillan, 1927. 1st ed. VG. *WORLDWIDE.* $16

Lovejoy, Joseph C. and Owen. MEMOIR OF THE REV. ELIJAH P. LOVEJOY...NY: John S. Taylor, 1838. 1st ed. 382pp. Orig cl sl worn, stained, repaired. Text foxing, else VG. Howes L522. *DIAMOND.* $125

Lovell, A.C.B. METEOR ASTRONOMY. Oxford: Clarendon Press, 1954. Blue cl, sl spotted, corner clipped from ffep, corners bumped, o/w Nice. *KNOLLWOOD.* $80

Lovell, Bernard. THE JODRELL BANK TELESCOPES. Oxford Univ Press, 1985. Fine in VG dj. *KNOLLWOOD.* $25

Lovesey, Peter. A CASE OF SPIRITS. London: Macmillan, 1975. 1st ed. Fine in dj. *MORDIDA.* $45

Lovesey, Peter. BERTIE AND THE TINMAN. London: Bodley Head, 1987. 1st ed. Fine in dj. *MORDIDA.* $30

Lovesey, Peter. MAD HATTER'S HOLIDAY. London: Macmillan, 1973. 1st ed. Fine in dj. *MORDIDA.* $50

Lovesey, Peter. ROUGH CIDER. London: Bodley Head, 1986. 1st ed. Signed. Fine in dj. *SILVER DOOR.* $35

Lovesey, Peter. SWING, SWING TOGETHER. NY: Dodd, 1976. 1st ed. As New in dj. *ELSE FINE.* $25

Lovesey, Peter. THE DETECTIVE WORE SILK DRAWERS. NY: Dodd, 1971. 1st ed. As New in dj. *ELSE FINE.* $35

Lovesey, Peter. THE LAST DETECTIVE. Bristol: Scorpion Press, 1991. 1st ed. 1/99 specially bound, numbered, signed. VF in acetate dj. *MORDIDA.* $135

Lovesey, Peter. THE TICK OF DEATH. NY: Dodd, 1974. 1st ed. As New in dj. *ELSE FINE.* $30

Lovesey, Peter. WAXWORK. London: Macmillan, (1978). 1st ed. Signed. Fine in Fine dj. *UNGER.* $35

Lovesey, Peter. WAXWORK. NY: Pantheon, 1978. 1st ed. As New in dj. *ELSE FINE.* $25

Lovesey, Peter. WOBBLE TO DEATH. London: Macmillan, 1970. 1st ed. Pages darkened o/w Fine in dj. *MORDIDA.* $125

Lovesey, Peter. WOBBLE TO DEATH. NY: Dodd, 1970. 1st ed, 1st bk. Fine; minor rubbing to dj. *ELSE FINE.* $45

Lovesey, Peter. WOBBLE TO DEATH. NY: Dodd Mead, 1970. 1st Amer ed. Fine in rubbed dj w/light staining on inner back flap. *MOR-DIDA.* $40

Lovett, Robert. EDITH WHARTON. NY: McBride, 1925. 1st ed. Fine in dj. *JUVELIS.* $75

Lovett, Robert. INFANTILE PARALYSIS IN MASSACHUSETTS DURING 1910. Boston, 1911. 154pp + numerous fldg maps and charts. *FYE.* $35

Lovett, Robert. THE TREATMENT OF INFANTILE PARALYSIS. Phila, 1916. 163pp. *FYE.* $125

Low, David. 'WITH ALL FAULTS'. Tehran: the Amate Press, 1973. 1st ed. With inscrip by Low. Fine in dj. *OAK KNOLL.* $45

Lowbury, Edward (ed). NIGHT RIDE AND SUNRISE. (Aberystwyth, Dyfed, Wales: Celtion, 1978). 1st ed. *CAPTAIN'S BOOK-SHELF.* $35

Lowden, Florence. A TRAVEL DIARY: EGYPT, PALESTINE AND GREECE 1929. (Chicago): Privately ptd (Lakeside Press), n.d. Japan vellum and stamped paper-covered boards. Frontis map, photos. Presentation inscrip. Fine. *SCHOYER'S.* $30

Lowe, Adolf, THE PRICE OF LIBERTY. A GERMAN ON CON-TEMPORARY BRITAIN. Hogarth Press. Day to Day Pamphlets No. 36, 1937. 1st ed. Wrappers. VG. *WOOLMER.* $35

Lowe, Percival G. FIVE YEARS A DRAGOON ('49 TO '54) AND OTHER ADVENTURES....Norman: Univ of Oklahoma, 1965. 1st ptg of new ed. Cl. VG in Good dj. *CONNOLLY & WADE.* $27.50

Lowell, Amy. WHAT'S O'CLOCK. Boston: Houghton Mifflin, 1925. 1st ed. Cl-backed boards, paper title labels. Fine in dj w/tiny chip from front panel and very shallow chip at head of spine. *CAPTAIN'S BOOKSHELF.* $125

Lowell, G. (ed). AMERICAN GARDENS. Boston, 1902. 112 photo plts. Orig dec cl w/garden design ptd in purple, gilt. Wear at corners, edges rubbed; spine frayed, darkened, minor soiling; bkpl removed. *SUTTON.* $275

Lowell, James Russell. CONVERSATIONS OF SOME OF THE OLD POETS. Cambridge, 1846. 2nd ed. NF. *POLYANTHOS.* $35

Lowell, James Russell. THE CATHEDRAL. Boston: Fields, Osgood, & Co, 1870. Spine tips rubbed, front hinge just starting, else VG w/pencilled gift inscript dated Dec. 25th, 1869. 1st ed. One of 3016. BAL 13135. *CHAPEL HILL.* $60

Lowell, Percival L. THE SOUL OF THE FAR EAST. NY: Macmillan, 1920 (1911). Good. *KNOLLWOOD.* $45

Lowell, Percival. THE EVOLUTION OF WORLDS. NY: Macmillan, 1910 (1909). 2nd ptg. Ex-lib in worn red cloth. *KNOLLWOOD.* $80

Lowell, Robert. FOR THE UNION DEAD. NY: Farrar Straus Giroux, (1964). 1st ed. Fine in Fine dj. *DERMONT.* $75

Lowell, Robert. IMITATIONS. NY: Farrar, Straus and Cudahy, (1961). 1st ed. Fine in Fine dj. *DERMONT.* $75

Lowell, Robert. LIFE STUDIES. NY: Farrar, Straus & Cudahy, (1959). Env tipped in at rear containing Lowell poem from mag, else About Fine in faintly soiled dj w/short closed tear. 1st Amer ed. *CHAPEL HILL.* $125

Lowell, Robert. PROMETHUS BOUND. NY: Farrar Straus Giroux, (1969). 1st ed. Owner name front pastedown (marked there where a sticker had covered it), signed. VG in price-clipped dj. *LOPEZ.* $175

Lowell, Robert. THE MILLS OF THE KAVANAUGHS. Cl. NY: Harcourt, Brace, (1951). 1st ed. Lt pencil annotations, o/w Fine in dj (sl worn, faded at spine). *JAFFE.* $125

Lowell, Robert. THE MILLS OF THE KAVANAUGHS. NY: Harcourt, Brace and Co., (1951). 1st ed. Fine in Fine dj. *DERMONT.* $200

Lowell, Robert. THE VOYAGE AND OTHER VERSIONS OF POEMS BY BAUDELAIRE. Sidney Nolan, illus. London: Faber & Faber, (1968). 1st ed. 1/200 specially bound, numbered, signed by Lowell and Nolan. Fine in slipcase. *CAPTAIN'S BOOKSHELF.* $450

Lowenfels, Walter (comp, ed). WALT WHITMAN'S CIVIL WAR. NY, 1960. 1st 1 vol ed. 335pp. Ex-lib. VG+. *PRATT.* $20

Lower, Mark A. ENGLISH SURNAMES....London 1843. 2nd ed. Illus. NF. *POLYANTHOS.* $75

Lowery, Irving E. LIFE ON THE OLD PLANTATION IN ANTE-BELLUM DAYS. Columbia, SC, 1911. 1st ed. Orig cl, some cover spotting. G. *McGOWAN.* $30

Lowman, Al (comp). PRINTER AT THE PASS: THE WORK OF CARL HERTZOG. San Antonio: The Univ of TX Institute of Texan Cultures, 1972. 1st ed. Fine. *WEBER.* $45

Lowndes, Mrs. Belloc. CRESSIDA: NO MYSTERY. NY: Alfred A. Knopf, 1930. 1st Amer ed. VG in dj (darkened spine, chipped, w/closed tears; sm strip missing back panel). *MORDIDA.* $35

Lowndes, Mrs. Belloc. VANDERLY'S ADVENTURE. NY: Jonathan Cape & Harrison Smith, 1931. 1st ed. Fine in VG dj w/faded spine; chipped; several short closed tears. *MORDIDA.* $40

Lowndes, R.A.W. MYSTERY OF THE THIRD MINE. Winston, 1959. VG in chipped dj. *MADLE.* $25

Lowndes, William Thomas. THE BIBLIOGRAPHER'S MANUAL OF ENGLISH LITERATURE. London: Bohn, 1857. 4 vols. Cloth boards, leather spine and tips, hinges rubbed. *DAWSON'S.* $100

Lowry, Malcolm. DARK AS THE GRAVE WHEREIN MY FRIEND IS LAID. NAL, 1968. 1st ed. Fine in dj (1" tear). *STAHR.* $35

Lowry, Malcolm. DARK AS THE GRAVE WHEREIN MY FRIEND IS LAID. NAL, (1968). 1st ed. Fine in dj with slight edge wear else NF. *BEBBAH.* $80

Lowry, Malcolm. OCTOBER FERRY TO GABRIOLA. World, 1970. 1st ed. Book Fine with dusty top edge in Fine dj except for delaminated striations, undoubtedly a publishing flaw. *BEBBAH.* $35

Lowry, Malcolm. OCTOBER FERRY TO GABRIOLA. World, 1970. 1st ed. Fine in a VG+, NF dj (coating wrinkled and puckered). *STAHR.* $30

Lowry, Malcolm. ULTRAMARINE. Phila: Lippincott (1962). 1st Amer ed. NF in VG+ dj. *DORN.* $95

Lowry, Malcolm. ULTRAMARINE. Phila/NY: J.B. Lippincott Company, (c1962). 1st Amer, 1st rev ed; 1st bk. Fine in dj, 2 sm scrapes. *HELLER.* $85

Lowry, Malcolm. UNDER THE VOLCANO. NY: Reynal & Hitchcock, 1947. 1st ed. Sl browning to the edges, else Fine in dj w/unnecessary internal mend; minimal wear to spine extrems, one corner. *CAPTAIN'S BOOKSHELF.* $500

Lowry, Malcolm. UNDER THE VOLCANO. NY: Reynal & Hitchcock, (1947). 1st ed. Covers sl soiled, spine sl sunned. NF. *CAPTAIN'S BOOKSHELF.* $75

Lowry, Malcolm. UNDER THE VOLCANO. NY: Reynal & Hitchcock, (1947). 1st ed. Orig grey cl. VG in price-clipped dj, lt chipping head of spine, 1" closed tear front panel. *CHAPEL HILL.* $600

Lowry, Martin. THE WORLD OF ALDUS MANUTIUS. Oxford: Blackwell, (1979). 1st ed. Inscribed. DJ. *WEBER.* $75

Lowry, Robert and William H. McCardle. A HISTORY OF MISSISSIPPI, FROM THE DISCOVERY OF THE GREAT RIVER...TO THE DEATH OF JEFFERSON DAVIS. Jackson: Henry, 1891. 1st ed, 2nd issue, w/errata. (12),5-648pp, errata leaf. Orig cl, sm paper label on lower spine, bkpl removed. Howes L540. *GINSBERG.* $150

Lowther, Charles C. DODGE CITY, KANSAS. Phila: Dorrance, (1940). Inscribed. Cl, dj. Fine. *SCHOYER'S.* $50

Lowther, E.H.N. A BIRD PHOTOGRAPHER IN INDIA. London, 1949. 78 photos. *SUTTON.* $56

Lowther, George. SUPERMAN. NY, (1942). 1st ed. Joe Shuster (illus). Plts. VG. *McCLINTOCK.* $195

Loy, Mina. THE LAST LUNAR BAEDEKER. Roger Conover (ed). Highlands, (NC): The Jargon Society, 1982. 1st ed. Dj. VF. *JAFFE.* $50

Loy, Mina. VIRGINS PLUS CURTAINS. Poems. Rochester: The Press of the Good Mountain, 1981. 1st ed. #48/80 ptd (though it has been reported that fewer than 40 were ever bound) on Fabriano Roma. Fine in wrappers w/paper label. *CAPTAIN'S BOOKSHELF.* $350

Luard, G.D. FISHING ADVENTURES IN CANADA AND U.S.A. London: Faber & Faber, (1950). Fine in dj. *ARTIS.* $50

Lubbock, Basil. THE DOWN EASTERS: AMERICAN DEEP-WATER SAILING SHIPS 1869-1929. Boston, 1929. 1st Amer ed. Orig cl. Fine. *LEFKOWICZ.* $100

Lubbock, Basil. THE LOG OF THE "CUTTY SARK." Boston & Glasgow, 1924. 1st ed. VG. *LEFKOWICZ.* $90

Lubbock, Perry. PORTRAIT OF EDITH WHARTON. NY: Appleton-Century, (1947). 1st ed. VG in dj. *JUVELIS.* $35

Lucas, A. and J.R. Harris. ANCIENT EGYPTIAN MATERIALS AND INDUSTRIES. London: Edward Arnold, (1962). 4th ed. Good. *ARCHAEOLOGIA.* $150

Lucas, A. FORENSIC CHEMISTRY AND SCIENTIFIC CRIMINAL INVESTIGATION. London, 1931. Rev 2nd ed. Ex-lib. NF. *POLYANTHOS.* $45

Lucas, June Richardson. THE CHILDREN OF FRANCE AND THE RED CROSS. NY, 1918. 1st ed. Signed. *FYE.* $75

Ludlam, F.H. and R.S. Scorer. CLOUD STUDY. London: John Murray, 1957 (1956). Good in dj. *KNOLLWOOD.* $22

Ludlow, James M. THE CAPTAIN OF THE JANIZARIES. NY, 1887. 404pp. *O'NEILL.* $40

Ludlow, Park. THE RED-SHANTY BOYS. Boston, (1871). Gilt-pict bds. NF. *POLYANTHOS.* $30

Ludlum, Robert. THE BOURNE IDENTITY. NY: Richard Marek, 1980. 1st ed. Fine in dj. *MORDIDA.* $40

Ludlum, Robert. THE CHANCELLOR MANUSCRIPT. Dial, 1977. 1st ed. About Fine in dj. Name. *STAHR.* $45

Ludlum, Robert. THE GEMINI CONTENDERS. Dial, 1976. 1st ed. Fine in dj. Signed bkpl pasted on ffep. *STAHR.* $75

Ludlum, Robert. THE HOLCROFT COVENANT. NY: Richard Marek, 1978. 1st ed. Fine in dj. *MORDIDA.* $40

Ludlum Robert. THE MATARESE CIRCLE. NY: Richard Marek, 1979. 1st ed. Edges lightly spotted o/w Fine in dj. *MORDIDA.* $35

Ludlum, Robert. THE MATLOCK PAPER. NY: Dial, 1973. 1st ed. Fine in NF dj w/3 tears. *BEASLEY.* $50

Luhan, Mabel Dodge. LORENZO IN TAOS. Knopf, 1932. 3rd ptg. VG. *OREGON*. $20

Luhan, Mabel Dodge. LORENZO IN TAOS. Knopf, 1935. 4th prtg. Sunning to spine, cvr edge wear else VG. *BEBBAH*. $22

Luhrs, Victor. THE GREAT BASEBALL MYSTERY. Barnes, 1966. 1st ed. VG in VG+ dj. *PLAPINGER*. $60

Lukach, Harry Charles. THE FRINGE OF THE EAST. London, 1913. *O'NEILL*. $110

Luke, Harry C. MOSUL AND ITS MINORITIES. London, 1925. ix,161pp. *O'NEILL*. $85

Luke, Harry C. THE CITY OF DANCING DERVISHES, AND OTHER SKETCHES AND STUDIES FROM THE NEAR EAST. London, 1914. Very Nice. *O'NEILL*. $65

Luke, Harry. FROM A SOUTH SEAS DIARY. 1938-1942. London: Nicholson & Watson, 1945. 1st ed. Fine in NF dj. *GREAT EPIC*. $45

Lukis, Pardey. TROPICAL HYGIENE FOR ANGLO-INDIANS AND INDIANS. Calcutta, 1914. 2nd ed. Scarce. *FYE*. $50

Lumholtz, Carl. NEW TRAILS IN MEXICO. NY: Scribner's, 1912. 2 fldg maps in pocket, 49 pp photo illus. Brown-stamped cl, moderate wear to tips and head and tail of spine, 1 gathering a bit sprung. *DAWSON'S*. $100

Lumholtz, Carl. NEW TRAILS IN MEXICO. NY: Scribners, 1912. 1st ed. Pict cl. 2 fldg maps in rear pocket (1 colored). Teg. Shelf wear, else Good. Ex-lib. *DIAMOND*. $45

Lumley, Brian. BENEATH THE MOORS. Sauk City, 1974. 1st ed. Fine in VG dj (slight rumpling, one tear). *McCLINTOCK*. $25

Lumley, Brian. BENEATH THE MOORS. Sauk City: Arkham House, 1974. 1st ed. Fine in Fine dj. *OTHER WORLDS*. $25

Lumley, Brian. THE CALLER OF THE BLACK. Sauk City: Arkham House, 1971. 1st ed. Front board nicked, dinged one spot, else Almost Fine in dj. *OTHER WORLDS*. $35

Lummis, Charles F. DATELINE FORT BOWIE, CHARLES FLETCHER LUMMIS REPORTS ON THE APACHE WAR. Norman, (1979). Ed by Don L. Thorp. 1st ed. Dj has faded spine, o/w Fine. *PRATT*. $25

Lummis, Charles F. GRAND CANYON NATIONAL PARK. National Park Series, 1919. Pict colored wraps, 32pp. VG+. *FIVE QUAIL*. $25

Lummis, Charles F. SOME STRANGE CORNERS OF OUR COUNTRY....Century Company, 1892. 1st ed. Dec cvr, frontis. Fine, bright, gift message. *AUTHORS OF THE WEST*. $75

Lumsden, James. THE SKIPPER PARSON ON THE BAYS AND BARRENS OF NEWFOUNDLAND. NY, (1905). 1st ed. VG. *ARTIS*. $25

Lund, Edward. HUNTERIAN LECTURES ON SOME OF THE INJURIES AND DISEASES OF THE NECK AND HEAD, THE GENITO-URINARY ORGANS, AND THE RECTUM. London, 1886. 1st ed. 116pp. 4 autotype photo illus. Scarce. *FYE*. $175

Lunn, Arnold. THE MOUNTAINS OF MY YOUTH. London: Oxford Univ Press, 1925. 1st ed. Minor shelfwear and spine lightening, else VG. *OLD LONDON*. $35

Lupton, Frederick. THE LAW RELATING TO DOGS. Stevens and Sons, 119, Chancery Lane (etc.), London, 1888. 1st, and only ed. Blank; half-title; title page; (v)-xii, (1)-160pp. Bound in at end is 32pp Stevens and Sons Catalogue of Law Works, dated January, 1888. 12mo. Well preserved, in orig crimson cl, gilt. Bit rubbed and faded, eps listing addit'l Stevens and Sons law publs. *BOSWELL*. $225

Lurie, Alison. FOREIGN AFFAIRS. NY: Random House, (1984). 1st trade ed. Fine in Fine dj. *LOPEZ*. $25

Lurie, Alison. THE WAR BETWEEN THE TATES. Random, 1974. 1st Amer ed. Fine. Dj price-clipped. *STAHR*. $15

Lurie, Alison. V.R. LANG: A MEMOIR. Munich: (Privately Ptd), 1959. 1st ed, 1st bk. Ltd to 300. Cover illus Edward Gorey. Inscribed and signed by Gorey. Some slight soiling to wrappers and wear to spine, upper hinge cracking. VG. *JUVELIS*. $600

Lurie, E. LOUIS AGASSIZ: A LIFE IN SCIENCE. Univ of Chicago Press, 1960. Dj near New. *BOOKCELL*. $45

Lusk, William Thompson. SCIENCE AND ART OF MIDWIFERY. NY: Appleton, 1896. New ed, rev, enl. VG. *SCHOYER'S*. $50

Lussan, Raveneau de. RAVENEAU DE LUSSAN, BUCCANEER OF THE SPANISH MAIN....Marguerite Eyer Wilbur (trans, ed). Cleveland: Arthur H. Clark Co, 1930. 1st ed in Eng. Map. Dj. Fine. *LEFKOWICZ*. $135

Lustgarten, Edgar. GAME FOR THREE LOSERS. London: Museum Press, (1952). 1st ed. Inscribed. Top edge sl spotted o/w VG in dj w/several short closed tears and small chip on back panel at spine corner. *MORDIDA*. $45

Luttig, John. JOURNAL OF A FUR-TRADING EXPEDITION ON THE UPPER MISSOURI 1812-1813....Stella Drumm (ed). St. Louis: Missouri Hist Soc, 1920. 1st ed, ltd to 365. Frontis, 5 plts, fldg map. Orig gilt stamped blue cl, lt blue boards. Front board soiled, corners bumped. Howes L572. VG. *OREGON*. $225

Lutyens, Edwin. FULBROOK. THE SKETCHBOOK...FOR A HOUSE BY EDWIN LUTYENS 1896-1899. Jane Brown (ed). 2 vols. (Marlborough): Libanus Press, 1989. 1st ed. Ltd to 300. Mint in cl slipcase. *JAFFE*. $500

Lutz, B. BRAZILIAN SPECIES OF HYLA. Austin, 1973. 7 plts. Dj. *SUTTON*. $45

Lutz, John. BETTER MOUSETRAPS. NY: St. Martin's Press, 1988. 1st ed. VF in dj. *MORDIDA*. $20

Lutz, John. DANCER'S DEBT. NY: St. Martin's Press, 1988. 1st ed. Fine in dj. *MORDIDA*. $20

Lutz, John. KISS. NY: Holt, 1988. 1st ed. Review copy, signed. Fine in dj. *SILVER DOOR*. $35

Lutz, John. LAZARUS MAN. NY: William Morrow, 1979. 1st ed. Fine in dj. *MORDIDA*. $25

Lutz, John. SCORCHER. NY: Henry Holt, 1987. 1st ed. VF in dj. *MORDIDA*. $20

Lutz, John. THE SHADOW MAN. NY: William Morrow, 1981. 1st ed. Fine in dj. *MORDIDA*. $25

Lutz, John. TROPICAL HEAT. NY: Henry Holt, 1986. 1st ed. VF in dj. *MORDIDA*. $20

Luvaas, Jay and Harold W. Nelson (eds). THE U.S. ARMY WAR COLLEGE GUIDE TO THE BATTLE OF GETTYSBURG. Carlisle, PA: 1986. 1st ed. 233pp. VF in dj. *PRATT*. $20

Luvaas, Jay. THE MILITARY LEGACY OF THE CIVIL WAR. Chicago, (1959). 1st ed. Light dj wear o/w VG+. *PRATT*. $35

Luxan, Diego Perez de. EXPEDITION INTO NEW MEXICO MADE BY ANTONIO DE ESPEJO 1582-1583: AS REVEALED IN THE JOURNAL OF DIEGO PEREZ DE LUXAN....Quivira Soc Pubs, vol I. LA: Quivira Society, 1929. George Peter Hammond and Agapito Rey (trans, eds). One of 500 numbered. 16 full-pg plts of photogr, 2 fldg maps. Ex-lib, bound in pub's orig paper boards. Sl wear to cvr, interior NF. *LAURIE*. $130

Luxmoore, Chas. F.C. "SALTGLAZE," London: The Holland Press. N.d. (circa 1970, rprt of 1924 ed). Black cl. *KARMIOLE*. $50

Lyall, Gavin. THE SECRET SERVANT. NY: Viking, 1980. 1st Amer ed. Fine in NF dj. *SILVER DOOR*. $25

Lybyer, Albert H. THE GOVERNMENT OF THE OTTOMAN EMPIRE IN THE TIME OF SULEIMAN THE MAGNIFICENT. Cambridge, 1913. *O'NEILL*. $45

Lydekker, R. A HANDBOOK TO THE CARNIVORA PT. L, CATS, CIVETS & MONGOOSES. London, 1896. 1st ed. VG+. *MIKESH.* $50

Lydekker, Richard. A HAND-BOOK TO THE MARSUPIALIA AND MONOTREMATA. London, 1896. 3/4 lea, worn top & bottom of spine extremities & along front hinge. NF. *POLYANTHOS.* $50

Lydekker, Richard. A HANDBOOK TO THE BRITISH MAMMALIA. London, 1896. 32 color plts. 3/4 lea, rubbed at spine extremities & hinges. NF. *POLYANTHOS.* $50

Lydston, G. Frank. ADDRESSES AND ESSAYS. Chicago, 1892. 2nd ed. 289pp. Scarce. *FYE.* $75

Lydston, G. Frank. PANAMA AND THE SIERRAS. Chicago: Riverton, 1900. 1st ed. 1/20 inscribed. Orig bright blue gilt stamped cl. *CONNOLLY & WADE.* $145

Lyell, Sir Charles. A SECOND VISIT TO THE UNITED STATES OF NORTH AMERICA. 2 vols. NY: Harper & Brothers, 1849. 1st Amer ed. 273pp;287pp, ads. Orig ptd wraps soiled, chipped. Minor dampstaining. *PARMER.* $175

Lyeskov, Nicolai. THE SENTRY AND OTHER STORIES. NY: Knopf, 1923. 1st ed. 1st collection of author's work to appear in English. NF in dj. *LAME DUCK.* $100

Lyford, William G. THE WESTERN ADDRESS DIRECTORY: CONTAINING THE CARDS OF MERCHANTS...IN PITTSBURGH, (PA)...ST. LOUIS, (MO.)...Baltimore: Printed by Jos. Robinson, 1837. 1st ed. 468pp. Modern boards, leather spine w/leather label. Nice. Howes L576. Interleaved throughout w/business cards on vari-colored leaves. *GINSBERG.* $1000

Lyle, Donald. NEURO-OPHTHALMOLOGY. Springfield, 1945. 1st ed. 234 illus. Scarce. *FYE.* $75

Lyman, Chester S. AROUND THE HORN TO THE SANDWICH ISLANDS AND CALIFORNIA 1845-1850. New Haven: Yale Univ Press, 1924. *PARMER.* $160

Lyman, George D. JOHN MARSH, PIONEER. THE LIFE STORY....NY: Charles Scribner's Sons, 1930. 1st ed. Paste on (bkpl?) removed. Shelfwear, overall VG. Inscribed. *PARMER.* $60

Lyman, George D. RALSTON'S RING: CALIFORNIA PLUNDERS THE COMSTOCK LODE. NY: Scribner's, 1937. 1st ed. Good. *LAURIE.* $20

Lyman, George D. THE SAGA OF THE COMSTOCK LODE BOOM DAYS IN VIRGINIA CITY. NY: Scribner's, 1934. Fine in VG dj. *CONNOLLY & WADE.* $27.50

Lyman, George D. THE SAGA OF THE COMSTOCK LODE. Scribner's, 1934. 1st ed. Good. Cvrs sl spotted. *VARNER.* $20

Lyman, Henry. ARTIFICIAL ANAESTHESIA AND ANAESTHETICS. NY, 1881. 1st ed. *FYE.* $150

Lyman, Henry. INSOMNIA; AND OTHER DISORDERS OF SLEEP. Chicago, 1885. 1st ed. *FYE.* $75

Lynch, James. WITH STEVENSON TO CALIFORNIA. Oakland: Biobooks, (1954). One of 500. 1st pub 1896. Fldg map. Unopened. Fine. *LAURIE.* $37.50

Lynch, Jeremiah. THREE YEARS IN THE KLONDIKE. Chicago: Lakeside Press, 1967. Lakeside Classic reprint. Fine. *BLUE DRAGON.* $25

Lynch, Jeremiah. THREE YEARS IN THE KLONDIKE. Dale L. Morgan (ed). London, n.d. (Circa 1904). 1st Amer ed. (Chicago, 1967). Lakeside Classic #65 with the gift card laid in. Fine. *PRATT.* $40

Lynch, R.I. THE BOOK OF THE IRIS. London, 1904. 1st ed. Cloth. Spine dulled, scuffing; lt foxing. *SUTTON.* $35

Lynch, William F. NARRATIVE OF THE UNITED STATES' EXPEDITION TO THE RIVER JORDAN AND THE DEAD SEA. Phila: Lee and Blanchard, 1849. New and corrected ed. Fldg maps. Binding broken, text browned, lower border dampstained. *HUDSON.* $50

Lynn, Elizabeth. WATCHTOWER. Berkley, 1979. 1st ed. Fine in dj. *MADLE.* $25

Lyon, James. FOUR ESSAYS ON THE RIGHT AND PROPRIETY OF SECESSION BY SOUTHERN STATES. BY A MEMBER OF THE BAR OF RICHMOND. Richmond, 1861. 1st ed. 55pp. Later paper boards, label lacking. Howes L591. *GINSBERG.* $500

Lyons, Arthur. AT THE HANDS OF ANOTHER. Holt, 1983. 1st ed. VF, dj. Signed, inscribed, dated. *STAHR.* $35

Lyons, Arthur. AT THE HANDS OF ANOTHER. NY: HRW, 1983. VF in dj. *ELSE FINE.* $30

Lyons, Arthur. CASTLES BURNING. NY: Holt, 1980. 1st ed. Signed. VF in dj. *SILVER DOOR.* $37.50

Lyons, Arthur. DEAD RINGER. Mason Charter, 1977. 1st ed. Fine, dj. Signed. Two small rubbed spots. *STAHR.* $45

Lyons, Arthur. HARD TRADE. NY: Holt, (1981). 1st ed, As New in dj. *CAPTAIN'S BOOKSHELF.* $30

Lyons, Arthur. HARD TRADE. NY: Holt, (1981). 1st ed. Inscribed. Fine in Fine dj. *UNGER.* $40

Lyons, Arthur. HARD TRADE. NY: HRW, 1981. 1st ed. VF in dj. *ELSE FINE.* $40

Lyons, Arthur. THE DEAD ARE DISCREET. London: Robson, (1977). 1st English ed. Signed. Fine in price-clipped dj. *UNGER.* $100

Lyons, C. SALMON & OUR HERITAGE, THE STORY OF A PROVINCE (BC) & AN INDUSTRY. Vancouver, BC, 1969. 1st ed. Fine in NF dj. *MIKESH.* $65

Lyons, Dorothy. DARK SUNSHINE. NY: Harcourt Brace, 1951. 1st ed. VG in Fair dj. *OCTOBER FARM.* $25

Lysaght, A.M. (ed.) JOSEPH BANKS IN NEWFOUNDLAND AND LABRADOR, 1766. Berkeley: Univ of CA Press. (1971). 1st ed. 4 fldg facs. Dj. *KARMIOLE.* $65

Lytle, Andrew Nelson. BEDFORD FORREST AND HIS CRITTER COMPANY. NY: Minton, Balch, 1931. 1st ed, 1st issue, 1st bk. 3,000 ptd. Orig black cl w/paper labels. Innocuous bump to one corner, but superb in modestly soiled dj rubbed at head of spine. *CHAPEL HILL.* $650

Lytle, Andrew. A NAME FOR EVIL. Indianapolis: Bobbs Merrill, (1947). 1st ed. Fine in dj (2 sm chips). Signed. *CAPTAIN'S BOOKSHELF.* $225

Lytle, Andrew. A NAME FOR EVIL. Indianapolis: Bobbs-Merrill, 1947. 1st ed. Fine; lt wear to dj extrems. *ELSE FINE.* $200

Lytle, Andrew. A NOVEL, A NOVELLA AND FOUR STORIES. (NY): McDowell Obolensky, (1958). 1st ed. Fine in rubbed dj. Signed. *CAPTAIN'S BOOKSHELF.* $75

Lytle, Andrew. A NOVEL, A NOVELLA AND FOUR STORIES. NY: McDowell, Obolensky, 1958. 1st ed. Fine in Fine dj, lt wear spine head. *BEASLEY.* $60

Lytle, Andrew. A WAKE FOR THE LIVING. NY: Crown, (1975). 1st ed. Fine in dj (some wear). Signed. *CAPTAIN'S BOOKSHELF.* $60

Lytle, Andrew. ALCHEMY. Winston-Salem: Palaemon Press, (1979). 1st Amer ed. 1/300 signed. Fine as published w/o dj. *DORN.* $35

Lytton, David. THE GODDAM WHITE MAN. NY, 1961. 1st ed. Cheap paper sl edge browned as usual. Dj little edge rubbed, 2 tiny chips. Author's 1st bk. *POLYANTHOS.* $35

M

M'Clellan, R. Guy. REPUBLICANISM IN AMERICA: A HISTORY OF THE COLONIAL AND REPUBLICAN GOVERNMENTS OF THE UNITED STATES...SF: R.J. Trumbull, 1869. 1st ed. Deluxe copy with full count of engrs present. 21 plts w/all tissue guards present. Full lea w/black labels. NF. *CONNOLLY & WADE*. $185

M'Clintock, Francis Leopold. THE VOYAGE OF THE 'FOX' IN ARCTIC SEAS....London: John Murray, 1859. 1st ed, and scarce thus. (xxviii), 403, 1 ad pp. Modern half calf, antique style. *LEFKOWICZ*. $200

M'Collester, Sullivan H. ROUND THE GLOBE IN OLD AND NEW PATHS. Boston, 1890. (vii),354pp. *O'NEILL*. $40

M'Ewen, George. THE CULTURE OF THE PEACH AND NECTARINE. London: Groombridge, 1859. 52pp. VG. One hand-colored plate of a peach. *AMERICAN BOTANIST*. $75

M'Intire, James. A NEW TREATISE ON THE USE OF THE GLOBES...Baltimore: E.J. Coale, 1826 (1823). 2nd ed. Very worn leather. 1 plt (of 3) missing. *KNOLLWOOD*. $45

M'Lehose, W.C. (ed.) THE CORRESPONDENCE BETWEEN BURNS AND CLARINDA. (Edinburgh: William Tait; London: Simpkin, Marshall; and Dublin: John Cumming, 1843). First Authorized and First Complete Edition. Orig emb cloth, gilt spine. Engr frontis, extra engr title. Joints and extremities sl worn, but the binding quite clean, smooth, and appealing. Hinge cracked before title page, trivial discoloration here and there; excellent internally. *PIRAGES*. $125

M'Robert, Patrick. A TOUR THROUGH PART OF THE NORTH PROVINCES OF AMERICA....(Phila., 1935). Facsimile of 1776 orig ed. Orig boards w/ptd paper label on front cvr. Howes M187. *GINSBERG*. $50

Mabie, Hamilton Wright. THE WRITERS OF KNICKERBOCKER, NEW YORK. NY: The Grolier Club. 1912. Ltd to 300. Slipcase (chipped). Bkpl. *KARMIOLE*. $65

Mabie, Hamilton. MYTHS EVERY CHILD SHOULD KNOW. GC ptg. 224pp. Illus by Mary Frye. VG w/sl edgewear, bright color cvr pict *BEBBAH*. $25

Mac Orlan, Pierre. ON BOARD THE MORNING STAR. Boni, 1924. 1st ed. 120pp. Woodcuts by Daragnes. Trans Malcolm Cowley. VG. *BEBBAH*. $40

MacArthur, Arthur. AFTER THE AFTERNOON. Appleton, 1941. Fine in dj. *MADLE*. $50

Macarthur, Blanche and Jennie Moore. LESSONS IN FIGURE PAINTING IN WATER COLORS. London, Paris, NY: (Cassell, Petter, Galpin & Co), n.d. (ca 1880). Pub's grn cl w/gilt titling. 16 water color plts tipped to pp. VG. *BOOK BLOCK*. $190

Macartney, Clarence Edward. LINCOLN AND HIS CABINET. NY: Scribner's, 1931. 1st ptg. 8 plts. *SCHOYER'S*. $15

Macartney, Clarence. GRANT AND HIS GENERALS. NY: McBride, (1953). 2nd ptg. Dj. Fine. *SCHOYER'S*. $20

Macauley, Rose. FABLED SHORE: FROM THE PYRENEES TO PORTUGAL. NY: Farrar, Straus, (1949). 1st ed. Chipped dj, o/w VG. *SCHOYER'S*. $15

MacBride, Thomas H(ouston). IN CABINS AND SODHOUSES. Iowa City: State Hist Soc of Iowa, 1928. 1st ed. Teg, deckled pgs. Wine red w/gilt dec cl. Corners and extrems bit worn, else VG. *CONNOLLY & WADE*. $75

MacCallum, William. A TEXT-BOOK OF PATHOLOGY. Phila, 1916. 1st ed. *FYE*. $150

MacClure, Victor. THE ARK OF THE COVENANT. Harpers, 1924. 1st ed. VG. *MADLE*. $50

MacClure, Victor. ULTIMATUM. London, 1924. 1st British ed. VG. *MADLE*. $50

MacCormack, Samuel. A VIEW OF THE STATE OF PARTIES IN THE UNITED STATES OF AMERICA...Edinburgh, 1812. 2nd ed, w/additions, corrections. 167,(5)pp. New cl w/leather label on spine. Howes V95. *GINSBERG*. $150

MacDonald, Aeneas. WHISKY. GC: Henry & Longwell, 1930. 1/307 numbered, signed by Morley and MacDonald. NF w/o dj (as issued?). *LOPEZ*. $75

MacDonald, Donald. A HISTORY OF PLATINUM. London: Johnson Matthey & Co. 1960. 1st ed. Dj. Fine. *KARMIOLE*. $65

MacDonald, George. THE GOLDEN KEY. Pictures Maurice Sendak, afterword W.H. Auden. NY: Farrar Straus & Giroux, (1967). 1st thus. Fine in dj. Signed by Sendak in 1978. *CAPTAIN'S BOOKSHELF*. $60

MacDonald, Hugh. JOHN DRYDEN, A BIBLIOGRAPHY OF EARLY EDITIONS AND OF DRYDENIANA. Oxford: The Clarendon Press, 1939. 1st ed. VG. *WEBER*. $125

MacDonald, John D. A TAN AND SANDY SILENCE. Phila: J.B. Lippincott, 1979. 1st Amer hb ed. Sm stain base of spine, o/w Fine in dj w/sm internal stain; nicks, wear). *MORDIDA*. $90

MacDonald, John D. BRIGHT ORANGE FOR THE SHROUD. Phila: Lippincott, 1972. 1st ed. Fine in price-clipped dj. *ELSE FINE*. $250

MacDonald, John D. CONDOMINIUM. Phila: J.B. Lippincott, 1977. 1st ed. Inscribed. Fine in dj w/few short closed tears and nicks. *MORDIDA*. $185

MacDonald, John D. DEAD LOW TIDE. London: Hale, 1976. 1st hb ed. As New in price clipped dj. *ELSE FINE*. $35

MacDonald, John D. MURDER FOR THE BRIDE. London: Hale, 1977. 1st hb ed. As New in dj. *ELSE FINE*. $50

MacDonald, John D. NIGHTMARE IN PINK. Phila: J.B. Lippincott, 1976. 1st Amer hb ed. Fine in dj w/minor rubbing at edges. *MORDIDA*. $165

MacDonald, John D. NIGHTMARE IN PINK. Phila: Lippincott, 1976. 1st ed. Fine; minor rubs dj extrems. *ELSE FINE*. $200

MacDonald, John D. NO DEADLY DRUG. GC: Doubleday, 1968. 1st ed. Fine in dj w/couple of tiny tears. *MORDIDA*. $45

MacDonald, John D. NO DEADLY DRUG. NY: Doubleday, (1968). 1st ed. Fine in very lightly soiled dj. *UNGER*. $65

MacDonald, John D. ONE FEARFUL YELLOW EYE. Phila: J.B. Lippincott, 1977. 1st Amer hb ed. Fine in dj w/rubbing. *MORDIDA*. $185

MacDonald, John D. PLEASE WRITE FOR DETAILS. NY: Simon and Schuster, 1959. 1st ed. Pp darkened o/w VG in price-clipped dj (chipped, frayed spine ends; sl faded spine; wear). *MORDIDA*. $40

MacDonald, John D. PLEASE WRITE FOR DETAILS. NY: Simon & Schuster, 1959. 1st ed. VF; sl wear at dj extrems. *ELSE FINE*. $200

MacDonald, John D. SEVEN. London: Hale, 1974. 1st hb ed. As New in price clipped dj. *ELSE FINE*. $40

MacDonald, John D. SLAM THE BIG DOOR. Greenwich, CT: Fawcett, (1960). 1st ed. Owner's name on front page, pages a bit tanned, else Fine, unworn in wrappers as issued. *BETWEEN COVERS*. $45

MacDonald, John D. THE ANNEX AND OTHER STORIES. Helsinki: Eurographica, 1987. 1st of this ed. Ltd to 350 signed by Macdonald. Ptd wraps. Mint. *JAFFE*. $175

MacDonald, John D. THE BRASS CUPCAKE. London: Robert Hale, 1974. 1st hb ed. VF in price-clipped dj. *MORDIDA*. $45

MacDonald, John D. THE DREADFUL LEMON SKY. Phila: J.B. Lippincott, 1974. 1st ed. Fine in dj. *MORDIDA*. $65

MacDonald, John D. THE DREADFUL LEMON SKY. Phila: Lippincott, 1974. 1st ed. Fine; minor rubs dj extrems. *ELSE FINE.* $65

MacDonald, John D. THE EMPTY COPPER SEA. London: Hale, 1979. 1st Brit ed. About Fine in dj. *SILVER DOOR.* $22.50

MacDonald, John D. THE EMPTY COPPER SEA. Phila: Lippincott, 1978. 1st ed. VF in dj. *ELSE FINE.* $35

MacDonald, John D. THE GIRL, THE GOLD WATCH & EVERYTHING. London: Hale, 1974. 1st hb ed. VF in dj. *ELSE FINE.* $40

MacDonald, John D. THE GIRL, THE GOLD WATCH AND EVERYTHING. London: Robert Hale, 1974. 1st hb ed. VF in price-clipped dj. *MORDIDA.* $45

Macdonald, John D. THE LONG LAVENDER LOOK. London: Hale, (1972). 1st UK ed, 1st hb ed. As New in dj. *CAPTAIN'S BOOKSHELF.* $50

MacDonald, John D. THE LONG LAVENDER LOOK. London: Hale, 1972. 1st hb ed. As New in clipped dj. *ELSE FINE.* $45

MacDonald, John D. THE LONG LAVENDER LOOK. London: Robert Hale, 1972. 1st hb ed. VF in price-clipped dj. *MORDIDA.* $45

MacDonald, John D. THE QUICK RED FOX. Phila: Lippincott, 1974. 1st ed. Fine, short creased tear in bottom edge of bright dj. *ELSE FINE.* $225

Macdonald, John D. THE SCARLET RUSE. London: Hale, (1975). 1st UK ed, 1st hb ed. As New in dj. *CAPTAIN'S BOOKSHELF.* $50

MacDonald, John D. THE SCARLET RUSE. London: Hale, 1975. 1st hb ed. As New in dj. *ELSE FINE.* $50

MacDonald, John D. THE SCARLET RUSE. NY: Lippincott & Crowell, 1980. 1st Amer hb ed. VF in dj. *MORDIDA.* $125

MacDonald, John D. THE TURQOISE LAMENT. London: Robert Hale, 1975. 1st Eng ed. VF in dj. *MORDIDA.* $45

MacDonald, John D. YOU LIVE ONCE. London: Hale, 1976. 1st hb ed. As New in dj. *ELSE FINE.* $35

MacDonald, John D. YOU LIVE ONCE. London: Robert Hale, 1976. 1st hb ed. VF in dj. *MORDIDA.* $45

MacDonald, John Ross (pseud of Kenneth Millar). FIND A VICTIM. NY: Knopf, 1954. 1st ed. 2pp ink-stained o/w VG in sl soiled dj w/scrape front panel; internal tape mends; short closed tears. *MORDIDA.* $95

MacDonald, John Ross (pseud of Kenneth Millar). THE IVORY GRIN. NY: Knopf, 1952. 1st ed. Fine in VG dj w/chipped spine ends, corners; several short closed tears. *MORDIDA.* $185

MacDonald, John. RAPE, OFFENDERS AND THEIR VICTIMS. Springfield, 1971. 1st ed. Dj. *FYE.* $50

MacDonald, John. THE MOVING TARGET. NY: Alfred A. Knopf, 1949. 1st ed. Fine in VG bright unfaded dj w/closed tears, chips at spine ends and at corners, and light stain on back panel. *MORDIDA.* $650

MacDonald, Philip. FINGERS OF FEAR. London: Collins Crime Club, 1953. 1st ed. Fine in Fine dj but for chips at lower spine, few short tears. *BEASLEY.* $50

MacDonald, Philip. THE LINK. GC: Doubleday, 1930. 1st US ed. Fine in NF dj w/few tears. *BEASLEY.* $125

MacDonald, Philip. THE POLFERRY RIDDLE. NY: Doubleday, 1931. 1st Amer ed. Minor wear but Nice. *SILVER DOOR.* $25

MacDonald, Ross (pseud of Kenneth Millar). A COLLECTION OF REVIEWS. Northridge: Lord John Press, 1979. 1st ed. One of 300 numbered, signed. VF w/o dj as issued. *MORDIDA.* $100

MacDonald, Ross (pseud of Kenneth Millar). ARCHER AT LARGE. Knopf, 1970. 1st ed. NF in dj, sm tear on front; spine sl sunned. *STAHR.* $35

MacDonald, Ross (pseud of Kenneth Millar). ARCHER IN HOLLYWOOD. NY: Knopf, 1967. 1st ed. NF in dj. *ELSE FINE.* $45

MacDonald, Ross (pseud of Kenneth Millar). ARCHER IN JEOPARDY. Knopf, 1979. 1st. Fine. Dj has two small bumps. *STAHR.* $30

MacDonald, Ross (pseud of Kenneth Millar). ARCHER IN JEOPARDY. NY: Alfred A. Knopf, 1979. Omnibus ed. Faint rmdr stamp top edge, o/w Fine in dj. *MORDIDA.* $30

MacDonald, Ross (pseud of Kenneth Millar). BLACK MONEY. NY: Knopf, 1966. 1st ed. Fine, minor rubs at dj edges. *ELSE FINE.* $175

MacDonald, Ross (pseud of Kenneth Millar). FIND A VICTIM. NY: Knopf, 1954. 1st ed. Bkpl. NF in lightly worn dj. *ELSE FINE.* $275

MacDonald, Ross (pseud of Kenneth Millar). LEW ARCHER, PRIVATE INVESTIGATOR. NY: Mysterious Press, 1977. 1/250 numbered/signed. As New in ptd acetate dj, linen slipcase. *DERMONT.* $150

MacDonald, Ross (pseud of Kenneth Millar). LEW ARCHER PRIVATE INVESTIGATOR. NY: Mysterious, (1977). 1st ed. One of 250 signed. Fine in acetate jacket in pub's slipcase. *UNGER.* $200

MacDonald, Ross (pseud of Kenneth Millar). LEW ARCHER: PRIVATE INVESTIGATOR. NY: Mysterious Press, 1977. 1st ed. Fine in dj. *MORDIDA.* $45

MacDonald, Ross (pseud of Kenneth Millar). MEET ME AT THE MORGUE. NY: Knopf, 1953. 1st ed. NF, bright, unfaded dj has minor wear to top edge of rear panel. *ELSE FINE.* $400

MacDonald, Ross (pseud of Kenneth Millar). ON CRIME WRITING. Santa Barbara: Capra Press, 1973. 1/250 numbered (entire hb ed), signed. Fine. *LOPEZ.* $85

MacDonald, Ross (pseud of Kenneth Millar). SELF-PORTRAIT. Capra, 1981. 1/250 numbered, signed by author and Eudora Welty, who contributed foreword. About Fine. *DERMONT.* $125

MacDonald, Ross (pseud of Kenneth Millar). SELF-PORTRAIT. Santa Barbara: Capra Press, 1981. 1/250 numbered. Foreword by Eudora Welty. Signed by MacDonald and Welty. Bound in full leather; Fine w/o dj as issued. *LOPEZ.* $175

MacDonald, Ross (pseud of Kenneth Millar). SELF-PORTRAIT: CEASELESSLY INTO THE PAST. Foreword by Eudora Welty. Santa Barbara: Capra Press, 1981. 1st ed. Bump at top of spine, o/w Fine in dj w/wrinkling. *MORDIDA.* $30

MacDonald, Ross (pseud of Kenneth Millar). SELF-PORTRAIT: CEASELESSLY INTO THE PAST. With a forward by Eudora Welty. Santa Barbara: Capra Press, 1981. 1st ed. One of 250 numbered, signed. VF w/o dj as issued. *MORDIDA.* $150

MacDonald, Ross (pseud of Kenneth Millar). SLEEPING BEAUTY. London: Collins, (1973). 1st Eng ed. Slight wear to dj. VG. *JUVELIS.* $25

MacDonald, Ross (pseud of Kenneth Millar). THE BARBAROUS COAST. NY: Knopf, 1956. 1st ed. Just About Fine in very lightly soiled dj. Nice. *CAPTAIN'S BOOKSHELF.* $175

MacDonald, Ross (pseud of Kenneth Millar). THE BLUE HAMMER. NY: Alfred A. Knopf, 1976. 1st ed. Sl fading, o/w Fine in dj. *MORDIDA.* $30

MacDonald, Ross (pseud of Kenneth Millar). THE CHILL. London: Collins Crime Club, 1964. 1st ed. NF, dj has minor edgewear. *ELSE FINE.* $45

MacDonald, Ross (pseud of Kenneth Millar). THE DOOMSTERS. London: Cassell, 1958. 1st ed. Fine, moderate edgewear, small chips to upper spine corners of dj. *ELSE FINE.* $100

MacDonald, Ross (pseud of Kenneth Millar). THE FAR SIDE OF THE DOLLAR. NY: Alfred A. Knopf, 1965. 1st ed. Fine in VG price-clipped dj (closed tears, wear, crease-tear and ring-mark). *MORDIDA.* $100

MacDonald, Ross (pseud of Kenneth Millar). THE GALTON CASE. NY: Knopf, 1959. 1st ed. Fine in bright dj (tiny nick at upper edge of rear panel, spine fold, o/w also Fine). *LOPEZ.* $350

MacDonald, Ross (pseud of Kenneth Millar). THE GOODBYE LOOK. Knopf, 1969. 1st ed, Fine in dj. *STAHR.* $60

MacDonald, Ross (pseud of Kenneth Millar). THE GOODBYE LOOK. Knopf, 1969. 1st ed. Fine in price-clipped dj, sl sunned spine. *STAHR.* $45

MacDonald, Ross (pseud of Kenneth Millar). THE GOODBYE LOOK. London: Collins, (1969). 1st Eng ed. VG in dj w/light wear. *JUVELIS.* $35

MacDonald, Ross (pseud of Kenneth Millar). THE INSTANT ENEMY. London: Collins, (1963). 1st Eng ed. NF in VG dj. *JUVELIS.* $50

MacDonald, Ross (pseud of Kenneth Millar). THE INSTANT ENEMY. NY: Alfred A. Knopf, 1968. 1st ed. Fine in dj. *MORDIDA.* $90

MacDonald, Ross (pseud of Kenneth Millar). THE INSTANT ENEMY. NY: Knopf, (1968). 1st ed. NF with Goldstone bkpl in NF dj. *UNGER.* $85

MacDonald, Ross (pseud of Kenneth Millar). THE INSTANT ENEMY. NY: Knopf, 1968. 1st ed. Fine in dj. *ELSE FINE.* $175

MacDonald, Ross (pseud of Kenneth Millar). THE MOVING TARGET. Boston: Gregg, 1979. 1st ed by this pub. VF in dj. *SILVER DOOR.* $25 .

MacDonald, Ross (pseud of Kenneth Millar). THE WYCHERLY WOMAN. London: Collins Crime Club, 1962. 1st Eng ed. Fine in dj (internal tape mend; wear). *MORDIDA.* $45

MacDonald, Sheila. MY AFRICAN GARDEN. NY: The Century Co. (1928). 1st ed. *KARMIOLE.* $30

Mace, Arthur C. and Herbert E. Winlock. THE TOMB OF SENEBTISI AT LISHT. NY: Metropolitan Museum of Art, 1916. 1st ed, ltd to 1000. Metropolitan Museum of Art Egyptian Expedition, Vol. I. 35 plts (3 color). 1/2 calf. Good. *ARCHAEOLOGIA.* $650

Mace, Jean. THE HISTORY OF A MOUTHFUL OF BREAD: AND ITS EFFECT ON THE ORGANIZATION OF MEN AND ANIMALS. NY, 1868. 1st Amer ed. *FYE.* $75

Macfarlan, Allan (ed). AMERICAN INDIAN LEGENDS. LA: LEC at the Ward Ritchie Press, 1968. One of 1500 illus, signed by Everett Gee Jackson. Fine in slipcase. *CAPTAIN'S BOOKSHELF.* $125

MacFarlane, Charles. LIFE OF NAPOLEON BONAPARTE. London: Routledge, 1880. 3rd ed. 12mo, xi,368pp. Contemp full morocco. Dec spine gilt. Marbled eps & fore-edges. Slight cover wear. Front cover reattached, o/w VG. *DIAMOND.* $35

MacFarlane, J. AN AMERICAN GEOLOGICAL RAILWAY GUIDE...DESCRIPTION OF EACH OF THE FORMATIONS. Appleton, 1879. 216pp. Front cvr soiling o/w VG. *BOOKCELL.* $50

MacFie, Harry. WASA-WASA. NY, (1951). 1st ed. VG in dj. *ARTIS.* $15

MacFie, Harry. WASA-WASA. NY: W.W. Norton & Company, Inc., 1951. 1st ed. VG in similar dj. *PARMER.* $30

MacGrath, Harold. THE CELLINI PLAQUE. GC: Doubleday-Page, 1925. 1st ed. VF, minor edgewear, some closed tears to pict dj. *ELSE FINE.* $50

MacGregor, Frances C. TWENTIETH CENTURY INDIANS. NY, 1941. 1st ed. Foreword by Clark Wissler. *HEINOLDT.* $15

Macgregor, Frances et al. FACIAL DEFORMITIES AND PLASTIC SURGERY, A PSYCHOSOCIAL STUDY. Springfield, 1953. 1st ed. *FYE.* $50

MacGregor, J. M. THE ROB ROY ON THE JORDAN, NILE, RED SEA AND GENNESARETH, ETC. A CANOE CRUISE....London, 1869. 13, 474pp. 4 litho color plts; 8 plts maps, 1 fldg, many woodcuts. Handsomely bound 1/2 composition leather, dec eps papers by Kushner of Paterson, NJ. Contents Fine. *HEINOLDT.* $75

MacGregor, J. THE ROB ROY ON THE JORDAN, NILE, RED SEA, AND GENNESARETH, & C. NY, 1870. 464pp. Nice. *O'NEILL.* $50

Machado, Antonio. CANCIONES. Robert Bly (trans). West Branch, Iowa: The Toothpaste Press, (1980). 1st ed. One of 150 ptd on Rives & hand-bound by Constance Sayre of the Black Oak Bindery, this copy hors commerce, inscribed. Boards. VF. *JAFFE.* $150

Machen, Arthur. BRIDLES & SPURS. Cleveland: The Rowfant Club, 1951. 1st ed. #44/178. Linen-backed grn boards; paper label. Spine, else Fine in sl slipcase. *CAPTAIN'S BOOKSHELF.* $175

Machen, Arthur. HOUSE OF SOULS. Knopf, 1922. 1st ed. Near VG. *MADLE.* $60

Machen, Arthur. ORNAMENTS IN JADE. NY, 1924. Ltd ed. 1000 numbered, designed by T.M. Cleland. Printed by the Pynson Printers. Signed. This is the Press Copy. Uncut. Spine label sl rubbed, tiny nick side spine rear cover. Fine. *POLYANTHOS.* $75

Machen, Arthur. ORNAMENTS IN JADE. NY: Knopf, 1924. 1st ed. One of 1000 signed, numbered. Spine ends torn, paper spine label effaced else Good to VG. *OTHER WORLDS.* $30

Machen, Arthur. THE ANATOMY OF TOBACCO. Knopf, 1926. 1st US ed. VG in sl chipped, worn dj. *MADLE.* $75

Machen, Arthur. THE BOWMEN. Putnam, 1915. VG. *MADLE.* $35

Machen, Arthur. THE CHRONICLE OF CLEMENDY. Carbonnek: Privately Ptd for the Society of Pantegruelists, 1923. Front hinge cracked, small corner dampstain on 1st 50 or so pages, but almost VG. 1st this ed. #192 of 1050 signed. *CHAPEL HILL.* $35

Machen, Arthur. THE CHRONICLE OF CLEMENDY. Privately ptd, 1923. One of 1050 numbered, signed. VG. *MADLE.* $100

Machen, Arthur. THE GREEN ROUND. Arkham House, 1968. VF in dj. *MADLE.* $80

Machen, Arthur. THE SHINING PYRAMID. Chicago, 1923. Ltd ed, 56/850 (of 875). Teg, uncut, bkpl, tiny edge piece missing, ffep. NF. *POLYANTHOS.* $50

Machen, Arthur. THE THREE IMPOSTERS. London: John Lane, 1895. 1st ed. Edges darkened o/w VG in cl covered boards w/gold-stamped lettering on spine. *MORDIDA.* $175

Machetanz, Sara. THE HOWL OF THE MALEMUTE. NY: Sloane Assoc, 1961. 1st ed. VG in VG- dj. *BLUE DRAGON.* $25

Macilwain, George. MEMOIRS OF JOHN ABERNETHY, F.R.S. WITH A VIEW OF HIS LECTURES, WRITINGS, AND CHARACTER. NY, 1853. 1st ed. 434pp. *FYE.* $75

MacInnes, Colin. CITY OF SPADES. NY: Macmillan, 1958. 1st ed. Fine; lt rubbing dj spine ends. *ELSE FINE.* $45

MacInnes, Colin. THREE YEARS TO PLAY. NY: FSG, 1970. 1st ed. As New in dj. *ELSE FINE.* $30

MacInnes, Colin. WESTWARD TO LAUGHTER. Farrar, Straus & Giroux, 1970. 1st Amer ed. Fine in dj. Dj spine sl darkened. *STAHR.* $20

MacInnes, Colin. WESTWARD TO LAUGHTER. London: McGibbon & Kee, 1969. 1st ed. Fine in dj. *ELSE FINE.* $40

MacInnes, Colin. WESTWARD TO LAUGHTER. NY: FSG, 1970. 1st ed. As new in dj. *ELSE FINE.* $30

MacInnes, Helen. NORTH FROM ROME. NY: Harcourt Brace, 1958. 1st ed. Inscribed. VG in dj w/chipped spine ends and corners, chip on back panel, wear along folds and several short closed tears. *MORDIDA.* $25

MacInnes, Helen. PRAY FOR A BRAVE HEART. NY: Harcourt Brace, 1955. 1st ed. Inscribed. VG in price-clipped dj w/faded spine, chipping at top of spine, several short closed tears and chipping at corners. *MORDIDA*. $25

Macintyre, Captain Donald. THE PRIVATEERS. London: Paul Elek Ltd., 1975. 1st ed. Fine in VG dj. *PARMER*. $20

Macirone, Francis. FACTS RELATING TO THE FALL AND DEATH OF JOACHIM MURAT...London, 1817. 3rd ed. 3/4 lea. Teg. NF. *POLYANTHOS*. $75

Mack, Connie. CONNIE MACK'S BASEBALL BOOK. Knopf, 1950. 2nd ptg. Signed. VG in VG dj. *PLAPINGER*. $45

Mackay, Malcolm S. COW RANGE AND HUNTING TRAIL. Putnam, 1925. 1st ed. Dk grn cl. Fine. *VARNER*. $200

Mackay-Smith, Alexander. THE AMERICAN FOXHOUND 1747-1967. Millwood: The American Foxhound Club, 1968. 1st and only ed, this no. 283 of 1000. Signed presentation. VG. *OCTOBER FARM*. $425

Mackenzie, Alexander Slidell. LIFE OF STEPHEN DECATUR. Boston: Charles C. Little and James Browne, 1846. 1st ed. Engr title, port, facs. Orig cl, lib label, but VG. *LEFKOWICZ*. $60

Mackenzie, Alexander. ALEXANDER MACKENZIE'S VOYAGE TO THE PACIFIC OCEAN IN 1793. Chicago: Lakeside Press, Christmas, 1931. 1st ed thus. Fldg map. VF. *CONNOLLY & WADE*. $37.50

Mackenzie, Alexander. VOYAGES FROM MONTREAL, ON THE RIVER ST. LAWRENCE THROUGH THE CONTINENT OF NORTH AMERICA.... London: Ptd for T. Cadell, Jun. and W. Davies, 1801. 1st ed. 3 maps. Leather spine restored w/orig spine laid on. Crnrs worn. Lt foxing. Respectable. Bkpls. Howes M133. *PARMER*. $3000

Mackenzie, Compton. CARNIVAL. NY: D. Appleton, 1913. Inscribed. VG w/o dj. *LOPEZ*. $45

Mackenzie, Compton. GREEK MEMORIES. London, 1939. xxiii,455pp. Reissue. *O'NEILL*. $30

Mackenzie, Compton. WIND OF FREEDOM. London, 1943. xi,276pp. 1st ed. *O'NEILL*. $35

Mackenzie, Donald A. EGYPTIAN MYTH AND LEGEND, WITH HISTORICAL....London: Gresham, n.d. (ca. 1920). 38 plts, fldg plt. Sl rubbed, covers sl affected by dampness, bumped, o/w Good. *WORLDWIDE*. $35

Mackenzie, G. Muir and A.P. Irby. TRAVELS IN THE SLAVONIC PROVINCES OF TURKEY-IN-EUROPE. 2 vols. London: Daldy, Isbiter, 1877. 2nd ed, rev. xvii;313; iii;342pp. 20 plts (1 fldg), fldg color map. Orig cl, edges rubbed, spine frayed, sl shaken. Ex-lib, o/w Good. *WORLDWIDE*. $150

MacKenzie, John. AUSTRAL AFRICA. London: Sampson Low, Marston, Searle, Rivington, 1887. 2 vols. 1st ed. xii,515pp; viii,525pp, 8vo. 2 fldg maps. Orig cl, rubbed & scuffed, top & bottom of spine sl torn, corners bumped. Map in vol 2 sl torn. VG ex-lib. *WORLDWIDE*. $125

Mackenzie, Morell. DISEASES OF THE PHARYNX, LARYNX, AND TRACHEA. NY, 1880, 440pp. With DISEASES OF THE OESOPHAGUS, NOSE AND NASO-PHARYNX. NY, 1884. 550pp. 1st Amer eds. Orig grn and yellow cloth bindings, as issued. *FYE*. $150

MacKenzie, R. Shelton. LIFE OF CHARLES DICKENS. Phila: T.B. Peterson, (1870). 1st ed. 8vo, 484pp, green cloth with gilt motif of Dickens on spine, one bkpl inside cover, one removed front endpaper. Fine. *GREAT EXPECTATIONS*. $37.50

MacKenzie, William Douglas. SOUTH AFRICA. ITS HISTORY, HEROES AND WARS. Oakland, CA: Occidental, (1900). 1st ed. Fldg map laid in. Cvrs faded, a bit soiled; hole in pp 219-220 w/some loss of text, else Good. *WREDEN*. $50

Mackenzie, William. THE PHYSIOLOGY OF VISION. London, 1841. 1st ed. Recent cloth w/new eps, lib perforation stamp on title, o/w Fine. *FYE*. $100

Mackersey, Ian. RESCUE BELOW ZERO. NY: W.W. Norton, 1954. 1st ed. VG in soiled, worn dj. *PARMER*. $30

Mackinney, Loren. EARLY MEDIEVAL MEDICINE WITH SPECIAL REFERENCE WITH FRANCE AND CHARTRES. Baltimore, 1937. 1st ed. *FYE*. $75

Mackinnon, Lilias. MUSIC BY HEART. London, NY, and Toronto: Oxford Univ Press, 1938. 1st ed. Dj. Fine. *WEBER*. $20

Mackworth-Praed, C.W. and C.H.B. Grant. BIRDS OF EASTERN AND NORTH EASTERN AFRICA. NY, 1980 (1957; 1960). 2nd ed. 96 colored plts. 2 vols. Minimal wear. *SUTTON*. $135

Maclay, Edgar S. (ed). JOURNAL OF WILLIAM MACLAY, U.S. SENATOR ...1789-1791. NY, 1890. 1st ed. Teg. Sl cvr wear. Lacks fly, o/w text VG. *DIAMOND*. $45

Maclay, Edgar S. MOSES BROWN, CAPTAIN U.S.N. NY: Baker, (1904). 1st ed. Orig pict cl, spine lightly faded. *GINSBERG*. $75

Maclay, Edgar Stanton. A HISTORY OF AMERICAN PRIVATEERS. NY, 1899. 1st ed. xl, 519 pp. 14 plts. Slight stain on lower joint. *LEFKOWICZ*. $110

Maclay, Edgar Stanton. A HISTORY OF THE UNITED STATES NAVY, from 1775 to 1898. Technical Revision by Lieutenant Roy C. Smith. New ed, rev, enl. NY: D. Appleton & Co. (1898). 2 vols. Pub's brn calf over marbled boards, gilt spines. Teg. *KARMIOLE*. $75

Maclay, John. OTHER ENGAGEMENTS. Dream House, 1987. 1st ed. As New. *MADLE*. $25

MacLean, Alistair. BEAR ISLAND. London: Collins, 1971. 1st ed. Very NF in dj. *SILVER DOOR*. $35

MacLean, Alistair. CAPTAIN COOK. GC: Doubleday & Co., 1972. 1st ed. VG. *PARMER*. $30

MacLean, Alistair. FORCE 10 FROM NAVARONE. GC: Doubleday, 1968. 1st ed. Fine in price clipped dj. *ELSE FINE*. $25

MacLean, Alistair. FORCE 10 FROM NAVARONE. London: Collins, 1968. 1st ed. Fine in dj. *ELSE FINE*. $35

MacLean, Alistair. H.M.S. ULYSSES. GC: Doubleday, 1956. 1st ed, 1st bk. Fine; dj, lt edgewear. *ELSE FINE*. $35

MacLean, Alistair. RIVER OF DEATH. London: Collins, 1981. 1st ed. Fine in dj. *SILVER DOOR*. $25

MacLean, Alistair. SANTORINI. London: Collins, 1986. 1st ed. Fine in dj. *SILVER DOOR*. $25

MacLean, Alistair. THE WAY TO DUSTY DEATH. London: Collins, 1973. 1st ed. Fine in dj. *SILVER DOOR*. $35

MacLean, Charles. THE WATCHER. Simon & Schuster, 1982. 1st ed. Fine in dj. *MADLE*. $50

Maclean, Hector. POPULAR PHOTOGRAPHIC PRINTING PROCESSES. London: L. Upcott Gill. 1898. 1st ed. (6),168pp. Frontis, 2 plts. Presentation, inscribed in 1898. Bound in 1/2 calf over brown cl, dec gilt spine, leather spine label. Orig dec brown cl covers and spine bound in at back. Teg. *KARMIOLE*. $100

Maclean, J. Kennedy and Walker J. McSpadden. HEROES OF THE FARTHEST NORTH AND FARTHEST SOUTH. NY: Thomas Y. Crowell Company, c. 1923. Rev ed. 2 fldg maps. Wear and soiling, interior VG. *PARMER*. $35

Maclean, J.P. MASTODON, MAMMOTH, AND MAN. 9 illus. Cincinnati, 1880. 2nd ed. 84pp. Orig gilt-stamped cl. Lt soiling, institutional bkpl, # sticker on spine. *SUTTON*. $95

Maclean, Norman. A RIVER RUNS THROUGH IT AND OTHER STORIES. Chicago: Univ of Chicago Press, (1976). Fine in price-clipped dj (few tiny nicks). One of only 1577 ptd. *CAPTAIN'S BOOK-SHELF*. $600

MacLean, Norman. A RIVER RUNS THROUGH IT. Chicago: Univ of Chicago Press, (1976). 1st ed. Owner name fep, o/w Fine in dj (bit of edgewear, faint spot of discoloration on front panel). *LOPEZ.* $650

Maclean, Norman. A RIVER RUNS THROUGH IT. West Hatfield: Pennyroyal Press, (1989). One of 200 in 1/4 red morocco over marbled boards. Barry Moser (illus). Mint. Signed by Maclean and Moser. *CAPTAIN'S BOOKSHELF.* $350

Macleish, Archibald. FRESCOES FOR MR. ROCKEFELLER'S CITY. NY: John Day, 1933. 1st ed. Signed. Wraps. John Day Pamphlet No. 29, NF w/erasure on half-title. *BEASLEY.* $100

MacLeod, Fiona (pseud of William Sharp). THE MOUNTAIN LOVERS. (Boston: Roberts Bros. and London: John Lane, 1895). 1st ed. Cover and title page decs by Aubrey Beardsley. Evidence of bkpl removal, spine sl dulled, o/w Fine. *PIRAGES.* $50

MacLeod, Norman. THE BITTER ROOTS. Smith & Durrell, 1941. 1st ed. VG, chipped & taped dj. *AUTHORS OF THE WEST.* $50

Maclise, Joseph. SURGICAL ANATOMY. Phila, 1870. Orig cloth. Folio, 156pp. VF. Stone engrvs. *FYE.* $500

Maclure, William. OPINIONS ON VARIOUS SUBJECTS, DEDICATED TO THE INDUSTRIOUS PRODUCERS. VOLUME ONE. New Harmony, IN: School Press, 1831. 1st ed. 483pp. Contemp leather and boards, hinges strengthened. Howes M162. *GINSBERG.* $1250

Macmichael, William. THE GOLD-HEADED CANE. NY, 1926. 261pp. *FYE.* $45

Macmillan, Donald B. ETAH AND BEYOND. Boston, 1927. 1st ed. VG. *ARTIS.* $35

Macmillan, Donald B. FOUR YEARS IN THE WHITE NORTH. Boston: Hale, Cushman & Flint, 1933. Good+. *BLUE DRAGON.* $35

Macmillan, Donald B. FOUR YEARS IN THE WHITE NORTH. NY: Harper & Brothers, 1918. 1st ed. Cl sl sunned and faded else VG. *GREAT EPIC.* $65

Macmillan, Donald B. FOUR YEARS IN THE WHITE NORTH. New and Revised Ed. Boston: The Medici Soc of America. 1925. *KARMIOLE.* $60

Macmillan, Donald B. FOUR YEARS IN THE WHITE NORTH. NY, London: Harper & Bros, 1918. Spine faded, brds mottled. *PARMER.* $45

Macmillan, Harold. RECONSTRUCTION. A PLEA FOR A NATIONAL POLICY. London, 1933. 1st ed, 1st bk. Inscribed. Cvrs sl stained. Spine darkened, gilt dull, o/w VG. *DIAMOND.* $75

Macmillan, Laura (comp). THE NORTH CAROLINA PORTRAIT INDEX 1700-1860. Chapel Hill, (1963). 1st ed. Patron's ed, One of 100 specially-bound. Fine. *CAPTAIN'S BOOKSHELF.* $200

Macmillan, Miriam. GREEN SEAS AND WHITE ICE. NY, (1948). Signed. VG in dj. *ARTIS.* $15

Macmillan, Miriam. GREEN SEAS AND WHITE ICE. NY: Dodd, Mead & Co, 1948. VG in Good dj. *BLUE DRAGON.* $15

MacMinn, Edwin. ON THE FRONTIER WITH COLONEL ANTES; OR, THE STRUGGLE FOR SUPREMACY...IN PENNSYLVANIA. Camden, NJ, 1900. 1st ed. Orig dec cloth. One of 1000. *GINSBERG.* $150

Macnish, Robert. AN INTRODUCTION TO PHRENOLOGY, IN THE FORM OF QUESTION AND ANSWER, WITH AN APPENDIX, AND COPIOUS ILLUSTRATIVE NOTES. Boston, 1836. 1st Amer ed. 135pp. *FYE.* $75

Macomb, J.N. REPORT OF THE EXPLORING EXPEDITION FROM SANTA FE, NM TO THE JUNCTION OF THE GRAND AND GREEN RIVERS OF THE GREAT COLORADO OF THE WEST IN 1859. Under the Direction of Capt. J.N. Macomb, with Geological Report by Prof. J.S. Newberry. Wash, GPO, 1876.

146pp, plts, fldg map. In orig brwn binding. Minor shelfwear, small spots back cover. Very light foxing to contents. Plts very clean,; colored plts with tissue guards are perfect. Map appears virtually untouched. *FIVE QUAIL.* $975

MacOrlan, Pierre. ON BOARD THE MORNING STAR. Boni, 1924. 1st ed. Trans by Malcolm Cowley. VG. *BEBBAH.* $40

Macoun, J. and J.M. Macoun. CATALOGUE OF CANADIAN BIRDS. Ottawa, 1909. 2nd ed. Buckram. Rubbed at edges; bkpl. *SUTTON.* $60

Macpherson, H.B. THE HOME-LIFE OF A GOLDEN EAGLE. London, 1910. 2nd ed. Later buckram. 32 mounted plts. Scattered lt foxing; institutional bkpl. *SUTTON.* $47

MacQuarrie, Hector. TAHITI DAYS. NY: George H. Doran, 1920. Cloth worn, spine chip at heel, pencil inscrip on title page. *PARMER.* $35

Macray, William Dunn. ANNALS OF THE BODLEIAN LIBRARY, OXFORD, A.D. 1598—A.D. 1867. London, Oxford, Cambridge: Rivingtons, 1868. 1st ed. Orig cl w/new cl spine but orig cloth spine title preserved. Letter mounted to fep; bkpl. *OAK KNOLL.* $55

Macready, Jonathan. A TREATISE ON RUPTURES. London, 1893. 1st ed. 442pp. 24 Fine lithographic plts. Exceptionally Fine. *FYE.* $150

MacWethy, Lou D. BATTLE OF KLOCK'S FIELD, OCTOBER 19, 1780 and: Dailey, N.P. BATTLE OF STONE ARABIA. Enterprise & News, St. Johnsville, NY, 1930. 17pp (small print-double columns). Wraps. *HEINOLDT.* $15

Madden, David. BIJOU. NY: Crown, (1974). Uncorrected proof. Signed. Light dust soiling of covers else Fine in wraps. *DORN.* $85

Madden, David. CASSANDRA SINGING. NY: Crown, (1969). 1st Amer ed. Inscribed. Small owner's sticker else NF in dj. *DORN.* $50

Madden, David. ON THE BIG WIND. NY: Holt, Rinehart and Winston, (1980). Adv rev copy with slip. Inscribed. NF in dj. *DORN.* $50

Madden, David. THE NEW ORLEANS OF POSSIBILITIES. Baton Rouge: Louisiana State Univ, (1982). 1st Amer ed. Signed. Fine in dj. *DORN.* $40

Madden, David. THE POETIC IMAGES IN 6 GENRES. Carbondale: Southern Illinois Univ Press, (1969). 1st Amer ed. Inscribed. Fine in dj. *DORN.* $45

Madden, Henry Miller. XANTUS, HUNGARIAN NATURALIST. Palo Alto: Books of the West, 1949. 1st ed. 6 plts. Fine in VG dj. *OREGON.* $90

Madis, George. THE WINCHESTER HANDBOOK. Ann Arbor: Edward Brothers, 1981. Stated 1st ed. Signed. Fine, not pub w/dj. *BACKMAN.* $25

Madison, Virginia. THE BIG BEND COUNTRY OF TEXAS. Univ of NM, 1955. 1st ed. Fine in sl chipped dj. *VARNER.* $30

Madsen, David. BLACK PLUME: THE SUPPRESSED MEMOIRS OF EDGAR ALLAN POE. NY: Simon and Schuster, 1980. 1st ed. Fine in dj. *MORDIDA.* $35

Maeterlinck, Maurice. THE CHILDREN'S LIFE OF THE BEE. Dodd, Mead, 1920. 192pp. Edward Detmold illus. VG+. Color cvr pict pastedown. *BEBBAH.* $25

Magendie, Franscois. SUMMARY OF PHYSIOLOGY. Trans. from the French by John Revere. Baltimore, 1822. 1st Eng trans. 430pp. Recent buckram w/new eps. Contents Fine. *FYE.* $250

Magnus, Hugo. SUPERSTITION IN MEDICINE. NY, 1905. 1st Eng trans. *FYE.* $65

Magnus, Hugo. SUPERSTITION IN MEDICINE. NY, 1905. 1st Eng trans. *FYE.* $65

Magnuson, Daniel. PETER THOMPSON'S NARRATIVE OF THE LITTLE BIGHORN CAMPAIGN 1876. Glendale: A.H. Clark, 1974. Fldg map. 1st ed. VF. *OREGON.* $65

Magoffin, Susan Shelby. DOWN THE SANTA FE TRAIL AND INTO MEXICO. New Haven: Yale Univ Press, 1926. Fldg map. Bkpl, sm sticker, sl rubbed. VG. *PARMER.* $125

Magoun, F. Alexander. THE FRIGATE CONSTITUTION AND OTHER HISTORIC SHIPS. Salem, 1928. Pub. 16. 30 plts. Worn dj. *LEFKOWICZ.* $250

Magoun, F. Alexander. THE FRIGATE CONSTITUTION AND OTHER HISTORIC SHIPS. Salem: Marine Research Society, 1928. Blue cl. Tipped in "Certificate." 30 plts, 16 two-pg plans. Marine Research Soc Pub No 16. Some spotting, lt overall wear, generally VG. *PARMER.* $195

Mahan, A.T. THE INFLUENCE OF SEA POWER UPON THE FRENCH REVOLUTION AND EMPIRE 1793-1812. Boston: Little, Brown, and Co, 1894. 3rd ed. 2 vols. Bright, NF set. *PARMER.* $150

Mahan, Alfred Thayer. THE LIFE OF NELSON....Boston, 1897. 1st ed. 2 vols. (xxviii),454; xvi,427pp. Orig cl, sm tear to spine of 1st vol, still NF. *LEFKOWICZ.* $125

Mahan, James Curtis. MEMOIRS OF JAMES CURTIS MAHAN. Lincoln, NE: Franklin, (1919). 1st ed. Port. Orig cl. *GINSBERG.* $125

Mahon, P.J. and J.M. Hayes. TRIALS AND TRIUMPHS OF THE CATHOLIC CHURCH IN AMERICA. Chicago: J.S. Hyland (1907). 2 vols. VG. *AARD.* $75

Mailer, Norman. A FRAGMENT FROM VIETNAM. Helsinki: Eurographica, 1985. 1st ed. Ltd to 350 signed by Mailer. Ptd wraps. Mint. *JAFFE.* $175

Mailer, Norman. CANNIBALS AND CHRISTIANS. NY: Dial, 1966. 1st ed. Blue cl. Fine in rubbed dj. *ARCHER.* $22.50

Mailer, Norman. HARLOT'S GHOST. NY: RH, (1991). 1st ed. Signed. Fine in dj. *LOPEZ.* $85

Mailer, Norman. MARILYN MONROE. NY: Grosset & Dunlap, 1973. 1st ed. VG in heavily edgeworn dj. *AKA.* $30

Mailer, Norman. OF A SMALL AND MODEST MALIGNANCY, WICKED AND BRISTLING WITH DOTS. California: Lord John Press, 1980. Ltd ed, 92/300 on Mohawk Superfine, signed. Cloth backed marbled boards. Mint in NF box. *POLYANTHOS.* $95

Mailer, Norman. THE EXECUTIONER'S SONG. Boston: Little, Brown, (1979). 1st ed. Orig blue cl. Fine in dj. *CHAPEL HILL.* $40

Mailer, Norman. THE EXECUTIONER'S SONG. Boston: Little, Brown, (1979). 1st ed. NF in dj. *LOPEZ.* $40

Mailer, Norman. THE LAST NIGHT. A STORY. NY: Targ Editions, 1984. Ltd ed, 250 only, signed. Uncut. Pub card laid in. Fine in like dj. *POLYANTHOS.* $125

Mailer, Norman. THE LAST NIGHT. NY: Targ Editions. 1984. Ltd to 250 signed. Fine. *KARMIOLE.* $100

Mailer, Norman. THE NAKED AND THE DEAD. NY, 1948. 1st ed, 1st bk. Extremities, spine and corners very sl bumped. Fine in dj (3-1/2" x 1-1/2" piece missing top edge front panel, few edge chips, little edge rubbed). *POLYANTHOS.* $100

Mails, Thomas E. THE PUEBLO CHILDREN OF THE EARTH MOTHER. GC: Doubleday & Co, 1983. 2 vols. 1st ed. New in djs, cl slipcase. *PARMER.* $150

Maimonides, Moses. ON THE CAUSES OF SYMPTOMS. Ed. by J.O. Leibowitz & S. Marcus. Berkeley, 1974. 1st Eng trans. Dj. *FYE.* $65

Maine, Sir Henry. VILLAGE-COMMUNITIES IN THE EAST AND WEST....4th ed. London: John Murray, 1881. xii,413pp, ads, pub's catalogue. Inscribed. Spine faded, sl spine tip wear. Cvrs sl stained. Bkpl. Contents VG. *DIAMOND.* $250

Maisel, Albert. THE WOUNDED GET BACK. NY, 1944. 1st ed. Dj. *FYE.* $45

Maitland, Sir J. Ramsay Gibson. THE HISTORY OF HOWIETOUN...FROM 1873 TO THE PRESENT TIME....PART 1. J.R. Guy, Stirling, N.B. 1887. 1st ed. (24)278pp. Frontis. Uncut, gilt cl. VG. *ARTIS.* $85

MAJESTY IN FLIGHT. London, 1984. Ron Van Der Meer. Moveable bk. *BOOKFINDERS INTL.* $30

Majno, Guido. THE HEALING HAND: MAN AND WOUND IN THE ANCIENT WORLD. Cambridge, 1975. 1st ed. *FYE.* $45

Major, Clarence. ALL-NIGHT VISITORS. NY: Olympia Press, (1969). 1st ed. Adv rev copy of scarce 1st book. NF in sl rubbed dj. *LOPEZ.* $125

Major, Clarence. EMERGENCY EXIT. NY: Fiction Collective, (1979). 1st ed. Hb issue. Fine in Fine dj. *LOPEZ.* $35

Major, Ralph. A HISTORY OF MEDICINE. Springfield, 1954. 1st ed. 2 vols. 1155pp. Scarce. *FYE.* $175

Major, Ralph. CLASSIC DESCRIPTIONS OF DISEASE WITH BIOGRAPHICAL SKETCHES OF THE AUTHORS. Springfield, 1932. 1st ed. *FYE.* $75

Major, Ralph. FATAL PARTNERS, WAR AND DISEASE. NY, 1941. 1st ed. *FYE.* $50

Majors, Alexander. SEVENTY YEARS ON THE FRONTIER. Minneapolis: Ross & Haines, 1965. Ltd ed of 2000. Fine in Good dj. *CONNOLLY & WADE.* $40

Makins, George. SURGICAL EXPERIENCES IN SOUTH AFRICA, 1899-1900. London, 1913. 2nd ed. 504pp. 105 illus. Ex-lib. *FYE.* $125

Makkleson, Ejnar. LOST IN THE ARCTIC. London: Heinemann, 1913. Grn cl w/silver centerpiece. 1st ed. Frontis, fldg map. Bright, VG. *CHAPEL HILL.* $135

Makower, Stanley V. THE MIRROR OF MUSIC. London: John Lane, 1895. Front hinge just starting at top, but VG. 1st ed. *CHAPEL HILL.* $90

Makriyannis. THE MEMOIRS OF GENERAL MAKRIYANNIS 1797-1864. London, 1966. H.A. Lidderdale (ed). Dj. *O'NEILL.* $35

Malamud, Bernard. A NEW LIFE. NY: FSC, 1961. 1st ed. Fine in dj, usual lt age darkening on spine. *ELSE FINE.* $75

Malamud, Bernard. IDIOTS FIRST. NY: Farrar Straus, 1963. 1st ed. Fine; short tear, minor edgewear to dj. *ELSE FINE.* $40

Malamud, Bernard. PICTURES OF FIDELMAN. NY: FSG, 1969. 1st ed. NF; closed tear at bottom spine fold of dj. *ELSE FINE.* $35

Malamud, Bernard. PICTURES OF FIDELMAN. Spiral-bound ptd wrappers. NY: Farrar Straus & Giroux, (1968). Uncorrected proof. Some pencil scoring in margins, top of front wrapper sl faded, o/w Fine. Rare. *JAFFE.* $225

Malamud, Bernard. THE ASSISTANT. NY: Farrar, Straus and Cudahy, (1957). 1st ed, 1st issue, w/reviews of The Natural on rear panel. Orig cl-backed brn boards. NF in VG dj, spine ends tape-repaired on verso. Inscribed. *CHAPEL HILL.* $200

Malamud, Bernard. THE FIXER. NY: Farrar Straus Giroux, (1966). 1st ed. NF in dj. *LOPEZ.* $40

Malamud, Bernard. THE MAGIC BARREL. NY: Farrar, Straus & Cudahy, (1958). 1st ed. Orig cl-backed boards. NF in sl spine-faded, VG dj, 1/2" closed tear top of rear panel. Signed. *CHAPEL HILL.* $200

Malamud, Bernard. THE NATURAL. London: Eyre & Spottiswoode, 1963. 1st Eng ed, 1st bk (w/notes on baseball not included in Amer ed). Fine in price clipped dj. *HELLER.* $150

Malamud, Bernard. THE NATURAL. NY: Harcourt, (1952). 1st ed, 1st bk. Fine in blue cloth and dj (rather deeply price clipped to the point of just touching the "l" in Natural on the front flap) w/a 1/8" chip from the head of the spine and a short tear. Signed. *CAPTAIN'S BOOKSHELF.* $1250

Malamud, Bernard. THE NATURAL. NY: Harcourt, Brace, (1952). 1st ed, 1st bk. Orig blue boards. NF in price-clipped dj. Signed ffep. *CHAPEL HILL.* $750

Malamud, Bernard. THE NATURAL. NY: Harcourt Brace, (1952). 1st ed. Fine in dj (tiny bit of rubbing). *LOPEZ.* $850

Malamud, Bernard. THE STORIES OF BERNARD MALAMUD. NY: Farrar, Straus, Giroux, (1983). 1st ed. One of a specially bound ltd ed, signed. Mint in pub's slipcase, orig plastic shrinkwrap. *CHAPEL HILL.* $200

Malamud, Bernard. THE TENANTS. NY: FSG, 1971. 1st ed. As New in dj. *ELSE FINE.* $50

Malamud, Nathan. ATLAS OF NEUROPATHOLOGY. Berkeley, 1957. 1st ed. Ex-lib. *FYE.* $40

Malcolm, George and Maxwell, Aymer. GROUSE AND GROUSE MOORS. London: A&C Black, 1910. 1st ed. Small tears top and base of spine, some edgewear, thus G+ only. Scarce. *OLD LONDON.* $50

Malcolm, John. A BACK ROOM IN SOMERS TOWN. NY: Scribner's, (1984). 1st US ed. Fine in Fine dj. *UNGER.* $30

Malcolm, John. MORTAL RUIN. NY: Scribner's, 1988. 1st Amer ed. Rev copy signed. Pub slip. VF in dj. *SILVER DOOR.* $37.50

Malcolm, John. THE GODWIN SIDEBOARD. London: Collins Crime Club, 1984. 1st ed. VF in dj. *MORDIDA.* $35

Malcolm, John. THE GWEN JOHN SCULPTURE. London: Collins Crime Club, 1985. 1st ed. Fine in dj w/short tears, wear. *MORDIDA.* $30

Malcolm, John. WHISTLER IN THE DARK. NY: Scribner's, (1986). 1st US ed. Fine in Fine dj. *UNGER.* $30

Malcolmson, Anne. SONG OF ROBIN HOOD. Houghton Mifflin, 1947. 1st ed. 123pp. Illus by Virginia Lee Burton. Corner bumps, small stain to upper corner of four leaves, VG+ w/silver & red on black dec cvrs. Dj has edgewear, spine chips, 1.5" x 2.5" piece missing lower edge, but still Good+. *BEBBAH.* $150

Malden, R.H. NINE GHOSTS. London, 1947. Fine in NF dj. *MADLE.* $75

Malden, R.H. NINE GHOSTS. London, 1947. VG in most of dj. *MADLE.* $45

Male, Emile. THE EARLY CHURCHES OF ROME. David Buxton (trans). London: Ernest Benn Ltd, 1960. 1st Eng ed. Dj, slipcase. *KARMIOLE.* $45

Malet, Lucas. THE GATELESS BARRIER. Dodd-Mead, 1900. 1st ed. VG. *MADLE.* $35

Malgaigne, J.F. SURGERY AND AMBROISE PARE. Norman, 1965. 1st Eng trans. *FYE.* $100

Malin, James C. INDIAN POLICY AND WESTWARD EXPANSION. Lawrence, Kansas, 1921. 108pp. Wraps. VG. *PRATT.* $35

Malinowski, Bronislaw. THE SEXUAL LIFE OF SAVAGES IN NORTH-WESTERN MELANESIA. 3rd ed, 2nd imp. London: George Routledge & Sons, Ltd. 1932. Fine in dj. *KARMIOLE.* $100

Mall, Thomas. THE HISTORY OF THE MARTYRS EPITOMISED.... Boston: Rogers & Fowle. 1747. 1st Amer ed. 2 vols bound in one. (16),267,(5); (4),xii,292,(4)pp. Index in each vol. Contemp calf, front hinge cracked but holding soundly. *KARMIOLE.* $350

Mallan, Lloyd, SUITING UP FOR SPACE. NY: John Day, 1971. Ex-lib in dj; pocket removed, stamps, spine label, tape marks. Good. *KNOLLWOOD.* $25

Mallet, Capt. Thierry. GLIMPSE OF THE BARREN LAND. NY: Privately ptd for The Revillon Freres, 1930. 1st ed. Signed presenta-

tion letter incl, and signed by the mgr (?) of the NY store and a "Compliments of Revillon Freres" card. VG (lt scuff mk on cvr. (Probably not pub w/dj.) *BACKMAN.* $40

Mallis, Arthur. AMERICAN ENTOMOLOGISTS. New Brunswick, NJ: Rutgers Univ Press, (1971). 1st ed. Fine- in VG dj. *AARD.* $30

Mallowan, Agatha Christie (Agatha Christie). STAR OVER BETHLEHEM. London: Collins, 1965. 1st ed. Inscription, o/w Fine in dj w/short closed tear. *MORDIDA.* $30

Malmin, Gunnar J. (ed). AMERICA IN THE FORTIES, (1840's). LETTERS OF....Norwegian-Amer Hist Assoc, U of Minn (1929), 1st ed. Frontis. Dj frayed. *HEINOLDT.* $12

Malone, Michael. DELECTABLE MOUNTAINS. NY: RH, (1976). 1st ed. VF in dj. Signed. *CAPTAIN'S BOOKSHELF.* $100

Malone, Michael. DINGLEY FALLS. NY: Harcourt Brace, 1980. 1st ed. Fine in dj. *MORDIDA.* $75

Malone, Michael. DINGLEY FALLS. NY: Harcourt Brace Jovanovich, 1980. 1st ed. VF in dj. *ELSE FINE.* $45

Malone, Michael. HANDLING SIN. Boston: LB, 1986. 1st ed. Fine in sl rubbed dj. Signed. *CAPTAIN'S BOOKSHELF.* $50

Malone, Michael. MONTANA, A HISTORY OF TWO CENTURIES. Univ of WA, (1976). 1st ed. VF in VF dj. *OREGON.* $25

Malone, Michael. PAINTING THE ROSES RED. NY: Random House, (1974). 1st ed, 1st bk. Fine in dj. *BERNARD.* $125

Malone, Michael. PAINTING THE ROSES RED. Random House, 1974. 1st ed. VG or better in dj. Bk cvr has been bent; dj shows light wear. *STAHR.* $35

Malone, Michael. TIME'S WITNESS. Boston: Little Brown, (1989). 1st ed. Rmdr mk. Fine in dj. Signed. *CAPTAIN'S BOOKSHELF.* $35

Malone, Michael. TIME'S WITNESS. Boston: Little Brown, 1989. 1st ed. VF in dj. *MORDIDA.* $30

Malone, Michael. UNCIVIL SEASONS. NY: Delacorte, (1983). 1st ed. Fine in dj, some rubbing. Signed. *CAPTAIN'S BOOKSHELF.* $50

Malone, Michael. UNCIVIL SEASONS. NY: Delacorte, 1983. 1st ed. VF in dj. *ELSE FINE.* $45

Malouf, David. AN IMAGINARY LIFE. London: Chatto, 1978. 1st UK. Fine in dj. *CAPTAIN'S BOOKSHELF.* $40

Malouf, David. BICYCLE. (St. Lucia): Univ of Queensland Press, (1970). 1st ed. NF. Inscribed. Issued only in wrapper. *LOPEZ.* $250

Maltby, Charles. THE LIFE AND PUBLIC SERVICES OF ABRAHAM LINCOLN. Stockton, CA: Daily Independent Steam Power Print. 1884. 1st ed. 326pp. Orig black cl. *KARMIOLE.* $60

Malthus, T. AN ESSAY ON THE PRINCIPLE OF POPULATION OR A VIEW....London: Reeves & Turner, 1878. 8th ed. 551pp, mostly unopened. VG. *BOOKCELL.* $150

Maltz, Albert. BLACK PIT. A PLAY. NY, (1935). 1st ed. Cvrs sl soiled. Dj w/piece missing, chips, edge rubbed. Author's 1st bk. *POLYANTHOS.* $35

Maltz, Albert. THE CROSS AND THE ARROW. Boston: Little Brown, 1944. 1st ed. Fine in very lightly used dj. *BEASLEY.* $50

Maltz, Maxwell. EVOLUTION OF PLASTIC SURGERY. NY, 1946. 1st ed. 368pp. Very Rare. *FYE.* $350

Man, Felix H. 150 YEARS OF ARTISTS' LITHOGRAPHS, 1803-1953. London: William Heinemann Ltd., (1953). 125 plts. Dj chipped. *OAK KNOLL.* $75

Manatt, J. Irving. AEGEAN DAYS. Boston: Houghton Mifflin, 1914. Lacks ffep. *SCHOYER'S.* $35

Mandelstam, Osip. JOURNEY TO ARMENIA. (London): Next Editions, (1980). Spiral bound in stiff red, white and black pict wraps. NF. *ROBBINS.* $40

Manford, Erasmus. TWENTY-FIVE YEARS IN THE WEST. Chicago: Erasmus Manford, 1875. 1st pub in 1867. Cover shows wear, still Good and tight. LAURIE. $30

Manfred, Frederick. CONQUERING HORSE. NY: McDowell, (1959). 1st ed. Fine in dj nicked at spine ends. UNGER. $50

Manfred, Frederick. GREEN EARTH. Crown, (1977). 1st ed. Inscribed, signed. Boards. Fine in dj. AUTHORS OF THE WEST. $35

Manfred, Frederick. KING OF SPADES. NY: Trident, (1966). 1st ed. Fine in very lightly soiled dj. UNGER. $65

Manfred, Frederick. KING OF SPADES. Trident, 1966. 1st ed. Signed. Fine in Nice chipped dj. AUTHORS OF THE WEST. $40

Manfred, Frederick. RIDERS OF JUDGMENT. NY: Random House, (1957). 1st ed. Signed. VG in dj. LOPEZ. $75

Manfred, Frederick. THE MAN WHO LOOKED LIKE THE PRINCE OF WALES. Trident, 1965. 1st ed. Inscribed, signed. Bkpl, Fine in dj. AUTHORS OF THE WEST. $35

Mangelsdorf, Tom. A HISTORY OF STEINBECK'S CANNERY ROW. Santa Cruz: Western Tanager Press, (1986). 1st ed. Fine in Fine dj. BOOK MARKET. $20

Mangione, Jerre. THE DREAM AND THE DEAL. THE FEDERAL WRITERS PROJECT 1935-1943. Boston: Little, Brown, 1972. 1st ed. Fine in Fine dj. BEASLEY. $35

Manigualt, Arthur Middleton. A CAROLINIAN GOES TO WAR, THE CIVIL WAR NARRATIVE OF ARTHUR MIDDLETON MANIGUALT, BRIGADIER GENERAL, CSA. Columbia, (1983). 1st ed. VG+. PRATT. $30

Manigualt, Edward. SIEGE TRAIN, THE JOURNAL OF A CONFEDERATE ARTILLERYMAN IN THE DEFENSE OF CHARLESTON. Columbia, (1986). Ed by Warren Ripley. 1st ed. Light dj wear o/w Fine. PRATT. $25

Manly, William Lewis. DEATH VALLEY IN '49. LA: Borden, 1949. Centennial 1st ed. NF. Howes M-255. CONNOLLY & WADE. $37.50

Manly, William Lewis. DEATH VALLEY IN '49. NY/Santa Barbara, 1929. NF. FIVE QUAIL. $40

Manly, William Lewis. DEATH VALLEY IN '49. San Jose, CA, 1894. 1927 reprint ed by Milo Milton Quaife. Lakeside Classic #25. Fldg map. VG. PRATT. $50

Manly, William Lewis. THE JAYHAWKER'S OATH AND OTHER SKETCHES. Ed by Arthur Woodward. LA, 1949. 1st ed. Fldg map. VF in VG dj (some repairs). FIVE QUAIL. $75

Mann, Albert William (comp). HISTORY OF THE FORTY-FIFTH REGIMENT, MASSACHUSETTS VOLUNTEER MILITIA. (Boston, 1908). 1st ed. Inner hinges strengthened. VG, bright, aeg. McGOWAN. $95

Mann, Ambrose Dudley. "MY EVER DEAREST FRIEND." THE LETTERS OF A. DUDLEY MANN TO JEFFERSON DAVIS, 1869-1889. Tuscaloosa, AL, 1960. 1st ed, ltd to 450. Wrappers, margins little sunned, else NF. McGOWAN. $75

Mann, Arthur, BASEBALL CONFIDENTIAL. McKay, 1951. 1st ed. Good+ in VG dj. PLAPINGER. $35

Mann, Edward. A MANUAL OF PSYCHOLOGICAL MEDICINE AND ALLIED NERVOUS DISEASES. Phila, 1883. 1st ed. 699pp. 2 photo illus. FYE. $200

Mann, Erika. SCHOOL FOR BARBARIANS. NY: Modern Age, (1938). Simultaneous pb prtg. Light foxing some pages, VG. Signed. BETWEEN COVERS. $250

Mann, Erika. THE LIGHTS GO DOWN. NY: F & R, (1940). 1st ed. Boards a bit soiled, some wrinkling to front fly, thus VG in VG dj w/light chipping. BETWEEN COVERS. $125

Mann, Etta Donnan. FOUR YEARS IN THE GOVERNOR'S MANSION OF VIRGINIA, 1910-1914. Dietz, 1937. 1st ed. VG in Fair dj. BOOK BROKER. $25

Mann, Garciela. THE 12 PROPHETS OF ALEIJAHINHO. Austin: Univ of TX Press, (1967). Chipped dj. SILVER. $25

Mann, Heinrich. YOUNG HENRY OF NAVARRE. NY: Knopf (1937). 1st Amer ed. Top edge sl sunned else Fine in VG dj. DORN. $50

Mann, Heinrich. YOUNG HENRY OF NAVARRE. NY: Knopf, 1937. 1st US ed. Inscribed to American novelist Bryher. Some spotting and staining to cl, else VG in dj. Uncommon. LAME DUCK. $750

Mann, Ida. DEVELOPMENTAL ABNORMALITIES OF THE EYE. Cambridge, 1937. 1st ed. 284 illus. Dj. FYE. $100

Mann, Kathleen. PEASANT COSTUME IN EUROPE. London, 1935. 2nd ed. NF. POLYANTHOS. $35

Mann, Klaus. ALEXANDER. NY: Brewer & Warren, 1930. 1st ed. VG+ in VG dj. Scarce in dj. LAME DUCK. $150

Mann, Klaus. JOURNEY INTO FREEDOM. NY: Knopf, 1936. 1st ed. Cl sl stained on front panel, else NF in spine faded NF dj. Uncommon. LAME DUCK. $85

Mann, Peggy and Vivian W. Siegal. THE MAN WHO BOUGHT HIMSELF. NY: Macmillan, 1975. 1st ed. Fine in VG dj. CONNOLLY & WADE. $25

Mann, R.K. THE LIFE, ADVENTURES, AND POLITICAL OPINIONS OF FREDERICK GUSTAVUS BURNABY. London, 1882. 1/4 morocco, gilt. 122pp. Bkpl, stamp. O'NEILL. $60

Mann, Thomas. DEATH IN VENICE. NY: LEC, 1972. One of 1500 illus, signed by Felix Hoffmann. Fine in slipcase. CAPTAIN'S BOOK-SHELF. $100

Mann, Thomas. FREUD, GOETHE, WAGNER. NY: Knopf, 1937. 1st US ed One page roughly opened, nicks at spinal extremities, else NF, lacking dj. CAPTAIN'S BOOKSHELF. $50

Mann, Thomas. JOSEPH THE PROVIDER. NY, 1944. 1st ed. Fine in dj. POLYANTHOS. $45

Mann, Thomas. THE TRANSPOSED HEADS. NY: Knopf, 1941. 1st US ed. Trans by H.T. Lowe-Porter. Fine in dj, an especially Nice copy. BERNARD. $40

Mann, Thomas. THE TRANSPOSED HEADS. NY: Knopf, 1941. Wraps, Adv reading copy. VG w/"Sample Copy" stamped on top edge; front wrap starting to separate. BEASLEY. $200

Mann, Thomas. YOUNG JOSEPH. NY: Alfred A. Knopf. 1939. H.T. Lowe-Porter (trans). "Fourth Printing." Extremities sl rubbed. Signed, dated. KARMIOLE. $150

Mannin, Ethel. LAND OF THE CRESTED LION....London: Adventurers Club (1954). 1st ed. VG in dj. SECOND LIFE. $25

Manning, Frederic. SCENES & PORTRAITS. London: Peter Davies, 1930. 1st ed. Some minor foxing of edges, else Fine in a dj that has some chipping at top and bottom of spine. WOOLMER. $75

Manning, Thomas G. GOVERNMENT IN SCIENCE. THE USGS, 1867-1894. Univ Kentucky Press, 1967. FIVE QUAIL. $30

Mannix, Daniel P. A SPORTING CHANCE. NY: Dutton, 1967. 2nd prtg. Dj. OLD LONDON. $20

Mannix, Daniel. THE FOX AND THE HOUND. NY: Dutton, 1967. 1st ed. Good+. OCTOBER FARM. $25

Mansfield, Edward D. LIFE AND SERVICES OF GENERAL WINFIELD SCOTT. NY: A.S. Barnes & Co., 1852. 538pp. Frontis. Soiled cl, shelf wear. SCHOYER'S. $30

Mansfield, Edward D. THE MEXICAN WAR: A HISTORY OF ITS ORIGIN. NY: A.S. Barnes & Co, 1848. 1st ed. 323pp, cloth. Spine torn, minor foxing, stains to several pp. GIBBS. $45

Mansfield, Katherine. IN A GERMAN PENSION. London: Stephen Swift, (1911). 1st ed. Dec grn cl, pub's emb compliments on title pg. Beautiful copy. Preserved in a half-morocco custom case, faded at spine. CAPTAIN'S BOOKSHELF. $850

Mansfield, Katherine. SOMETHING CHILDISH AND OTHER STORIES. London: Constable & Co, (1924). 1st ed, 2nd issue. Badly chipped torn dj fading on edges, lacking a portion in front. *SCHOYER'S.* $20

MANUAL FOR THE MEDICAL DEPARTMENT, UNITED STATES ARMY, 1916. NY, 1917. *FYE.* $50

MANUAL FOR THE MEDICAL DEPARTMENT. 1906. COMPILED UNDER THE DIRECTION OF THE SURGEON GENERAL. Washington, 1906. *FYE.* $50

Mapes, David P. HISTORY OF THE CITY OF RIPON, AND OF ITS FOUNDER, DAVID P. MAPES. Milwaukee, 1873. 1st ed. Frontis, (2),281pp ,2 full-pg etchings. 12 mo. Rust cl, showing edgewear, else VG. Scarce. *CONNOLLY & WADE.* $100

Mapp, Alf J., Jr. FROCK COATS AND EPAULETS. NY, (1963). 1st ed. 501pp. VG in dj. *PRATT.* $30

Marbarger, John P. (ed). SPACE MEDICINE, THE HUMAN FACTOR. Urbana: Univ of IL Press, 1951. VG in beige cl; bkpl. *KNOLLWOOD.* $40

Marcade, Jean. EROS KALOS. Geneva et al: Nagel (1962). Tipped-in color plts, some fldg. Shaken. *SCHOYER'S.* $25

March, William. COMPANY K. (NY): Harrison Smith & Robert Haas, 1933. 1st ed. 1st bk. Orig grn cl. Name, else Fine in orig glassine jacket w/ptd paper flaps (and a few tears). *CHAPEL HILL.* $300

MARCO POLO. London, 1962. Kubasta. 2 pg pop-up of Marco Polo. Pop-up bk. *BOOKFINDERS INTL.* $150

Marcou, Jules. LIFE, LETTERS, AND WORKS OF LOUIS AGASSIZ. Westmead, England, 1972. Facs of 1896 ed. 2 vols in 1. *FYE.* $30

Marcy, Henry. THE ANATOMY AND SURGICAL TREATMENT OF HERNIA. NY, 1892. 1st ed. 1/2 leather, 4to, 421pp. 66 full page heliotype and lithographic plts, 6 colored. VF. Scarce. *FYE.* $500

Marcy, Randolph B. and George B. McClellan. EXPLORATION OF THE RED RIVER OF LOUISIANA IN THE YEAR 1852. Washington: Robert Armstrong, 1853. Lacks botany plt no. XVIII and both maps, issued separately. Wear at extremities, some foxing, still presentable. Howes M-276. *LAURIE.* $50

Marcy, Randolph B. BORDER REMINISCENCES. NY, 1871. 2nd prtg, (1872). 396pp & ads. VG. *PRATT.* $85

Marcy, Randolph B. THIRTY YEARS OF ARMY LIFE ON THE BORDER. NY, 1866. 1st ed. Rebacked w/part of orig backstrip. Sl cvr wear. Few page margins frayed. Little soiling or staining on some page margins, o/w VG. Howes M280. *DIAMOND.* $85

Marcy, Randolph B. THIRTY YEARS OF ARMY LIFE ON THE BORDER. NY: Harper & Brothers, 1866. 1st ed. Sl spine wear, but Superior. *HUDSON.* $150

Marden, Philip S. GREECE & THE AEGEAN ISLANDS. Boston, 1907. 1st ed. xv,386pp. *O'NEILL.* $30

Marden, Philip S. TRAVELS IN SPAIN. Boston & NY: Houghton Mifflin Co. 1910. Sl nibbled fep. Bumped, rubbed corners. *SCHOYER'S.* $25

Marett, Robert Ranulph. A JERSEYMAN AT OXFORD. London, NY, Toronto: Oxford Univ Press, 1941. 1st ed. Dj. Fine. *WEBER.* $20

Margolies, Joseph (ed). STRANGE AND FANTASTIC STORIES. Whittlesey House, 1946. 1st ed. Fine in dj. *MADLE.* $35

Margolioth, H.M. (ed). THE POEMS & LETTERS OF ANDREW MARVELL. London, 1912. 2nd ed. 2 vols. Dj of vol 2 has chip bottom of sp. NF. *POLYANTHOS.* $50

Margotta, Roberto. THE STORY OF MEDICINE. NY, 1968. 1st ed. Dj. *FYE.* $50

MARGRET HOWTH. (By Rebecca Harding Davis.) Boston: Ticknor and Fields, 1862. 1st ed. Brown cl, sl faded, esp on spine, w/some bleached out areas on back, quite sturdy. VG. *SCHOYER'S.* $150

Mariani, Angelo. COCA AND ITS THERAPEUTIC APPLICATION. NY, 1890. 1st ed. Inscribed. Scarce. *FYE.* $250

Marion and Co. PRACTICAL GUIDE TO PHOTOGRAPHY. New Edition Revised and Enlarged. London: Marion & Co. 1887. viii,230pp. Numerous text figures. 1/2 maroon calf over blue cl, dec gilt spine, leather spine label. *KARMIOLE.* $100

Marion, F. THE WONDERS OF OPTICS. NY: Charles Scribner, 1869. Charles W. Quin (ed). Blindstamped red cl, gilt dec spine; Bumping, wear, fraying, stain o/w Good. *KNOLLWOOD.* $40

Maris, Roger and Jim Ogle. ROGER MARIS AT BAT. Duell, Sloan & Pearce, 1962. 1st ed. VG in VG+ dj. *PLAPINGER.* $60

Maritis, Giovanni. TRAVELS IN THE ISLAND OF CYPRUS. London, 1971. Claude D. Cobham (trans). *O'NEILL.* $30

Markham, Albert Hastings. LIFE OF SIR JOHN FRANKLIN AND THE NORTH-WEST PASSAGE. London: George Philip & Son, 1891. 6 maps (4 in color, 1 fldg). Some minor wear, sl dusty, else VG. *PARMER.* $125

Markham, Albert Hastings. THE GREAT FROZEN SEA: A PERSONAL NARRATIVE...VOYAGE OF THE 'ALERT' DURING THE ARCTIC EXPEDITION OF 1875-6. London: Daldy, Isbister & Co, 1878. 1st ed. xx,440pp. Fldg map. Orig blue dec cl, gilt titles. Rubbing edges, joints, spine darkened a bit, lt foxing. Inscription, else VG. *PARMER.* $425

Markham, Beryl. THE SPLENDID OUTCAST. SF: North Point, 1987. Uncorrected proof. Fine in wraps. *LOPEZ.* $30

Markham, E. CLEMATIS. London, (1935). Cloth, pp yellowed, name stamp. Dj, sm piece missing. *SUTTON.* $40

Markham, Henry H. RESOURCES OF CALIFORNIA. Sacramento, 1893. 15 plts. Spine chipped, o/w VG. *BOHLING.* $125

Markham, Robert. COLONEL SUN. London: Jonathan Cape, 1968. 1st ed. Fine in dj (tiny tear). *MORDIDA.* $30

Markham, Sidney. COLONIAL ARCHITECTURE OF ANTIQUA, GUATEMALA. Phila: American Phil Soc, 1966. 1st ed. Ltd to 2000. Good in dj. *SILVER.* $50

Marks, Henry K. UNDERTOW. NY: Harper, (1923). 1st ed. Dj flaws. Fine. *MUELLER.* $25

Marks, J. (pseud of Jamake Highwater). MICK JAGGER. NY: Curtis, (1973). Pb orig. Fine in wrappers w/tiny nick at base of spine. *LOPEZ.* $50

Marks, J. (pseud of Jamake Highwater). ROCK AND OTHER FOUR LETTER WORDS. (NY): (Bantam), (1968). 1st book, a pb orig. Spine creased, o/w VG in wrappers. *LOPEZ.* $50

Markstein, George. THE COOLER. London: Souvenir Press, 1974. 1st ed. Fine in dj. *MORDIDA.* $45

Markus, Julia. AMERICAN ROSE. Boston: Houghton Mifflin, 1980. 1st ed. Inscribed. Fine in NF dj. *LOPEZ.* $35

Markus, Julia. AMERICAN ROSE. Rev copy. Signed. Fine in dj. *LOPEZ.* $30

Marland, Michael (ed). THE TIMES AUTHORS NUMBER 3: DYLAN THOMAS. (London: London Times, 1970). 1st ed. Loose sheets of various sizes laid into pub's folder, plastic bag. Fine. *CHAPEL HILL.* $45

Marlowe, George Francis. CHURCHES OF OLD NEW ENGLAND. NY, 1947, 1st ed. *HEINOLDT.* $12

Marlowe, George Francis. COACHING ROADS OF OLD NEW ENGLAND. NY: Macmillan, 1945. 1st prtg. VG in VG dj. *OCTOBER FARM.* $45

Marlowe, Kenneth. MR. MADAM. Sherbourne Press (1964). 1st ed. VG in VG dj. *AARD.* $20

Marlowe, Stephen. DRUM BEAT-BERLIN. Greenwich: Fawcett Publications, 1964. 1st ed. Pb orig. Gold Medal #1420. VF unread in wrappers. *MORDIDA.* $25

Marlowe, Stephen. DRUM BEAT-DOMINIQUE. Greenwich: Fawcett Pubs, 1965. 1st ed. Pb orig. Gold Medal #1508. VF unread in wrappers. *MORDIDA.* $25

Marlowe, Stephen. DRUM BEAT-MARIANNE. Greenwich: Fawcett Pubs, 1968. 1st ed. Pb orig. Gold Medal #1909. Fine in wrappers. *MORDIDA.* $20

Marlowe, Stephen. PERIL IS MY PAY. Greenwich: Fawcett Pubs, 1960. 1st ed. Pb orig. Gold Medal #1018. Crease, wrinkled, o/w VG in wrappers. *MORDIDA.* $20

Marlowe, Stephen. TERROR IS MY TRADE. Greenwich: Fawcett Publications, 1958. 1st ed. Pb orig. Gold Medal #813. Crease front cvr, o/w VG in wrappers. *MORDIDA.* $20

Marlowe, Stephen. THE SECOND LONGEST NIGHT. NY: Fawcett Publications, 1955. 1st ed. Pb orig. Gold Medal no. 523. Stain on front cover o/w VG in wrappers. *MORDIDA.* $20

Marmelszadt, Willard. MUSICAL SONS OF AESCULAPIUS. NY, 1946. 1st ed. 116pp. Scarce. *FYE.* $150

Marmelszadt, Willard. MUSICAL SONS OF AESCULAPIUS. NY: Froben Pr, 1946. Gilt blue cl. VG+. Inscribed. *SMITHFIELD.* $115

Marquand, J.P. STOPOVER: TOKYO. Boston: Little, Brown, 1957. 1st ed. Edges spotted and stained, o/w VG in dj w/wear, chips, tears. *MORDIDA.* $30

Marquez, Gabriel Garcia. See Garcia Marquez, Gabriel.

Marquis, Don. DANNY'S OWN STORY. GC, NY: Doubleday, Page, 1912. Orig grn cl w/mounted cvr illus. Gift inscript in verse, front hinge cracked, else VG. 1st ed. *CHAPEL HILL.* $60

Marquis, Don. DANNY'S OWN STORY. NY, 1912. 1st ed. Author's 1st bk. Spine sl rubbed. NF. *POLYANTHOS.* $65

Marquis, Donald M. IN SEARCH OF BUDDY BOLDEN: FIRST MAN OF JAZZ. Baton Rouge: Louisiana State Univ, (1978). Owner name blocked out in felt tip, o/w Fine in sl used dj. *AKA.* $35

MARRIAGE, A NOVEL. (By Susan Ferrier.) Edinburgh and London: Wm. Blackwood and John Murray, 1818. 1st ed. 3 vols. Small 12mo, bound in early half-Russia. (DNB). VG, scarce. *HARTFIELD.* $295

Marriott, Alice. HELL ON HORSES AND WOMEN. Norman, 1953. 1st ed. Fine in moderately worn, price-clipped dj. *BAADE.* $50

Marriott, Alice. THE TEN GRANDMOTHERS. Norman: Univ of OK Press, 1945. 1st ed. VG in dj. *LOPEZ.* $45

Marriott, Alice. THE VALLEY BELOW. Norman: Univ of Oklahoma Press, 1949. 1st ed. VG. *BURCHAM.* $35

Marryat, Captain (Frederick). MONSIEUR VIOLET. London: Thomas Hodgson, (c. 1849). 303pp. Pict boards, light wear to boards, rfep creased. *DAWSON'S.* $50

Marryat, Frederick. A DIARY IN AMERICA. (Part I). In Three Volumes. (Part Second. In Three Volumes.) London: Ptd for Longman, Orme, Brown, Green & Longmans. 1839. 1st ed. Two series complete in 6 vols. 2 fldg maps. 19th-c calf over marbled boards, gilt spines, brown lea spine labels; some spine extrems chipped, cvrs rubbed. Half-titles in all vols. Howes M300 and M301. *KARMIOLE.* $350

Marryat, Frederick. PETER SIMPLE. (London: Printed by Robert MacLehose & Co. Ltd. at the Univ Press, Glasgow, for Constable & Company, 1929). 2 vols. One of 750. Scattered light foxing, o/w Fine. *PIRAGES.* $50

Marryat, Frederick. POOR JACK. London: Longman, Orme.., 1840. Illus by Clarkson Stanfield. 1st ed. x,384pp. Engraved frontis, plts and illus. 3/4 calf, marbled boards, red leather label on paneled spine, gilt. Sm crack in front joint, extrems a bit worn, cvrs rubbed, else VG. *WREDEN.* $100

Marryat, Frederick. SNARLEYVOW; OR THE DOG FIEND. Phila: Carey & Hart, 1837. 1st ed. 2 vols. Orig boards, spine labels sl deteriorated, foxing throughout, chip to head of spine of vol II, staining to boards. Author's pencilled presentation to second blank of vol I. VG. *LAME DUCK.* $350

Mars, G.C. (ed). BRICKWORK IN ITALY. Chicago: Amer Face Brick Assoc, 1925. Full-pg map, 20 plts. From lib of Marcus Reynolds, in his binding. Bound in brown morocco backed rust brown cl, bumped, joints rubbed, name. Internally NF. *BLUE MOUNTAIN.* $45

Mars, G.C. (ed). BRICKWORK IN ITALY. Chicago: Amer Face Brick Assoc, 1925. A little smudged. Tipped-in errata slip. *SCHOYER'S.* $40

Marsh, James. FOUR YEARS IN THE ROCKIES, OR THE ADVENTURES OF ISAAC P. ROSE. Longs, n.d. (ca 1951). VF in VG dj. *OREGON.* $60

Marsh, James. FOUR YEARS IN THE ROCKIES, OR THE ADVENTURES OF ISAAC P. ROSE. New Castle, PA: W.B. Thomas, 1884. Frontis. Orig red pict cl w/sl wear, spotting. Howes M306. *OREGON.* $600

Marsh, Ngaio and Dr. Henry Jellett. THE NURSING HOME MURDER. NY: Sheridan House, 1941. 1st Amer ed. VG in dj w/internal and external tape mends and chipping at base of spine and at corners. *MORDIDA.* $85

Marsh, Ngaio. BLACK BEECH & HONEYDEW: AN AUTOBIOGRAPHY. London: Collins, 1966. 1st ed. Fine in dj. *MORDIDA.* $65

Marsh, Ngaio. CLUTCH OF CONSTABLES. London: Collins, 1968. 1st ed. NF in dj. *SILVER DOOR.* $20

Marsh, Ngaio. OPENING NIGHT. London: Collins Crime Club, 1951. 1st ed. Fine in VG dj w/crease-tear on front panel, several short closed tears, and fraying at top of spine. *MORDIDA.* $35

Marsh, Ngaio. TIED UP IN TINSEL. Boston: Little Brown, 1972. 1st ed. Fine in close to fine dj. *BEASLEY.* $25

Marshall, Christopher. PASSAGES FROM THE REMEMBRANCER OF CHRISTOPHER MARSHALL. EDITED BY WILLIAM DUANE. Phila., 1839. 1st ed. 124,(16)pp, errata slip. New cl. Howes M310. *GINSBERG.* $125

Marshall, Edison. DIAN OF THE LOST LAND. Grosset, 1935. Fine in frayed, internally repaired dj. *MADLE.* $35

Marshall, Edison. EARTH GIANT. Doubleday, 1960. 1st ed. NF in frayed dj. *MADLE.* $37

Marshall, Edison. OGDEN'S STRANGE STORY. Kinsey, 1934. 1st ed. Near VG. *MADLE.* $30

Marshall, Edison. THE DEADFALL. Cosmopolitan, 1927. 1st ed. Fine in sl frayed dj. *MADLE.* $30

Marshall, Edison. THE LIGHT IN THE JUNGLE. Burt, n.d. VG in chipped dj. *MADLE.* $25

Marshall, Edison. THE SLEEPER OF THE MOONLIT RANGES. NY, 1925. 1st ed. NF. *ARTIS.* $15

Marshall, F.H. CATALOGUE OF THE JEWELLERY, GREEK, ETRUSCAN, AND ROMAN, IN THE DEPARTMENTS OF ANTIQUITIES, BRITISH MUSEUM. London: British Museum, 1911. 1st ed. 97 figs, 73 plts. Good. *ARCHAEOLOGIA.* $650

Marshall, J.F. THE BRITISH MOSQUITOS. London, 1938. 20 plts. *SUTTON.* $60

Marshall, Jim. SWINGING DOORS. Seattle: Frank McCaffrey, (1949). Edgetears to dj. *AKA.* $35

Marshall, John. ROYAL NAVAL BIOGRAPHY; OF PETER HEYWOOD, ESQ. NY: (Pr. pr., n.d., but ca 1937). Orig cl. Fine. *LEFKOWICZ.* $50

Marshall, John. THE LIFE OF WASHINGTON. 2nd ed, rev, corrected. 2 vols. Phila: James Crissy, 1832. iv,460,42,viii; 448,32,v. Frontis vol I. Owner sig both vols, clippings pasted to eps. Orig 3/4 leather w/marbled boards, joints tender. Foxing. *SCHOYER'S.* $65

Marshall, Logan. HINDENBURG'S MARCH INTO LONDON. Winston, 1916. 1st US ed. NF in wraps. *MADLE.* $75

Marshall, Mrs. A.B. FANCY ICES. (London: Marshall's School of Cookery and Simpkin, Marshall, Hamilton, Kent & Co., [1894]). viii, 238, 30 pp (including the ads at back). 1st ed . Orig blue cl, gilt stamped titling, illus on front cover. VF. *PIRAGES.* $150

Marshall, Mrs. A.B. FANCY ICES. London: Marshall's School of Cookery, (1894). vi,(2),238pp,30pp ads. Blue buckram boards w/title, design front cover. Spine darkened, edges worn. VG. *HELLER.* $165

Marshall, Orsamus H. THE HISTORICAL WRITINGS OF THE LATE ORSAMUS H. MARSHALL....Albany, NY: Munsell, 1887. 1st ed. (24),500pp. Frontis, map. Orig cl, paper label on spine, bkpl removed. Howes M319. *GINSBERG.* $125

Marshall, Otto Miller. THE WHAM PAYMASTER ROBBERY. Pima, AZ: Pima Chamber of Commerce, 1967. 1st ed. VF in wraps. *GIBBS.* $25

Marshall, Paule. SOUL CLAP HANDS AND SING. NY: Atheneum, 1961. 1st ed. Signed. Fine in Fine dj w/sun darkening to spine. *BEASLEY.* $225

Marshall, Robert. ARCTIC WILDERNESS. Berkeley: Univ of California Press, 1956. 1st ed. VG in VG- dj. *BLUE DRAGON.* $27.50

Marshall, Scout J.T. THE MILES EXPEDITION OF 1874-1875. Austin, 1971. Ed by Lonnie White. 1st ed. Signed by White. VG+. *PRATT.* $30

Marshall, William. MANILA BAY. NY: Viking, 1986. 1st Amer ed. Signed. VF in dj. *SILVER DOOR.* $35

Marshall, William. PERFECT END. NY: Holt, 1983. 1st Amer ed. Signed. VF in dj. *SILVER DOOR.* $35

Marshall, William. THIN AIR. London: Hamilton, 1977. 1st ed. Signed. VG+ in dj. *SILVER DOOR.* $35

Marshall-Cornwall, Gen. Sir James. GRANT AS MILITARY COMMANDER. NY: Van Nostrand, 1970. 1st ed. NF. *ARCHER.* $22.50

Marston, E. SKETCHES OF BOOKSELLERS OF OTHER DAYS. London: Sampson Low, Marston & Co, 1901. 1st ed. Cvrs sl soiled, endpapers replaced, else Good. *WREDEN.* $40

Marston, Edward. THE MERRY DEVILS. NY: St. Martin's, 1990. 1st Amer ed. Review copy, signed. Pub's slip laid in. Fine in dj. *SILVER DOOR.* $35

Marston, John. THE METAMORPHOSIS OF PIGMALION'S IMAGE. Waltham St. Lawrence, 1926. One of 325. Engr by Rene Ben Sussan. 18 pages + 2 full-pg color engr. Light soiling to spine. *DAWSON'S.* $75

Marston, Muktuk (Marvin). MEN OF THE TUNDRA. NY: October House, (1972, 69). 2nd printing. Fine- in VG dj. *AARD.* $20

Marti-Ibanez, Felix. A PRELUDE TO MEDICAL HISTORY. NY, 1961. 1st ed. Dj. *FYE.* $30

Marti-Ibanez, Felix. THE EPIC OF MEDICINE. NY, 1962. 1st ed. *FYE.* $40

Marti-Ibanez, Felix. THE SHIP IN THE BOTTLE AND OTHER ESSAYS. NY, 1968. 1st ed. Dj. *FYE.* $30

Martin, A.C. and F.M. Uhler. FOOD OF GAME DUCKS IN THE UNITED STATES AND CANADA. Washington, DC: USDA. Tech Bull #634, March 1939. 1st ed. Name, date received noted on cvr. Ptd wraps. Fine. *CONNOLLY & WADE.* $45

Martin, Benjamin Ellis. IN THE FOOTPRINTS OF CHARLES LAMB. NY: Charles Scribner's Sons, 1890. VG. *WEBER.* $45

Martin, Bill and John Archambault. WHITE DYNAMITE AND CURLY KIDD. HRW, (1986). 1st ed. Signed by authors. Fine in Fine dj. *BEBBAH.* $30

Martin, Christopher. DAMN THE TORPEDOES, THE STORY OF AMERICA'S FIRST ADMIRAL, DAVID GLASGOW FARRAGUT. NY, (1970). 1st ed. 280pp. VG+ in dj. *PRATT.* $22.50

Martin, Cy. THE SAGA OF THE BUFFALO. NY: Hart, (1973). 1st ed. Fine in VG dj. *OREGON.* $35

Martin, David. TETHERED. Holt Rinehart Winston, 1979. 1st ed. Fine in dj worn at head of spine. *STAHR.* $35

Martin, David. THE CRYING HEART TATTOO. NY: Holt, (1982). 1st ed. Fine in Fine dj. *UNGER.* $35

Martin, Douglas D. TOMBSTONE'S EPITAPH. Albuquerque: Univ of NM, 1953. Wine cl, silver dec. Fine. *CONNOLLY & WADE.* $25

Martin, Douglas D. YUMA CROSSING. Albuquerque: Univ of NM, 1954. 1st ed. Tan & grn cl. NF in very chipped dj. *CONNOLLY & WADE.* $25

Martin, Edward Winslow. HISTORY OF THE GRANGE MOVEMENT, OR THE FARMER'S WAR AGAINST MONOPOLIES. Phila et al, National Pub. Co. (1873) 534pp+10pp ads. Full lea. Split along front hinge & repaired. VG. *BOHLING.* $35

Martin, Edward Winslow. THE LIFE AND PUBLIC SERVICE OF SCHUYLER COLFAX. NY, 1868. 512pp. Ex-lib. VG. *PRATT.* $40

Martin, Franklin H. SOUTH AMERICA FROM A SURGEON'S POINT OF VIEW. NY: Fleming H. Revell, 1922. 1st ed. VG. Lt wear to blue cl. *PARMER.* $20

Martin, G.C. & F.J. Katz. GEOLOGY AND COAL FIELDS OF THE LOWER MATANUSKA VALLEY ALASKA. Washington, 1912. Several color fold-out maps bound in and in rear pocket. Wraps worn at spine. Interior and maps VG. *ARTIS.* $20

Martin, George R.R. THE ARMAGEDDON RAG. Poseidon, 1983. 1st ed. Fine in sl frayed dj. *MADLE.* $25

Martin, H.T. CASTOROLOGIA OF THE HISTORY AND TRADITIONS OF THE CANADIAN BEAVER. London, 1892. 14 plts. 238pp. Orig gilt dec cl. Sm tears head of spine; some signs of dampness, mostly to spine, eps. Ex-lib. Scarce. *SUTTON.* $115

Martin, John C. LEST WE FORGET: A CHRONICLE OF IMPORTANT EVENTS OF THE CIVIL WAR. (Madison, WI, ca. 1920). Frontis. Signed. *GINSBERG.* $100

Martin, Milton Fox. TROUT LORE. NY: Duell Sloan Pearce, (1942). 1st ed. Photos. Fine in Fine- dj. *AARD.* $25

Martin, Percy F. EGYPT OLD AND NEW: NY: Doran 1923. Spine faded. Tipped-in photos, fldg map. *SCHOYER'S.* $45

Martin, Percy. MEXICO'S TREASURE HOUSE (GUANAJUATO). NY: Cheltenham Press, 1906. 1st ed. 44pp b/w plts, 6 panoramic fldouts, 2 maps. Cl fading, some soiling. Contents Good. *SILVER.* $40

Martin, R(obert) Montgomery. HISTORY OF AUSTRAL-ASIA. London: John Mortimer, 1836. 371pp. 12mo. Red cl stamped in gilt. Ex-lib. Some leaves loose, others repaired. 2 double-pg maps. *SCHOYER'S.* $40

Martin, Tyrone G. A MOST FORTUNATE SHIP: A NARRATIVE HISTORY OF "OLD IRONSIDES". Chester, Conn., (1980). 1st ed. Fine in dj. Signed. *LEFKOWICZ.* $60

Martin, Valerie. A RECENT MARTYR. Boston: Houghton Mifflin, 1987. 1st ed. Uncorrected proof copy. Signed. Fine in wrappers. *LOPEZ.* $50

Martindale, Charles. LOUGHERY'S DEFEAT AND PIGEON ROOST MASSACRE, WITH INTRODUCTORY SKETCH. Indianapolis: Bowen-Merrill, 1888. 32pp. Orig printed wrappers, chipped. Indiana Hist Soc Pamphlets #4. *GINSBERG.* $50

Martindale, W. THE EXTRA PHARMACOPOEIA....1890. 6th ed. Full leather scuffed, tears to spine ends; pp staining, chipping; pp yellowed. *SUTTON.* $35

Martineau, Harriet. DEERBROOK. NY: Harper, 1839. 1st US ed. 2 vols. Leather backed paper boards (lib bkpls) some foxing. VG, tight set. Bks are different heights. *SECOND LIFE.* $125

Martineau, Harriet. THE ENGLISH LAKE DISTRICT. 5th ed. Windermere: J. Garnett. London: Simpkin, Marshall & Co. 1876. 1st ed. (2),xiv,368,xxpp. Index. Maps, plans (some color), fldg map in rear pocket; views (some fldg). Cvrs soiled, lightly frayed. *KARMIOLE.* $45

Martinson, Harry. ANIARA. NY, 1963. 1st Amer ed. W/2 record set. Albums Fine w/slight wear to album cover; book Fine in lightly used dj. *McCLINTOCK.* $125

Martof, B.S. et al. AMPHIBIANS & REPTILES OF THE CAROLINAS & VIRGINIA. Chapel Hill, NC: Univ of NC, 1980. Fine. *MIKESH.* $27.50

Martyr, Weston. THE SOUTHSEAMAN. Edinburgh and London: William Blackwood, 1928. New ed. Some shelfwear. *PARMER.* $30

Marvin, Frederic Rowland. THE EXCURSIONS OF A BOOK-LOVER. Boston: Sherman, French & Co, 1910. 1st ed. A few small spots on cvrs, bkpl skillfully removed, light pencilling in margins of 3pp, else VG. *WREDEN.* $25

Marx, Groucho. THE GROUCHO LETTERS: LETTERS FROM & TO GROUCHO MARX. NY: Simon & Schuster, (1967). 1st ed. Owner's inscrip, else NF in lightly worn dj. *AKA.* $30

MARY PUTNAM JACOBI, M.D. A PATHFINDER IN MEDICINE WITH SELECTIONS FROM HER WRITINGS AND A COMPLETE BIBLIOGRAPHY. NY, 1925. 1st ed. *FYE.* $100

Marzails, Frank T. LIFE OF CHARLES DICKENS. Phila: John D. Morris, (c. 1900). 8vo, red cloth with lea spine label, bkpl, ltd to 1000; unopened. Fine. *GREAT EXPECTATIONS.* $27.50

Masefield, John (ed). LYRICS OF BEN JOHNSON BEAUMONT AND FLETCHER. London: Grant Richards, 1906. 1st ed. Teg, uncut and partly unopened. Vellum binding w/leather ties. Spine little sunned and rubbed. Fine. *POLYANTHOS.* $35

Masefield, John. A LETTER FROM PONTUS & OTHER VERSE. London: Heinemann, (1936). NF in dj. 1st ed. *CHAPEL HILL.* $35

Masefield, John. REYNARD THE FOX, OR THE GHOST HEATH RUN. NY: Macmillan, 1921. 16 plts. 1st illus. U.S. ed. VG in Good dj. *OCTOBER FARM.* $65

Masefield, John. REYNARD THE FOX. NY: Macmillan, 1919. 1st ed. Owner name, front hinge starting, but VG. *CHAPEL HILL.* $45

Masefield, John. THE COLLECTED POEMS. Frontis, cl w/leather label. London: Heinemann, 1923. 1st ed. Ltd to 530, this signed by Masefield with a verse. Fine in evenly dust-soiled dj. *JAFFE.* $125

Masefield, John. THE WANDERER OF LIVERPOOL. NY: Macmillan, 1930. 1st ed. One of 350 numbered, signed. Color frontis, 32 plts, 4 plans (3 fldg). Orig boards, extrems rubbed. *LEFKOWICZ.* $150

Mason, A.E.W. AT THE VILLA ROSE. London: Hodder and Stoughton, 1910. 1st ed. Names on front pastedown o/w VG in cloth-covered boards w/gold-stamped titles on spine. *MORDIDA.* $85

Mason, A.E.W. THE BROKEN ROAD. NY: Scribner's, 1907. 1st US ed. Fine and bright. Name. *BEASLEY.* $25

Mason, A.E.W. THE HOUSE IN LORDSHIP LANE. London: Hodder & Stoughton, 1946. Fine; lt edgewear to dj. *ELSE FINE.* $60

Mason, A.E.W. THE HOUSE IN LORDSHIP LANE. NY: Dodd-Mead, 1946. 1st ed. Fine; price clipped dj has lt wear. *ELSE FINE.* $40

Mason, A.E.W. THE PRISONER IN THE OPAL. GC: Doubleday Crime Club, 1928. 1st ed. VF; narrow chips spine ends of dj. *ELSE FINE.* $65

Mason, Anita. BETHANY. London: Hamish Hamilton, (1981). 1st ed. Inscribed. Fine in dj. *LOPEZ.* $45

Mason, Bobbie Ann, SHILOH AND OTHER STORIES. Harper, 1982. 1st ed. VF in dj. *STAHR.* $65

Mason, Bobbie Ann. IN COUNTRY. Harper & Row, 1985. 1st ed. VF in dj. *STAHR.* $20

Mason, Bobbie Ann. IN COUNTRY. London: Chatto & Windus, (1986). 1st UK ed. Fine in dj. *CAPTAIN'S BOOKSHELF.* $25

Mason, Bobbie Ann. IN COUNTRY. NY: H&R, (1985). 1st ed. Rev copy. Inscribed. Fine in dj. *LOPEZ.* $75

Mason, Bobbie Ann. LOVE LIFE. London: Chatto & Windus, (1989). 1st Eng ed. Signed. Fine in Fine dj. *LOPEZ.* $50

Mason, Bobbie Ann. LOVE LIFE. Ptd wrappers. NY: Harper, (1989). Uncorrected proof. VF. *JAFFE.* $125

Mason, Bobbie Ann. NABOKOV'S GARDEN. Ann Arbor: Ardis, (1974). 1st ed. Dj. VF. *JAFFE.* $250

Mason, Bobbie Ann. SHILOH AND OTHER STORIES. NY: H&R (1982). 1st ed. Fine in dj. *LOPEZ.* $75

Mason, Bobbie Ann. SHILOH AND OTHER STORIES. NY: Harper, 1982. 1st ed. Fine but for few checkmarks on contents page, in NF dj (few tears, internal mends). *BEASLEY.* $35

Mason, Bobbie Ann. SHILOH AND OTHER STORIES. NY: Harper, 1982. 1st ed. 1st bk. VF; minor rub to dj. *ELSE FINE.* $60

Mason, Bobbie Ann. SHILOH AND OTHER STORIES. NY: Harper, (1982). Uncorrected proof. Fine in wraps. *CAPTAIN'S BOOKSHELF.* $175

Mason, Bobbie Ann. SHILOH AND OTHER STORIES. Ptd wrappers. NY: Harper & Brothers, (1982). Uncorrected proof. VF. *JAFFE.* $350

Mason, Bobbie Ann. SPENCE + LILA. NY: H&R, (1988). 1st ed. Signed by Mason and illus. LaNelle Mason. Fine in dj. *LOPEZ.* $50

Mason, Bobbie Ann. SPENCE & LILA. London: Chatto & Windus, (1989). 1st ed. Fine in dj. *CAPTAIN'S BOOKSHELF.* $20

Mason, Edward G. EARLY CHICAGO AND ILLINOIS. Chicago, 1890. 1st ed. (25),521pp, uncut. Orig cl. Chicago Hist Soc Colls V.4. Small piece clipped from title page, no text affected. *GINSBERG.* $100

Mason, F. van Wyck. PROUD NEW FLAGS. Phila, (1951). 1st ed. Dj spine faded, o/w VG+. *PRATT.* $15

Mason, Gene W. MINUS THREE. Englewood Cliffs: Prentice-Hall, 1970. 1st ed. NF in VG dj. *PARMER.* $35

Mason, Gregory. SOUTH OF YESTERDAY. NY: Holt, (1940). 1st ed. *SILVER.* $30

Mason, John. A PRACTICAL COURSE IN BOOKCRAFTS AND BOOKBINDING. Leicester: Backus, (1947). 2nd ed. *OAK KNOLL.* $85

Mason, Michael H. PARADISE OF FOOLS. London: Hodder and Stoughton, 1936. Fldg map. Spine faded. Bkpl. *SCHOYER'S.* $35

Mason, Michael H. WHERE TEMPESTS BLOW—UPON THE LAND OF MAGELLAN. London: Hodder & Stoughton, 1933. 2nd prtg. VG, lt foxing. *PARMER.* $45

Mason, Philip. THE BIRTH OF A DILEMMA—THE CONQUEST AND SETTLEMENT OF RHODESIA. London: Oxford Univ Press, 1958. 1st ed. VG in VG dj. *GREAT EPIC.* $40

Mason, Richard. THE GENTLEMAN'S NEW POCKET FARRIER. Phila: Grigg & Elliot, 1841. Leatherbound. Spine repaired with cloth. Good. *OCTOBER FARM.* $95

Mason, Richard. THE GENTLEMAN'S NEW POCKET FARRIER. Richmond: Peter Cottom, 1825. 3rd Ed, Enlarged and Improved. 12mo. 228pp. 4 engr plts. Sound, but covers detached. *M & S.* $225

Mason, Steve. JOHNNY'S SONG: POETRY OF A VIETNAM VETERAN. NY: Bantam, (1986). 1st ed. Inscribed, signed. Fine in Fine dj. *AKA*. $40

Mason, Walt. UNCLE WALT. Chicago: (Geo. Matthew Adams), 1911. 1st ed, 2nd ptg. Pub's brn cl w/design by Will Bradley in orange, mustard yellow and black, and signed by the artist-designer. In orig Bradley designed dj (2 sm pieces missing from very top; hinge joining cvr to spine separated). Wonderful condition. Rare thus. *BOOK BLOCK*. $275

Mason, Walt. UNCLE WALT. Chicago: George Mathew Adams. 1910. 190pp. Frontis by John T. McCutcheon, illus by William Stevens. Arranged, dec by Will Bradley. Dec brown cl, designed, signed by Bradley, stamped in yellow, orange and black. Fine in dj (a bit chipped). *KARMIOLE*. $85

Maspero, G. MANUAL OF EGYPTIAN ARCHEOLOGY AND GUIDE TO THE STUDY OF ANTIQUITIES IN EGYPT. NY: Putnam's, 1926. *ARCHAEOLOGIA*. $45

Masson, Georgina. ITALIAN GARDENS. NY, (1961). 1st Amer ed. 2 colored, 211 photogravure plts. Cl. *SUTTON*. $135

Masson, Georgina. ITALIAN GARDENS. NY: Harry N. Abrams, Inc. (1961). 1st ed. Dj chipped. *KARMIOLE*. $100

Master. R.E.L. & Jean Houston. THE VARIETIES OF PSYCHEDELIC EXPERIENCE. NY: Holt Rinehart Winston, 1966. 1st ed. Bkpl. Dj price-clipped w/short tear, edgewear. *AKA*. $35

Masters, Edgar Lee. CHILDREN OF THE MARKETPLACE. NY: Macmillan, 1922. 1st ed. Inscribed. VG, lacking dj. *LOPEZ*. $45

Masters, Edgar Lee. LEE, A DRAMATIC POEM. NY: Macmillan, 1926. #111/250, signed. Unopened; no wrapper, as issued. VG+. *BOHLING*. $200

Masters, Edgar Lee. LEE. A DRAMATIC POEM. NY: Macmillan, 1926. 1st ed. Inscribed. VG, lacking dj. *LOPEZ*. $65

Masters, Edgar Lee. LEE; A DRAMATIC POEM. NY, 1926. 1st ed. Dj chipped o/w VG. *PRATT*. $50

Masters, Edgar Lee. SPOON RIVER ANTHOLOGY. London: T. Werner Laurie Ltd, (nd). 1st Eng ed of illus ed, w/new poems. 1/4 imitation vellum, gray paper boards. Macmillan sheets w/Laurie cancel title-page. NF. *HELLER*. $100

Masters, Edgar Lee. SPOON RIVER ANTHOLOGY. NY, 1942. Boardman Robinson (illus). LEC. #10/1500. Signed by author, illus. Backstrip yellowed. Box worn o/w VG. *ARTIS*. $75

Masters, Edgar Lee. SPOON RIVER ANTHOLOGY. NY: Macmillan, 1915. Rear hinge just starting, but fresh, superb. Custom blue cl clamshell box w/black morocco spine. 1st ed, 1st issue measuring exactly 7/8" across the top. Bkpl, "duplicate withdrawn" lib ticket. *CHAPEL HILL*. $395

Masters, Edgar Lee. STARVED ROCK. NY: Macmillan, 1919. Gift inscript, else VG. 1st ed. *CHAPEL HILL*. $50

Masters, Edgar Lee. THE GREAT VALLEY. NY: Macmillan, 1916. Bkpl, bkseller's label, but Fine. 1st ed. *CHAPEL HILL*. $65

Masters, Edgar Lee. THE LIVING THOUGHTS OF EMERSON. NY: Longmans, Green, 1940. 1st ed. Fine in VG+ dj w/very slight loss at crown. *BETWEEN COVERS*. $85

Masters, Edgar Lee. THE TALE OF CHICAGO. NY: Putnam's, 1933. 1st ed. Good. Uncommon. *CONNOLLY & WADE*. $18.50

Masters, Edgar Lee. VACHEL LINDSAY: A POET IN AMERICA. Scribner's, 1935. 1st ed. Fine in dj. *AUTHORS OF THE WEST*. $20

MASTERS OF PHOTOGRAPHY 1844-1954. NY: Scott Elliott Gallery, (ca. 1960). 1st ed. 21 sheets laid into pub's folder. About Fine. *CHAPEL HILL*. $40

Masterson, V.V. THE KATY RAILROAD AND THE LAST FRONTIER. Norman: Univ of OK Press, 1952. 1st ed. Fine in chipped dj. *GIBBS*. $25

Mastin, John. THROUGH THE SUN IN AN AIRSHIP. London, 1909. 1st ed. Good+. *MADLE*. $30

Matera, Lia. A RADICAL DEPARTURE. NY: Bantam Books, 1988. 1st ed. Pb orig. Inscribed. VF, unread in wrappers. *MORDIDA*. $30

Mathe, Jean. LEONARDO DA VINCI: ANATOMICAL DRAWINGS. Barcelona, 1978. 1st ed. Dj. *FYE*. $60

Matheny, H.E. MAJOR GENERAL THOMAS MALEY HARRIS...A MEMBER OF THE MILITARY COMMISSION. Parson's: McClain, 1963. 1st ed. Fine. *ARCHER*. $25

Mather, Cotton. MAGNALIA CHRISTI AMERICANA; OR, THE ECCLESIASTICAL HISTORY OF NEW ENGLAND...WITH AN INTRODUCTION AND OCCASIONAL NOTES...TO WHICH IS ADDED A MEMOIR...ALSO, A COMPREHENSIVE INDEX. Hartford, 1853-1855. 2 vols. (43),13-626; 682pp. Port. Orig cl. Howes M391. *GINSBERG*. $175

Mathes, W. Michael (trans, ed). THE CONQUISTADOR IN CALIFORNIA: 1535....LA: Dawson's Book Shop, 1973. Ltd to 500. Facs photo illus, map in rear pocket. *SILVER*. $35

Matheson, Richard Christian. SCARS. LA: Scream Press, 1987. 1st ed. One of 250 signed, numbered. Fine (w/o dj as issued) in slipcase. *OTHER WORLDS*. $125

Matheson, Richard Christian. SCARS. LA: Scream Press, 1987. 1st ed. Fine in dj. *OTHER WORLDS*. $35

Matheson, Richard. A STIR OF ECHOES. Lippincott, 1958. 1st ed. Good+. *MADLE*. $25

Matheson, Richard. BORN OF MAN AND WOMAN: TALES OF SCIENCE FICTION AND... Phila: Chamberlain Press, 1954. 1st ed. Portion of spine (bk and dj) bumped/creased, remains of paper label ffep else NF in dj. *OTHER WORLDS*. $150

Matheson, Richard. HELL HOUSE. NY: Viking, 1971. 1st ed. NF in very close to Fine dj. *BEASLEY*. $150

Matheson, Richard. HELL HOUSE. NY: Viking Press, (1971). 1st ed. Name, address on flyleaf, o/w NF in price clipped dj. *BERNARD*. $175

Matheson, Richard. HELL HOUSE. Viking, 1971. 1st ed. Fine in dj w/small chip, short closed tear foot of spine. *STAHR*. $150

Matheson, Richard. HELL HOUSE. Viking, 1971. 1st ed. VG in dj. *MADLE*. $185

Matheson, Richard. I AM LEGEND. NY: Gold Medal Books, July 1954. 1st ptg pb orig. Front cvr creased, else VG+ in paper wraps. *BERNARD*. $45

Matheson, Richard. I AM LEGEND. NY: Walker & Co, (1970). 1st hb ed. Fine in NF dj (sm tear). *BERNARD*. $175

Matheson, Richard. THE BEARDLESS WARRIORS. Little-Brown, 1960. 1st ed. VG in frayed, dusty dj. *MADLE*. $100

Matheson, Richard. THIRD FROM THE SUN. NY: Bantam Books, 1955. NF in paper wraps. *BERNARD*. $25

Matheson, Richard. WHAT DREAMS MAY COME. NY, 1978. 1st ed. NF in VG+ dj. Scarce. *PETTLER*. $150

Matheson, Richard. WHAT DREAMS MAY COME. Putnam, 1978. 1st ed. Fine in dj. *MADLE*. $100

Mathew, B. THE CROCUS, A REVISION OF THE GENUS CROCUS (IRIDACEAE). Portland, 1983. 96 colored plts. Hb. Dj. *SUTTON*. $50

Mathews, (Anne). MEMOIRS OF CHARLES MATHEWS, COMEDIAN. London: Richard Bentley, 1839. 2nd ed. 4 vols. Later half green morocco, bit of wear to vol III; vols I and III uniform; vols II and IV uniform; spines elaborately gilt to compartments; some rubbing to two volumes; engr frontis to each vol; 13 engr plts to text; teg. VG. *DRAMATIS PERSONAE*. $135

Mathews, (Charles). MEMOIRS OF THE YOUTHFUL DAYS OF MR. MATHEWS... London: Duncombe, n.d. (1822). 2nd ed. Narrow 12mo; quarter morocco; gilt; upper cover detached; hand-colored, folding frontis; orig wraps bound in; uncut. VG. *DRAMATIS PERSONAE.* $90

Mathews, (Charles). MR. MATHEWS' COMIC ANNUAL FOR 1833. (London): W. Holmes, n.d. (c. 1833). Narrow 12mo; half morocco, gilt; worn; orig blue printed wraps bound in; hand-colored, fldg frontis; corner of title chipped; uncut. VG. *DRAMATIS PERSONAE.* $95

Mathews, (Charles). SKETCHES OF MR. MATHEWS'S TRIP TO AMERICA. London: J. Limbird, n.d. (1824). 12mo; later cloth, orig printed wraps bound in; upper wrap laid down; fldg, hand-colored frontis by R. Cruikshank, containing four illus, embrowned; uncut. VG. *DRAMATIS PERSONAE.* $110

Mathews, John Joseph. TALKING TO THE MOON. Chicago: Univ of Chicago Press, (1945). 1st ed. Owner inscrip, sl cocked, worn at spine ends. Good only, lacking dj. *LOPEZ.* $40

Mathews, John Joseph. THE OSAGES, CHILDREN OF THE MIDDLE WATERS. Univ of OK, (1961). 1st ed. VF in Fine dj. *OREGON.* $50

Mathews, John Joseph. THE OSAGES: CHILDREN OF THE MIDDLE WATERS. Norman: Univ of OK, 1973. Vol 60 in Civilization of Amer Indian series. Signed. Fine in Fine dj. *CONNOLLY & WADE.* $50

Mathews, John Joseph. WAH' KON-TAH. Norman: Univ of OK Press, 1932. 1st ed. VG in dj. *LOPEZ.* $35

Mathews, John Joseph. WAH' KON-TAH: THE OSAGE AND THE WHITE MAN'S ROAD. Norman: Univ of OK, 1932. 1st ed, 1st bk. Fldg map. NF in Good dj. *CONNOLLY & WADE.* $37.50

Mathews, John Joseph. WAH'KON-TAH, THE OSAGE AND THE WHITE MAN'S ROAD. Norman, 1932. 1st ed. Minor dj chipping o/w VG. *PRATT.* $30

Mathews, John Joseph. WAH'KON-TAH. Univ of OK Press, 1932. 1st ed. Spine sl sunned, o/w VG. *DIAMOND.* $25

Mathews, M.M. (ed). A DICTIONARY OF AMERICANISMS ON HISTORICAL PRINCIPLES. Univ of Chicago, 1956. 3rd ptg. Fine in chipped dj. *VARNER.* $75

Mathewson, Christy. PITCHING IN A PINCH. Grosset & Dunlap reprint. VG, w/o dj. *PLAPINGER.* $55

Mathewson, Christy. PITCHING IN A PINCH. Putnam, 1912. 1st ed. Good+. *PLAPINGER.* $300

Mathewson, Christy. WON IN THE NINTH. R.J. Bodmer, 1910. 1st novel. Good+ without dj as issued. *PLAPINGER.* $100

Mathieson, Theodore. THE GREAT "DETECTIVES." Intro. by Ellery Queen. NY: Simon and Schuster, 1960. 1st ed. Advance review, slip laid in. Pp darkened; couple pp have short tear and sm chip, o/w VG in dj, short closed tear. *MORDIDA.* $35

Mathis, Edward. ANOTHER PATH, ANOTHER DRAGON. NY: Charles Scribner's Sons, 1988. 1st ed. VF in dj. *MORDIDA.* $25

Mathis, Edward. DARK STREAKS AND EMPTY PLACES. NY: Charles Scribner's Sons, 1986. 1st ed. VF in dj. *MORDIDA.* $30

Mathis, Edward. FROM A HIGH PLACE. NY: Charles Scribner's Sons, 1985. 1st ed. VF in dj. *MORDIDA.* $30

Mathis, Edward. NATURAL PREY. NY: Charles Scribner's Sons, 1987. 1st ed. VF in dj. *MORDIDA.* $27.50

Mathis, Edward. ONLY WHEN SHE CRIES. NY: Berkley, 1989. 1st ed. Pb orig. VF, unread in wrappers. *MORDIDA.* $20

Mathis, Edward. THE BURNED WOMAN. NY: Charles Scribner's Sons, 1989. 1st ed. VF in dj. *MORDIDA.* $22.50

Matson, Donald. THE TREATMENT OF ACUTE CRANIOCEREBRAL INJURIES DUE TO MISSILES. Springfield, 1948. 1st ed. *FYE.* $30

Matson, Simnon E. (ed). THE BATTLE OF BEECHER ISLAND, FOUGHT SEPTEMBER 17, 18, 1868. Wray, CO, (1960). 1st ed. 124pp. Pict wraps. Fine. *PRATT.* $20

Mattes, Merrill J. INDIANS, INFANTS AND INFANTRY. ANDREW & ELIZABETH BURT ON THE FRONTIER. Denver, 1960. 1st ed. Sl dj wear and chipping o/w VG. *PRATT.* $40

Mattes, Merrill J. INDIANS, INFANTS AND INFANTRY. Denver: Old West Publishing, 1960. 1st ed. Fine in Fine dj. *BOOK MARKET.* $30

Mattes, Merrill. INDIANS, INFANTS, AND INFANTRY. ANDREW AND ELIZABETH BURT ON THE FRONTIER. Denver: Old West, (1960). 1st ed. VF in F dj. *OREGON.* $40

Matteson, Mrs. Antoinette. THE OCCULT FAMILY PHYSICIAN; AND BOTANIC GUIDE TO HEALTH. Buffalo, N.Y.: Published by the Author, 1894. 1st ed. 8vo. 317,(5)pp. Port of the Authoress. Orig cloth, quite stained. Inner hinges broken. Sound. *M & S.* $125

Matthes, Francois Emile. FRANCOIS MATTHES AND THE MARKS OF TIME: YOSEMITE AND THE HIGH SIERRA. Fritiof Fryxell (ed). SF: Sierra Club, (1962). 1st ed. Dj chipped at extrems, o/w VG. *LAURIE.* $35

Matthew, James E. THE LITERATURE OF MUSIC. London: Elliot Stock, 1896. 1st ed. Orig grn cl, beveled edges. *OAK KNOLL.* $35

Matthews, Frederick C. AMERICAN MERCHANT SHIPS 1850-1900. (-SERIES TWO) Salem, 1930 -31. Pubs. 21 & 23. 2 vols. Fine set, in djs. Vols separately pub. *LEFKOWICZ.* $300

Matthews, Henry. THE DIARY OF AN INVALID. London, 1820. 2nd ed. 516pp. Recent cloth-backed boards, new eps. *FYE.* $150

Matthews, James N. MY HOLIDAY; HOW I SPENT IT...1896. Buffalo: Taylor and NY: Hurd & Houghton, 1867. 1st ed. Teg. Very Nice. *SECOND LIFE.* $45

Matthews, L.H. WANDERING ALBATROSS, ADVENTURES...SOUTHERN OCEAN. London, 1951. Some fading to spine; dj w/pieces missing. *SUTTON.* $25

Matthews, Leslie. HISTORY OF PHARMACY IN BRITAIN. Edinburgh, 1962. 1st ed. *FYE.* $75

Matthews, P.W. and Anthony W. Tuke. HISTORY OF BARCLAYS BANK LIMITED. London: Blades, East & Blades Ltd. 1926. 1st ed. 70 plts. Grn cl, gilt spine, gilt emblem on front cvr. Teg. Bkpls. *KARMIOLE.* $100

Matthews, Patrick (ed). THE PURSUIT OF MOTHS AND BUTTERFLIES—AN ANTHOLOGY. London: Chatto & Windus, 1957. 1st ed. Fine- in VG+ dj. *AARD.* $25

Matthews, W.H. MAZES AND LABYRINTHS. London: Longmans, Green, 1922. 1st ed. Illus. Label and rear cover soiled, corners worn, frontis and 2pp of prelims stained, withal Good. *WREDEN.* $50

Matthews, William F. BOOKBINDING, A MANUAL FOR THOSE INTERESTED IN THE CRAFT OF BOOKBINDING. NY: E.P. Dutton Co., n.d. 1st US ed. Ink inscrip ffep, dj chipped. *OAK KNOLL.* $65

Matthias, Benjamin. THE POLITICIAN'S REGISTER...Phila: Key and Biddle, 1835. 1st ptg. 104pp. Orig ptd boards w/new leather reback. *SCHOYER'S.* $100

Matthiessen, Peter. AFRICAN SILENCES. NY: Random House, (1991). Uncorrected proof. Ptd wraps. VF. *JAFFE.* $50

Matthiessen, Peter. AT PLAY IN THE FIELDS OF THE LORD. NY: Random House (1965). 1st ed. Fine in price-clipped but Fine dj (sl uniform tanning to spine). *LOPEZ.* $100

Matthiessen, Peter. AT PLAY IN THE FIELDS OF THE LORD. NY: Random House (1965). 1st ed. VG+ in dj (sm edge chips). *DORN.* $75

Matthiessen, Peter. BLUE MERIDIAN, THE SEARCH FOR THE GREAT WHITE SHARK. NY: Random, 1971. Illus. Silver dec cl. NF in VG+ dj. *MIKESH.* $22.50

Matthiessen, Peter. FAR TORTUGA. NY: Random House, (1975). 1st ed. Fine in NF dj. *JUVELIS.* $50

Matthiessen, Peter. FAR TORTUGA. NY: Random House (1975). 1st ed. NF in price-clipped NF dj. *DORN.* $50

Matthiessen, Peter. IN THE SPIRIT OF CRAZY HORSE. NY: Viking, (1983). 1st ed. NF in dj. *LOPEZ.* $200

Matthiessen, Peter. IN THE SPIRIT OF CRAZY HORSE. NY: Viking, 1983. 1st ed. Fine but for rmdr marks bottom edge, in Fine dj w/crease on flap. *BEASLEY.* $100

Matthiessen, Peter. IN THE SPIRIT OF CRAZY HORSE. NY: Viking, (1983). 1st ed. Fine in NF dj. *LOPEZ.* $225

Matthiessen, Peter. IN THE SPIRIT OF CRAZY HORSE. Viking, 1983. 1st ed. Fine in dj. *STAHR.* $175

Matthiessen, Peter. MEN'S LIVES. London: Collins Harvill (1988). 1st Eng ed. Fine in dj. *LOPEZ.* $60

Matthiessen, Peter. MEN'S LIVES. THE SURFMEN & BAYMEN OF THE SOUTH FORK. 2 vols. (NY: Rock Foundation, 1986). 1st ed. Mint. Cl, slipcase. *JAFFE.* $350

Matthiessen, Peter. NINE-HEADED DRAGON RIVER; ZEN JOURNAL 1969-1982. Boston: Shambhala (1986). Uncorrected proof. Fine in wraps. *DORN.* $75

Matthiessen, Peter. ON THE RIVER STYX & OTHER STORIES. NY: Random House, (1989). Uncorrected proof. Fine in wraps. *CAPTAIN'S BOOKSHELF.* $100

Matthiessen, Peter. ON THE RIVER STYX. NY: Random House, 1989. 1st ed. Fine. *SMITH.* $30

Matthiessen, Peter. OOMINGMAK, THE EXPEDITION OF THE MUSK OX ISLAND IN THE BERING SEA. Hastings, (1967). 1st ed. Faint pinkish patch on title page else VG. *BEBBAH.* $25

Matthiessen, Peter. OOMINGMAK. NY: Hastings, (1967). 1st ed. Fine in dj that is sl spine-faded. *LOPEZ.* $55

Matthiessen, Peter. OOMINGMAK. NY: Hastings House (1967). 1st ed. NF in dj. *DORN.* $60

Matthiessen, Peter. RACE ROCK. NY: Harper, 1954. 1st ed. Author's 1st book. Spine quite sunned, o/w Fine in worn, chipped dj. *BEASLEY.* $40

Matthiessen, Peter. RADITZER. Viking, 1961. 1st ed. VG or better. Dj worn and chipped, esp. at spine ends. *STAHR.* $40

Matthiessen, Peter. SAL SI PUEDES. NY: Random House, (1969). 1st ed. Orig black cl. Pencilled name, address erased ffep, else Fine in dj. Signed. *CHAPEL HILL.* $85

Matthiessen, Peter. SAL SI PUEDES. NY: Random House, (1969). 1st ed. Signed. "H" mark on fep, o/w NF in price-clipped dj. *LOPEZ.* $75

Matthiessen, Peter. SAL SI PUEDES: CESAR CHAVEZ AND THE NEW AMERICAN REVOLUTION. NY: Random House (1969). 1st ed. Bkstore stamp, top edge sunned else NF in NF dj. *DORN.* $50

Matthiessen, Peter. SEAL POOL. GC: Doubleday, (1972). 1st ed. Fine in pict boards, lacking dj. Very scarce. *BETWEEN COVERS.* $150

Matthiessen, Peter. SEAL POOL. GC: Doubleday, (1972). Trade ed. NF in pict boards. *DORN.* $120

Matthiessen, Peter. THE CLOUD FOREST. NY: Viking, 1961. 1st ed. 1 corner sl bumped else Fine in dj (very lightly rubbed, tiny chip). *CAPTAIN'S BOOKSHELF.* $125

Matthiessen, Peter. THE CLOUD FOREST. NY: Viking, 1961. Advance review copy. Owner name front pastedown, o/w VG in dj. *LOPEZ.* $150

Matthiessen, Peter. THE SHOREBIRDS OF NORTH AMERICA. NY: Viking, (1967). 1st ed. Small bkpl front pastedown, o/w Fine in NF dj. *LOPEZ.* $150

Matthiessen, Peter. THE SHOREBIRDS OF NORTH AMERICA. NY: Viking, (1967). Ltd ed. One of 350 signed by Matthiessen, Robert Verity Clem (illus), Gardner D. Stout (ed), Ralph S. Palmer (provided species accounts). Full leather. 32 full-pg color repros. Minor spotting to binding, but Fine. *CAPTAIN'S BOOKSHELF.* $1000

Matthiessen, Peter. THE SHOREBIRDS OF NORTH AMERICA. NY: Viking, 1967. 1st ed. Fine in NF dj (few traces of edge wear). *BEASLEY.* $150

Matthiessen, Peter. THE SNOW LEOPARD. Franklin Center: Franklin Library, 1978. True 1st ed. Leatherbound ltd ed, w/special intro by author. Fine. *LOPEZ.* $150

Matthiessen, Peter. THE SNOW LEOPARD. Franklin Mint, 1978. Ltd ed. Fine. *MIKESH.* $95

Matthiessen, Peter. THE SNOW LEOPARD. London: Chatto & Windus, 1979. 1st Eng ed. Fine in NF dj. *LOPEZ.* $65

Matthiessen, Peter. THE SNOW LEOPARD. NY: Viking, (1978). 1st ed. Fine in NF dj. *LOPEZ.* $65

Matthiessen, Peter. THE TREE WHERE MAN WAS BORN. NY: Dutton, 1972. 1st ed. Fine in NF dj. The publisher's edition, in brown cloth, as opposed to the book club edition in tan paper boards. *LOPEZ.* $65

Matthiessen, Peter. THE TREE WHERE MAN WAS BORN. With Eliot Porter's The African Experience. NY: Dutton (1972). True 1st ed in dk brn cl w/the priced dj. NF in creased dj. *DORN.* $75

Matthiessen, Peter. THE WIND BIRDS. Robert Gillmor (illus). Cl-backed boards. NY: Viking, (1973). 1st ed. Fine in dj (1 closed tear). *JAFFE.* $75

Matthiessen, Peter. UNDER THE MOUNTAIN WALL, A CHRONICLE OF TWO SEASONS IN THE STONE AGE. Viking, 1962. 1st ed. VG+ in VG+ dj. *BEBBAH.* $35

Matthiessen, Peter. WILDLIFE IN AMERICA. (NY): Viking, (1987). Revised reissue. Fine in dj. *LOPEZ.* $35

Matthiessen, Peter. WILDLIFE IN AMERICA. NY: Viking, 1987. Rev, updated ed. 8 color plts, 16 monochrome. VF in VF dj. *CONNOLLY & WADE.* $25

Maude, H.E. SLAVERS IN PARADISE. Stanford: Stanford Univ Press, 1981. 1st Amer. ed. New in dj. *PARMER.* $25

Maugham, R.C.F. AFRICA AS I HAVE KNOWN IT. Nyasaland-East Africa-Liberia-Senegal. London: John Murray, 1929. 1st ed. Minor rubbing & scratches, cvrs, minor foxing else VG+. *GREAT EPIC.* $115

Maugham, W. Somerset with David Gray. SMITH. NY: Duffield, 1911. 1st ed. NF. *ELSE FINE.* $125

Maugham, W. Somerset. AH KING. GC: Doubleday Doran, 1933. 1st US ed. VG+ in Fair dj. *AARD.* $30

Maugham, W. Somerset. ASHENDEN OR THE BRITISH AGENT. London: Heinemann, 1928. 1st ed. Fine, lacks dj. *CAPTAIN'S BOOKSHELF.* $150

Maugham, W. Somerset. ASHENDEN: OR THE BRITISH AGENT. GC: Doubleday-Doran, 1928. 1st ed. Name. Small split at spine head, else Fine. Dj lightly worn; neatly but unnecessarily reinforced along internal edges w/brown paper tape. *ELSE FINE.* $450

Maugham, W. Somerset. BOOKS AND YOU. London: William Heinemann, (1940). 1st ed. NF. *WREDEN.* $20

Maugham, W. Somerset. CAKES AND ALE. London: William Heinemann Ltd, 1930. 1st ed. Fine in blue cl. Cream ptd dj chipped and spine darkened. *JUVELIS.* $100

Maugham, W. Somerset. DON FERNANDO; OR VARIATIONS ON SOME SPANISH THEMES. GC: Doubleday-Doran, 1935. 1st ed. Fine; minor edgewear, narrow chips at dj spine ends. *ELSE FINE.* $65

Maugham, W. Somerset. OF HUMAN BONDAGE. New Haven: LEC, 1938. 2 vols. One of 1500 illus, signed by John Sloane. Spines sl sunned, else Fine set lacking slipcase. *CAPTAIN'S BOOKSHELF.* $350

Maugham, W. Somerset. STRICTLY PERSONAL. GC: Doubleday, 1941. 1st ed. One of 515 specially bound, signed. Fine in slipcase. *CAPTAIN'S BOOKSHELF.* $200

Maugham, W. Somerset. THE BOOK-BAG. Florence: G. Orioli, 1932. One of 700 signed. Bkpl on front fly, a little darkening at edges of paper covered boards, else About Fine in VG dj w/darkened spine; long but unobtrusive tear on front panel. *BETWEEN COVERS.* $175

Maugham, W. Somerset. THE CASUARINA TREE. London: William Heinemann Ltd, 1926. 1st ed. Inscribed. Blue cl, some wear. Good. *JUVELIS.* $125

Maugham, W. Somerset. THE EXPLORER. NY, 1909. 1st U.S. and 1st illus ed. Spine little cocked, extremities little rubbed, rear cover edges little sunned. NF. Scarce. *POLYANTHOS.* $75

Maugham, W. Somerset. THE LAND OF THE BLESSED VIRGIN. London: Heinemann, 1905. 1st ed. Frontis. Orig linen-backed lt blue boards. VG, unopened. *CHAPEL HILL.* $350

Maugham, W. Somerset. THE LETTERS OF WILLIAM SOMERSET MAUGHAM TO LADY JULIET DUFF. Pacific Palisades: Rasselas Press, 1982. Loren R. Rothschild (ed, inscrip). 1st ed. Fine. *BEASLEY.* $100

Maugham, W. Somerset. THE MAUGHAM READER. GC: Doubleday, 1950. 1st ed. Inscribed. VG, lacking dj. *LOPEZ.* $100

Maugham, W. Somerset. THE MOON AND SIXPENCE. NY: George H. Doran. (1919). Brown cl, spine a bit faded. 1st Amer ed. The variant with Maugham's name misspelled "Maughan" on front cover and spine. *KARMIOLE.* $125

Maunder, E. Walter. ASTRONOMY WITHOUT A TELESCOPE. London: Knowledge Office, 1902. Silver gilt illus blue cl. Corners bumped & worn, rear edge of spine fraying, owner's name label. *KNOLLWOOD.* $50

Maurer, David & Victor Vogel. NARCOTICS AND NARCOTIC ADDICTION. Springfield, 1954. 1st ed. *FYE.* $25

Maurice, Major General Sir Frederick. STATESMEN AND SOLDIERS OF THE CIVIL WAR, A STUDY OF THE CONDUCT OF THE WAR. Boston, 1926. 1st ed. VG+. *PRATT.* $42.50

Maurice, Major-General Sir Frederick. ROBERT E. LEE, THE SOLDIER. Boston, 1925. 1st ed. 313pp. VG+. *PRATT.* $37.50

Mauriceau, A.M. THE MARRIED WOMAN'S PRIVATE MEDICAL COMPANION...NY, 1854. With a printed slip pasted to the inside front cover. 16mo. 13,238pp. Orig cloth. Very Nice. *M & S.* $200

Maurois, Andre. CHELSEA WAY. Trans by Hamish Miles. London: Elkin Mathews & Marrot, 1930. Light offsetting to eps, else NF. 1st ed in Eng. #384 of 530 signed. *CHAPEL HILL.* $75

Maury, Dabney H. RECOLLECTIONS OF A VIRGINIAN IN THE MEXICAN, INDIAN, AND CIVIL WAR. Scribners, 1894. 1st ed. 279pp, frontis. Rear hinge tear, interior soil. Ex-lib. Good+. *BOOK BROKER.* $75

Maury, M.F. THE PHYSICAL GEOGRAPHY OF THE SEA. Harper & Bros., 1855. 3rd ed. Ex-lib copy, no internal markings except on title page, fep, pastedown. 8 fldg plts. Good+. *MAD DOG.* $40

Maury, M.F. THE PHYSICAL GEOGRAPHY OF THE SEA. NY: Harper & Bros, 1855. 3rd ed. 281pp; 12 plts. Gilt blue pict cl. VG+. *SMITHFIELD.* $80

Maury, Matthew Fontaine. PHYSICAL GEOGRAPHY OF VIRGINIA. NY: Van Nostrand, 1869. 2nd ed. 2 (of 3) fldg maps. Orig

wraps repaired, rear wrap and backstrip defective, 1 map repaired, o/w contents Good. *DIAMOND.* $75

Mawe, T. and J. Abercrombie. EVERY MAN HIS OWN GARDENER....London, 1822. 22nd ed. Pp vii,(1),726. Contemp leather, modern calf spine. Minor worming at rear w/loss of few letters. Lt staining, offsetting prelim pp, eps renewed. *SUTTON.* $110

Mawson, Sir Douglas. HOME OF THE BLIZZARD. London/Phila: Heinemann/Lippincott, n.d. 2 vols. Errata, pp xxx,349; pp xiii,338. 3 fldg maps. Orange cl, black titles. Some foxing to edges, eps renewed. Shelfwear, lt soil. *PARMER.* $550

Maxfield, Archibald. OBSERVATIONS ON ULCERS OF THE LEGS, AND OTHER PARTS SHEWING THAT THE MOST OBSTINATE AND INTRACTABLE CASES MAY BE SPEEDILY CURED BY MILD METHODS OF TREATMENT. London, 1842. 1st ed. 80pp. *FYE.* $100

Maxson, Louis. SPINAL ANESTHESIA. Phila, 1938. 1st ed. *FYE.* $45

Maxwell, A.E. JUST ANOTHER DAY IN PARADISE. GC: Doubleday, 1985. 1st ed. Fine in dj. *MORDIDA.* $40

Maxwell, A.E. JUST ANOTHER DAY IN PARADISE. NY: Doubleday, 1985. 1st ed. Signed. Fine in dj. *SILVER DOOR.* $35

Maxwell, A.E. THE FROG & THE SCORPION. NY: Doubleday, 1986. Uncorrected proof copy. Signed by both authors. Lt cover crease o/w Fine in wrappers. *SILVER DOOR.* $30

Maxwell, Marius. STALKING BIG GAME WITH A CAMERA IN EQUATORIAL AFRICA....NY: The Century Company,1924. 1st ed. Very minor wear extremes. Some minor page dampstaining. Front and rear hinges starting else Near VG. *GREAT EPIC.* $95

Maxwell, Marius. STALKING BIG GAME WITH CAMERA IN EQUATORIAL AFRICA WITH A MONOGRAPH ON THE AFRICAN ELEPHANT. NY & London: Century, 1924. Dec cl. Fine. *MIKESH.* $60

Maxwell, W.H. WILD SPORTS OF THE WEST OF IRELAND. London and Glasgow, 1892. New ed. Wear, bkpl removal, else VG. *OLD LONDON.* $50

Maxwell, William Quentin. LINCOLN'S FIFTH WHEEL, THE POLITICAL HISTORY OF THE U.S. SANITARY COMMISSION. NY, 1956. 1st ed. 372pp. Inscribed. VG+ in dj. *PRATT.* $40

Maxwell, William. ANCESTORS. NY: Knopf, 1971. 1st ed. Remainder stamp bottom edge of pages, o/w Fine in Fine dj. *LOPEZ.* $40

Maxwell, William. BILLIE DYER. NY: Knopf, 1992. Uncorrected proof. Fine. *LOPEZ.* $35

Maxwell, William. THE CHATEAU. NY: Knopf, 1961. 1st ed. Owner's name, sl rubbing to spine ends, o/w Fine in lightly used dj. *BEASLEY.* $40

Maxwell, William. THE HEAVENLY TENANTS. NY: Harper & Brothers, (1946). 1st ed. VG in Good dj. *LOPEZ.* $85

Maxwell, William. THE HEAVENLY TENANTS. NY: Harpers, (1946). 1st ed. Fine in dj. *DERMONT.* $125

Maxwell, William. THE OLD MAN AT THE RAILROAD CROSSING AND OTHER TALES. NY: Knopf, 1966. 1st ed. Spine very sl cocked, o/w NF in dj. *LOPEZ.* $55

May, Earl Chapin. THE CANNING CLAN. NY: Macmillan, 1937. 1st ed. 10 plts. Fine in chipped, scarce, foil-covered dj. *CONNOLLY & WADE.* $65

May, Julian. THE GOLDEN TORC. Houghton-Mifflin, 1982. 1st ed. Fine in dj. Review slip. Signed. *MADLE.* $35

May, Julian. THE MANY-COLORED LAND. Houghton, 1981. 1st ed. Fine in dj. Signed. *MADLE.* $30

May, Julian. THE NON-BORN KING. Houghton-Mifflin, 1982. 1st ed. Fine in dj. Review slip. Signed. *MADLE.* $35

May, Margaret (trans). GALEN ON THE USEFULNESS OF THE PARTS OF THE BODY. Ithaca, 1968. 1st Eng trans. 2 vols. Slipcase. *FYE.* $150

May, Peter. HIDDEN FACES. London: Piatkus, 1981. 1st ed. Fine in price-clipped dj. *MORDIDA.* $25

May, Ralph. EARLY PORTSMOUTH HISTORY. Boston: Goodspeeds, 1926. 1st ed. Orig cl. *GINSBERG.* $85

Mayall, R. Newton & Margaret W. SUNDIALS, HOW TO KNOW, USE, AND MAKE THEM. Cambridge, MA: Sky Publishing, 1973 (1938). 2nd ed., 1st prtg. VG in dj. *KNOLLWOOD.* $30

Mayer, Alfred M. (ed) SPORT WITH GUN AND ROD IN AMERICAN WOODS AND WATERS. NY: Century Co, (1883). 1st ed. Precedes Eng ed, which appeared in 2 vols. 2 bkpls, name stamps. VG+. *AARD.* $150

Mayer, Brantz. MEXICO AS IT WAS AND AS IT IS. NY & London & Paris: J. Winchester & Wiley and Putnam, 1844. 1st ed. 35 plts, gilt pict cl. Light chipping to top and bottom of spine, foxing, several edges rubbed, signature. *ARCHAEOLOGIA.* $150

Mayer, Brantz. TAH-GAH-JUTE, or LOGAN AND CAPTAIN MICHAEL CRESOP. Baltimore, 1st ed. 86pp plus errata. Number stamp on bottom title pg. Rebound by hand in new buckram. *HEINOLDT.* $45

Mayer, Charles. JUNGLE BEASTS I HAVE CAPTURED. GC: Doubleday Page, 1924. 1st ed. VG. *AARD.* $25

Mayer, Mercer. EAST OF THE SUN AND WEST OF THE MOON. NY: Four Winds, (1980). 1st ed. Cl, gold dec. Inscribed. Fine in VG dj. *ACADEMIC LIBRARY.* $30

Mayer, Tom. THE WEARY FALCON. Boston: Houghton Mifflin Co, 1971. 1st ed. Fine in Fine dj, sl rubbing head, foot of backstrip. *HELLER.* $95

Maynard, C.J. A MANUAL OF NORTH AMERICAN BUTTERFLIES. Boston, 1891. 1st ed. 10 hand-colored plts. Rubbed, remains of paper label on spine, 1 pl detached and w/small tear, bkpl. *SUTTON.* $135

Maynard, Joe, and Barry Miles. WILLIAM S. BURROUGHS, A BIBLIOGRAPHY. 1953-73. Charlottesville: Univ Press of Virginia, 1978. 1st ed. Fine, issued w/o dj. *BEASLEY.* $25

Maynard, L.W. BIRDS OF WASHINGTON AND VICINITY. Washington, 1898. Some wear at corners; ex-lib. *SUTTON.* $27

Mayne, Peter. THE ALLEYS OF MARRAKESH. Boston: Little, Brown, 1953. 1st ed. Review copy with slip. As New in Fine+ dj. *GREAT EPIC.* $35

Mayne, Peter. THE NARROW SMILE. London: John Murray, 1955. 1st ed. Grn cl. NF, chipped dj. *PARMER.* $20

Mayne, R.C. FOUR YEARS IN BRITISH COLUMBIA AND VANCOUVER ISLAND. London: John Murray, 1862. 1st ed. 1 fldg map. Bound in full cl, stamped in gilt. Minor defects to binding, margin of one plt repaired, else VG. *LAURIE.* $400

Mayo, Herbert. OBSERVATIONS ON INJURIES AND DISEASES OF THE RECTUM. London, 1833. 1st ed. 1/4 leather, 220pp. 1" missing from top of spine, o/w VG. *FYE.* $100

Mayo, J.K. WOLF'S HEAD. London: Collins Harvill, 1987. 1st ed. Signed. Fine in price-clipped dj. *MORDIDA.* $40

Mayor, A. Hyatt. ARTISTS & ANATOMISTS. NY, 1984. 1st ed. Dj. *FYE.* $40

Mayor, Archer. BORDERLINES. NY: G.P. Putnam's Sons, 1990. 1st ed. Fine in dj. *MORDIDA.* $20

Maziere, Francis. EXPEDITION TUMAC-HUMAC. GC: Doubleday, 1955. 1st ed. Almost Fine in VG dj. *AARD.* $20

Mazor, Julian. WASHINGTON AND BALTIMORE. NY: Knopf, 1968. 1st ed, 1st book. One corner bumped, o/w Fine in VG dj, w/chip. *LOPEZ.* $25

McAlexander, Hubert, ed. CONVERSATIONS WITH PETER TAYLOR. Jackson: Univ Press of Mississippi, (1987). 1st ed. Fine in dj. Signed by Taylor. *CAPTAIN'S BOOKSHELF.* $40

McAllester, David P. PEYOTE MUSIC. NY: Viking Fund, 1949. 62 plts. Good. *ARCHAEOLOGIA.* $45

McAllister, Anna. ELLEN EWING, WIFE OF GENERAL SHERMAN. NY, 1936. 1st ed. 379pp. VG+ *PRATT.* $35

McAllister, James Gray. SKETCH OF CAPTAIN THOMAS MCALLISTER, CO. A., 27TH VIRGINIA REGIMENT. Petersburg, VA, 1896. 1st ed, ptd for priv distribution. Wrappers. VG. *McGOWAN.* $125

McAlmon, Robert. BEING GENIUSES TOGETHER 1920-1930. Revised and w/Supplementary Chapters by Kay Boyle. London: Michael Joseph, (1970). 1st UK ed thus. Fine in dj. Signed by Boyle. *CAPTAIN'S BOOKSHELF.* $75

McArthur, Lewis A. OREGON GEOGRAPHIC NAMES. Portland: Oregon Historical Soc, 1974. 4th ed, rev, enl. VG in Good dj. *CONNOLLY & WADE.* $20

McArthur, Lewis. OREGON GEOGRAPHIC NAMES. Binfords & Mort, 1944. 2nd ed. VF in Good+ dj. *OREGON.* $25

McAuley, Ed. BOB LEMON—THE WORK HORSE. Barnes, 1951. 1st ed. VG. *PLAPINGER.* $40

McBain, Ed & Craig Rice. THE APRIL ROBIN MURDERS. Random House, 1958. 1st ed. NF. Dj chipped at spine ends. *STAHR.* $20

McBain, Ed. ANOTHER PART OF THE CITY. NY: Mysterious Press, 1986. 1st ed. New in slipcase. #176/250 signed. *ELSE FINE.* $50

McBain, Ed. BEAUTY & THE BEAST. NY: HRW, 1982. 1st ed. As New in dj. *ELSE FINE.* $30

McBain, Ed. BREAD. NY: Random House, 1974. 1st ed. VF in dj. *MORDIDA.* $35

McBain, Ed. EIGHT BLACK HORSES. NY: Arbor, 1985. 1st ed. Review copy, signed. Pub's slip laid in. VF in dj. *SILVER DOOR.* $35

McBain, Ed. EIGHT BLACK HORSES. NY: Arbor, 1985. 1st ed. New in slipcase. #35/300, signed. *ELSE FINE.* $50

McBain, Ed. EVEN THE WICKED. By Richard Marsten. NY: Permabooks, 1958. 1st ed. Pb orig. Fine in wrappers. *MORDIDA.* $35

McBain, Ed. GOLDILOCKS. NY: Arbor, 1977. 1st ed. Fine; minor edgetears to dj. *ELSE FINE.* $25

McBain, Ed. GOLDILOCKS. NY: Arbor House, 1977. 1st ed. Fine in dj. *MORDIDA.* $35

McBain, Ed. GUNS. NY: Random House, 1976. 1st ed. Fine in price-clipped dj. *MORDIDA.* $25

McBain, Ed. HAIL TO THE CHIEF. NY: Random House, 1973. 1st ed. Fine in dj. *MORDIDA.* $35

McBain, Ed. JACK & THE BEANSTALK. NY: HRW, 1984. 1st ed. VF in dj. *ELSE FINE.* $25

McBain, Ed. JIGSAW. GC: Doubleday, 1970. 1st ed. Fine in dj. *MORDIDA.* $40

McBain, Ed. JIGSAW. GC: Doubleday, 1970. 1st ed. Fine in dj. *ELSE FINE.* $45

McBain, Ed. KILLER'S PAYOFF. NY: Permabooks, 1958. 1st ed. Pb orig. Fine, unread, in wrappers. *MORDIDA.* $45

McBain, Ed. LIKE LOVE. NY: Simon & Schuster, 1962. 1st ed. Few stain spots on bottom edge o/w Fine in dj w/some tiny tears and nicks. *MORDIDA.* $45

McBain, Ed. POISON. NY: Arbor, 1986. 1st ed. Proof copy. Fine in wraps. *ELSE FINE.* $30

McBain, Ed. RUMPLESTILTSKIN. NY: Viking, 1981. 1st ed. Fine in dj. *ELSE FINE.* $25

McBain, Ed. SADIE WHEN SHE DIED. GC: Doubleday, 1972. 1st ed. Fine in VG price-clipped dj (rubbed front panel; wear). *MORDIDA.* $25

McBain, Ed. THE 87TH SQUAD. NY: Simon & Schuster, 1960. 1st hb ed. Usual page browning. Fine; minor rubs at dj spine ends. *ELSE FINE.* $65

McBain, Ed. THE INTERVIEW AND OTHER STORIES. Helsinki: Finland, 1986. 1st of this ed. Ltd to 350 signed by McBain. Ptd wraps. Mint. *JAFFE.* $175

McBain, Ed. WHERE THERE'S SMOKE. NY: Random House, 1975. 1st ed. Inscribed. Goldstone bkpl on front pastedown. Fine in dj. *MORDIDA.* $35

McBain, Ed. WHERE THERE'S SMOKE. NY: Random House, 1975. 1st ed. Fine in dj. *ELSE FINE.* $25

McBride, Henry (et al). JOHN MARIN. MOMA. NY, (1936). 1st ed. Cloth. VG. *ARTIS.* $27.50

McCaffrey, Anne. DRAGONQUEST. Del Rey, 1979. 1st hb ed. Fine in dj. *MADLE.* $35

McCaffrey, Anne. THE WHITE DRAGON. Del Rey, 1978. 1st ed. Fine in dj. *MADLE.* $35

McCallum, John. THE TIGER WORE SPIKES. Barnes, 1956. 1st ed. VG in Fine dj. *PLAPINGER.* $45

McCammon, Robert R. MYSTERY WALK. NY: Holt Rinehart & Winston, (1983). 1st ed. Trace of wear else Fine in dj. *OTHER WORLDS.* $75

McCammon, Robert R. SWAN SONG. Arlington Heights: Dark Harvest, 1989. 1st hb ed. Trade issue. Bkpl, rear cover scratched else Fine in Fine dj. *OTHER WORLDS.* $32.50

McCammon, Robert R. USHER'S PASSING. NY: Holt Rinehart & Winston, (1984). 1st ed. Signed. NF in Fine dj. *OTHER WORLDS.* $50

McCann, Capt. Irving Goff. WITH THE NATIONAL GUARD ON THE BORDER: OUR NATIONAL MILITARY PROBLEM. St. Louis, 1917. Orig cl. 1st ed. *GINSBERG.* $125

McCarry, Charles. THE BRIDE OF THE WILDERNESS. NY: Nal, (1988). 1st ed. VF in VF dj. *UNGER.* $35

McCarry, Charles. THE MIERNIK DOSSIER. London: Hutchinson, 1974. 1st Brit ed. Fine in dj. *SILVER DOOR.* $27.50

McCarry, Charles. THE MIERNIK DOSSIER. NY: SRP, (1973). 1st ed. Fine, slight spine fade to dj spine. *ELSE FINE.* $50

McCarry, Charles. THE TEARS OF AUTUMN. NY: Saturday Review, (1975). 1st ed. NF in NF dj. *UNGER.* $50

McCarthy, Cormac. ALL THE PRETTY HORSES. NY: Knopf, 1992. Uncorrected proof. Fine in wraps. *CAPTAIN'S BOOKSHELF.* $150

McCarthy, Cormac. ALL THE PRETTY HORSES. NY: Knopf, 1992. Advance presentation issue. Fine in orig dec wraps enclosed in fldg card box. Signed. *CAPTAIN'S BOOKSHELF.* $175

McCarthy, Cormac. BLOOD MERIDIAN. NY: Random House, (1985). Fine in dj. 1st ed. *CHAPEL HILL.* $35

McCarthy, Cormac. BLOOD MERIDIAN. NY: Random House, 1985. 1st ed. Fine in Fine dj w/tiny rub at spine fold. *BEASLEY.* $75

McCarthy, Cormac. BLOOD MERIDIAN. NY: RH, (1985). Uncorrected proof. Fine in wraps. *CAPTAIN'S BOOKSHELF.* $225

McCarthy, Cormac. OUTER DARK. NY: RH, (1968). 1st ed. Paperclip removal; name erasure ffep o/w Fine in dj (edge nicks, short tear). *CAPTAIN'S BOOKSHELF.* $200

McCarthy, Cormac. OUTER DARK. NY: RH, (1968). 1st ed. NF in defective dj. *LOPEZ.* $40

McCarthy, Cormac. SUTTREE. NY: Random House, (1979). 1st ed. Review copy with pub's letter. Fine in Fine dj. *UNGER.* $125

McCarthy, Cormac. SUTTREE. NY: RH, (1979). 1st ed. Fine in dj with 2 minute nicks; w/o rmdr mk and spine fading which usually plague this title. *CAPTAIN'S BOOKSHELF.* $125

McCarthy, Cormac. THE ORCHARD KEEPER. NY: Random House, (1965). 1st ed, 1st bk. Fine in sl yellowed dj (few sm edge tears heel of spine). *CAPTAIN'S BOOKSHELF.* $750

McCarthy, Cormac. THE ORCHARD KEEPER. NY: Random House, (1965). Advance reading copy. Lt soiling, tiny tear, else NF in wraps. *CAPTAIN'S BOOKSHELF.* $450

McCarthy, Mary. BIRDS OF AMERICA. NY: Harcourt Brace, 1971. 1st ed. NF. *SMITH.* $30

McCarthy, Mary. HANOI. London: Weidenfeld & Nicolson, (1968). 1st British ed (only hb ed). Lt wear to dj (sm ugly tear rear panel; foxing, ink on page edges). *AKA.* $45

McCarthy, Mary. THE GROUP. Franklin Center: Franklin Library, 1978. Franklin Library leatherbound ltd ed, signed. Fine. *LOPEZ.* $65

McCarthy, Mary. THE OASIS. NY, 1949. 1st ed. Fine. Small dj tear side spine front panel, little edge rubbed. *POLYANTHOS.* $30

McCartney, John. THE STORY OF A GREAT HORSE CRESCEUS 2:02 1/4. Indianapolis: Hollenbeck, 1902. Good+. *OCTOBER FARM.* $25

McCarty, John L. MAVERICK TOWN. THE STORY OF OLD TASCOSA. Norman: Univ of OK, 1946. 1st ed. Pict cl. Fine in dj. *CONNOLLY & WADE.* $55

McCarty, John. MAVERICK TOWN, THE STORY OF OLD TOSCOSA. Univ of OK Press, 1946. 1st ed. Fine in NF dj. *VARNER.* $35

McCaslin, Rev. R. PLAIN GROVE: A HISTORY OF ITS EARLY SETTLEMENT. Claremont, NH: Claremont Mfg. Co., 1884. 1st ed. 272pp, boards. NF. *ARCHER.* $40

McCauley, J.E. A STOVE-UP COWBOY'S STORY. Austin, 1943. 1st ed. Ltd to 700. VG. Owner inscrip. *VARNER.* $100

McCauley, Lois B. MARYLAND HISTORICAL PRINTS 1752 to 1889. Baltimore: MD Hist Soc, (1975). 1st ed. 338 illus, 32 in color. Fine in dj. *CAPTAIN'S BOOKSHELF.* $175

McClellan, Elisabeth. HISTORIC DRESS IN AMERICA 1800-1870. Phila: George W. Jacobs & Co, (1910). Blue cl stamped in gilt, sl rubbed, shaken. Lacks ffep. Soiled o/w VG. *SCHOYER'S.* $50

McClellan, George B. ARMY OF THE POTOMAC. REPORT OF MAJOR-GENERAL GEORGE B. MCCLELLAN, AUG. 4, 1863. NY: Sheldon & Co, 1864. 1st ed. Only 250 printed. Fldg map. Orig cl cvrs sl worn. Rebacked w/new cl and spine label. Text VG. Inscribed. *DIAMOND.* $450

McClellan, George B. MCCLELLAN'S OWN STORY, THE WAR FOR THE UNION. NY, 1887. 1st ed. 678pp. Minor water damage, o/w VG+. *PRATT.* $75

McClellan, George B. MCCLELLAN'S OWN STORY. NY, 1887. 1st ed. Orig lib calf cvrs sl worn and stained. Rebacked. Ffep and 12pp margins chipped, o/w contents VG. *DIAMOND.* $45

McClellan, George. ANATOMY IN ITS RELATION TO ART. Phila, 1901. 1st ed. 142pp + 125 plts. Backstrip worn, hinges cracked and glued. Contents Fine. Scarce. *FYE.* $300

McClellan, George. REGIONAL ANATOMY IN ITS RELATION TO MEDICINE AND SURGERY. Phila, 1892. 2 vols. 436pp. Illus. *FYE.* $250

McClellan, H.B. I RODE WITH JEB STUART. Bloomington, IN: Indiana Univ, 1958. 1st ed. NF in VG dj. *CONNOLLY & WADE.* $37.50

McClelland, Gordon T. and Jay Last. CALIFORNIA ORANGE BOX LABELS. Beverly Hills: Hillcrest, 1985. As new in dj. *MAD DOG.* $25

McClintock, Capt. IN THE ARCTIC SEAS. Phila: Porter & Coates, nd (c1880). Rprt. (23)375pp. Frontis. Embossed cl, cheap paper, NF. *ARTIS.* $22.50

McClung, Col. D. W. CENTENNIAL ANNIVERSARY OF THE CITY OF HAMILTON, OHIO, SEPTEMBER 17-19, 1891...Hamilton, Ohio: 1892. 1st ed. 322pp. Orig cl, sm paper label on spine, bkpl removed. *GINSBERG*. $75

McClung, John A. SKETCHES OF WESTERN ADVENTURE. Cincinnati: J.A. James & Co, 1839. Woodcut frontis, orig calf, rather foxed. Howes M46. *HUDSON*. $500

McClure, Capt. WITH STANLEY IN AFRICA. NY: Worthington, 1891. 1st ed. 297pp. Spine reinforced w/clear tape, internally VG ex-lib. *WORLDWIDE*. $40

McClure, James. THE ARTFUL EGG. London: Macmillan, 1984. 1st Eng ed. VF, dj. *STAHR*. $35

McClure, Michael. FOR ARTAUD. (NY: Totem Press, 1959). 1st ed. Pub as Blue Plate #2. Signed w/abstract ink drwg on front cover. Owner's name and holograph poem, else Fine in wrappers. *CAPTAIN'S BOOKSHELF*. $150

McClure, Michael. FOR ARTAUD. (NY: Totem Press, 1959). 1st ed. Pub as Blue Plate #2. Fine in wrappers. *CAPTAIN'S BOOKSHELF*. $50

McClure, Michael. HAIL THEE WHO PLAY. LA: Black Sparrow Press, 1968. 1st ed. 1/75 hardbound, signed, w/orig drawing. Fine w/o dj, as issued. *CAPTAIN'S BOOKSHELF*. $75

McClure, Michael. LITTLE ODES. Jan-March 1961. (NY: Poet's Press, 1968). 1st ed. 1/150 signed. Fine in wrappers. *CAPTAIN'S BOOKSHELF*. $75

McClure, Michael. LOVE LION BOOK. SF: Four Seasons Foundation, 1966. 2nd ptg. NF in wrappers. *CAPTAIN'S BOOKSHELF*. $15

McClure, Michael. MUSCLED APFLE SWIFT. Sacramento: Runcible Press, n.d. Pirated ed. 1/350. NF in stapled wrappers. *CAPTAIN'S BOOKSHELF*. $50

McClure, Michael. PASSAGE. Big Sur: Jonathan Williams, 1956. 1st ed, 1st bk. One of 200 ptd as Jargon 20. Fine in wrappers. *CAPTAIN'S BOOKSHELF*. $450

McClure, Michael. PLANE POEMS. NY: Phoenix Book Shop, 1969. About Fine. 1st ed. #41 of 100 numbered signed. *CHAPEL HILL*. $50

McClure, Michael. STAR. Poems. NY: Grove, (1970). 1st ed. Fine in dj. *CAPTAIN'S BOOKSHELF*. $35

McClure, Michael. THE ADEPT. NY: Delacorte, (1971). 1st ed. Fine in dj. *CAPTAIN'S BOOKSHELF*. $35

McClure, Michael. THE BEARD. Intro Norman Mailer. (SF): Coyote, 1967. 1st ed. Fine in wrappers. *CAPTAIN'S BOOKSHELF*. $40

McClure, Michael. THE BLOSSOM OR BILLY THE KID. (Milwaukee: Great Like Books, 1967). 1st ed. 1/525 numbered. Fine in wrappers. *CAPTAIN'S BOOKSHELF*. $35

McClure, Michael. THE CHERUB. LA: Black Sparrow Press, 1970. 1st ed. 1/250 signed. Light soiling to boards, else Fine in acetate dj. *CAPTAIN'S BOOKSHELF*. $50

McClure, Michael. THIRTEEN MAD SONNETS. (Milan: Serigrafia Pezzoli), 1964. 1st ed. 1/299. Photos Ettope Sottsass. Slight fading to front panel, else Fine in wrappers. *CAPTAIN'S BOOKSHELF*. $125

McClure. A(lexander) K(elly). ABRAHAM LINCOLN AND MEN OF WAR-TIMES. Phila: Times Pub Co, 1892. Stated 2nd ed (ptg). Pict cl *SCHOYER'S*. $25

McCluskey, John. LOOK WHAT THEY DONE TO MY SONG. NY: Random House, 1974. 1st ed, 1st bk. Fine, minor wear at dj spine ends. *ELSE FINE*. $60

McCluskey, John. LOOK WHAT THEY DONE TO MY SONG. NY: Random House, (1974). 1st ed. Fine in NF dj w/creases. *LOPEZ*. $25

McCombe, Leonard (photographer). NAVAHO MEANS PEOPLE. Cambridge: Harvard Univ Press, 1951. Text by Evon Z. Vogt and Clyde Kluckhohn. 1st ed. Spine sunned, o/w Fine. *LAURIE*. $60

McConkey, Harriet E. Bishop. DAKOTA WAR WHOOP. Chicago: R.R. Donnelly, Christmas, 1965 (1864). Lakeside Classic. 1st ed thus Dale L. Morgan (ed). Blue cl, gilt. Fine. *CONNOLLY & WADE*. $25

McCook, H.C. TENANTS OF AN OLD FARM. NY, 1885. 2nd ed. Some spotting, light soiling. *SUTTON*. $65

McCord, Howard. SOME NOTES TO GARY SNYDER'S MYTHS & TEXTS. Sand Dollar, 1971. 1st trade. Fine in wraps. *STAHR*. $10

McCordock, Robert Stanley. THE YANKEE CHEESE BOX. NY, (1938). 1st ed. 470pp. Dj worn, minor cvr soiling o/w VG+. *PRATT*. $50

McCorkle, Jill. CRASH DIET. Chapel Hill: Algonquin (1992). Uncorrected proof. Fine in wraps. *DORN*. $40

McCorkle, Jill. FERRIS BEACH. Chapel Hill: Algonquin, (1990). Uncorrected proof. Signed. Fine in wraps. *DORN*. $60

McCorkle, Jill. FERRIS BEACH. Chapel Hill: Algonquin, (1990). 1st trade ed. Signed. Fine in dj. *DORN*. $35

McCorkle, Jill. FERRIS BEACH. Chapel Hill: Algonquin, 1990. 1st ed. Signed. Fine in Fine dj. *ROBBINS*. $35

McCorkle, Jill. JULY 7TH. Algonquin, 1984. 1st ed. Fine in dj. *STAHR*. $100

McCorkle, Jill. JULY 7TH. Chapel Hill: Algonquin, (1984). 1st Amer ed. Signed. Scarce. Fine in dj. *DORN*. $80

McCorkle, Jill. TENDING TO VIRGINIA. Algonquin, 1987. 1st ed. VF in dj. *STAHR*. $145

McCorkle, Jill. TENDING TO VIRGINIA. Chapel Hill: Algonquin, (1987). 1st Amer ed. Signed. Fine in dj. *DORN*. $45

McCorkle, Jill. TENDING TO VIRGINIA. Chapel Hill: Algonquin, 1987. 1st ed. Fine in dj. Signed. *CAPTAIN'S BOOKSHELF*. $40

McCorkle, Jill. THE CHEERLEADER. Chapel Hill: Algonquin, (1984). 1st Amer ed. Signed. Fine in dj. Scarce. *DORN*. $80

McCormick, Cyrus. THE CENTURY OF THE REAPER....Boston: Houghton Mifflin, 1931. 1st ed. Fine in Good dj. *CONNOLLY & WADE*. $50

McCormick, Donald. WHO'S WHO IN SPY FICTION. London: Elm Tree, 1977. 1st ed. Fine in NF dj. *SILVER DOOR*. $25

McCormick, H.H. LANDSCAPE ART, PAST AND PRESENT. NY, 1923. One of 1200. 56 photogravure plts. Orig cl spine, paper covered boards. Some wear at corners, spine sl soiled, scuffed. *SUTTON*. $185

McCormick, Jay. NOVEMBER STORM. NY, 1943. 1st ed. Signed. Fine in dj. *ARTIS*. $20

McCormick, John. THE COMPLETE AFICIONADO. Cleveland: World Pub, (1967). 1st ed. Chipped dj. *SILVER*. $20

McCormick, Richard C. ARIZONA: ITS RESOURCES AND PROSPECTS. NY, 1865. 1st ed. 22pp. Fldg map. Orig ptd wrappers. Howes M65. *GINSBERG*. $125

McCormick, Richard C. ARIZONA: ITS RESOURCES AND PROSPECTS. NY: D. Van Nostrand, 1865. 22pp, fldg map, 9 1/4 x 6", ptd wrappers. 1" tear to front cover, wrappers starting to separate along spine. *DAWSON'S*. $150

McCormick, Richard C. VISIT TO THE CAMP BEFORE SEVASTOPOL. NY: Appleton, 1855. 4th Thousand. 212pp,4pp pub ads. Orig cl stamped in blind and gilt, faded on spine. Fldg frontis, 8 litho illus, some double-pg, all foxed. *SCHOYER'S*. $65

McCormick, Robert R. THE WAR WITHOUT GRANT. NY, 1950. 1st ed. 245pp; fldg color maps. Light dj wear o/w Fine. *PRATT*. $40

McCormick, Robert R. THE WAR WITHOUT GRANT. NY, 1950. 1st ed. Many fine, fldg maps. Fine in NF dj (sl edgewear). *McCLINTOCK*. $35

McCosker, M. J. THE HISTORICAL COLLECTION OF IN-SURANCE COMPANY OF NORTH AMERICA. Phila: Ins Co of North America, 1945. VG. *BACKROOM*. $30

McCoy, Horace. 4 NOVELS. London: Zomba Books, 1983. Omnibus ed. VF in dj. *MORDIDA*. $25

McCoy, Horace. NO POCKETS IN A SHROUD. London: Arthur Barker, (1938). Fourth UK ptg. Inscribed. Binding cocked; dj worn but present. *LOPEZ*. $200

McCoy, Horace. THEY SHOOT HORSES, DON'T THEY? NY, 1948. 1st pb ed. VG+ in wrappers. *PETTLER*. $15

McCoy, Joseph G. CATTLE TRADE OF THE WEST AND SOUTHWEST. Columbus, 1951. Long's Book Store Reprint. Fine in sl chipped and soiled dj. *BAADE*. $50

McCoy, Joseph G. HISTORIC SKETCHES OF THE CATTLE TRADE OF THE WEST AND SOUTHWEST. Kansas City, MO, 1874. 1st ed. (6),427,(24)pp. Orig cl. State A, w/head of Texas longhorn emb on front cover. Some fading to spine and covers as usual. Howes M72. *GINSBERG*. $1750

McCoy, Joseph G. HISTORIC SKETCHES OF THE CATTLE TRADE OF THE WEST & SOUTHWEST. Kansas City: Ramsey, Millet, Hudson, 1874. 1st ed. 427pp + 24pp ads. Frontis, ads on eps. Binding state B. Lacking ffep, corner and spine edge wear, some foxing. Overall VG. Rare. Howes M72. *OREGON*. $1200

McCracken, Harold. ALASKA BEAR TRAILS. NY: Doubleday, 1931. Photos, plts. Dec cl. VG. *MIKESH*. $95

McCracken, Harold. FREDERICK REMINGTON. Phila, 1947. NF. *POLYANTHOS*. $60

McCracken, Harold. GEORGE CATLIN AND THE OLD FRON-TIER. Dial, 1959. 1st trade ed. Fine in VG dj. *OREGON*. $45

McCracken, Harold. GEORGE CATLIN AND THE OLD FRON-TIER. NY, 1959, 1st trade ed. 216pp; 36 color plts, 130 b/w illus. Dj. *HEINOLDT*. $40

McCracken, Harold. GEORGE CATLIN AND THE OLD FRON-TIER. NY: Dial, 1959. 1st ed. Boards sl bowed o/w Fine in VG rubbed price-clipped dj. *ARCHER*. $35

McCracken, Harold. GEORGE CATLIN AND THE OLD FRON-TIER. NY: Dial Press, 1959. 1st ed. Dj sl chipped at extremities, else VG. *LAURIE*. $75

McCracken, Harold. GOD'S FROZEN CHILDREN. GC: Doubleday, Doran, 1930. 291 pp. 1st ed. Cl smudgy, sunned, small dampstain front cvr, else Near VG. *GREAT EPIC*. $35

McCracken, Harold. HUNTERS OF THE STORMY SEA. London: Oldbourne, 1957. 1st ed. Minor bump front cvr bottom corner, slight fore-edge foxing else NF in Fine dj. *GREAT EPIC*. $65

McCracken, Harold. PORTRAIT OF THE OLD WEST, WITH A BIOGRAPHICAL CHECK LIST OF WESTERN ARTISTS. NY: McGraw-Hill, (1952). 1st ed. Fine in dj. *LAURIE*. $50

McCracken, Harold. PORTRAIT OF THE OLD WEST. McGraw-Hill, 1952. 1st ed. Fine in VG dj. *VARNER*. $40

McCracken, Harold. PORTRAIT OF THE OLD WEST. NY, 1952. 1st ed. Gift inscrip. Slight soiling to covers, o/w VG in badly chipped dj. *BAADE*. $40

McCracken, Harold. THE BEAST THAT WALKS LIKE A MAN, THE STORY OF THE GRIZZLY BEAR. London: Oldbourne, 1957. VG+. *MIKESH*. $27.50

McCracken, Harold. THE BEAST THAT WALKS LIKE A MAN, THE STORY OF THE GRIZZLY BEAR. GC, NY, 1955. 1st ed. VG+. *MIKESH*. $25

McCracken, Harold. THE LAST OF THE SEA OTTERS. Phila: J.B. Lippincott, 1942. Third impression. NF in VG dj. *GREAT EPIC*. $35

McCrea, Tully. DEAR BELLE, LETTERS FROM A CADET & OF-FICER TO HIS SWEETHEART 1858-1865. Middletown, (1965). Ed by Catherine S. Crary. 1st ed. Light dj wear o/w Fine. *PRATT*. $35

McCreery, William B. MY EXPERIENCES AS A PRISONER OF WAR, AND ESCAPE FROM LIBBY PRISON. Detroit, 1893. 1st ed. Wrappers, backstrip lacking, small embossed lib stamp. *McGOWAN*. $37.50

McCrumb, Sharyn. BIMBOS OF THE DEATH SUN. Lake Geneva: TSR, Inc., 1987. 1st ed. Pb orig. Inscribed. Crease on spine and sl rubbing, o/w Fine in wrappers. *MORDIDA*. $30

McCrumb, Sharyn. IF EVER I RETURN, PRETTY PEGGY-O. NY: Charles Scribner's Sons, 1990. 1st ed. VF in dj. *MORDIDA*. $20

McCrumb, Sharyn. IF EVER I RETURN, PRETTY PEGGY-O. NY: Scribner's, (1990). 1st ed. Signed. VF in VF dj. *UNGER*. $40

McCrumb, Sharyn. PAYING THE PIPER. NY: Ballantine, 1988. 1st ed. Pb orig. Stamp, o/w Fine in wrappers. *MORDIDA*. $25

McCrumb, Sharyn. SICK OF SHADOWS. NY: Avon, 1984. 1st ed., 1st mystery. Pb orig. Fine, unread, in wrappers. *MORDIDA*. $35

McCrumb, Sharyn. THE WINDSOR KNOT. NY: Ballantine Books, 1990. 1st ed. VF in dj. *MORDIDA*. $20

McCullers, Carson. CLOCK WITHOUT HANDS. Boston: Houghton Mifflin Co, 1961. 1st ed. Fine in price clipped dj w/cellophane window. *HELLER*. $75

McCullers, Carson. SWEET AS A PICKLE AND CLEAN AS A PIG. Boston: Houghton Mifflin, 1964. 1st ed. NF in dj chipped top of backstrip, lower right corner. *HELLER*. $100

McCullers, Carson. THE MORTGAGED HEART. Ed. by Margarita G. Smith. Boston: Houghton Mifflin, 1971. 1st ed. Fine in NF dj. (spine a little sunned from peach to pink as usual). *CHAPEL HILL*. $30

McCullers, Carson. THE SQUARE ROOT OF WONDERFUL. London: Cresset Press, 1958. 1st Eng ed. Fine in price clipped dj. *HELLER*. $85

McCurrach, J.C. PALMS OF THE WORLD. NY, 1960. Cl, some fraying, fading to lower extrems. Ex-lib, dj. *SUTTON*. $47

McCutchan, Philip. TALL SHIPS. NY: Crown Publishers, Inc., 1976. 1st ed. NF in VG dj. *PARMER*. $20

McCutchan, Philip. THE DRAKOTNY. London: Harrap, 1971. 1st ed. Fine in dj. *SILVER DOOR*. $25

McCutcheon, George Barr. BOOKS ONCE WERE MEN. NY: Dodd, Mead & Co., 1931. Fine, in generally Good box. *WREDEN*. $20

McCutcheon, George Barr. COWARDICE COURT. G&D, 1906. VG+. *BEBBAH*. $22

McCutcheon, George Barr. THE PRINCE OF GRAUSTARK. NY: Dodd Mead, 1914. 1st ed. Prev owner's name. Fine-. *AARD*. $12.50

McCutcheon, John T. IN AFRICA: HUNTING ADVENTURES IN THE BIG GAME COUNTRY. Indianapolis: Bobbs-Merrill, 1910. 1st ed. Sl shaken, corners rubbed, first few leaves sl smudged, o/w VG ex-lib. *WORLDWIDE*. $125

McDaniel, Bruce W. THE DESERT GOD'S CRUCIBLE. Boston: Richard G. Badger The Gorham Press, (1926). Mint in Mint dj. *BOOK MARKET*. $60

McDaniel, Ruel. VINEGARROON. Kingsport, TN, 1936. 1st ed. Cloth. Fine in dj. *GIBBS*. $25

McDaniels, Ruel. VINEGARROON. Kingsport: Southern, 1936. 1st ed. Orig pict cl. Early newspaper clipping tipped in. Last few pgs show small stain on edge of leaves, affecting nothing. Minor edgewear. VG. *CONNOLLY & WADE*. $35

McDermand, Charles. WATERS OF THE GOLDEN TROUT COUNTRY. NY: G.P. Putnam's Sons, 1946. 2nd impression. VG in VG dj w/light edge wear. *BACKMAN*. $28

McDermott, Alice. THAT NIGHT. NY: Farrar, Straus & Giroux, (1987). 1st ed, 2nd book. Fine in dj. *BERNARD*. $35

McDermott, J.F. (ed). FRENCHMEN AND FRENCH WAYS IN THE MISSISSIPPI VALLEY. Univ of IL, 1969. 1st ed. Fine in VG dj. *VARNER*. $20

McDermott, John. FRENCHMEN & FRENCH WAYS IN THE MISSISSIPPI VALLEY. Univ of IL, 1969. 1st ed. VF in VF dj. *OREGON*. $25

McDermott, John. GEORGE CALEB BINGHAM, RIVER PORTRAITIST. Univ of OK, (1959). 1st ed. 79 plts. VF in VG dj. *OREGON*. $60

McDermott, John. PRIVATE LIBRARIES IN CREOLE SAINT LOUIS. Baltimore: Johns Hopkins Press, 1938. Cvrs a bit scuffed, top of label chipped, else internally Fine. *WREDEN*. $35

McDermott, John. PRIVATE LIBRARIES IN CREOLE SAINT LOUIS. Johns Hopkins, 1938. 1st ed. Fine. *OREGON*. $100

McDermott, John. THE EARLY HISTORIES OF ST. LOUIS. St. Louis Hist Documents Foundation, 1952. 1st ed. VF in Good+ dj. *OREGON*. $50

McDermott, John. THE FRENCH IN THE MISSISSIPPI VALLEY. Univ of IL, 1965. 1st ed. VF in VG dj. *OREGON*. $35

McDermott, John. THE SPANISH IN THE MISSISSIPPI VALLEY, 1762-1804. Univ of IL, (1974). 1st ed. VF in VF dj. *OREGON*. $35

McDermott, John. TRAVELERS ON THE WESTERN FRONTIER. Univ of IL, (1970). 1st ed. VF in Fine dj. *OREGON*. $35

McDonald, Frederic W. IN A NOOK WITH A BOOK. Cincinnati: Jennings & Graham, (190?). Fine. *WREDEN*. $20

McDonald, Frederic W. RECREATIONS OF A BOOK-LOVER. London: Hodder and Stoughton, 1911. 1st ed. Extrems rubbed, sm stain rear cover, else Good. *WREDEN*. $25

McDonald, Gregory. FLETCH & THE MAN WHO. London: Gollancz, 1983. 1st Brit & 1st hardcover ed. Rev copy with pub slip. VF in dj. *SILVER DOOR*. $30

McDonald, Gregory. FLETCH & THE WIDOW BRADLEY. London: Gollancz, 1981. 1st British ed. VF in dj. *SILVER DOOR*. $35

McDonald, Jerry. NORTH AMERICAN BISON, THEIR CLASSIFICATION AND EVOLUTION. Berkeley: Univ of CA, (1981). 1st ed. VF in VF dj. *OREGON*. $45

McDonough, James Lee. CHATTANOOGA—A DEATH GRIP ON THE CONFEDERACY. Knoxville, (1984). 1st ed. 217pp. VG+ in dj. *PRATT*. $27.50

McDougal, Henry Clay. RECOLLECTIONS, 1844-1909. Kansas City, 1910. 1st ed. *GINSBERG*. $75

McDougall, J. FOREST, LAKE & PRAIRIE: TWENTY YEARS OF FRONTIER LIFE IN WESTERN CANADA 1842-1862. Toronto: W. Briggs, (1910). 2nd ed. Gilt dec cl. VG+. *MIKESH*. $47.50

McDougall, John. SADDLE, SLED AND SNOWSHOE....Cincinnati: Jennings & Graham, (1896). VG. *ARTIS*. $35

McDowell, Frank & Carl Enna (eds). SURGICAL REHABILITATION IN LEPROSY AND IN OTHER PERIPHERAL NERVE DISORDERS. Baltimore, 1974. 1st ed. *FYE*. $75

McDowell, Michael. TOPLIN. Santa Cruz: Scream Press, 1985. 1st ed. One of 250 signed, numbered. Fine in Fine dj in slipcase. *OTHER WORLDS*. $125

McEacharn, N. THE VILLA TARANTO, A SCOTSMAN'S GARDEN IN ITALY. London, 1954. Cloth. Dj, tears. *SUTTON*. $45

McEiligott, James N. THE AMERICAN DEBATER. Chicago: S.C. Griggs & Co, 1863. Rev, enl ed. Frontis, orig cl. *KARMIOLE*. $50

McElory, John. THIS WAS ANDERSONVILLE...Ed by Roy Meredith. NY: McDowell, Obolensky, 1957. 1st ed. VG in Good+ dj. *CONNOLLY & WADE*. $45

McElroy, Joseph G. THE BATTLE OF CHICKAMAUGA. N.p., (1895). 1st ed. Wrappers. NF. *McGOWAN*. $27.50

McElroy, Joseph. A SMUGGLER'S BIBLE. NY: Harcourt, Brace & World, (1966). 1st ed, 1st book. Adv prepub copy in stiff ppwrps. Right mid-edge of spine has 1/2" cut through to inner hinge; cover lightly soiled o/w VG. *BERNARD*. $225

McElroy, Joseph. A SMUGGLER'S BIBLE. NY: HB&W, (1966). Advance copy in ptd wraps. Just About Fine and uncommon, thus. *CAPTAIN'S BOOKSHELF*. $275

McElroy, Joseph. ANCIENT HISTORY. NY: Knopf, 1971. 1st ed. Inscribed, ALS laid in. VG. *SMITH*. $175

McElroy, Joseph. ANCIENT HISTORY: A PARAPHRASE. NY: Knopf, 1971. 1st ed. Fine in Fine dj. *BEASLEY*. $65

McElroy, Joseph. HIND'S KIDNAP. NY: Harper, 1969. 1st ed. Fine in Fine dj. *BEASLEY*. $125

McElroy, Joseph. LOOKOUT CARTRIDGE. NY: Knopf, 1974. 1st ed. Fine in Fine dj, w/usual tendency to curl at top edge. *BEASLEY*. $50

McElroy, Joseph. LOOKOUT CARTRIDGE. NY: Knopf, 1974. 1st ed. Fine in very lightly used dj w/few tiny tears. *CAPTAIN'S BOOKSHELF*. $35

McElroy, Joseph. PLUS. NY: Knopf, 1977. 1st ed. Uncorrected proof copy in wrappers. Signed. *LOPEZ*. $175

McElroy, Robert. JEFFERSON DAVIS, THE UNREAL AND THE REAL. 2 vols. NY, 1937. 1st ed. 783pp. Ex-lib. Rebound. VG+. *PRATT*. $47.50

McEwan, Ian. FIRST LOVE, LAST RITES. Random House, 1975. 1st Amer ed. VF in dj. *STAHR*. $45

McEwan Ian. IN BETWEEN THE SHEETS & OTHER STORIES. Simon and Schuster, 1978. 1st ed. Fine in dj. Signed. Rmdr stamp. *STAHR*. $60

McEwan, Ian. IN BETWEEN THE SHEETS. NY: Simon & Schuster, (1978). 1st Amer ed. Signed. NF in dj. *LOPEZ*. $50

McEwan, Ian. THE CHILD IN TIME. Boston: Houghton Mifflin, (1990). 2nd ptg of Amer ed. Inscribed, note from secretary laid in. Fine in dj. *LOPEZ*. $45

McEwan, Ian. THE CHILD IN TIME. Houghton Mifflin, 1987. Uncorrected proof of 1st Amer ed. VF in wraps. *STAHR*. $25

McEwan, Ian. THE COMFORT OF STRANGERS. NY: Simon & Schuster, (1981). 1st ed. Signed. Fine in dj. *LOPEZ*. $85

McEwan, Ian. THE COMFORT OF STRANGERS. Simon and Schuster, 1981. 1st Amer ed. VF in dj. *STAHR*. $15

McEwan, Ian. THE COMFORT OF STRANGERS. Simon and Schuster, 1981. 1st Amer ed. VF in dj. Signed. *STAHR*. $60

McEwan, Ian. THE COMFORT OF STRANGERS. Simon and Schuster, 1981. Uncorrected proof of Amer ed. Fine in yellow wraps. *STAHR*. $60

McEwan, Ian. THE INNOCENT. Doubleday, 1990. Advance reading copy of Amer ed. Fine in dec wraps. Letter to bkseller laid in. *STAHR*. $35

McEwan, Ian. THE INNOCENT. London: Cape, (1990). Fine in Fine dj. Signed. *LOPEZ*. $85

McFall, David. DARKIE AND OTHERS. (Asheville, NC: The Inland Press, 1930). 1st ed. Orig ptd wraps. Yapp edges worn, traces of foxing, but VG. *CHAPEL HILL*. $40

McFarland, Asa. AN OUTLINE OF BIOGRAPHY AND RECOLLECTION. Concord, 1880. 1st ed. 144,(1)pp. Port, orig cl. *GINSBERG*. $50

McFarling, Lloyd. EXPLORING THE NORTHERN PLAINS, 1804-1876. Caxton, 1955. 1st ed. Dampstain bottom spine. Good+ in Good+ dj. *OREGON.* $35

McFee, William. THE HARBOURMASTER. GC, NY: Doubleday, 1931. 1st ed, 1/377 signed. Fine, unopened. *JUVELIS.* $70

McFee, William. THE HARBOURMASTER. GC: Doubleday Doran, 1932. 1st ed. Spine lettering dull, VG in bright, externally Fine dj (front flap chipped). Scarce glassine dj overlay. *BERNARD.* $45

McGaw, William Cochran. SAVAGE SCENE, THE LIFE AND TIMES OF JAMES KIRKER, FRONTIER KING. NY, (1972). 1st ed. 242pp. Fine in dj. *PRATT.* $25

McGaw, William. SAVAGE SCENE...JAMES KIRKER, FRONTIER KING. Hastings House, (1972). 1st ed. VF in VF dj. *OREGON.* $35

McGill, William M. CAVERNS OF VIRGINIA. Univ of VA Press, 1933. Spine severed. Sm insect holes; spot. VG. *BOOK BROKER.* $75

McGinley, Rev. Wm. A. RECEPTION OF LIEUT. A.W. GREELY, U.S.A., AND HIS COMRADS, AND OF THE ARCTIC RELIEF EXPEDITION....Washington: GPO, 1884. VG (spine chipped, edges soiled). *PARMER.* $125

McGlashan, M. Nona. GIVE ME A MOUNTAIN MEADOW. Fresno: Valley Publishers, 1977. 1st ed. 248pp & loose leaf index signed. Fine in Fine dj. *BOOK MARKET.* $20

McGovern, James. CROSSBOW AND OVERCAST. NY: Wm. Morrow, 1964. VG in sl worn dj. *KNOLLWOOD.* $23

McGrath, Patrick. BLOOD AND WATER AND OTHER TALES. NY: Poseidon, (1988). 1st ed. Fine in dj. *CAPTAIN'S BOOKSHELF.* $45

McGraw, Blanche (Mrs. John). THE REAL MCGRAW. McKay, 1953. Arthur Mann (ed). 1st ed. Inscribed. VG in VG dj. *PLAPINGER.* $140

McGraw, John. HOW TO PLAY BASEBALL. Harper, 1914. 1st ed. Good. *PLAPINGER.* $110

McGraw, John. MY THIRTY YEARS IN BASEBALL. Boni & Liveright, 1923. 1st ed. VG. *PLAPINGER.* $200

McGuane, Thomas. AN OUTSIDE CHANCE: ESSAYS ON SPORT. NY: Farrar Straus & Giroux, (1980). 1st ed. Review copy, slip laid in. Fine in dj. Signed. *CAPTAIN'S BOOKSHELF.* $75

McGuane, Thomas. KEEP THE CHANGE. Boston: Houghton Mifflin Co./Seymour Lawrence, 1984. One of ltd ed of 150 signed. New, issued w/o dj, in slipcase. *BERNARD.* $100

McGuane, Thomas. KEEP THE CHANGE. Boston: Houghton Mifflin/SL, 1989. 1st ed. 1/150 numbered, signed. Fine w/o dj, as issued, in cl slipcase. *LOPEZ.* $125

McGuane, Thomas. KEEP THE CHANGE. Houghton Mifflin, 1989. Advance reading copy. Fine in dec wraps. *STAHR.* $30

McGuane, Thomas. NINETY-TWO IN THE SHADE. London: Collins, 1974. 1st UK ed. Fine in dj. Signed. *CAPTAIN'S BOOKSHELF.* $125

McGuane, Thomas. NINETY-TWO IN THE SHADE. London: Collins, 1974. 1st UK ed. Fine in price clipped dj. *BERNARD.* $35

McGuane, Thomas. NOBODY'S ANGEL. NY: Random House, 1981. 1st ed. NF. *SMITH.* $25

McGuane, Thomas. NOBODY'S ANGEL. NY: RH, (1982). Uncorrected proof. Fine in red wraps. Custom fldg case. *CAPTAIN'S BOOKSHELF.* $150

McGuane, Thomas. NOTHING BUT BLUE SKIES. Boston: Houghton Mifflin, 1992. Adv uncorrected proof. Fine in pict wrappers. *CAPTAIN'S BOOKSHELF.* $45

McGuane, Thomas. PANAMA. Farrar Straus Giroux, 1978. Fine in VG dj. *BEBBAH.* $18

McGuane, Thomas. PANAMA. NY: Farrar Straus Giroux, (1978). 1st ed. Signed. Fine in Fine dj. *DERMONT.* $30

McGuane, Thomas. PANAMA. NY: FS&G, (1978). 1st state of uncorrected proof in tall grn wraps. Fine in custom fldg case. *CAPTAIN'S BOOKSHELF.* $200

McGuane, Thomas. SOMETHING TO BE DESIRED. NY: Random House, 1984. 1st ed. Fine in dj. *ARCHER.* $20

McGuane, Thomas. THE BUSHWACKED PIANO. NY: Simon and Schuster, 1971. 1st ed. Fine but for owner's name, in NF dj w/short tear. *BEASLEY.* $75

McGuane, Thomas. THE BUSHWHACKED PIANO. NY: S&S, (1971). Uncorrected proof. Fine in ptd yellow wraps. *CAPTAIN'S BOOKSHELF.* $675

McGuane, Thomas. THE SPORTING CLUB. NY: S&S, 1969. Uncorrected proof of 1st bk. Just About Fine in ptd yellow wraps. Custom fldg case. *CAPTAIN'S BOOKSHELF.* $750

McGuane, Thomas. THE SPORTING CLUB. NY: Simon & Schuster, (1968). 1st ed, 1st book. Signed by McGuane on bookplate tipped in on flyleaf. NF in dj which is very lightly soiled on rear panel. *BERNARD.* $100

McGuane, Thomas. TO SKIN A CAT. NY, 1986. 1st ed. VF in dj. *PETTLER.* $25

McGuane, Thomas. TO SKIN A CAT. NY: Dutton/SL, (1986). 1st ed. Signed. Fine in Fine dj. *LOPEZ.* $45

McGuire, C.E. CATHOLIC BUILDERS OF THE NATION. 5 vols. Boston, 1923. 1st ed. VG. *ARTIS.* $55

McGuirre, Harry (compiler). TALES OF ROD AND GUN. NY: Macmillan Co, 1931. 1st ed. VG in Poor dj. *BACKMAN.* $25

McHale, Tom. PRINCIPATO. NY: Viking, (c1970). 1st bk. Unrevised proofs. Confidential. Viking letter laid in. NF in ptd wraps. *HELLER.* $60

McHugh, Tom. TIME OF THE BUFFALO. NY, 1972, 1st ed. *HEINOLDT.* $15

McHugh, Vincent. I AM THINKING OF MY DARLING. Simon & Schuster, 1943. Fine in dj. *MADLE.* $35

McIlhany, Edward W. RECOLLECTIONS OF A '49ER. A QUAINT AND THRILLING NARRATIVE....Kansas City, Mo., 1908. 1st ed. Orig cl. Howes M111. *GINSBERG.* $150

McIlhenny, E.A. BIRD CITY. Boston, 1934. Fldg photo. Some gilt lettering worn away; bkpl; glue residue on eps. *SUTTON.* $35

McIlhenny, E.A. THE AUTOBIOGRAPHY OF AN EGRET. Stiff wraps, dj (chipped), NY, 1939. *SUTTON.* $25

McIlvaine, Mable. REMINISCENCES OF CHICAGO DURING THE CIVIL WAR. NY, (1967). 1st ed. 194pp. VG+ in dj. *PRATT.* $17.50

McIlvanney, William. A GIFT FROM NESSUS. London: E&S, 1968. 1st ed. Fine in dj. *ELSE FINE.* $40

McIlvanney, William. LAIDLAW. NY: Pantheon, 1977. 1st ed. Fine in dj. *ELSE FINE.* $30

McIlvanney, William. THE PAPERS OF TONY VEITCH. London: Hodder, 1983. 1st ed. About Fine in dj. *SILVER DOOR.* $25

McIlwraith, T. THE BIRDS OF ONTARIO, BEING A CONCISE ACCOUNT OF EVERY SPECIES...IN ONTARIO. Toronto, 1894. 426pp. Orig gilt-dec cl. Sm tears head of spine; institutional bkpl, sticker on spine; pp yellowed. Bright. *SUTTON.* $65

McInerney, Jay. BRIGHT LIGHTS, BIG CITY. Vintage, 1984. 1st. NF, wraps. Lower, right front corner bumped. No adverts on ffep. *STAHR.* $20

McInerney, Jay. BRIGHTNESS FALLS. NY: Knopf, 1992. Wraps. Advance reading copy. Fine in Fine ptd folding box. *BEASLEY.* $35

McInerney, Jay. RANSOM. NY: Vintage Contemporaries, 1985. 1st ed. Fine in Fine dj, wrinkles on spine. *BEASLEY.* $40

McInerney, Jay. STORY OF MY LIFE. NY: Atlantic, (1988). 1st ed. Signed. VF in VF dj. *UNGER*. $40

McIntosh, Christopher. ELIPHAS LEVI AND THE FRENCH OCCULT REVIVAL. NY: Weiser, (1974). 1st US ed. VG+ in VG dj. *BLUE DRAGON*. $45

McIntosh, J.T. ONE IN THREE HUNDRED. Doubleday, 1954. 1st ed. VG in chipped dj. *MADLE*. $25

McIntyre, A.R. CURARE, ITS HISTORY, NATURE, AND CLINICAL USE. Chicago, 1947. 2 pp creased. Worn dj. *SUTTON*. $37

McIntyre, Vonda. DREAMSNAKE. Boston: HM, 1978. 1st ed. Fine; minor edgewear to dj. *ELSE FINE*. $75

McIntyre, Vonda. FIREFLOOD AND OTHER STORIES. Houghton-Mifflin, 1979, 1st ed. Fine in dj. Inscribed to George O. Smith. *MADLE*. $40

McKay, Claude. BANJO. NY & London: Harper & Bros., 1929. 1st ed. Bottom of spine dull; bookplt o/w VG in dj missing bottom of spine & chipped at top spine edge; spine faded; front panel has faded wide band. Dj. *BERNARD*. $150

McKay, Claude. BANJO. NY: Harper, 1929. 1st ed. Spine dulled, else lightly worn in lightly used dj w/tears and small chips. *BEASLEY*. $300

McKay, Claude. BANJO: A STORY WITHOUT A PLOT. NY and London: Harper & Brothers, 1929. 1st ed. 1/2 cl, dec paper boards. VG w/o dj. *HELLER*. $75

McKean, Hugh F. THE "LOST" TREASURES OF LOUIS COMFORT TIFFANY. GC, NY: Doubleday, 1980. Dj. *KARMIOLE*. $60

McKearin, Helen and George. TWO HUNDRED YEARS OF AMERICAN BLOWN GLASS. NY: Crown, 1962. 10th prtg. VG in dj. *BACKROOM*. $30

McKee, Edwin D. ANCIENT LANDSCAPES OF THE GRAND CANYON REGION. Self-pub, 1931. 1st ed. Grn stiff pict wraps, 50pp, illus. VG+. *FIVE QUAIL*. $25

McKee, Irving. "BEN-HUR" WALLACE, THE LIFE OF GENERAL LEW WALLACE. Berkeley, 1947. 1st ed. Minor cover wear o/w Fine. *PRATT*. $40

McKelvey, S.D. BOTANICAL EXPLORATION OF THE TRANS-MISSISSIPPI WEST, 1790-1850. Jamaica Plain, 1955. 6 fldg maps, 3 full-pg maps, 2 maps rear pocket. Cl, glassine dj. *SUTTON*. $250

McKenna, James A. BLACK RANGE TALES. Chicago (1965). Facsimile of 1936 1st ed. Intro Shane Leslie. *HEINOLDT*. $20

McKenna, James A. BLACK RANGE TALES. NY, 1936. 1st ed. 320pp. Some surface wear, bkpl or pocket removed inside rear cover (but no other ex-lib markings evident). About Good+. *FIVE QUAIL*. $50

McKenna, James B. A SPANIARD IN THE PORTUGUESE INDIES. Cambridge: Harvard Univ Press, 1967. 1st ed. New in lightly rubbed dj. *PARMER*. $30

McKillup, Patricia. STEPPING FROM THE SHADOWS. Atheneum, 1982. 1st ed. Fine in dj. *MADLE*. $30

McKinlay, William Laird. KARLUK—THE GREAT UNTOLD STORY OF THE ANTARCTIC EXPLORATION. London: George Weidenfeld and Nicolson, 1976. 1st ed. VG in similar dj. *PARMER*. $40

McKinley, Captain Ashley. THE SOUTH POLE PICTURE BOOK. NYH: S.W. Miller, (1934). Wraps. Good+. *BLUE DRAGON*. $25

McKinney, E.P. IRIS IN THE LITTLE GARDEN. Boston, 1927. Cl, sm stain upper edge front cvr; name. *SUTTON*. $25

McKready, Kelvin. A BEGINNER'S STAR-BOOK, AN EASY GUIDE TO THE STARS...NY: G.P. Putnam's Sons, 1923 (1912). 2nd ed, rev. Corners bumped & worn, envelope laid in containing newspaper clippings. Good. *KNOLLWOOD*. $40

McLanahan, Ed. FAMOUS PEOPLE I HAVE KNOWN. NY: Farrar Straus Giroux (1985). 1st ed. Owner inscrip, else Fine in dj. *SECOND LIFE*. $35

McLaurin, Tim. KEEPER OF THE MOON. NY: Norton, (1991). Uncorrected proof. Fine in wraps. *DORN*. $35

McLaurin, Tim. WOODROW'S TRUMPET. NY: Norton, (1989). Uncorrected proof. Fine in ptd wrappers. *CAPTAIN'S BOOKSHELF*. $25

McLoughlin, Emmett. AN INQUIRY INTO THE ASSASSINATION OF ABRAHAM LINCOLN. NY, (1963). 1st ed. 190pp. Lt dj wear, o/w Fine. *PRATT*. $35

McLuhan, Marshall and Quentin Fiore. THE MEDIUM IS THE MASSAGE. NY: Random House. 1967. 1st ptg. Dj. *KARMIOLE*. $65

McLuhan, Marshall. THE GUTENBERG GALAXY. Canada, 1962. 1st ed. Signed presentation. Bottom edge sl rubbed. Fine in dj (extremities little chipped, edge rubbed). *POLYANTHOS*. $75

McLuhan, T. C. TOUCH THE EARTH. NY, 1971, 5th ed. Dj. *HEINOLDT*. $25

McMalion, John R. THE WRIGHT BROTHERS: FATHER OF FLIGHT. Boston: Little, Brown, 1930. 1st ed. Fine in Fine dj. *BOOK MARKET*. $40

McManus, James. CHIN MUSIC. Crown, 1985. 1st ed. Fine in dj. *STAHR*. $35

McMaster, S.W. 60 YEARS ON THE UPPER MISSISSIPPI. MY LIFE AND EXPERIENCES. Rock Island, IL, 1893 (i.e. 1895). Wrappers edgeworn, slight rounding of corners. Good. Howes M169. *BOHLING*. $450

McMeen, Samuel and Kempster Miller. TELEPHONY...Chicago: Amer Technical Society. 1923 rev ed. Fine. *MAD DOG*. $45

McMillan, Terry. WAITING TO EXHALE. NY: Viking, 1992. 1st ed. Signed. Fine in Fine dj. *BEASLEY*. $45

McMurtrie, Douglas. A HISTORY OF PRINTING IN THE UNITED STATES. Volume 11. NY: R. R. Bowker Co., 1936. 1st ed. Front leaf yellowed from newspaper article. *OAK KNOLL*. $150

McMurtrie, Douglas. AMERICAN TYPE DESIGN IN THE TWENTIETH CENTURY WITH SPECIMENS....Chicago: Ballou, 1924. Gold stamped boards, cloth spine. Dj chipped. *DAWSON'S*. $50

McMurtrie, Douglas. THE GENERAL EPISTLE OF THE LATTER DAY SAINTS. DATED: WINTER QUARTERS, NEBRASKA, DECEMBER 23, 1847, AND CONSTITUTING THE EARLIEST KNOWN EXAMPLE OF PRINTING IN THE PRESENT STATE OF NEBRASKA. Containing a Complete Facsimile of the Original Edition of the Epistle. Chicago: The Black Cat Press, 1935. One of 120. Few spots on covers. *OAK KNOLL*. $75

McMurtrie, Douglas. THE GOLDEN BOOK. Chicago, 1927. Gilt-pict bds. NF. *POLYANTHOS*. $100

McMurtrie, Douglas. THE GOLDEN BOOK...NY: Covici-Friede, (1927,34). 3rd ed. VG. *AKA*. $25

McMurtry, Larry. ALL MY FRIENDS ARE GOING TO BE STRANGERS. NY: S&S, (1972). 1st ed. Fine in dj. *LOPEZ*. $100

McMurtry, Larry. ANYTHING FOR BILLY. NY: Simon & Schuster, (1988). 1st ed. Cl-backed boards, dj. VF. *JAFFE*. $50

McMurtry, Larry. ANYTHING FOR BILLY. NY: Simon & Schuster, (1988). 1st ed. Signed. NF in dj. *OUTPOST*. $50

McMurtry, Larry. ANYTHING FOR BILLY. NY: Simon & Schuster, (1988). Uncorrected proof. Ptd wraps. VF. *JAFFE*. $150

McMurtry, Larry. ANYTHING FOR BILLY. NY: Simon & Schuster, (1988). 1st ed. Fine in Fine dj. *LOPEZ*. $30

McMurtry, Larry. BUFFALO GIRLS. NY: Simon & Schuster, (1990). 1st ed. Signed. Fine in Fine dj. *LOPEZ*. $55

McMurtry, Larry. CADILLAC JACK. A NOVEL. Cl-backed boards, dj. NY: Simon & Schuster, (1982). 1st ed. VF. *JAFFE*. $45

McMurtry, Larry. CADILLAC JACK. NY: Simon & Schuster, (1982). 1st ed. Remainder mark, o/w Fine in NF price-clipped dj. *LOPEZ*. $35

McMurtry, Larry. DESERT ROSE. NY: Simon & Schuster, (1983). 1st ed. Remainder mark, o/w Fine in dj. *LOPEZ*. $45

McMurtry, Larry. DESERT ROSE. NY: Simon & Schuster, 1983. 1st ed. Fine. *SMITH*. $40

McMurtry, Larry. FILM FLAM. NY: Simon & Schuster, (1987). 1st ed. Fine in dj. *LOPEZ*. $40

McMurtry, Larry. FLIM FLAM. NY: Simon & Schuster, (1987). Uncorrected proof. Tiny spot front cover, o/w Fine. *LOPEZ*. $100

McMurtry, Larry. HORSEMAN, PASS BY. NY: Harper, (1961). 1st ed. Prev owner's name, o/w Fine in NF dj. *LOPEZ*. $850

McMurtry, Larry. IN A NARROW GRAVE. Austin: Encino Press, 1968. 1/250 numbered, signed. Inscribed. Fine. Cl slipcase. *LOPEZ*. $1,500

McMurtry, Larry. IT'S ALWAYS WE RAMBLED: AN ESSAY ON RODEO. NY: Hallman, 1974. 1/300 numbered, signed. Lt creasing, spotting along front inner spine. NF. *LOPEZ*. $400

McMurtry, Larry. IT'S ALWAYS WE RAMBLED: AN ESSAY ON RODEO. NY: Frank Hallman, 1974. 1st ed. 1/300 numbered, signed. Fine w/o dj, as issued. *CAPTAIN'S BOOKSHELF*. $300

McMurtry, Larry. LEAVING CHEYENNE. NY: Harper & Row, (1963). 1st ed. NF in dj (uniformly faded on spine and has tape shadows on flap edges from a former jacket protector. *LOPEZ*. $650

McMurtry, Larry. LONESOME DOVE. NY, 1985. 1st ed. Date on front pastedown (hidden by dj flap). Fine in dj. *PETTLER*. $165

McMurtry, Larry. LONESOME DOVE. NY: S&S, (1985). 1st ed. Fine in Fine dj. *UNGER*. $200

McMurtry, Larry. LONESOME DOVE. NY: Simon & Schuster, (1985). 1st ed. Fine (rm on bottom edge) in dj. *CAPTAIN'S BOOKSHELF*. $150

McMurtry, Larry. LONESOME DOVE. NY: Simon & Schuster, (1985). Uncorrected proof. Ptd wraps. VF. *JAFFE*. $375

McMurtry, Larry. LONESOME DOVE. Simon & Schuster, (1985). 1st ed. Boards. Fine in dj. *AUTHORS OF THE WEST*. $175

McMurtry, Larry. LONESOME DOVE. Simon and Schuster, 1985. 1st ed. NF in Fine dj. Binding bit loose. *STAHR*. $100

McMurtry, Larry. MOVING ON. NY: Simon & Schuster, (1970). 1st ed. Fine in NF dj. *LOPEZ*. $100

McMurtry, Larry. MOVING ON. NY: Simon & Schuster, (1970). 1st ed. Fine in dj and uncommon, thus. Inscribed. *CAPTAIN'S BOOKSHELF*. $200

McMurtry, Larry. MOVING ON. Simon and Schuster, 1970. 1st ed. NF in dj. Bk sl cocked; dj chipped. *STAHR*. $75

McMurtry, Larry. SOME CAN WHISTLE. NY, 1989. 1st ed. Signed. Fine in like dj. *POLYANTHOS*. $35

McMurtry, Larry. SOME CAN WHISTLE. Simon & Schuster, (1989). 1st ed. Fine in Fine dj. *BEBBAH*. $25

McMurtry, Larry. SOMEBODY'S DARLING. NY: S&S(1978). 1st ed. Fine in Fine dj. *LOPEZ*. $50

McMurtry, Larry. SOMEBODY'S DARLING. NY: Simon & Schuster, (1978). 1st ed. Signed. Rmdr stamp, o/w NF in dj. *LOPEZ*. $85

McMurtry, Larry. SOMEBODY'S DARLING. NY: Simon & Schuster, 1978 1st ed. Bkpl, remainder mark, o/w NF. *SMITH*. $50

McMurtry, Larry. TERMS OF ENDEARMENT. NY: S&S, (1975). 1st ed. Fine in NF dj. *UNGER*. $75

McMurtry, Larry. TERMS OF ENDEARMENT. NY: S&S(1975). 1st ed. Cheap paper browning as usual o/w Fine in dj. *LOPEZ*. $75

McMurtry, Larry. TEXASVILLE. NY: S&S, (1987). 1st ed. Signed. Fine in Fine dj. *UNGER*. $75

McMurtry, Larry. TEXASVILLE. NY: Simon & Schuster, (1987). 1st ed. Signed. Rmdr mark, o/w Fine in Fine dj. *LOPEZ*. $65

McMurtry, Larry. TEXASVILLE. NY: Simon & Schuster, (1987). 1st ed. Slight staining bottom page edges, o/w Fine in Fine dj. *LOPEZ*. $25

McMurtry, Larry. TEXASVILLE. Simon and Schuster, 1987. 1st ed. Fine in dj. *STAHR*. $25

McMurtry, Larry. THE DESERT ROSE. NY: Simon & Schuster, 1983. 1st ed. VF in slipcase. 1/250 signed. *ELSE FINE*. $200

McMurtry, Larry. THE DESERT ROSE. Simon & Schuster, (1983). 1st ed. Fine in Fine dj. *BEBBAH*. $50

McMurtry, Larry. THE LAST PICTURE SHOW. NY: Dial, (1966). 1st ed. NF/Fine in NF mildly soiled dj. *UNGER*. $300

McMurtry, Larry. THE LAST PICTURE SHOW. NY: Dial, 1966. Orig tan cl. Bright and just About Fine in dj. 1st ed. *CHAPEL HILL*. $400

McMurty, Larry. THE LAST PICTURE SHOW. NY: Dial, 1966. 1st ptg. VG, dj. *BURCHAM*. $200

McNally, Dennis. DESOLATE ANGEL. NY: Random House, (1979). 1st ptg. VF in lightly Rubbed dj. *AKA*. $30

McNamara, Brooks. STEP RIGHT UP: AN ILLUSTRATED HISTORY OF THE AMERICAN MEDICINE SHOW. GC, NY, 1976. 1st ed. Dj. Ex-lib. *FYE*. $40

McNaspy, C.J. LOST CITIES OF PARAGUAY. Chicago: Loyola Univ Press, (1982). 1st ed. Chipped dj. *SILVER*. $35

McNeal, T.A. WHEN KANSAS WAS YOUNG. NY: Macmillan, 1922. 1st ed. Slight edgewear. Clean, tight, VG. Scarce. *CONNOLLY & WADE*. $67.50

McNeal, Tom. TOM McNEAL'S FABLES. KANSAS STORIES. Topeka, 1900. 1st ed. Fine. *VARNER*. $50

McNeer, Kay and Lynd Ward. THE WOLF OF LAMBS LANE. Houghton Mifflin, 1967. 1st ed. 64pp. Illus by Ward. Red mark to back edge else, NF in VG+ dj w/2 short closed edge tears, small skinned patch. *BEBBAH*. $30

McNeile, H.C. BULLDOG DRUMMOND AT BAY. GC: Doubleday Crime Club, 1935. 1st ed. Fine. *ELSE FINE*. $30

McNeile, H.C. BULLDOG DRUMMOND RETURNS. GC: Doubleday Crime Club, 1932. 1st ed. Fine. *ELSE FINE*. $30

McNeile, H.C. BULLDOG DRUMMOND STRIKES BACK. GC: Doubleday Crime Club, 1933. 1st ed. Name. Fine; lt edgewear to dj. *ELSE FINE*. $110

McNeile, H.C. BULLDOG DRUMMOND'S THIRD ROUND. NY: Doran, 1924. 1st ed. Fine. *ELSE FINE*. $40

McNeile, H.C. CHALLENGE. GC: Doubleday Crime Club, 1937. 1st ed. Fine. *ELSE FINE*. $25

McNeile, H.C. THE BLACK GANG. NY: Doran, 1922. 1st ed. Inner hinges starting, else Fine. *ELSE FINE*. $35

McNeile, H.C. THE FEMALE OF THE SPECIES. GC: Doubleday Crime Club, 1928. 1st ed. Fine. *ELSE FINE*. $35

McNeile, H.C. THE FINAL COUNT. NY: Doran, 1926. 1st ed. Fine. *ELSE FINE*. $40

McNeill, John Charles. LYRICS FROM COTTON LAND. Charlotte, NC: Stone Publishing Co, (1922). 2nd ed. Orig red bandanna cl w/mounted cover illus. Spine a trifle sunned, emb stamp, but lovely. *CHAPEL HILL*. $45

McNeill, William. PLAGUES AND PEOPLES. GC, 1976. 1st ed. Dj. *FYE*. $25

McNichols, Charles. CRAZY WEATHER. NY, 1944. 1st ed. Bkpl removed, else VG+ in VG dj. *FIVE QUAIL*. $15

McNickle, D'Arcy and Harold E. Fey. INDIANS AND OTHER AMERICANS. NY: Harper, (1959). 1st ed. VG in price-clipped dj. *LOPEZ*. $50

McNickle, D'Arcy. INDIAN MAN. Bloomington: Indiana Univ Press, 1971). 1st ed. Fine in NF dj. *LOPEZ*. $55

McNickle, D'Arcy. RUNNER IN THE SUN. Phila: Winston, (1954). 1st ed. VG in dj. *LOPEZ*. $85

McNickle, D'Arcy. THEY CAME HERE FIRST. Phila: Lippincott, (1949). 1st ed. Owner inscrip, o/w VG, lacking dj. *LOPEZ*. $40

McNickle, D'Arcy. WIND FROM AN ENEMY SKY. SF: H&R, (1978). 1st ed. VG in sl edgeworn dj. *LOPEZ*. $30

McNitt, Frank. THE INDIAN TRADERS. Univ of OK, (1962). 1st ed. Frontis. VF in Fine dj. *OREGON*. $50

McNitt, Frank. THE INDIAN TRADERS. Univ of OK Press, 1963. 2nd ptg. Fine in VG dj. *VARNER*. $25

McOmie, Prof. A.M. et al. THE ARIZONA STRIP. State of AZ, 1915. Grey wraps, 39pp, many photos. Fine. *FIVE QUAIL*. $65

McPhee, John and Galen Rowell. ALASKA: IMAGES OF THE COUNTRY. SF: Sierra Club Books, (1981). Limited 1st ed, signed by McPhee & Rowell. VG+. *BLUE DRAGON*. $45

McPhee, John. A ROOMFUL OF HOVINGS AND OTHER PROFILES. NY: FSG, 1968. 1st ed. Name. NF in dj. *ELSE FINE*. $85

McPhee, John. A ROOMFUL OF HOVINGS. NY: Farrar Straus Giroux, (1968). 1st ed. Fine in dj. *LOPEZ*. $125

McPhee, John. A SENSE OF WHERE YOU ARE. NY: Farrar, Straus & Giroux, (1965). 1st ed. Fine in price-clipped dj, sl rubbed, faded at spine. *JAFFE*. $225

McPhee, John. A SENSE OF WHERE YOU ARE. NY: Farrar, Straus & Giroux, (1978). 2nd ed, w/new note. Dj. Mint. *JAFFE*. $45

McPhee, John. A SENSE OF WHERE YOU ARE. NY: FSG (1965). 1st ed. Edges sunned else Fine in dj (1/2" fold tear else NF). *DORN*. $175

McPhee, John. ANNALS OF THE FORMER WORLD. NY: FSG (1983). Ltd ed. 1/450 numbered. Signed. VF in slipcase. *LOPEZ*. $125

McPhee, John. COMING INTO THE COUNTRY. NY: Farrar, Straus & Giroux, (1977). 1st ed. Bottom edge sl bumped o/w NF in Fine dj. *BERNARD*. $50

McPhee, John. GIVING GOOD WEIGHT. NY: FSG, (1979). 1st ed. Fine in dj which has creased rear flap. *BERNARD*. $17.50

McPhee, John. GIVING GOOD WEIGHT. NY: Farrar, Straus, Giroux (1979). 1st ed. Adv rev copy with promo slip and photo. Spotting top edges, o/w Fine in NF dj. *AKA*. $35

McPhee, John. GIVING GOOD WEIGHT. NY: Farrar, Straus, Giroux, 1979. 1st ed. Fine, rubbed dj. *PARMER*. $20

McPhee, John. GIVING GOOD WEIGHT. NY: FSG, 1979. 1st ed. VF in dj. *ELSE FINE*. $30

McPhee, John. IN SUSPECT TERRAIN. NY: Farrar, Straus, Giroux (1979). 1st ed. Fine in rubbed, sl wrinkled dj. *AKA*. $30

McPhee, John. IN SUSPECT TERRAIN. NY: FSG, 1983. 1st ed. Fine in dj. *ELSE FINE*. $40

McPhee, John. LA PLACE DE LA CONCORDE SUISSE. NY: Farrar, Straus & Giroux, (1984). 1st ed. New in dj. *BERNARD*. $20

McPhee, John. LA PLACE DE LA CONCORDE SUISSE. NY: FSG (1984). Ltd ed. 1/200 numbered. Signed. Fine in slipcase. *LOPEZ*. $125

McPhee, John. LEVELS OF THE GAME. NY, 1969. 1st ed. Fine in price-clipped dj. *PETTLER*. $50

McPhee, John. LEVELS OF THE GAME. NY: FSG, 1969. 1st ed. Review copy, slip laid in. VF in dj. *ELSE FINE*. $85

McPhee, John. LOOKING FOR A SHIP. NY: Farrar, Straus & Giroux, (1990). 1st ed. Publisher's business reply card folded & laid in. New in dj. *BERNARD*. $20

McPhee, John. ORANGES. NY: FSG (1967). 1st ed. NF in dj. *LOPEZ*. $85

McPhee, John. THE CROFTER & THE LAIRD. NY: FSG, 1970. 1st ed. Fine in dj. Very scarce. *ELSE FINE*. $95

McPhee, John. THE DELTOID PUMPKIN SEED. NY: Farrar, Straus & Giroux, (1973). 1st ed. NF in dj. *BERNARD*. $35

McPhee, John. THE SURVIVAL OF THE BARK CANOE. NY: Farrar, Straus, (1975). 1st ed. Fine in NF dj with small closed tear rear panel. *UNGER*. $200

McPhee, John. WIMBLEDON: A CELEBRATION. NY, 1972. 1st ed. NF in VG dj. *PETTLER*. $35

McPhee, John. WIMBLEDON: A CELEBRATION. NY, (1972). 1st ed. Fine in dj. Signed. *CAPTAIN'S BOOKSHELF*. $100

McPhee, John. WIMBLEDON: A CELEBRATION. NY, 1972. 1st ed. Fine in dj with few small rubbed spots. *STAHR*. $45

McPherson, James Alan and Miller Williams, eds. RAILROAD. NY: Random House, (1976). Fine in dj. *LOPEZ*. $85

McPherson, James Alan. ELBOW ROOM. Boston: Little, Brown, (1977). 1st ed. Fine in dj. Signed. *CAPTAIN'S BOOKSHELF*. $150

McPherson, James Alan. ELBOW ROOM. Boston: Little, Brown, (1977). 1st ed. Fine in sl edgeworn dj. *LOPEZ*. $85

McPherson, James Alan. HUE AND CRY. Boston: A-LB, 1969. 1st ed, 1st bk. VF, minor rubs to dj extremities. *ELSE FINE*. $100

McPherson, James Alan. HUE AND CRY. Boston: Little, Brown, (1969). 1st ed. NF in dj. *LOPEZ*. $150

McPherson, James Alan. HUE AND CRY. Boston: Little, Brown, (1969). 1st ed. Fine in dj w/touch of rubbing to spine lettering. *BETWEEN COVERS*. $200

McReynolds, Edwin R. OKLAHOMA, A HISTORY OF THE SOONER STATE. U of Okla (1954), 1st ed, dj. *HEINOLDT*. $25

McTaggart, M.F. FROM COLONEL TO SUBALTERN. SOME KEYS FOR HORSE-OWNERS. London & NY: Country Life & Scribner's, 1928. 1st US ed. VG in Good dj. *OCTOBER FARM*. $25

McTaggart, M.F. STABLE AND SADDLE. NY: Scribner's, 1930. 1st U.S. ed. VG in Good dj. *OCTOBER FARM*. $25

McTaggart, M.F. STABLE AND SADDLE. NY: Scribner's, 1930. Minor edgewear to extremities, else VG. *OLD LONDON*. $65

McVail, John. VACCINATION VINDICATED: BEING AN ANSWER....London, 1887. 1st ed. 176pp. Inscribed. *FYE*. $100

McVicker, Mary Louise. THE WRITINGS OF J. FRANK DOBIE: A BIBLIOGRAPHY. Lawton, OK: Museum of the Great Plains, 1968. 1st ed. As New. *GIBBS*. $30

McWilliam, James. MEDICAL HISTORY OF THE EXPEDITION TO THE NIGER DURING THE YEARS 1841-2 COMPRISING AN ACCOUNT OF THE FEVER WHICH LED TO ITS ABRUPT TERMINATION. London, 1843. 1st ed. 287pp + fldg map. Ffep lacking, plt foxed. Private dec lib stamp on title. *FYE*. $600

McWilliams, Carey. CALIFORNIA: THE GREAT EXCEPTION. NY: Current Books/A.A. Wyn, 1949. 1st ed. Cl in lightly chipped dj. *DAWSON'S*. $30

McWilliams, Carey. LOUIS ADAMIC AND SHADOW AMERICA. LA: Whipple, (1935). 1st ed. Owner's name. About Fine in lightly browned dj. *AKA*. $50

McWilliams, Carey. NORTH FROM MEXICO. Phila: J.B. Lippincott, 1949. Cl in lightly chipped dj. *DAWSON'S*. $40

McWilliams, Carey. SOUTHERN CALIFORNIA COUNTRY: AN ISLAND ON THE LAND. NY: Duell, Sloan & Pearce, (1946). 1st ed. Grn-stamped cl in lightly chipped dj. Signed. *DAWSON'S*. $40

Meacham, Charles M. A HISTORY OF CHRISTIAN COUNTY KENTUCKY FROM OXCART TO AIRPLANE....Nashville, 1930. 1st ed. Orig cl, spine faded. GINSBERG. $100

Mead, Charles W. THE MUSICAL INSTRUMENTS OF THE INCA. NY: American Museum Press, 1924. Pp. 313-347 (uncut), 8 figs, 5 plts. Tattered wraps. Good. ARCHAEOLOGIA. $35

Mead, Frederick S. HARVARD'S MILITARY RECORD IN THE WORLD WAR. Boston, 1921. Name index. Good. ARTIS. $22.50

Mead, G.R.S. SOME MYSTICAL ADVENTURES. London: Watkins, 1910. 1st ed. VG. BLUE DRAGON. $65

Mead, Margaret. AN ANTHROPOLOGIST AT WORK: WRITINGS OF RUTH BENEDICT. Boston: Houghton Mifflin/Riverside Press, Cambridge, 1959. 1st ed. NF in Good dj. CONNOLLY & WADE. $45

Mead, Peter. AN ELEMENTARY TREATISE ON AMERICAN GRAPE CULTURE AND WINE MAKING. NY: Harper, 1867. 1st ed. Ex-lib, some external wear. Good. SECOND LIFE. $150

Meade, L.T. THE MEDICINE LADY. NY: Cassell Pub Co, 1892. 1st US ed, 1st bk. Dec cl. VG. BURCHAM. $200

Meadows, Paul. JOHN WESLEY POWELL. Lincoln, 1952. Blue wraps, 106pp. Fine. FIVE QUAIL. $30

Meakin, Budgett. LIFE IN MOROCCO AND GLIMPSES BEYOND. London: Chatto & Windus, 1905. 1st ed. 24 plts. Sl rubbed, spine frayed, unevenly faded, eps sl soiled, o/w VG ex-lib. WORLDWIDE. $40

Means, Philip. FALL OF THE INCA EMPIRE AND THE SPANISH RULE IN PERU: 1530-1780. NY: Scribner's, 1932. 1st ed. Fldg map. Gilt lettering to spine. Chipped dj. SILVER. $40

Meany, Tom et al. BOSTON RED SOX. Barnes, 1956. 1st ed. Fine in Fine dj. PLAPINGER. $50

Meany, Tom et al. MILWAUKEE'S MIRACLE BRAVES. A.S. Barnes, 1954. 1st ed. Fine in VG+ dj. PLAPINGER. $45

Meany, Tom. JOE DIMAGGIO—YANKEE CLIPPER. Barnes, 1951. 1st ed. VG. PLAPINGER. $45

Meany, Tom. MILWAUKEE'S MIRACLE BRAVES. A.S. Barnes, 1954. 1st ed. VG+ in Fine dj. PLAPINGER. $50

Meany, Tom. RALPH KINER—THE HEIR APPARENT. Barnes, 1951. 1st ed. Fine. PLAPINGER. $40

Meany, Tom. TED WILLIAMS—HITTING UNLIMITED. Barnes, 1951. VG. PLAPINGER. $45

Meany, Tom. THE MAGNIFICENT YANKEES. Barnes, 1952. 1st ed. VG in Fine dj. PLAPINGER. $60

Meany, Tom. THE YANKEE STORY. Dutton, 1960. VG in VG+ dj. PLAPINGER. $40

Mearns, David C. THE LINCOLN PAPERS. 2 vols. GC, 1948. 1st ed. 681pp. Fine. PRATT. $25

Mearns, David C. THE LINCOLN PAPERS. GC: Doubleday, 1948. Stated 1st ed. Chipped djs, in orig slipcase. SCHOYER'S. $25

Mearns, David C. THE LINCOLN PAPERS. GC: Doubleday, 1948. 1st ed. 2 vols. Fine in dj. Vol I dj, sl chipped; Vol II dj, Fine. In lightly rubbed slipcase. CONNOLLY & WADE. $55

Mecklenburg, George. THE LAST OF THE OLD WEST. Washington, D.C.: Capital Book, (1927). 1st ed. Signed. Dj shows wear at extremities, o/w VG. LAURIE. $50

MEDICAL CLASSICS. Baltimore, 1936-1941. 1st and only ed. Vols. 1-5, 1/2 leather. FYE. $900

MEDICAL ESSAYS: COMPILED FROM REPORTS TO THE BUREAU OF MEDICINE AND SURGERY, BY MEDICAL OFFICERS OF THE U.S. NAVY. Washington, 1873. 1st ed. 1/4 leather, 345pp. Scarce. FYE. $250

MEDICAL LEAVES 1939. Chicago, 1939. 1st ed. Scarce. FYE. $100

Medway, L. and D.R. Wells. THE BIRDS OF THE MALAY PENINSULA. Vol V. 25 colored plts. London, 1976. SUTTON. $135

Medwin, Thomas. CONVERSATIONS OF LORD BYRON...London, 1824. Fldg facs as frontis. New cl and boards. Uncut. O'NEILL. $50

Medwin, Thomas. JOURNAL OF THE CONVERSATIONS OF LORD BYRON...NY: Wilder and Campbell, 1824. 1st Amer ed. Small 8vo, 304pp. Handsome recent 3/4 lea, marbled boards, panelled spine, gilt on red lea label. Fldg facs letter, early pencil note verso of front flyleaf. Excellent. HARTFIELD. $295

Meehan, Thomas. AMERICAN HANDBOOK OF ORNAMENTAL TREES. Phila, 1853. Backstrip partially loose, corners scuffed, spot on rear cvr, sl foxing. SUTTON. $125

Meehan, Thomas. AMERICAN HANDBOOK OF ORNAMENTAL TREES. Phila: Lippincott, Gambo, 1853. 1st ed. 257pp. Foxing, names in pencil Good. SECOND LIFE. $135

Meehan, Thomas. WAYSIDE FLOWERS. Phila, 1881. 31 chromolitho plts. Orig gilt dec cl (some corner wear, spine ends frayed, inner hinges cracked). Some pp yellowing, pl offsetting, spotting rear cvr; plts mostly clean. SUTTON. $285

Meek, M.R.D. A MOUTHFUL OF SAND. London: Collins Crime Club, 1988. 1st ed. VF in dj. MORDIDA. $35

Meek, M.R.D. A WORM OF DOUBT. London: Collins Crime Club, 1987. 1st ed. VF in dj. MORDIDA. $30

Meek, M.R.D. HANG THE CONSEQUENCES. London: Collins Crime Club, 1984. 1st ed. Fine in sl rubbed dj. MORDIDA. $30

Meek, M.R.D. IN REMEMBRANCE OF ROSE. London: Collins Crime Club, 1986. 1st ed. VF in dj. MORDIDA. $35

Meek, M.R.D. IN REMEMBRANCE OF ROSE. NY: Scribner, 1987. 1st Amer ed. Rev copy. Pub's slip laid in. Fine in dj. SILVER DOOR. $25

Meek, M.R.D. THE SPLIT SECOND. London: Collins, 1985. 1st ed. VF in dj. SILVER DOOR. $25

Meek, M.R.D. THE SPLIT SECOND. London: Collins Crime Club, 1985. 1st ed. VF in dj. MORDIDA. $35

Meek, Stephen. THE AUTOBIOGRAPHY OF A MOUNTAIN MAN, 1805-1889. Pasadena: Dawson, 1948. 1st ed, Ltd to 300. Fine. OREGON. $80

Meeker, Ezra. THE BUSY LIFE OF EIGHTY-FIVE YEARS OF EZRA MEEKER: VENTURES AND ADVENTURES... (AND) THE OREGON TRAIL... Seattle: Pub by author, (1916). 1st ed. Presentation, signed. VG. LAURIE. $50

Meginness, J.F. OTZINACHSON: A HISTORY OF THE WEST BRANCH VALLEY OF THE SUSQUEHANNA...Williamsport, Pa. Gazette & Bulletin, 1889. Rev ed. 1 fldg map. Half leather. Hinges cracked & glued, leather chipped. interior fine. OREGON. $60

Meginness, John F. BIOGRAPHY OF FRANCIS SLOCUM. THE LOST SISTER OF WYOMING. Williamsport, PA, 1891. 6 plts. Marbled boards, 1/4 calf, raised bands, leather labels. 500 ptd. Howes M479. CULLEN. $225

Megrue, Roi Cooper. UNDER COVER. Boston: Little Brown, 1914. 1st ed. Spine lettering flaked, VG+, no dj. ELSE FINE. $35

Mehl, Ernest. THE KANSAS CITY ATHLETICS. Holt, 1956. 1st ed. Good+ in VG dj. PLAPINGER. $45

Mehta, Gita. KARMA KOLA: MARKETING THE MYSTIC EAST. NY: Simon & Schuster, (1979). 1st ed. 201pp. NF in lightly worn dj. AKA. $35

Meigs, Arthur. A STUDY OF THE HUMAN BLOOD-VESSELS IN HEALTH AND DISEASE. Phila, 1907. 1st ed. 136pp. 103 photomicrographs. Scarce. FYE. $150

Meigs, Arthur. THE ORIGIN OF DISEASE, ESPECIALLY OF DISEASE RESULTING FROM INTRINSIC AS OPPOSED TO

EXTRINSIC CAUSES. Phila, 1897. 1st ed. Photomicrographs. Ex-lib. Very Rare. *FYE.* $175

Meigs, Charles. ON THE NATURE, SIGNS, AND TREATMENT OF CHILDBED FEVERS. Phila, 1854. 1st ed. Fine. *FYE.* $300

Meigs, Elizabeth. THE SILVER QUEST. Indianapolis: Bobbs-Merrill, 1949. 1st ed. VG in Good dj. *OCTOBER FARM.* $15

Meigs, J. Forsyth. A HISTORY OF THE FIRST QUARTER OF THE SECOND CENTURY OF THE PENNSYLVANIA HOSPITAL. Phila, 1877. 1st ed. 3 engrvd plts. Ex-lib. Scarce. *FYE.* $45

Meigs, J. Forsyth. A PRACTICAL TREATISE ON THE DISEASES OF CHILDREN. Phila, 1858. 3rd ed. Full leather, 724pp. *FYE.* $75

Meigs, John Forsyth. THE STORY OF THE SEAMAN. Phila: J.B. Lippincott Co. 1924. 1st ed. 2 vols. *KARMIOLE.* $75

Meigs, Peveril. THE DOMINICAN MISSION FRONTIER OF LOWER CALIFORNIA. Berkeley: Univ of CA, 1935. 1st ed. VG. Scarce. *CONNOLLY & WADE.* $95

Meinertzhagen, Colonel Richard. MIDDLE EAST DIARY 1917-1956. NY, 1960. Dj. *O'NEILL.* $85

Meisel, M. A BIBLIOGRAPHY OF AMERICAN NATURAL HISTORY. 3 vols. Hafner, 1967 facs of 1924 ed. As New in dj. *BOOK-CELL.* $400

Meldgaard, Jorgen. ESKIMO SCULPTURE. NY: Clarkson Potter, (1960). 1st Eng ed. VG in Good dj. *BLUE DRAGON.* $25

Meline, James F. TWO THOUSAND MILES ON HORSEBACK. NY: Hurd and Houghton, 1867. Lrg fldg map, tables. Bkpl, fly leaf damage. *HUDSON.* $100

Meline, James F. TWO THOUSAND MILES ON HORSEBACK. NY, 1867. 1st ed. Cvrs sl stained & shelfworn. Rebacked. Lacks map called for in Howes. Few pencil marks, o/w VG. Howes M488. *DIAMOND.* $50

Meltzer, Milton. HUNTED LIKE A WOLF, THE STORY OF THE SEMINOLE WAR. NY, (1972). 1st ed. 216pp. Dj wear, o/w Fine. *PRATT.* $20

Melville, George W. IN THE LENA DELTA. Boston: Houghton Mifflin, 1885. NF. *ARTIS.* $85

Melville, Herman. BILLY BUDD. BENITO CERENO. Illus by Robert Shore. NY: Ptd for the Members of LEC, 1965. Ed ltd to 1500 numbered, signed by Shore. Slipcase. *KARMIOLE.* $50

Melville, Herman. MARDI: AND A VOYAGE THITHER. (NY: Harper & Brothers, 1849). 2 vols. 1st Amer ed (intended to be published simultaneously with the Brit ed, but following it by a few days). Orig cl. With 4 leaves of ads at back of vol 2. BAL 13658. The usual sprinkled foxing on text and end papers; 3 spine ends flush with text block (the 4th a bit frayed), corners somewhat worn, o/w very clean. Excellent. *PIRAGES.* $1500

Melville, Herman. MARDI: AND A VOYAGE THITHER. NY: Harper, 1849. 1st ed. 2 vols. Orig purple cl stamped in blind. Spines faded to brown, scattered moderate foxing throughout, name inked out in ink on ffep of Vol 1. VG set. *CAPTAIN'S BOOKSHELF.* $900

Melville, Herman. MOBY DICK OR THE WHALE. Illus Rockwell Kent. NY: Random House, 1930. 1st ed, thus. Fine in lightly chipped dj w/several tears at folds. *CAPTAIN'S BOOKSHELF.* $200

Melville, Herman. MOBY DICK, OR THE WHALE. NY: Random House, 1930. 1st trade ed, ptd at the Lakeside Press, Chicago. Rockwell Kent (illus). Incl orig watercolor port by Leonard Baskin on fore-edge of bk. Fine in NF dj. *SECOND LIFE.* $700

Melville, Herman. OMOO. NY: Dodd, Mead, 1924. Illus by Mead Schaeffer. Lt foxing, dj chipped. VG. *WEBER.* $100

Melville, Herman. OMOO. NY: Harper & Brothers, 1847. 1st Amer ed, pict cloth. VG with light wear at extremities of spine but with gilt stamping still bright, both on spine and front cover. *LOPEZ.* $1,750

Melville, Herman. OMOO. Oxford: LEC, 1961. One of 1500 illus, signed by Reynolds Stone. Fine in slipcase. *CAPTAIN'S BOOKSHELF.* $150

Melville, Herman. OMOO: A NARRATIVE....NY: Harper & Bros, 1847. 389pp, (9),16pp ads. Orig grn cl w/gilt dec spine, gilt ship on front cvr. Barely discernible 1/2" nick at head of spine, else bright, practically Fine copy. Early ownshp sig on front fly. 1st Amer ed. Rare in this cond. BAL 13656. *CHAPEL HILL.* $4,000

Melville, Herman. PIERRE; OR THE AMBIGUITIES. NY: Harper & Brothers, 1852. 1st ed. Brn blind-stamped cl (expertly rebacked, new endleaves, foxed). Owner ink stamp. BAL 13666. *WEBER.* $650

Melville, Herman. REDBURN: HIS FIRST VOYAGE. NY: Harper & Bros, 1849. 390pp, (4), 11, (1), 2pp ads. Orig dk blue-grn cl. Eps somewhat darkened as usual with this title, moderately heavy foxing throughout, o/w clean, VG to NF. Cl fresh and minimally rubbed. "Wilson Collection" (Carroll Wilson) stamped on ffep. 1st Amer ed. According to BAL 13660, copies of the 1st ptg have only 10pp ads, while copies w/more pp of ads (as in this copy) are from the 2nd ptg. Schwartz, however, designates copies w/the present configuration of ads as the 1st issue. Either way, very difficult to locate in such nice cond. *CHAPEL HILL.* $3,500

Melville, Herman. REDBURN: HIS FIRST VOYAGE. (NY: Harper & Brothers, 1849). 390 pp, (9) leaves (ads). 1st Amer ed (extended ads). Original purple cloth. BAL 13660. A little cocked, spine evenly faded, corners and spine ends a bit worn, covers somewhat soiled and mottled, but binding solid. End papers oxidized, intermittent foxing. Extremely Good. *PIRAGES.* $850

Melville, Herman. THE CONFIDENCE MAN. NY: Dix, Edwards, 1857. 1st ed, 1st issue, with "Miller & Holman" on right page. Cloth worn at extremities of spine and at tips of covers; front hinge with small cracks to endsheets, else VG; gift inscrip (from 1864) on ffep. *LOPEZ.* $1,500

Melville, Herman. THE PIAZZA TALES. NY: Dix & Edwards, 1856. Lower corners bumped, spine extremities rubbed, scattered light foxing. VG. 1st ed. Amer naturalist John Bachman's copy w/pencilled sig "Jno Bachman, 1856." BAL13669. *CHAPEL HILL.* $2,800

Melville, James. A SORT OF SAMURAI. London: Secker, 1981. 1st ed. Signed. NF in dj. *SILVER DOOR.* $35

Melville, James. THE IMPERIAL WAY. London: Deutsch, 1986. 1st ed. Signed. Fine in dj. *SILVER DOOR.* $35

Melville, Lewis. STAGE FAVOURITES OF THE 18TH CENTURY. London: Hutchinson, nd. (1928). 1st Eng ed. VG-. *AARD.* $20

Memmi, Albert. THE LIBERATION OF THE JEW. NY: Orion, (1966). 1st ed. 303pp. Dj edgeworn. *AKA.* $25

MEMOIR OF JOHN HOWE PEYTON, IN SKETCHES....TOGETHER WITH SOME OF HIS...LETTERS, ETC. Staunton: Blackburn, 1894. 1st ed. (6),297pp. Orig cl, sm gouge in front cover, light soiling. One page ALS. Presentation. Howes P278. *GINSBERG.* $150

MEMOIR OF SUSAN DIMOCK, RESIDENT PHYSICIAN OF THE NEW ENGLAND HOSPITAL FOR WOMEN AND CHILDREN. Boston: 1871. Good+. *SMITHFIELD.* $35

MEMOIRS OF AN INFANTRY OFFICER. (By Siegfried Sassoon.) London, 1930. 1st ed. Fine in dj (spine very sl sunned, extremities few tiny tears). *POLYANTHOS.* $300

MEMOIRS OF AN INFANTRY OFFICER. (By Siegfried Sassoon.) London: Faber & Faber, (1930). 1st ed, 2nd issue, w/page edges trimmed. Orig blue cl. Fine in NF dj, sm small chips, tears. *CHAPEL HILL.* $200

MEMOIRS OF ANDREW JACKSON. Compiled by a citizen of Massachusetts. Phila: (Collins, printers), 1840. 334pp. Engr frontis. Contemp full calf w/spine label. *SCHOYER'S.* $45

MEMOIRS OF MODERN PHILOSOPHERS. (By Elizabeth Hamilton.) In two vols. Dublin: Smith for Wogan et. al, 1800. 1st Dublin ed. (Same yr as 1st ed). Contemp sheep, rebacked. 300,300pp. VG. *SECOND LIFE.* $500

MEMOIRS OF THE PHILADELPHIA SOCIETY FOR PROMOTING AGRICULTURE. Vol 1. Phila, 1808. 2 plts, 6 woodcuts; fldg chart w/some tears. Pp (2),lxv,331; 38; 84;(17pp-index); (1). Contemp full sheep worn, scuffed; tear to front flyleaf. Foxing, pp browning, some bending to corner of rear cvr. *SUTTON.* $385

MEMORANDUM ON THE SUBJECT OF THE EARL OF ELGIN'S PURSUITS IN GREECE. London, 1815. 2nd ed, corrected. Recent 1/4 calf. 100pp. Uncut. Half-title. *O'NEILL.* $150

MEMORIAL AND BIOGRAPHICAL HISTORY OF THE COUNTIES OF FRESNO, TULARE AND KERN, CALIFORNIA...Chicago: Lewis Publ Co, n.d. 3 photoview plts. Lea cvrs reattached, worn & sl defective. Rebacked w/new cl. Little foxing on some pages, o/w contents VG. *DIAMOND.* $150

MEMORIAL OF COLONEL JOHN STANTON SLOCUM FIRST COLONEL OF THE SECOND RHODE ISLAND VOLUNTEERS, WHO FELL IN THE BATTLE OF BULL RUN, VA, JULY 21, 1861. Providence, 1886. 1st ed. Wrappers, minor chipping, else VG to NF. *McGOWAN.* $45

Menaboni, Athos and Sara. MENABONI'S BIRDS. Rinehart, (c. 1950). 1st ed. VG. *BOOK BROKER.* $35

Mencken, August. BY THE NECK: A BOOK OF HANGINGS. Hastings, 1942. 1st ed. Fine in Good dj. *VARNER.* $25

Mencken, H.L. A BOOK OF BURLESQUES. NY: Knopf, (1924). 5th prtg. VG. Inscribed. *CAPTAIN'S BOOKSHELF.* $60

Mencken, H.L., and Robert Reives La Monte. MEN VERSUS THE MAN. A CORRESPONDENCE BETWEEN ROBERT REIVES LA MONTE AND H. L. MENCKEN. NY: Holt, 1910. 1st ed. Fine w/owner's name. *BEASLEY.* $125

Mencken, H.L. CHRISTMAS STORY. NY: Knopf, 1946. Fine in price-clipped, NF dj (2 letters inkstamped on rear panel). 1st ed. *CHAPEL HILL.* $65

Mencken, H.L., George Jean Nathan and Willard Huntington Wright. EUROPE AFTER 8:15. NY: John Lane, 1914. 1st ed. Owner's stamp title page, very slight dulling to spine, o/w Fine. *BEASLEY.* $150

Mencken, H.L. IN DEFENCE OF WOMEN. London: Cape, 1923. 1st UK ed. Inscribed by author. Close to Fine. *BEASLEY.* $300

Mencken, H.L. IN DEFENSE OF WOMEN. NY: Philip Goodman, 1918. Correct 1st ptg. w/"Ppilip Goodman" for "Philip Goodman" on title page. NF but for soiling to rear board and dulled spine. *BEASLEY.* $200

Mencken, H.L. MINORITY REPORT: H.L. MENCKEN'S NOTEBOOKS. NY: Knopf, 1956. 1st ed. NF in Near VG dj. *ARCHER.* $20

Mencken, H.L. NEWSPAPER DAYS 1899-1906. NY: Knopf, 1941. 1st ed. Fine in Very NF dj w/one tiny chip, some very light edgewear. *BETWEEN COVERS.* $125

Mencken, H.L. THE ARTIST: A DRAMA WITHOUT WORDS. Boston: Luce, 1912. 1st ed. Pict boards. Slight wear to head of spine; long nonauthorial inscription. VG, bkpl. *CAPTAIN'S BOOKSHELF.* $150

Mencken, H.L. THE VINTAGE MENCKEN. Gathered by Alistair Cooke. NY: Vintage, 1955. 1st Vintage ed. NF in wraps. *CAPTAIN'S BOOKSHELF.* $15

Mencken, H.L. TREATISE ON THE GODS. NY: Knopf, 1930. 1st ed. 1/375 specially bound, signed. Spine a bit discolored, NF (owner sig), lacking slipcase. *CAPTAIN'S BOOKSHELF.* $150

Mende, Elsie Porter with Henry Greenleaf Pearson. AN AMERICAN SOLDIER AND DIPLOMAT, HORACE PORTER. NY, 1927. 1st ed. 390pp. Ex-lib. VG. *PRATT.* $30

Mendell, G.H. REPORT ON THE VARIOUS PROJECTS FOR THE WATER SUPPLY OF SAN FRANCISCO, CAL....SF: Spaulding & Barto, 1877. Fldg maps and diagrams all present. Errata slip bound in before title pg. 1/2 leather, marble paper boards. VG. *LAURIE.* $600

Mendenhall, Walter C. GROUND WATERS OF THE INDIO REGION, WITH A SKETCH....Washington: GPO, 1909. Water Supply Paper 225. VG to Fine, map present in end pocket. *BOOK MARKET.* $60

Mendenhall, Walter C. SOME DESERT WATERING PLACES IN SOUTHEASTERN CALIFORNIA AND SOUTHWESTERN NEVADA. Washington: GPO, 1909. Water Supply Paper 224. Map present in endpocket. Fine. *BOOK MARKET.* $90

Menefee, George W. COW TALK: THE MEMOIRS OF...AN EARLY DAY CATTLEMAN OF THE SOUTHWEST. Recorded by Lottie W. Reddert. Privately ptd, 1975. 1st ed. Wrappers. *CONNOLLY & WADE.* $22.50

Menninger, E.A. EDIBLE NUTS OF THE WORLD. Stuart, 1977. Cl w/cover spotting; lt foxing to fep, spotted dj. Signed. *SUTTON.* $65

Menpes, Dorothy. BRITTANY. A&C Black, 1905. 1st ed. 20s Series. Spine sl sunned, else VG-NF. *OLD LONDON.* $75

Menpes, Mortimer. JAPAN—A RECORD IN COLOUR. A&C Black. 1905 reprint. 20s Series. NF. *OLD LONDON.* $45

Mercer, A.A. BANDITTI OF THE PLAINS, OR, THE CATTLEMEN'S INVASION OF WYOMING IN 1892. James Mitchell Clarke. SF: Grabhorn Press, 1935. *HEINOLDT.* $125

Mercer, A.A. BANDITTI OF THE PLAINS, OR, THE CATTLEMEN'S INVASION OF WYOMING IN 1892. Univ of Oklahoma Press, 1954. 2nd prtg. NF in dj. *DIAMOND.* $15

Mercer, A.A. THE BANDITTI OF THE PLAINS OR THE CATTLEMEN'S INVASION OF WYOMING IN 1892 (THE CROWNING INFAMY OF THE AGES). Norman: Univ of OK, 1955. Fine in Fine dj. *CONNOLLY & WADE.* $25

Mercer, Henry C. ANCIENT CARPENTERS' TOOLS. PA: Horizon Press, 1975. 5th ed. VG. *BACKROOM.* $75

Meredith, George. DIANA OF THE CROSSWAYS. London: Chapman & Hall, 1853. 3 vols. Bkpls removed, some hinges cracked or starting, o/w Near VG. 1st complete bk ed. *CHAPEL HILL.* $150

Meredith, George. POEMS. The Empty Purse, with Odes to the Comic Spirit....London: Macmillan, 1892. NF. 1st ed. *CHAPEL HILL.* $50

Meredith, Grace E. GIRL CAPTIVES OF THE CHEYENNES: A TRUE STORY.... LA: Gem, 1927. Signed presentation by sister of one of the captives. 1st ed. Frontis, 2pp map, 12 plts, errata slip on pg 93. Red cl w/gilt, Fine. *CONNOLLY & WADE.* $145

Meredith, Roy. MR. LINCOLN'S CAMERA MAN. MATHEW B. BRADY. NY: Scribner's, 1946. 1st ed. VG. *ARTIS.* $30

Meredith, William. LOVE LETTERS FROM AN IMPOSSIBLE LAND. New Haven: Yale Univ Press, 1944. 1st ed. Spine a bit darkened, else Fine but lacking dj. Inscribed. Author's 1st book. *WOOLMER.* $150

Meredith, William. THE OPEN SEA AND OTHER POEMS. NY: Knopf, 1958. 1st ed. Fine, lacking dj. Inscribed. *WOOLMER.* $85

Mereness, Newton D. MARYLAND AS A PROPRIETARY PROVINCE. NY, 1901. Orig cl. 1st ed. Howes M533. *GINSBERG.* $75

Merfield, Fred G. GORILLA HUNTER. NY: Farrar, Straus, 1956. 1st ed. Fine in NF dj. *GREAT EPIC.* $30

Merfield, Fred G. GORILLAS WERE MY NEIGHBOURS. London/NY/Toronto: Longhman's, Green and Co, 1956. 1st ed. VG+ in VG dj. *BACKMAN.* $32

Merimee, Prosper. CARMEN AND LETTERS FROM SPAIN. Paris: Harrison of Paris, (1931). 1/595 on Rives, from a total of 645. In brn slipcase. *JUVELIS.* $100

Merimee, Prosper. CARMEN. NY: LEC, 1941. Illus by Jean Charlot. Ed ltd to 1500 numbered, signed by Charlot. Slipcase. *KARMIOLE.* $100

Merington, Marguerite (ed). THE CUSTER STORY, THE LIFE AND INTIMATE LETTERS OF GENERAL CUSTER AND HIS WIFE ELIZABETH. NY, (1950). 1st ed. Fine in dj. *PRATT.* $27.50

Meriwether, David. MY LIFE IN THE MOUNTAINS & ON THE PLAINS. Robert Griffen (ed). Univ of OK, (1965). 1st ed. Signed presentation from Griffen. VF in VG dj. *OREGON.* $45

Merk, Frederick (ed). FUR TRADE AND EMPIRE: GEORGE SIMPSON'S JOURNAL....Cambridge, 1931. Fldg map in rear pocket. Orig cl. Howes M536. Oscar Handlin's copy. *GINSBERG.* $125

Merkley, Christopher. BIOGRAPHY OF CHRISTOPHER MERKLEY. Salt Lake, 1887. 1st ed, 46pp, orig pink wraps. VG. *BENCHMARK.* $75

Merli, Frank J. GREAT BRITAIN AND THE CONFEDERATE NAVY 1861-1865. Bloomington, 1970. 1st ed. Fine in dj. *PRATT.* $32.50

Merrell, William Howard. FIVE MONTHS IN REBELDOM; OR NOTES FROM THE DIARY OF A BULL RUN PRISONER, AT RICHMOND. Rochester, NY, 1862. 1st ed. Wrappers lacking, else VG. *McGOWAN.* $125

Merriam, Alan P. ETHNOMUSICOLOGY OF THE FLATHEAD INDIANS. NY: Werner-Gren Foundation for Anthropological Research, 1967. Viking Fund Publ in Anthropology #44. Subscriber ed. 29 plts. Stiff wrappers. Fine. *CONNOLLY & WADE.* $55

Merriam, C. Hart. RESULTS OF A BIOLOGICAL SURVEY OF THE SAN FRANCISCO MOUNTAIN REGION AND DESERT OF THE LITTLE COLORADO, ARIZONA. Washington: USDA, 1890. 8vo, 3/4 black lea, 136pp, 5 double-page colored maps, 13 plts, figures. Maps pristine. Leather binding somewhat shabby. Internally NF. *FIVE QUAIL.* $125

Merriam, C. Hart. THE DAWN OF THE WORLD. Cleveland: The Arthur H. Clark Co, 1910. 15 full-pg illus. Cloth, silverfishing to covers. *DAWSON'S.* $75

Merriam, Florence. MY SUMMER IN A MORMON VILLAGE. Boston, 1894. 1st ed. NF. *BENCHMARK.* $45

Merriam, George. THE LIFE & TIMES OF SAMUEL BOWLES. Century Co, 1885. 2 vols. 1st ed. Fine. *OREGON.* $40

Merriam, George. THE LIFE AND TIMES OF SAMUEL BOWLES. NY: 1885. 2 vols. 1st ed. Orig cl. Lib bkpls. *GINSBERG.* $75

Merriam, H.G. WAY OUT WEST. RECOLLECTIONS & TALES. Univ of OK, (1969). 1st ed. VF in VF dj. *OREGON.* $25

Merrien, Jean. LONELY VOYAGERS. NY: G.P. Putnam's Sons, 1954. 1st Amer. ed. VG in lightly worn dj. *PARMER.* $35

Merrill, James. BRAVING THE ELEMENTS. Poems. NY: Atheneum, 1972. 1st ed. Fine in dj. *CAPTAIN'S BOOKSHELF.* $50

Merrill, James. BRONZE. (NY): Nadja, (1984). 1st ed. 1/150 in boards, signed. Fine. *CAPTAIN'S BOOKSHELF.* $125

Merrill, James. DIVINE COMEDIES. NY: Atheneum, 1976. 1st ed. Fine in dj. *CAPTAIN'S BOOKSHELF.* $35

Merrill, James. FIRST POEMS. NY: Alfred A. Knopf, 1951. 1st ed. 1/999 numbered. Spine a bit rubbed; VG (owner sig) in lightly worn and soiled dj. Inscribed. *CAPTAIN'S BOOKSHELF.* $200

Merrill, James. FIRST POEMS. NY: Knopf, 1951. One of 990 numbered. Author's 1st commercially published book. Spine sl faded, else Fine, lacking dj. Prev owner's sig. *WOOLMER.* $125

Merrill, James. FROM THE FIRST NINE. NY: Atheneum, 1982. 2nd ptg. Signed. Fine in Fine dj. *LOPEZ.* $20

Merrill, James. MARBLED PAPER. Salem, Oregon: Seluzicki, 1982. 1st ed. Ltd to 200 signed. Emb wraps. Mint. *JAFFE.* $100

Merrill, James. MARBLED PAPER. Salem: Seluzicki, 1972. 1st ed. 1/200 signed. Fine in wrappers. *CAPTAIN'S BOOKSHELF.* $125

Merrill, James. METAMORPHOSIS OF 741. Pawlet, VT: Banyan Press, 1977. 1st ed. 1/440. Fine in wrappers and env. *CAPTAIN'S BOOKSHELF.* $100

Merrill, James. NIGHTS AND DAYS. (London): Chatto & Windus/ Hogarth Press, 1966. 1st UK ed. Fine in price-clipped dj sl darkened at the spine. *CAPTAIN'S BOOKSHELF.* $35

Merrill, James. NIGHTS AND DAYS. Poems. NY: Atheneum, 1966. 1st ed. Fine in dj w/short tear. *CAPTAIN'S BOOKSHELF.* $75

Merrill, James. NIGHTS AND DAYS. Poems. NY: Atheneum, 1966. 1st ed, wrappered issue. Fine in lightly rubbed wrappers. *CAPTAIN'S BOOKSHELF.* $15

Merrill, James. PLAYS OF LIGHT. (Ann Arbor: Laurence Scott, 1984). 1st ed. 1/175 signed. Folio. VF in marbled wrappers. *CAPTAIN'S BOOKSHELF.* $225

Merrill, James. PLAYS OF LIGHT. Frontis, marbled wrappers w/ptd label, manila env. (Ann Arbor, MI: Laurence Scott, 1984). 1st ed. Ltd to 175 signed. Mint. *JAFFE.* $250

Merrill, James. SELECTED POEMS. (London): Chatto & Windus/ Hogarth Press, 1961. 1st ed. Fine in dj. *CAPTAIN'S BOOKSHELF.* $100

Merrill, James. THE COUNTRY OF A THOUSAND YEARS OF PEACE AND OTHER POEMS. NY: Knopf, 1959. 1st ed. Fine in very lightly rubbed dj. *CAPTAIN'S BOOKSHELF.* $125

Merrill, James. THE FIRE SCREEN. NY: Atheneum, 1969. 1st ed. Fine in wrappers, as issued. *CAPTAIN'S BOOKSHELF.* $45

Merrill, James. THE FIRE SCREEN. NY: Atheneum, 1969. 1st ed. Orig ptd wraps. VG. *CHAPEL HILL.* $30

Merrill, James. THE IMAGE MAKER. A Play in One Act. (NY): Sea Cliff Press, (1986). 1st ed. 1/220, signed. Fine in cloth w/paper label w/o dj, as issued. *CAPTAIN'S BOOKSHELF.* $100

Merrill, James. THE REBEL SHORE. Boston, (1957). 1st ed. Dj has a little wear o/w VG+. *PRATT.* $32.50

Merrill, James. THE SERAGLIO. NY: Knopf, 1957. 1st ed, 1st novel. Fine in lightly worn price-clipped dj. Inscribed. *CAPTAIN'S BOOKSHELF.* $125

Merrill, James. TWO POEMS FROM THE CUPOLA AND THE SUMMER PEOPLE. (London): Chatto & Windus/ Hogarth Press, (1972). 1st ed. Fine in dj. *CAPTAIN'S BOOKSHELF.* $60

Merrill, James. VIOLENT PASTORAL. No. 13 of 100 set and printed by hand by The Adams House & Lowell House Printers . . . June 1965. Wrappers. Fine. *WOOLMER.* $450

Merrill, James. WATER STREET. Poems. NY: Atheneum, 1962. 1st ed, wrappered issue. NF in ptd wrappers. *CAPTAIN'S BOOKSHELF.* $35

Merrill, Judith. SHADOW ON THE HEARTH. Doubleday, 1950. 1st ed. NF in sl chipped, frayed dj. *MADLE.* $35

Merrill, S. THE MOOSE BOOK. NY: Dutton, (1920). 2nd ed. Photos, drawings. Gilt dec. VG. *MIKESH.* $60

Merritt, A. 7 FOOTPRINTS TO SATAN. NY: Boni and Liveright, 1928. 1st ed. NF but for fraying spine ends and sl shakiness. *BEASLEY.* $100

Merritt, A. DWELLERS IN THE MIRAGE & THE FACE IN THE ABYSS. Liveright, 1953. Rear of dj tape-stained, else Fine. *MADLE.* $35

Merritt, A. THE FOX WOMAN AND OTHER STORIES. NY, (1949). Avon #214. 1st (and only) ed. Wraps. VG+ w/no spine creasing. *McCLINTOCK.* $20

Merritt, A. THE FOX WOMAN. Avon, 1949. 1st ed. Near VG in wraps. *MADLE.* $25

Merritt, A. THE FOX WOMAN. Avon, 1949. One of 300 hb by Fantasy Press pub Lloyd Eshbach. Pp yellowed as usual, else Fine in the ptd white dj. MADLE. $300

Merritt, A. THE MOON POOL. Liveright, n.d. (1930s) Fine in sl frayed dj. MADLE. $50

Merritt, A. THE MOON POOL. NY: Avon 370, 1951. Wraps. 1st Avon paperback ed. Fine. BEASLEY. $30

Merritt, Benjamin Dean. THE ATHENIAN CALENDAR IN THE FIFTH CENTURY...Cambridge: Harvard Univ Press, 1928. 2 fldg plates rear pocket. Bkpl. ARCHAEOLOGIA. $150

Merritt, John. BARONETS AND BUFFALO. Missoula Mountain Press, 1986. 1st ed. VF in VF dj. OREGON. $16

Mersfelder, L.C. COWBOY-FISHERMAN-HUNTER. TRUE STORIES OF THE GREAT SOUTHWEST. Kansas City: Brown-White-Lowell Press, 1951. 2nd ed, rev and enrlgd. Fldg map. VG in Good dj. CONNOLLY & WADE. $45

Merton, Thomas. NEW SEEDS OF CONTEMPLATION. (NY, 1961). 1st ed. New Directions imprint. NF. McCLINTOCK. $12.50

Merton, Thomas. ORIGINAL CHILD BOMB. Illus Emil Antonucci, black boards with ptd label, acetate dj. (Norfolk, CT): New Directions, (1962). 1st ed. Ltd to 500 signed. Base of spine sl rubbed, o/w Fine. JAFFE. $450

Merton, Thomas. ORIGINAL CHILD BOMB. N.p.: New Directions, 1962. 1st ed, ltd to 8,000. Sl bumped & rubbed, o/w VG+ w/o dj as issued. ARCHER. $40

Merton, Thomas. SEASONS OF CELEBRATION. NY: Farrar Straus & Giroux, (1965). 1st ed. Fine in dj. CAPTAIN'S BOOKSHELF. $35

Merton, Thomas. SEEDS OF DESTRUCTION. Farrar Straus Giroux, 1964. 1st ed. VG in VG dj with barely noticeable tape at edge. BEBBAH. $28

Merton, Thomas. THE CHRISTMAS SERMONS OF BL. GUERRIC OF IGNY. (Abbey of Gethsemani, 1959). 1st ed. NF. McCLINTOCK. $65

Merton, Thomas. THE LIVING BREAD. NY, (1956). 1st ed. VG in dj. McCLINTOCK. $25

Merton, Thomas. THE SECULAR JOURNAL OF THOMAS MERTON. NY, (1959). 1st ed. Fine in VG dj. McCLINTOCK. $25

Merton, Thomas. THE SECULAR JOURNAL OF THOMAS MERTON. NY: FSC, 1959. 1st ed. NF in VG dj (1" tear, a bit soiled). ARCHER. $25

Merton, Thomas. THE SEVEN STOREY MOUNTAIN. NY: Harcourt, Brace & Company, (1948). 1st ed. Rare white binding & first state dj (on back, Merton "is second from the left" in one of the photos). White cl. Fine in sl soiled dj (tiny chip, short closed tear). JAFFE. $2250

Merton, Thomas. THE TEARS OF THE BLIND LION. NY: New Directions, 1949. Uncommon cl ed. Fine but name oblit. on fep, and small darkened area at head of spine, in lightly used dj (tiny chip at head of lightly sunned and lightly worn spine). BEASLEY. $35

Merton, Thomas. THE TEARS OF THE BLIND LION. NY: New Directions, (1949). 1st ed. Fine in price clipped dj (spine and edges little sunned). POLYANTHOS. $45

Merton, Thomas. THE TOWER OF BABEL. Gerhard Marcks (illus). (Norfolk, CT: New Directions, 1957). 1st ed. One of 250 numbered, ptd on hand press of Richard Von Sichowsky in Hamburg & signed by Merton & Marcks. Orig boards, slipcase. Fine. JAFFE. $1750

Merton, Thomas. THE WATERS OF SILOE. NY: Harcourt, Brace, (1949). 1st ed. Orig blue cl. Fine in dj. CHAPEL HILL. $50

Merton, Thomas. THIRTY POEMS. Norfolk: New Directions, 1944. 1st ed, 1st bk. Wraps in dj. Fine in NF dj (tear at flap fold, tiny vermin holes at spine). BEASLEY. $100

Merton, Thomas. WHAT ARE THESE WOUNDS? Milwaukee: Bruce Pub Co, (1950). VG. BLUE DRAGON. $27.50

Merullo, Roland. LEAVING LOSAPAS. Boston: Houghton Mifflin, 1991. 1st ed. Signed. Fine in dj. LOPEZ. $45

Merwin, Henry Childs. THE LIFE OF BRET HARTE WITH SOME ACCOUNT....Houghton Mifflin, 1911. 1st ed. Teg. VG+, bkpl. AUTHORS OF THE WEST. $17.50

Merwin, Sam. THE HOUSE OF MANY DOORS. Doubleday, 1951. 1st ed. Fine in dj. MADLE. $35

Merwin, W.S. (ed). WEST WIND. Self-wrappers, stapled as issued. (London): Poetry Bk Soc, Christmas 1961. 1st ed. Dusty, but VG. JAFFE. $75

Merwin, W.S. A MASK FOR JANUS. New Haven: Yale, 1952. 1st ed, 1st bk. One corner sl bumped, else Fine in lightly rubbed and soiled dj (few tiny tears). CAPTAIN'S BOOKSHELF. $225

Merwin, W.S. (trans). THE SATIRES OF PERSIUS. Bloomington: Indiana Univ Press, 1961. 1st ed. Fine but for owner's name, in NF dj (few tiny tears). BEASLEY. $40

Metcalf, Arthur. THE GREEN DEVIL. Pilgrim Press, 1912. 1st ed. Near VG. Signed. MADLE. $25

Metcalf, Paul. BOTH. (N.p.): The Jargon Society, 1982. 1st ed. Signed. Fine in dj. LOPEZ. $55

Metcalf, Paul. THE MIDDLE PASSAGE. Highlands: The Jargon Society, 1976. 1st ed. Signed. Fine in wrappers, in dj. LOPEZ. $35

Metcalfe, John. THE FEASTING DEAD. Arkham House, 1954. 1st ed. Fine in dj. MADLE. $175

Metcalfe, John. THE SMOKING LEG. London, 1927. Edge-wear, else VG. MADLE. $40

Metcalfe-Shaw, Gertrude E. ENGLISH CARAVANNERS IN THE WILD WEST. Edinburgh, 1926. 1st ed. Fldg map. VG. DIAMOND. $45

Metchnikoff, Elie. THE NATURE OF MAN, STUDIES IN OPTIMISTIC PHILOSOPHY. London, 1903. 1st Eng trans. FYE. $100

Meteyard, Eliza. WEDGEWOOD TRIO. Merion, PA: Buten Museum of Wedgewood, 1967. 1st ed. VG. BACKROOM. $30

Metz, Leon Claire. JOHN SELMAN, GUNFIGHTER. Norman, (1966). 2nd ed, (1980). Fine in dj. PRATT. $27.50

Metz, Leon Claire. JOHN SELMAN: TEXAS GUNFIGHTER. NY, 1966. 1st ed. Fine in very slight edgeworn dj w/scratch on front. BAADE. $35

Metz, Leon Claire. THE SHOOTERS. El Paso: Mangan Books, 1976. 1st ed. Presentation, signed. Fine in dj. LAURIE. $40

Metzger, Berta. TALES TOLD IN HAWAII. NY: FRederick Stokes, 1929. 116pp. 1st ed. Illus by Verna Tallman. Fine in Near VG dj. GREAT EPIC. $55

Metzner, Ralph (ed). ECSTATIC ADVENTURE. NY: Macmillan, 1968. 1st ed. 306pp. VG in sl chipped dj. AKA. $28

Mewshaw, Michael. WAKING SLOW. London: Constable, (1973). 1st Eng ed. Signed. NF in sl age darkened dj. LOPEZ. $40

Meyer, Georg Hermann von. THE ORGANS OF SPEECH AND THEIR APPLICATION IN THE FORMATION OF ARTICULATE SOUNDS. London, 1892. 2nd ed. FYE. $75

Meyer, Hazel. THE GOLD IN TIN PAN ALLEY. Phila: Lippincott, (1958). 1st ed. VG in VG dj. AARD. $20

Meyer, Howard N. LET US HAVE PEACE, THE LIFE OF ULYSSES GRANT. NY, (1966). 1st ed. Small tear on dj, o/w Fine. PRATT. $20

Meyer, Joseph. NATURE'S REMEDIES: EARLY HISTORY AND USES OF BOTANIC DRUGS AS REVEALED IN THE LEGENDS AND ANECDOTES OF ANCIENT TIMES. Hammond, 1934. 1st ed. FYE. $40

Meyer, Karl. THE PLUNDERED PAST. NY: Atheneum, 1973. 1st ed. Good in chipped dj. *SILVER.* $20

Meyer, L. MODERN THEORIES OF CHEMISTRY. London: Longmans, Green, 1888. 1st Eng ed. 587pp. New end leaves, rebacked with orig backstrip label. Good. *BOOKCELL.* $80

Meyer, Roy. THE VILLAGE INDIANS OF THE UPPER MISSOURI....Univ of NE, (1977). 1st ed. VF in VF dj. *OREGON.* $35

Meyer, Samuel A. 50 GOLDEN YEARS. A HISTORY OF THE CITY OF NEWPORT BEACH. 1906-1956. Newport Harbor Publ: 1957. 1st ed. 72 plts. Gilt emb blue cl. Edgewear. VG. *CONNOLLY & WADE.* $55

Meyer, Willi and Victor Schmeiden. BIER'S HYPEREMIC TREATMENT IN SURGERY, MEDICINE, AND THE SPECIALTIES. Phila, 1908. 1st ed. *FYE.* $60

Meyer, William H. NAVAL SKETCHES OF THE WAR IN CALIFORNIA. Ltd ed of 1000. Colored plts. Orig boards w/lea backstrip, chipped. *GINSBERG.* $300

Meyers, William H. and Dudley W. Knox. NAVAL SKETCHES OF THE WAR IN CALIFORNIA. Intro Franklin D. Roosevelt. NY: Random House. 1939. Ltd to 1000 ptd by the Grabhorn Press. Fine. *KARMIOLE.* $300

Meyers, William H. JOURNAL OF A CRUISE TO CALIFORNIA AND THE SANDWICH ISLANDS..1841-1844. SF: Grabhorn Press, 1955. One of 400. John Haskel Kemble (ed). 11 color plts. 1/2 morocco, cl. Lt rubbing to cvrs, else Excellent. *PARMER.* $325

Meynell, Alice. HEARTS OF CONTROVERSY. London: Burns & Oates (1917). 1st ed. Spine darkened, sl worn. VG. *SECOND LIFE.* $35

Meynell, Alice. POEMS. NY: Scribners, 1913. 1st US ed. Uncut. Collected ed. Spine sl soiled, VG. *SECOND LIFE.* $30

Meynell, Alice. THE CHILDREN. NY: John Lane, 1897. 1st ed. Uncut, teg, grn stamped cl binding (rubbed). VG. *SECOND LIFE.* $75

Meynell, Francis. MY LIVES. NY, 1971. 1st ed. Signed presentation. Fine in dj (very small piece missing top edge rear panel). *POLYANTHOS.* $45

Meyrick, Samuel Rush, & Charles Hamilton Smith. THE COSTUME OF THE ORIGINAL INHABITANTS OF THE BRITISH ISLANDS, FROM THE EARLIEST PERIODS TO THE SIXTH CENTURY; TO WHICH IS ADDED, THAT OF THE GOTHIC NATIONS...London: Ptd by William Bulmer, Shakespeare Press, pub by R. Havell, 1815. 1st ed. Folio. 59pp. Hand colored frontis, 24 hand colored plts. Orig full dk grn straight-grain morocco stamped in blind and gilt, aeg; some scuffing, but all restored, expertly repaired w/new matching spine. Bkpls. Fine. *WEBER.* $1,250

Meyrink, Gustav. THE GOLEM. Houghton-Mifflin, 1928. 1st US ed. VG. *MADLE.* $35

Michael, A.C. AN ARTIST IN SPAIN. London: Hodder & Stoughton, n.d. (c. 1914). 26 tipped-in plts. Attractive. *SCHOYER'S.* $40

Michaels, Barbara. AMMIE, COME HOME. NY: Meredith Press, 1968. 1st ed. Fine in dj w/tiny wear at spine ends and at corners. *MORDIDA.* $45

Michaels, Barbara. GREYGALLOWS. London: Souvenir, 1974. 1st British ed. Signed. Fine in dj. *SILVER DOOR.* $37.50

Michaels, Barbara. HERE I STAY. NY: Congdon & Weed, (1983). 1st ed. VF in VF dj. *UNGER.* $45

Michaels, Barbara. HERE I STAY. NY: Congdon & Weed, 1983. 1st ed. Fine in dj w/closed tear, crease. *MORDIDA.* $32.50

Michaels, Barbara. SOMEONE IN THE HOUSE. NY: Dodd Mead, 1981. 1st ed. Inscribed. Fine in dj. *MORDIDA.* $65

Michaels, Barbara. SONS OF THE WOLF. NY: Meredith Press, 1967. 1st ed. VF in dj. *MORDIDA.* $100

Michaels, Barbara. THE GREY BEGINNING. NY: Congdon & Weed, (1984). 1st ed. VF in price-clipped dj. *UNGER.* $45

Michaels, Barbara. THE GREY BEGINNING. NY: Congdon & Weed, 1984. 1st ed. VF in dj. *MORDIDA.* $35

Michaels, Barbara. THE WALKER IN THE SHADOWS. NY: Dodd Mead, 1979. 1st ed. Fine in dj. *MORDIDA.* $85

Michaels, Barbara. THE WIZARD'S DAUGHTER. NY: Dodd Mead, 1980. 1st ed. Fine in dj (short closed tear base of spine; faint crease front panel). *MORDIDA.* $40

Michaels, Barbara. WAIT FOR WHAT WILL COME. NY: Dodd Mead, 1978. 1st ed. Fine in dj w/crease-tear, couple short closed tears. *MORDIDA.* $65

Michalowski, Kazimieriz. ART OF ANCIENT EGYPT. NY: Harry N. Abrams, 1968. 1st ed. 145 color illus, 150 plans and charts. Spine bumped. Good. *ARCHAEOLOGIA.* $175

Michelangelo, Buonarotti. THE LETTERS OF MICHELANGELO. Ed by E.H. Ramsden. In 2 Vols. Vol One 1496-1534. (Vol Two 1537-1563). (Stanford): Stanford Univ Press. 1963. 1st ed. 2 fldg tables. Fine in slipcase. *KARMIOLE.* $75

Michelet, Jules. SATANISM AND WITCHCRAFT. NY, 1939. Dj. Fine. *POLYANTHOS.* $45

Michener, James A. ABOUT CENTENNIAL: SOME NOTES ON THE NOVEL. Random House, (1974). 1st ltd ed of 3,200. Ep maps. Fine in dj. *AUTHORS OF THE WEST.* $40

Michener, James A. ALASKA. NY: Random House, 1988. 1st ed. Fine in slipcase. One of 1000 signed. *ELSE FINE.* $90

Michener, James A. and A. Grove Day. RASCALS IN PARADISE. NY: RH, (1957). 1st ed. Fine in dj. *CAPTAIN'S BOOKSHELF.* $125

Michener, James A. CARAVANS. NY: Random House, 1963. 1st ed. NF in NF dj. *BEASLEY.* $45

Michener, James A. CARAVANS. NY: Random House, 1963. 1st ed. Fine, minor wear to spine heel of price clipped dj. *ELSE FINE.* $60

Michener, James A. CENTENNIAL. NY: Random House, 1974. 1st ed. Fine but for owner's name, a little spattering to bottom edge, in NF dj w/few small tears. *BEASLEY.* $40

Michener, James A. CENTENNIAL. Random House, (1974). 1st ed. Ep maps. Fine in dj. *AUTHORS OF THE WEST.* $20

Michener, James A. COLLECTORS, FORGERS—AND A WRITER: A MEMOIR. NY: Targ Editions, 1983. 1st ed, 1/250. Signed. *JUVELIS.* $90

Michener, James A. COLLECTORS, FORGERS—AND A WRITER: A MEMOIR. NY: Targ Editions, 1983. 1st ed. One of 250 signed. Cl, slipcase. VF. *JAFFE.* $175

Michener, James A. HAWAII. NY: Random House, 1959. 1st ed. Fine minor wear at spine heel of price-clipped dj. *ELSE FINE.* $75

Michener, James A. JAPANESE PRINTS FROM THE EARLY MASTERS TO THE MODERN. Rutland/Tokyo: Charles E. Tuttle, 1959. 1st ed. 257 plates, 55 in full color. NF. *SMITH.* $125

Michener, James A. KENT STATE: WHAT HAPPENED AND WHY. NY: Random House, 1971. 1st ed. Fine, minor wear at dj spine heel. *ELSE FINE.* $85

Michener, James A. LEGACY. NY: Random House, 1987. Wraps. Adv uncorrected proofs. NF. *BEASLEY.* $30

Michener, James A. POLAND. NY: Random House, 1983. 1st ed. Signed, ltd ed, one of 500. VF in slipcase. *ELSE FINE.* $150

Michener, James A. SAYONARA. NY: Random, 1954. 1st ed. Name. VF, an exceptional example of the dj, no spine fade of laminate peeling. *ELSE FINE.* $125

Michener, James A. SPACE. NY: Random House 1982. 1st ed. Signed, ltd ed. One of 500. VF in slipcase. *ELSE FINE.* $150

Michener, James A. TEXAS. (New York: Random House, [1985]). 1st ed. One of 1000 specially bound signed by Michener. Mint in slipcase. *PIRAGES.* $125

Michener, James A. TEXAS. NY: Random House, 1985. 1st ed. Fine in dj. *GIBBS.* $17.50

Michener, James A. TEXAS. NY: Random House, 1985. 1st ed, ltd to 1,000 signed. Fine in Fine slipcase. *BOOK MARKET.* $100

Michener, James A. THE BRIDGE AT ANDAU. NY: Random, 1957. 1st ed. Name. Fine in dj. *ELSE FINE.* $60

Michener, James A. THE BRIDGES AT TOKO-RI. NY: Random, 1953. 1st ed. VF, minor rubs at spine corners of the dj. *ELSE FINE.* $115

Michener, James A. THE EAGLE AND THE RAVEN. Austin: State House Press, (1990). 1st ed. One of 350 numbered, signed by author and illus Shaw. VF in pub's slipcase. *UNGER.* $125

Michener, James A. THE FIRES OF SPRING. Sydney: Dymock's Book Arcade Limited, 1950. 1st Australian ed. Dampstain extending across bottom corner, affecting pages, boards and back panel of dj, else VG in internally repaired About VG dj w/small chips and soiling. *BETWEEN COVERS.* $150

Michener, James A. THE NOVEL. NY: RH, (1991). Uncorrected proof. Fine in wrappers. *LOPEZ.* $30

Michener, James A. THE QUALITY OF LIFE. James B. Wyeth (illus). Ptd boards w/pict label, slipcase. (Phila): Girard Bank, 1970. 1st ed. Signed. VF. *JAFFE.* $100

Michener, James A. THE SOURCE. NY: Random House, 1965. 1st ed. Fine but for owner's name, date, in lightly used dj. *BEASLEY.* $50

Michener, James A. THE VOICE OF ASIA. NY: Random, 1951. 1st ed. Name. VF, dj has minute rubs at spine corner. *ELSE FINE.* $165

Michener, James A. THE WATERMEN: SELECTIONS FROM CHESAPEAKE. NY, (1979). 1st ed. Signed. Fine in like dj. *POLYANTHOS.* $45

MICHIGAN. A GUIDE TO THE WOLVERINE STATE. NY: Oxford Univ Press, (1943). 2nd prtg. Lacks rear pocket map. Good. *ARTIS.* $17.50

Middlebrook, Louis F. SEALS OF MARITIME NEW ENGLAND. Salem: The Essex Institute, 1926. Very nice. *PARMER.* $50

Middleton, Arthur Pierce. TOBACCO COAST: A MARITIME HISTORY OF THE CHESAPEAKE BAY IN THE COLONIAL ERA. Mariner's Museum, 1953. *BOOK BROKER.* $75

Middleton, John and E.H. Winter (eds). WITCHCRAFT AND SORCERY IN EAST AFRICA. London: Routledge & Kegan Paul, (1963). 2nd imp. 1964. NF in VG dj. *ACADEMIC.* $30

Middleton, W.E. Knowles. A HISTORY OF THE THEORIES OF RAIN AND OTHER FORMS OF PRECIPITATION. NY: Franklin Watts, 1966 (UK 1965). 1st US ed. Rear board sl faded, front board very sl warped. Good. *KNOLLWOOD.* $29

Midhat Bey, Ali Haydar. THE LIFE OF MIDHAT PASHA. London, 1903. Portraits. xii,292pp. Uncut. *O'NEILL.* $70

Miers, Earl Schenck (ed). TRIAL BY WILDERNESS. Kingsport, TN: Privately ptd, Kingsport Press, 1957. Ltd to 1500. Slipcase. Fine. *CONNOLLY & WADE.* $40

Miers, Earl Schenck. THE AMERICAN CIVIL WAR, A POPULAR ILLUSTRATED HISTORY OF THE YEARS 1861-1865 AS SEEN BY THE ARTIST-CORRESPONDENTS WHO WERE THERE. NY, 1961. Minor dj wear o/w VG+. *PRATT.* $35

Miers, Earl Schenck. THE WEB OF VICTORY, GRANT AT VICKSBURG. NY, (1955). 1st ed. 329pp. Dj chipped w/faded spine, o/w VG. *PRATT.* $25

Miers, Earl Schenck. THE GREAT REBELLION. Cleveland, (1958). 1st ed. Dj. VG. *PRATT.* $30

Miers, Henry A. YUKON: A VISIT TO THE YUKON GOLD-FIELDS. N.p, 1901. Ptd wrappers, wrappers separated at spine. *DAWSON'S.* $100

Migot, Andre. THIN EDGE OF THE WORLD. Boston: Little Brown, (1956). 1st Amer ed. VG in dj. *ARTIS.* $15

Mihalic, Slavko. ATLANTIS. (NY: Greenfield Center, 1983). Simic, Charles and Peter Kastmiler (trans). 1st US ed. Fine in wrappers. *CAPTAIN'S BOOKSHELF.* $20

Mikkelsen, Ejnar. MIRAGE IN THE ARCTIC. London: Rupert Hart-Davis, 1955. 1st ed. NF in NF dj. *GREAT EPIC.* $45

Mikkelson, Ejnar. CONQUERING THE ARCTIC ICE. Phila, n.d. (c1930). Spine frayed, spot on front cvr, 2pp soiled. *ARTIS.* $65

Mikkelsen, Ejnar. FROZEN JUSTICE. NY, 1922. 1st ed. Trans. from the Danish by A.G. Jayne. Dj badly chipped, o/w VG. *ARTIS.* $45

Mikolowski, Ken. THANK YOU, CALL AGAIN. Illus Ann Mikolowski, map wrappers. Mt. Horeb: Perishable Press, 1973. 1st ed. Ltd to 120. Signed by Walter Hamady. Fine. *JAFFE.* $150

Mikovaro, E. THE BOOK OF PIRATES. Whitman, (1932). Near 4to. 95pp. Illus by G.R. Taylor. Edgewear. VG w/bright pict paper-covered boards. *BEBBAH.* $25

Milburn, William Henry. THE PIONEERS, PREACHERS AND PEOPLE OF THE MISSISSIPPI VALLEY. NY: Derby & Jackson, 1860. Front hinge cracked, fly leaf gone, foxing. *HUDSON.* $50

Milburn, William Henry. THE RIFLE, AXE AND SADDLEBAGS, AND OTHER PLEASURES. NY: Derby and Jackson, 1857. 1st ed. Frontis, 309pp. 12mo. Orig blind-stamped beige cl. Minor wear. VG. *CONNOLLY & WADE.* $75

Miles, Alexander. SURGICAL WARD WORK AND NURSING. London, 1899. 2nd ed. 288pp. 333 illus. Scarce. *FYE.* $200

Miles, George W. BIENNIAL REPORT OF THE COMMISSIONER OF FISHERIES AND GAME OF INDIANA. Indianapolis, 1913. 16 color plts, fldg map. Good. *ARTIS.* $30

Miles, Henry Downes, PUGILISTICA. Edinburgh: John Grant, 1906. 1st ed. 3 vols. Some wear to extremities, minor foxing, else VG. *OLD LONDON.* $350

Miles, Keith. BULLET HOLE. NY: Harper, 1987. 1st Amer ed. Review copy, signed. Pub's slip laid in. VF in dj. *SILVER DOOR.* $35

Miles, Nelson A. ANNUAL REPORT MAJOR GENERAL MILES, WAR DEPT, YEAR ENDING JUNE 30, 1898. Washington, GPO, 1899. 720pp. Many fldg maps. Rebound in new buckram. Contents Fine. *HEINOLDT.* $50

Miles, Nelson A. PERSONAL RECOLLECTIONS AND OBSERVATIONS OF GENERAL NELSON A. MILES. Chicago: the Werner Co., 1896. 1st issue, w/the portrait listing the author as "General". Howes M595. *KARMIOLE.* $125

Miles, Nelson A. PERSONAL RECOLLECTIONS AND OBSERVATIONS OF...Chicago, 1896. 1st ed. 590pp. Port (rank given as "Mag. -Gen."), plts. Orig pict cl, bright cover, spine a little faded. *GINSBERG.* $150

Miles, William. JOURNAL OF THE SUFFERINGS AND HARDSHIPS OF CAPT. PARKER H. FRENCH'S OVERLAND EXPEDITION TO CALIFORNIA. (NY, 1916). Orig ptd wrappers. Facsimile reprint. Howes M597. One of 250. *GINSBERG.* $50

MILITARY HISTORY OF OHIO, ITS BORDER ANNALS...INDIAN WARS...WAR OF 1812...MEXICAN WAR...WAR OF REBELLION. NY, 1886. Cvr worn, spine repaired. VG. *HEINOLDT.* $50

Mill, John Stuart. A SYSTEM OF LOGIC, RATIOCINATIVE AND INDUCTIVE, ETC. NY: Harper, 1848. 1st Amer ed. Brown cloth, tooled in blind. Light scattered foxing, else Fine. *CAPTAIN'S BOOKSHELF.* $200

Mill, John Stuart. AUTOBIOGRAPHY. London: Longman's, Green, Reader, and Dyer, 1873. 1st ed, 1st issue (without errata). Green cl. vi, 313 & (1)pp & 2 ads. VG. *BLUE MOUNTAIN.* $250

Mill, John Stuart. CONSIDERATIONS ON REPRESENTATIVE GOVERNMENT. NY: Harper & Bros. 1862. 1st Amer ed. 366pp. + 6 pp ads. Orig blue cl, spine faded. *KARMIOLE.* $85

Mill, John Stuart. THE SUBJECTION OF WOMEN. NY: Appleton, 1870. 2nd US ed. VG. *SECOND LIFE.* $125

Millais, J.G. NEWFOUNDLAND AND ITS UNTRODDEN WAYS. London: Longmans, Green and Co, 1907. 1st ed. 6 photogravure plts. Cvrs worn, bumped; gilt faded; internal soiling. *PARMER.* $250

Millar, Kenneth. BLUE CITY. NY: Knopf, 1947. 1st ed. VG in sl darkened dj w/minor wear at spine ends and corners, couple of small scrapes along spine and few nicks. *MORDIDA.* $200

Millar, Kenneth. BLUE CITY. NY: Knopf, 1947. Orig red cl. Former owner's ink stamp, but VG in dj (couple of small chips and tears, modest soiling). 1st ed. *CHAPEL HILL.* $275

Millar, Margaret. EXPERIMENT IN SPRINGTIME. NY: Random House, 1947. 1st ed. Fine; lt wear dj spine ends. *ELSE FINE.* $45

Millar, Margaret. HOW LIKE AN ANGEL. NY: Random House, 1962. 1st ed. Fine in dj w/closed tears, wear). *MORDIDA.* $27.50

Millar, Margaret. ROSE'S LAST SUMMER. Random, (1952). 1st ed. VG+ in VG dj with edgewear, rubs. *BEBBAH.* $35

Millar, Margaret. THE BIRDS AND BEASTS WERE THERE. NY: Random House, 1967. 1st ed. Nice association inscription. VG. *SMITH.* $50

Millar, Margaret. THE CANNIBAL HEART. Random, (1949). 1st ed. VG in dj with chipping at spine ends, wear, else VG. *BEBBAH.* $20

Millar, Margaret. THE IRON GATES. NY: Random House, 1945. 1st ed. NF in VG dj. *ARCHER.* $35

Millar, Margaret. THE IRON GATES. NY: Random House, 1948. 1st ed. VF; lt rubbing extrems of unfaded red dj. *ELSE FINE.* $65

Millard, David. A JOURNAL OF TRAVELS IN EGYPT, ARABIA...DURING 1841-2. NY: Ptd for H. Ludwig, 1847. 3rd ed. 348pp. Full lea, rubbed, edges frayed, spine chipped, front cover detached, sl foxed and spotted, o/w Good. *WORLDWIDE.* $65

Millard, Olive. UNDER MY THUMB. London: C. Johnson, (1952). 1st ed. VG+ in VG dj. *AARD.* $30

Millay, Edna St. Vincent. MINE THE HARVEST. NY: Harper & Bros, (1954). Top edge sunned, else Fine in price-clipped, VG dj. 1st ed. *CHAPEL HILL.* $40

Millay, Edna St. Vincent. THE BUCK IN THE SNOW AND OTHER POEMS. NY, 1928. Ltd ed, 292/515 only signed. Top spine very small chip. Fine in glassine dj in Fine box. *POLYANTHOS.* $150

Millay, Edna St. Vincent. THE PRINCESS MARRIES THE PAGE. Harper, 1932. 1st ed. 51pp. Illus by J. Paget-Fredericks. VG+ in VG+ dj. *BEBBAH.* $35

Millay, Edna St. Vincent. THE PRINCESS MARRIES THE PAGE. NY: Harper, 1937. 1st ed. Bound in pub's full limp calf binding. Little rubbed, else VG. *SECOND LIFE.* $65

Miller, Alfred Jacob. THE WEST OF ALFRED JACOB MILLER (1837). Univ of OK Press, (1951). 1st ed. Fine. *AUTHORS OF THE WEST.* $60

Miller, Amy. SHAKER HERBS. NY: Clarkson, 1976. Dj worn, else VG. *AMERICAN BOTANIST.* $40

Miller, Annie Louise. ACROSS THREE OCEANS: A WOMAN'S TOUR OF THE WORLD. Lincoln: State Journal, n.d. (1910). 1st ed. 192pp. Map. Red cl, dec in gilt. Worn on extrems. Damp mk, not affecting internal condition at all, else VG. *CONNOLLY & WADE.* $35

Miller, Arthur and Inge Morath. IN THE COUNTRY. NY: Viking, (1977). 1st ed. Signed by Miller. VG in dj. *LOPEZ.* $65

Miller, Arthur. AFTER THE FALL. Cl, glassine dj, slipcase. NY: Viking, (1964). 1st ed. Ltd to 500 signed. VF. *JAFFE.* $150

Miller, Arthur. AFTER THE FALL. NY, (1964). 1st ed. Fine in dj. *McCLINTOCK.* $25

Miller, Arthur. DEATH OF A SALESMAN. Cl, cl slipcase. NY: Viking, (1981). Special illus ltd ed. Ltd to 500 signed. Fine. *JAFFE.* $125

Miller, Arthur. DEATH OF A SALESMAN. NY: Viking, 1949. 1st ed. Fine in dj (touch of wear to spinal extremities, very small tear). *CAPTAIN'S BOOKSHELF.* $250

Miller, Arthur. THE MURAL PAINTING OF TEOTIHUACAN. Washington: Dumbarton Oaks, 1973. 1st ed. Good in dj. *SILVER.* $35

Miller, Arthur. TIMEBENDS. Franklin Center: Franklin Library, 1987. 1st ed. One of an unspecified number signed. Fine in full lea. *BETWEEN COVERS.* $65

Miller, Byron S. SAIL, STEAM AND SPLENDOUR. Times Books (1977), 1st ed, dj. *HEINOLDT.* $30

Miller, Clive. THIS PASSING NIGHT. London: Secker and Warburg, 1963. 1st UK ed. Fine in Fine dj. *BEASLEY.* $25

Miller, Clive. THIS PASSING NIGHT. NY: H&R, (1962). 1st ed. Inscribed. VG in dj. *LOPEZ.* $25

Miller, David E. HOLE IN THE ROCK. AN EPIC IN THE COLONIZATION OF THE GREAT AMERICAN WEST. Salt Lake City: Univ of UT, 1966. Fine in VG dj. *CONNOLLY & WADE.* $45

Miller, David Humphreys. CUSTER'S FALL, THE INDIAN SIDE OF THE STORY. NY, (1957). 1st ed. VG in dj. *PRATT.* $65

Miller, Don and Stan Cohen. MILITARY & TRADING POSTS OF MONTANA. Missoula, MT, (1971). 1st ed. Wraps. Fine. *PRATT.* $20

Miller, Francis T. (ed). THE PHOTOGRAPHIC HISTORY OF THE CIVIL WAR. 10 vols. NY, 1911. 1st ed. Illus, maps, pict cloth. One vol has small tear at top of spine and another a little chipping at bottom of spine o/w at least VG. Most vols VG+. *PRATT.* $385

Miller, Francis T. (ed). THE PHOTOGRAPHIC HISTORY OF THE CIVIL WAR. In Ten Vols....NY: The Review of Reviews Co. 1911-12. 10 vols. Fine set. *KARMIOLE.* $375

Miller, Francis T. PORTRAIT LIFE OF LINCOLN. Springfield, MA: The Patriot Publishing Company, 1910. 1st ed. Sl soiling. *HUDSON.* $45

Miller, Francis T. THE WORLD IN THE AIR. 2 vols. NY: Putnam's, 1930. 1st ed. Backstrips dull, Good. *ARTIS.* $75

Miller, Francis T. THE WORLD IN THE AIR....NY: Putnam, 1930. 1st ed. 2 vols. Orig cl, bkpl removed, emb lib stamp, white numbers on spine. *GINSBERG.* $200

Miller, Francis W. CINCINNATI'S BEGINNINGS...CHIEFLY FROM HITHERTO UNPUBLISHED DOCUMENTS. Cincinnati: Thomson, 1880. 1st ed. (9),235,(4)pp. Orig gold stamped cl, paper label on spine, bkpl removed. Howes M604. *GINSBERG.* $150

Miller, Genevieve. THE ADOPTION OF INOCULATION FOR SMALLPOX IN ENGLAND AND FRANCE. Phila, 1957. 1st ed. *FYE.* $50

Miller, Henry and Bezalel Schatz. INTO THE NIGHT LIFE. (Berkeley, California: Henry Miller and Bezalel Schatz, [1947]). 37 serigraphed leaves. One of 800 (but most destroyed). Signed by Miller and Schatz. Orig serigraphed cl. Slipcase. Serigraphed throughout. Mint. *PIRAGES.* $1200

Miller, Henry. BLACK SPRING. NY: Grove, 1963. 1st ed. VF; minor rub to dj. *ELSE FINE.* $20

Miller, Henry. BLACK SPRING. NY: Grove Press, (1963). 1st Amer ed. VG in rubbed dj. *WREDEN.* $45

Miller, Henry. BLACK SPRING. Paris: The Obelisk Press, (1936). 1st ed. Dec wraps. VG in buckram slipcase. *JUVELIS.* $750

Miller, Henry. BOOK OF FRIENDS. Santa Barbara: Capra Press, 1976. 1st ed. NF. *SMITH.* $20

Miller, Henry. BOOKS IN MY LIFE. New Directions, 1952. 1st issue, w/photos tipped in, list of illus, notice of further vols (never pub). (2nd issue lacks the photos & had title page excised w/another of different stock tipped-in; (therefore lacks list of illus, mention of further vols). Pencil underlining on 2 or 3pp. Lt foxing ep. Dj edges, spine browned, edge tears, chips, price clipped. Signed. About VG in Good dj. *AKA.* $150

Miller, Henry. FIRST IMPRESSION OF GREECE. Santa Barbara: Capra Press, 1973. 1st ed. One of 250 numbered. Picture of Miller tipped in at rear. Signed. As New. *WREDEN.* $75

Miller, Henry. GREECE. Drawings by Anne Poor. NY: A Studio Book. The Viking Press. (1964). 1st ed. Pres copy, inscribed. Spine lightly faded. Dj. *KARMIOLE.* $125

Miller, Henry. GREECE. NY, 1964. Dj. 1st ed. *O'NEILL.* $25

Miller, Henry. GREECE. NY: Viking, (1964). 1st ed. Inscribed. Fine in VG dj. *JUVELIS.* $100

Miller, Henry. MONEY AND HOW IT GETS THAT WAY. Paris: Booster Broadside No. 1, 1938. 1st ed. Pub. in Sept. 1938. Printed wrappers. Very NF. *SMITH.* $350

Miller, Henry. MY BIKE & OTHER FRIENDS. Santa Barbara: Capra, (1978). #8 of 250 signed. Fine in Fine dj. *UNGER.* $90

Miller, Henry. NOTES ON AARON'S ROD. Santa Barbara: Black Sparrow, (1980). 1st ed. One of 276 signed. Illus boards. Fine in acetate dj as issued. *UNGER.* $90

Miller, Henry. ORDER AND CHAOS CHEZ HANS REICHEL. Tucson: Loroyn Press, (1966). 1/1399 from a total ed of 1524 w/letter from pub laid in. Dec boards, ptd dj, pub's box. NF. *JUVELIS.* $100

Miller, Henry. PLEXUS. THE ROSY CRUCIFIXION. BOOK TWO. NY, 1965. Grove Press. Complete Paris ed. 1st ed. Signed. Printed wraps. Rear wrap little soiled. Fine. *POLYANTHOS.* $45

Miller, Henry. SEXUS. Paris: Obelisk, 1949. 1st ed. 2 vols. 1/3000. Green cl w/o djs, as issued. VG+. *LAME DUCK.* $125

Miller, Henry. THE AMAZING AND INVARIABLE BEAUFORD DELANEY. NY: Alicat Bookshop, (1945). Ltd ed, 750. This copy specially signed. Pict wraps. Spine rubbed, corner crease rear wrapper. NF. *POLYANTHOS.* $75

Miller, Henry. THE HENRY MILLER READER. Norfolk: New Directions, 1959. 1st ed. Fine; small stain on rear, light edgewear to dj. *ELSE FINE.* $20

Miller, Henry. THE PAINTINGS OF HENRY MILLER....Santa Barbara: Capra (1973). 1st ed. Navy blue cl. Fine in sl soiled slipcase. *AKA.* $100

Miller, Henry. THE WORLD OF LAWRENCE. Santa Barbara: Capra Press, 1980. 1st ed. One of 250 numbered, specially bound, signed. As New, w/o dj as issued. *SMITH.* $125

Miller, Henry. TROPIC OF CANCER. Paris: Obelisk Press, 1934. 1st ed. Wraps. Inscribed to Leviticus Lyon in 1934, in Paris. Front wrap chipped and reattached, spine and rear wrap missing. Very Scarce w/such an early inscription. In handsome custom box. *BEASLEY.* $1200

Miller, Henry. TROPIC OF CAPRICORN. (New York: Grove Press, [1961]). 1st Amer ed. Extremely Fine in dj. *PIRAGES.* $75

Miller, Henry. TWO LETTERS FROM GREECE. GEORGE SEFERIS TO HENRY MILLER. Athens, 1990. 1/750. *O'NEILL.* $35

Miller, Heyman. CENTRAL AUTONOMIC REGULATIONS IN HEALTH AND DISEASE WITH SPECIAL REFERENCE TO THE HYPOTHALAMUS. NY, 1942. 1st ed. *FYE.* $50

Miller, Isabelle. SILVER BY NEW YORK MAKERS: LATE 17TH CENTURY TO 1900. NY: MMA, 1938. One of 100. VG+. Wraps. *BACKROOM.* $30

Miller, James Knox Polk. Ed by Andrew F. Rolle. THE ROAD TO VIRGINIA CITY, THE DIARY OF JAMES KNOX POLK MILLER. Norman, (1960). 1st ed. Dj wear o/w VG+. *PRATT.* $30

Miller, James. THE PRACTICE OF SURGERY. Phila, 1846. 1st Amer ed. Full leather, 496pp. VF. *FYE.* $150

Miller, James. THE PRINCIPLES OF SURGERY. Edinburgh, 1844. 1st ed. 716pp. Inner hinges cracked, name torn from title page, not affecting prtg. Ex-lib. *FYE.* $175

Miller, Joaquin. FIRST FAM'LIES IN THE SIERRAS. London: George Routledge & Sons. 1875. 1st ed. (10),152,(2)pp. Orig pict color boards, extrems worn. Inscrip dated Feb. 27, 1905 signed by Miller. BAL 13758. True 1st ed, predating the Amer. One of Miller's scarcest books. *KARMIOLE.* $450

Miller, Joaquin. IN CLASSIC SHADES AND OTHER POEMS. Chicago: Belford-Clarke, 1890. 1st ed. Grn dec cover, spine. Blindstamp and gilt. Fine. *CONNOLLY & WADE.* $50

Miller, Joaquin. LIFE AMONGST THE MODOCS: UNWRITTEN HISTORY. London: Richard Bentley & Son, 1873. 1st ed, unlisted binding. Orig cocoa brown cl partially faded. Little corner wear. Rebacked w/gilt title of orig backstrip. Contents VG. Howes M608. BAL 13755. Cvrs not bevelled. Spine lettered: LIFE / AMONGST / THE MODOCS / MILLER /. Uncoated eps. *DIAMOND.* $125

Miller, Joaquin. SHADOWS OF SHASTA. Chicago: Jansen, McClurg, 1881. 184pp,16pp ads. 1st ed. VG. *OREGON.* $95

Miller, Joaquin. SONGS OF THE SUN-LANDS. Boston: Roberts Bros, 1873. 1st Amer ed. 212,4pp ads. Teg, brown cl w/gilt dec. Wear on all edges of spine. Good to VG. *CONNOLLY & WADE.* $35

Miller, Joaquin. SONGS OF THE SUNLANDS. Boston: Roberts Bros, 1875. Signed presentation, w/add'l autograph letter, signed, tipped on ffep. VG. *CULLEN.* $140

Miller, Joaquin. THE BUILDING OF THE CITY BEAUTIFUL. Trenton: Albert Brandt, 1905. 1st ed. Frontis, 243,(5)pp. Book adv. Teg, deckle edges. Red ribbed cl. Gilt dec spine & covers. NF. *CONNOLLY & WADE.* $55

Miller, John C. ORIGINS OF THE AMERICAN REVOLUTION. Boston, 1943, 1st ed. Illus Eric Simon. Dj worn and chipped. *HEINOLDT.* $35

Miller, Joseph. ARIZONA: THE LAST FRONTIER. Hastings House, (1956). 1st ed. VG in VG dj. *OREGON.* $30

Miller, Joseph. MONUMENT VALLEY AND THE NAVAJO COUNTRY: ARIZONA-UTAH. NY: Hastings, 1951. 1st ed. Cloth. NF in NF dj. *CONNOLLY & WADE.* $30

Miller, Leo. IN THE WILDS OF SOUTH AMERICA. NY, 1918. NF. *POLYANTHOS.* $60

Miller, Max. FOG AND MEN ON THE BERING SEA. NY: E.P. Dutton, 1936. 1st ed. Spine darkened; a portion of dj affixed to rear pastedown. *PARMER.* $20

Miller, Nina Hull. SHUTTER'S WEST. Denver: Sage, 1962. 1st ed. VG in VG dj. *CONNOLLY & WADE.* $20

Miller, Olive Beaupre. ENGINES AND BRASS BANDS. Book House & Doubleday, Doran, 1933. Stated 1st ed. 376pp. Corner bumps, sl wear, soil but VG. *BEBBAH.* $25

Miller, Olive Beaupre. LITTLE PICTURES OF JAPAN. Book House, 1952 ptg. 4to. 191pp. Illus by Katharine Sturges. Faint stain to circular cvr pict pastedown but VG+. *BEBBAH.* $30

Miller, Olive Beaupre. MY BOOK HOUSE. Chicago, 1948. 13 volumes, all VG to NF. All blue cloth w/color pict pastedown. Illus. 13th volume is Parent's Guidebook. Volumes. *BEBBAH.* $125

Miller, Polly and Leon Gordon Miller. LOST HERITAGE OF ALASKA. Cleveland: World Pub. Co, (1967). 1st prtg. Inscribed by both authors. VG in VG- dj. *BLUE DRAGON.* $35

Miller, Richard Briscoe. SLAVERY AND CATHOLICISM. Durham, NC, ca 1957. 1st ed. Orig cl. Shaken, else VG w/prospectus. *McGOWAN.* $75

Miller, Richard. BOHEMIA. THE PROTOCULTURE THEN AND NOW. Chicago: Nelson-Hall, 1977. 1st ed. Fine in very lightly used dj (wear at rear flap fold). *BEASLEY.* $25

Miller, Ronald Dean. SHADY LADIES OF THE WEST. Westernlore, 1964. 1st ed. Fine in Fine dj. *OREGON.* $35

Miller, W. Henry. PIONEERING NORTH TEXAS. San Antonio: The Naylor Co, 1953. 1st ed. Fine. *GIBBS.* $75

Miller, Wade. BRANDED WOMEN. NY: Fawcett Pubs, 1952. 1st ed. Pb orig. Gold Medal #257. Rubbing, o/w Fine in wrappers. *MORDIDA.* $22.50

Miller, Wade. MAD BAXTER. NY: Fawcett Pubs, 1955. 1st ed. Pb orig. Gold Medal #469. Short scrape on front cover and edges sl rubbed, o/w Fine in wrappers. *MORDIDA.* $22.50

Miller, Wade. THE BIG GUY. NY: Fawcett Pubs, 1953. 1st ed. Pb orig. Gold Medal #279. Back cover soiled, o/w VG in wrappers. *MORDIDA.* $20

Miller, Wade. UNEASY STREET. NY: Farrar Straus, 1948. 1st ed. VG in dj w/chipping at top of spine and at corners and a sl faded spine. *MORDIDA.* $25

Miller, Walter. A CANTICLE FOR LEIBOWITZ. Phila: Lippincott, (1960). 1st ed. Fine in bright, fresh dj (chip upper edge rear panel o/w NF). Inscribed. *LOPEZ.* $2500

Miller, Warren. THE COOL WORLD. Boston: Little-Brown, 1959. 1st ed. Fine in dj. *ELSE FINE.* $50

Millett, Kate. SITA. NY: Farrar Straus Giroux, 1977. 1st ed. Fine. *SMITH.* $25

Millikan, R.A. THE AUTOBIOGRAPHY OF ROBERT A. MILLIKAN. London: McDonald, 1951. Good in worn dj. *KNOLLWOOD.* $45

Millikan, R.A. THE ELECTRON. Univ of Chicago Press, 1918 (1917). VG. *KNOLLWOOD.* $75

Millman, Lawrence. OUR LIKE WILL NOT BE THERE AGAIN. Boston: Little Brown, (1977). 1st ed. Signed. Fine in dj. *LOPEZ.* $25

Mills, Anson. MY STORY. Washington, DC: Privately ptd, 1918. 1st ed. Orig limp cloth. VG. Presentation copy. *McGOWAN.* $150

Mills, Charles K. HARVEST OF BITTER REGRETS. Glendale, 1985. 1st ed. 432pp. Fine. *PRATT.* $30

Mills, Clarence A. CLIMATE MAKES THE MAN. NY: Harper, (1942). 1st ed. Fine- in VG- dj. *AARD.* $25

Mills, E.A. BIRD MEMORIES OF THE ROCKIES. Boston & NY, 1931. 1st ed. VG+. *MIKESH.* $30

Mills, Enos A. THE SPELL OF THE ROCKIES. London: Constable, 1912. 1st Brit ed. Pict eps, frontis, 10 plts photos. Pict cl, gilt. Fine in Very rare dj. *CONNOLLY & WADE.* $95

Mills, Samuel J. REPORT OF A MISSIONARY TOUR THROUGH THAT PART OF THE UNITED STATES WHICH LIES WEST OF THE ALLEGANY MOUNTAINS. Andover: Flagg & Gould, 1815. 64pp, modern brown cloth, gilt spine title. Paper quite darkened, else VG. Howes M629. *BOHLING.* $450

Mills, Stephen O. and James W. Phillips. SOURDOUGH SKY. Seattle: Superior, 1969. 1st ed. Fine in VG dj. Inscribed. *PARMER.* $45

Millspaugh, Charles F. AMERICAN MEDICINAL PLANTS; AN ILLUSTRATED AND DESCRIPTIVE GUIDE....2 vols. NY & Phila, 1887. 1st ed. 180 colored plts. Leather very worn and scuffed;

hinges of Vol I split, front cvr, title pg Vol II detached; plts, text very clean. *SUTTON.* $1,450

Milne, A.A. BY WAY OF INTRODUCTION. Cl-backed batik boards. NY: Dutton, (1929). 1st ed. Ltd to 166. VF in lightly soiled slipcase. *JAFFE.* $350

Milne, A.A. FOUR DAYS' WONDER. NY, (1933). 1st ed. Vertical crease 2 ffeps, spine little sunned. NF. *POLYANTHOS.* $30

Milne, A.A. NOW WE ARE SIX. Illus E.H. Shepard. London: Methuen & Co., (1927). 1st trade ed. Gold-stamped cloth in dj w/tiny chipping, sl offset on half-title from laid-in catalogue descrip. Bkpl. *DAWSON'S.* $250

Milne, A.A. POOH'S POT OF HONEY. Dutton, (1968). Stated 1st ed. Four miniature books in djs each 47pp. Boxed. Illus Ernest Shepard. Fine in Fine djs, slipcase NF. *BEBBAH.* $35

Milne, A.A. TEDDY BEAR AND OTHER SONGS FROM "WHEN WE WERE VERY YOUNG" BY MILNE. NY, 1926. Music by H. Fraser-Simson. Illus by E.H. Shepard. VG-NF. *POLYANTHOS.* $45

Milne, A.A. THE HOUSE AT POOH CORNER. E. H. Shepard (decs). Pict cl. London: Methuen, (1928). 1st ed. Fine, sl rubbed dj. *JAFFE.* $500

Milne, A.A. THE HOUSE AT POOH CORNER. London, 1928. 1st ed. Ernest H. Shepard (decs). Spine and two edges rear cover little sunned. Fine in dj (spine sunned, very small piece missing top, lower spine sl chipped, few tiny edge chips w/very small edge tear). *POLYANTHOS.* $300

Milne, A.A. THE KING'S BREAKFAST. London: Methuen (1925). Orig cl backed boards and sl soiled paper label, uncut and partially unopened. One of 100 signed. Nice. *SECOND LIFE.* $650

Milne, A.A. THE SECRET. NY: Fountain, London: Methuen, 1929. 1st ed. Cl and paper label. One of 742 signed. Nice. *SECOND LIFE.* $95

Milne, A.A. TOAD OF TOAD HALL. London: Methuen, (1929). 1st ed. Slight offsetting from dj flaps, else Fine in Very NF dj, very sl soiled, with a few negligible short tears. *BETWEEN COVERS.* $350

Milne, A.A. WHEN WE WERE VERY YOUNG. Dutton, 1924. 1st Amer ed. 12mo. 100pp. Illus by Ernest H. Shephard. Slight edgewear. VG+. Gilt dec, lettering on cvr. *BEBBAH.* $90

Milne, A.A. WINNIE THE POOH. London: Methuen & Co., (1926). 1st trade ed. Illus E.H. Shepard. Gold-stamped cl. Bkpl. *DAWSON'S.* $150

Milne, A.A. WINNIE-THE-POOH. Ernest H. Shepard (decs). Gilt-dec grn cl. London: Methuen, (1926). 1st trade ed. Front flap of dj clipped, o/w Fine. *JAFFE.* $1250

Milne, E.A. SIR JAMES JEANS, A BIOGRAPHY. Cambridge Univ Press, 1952. 2 plts. VG. *KNOLLWOOD.* $40

Milner, Alfred. ENGLAND IN EGYPT. London: Arnold, 1894. New ed. Fldg map. Sl rubbed, extremities frayed, fore-edge of leaves sl spotted, o/w VG. *WORLDWIDE.* $45

Milner, Duncan C. LINCOLN AND LIQUOR. 2nd ed, w/supplement. Chicago: W.P. Blessing Co., n.d. (1926). Port. *SCHOYER'S.* $30

Milner, Henry Ernest. THE ART AND PLANNING OF LANDSCAPE GARDENING....London: By the author, 1890. 1st ed. 116pp. Orig grn cl (wear on spine). Occasional stains. 21 plts. *SECOND LIFE.* $150

Milosz, Czeslaw. SELECTED POEMS. Helsinki: Eurographica, 1986. 1st of this ed. Ltd to 350 signed. Ptd wraps. Mint. *JAFFE.* $150

Milosz, Czeslaw. THE CAPTIVE MIND. NY: LEC, (1983). One of 1500 illus, signed by Janusz Kapusta and Milosz. Fine in sl nicked slipcase. *CAPTAIN'S BOOKSHELF.* $125

Milton, John. POEMS IN ENGLISH. Illus William Blake. London: Nonesuch Press, 1926. 1/1450. 2 vols. Some offsetting to eps both vols, else Fine set. *CAPTAIN'S BOOKSHELF.* $200

Milton, John. THE MASQUE OF COMUS. (LEC, 1954). One of 1500. 6 full-leaf color plts by Edmund Dulac. VF (slipcase a little worn). This is the final work by Dulac, who died before he could sign the colophon. As a result this is one of the very few unsigned LEC books. *PIRAGES.* $225

Milton, John. THE MASQUE OF COMUS. Prefaces by Mark Van Doren and Hubert Fox. Cambridge U, England, n/d. 71pp; 6 plts in color by Edmund Dulac. Marbled boards, slipcase. *HEINOLDT.* $35

Milton, John. THE MASQUE OF COMUS. THE POEMS. Illus Edmund Dulac. Parchment backed marbled boards, tissue dj, slipcase. Cambridge: LEC, 1954. One of 1500 ptd at the Univ Press. Fine. *JAFFE.* $150

Milton, John. THE MASQUE OF COMUS....Cambridge: LEC, 1954. One of 1500 illus by Edmund Dulac. Parchment-backed marbled boards. Fine in slipcase. *CAPTAIN'S BOOKSHELF.* $150

Milton, Viscount; Cheadle, W. B. THE NORTH-WEST PASSAGE BY LAND...AN EXPEDITION FROM THE ATLANTIC TO THE PACIFIC...London: Cassell, Petter, and Galpin, ca 1865. Edges worn, brds rubbed, hinges cracked but holding, ownr's inscrip. *PARMER.* $75

Miltoun, Francis. ITALIAN HIGHWAYS AND BYWAYS FROM A MOTOR CAR. London: Hodder & Stoughton, 1909. Some owner markings. 2 fldg maps. *SCHOYER'S.* $45

Mindlin, Henrique E. MODERN ARCHITECTURE IN BRAZIL. NY: Reinhold Pub Corp, (1956). 1st Eng lang ed. Dj. *KARMIOLE.* $45

Miner, H.S. ORCHIDS. Boston, 1885. 24 chromolithos. Orig wrappers (backstrip missing, sheets loose, pp very clean, teg). Orig gilt, pict cl fldg case (some wear at corners, some cracking and splitting at edges of spine & joints). *SUTTON.* $675

Mines, Samuel (comp). THE BEST STARTLING STORIES. NY: Henry Holt, (1953). 1st ed. Dj. Fine. *WEBER.* $25

Mingus, Charles. BENEATH THE UNDERDOG. Knopf, 1971. 1st ed. Fine in dj. *STAHR.* $45

Mingus, Charles. BENEATH THE UNDERDOG. NY: Knopf, 1971. 1st ed. VG in VG dj. *AKA.* $30

MINNESOTA ARROWHEAD COUNTRY. Chicago, 1941. American Guide Series. WPA guides. 1st ed, no dj. *SCHOYER'S.* $35

MINNESOTA. A STATE GUIDE. NY, 1938. 1st edn. Fldg maps. Cvrs sl stained, o/w VG. *DIAMOND.* $35

MINNESOTA. NY, 1938. American Guide Series. WPA guide. 1st ptg, w/fldg map and dj. *SCHOYER'S.* $70

Minnigh, L.W. GETTYSBURG, WHAT THEY DID HERE...(n.p.), 1924. 168pp & ads. Wear to pict cover o/w VG. *PRATT.* $22.50

Mintz, Lannon. THE TRAIL BIBLIOGRAPHY OF THE TRAVELLERS ON THE OVERLAND TRAIL TO CALIFORNIA....1841-1864. Albuquerque: Univ of NM Press, (1987). 1st ed. Fine in Fine dj. *BOOK MARKET.* $30

MIRIAM COFFIN, OR, THE WHALE-FISHERMEN: A TALE. (By Joseph C. Hart.) NY: Carvill, (etc.) 1834. 1st ed of 1st Amer whaling novel. 2 vols. Orig cl, bindings waterstained and once bubbled (expertly restored), spine label on vol 2 a replacement, some foxing and dampstaining throughout, but still a Good set. *LEFKOWICZ.* $800

Mirsky, Jeannette. THE WESTWARD CROSSINGS, BALBOA, MACKENZIE, LEWIS & CLARK. Knopf, 1946. 1st ed. Fine in VG dj. *OREGON.* $30

MISCELLANEOUS POEMS, By a Lady of Charleston, S.C. (By Eliza Crawley Murden.) NY: The Author, 1827. 2nd ed. 179pp. Contemp cl-backed boards. Spine worn, foxing, eps lacking, still Good to VG of a fragile item. *CHAPEL HILL.* $150

Miser, Hugh D. THE SAN JUAN CANYON, SOUTHEASTERN UTAH. GEOGRAPHIC AND HYDROGRAPHIC RECON-

NAISSANCE. USGS Water-Supply Paper 538. 1924. v,80pp. Photo plts, fldg maps or charts. VG. *FIVE QUAIL.* $65

Mishima, Yukio. ACTS OF WORSHIP. NY: Kodansha, 1989. Uncorrected proof. NF in wraps, nick along fore-edge of rear cvr. *LOPEZ.* $25

Mishima, Yukio. AFTER THE BANQUET. NY: Knopf (1963). 1st Amer ed. Fine in dj. *DORN.* $50

Mishima, Yukio. AFTER THE BANQUET. NY: Knopf, 1963. 1st Amer ed. Fine in dj. *JUVELIS.* $75

Mishima, Yukio. CONFESSIONS OF A MASK. (Norfolk, CT:) New Directions, 1958. 1st Amer ed. NF in dj. *JUVELIS.* $150

Mishima, Yukio. CONFESSIONS OF A MASK. NY: New Directions (1958). 1st Amer ed. Fine in dj. *DORN.* $45

Mishima, Yukio. DEATH IN MIDSUMMER AND OTHER STORIES. (Norfolk, CT:) New Directions, (1966). 1st Amer ed. Fine in dj. *JUVELIS.* $75

Mishima, Yukio. FIVE MODERN NO PLAYS. NY: Knopf, 1957. 1st Amer ed. Fine in dj. *JUVELIS.* $75

Mishima, Yukio. FORBIDDEN COLORS. NY: Knopf, 1968. 1st ed. Fine in dj. *JUVELIS.* $75

Mishima, Yukio. FORBIDDEN COLORS. NY: Knopf, 1968. 1st ed. Fine in just About Fine dj. *BEASLEY.* $40

Mishima, Yukio. ORDEAL BY ROSES. (NY:) Aperture, (1985). 1st ed. Fine in dj. *JUVELIS.* $75

Mishima, Yukio. RUNAWAY HORSES. (NY: Knopf, 1973.) 1st Amer ed. Fine in dj. *JUVELIS.* $75

Mishima, Yukio. RUNAWAY HORSES. Knopf, 1973. 1st Amer ed. Fine to VF in dj (sm rubbed spot). *STAHR.* $25

Mishima, Yukio. SPRING SNOW. (NY: Knopf, 1972.) 1st ed. Fine in dj. *JUVELIS.* $75

Mishima, Yukio. SPRING SNOW. Knopf, 1972. 1st Amer ed. Fine in dj. *STAHR.* $25

Mishima, Yukio. THE "SEA OF FERTILITY" TETROLOGY. NY: Knopf (1972-74). 1st eds. 4 vols. VG+ to Fine in similar djs. *DORN.* $200

Mishima, Yukio. THE DECAY OF THE ANGEL. (NY: Knopf, 1974.) 1st Amer ed. Fine in dj. *JUVELIS.* $75

Mishima, Yukio. THE SAILOR WHO FELL FROM GRACE WITH THE SEA. NY: Knopf (1965). 1st Amer ed. Fine in NF dj. *DORN.* $85

Mishima, Yukio. THE SAILOR WHO FELL FROM GRACE WITH THE SEA. NY: Knopf, 1965. 1st Amer ed. Fine in dj. *JUVELIS.* $125

Mishima, Yukio. THE SAILOR WHO FELL FROM GRACE WITH THE SEA. NY: Knopf, 1965. 1st ed. Fine in dj. *LOPEZ.* $125

Mishima, Yukio. THE SOUND OF WAVES. NY: Knopf, 1956. 1st ed. Inscribed. Lt shelfwear to bk, edgewear to dj. VG in dj. *LOPEZ.* $950

Mishima, Yukio. THE SOUND OF WAVES: A LOVE STORY. NY: Knopf, 1956. 1st Amer ed. Fine in dj. *JUVELIS.* $150

Mishima, Yukio. THE TEMPLE OF DAWN. NY: Knopf, 1973. 1st Amer ed. Fine in dj. *JUVELIS.* $75

Mishima, Yukio. THE TEMPLE OF THE GOLDEN PAVILION. NY: Knopf, 1959. 1st Amer ed. Fine in dj. *JUVELIS.* $75

Mishima, Yukio. THE WAY OF THE SAMURAI. NY: Basic Books, Inc, 1977. 1st Amer ed. Fine in dj. *JUVELIS.* $75

Mishima, Yukio. THIRST FOR LOVE. NY: Knopf (1969). 1st ed. Fine in Fine price-clipped dj. *DORN.* $45

Mishima, Yukio. THIRST FOR LOVE. NY: Knopf, 1969. 1st ed. Fine in NF dj. *BEASLEY.* $35

Mishima, Yukio. THIRST FOR LOVE. NY: Knopf, 1969. 1st Amer ed. Fine in dj. *JUVELIS*. $75

MISSION FURNITURE, HOW TO MAKE IT. Part I. (Part Two). Popular Mechanics Handbooks. Chicago: Popular Mechanics Co. (1909 and 1910). 2 vols. Each vol w/6 pgs ads at back. Vol I in red cl stamped in black; vol II, blue cl, gilt. Cvrs sl soiled. Scarce. *KARMIOLE*. $75

MISSOURI. NY, (1941). American Guide Series. WPA guide. 1st ptg, lacks dj. *SCHOYER'S*. $40

Mitchell, B.W. TRAIL LIFE IN THE CANADIAN ROCKIES. NY: Macmillan, 1924. 1st ed. VG. *ARTIS*. $30

Mitchell, Betty L. EDMUND RUFFIN. Bloomington, IN, (1981). 1st ed. Fine in NF dj. *McGOWAN*. $30

Mitchell, Carleton. ISLANDS TO WINDWARD: CRUISING THE CARIBBEES. Toronto, NY, and London: D. Van Nostrand, (1948). Dj. VG. *WEBER*. $100

Mitchell, Charles A. THE EXPERT WITNESS...CIVIL ACTIONS & HISTORY. NY, 1923. 1st US ed. Spine faded, o/w VG. *DIAMOND*. $35

Mitchell, Edwin Valentine. MOROCCO BOUND. NY: Farrar & Rinehart, (1929). 1st ed. Fine. *WREDEN*. $20

Mitchell, Edwin Valentine. THE HORSE & BUGGY AGE IN NEW ENGLAND. NY: Coward McCann, 1937. 1st prtg. VG. *OCTOBER FARM*. $30

Mitchell, Emerson Blackhorse & T.D. Allen. MIRACLE HILL. Norman: Univ of OK Press, (1967). 1st ed. Signed by both authors. Fine in NF, price-clipped dj. *LOPEZ*. $65

Mitchell, Gladys. ADDERS ON THE HEATH. London House, 1963. 1st Amer ed. VG+ in VG dj. *BEBBAH*. $25

Mitchell, Gladys. SPEEDY DEATH. NY: MacVeagh/Dial, 1929. 1st US ed of 1st bk. Fine in Good to VG dj w/internal mending and rejoining of sections. *BEASLEY*. $125

Mitchell, Gladys. UNCOFFIN'D CLAY. London: Michael Joseph, 1980. 1st ed. Fine in dj w/sm internal tape mend; short tear. *MORDIDA*. $40

Mitchell, J. Leslie. THE LOST TRUMPET. Bobbs-Merrill, 1932. 1st US ed. Fine in a dj (sm chip top of spine). *MADLE*. $85

Mitchell, J. Leslie. THREE GO BACK. Bobbs-Merrill, 1932. 1st US ed. VG. *MADLE*. $25

Mitchell, J.A. DROWSY. Stokes, 1917. 1st ed. VG. *MADLE*. $32

Mitchell, Joseph. THE BOTTOM OF THE HARBOR. Boston & Toronto: Little, Brown & Co., (1959). 1st ed. Fine in VG+ dj which is sl worn at edges. *BERNARD*. $75

Mitchell, Margaret J. THE FIRELESS COOK BOOK. NY, 1909. NF. *POLYANTHOS*. $45

Mitchell, Margaret. GONE WITH THE WIND. NY: LEC, l968. One of 1500. 2 vols. Illus, signed by George Groth. Fine in slipcase. *CAPTAIN'S BOOKSHELF*. $250

Mitchell, Margaret. GONE WITH THE WIND. NY: Macmillan, (1936). 1st ed (May, 1936) in 1st issue dj. VG in a price-clipped dj (minor edgewear, internally strengthened). *LOPEZ*. $2750

Mitchell, Margaret. MARGARET MITCHELL'S GONE WITH THE WIND LETTERS, 1936-1949. NY: Macmillan, (1976). Ed by Richard Harwell. Fine in two djs. 1st ed. *CHAPEL HILL*. $45

Mitchell, Maria. LIFE, LETTERS, AND JOURNALS. Phebe Mitchell Kendall (comp). Boston: Lee and Shepard, 1896. 1st ed. Wear top of spine, front hinge loose. Good. *SECOND LIFE*. $65

Mitchell, Mary. DIVIDED TOWN, A STUDY OF GEORGETOWN, D.C. DURING THE CIVIL WAR. Barre, MA, 1968. 1st ed. 193pp. VG+ in dj. *PRATT*. $25

Mitchell, Nahum. HISTORY OF THE EARLY SETTLEMENT OF BRIDGEWATER...INCLUDING AN EXTENSIVE FAMILY REGISTER. Boston, 1840. 1st ed. 402pp. Orig boards, cl spine, ptd paper label on spine. Howes M681. *GINSBERG*. $125

Mitchell, Peter. GREAT FLOWER PAINTERS. Woodstock, NY: Overlook Press, (1973). Dj. Fine. *WREDEN*. $55

Mitchell, S. Augustus. ILLINOIS IN 1837. Phila: Mitchell, 1837. 2nd issue, w/1838 on cover. Fldg frontis map. Light wear, staining; map w/some reinforcements on folds from reverse; light lib stamp, light foxing throughout. Howes M689. *BOHLING*. $350

Mitchell, S. Weir (ed). FIVE ESSAYS BY JOHN KEARSLEY MITCHELL, M.D. Phila, 1859. 1st ed. 371pp. Spine rubbed, w/hinges reinforced, one section starting. *FYE*. $200

Mitchell, S. Weir. CIRCUMSTANCE. NY, 1901. 1st ed. *FYE*. $35

Mitchell, S. Weir. CONSTANCE TRESCOT. NY: Century, 1905. 1st ed. 384pp. Blue cl over boards. Text sl yellowed, else VG. *BOOKMINE*. $40

Mitchell, S. Weir. DOCTOR AND PATIENT. Phila, 1889. 3rd ed. *FYE*. $75

Mitchell, S. Weir. DOCTOR AND PATIENT. Phila 1904. 4th ed. *FYE*. $50.

Mitchell, S. Weir. FAR IN THE FOREST: A STORY. Phila, 1889. 1st ed. *FYE*. $50

Mitchell, S. Weir. FAT AND BLOOD: AND HOW TO MAKE THEM. Phila, 1878. 2nd ed. *FYE*. $150

Mitchell, S. Weir. FRANCIS DRAKE, A TRAGEDY OF THE SEA. Boston, 1893. 1st ed. White boards soiled. *FYE*. $75

Mitchell, S. Weir. HUGH WYNNE, FREE QUAKER: SOMETIME BREVET LIEUTENANT COLONEL ON THE STAFF OF HIS EXCELLENCY GEORGE WASHINGTON. NY, 1897. 1st ed., 2nd prtg. 2 vols. Scarce. *FYE*. $75

Mitchell, S. Weir. LECTURES ON DISEASES OF THE NERVOUS SYSTEM, ESPECIALLY IN WOMEN. Phila, 1881. 1st ed. 238pp. Ex-lib. The publisher's ads have been removed from the back. Very scarce. *FYE*. $300

Mitchell, S. Weir. LITTLE STORIES. NY, 1903. 1st ed. *FYE*. $60

Mitchell, S. Weir. SOME RECENTLY DISCOVERED LETTERS OF WILLIAM HARVEY WITH OTHER MISCELLANEA WITH A BIBLIOGRAPHY OF HARVEY'S WORKS BY CHARLES PERRY FISHER. Phila, 1912. 1st ed. Wrappers. *FYE*. $100

Mitchell, S. Weir. THE AUTOBIOGRAPHY OF A QUACK AND THE CASE OF GEORGE DEDLOW. NY, 1900. 1st ed. *FYE*.$50

Mitchell, S. Weir. THE COLLECTED POEMS. NY, 1896. 1st ed. *FYE*. $100

Mitchell, S. Weir. THE COMFORT OF THE HILLS AND OTHER POEMS. NY, 1910. 1st ed. Scarce. *FYE*. $50

Mitchell, S. Weir. THE GUILLOTINE CLUB & OTHER STORIES. NY: Century, 1910. 1st ed. Brief inscription. NF, green & gilt Art Nouveau binding. *ELSE FINE*. $45

Mitchell, S. Weir. THE RED CITY. NY: Century, 1908. 1st ed. Covers little soiled, else VG. *SECOND LIFE*. $35

Mitchell, W.A. LINN COUNTY, KANSAS: A HISTORY. 1928. 1st ptg. Fine. *VARNER*. $50

Mitchell, W.O. THE VANISHING POINT. Macmillan of Canada, (1973). 1st Canadian ed. Signed. Fine, clean chipped dj. *AUTHORS OF THE WEST*. $25

Mitchell-Hedges, F.A. BATTLES WITH GIANT FISH. London: Duckworth, 1924. 2nd imp. Cover wear, else G+. *OLD LONDON*. $35

Mitchell-Hedges, F.A. BATTLES WITH MONSTERS OF THE SEA. London and NY: D. Appleton-Century Co., 1937. 1st ed. Cover wear, else VG. *OLD LONDON*. $35

Mitchiner, Philip and E.M. Cowell. MEDICAL ORGANISATION AND SURGICAL PRACTICE IN AIR RAIDS, London, 1939. 1st ed, reprinted. Photo illus. Scarce. *FYE.* $75

Mitford, Mary Russell. OUR VILLAGE...ILLUSTRATED. London: Sampson, Low.., 1879. xi,170pp. Engr frontis, pict title. Full grn morocco, gilt, inside gilt dentelles, marbled eps, aeg. VF. *WREDEN.* $235

Mitford, Nancy. DON'T TELL ALFRED. London: Hamilton, (1960). 1st ed. Fine. *SECOND LIFE.* $25

Mitford, Nancy. LOVE IN A COLD CLIMATE. NY: Random House, (1949). 1st US ed. Nice in price clipped dj. *SECOND LIFE.* $35

Mitford, Nancy. THE BLESSING. NY: Random House, (1951). 1st US ed. Fine. *SECOND LIFE.* $25

Mitscherlich, A. & F. Mielke. DOCTORS OF INFAMY: THE STORY OF THE NAZI MEDICAL CRIMES. NY; H. Schuman, 1949. 1st ed. Boards a trifle soiled, o/w Fine. *ARCHER.* $45

Mitton, G.E. BUCKINGHAMSHIRE AND BERKSHIRE. A&C Black, 1920. 1st ed. 20s Series. Slight wear, minor fading, some spotting, but VG. *OLD LONDON.* $45

Mitton, G.E. NORMANDY. A&C Black, 1905. 1st ed. 10s Series. VG-NF. *OLD LONDON.* $65

Mochi, U. and D. MacClintock. NATURAL HISTORY OF ZEBRAS. NY, 1976. NF in VG+ dj. *MIKESH.* $25

Mochi, Ugo & T. Donald Carter. HOOFED MAMMALS OF THE WORLD. NY: Scribner, 1953. 1st (A) ed. Corners bumped. VG. *OCTOBER FARM.* $195

Mockingbird, Jon. THE WOKOSANI ROAD. NY: Exposition Press, (1963). 1st ed. NF in dj. Presumably very scarce. *LOPEZ.* $85

MODERN GHOSTS. Harper, 1890. 1st ed. VG. *MADLE.* $50

MODERN ROSES IV. J. Horace McFarland Company and the American Rose Society (comp). Harrisburg, 1952. 31 plts. Cl, lt spotting of cvrs; pencil notes, bkpl. *SUTTON.* $30

MODERN TRAVELLER: GREECE. London: Ptd for James Duncan, 1826. (By Josiah Conder.) 2 vols. 3/4 lea, rubbed. Joints weak, vol 2. Frontis map, 7 plts, several w/dampstains. Bkpl. *SCHOYER'S.* $60

Moehring, Eugene P. and Arlene Deylin (eds). THE CIVIL WAR EXTRA. NY, 1975. 1st ed. 310pp. Dj w/light wear, small tear, o/w VG+. *PRATT.* $35

Moffit and Wayland. GEOLOGY OF THE NUTZOTIN MOUNTAINS, ALASKA AND GOLD DEPOSITS NEAR NABESNA. Washington, 1943. 4 color fold-out maps in rear pocket, 1 in text. Wraps worn at spine. *ARTIS.* $20

Mogelever, Jacob. DEATH TO TRAITORS, THE STORY OF GENERAL LAFAYETTE BAKER....GC, 1960. 1st ed. 429pp. Dj wear, o/w Fine. *PRATT.* $37.50

Mohr, C. PLANT LIFE OF ALABAMA....Washington, 1901. Colored map, 12 plts. 1/2 leather w/brittleness and wear, inner joint cracked. Ex-lib. *SUTTON.* $50

Mohr, Max. PIMPUS AND CAXA OR THE NORTH POLE FLYERS. London/NY: Samuel French, 1927. Wrappers. Owner's signature, else Fine. *PARMER.* $50

Mohr, Nicolaus. EXCURSION THROUGH AMERICA. Ray A. Billington (ed). Chicago, 1973 (Lakeside Classic). Fldg map. Fine. *BOHLING.* $25

Moises, Rosalio with J.H. Kelley and Wm. C. Holden. THE TALL CANDLE. THE PERSONAL CHRONICLE OF A YAQUI INDIAN. Lincoln: Univ of NE, 1971. 1st ed. Fldg chart. Fine in Fine dj. *CONNOLLY & WADE.* $40

Mojtabai, A.G. MUNDOME. NY: Simon & Schuster, (1974). 1st ed. Signed. VG in dj. *LOPEZ.* $50

Moldenke, Charles E. THE NEW YORK OBELISK. NY, 1891. NF. *POLYANTHOS.* $35

Mollhausen, Baldwin. DIARY OF A JOURNEY FROM THE MISSISSIPPI TO THE COASTS OF THE PACIFIC WITH A UNITED STATES GOVERNMENT EXPEDITION. London, 1858. 2vols. xxx,(2),352,x,(2),397pp. Mrs. Percy Sinnet (trans), Alexander von Humboldt (intro). Fldg map, many chromolithos. Full contemp calf, raised bands w/gilt. Nice set. Howes M713. *GINSBERG.* $1500

Molloy, J. Fitzgerald. THE LIFE AND ADVENTURES OF EDMUND KEAN, TRAGEDIAN, 1787-1833. With a Portrait. London: Downey & Co, 1897. Orig dec cl sl scuffed, soiled. Bkpl. *DRAMATIS.* $35

Molloy, J. Fitzgerald. THE LIFE AND ADVENTURES OF EDMUND KEAN, TRAGEDIAN. 1787-1833. London: Ward and Downey, 1888. 1st ed. 2 vols. Orig gilt dec cl. *DRAMATIS.* $100

Molyneux, Peter. THE ROMANTIC STORY OF TEXAS. NY & Dallas: Cordova Pr, 1936. 1st ed. VG. *DIAMOND.* $25

Momaday, N. Scott (ed). THE COMPLETE POEMS OF FREDERICK GODDARD TUCKERMAN. NY: Oxford, 1965. NF in sl edgeworn dj. *LOPEZ.* $100

Momaday, N. Scott. ANGLE OF GEESE AND OTHER POEMS. (Boston): Godine, (1974). 1st ed. Fine w/o dj, as issued. *LOPEZ.* $35

Momaday, N. Scott. HOUSE MADE OF DAWN. (Franklin Center: Franklin Library, 1977). Ltd ed reissue. *LOPEZ.* $40

Momaday, N. Scott. HOUSE MADE OF DAWN. NY: H&R, (1968). 1st ed. Fine in Fine dj. *LOPEZ.* $150

Momaday, N. Scott. THE NAMES. NY: H&R, (1976). 1st ed. VG in dj w/bit of edgewear. *LOPEZ.* $25

Momaday, N. Scott. THE WAY TO RAINY MOUNTAIN. (Albuquerque): Univ of NM, (1969). 1st ed. Name, o/w Fine in NF dj. *LOPEZ.* $100

Monaghan, Jay (ed). THE BOOK OF THE AMERICAN WEST. Messner, (1963). 1st ed. Fine in VG dj. *OREGON.* $45

Monaghan, Jay. CUSTER, THE LIFE OF GENERAL GEORGE ARMSTRONG CUSTER. Boston, (1959). 1st ed. 469pp. Dj wear and chipping o/w VG. *PRATT.* $55

Monaghan, Jay. CUSTER: THE LIFE OF GENERAL GEORGE ARMSTRONG CUSTER. Boston: Little Brown, 1959. 1st ed. Sl fade backstrip. NF. *CONNOLLY & WADE.* $30

Monaghan, Jay. LAST OF THE BADMEN....Bobbs-Merrill, 1946. Fine in sl chipped dj. *VARNER.* $22.50

Monahan, Florence. WOMEN IN CRIME. NY: Washburn, (1941). 1st ed. Lacks fep, o/w VG. *SECOND LIFE.* $30

Monardes, Nicholas. JOYFULL NEWS OUT OF THE NEW FOUNDE WORLDE WRITTEN IN SPANISH BY NICHOLAS MONARDES, PHYSICIAN OF SEVILLE AND ENGLISHED BY JOHN FRAMPTON, MERCHANT ANNO 1577. London, 1925. 2 vols. 177, 188pp. *FYE.* $225.

Moncrieff, A.R. Hope. A BOOK ABOUT AUTHORS. London: Adam and Charles Black, 1914. 1st ed. Slip removed from ffep, o/w Fine. Sir James Balfour's copy, w/his bkpl. *WREDEN.* $35

Moncrieff, A.R. Hope. BONNIE SCOTLAND. A&C Black. 1912 reprint. VG-NF. *OLD LONDON.* $55

Moncrieff, A.R. Hope. LONDON. A&C Black, 1924 (book dated 1923). 1st ed (this series). W/o dj, else VG indeed. *OLD LONDON.* $25

Moncrieff, A.R. Hope. MIDDLESEX. A&C Black, 1907. 1st ed. 7s 6d Series. VG-NF. *OLD LONDON.* $75

Moncrieff, A.R. Hope. SCOTLAND. A&C Black, 1922. 2nd ed, rev. Dj poor, else VG. *OLD LONDON.* $20

Moncrieff, William T. PARIS & LONDON. NY: E.M. Murden, 1828. 1st Amer ed. 16mo; orig printed wraps; engr frontis; uncut. VG. *DRAMATIS PERSONAE.* $30

Mondor, Henri. DOCTORS & MEDICINE IN THE WORKS OF DAUMIER: NOTES AND CATALOGUE BY JEAN AD-HEMAR. NY, 1981. Dj. *FYE.* $40

Monell, S.H. THE TREATMENT OF DISEASE BY ELECTRIC CURRENT. NY, 1900. 2nd ed. Woodcut illus. *FYE.* $150

Moninger, John. EVERYTHING FOR THE GREENHOUSE. Chicago: Moninger, 1913. VG. *AMERICAN BOTANIST.* $40

Monroe, Anne Shannon. THE WORLD I SAW. NY: Doubleday, Doran, 1928. 1st ed. Nice in dj. *SECOND LIFE.* $30

Monroe, James. MESSAGE FROM THE PRESIDENT...TRANS-MITTING COPIES...IN RELATION TO THE SEMINOLE WAR. Wash., 1818. 1st ed. 165pp. 1/2 morocco. Howes S281. *GINSBERG.* $250

Monroe, John. THE AMERICAN BOTANIST, AND FAMILY PHYSICIAN....Compiled by Silas Gaskill. Wheelock, (VT): Morrison, 1824. 1st ed? 203pp. Orig calf backed paper cvr boards (worn, lacking some of plain paper). Foxing, lacks edge of final blanks). Not bad. *SECOND LIFE.* $365

Monroe, Neil. THE CLYDE. A&C Black, 1907. 1st ed. 20s Series. Slight chipping top of spine, spine somewhat sunned. VG. *OLD LONDON.* $75

Monroe, Will S. BULGARIA AND HER PEOPLE. Boston, 1914. xxi,419pp. Uncut. *O'NEILL.* $30

MONSTER ISLAND. London, 1981. Van Der Meer (illus), Lokvig, Strejan (engs). One minor monster on pg 1 with sl arthritic neck, o/w all in good shape. Moveable bk. *BOOKFINDERS INTL.* $25

Montague, C.E. A WRITER'S NOTES ON HIS TRADE. London: Chatto & Windus, 1930. 1st ed. 1/750, signed. Spine sl sunned, minor wear to extremities. VG. *JUVELIS.* $35

Montague, C.E. RIGHT OFF THE MAP. Doubleday, 1927. 1st ed. VG in most of dj. *MADLE.* $25

Montague, Mary Wortley. LETTERS OF... WRITTEN DURING HER TRAVELS....New ed. London: Ptd for the bksellers, 1793. 2 vols in one. Orig calf, leather spine label. Front joint quite weak, some old worming. Foxing, o/w VG. *SCHOYER'S.* $40

Montague, Sydney R. NORTH TO ADVENTURE. NY: McBride, (1939). 1st ed. Cl edgeworn. Good. *ARTIS.* $15

Montaignes, Francois. THE PLAINS...EXPEDITION OF EX-PLORATION IN 1845...Univ of OK, (1972). 1st ed. VF in VF dj. *OREGON.* $35

Montale, Eugenio. MOTETS. (Iowa City): Windover Press, 1981. Wright Charles (trans). One of 220. Fine w/o dw, as issued. *CAPTAIN'S BOOKSHELF.* $50

Montale, Eugenio. SELECTED ESSAYS. G. Singh (trans). Manchester, UK: Carcanet, (1978). 1st ed. Fine in dj. *CAPTAIN'S BOOKSHELF.* $30

MONTANA, A STATE GUIDE BOOK. Viking, 1939. 1st ed. Fine in chipped dj. *VARNER.* $50

Montecino, Marcel. CROSSKILLER. NY: Arbor House, 1988. 1st ed, 1st bk. VF in dj. *ELSE FINE.* $85

Montecino, Marcel. THE CROSSKILLER. Arbor House, 1988. 1st ed. Fine in price-clipped dj. Bkpl front pastedown. *STAHR.* $75

Monteilhet, Hubert. ANDROMACHE, OR, THE INADVERTENT MURDER. Simon and Schuster, 1970. 1st Amer ed. About Fine in dj. *STAHR.* $15

MONTEREY PENINSULA. Palo Alto, (1941). American Guide Series. WPA guide. 1st w/dj. *SCHOYER'S.* $45

MONTEREY PENINSULA. Stanford, (1946). 2nd ed. F in VG dj. *OREGON.* $35

Montgomery, Charles. AMERICAN FURNITURE: THE FEDERAL PERIOD. NY: Bonanza, 1978. 2nd ptg. VG in VG dj. *BACKROOM.* $250

Montgomery, Florence. PRINTED TEXTILES. NY: Viking, 1970. 1st ed. VG in dj. *BACKROOM.* $325

Montgomery, Frances. BILLY WHISKERS' GRANDCHILDREN. Illus by Hugo Von Hofsten. Chicago: The Saalfield Pub Co, (1909). 6 full-pg color plts. Grn cl w/gilt billy-goat and title on front cvr. Dj chipped, worn. *KARMIOLE.* $50

Montgomery, Frances. BILLY WHISKERS' PRANKS. Saalfield, (1925). 148pp. Illus by Frances Brundage. Cvr dec in gilt & black on brick colored cloth. Edgewear. VG+. *BEBBAH.* $28

Montgomery, Marion. DARRELL. NY: Doubleday, (1964). 1st Amer ed. Inscribed. NF in dj. *DORN.* $125

Montgomery, Marion. FUGITIVE. NY: Harper & Row, (1974). 1st Amer ed. Signed. Also laid in is a TLS from Harper & Row ed to Andrew Lytle presenting him with a copy. Fine in dj. *DORN.* $65

Montgomery, Marion. STONES FROM THE RUBBLE. Memphis: Argus Books, (1965). 1st Amer ed. Signed. Fine in dj. *DORN.* $50

Montgomery, Marion. THE WANDERING OF DESIRE. NY: Harper, (1962). 1st Amer ed. Inscribed. Fine in dj. *DORN.* $100

Monti, Franco. PRECOLUMBIAN TERRACOTTAS. London: Paul Hamlyn, c. 1969. Eng ed. Unpleasant stain. Dj very worn. *PARMER.* $25

Montule, Edouard de. TRAVELS IN AMERICA 1816-1817. Bloomington: Indiana Univ Press, 1951. 1st trade ed. Edward D. Seeber (trans). Corners bumped, some minor wear. *PARMER.* $35

Moody, Ralph. RIDERS OF THE PONY EXPRESS. Boston: Houghton Mifflin/Riverside Press, 1958. North Star Book #6. VF pict cl in VG dj. *CONNOLLY & WADE.* $25

Moody, Ralph. STAGECOACH WEST. NY: Crowell, 1967. 1st prtg. Back cover spotted, o/w VG in Good dj. *OCTOBER FARM.* $38

Moody, Susan. PENNY ROYAL. London: Macmillan, 1986. 1st ed. Signed. Fine in dj. *MORDIDA.* $37.50

Moody, Susan. PENNY WISE. London: Michael Joseph, 1988. 1st ed. Fine in dj. *MORDIDA.* $45

Moon, Sheila. A MAGIC DWELLS. Middletown: Wesleyan Univ Press, (1970). 1st ed. Fine in dj. *LOPEZ.* $45

Moon, William Least Heat. See Heat Moon, William Least.

Mooney, Ted. EASY TRAVEL TO OTHER PLANETS. NY: Farrar, Straus & Giroux, (1981). 1st ed, 1st book. Fine in dj. *BERNARD.* $25

Moorcock, Michael. A CURE FOR CANCER. Holt, 1971. 1st ed. Fine dj. *MADLE.* $22

Moorcock, Michael. THE SAILOR ON THE SEAS OF FATE. London, 1976. 1st ed. Fine in dj. *MADLE.* $30

Moore, A. BRITISH MOSQUITOES AND HOW TO EXTER-MINATE THEM. London: Hutchinson, 1925. 29 plts. Fine in VG dj. *MAD DOG.* $20

Moore, Brian. BLACK ROBE. London: Cape (1985). NF in dj. Signed. *LOPEZ.* $125

Moore, Brian. FERGUS. NY: Holt, 1970. 1st US ed. Fine in close to Fine dj w/some offsetting from book to dj. *BEASLEY.* $30

Moore, Brian. LIES OF SILENCE. (London): London Limited Editions, (1990). 1/150 numbered, signed. Fine in pub's plain glassine dj. *LOPEZ.* $125

Moore, Brian. LIES OF SILENCE. Doubleday, 1990. Advance reading copy. Fine in beige wraps w/brown type and border. Promo letter laid in. *STAHR.* $30

Moore, Brian. THE EMPEROR OF ICE CREAM. NY: Viking, 1965. 1st ed. As New in dj. *ELSE FINE.* $45

Moore, Brian. THE GREAT VICTORIAN COLLECTION. NY: FSG, 1975. 1st ed. As New in dj. *ELSE FINE.* $25

Moore, Brian. THE LUCK OF GINGER COFFEY. Andre Deutsch, 1960. 1st Eng ed. About Fine in a price-clipped dj. *STAHR.* $100

Moore, Brian. THE LUCK OF GINGER COFFEY. Atlantic-Little, Brown, 1960. 1st ed. About Fine in sl worn dj w/sunned spine. *STAHR.* $60

Moore, C.L. DOOMSDAY MORNING. Doubleday, 1957. 1st ed. Fine in frayed dj. *MADLE.* $75

Moore, C.L. SHAMBLEAU AND OTHERS. NY: Gnome Press, (1953). 1st ed. Boards quite worn; contents tight, clean in edgeworn dj missing 1/3 rear panel, rear flap. *OTHER WORLDS.* $35

Moore, C.L. SHAMBLEAU AND OTHERS. NY: Gnome Press, 1953. 1st ed. Rear cvr sl spotted. Fine in dj w/3 tiny edge tears. *POLYANTHOS.* $100

Moore, C.L. SHAMBLEAU. Gnome Press, 1953. 1st ed. VF in Fine dj. *MADLE.* $150

Moore, Charles. THE FAMILY LIFE OF GEORGE WASHINGTON. Boston: 1926. 1st ed. Orig boards, cloth spine. Orig prospectus laid in. One of 375 numbered, boxed. *GINSBERG.* $125

Moore, Charles. THE NORTHWEST UNDER THREE FLAGS, 1635-1796. NY, 1900, 1st ed. 5 maps. Auto presentation. Worn top & bottom spine. Spine darkened. *HEINOLDT.* $30

Moore, Elaine. WINNING YOUR SPURS. Boston: Little, Brown, 1954. 1st ed. Eps foxed, o/w VG in Good dj. *OCTOBER FARM.* $25

Moore, Francis Roy. WAPELLO CHIEF: A TALE OF IOWA. Cedar Rapids: Torch, 1938. 1st ed. Blue cl, gilt. VG. Scarce. *CONNOLLY & WADE.* $60

Moore, Frank. SPEECHES OF ANDREW JOHNSON...Boston: Little, Brown, 1865. Frontis. *SCHOYER'S.* $40

Moore, Frank. WOMEN OF THE WAR; THEIR HEROISM AND SELF-SACRIFICE. Hartford, 1867. 1st ed. 596pp. *FYE.* $100

Moore, George. A STORY-TELLER'S HOLIDAY. London: (Privately ptd), 1918. One of 1000 (#326) signed. Pub's parchment over gray-grn boards w/paper spine label Orig dj w/paper spine label (tear at joint, some fading; stain). Unopened, untrimmed. *BOOK BLOCK.* $40

Moore, George. IMPRESSIONS AND OPINIONS. London: T. Werner Laurie, 1913. 2nd Eng ed, revised. Some minor foxing, else VG. *WOOLMER.* $35

Moore, George. IN SINGLE STRICTNESS. London: Heinemann, 1922. One of 1,030 signed by author. Spine a touch darkened, else just about Fine. *WOOLMER.* $75

Moore, George. IN SINGLE STRICTNESS. NY: (Privately ptd by Boni & Liveright), 1922. One of 1050 signed on colophon. Pub's white parchment spine over blue boards, w/gilt-stamped leather spine label; in pub's dj lettered on spine (sl faded; 1/2" straight tear). Couple of 1st leaves have faint spots. An untrimmed, largely unopened. *BOOK BLOCK.* $35

Moore, George. PARNELL AND HIS ISLAND. Ptd stiff wrappers. London: Sonnenschein, 1887. 1st ed, simultaneous wrappered issue. Fragile: binding has deteriorated (spine worn away, front cvr detached); lightly soiled. Still useful. Rare, preserved in 1/2 morocco slipcase. *JAFFE.* $250

Moore, George. THE BROOK KERITH. A SYRIAN STORY. London: T. Werner Laurie, 1916. One of 250 signed by author. Spine a little darkened, else just about Fine. Uncut and unopened. *WOOLMER.* $75

Moore, George. THE MAKING OF AN IMMORTAL. NY: The Bowling Green Press; London: Faber & Gwyer, Ltd, 1927. 1st ed. 1/1240 signed. VG in orig boards w/chipped label. *JUVELIS.* $40

Moore, George. ULICK AND SORACHA. NY: Issued for Subscribers Only by Boni and Liveright, 1926. One of 1,250 numbered, signed. Dj; unopened. Pub's slipcase. Bkpl of Estelle Doheny. Fine. *WEBER.* $50

Moore, James. HISTORY OF THE COOPER SHOP VOLUNTEER REFRESHMENT SALOON. Phila: James B. Rodgers, 1866. Rubbed, backstrip repaired, internally very nice, engraved frontis. *MAD DOG.* $40

Moore, James. KILPATRICK AND OUR CAVALRY: COMPRISING A SKETCH OF THE LIFE OF GENERAL KILPATRICK....NY: Widdleton, 1865. 1st ed. 245,(4)pp. Orig dec cl, faded. Inscribed presentation from Mrs. Julia E. Kilpatrick. Howes M774. *GINSBERG.* $100

Moore, John. A JOURNAL DURING A RESIDENCE IN FRANCE. London: G.G.J. & J. Robinson, 1793. 2 vols. 1st ed. 8vo, 502; 617,(5)pp, hand-colored fldg map in vol 2. Contemp tree calf covers somewhat worn. Front covers reattached. Inscription in vol 2; bkplts in both vols. VG. *DIAMOND.* $250

Moore, John. A VIEW OF SOCIETY AND MANNERS IN ITALY, With Anecdotes Relating to Some Eminent Characters. Boston (England): David West and Ebonezer Larkin, 1792. Large thick 8vo, 512pp. Recent fine rebinding in full polished calf, blind fillets, raised bands, gilt, gilt on dark grn lea title. Title-page repaired, unobtrusive lib stamp, very light foxing. Nice. *HARTFIELD.* $195

Moore, Joseph. PENICILLIN IN SYPHILIS. Springfield, 1946. 1st ed. *FYE.* $75

Moore, Lorrie. SELF-HELP. NY: Knopf, 1986. 1st ed, 1st novel. Fine in Fine dj. *ROBBINS.* $20

Moore, Marianne. POEMS. London: The Egoist Press, 1921. 1st ed, 1st bk. Orig patterned wraps, paper label. Dots of foxing, but NF. *CHAPEL HILL.* $750

Moore, Marianne. PUSS IN BOOTS, THE SLEEPING BEAUTY & CINDERELLA. Macmillan, 1963. 1st ed. Illus Eugene Karlin. NF in VG+ dj. *BEBBAH.* $30

Moore, Marianne. SELECTED FABLES OF LA FONTAINE. London: Faber, (1955). 1st ed. One of 2000 ptd. Comp copy from T. S. Eliot, w/Faber's slip bearing Eliot's typed-in name, tipped in at front. Fine in evenly darkened dj. *JAFFE.* $150

Moore, Marianne. TELL ME, TELL ME: GRANITE, STEEL AND OTHER TOPICS. New Poems and Prose. NY: Viking, (1966). 1st ed. VG in NF dj. *SCHOYER'S.* $35

Moore, Marianne. THE PANGOLIN AND OTHER VERSE. Dec boards. (London): Brendin Pub Co, 1936. 1st ed. One of only 120 ptd at Curwen Press. The Press's own copy, w/sm bkpl on front endsheet. Fine. *JAFFE.* $1250

Moore, Mavis. PONY FOR A PRIZE. NY: Macmillan, 1951. 1st prtg. VG in Good dj. *OCTOBER FARM.* $15

Moore, McCornack, and McCready. THE STORY OF EUGENE. NY: Stratford House, 1949. 1st ed. Fine. Scarce. *OREGON.* $70

Moore, Merrill. FUGITIVE SONNETS. Aldington, Kent (UK): The Hand and Flower Press, (1953). 1st ed. VG in ptd wraps. Inscribed. *CAPTAIN'S BOOKSHELF.* $50

Moore, Merrill. ILLEGITIMATE SONNETS. NY: Twayne, (1950). 1st ed. Orig brownish red cl. Fine in VG dj. Inscribed. Eps illus w/6 cartoons by Edward Gorey—his 1st commercial bk appearance. *CHAPEL HILL.* $100

Moore, Merrill. POEMS FROM THE FUGITIVE (1922-1926). (NY: Ptd by the Beekman Hill Press, 1936). 1st ed. Inscribed. Orig ptd self-wraps. NF. *CHAPEL HILL.* $95

Moore, Merrill. SIX SIDES TO A MAN. Louis Untermeyer (epilogue). NY: Harcourt, Brace, (1935). 1st ed. Adv rev copy, slip tipped in. Inscribed. Orig black cl. Fine. *CHAPEL HILL.* $150

Moore, Merrill. SIX SIDES TO A MAN. NY: Harcourt, Brace (1935). 1st ed. Inscribed. VG in chipped dj. *DORN.* $60

Moore, Merrill. SONNETS FROM THE FUGITIVE. (Boston: Caduceus Press, 1937). 1st ed. NF in wraps. Signed twice. *CAPTAIN'S BOOKSHELF.* $60

Moore, Merrill. SONNETS. Reprtd from Sewanee Review, 1928-1935. Sewanee, TN: The Univ Press, 1938. 1st ed. Presentation, inscribed. Orig ptd wraps. Title, last pgs little browned from acidic wraps, bkpl removed, sm inkstamp front wrap. VG. *CHAPEL HILL.* $80

Moore, N. Hudson. OLD PEWTER, BRASS, COPPER & SHEFFIELD PLATE. NY, (1933). NF. *POLYANTHOS.* $30

Moore, N. Hudson. THE LACE BOOK. NY: Stokes, (1904). 1st ed. 70 engrs. 206pp. Fine. *SECOND LIFE.* $50

Moore, Nathaniel Fish. DIARY OF A TRIP FROM NEW YORK TO THE FALLS OF ST. ANTHONY IN 1845. Univ of Chicago, 1946. 1st ed. Fine in VG dj. *ARTIS.* $15

Moore, Norman. THE HISTORY OF THE STUDY OF MEDICINE IN THE BRITISH ISLES. Oxford, 1908. 1st ed. *FYE.* $100

Moore, Opha. HISTORY OF FRANKLIN COUNTY, OHIO. In 3 vols. Topeka, Indianapolis: Historical Pub Co., 1930. 24 plts; 51 plts; 48 plts. Some waterstaining; sturdy. *BOHLING.* $150

Moore, Phil H. WITH GUN AND ROD IN CANADA. NY & Boston, 1922. Photos. Signed. Sl soiled buckram. Good. *CULLEN.* $70

Moore, T.W. TREATISE AND HAND-BOOK OF ORANGE CULTURE IN FLORIDA, LOUISIANA AND CALIFORNIA. NY and Jacksonville, 1886. 4th ed. Orig orange cl w/some edge wear and scuffing. 2pp browned by newspaper clipping. *SUTTON.* $50

Moore, Terris. MT. MCKINLEY: THE PIONEER CLIMBS. College: Univ of Alaska Press, (1967). VG in VG dj. *BLUE DRAGON.* $35

Moore, Vandi. BRANDS ON THE BOSWELL. A NARRATIVE HISTORY....Glendo, WY: High Plains Press, 1986. 1st ed, signed, inscribed. Fine in VG dj. *GIBBS.* $25

Moore, W.C. DISEASES OF BULBS. London, 1939. Boards. Names on cvr. Soiled, spine ends worn, name stamps. *SUTTON.* $30

Moore, Ward. GREENER THAN YOU THINK. Sloane, 1947. 1st ed. NF in sl chipped dj. *MADLE.* $30

Moore, Wilfred G. and Robert M. Burtt. JIMMIE ALLEN IN THE AIR MAIL ROBBERY. Racine, WI, (1936). 1st ed. Big Little Book #1143. Front cover soil, else VG. *McCLINTOCK.* $10

Moore, Winston and Marian. OUT OF THE FRYING PAN. LA: De Vorss & Co, (1939). Black-stamped cl in dj. *DAWSON'S.* $50

Moorehead, Alan. FATAL IMPACT. NY: Harper & Row, 1966. 1st ed. NF in VG dj. *PARMER.* $17.50

Moorehead, John. TRAUMATIC SURGERY. Phila, 1918. 1st ed. Photo, x-ray illus. *FYE.* $60

Moorehead, Warren K. A REPORT ON THE ARCHAEOLOGY OF MAINE. Andover: The Andover Press. 1922. 1st ed. 272pp+8 maps and plans. Text includes 13 other maps and plans (some fldg). *KARMIOLE.* $65

Moorehead, Warren King. ARCHAEOLOGY OF THE ARKANSAS RIVER VALLEY. New Haven: Yale Univ Press, 1931. Corner bumped, minor staining at lower margins. W/supplementary papers by J.B. Thoburn and C. Peabody. Good. *ARCHAEOLOGIA.* $125

Moorey, P.R.S. ANCIENT PERSIAN BRONZES IN THE ADAM COLLECTION. London: Faber & Faber, (1974). 12 figs, 2 maps. Dj. Good. *ARCHAEOLOGIA.* $85

Moorhead, Alan. END IN AFRICA. NY & London: Harper & Bros, (1943). 1st ed. Dj poor. *SCHOYER'S.* $20

Moorhead, Max L. THE PRESIDIO. Norman: Univ of OK, 1975. 1st ed. Fine in NF dj. *CONNOLLY & WADE.* $30

Moorhead, Max. NEW MEXICO'S ROYAL ROAD. Univ of OK, (1958). 1st ed. VG in VG dj. *OREGON.* $40

Moors, H.J. WITH STEVENSON IN SAMOA. London: T. Fisher Unwin. 1910. 1st ed. Frontis, 42 plts. Blue cl, gilt; spine extrems lightly rubbed. *KARMIOLE.* $30

Moraga, Gabriel. THE DIARY OF ENSIGN GABRIEL MORAGA'S EXPEDITION OF DISCOVERY IN THE SACRAMENTO VALLEY, 1808. LA: Glen Dawson, 1957. One of 300 . Donald C. Cutter (trans, ed). Fldg map, boards w/cl spine. *DAWSON'S.* $45

Morand, Paul. BLACK MAGIC. NY, 1929. Hamish Miles, trans. 1st ed. Aaron Douglas (illus). Fine in like dj. *POLYANTHOS.* $75

Morand, Paul. EARTH GIRDLED. London: Alfred A. Knopf. 1928. 1st ed. Dj chipped. *KARMIOLE.* $30

Morant, George Souile de. CHINESE LOVE TALES. NY: Three Sirens Press, 1935. VG. *JUVELIS.* $50

Morassi, Antonio. ART TREASURES OF THE MEDICI. London: The Abbey Library. (1969). 1st ed. 55 mounted color plts, 8 b/w illus. Dj. *KARMIOLE.* $60

MORE PLEASANT SURPRISES. London, (1890s). Fred Weatherly and Ernest Nister. 8 disappearing pictures. Tabs reinforced. Strip of reinforcing tape between last 2pp. Moveable bk. *BOOKFINDERS INTL.* $800

More, Sir Thomas. UTOPIA. NY: LEC, 1934. Ltd to 1500 ptd at the Rudge Press under the supervision of Bruce Rogers, who has signed the ed. 1/4 vellum, dec boards. Fine in very sl split slipcase. *JAFFE.* $175

Moreau, F.J. A PRACTICAL TREATISE ON MIDWIFERY: EXHIBITING THE PRESENT ADVANCED STATE OF THE SCIENCE. Trans from the French by Thomas Forrest Betton and ed. by Paul B. Goddard. Phila, 1844. 1st Eng trans. Folio, orig cloth rebacked. 235pp + 80 engrvd plts. *FYE.* $600

Moreland, Arthur. DICKENS LANDMARKS IN LONDON. Foreword by Sir Henry F. Dickens. London, (1931). 1st ed. 2 maps. Pict boards. Corners sl bumped, o/w VG in sl chipped, stained, repaired pict dj. *DIAMOND.* $75

Moreland, George. BALLDOM. Balldom, 1914. 29pp supplement updating through 1916 laid in. Good+ without dj. *PLAPINGER.* $100

Morey, Chas Rufus. MEDIEVAL ART. NY: Norton, (1942). Dj worn at edges. *ARTIS.* $20

Morey, Walts. RUNAWAY STALLION. NY: Dutton, 1973. 1st ed. Fine in Fine dj. *OCTOBER FARM.* $18

Morgan, A. T. YAZOO; OR, ON THE PICKET LINE OF FREEDOM IN THE SOUTH....Wash., 1884. 1st ed. 512pp. Orig cl. Howes M795. *GINSBERG.* $125

Morgan, A.T. YAZOO, OR ON THE PICKET LINE OF FREEDOM IN THE SOUTH. Washington, 1884. 1st ed. 512pp. Minor cvr wear and staining o/w VG+. *PRATT.* $125

Morgan, Anna. THE ART OF SPEECH AND DEPORTMENT. Chicago: A. C. McClurg & Co., 1926. 1st ed. Fine. *OLD LONDON.* $25

Morgan, Charles. THE FOUNTAIN. NY: Knopf, 1932. 1st US ed. Prev owner's name. Fine- in VG- dj. *AARD.* $20

Morgan, Dale and Carl I. Wheat. JEDEDIAH SMITH AND HIS MAPS OF THE AMERICAN WEST. SF: CA Hist Soc, 1954. 1st ed, ltd to 530. 7 fldg maps (3 rear pocket). 1st pub of "Fremont-Gibbs-Smith" map. VG. *OREGON.* $750

Morgan, Dale and Eleanor Towles Harris (eds). THE ROCKY MOUNTAIN JOURNALS OF WILLIAM MARSHALL ANDERSON. THE WEST IN 1834. Huntington, 1967. 1st ed, ptd in ed of 1500. Frontis. VF in VF dj. *OREGON.* $125

Morgan, Dale. JEDEDIAH SMITH AND THE OPENING OF THE WEST. Bobbs-Merrill, 1953. 1st ed. Fine in Fine dj. *VARNER.* $75

Morgan, Dale. JEDEDIAH SMITH AND THE OPENING OF THE WEST. Bobbs Merrill, (1953). 1st ed. Frontis. Green cl. VG in VG dj. Signed. Fep about 1/8" short. *OREGON.* $135

Morgan, Dale. JEDIDIAH SMITH AND THE OPENING OF THE WEST. Bobbs Merrill, (1953). Blue cl. 1st ed. VG in VG dj. *OREGON.* $115

Morgan, Dale. THE HUMBOLDT, HIGHROAD OF THE WEST. Farrar & Rinehart, (1943). 1st ed. VG. *OREGON.* $45

Morgan, Dale. THE WEST OF WILLIAM H. ASH-LEY...RECORDED IN THE DIARIES AND LETTERS OF WILLIAM H. ASHLEY AND HIS CONTEMPORARIES, 1822-1838. Old West Pub, 1964. 1st ed. Frontis, 26 plts, fldg map, 2 facs. 1/250 deluxe, ltd ed (this unsigned). 1/2 calf & linen w/morocco spine label; matching linen slipcase. VF in VF case. *OREGON.* $500

Morgan, Dale. THE WEST OF WILLIAM H. ASH-LEY...RECORDED IN THE DIARIES AND LETTERS OF WILLIAM H. ASHLEY AND HIS CONTEMPORARIES, 1822-1838. Denver, 1964. Pict buckram. 1st trade ed. VF. *OREGON.* $200

Morgan, Frederick. REFRACTIONS. Omaha: Abattoir Editions, Univ of NE. 1981. Ed ltd to 290 numbered. Fine. *KARMIOLE.* $35

Morgan, George H. ANNALS, COMPRISING MEMOIRS, INCIDENTS, AND STATISTICS OF HARRISBURG, FROM THE PERIOD OF ITS FIRST SETTLEMENT...Harrisburg: Brooks, 1858. 1st ed. (2),400,(2)pp. Orig cl, joints expertly mended. Howes M796. *GINSBERG.* $125

Morgan, James Morris. RECOLLECTIONS OF A REBEL REEFER. Boston: 1917. 1st ed. Orig dec cl. Howes M798. *GINSBERG.* $100

Morgan, James Morris. RECOLLECTIONS OF A REBEL REEFER. London, (1917). 1st Eng ed. 372pp. Index, pict. cloth. A little cvr wear o/w VG+. *PRATT.* $110

Morgan, James Morris. RECOLLECTIONS OF A REBEL REEFER. London: Constable, 1918. 1st Eng ed. Cvrs bit soiled, rubber stamp. *LEFKOWICZ.* $45

Morgan, John. EARLY ACTIVITIES IN THE UPPER FOUR TENTHS. Camden Hist Soc, 1948. 16pp, bound in pamphlet cover. *HEINOLDT.* $15

Morgan, John. THE LIFE AND ADVENTURES OF WILLIAM BUCKLEY. Sussex: Caliban, 19798. New in similar dj. *PARMER.* $30

Morgan, Lady (Sydney Owenson). LADY MORGAN'S MEMOIRS. London: Allen, 1862. 1st ed. 2 vols. Tall 8vo, viii,532; 552pp, index each vol. Full polished calf, raised bands, gilt, blind fillets, gilt on red lea labels, port frontis engr. Bkpl. VG. *HARTFIELD.* $295

Morgan, Lewis H. HOUSES AND HOUSE-LIFE OF THE AMERICAN ABORIGINES. Washington: GPO, 1881. Vol IV in "Contributions to North American Ethnology." 281pp, index. Spine dull, front hinge a bit tender, corners bumped; internally VG. *FIVE QUAIL.* $135

Morgan, Lewis H. THE AMERICAN BEAVER AND HIS WORKS. Phila: Lippincott, 1868. 1st ed. 330pp. Soiled. Fold-out diagrams, woodcuts, steel engrs. Presentation from author's nephew. VG, tight. *SECOND LIFE.* $150

Morgan, Lewis Henry. THE INDIAN JOURNALS 1859-62. Leslie White (ed). Univ of MI, (1959). 1st ed. 16 plts. VG in VG dj. *OREGON.* $65

Morgan, W.Y. A JOURNEY OF A JAYHAWKER. Topeka: Crane, 1905. Dec cl. Signed presentation. VG. *BURCHAM.* $50

Morgan, Willard D. (ed) THE COMPLETE PHOTOGRAPHER: A COMPLETE GUIDE...NY: Nat'l Education Alliance, Inc, 1942-1943. 1st ed. 10 vols complete w/index vol. Orig dec grn cl stamped in black and gold. Tissue dj's. Fine set. *KARMIOLE.* $175

Morgulis, Sergius. FASTING AND UNDERNUTRITION: A BIOLOGICAL AND SOCIOLOGICAL STUDY OF INANITATION. NY, 1923. *FYE.* $100

Morier, James. THE ADVENTURE OF HAJJI BABA OF ISPAHAN. NY: Random House, 1937. VG. *WORLDWIDE.* $16

Morier, James. THE ADVENTURES OF HAJJI BABA OF ISPAHAN. London & NY: Macmillan, 1895. lii,456pp. VG. *WORLDWIDE.* $45

Morison, Samuel Eliot (ed, trans). JOURNALS AND OTHER DOCUMENTS ON THE LIFE OF CHRISTOPHER COLUMBUS. NY: LEC, 1963. One of 1500 illus, signed by Lima de Freitas. Fine in slipcase. *CAPTAIN'S BOOKSHELF.* $175

Morison, Samuel Eliot. ADMIRAL OF THE OCEAN SEA...CHRISTOPHER COLUMBUS. Boston, 1942. 1st ed. 2 vols. orig cloth, djs. Fine set in worn in pub's box, spine of dj's sunned. Fine. *LEFKOWICZ.* $300

Morison, Samuel Eliot. OLD BRUIN. COMMODORE MATTHEW C. PERRY 1794-1858. Little Brown, (1967). 1st ed. VG in VG dj. *OREGON.* $35

Morison, Samuel Eliot. SAMUEL DE CHAMPLAIN. FATHER OF NEW FRANCE. Boston: Little, Brown, 1972. 1st ed. Inscribed. Near pristine. *PARMER.* $50

Morison, Samuel Eliot. THE MARITIME HISTORY OF MASSACHUSETTS 1783-1860. Boston & NY, 1921. 1st ed, 1st state, w/"scared codfish" on p 149. Frontis, 47 plts. VG. *LEFKOWICZ.* $75

Morison, Stanley. FIRST PRINCIPLES OF TYPOGRAPHY. NY: Macmillan Co., 1936. 1st separate ed. Dj. *DAWSON'S.* $75

Morison, Stanley. FIRST PRINCIPLES OF TYPOGRAPHY. NY: Macmillan. 1936. 1st ed. Fine in dj. *KARMIOLE.* $50

Morison, Stanley. FOUR CENTURIES OF FINE PRINTING. TWO HUNDRED AND SEVENTY-TWO EXAMPLES OF THE WORK...BETWEEN 1465 AND 1924. London: Benn, (1949). 2nd ed, rev, enl. One of 200 numbered of Edition De Luxe prepared for Collector's Bk Club. Fine. *JAFFE.* $225

Morley, Christopher. RUDOLPH AND AMINA, or THE BLACK CROOK. NY, (1930). 1st ed. Bkplt, else VG. *BOND.* $32.50

Morley, Christopher. THE GOLDFISH UNDER THE ICE. London: Elkin, Matthews, and Marrot, 1929. One of 530 signed. Dj. *DAWSON'S.* $50

Morley, Christopher. THE OLD MANDARIN. MORE TRANSLATIONS FROM THE CHINESE. (NY): Harcourt, Brace, 1947. Fine in price-clipped dj (touch of rubbing). 1st ed. *CHAPEL HILL.* $35

Morley, Christopher. WHERE THE BLUE BEGINS. Arthur Rackham. Phila: Lippincott, (1922). Reprint. 4 full-pg color plts. Fine lacking dj. Inscribed. *CAPTAIN'S BOOKSHELF.* $100

Morley, Christopher. WHERE THE BLUE BEGINS. London and NY: William Heinemann and Doubleday, Page, & Co., (1922). 1st ed. Illus Arthur Rackham. 2 full-pg color illus. Light soiling. *DAWSON'S.* $100

Morley, F.V. and Hodgson, J.S. WHALING NORTH AND SOUTH. NY: The Century Co., 1926. xviii + 235pp. 1st ed. Orig. gilt dec grey cl, gilt titles. Minor spots and fore-edge foxing. NF in VG dj. *GREAT EPIC.* $55

Morley, John. LIFE OF WILLIAM EWART GLADSTONE. London: Macmillan, 1903. 3 vols. 1st ed. Cl sl shelfworn, repaired. 9 plts. Foxing few pp, o/w VG. *DIAMOND.* $75

Morley, Margaret W. THE CAROLINA MOUNTAINS. Boston and NY: Houghton Mifflin Co.,1913. 1st ed. Minor smudges, some edgewear, but VG+. *OLD LONDON.* $65

Morley, S. Griswold. THE COVERED BRIDGES OF CALIFORNIA. Berkeley: Univ of CA, 1938. 1st ed. Cloth, silver letters. Fine. *CONNOLLY & WADE.* $45

Morley, Sylvanus. THE ANCIENT MAYA. Stanford Univ Press, (1958). 3rd ed. Good in chipped dj. *SILVER.* $25

Morrell, David. FIRST BLOOD. London: Barrie & Jenkins, 1972. 1st Eng ed. Inscribed. Fine in dj w/an internal tape repair and crease on spine. *MORDIDA.* $65

Morrell, David. FIRST BLOOD. NY: M. Evans, 1972. 1st ed. Bkseller's small label on fep. Fine in price-clipped dj. *MORDIDA.* $75

Morrell, David. TESTAMENT. Evans, 1975. 1st ed. Fine in sl rubbed dj. *MADLE.* $35

Morrell, David. THE LEAGUE OF NIGHT AND FOG. NY: E.P. Dutton, 1987. 1st ed. Fine in dj. *MORDIDA.* $20

Morrell, David. THE TOTEM. NY: Evans, 1979. 1st ed. VF in dj. *ELSE FINE.* $75

Morrell, David. THE TOTEM. NY: M. Evans, 1979. 1st ed. Remainder mark on bottom edge and initials on front pastedown o/w Fine in dj. *MORDIDA.* $30

Morrell, David. THE TOTEM: A NOVEL. NY: Evans, (1979). 1st ed. NF in Fine dj. *OTHER WORLDS.* $50

Morrell, Martha McBride. "YOUNG HICKORY." THE LIFE AND TIMES OF PRESIDENT JAMES K. POLK. NY: Dutton, (1949). Frontis. Stated 1st ed. Dj. *SCHOYER'S.* $30

Morrell, W.P. THE GOLD RUSHES. NY: Macmillan, 1941. 1st ed. Name, else Fine in sl chipped dj. *CONNOLLY & WADE.* $65

Morressy, John. UNDER A CALCULATING STAR. GC: Doubleday, 1975. 1st ed. Signed. Fine in NF dj. *LOPEZ.* $25

Morris, Ann Axtell. DIGGING IN YUCATAN. GC: Doubleday, Doran, 1943. 2 frontis. Inscription. Good. *ARCHAEOLOGIA.* $45

Morris, Charles. THE AUTOBIOGRAPHY OF COMMODORE CHARLES MORRIS, U.S. NAVY. Boston and Annapolis, 1880. 1st ed. 111 pp. Heliotype port. Orig ptd wrappers. Howes M822. *GINSBERG.* $150

Morris, Craig and Donald Thompson. HUANUCO PAMPA. NY: Thames & Hudson, (1985). 1st ed. 14 color, 126 b/w photo illus. Good in dj. *SILVER.* $30

Morris, Earl H. THE TEMPLE OF THE WARRIORS. NY: Charles Scribner's Sons, 1931. 1st ed. Spine faded; else VG. *PARMER.* $30

Morris, F.O. A HISTORY OF BRITISH BUTTERFLIES. London: G. Routledge, 1904. 9th ed. 79 full pg handcolored plts. 234pp,plts,addenda. Gilt dec cl. NF. *MIKESH.* $275

Morris, Frank and Edward Eames. OUR WILD ORCHIDS. NY: Scribners, 1929. 130 plates, 4 color. Fine in VG pict. dj. Signed presentation on fly. *CULLEN.* $100

Morris, Gouveneur. THE DIARY AND LETTERS OF....NY, 1888. 2 vols. 1st ed. Anne Cary Morris (ed). Orig cl. Howes M826. *GINSBERG.* $75

Morris, Henry. DESERT GOLD AND TOTAL PROSPECTING. Privately ptd, 1955. 1st ed. Fine in Fine dj. *BOOK MARKET.* $25

Morris, Lucile. BALD KNOBBERS. Caxton, 1939. 1st ed. Pict cl. VG. *OREGON.* $60

Morris, Lucile. BALD KNOBBERS. Caxton, 1939. 1st ed. Signed presentation. Fine in chipped dj. *VARNER.* $95

Morris, Maurice O'Connor. RAMBLES IN THE ROCKY MOUN-TAINS. London: Smith, Elder and Co, 1864. Little spotting of contents, but binding esp clean and bright. Howes M831. *HUDSON.* $250

Morris, Maurice O'Connor. RAMBLES IN THE ROCKY MOUN-TAINS. London, 1864. 1st ed. (8),264pp. Orig cl. Very nice. Howes M831. *GINSBERG.* $300

Morris, Paul C. AMERICAN SAILING COASTERS OF THE NORTH ATLANTIC. Chardon: Bloch and Osborn, 1973. Fldg drawing. NF. *PARMER.* $60

Morris, R.H., D.P. Abbott E.C. Haderlie et al. INTERTIDAL IN-VERTEBRATES OF CALIFORNIA. Stanford, (1980). Dj. *SUTTON.* $65

Morris, Robert (ed). COLLECTIONS OF THE WYOMING HIS-TORICAL SOCIETY, VOL. 1. Cheyenne, 1897. 1st ed. 353pp. Frontis. Comp copy signed. Corners, spine label worn; eps cracking at hinges, internally Fine. *OREGON.* $225

Morris, Robert. FREEMASONRY IN THE HOLY LAND. KY, 1879. Gilt-pict. NF. *POLYANTHOS.* $50

Morris, William and E. Belfort Bax. SOCIALISM, ITS GROWTH AND OUTCOME. London, 1893. 1st ed. Spine sl sunned, extremities very sl rubbed, front hinge starting. NF. *POLYANTHOS.* $35

Morris, William. CHANTS FOR SOCIALISTS. NY: New Horizon, 1935. 22pp. Wraps. *AKA.* $25

Morris, William. GOTHIC ARCHITECTURE: A LECTURE FOR THE ARTS AND CRAFTS EXHIBITION. London: Ptd by the Kelmscott Press at the New Gallery, 1893. Of ed. of 1500, this is 1/approx. 500 of 1st issue (w/misprint on p. 45, "Van Eyk"). Soiled. NF. *BLUE MOUNTAIN.* $450

Morris, William. THE EARTHLY PARADISE. Boston: Roberts, 1870-1871. 3 vols. 1st US ed. Bound in gold stamped grn cl. Some rippling to cl, else VG. *SECOND LIFE.* $85

Morris, Willie. GOOD OLD BOY. (London): Andre Deutsch, (1974). 1st ed. Fine in dj. Inscribed. *CAPTAIN'S BOOKSHELF.* $40

Morris, Willie. HOMECOMINGS. Jackson & London: Univ Press of Mississippi, (1989). 1st trade ed. Orig cl-backed blue boards. Fine in dj. Inscribed by author, illus. *CHAPEL HILL.* $100

Morris, Willie. HOMECOMINGS. Jackson & London: Univ. Press of Mississippi, (1989). 1st ed. #92 of 174 signed by author and artist William Dunlap. 4to. Orig cl-backed blue boards. As New in pub's slipcase. *CHAPEL HILL.* $75

Morris, Willie. HOMECOMINGS. Jackson: Univ Press of Mississippi, (1989). One of 174 specially bound, signed by Morris and Dunlap (artist). As New in slipcase. *CAPTAIN'S BOOKSHELF.* $75

Morris, Willie. NORTH TOWARD HOME. Boston: Houghton Mifflin, 1967. 1st ed. Orig black cl. Fine in lightly soiled dj. *CHAPEL HILL.* $45

Morris, Willie. THE COURTING OF MARCUS DUPREE. GC: Doubleday, 1983. 1st ed. About Fine in sl used dj (few short tears). Inscribed. *CAPTAIN'S BOOKSHELF.* $75

Morris, Willie. THE COURTING OF MARCUS DUPREE. GC: Doubleday, 1983. 1st ed. VF in dj. Inscribed. *CAPTAIN'S BOOKSHELF.* $100

Morris, Willie. THE LAST OF THE SOUTHERN GIRLS. Knopf, 1973. Advance reading copy. Fine in wraps. *STAHR.* $25

Morris, Willie. YAZOO. NY: Harper's Magazine Press, (1971). 1st ed. Orig beige cl. Fine in dj. Signed. *CHAPEL HILL.* $65

Morris, Willie. YAZOO: INTEGRATION IN A DEEP-SOUTHERN TOWN. NY: Harpers, (1971). 192pp. Price-clipped dj. Owner inscrip. *AKA.* $30

Morris, Wright. A CLOAK OF LIGHT. Franklin Center: Franklin Library, 1985. 1st ed. One of an unspecified number signed. Fine in full lea. *BETWEEN COVERS.* $50

Morris, Wright. ABOUT FICTION: REVERENT REFLEC-TIONS....Harper, (1975). 1st ed. Boards. Fine in dj. *AUTHORS OF THE WEST.* $20

Morris, Wright. MY UNCLE DUDLEY. NY: Harcourt Brace, 1942. 1st ed, 1st bk. NF in VG dj w/skinned spot in back, a 3/4" tear in front, lightly chipped & soiled. *ARCHER.* $650

Morris, Wright. THE HOME PLACE. NY: Scribners, 1948. 1st ed. NF (owner sig) in dj w/three-quarter inch chip head of spine. *CAPTAIN'S BOOKSHELF.* $125

Morris, Wright. THE MAN WHO WAS THERE. NY: Scribners, 1945. 1st ed. Fine in NF dj w/few short tears. *BEASLEY*. $200

Morris, Wright. THE MAN WHO WAS THERE. NY: Scribners, 1945. 1st ed. Fine in internally-mended dj (slight wear to spinal extremities). *CAPTAIN'S BOOKSHELF*. $100

Morris, Wright. THE WORKS OF LOVE. Knopf, 1952. 1st ed. Fine in dj. *AUTHORS OF THE WEST*. $40

Morris, Wright. WILL'S BOY. Harper & Row, 1981. Uncorrected proof. VF in wraps. *STAHR*. $25

Morrison, Arthur. CHRONICLES OF MARTIN HEWITT BEING THE SECOND SERIES OF THE ADVENTURES OF MARTIN HEWITT: INVESTIGATOR. London, 1895. 1st ed. Illus by D. Murray Smith. Pict cloth gilt, spine sunned, extremities and corners little rubbed. *POLYANTHOS*. $300

Morrison, Arthur. TALES OF MEAN STREETS. London: Methuen, (1894). 1st ed. Bound with 32pp of advertised books, this is NF. *UNGER*. $75

Morrison, Herbert Seymour. SONGS OF A SAILOR. Boston: Bruce Humphries, 1932. 1st ed. Inscribed, signed. VF in VG dj. *CONNOLLY & WADE*. $45

Morrison, J.S. and R.T. Williams. GREEK OARED SHIPS, 900-322 B.C. Cambridge: Cambridge Univ Press, 1968. 31 plts. Boards sl discolored, signature. Good. *ARCHAEOLOGIA*. $150

Morrison, John H. HISTORY OF AMERICAN STEAM NAVIGATION. NY, 1903. 1st ed. Orig cl. Bkpl. VG. *BOHLING*. $150

Morrison, Toni. BELOVED. London: Chatto & Windus, (1987). Uncorrected proof of 1st English ed. Orig ptd wraps. Fine. *CHAPEL HILL*. $100

Morrison, Toni. BELOVED. NY: Knopf, 1987. 1st ed. Fine in dj w/price sticker on rear panel. Inscribed. *CHAPEL HILL*. $100

Morrison, Toni. BELOVED. NY: Knopf, 1987. 1st ed. Fine in dj. *LOPEZ*. $40

Morrison, Toni. JAZZ. NY: Knopf, 1992. Uncorrected proof. Fine in wraps. *CAPTAIN'S BOOKSHELF*. $100

Morrison, Toni. SONG OF SOLOMON. London: Chatto & Windus, 1978. 1st Eng ed. Fine in Fine dj. *LOPEZ*. $45

Morrison, Toni. SONG OF SOLOMON. NY: Knopf, 1977. 1st ed. Orig black cl. Fine in dj (sl faded spine). *CHAPEL HILL*. $95

Morrison, Toni. SONG OF SOLOMON. NY: Knopf, 1977. Fine (faint remainder mark on top edge) in dj. Signed. *CAPTAIN'S BOOKSHELF*. $125

Morrison, Toni. SULA. NY: Knopf, 1972. 1st ed. Fine in dj. *CAPTAIN'S BOOKSHELF*. $450

Morrison, Toni. TAR BABY. NY: Knopf, 1981. 1st trade ed. Orig beige cl. Fine in dj. Signed by Morrison. *CHAPEL HILL*. $150

Morrison, Toni. TAR BABY. NY: Knopf, 1981. 1st trade ed. Fine in NF dj. Inscribed. *CHAPEL HILL*. $125

Morrison, Toni. TAR BABY. NY: Knopf, 1981. Uncorrected proof of 1st ed. Orig ptd light blue wraps. NF. *CHAPEL HILL*. $250

Morrison, Toni. THE BELOVED. Ptd wrappers. NY: Knopf, 1987. Uncorrected proof. VF. *JAFFE*. $150

Morrison, Toni. THE BLUEST EYE. London: Chatto & Windus, (1979). 1st Eng ed of 1st bk. Fine in Fine dj. *LOPEZ*. $100

Morrison, Toni. THE BLUEST EYE. London: Chatto & Windus, 1979. 1st UK ed. Fine in price-clipped dj. *CAPTAIN'S BOOKSHELF*. $100

Morrison, Toni. THE BLUEST EYE. London: Chatto & Windus, 1979. 1st UK ed. New in dj. *BERNARD*. $100

Morrison, Toni. THE BLUEST EYE. NY: Holt, (1970). 1st ed, 1st bk. Lt, thumb-sized spot front panel, else NF in VF dj. The likelihood that this bk, dj were married at an earlier date is strong. Morrison's sig tipped in. *CAPTAIN'S BOOKSHELF*. $750

Morrow, Bradford and Patrick McGrath (eds). THE NEW GOTHIC: A COLLECTION OF CONTEMPORARY GOTHIC FICTION. NY: Random House, (1991). 1st ed. As New in dj. *CAPTAIN'S BOOKSHELF*. $45

Morrow, Bradford. POSTHUMES. Dj by Roland Ginzel. (Santa Barbara): Cadmus Editions, 1982. 1st ed. Ltd to 150 numbered, signed by Morrow & Ginzel. Mint. *JAFFE*. $50

Morrow, Decatur Franklin. THEN AND NOW. REMINISCENCES AND HISTORICAL ROMANCE 1856-1865. Macon, GA, 1926. 1st ed. Wrappers. VG. *McGOWAN*. $45

Morrow, Elizabeth. THE PAINTED PIG. Knopf, 1956 ptg. Illus by Rene d'Harnoncourt. VG+ in VG+ dj w/3 tiny closed edge tears. Inscrip. *BEBBAH*. $32

Morrow, Elizabeth. THE RABBIT'S NEST. Macmillan, 1940. 1st ptg. Paperclip mk to front fly & front panel of dj. VG+ in VG+ dj w/tiny chips. *BEBBAH*. $25

Morrow, James. THE WINE OF VIOLENCE. Holt, 1981. 1st ed. Fine in dj. *MADLE*. $35

Morrow, James. THIS IS THE WAY THE WORLD ENDS: A NOVEL. NY: Holt, (1986). 1st ed. Signed. Almost Fine in nicked dj. *OTHER WORLDS*. $45

Morrow, Josiah (ed). LIFE AND SPEECHES OF THOMAS CORWIN. Cincinnati, 1896. 1st ed. 1/4 leather. Good, sound. *ARTIS*. $20

Morrow, Patrick D. BRET HARTE: LITERARY CRITIC. Bowling Green State Univ Popular Press, 1979. 1st ed. New list in dj. *AUTHORS OF THE WEST*. $10.95

Morse, A. Reynolds. DALI: A STUDY OF HIS LIFE AND WORK. NY: NY Graphic Society, 1958. 1st ed. Tipped in color plts, oversized, pict boards, shelfworn, else VG+ in ptd acetate dj (quite chipped & clear tape repaired). *PETTLER*. $125

Morse, A.P. MANUAL OF THE ORTHOPTERA OF NEW ENGLAND. Boston, 1920. 20 plts. Binder's buckram (insect tracings on covers, orig wrappers retained, 1 pg w/tear repaired, tears along gutters of 2 pp). *SUTTON*. $45

Morse, E.L. (ed). SAMUEL F.B. MORSE: HIS LETTERS & JOURNALS, 2 vols. Houghton Mifflin, 1914. VG. *BOOKCELL*. $65

Mortimer, John. SUMMER'S LEASE. Franklin Center: Franklin Lib, 1988. Leatherbound ltd ed. Fine. Signed. *LOPEZ*. $45

Morton, Anthony (John Creasey). ALIAS BLUE MASK. Phila: Lippincott, 1939. 1st ed. VF, minor edgewear to pict dj. *ELSE FINE*. $60

Morton, Bowditch. HANDBOOK OF FIRST AID TO THE INJURED. NY, 1884. 2nd ed. Woodcut illus. *FYE*. $40

Morton, Desmond and Reyinald H. Roy. TELEGRAMS OF THE NORTH-WEST CAMPAIGN, 1885. Toronto, 1972. 1st ed. Frontis, 5 maps. Orig cl. Champlain Soc. Pubs. 47. One of 1000 numbered. *GINSBERG*. $100

Morton, H.V. IN THE STEPS OF THE MASTER. Dodd, Mead, 1935. 2nd prtg. Dj chipped. *SCHOYER'S*. $15

Morton, J. SOUTHERN FLORICULTURE, A GUIDE. Clarksville, 1890. Orig gilt-stamped cl, some wear extrems, some speckling, soiling. Pp yellowed. *SUTTON*. $50

Morton, J. Sterling and Albert Watkins. HISTORY OF NEBRASKA FROM THE EARLIEST EXPLORATIONS OF THE TRANS-MISSISSIPPI REGION. Lincoln: Western Publishing and Engraving, 1918. 2nd ed. Cl w/leather spine and tips, light wear to extremities. *DAWSON'S*. $100

Morton, Joseph W., Jr. (ed). SPARKS FROM THE CAMPFIRE OR TALES OF THE OLD VETERANS. Phila, 1890. "New and Rev ed.," (1892). 648pp. Cover wear, hinges little tender, o/w VG+. *PRATT*. $45

Morton, Louis. THE WAR IN THE PACIFIC: STRATEGY AND COMMAND. Washington: Dept Army/USGPO, 1962. 1st ed. Fine. *ARCHER.* $25

Morton, Louis. THE WAR IN THE PACIFIC: THE FALL OF THE PHILIPPINES. Washington: Dept Army/USGPO, 1953. 1st ed. Bumped, lacks pocket map, o/w VG. *ARCHER.* $20

Morton, Oren F. A HISTORY OF ROCKBRIDGE COUNTY, VIRGINIA. Staunton, Va.: McClure, 1920. 1st ed. Orig cl, inner hinges strengthened, stain on rear cover. *GINSBERG.* $125

Morton, Oren F. ANNALS OF BATH COUNTY, VIRGINIA. Staunton, Va: McClure, 1917. 1st ed. Fldg map. Orig cl, sm paper label on spine, bkpl removed. *GINSBERG.* $75

Morton, Oren F. A HISTORY OF PENDLETON COUNTY, WEST VIRGINIA. Dayton, VA, 1910. 1st ed. Fldg map, plts. Orig cl, paper label on spine, lib bkpl, perf lib stamp on title pg. Howes M850. *GINSBERG.* $100

Morton, Samual George. TYPES OF MANKIND: OR, ETHNOLOGICAL RESEARCHES....Phila: Lippincott, Grambo, 1854. 1st ed. Small 4to, 738pp. Recent buckram. VG. *WORLDWIDE.* $225

Mosby, John Singleton. THE MEMOIRS OF COLONEL JOHN S. MOSBY. Boston, 1917. 1st ed. Spine trifle dull, else VG to NF. *McGOWAN.* $250

Mosel, Arlene. THE FUNNY LITTLE WOMAN. Dutton, (1972). Stated 1st ed. Illus, signed by Blair Lent. NF in VG dj w/few short closed edge tears. *BEBBAH.* $85

Moseley, Keith. STEAM LOCOMOTIVES. London, 1989. 3-D bk. *BOOKFINDERS INTL.* $15

Moser, Brian & Donald Tayler. THE COCAINE EATERS. NY: Tapliner, (1967). 1st Amer ed. Chipped dj. *SILVER.* $35

Moses, Anna Mary Robertson. GRANDMA MOSES. MY LIFE'S HISTORY. Otto Kallir (ed). (NY): Harper & Bros. (1952). Ltd to 270 numbered, signed. 1/2 red morocco over dec boards, gilt spine. Teg. Slipcase. Bkpl. *KARMIOLE.* $400

Moses, Michael. MASTER CRAFTSMEN OF NEWPORT. Tenafly, NJ: MMI Americana Press, 1984. NF in NF dj. *BACKROOM.* $125

Mosher, Howard Frank. DISAPPEARANCES. NY: Viking, (1977). Advance review copy. Top edge of pages sl spotted, o/w Fine in NF dj. *LOPEZ.* $75

Mosher, Howard Frank. WHERE THE RIVERS FLOW NORTH. NY: Viking, (1978). 1st ed. Inscribed. Fine in NF dj (few short edge tears). *LOPEZ.* $75

Moskowitz, Sam (ed). UNDER THE MOONS OF MARS. Holt, 1970. 1st ed. Fine in dj. *MADLE.* $35

Mosley, Walter. DEVIL IN A BLUE DRESS. NY: W.W. Norton, 1990. 1st ed. VF in dj. *MORDIDA.* $25

Mosoriak, Roy. THE CURIOUS HISTORY OF MUSIC BOXES. Chicago: Lightner, (1943). Cvrs a trifle faded, else Fine. *WREDEN.* $50

Moss, James E. DUELING IN MISSOURI HISTORY. Kansas City Posse of the Westerners, Kansas City, MO, 1966. Signed, ltd to 250. Fine. *VARNER.* $55

Moss, W. Stanley. A WAR OF SHADOWS. London, 1952. 240pp. 1st ed. *O'NEILL.* $25

Mosser, Marjorie. GOOD MAINE FOOD. NY: Doubleday, Doran, 1939. Intro and notes by Kenneth Roberts. 2nd ptg. Inscrip, offsetting to eps. Signed by Mosser and Roberts. Fine. *CHAPEL HILL.* $200

Mossman, Isaac Van Dorsey. A PONY EXPRESSMAN'S RECOLLECTIONS. Portland, OR): Champoeg Press. 1955. 56pp. Tipped-in photographic frontis, fldg map. Ed ltd to 500. *KARMIOLE.* $40

Mossman, Isaac. A PONY EXPRESSMAN'S RECOLLECTIONS. Portland: Champoeg Press, 1955. Fldg map inside rear cover. Ltd to 500. 1st ed. VF. *OREGON.* $60

Mosso, Angelo. FATIGUE. London, 1906. 1st Eng trans. *FYE.* $100

MOTHER GOOSE. Music by E.I. Lane. Colored lithos by J.L Webb. NY, 1888. VG-NF. *POLYANTHOS.* $75

Mothershead, Harmon Ross. THE SWAN LAND AND CATTLE COMPANY, LTD. Norman: Univ of OK Press, 1971. 1st ed. Fine in dj. *GIBBS.* $25

Motherwell, Robert. RECONCILIATION ELEGY. NY, (1980). 1st ed. Signed. Pict wraps. Fine. *POLYANTHOS.* $75

Motion, Andrew. INDEPENDENCE. Edinburgh: Salamandar, 1981. One of 600 clothbound. VF in dj. *WOOLMER.* $65

Motion, Andrew. THE PALE COMPANION. London: Viking, 1989. 1st ed. Fine in dj. *WOOLMER.* $40

Motley, Willard. LET NO MAN WRITE MY EPITAPH. NY: Random House, 1958. 1st ed. Fine but for slight fading to spine and edges, in NF dj. *BEASLEY.* $40

Motley, Willard. LET NO MAN WRITE MY EPITAPH. NY: Random House, (1958). 1st ed. VG in dj w/soiling and wear at edges, some crimping to lamination. *LOPEZ.* $25

Motley, Willard. LET NOON BE FAIR. NY: Putnam, (1966). 1st ed. Fine in dj w/short tear. *LOPEZ.* $40

Motley, Willard. WE FISHED ALL NIGHT. NY: Appleton, 1951. 1st ed. Fine in like dj (lt internal reinforcement). *BEASLEY.* $45

Mott, Ed(ward) (Harold). THE BLACK HOMER OF JIMTOWN. NY: Grosset & Dunlap, 1900. 1st ed. Orig grn cl w/mounted cover photo. Slight soiling, but VG. *CHAPEL HILL.* $95

Mott, Frank Luther. A HISTORY OF AMERICAN MAGAZINES, 1865-1885. Cambridge, 1970. *FYE.* $50

Mott, Frederick. THE DEGENERATION OF THE NEURONE. London, 1900. 1st ed. Illus. w/photomicrographs. *FYE.* $125

Moullin, C.W. Mansell. SURGERY. Phila, 1893. 2nd Amer ed. Full leather. 600 illus, color lithograph frontis. *FYE.* $100

Moulton, Forest Ray. AN INTRODUCTION TO CELESTIAL MECHANICS. NY: Macmillan, 1939 (1914), 2nd rev ed, 6th ptg. Good in maroon cl; spine faded, corners bumped. *KNOLLWOOD.* $35

Mounsey, A.H. A JOURNEY THROUGH THE CAUCASUA AND THE INTERIOR OF PERSIA 1872. London, 1872. Fldg map. Cl, rubbed, spine ends worn. xi,336pp. *O'NEILL.* $135

MOUNTAIN CLIMBING. Scribner's, 1897. 1st ed. VG-NF. *OLD LONDON.* $45

Mountfield, David. A HISTORY OF POLAR EXPLORATION. NY: Dial Press, 1974. 1st Dial ed. VG+ in VG dj. *BLUE DRAGON.* $25

Mountford, Charles P. BROWN MEN AND RED SAND. NY: Praeger (1952). 1st US ed. VG in Good dj. *AARD.* $20

MOVING PICTURES. London, 1985. Moveable bk. *BOOKFINDERS INTL.* $28

Mowat, Farley. A WHALE FOR THE KILLING. Toronto: McClelland and Stewart, (1972). 1st ed. Owner name, notations. Signed. VG in edgeworn dj. *LOPEZ.* $85

Mowat, Farley. PEOPLE OF THE DEER. Boston: Little, Brown. February 1952. viii + 344pp. 1st ed, second printing. Cl sunned top of spine. NF in Near VG dj. *GREAT EPIC.* $35

Mowris, James A. A HISTORY OF THE ONE HUNDRED AND SEVENTEENTH REGIMENT N.Y. VOLUNTEERS, (FOURTH ONEIDA). Hartford, 1866. 1st ed. Top of spine sl chipped, moderate foxing. VG to NF. *McGOWAN.* $165

Mowry, Jess. WAY PAST COOL. Farrar Straus Giroux, 1992. Advance reading copy. VF in dec wraps. *STAHR.* $35

Moyes, Patricia. BLACK WIDOWER. London: Collins Crime Club, 1975. 1st ed. Fine in dj. *MORDIDA.* $35

Moyes, Patricia. TO KILL A COCONUT. London: Collins Crime Club, 1977. 1st ed. Fine in dj. *MORDIDA.* $35

Moynihan, B. ABDOMINAL OPERATIONS. Phila, 1906. 2nd ed. *FYE*. $75

Moynihan, B. THE SPLEEN AND SOME OF ITS DISEASES. London, 1921. 1st ed. *FYE*. $100

Mphahlele, Ezekiel. THE WANDERERS. NY: Macmillan, (1971). 1st ed. Fine in Fine dj. *LOPEZ*. $35

MR. DUNN BROWNE'S EXPERIENCES IN FOREIGN PARTS. (By Samuel W. Fiske.) Boston, 1857. xii,300pp. *O'NEILL*. $45

MR. FACEY ROMFORD'S HOUNDS. (by Robert Smith Surtees). London: Bradbury, Agnew & Co, (1892?). Red 3/4 crushed morocco, marbled sides, eps; wide raised bands, gilt top. Hand colored title vignette, 2 uncolored plts, 24 hand colored plts by John Leech and H.K. Browne. Sl wear to joints, o/w Fine binding. Tear (repaired) at frontis; tear at leaf (unrepaired, no loss), o/w excellent internally. *PIRAGES*. $150

Mrabet, Mohammed. LOOK & MOVE ON. Ed by Paul Bowles. Santa Barbara: Black Sparrow, 1976. 1st ed. Fine in unptd dj as issued. One of 250 hb copies signed by Mrabet and Bowles. *BETWEEN COVERS*. $125

Mrabet, Mohammed. M'HASHISH. London: Peter Owen, (1988). Paul Bowles, trans. 1st UK ed, only issued in wrappers. Fine. *LOPEZ*. $45

Mrabet, Mohammed. THE BIG MIRROR. London: Peter Owen, (1989). Paul Bowles, trans. 1st UK ed, only issued in wrappers. Fine. *LOPEZ*. $45

Mrabet, Mohammed. THE LEMON. NY: McGraw-Hill, (1972). Paul Bowles, trans. 1st Amer ed. Fine in dj. *LOPEZ*. $35

Mudge, Jean McClure. CHINESE EXPORT PORCELAIN FOR THE AMERICAN TRADE 1785-1835. DE: Univ of Delaware Press, 1962. 1st ed. VG in dj. *BACKROOM*. $75

Muehry, Adolph. OBSERVATIONS ON THE COMPARATIVE STATE OF MEDICINE IN FRANCE, ENGLAND, AND GERMANY, DURING A JOURNEY INTO THESE COUNTRIES IN THE YEAR 1835. Phila, 1838. 128pp. Pamphlet, removed from bound vol. 1st Eng trans. *FYE*. $75

Mueller, Hans A. HOW I MAKE WOODCUTS & WOOD ENGRAVINGS. NY, 1945. Fine. *POLYANTHOS*. $45

Muench, Joyce and Josef. GRAND CANYON. A PICTORIAL INTERPRETATION. NY, 1950. Clean, bright in Good+ dj. *FIVE QUAIL*. $25

Muir, John (ed). PICTURESQUE CALIFORNIA: THE ROCKY MOUNTAINS AND THE PACIFIC SLOPE. 2 vols. NY & SF: J. Dewing Pub Co., (1888). 3/4 brown lea and cl (covers detached, lea scuffed and chipped). 120 plts. Marginal staining end of vol 1. Contents unusually bright and clean. *BLUE MOUNTAIN*. $650

Muir, John. A THOUSAND-MILE WALK TO THE GULF. Boston: Houghton Mifflin, 1916. 1st ed. Fine in VG (scarce) dj. *BOOK MARKET*. $225

Muir, John. A THOUSAND-MILE WALK TO THE GULF. Boston: Houghton Mifflin, 1916. Lg paper ed. Pub's (scarce) pict slipcase w/version of the trade ed dj tipped on. Ltd to 550. Fine. *BOOK MARKET*. $450

Muir, John. OUR NATIONAL PARKS. Boston & NY, (1902). Illus. Gilt dec cl, teg. VG+. *MIKESH*. $37.50

Muir, John. THE MOUNTAINS OF CALIFORNIA. NY: Century, 1922. New and enl ed. Frontis, 16 plts, map. Lengthy inscrip on fep. Gilt-emb, dec cl. Beautiful and Fine. Howes M880. *CONNOLLY & WADE*. $50

Muir, John. THE STORY OF MY BOYHOOD AND YOUTH. Boston, 1913. 1st ed. 10 illus on 9 plts. Minor shelfwear, spine stains & rear cvr marks, o/w NF. *DIAMOND*. $75

Muir, John. THE YOSEMITE. NY: The Century Co, 1912. 1st ed. 3 fldg maps, 32 full-pg photo illus. Pict cl, some wear to head of spine and upper tips. Corner of one map creased, faint spotting to lower corners of some leaves. *DAWSON'S*. $175

Muir, John. TRAVELS IN ALASKA. Boston: Houghton Mifflin Co,, (1915). 1st ed. Partially removed paper label on bottom of spine, glue/paper marks on fly, bkpl, else VG- in orig. dec. cover. *BLUE DRAGON*. $60

Muir, John. TRAVELS IN ALASKA. Boston: Houghton Mifflin Co. 1915. 1st ed. Frontis, 11 plts. Gray cl stamped in white, mounted color illus on front cvr; cl, few small spots. *KARMIOLE*. $125

Muir, John. TWO ESSAYS ON THE SIGHTS & SOUNDS OF THE SIERRA NEVADA. Ashland: Lewis Osborne, 1973. One of 1000 numbered. Fine in dj. *LAURIE*. $60

Muir, John Reid. THE LIFE AND ACHIEVEMENTS OF CAPTAIN JAMES COOK R.N., F.R.S. EXPLORER, NAVIGATOR, SURVEYOR AND PHYSICIAN. London and Glasgow: Blackie and Son, Limited, 1939. 1st ed. Small marginal tear in fldg map, bit of wear to covers, else VG. *PARMER*. $50

Muir, P.H. (ed). TALKS ON BOOK-COLLECTING. London: Cassell, (1952). 1st ed. Lt foxing, o/w Fine in sl soiled dj. *JAFFE*. $65

Mujica-Lainez, Manuel. BOMARZO. NY: Simon & Schuster, (1969). 1st ed. Bit of spotting on fore-edge of pages o/w NF in dj. *LOPEZ*. $45

Mukerji, Dhan. THE CHIEF OF THE HERD. Dutton, (1929). Stated 1st ed. 168pp. Illus by Mahlon Blaine. NF in VG dj w/chips, two small holes, small edge tear. *BEBBAH*. $35

Mukherjee, Bharati. JASMINE. NY: Grove Weidenfeld, (1989). 1st ed. Signed. Fine in Fine dj. *LOPEZ*. $45

Mukherjee, Bharati. WIFE. Boston: Houghton Mifflin, 1975. 1st ed. Fine in NF dj. *BEASLEY*. $125

Mulford, Clarence E. BAR-20. NY, 1907. Author's 1st bk. 1st ed, 2nd state, w/o "Blazing Star" in list of illus. 7 plts. Little silverfishing on cl. Dampstaining few pp margins. Name stamp on fly, o/w VG. *DIAMOND*. $75

Mulford, Clarence E. HOPALONG CASSIDY RETURNS. Doubleday, Pg & Co, 1924. 1st ed. Pict cvr. VG+. *AUTHORS OF THE WEST*. $30

Mulford, Clarence E. THE BAR 20 RIDES AGAIN. GC: Doubleday, (1926). 1st ed. VG+ in VG intact dj showing very mild wear considering age. Ink drawing by Paul Brown, back panel. *UNGER*. $225

Mulford, Prentice. PRENTICE MULFORD'S STORY...Oakland, (1953). 300pp. Frederic Remington illus. Orig cl. Howes M882. *GINSBERG*. $30

Mulisch, Harry. THE ASSAULT. NY: Pantheon Books, (1985). 1st US ed. 1st book pub. in US. Trans by Claire Nicolas White. New in dj. *BERNARD*. $20

Mullan, John. MINERS AND TRAVELERS GUIDE TO OREGON, WASHINGTON, IDAHO...VIA THE MISSOURI AND COLUMBIA RIVERS. ACCOMPANIED BY A GENERAL MAP OF THE MINERAL REGION...OF THE ROCKY MOUNTAINS. NY: W.M. Franklin, 1865. 1st ed. Colored fldg map. Orig gilt and blindstamped cloth. Map folds tape reinforced, a few repaired tears. Fine. Howes M885. *OREGON*. $500

Mullen, Stanley. KINSMEN OF THE DRAGON. Chicago: Shasta Publishers Co, (1951). 1st ed. Signed. VG in dj (several internally mended edge tears; sl wear). *BERNARD*. $100

Muller, Dan. CHICO OF THE +UP RANCH. Chicago, 1938. 1st ed. Former owner's gift inscrip. NF in chipped dj. *BAADE*. $37.50

Muller, Dan. HORSES. Chicago, (1936). 1st trade ed. Burlap cvrs. Fore-edge sl spotted, o/w NF. *DIAMOND*. $35

Muller, Fritz. THE LIVING ARCTIC. Toronto: Methuen, (1977). VG+ in VG- dj. *BLUE DRAGON*. $25

Muller, Marcia. EDWIN OF THE IRON SHOES. NY: McKay, (1977). 1st ed. Signed. Fine in Fine dj. *UNGER.* $60

Muller, Marcia. LEAVE A MESSAGE FOR WILLIE. NY: St. Martin's Press, 1984. 1st ed. Fine in dj w/some tiny tears and wear at top of spine. *MORDIDA.* $22.50

Muller, Marcia. LEAVE A MESSAGE FOR WILLIE. NY: St. Martin's, 1984. 1st ed. Signed. VF in dj. *SILVER DOOR.* $35

Muller, Marcia. THE CAVALIER IN WHITE. NY: St. Martin's, 1986. 1st ed. Rev copy signed. Fine in dj. *SILVER DOOR.* $35

Muller, Marcia. THE CAVALIER IN WHITE. NY: St. Martin's Press, 1986. 1st ed. Fine in dj. *MORDIDA.* $32.50

Muller, Marcia. THE SHAPE OF THE DEAD. NY: Mysterious Press, 1989. 1st ed. VF in dj. *MORDIDA.* $25

Muller, S. BEYOND CIVILIZATION. Chico: Brown Gold Pubs, 1952. Spiral bound in ptd wraps. Wraps lightly soiled, owner inscrip, else VG. *PARMER.* $25

Muller-Freienfels, Richard. THE EVOLUTION OF MODERN PSYCHOLOGY. New Haven, 1935. 1st Eng trans. *FYE.* $40

Mullett, Charles. PUBLIC BATHS AND HEALTH IN ENGLAND, 16TH-18TH CENTURY. Baltimore, 1946. 1st ed. Wrappers. *FYE.* $35.

Mullin, Willard (as told to Dave Camerer). A HAND IN SPORT. Barnes, 1958. 1st ed. Good+ in VG dj. *PLAPINGER.* $50

Mumey, Nolie. JAMES PIERSON BECKWOURTH, 1856-1866. Denver, 1957. 1st ed, ltd to 500 numbered, signed. Frontis, 25 plts. Bkpl. VF in VG dj. *OREGON.* $165

Mumey, Nolie. NATHAN ADDISON BAKER (1843-1934). Denver: Old West Pub., 1965. #60/500 signed. Most pp unopened. Fine. *ARCHER.* $60

Mumey, Nolie. NATHAN ADDISON BAKER (1843-1934). Old West, 1965. 1st ed, ltd to 500 signed, numbered. 11 plts. Facs in rear cvr pocket. Lea spine and cvr labels. VF. *OREGON.* $40

Mumey, Nolie. OLD FORTS AND TRADING POSTS OF THE WEST. BENT'S OLD FORT & BENT'S NEW FORT ON ARKANSAS RIVER. VOL. I (all pub). Denver: Artcraft, 1956. 1st ed. Ltd to 500 numbered, signed. Frontis, 36 plts (4 fldg), fldg map tipped to rear. Spine faded, o/w Fine. *OREGON.* $160

Mumey, Nolie. ROCKY MOUNTAIN DICK. Denver: Range Press, 1953. 1st ed. Signed, #295 of 500. Fine. *VARNER.* $95

Mumey, Nolie. THE ART AND ACTIVITIES OF JOHN DARE (JACK) HOWLAND...PIONEER. Johnson Pub, 1973. 1st ed, ltd to 350 signed, numbered. Buckram w/leather cvr and spine labels. VG in Fine slipcase. *OREGON.* $125

Mumey, Nolie. THE LIFE OF JIM BAKER 1818-1898....Denver: World Press, 1931. 1st ed, ltd. to 250 signed, this #54. Frontis, 34 plts. Bl cl & boards, paper spine, cvr labels. 1" break in cl at top of spine. Bkpl, stamp o/w VG. Howes M889. *OREGON.* $300

Mumey, Nolie. THE SINGING ARROW. Denver: Golden Bell, 1958. One of 1000 numbered, signed. Fine in lightly rubbed, NF dj. *LOPEZ.* $50

Mumey, Nolie. THE TETON MOUNTAINS THEIR HISTORY AND TRADITION. WITH, AN ACCOUNT..Denver: Artcraft Press, 1947. 1st ed, ltd to 700 numbered, signed. Frontis, fldg panorama, dbl pg map. Cl, boards, pict paper cvr label, spine label (quite corner chipped revealing that title was orig gilt stamped onto the spine). Rear eps adhered to each other o/w VG. *OREGON.* $190

Mumford, James. A NARRATIVE OF MEDICINE IN AMERICA. Phila, 1903. *FYE.* $100

Mumford, James. SURGICAL MEMOIRS AND OTHER ESSAYS. NY, 1908. *FYE.* $75.

Mumford, Lewis. THE CITY IN HISTORY. NY: Harcourt Brace World, 1961. 1st ed. Signed. Illus; offsetting to eps, pencil notes to rear fep, VG+ in spine faded dj. *LAME DUCK.* $125

Mumford, Lewis. THE STORY OF UTOPIAS. Intro Hendrik Willem Van Loon (illus). NY, (1922). 1st ed, 1st bk. Orig buckram & boards, pict paper label. Spine gilt almost rubbed off. Minor soiling on boards. Text NF. *DIAMOND.* $150

Mundy, Godfrey Charles. OUR ANTIPODES: OR, RESIDENCE AND RAMBLES IN THE AUSTRALASIAN COLONIES WITH A GLIMPSE OF THE GOLD FIELDS. London: Richard Bentley, 1852. 2nd ed. 3 vols. Orig. gilt dec. blue cloth. 8vo, xii, 410pp; viii, 405pp; viii, 431pp. Good with wear to all edges, spotting and soil. *PARMER.* $700

Mundy, Talbot. BLACK LIGHT. Indianapolis, 1930. 1st ed. Extrems sl rubbed, name. NF. *POLYANTHOS.* $35

Mundy, Talbot. EAST AND WEST. Appleton, 1937. 1st ed. NF in sl edge-rubbed dj. *MADLE.* $200

Mundy, Talbot. FULL MOON. Appleton, 1935. 1st ed. Chip to bottom of dj spine, else VG. *MADLE.* $150

Mundy, Talbot. JIMGRIM AND ALLAH'S PEACE. NY & London: D. Appleton-Century Co., 1936. 1st ed. VG+ in price clipped dj sl chipped at spine ends, also, lightly soiled on rear panel. Still very attractive dj. *BERNARD.* $175

Mundy, Talbot. JUNGLE JEST. Century, 1932. 1st ed. VG in chipped dj. *MADLE.* $150

Mundy, Talbot. KING OF THE KHYBER RIFLES. Bobbs-Merrill, 1916 1st ed, 2nd issue. *MADLE.* $30

Mundy, Talbot. OM—THE SECRET OF AHBOR VALLEY. Indianapolis, (1924). 1st ed. VG. *BOND.* $27.50

Mundy, Talbot. THE DEVIL'S GUARD. Bobbs-Merrill, 1926. 1st ed. VG. *MADLE.* $35

Mundy, Talbot. THE GUNGA SAHIB. Appleton, 1934. 1st ed. Fine in dj. *MADLE.* $225

Mundy, Talbot. THE IVORY TRAIL. Bobbs-Merrill, 1919. 1st ed. VG *MADLE.* $35

Mundy, Talbot. TROS OF SAMOTHRACE, NY & London: D. AppletonCentury, 1934. Yellow cl bumped, rubbed. Signed by Mundy. VG. *BLUE MOUNTAIN.* $125

Mundy, Talbot. TROS OF SAMOTHRACE. Appleton, 1934. 1st ed. Near VG. *MADLE.* $40

Mundy, Talbot. WINDS OF THE WORLD. Burt, n.d. VG in dj. *MADLE.* $35

Munford, Robert Beverley, Jr. RICHMOND HOMES AND MEMORIES. Richmond: Garrett and Massie, c1936. 1st ed. Frontis. Partial dj. *HUDSON.* $35

Munk, J.A. SOUTHWEST SKETCHES. NY: G.P. Putnam's, 1920. 1st ed. Fine. *BOOK MARKET.* $65

Munk, Joseph A. ACTIVITIES OF A LIFETIME. LA: Times Mirror, 1924. 1st ed. 8 plts. VG. *OREGON.* $100

Munn, H. Warner. THE BANNER OF JOAN. West Kingston: Grant, 1975. 1st ed. Fine in dj, some browning. *OTHER WORLDS.* $30

Munn, H. Warner. THE WEREWOLF OF PONKERT. Donald Grant, 1958. 1st ed. Sm stain to rear panel of sl dusty dj, else Fine. Signed. *MADLE.* $150

Munn, Henry Toke. PRAIRIE TRAILS AND ARCTIC BY-WAYS. London: Hurst and Blackett, Ltd., 1932. 2nd imp. Sl musty, some foxing at edges. Laid in is 1938 New Year Greeting from Munn. *PARMER.* $75

Munn, Henry Toke. TALES OF THE ESKIMO. London, n.d. 196pp, 19 photos. Dj lacks 1/2 of backstrip. VG. *ARTIS.* $45

Munnings, Sir Alfred. THE AUTOBIOGRAPHY OF...VOL. I, AN ARTIST'S LIFE. London: Museum Press, 1952. Ltr prtg. Good+ in Good dj. VOL. II, THE SECOND BURST. Ltr. prtg. Good+ in Good dj. VOL. III, THE FINISH. 1st prtg. VG in Good dj. Set of 3 vols. *OCTOBER FARM.* $325

Munro, Alice. FRIEND OF MY YOUTH. NY: Knopf, 1990. 1st ed. New in dj. *BERNARD.* $25

Munro, Alice. FRIEND OF MY YOUTH. NY: Knopf, 1990. Wraps, adv uncorrected proofs. Signed by author. Fine in NF slipcase w/a few tears. *BEASLEY.* $50

Munro, Alice. SOMETHING I'VE BEEN MEANING TO TELL YOU. Toronto: McGraw Hill Ryerson, Ltd, (1974). 1st ed. Fine in dj w/two tiny tears. *CAPTAIN'S BOOKSHELF.* $75

Munro, Alice. THE BEGGAR MAID: STORIES OF FLO AND ROSE. (London): Allen Lane, (1980). 1st UK ed. Base of spine bumped else NF in NF dj. *ROBBINS.* $25

Munro, Donald. CRANIO-CEREBRAL INJURIES THEIR DIAGNOSIS AND TREATMENT. London, 1938. 1st ed. *FYE.* $75

Munro, John. FREDERICK JAMES FURNIVALL, A VOLUME OF PERSONAL RECORD. London: Henry Frowde, Oxford Univ Press, 1911. 1st ed. *OAK KNOLL.* $55

Munro, Neil. AYRSHIRE IDYLLS. A&C Black, 1923. 7s 6d Series. 2nd ed. NF. *OLD LONDON.* $37.50

Munro, Neil. THE HISTORY OF THE ROYAL BANK OF SCOTLAND, 1727-1927. Edinburgh: R. & R. Clark. 1928. 1st ed. xviii,416pp. Cvrs somewhat soiled. Teg. *KARMIOLE.* $35

Munro-Fraser, J. P. HISTORY OF SOLANO COUNTY. SF: Wood, 1879. 1st ed. 503pp. Orig gold stamped half calf, sm paper label on lower spine; bkpl removed; small gouge on upper spine affecting a few letters. Howes M897. Scarce. *GINSBERG.* $650

Murari, Timeri. THE MARRIAGE. (Dehli/London): Macmillan, (1973). 1st ed, 1st novel. Inscribed. VG in lightly edgeworn dj. *LOPEZ.* $45

Murbarger, Nell. GHOSTS OF THE GLORY TRAIL. Palm Desert: Desert Magazine Press, (1956). 1st ed. VG in VG dj. *BOOK MARKET.* $35

Murbarger, Nell. GHOSTS OF THE GLORY TRAIL: INTIMATE GLIMPSES.... Palm Desert: Desert Magazine, 1956. 1st ed. Signed. NF. *CONNOLLY & WADE.* $45

Murchison, R.I. SILURIA. London: John Murray, 1867. 4th ed. 40 plts. Lacks geological map at end. Rebacked. Ex-lib, page margins sl shaved, o/w Good. *DIAMOND.* $45

Murchison, R.I. SILURIA: THE HISTORY OF...WITH A BRIEF SKETCH OF THE DISTRIBUTION OF GOLD....London: J. Murray, 1854. 1st ed. 523pp. 37 plts, some fldg. Fldg map. Orig cl. Lacks frontis map. Cvr worn, rear hinge starting. Lib bkpl, stamp, else Good. *SMITHFIELD.* $120

Murdoch, Angus. BOOM COPPER. NY: Macmillan, 1943. 1st ed. Taped, tattered dj. *ARTIS.* $22.50

Murdoch, Iris with J.B. Priestley. A SEVERED HEAD: A PLAY IN THREE ACTS. London: Chatto & Windus, 1964. 1st ed. VF in dj. *ELSE FINE.* $50

Murdoch, Iris. A FAIRLY HONOURABLE DEFEAT. Viking, 1970. 1st Amer ed. Fine in VF dj. *STAHR.* $20

Murdoch, Iris. A SEVERED HEAD. London: C&W, 1961. 1st ed. NF in dj w/few tiny chips. *LAME DUCK.* $200

Murdoch, Iris. A SEVERED HEAD. NY: Viking, 1961. 1st ed. Fine; trace of spine fading to dj. *ELSE FINE.* $40

Murdoch, Iris. AN ACCIDENTAL MAN. NY: Viking, 1972. 1st ed. As New in dj. *ELSE FINE.* $40

Murdoch, Iris. AN ACCIDENTAL MAN. Viking, 1971. 1st Amer ed. Fine in NF dj. Dj spine lightly sunned. *STAHR.* $15

Murdoch, Iris. AN UNOFFICIAL ROSE. NY: Viking, (1962). 1st US ed. VG+ in VG+ price clipped dj. *AARD.* $25

Murdoch, Iris. AN UNOFFICIAL ROSE. NY: Viking, 1962. 1st ed. Fine in dj. *ELSE FINE.* $35

Murdoch, Iris. AN UNOFFICIAL ROSE. Viking,1962. 1st ed. Fine in NF dj (sm chip head of spine). *STAHR.* $20

Murdoch, Iris. HENRY AND CATO. Viking, 1977. 1st Amer ed. Fine in dj. *STAHR.* $20

Murdoch, Iris. THE BLACK PRINCE. NY: Viking, 1973. 1st ed. As New in dj. *ELSE FINE.* $35

Murdoch, Iris. THE BOOK AND THE BROTHERHOOD. Franklin Center: Franklin Lib, 1988. Leatherbound ltd ed. Signed. *LOPEZ.* $85

Murdoch, Iris. THE GOOD APPRENTICE. Cl backed marbled boards, tissue dj. London: London Limited Editions, (1985). 1st ed. Ltd to 250 signed. VF. *JAFFE.* $150

Murdoch, Iris. THE MESSAGE TO THE PLANET. Cl backed marbled boards, tissue dj. London: London Limited Editions, (1989). 1st ed. Ltd to 150 signed. VF. *JAFFE.* $150

Murdoch, Iris. THE RED AND THE GREEN. London: Chatto & Windus, (1965). 1st ed. Owner stamp front and rear eps, o/w VF in dj. *LOPEZ.* $50

Murdoch, Iris. THE SACRED & PROFANE LOVE MACHINE. NY: Viking, 1974. 1st ed. As New in dj. *ELSE FINE.* $30

Murdoch, Iris. THE SEA, THE SEA. NY: Viking Press, (1978). 1st Amer ed. Fine in dj w/touch of rubbing. *CAPTAIN'S BOOKSHELF.* $40

Murdoch, Iris. THE TIME OF THE ANGELS. London: Chatto & Windus, 1966. Fine in dj. *LOPEZ.* $50

Murdoch, Iris. UNDER THE NET. NY: Viking, 1954. 1st ed. Small bkpl under dj flap. Fine; minor wear to dj. *ELSE FINE.* $100

Murdock, Charles A. A BACKWARD GLANCE AT EIGHTY. SF: Paul Elder, 1921. Ltd ed, signed. Fine. *WEBER.* $30

Murdock, Harold. THE NINETEENTH OF APRIL, 1775. Boston, 1925, 1st ed. Fldg map in rear. Dj, small piece missing from top of spine. Book Fine. *HEINOLDT.* $12

Murfin, James V. THE GLEAM OF BAYONETS. NY, (1965). 2nd prtg. A little dj wear but VG+. *PRATT.* $30

Murie, Adolph. A NATURALIST IN ALASKA. NY: Devin-Adair, 1961. 1st ed. Fine in Fine dj. *AARD.* $20

Murphy, Bob. DESERT SHADOWS. Billings, MT: Privately ptd, 1986. 1st ed. Fine in wraps. *BOOK MARKET.* $20

Murphy, Celeste. THE PEOPLE OF THE PUEBLO OR THE STORY OF SONOMA. Sonoma: W.L. and C.G. Murphy, 1935. 2nd prtg. Spine faded, overall wear, generally VG. *PARMER.* $65

Murphy, Celeste. THE PEOPLE OF THE PUEBLO. Sonoma: Privately ptd, 1935. 1st ed. 22 plts. Fine. *OREGON.* $125

Murphy, Edmund. HENRY DE TONTY. FUR TRADER OF THE MISSISSIPPI. Baltimore: Johns Hopkins, 1941. 1st ed. Frontis, 5 plts, 1 fldg map. Signed presentation. VG. *OREGON.* $90

Murphy, James L. AN ARCHAEOLOGICAL HISTORY OF THE HOCKING VALLEY. Ohio: Ohio Univ Press, (1975). 92 figs. Good in tattered dj. *ARCHAEOLOGIA.* $35

Murphy, James Leonidas. ALABAMA AND THE CHARLESTON CONVENTION OF 1860. Montgomery, AL, 1905. Alabama Hist Soc Reprint #36. Wrappers. NF. *McGOWAN.* $45

Murphy, James. THE GABBY HARNETT STORY. Exposition Press, 1983. 1st ed. VG+ in Fine dj. *PLAPINGER.* $55

Murphy, Joseph E. SOUTH TO THE POLE BY SKI. St. Paul: Marlor Press, 1990. 1st ed. NF in dj with small abrasion on front. *PARMER.* $30

Murphy, Robert Cushman. A DEAD WHALE OR A STOVE BOAT. Boston: (Houghton Mifflin), 1967. 1st ed. Pub's white cl w/greenish stamping. *BOOK BLOCK.* $25

Murphy, Robert Cushman. LOGBOOK FOR GRACE/WHALING BRIG DAISY, 1912-1913. NY: Macmillan Company, 1947. 1st ed. VG in worn dj. *PARMER.* $40

Murphy, Robert. THE PEREGRINE FALCON. Boston: Houghton Mifflin, 1963. 2nd prtg. NF in dj. *OLD LONDON.* $15

Murphy, Thomas D. THREE WONDERLANDS OF THE AMERICAN WEST. Boston: L.C. Page, 1912. 1st ed. 16 color plts, 32 b/w plts, 3 maps. Teg. NF. *CONNOLLY & WADE.* $80

Murphy, Thomas D. THREE WONDERLANDS OF THE AMERICAN WEST. With 16 repros in color from orig paintings by Thomas Moran, and 32 duogravures from photos. Also maps of the Yellowstone, Yosemite, and Grand Canyon regions. 1st ed. Boston, 1912. Grn cloth, teg, untrimmed. Promo leaflet about book laid in. VG+. *FIVE QUAIL.* $75

Murray, A.H. Hallam et al. SKETCHES ON THE OLD ROAD THROUGH FRANCE TO FLORENCE. NY: Dutton, 1905. 48 plts, 1 map. Orig cl, corners rubbed, spine torn; internally VG; teg. *WORLDWIDE.* $18

Murray, Albert. SOUTH TO A VERY OLD PLACE. NY: McGraw-Hill, (1971). 1st ed. Fine in NF dj. *LOPEZ.* $65

Murray, Albert. SOUTH TO A VERY OLD PLACE. NY: McGraw Hill, (c1971). 1st ed. Inscribed. Fine in dj. *HELLER.* $60

Murray, Albert. STOMPING THE BLUES. NY: McGraw-Hill, (1976). 1st ed. Fine in price-clipped Fine dj. *BETWEEN COVERS.* $60

Murray, Albert. THE OMNI-AMERICANS. NY: Outerbridge & Dienstfrey, 1970. 1st ed. Fine in NF dj. *BEASLEY.* $40

Murray, Amelia M. LETTERS FROM THE UNITED STATES, CUBA AND CANADA....2 vols in 1. NY, 1856. 1st Amer ed. 408pp. Dec cl cvrs worn, recolored. VG. *DIAMOND.* $45

Murray, Bruce and Eric Burgess. FLIGHT TO MERCURY. NY: Columbia Univer Press, 1977. VG in dj. *KNOLLWOOD.* $40

Murray, George W. A HISTORY OF GEORGE W. MURRAY, AND HIS LONG CONFINEMENT AT ANDERSONVILLE, GEORGIA. (Hartford, CT, 186?). 1st ed. Wrappers. VG. *McGOWAN.* $37.50

Murray, Hon. Amelia M. LETTERS FROM THE UNITED STATES, CUBA, AND CANADA. NY: Putnam, 1856. 1st US ed. Worn pub's cl. Bkpl, rear hinge tender. Initials on flyleaf bled through to title pg. Howes M-912. *SECOND LIFE.* $85

Murray, James Austin. THE WAR BIBLE OF THE MOMENT WRITTEN INTO COLLOQUIAL ENGLISH AND PURE SLANG...Chicago: J. Murray, 1914. #851/1000. 270pp, stiff wraps, aeg. Some shelfwear o/w VG. *ARCHER.* $22.50

Murray, John Middleton (ed). THE SCRAPBOOK OF KATHERINE MANSFIELD. London: Constable, (1939). 1st ed. Fine in dj (sl faded spine, minute edgewear). *CAPTAIN'S BOOKSHELF.* $50

Murray, Keith A. THE MODOCS AND THEIR WAR. Norman, (1969). 2nd ptg of 1st ed. 343pp. VG in dj. *PRATT.* $32.50

Murray, Margaret A. EGYPTIAN TEMPLES. London: Sampson Low, (1931). 64 plts. Good. *ARCHAEOLOGIA.* $45

Murray, Margaret Alice. EGYPTIAN SCULPTURE. London: Duckworth, (1930). 8 figs, 55 plts. Signature. Good. *ARCHAEOLOGIA.* $45

Murray, Margaret. MY FIRST HUNDRED YEARS. London: William Kimber, (1963). 1st ed. 5 plts. Dj. Signature. Good. *ARCHAEOLOGIA.* $45

Murray, P.D.F. BONES: A STUDY OF THE DEVELOPMENT AND STRUCTURE OF THE VERTEBRATE SKELETON. Cambridge, 1936. 1st ed. *FYE.* $50

Murray, Pauline. PLANNING AND PLANTING THE HOME GARDEN. NY: Orange Judd, 1932. Cloth lightly worn, else VG. *AMERICAN BOTANIST.* $25

Murray, Robert. FORT LARAMIE. VISIONS OF A GRAND OLD POST. Fort Collins: Old Army Press, (1974). 1st ed. Autographed ed of 250. VF in VF dj. *OREGON.* $60

Murray, William. THE GETAWAY BLUES. Bantam, 1990. Uncorrected proof. Fine in blue and white wraps. Signed. Promo postcard laid in. *STAHR.* $35

Murray, William. WHEN THE FAT MAN SINGS. NY: Bantam, 1987. 1st ed. Rev copy signed. Fine in dj. *SILVER DOOR.* $35

Murtha, Edwin. PAUL MANSHIP. NY: The Macmillan Co. 1957. 1st ed. Color frontis. 132 plts. Dj. *KARMIOLE.* $100

Musgrave, Clifford. REGENCY FURNITURE 1800 TO 1830. NY: Thomas Yoseloff. (1961). 1st ed. Dj. Bkpl. *KARMIOLE.* $40

Musial, Stan (as told to Bob Broeg). STAN MUSIAL—THE MAN'S OWN STORY. Doubleday, 1964. 1st ed. VG in VG dj. *PLAPINGER.* $40

Musick, James. ST. LOUIS AS A FORTIFIED TOWN. NARRATIVE...STRUGGLE FOR FUR TRADE OF MISSISSIPPI VALLEY....St. Louis: Privately ptd, 1941. 1st ed, ltd to 500. VG. *OREGON.* $150

Musil, Alois. IN THE ARABIAN DESERT. NY, 1930. xiv,339pp. *O'NEILL.* $85

Musson, Spencer C. THE UPPER ENGADINE. A&C Black, 1907. 1st ed. 6s Series. Lacks one plt, else VG-NF. *OLD LONDON.* $40

Mutch, Thomas A. GEOLOGY OF THE MOON. Princeton Univ Press, 1972 (1970), rev ed. VG in dj. *KNOLLWOOD.* $45

Mutch, Thomas et al. THE GEOLOGY OF MARS. Princeton, NJ: Princeton Univ Press, 1976. VG in dj w/corner clipped. *KNOLLWOOD.* $45

MY DOLL'S HOUSE. A Bancroft Pop-Up Model Book. London, 1963. 2 very nice pop-ups. Pop-up bk. *BOOKFINDERS INTL.* $28

MY PETS. Cleveland: World, (1929). Color pict boards and cl. Color dj. Mammoth series #1400. Fine in Good dj. *ARTIS.* $25

MY POP—UP BOOK OF BABY ANIMALS. London, 1982. Ann Grahame Johnstone. Sm tape repair on back 1 pg. Pop-up bk. *BOOKFINDERS INTL.* $25

Myers, Charles E. MEMOIRS OF A HUNTER. Davenport: Privately ptd, 1948. 1st ed. (10),309pp, 18 plts. Fine in NF dj. *CONNOLLY & WADE.* $50

Myers, Gustavus. HISTORY OF BIGOTRY IN THE UNITED STATES. NY: Random House, (1943). 1st ed. Fine in VG dj. *WREDEN.* $35

Myers, H.M. and P.V.N. LIFE AND NATURE UNDER THE TROPICS....NY, 1871. 1st ed. xvi,330pp, (2pp-ads). Orig cl. Lt overall wear and scuffing, occasional lt foxing, mostly to preliminary pp. *SUTTON.* $65

Myers, Henry. O KING, LIVE FOR EVER. NY: Crown, (1953). 1st ed. Presentation inscrip. Fine in sl used dj. *DERMONT.* $45

Myers, J.C. SKETCHES ON A TOUR THROUGH THE NORTHERN AND EASTERN STATES, THE CANADAS AND NOVA SCOTIA. Harrisonburg, 1849. 1st ed. 476pp. Contemp full calf, joints strengthened. Howes M932. *GINSBERG.* $150

Myers, John M. PIRATE, PAWNEE AND MOUNTAIN MAN, THE SAGA OF HUGH GLASS. Little, Brown, (1963). 1st ed. Fine in Fine dj. *OREGON.* $35

Myers, John Myers. SAN FRANCISCO'S REIGN OF TERROR. GC, 1966. 1st ed. Dj has light wear and small piece torn off, o/w Fine. *PRATT.* $22.50

Myers, John Myers. THE DEATH OF THE BRAVOS. Boston, 1962. 1st ed. Dj wear o/w VG+. *PRATT.* $25

Myers, John Myers. THE LAST CHANCE: TOMBSTONE'S EARLY YEARS. NY: E.P. Dutton & Co, 1950. 1st ed. Dj chipped at edges, else VG. *LAURIE.* $25

Myers, John. THE LAST CHANCE. TOMBSTONE'S EARLY YEARS. Dutton, (1950). 1st ed. Inscription, o/w VG in VG dj. *OREGON.* $35

Myers, P.V.N. REMAINS OF LOST EMPIRES. NY: Harper, 1875. 531pp. *O'NEILL.* $45

Myers, Robert Manson. HANDEL'S MESSIAH. NY: Macmillan, 1948. 1st ed. Prev owner's name. VG+ in Good dj. *AARD.* $20

Myers, Robert Manson. THE CHILDREN OF PRIDE. New Haven, (1972). Abridged ed, (1984). Lt dj wear, o/w Fine. *PRATT.* $32.50

Myerson, Joel. RALPH WALDO EMERSON; A DESCRIPTIVE BIBLIOGRAPHY. Univ of Pittsburgh Press, 1982. 1st ed. VG. *WEBER.* $110

Mylod, John. BIOGRAPHY OF A RIVER, THE PEOPLE AND LEGENDS OF THE HUDSON VALLEY. NY (1969), 1st ed, dj. *HEINOLDT.* $15

Myrick, David F. NEW MEXICO'S RAILROAD. Golden, CO: Railroad Museum, 1970. 1st ed. Fine in Fine dj. *BOOK MARKET.* $40

N

Nabokoff, Vladimir. LAUGHTER IN THE DARK. Indianapolis: Bobbs-Merrill, 1938. 1st ed. Fine in the variant brown binding; Fine dj. *BEASLEY.* $450

Nabokov, Peter. INDIAN RUNNING. Santa Barbara: Capra Press, 1981. Only issued in wrappers. VG. Signed. *LOPEZ.* $45

Nabokov, Vladimir. ADA. NY: McGraw-Hill (1969). 1st Amer ed. Fine in a NF dj. *DORN.* $45

Nabokov, Vladimir. BEND SINISTER. NY: Henry Holt, 1947. 1st ed. Part of spine lettering faded, "2" stamped on top edge, o/w VG in VG rubbed dj w/small tear. *ARCHER.* $80

Nabokov, Vladimir. BEND SINISTER. NY: Holt, (1947). Spine ends lightly bumped, else NF in severely price-clipped but bright dj (touch of soiling). 1st ed. *CHAPEL HILL.* $225

Nabokov, Vladimir. CONCLUSIVE EVIDENCE. NY: Harper, 1951. 1st ed. Fine w/sunned edges, in worn dj w/tears and small chips. *BEASLEY.* $100

Nabokov, Vladimir. DESPAIR. Putnam, 1966. 1st Amer ed. About Fine in dj (2 sm tears, lt wear). Neat bkpl removal. *STAHR.* $25

Nabokov, Vladimir. INVITATION TO A BEHEADING. (New York: G. P. Putnam's Sons, [1959]). 1st Amer ed. Upper corners bumped, o/w VF in VF dj. *PIRAGES.* $150

Nabokov, Vladimir. INVITATION TO A BEHEADING. NY, (1959). 1st ed. Rev slip laid in. Sl edge soiled. Dj w/sm tears, soiled, crease. *POLYANTHOS.* $45

Nabokov, Vladimir. LOLITA. 2 vols. Paris: Olympia Press, (1955). 1st ed, 1st issue. 5000 (estimate) in 1st prtg. Ptd wrappers. Fine set in linen clamshell box w/leather label. *JAFFE.* $1650

Nabokov, Vladimir. LOLITA. NY: Putnam, (1955). 1st US ed. NF in lightly used dj. *CAPTAIN'S BOOKSHELF.* $125

Nabokov, Vladimir. NABOKOV'S QUARTET. (NY): Phaedra, 1966. 1st ed. Owner's name o/w NF in VG dj. *LOPEZ.* $35

Nabokov, Vladimir. NABOKOV'S QUARTET. (NY): Phaedra, 1966. 1st ed. Discoloration to front pastedown (mainly under dj flap), else Fine in dj. *CAPTAIN'S BOOKSHELF.* $50

Nabokov, Vladimir. NIKOLAI GOGOL. Norfolk: New Directions, 1944. The correct 1st ed, w/all points. Fine but for sl traces of foxing, in close to Fine dj w/tiny internal mends. *BEASLEY.* $150

Nabokov, Vladimir. NOTES ON PROSODY. London: RKP, 1965. 1st UK ed. NF in VG+ in dj lightly soiled along spine. *LAME DUCK.* $100

Nabokov, Vladimir. PALE FIRE. NY: Putnam, 1962. 1st ed. NF in price clipped dj w/discolored spine. *LAME DUCK.* $125

Nabokov, Vladimir. PNIN. Melbourne, London, Toronto: Heinemann, (1957). 1st UK ed. Sl offset to eps, else Fine in dj (creased). *BERNARD.* $100

Nabokov, Vladimir. POEMS. GC: Doubleday, 1959. 1st ed. Binding shows some spotting, else About Fine (lg owner sig) in sl used dj. *CAPTAIN'S BOOKSHELF.* $125

Nabokov, Vladimir. THE DEFENSE. NY: Putnam, (1964). 1st Amer ed. VG in lightly soiled dj. *DORN.* $60

Nabokov, Vladimir. THE EYE. NY: Phaedra (1965). 1st Amer ed. 1st state bk and dj. Fine in VG dust-soiled dj, price sticker residue. *DORN.* $40

Nabokov, Vladimir. THE GIFT. London: Weidenfeld and Nicolson, (c1963). 1st English language British ed. Fine in dj. *HELLER.* $50

Nabokov, Vladimir. THE GIFT. NY: Putnam (1963). 1st Amer ed. NF in sl worn, VG dj. *LOPEZ.* $35

Nabokov, Vladimir. THE WALTZ INVENTION. (NY): Phaedra, 1966. 1st ed. Fine in NF 1st issue dj (faded spine). *BERNARD.* $75

Nabokov, Vladimir. TRANSPARENT THINGS. NY: McGraw-Hill (1972). 1st Amer ed. Fine in dj. *DORN.* $40

Nadeau, Remi A. THE WATER SEEKERS. GC, 1950. VG+ in VG dj. *FIVE QUAIL.* $75

Nadeau, Remi. CITY MAKERS. NY: Doubleday, 1948. 1st ed. Fine in VG dj. Signed. *BOOK MARKET.* $60

Nadeau, Remi. FORT LARAMIE AND THE SIOUX INDIANS. Prentice Hall, (1967). 1st ed. VF in VG dj. *OREGON.* $35

Naether, C.A. THE BOOK OF THE PIGEON. Phila, 1939. Worn dj. *SUTTON.* $40

Nagatsuka, Ryuji. I WAS A KAMAKAZE. NY: Macmillan, (1973, 72). 1st US ed. Fine in Fine- dj. (price-clipped) *AARD.* $20

Nagel, Otto. THE DRAWINGS OF KATHE KOLLWITZ. NY: Galerie St. Etienne, and Crown, (1972). Dj. Sig of J. Zeitlin. Scarce. *WEBER.* $275

Naipaul, Shiva. NORTH OF SOUTH. London: Andre Deutsch, 1978. 1st ed. Fine in Fine dj. *BEASLEY.* $50

Naipaul, Shiva. THE CHIP-CHIP GATHERERS. London: Deutsch, 1973. Uncorrected proof in salmon wraps. Worn, thus VG only. Scarce. *LAME DUCK.* $200

Naipaul, V.S. A BEND IN THE RIVER. NY: Knopf, 1979. 1st US ed. Fine in NF dj. *AKA.* $40

Naipaul, V.S. A TURN IN THE SOUTH. Boards, dj. (London): Deutsch, (1989). 1st Eng ed. Mint. *JAFFE.* $45

Naipaul, V.S. A TURN IN THE SOUTH. London, (1989). 1st ed. Fine in dj. Signed. *LOPEZ.* $65

Naipaul, V.S. A TURN IN THE SOUTH. NY: Knopf, 1989. 1st Amer ed. Signed. Fine in dj. *LOPEZ.* $85

Naipaul, V.S. AN AREA OF DARKNESS. NY: Macmillan, (1965). 1st Amer ed. Fine in NF dj (front flap creased). *LOPEZ.* $85

Naipaul, V.S. GUERILLAS. NY, 1975. 1st US ed. Fine in dj. *PETTLER.* $25

Naipaul, V.S. IN A FREE STATE. (London): Deutsch, (1971). 1st UK ed. Prev owner name, o/w Fine in price-clipped dj. *LOPEZ.* $125

Naipaul, V.S. IN A FREE STATE. Boards, dj. (London): Deutsch, (1971). 1st ed. VF. *JAFFE.* $85

Naipaul, V.S. INDIA: A MILLION MUTINIES NOW. Boards, dj. London: Heineman, (1990). 1st ed. Signed. Mint. *JAFFE.* $100

Naipaul, V.S. INDIA: A MILLION MUTINIES NOW. Cl-backed marbled boards, glassine dj. London: London Limited Editions, (1990). 1st ed. One of 150 signed. Mint. *JAFFE.* $150

Naipaul, V.S. INDIA: A MILLION MUTINIES NOW. London: London Limited Editions, 1990. Ltd ed, 39/150 only. Signed, specially bound. Mint in Mint orig tissue dj. *POLYANTHOS.* $75

Naipaul, V.S. INDIA: A MILLION MUTINIES NOW. NY: Viking, 1990. Wraps. Adv uncorrected proofs. Fine. *BEASLEY.* $50

Naipaul, V.S. MIGUEL STREET. NY: Vanguard, (1960). 1st Amer ed. NF in dj (light edgewear, unobtrusive tear front panel). *LOPEZ.* $175

Naipaul, V.S. MR. STONE AND THE KNIGHT'S COMPANION. Boards, dj. (London): Deutsch, (1963). 1st ed. VF. *JAFFE.* $225

Naipaul, V.S. THE ENIGMA OF ARRIVAL. (NY): Viking, (1987). 1st ed. Fine in dj. *LOPEZ.* $30

Naipaul, V.S. THE ENIGMA OF ARRIVAL. NY: Knopf, 1987. Wraps. Adv uncorrected proofs. Fine. *BEASLEY.* $100

Naipaul, V.S. THE LOSS OF EL DORADO. (London): Deutsch, (1969). 1st Eng ed. Advance comp copy with slip laid in. Fine in dj. *LOPEZ.* $175

Naipaul, V.S. THE MYSTIC MASSEUR. NY, 1959. 1st US ed, 1st bk. NF in dj. Scarce in this condition. *PETTLER.* $90

Naipaul, V.S. THE MYSTIC MASSEUR. NY: Vanguard Press, (1959). 1st US ed of 1st bk. NF in VG dj (2" tear; sl spine wear). *BERNARD.* $60

Naipul, V.S. THE MIMIC MEN. NY: Macmillan, 1967. 1st US ed. Fine in VG dj. *ARCHER.* $25

Nakayama, Shigeru. A HISTORY OF JAPANESE ASTRONOMY, CHINESE BACKGROUND AND WESTERN IMPACT. Cambridge: Harvard Univ Press, 1969. Black mark bottom page edges, else Like New in dj. *KNOLLWOOD.* $28

Nalle, Ouida Ferguson. THE FERGUSONS OF TEXAS OR "TWO GOVERNORS FOR THE PRICE OF ONE." San Antonio: The Naylor Co, 1946. 1st ed. Fldg genealogical chart. Fine in chipped dj. *GIBBS.* $45

Nancrede, Charles. LECTURES UPON THE PRINCIPLES OF SURGERY. Phila, 1899. 1st ed. *FYE.* $75

Nansen, Fridtjof. FARTHEST NORTH. 2 vols bound together. London, 1898. Pl, portrait, fldg map. 1st pg has stains from colored litho opposite. Cvr wear. *HEINOLDT.* $40

Nansen, Fridtjof. FARTHEST NORTH. In Two Volumes. NY: Harper & Bros. 1897. 1st ed. 2 vols. Lg. 8vo. xiv,588; xii,730pp, 4pp ads. Index. 4 fldg maps in 2 pockets of vol 1. *KARMIOLE.* $175

Nansen, Fridtjof. THE FIRST CROSSING OF GREENLAND. London: Longmans, Green, & Co, 1897. New ed. Ex-lib lightly marked. Good, sound. *BLUE DRAGON.* $45

Nanton, Paul. ARCTIC BREAKTHROUGH. FRANKLIN'S EXPEDITIONS, 1819-1847. Toronto: Clarke, Irwin, 1970. 1st Canadian ed. Fine in Fine dj. *AARD.* $20

Nanton, Paul. ARCTIC BREAKTHROUGH. FRANKLIN'S EXPEDITIONS 1819-1847. Toronto: Clarke, Irwin, 1970. 1st ed. VG in similar dj. Autographed. *PARMER.* $35

Naphegyi, G. GHARDAIA; OR NINETY DAYS AMONG THE B'NI MOZAB. NY: G.P. Putnam. 1871. 1st ed. 348pp. Orig purple cl, gilt. *KARMIOLE.* $75

Nares, Sir G(eorge) S(trong). NARRATIVE OF A VOYAGE TO THE POLAR SEA DURING 1875-6 IN H.M. SHIPS 'ALERT'

AND 'DISCOVERY.'....H.W. Feilden (ed). London: Sampson Low, Marston, Searle, & Rivington, 1878. 1st ed. 2 vols. 2 fldg maps (1 w/crease tears), 6 mounted woodburytypes. Minor soiling; sl interior wear. *PARMER.* $600

Nasatir, A.P. (ed). A FRENCH JOURNALIST IN THE CALIFORNIA GOLD RUSH. Georgetown, CA: Talisman Press, 1964. 1st ed. Fine. *OREGON.* $55

Nasatir, Abraham. BEFORE LEWIS AND CLARK...HISTORY OF THE MISSOURI 1785-1804. St. Louis Hist Documents Foundation, 1952. 2 vols. 1st ed. 5 fldg maps. VF in VF dj. *OREGON.* $200

Nasby, Petroleum V. (pseud of David Ross Locke). "SWINGIN ROUND THE CIRKLE." Boston: Lee and Shepard, 1867. 1st ed. 8 plts. Orig cl, wear at spine. *SCHOYER'S.* $45

Nash, Ann. CABBAGES AND CRIME. Doubleday, 1945. 1st ed. VG in dj with few chips. *BEBBAH.* $18

Nash, Jay Robert. LOOK FOR THE WOMAN. NY: Evans, (1981). VG in dj. *SCHOYER'S.* $25

Nash, Jay Robert. LOOK FOR THE WOMAN. NY: Evans, 1981. 1st ed. Fine in Fine dj. *BEASLEY.* $30

Nash, Ogden. GOOD INTENTIONS. Boston: Little Brown, 1942. 1st ed. VF; minor wear, a little age darkening at dj extremities. *ELSE FINE.* $45

Nash, Ogden. HAPPY DAYS. NY: Simon & Schuster, 1933. 1st ed. Bkpl, offsetting to fep from newspaper clipping, else Fine. Light aging, tiny chips corners of dj spine. *ELSE FINE.* $100

Nash, Paul. OUTLINE: AN AUTOBIOGRAPHY....London: Faber and Faber Ltd, 1949. 50 plts. Blue buckram boards, dj. VG. *HELLER.* $125

Nash, Wallis. OREGON: THERE AND BACK IN 1877. London: Macmillan, 1878. 1st ed. Double pp color map, 9 plts. Ex-lib, spine darkened, ends and hinges reinforced. Good+. *OREGON.* $37.50

Nash, Wallis. TWO YEARS IN OREGON. Appleton, 1882. 2nd ptg. Fine. *OREGON.* $60

Nash, Wallis. TWO YEARS IN OREGON. NY: Appleton, 1882. 1st ed. 311pp. Spine soiled. Rear ep sl torn, o/w VG. *DIAMOND.* $75

Nash, Wallis. TWO YEARS IN OREGON. NY: D. Appleton & Co, 1882. 1st ed. Ex-lib but still VG. *LAURIE.* $50

Nasmyth, James and James Carpenter. THE MOON, CONSIDERED AS A PLANET, A WORLD, AND A SATELLITE, London: John Murray, 1903 (1874). 4th ed. 25 plts. Corners bumped, minor spotting of boards, eps browned. Good. *KNOLLWOOD.* $75

Nasnaga. INDIANS' SUMMER. NY: H&R, (1975). 1st ed. Fine in NF dj. *LOPEZ.* $45

Nasr, Seyyed Hossein. PERSIA. BRIDGE OF TURQUOISE. Boston: NY Graphic Soc, 1975. 1st ed. Dj. NF. *WORLDWIDE.* $125

Nast, Thomas. MISS COLUMBIA'S PUBLIC SCHOOL OR WILL IT BLOW OVER? NY: Francis B. Felt, 1871. Lt wear extrems. Orig gilt lettered cl. *CULLEN.* $100

Nast, Thomas. THE FIGHT AT DAME EUROPA'S SCHOOL. NY: Francis B. Felt, (1871). 1st ed. Bright in orig gilt-lettered cl. *CULLEN.* $100

Nathan, George Jean. BEWARE OF PARENTS. NY: Farrar & Rinehart, (1943). 1st ed. Dj. Fine. *MUELLER.* $35

Nathan, George Jean. LAND OF THE PILGRIM'S PRIDE. NY: Knopf, 1927. 1st ed. Dj. Fine. *MUELLER.* $25

Nathan, George Jean. THE AUTOBIOGRAPHY OF AN ATTITUDE. NY: Knopf, 1925. 1st ed. Dj. Fine. *MUELLER.* $30

Nathan, George Jean. THE AVON FLOWS. NY: Random House, (1937). 1st ed. Dj tear. Fine. *MUELLER.* $20

Nathan, Robert. JOURNEY OF TAPIOLA. NY: Knopf, 1938. 1st ed. Spine very sl darkened, else Fine in VG dj w/slight chipping, bit of darkening on spine. BETWEEN COVERS. $35

Nathan, Robert. TAPIOLA'S BRAVE REGIMENT. NY: Knopf, 1941. Adv reading copy in self wraps w/slip. Two faint coffee rings on front wrap, spine darkened, wrinkled. VG. BETWEEN COVERS. $50

Nathan, Robert. THE CONCERT. NY: House of Books, 1940. 1/250. Signed, ltd. ed. VF in pub's glassine dj, sl age darkened but still Fine. LOPEZ. $65

Nathan, Robert. YOUTH GROWS OLD. NY: Robert M. McBride Co. 1922. 1st ed. 54pp. Black cl. Nice dj. KARMIOLE. $65

NATURE. (By Ralph Waldo Emerson.) Boston: James Munroe & Co., 1836. 8vo, 95pp. Orig dk brown cl. Modest wear to corners and spine tips, Very light scattered foxing, Emerson postage stamp tipped to ffep, but VG. Bright, appealing, w/signature of "M. Wells, Whitesboro, 1842." 1st ed, 2nd state, w/pp 94 correctly paged. Clipped signature of "Emerson" is tipped in at title page, but this is apparently not in the author's hand. Pinkish-tan eps. This copy 5/16" shorter than other copies examined. BAL 5181. CHAPEL HILL. $1,500

Naunyn, B. A TREATISE ON CHOLELITHIASIS. London, 1896. 1st Eng trans. FYE. $100

NAVAL ACTIONS, AND OPERATIONS AGAINST CUBA AND PORTO RICO, 1593-1815. Boston: 1901. Orig cl. 1st ed. GINSBERG. $75

NAVAL SKETCHES OF THE WAR IN CALIFORNIA: REPRODUCING TWENTY-EIGHT DRAWINGS MADE IN 1846-47 BY WILLIAM H. MEYERS....NY: Random House, 1939. One of 1000. 28 full-pg color illus. Marbled boards, lea spine, lea spine label. Faint spot bottom of spine, slight rubbing part of spine. DAWSON'S. $300

Naville, Edouard. AHNAS EL MEDINEH (HERACLEOPOLIS MAGNA) WITH CHAPTERS....Tylor, J.J. and F. Griffith. THE TOMB OF PAHERI AT EL KAB. London: Kegan Paul, Trench, Trubner, Quaritch, 1894. 1st ed. (12),40,viii,35pp, folio. 28 plts, 8 fldg. Orig boards w/cl spine, edges rubbed, o/w VG. Ex-lib w/number on spine. WORLDWIDE. $65

Naville, Edouard. THE FESTIVAL-HALL OF OSORKON II IN THE GREAT TEMPLE OF BUBASTIS (1887-1889). London: Kegan Paul, Trench, Trubner, 1892. 1st ed, 39 plts. 19 fldg. Orig boards w/cl spine, edges rubbed, spine frayed, o/w VG. Ex-lib w/number on spine. WORLDWIDE. $95

Naylor, Gloria. LINDEN HILLS. Pict wrappers. NY: Ticknor & Fields, 1985. Advance copy of 1st ed. Signed. Mint. JAFFE. $150

Naylor, Gloria. LINDEN HILLS. Ticknor & Fields, 1985. Advance reading copy. Fine in dec. wraps. STAHR. $60

Naylor, Gloria. LINDEN HILLS. Ticknor & Fields, 1985. Fine in Fine dj. BEBBAH. $20

Naylor, Gloria. MAMA DAY. NY: Ticknor & Fields, 1988. Advance copy of the 1st ed. Signed. Wraps. Mint. JAFFE. $125

Naylor, Gloria. THE WOMEN OF BREWSTER PLACE. NY: Viking, (1982). 1st ed of 1st bk. Fine in dj. Scarce. BERNARD. $400

Naylor, Gloria. THE WOMEN OF BREWSTER PLACE. NY: Viking, (1982). 1st ed. Rmdr stamping bottom edge of pp, o/w NF in dj. LOPEZ. $350

Naylor, Gloria. THE WOMEN OF BREWSTER PLACE. Ptd wrappers. NY: Viking, (1982). Uncorrected proof. Signed. VF, rare proof. JAFFE. $1000

Neal, E. Virgil and C.S. Clark (eds). HYPNOTISM AND HYPNOTIC SUGGESTION. Rochester, NY, (1906). 1st ed. DIAMOND. $45

Neal, Larry. BLACK BOOGALOO (NOTES ON BLACK LIBERATION). (SF): Journal of Black Poetry Press, (1969). 1st ed. Wrap-

pers a bit tanned, little rubbing, else NF. Very uncommon. BETWEEN COVERS. $100

Neale, John Preston. THE HISTORY AND ANTIQUITIES OF WESTMINSTER ABBEY AND HENRY THE SEVENTH'S CHAPEL. London: Willis & Sotheran. 1856. xviii,112pp. 85 engr. Orig calf spine over grn cl; corners sl worn. KARMIOLE. $200

Neale, Rev. J.M. NOTES, ECCLESIOLOGICAL AND PICTURESQUE, ON ALMATIA, CROATIA, ISTRIA, STYRIA....London, 1861. Fldg frontis, 3 plts. viii,208pp. O'NEILL. $75

Nearing, Helen and Scott. THE MAPLE SUGAR BOOK. NY: John Day, (1950). 1st ed (?) Inscribed by authors. SECOND LIFE. $45

Nearing, Scott. EDUCATIONAL FRONTIERS. A BOOK ABOUT SIMON NELSON PATTEN AND OTHER TEACHERS. Privately printed, 1925. 1/170, numbered and signed by the author. NF, probably issued w/out dj. Quite uncommon. BEASLEY. $100

Neatby, Leslie H. IN QUEST OF THE NORTHWEST PASSAGE. NY: Crowell Co, (1958). 1st Amer ed. VG in Good dj. BLUE DRAGON. $25

Neatby, Leslie. CONQUEST OF THE LAST FRONTIER. Athens: Ohio Univ, (1966). 1st ed. 4 double pp maps. Fine in Fine dj. OREGON. $30

Needham, I.G. and H.B. HEYWOOD. A HANDBOOK OF THE DRAGONFLIES OF NORTH AMERICA. Springfield, 1929. Spine faded. SUTTON. $45

Needham, Joseph. A HISTORY OF EMBRYOLOGY. NY, 1959. Ex-lib. FYE. $75

Neeser, Robert Wilden. STATISTICAL AND CHRONOLOGICAL HISTORY OF THE UNITED STATES NAVY 1775-1907. NY, 1909. 1st ed. 2 vols. (viii),153; (vi),487pp. Cvrs very worn, spine of Vol 1 torn. LEFKOWICZ. $225

Neff, Robert and Anthony Connor. BLUES. Boston: Godine, 1975. 1st ed. Issued in wraps and cloth, this being the wraps issue. About Fine. BEASLEY. $35

Neftel, William. GALVANO-THERAPEUTICS. NY, 1873. 1st ed. 161pp. Scarce. FYE. $125

Negovskii, V.A. RESUSCITATION AND ARTIFICIAL HYPOTHERMIA. NY, 1962. 1st Eng trans. FYE. $50

Neihardt, John G. POETIC VALUES: THEIR REALITY....Macmillan, 1925. 1st ed. Fine, bright. AUTHORS OF THE WEST. $40

Neihardt, John G. SONG OF HUGH GLASS. NY, 1915. 1st ed. 8 pp ads. Bright. HEINOLDT. $25

Neihardt, John G. THE SONG OF HUGH GLASS. Macmillan, 1915. 1st ed. Fine, name, address. AUTHORS OF THE WEST. $60

Neihardt, John G. WHEN THE TREE FLOWERED. NY: Macmillan, 1951. 1st ed. VG in edgeworn dj. LOPEZ. $25

Neihardt, John. THE SPLENDID WAYFARING...JEDEDIAH SMITH & HIS COMRADES...Macmillan, 1920. 1st ed. Frontis, 16 plts. VG. OREGON. $55

Neil, James. PALESTINE EXPLORED WITH VIEW TO ITS PRESENT NATURAL FEATURES. London: James Nisbet, 1888. Frontis. Good. ARCHAEOLOGIA. $45

Neill, Edward D. MATERIALS FOR THE FUTURE HISTORY OF MINNESOTA. St. Paul: Brown, 1856. 1st ed. 142,(17)pp. Frontis. Contemp half morocco, front orig ptd wrapper laid in. Emb lib stamp. Howes N42. GINSBERG. $125

Neill, Edward D. THE HISTORY OF MINNESOTA...Phila & Minneapolis, 1873. 2nd ed. 2 fldg maps. Contemp lib calf. Rebacked. Inner front hinge reinforced. Rear hinge starting. Few small tears on fldg maps, o/w VG. DIAMOND. $75

Neill, John. OUTLINES OF THE ARTERIES: WITH SHORT DESCRIPTIONS. Phila, 1852. 2nd ed. 28pp + 7 color plts. FYE. $100

Neill, Patrick. THE FRUIT, FLOWER, AND KITCHEN GARDEN. Phila, 1851. Orig cl worn at extrems, spine ends partially perished, foxed. Ex-lib. *SUTTON*. $45

Neill, Patrick. THE FRUIT, FLOWER AND KITCHEN GARDEN. Phila: Baird, 1851. 4th ed. 427pp. Head and tail of spine rubbed, feps removed, else Very Sound. *AMERICAN BOTANIST*. $40

Neilsen, Waldo. RIGHT-OF-WAY. A GUIDE TO ABANDONED RAILROADS IN THE UNITED STATES. Bend, OR: Old Bottle Magazine, c1974. Pict wraps. Labels removed from cover. Scarce. *HUDSON*. $35

Neilson, Charles. ORIGINAL, COMPILED AND CORRECTED ACCOUNT OF BURGOYNE'S CAMPAIGN AND THE MEMORABLE BATTLES.... (Munsell, Albany orig 1844) Reprint author, Bemis Heights, 1926. Errata pg. Spine faded. *HEINOLDT*. $20

Nelson, Bruce. LAND OF THE DACOTAHS. U of Minn, Minneapolis (1946), 1st ed. Cover dull, top of spine worn. *HEINOLDT*. $18

Nelson, Herbert B. THE LITERARY IMPULSE IN PIONEER OREGON. Corvallis: OR State College at the College Press, 1948. 1st ed. Fldg map; plts. Ptd wrappers. NF. *CONNOLLY & WADE*. $37.50

Nelson, J. Raleigh. LADY UNAFRAID. Caxton, 1952. 1st ed. Fine in chipped dj. *ARTIS*. $30

Nelson, James G. THE EARLY NINETIES, A VIEW FROM THE BODLEY HEAD. Cambridge: Harvard Univ Press, 1971. 1st ed. Cl, dj. *OAK KNOLL*. $25

Nelson, John Louw. RHYTHM FOR RAIN. Boston, 1937. 1st ed. VG+. *DIAMOND*. $35

Nelson, John Louw. RHYTHM FOR RAIN. Boston: Houghton Mifflin, 1937. 1st ed. Dj worn, o/w Good. *LAURIE*. $35

Nelson, Paul. CARGO. (Iowa City): Stone Wall Press/Seamark Press, 1972. 1st ed. Ltd to 250. Cl, w/ptd label. Fine. *JAFFE*. $75

Nelson, Truman. THE OLD MAN, JOHN BROWN AT HARPER'S FERRY. NY, 1973. 1st ed. 304pp. Fine in dj. *PRATT*. $27.50

Nelson, William Hamilton. ALLURING ARIZONA. SF, 1927. 3rd ed. Inscribed. Fine in VG dj. *FIVE QUAIL*. $15

Nemerov, Howard. FIGURES OF THOUGHT. Boston: Godine (n.d.). Uncorrected proof. Signed. Fine in wraps. *DORN*. $65

Nemerov, Howard. GUIDE TO THE RUINS. NY: Random House, (1950). Adv rev copy w/slip. Fine in sl worn dj. *DORN*. $70

Nemerov, Howard. JOURNAL OF THE FICTIVE LIFE. New Brunswick: Rutgers (1965). 1st ed. VG in dj (edgewear, chips). *DORN*. $25

Nemerov, Howard. MIRRORS & WINDOWS: POEMS. Chicago: Univ of Chicago Press (1958). 1st ed. Inscribed. VG in sl worn dj. *DORN*. $60

Nemerov, Howard. NEW AND SELECTED POEMS. Chicago: Univ of Chicago Press (1960). 1st ed. Inscribed. NF in dj. *DORN*. $60

Nemerov, Howard. THE MELODRAMATISTS. NY, 1949. 1st ed. Bkpl, bkst sticker, else VG in bit chipped dj. *PETTLER*. $40

Nemerov, Howard. THE SALT GARDEN. Boston: Little, Brown (1955). 1st ed. Inscribed. Black paper covering chipped, rubbed. Dj shows lt use. *DORN*. $50

Nemerov, Howard. THE WESTERN APPROACHES: POEMS 1973-75. Chicago: Univ of Chicago Press (1975). 1st ed. Signed. Fine in dj. *DORN*. $45

Nemerov, Howard. THE WINTER LIGHTNING. London: Rapp & Whiting (1968). 1st Eng ed. Inscribed. Fine in dj. *DORN*. $45

Nernst, Walter. THEORETICAL CHEMISTRY FROM THE STANDPOINT OF AVOGADRO'S RULE & THERMODYNAMICS. London, 1895. 1st Eng trans. 697pp. Exceptionally Fine. *FYE*. $200

Neruda, Pablo. LET THE RAIL SPLITTER AWAKE AND OTHER POEMS. NY: Masses & Mainstreams (1950). 1st Amer ed. Fine in NF dj (sm chip). *DORN*. $150

Neruda, Pablo. MEMOIRS. NY, 1977. 1st ed. Fine in dj w/edge tear rear panel. *POLYANTHOS*. $25

Neruda, Pablo. SPLENDOR AND DEATH OF JOAQUIN MURIETA. NY: FSG (1972). 1st Amer ed. Fine in price-clipped dj. *DORN*. $30

Nesbitt, Francis E. ALGERIA AND TUNIS. A&C Black, 1906. 1st ed. 20s Series. NF. *OLD LONDON*. $165

Nesbitt, L.M. DESERT AND FOREST: THE EXPLORATION OF ABYSSINIAN DANAKIL. London: Alden Press, 1934. 2nd ed. Fldg map. Good. *WORLDWIDE*. $14

Netter, Frank. A COMPILATION OF PAINTINGS ON THE NORMAL AND PATHOLOGICAL ANATOMY OF THE NERVOUS SYSTEM. Summit, NJ, 1968. 1st ed. *FYE*. $50

Netter, Frank. THE CIBA COLLECTION OF MEDICAL ILLUSTRATIONS. Summit, NJ, 1948. 1st ed. Scarce. *FYE*. $75

Netter, Frank. THE CIBA COLLECTION OF MEDICAL ILLUSTRATIONS. VOLUMES 1-6 (IN 8). Summit, NJ, 1975. Slipcase. *FYE*. $200

Nettle, Richard. THE SALMON FISHERIES OF THE ST. LAWRENCE AND ITS TRIBUTARIES. Montreal: John Lovell, 1857. 1st ed. 12mo. 144pp. Orig cloth. Copyright slip pasted to verso of title. Lib stamp on title, institutional bkplt inside front cover, but Very Nice. *M & S*. $550

Neuburger, Max. BRITISH MEDICINE AND THE VIENNA SCHOOL, CONTACTS AND PARALLELS. London, 1943. 1st ed. *FYE*. $75

Neuburger, Max. THE HISTORICAL DEVELOPMENT OF EXPERIMENTAL BRAIN AND SPINAL CORD PHYSIOLOGY BEFORE FLOURENS. Baltimore, 1981. 1st Eng trans. *FYE*. $50

Neugeboren, Jay. LISTEN RUBEN FONTANEZ. Boston: Houghton Mifflin, 1968. 1st ed. Bkpl. Signed. Fine in NF dj. *LOPEZ*. $35

Neugeboren, Jay. PARENTHESES. NY: Dutton (1970). 1st ed. Inscribed. NF in dj. *LOPEZ*. $30

Neugeboren, Jay. SAM'S LEGACY. NY: HRW (1974). 1st ed. Inscribed. Very light stain bottom edge of fep o/w NF in dj. *LOPEZ*. $25

Neville, A.W. THE RED RIVER VALLEY: THEN AND NOW. Paris: (North Texas Publishing Co.), 1948. One of 2,000. Fine in dj. *LAURIE*. $125

Nevins, Allan. FORD: THE TIMES, THE MAN, THE COMPANY. NY: Scribner's, 1954. 1st ed. Fine in Fine dj. *BOOK MARKET*. $50

Nevins, Allan. FREMONT. THE WEST'S GREATEST ADVENTURER. NY: Harper & Bros. 1928. 1st ed. 2 vols and 62 plts. Maroon cl stamped in white. Djs. Scarce in this fine condition. *KARMIOLE*. $100

Nevins, Allan. FREMONT: THE WEST'S GREATEST ADVENTURER. NY: Harper, 1928. 1st ed. 2 vols. Blue cl, gilt. VG. *CONNOLLY & WADE*. $90

Nevins, Allan. THE WAR FOR THE UNION. 4 vols. NY, 1959, 1960 & 1971. 1st eds. 436, 557, 532 & 448pp. Vol. I inscribed. A little dj wear, chipping; one vol has faded dj spine o/w Fine. *PRATT*. $95

Nevins, Francis M., Jr. ROYAL BLOODLINES: ELLERY QUEEN....Bowling Green: Bowling Green Univ Press, 1974. 1st ed. VF w/o dj as issued. Contains a Queen checklist. *MORDIDA*. $35

NEW HAMPSHIRE. Boston, 1938. American Guide Series. Light chipping to dj. Maps. NF. *POLYANTHOS*. $40

NEW MEXICO, A GUIDE TO THE COLORFUL STATE. Hastings House, 1940. 1st ed. American Guide Series. VG. *OREGON*. $45

NEW STORIES FROM THE CHAPBOOK....Chicago, 1898. Pub's pink cl w/figures of 3 "Sandwich Men." The colors employed are red and black; design appears on both covers; spine stamped w/solid red (for the 1st series, solid blue), with the lettering dropped out in the pink. 1/4" reinforcement to a split in head of spine. Ptd at Lakeside Press in Caslon types on laid paper. *BOOK BLOCK.* $150

Newberry, Julia. JULIA NEWBERRY'S DIARY. Norton, NY (1933). Frontis. Spine faded, spot on front cover. *HEINOLDT.* $10

Newby, Eric. A SHORT WALK IN THE HINDU KUSH: London: Secker & Warburg, 1958. 1st ed. 2 fldg maps. In torn badly chipped dj. *SCHOYER'S.* $60

Newcomb, Raymond Lee. OUR LOST EXPLORERS...THE JEAN-NETTE ARCTIC EXPEDITION. Hartford: American Pub Co, 1883. VG. *WEBER.* $75

Newcomb, Rexford. OLD KENTUCKY ARCHITECTURE. NY: William Helburn, 1940. 1st ed. 130 plts. Owner's inscrip on ffep. Blue cl. *KARMIOLE.* $45

Newcomb, Rexford. THE COLONIAL AND FEDERAL HOUSE: HOW TO BUILD AN AUTHENTIC COLONIAL HOUSE. Phila: Lippincott, 1933. 1st ed. NF. *CAPTAIN'S BOOKSHELF.* $50

Newell, Charles Martin. KAMEHAMEHA, THE CONQUERING KING...A ROMANCE OF HAWAII. NY and London: G.P. Putnam's Sons, 1885. 1st ed. viii,399pp. Frontis, facs letter. Olive grn cl stamped in black, very sl rubbed at corners. Owner sig. *WEBER.* $75

Newell, Peter. THE ROCKET BOOK. NY: Harpers, (1912). 1st ed. Some light soiling to some pgs, binding, but VG (pict label affixed to front panel being lightly chipped). *CAPTAIN'S BOOKSHELF.* $75

Newell, Robert. ROBERT NEWELL'S MEMORANDA: TRAVELS IN TERITORY OF MISSOURIE. Dorothy Johanson (ed). Portland: Champoeg Press, 1959. 1st ed, ltd to 1000. Frontis, 1 fldg map. Fine. *OREGON.* $60

Newhafer, Richard. NO MORE BUGLES IN THE SKY. NY: NAL, (1966). Stated 1st ed. Dj edgeworn, few edge chips, tears. VG+ in VG dj. *AKA.* $60

Newhall, Nancy. TIME IN NEW ENGLAND. NY: Oxford, 1950. 1st ed. Fine in lightly used dj. *CAPTAIN'S BOOKSHELF.* $100

Newhall, Ruth Waldo. THE NEWHALL RANCH. San Marino: Huntington, 1958. 1st ed. Fine in Fine dj. *CONNOLLY & WADE.* $75

Newhall, Ruth. THE NEWHALL RANCH. San Marino: Huntington, 1958. 1st ed. VG. *OREGON.* $60

Newhouse, Edward. ANYTHING CAN HAPPEN. NY: Harcourt, 1941. 1st ed. Fine in About Fine dj. *BEASLEY.* $75

Newman, Charles. A CHILD'S HISTORY OF AMERICA. Chicago: Swallow Press, (1973). 1st ed. Inscribed. Fine in NF dj. *LOPEZ.* $65

Newman, Charles. THE EVOLUTION OF MEDICAL EDUCA-TION IN THE NINETEENTH CENTURY. London, 1957. 1st ed. *FYE.* $100

Newman, Isidora. THE LEGEND OF THE ORANGE BLOSSOM AND OTHER FAIRY FLOWERS. Whitman, (1926). Un-paginated. Illus, 4 color plates by Willy Pogany. Paper-covered boards w/color illus. Edgewear, crease to rear cvr but VG+. *BEBBAH.* $40

Newman, John Henry. A LETTER TO THE REV. E.B. PUSEY. London, 1866. Wraps. VG-NF. *POLYANTHOS.* $45

Newman, John P. THE THRONES AND PALACES OF BABYLON AND NINEVEH FROM SEA TO SEA. NY: Nelson & Phillips: Cincinnati: Hitchcock & Walden, 1876. 1st ed. 455pp. Good. *WORLDWIDE.* $35

Newman, Tillie Karns. THE BLACK DOG TRAIL. Boston: Chris-topher, 1957. 1st ed. Inscribed. Name, else VF in VG dj. *CONNOLLY & WADE.* $37.50

Newmark, Harris. SIXTY YEARS IN SOUTHERN CALIFORNIA 1853-1913. Boston: Houghton Mifflin, 1930. 1st of this ed. Fine in Fine dj. *BOOK MARKET.* $100

Newsholme, Arthur. EVOLUTION OF PREVENTIVE MEDICINE. Baltimore, 1927. 1st Amer ed. *FYE.* $75

Newson, T.M. PEN PICTURES OF ST. PAUL, MINNESOTA, AND BIOGRAPHICAL SKETCHES OF OLD SET-TLERS...TO...1857. Vol I. St. Paul: Pub by author, 1886. 1st ed. Slight water staining at front edge, still VG. *LAURIE.* $125

Newton, A. and H. Gadow. A DICTIONARY OF BIRDS. London, 1893-96. Institutional bkpl, sticker on spine, cheap issue, un-abridged. *SUTTON.* $60

Newton, A. Edward. A MAGNIFICENT FARCE AND OTHER DIVERSIONS OF A BOOK-COLLECTOR. Boston, (1921). 1st ed. Bkpl; spine sl rubbed, little offsetting inside cvrs and feps. Uncut. *POLYANTHOS.* $30

Newton, A. Edward. BIBLIOGRAPHY AND PSEUDO-BIBLIOG-RAPHY. Phila: Univ of Pennsylvania Press, 1936. 1st ed. Fine in VG dj. *WREDEN.* $25

Newton, A. Edward. END PAPERS. Boston: Little, Brown, 1933. 1st ed. Frontis, advance review, slip laid in. Spine browned. VG in NF dj. *BERNARD.* $60

Newton, A. Edward. THE AMENITIES OF BOOK COLLECTING AND KINDRED AFFECTIONS. Boston: Atlantic Monthly, 1918. 1st ed, 1st issue w/o index, but lacking errata slip. Fine in sl worn, dust-soiled dj. *JAFFE.* $100

Newton, A. Edward. THIS BOOK COLLECTING GAME. Boston, 1928, 2nd ptg. Colored frontis. *HEINOLDT.* $10

Newton, H. Chance. CRIME AND THE DRAMA; OR, DARK DEEDS DRAMATIZED. London, (1927). 1st ed. Spine sl faded. Sm repair to cl, else VG. *DIAMOND.* $35

Newton, Helmut. BIG NUDES. NY, 1982. Dj. Fine. *POLYANTHOS.* $65

Newton, Helmut. SLEEPLESS NIGHTS. NY, 1978. Dj. Fine. *POLYAN-THOS.* $65

Newton, Helmut. WHITE WOMEN. (NY): Stonehill. (1976). 1st ed. Dj. Pres copy signed by Newton. *KARMIOLE.* $150

Newton, Huey. REVOLUTIONARY SUICIDE. NY: Harcourt, 1973. 1st ed. Fine in Fine dj. *BEASLEY.* $45

Newton, Huey. REVOLUTIONARY SUICIDE. NY: Harcourt, Brace, Jovanovich, (1973). 1st ed. Dj. *AKA.* $30

Newton, Joseph Fort. LINCOLN AND HERNDON. Cedar Rapids: The Torch Press, 1910. 1st ptg. 8 plts. Pict cl. Inscription partially erased. *SCHOYER'S.* $40

Newton, Rev. Richard. 60 ILLUSTRATED RAMBLES IN BIBLE LANDS. Phila, 1875. 254pp. 1st ed. *O'NEILL.* $75

NIAGARA FALLS. Portland, ME, c. 1890. Album accordion folder, 13pp. Souvenir bk. Contents VG, cover wear. *HEINOLDT.* $18

Niatum, Duane. ASCENDING RED CEDAR MOON. NY: H&R, (1973). 1st ed, 1st book. NF in VG dj, lt edgewear. *LOPEZ.* $35

Niatum, Duane. DIGGING OUT THE ROOTS. NY: H&R, (1977). 1st ed. Fine in dj w/crease. *LOPEZ.* $35

Niatum, Duane. SONGS FOR THE HARVESTER OF DREAMS. Seattle: Univ of WA Press, (1981). 1st ed. Fine in NF dj. *LOPEZ.* $40

Nice, Margaret Morse. THE WATCHER AT THE NEST. NY: Mac-millan, 1939. 1st ed. Fine- in VG+ dj. *AARD.* $20

Nichol, J.R. STEPPING STONES TO THE SOUTH POLE. Sydney: Angus & Robertson, (1948). 1st ed. VG+ in VG- dj. *BLUE DRAGON.* $25

Nicholas, George. A LETTER FROM...JUSTIFYING THE CON-DUCT...AND CORRECTING CERTAIN FALSE STATE-MENTS...Phila.: Carey, 1799. 39pp (p39 in facs). New cl w/leather label. Howes N136. "William Findlay" in ink on title page. *GINSBERG.* $150

Nichols, Alice. BLEEDING KANSAS. NY, 1954. 1st ed. VG+ in dj. *PRATT.* $30

Nichols, Alice. BLEEDING KANSAS. NY: Oxford, 1954. 1st ed. F in dj w/tears. *OREGON.* $30

Nichols, Beverley (selected by). A BOOK OF OLD BALLADS. London: Hutchinson, 1934. Illus by H.M. Brock. Cl, gold lettering. 16 color plts. VG. *ACADEMIC LIBRARY.* $40

Nichols, H.C.M. BIRDS OF MARSH AND MERE AND HOW TO SHOOT THEM. London: Heath Cranton, 1928. "Cheap" ed. Half brown lea. Ex-lib with minor stampings and pocket removal marks. G+. *OLD LONDON.* $30

Nichols, James L. THE CONFEDERATE QUARTERMASTER IN THE TRANS-MISSISSIPPI. Austin, (1964). 1st ed. VG+. *PRATT.* $25

Nichols, John. A GHOST IN THE MUSIC. Holt, 1979. 1st ed. Fine in dj. Signed, inscribed, and dated (5/8/87). *STAHR.* $45

Nichols, John. A GHOST IN THE MUSIC. NY: Holt, Rinehart Winston, 1979. 1st ed. Proof. NF in wraps. *SMITH.* $35

Nichols, John. A GHOST IN THE MUSIC. NY: HRW, 1979. 1st ed. Fine in Fine dj (very sl rubbed along joint). *ARCHER.* $25

Nichols, John. AMERICAN BLOOD. NY: Holt, (1987). 2nd ptg. Fine in Fine dj. *AKA.* $35

Nichols, John. AN ELEGY FOR SEPTEMBER. NY: Henry Holt & Co., (1992). 1st ed. Signed. New in dj. *BERNARD.* $35

Nichols, John. THE MILAGRO BEANFIELD WAR. NY: Holt, (1974). 1st ed. A few very small spots on top and fore-edges, else just About Fine in lightly used dj. *CAPTAIN'S BOOKSHELF.* $125

Nichols, John. THE NIRVANA BLUES. NY: Holt, Rinehart & Winston, (1981). 1st ed. Signed. Fine in NF dj which has a small scrape at bottom spine edge. *BERNARD.* $60

Nichols, John. THE WIZARD OF LONELINESS. NY: G.P. Putnam's, (1966). 1st ed, 2nd book. Signed. Spine lettering dull o/w VG in dj which is worn at edges & with a couple of short, internally mended tears. *BERNARD.* $85

Nichols, Leigh (pseud of Dean R. Koontz). THE DOOR TO DECEMBER. London: Inner Circle, 1987. 1st hardcover ed. As New in dj. *ELSE FINE.* $65

Nichols, Robert and Jim Tully. TWENTY BELOW. London: Robert Holden, 1927. 1/100, numbered and signed by Nichols. *BEASLEY.* $75

Nichols, Roger L. GENERAL HENRY ATKINSON, A WESTERN MILITARY CAREER. Norman, (1965). 1st ed. Fine in dj. *PRATT.* $32.50

Nichols, Roy Franklin. FRANKLIN PIERCE. Phila: Univ of PA Press, 1931. 10 plts. Heavy offsetting from laid-in review on 2pp. Spine type rubbed off. *SCHOYER'S.* $35

Nicholson, George (ed). THE ILLUSTRATED DICTIONARY OF GARDENING. 4 vols. Supplement bound-in back of Vol 4. London, (c. 1890). 4 colored plts. Orig gilt-dec cl, sl cracking of 2 inner hinges. Nice ex-lib. *SUTTON.* $145

Nicholson, George (ed). THE ILLUSTRATED DICTIONARY OF GARDENING. NY and London: Penman, (1890). 1st ed. 4 vols. 544; 544; 537; 608pp, aeg, grn cl. 19 colored plts. Loose hinges. VG. *SECOND LIFE.* $150

Nicholson, Harold. SWEET WATERS. Boston: Houghton Mifflin, 1922. 1st US ed. Apparently a lending lib copy with rear pocket removed but with no other signs of library usage. Spine faded, else VG. Dj not present; nine-line blurb from dj pasted inside front cover. Scarce in any condition. *WOOLMER.* $75

Nicholson, Peter. THE CARPENTER'S NEW GUIDE...A NEW ED...REVISED BY ARTHUR ASHPITEL. Together with Practi-

cal Rules on Drawing, by George Pyne. London: Lockwood & Co. N.d. (circa 1857). 3 parts in 1. 80;32;80pp+74 engr plts. Orig maroon cl, blind-stamped, gilt spine; spine extrems, corners frayed. *KARMIOLE.* $150

Nicholson, Renton. AUTOBIOGRAPHY OF A FAST MAN. Pub for the Proprietors, London, 1863. 2nd ed. Title pg;leaf;(1)-380pp. 8vo. Attractive, bound in early 3/4 calf over marbled boards, a bit rubbed and embrowned, but still quite nice. *BOSWELL.* $350

Nicholson, Watson. THE HISTORICAL SOURCES OF DEFOE'S JOURNAL OF THE PLAGUE YEAR. Boston, 1919. *FYE.* $50

Nickell, J.M. J.M. NICKELL'S BOTANICAL READY REFERENCE. Chicago, 1881. Limp leather very scuffed, pieces missing from spine, upper edge back cover; eps very soiled, cracked; text mostly clean. *SUTTON.* $45

Nicol, John. THE LIFE AND ADVENTURES OF JOHN NICOL, MARINER. Edinburgh: William Blackwood; London: T. Cadell, 1822. 1st ed. (xii) 215 pp. Port. Modern half morocco, a few spots of foxing, but surprisingly clean and attractive, w/half-title. *LEFKOWICZ.* $700

Nicolay, John G. THE OUTBREAK OF REBELLION-CAMPAIGNS OF THE CIVIL WAR, VOL. I. NY, 1881. 1st ed. 220pp & ads. VG. *PRATT.* $35

Nicoll, Bruce H. and Ken R. Keller. SAM MCKELVIE, SON OF THE SOIL. Lincoln: Johnson, 1954. 1st ed. Fine. *CONNOLLY & WADE.* $30

Nicollet, Joseph N. REPORT INTENDED TO ILLUSTRATE A MAP OF THE HYDROGRAPHIC BASIN OF THE UPPER MISSISSIPPI RIVER. Wash, SD237, 1843. 1st ed. 170pp. Fldg map. 1/2 morocco, orig blue ptd front wrapper bound in. Also incl "A Sketch of the Early History of St. Louis. Howes N152. *GINSBERG.* $375

Nicolson, Harold. JOURNEY TO JAVA. GC: Doubleday, 1958. 1st ed. NF in NF dj. *GREAT EPIC.* $35

Nicolson, John (ed). THE ARIZONA OF JOSEPH PRATT ALLYN. LETTERS FROM A PIONEER JUDGE. Tucson, 1974. VF in Fine dj. *FIVE QUAIL.* $12.50

Nicosia, Gerald. MEMORY BABE: A CRITICAL BIOGRAPHY OF JACK KEROUAC. NY: Grove, (1983). 1st ed. VF in dj. *AKA.* $30

Niecks, Frederick. FREDERICK CHOPIN AS MAN AND MUSICIAN. London: Novello, 1890. 2 vols. Sl shelfwear, mostly unopened. VG. *BANCROFT.* $22

Niedecker, Lorine. NORTH CENTRAL. London: Fulcrum, (1968). 1st ed, regular issue. Fine in dj. *CAPTAIN'S BOOKSHELF.* $125

Niedecker, Lorine. T&G: THE COLLECTED POEMS (1936-1966). Penland: The Jargon Society, 1968. One of 2000 pub as Jargon 48. Fine in wraps. *CAPTAIN'S BOOKSHELF.* $50

Nieman, S.I. JUDAH BENJAMIN, MYSTERY MAN OF THE CONFEDERACY. Indianapolis, (1963). 1st ed. Inscribed. VG+ in dj. *PRATT.* $45

Nietzsche, Friedrich. MY SISTER AND I. NY: Boar's Head Books, 1953. Trans by Dr. Oscar Levy. VG in worn dj. *WREDEN.* $35

Nietzsche, Friedrich. THUS SPAKE ZARATHUSTRA. Thomas Common (trans), Henry David Aiken (intro). NY: LEC, 1964. One of 1500 w/decs by Arnold Bank. Fine in slipcase. *CAPTAIN'S BOOK-SHELF.* $75

Nightingale, Florence. LETTERS FROM EGYPT. A JOURNEY ON THE NILE, 1849-1850. NY: Weidenfeld & Nicolson, (1987). Color frontis. Dj. Good. *ARCHAEOLOGIA.* $35

Nightingale, Florence. NOTES ON NURSING: WHAT IT IS, AND WHAT IT IS NOT. London (1860). 1st ed. 79pp. This early ptg includes phrase "the right of Translation is reserved" on title page but appeared before printer's errors were corrected in text. *FYE.* $400

Nightingale, Florence. NOTES ON NURSING; WHAT IT IS, AND WHAT IT IS NOT. NY: D. Appleton and Company, 1860. 1st Amer ed. 140 pgp,4pp pub's cat. Sl wear to head, tail of spine. Occasional minor foxing. Carte-de-visite w/engr port laid in. Fine, tight. *BLUE MOUNTAIN.* $275

Nightingale, Florence. SELECTED WRITINGS OF FLORENCE NIGHTINGALE. Lucy Ridgley Seymer (comp). NY, 1954. 1st ed. *FYE.* $50

Niklaus, Thelma. HARLEQUIN. NY: George Braziller, Inc, 1956. Dj chipped, rubbed. *KARMIOLE.* $40

Nikolic, Djordje. KEY TO DREAMS ACCORDING TO DJORDJE. Chicago: Elpenor, (1978). 1st ed. Fine in dj. *CAPTAIN'S BOOKSHELF.* $35

Niles, George. PELLAGRA, AN AMERICAN PROBLEM. Phila, 1912. 1st ed. Photo illus. Inner hinges cracked. Scarce. *FYE.* $75

Niles, Rena and John Jacob. MR. POOF'S DISCOVERY. Blue cl w/paper label. Lexington, (KY): Bur Press, (1947). 1st ed. Fine. *JAFFE.* $75

Nimmo, Joseph, Jr. TREASURY DEPARTMENT. REPORT ON THE INTERNAL COMMERCE OF THE UNITED STATES...Wash., 1885. 562pp. 5 fldg maps, tables. Full modern morocco. Howes N158. *GINSBERG.* $1000

Nin, Anais. CHILDREN OF THE ALBATROSS. Dutton, 1947. 1st ed. About Fine in dj (sl worn; missing piece at head of spine). *STAHR.* $25

Nin, Anais. DIARY. VOLUME SIX 1955-1966. NY & London: Harcourt Brace Jovanovich, (1976). 1st ed. VG in dj. *SCHOYER'S.* $20

Nin, Anais. HENRY AND JUNE. San Diego et al: Harcourt Brace Jovanovich, (1986). 1st ed. Fine in dj. *SCHOYER'S.* $20

Nin, Anais. HOUSE OF INCEST. NY: Gemor Press (1947). 1st Amer ed. Pict orange cl. Issued w/o dj. Wear top of spine else VG. *DORN.* $95

Nin, Anais. WINTER OF ARTIFICE. Paris: Obelisk, (1939). 1st ed. VF in wrappers, w/o dj, as issued. *CAPTAIN'S BOOKSHELF.* $250

NINE YEARS OF DEMOCRATIC RULE IN MISSISSIPPI: BEING NOTES...FROM THE BEGINNING OF THE YEAR 1838, TO THE PRESENT TIME. (By H. E. Van Winkle.) Jackson, MS: Palmer, 1847. 1st ed. (12),304pp. Contemp full calf, red leather label on spine. Howes V45. *GINSBERG.* $750

Nininger, H.H. OUR STONE-PELTED PLANET, A BOOK ABOUT METEORS AND METEORITES. Boston: Houghton Mifflin, 1933 (1933). VG. *KNOLLWOOD.* $40

Nininger, H.H. OUT OF THE SKY, AN INTRODUCTION TO METEORITICS. Univ of Denver Press, 1952. VG in worn dj. *KNOLLWOOD.* $48

Nishimura, Hideo et al., PRENATAL DEVELOPMENT OF THE HUMAN WITH SPECIAL REFERENCE TO CRANIOFACIAL STRUCTURES: AN ATLAS. Bethesda, 1977. 1st ed. 161 illus. Lib stamp on title, o/w Fine. *FYE.* $75

Nissenson, Hugh. A PILE OF STONES. NY: Charles Scribner's Sons, (c1965). 1st ed, 1st bk. Inscribed. Corners sl bumped, o/w Fine in dj, short tears. *HELLER.* $55

Nissenson, Hugh. MY OWN GROUND. NY: Farrar Straus Giroux, (1976). 1st ed. Inscribed. NF in dj. *LOPEZ.* $35

Nissenson, Hugh. THE TREE OF LIFE. NY: H&R, (1985). 1st ed. Rev copy. Signed. Fine in Fine dj. *LOPEZ.* $35

Niven, John. CONNECTICUT FOR THE UNION, THE ROLE OF THE STATE IN THE CIVIL WAR. New Haven, 1965. 1st ed. VG+ in dj. *PRATT.* $40

Niven, John. GIDEON WELLES, LINCOLN'S SECRETARY OF THE NAVY. NY, 1973. 1st ed. Light dj wear with crease down front o/w Fine. *PRATT.* $30

Niven, Larry. A GIFT FROM EARTH. NY: Walker, 1970. 1st ed. Signed. Fine in dj. *ELSE FINE.* $70

Niven, Larry. A WORLD OUT OF TIME. Holt, 1976. 1st ed. Fine in dj. *MADLE.* $35

Niven, Larry. RINGWORLD. Holt, 1977. 1st US hb ed. Fine in dj. *MADLE.* $75

Niven, Larry. THE MAGIC GOES AWAY. Ace, 1978. 1st ltd, signed hb ed. Fine in dj. *MADLE.* $37

Nixon, Howard M. ROYAL ENGLISH BOOKBINDINGS IN THE BRITISH MUSEUM. London: British Museum, 1957. Paper wrappers. *OAK KNOLL.* $25

Nixon, Howard M. SIXTEENTH-CENTURY GOLD-TOOLED BOOKBINDINGS IN THE PIERPONT MORGAN LIBRARY. New York: Pierpont Morgan Library, 1971. 1st ed. Cloth. *OAK KNOLL.* $350

Nixon, Oliver W. HOW MARCUS WHITMAN SAVED OREGON. Chicago, 1895. Slight rubbing. VG. *POLYANTHOS.* $40

Nixon, Richard M. THE CHALLENGES WE FACE. NY: McGraw-Hill, 1960. 1st ed, 1st book. NF in VG sl chipped & rubbed dj. *ARCHER.* $55

Noble, Carl. JUGHEADS BEHIND THE LINES. Caldwell: Caxton Press, (1938). 1st ed. VG in Good+ dj. *OREGON.* $20

Noble, Daniel. THE BRAIN AND ITS PHYSIOLOGY- A CRITICAL DISQUISITION ON THE METHODS OF DETERMINING THE RELATIONS SUBSISTING BETWEEN THE STRUCTURE AND FUNCTIONS OF THE ENCEPHALON. London, 1846. 1st ed. Orig boards rebacked with binder's tape, 1st 4 leaves detached w/edges chipped, ex-lib. *FYE.* $150

Noble, Frederic Perry. THE REDEMPTION OF AFRICA: A STORY OF CIVILIZATION. Chicago, NY: Revell, 1899. 2 vols. 1st ed. xxvii, 474pp; vii,475-856pp. 5 fldg maps, 2 maps in back pocket, one should have been frontis. Orig cl, sl rubbed, o/w VG ex-lib. *WORLDWIDE.* $85

Noble, John. OFFICIAL HANDBOOK. HISTORY...OF THE CAPE OF GOOD HOPE. London: Donald Currie; Cape Town: W. A. Richards, 1886. 2 fldg tables, 25 plts and maps, some fldg, and incl 6 chromolitho plts. (The London imprint is pasted on.) Orig color-litho boards, rubbed, ep ads. *LEFKOWICZ.* $125

Noel, Baptist W. THE REBELLION IN AMERICA. London: Nesbet, 1863. 1st ed. (20),494,(2)pp. Orig cl. Howes N166. *GINSBERG.* $125

Noguchi, Thomas T. and Arthur Lyons. UNNATURAL CAUSES. NY: Putnam, 1988. 1st ed. Review copy, pub's slip laid in. Signed by Lyons. VF in dj. *SILVER DOOR.* $35

Noice, Harold. WITH STEFANSSON IN THE ARCTIC. London: George G. Harrap, 1925. VG. *PARMER.* $35

Nolan, Alan T. THE IRON BRIGADE. Berrien Springs, 1983. 3rd ed. VF in dj. *ARTIS.* $25

Nolan, William F. (ed). RAY BRADBURY REVIEW 1952. 1st ed. VG in wraps. *MADLE.* $40

Nolan, William F. DASHIELL HAMMETT: A CASEBOOK. Santa Barbara: McNally & Loftin, (1969). 1st ed. Fine in dj. *CAPTAIN'S BOOKSHELF.* $75

Nolan, William F. DASHIELL HAMMETT: A CASEBOOK. Santa Barbara: McNally & Loftin, 1969. 1st ed. VF in dj. *MORDIDA.* $65

Nolan, William F. THE BLACK MASK BOYS. NY: Morrow, 1985. 1st ed. Signed. Fine in dj. *SILVER DOOR.* $45

Nolte, Vincent. FIFTY YEARS IN BOTH HEMISPHERES. NY: Redfield, 1854. 1st Amer ed, 1st Eng trans. (4),(22),(11)-484,(4)pp. Orig cl. Howes N169. *GINSBERG.* $150

Norden, Pierre. CONAN DOYLE—A BIOGRAPHY. NY: Holt, 1967. 1st Amer ed. Illus. Fine in dj. *SILVER DOOR.* $25

Nordenskiold, A.E. THE VOYAGE OF THE "VAGA" ROUND ASIA AND EUROPE. London, 1881. Trans by A. Leslie. 2 vols. 11 fldg maps. Wear at extrems, ink inscrip on half titles, some foxing, hinges starting. SUTTON. $150

Nordenskiold, Erik. THE HISTORY OF BIOLOGY. L.B. Eyre (trans). London: Kegan Paul et al, 1929. 1st British ed. Blue cl. VG. SMITHFIELD. $72

Nordenskiolo, G. THE CLIFF DWELLERS OF THE MESA VERDE, SOUTHWESTERN COLORADO: THEIR POTTERY AND IMPLEMENTS. Trans D. Lloyd Morgan. (iii),174pp,iv pp index. 94 figs, 51 plts (1 color, most w/letterpress). Bound with: RETZIUS, G. APPENDIX: HUMAN REMAINS FROM THE CLIFF DWELLINGS OF THE MESA VERDE. Stockholm & Chicago: P.A. Norstadt, 1893. 1st ed in Eng simultaneous w/Swedish ed. xi + 10 double pp plts, map, folio, 3/4 cl. ARCHAEOLOGIA. $1,500

Nordenskjold, Otto and Ludwig Mecking. THE GEOGRAPHY OF THE POLAR REGIONS. NY: Amer Geographical Soc, 1928. VG (some soiling, wear to orig grey wraps). PARMER. $35

Nordhoff, Charles and James N. Hall. BOTANY BAY. Boston: Atlantic-Little Brown, 1941. Adv rev copy w/slip laid in. Fine in lightly used dj w/chip at head of bit darkened spine. BEASLEY. $75

Nordhoff, Charles and James Norman Hall. MUTINY ON THE BOUNTY. Boston, 1932. 1st ed. Rubbed, dj (lg piece torn from top), some slight damage to margin of one leaf. Uncommon in 1st ptg. LEFKOWICZ. $50

Nordhoff, Charles and James Norman Hall. PITCAIRN'S ISLAND. Boston: Little, Brown, 1934. Brownish orange cl. Fine in price--clipped, NF pict dj (1 very small corner chip and two or three short closed tears on rear panel). 1st ed. CHAPEL HILL. $200

Nordhoff, Charles. CALIFORNIA: A BOOK FOR TRAVELLERS. NY: Harper & Brothers, 1874. Blue cl rubbed. HUDSON. $75

Nordhoff, Charles. CALIFORNIA: FOR HEALTH, PLEASURE AND RESIDENCE. NY, 1872, 1st ed. Rebound, old cover transposed. HEINOLDT. $18

Nordhoff, Charles. CALIFORNIA: FOR HEALTH, PLEASURE AND RESIDENCE. NY: Harper & Bros, 1872. 1st ed. Frontis map, (v),12-255,(5),2-5 pp. Backstrip reinforced at top and bottom. Orig gilt stamped cl. Some wear, else Fine. CONNOLLY & WADE. $125

Nordhoff, Charles. NORTHERN CALIFORNIA, OREGON AND THE SANDWICH ISLANDS. NY: Harper & Brothers, 1874. 1st ed. Lightly foxed. HUDSON. $95

Nordhoff, Charles. PENINSULAR CALIFORNIA. NY: Harper & Brothers, 1888. Double pp map in text. Shaken. HUDSON. $75

Nordyke, Lewis. GREAT ROUNDUP....Morrow, 1955. 1st ed. Fine in NF dj. VARNER. $60

Norfleet, J. Frank. NORFLEET. Ft. Worth, 1924. VG. ARTIS. $15

Norman, B.M. RAMBLES IN YUCATAN. NY: J. & H. G. Langley, 1843. 2nd ed. 304pp, ads, plts. Orig brn emb, gilt spine titles and cover dec. Professionally re-backed, orig spine laid down, some internal foxing, else VG. PARMER. $300

Norman, Charles. THE CASE OF EZRA POUND. NY: Bodley Press, (1948). 1st ed. Orig ptd lt blue wraps. Owner name, but VG. CHAPEL HILL. $30

Norman, Henry. ALL THE RUSSIAS. NY: Charles Scribner's Sons. 1902. 1st ed. KARMIOLE. $50

NORMAN ROCKWELL, SPECIAL DAYS COME TO LIFE. NY, 1987. Pop-up bk. BOOKFINDERS INTL. $20

Norman, William M. A PORTION OF MY LIFE; BEING A SHORT & IMPERFECT HISTORY WRITTEN WHILE A PRISONER OF WAR ON JOHNSON'S ISLAND, 1864. Winston-Salem, 1959. 1st ed. VG+ in dj. PRATT. $27.50

Norris, Frank. BLIX. Doubleday and McClure, 1899. 1st ed. Tan pict cl, stamped in orange. VG, bkpl. AUTHORS OF THE WEST. $35

Norris, Frank. MCTEAGUE. A STORY OF SAN FRANCISCO. NY, 1899. 1st ed, 2nd issue. Orig cl cvrs sl stained. Part of rear cvr faded. Little shelfwear. Inner hinges repaired. Erasures on front fly & pastedown. Text sl shaken, o/w VG. DIAMOND. $100

Norris, Frank. MORAN OF THE LADY LETTY. NY, 1898. 1st ed. Dec blind-stamped cl printed in orange. Spine & cvr lettering rubbed. Small dampstain some page margins. Little soiling on some pp, o/w VG. DIAMOND. $75

Norris, Frank. THE LETTERS OF FRANK NORRIS. SF: The Book Club of California, 1956. Ltd ed, 350 printed by Edwin and Robert Grabhorn for the Colt Press. Franklin Walker (ed). Frontis. Fine. POLYANTHOS. $150

Norris, Hoke. ALL THE KINGDOMS OF EARTH. NY: Simon & Schuster, (1956). 1st ed. 1st bk. Minor crimp in spine, else Fine in dj. CHAPEL HILL. $35

North, Arthur W. CAMP AND CAMINO IN LOWER CALIFORNIA. NY, 1910, 1st ed. Spine faded. Map. HEINOLDT. $35

North, John Ringling and Alden Hatch. THE CIRCUS KINGS. GC: Doubleday, 1960. 1st ed. Review slip laid in. Fine in Fine dj. AARD. $25

North, Luther. MAN OF THE PLAINS, RECOLLECTIONS OF LUTHER NORTH, 1856-1882. Lincoln, 1961. Ed by Donald F. Danker. 1st ed. Lt dj wear o/w Fine. PRATT. $22.50

North, M.L. SARATOGA WATERS; Or, The Invalid at Saratoga. NY: M.W. Dodd. 1840. 1st ed. 70pp. Orig brn cl. Fine. KARMIOLE. $60

North, Mary M. A PRAIRIE SCHOONER....Neale, 1902. 1st ed (?). Fine. Scarce. VARNER. $35

North, Mary Remsen. DOWN THE COLORADO. By a Lone Girl Scout. NY, 1930. 1st ed. Orange cl, illus; xiii,164pp. Very scarce. Cover corners rubbed, spine sunburned, wear to heel and head of backstrip, else VG+. FIVE QUAIL. $45

North, Sterling. PLOWING ON SUNDAY. NY: MacMillan, 1934. 1st ed. NF in lightly edgeworn dj (short tear). CAPTAIN'S BOOKSHELF. $50

North, Thomas. FIVE YEARS IN TEXAS; OR, WHAT YOU DID NOT HEAR DURING THE WAR FROM JANUARY 1861 TO JANUARY 1865. Cincinnati: Elm Street Printing Company, 1870. 1st ed. Cloth moderately worn, extremities frayed, boards exposed at lower corners, shaken. Howes N193. BOHLING. $350

Northe, James Neill (ed). LAND OF GOLD (TIERRA DE ORO): AN ANTHOLOGY. Ontario, CA: Herald-Silhouettes Press, 1934. 1st ed. Inscribed. Ltd ed, #74 of 500. Musty, but still bright and Fine. Very scarce. CONNOLLY & WADE. $200

Northend, Mary H. COLONIAL HOMES AND THEIR FURNISHINGS. Boston: LB, 1912. 1st ed. Fine. CAPTAIN'S BOOKSHELF. $75

Northrop, N.B. PIONEER HISTORY OF MEDINA COUNTY. Medina, Ohio: Geo. Redway, printer, 1861. 224pp. Orig black cl, chipped. Howes N200. GINSBERG. $100

Northrup, Solomon. NARRATIVE OF; A CITIZEN OF NEW YORK, KIDNAPPED IN WASHINGTON CITY IN 1841, AND RESCUED IN 1853. Auburn, NY: Derby and Miller, 1853. 17th thousand. Worn, corners bumped and worn, quite foxed, some small dampstains, chips to couple of pp not affecting text, one signature sprung. Scarce. BETWEEN COVERS. $100

NORTHWEST COAST OF AMERICA & CALIFORNIA: 1832. LETTERS....LA: Ptd for Glen Dawson, 1959. Ed ltd to 180. Owner inscrip fep, else Fine. KARMIOLE. $45

Norton, Andre (ed). SPACE PIONEERS. World, 1954. 1st ed. Fine in frayed dj. MADLE. $175

Norton, Andre (ed). SPACE SERVICE. World, 1953. 1st ed. NF in dj. *MADLE*. $200

Norton, Andre. 'WARE HAWK. Atheneum, 1983. 1st ed. Fine in dj. Signed. *MADLE*. $55

Norton, Andre. ANDROID AT ARMS. Harcourt, 1971. 1st ed. VG in NF dj. *MADLE*. $60

Norton, Andre. AT SWORD'S POINT. Harcourt, 1954. 1st ed. VG in chipped dj. *MADLE*. $135

Norton, Andre. CATSEYE. Harcourt, 1961. 1st ed. VG in used dj. *MADLE*. $45

Norton, Andre. DARK PIPER. Harcourt, 1968. 1st ed. Fine in dj. *MADLE*. $75

Norton, Andre. DREAD COMPANION. Harcourt, 1970. 1st ed. Fine in dj. *MADLE*. $35

Norton, Andre. DREAD COMPANION. Harcourt, 1970. 1st ed. Fine in dj. Signed. *MADLE*. $60

Norton, Andre. FLIGHT IN VIKTOR. Tor, 1986. 1st ed. Fine in dj. Signed. *MADLE*. $45

Norton, Andre. FORERUNNER FORAY: THE SECOND VENTURE Doherty, 1985. 1st ed. Fine in dj. Signed. *MADLE*. $45

Norton, Andre. GALACTIC DERELICT. World, 1959. 1st ed. Ex-lib. VG in NF dj. *MADLE*. $50

Norton, Andre. GARAN THE ETERNAL. F.P.C.I., 1972. 1st ed. As New. *MADLE*. $35

Norton, Andre. HERE ABIDE MONSTERS. Atheneum, 1973. 1st ed. Fine in dj. *MADLE*. $40

Norton, Andre. HORN CROWN. S.F.B.C., 1981. Fine in dj. Signed. *MADLE*. $25

Norton, Andre. ICE CROWN. Viking, 1970. 1st ed. VG in dj. *MADLE*. $40

Norton, Andre. JUDGMENT ON JANUS. Harcourt, 1963. 1st ed. NF in dj. *MADLE*. $80

Norton, Andre. KNAVE OF DREAMS. Viking, 1975. 1st ed. Fine in dj. Signed. *MADLE*. $55

Norton, Andre. NIGHT OF MASKS. Harcourt, 1964. 1st ed. Fine in dj. *MADLE*. $85

Norton, Andre. NO NIGHT WITHOUT STARS. London, 1976. 1st British ed. Fine in dj. Inscribed. *MADLE*. $50

Norton, Andre. OPERATION TIME SEARCH. Harcourt, 1967. 1st ed. Fine dj. *MADLE*. $75

Norton, Andre. ORDEAL IN OTHERWHERE. World, 1964. 1st ed. NF in dj. *MADLE*. $85

Norton, Andre. OUTSIDE. Walker, 1974. 1st ed. Fine in dj. *MADLE*. $30

Norton, Andre. POSTMARKED THE STARS. Harcourt, 1969. 1st ed. NF in sl frayed dj. *MADLE*. $50

Norton, Andre. QUAG KEEP. Atheneum, 1978. 1st ed. Fine in dj. Signed. *MADLE*. $50

Norton, Andre. QUEST CROSSTIME. Viking, 1965. 1st ed. NF in frayed dj. *MADLE*. $65

Norton, Andre. RED HART MAGIC. Crowell, 1976. 1st ed. Fine in dj. Signed. *MADLE*. $60

Norton, Andre. SHADOW HAWK. Harcourt, 1960. 1st ed. Chip in dj, else NF. *MADLE*. $90

Norton, Andre. SHADOW HAWK. Harcourt, 1960. 1st ed. Ex-lib. Good+ in frayed, taped dj. *MADLE*. $25

Norton, Andre. STAND TO HORSE. Harcourt, 1956. 1st ed. NF. *MADLE*. $50

Norton, Andre. THE GATE OF THE CAT. Ace, 1987. 1st ed. Fine in dj. Signed. *MADLE*. $45

Norton, Andre. THE IRON CAGE. Viking, 1974. 1st ed. Fine in dj. *MADLE*. $35

Norton, Andre. THE JARGOON PARD. Atheneum, 1974. 1st ed. Fine in dj. *MADLE*. $35

Norton, Andre. THE OPAL-EYED FAN. Dutton, 1977. 1st ed. Fine in dj. Signed. *MADLE*. $60

Norton, Andre. THE STARS ARE OURS. World, 1954. 1st ed. Near VG in chipped Finlay dj. *MADLE*. $65

Norton, Andre. THE X FACTOR. Harcourt, 1965. 1st ed. Fine in dj. *MADLE*. $85

Norton, Andre. VICTORY ON JANUS. Harcourt, 1966. 1st ed. Fine in dj. *MADLE*. $100

Norton, Andre. WRAITHS OF TIME. Atheneum, 1976. 1st ed. Fine in dj. *MADLE*. $50

Norton, Doreen. THE PALOMINO HORSE. LA: Borden, 1949. 1st ed. VG in Good dj. *OCTOBER FARM*. $125

Norton, Edward Quincy. CONSTRUCTION TUNING AND CARE OF THE PIANO-FORTE. Boston: Ditson, 1887. 1st ed. Cl backed ptd boards. *SECOND LIFE*. $75

Norton, Henry K. THE STORY OF CALIFORNIA FROM THE EARLIEST DAYS TO THE PRESENT. Chicago: McClurg, 1913. 1st ed. Fldg map. Orig red buckram, gilt. Pgs preceding, following plts exhibit foxing on margins. Minor shelf wear. Map is Fine. Tight, clean, About Fine. *CONNOLLY & WADE*. $45

Norton, Roy. THE TOLL OF THE SEA. NY: Appleton, 1909. Appleton "(1)" at end of text. Cream colored stamping somewhat rubbed, o/w VG in orig blue cl. *HELLER*. $65

Noshy, Ibrahim. THE ARTS IN PTOLEMAIC EGYPT: A STUDY OF GREEK AND EGYPTIAN INFLUENCES IN PTOLEMAIC ARCHITECTURE AND SCULPTURE. London: Oxford Univ Press, 1937. 18 plts. Covers soiled. Good. *ARCHAEOLOGIA*. $250

Nossiter, Harold. SOUTHWARD HO! BEING THE LOG OF THE 35 TON SCHOONER YACHT SIRIUS FROM ENGLAND TO AUSTRALIA. Boston: Charles E. Lauriat, 1938. 1st ed. Minor browning else NF in dj. *GREAT EPIC*. $45

NOTES FROM THE NEW UNDERGROUND. NY: Viking, (1968). 1st ed. VG in dj. *LOPEZ*. $45

Nott, Charles C. SKETCHES OF THE WAR. NY, 1863. *POLYANTHOS*. $60

Nott, Josiah Clark and George Gliddon. TYPES OF MANKIND. Phila, 1854. 1st trade ed. 738pp + charts. Front board nearly detached. *FYE*. $200

Nourse, Alan. TROUBLE ON TITAN. Winston, 1954. 1st ed. VG in frayed dj. *MADLE*. $45

Nourse, J.E. AMERICAN EXPLORATIONS IN THE ICE ZONES. Boston: D. Lothrup Co, c. 1884. 3rd ed. 624pp, 6 maps, 1 double pg. Elaborately dec cl in silver and black. *PARMER*. $95

Novak, Joseph (pseud of Jerzy Kosinski). THE FUTURE IS OURS, COMRADE. GC: Doubleday, 1960. 1st ed, 1st bk. Orig grey cl. Unobtrusive dampstain, bkseller label at rear, still VG in dj. Signed. *CHAPEL HILL*. $350

Nowell, Elizabeth. THOMAS WOLFE. NY, 1960. Dj. *HEINOLDT*. $15

Nowlan, Phil and Dick Calkins. THE ADVENTURES OF BUCK ROGERS. Whitman Big Big Book, 1934. 1st ed. VG. *MADLE*. $85

Noyes, A.J. IN THE LAND OF CHINOOK, OR THE STORY OF BLAIN COUNTY. Helena: State Pub Co, (1917). 1st ed. 24 plts. VF. Howes N218. *OREGON*. $250

Noyes, Alfred. THE ENCHANTED ISLAND. Stokes, n.d. VG. Inscribed. *MADLE*. $75

Noyes, Alfred. WALKING SHADOWS. Stokes, 1918. 1st ed. VG. *MADLE.* $35

Noyes, Henry. A TREATISE ON THE DISEASES OF THE EYE. NY, 1881. 1st ed. 362pp + 2 chromolithographic plts. *FYE.* $50

Noyes, Katharine M. JESSE MACY: AN AUTOBIOGRAPHY. Springfield, IL, Baltimore: Thomas, 1933. 1st ed. *GINSBERG.* $75

Nugent, Maria. LADY NUGENT'S JOURNAL OF HER RESIDENCE IN JAMAICA. Kingston: Jamaica: Institute of Jamaica, 1966. Wright, Philip (ed). 4th rev ed. VG in chipped dj. *SCHOYER'S.* $17.50

Nunan, Thomas. DIARY OF AN OLD BOHEMIAN. SF: Wagner, 1927. 1st ed. Tape repair on 4pp. Blue cl, pict covers. VG. Scarce. *CONNOLLY & WADE.* $25

Nunis, Doyce (ed). LOS ANGELES AND ITS ENVIRONS IN THE 20TH CENTURY. A BIBLIOGRAPHY OF A METROPOLIS. LA: Ward Ritchie Press, 1973. 1st ed. Fine in Fine dj. *BOOK MARKET.* $30

Nunis, Doyce (ed). THE GOLDEN FRONTIER: THE RECOLLECTIONS OF HERMAN FRANCIS REINHART, 1851-1869. Austin: Univ of Texas Press, (1962). 1st ed. VG in dj. *LAURIE.* $30

Nunis, Doyce. ANDREW SUBLETTE, ROCKY MOUNTAIN PRINCE 1813-1853. LA: Dawson, 1960. 1st ed. Ltd to 330. VG. *OREGON.* $75

Nunis, Doyce. THE TRIALS OF ISAAC GRAHAM. LA: Dawson's, 1967. 1st ed. Ltd to 300. VF. *OREGON.* $65

NURSERY RHYME POP-UP BOOK. London, (1950s). Moveable bk. *BOOKFINDERS INTL.* $70

NURSERY RHYMES. London, (1970's). Pop-up bk. *BOOKFINDERS INTL.* $25

NURSERY RHYMES. NY: McLoughlin Brothers, n.d. One of "Aunt Louisa's Big Picture Books." Pict wraps sewn at spine. Small hole few pp, o/w NF, (sl foxing, wear to wrappers). *JAFFE.* $125

Nuttall, T. A MANUAL OF THE ORNITHOLOGY OF THE UNITED STATES AND CANADA. THE LAND BIRDS AND THE WATER BIRDS. Boston, 1832-34. 114 woodcuts. 2 vols. Pp vi,693; vii,627. Contemp cl. Very worn; hinges cracked & tender; heads of spines torn; vol 2 shaken w/some signatures nearly loose; foxed; lt dampstaining few pp; pp 311 & 312 missing. *SUTTON.* $75

Nuttall, T. A POPULAR HANDBOOK OF THE BIRDS OF THE UNITED STATES AND CANADA, REVISED AND ANNOTATED BY M. CHAMBERLAIN. Boston, (1903). New ed. 20 colored plts, 173 woodcuts. 2 vols in 1. Rubbed at extremities, spotting to upper front cvr; inner hinges cracked; pp yellowed. *SUTTON.* $40

Nuttall, T. A POPULAR HANDBOOK OF THE ORNITHOLOGY OF EASTERN NORTH AMERICA, REVISED AND ANNOTATED BY M. CHAMBERLAIN. Boston, 1897 (1896). 20 colored plts, 172 woodcuts. 2 vols. Soiled; institutional bkpls, sticker on spines. *SUTTON.* $48

Nuttall, Thomas. JOURNEY OF TRAVELS INTO THE ARKANSAS TERRITORY DURING THE YEAR 1819. Savoie Lottinville (ed). Univ of OK, (1980). 1st ed thus. VF in VF dj. *OREGON.* $35

Nutting, Wallace. MAINE BEAUTIFUL. Framingham, MA: Old America Co., 1924. 1st ed. Spine sunned o/w VG. *ARCHER.* $20

Nutting, Wallace. NEW HAMPSHIRE BEAUTIFUL. Framingham, MA: Old America Co., 1923. 1st ed. Spine sunned, couple of damp spots, o/w VG. *ARCHER.* $20

Nye, Edgar Wilson (Bill). A GUEST AT THE LUDLOW AND OTHER STORIES. 1897. Pict cvr, gilt. Teg. Fine. *AUTHORS OF THE WEST.* $25

Nye, Nelson. HORSE THIEVES. NY: Evan, (1987). 1st ed. Inscribed. Fine in Fine dj. *UNGER.* $45

Nye, Nelson. PISTOLS FOR HIRE. NY: Macmillan, (1941). 1st ed, 1st bk. Inscribed. VG, foxed, in a VG dj with tape traces to spine ends. *UNGER.* $125

Nye, Robert. FALSTAFF. London: Hamish Hamilton, (1976). 1st ed. Fine in dj. *CAPTAIN'S BOOKSHELF.* $60

Nye, Wilbur Sturtevant. CARBINE AND LANCE: THE STORY OF OLD FORT SILL. Norman, 1937. Oxidation on eps from formerly laid in newspaper, o/w VG. *BAADE.* $75

Nye, Wilbur Sturtevant. CARBINE & LANCE: THE STORY OF OLD FORT SILL. Norman: Univ of OK Press, 1943. 6th ptg, 1951. Nearly fine in dj/w light wear. *BOHLING.* $30

Nye, Wilbur Sturtevant. CARBINE & LANCE: THE STORY OF OLD FORT SILL. Norman, 1937. 3rd ed (1969). 361pp. Dj wear w/small piece missing from back o/w Fine. *PRATT.* $35

Nye, Wilbur Sturtevant. PLAINS INDIANS RAIDERS. Norman: Univ of OK Press, (1968). 1st ed. Cl, dj. VG. *SCHOYER'S.* $40

Nylander, Carl. THE DEEP WELL. London: George Allen and Unwin, (1969). Dj. Good. *ARCHAEOLOGIA.* $25

Nyren, John. THE YOUNG CRICKETER'S TUTOR. London: The Dropmore Press, 1948. Ltd ed (396/750 only). Fine in NF dj. *OLD LONDON.* $40

O

O. HENRY MEMORIAL AWARD PRIZE STORIES OF 1946. GC: Doubleday, 1946. 1st ed. Offsetting from newspaper article on feps, o/w Fine in dj. *JAFFE.* $40

O. HENRY MEMORIAL AWARD PRIZE STORIES OF 1947. GC: Doubleday, 1947. Herschel Brickell (ed). 1st ed. Fine in dj. *JAFFE.* $40

O. Henry. See Henry, O.

O' Malley, C.D. MICHAEL SERVETUS: A TRANSLATION OF HIS GEOGRAPHICAL, MEDICAL AND ASTROLOGICAL WRITINGS WITH INTRODUCTIONS AND NOTES. Phila, 1953. 1st ed. *FYE.* $75

O'Brian, Patrick. DESOLATION ISLAND. NY: Stein & Day, 1978. 1st ed. VF in dj. *ELSE FINE.* $35

O'Brian, Patrick. THE LETTER OF MARQUE. NY: Norton, 1990. 1st ed. VF in dj. Adv copy, pub letter laid in. *ELSE FINE.* $25

O'Brien, Flann. THE HARD LIFE. NY: Pantheon, (1962). 1st Amer ed. Fine in lightly worn dj. *DORN.* $50

O'Brien, Flann. THE HARD LIFE. Pantheon, 1962. 1st Amer ed. Fine in dj (sl chipped foot of spine). *STAHR.* $65

O'Brien, Flann. THE POOR MOUTH (AN BEAL BOCHT). A BAD STORY ABOUT THE HARD LIFE. Ed by Myles na Gopaleen (Flann O'Brien), trans by Patrick C. Power, illus by Ralph Steadman. Orig burlap. London: Bernard Jacobsen in association w/Hart Davis, MacGibbon, (1973). 1st illus ed. One of 130 numbered signed by Steadman, a separate signed print (1/150) laid in. Fine. *JAFFE.* $1000

O'Brien, Frank G. MINNESOTA PIONEER SKETCHES. Minneapolis: H. H. S. Rowell, 1904. 1st ed. Red cl. Scarce. Fine. *WEBER.* $125

O'Brien, Geoffrey. HARDBOILED AMERICA....NY: Van Nostrand, 1981. 1st ed. VF in dj. *SILVER DOOR.* $50

O'Brien, Jack. ALONE ACROSS THE TOP OF THE WORLD. Phila: Winston (1935). Inscribed. Fine in VG dj. *AARD.* $25

O'Brien, Jack. ALONE ACROSS THE TOP OF THE WORLD....Chicago: Winston, 1935. 1st ed. 7 plts. Inscribed. Fine in scarce, Good+ dj. *CONNOLLY & WADE.* $42.50

O'Brien, Patrick. THE REVERSE OF THE MEDAL. London: Collins, 1986. 1st ed. VF in dj. *ELSE FINE.* $40

O'Brien, Robert. CALIFORNIA CALLED THEM: A SAGA OF GOLDEN DAYS AND ROARING CAMPS. NY: McGraw-Hill, (1951). Signed. Dj chipped at extremities, else Fine. *LAURIE.* $15

O'Brien, Tim. GOING AFTER CACCIATO. (NY): Delacorte/Lawrence, (1978). 1st ed. Signed. NF in dj. *LOPEZ.* $175

O'Brien, Tim. GOING AFTER CACCIATO. London: Cape (1978). 1st Eng ed. Fine in dj. *DORN.* $45

O'Brien, Tim. GOING AFTER CACCIATO. London: Cape, 1978. First UK ed. Signed. Fine in dj. *LOPEZ.* $85

O'Brien, Tim. IF I DIE IN A COMBAT ZONE. (NY): Delacorte, (1973). 1st ed. Faint tape shadows front and rear pastedowns, presumably from earlier dj protector; very sl fading to edges of boards, o/w VF in Fine dj. Signed. *LOPEZ.* $850

O'Brien, Tim. IF I DIE IN A COMBAT ZONE. London: Calder & Boyars (1973). 1st Eng ed. Signed. Fine in dj. *DORN.* $150

O'Brien, Tim. IF I DIE IN A COMBAT ZONE. (London: Calder & Boyars, 1973). 1st Eng ed. Signed. Fine in Fine dj. *LOPEZ.* $200

O'Brien, Tim. NORTHERN LIGHTS. London: Boyars, (1976). 1st Eng ed. 1/900. Signed. Fine in Fine dj. *LOPEZ.* $200

O'Brien, Tim. NORTHERN LIGHTS. London: Marion Boyars, (1976). 1st UK ed. Only 900 copies. New in dj. *BERNARD.* $75

O'Brien, Tim. SPEAKING OF COURAGE. Santa Barbara, CA: Neville, 1980. 1st ed. 1/300 numbered, signed. Fine. *JUVELIS.* $50

O'Brien, Tim. SPEAKING OF COURAGE. Santa Barbara: Neville, (1980). 1st ed. One of 300 numbered, signed. Fine in acetate dj. *UNGER.* $75

O'Brien, Tim. THE NUCLEAR AGE. NY: Knopf (1985). 1st ed. Signed. Fine in dj. *DORN.* $50

O'Brien, Tim. THE NUCLEAR AGE. NY: Knopf, 1985. 1st ed. Signed. Fine in Fine dj. *LOPEZ.* $65

O'Brien, Tim. THE NUCLEAR AGE. Oregon: Press-22, 1981. Ltd ed, 1/125 only, signed. Printed self-wraps. Fine. *POLYANTHOS.* $30

O'Brien, Tim. THE THINGS THEY CARRIED. Boston: Houghton Mifflin/SL, 1990. 1st ed. Signed. Fine in dj. *LOPEZ.* $75

O'Callaghan, John Cornelius. HISTORY OF THE IRISH BRIGADES IN THE SERVICE OF FRANCE. NY, 1887. 4th ed. Fldg map. VG-NF. *POLYANTHOS.* $45

O'Connell, D.J.K. THE GREEN FLASH AND OTHER LOW SUN PHENOMENA. Amsterdam: North Holland Pub Col, Vatican Observatory, 1958. Spine faded, o/w VG in slipcase. *KNOLLWOOD.* $60

O'Connor, Edwin. THE EDGE OF SADNESS. Boston: Little, Brown, (1961). 1st ed. NF in VG dj, internally strengthened w/tape. *LOPEZ.* $30

O'Connor, Feargus. A PRACTICAL WORK ON THE MANAGEMENT OF SMALL FARMS. Manchester: Heywood, 1846. 4th ed. Uncut in pub's spotted cl. Good. *SECOND LIFE.* $75

O'Connor, Flannery (ed). DEATH OF A CHILD. London: Catholic Book Club, (1961). 1st UK ed of A MEMOIR OF MARY ANN. NF in lightly used dj w/closed tear, small snag on bottom edge. *ROBBINS.* $60

O'Connor, Flannery. A GOOD MAN IS HARD TO FIND. NY: Harcourt Brace, (1955). 1st ed. Fine in bright, Fine dj. Signed. In custom 1/4 lea clamshell box. *LOPEZ.* $5,000

O'Connor, Flannery. A GOOD MAN IS HARD TO FIND. Cl. NY: Harcourt, Brace, (1955). 1st ed. Fine in radically price-clipped dj. *JAFFE.* $375

O'Connor, Flannery. A GOOD MAN IS HARD TO FIND. NY: HB, (1955). 1st ed. Edges of black boards sl rubbed, as usual, else Fine in dj (shallow chipping to spinal extremities). Magenta circle on

spine of dj is less faded than is normal with this title. *CAPTAIN'S BOOKSHELF.* $500

O'Connor, Flannery. EVERYTHING THAT RISES MUST CONVERGE. NY: Farrar, 1965. 1st ed. About Fine in Fine dj. *BEASLEY.* $125

O'Connor, Flannery. EVERYTHING THAT RISES MUST CONVERGE. NY: Farrar, Straus & Giroux, (1965). 1st ed. Fine in NF dj which is sl rumpled at top of spine. *BERNARD.* $125

O'Connor, Flannery. EVERYTHING THAT RISES MUST CONVERGE. NY: Farrar, Straus & Giroux, (1965). 1st ed. Dj. Fine. *JAFFE.* $250

O'Connor, Flannery. MYSTERIES AND MANNERS. NY: Farrar, 1969. 1st ed. Fine in Fine dj w/trace of wrinkling at foot of spine. *BEASLEY.* $65

O'Connor, Flannery. MYSTERY AND MANNERS. London: Faber, 1972. 1st Eng ed. Boards, dj. Fine. *JAFFE.* $100

O'Connor, Flannery. MYSTERY AND MANNERS. NY: Farrar Straus Giroux, (1969). Sally & Robert Fitzgerald (eds). 1st ed. Dj. VF. *JAFFE.* $100

O'Connor, Flannery. NEW SIGNATURES. Alan Swallow (ed). Prairie City, Illinois: The Press of James A. Decker, (1947). 1st ed. Variant binding ptd in blue down spine. Incl poem by John Hollander. Fine in sl nicked dj. *JAFFE.* $475

O'Connor, Flannery. THE ARTIFICIAL NIGGER AND OTHER TALES. Boards. London: Spearman, 1957. 1st Eng ed. of A Good Man Is Hard To Find. Fine in internally reinforced dj. *JAFFE.* $225

O'Connor, Flannery. THE COMPLETE STORIES. NY: Farrar Straus & Giroux, (1971). 1st ed. Dj. VF. *JAFFE.* $250

O'Connor, Flannery. THE COMPLETE STORIES. NY: Farrar Straus & Giroux, (1971). Uncorrected proof. Bump at heel of spine, else Fine in wrappers. *CAPTAIN'S BOOKSHELF.* $250

O'Connor, Flannery. THE HABIT OF BEING. Sally Fitzgerald (ed). NY: Farrar Straus Giroux, (1979). 1st ed. Dj. VF. *JAFFE.* $50

O'Connor, Flannery. THE HABIT OF BEING: LETTERS OF FLANNERY O'CONNOR. Ed by Sally Fitzgerald. NY: Farrar Straus & Giroux, (1978). Uncorrected proof. NF in wrappers w/sl faded spine and O'Connor's name written in ink on spine. *CAPTAIN'S BOOKSHELF.* $200

O'Connor, Flannery. THE VIOLENT BEAR IT AWAY. (London): Longmans, (1960). 1st Eng ed. Boards. Fine in sl soiled dj. *JAFFE.* $150

O'Connor, Flannery. WISE BLOOD. NY: Harcourt, (1952). 1st ed, 1st bk. Light wear spinal extremities w/tiny tear head of spine, else remarkably fresh and bright in dj unfaded at spine, but w/shallow edge chipping. *CAPTAIN'S BOOKSHELF.* $800

O'Connor, Flannery. WISE BLOOD. NY: Harcourt, Brace, (1952). 1st ed, 1st bk. Orig yellow boards. NF in dj, couple tiny chips, clean tears. *CHAPEL HILL.* $850

O'Connor, Flannery. WISE BLOOD. NY: Harcourt, Brace & Co., (1952). 1st ed, 1st book. Clean, bright copy. *ROBBINS.* $400

O'Connor, Flannery. WISE BLOOD. Yellow boards, dj. NY: Harcourt, Brace, (1952). 1st ed. VF. *JAFFE.* $1750

O'Connor, Frank. GUESTS OF THE NATION. London: MacMillan, 1931. 1st ed, 1st bk. Touch of sunning to head of spine, light offsetting to eps, else Fine in dj sl worn at spinal extremities and w/spine very sl faded. *CAPTAIN'S BOOKSHELF.* $450

O'Connor, Frank. SHAKESPEARE'S PROGRESS. Cleveland: World, 1960. Ed ltd to 975. Fine in slipcase. *ARCHER.* $30

O'Connor, Frank. THE ART OF THE THEATRE. Dublin: Maurice Fridberg, 1947. 1st ed. VG+ to NF. Wraps. Name. *BEASLEY.* $45

O'Connor, Jack. COMPLETE BOOK OF RIFLES AND SHOT-GUNS. NY: Outdoor Life/Harper & Bros, 1961. 1st ed. VG+ in VG dj. *BACKMAN.* $25

O'Connor, Jack. SHEEP & SHEEP HUNTING, THE DEFINITIVE BOOK ON THE WILD SHEEP. NY, 1974. 1st ed. Fine in Fine dj. *MIKESH.* $125

O'Connor, Jack. THE ART OF HUNTING BIG GAME IN NORTH AMERICA. NY: Outdoor Life, 1967. 1st ed, 1st ptg. Fine in VG dj. *BACKMAN.* $28

O'Connor, Jack. THE BEST OF JACK O'CONNOR. Clinton: Amwell Press, 1977. 1st trade ed, slipcased. VG, not pub w/dj. *BACKMAN.* $35

O'Connor, Jack. THE BIG GAME ANIMALS OF NORTH AMERICA. NY: Outdoor Life/Charles Scribner's Sons, 1977. 1st prtg of rev 2nd ed. VG+ in Good+ dj. *BACKMAN.* $25

O'Connor, Jack. THE HUNTING RIFLE. NY: Winchester Press, 1970. 1st ed. Fine in Fine dj. *BACKMAN.* $30

O'Connor, Jack. THE RIFLE BOOK. NY: Knopf, (1949), 1953. 1st ed, 4th prtg. Bkpl. VG in Poor dj. *BACKMAN.* $30

O'Connor, Jack. THE RIFLE BOOK. NY: Knopf, 1964. 1st prtg of rev 2nd ed. VG+ in VG dj. *BACKMAN.* $30

O'Connor, Jack. THE SHOTGUN BOOK. NY: Knopf, 1965. 1st ed. Dj VG. Red cl, gilt. Fine. *CONNOLLY & WADE.* $60

O'Connor, Philip F. STEALING HOME. Knopf, 1979. 1st ed. Fine in dj. Rmdr stamp. *STAHR.* $15

O'Connor, Richard. BAT MASTERSON. Doubleday, 1957. 1st ed. VG in Fair dj. *OREGON.* $17.50

O'Connor, Richard. HIGH JINKS ON THE KLONDIKE. Bobbs-Merrill, (1954). 284pp. 1st ed. VG in G+ dj. *OREGON.* $25

O'Connor, Richard. HIGH JINKS ON THE KLONDIKE. Indianapolis: Bobbs-Merrill, 1954. NF in bright, VG dj. *CONNOLLY & WADE.* $25

O'Connor, Richard. PAT GARRETT. A BIOGRAPHY. NY: Doubleday & Co, 1960. Cloth. VF. 1st ed. *GIBBS.* $27.50

O'Conor, J.F.X. FACTS ABOUT BOOKWORMS. London: Suckling & Co, 1898. One of 750 numbered. Strong counterattack by silverfish launched on rear cover, else VG. *WREDEN.* $50

O'Cotter, Pat. RHYMES OF A ROUGHNECK. Seward, AK: O'Cotter, 1918. 1st ed. Presentation copy, inscribed, dated and signed. Little rubbed at extremes. *MUELLER.* $45

O'Crouley, Pedro Alonso. A DESCRIPTION OF THE KINGDOM OF NEW SPAIN. Sean Galvin, (ed, trans). (SF): John Howell, 1972. 23 full-pg plts; map placed in a pocket inside rear cvr. Fine in sl worn dj. *LAURIE.* $75

O'Donnell, Bernard. THE OLD BAILEY AND ITS TRIALS. London, (1950). 1st ed. 9 plts. Spine sl faded. 2 stains fore-edge. Sm hole, slight wear 1p, o/w text VG. *DIAMOND.* $25

O'Donnell, E.P. GREEN MARGINS. Boston: Houghton Mifflin, 1936. 1st ed, 1st bk. Spine somewhat discolored, else Fine in wraparound dj w/slight fading to spine. *CAPTAIN'S BOOKSHELF.* $50

O'Donnell, E.P. THE GREAT BIG DOORSTEP. Boston: Houghton Mifflin, 1941. 1st ed. NF in a lightly rubbed, sl spine faded dj. 1 page TLS laid in w/closure in holograph. *CAPTAIN'S BOOKSHELF.* $75

O'Donnell, Georgene. MINIATURIA: THE WORLD OF TINY THINGS. Chicago: Lightner Pub Co, (1943). 1st ed. Signed. VG. *WREDEN.* $40

O'Donnell, Lillian. DEATH SCHUSS. NY: Abelard-Schuman, 1963. 1st ed. Fine in lightly soiled dj, sl faded spine. *MORDIDA.* $40

O'Donnell, Peter. MODESTY BLAISE—I, LUCIFER. London: Souvenir, 1967. 1st ed. Fine in dj. *SILVER DOOR.* $25

O'Donnell, Peter. PIECES OF MODESTY. NY: Mysterious Press, 1986. 1st hc ed. New in slipcase. #176/200 signed. *ELSE FINE.* $60

O'Faolain, Julia. WE MIGHT SEE SIGHTS! AND OTHER STORIES. London: Faber and Faber, (1968). 1st ed, 1st bk. Fine in price clipped dj. *HELLER.* $70

O'Flaherty, Liam. THE FAIRY GOOSE AND TWO OTHER STORIES. NY: Crosby Gaige; London: Faber & Gwyer, Ltd, 1927. 1st ed. 1/1190 signed. Paper label sl chipped, corners bumped, else VG. Unopened. *JUVELIS.* $50

O'Hara, Frank. LUNCH POEMS. SF: City Lights, (1964). 1st ed. Pocket Poets Series No. 19. Sides spine little rubbed, tiny edge nick. Fine. *POLYANTHOS.* $25

O'Hara, Frank. MEDITATIONS IN AN EMERGENCY. NY: Grove Press, (1957). 1st Grove ed. Price inked out on front wraps, else Fine in ptd wrap. *CAPTAIN'S BOOKSHELF.* $35

O'Hara, Frank. MEDITATIONS IN AN EMERGENCY. NY: Grove Press, (1957). 1st ed. 1/75 clothbound. Fine in a very lightly soiled slipcase. *CAPTAIN'S BOOKSHELF.* $1250

O'Hara, Frank. SECOND AVENUE. NY: Totem/Corinth, (1960). 1st ed. 1st issue w/red and black cover drawing by Larry Rivers and signed by him. Fine. *POLYANTHOS.* $55

O'Hara, John. APPOINTMENT IN SAMARRA. NY: Harcourt, Brace, Jovanovich, (c1934). 1st ed, 1st bk. Corners sl bumped, o/w Fine, w/o dj. *HELLER.* $100

O'Hara, John. APPOINTMENT IN SAMARRA. NY: Modern Library, (1953). 1st ML ed. About Fine in dj rubbed at outer rear joint, spinal extremities. *CAPTAIN'S BOOKSHELF.* $30

O'Hara, John. HOPE OF HEAVEN. Harcourt, 1938. 1st ed. VG or better. Sl cocked. *STAHR.* $15

O'Hara, John. HOPE OF HEAVEN. NY: Harcourt, Brace & Co., (1938). 1st ed. NF in VG dj which has 2 short tears & wear at edges, but still an attractive dj. *BERNARD.* $85

O'Hara, John. SERMONS AND SODA WATER. NY: Random House (1960). 1st ed. 3 vols, signed on tipped-in leaf. Fine in NF slipcase. *LOPEZ.* $175

O'Hara, John. THE INSTRUMENT. NY: Random House, (1967). 1st ed. Fine in dj. *SECOND LIFE.* $25

O'Hara, John. THE INSTRUMENT. NY: Random House, 1967). 1/300 numbered, signed. Fine in acetate dj, pub's plain slipcase. *LOPEZ.* $125

O'Hara, John. THE LOCKWOOD CONCERN. NY: Random House, (1965). 1st ed. Fine in dj. *SECOND LIFE.* $25

O'Hara, John. WAITING FOR WINTER. NY: Random House, (1966). 1st ed. Fine in dj. *SECOND LIFE.* $25

O'Kane, Walter C. SUN IN THE SKY. Univ of OK Press, 1950. 1st ed. Fine in Fine dj. *VARNER.* $35

O'Kane, Walter C. SUN IN THE SKY: THE HOPI INDIANS OF THE ARIZONA MESA LANDS. Norman: Univ of OK, 1950. 1st ed. Fine in Fine dj. *CONNOLLY & WADE.* $45

O'Kane, Walter C. THE HOPIS. Univ of OK Press, 1953. 1st ed. Fine in Fine dj. *VARNER.* $35

O'Keefe, John. THE HIGHLAND REEL. Boston: for Wm. P. and L. Blake, 1797. 12mo; disbound; sl embrowning. VG. *DRAMATIS PERSONAE.* $50

O'Keefe, John. THE PRISONER AT LARGE. Phila: Henry Taylor, 1791. 12mo; disbound; uncut. VG. *DRAMATIS PERSONAE.* $50

O'Malley, Austin. THE ETHICS OF MEDICAL HOMICIDE AND MUTILATION. NY, 1922. *FYE.* $75

O'Meara, James. BRODERICK AND GWIN: THE MOST EXTRAORDINARY CONTEST FOR A SEAT IN THE

SENATE...SF, 1881. 1st ed. (10),254pp, lacks a fly leaf. Orig cl. Howes 083. *GINSBERG*. $125

O'Meara, Walter. DAUGHTERS OF THE COUNTRY. Harcourt, (1968). 1st ed. Fine in Fine dj. *OREGON*. $50

O'Meara, Walter. DAUGHTERS OF THE COUNTRY. NY, (1968). 1st ed. Dj. VG. *PRATT*. $35

O'Neal, Bill. ENCYCLOPEDIA OF WESTERN GUN-FIGHTERS. Norman, 1979. 1st ed. Fine in sl worn dj. *BAADE*. $65

O'Neal, Bill. HENRY BROWN, THE OUTLAW-MARSHALL. College Station, TX: Early West, (1980). 1st ed, ltd to 1,500. Fine in Fine dj. *BOOK MARKET*. $18

O'Neal, William B. PRIMITIVE INTO PAINTER: LIFE AND LETTERS OF JOHN TOOLE. Univ of VA Press, 1960. VG in Good dj. *BOOK BROKER*. $65

O'Neil, James B. THEY DIE BUT ONCE. THE STORY OF A TEJANO. NY: Knight, 1935. 1st ed. VG in Fine dj. *OREGON*. $85

O'Neil, James B. THEY DIE BUT ONCE....Knight, 1935. 1st ed. Fine. *VARNER*. $30

O'Neill, Charles. WILD TRAIN, THE STORY OF THE ANDREW RAIDERS. NY, (1956). 1st ed. 482pp. Dj. VG+. *PRATT*. $45

O'Neill, Dan (ed). THE NEW CATHOLICS: CONTEMPORARY CONVERTS TELL THEIR STORY. NY: Crossroad, (1987). Foreword by Walker Percy. 1st ed. Fine in dj. *CAPTAIN'S BOOKSHELF*. $35

O'Neill, Eugene G. A TOUCH OF THE POET. New Haven, CT: Yale Univ Press, 1957. 1st ed. Fine in sl rubbed dj. *JAFFE*. $65

O'Neill, Eugene G. ALL GOD'S CHILLUN GOT WINGS And WELDED. NY: Boni & Liveright, (1924). Former owner's sig, corners bumped, but VG. 1st ed. *CHAPEL HILL*. $45

O'Neill, Eugene G. ALL GOD'S CHILLUN GOT WINGS and WELDED. Cl-backed boards. NY: Boni & Liveright, (1924). 1st ed. One of 3200 ptd. Fine in dj (sl worn head of spine). *JAFFE*. $275

O'Neill, Eugene G. DESIRE UNDER THE ELMS. NY: Boni & Liveright, 1925. 1st separate bk ed. One of 2000 ptd. Fine in dj (sl wear, darkening of spine). *JAFFE*. $275

O'Neill, Eugene G. MARCO MILLIONS. Parchment backed dec boards. NY: Boni & Liveright, 1927. 1st ed. Ltd to 450 signed. Slipcase a trifle rubbed, tissue dj a bit edge-worn, but still exceptionally Fine, bright. *JAFFE*. $500

O'Neill, Eugene G. THE ICEMAN COMETH. (LEC, 1982). One of 2000, signed by the artist, Leonard Baskin. Mint in slipcase. *PIRAGES*. $125

O'Neill, Eugene G. THE ICEMAN COMETH. NY: LEC, 1982. One of 2000 illus, signed by Leonard Baskin. Orig litho by Baskin tipped in at rear. Fine in slipcase. *CAPTAIN'S BOOKSHELF*. $125

O'Neill, Eugene G. THIRST AND OTHER ONE-ACT PLAYS. Cl-backed boards w/paper labels. Boston: The Gorham Press, (1914). 1st ed. One of 1000 ptd. Spine dust-soiled, bkpl, lower right corner of title-pg sl torn, o/w Good. *JAFFE*. $150

O'Neill, Eugene G. THIRST. Boston: The Gorham Press, (1914). 1st ed. 1,000 copies of 1st book. Spine darkened, endpapers sl browned o/w VG. *BERNARD*. $225

O'Reilly, Harrington. FIFTY YEARS ON THE TRAIL, A TRUE STORY OF WESTERN LIFE. London: Chatto, 1889. 1st ed. xvi,381pp. Orig pict wraps bound into 1/2 morocco, marbled eps, aeg. Signed presentation. Fine. Howes O120. *OREGON*. $220

Oakley, Amy. CLOUD LANDS OF FRANCE. NY: Century, 1927. 1st ed. Minor wear to extremities, else VG-NF. *OLD LONDON*. $50

Oates, Joyce Carol (ed). THE BEST AMERICAN ESSAYS 1991. NY: Ticknor & Fields, 1991. Uncorrected proof. Fine in wrappers. *CAPTAIN'S BOOKSHELF*. $60

Oates, Joyce Carol. A GARDEN OF EARTHLY DELIGHTS. NY: Vanguard, 1967. Fine in dj. *ELSE FINE*. $135

Oates, Joyce Carol. A MIDDLE-CLASS EDUCATION. NY: Albondocani Press, 1980. Ltd ed, 164/326 signed. Hand-sewn wraps are French marble paper. Pub announcement laid in. Fine. *POLYANTHOS*. $45

Oates, Joyce Carol. ALL THE GOOD PEOPLE I'VE LEFT BEHIND. Santa Barbara: Black Sparrow, 1979. One of 300 signed. Fine in cl-backed patterned boards. *CAPTAIN'S BOOKSHELF*. $60

Oates, Joyce Carol. ANGEL OF LIGHT. NY: Dutton, (1981). 1st ed. Bkpl tipped in identifying it as one of "no more than 500 copies" numbered and signed. Fine in Fine dj. *LOPEZ*. $40

Oates, Joyce Carol. BY THE NORTH GATE. NY: The Vanguard Press, Inc, (1963). 1st ed, 1st bk. Fine in dj. *JUVELIS*. $250

Oates, Joyce Carol. CELESTIAL TIMEPIECE. Dallas: Pressworks, (1980). Ltd to 350, this copy unnumbered, w/illus laid in, rather than tipped in. Signed by author and illustrator. Fine in plain acetate dj. *LOPEZ*. $45

Oates, Joyce Carol. CHILDWOLD. Vanguard, 1976. 1st ed. Fine in dj. *STAHR*. $25

Oates, Joyce Carol. CROSSING THE BORDER: FIFTEEN TALES. NY: Vanguard, 1976. 1st ed. Fine; tiny scratch dj spine. *ELSE FINE*. $65

Oates Joyce Carol. CYBELE. Santa Barbara: Black Sparrow Press, 1979. 1st ed. 1/50 signed. Fine in slipcase. *CAPTAIN'S BOOKSHELF*. $100

Oates, Joyce Carol. CYBELE. Santa Barbara: Black Sparrow Press, 1979. 1st ed. Ltd, signed, deluxe issue. 1/50 from a total of 1,350. Pub's slipcase. Fine in acetate dj. *JUVELIS*. $200

Oates, Joyce Carol. CYBELE. Santa Barbara: Black Sparrow Press, 1979. One of 300 numbered, signed. Fine in cl-backed dec boards. *CAPTAIN'S BOOKSHELF*. $60

Oates, Joyce Carol. DAISY. Santa Barbara: Black Sparrow Press, 1977. 1st ed. 1/170 ltd, signed from total issue of 230. Fine in acetate dj. *JUVELIS*. $150

Oates, Joyce Carol. DO WITH ME WHAT YOU WILL. NY, (1973). 1st ed. VF in VG dj. *BOND*. $65

Oates, Joyce Carol. DO WITH ME WHAT YOU WILL. NY: Vanguard, 1973. 1st ed. As New in dj. *ELSE FINE*. $40

Oates, Joyce Carol. DREAMING OF AMERICA AND OTHER POEMS. N.p.: Aloe Editions, 1973. 1st ed. 1/150 signed. Fine in wraps w/ptd paper label. *CAPTAIN'S BOOKSHELF*. $75

Oates, Joyce Carol. EXPENSIVE PEOPLE. NY: Vanguard, (1968). 1st ed. Fine in lightly rubbed dj. *DORN*. $80

Oates, Joyce Carol. IN CASE OF ACCIDENTAL DEATH. Cambridge: Pomegranate, 1972. NF but for few folds. 1/250 numbered, signed. *BEASLEY*. $75

Oates, Joyce Carol. LIVES OF THE TWINS BY ROSAMOND SMITH. NY: Simon & Schuster, (1987). 1st ed. Grey and blue boards, dj. Fine. *JUVELIS*. $75

Oates, Joyce Carol. LOVE AND ITS DERANGEMENTS POEMS. Baton Rouge, LA: Louisiana State Univ Press, (1970). 1st ed. Red cl, black dj. Fine. *JUVELIS*. $100

Oates, Joyce Carol. MARRIAGES AND INFIDELITIES. NY: Vanguard, 1972. 1st ed. As New; minor edgewear to dj. *ELSE FINE*. $30

Oates, Joyce Carol. MARYA: A LIFE. Franklin Center: Franklin Library, 1986. 1st ed. One of an unspecified number signed. Fine in full lea. *BETWEEN COVERS*. $85

Oates, Joyce Carol. MARYA: A LIFE. NY: Dutton, (1986). Signed. Fine in dj. *DORN*. $40

Oates, Joyce Carol. QUEEN OF THE NIGHT. Northridge: Lord John, 1979. 1/300 numbered, signed. Fine w/o dj, as issued. *LOPEZ.* $65

Oates, Joyce Carol. SEASON OF PERIL. Santa Barbara: Black Sparrow Press, 1977. 1st ed. 1/200 numbered and signed from a total issue of 260. Red boards. Fine in acetate dj. *JUVELIS.* $100

Oates, Joyce Carol. SMALL AVALANCHES AND OTHER STORIES. Helsinki: Eurographica, (1989). 1st ed. Ltd to 350 signed. Ptd wraps. Mint. *JAFFE.* $150

Oates, Joyce Carol. SOLSTICE. NY: Dutton, (1985). 1st ed. Signed. Fine in dj. *DORN.* $40

Oates, Joyce Carol. SON OF THE MORNING. NY: Vanguard, 1978. 1st ed. As New in dj. Publicity photo laid in. *ELSE FINE.* $25

Oates, Joyce Carol. THE ASSASSINS. NY: Vanguard, 1975. 1st ed. As New in dj. *ELSE FINE.* $30

Oates, Joyce Carol. THE GODDESS AND OTHER WOMEN. NY: Vanguard Press, (c1974). 1st ed. Inscribed, a.l.s laid in. NF in sl darkened white dj. *HELLER.* $60

Oates, Joyce Carol. THE GODDESS AND OTHER WOMEN. NY: Vanguard, 1974. 1st ed. VF in dj. *ELSE FINE.* $25

Oates, Joyce Carol. THE HOSTILE SUN--THE POETRY OF D.H. LAWRENCE. LA: Black Sparrow, 1973. Trade ed. in wrappers. Signed. Fine. *LOPEZ.* $35

Oates, Joyce Carol. THE LAMB OF ABYSSALIA. Karyl Klopp (illus), cl-backed dec boards, acetate dj. (N.p.): Pomegranate Press, 1979. 1st ed. One of 50 deluxe signed by Oates & Klopp. VF. *JAFFE.* $185

Oates, Joyce Carol. THE POISONED KISS. NY: Vanguard, 1975. 1st ed. VF in dj. *ELSE FINE.* $35

Oates, Joyce Carol. THE SEDUCTION & OTHER STORIES. LA: Black Sparrow, 1975. One of 350 handbound in boards. Fine in glassine dj. Signed. *BETWEEN COVERS.* $85

Oates, Joyce Carol. THE WHEEL OF LOVE. NY: Vanguard, 1965. 1st ed. Bkpl. Rear cover sl dampmarked. VG+ in dj. *ELSE FINE.* $35

Oates, Joyce Carol. THEM. NY: The Vanguard Press, (1969). 1st ed. Orig blue cl. NF in VG dj, some wear along top edge. Inscribed. *CHAPEL HILL.* $150

Oates, Joyce Carol. THEM. NY: Vanguard (1969). 1st ed. NF in sl worn, VG dj. *LOPEZ.* $65

Oates, Joyce Carol. THEM. NY: Vanguard, (1969). 1st ed. Fine; narrow chip at spine heel of price clipped dj. *ELSE FINE.* $65

Oates, Joyce Carol. TRIUMPH OF THE SPIDER MONKEY. Santa Barbara: Black Sparrow, 1976. One of 350 handbound in boards. Fine in glassine dj. Signed. *BETWEEN COVERS.* $85

Oates, Joyce Carol. UPON THE SWEEPING FLOOD AND OTHER STORIES. NY: Vanguard Press, (c1966). 1st ed. Corners sl bumped, o/w Fine in dj (sl rubbed head, foot of backstrip). *HELLER.* $75

Oates, Joyce Carol. WONDERLAND. NY: Vanguard, (1971). 1st ed. Signed. Fine in VG dj (sm closed tear and very light use). *DORN.* $70

Oates, Joyce Carol. WONDERLAND. NY: Vanguard, 1971. 1st ed. As New in dj. *ELSE FINE.* $40

Oates, Joyce Carol. YOU MUST REMEMBER THIS. Franklin Center: Franklin Lib, 1987. Leatherbound ltd ed. Fine. Signed. *LOPEZ.* $85

Oates, Stephen B. VISIONS OF GLORY, TEXANS ON THE SOUTHWESTERN FRONTIER. Norman, (1970). 1st ed. 217pp. Fine in dj. *PRATT.* $25

Oates, Stephen B. WITH MALICE TOWARDS NONE, THE LIFE OF ABRAHAM LINCOLN. NY, (1977). 1st ed. 492pp. Dj wear, o/w VG+. *PRATT.* $35

Oats, Sergeant (pseud of John B. Vaughter). PRISON LIFE IN DIXIE. Chicago, 1880. 1st ed. 209pp & ads. A little cvr soiling and chipping but VG. *PRATT.* $75

Oberndorf, Clarence. THE PSYCHIATRIC NOVELS OF OLIVER WENDELL HOLMES. NY, 1944. 1st ed. *FYE.* $30

Oberth, Hermann. THE MOON CAR. NY: Harper, 1959. 1st ed. Trans by Willy Ley. Ex-lib in dj; internally clean & tight. *KNOLLWOOD.* $35

Obojski, Robert. BUSH LEAGUE. Macmillan, 1975. 1st ed. Fine in Fine dj. *PLAPINGER.* $35

Obojski, Robert. THE RISE OF JAPANESE BASEBALL POWER. Chilton, 1975. 1st ed. Fine in VG sunned dj. *PLAPINGER.* $65

Ochsner, Albert and Nelson Percy. A NEW CLINICAL SURGERY. Chicago, 1911. 3rd ed. *FYE.* $75

Ochsner, Albert and Ralph Thompson. THE SURGERY AND PATHOLOGY OF THE THYROID AND PARATHYROID GLANDS. St. Louis, 1913. 1st ed. *FYE.* $100

Ochsner, Albert. CLINICAL SURGERY. Chicago, 1902. 1st ed. Numerous Fine plts. *FYE.* $100

Ochsner, Albert. THE ORGANIZATION, CONSTRUCTION, AND MANAGEMENT OF HOSPITALS WITH NUMEROUS PLANS AND DETAILS. Chicago, 1907. 1st ed. 600pp. 339 illus. *FYE.* $250

Odell, George C.D. ANNALS OF THE NEW YORK STAGE. NY: Columbia Univ Press, 1927-1949. 15 vols. 4to; gilt-stamped cloth; some fading and light soiling to spines, a few covers dusty or lightly soiled; profusely illus. VG. *DRAMATIS PERSONAE.* $1,100

Oden, Bill. EARLY DAYS ON THE TEXAS-NEW MEXICO PLAINS. Edited by J. Evetts Haley. Canyon: Palo Duro Press, 1965. One of 750. NF. *LAURIE.* $50

Odens, Peter. FIRE OVER YUMA. Yuma, 1966. Signed. VG in wraps. *FIVE QUAIL.* $10

Odum, Howard W. COLD BLUE MOON. Indianapolis: Bobbs-Merrill, (1931). 1st ed. Orig black cl. Emb stamp, else VG in pict dj. *CHAPEL HILL.* $65

Odum, Howard W. RAINBOW ROUND MY SHOULDER. Indianapolis: Bobbs-Merrill, (1928). 1st ed. VG in dj missing large piece bottom edge of front panel. *LOPEZ.* $75

Oemler, A. TRUCK-FARMING AT THE SOUTH, A GUIDE....NY, 1884 (1883). Orig cl, lt wear to extrems; ex-lib. *SUTTON.* $35

Oesterlen, F. MEDICAL LOGIC. London, 1855. 1st Eng trans. *FYE.* $75

Offenbach, Jacques. ORPHEUS IN AMERICA: OFFENBACH'S DIARY. Bloomington: IN Univ, 1957. 1st ed. Fine in Good+ dj. *CONNOLLY & WADE.* $25

OFFICIAL BRAND BOOK OF THE STATE OF MISSOURI. Missouri Department of Agriculture, 1974. 1st ed. Fine. *CONNOLLY & WADE.* $20

OFFICIAL BRAND BOOK OF THE STATE OF NEVADA... REVISED TO JULY 1, 1941. Reno: State Depart of Agriculture, (1941). Ptd wrappers w/cl spine, remains of sticker on corner of title pg. *DAWSON'S.* $40

OFFICIAL BRAND BOOK OF THE STATE OF WYOMING, 1956. Cheyenne: Live Stock & Sanitary Board of Wyoming (1956). Gold-stamped fabricoid. *DAWSON'S.* $25

Ogan, Lew. HISTORY OF VINTON COUNTY, OHIO. McArthur, OH, (1954). VG but for snag in spine. *BOHLING.* $50

Ogilvie, W.H. WAR PRIMER ON WOUND INFECTION, ITS CAUSES, PREVENTION AND TREATMENT. London, 1940. 1st ed. Wrappers. *FYE.* $50

Ogilvie, Will. A HANDFUL OF LEATHER. NY: Scribner's, 1928. 1st ed. VG in Good dj. *OCTOBER FARM.* $85

Ogilvie, Will. GALLOPING SHOES. London: Constable, 1922. Signed presentation. VG. *OCTOBER FARM.* $125

Ogilvie, Will. GALLOPING SHOES. London: Constable, 1928. VG in Good dj. *OCTOBER FARM.* $85

Ogilvie, Will. OVER THE GRASS. London: Constable, 1925. 1st ed. Laid in, a notice of an exhibition of Edward's paintings for this book, and for "Hunting Songs". VG in Fair dj. *OCTOBER FARM.* $95

Oglesby, Catharine. MODERN PRIMITIVE ARTS OF MEXICO, GUATEMALA, & THE SOUTHWEST. Whittlesey House, (1939). 1st ed. VG in VG dj. *OREGON.* $55

Oglesby, Richard. MANUEL LISA AND THE OPENING OF THE MISSOURI FUR TRADE. Univ of OK, (1963). 1st ed. VF in VG dj. *OREGON.* $50

Oh, Sadaharu and David Falkner. SADAHARU OH: A ZEN WAY OF BASEBALL. NY: Times Books, (1984). 1st ed. Fine in dj. *CAPTAIN'S BOOKSHELF.* $35

Ohrlin, Glenn. THE HELL-BOUND TRAIN: A COWBOY SONGBOOK. Univ of IL Press, (1973). 1st ed. Record laid in. New in dj. *AUTHORS OF THE WEST.* $20

Okie, Howard Pitcher. OLD SILVER AND SHEFFIELD PLATE. GC: Doubleday, Doran, 1928. 1st ed. 25 full-pg illus. NF in slipcase. *CAPTAIN'S BOOKSHELF.* $75

OKODAKICIYE WOCEKIYE WOWAPI KIN: THE BOOK OF COMMON PRAYER. NY: NY Bible and Common Prayer Soc for the Indian Commission of the Protestant Episcopal Church, 1878. 1st ed. xxii,664pp. Orig blindstamped brn cl w/gilt letters on spine. VG. Rare. *CONNOLLY & WADE.* $300

Okrent, Daniel and Harris Lewine (eds). THE ULTIMATE BASEBALL BOOK. Houghton-Mifflin, 1979. 1st ed. Fine in VG dj. *PLAPINGER.* $65

Okri, Ben. STARS OF THE NEW CURFEW. (N.p.): Viking, (1989). Uncorrected proof of 1st Amer ed. Fine. *LOPEZ.* $30

Okri, Ben. THE FAMISHED ROAD. NY: Nan Talese/ Doubleday, (1991). 1st US ed. As New in dj. Signed. *CAPTAIN'S BOOKSHELF.* $75

Olcott, Henry S. SORGHO AND IMPHEE, THE CHINESE AND AFRICAN SUGAR CANES. 6th ed. NY: A.O. Moore, 1858. Spine faded. *KARMIOLE.* $75

OLD PLYMOUTH: A GUIDE TO ITS LOCALITIES AND OBJECTS OF INTEREST. Plymouth, MA, 1888, 4th ed. 104pp, 16pp ads. Bound in new buckram. *HEINOLDT.* $15

Old Sleuth. THE GREAT RIVER MYSTERY, OR, IN THE CLUTCHES OF A BEAUTIFUL BLACKMAILER. Cleveland: Arthur Westbrook, 1909. 1st ed. Pb orig. Adventure Series no. 87. Short closed tear on back panel o/w VG in pict wrappers. *MORDIDA.* $25

OLD THINGS AND NEW; Or, Ancient Fables....Baltimore: Pub by Joseph N. Lewis, 1835. 1st ed. 51pp. Early 20th century 1/4 calf and boards. Traces of lt foxing, but Nice. *CHAPEL HILL.* $125

Olden, Sarah Emilia. THE PEOPLE OF TIPI SAPA. (The Dakotas). Tipi Sapa Mitaoyate Kin. Milwaukee, WI: Morehouse Pub Co. 1918. 1st ed. xxiv,158pp. Frontis port, 20 photogr plts. Spine lightly stained. *KARMIOLE.* $50

Older, Fremont. MY OWN STORY. NY: Post-Enquirer, 1925. 1st ed thus. John D. Barry (intro). Frontis. Grey, stiff wraps, sunned on spine. Small chip head of spine, else Fine. *CONNOLLY & WADE.* $35

Oldham, J. Basil. ENGLISH BLIND-STAMPED BINDINGS. Cambridge: Univ Press, 1952. Ed ltd to 750. 61 leaves of collotype plts. Fine in somewhat torn and chipped dj. *KARMIOLE.* $250

Oldroyd, Osborn Hamiltine. A SOLDIER'S STORY OF THE SIEGE OF VICKSBURG FROM THE DIARY OF OSBORN H.

OLDROYD....Springfield, IL: Privately ptd, 1885. 1st ed. Rubbing to spine ends, corners, else VG to NF. Presentation slip, inscribed. *McGOWAN.* $250

Olin, W.H. AMERICAN IRRIGATION FARMING. A SYSTEMATIC....Chicago: McClure, 1913. 1st ed. Frontis. NF. *CONNOLLY & WADE.* $42.50

Oliphant, J. Orin. ON THE CATTLE RANGES OF THE OREGON COUNTRY. Univ of WA, (1968). 1st ed. VF in VF dj. *OREGON.* $50

Oliphant, Laurence. THE RUSSIAN SHORES OF THE BLACK SEA IN THE AUTUMN OF 1852....NY: Redfield, 1854. 1st US ed, from the 3rd London ed. 266pp. 2 maps (1 fldg). Ex-lib, o/w VG. *WORLDWIDE.* $65

Oliphant, Lawrence. MINNESOTA AND THE FAR WEST. Edinburgh, 1855. 1st ed. (14),306,(16)pp. Fldg map at rear, 7 plts, woodcuts in text. Orig dec cl. Howes 064. *GINSBERG.* $300

Oliva, Leo E. SOLDIERS ON THE SANTA FE TRAIL. Univ of OK Press, 1967. 1st ed. Inscribed. Fine in NF dj. *VARNER.* $40

Oliver, Andrew (ed). THE JOURNAL OF SAMUEL CURWEN, LOYALIST. 2 Vols. Harvard Univ Press, 1972. 1st ed. VF in djs. *ARTIS.* $25

Oliver, Chad. SHADOWS IN THE SUN. Ballantine, 1954. 1st ed. NF in sl foxed, chipped dj. Inscribed. *MADLE.* $500

Oliver, Edith Patton. MISS ANNA. Oak Brook: Broland Pub, 1967. 1st ed. Dj chipped, worn. Dust, else VG. Inscribed. *PARMER.* $65

Oliver, Harry. DESERT ROUGH CUTS. A HAYWIRE HISTORY OF THE BOREGO DESERT. LA: Ward Ritchie, 1938. 1st ed. Fragile. Cloth backstrip over paper-covered boards w/Oliver woodcut. Cloth backstrip of flimsy material, showing age. VG, scarce. *CONNOLLY & WADE.* $75

Oliver, Herman. GOLD AND CATTLE COUNTRY. Binfords & Mort, 1961. E.R. Jackman (ed). 1st ed. VG in Fine dj. *OREGON.* $25

Oliver, Herman. GOLD AND CATTLE COUNTRY. Portland, 1961. 1st ptg. Signed. Fine in Fine dj. *VARNER.* $45

Oliver, Jean. ARCHITECTURE OF THE KIDNEY IN CHRONIC BRIGHT'S DISEASE. NY, 1939. 1st ed. 195pp + plts. *FYE.* $100

Oliver, Paul. BLUES FELL THIS MORNING. NY: Horizon, 1961. 1st US ed. Fine in Fine dj but for a few chips. *BEASLEY.* $50

Olivier, Laurence. CONFESSIONS OF AN ACTOR. NY: S&S, (1982). 1st ed. Inscribed. Fine in Fine dj. *UNGER.* $125

Olmstead, A.T. HISTORY OF PALESTINE AND SYRIA TO THE MACEDONIAN CONQUEST. NY & London: Scribner's. 1931. 1st ed. Fldg map. A little rubbed, spine worn, pencil underlining. *SCHOYER'S.* $40

Olmstead, Robert. RIVER DOGS. NY: Vintage, (1987). Uncorrected proof. Fine in wraps, promo letter laid in. *LOPEZ.* $45

Olsen, D.B. BRING THE BRIDE A SHROUD. GC: Doubleday Crime Club, 1945. 1st ed. Fine in VG dj w/sl faded spine, wear and nicks; sm chip. *MORDIDA.* $32.50

Olsen, D.B. DEATH WALKS ON CAT FEET. GC: Doubleday Crime Club, 1956. 1st ed. Fine in sl soiled dj, couple short closed tears. *MORDIDA.* $32.50

Olsen, Tillie. TELL ME A RIDDLE. Phila: Lippincott, 1961. 1st ed. Fine in modestly used dj. *DERMONT.* $200

Olsen, Tillie. TELL ME A RIDDLE. Phila/NY: Lippincott, 1961. 1st ed. Very faint foxing to fore-edge, else Fine in Very NF dj, sl spine faded, w/remnant of pencilled number top of spine. *BETWEEN COVERS.* $350

Olson, Charles. ARCHEOLOGIST OF MORNING. NY: Cape Goliard/Grossman, 1970. 1st ed, 1st issue. Fine in dj (lt crease). *AKA.* $250

Olson, Charles. CALL ME ISHMAEL. NY: Reynal & Hitchcock, (1947). 1st ed, 1st bk. Shelfwear, cup stain, spine sl sunstruck. VG. *AKA*. $90

Olson, Charles. CALL ME ISHMAEL. NY: Reynal & Hitchcock, 1947. Fine but for sunning, lacking dj. *BEASLEY*. $35

Olson, Charles. CHARLES OLSON IN CONNECTICUT: LAST LECTURES. Grn boards. Iowa City: Windhover Press, 1974. 1st ed. Ltd to 220. Fine. *JAFFE*. $65

Olson, Charles. HUMAN UNIVERSE AND OTHER ESSAYS. NY: Grove, 1967. 1st ed. Fine in Fine dj. *BEASLEY*. $40

Olson, Charles. SOME EARLY POEMS. Iowa City: Windhover Press, 1973. 1st ed. Ltd to 300. Cl backed boards. Fine. *JAFFE*. $75

Olson, Charles. STOCKING CAP. A STORY. Self wrappers, stitched as issued. (SF: Grabhorn-Hoyem for Donald Allen), Christmas 1966. 1st ed. One of 100 ptd. Fine. *JAFFE*. $225

Olson, Charles. THE MAXIMUS POEMS. Cl w/pict labels on cvrs & spine. NY: Jargon/Corinth Books, 1960. 1st ed, hardbound issue. One of 75 numbered bound in cl out of total hb issue of 101 (incl 26 signed by Olson). Outer margin of back cvr sl dampstained, o/w Fine. *JAFFE*. $150

Olson, James. HISTORY OF NEBRASKA. Univ of NE, 1955. 1st ed. Signed. Fine. *OREGON*. $40

Olson, James. J. STERLING MORTON. Lincoln: Univ of NE Press, 1942. 1st ed. Signed. Lacks ffep, small gouge in back. VG in Good dj. *ARCHER*. $15

Olson, Reuel Leslie. THE COLORADO RIVER COMPACT. LA, 1926. xxiv, 527pp; 1st ed. Ex-lib, minimal markings. *FIVE QUAIL*. $45

Olsson, A.A. MOLLUSKS OF THE TROPICAL EASTERN PACIFIC.... PANAMIC-PACIFIC PELECYPODA. Ithaca, 1961. 86 plts. Wrappers (name blackened out on spine) o/w Nice ex-lib. *SUTTON*. $50

Olsson, Jan. WELCOME TO TOMBSTONE. London: Elek Books, 1956. 1st ed. Fine in dj. *GIBBS*. $40

Olsson, Jan. WELCOME TO TOMBSTONE. London: Elek Books, (1956). 1st ed. VF in VF dj. *OREGON*. $25

Omand, W.T. BELGIUM. A&C Black, 1908. 1st ed. Later imp (red shield). 20s Series. VG-NF. *OLD LONDON*. $85

Omang, Joanne. INCIDENT AT AKABAL. Boston: HMCo. (1992). Uncorrected proof. Fine in wraps. *DORN*. $25

Omond, G.W.T. BRABENT AND EAST FLANDERS. A&C Black, n.d. (1907). 1st ed. 7s 6d Series. Minor cover stain, some foxing, else VG. *OLD LONDON*. $40

Omond, G.W.T. BRUGES AND WEST FLANDERS. A&C Black, 1906. 1st ed. 10s Series. VG-NF. *OLD LONDON*. $40

Omond, G.W.T. LIEGE AND THE ARDENNES. A&C Black, 1908. 1st ed. 7s 6d Series. Minor spotting, slight wear, but VG indeed. *OLD LONDON*. $75

Ondaatje, Michael. COMING THROUGH SLAUGHTER. London, 1979. 1st ed, 1st bk. Signed. Fine in price clipped dj. *POLYANTHOS*. $65

Ondaatje, Michael. COMING THROUGH SLAUGHTER. London: Boyars, (1979). 1st ed. Signed. Fine in dj. *LOPEZ*. $100

Ondaatje, Michael. COMING THROUGH SLAUGHTER. NY: Norton, 1976. 1st ed. VF; faint sticker shadow on dj. *ELSE FINE*. $45

Ondaatje, Michael. IN THE SKIN OF A LION. (Toronto): McClelland and Stewart, (1987). Correct 1st ed. Fine in Fine dj. Signed. *LOPEZ*. $65

Ondaatje, Michael. IN THE SKIN OF THE LION. NY: Knopf, 1987. 1st Amer Ed. Fine in dj. Signed. *CAPTAIN'S BOOKSHELF*. $75

Ondaatje, Michael. RAT JELLY AND OTHER POEMS 1963-78. London: Boyers, 1980. 1st ed. VF in dj. *ELSE FINE*. $35

Ondaatje, Michael. RAT JELLY AND OTHER POEMS 1963-78. London, 1980. 1st ed. Signed. Fine in like dj. *POLYANTHOS*. $55

Ondaatje, Michael. THE CINNAMON PEELER SELECTED POEMS. NY: Knopf, 1991. 1st Amer ed. Signed. *CAPTAIN'S BOOKSHELF*. $45

Ondaatje, Michael. THE COLLECTED WORKS OF BILLY THE KID. NY: Norton, (1974). 1st US ed. Errata slip laid in. NF in sl soiled dj. *BERNARD*. $30

Ondaatje, Michael. THE COLLECTED WORKS OF BILLY THE KID. London: Boyars, (1981). 1st Eng ed. Signed. Fine in dj. *LOPEZ*. $75

Ondaatje, Michael. THE COLLECTED WORKS OF BILLY THE KID. London, 1981. 1st ed. Signed. Fine in price clipped dj. *POLYANTHOS*. $55

Ondaatje, Michael. THE ENGLISH PATIENT. NY: Knopf, 1992. 1st Amer ed. As New in dj. Signed. *CAPTAIN'S BOOKSHELF*. $60

Ondaatje, Michael. THERE'S A TRICK WITH A KNIFE I'M LEARNING TO DO. NY: Norton, (1979). Inscribed. Fine in Fine dj. *LOPEZ*. $85

ONE HUNDRED YEARS OF BOOK AUCTIONS, 1807-1907 BEING A BRIEF RECORD OF THE FIRM OF HODGSON AND CO.. London. n.p., 1908. 53pp. Printed for priv circ; scarce. Soiling of outer paper wrappers. *OAK KNOLL*. $85

Onslow-Ford, Gordon. PAINTING IN THE INSTANT. London: Thames and Hudson, 1964. 1st ed. Holograph facs notebook. Issued w/o dj? Fine. Uncommon. *BEASLEY*. $100

Onstott, Kyle with Lance Horner. THE TATTOOED ROOD. Middleburg: Denlinger's, 1960. 1st ed. Fine in dj. *ELSE FINE*. $45

Onstott, Kyle. BEEKEEPING AS A HOBBY. Harper & Bros., 1941. 1st ed. Fine in VG Dj. *MAD DOG*. $15

Onstott, Kyle. DRUM. NY: Dial, 1962. 1st ed. Fine; minor wear to dj. *ELSE FINE*. $35

Oppe, A.P. THE WATER-COLOURS OF TURNER, COX & DE WINT. London: Halton & Truscott Smith, Ltd. 1925. 1st ed. 34 tipped-in color plts, each w/tissue guard. *KARMIOLE*. $75

Oppe, A.P. THOMAS ROWLANDSON. HIS DRAWINGS & WATER-COLORS. Geoffrey Holme (ed). London: The Studio, 1923. 16 color, 75 monochrome tipped-in plts, full vellum, unptd dj. London: The Studio, 1923. 1st ed. One of 200 specially bound. Fine, bright in worn fldg chemise. *JAFFE*. $200

Oppen, George. COLLECTED POEMS. (NY): New Directions, (1975). 1st ed. Fine in dj. *BERNARD*. $35

Oppenheim, E. Philips. THE MAYOR ON HORSEBACK. Boston: Little, Brown, 1937. 1st ed. Fine in dj w/short closed tear back panel. Exceptional. *MORDIDA*. $85

Oppenheim, E. Phillips. GENERAL BESSERLEY'S PUZZLE BOX. Boston: Little Brown, 1935. 1st ed. VF in dj. *ELSE FINE*. $45

Oppenheim, E. Phillips. GENERAL BESSERLEY'S SECOND PUZZLE BOX. Boston: Little Brown, 1940. 1st ed. VF; dj spine sl age darkened. *ELSE FINE*. $35

Oppenheim, E. Phillips. SLANE'S LONG SHOTS. Little, Brown, 1930. 1st Amer ed. Good with staining to lower corner of front, rear boards in spine-darkened dj with closed edge tear, chips. *BEBBAH*. $18

Oppenheim, E. Phillips. THE BATTLE OF BASINGHALL STREET. Boston, 1935. 1st ed. Fine w/o dj. *BOND*. $35

Oppenheim, E. Phillips. THE BATTLE OF BASINGHALL STREET. Boston: Little-Brown, 1935. 1st ed. Fine; dj w/minor chips. *ELSE FINE*. $35

Oppenheim, E. Phillips. THE BIRD OF PARADISE. London: Hodder & Stoughton, 1936. 1st ed. Spine letters flaking, else Fine. Dj chipped at spine ends. *ELSE FINE*. $60

Oppenheim, E. Phillips. THE COLOSSUS OF ARCADIA. Boston: Little Brown, 1938. 1st ed. VF in dj w/minor edgewear. *ELSE FINE.* $40

Oppenheim, Hermann. DISEASES OF THE NERVOUS SYSTEM. Phila, 1904. 2nd Amer ed. Shaken. *FYE.* $75

Oppenheim, James. THE NINE-TENTHS. NY: Harper, 1911. 1st ed. VG w/considerable rubbing. *BEASLEY.* $75

Oppenheimer, Heinrich. MEDICAL AND ALLIED TOPICS IN LATIN POETRY. London, 1928. 1st ed. Underlining in a few leaves, backstrip rubbed. *FYE.* $75

Oppenheimer, Seymour. THE SURGICAL TREATMENT OF CHRONIC SUPPURATION OF THE MIDDLE EAR AND MASTOID. Phila, 1906. 1st ed. *FYE.* $200

Opper, F(rederick B.). WILLIE AND HIS PAPA AND THE REST OF THE FAMILY. NY: Grosset & Dunlap, (1901). Cl w/pict boards, rubbed, some staining, contents Fine. *SCHOYER'S.* $65

Oppert, Ernest. FORBIDDEN LAND; VOYAGES OT THE COREA. NY: Putnam's, 1880. (xx), (351)pp. Blue cl stamped in gilt, a little rubbed, spotted and shaken. double-pg frontis. Lacks both charts. *SCHOYER'S.* $60

Optic, Oliver (pseud of William Adams). THE BLUE AND THE GRAY—ON LAND AN UNDIVIDED UNION. Boston: Lee and Shephard, 1899. 1st ed. Fine. *BOOK MARKET.* $35

Orcutt, William Dana. FROM MY LIBRARY WALLS. London: John Murray, (1946). 1st Eng ed. John Roland Abbey's copy, w/his bkpl. Front cover dampstained, else Good in soiled dj. *WREDEN.* $30

Orcutt, William Dana. ROBERT CAVELIER DE LA SALLE AND HIS DISCOVERY OF THE MISSISSIPPI RIVER. Chicago, 1904. Author's 1st bk. NF. *POLYANTHOS.* $55

Orcutt, William Dana. THE MAGIC OF THE BOOK. Boston: Little, Brown, 1930. 1st trade ed. Light pencilling on prelims, o/w Fine. *WREDEN.* $65

Orczy, (Emmuska), Baroness. ELDORADO. London: Hodder & Stoughton, (1913). Owner's sig, else VG. 1st ed. *CHAPEL HILL.* $50

Ordronaux, John. REGIMEN SANITATIS SALERNITANUM. CODE OF HEALTH OF THE SCHOOL OF SALERNUM. Phila, 1870. 1st ed. 4to, 167pp. Backstrip chewed w/1" piece missing from tail of spine. Contents Fine. *FYE.* $100

Ordway, Frederick I. and Mitchell R. Sharpe. THE ROCKET TEAM. NY: T.Y. Crowell, 1979. VG w/dj. *KNOLLWOOD.* $36

Oregon Pioneer Association. 49TH ANNUAL REUNION...1921. 1st ed. Orig wraps. Fine. *OREGON.* $40

Oregon Pioneer Association. TRANSACTIONS OF THE 15TH ANNUAL REUNION. PORTLAND, OR. JUNE 15TH, 1887. 1st ed. Orig wraps, spine chipping. VG. *OREGON.* $30

OREGON. END OF THE TRAIL. Portland, OR, (1940). 1st ed. Fldg map in envelope. Shelfworn, spine soiled. Spine gilt dull, o/w VG. *DIAMOND.* $35

Orellana, Sandra. INDIAN MEDICINE IN HIGHLAND GUATEMALA: THE PRE-HISPANIC AND COLONIAL PERIODS. Albuquerque, 1987. 1st ed. Dj. *FYE.* $25

Orem, Preston D. BASEBALL 1845-1881. Self-pub, 1961. 1st ed. Fine. *PLAPINGER.* $70

Orfield, Lester B. CRIMINAL PROCEDURE FROM ARREST TO APPEAL. NY & London, 1947. Orig buckram. NF in dj. *DIAMOND.* $45

Orians, G.H. BLACKBIRDS OF THE AMERICAS. Seattle, 1985. Dj. *SUTTON.* $30

Orlofsky, Patsy & Myron. QUILTS IN AMERICA. NY: McGraw-Hill, 1974. VG to NF in VG to NF dj. *BACKROOM.* $450

Ormsbee, Thomas. THE WINDSOR CHAIR. NY: Deerfield Books, Inc, 1962. 1st ed. VG in dj. *BACKROOM.* $50

Ornduff, Donald. THE HEREFORD IN AMERICA. A HISTORY OF THE BREED'S PROGRESS. Kansas City, 1960. 2nd ed. VG in Good+ dj. *OCTOBER FARM.* $30

Orr, H. Winnett. ON THE CONTRIBUTIONS OF HUGH OWEN THOMAS, SIR ROBERT JONES, AND JOHN RIDLON TO MODERN ORTHOPEDIC SURGERY. Springfield, 1949. 1st ed. *FYE.* $75

Orrin, H.C. FASCIAL GRAFTING IN PRINCIPLE AND PRACTICE, AN ILLUSTRATED MANUAL OF PROCEDURE AND TECHNIQUE. London, 1928. 1st ed. Ex-lib. *FYE.* $100

Orth, Samuel O. A HISTORY OF CLEVELAND, OHIO. 3 vols. Chicago: Clarke, 1910. 1st ed. Half-leather, aeg. VG to NF. *ARCHER.* $135

Ortiz, Alfonso (ed). HANDBOOK OF NORTH AMERICAN INDIANS, VOLUME 9 (only): SOUTHWEST. Washington: Smithsonian Institution, 1979. Good. *ARCHAEOLOGIA.* $85

Ortiz, Fernando. CUBAN COUNTERPOINT: TOBACCO AND SUGAR. NY: Knopf, 1947. 1st ed. Chipped dj. *SILVER.* $30

Ortiz, Roxanne Dunbar. THE GREAT SIOUX NATION. (NY/Berkeley): American Indian Treaty Council Information Center/Moon Books, (1977). One of 5,000 of the issue in wrappers (there were 1,000 hardcovers). VG. *LOPEZ.* $75

Ortiz, Simon J. A GOOD JOURNEY. Berkeley: Turtle Island, 1977. Issue in wrappers. One of 1/2000. VG. *LOPEZ.* $35

Ortiz, Simon J. FROM SAND CREEK. Oak Park: Thunder's Mouth Press, (1981). 1st ed. Fine in wrappers, as issued. *LOPEZ.* $35

Ortiz, Simon J. GOING FOR THE RAIN. NY: H&R, (1976). 1st ed. VG in wrappers, as issued. *LOPEZ.* $45

Orton, Joe. ENTERTAINING MR. SLOANE. London: HH, 1964. 1st ed of author's 1st bk. VG+ in VG dj w/small chip to rear panel. Inscribed to Peter (Willes). *LAME DUCK.* $1250

Orwell, George (pseud of Eric Arthur Blair). DOWN AND OUT IN PARIS AND LONDON. NY & London: Harper & Bros, 1933. 1st Amer ed. Orig lavender cl. Minor staining edges last few pgs, o/w About Fine in VG pict dj, chip, few tears. Quite scarce in dj. *CHAPEL HILL.* $1,200

Orwell, George. ANIMAL FARM. NY: Harcourt, Brace and Co., (1946). Advance, Confidential Copy in gray ptd wrappers of the 1st Amer ed. Clean, showing light use only. *DERMONT.* $400

Orwell, George. KEEP THE ASPIDISTRA FLYING. London, 1936. 1st ed. Spine sunned, extremities minimally rubbed, covers little soiled. NF. Very Scarce. *POLYANTHOS.* $150

Orwell, George. NINETEEN EIGHTY-FOUR. London: Secker & Warburg, 1949. 1st ed, in preferred red dj (also issued in grn). Orig grn cl. VG in heavily faded, somewhat rubbed dj, chipping to corners and spine ends; abraded spot rear joint. Scarce. *CHAPEL HILL.* $450

Orwell, George. NINETEEN EIGHTY-FOUR. London: Secker & Warburg, 1949. 1st ed, in the variant grn dj (no priority). Few short closed tears in dj, o/w Fine. *JAFFE.* $850

Orwell, George. NINETEEN EIGHTY-FOUR. London: Secker & Warburg, 1949. Orig grn cl. Nearly Fine in VG grn dj (light rubbing, very small chip at head of spine affecting no lettering). 1st ed. *CHAPEL HILL.* $500

Orwell, George. NINETEEN EIGHTY-FOUR. NY: Harcourt, Brace, (1949). 1st Amer ed. Orig grey cl. Fine in NF dj. Excellent. In preferred red dj (also issued in blue jacket, probably later). *CHAPEL HILL.* $250

Orwell, George. NINETEEN EIGHTY-FOUR. NY: Harcourt, Brace & Co, (1949). 1st US ed. Advance prepub of 1st US ed in wraps. Spine sl cocked & cvr sl soiled, else VG. *BERNARD.* $375

Orwell, George. SHOOTING AN ELEPHANT. London: Secker and Warburg, 1950. 1st ed. Orig grn cl. VG in dj. *CHAPEL HILL.* $200

Orwell, George. THE COLLECTED ESSAYS, JOURNALISM AND LETTERS. Sonia Orwell & Ian Angus (eds). 4 vols. London: Secker, (1968). 1st eds. Dj. Fine set. *JAFFE.* $300

Osborn, Campbell. LET FREEDOM RING. Tokyo: Inter-nation Co, (1954). 1st ed. Map. Fine in VG dj. *OREGON.* $60

Osborn, H. INSECTS AFFECTING DOMESTIC ANIMALS. Washington, 1906. 5 plts. Later cloth binding worn at corners, newspaper clippings glued in, hinges cracked. Inscrip by author. *SUTTON.* $38

Osborn, H.S. THE NEW DESCRIPTIVE GEOGRAPHY OF PALESTINE. Oxford, OH, 1877. 309pp. *O'NEILL.* $45

Osborn, Karen. PATCHWORK. San Diego: Harcourt, Brace & Jovanovich, (1991). 1st Amer ed. Signed. Fine in dj. *DORN.* $35

Osborn, Sherard. STRAY LEAVES FROM AN ARCTIC JOURNAL; OR, EIGHTEEN MONTHS IN THE POLAR REGIONS. London: Longman, Brown, Green, and Longmans, 1852. 1st ed. (x), 320 pp. Fldg map, 3 color plts. Contemp red polished calf, spine gilt, obtrusive dampstain throughout. *LEFKOWICZ.* $275

Osborne, David (pseud of Robert Silverberg). INVISIBLE BARRIERS. NY: Avalon Books, (c1958). Fine in dj, 2 short tears. *HELLER.* $50

Osborne, John. A BOND HONOURED. London: Faber and Faber, 1966. 1st ed. Fine in dj. *JUVELIS.* $40

Osgood, Cornelius. WINTER. NY, (1953). 1st ed. Fine in dj. *ARTIS.* $15

Osgood, Cornelius. WINTER. NY: W.W. Norton, 1953. 1st ed. VG in darkened, chipped dj. *PARMER.* $25

Osgood, Ernest Staples (ed). THE FIELD NOTES OF CAPTAIN WILLIAM CLARK 1803-1805. Yale, 1964. 1st ed. Fine in VG dj. *OREGON.* $300

Osgood, Henry O. SO THIS IS JAZZ. Boston, 1926. VG. *POLYANTHOS.* $75

Osgood, Herbert L. THE AMERICAN COLONIES IN THE EIGHTEENTH CENTURY. NY, 1924. 1st ed. 4 vols. Orig cl, light discoloration on some rear covers. Howes 0132. *GINSBERG.* $100

Oskison, John M. A TEXAS TITAN. GC: Doubleday Doran, 1929. 1st ed. NF, lacking dj. *LOPEZ.* $45

Oskison, John M. BLACK JACK DAVY. NY: Appleton, 1926. 1st ed. Owner name fep, o/w VG in VG dj. *LOPEZ.* $150

Oskison, John M. WILD HARVEST. Chicago: White House, (1925). 2nd ed. 1st book. Rmdr imprint and binding, apparently using the orig pub's 2nd prtg sheets. NF in VG dj, somewhat spine-faded, chipped. *LOPEZ.* $200

Osler, W. A CONCISE HISTORY OF MEDICINE. Baltimore, 1919. 1st ed. *FYE.* $125

Osler, W. AEQUANIMITAS WITH OTHER ADDRESSES. London, 1904. 1st British ed. 389pp. Extremities of binding rubbed. Overall, VG. Scarce. *FYE.* $250

Osler, W. AEQUANIMITAS WITH OTHER ADDRESSES. Phila, 1925. 2nd ed. *FYE.* $40

Osler, W. AN ALABAMA STUDENT AND OTHER BIOGRAPHICAL ESSAYS. NY, 1908. 1st ed, 1st ptg. 334pp. *FYE.* $225

Osler, W. MAN'S REDEMPTION OF MAN. NY, 1913. 1st ed. 1" by 1/4" crush mark on front cover, o/w Fine. *FYE.* $125

Osler, W. ON CHOREA AND CHOREIFORM AFFECTIONS. Phila, 1894. 1st ed. 125pp. VF. Very rare. *FYE.* $1,000

Osler, W. SCIENCE AND IMMORTALITY (THE INGERSOLL LECTURE, 1904). Boston: Houghton Mifflin, 1904. 1st ed. Red cl cvr sl worn, contents VG. *SMITHFIELD.* $63

Osler, W. SCIENCE AND IMMORTALITY. Boston, 1905. 1st ed, reprinted. 54pp. *FYE.* $80

Osler, W. SCIENCE AND IMMORTALITY. Boston: Houghton Mifflin, 1904. 1st ed. Red cl cvr sl worn; contents VG. *SMITHFIELD.* $70

Osler, W. THE EVOLUTION OF MODERN MEDICINE. New Haven, 1929. 1st ed, 4th ptg. 243pp. VF. Scarce. *FYE.* $150

Osler W. THE EVOLUTION OF MODERN MEDICINE. New Haven, 1921. 1st ed. 243pp. *FYE.* $250

Osler, W. THE OLD HUMANITIES AND THE NEW SCIENCE. Boston, 1920. 64pp. Intro by Harvey Cushing. Portrait of Osler. *FYE.* $100

Osler, W. THE PRINCIPLES AND PRACTICE OF MEDICINE. NY, 1892. 1st ed, 2nd ptg. 1079pp. Exceptionally Fine in orig brown cloth. Rare in Fine condition. *FYE.* $1250

Osler, W. THE PRINCIPLES AND PRACTICE OF MEDICINE. NY, 1892. 1st ed., 1st prtg. 1079pp. Full leather. Orig boards skillfully rebacked in matching leather w/orig label, new eps. Ads dated Nov. 1891. *FYE.* $1750

Osler, W. THE PRINCIPLES AND PRACTICE OF MEDICINE. NY, 1912. 8th ed. Shaken, inner hinges cracked. *FYE.* $75

Osler, W. THE PRINCIPLES AND PRACTICE OF MEDICINE. NY, 1892. 1st ed, not 1st ptg. 1079pp. Orig grn cloth. Shaken, inner hinges cracked, 1/2" piece missing from top of spine. Contents VG. *FYE.* $650

Osler W. THE PRINCIPLES AND PRACTICE OF MEDICINE. NY, 1897. 2nd ed. *FYE.* $250

Osler, W. THE PRINCIPLES AND PRACTICE OF MEDICINE. NY: Appleton, 1901. 3rd ed. Recased, paper spine label. Near VG. *SMITHFIELD.* $80

Osler, W. UNITY, PEACE, AND CONCORD. A FAREWELL ADDRESS TO THE MEDICAL PROFESSION IN THE UNITED STATES. Oxford, 1905. 1st ed. Wrappers. 22pp. Scarce. *FYE.* $150

Osmond, Humphry and Bernard Aaronson (eds). PSYCHEDELICS. Cambridge: Schenkman, 1971. 1st ed. VG in dj. *LOPEZ.* $40

Ostrander, A.B. AFTER 60 YEARS. Seattle, (1925). 1st ed. 120pp, illus. Pict wraps. VG+. *PRATT.* $100

Oswald, Felix. ALONE IN THE SLEEPING-SICKNESS COUNTRY. London: Kegan Paul, Trench, Trubner & Co. Ltd., 1915. 1st ed. Ex-lib spine label carefully removed, foxing, else VG. *GREAT EPIC.* $55

Oswald, Felix. THE POISON PROBLEM OR THE CAUSE AND CURE OF INTEMPERANCE. NY, 1887. 1st ed. *FYE.* $40

Oswald, Felix. VACCINATION A CRIME, WITH COMMENTS ON OTHER SANITARY SUPERSTITIONS. NY, 1901. 1st ed. 1/2 lea. *FYE.* $75

Oswald, Richard. RICHARD OSWALD'S MEMORANDUM ON THE FOLLY OF INVADING VIRGINIA. Charlottesville, 1953. Robinson, W. Stitt Jr. (ed). 1st ed. Colored frontis. Orig cl backed boards. One of 750. *GINSBERG.* $60

Oswald, Richard. MEMORANDUM ON THE FOLLY OF INVADING VIRGINIA. Univ of VA, 1953. Ltd 750. Robinson W. Stitt, Jr. (ed). Colored frontis & map. *HEINOLDT.* $15

Otero, Miguel Antonio. THE REAL BILLY THE KID WITH NEW LIGHT ON THE LINCOLN COUNTY WAR. NY: Rufus Rockwell Wilson Inc, 1936. 1st ed. Fine. *GIBBS.* $110

Otis, Elwell S. THE INDIAN QUESTION. NY: Sheldon and Co, 1878. 1st ed. Fine. *LAURIE.* $90

Otis, Philo Adams. THE CHICAGO SYMPHONY ORCHESTRA. Chicago: Clayton F. Summy Co. (1924). 1st ed. 466pp. Blue cl, gilt. Scarce. *KARMIOLE.* $45

OTIS' LETTERS IN DEFENCE OF THE HARTFORD CONVENTION, AND THE PEOPLE OF MASSACHUSETTS. (By Harry Gray Otis.) Boston, 1824. Enl, best ed. (7),103pp, untrimmed. Sewn as issued, title page expertly mended, a few letters affected of pub's name. Howes 0143. *GINSBERG.* $75

Otteson, Stuart. THE BOLT ACTION: A DESIGN ANALYSIS. NY: Winchester Press, 1976. 1st ed. Fine in Fine dj. *BACKMAN.* $25

Ottley, Roi and William J. Weatherby, (eds). THE NEGRO IN NEW YORK. AN INFORMAL SOCIAL HISTORY. NY & Dobbs Ferry: NYPL & Oceana, 1967. 1st ed. Fine in lightly used dj. *BEASLEY.* $75

Ottley, Roi. BLACK ODYSSEY. THE STORY OF THE NEGRO IN AMERICA. NY: Scribners, 1948. 1st ed. VG in Good dj. *CONNOLLY & WADE.* $28.50

Otto, Eberhard. ANCIENT EGYPTIAN ART: THE CULTS OF OSIRIS AND AMON. NY: Harry N. Abrams, (1967). 16 color illus. Dj. Good. *ARCHAEOLOGIA.* $95

Otto, Whitney. HOW TO MAKE AN AMERICAN QUILT. NY: Villard, (1991). 1st ed. Signed. VF in VF dj. *UNGER.* $45

OUR ACRE AND ITS HARVEST, HISTORICAL SKETCH OF THE SOLDIER'S AID SOCIETY OF NORTHERN OHIO. Cleveland, 1869. 1st ed. 511pp. VG. *PRATT.* $60

OUR COAL AND COAL-PITS...By a traveller underground. (By John R. Leifchild.) London: Longman, Brown, 1862. 2nd ed. Prize bkpl, slight cover wear. Contents Good. *DIAMOND.* $45

OUR CRUISE! THE INNS (sic.) AND OUTS OF IT. BEING A JOURNAL OF THE U.S. SHIP SAVANNAH'S CRUISE....NY: Hall & Maigne, 1856. (By J.P. Forde.) 1st ed, and apparently the only ed. 190,(1)pp. Orig cl, cvrs blindstamped w/Jack Tar leaning on capstan, rubbed; lacking ffep, corner torn from title pg, sl affecting one letter in the imprint, foxing throughout. *LEFKOWICZ.* $225

Oursler, Fulton. SANDALWOOD. NY: Macaulay, (1925). 1st ed. Dj. Fine. *MUELLER.* $100

Ousby, Ian. BLOODHOUNDS OF HEAVEN: THE DETECTIVE IN ENGLISH FICTION. Cambridge: Harvard Univ Press 1976. 1st ed. Fine in price-clipped dj w/minor wear at spine ends and at corners. *MORDIDA.* $65

Ouseley, William G. REMARKS ON THE STATISTICS AND POLITICAL INSTITUTIONS...WITH SOME OBSERVATIONS....TO WHICH ARE ADDED STATISTICAL TABLES. Phila., Carey, 1832. 1st ed. 227pp. Orig boards, paper label on spine, faded. Howes 0157. *GINSBERG.* $150

OUTCROPPINGS. (Ed anonymously by Bret Harte.) SF: A. Roman, NY: Widdleton, 1866. 1st ed. 144pp. Blue cl w/stamping, little wear to head of spine. VG, tight. BAL 7238, state A (sequence undetermined) w/"sraining" p. 70, w/o ornament on p f and w/o pub's imprint on heel of spine. Bkpl. Nice. Scarce. *SECOND LIFE.* $250

OVERLAND RED: A ROMANCE OF THE MOONSTONE CANON TRAIL. (by Knibbs, Henry Herbert). Boston: Houghton Mifflin, 1914. Signed. Black-stamped cl, sl cocked, spine lightly sunned, tips a bit bumped, owner inscription. *DAWSON'S.* $50

Overton, Richard C. BURLINGTON WEST. Cambridge: Harvard Univ Press, 1941. 1st ed. VG in cl, badly torn dj. *SCHOYER'S.* $20

Overton, Richard C. BURLINGTON WEST. Cambridge, Harvard U., 1941. 1st ed. Orig cl. Spine faded, rear board dampstained, VG interior. *BOHLING.* $35

Overy, Paul. KANDINSKY: THE LANGUAGE OF THE EYE. NY & Washington: Praeger (1960). Lt grn cl (bottom of spine chipped). Dj (spine chipped, sm piece torn). NF *BLUE MOUNTAIN.* $45

Owen, D.F. TROPICAL BUTTERFLIES. Oxford, 1971. Sticker removed from title. *SUTTON.* $50

Owen, David Dale. REPORT OF A GEOLOGICAL SURVEY OF WISCONSIN, IOWA AND MINNESOTA; AND...A PORTION OF NEBRASKA TERRITORY... Phila: Lippincott Co, 1852. 1st ed. 2 vols. 638pp text (vol I) & plts (vol II); incl 3 fldg maps, 27 plts, 19 sections. Cvrs have faded areas, else VG+ set. *SMITHFIELD.* $245

Owen, Frank. A HUSBAND FOR KUTANI. Furman, 1938. 1st ed. NF in frayed dj. *MADLE.* $40

Owen, Guy. SEASON OF FEAR. NY: Random House, (1960). 1st ed. Fine in dj (nominal rubbing at foot of spine). *CHAPEL HILL.* $45

Owen, Guy. THE GUILTY & OTHER POEMS. (Lanham, MD: Goosetree Press, 1964). 1st ed. Orig ptd self-wraps, cover-title. Fine. *CHAPEL HILL.* $40

Owen, Guy. THE WHITE STALLION AND OTHER POEMS. Winston-Salem, NC: John F. Blair, (1969). 1st ed. Orig grn cl. Fine in price-clipped, NF dj (couple of stickers removed). *CHAPEL HILL.* $20

Owen, John. THE JOURNALS AND LETTERS OF MAJOR JOHN OWEN...THE BUILDING OF FORT OWEN...RELATIONS WITH THE INDIANS...NY, 1927. Ed ltd to 500. 2 vols. 2 maps, 30 plts. Orig cl, spines a trifle faded. Seymour Dunbar (trans, ed). Howes 0163. *GINSBERG.* $200

Owen, Maggie. THE BOOK OF MAGGIE OWEN. Indianapolis: Bobbs Merrill (1941). 1st ed. VG+ in Good dj. *AARD.* $25

Owen, Narcisse. MEMOIRS...1831-1901. (Wash., ca 1907). 126pp. 1st ed. Frontis, photographic plts. Orig grn cl. Presentation copy from Robert L. Owen. Howes 0164. *GINSBERG.* $350

Owen, Robert Dale. FOOTFALLS ON THE BOUNDARY OF ANOTHER WORLD. Phila: J.B. Lippincott. 1860. 1st ed. 528pp. 1/2 calf over marbled boards; marbled edges. *KARMIOLE.* $50

Owen, Russell. THE ANTARCTIC OCEAN. NY: Whittlesey House, (1941). 1st ed. Name stamp on title page, else VG in Good dj. *BLUE DRAGON.* $30

Owen, Thomas P. REVOLUTIONARY SOLDIERS IN ALABAMA: BEING A LIST OF NAMES....Montgomery, 1911. 1st ed. Orig printed wrappers. *GINSBERG.* $40

Owens, Fern Royer. SKY PILOT OF ALASKA. Mountain View, (1949). 1st ed. Fine in dj. *ARTIS.* $15

Owsley, Frank Lawrence. THE C.S.S. FLORIDA. Phila, (1965). 1st ed. Fine in NF dj. *McGOWAN.* $85

Oxford and Asquith, Earl of. FIFTY YEARS OF BRITISH PARLIAMENT. 2 vols. Boston, 1926. 1st Amer ed. 16 plts w/tissue guards. Teg. VG. *DIAMOND.* $45

Oyabe, Jenichiro. A JAPANESE ROBINSON CRUSOE. Boston: Pilgrim Press, (1898). 1st (?) ed. 219pp. Fine. *AARD.* $45

Ozick, Cynthia. BLOODSHED AND THREE NOVELLAS. NY: Knopf, 1976. 1st ed. Signed & dated. New in dj. *BERNARD.* $40

Ozick, Cynthia. METAPHOR AND MEMORY. Ptd wrappers. NY: Knopf, 1989. Uncorrected proof. VF. *JAFFE.* $45

Ozick, Cynthia. THE CANNIBAL GALAXY. NY: Knopf, 1983. Uncorrected proof. White wrappers very sl soiled, o/w Fine. *JAFFE.* $65

Ozick, Cynthia. THE MESSIAH OF STOCKHOLM. NY: Knopf, 1987. Uncorrected proof. Fine in wraps, pub's sheet stapled inside front cvr. *LOPEZ.* $25

Ozick, Cynthia. THE PAGAN RABBI & OTHER STORIES. NY: Knopf, 1971. 1st ed, 2nd book. NF in price clipped dj which is very lightly soiled on rear panel. *BERNARD.* $45

Ozick, Cynthia. TRUST. (London): MacGibbon & Kee, (1966). 1st UK ed, 1st book. Bottom edge bumped o/w NF in lightly soiled dj. *BERNARD.* $75

P

Pabor, William E. COLORADO AS AN AGRICULTURAL STATE. NY: OJ, 1883. 1st ed. Staining to ep, o/w nice. *SECOND LIFE.* $65

Pacific Stars and Stripes. DATELINE ASIA: 25 YEARS OF HISTORY. N.p.: (Pacific Stars and Stripes), (1970). 1st ed. NF in sl stained dj, sm edgetears. *AKA.* $50

Pack, George and A.H. Davis. BURNS: TYPES, PATHOLOGY AND MANAGEMENT. Phila, 1930. 1st ed. Photo illus. *FYE.* $100

Packard, A.S. FIFTH REPORT OF THE UNITED STATES ENTOMOLOGICAL COMMISSION. Washington, 1890. 40 plts. Half calf. Ex-lib. *SUTTON.* $65

Packard, A.S. GUIDE TO THE STUDY OF INSECTS. NY, 1883. 8th ed. *SUTTON.* $48

Packard, A.S. GUIDE TO THE STUDY OF INSECTS....Salem, 1869. 1st ed. 11 plts. Worn, front hinge cracked, occasional pencil notations. Ex-lib. *SUTTON.* $60

Packard, A.S. HALF HOURS WITH INSECTS. Boston, 1877. Nice ex-lib copy. *SUTTON.* $37

Packard, F.R. THE HISTORY OF MEDICINE IN THE UNITED STATES. Lippincott, 1901. 1st ed. Good. *BOOKCELL.* $60

Packard, Francis. SOME ACCOUNT OF THE PENNSYLVANIA HOSPITAL FROM ITS FIRST RISE TO THE BEGINNING OF THE YEAR 1938. Phila, 1938. 1st ed. *FYE.* $75

Packard, Joseph. RECOLLECTIONS OF A LONG LIFE. Byron S. Adams, 1902. Cvr worn; tears to spine; foxing. *BOOK BROKER.* $35

Packer, Vin. DARK INTRUDER. NY: Fawcett Pubs, 1952. 1st ed. Pb orig. Gold Medal #250. Spine edges worn, o/w Fine in wrappers. *MORDIDA.* $30

Packer, Vin. SPRING FIRE. NY: Fawcett Publications, 1952. 1st ed. Pb orig. Gold Medal #222. Fine, unread in wrappers. *MORDIDA.* $40

Packer, Vin. THE EVIL FRIENDSHIP. NY: Fawcett Pubs, 1958. 1st ed. Pb orig. Gold Medal #797. Fine, unread in wrappers. *MORDIDA.* $35

Paddack, William C. LIFE ON THE OCEAN OR THIRTY-FIVE YEARS AT SEA. Cambridge: For the author, 1893. 1st ed. (xiv),242pp. *LEFKOWICZ.* $100

PADDINGTON AND THE SNOW BEAR. 1981. Michael Bond. Pop-up bk. *BOOKFINDERS INTL.* $15

PADDINGTON'S POP UP BOOK. London, 1977. Pop-up bk. *BOOK-FINDERS INTL.* $55

Paden, Irene D. and Margaret E. Schlichtmann. THE BIG OAK FLAT ROAD. SF: (Emil P. Schlichtmann), 1955. One of 1000. Fldg map. Cloth. *DAWSON'S.* $50

Padgett, Lewis. THE DAY HE DIED. Duell-Sloan, 1947, 1st ed. Near VG. *MADLE.* $25

Page, Anthea. EGYPTIAN SCULPTURE, ARCHAIC TO SAITE, FROM THE PETRI COLLECTION. Warminster: Aris & Phillips, (1976). 1 fig. Dj. Good. *ARCHAEOLOGIA.* $125

Page, Elisabeth. WILD HORSES AND GOLD. NY: Farrar & Rinehart, 1932. 1st ed. VG. *OCTOBER FARM.* $35

Page, Elizabeth. WILD HORSES AND GOLD: FROM WYOMING TO THE YUKON. NY: Farrar & Rinehart, (1932). 1st ed. VG. *LAURIE.* $60

Page, Elizabeth. WILD HORSES AND GOLD: FROM WYOMING TO THE YUKON. NY: Farrar & Rinehart, (1932). 1st ed. VG. *BLUE DRAGON.* $37.50

Page, Irvine. CHEMISTRY OF THE BRAIN. Springfield, 1937. 1st ed. *FYE.* $60

Page, Marco. FAST COMPANY: NY: Dodd-Mead, 1938. 1st ed. Fine, lt wear at dj spine ends. *ELSE FINE.* $325

Page, Marco. THE SHADOWY THIRD. NY: Dodd Mead, 1946. 1st ed. Edges lightly spotted o/w VG in dj w/faded spine, wear at spine ends and at corners, some wrinkling on back panel and wear along folds. *MORDIDA.* $25

Page, Thomas Nelson. BRED IN THE BONE. NY: Scribner's, 1904. 1st ed. Orig grn cl, teg. Binding a trifle soiled, else bright, Almost Fine; partly unopened. *CHAPEL HILL.* $40

Page, Thomas Nelson. GORDON KEITH. NY: Scribner's, 1903. 1st ed. Orig dec blue cl. Owner ink stamp, initials, else VG. *CHAPEL HILL.* $35

Page, Thomas Nelson. IN OLE VIRGINIA. NY: Scribner's, 1887. 1st ed, 1st prtg. 1st bk. 230pp,(12)pp ads. Orig dec grn cl. One corner lightly bumped, but Nice. Custom grn cl chemise, 1/4 morocco slipcase. *CHAPEL HILL.* $150

Page, Thomas Nelson. JOHN MARVEL ASSISTANT. NY: Scribner's, 1909. 1st ed, 1st state. Orig grn cl. Gift inscrip, else NF. *CHAPEL HILL.* $35

Page, Thomas Nelson. TWO LITTLE CONFEDERATES. NY, 1888. 1927 reprint. 169pp, illus, pict. cloth. Minor cvr wear o/w Fine. *PRATT.* $27.50

Paget, James. LECTURES ON SURGICAL PATHOLOGY. Phila, 1854. 1st Amer ed. Full leather. Backstrip rubbed, label missing. Contents Fine. *FYE.* $50

Paget, John. PARADOXES AND PUZZLES. Edinburgh, London: William Blackwood and Sons, 1874. Later brn buckram. VG. *WEBER.* $45

Paher, Stanley W. COLORADO RIVER GHOST TOWNS. Las Vegas, 1976. Signed. Fine in NF dj. *FIVE QUAIL.* $35

Paher, Stanley W. LAS VEGAS. AS IT BEGAN—AS IT GREW. Las Vegas: Nevada Publications, 1971. 1st ed. Signed. VG. *CONNOLLY & WADE.* $50

Paige, D.D. (ed). THE LETTERS OF EZRA POUND. London: Faber & Faber (1951). 1st Eng ed. Fine in dj. *DORN.* $55

Paige, Sachel (as told to David Lipman). MAYBE I'LL PITCH FOREVER. Doubleday, 1962. 1st ed. VG in Fine dj. *PLAPINGER.* $50

Paillard, Jean Sant-Fort. UNDERSTANDING EQUITATION. GC: Doubleday, 1974. 1st ed. VG in Good+ dj. *OCTOBER FARM.* $20

Pain, Barry. MORE STORIES. London, 1930. 1st ed. VG. *MADLE.* $75

Pain, Howard. THE HERITAGE OF UPPER CANADIAN FURNITURE. Toronto: Key Porter Books, 1984. 2nd ed. NF in dj. *BACKROOM.* $55

Paine, Albert Bigelow. MARK TWAIN, A BIOGRAPHY. 4 vols. Harper, 1912. 1st ed. 55 plts (Vol 1 lacks 1 plt), 8 part fldg pl. VG. *OREGON.* $50

Paine, Caroline. TENT AND HAREM: NOTES OF AN ORIENTAL TRIP. NY, 1859. x,300pp. Clean. *O'NEILL.* $50

Paine, Lauran. TEXAS BEN THOMPSON. LA, 1966. 1st ed. Fine in Fine dj. *VARNER.* $35

Paine, Martyn. LETTERS ON THE CHOLERA ASPHYXIA, AS IT HAS APPEARED IN THE CITY OF NEW-YORK: ADDRESS TO JOHN C. WARREN, M.D., OF BOSTON AND ORIGINALLY PUBLISHED IN THAT CITY TOGETHER WITH OTHER LETTERS, NOT BEFORE PUBLISHED. NY, 1832. 1st ed. 160pp. *FYE.* $150

Paine, Martyn. THE INSTITUTES OF MEDICINE. NY, 1847. 1st ed. Full leather, 826pp. *FYE.* $100

Paish, Sir George. THE WAY OUT. NY: Putnam, (1937). 1st ed. Edgetears, o/w bright dj. *AKA.* $30

Paleologue, Maurice. AN INTIMATE JOURNAL OF THE DREYFUS CASE. NY, (1957). Cloth. NF in dj. *DIAMOND.* $25

PALESTINE; OR, THE HOLY LAND. (By Josiah Conder.) London: James Duncan, 1824. 3/4 lea, rubbed. Fldg map, 2 plts (1 waterstained), 1 plan. Bkpls. *SCHOYER'S.* $50

Paley, Grace. ENORMOUS CHANGES AT THE LAST MINUTE. NY: Farrar, Straus, Giroux, (1974). 1st ed. Orig cl. Signed. Virtually mint in dj. *PIRAGES.* $125

Paley, Grace. LATER THE SAME DAY. NY: Farrar Straus Giroux, (1985). 1st ed. Signed. Fine in Fine dj. *LOPEZ.* $45

Paley, Grace. LATER THE SAME DAY. NY: FS&G, (1985). Uncorrected proof. Fine in ptd wraps. *CAPTAIN'S BOOKSHELF.* $25

Paley, Grace. THE LITTLE DISTURBANCES OF MAN. GC: Doubleday, 1959. 1st ed. Orig cl. Virtually Mint in excellent dj (sl soiled, sunned, missing sm chip). Signed. *PIRAGES.* $175

Paley, Grace. THE LITTLE DISTURBANCES OF MAN. GC: Doubleday, 1959. 1st ed, 1st bk. Owner sig. One corner sl bumped, else Fine in dj. Signed. *CAPTAIN'S BOOKSHELF.* $175

Palgrave, William Gifford. ESSAYS ON EASTERN QUESTIONS. London, 1872. *O'NEILL.* $75

Palgrave, William Gifford. PERSONAL NARRATIVE OF A YEAR'S JOURNEY THROUGH CENTRAL AND EASTERN ARABIA (1862-63). London, 1869. Fldg map (repaired). 421pp. *O'NEILL.* $60

Palladino, L.B. INDIAN AND WHITE IN THE NORTHWEST. Lancaster, PA, 1922. 2nd ed. Frontis, 38 plts. Leatherette. Edges marbled. VG. Howes P40. *OREGON.* $75

Pallas, Peter S. TRAVELS THROUGH THE SOUTHERN PROVINCES OF THE RUSSIAN EMPIRE, IN THE YEARS 1793 AND 1794. London, 1812. 2nd ed. 50 engr plts (of 52), 26 fldg, 42 hand-colored. 28 vignettes (24 hand-colored) and 2 fldg maps. 2 vols. Newly rebound in half calf, raised bands, gilt, orig boards retained. xxiii,552; xxxii,523pp. VF, lacking only plts 19 & 20 in vol 1. *O'NEILL.* $750

Pallas, Peter Simon. BERING'S SUCCESSORS. 1745-1780. Seattle: Univ of Washington Press, 1948. 2 fldg maps. VG+. *PARMER.* $85

Pallen, Conde. CRUCIBLE ISLAND. Manhattanville, 1919. 1st ed. VG. *MADLE.* $50

Palmer, B.W. FAVORITE PRESCRIPTIONS OF DISTINGUISHED PRACTITIONERS WITH NOTES ON TREATMENT. NY, 1884. *FYE.* $50

Palmer, E.H. THE DESERT OF THE EXODUS. NY: Harper, 1872. 470pp,2pp pub ads. Light blue cl stamped in black and gilt, badly discolored. Eps discolored from old mold stains. 5 maps, (3 fldg), numerous full-page plts, cuts in text. w.a.f. *SCHOYER'S.* $35

Palmer, E.H. THE DESERT OF THE EXODUS. JOURNEYS ON FOOT IN THE WILDERNESS OF THE FORTY YEARS' WANDERINGS. Cambridge, 1871. Frontis in color, map, tinted plts and llus. Minor tears in maps professionally repaired. 2 vols. New cl, spine gilt, gilt devices from orig. covers retained. xx,280pp; 297pp. Uncut. Beautiful. *O'NEILL.* $300

Palmer, Edwin O. HISTORY OF HOLLYWOOD. Hollywood: Edwin O. Palmer, 1938. 2nd ed. Gold stamped fabricoid. Inscribed. *DAWSON'S.* $150

Palmer, Harry et al. ATHLETIC SPORTS IN AMERICA, ENGLAND, AND AUSTRALIA. Hubbard Bros., 1889. VG. Minor hinge wear, pages browning, still Very Nice copy without dj as issued. *PLAPINGER.* $550

Palmer, R.S. (ed). HANDBOOK OF NORTH AMERICAN BIRDS. VOL. 1. LOONS THROUGH FLAMINGOS. New Haven, 1976 (1962). 7 colored plts (incl double-pg color chart). *SUTTON.* $60

Palmer, Robert. DEEP BLUES. NY: Viking, (1981). NF in NF dj. *AKA.* $35

Palmer, Robert. DEEP BLUES. NY: Viking, 1981. 1st ed. Fine in Fine dj. *BEASLEY.* $35

Palmer, Sir Richmond. THE BORNU SAHARA AND SUDAN. London: Murray, 1936. viii,296pp. Uncut. Scribbling on ep, else VG. One of 500. *O'NEILL.* $185

Palmer, Stuart and Fletcher Flora. HILDEGARD WITHERS MAKES THE SCENE. NY: Random House, 1969. 1st ed. Mark on copyright pg, o/w Fine in price-clipped dj. *MORDIDA.* $25

Palmer, Stuart. THE GREEN ACE. NY: Morrow, 1950. 1st ed. Name. Fine, minor wear to spine top of pict dj. *ELSE FINE.* $65

Palmer, W.T. THE ENGLISH LAKES. A&C Black, 1908. 2nd ed. Non-authorial inscrip ffep, else VG. *OLD LONDON.* $55

Palmer, W.T. THE ENGLISH LAKES. A&C Black, 1925. 1st ed (this series). Dj Good, else VG-NF. *OLD LONDON.* $35

Palmer, W.T. THE ENGLISH LAKES. London: Adam and Charles Black, 1908. Painted by A. Heaton Cooper. Cvrs sl soiled, else Fine. *WREDEN.* $25

Palmquist, Peter. FINE CALIFORNIA VIEWS. THE PHOTOGRAPHS OF A.W. ERICSON. Eureka, Interface Calif. (1975). 1st ed. F in F dj. *OREGON.* $40

Palomares, Jose Francisco. MEMOIRS. Trans by Thomas Workman Temple II. LA: Glen Dawson, 1955. One of 205. Ptd boards w/cl spine; lt soiling. *DAWSON'S.* $60

Paltock, Robert. THE LIFE AND ADVENTURES OF PETER WILKINS. London: (Reeves & Turner), 1884. 2 vols. 3/4 natural vellum over blue boards; leather spine labels. Minor occasional foxing at very beginning of vol 1, but very fresh, largely unopened. *BOOK BLOCK.* $175

Pammel, L.H. et al. HONEY PLANTS OF IOWA. Des Moines, 1930. Colored frontis. Rear hinge cracked. *SUTTON.* $50

Pancake, Breece D'J. THE STORIES OF BREECE D'J PANCAKE. Boston: Atlantic, Little, Brown, (1983). 1st ed. Fine in dj. *DORN.* $50

Pancoast, Joseph. A TREATISE ON OPERATIVE SURGERY, COMPRISING A DESCRIPTION OF THE VARIOUS PROCESSES OF THE ART. Phila, 1844. 1st ed. 2000 copies. 4to, 1/2 leather, 380pp. 80 stone engrvd plts. Scattered foxing as usual. Quite rare. *FYE.* $1,250

Panek, LeRoy L. THE SPECIAL BRANCH: THE BRITISH SPY NOVEL 1890-1980. Bowling Green: Bowling Green Popular Press, 1981. 1st ed. VF in dj. *MORDIDA.* $35

Pangborn, Edgar. A MIRROR FOR OBSERVERS. Doubleday, 1954. 1st ed. Fine in sl frayed dj. *MADLE.* $150

Pangborn, Edgar. DAVY. St Martin's, 1964. 1st ed. Fine in dj. *MADLE.* $100

Pangborn, Edgar. WEST OF THE SUN. Doubleday. 1953. 1st ed. NF in dj. *MADLE.* $50

Pannell, Walter. CIVIL WAR ON THE RANGE: AN HISTORICAL ACCOUNT. LA: Welcome News, (1943). 1st ed. Pict wraps. VG. *OUTPOST.* $12.50

PANORAMA PICTURES. London: Nister, (1890s). Sm card in front states, "Oct. 9, 1894." Reinforcing tape front, rear inside spine. 5 movables. Outstandingly Good condition. Pop-up bk. *BOOKFINDERS INTL.* $900

Pantazzi, Ethel G. ROUMANIA IN LIGHT & SHADOW. Toronto, (1919). Uncut. Pres inscrip by author. *O'NEILL.* $30

Panum, Peter. OBSERVATIONS MADE DURING THE EPIDEMIC OF MEASLES ON THE FAROE ISLANDS IN THE YEAR 1846. NY, 1940. 1st Eng trans. *FYE.* $60

Papageorgiou, Athanasius. ICONS OF CYPRUS. Paris et al: Nagel (1969). 89 color plates. Fine in dj, slipcase. *SCHOYER'S.* $75

Papanicolaou, George. ATLAS OF EXFOLIATIVE CYTOLOGY (WITH) SUPPLEMENTS ONE AND TWO. Cambridge, 1954-1963. 1st eds. 2 vols. Ex-lib. *FYE.* $125

Papus. THE TAROT OF THE BOHEMIANS. London, 1910. Rev ed. Teg. NF. *POLYANTHOS.* $60

PAPYRO-PLASTICS, OR THE ART OF MODELLING IN PAPER. D. Boileau (trans). 3rd ed. London: (Boosey), 1830. Full crushed burgundy oasis niger w/gilt border. Spine w/5 raised bands and gilt dec. 22 engr plts, incl hand-colored frontis, many of which fold out. Some plts have lt browning, sl wear. *BOOK BLOCK.* $295

Paracelsus. FOUR TREATISES OF THEOPHRASTUS VON HOHENHEIM CALLED PARACELSUS. Baltimore, 1941. 1st ed. 256pp. *FYE.* $100

Paracelsus. SELECTED WRITINGS. NY, 1951. Jolande Jacobi (ed). 1st Eng trans. *FYE.* $75

Paramore, Edward E, Jr. THE BALLAD OF YUKON JAKE. NY: Coward McCann, 1928. 1st ed. Scarce pict dj, chipped on front top edge only, else VG. Pict boards and contents, Fine. *CONNOLLY & WADE.* $75

Paramore, Edward E. THE BALLAD OF YUKON JAKE. NY: Coward-McCann, (c1928). Hogarth, Jr. (illus, pseud of Rockwell Kent). 1st ed. Ink initials, date, o/w Fine in price clipped dj externally reinforced top, bottom edge. *HELLER.* $75

Pardoe, Julia. THE LIFE OF MARIE DE MEDICIS....NY: Scribner & Welford, 1890. New Ed. 4 vols. 21 illus. Uncut, Bound in cl. Good set. One half title separate. *SECOND LIFE.* $65

Pare, Ambroise. THE APOLOGIE AND TREATISE OF AMBROISE PARE CONTAINING THE VOYAGES MADE INTO DIVERSE PLACES WITH MANY OF HIS WRITINGS UPON SURGERY. Chicago, 1952. Ed by Geoffrey Keynes. 1st ed. *FYE.* $50

Paretsky, Sara. BITTER MEDICINE. London: Gollancz, 1987. 1st British ed. Review copy, signed. Pub's slip laid in. Fine in dj. *SILVER DOOR.* $37.50

Paretsky, Sara. BITTER MEDICINE. Morrow, 1987. 1st ed. VF in dj. *STAHR.* $45

Paretsky, Sara. BLOOD SHOT. NY: Delacorte, (1988). 1st ed. Signed. VF in VF dj. *UNGER.* $60

Paretsky, Sara. BLOOD SHOT. NY: Delacorte Press, 1988. 1st Amer ed. Fine in dj. *MORDIDA.* $35

Paretsky, Sara. BURN MARKS. NY: Delacorte, (1990). 1st ed. Signed. Fine in Fine dj. *UNGER.* $50

Paretsky, Sara. BURN MARKS. NY: Delacorte Press, 1990. 1st ed. Fine in dj. *MORDIDA.* $30

Paretsky, Sara. GUARDIAN ANGEL. NY: Delacorte, (1992). 1st ed. Signed. VF in VF dj. *UNGER.* $40

Paretsky, Sara. INDEMNITY ONLY. NY: Dial Press, 1982. 1st ed, 1st bk. Signed. Fine, minor wear at dj spine top. *ELSE FINE.* $1,000

Paretsky, Sara. KILLING ORDERS. NY: William Morrow, 1985. 1st ed. Crease on fep o/w Fine in dj. *MORDIDA.* $50

Parisot, Rev. R. P. THE REMINISCENCES OF A TEXAS MISSIONARY. San Antonio, 1899. 1st ed. 277,(5),(6)pp. Orig cl, very nice. Howes P67. *GINSBERG.* $150

Park, Clyde W. MORGAN. THE UNPREDICTABLE. (Cincinnati, 1959). 1st ed. VG. Scarce. *McGOWAN.* $75

Park, Mungo. THE LIFE AND TRAVELS OF MUNGO PARK. NY: Harper, 1844. xii + 248pp. Orig cl, rubbed, spine frayed, foxing, some smudged pages, o/w Good ex-lib. *WORLDWIDE.* $30

Park, Roswell. SELECTED PAPERS, SURGICAL AND SCIENTIFIC. Buffalo, 1914. 1st ed. Scarce. *FYE.* $100

Parke, J. Richardson. HUMAN SEXUALITY, A MEDICO-LITERARY TREATISE. Phila: Professional Pub, 1912. VG, tight. *SECOND LIFE.* $35

Parker, Dorothy. AFTER SUCH PLEASURES. NY: The Viking Press, 1933. 1st ed. Signed, ltd ed in slipcase. #189 of 250. Spine darkened, slipcase Good only. Book is VG. *SMITH.* $125

Parker, Eric. ELEMENTS OF SHOOTING. London: The Field Press, 1930. Probably 1st ed. VG-NF. *OLD LONDON.* $35

Parker, Eric. SHOOTING DAYS. London: Philip Allan, 1932. New ed. Some wear top and base of spine, corners sl bumped, else VG+. *OLD LONDON.* $25

Parker, G.H. ANIMAL COLOUR CHANGES AND THEIR NEUROHUMOURS. Cambridge, 1948. Eps yellowed, dj worn. *SUTTON.* $40

Parker, Joan H. & Robert B. THREE WEEKS IN SPRING. Houghton, 1978. 1st ed. Fine. Dj mildly scuffed. *STAHR.* $35

Parker, Nathan H. IOWA AS IT IS IN 1855. Chicago: Keen and Lee, 1855. 1st ed. 9 plts incl frontis, tables. Howes P83. *HUDSON.* $125

Parker, Nathan H. IOWA AS IT IS IN 1856. Chicago: Keen and Lee; Phila: DeSilver, 1856. 2nd ptg. (3)pp ads,264pp. 9 plts, 1 hand-colored fldg map. Ex-lib in orig cl, dec gilt spine rubbed. Howes P-83. *SCHOYER'S.* $125

Parker, Nathan H. THE MINNESOTA HANDBOOK, FOR 1856-7. Boston: John P. Jewett & Co. 1857. 1st ed. 12mo. viii,160pp. Fldg map. Orig. blue cloth, gilt; spine faded. *KARMIOLE.* $150

Parker, Nathan H. THE MINNESOTA HANDBOOK, FOR 1856-7...Boston, 1857. 1st ed. 159,(1)pp. Fldg map. Orig cl. Howes P85. *GINSBERG.* $175

Parker, Neville P. JOHN SINGLETON COPLEY. AMERICAN PORTRAITS: OIL, PASTEL AND MINIATURE WITH BIOGRAPHICAL SKETCHES. Boston, 1938. NF. *POLYANTHOS.* $100

Parker, Robert B. A CATSKILL EAGLE. Delacorte, (1985). 1st prtg. Signed. Fine in Fine dj. *BEBBAH.* $25

Parker, Robert B. A CATSKILL EAGLE. Delacorte, 1985. 1st ed. Fine in dj. Rmdr spray. *STAHR.* $15

Parker, Robert B. A SAVAGE PLACE. NY: Delacorte/Seymour Lawrence, 1981. 1st ed. Inscribed. VF in price-clipped dj. *MORDIDA.* $45

Parker, Robert B. CEREMONY. NY: Delacorte/Seymour Lawrence, 1982. 1st ed. VF in dj. *MORDIDA.* $35

Parker, Robert B. CRIMSON JOY. Delacorte, 1988. Uncorrected proof. Fine. Wraps. Signed on bkpl. *STAHR.* $50

Parker, Robert B. CRIMSON JOY. NY: Delacorte, 1988. 1st ed, one of 250 specially bound, numbered, signed. Fine in Fine slipcase. *BEASLEY.* $75

Parker, Robert B. CRIMSON JOY. NY: Delacorte Press, 1988. 1st ed. One of 250 numbered, specially bound, signed. VF in slipcase w/o dj as issued. *MORDIDA.* $100

Parker, Robert B. EARLY AUTUMN. Delacorte, 1981. 1st ed. Fine in dj w/few short tears and rubbed spots. Signed & inscribed. *STAHR.* $45

Parker, Robert B. GOD SAVE THE CHILD. Boston: Houghton Mifflin, 1974. 1st ed. Fine in dj (sl faded spine; short closed tear). *MORDIDA.* $225

Parker, Robert B. GOD SAVE THE CHILD. London: Deutsch, 1975. 1st British ed. Fine in dj. *SILVER DOOR.* $150

Parker, Robert B. LOOKING FOR RACHAEL WALLACE. NY: Delacorte/Seymour Lawrence, 1980. 1st ed. Signed. VF in dj. *MORDIDA.* $85

Parker, Robert B. LOOKING FOR RACHEL WALLACE. Delacorte, (1980). 1st ed. Fine in Fine price-clipped dj. *BEBBAH.* $30

Parker, Robert B. LOOKING FOR RACHEL WALLACE. NY: Delacorte, 1980. 1st ed. VF in dj. *ELSE FINE.* $75

Parker, Robert B. LOVE AND GLORY. NY: Delacrote, /1983. 1st ed. VF in dj. *ELSE FINE.* $50

Parker, Robert B. LOVE AND GLORY. NY: Delacorte/Seymour Lawrence, 1983. 1st ed. Fine in dj w/tiny wear. *MORDIDA.* $25

Parker, Robert B. MORTAL STAKES. Boston: Houghton Mifflin, 1975. 1st ed. Inscribed. Fine in dj (sl faded spine; wear at corners). *MORDIDA.* $225

Parker, Robert B. MORTAL STAKES. London: Deutsch, (1976). 1st English ed. Signed. Fine in Fine dj. *UNGER.* $100

Parker, Robert B. PALE KINGS AND PRINCES. Delacorte, 1987. Uncorrected proof. VF. Red wraps. Signed on bkpl numbered 387/500; presentation slip. *STAHR.* $45

Parker, Robert B. PALE KINGS AND PRINCES. NY: Delacrote, 1987. 1st ed. Signed, ltd, #23 of 250. VF in slipcase. *ELSE FINE.* $125

Parker, Robert B. PERCHANCE TO DREAM. NY: Putnam, 1991. 1st ed. Fine in dj. *ELSE FINE.* $20

Parker, Robert B. PERCHANCE TO DREAM. Putnam's, 1991. Uncorrected proof. Fine in grey wraps. *STAHR.* $45

Parker, Robert B. PLAYMATES. NY: G.P. Putnam's Sons, 1989. 1st ed. One of 250 numbered, specially bound, signed. VF in slipcase w/o dj as issued. *MORDIDA.* $75

Parker, Robert B. PROMISED LAND. Houghton Mifflin, 1976. 1st ed. VG in dj (browning at flyleaf and spine folds). Bk is Fine but for list of words in pencil and ink on rear endpaper and pastedown. *STAHR.* $75

Parker, Robert B. STARDUST. London: Viking, 1991. 1st British ed. Review copy, pub's slip laid in. Fine in dj. *SILVER DOOR.* $27.50

Parker, Robert B. TAMING A SEA-HORSE. Delacorte Press, 1986. Uncorrected proof. Fine in grey-green wraps. Signed on bkpl. *STAHR.* $45

Parker, Robert B. THE GODWULF MANUSCRIPT. Boston: Houghton Mifflin Co., 1974. 1st ed. 7,500 copies of 1st book. Signed. Some light foxing on half-title page o/w VG+ in dj which is very lightly soiled. *BERNARD.* $300

Parker, Robert B. THE GODWULF MANUSCRIPT. Boston: Houghton Mifflin, 1974. 1st ed. VG+ in dj w/several edge tears and showing wear. *LAME DUCK.* $150

Parker, Robert B. THE JUDAS GOAT. Boston: Houghton Mifflin, 1978. 1st ed. Fine in dj. *MORDIDA.* $85

Parker, Robert B. THE WIDENING GYRE, A SPENSER NOVEL. (NY): Delacorte Press, (c1983). 1st ed. Inscribed. Sm crease ffep, o/w Fine in dj. *HELLER.* $60

Parker, Robert B. VALEDICTION. Delacorte, 1984. 1st ed. VF in dj. Signed. *STAHR.* $35

Parker, Robert B. VALEDICTION. London: Severn, 1986. 1st British hb ed. Fine in dj. *SILVER DOOR.* $25

Parker, Robert B. WILDERNESS. Delacorte Press, 1979. 1st ed. Fine in dj. Signed & inscribed. Remainder mark. *STAHR.* $60

Parker, Robert B. WILDERNESS. NY: Delacorte/Seymour Lawrence, 1979. 1st ed. Inscribed. VF in dj. *MORDIDA.* $45

Parker, Samuel. JOURNAL OF AN EXPLORING TOUR BEYOND THE ROCKY MOUNTAINS. Ithaca, NY: Andrus,

Woodruff & Gauntlett, 1844. 4th ed. Fldg map. Orig cl shaken, stained, front fly leaf lacking, browned. Howes P89. *HUDSON.* $295

Parker, Samuel. JOURNAL OF AN EXPLORING TOUR BEYOND THE ROCKY MOUNTAINS. Ross & Haines, 1967. 1st ed, ltd to 2000. Fldg map laid in. VF in VF dj. Howes P89. *OREGON.* $40

Parker, T. Jefferson. LAGUNA HEAT. NY: St. Martin's Press, 1985. 1st ed. Sm stain fore-edge, o/w Fine in dj with minor wear. *MORDIDA.* $30

Parker, T. Jefferson. LITTLE SAIGON. St. Martin's, 1988. 1st ed. VF, dj. Signed, inscribed, dated. *STAHR.* $35

Parker, William B. NOTES TAKEN DURING THE EXPEDITION COMMANDED BY CAPT. R. B. MARCY...IN THE SUMMER AND FALL OF 1854. Phila., Hayes & Zell, 1856. 1st ed. 242,(1),6 ads. Orig brown cl, pubs' names on sides in blind, title in gilt on backstrip, minor repair to extremities of spine. Howes P91. *GINSBERG.* $750

Parker, William H. PARKER ON POLICE. Springfield: Charles C. Thomas, (1957). O.W. Wilson (ed). Cl in sl soiled dj, few marginal notes in pencil, bottom tips bumped. *DAWSON'S.* $75

Parkerson, A.C. HOW UNCLE SAM FIGHTS; OR MODERN WARFARE. Baltimore: R.H. Woodward Co., 1898. Fine. *OREGON.* $40

Parkes, H.B. THE PRAGMATIC TEST. SF: Colt Press (1941). 1st ed. Full linen w/ptd paper label. Spine a little faded else Fine in lightly chipped dj. *CAPTAIN'S BOOKSHELF.* $60

Parkhill, Forbes. THE BLAZED TRAIL OF ANTOINE LEROUX. LA: Westernlore, 1965. 1st ed. VG in Fine dj. *OREGON.* $45

Parkhill, Forbes. THE WILDEST OF THE WEST. NY: Henry Holt and Co, 1951. 1st ed. Fine in Good, faded dj. *GIBBS.* $25

Parkin, Charles M. THE ROCKET HANDBOOK FOR AMATEURS, AN ILLUSTRATED GUIDE. NY: John Day, 1959. Good. *KNOLLWOOD.* $30

Parkins, Leroy. THE HARVARD, MEDICAL SCHOOL AND ITS CLINICAL OPPORTUNITIES. Boston, 1916. 1st ed. *FYE.* $30

Parkinson, C. Northcote. THE LIFE AND TIMES OF HORATIO HORNBLOWER. London, (1971). 1st ed. Fine in VG dj. *McCLINTOCK.* $17.50

Parkinson, Sydney. A JOURNAL OF A VOYAGE TO THE SOUTH SEAS, IN HIS MAJESTY'S SHIP, THE ENDEAVOR...ON HIS LATE EXPEDITION WITH DR. SOLANDER, ROUND THE WORLD. EMBELLISHED WITH VIEWS AND DESIGNS, DELINEATED BY THE AUTHOR, AND ENGRAVED BY CAPITAL ARTISTS. London: Printed for Stanfield Parkinson (ed), sold by Messrs. Richardson and Urquhart, at the Royal Exchange; Evans, in Pater-Noster Row; Hooper, on Ludgate-Hill; Murray, in Fleet-Street; Leacroft, at Charing-Cross; and Riley, in Curzon-Street, May-Fair, 1773. 1st ed. 13 1/8" x 10 1/4." xxiii,212pp, errata, directions to binder. Frontis port, 27 Fine engr plts. Contemp calf w/some scuffing and wear, expertly rebacked. Some offsetting from plts, occasional spot. Fine. *PARMER.* $6500

Parkman, Francis. THE BOOK OF ROSES. Boston: J.E. Tilton and Company, 1866. 1st ed. Orig cl. NF. BAL 15453. *JUVELIS.* $75

Parkman, Francis. FRANCE AND ENGLAND IN NORTH AMERICA. Boston: Little, Brown and Company, 1869. 1st ed. Issued as Part 3 of series, separate in itself. Map. Howes P98. *HUDSON.* $50

Parkman, Francis. THE DISCOVERY OF THE GREAT WEST. Little, Brown, & Co, 1869. 1st ed. Fine, bright, gilt-stamped orig grn cl. *AUTHORS OF THE WEST.* $200

Parkman, Francis. THE OREGON TRAIL. Boston, 1892. 1st illus ed by Remington. 411pp. Orig leather cover rebacked in brown buckram by professional hand binder. Small piece of tissue guard stuck to title pg. *HEINOLDT.* $75

Parkman, Francis. THE OREGON TRAIL. Illus by Thomas Hart Benton. Doubleday, Doran, 1945. 1/1000 numbered/signed by artist. Spine a tad darkened, o/w Fine. *DERMONT.* $150

Parkman, Francis. THE OREGON TRAIL. London: Folio Society, 1973. 1st folio ed. Dec boards. Fine in Fine slipcase. *AUTHORS OF THE WEST.* $40

Parkman, Francis. VASSALL MORTON: A NOVEL. Boston: Phillips Sampson and Company, 1856. 1st ed. Some wear, edges lightly browned and stained. Generally VG. *JUVELIS.* $50

Parkman, John. THE OREGON TRAIL. Phila, (1931). Frontis, 15 plts. Bottom of spine shelfworn, much gilt on cover flaked off o/w VG. *OREGON.* $35

Parks, Gordon. GORDON PARKS: WHISPERS OF INTIMATE THINGS. NY: Viking, (1971). 1st ed. Fine in lightly used dj. *AKA.* $25

Parks, Gordon. THE LEARNING TREE. (London): Hodder and Stoughton, (1964). 1st Eng ed, 1st bk. Fine in dj w/pub's price stickers. Sl soiling back panel. *HELLER.* $50

Parks, Gordon. THE LEARNING TREE. NY: H&R, (1963). 1st ed. Inscribed. NF in VG dj. *LOPEZ.* $75

Parley, Peter (pseud of Samuel Griswold Goodrich). FAGGOTS FOR THE FIRESIDE. NY: Appleton, 1855. 1st ed. Rebacked w/orig backstrip. Wear, staining; foxing in contents. Bkpl & card pocket removed o/w Good. *DIAMOND.* $35

Parmer, Charles. MURDER AT THE KENTUCKY DERBY. GC: Doubleday Crime Club, 1942. 1st ed. Lt dampstain back cvr, o/w Fine in dj w/dampstain, smudge. *MORDIDA.* $45

Parrish, Anne. FLOATING ISLAND. Harpers, (1930). Stated 1st ed. 265pp. Illus by author. Slight edgewear, soiling to forward edge and back edge but VG w/cvr pict pastedown. *BEBBAH.* $35

Parrish, Randall. BETH NOVELL: A ROMANCE OF THE WEST. A.C. McClurg & Co, 1907. 1st ed. Frontis by N.C. Wyeth. Dec cvr. VG+. *AUTHORS OF THE WEST.* $35

Parrish, Randall. WHEN WILDERNESS WAS KING: A TALE OF THE ILLINOIS COUNTRY. A.C. McClurg. 1904. 1st ed. 6 full color illus. Pict cvr. Faint stamp, else Fine. *AUTHORS OF THE WEST.* $25

Parry, Ann. PARRY OF THE ARCTIC. London: Chatto & Windus, 1963. VG in worn dj. *PARMER.* $30

Parry, Leonard (ed). TRIAL OF DR. SMETHHURST. Edinburgh & London: William Hodge, (1931). Small cvr stain. Minor cvr rubbing, o/w VG. Ex-lib. *DIAMOND.* $25

Parsons, A(lbert) R. ANARCHISM: ITS PHILOSOPHY AND SCIENTIFIC BASIS. Chicago: Mrs. A.R. Parsons, 1887. 1st ed. Ex-libris signs, including small label at corner of front board and a few rubber stamp marks, small perforations, etc. No pockets or pocket removal, boards Quite Nice but for sticker. *BEASLEY.* $300

Parsons, John E. THE FIRST WINCHESTER. NY: Morrow, 1955. Pict cl; dj. *SCHOYER'S.* $35

Parsons, John Herbert. AN INTRODUCTION TO THE STUDY OF COLOUR VISION. Cambridge, 1915. 1st ed. Ex-lib. *FYE.* $75

Parsons, John Herbert. AN INTRODUCTION TO THE THEORY OF PERCEPTION. Cambridge, 1927. 1st ed. Dj. *FYE.* $150

Parsons, Lee et al. THE FACE OF ANCIENT AMERICA. THE WALLY & BRENDA ZOLLMAN COLLECTION....Indianapolis: IMA/IU Press, (1988). 1st ed, ltd to 1000. Good in dj. *SILVER.* $55

Parsons, M. ENGLISH HOUSE GROUNDS. NY, 1924. E. Clute (ed). Cl-backed, paper covered boards; sl wear, soiling. Inscribed. *SUTTON.* $65

Parsons, Marion Randall. OLD CALIFORNIA HOUSES. Berkeley, LA: Univ of CA Press, 1952. Inscription. Cl w/paper label in dj, bkpl. *DAWSON'S.* $35

Parsons, Marion Randall. OLD CALIFORNIA HOUSES. Berkeley: Univ of CA, 1952. 1st ed. Olive cl, paper wrap-around label. Faded on spine, else NF. *CONNOLLY & WADE.* $35

Parsons, S.B. PARSONS ON THE ROSE. NY, 1869. Rev ed. Gilt dec cl, some wear at extrems. Browning of title, pencil marks in text. *SUTTON.* $45

Parsons, Samuel. LANDSCAPE GARDENING. NY: Putnam, 1900. 1st ed. Frontis loose. VG. *SECOND LIFE.* $60

Parsons, Talcott and Kenneth B. Clark (eds). THE AMERICAN NEGRO. Boston: Houghton Mifflin, 1966. 1st ed. NF in like dj. *CAPTAIN'S BOOKSHELF.* $75

Parsons, Usher. BOYLSTON PRIZE DISSERTATIONS ON 1. INFLAMMATION OF THE PERIOSTIUM. 2. ENEURSIS IRRATATA. 3. CUTANEOUS DISEASES. 4. CANCER OF THE BREAST. ALSO REMARKS ON MALARIA. Boston, 1839. 1st ed. 248pp. *FYE.* $100

Parsons, Usher. DIRECTIONS FOR MAKING ANATOMICAL PREPARATIONS. Phila: Carey & Lea, 1831. 1st ed. xxiv,316pp,4 plts. Rebound in calf over boards. *KARMIOLE.* $150

Parsons, William B. ROBERT FULTON & THE SUBMARINE. Columbia Univ Press, 1922. VG+. *BOOKCELL.* $30

Parsons, William B. ROBERT FULTON AND THE SUBMARINE. NY: Columbia Univ Press, 1922. 1st ed. NF. *PARMER.* $95

Parton, James. GENERAL BUTLER IN NEW ORLEANS: HISTORY OF....NY: Mason Bros, 1864. 2 frontis, 661,(1)pp, index, ad. 12mo. Orig grn textured cl. Edge wear, else tight and clean, Good to VG. *CONNOLLY & WADE.* $60

Parton, James. SMOKING AND DRINKING. Boston, 1868. 1st ed. *FYE.* $100

Pascal, Blaise. LES PENSEES. Martin Turnell (trans), Ismar David (illus). Bloomfield, CT: LEC, 1971. White cl. 1/1500. Signed by artist. *SECOND LIFE.* $45

Pasternak, Boris. I REMEMBER. (NY): Pantheon, (1959). Trans by David Magarshack. Owner's sig, else Fine in price-clipped dj (moderate rubbing, sl sunned spine). 1st ed in English. *CHAPEL HILL.* $35

PASTORAL FROM WALT DISNEY'S FANTASIA. NY: Harper, (1940). 1st ed. Pict boards and cl. Corners sl rubbed, o/w Fine. *ARTIS.* $45

Patchen, Kenneth. BEFORE THE BRAVE. NY, Random House, (1936). 1st ed. One of 1000. Spine faded, lt wear; spot on cvr. Interior Fine. *McCLINTOCK.* $25

Patchen, Kenneth. CLOTH OF THE TEMPEST. NY: Harper, (1943). 1st ed. NF in black cl w/paper labels in dj sunned at spine. *CAPTAIN'S BOOKSHELF.* $125

Patchen, Kenneth. FABLES AND OTHER LITTLE TALES. Karlsruhe/ Baden: Jonathan Williams, 1953. 1st ed. 1/450. Pub as Jargon 6. Fine in lightly soiled wrappers w/two small stains. *CAPTAIN'S BOOKSHELF.* $125

Patchen, Kenneth. SLEEPERS AWAKE. (NY: Padell, 1946). 1st trade ed. Fine in lightly rubbed dj (few tiny tears). *CAPTAIN'S BOOKSHELF.* $150

Patchen, Kenneth. THE JOURNAL OF ALBION MOONLIGHT. NY: New Directions, 1961. 1st ed, 2nd ptg in wraps. Inscribed. Rubber stamped. NF. *SMITH.* $60

Patchen, Kenneth. THE JOURNAL OF ALBION MOONLIGHT. NY: United Book Guild, 1944. 1st thus. VG or better in worn, rubbed dj missing 2" piece foot of spine. *STAHR.* $60

Patchett, M.E. SPACE CAPTIVES OF THE GOLDEN MEN. Bobbs-Merrill, 1953. 1st US ed. Fine in dj. *MADLE.* $50

Pater, Walter. THE MARRIAGE OF CUPID AND PSYCHE FROM THE GOLDEN ASS OF LUCIUS APULEIUS. NY: LEC, 1951. One of 1500 illus, signed by Edmund Dulac. Full parchment. Spine darkened, else NF in a VG slipcase. *CAPTAIN'S BOOKSHELF.* $175

Pater, Walter. THE MARRIAGE OF CUPID AND PSYCHE. RETOLD BY WALTER PATER. NY: LEC, 1951. Illus by Edmund Dulac. Full parchment in matching slipcase. One of 1500 designed by Warren Chappell, signed by Dulac. Fine. *JAFFE.* $225

Paterson, John M. (ed). TRIAL OF JOHN JASPER FOR THE MURDER OF EDWIN DROOD. Phila: Phila Branch of the Dickens Fellowship, 1914. 1st ltd ed. 8vo, 152pp, illus, #157 of 500, signed by editor Paterson on limitation page and again as a presentation copy on fly. Inscribed. Blue cloth. Paper spine label sl chipped. VG+. *GREAT EXPECTATIONS.* $25

Paton, Alan. CRY, THE BELOVED COUNTRY. Franklin Center: Franklin Library, 1978. Franklin Library reissue, w/new intro by author. Signed. Leatherbound, silk eps, silk marker; aeg. Fine. *LOPEZ.* $100

Paton, David. ANIMALS OF ANCIENT EGYPT. Princeton: Princeton Univ Press, 1925. 1 corner bumped, boards stained, materials for a "Sign List" of Egyptian Hieroglyphs "E" only. Good. *ARCHAEOLOGIA.* $175

Paton, John G. JOHN G. PATON, MISSIONARY TO THE NEW HEBRIDES. London: Hodder and Stoughton, 1889. 4th ed., 1st Part; 3rd ed., 2nd Part. 2 vols. VG with minor wear. *PARMER.* $50

Patrick, Marsena Rudolph. INSIDE LINCOLN'S ARMY, THE DIARY OF MARSENA RUDOLPH PATRICK, PROVOST MARSHALL GENERAL, ARMY OF THE POTOMAC. Ed by David S. Sparks. NY, (1964). 1st ed. 536pp. Piece missing from dj, o/w VG+. *PRATT.* $40

Patten, William & Walker McSpadden. THE BOOK OF BASEBALL. Collier, 1911. Signed. Good, without dj as issued. Hinges, spine repaired. *PLAPINGER.* $375

Patterson, Haywood, and Earl Conrad. SCOTTSBORO BOY. GC: Doubleday, 1950. 1st ed. Fine in NF dj w/short tear, lightly darkened spine. *BEASLEY.* $65

Patterson, J.H. IN THE GRIP OF THE NYIKA...BRITISH EAST AFRICA. NY: Macmillan, 1909. 1st US ed. VG. *AARD.* $90

Patterson, J.H. THE MAN-EATERS OF TSAVO. London: Macmillan, 1908. 4th ptg. Near VG ex-lib. *WORLDWIDE.* $15

Patterson, James Medill. A LITTLE BROTHER OF THE RICH. Chicago: Reilly & Britton, 1908. 1st ed. Fine w/a little rubbing. *BEASLEY.* $75

Patterson, R.L. THE SAGE GROUSE IN WYOMING. Denver: Sage, 1952. VG. Signed presentation. *MIKESH.* $45

Patterson, R.M. THE BUFFALO HEAD. NY: Wm. Sloane, 1961. 1st ed. VG in VG dj. *CONNOLLY & WADE.* $27.50

Patterson, Raymond R. 26 WAYS OF LOOKING AT A BLACK MAN. NY: Award Books, (1969). Pb orig. NF in wrappers. *LOPEZ.* $45

Patterson, Robert. A NARRATIVE OF THE CAMPAIGN IN THE VALLEY THE SHENANDOAH IN 1861. Phila, 1865. 1st ed. 195pp. Illus. Inscribed to Colonel Fellows, 1st New Hampshire Vols., who served under Gen. Patterson. Laid in is a personal letter from the general to the same officer. VG. *PRATT.* $200

Pattie, James O. THE PERSONAL NARRATIVE OF JAMES O. PATTIE OF KENTUCKY EDITED BY TIMOTHY FLINT. Lakeside Classic, 1930. VG. Howes P123. *OREGON.* $30

Pattullo, George. ALWAYS NEW FRONTIERS. Pattulo, (1951). 1st ed. Label signed, glued in. Fine in dj. *AUTHORS OF THE WEST.* $25

Paul, Eden and Cedar (trans). A YOUNG GIRL'S DIARY. London: George Allen & Unwin, (1921). Edges freckled, sl soiled. *WEBER.* $65

Paul, Eliot. A GHOST TOWN ON THE YELLOWSTONE. NY: Random House, 1948. 1st ed. NF in Good dj. *CONNOLLY & WADE.* $25

Paul, Elliot. THE BLACK AND THE RED. Random, (1956). 1st ed. VG with grease pencil marks on endpaper in VG+ dj with edgewear. *BEBBAH.* $20

Paul, Elliot. THE STARS AND STRIPES FOREVER. NY: Random House, 1939. 1st ed. Fine, minor edgewear to price clipped dj. *ELSE FINE.* $50

Paul, Elliot. WAYLAID IN BOSTON. NY: Random House, 1953. 1st ed. VF in dj. *MORDIDA.* $65

Paul, Elliot. WAYLAID IN BOSTON. Random, (1953). 1st ed. VG with edgewear in VG dj. *BEBBAH.* $25

Paul, Raymond. THE THOMAS STREET HORROR. NY: Viking Press, 1982. 1st ed. Fine in dj. *MORDIDA.* $25

Paul Wilhelm. PAUL WILHELM...TRAVELS IN NORTH AMERICA 1822-1824. Savoie Lottinville (ed). Norman: Univ of OK, (1973). 1st ed. thus. VF in VF dj. Howes P130. *OREGON.* $50

Paulding, James Kirke. THE LION OF THE WEST: RETITLED THE KENTUCKIAN, OR....Rev by John A. Stone, Wm. B. Bernard. Ed by James N. Tidwell. Stanford: Stanford Univ, 1954. 1st ed. Fine in About Fine dj. *CONNOLLY & WADE.* $50

Pauley, Art. HENRY PLUMMER, LAWMAN AND OUTLAW. White Sulphur Springs, MT: The Meagher County News, 1980. 1st ed. Fine in dj. *GIBBS.* $35

Paull, H.M. LITERARY ETHICS. London, (1928). 1st ed. Spine, part of cvrs faded, o/w VG in dj. *DIAMOND.* $35

Paullin, Charles O. COMMODORE JOHN RODGERS...1773-1838. A BIOGRAPHY. Cleveland, Clark, 1910. 1st ed. 434pp. Orig cl. *GINSBERG.* $100

Pausch, Georg. JOURNAL OF CAPTAIN PAUSCH...DURING THE BURGOYNE CAMPAIGN. W.L. Stone (ed, trans). Albany, 1886. 1st ed. (14),186pp. Orig cl, faded paper label on spine. Howes P140. *GINSBERG.* $150

Pavlov, Ivan. CONDITIONED REFLEXES: AN INVESTIGATION OF THE PHYSIOLOGICAL ACTIVITY OF THE CEREBRAL CORTEX. Trans. and ed. by G.V. Anrep. Oxford, 1927. 1st Eng trans. Ex-lib. *FYE.* $150

Pavlov, Ivan. LECTURES ON CONDITIONED REFLEXES. VOLUME 1. NY, 1941. *FYE.* $50

Pavlov, Ivan. THE WORK OF THE DIGESTIVE GLANDS. London, 1910. 2nd Eng ed. VF. *FYE.* $200

Paxton, Harry. THE WHIZ KIDS. McKay, 1950. 1st ed. Good+ in VG dj. Scarce. *PLAPINGER.* $125

Paxton, J. A POCKET BOTANICAL DICTIONARY....London, 1853 (1849). 2nd ed. Orig gilt dec cl, spine ends frayed. Ex-lib. *SUTTON.* $45

Payne, Cecilia. THE STARS OF HIGH LUMINOSITY. Pub for Harvard College Observatory by McGraw-Hill, NY, 1930, 1st ed. Good in maroon cl; stains on eps. *KNOLLWOOD.* $60

Payne, Darwin. OWEN WISTER. Dallas: Southern Methodist Univ Press, 1985. 1st ed. Fine in Fine dj. Name, address, note on title page. *BACKMAN.* $25

Payne, Doris Palmer. CAPTAIN JACK, MODOC RENEGADE. Portland, (1938). 1st ed. 259pp. VG in dj. *PRATT.* $45

Payne, Edward F. THE CHARITY OF CHARLES DICKENS. Boston: The Bibliophile Society, (1929). 1st ltd ed. Tall 8vo, full calf, one of 425, light wear. VG+. *GREAT EXPECTATIONS.* $70

Payne, Edward F. THE ROMANCE OF CHARLES DICKENS AND MARIA BEADNELL WINTER. Boston: The Bibliophile

Society, (1929). 1st ltd ed. Tall 8vo, full calf, one of 425. VG+. *GREAT EXPECTATIONS*. $75

Payne, H.T. GAME BIRDS AND GAME FISHES OF THE PACIFIC COAST. LA: News Pub Co, (1913). 4pp ads. Black-stamped cl, a little loose in binding; lt wear to extrems. *DAWSON'S*. $50

Payson, George. THE NEW AGE OF GOLD; OR, THE LIFE AND ADVENTURES OF ROBERT DEXTER ROMAINE....Boston: Phillips, 1856. 1st ed. 403,(4)pp. Orig cl, emb lib stamp, bkpl. Howes P154. *GINSBERG*. $100

Paz, Octavio. ALTERNATING CURRENT. NY: Viking (1973). 1st Amer ed. Lt sunning top of spine else Fine in dj. *DORN*. $40

Paz, Octavio. IN THE MIDDLE OF THIS PHASE AND OTHER POEMS. Trans by Eliot Weinberger. Helsinki: Eurographica, 1987. 1st of this ed. Ltd to 350 signed. Ptd wrappers. Mint. *JAFFE*. $150

Paz, Octavio. ONE EARTH, FOUR OR FIVE WORLDS: REFLECTIONS....NY: HBJ (1985). 1st Amer ed. Signed. Fine in dj. *DORN*. $65

Peabody, Robert. HOSPITAL SKETCHES. Boston, 1916. 1st ed. Scarce. *FYE*. $45

Peake, James. RUDIMENTARY TREATISE ON SHIP BUILDING, FOR THE USE OF BEGINNERS. London: John Weale, 1849. 1st ed. Grn cl, paste on cvr label. 6 fldg plts. Some spotting to orig flexible cl cvrs; interior tight. *PARMER*. $475

Peake, Mervyn. THE GORMENGHAST TRILOGY. NY: Weybright & Talley, (1967). 1st ed thus. 3 vols. Each just About Fine in djs. *CAPTAIN'S BOOKSHELF*. $75

Peake, Mervyn. TITUS ALONE. London, 1959. 1st ed. Fine in dj. *MADLE*. $200

Peake, Mervyn. TITUS GROAN. NY, (1946). 1st ed. NF in dj, spine missing pieces, few edge chips, tears at flap folds. Author's 1st bk. *POLYANTHOS*. $40

Peake, Mervyn. TITUS GROAN. Reynal, 1946. 1st US ed. VG in worn dj. *MADLE*. $60

Peake, Ora Brooks. A HISTORY OF THE UNITED STATES INDIAN FACTORY SYSTEM, 1795-1822. Denver: Sage Books, 1954. 1st ed. 1 pl. VF in VF dj. *OREGON*. $75

Peake, Ora Brooks. THE COLORADO RANGE CATTLE INDUSTRY. A.H. Clark, 1937. 1st ed. Fine. *VARNER*. $150

Peake, Ora Brooks. THE COLORADO RANGE CATTLE INDUSTRY. Glendale: The Arthur H. Clark Co, 1937. 1st ed. Fldg maps. Fine. *GIBBS*. $135

Peale, Rembrandt. AN HISTORICAL DISQUISITION ON THE MAMMOTH, OR GREAT AMERICAN INCOGNITUM....1 pl. London, 1803. Pp v,(1),91. 19th-c, 1/2 leather w/marbled boards, eps. Rubbed at edges of leather; front hinge tender; some dark spots on last three pp, bkpl. *SUTTON*. $535

Pearce, M.L. and L.M. Homsher. THE GHOST TOWNS OF WYOMING. NY, 1956. 1st ed. Inscribed by both authors. Fine in Fine dj. *VARNER*. $45

Pearce, Michael. THE MAMUR ZAPT AND THE RETURN OF THE CARPET. London: Collins Crime Club, 1988. 1st ed. Fine in dj w/tiny wear at base of spine. *MORDIDA*. $75

Pearce, T.M. and A.P. Thomason (eds). SOUTHWESTERNERS WRITE: THE AMERICAN SOUTHWEST IN STORIES. Univ of NM Press, 1946. 1st ed. Dec eps. Fine in dj. *AUTHORS OF THE WEST*. $35

Pearce, Thomas M. et al (eds). AMERICA IN THE SOUTHWEST. Univ of NM, 1933. 1st ed. Fine. *VARNER*. $45

Pearce, Thomas M. et al (eds). AMERICA IN THE SOUTHWEST: A REGIONAL HISTORY. Albuquerque: Univ Press, 1933. 1st ed. VF, scarce. *CONNOLLY & WADE*. $75

Pearce, W.M. THE MATADOR LAND AND CATTLE COMPANY. Univ of OK Press, 1964. 1st ed. Fine in NF dj. *VARNER*. $40

Pearce, Walter. PAINTING AND DECORATING. London: (Chas. Griffin), n.d. (1902). 2nd rev, enl ed. 4 color plts. Pub's pebbled chocolate cl w/gilt titling. VF. *BOOK BLOCK*. $225

PEARL HARBOR ATTACK. HEARINGS BEFORE THE JOINT COMMITTEE ON THE INVESTIGATION OF THE PEARL HARBOR ATTACK, CONGRESS OF THE UNITED STATES, SEVENTY-NINTH CONGRESS, FIRST SESSION, PURSUANT TO S. CON. RES. 27, A CONCURRENT RESOLUTION AUTHORIZING AN INVESTIGATION OF THE ATTACK ON PEARL HARBOR ON DECEMBER 7, 1941, AND EVENTS AND CIRCUMSTANCES RELATING THERETO...Wash: GPO, 1946. 39 parts, and final report (SD244). 1st ed. Orig printed wrappers. Complete file of all published. *GINSBERG*. $1500

PEARL OF GREAT PRICE. Salt Lake, 1878. 1st Amer. ed. (2nd ed.), 71pp, orig brown cloth sl worn, folding facs, lacks ffep, hinges and spine soft, interior tight and clean. *BENCHMARK*. $250

Pears, Sir Edwin. FORTY YEARS IN CONSTANTINOPLE. London, 1916. Spine darkened. *O'NEILL*. $55

Pears, Sir Edwin. LIFE OF ABDUL HAMID. NY: Holt, 1917. Frontis. Orig cl, sl rubbed, spine sl frayed, a few underscorings and notes in pencil, o/w VG. *WORLDWIDE*. $45

Pearsall, Clarence E. et al. THE QUEST FOR QUAL-A-WA-LOO (HUMBOLDT BAY): A COLLECTION....Oakland: Holmes, 1966. VF. *CONNOLLY & WADE*. $45

Pearsall, Robert and Ursula Spier Erickson. THE CALIFORNIANS: WRITINGS. 2 vols. Hesperian House, (1961). 1st ed. Fine in dj. *AUTHORS OF THE WEST*. $40

Pearsall, Ronald. CONAN DOYLE: A BIOGRAPHICAL SOLUTION. London: Weidenfeld and Nicolson, 1977. 1st ed. Fine in dj. *MORDIDA*. $45

Pearsall, Ronald. THE WORM IN THE BUD: THE WORLD OF VICTORIAN SEXUALITY. Macmillan, 1969. 1st ed. Fine in Fine dj. *MAD DOG*. $15

Pearson, Edmund. DIME NOVELS, or FOLLOWING AN OLD TRAIL IN POPULAR LITERATURE. Boston, 1929, 1st ed. 1/2" tear on spine. *HEINOLDT*. $20

Pearson, Edmund. QUEER BOOKS. London: Constable, 1929. Cvrs soiled, front hinge cracked, shaken, else Good. *WREDEN*. $15

Pearson, Hesketh. OSCAR WILDE: HIS LIFE AND WIT. NY: Harper & Bros, 1946. 1st ed. Sl cocked, spine sunned o/w VG+. *ARCHER*. $12.50

Pearson, James Larkin. FIFTY ACRES AND OTHER SELECTED POEMS. Wilkesboro, NC: Pearson Pub Co, 1937. 1st ed thus, enl by 44 pgs over 1933 ed. Inscribed. Orig blue cl. VG+. *CHAPEL HILL*. $65

Pearson, John. THE LIFE OF IAN FLEMING. NY, (1966). 1st ed. Fine in NF price clipped dj. *POLYANTHOS*. $30

Pearson, John. THE LIFE OF IAN FLEMING. London, (1966). 1st ed. NF in sl chipped dj. *DIAMOND*. $25

Pearson, John. PRINCIPLES OF SURGERY. Boston, 1832. 1st Amer ed. 1/2 leather, 122pp. *FYE*. $75

Pearson, Karl. THE GRAMMAR OF SCIENCE. London, 1900. 2nd ed. *FYE*. $60

Pearson, L. and B.H. Warren. DISEASES AND ENEMIES OF POULTRY. 2 vols in 1. Harrisburg, 1897. 95 colored, 8 b/w plts. 3/4 leather w/edge and corner wear, some scuffing. Few plts show signs of pp sticking. *SUTTON*. $165

Pearson, Ridley. THE SEIZING OF YANKEE GREEN MALL. NY: St. Martin's Press, 1987. 1st ed. VF in dj. *MORDIDA*. $25

Pearson, Ridley. UNDERCURRENTS. NY: St. Martin's Press, 1988. 1st ed. Fine in dj. *MORDIDA*. $25

Pearson, T.R. GOSPEL HOUR. NY: Morrow, (1991). 1st Amer ed. Signed. Fine in dj. *DORN*. $35

Pearson, T.R. OFF FOR THE SWEET HEARAFTER. NY: Linden, (1986). 1st Amer ed. Signed. Rem stamp bottom edge else Fine in dj. *DORN*. $40

Pearson, T.R. OFF FOR THE SWEET HEREAFTER. NY: Linden (1986). Uncorrected proof. Cigarette hole top front cvr (affecting 5pp) else VG in wraps. *DORN*. $20

Pearson, T.R. THE LAST OF HOW IT WAS. NY: Linden (1987). Uncorrected proof. NF in wraps. *DORN*. $35

Pearson, T.R. THE LAST OF HOW IT WAS. NY: Linden, (1987). 1st Amer ed. Signed. Rem stamp bottom edge else Fine in dj. *DORN*. $40

Peary, Josephine D. THE SNOW BABY. NY: Frederick A. Stokes Co, 1901. Wear, soiling; some internal markings. Pict dec cl, photo pasted on. *PARMER*. $75

Peary, Robert E. NEAREST THE POLE. NY: Doubleday, Page & Co, 1907. 1st ed. VG. *BLUE DRAGON*. $125

Peary, Robert E. NORTHWARD OVER THE "GREAT ICE". NY: Frederick A. Stokes Co., 1898. 1st ed. 2 vols. Spines faded. *LEFKOWICZ*. $150

Peary, Robert E. NORTHWARD OVER THE "GREAT ICE". NY: Frederick A. Stokes Co, 1898. 1st ed. Blue cl. Spines darkened; else VG set. *PARMER*. $200

Peary, Robert E. SNOWLAND FOLK. NY: Frederick A. Stokes Co, 1904. Pencilling. Cvrs soiled. News clipping tipped in. *PARMER*. $75

Peary, Robert E. THE NORTH POLE. NY, 1910. 1st ed. 8 hand-colored photos; fldg color map. Pict cl. Tattered dj laid in. Shelfwear o/w VG. *ARTIS*. $85

Peary, Robert E. THE NORTH POLE. NY: Stokes, September 1910. 1st trade ed. Theodore Roosevelt (intro). 8 full-pg color plts, 64pp b/w photos. Facs of Notebook Observations in Appen. II. Fldg map at rear. Bright, very clean w/no damage or wear to map. Wear to extrems, else Fine. *CONNOLLY & WADE*. $125

Peary, Robert E. THE NORTH POLE; ITS DISCOVERY IN 1909....NY: Frederick A. Stokes Co., 1910. 2nd ed. Fldg map tipped-in at back. Nice, bright. *KARMIOLE*. $100

Peattie, Donald Culcross (ed). AUDUBON'S AMERICA: THE NARRATIVES AND EXPERIENCES OF JOHN JAMES AUDUBON. Boston: Houghton Mifflin, 1940. 1st ed. Frontis, x,329pp,16 double-pg, full color plts. Blue cl, red and silver inset on cover and spine. Minor edgewear, spine sl faded, else NF. Contents Fine. *CONNOLLY & WADE*. $50

Peattie, Donald Culcross (ed). AUDUBON'S AMERICA. Boston, 1940. Ltd to 3025, signed. 17 facs. Glassine dj, slipcase (worn). *SUTTON*. $95

Peattie, Donald Culcross. IMMORTAL VILLAGE. Chicago: Univ of Chicago Press, (1945). Paul Landacre illus. One of 500 signed by author, illus. Dj price clipped. *DAWSON'S*. $175

Peattie, Donald Culcross. THE ROAD OF A NATURALIST. Boston: Houghton Mifflin, 1941. 1st ed. Fine in Fine dj. *BOOK MARKET*. $35

Peattie, Roderick (ed) THE INVERTED MOUNTAINS. CANYONS OF THE WEST. NY, 1948. NF in VG+ dj. *FIVE QUAIL*. $30

Peattie, Roderick (ed). THE INVERTED MOUNTAINS. NY: Vanguard, 1948. 1st ed. VG. *CONNOLLY & WADE*. $25

Peavey, John R. FROM THE THORNY HILLS OF DUVAL TO THE SLEEPY RIO GRANDE. Brownsville, TX: Springman-King, 1963. 1st ed. Inscribed, signed, dated. VG. *CONNOLLY & WADE*. $37.50

Peck, Ellen M. H. TRAVELS IN THE FAR EAST. NY: Crowell (1909). Grn cl dec in gilt. Joints weak. *SCHOYER'S*. $30

Peck, George W. HOW PRIVATE GEO. W. PECK PUT DOWN THE REBELLION, OR THE FUNNY EXPERIENCES OF A RAW RECRUIT. Chicago: Belford, Clarke, 1887. 1st ed. Frontis, ix,316,(4),adverts, 15 plts. Thick 12mo. Brown dec cl w/black and gilt on cover and spine. VG. *CONNOLLY & WADE*. $40

Peck, George. WYOMING....NY: Harper, 1858. 1st ed. Pub's cl. *SECOND LIFE*. $65

Peck, Henry L. THE PROUD HERITAGE OF LE FLORE COUNTY: A HISTORY OF AN OKLAHOMA COUNTY. Muskogee: Hoffman, 1967. 3rd ed. Frontis, 20 photo plts. Sturdy black cl, rounded corners, decs in gilt. Fine. *CONNOLLY & WADE*. $65

Peck, Herbert. THE BOOK OF ROOKWOOD POTTERY. Tucson, AZ: Herbert Peck, 1968. VG in dj. *BACKROOM*. $45

Peck, Taylor. ROUND-SHOT TO ROCKETS. Annapolis, 1949. 1st ed. Light dj wear o/w Fine. *PRATT*. $37.50

Peck, Walter Edwin (ed). SEVENTEEN LETTERS OF GEORGE NOEL BYRON, LORD BYRON...1811-1817. One of ltd ed of 475 on all rag paper. Uncut and unopened. *O'NEILL*. $45

Peckham, Howard H. CAPTURED BY INDIANS, TRUE TALES OF PIONEER SURVIVORS. New Brunswick, (1954). 1st ed. 238pp. Dj has a little wear, small piece torn from front, o/w Fine. *PRATT*. $32.50

Peel, C.V.A. THE ZOOLOGICAL GARDENS OF EUROPE, THEIR HISTORY & CHIEF FEATURES. London: Robinson, 1903. Illus. Gilt dec cl. Good+. *MIKESH*. $47.50

Peet, Mary Rockwood. SAN PASQUAL: A CRACK IN THE HILLS. Culver City: The Highland Press, 1949. 10pp photo illus. Cl in worn dj. *DAWSON'S*. $35

Peet, T. Eric. ROUGH STONE MONUMENTS AND THEIR BUILDERS. London & NY: Harper & Brothers, 1912. Frontis. 22 figs, 2 plts. Good. *ARCHAEOLOGIA*. $35

Peirce, A.C. A MAN FROM CORPUS CHRISTI OR THE ADVENTURES OF TWO BIRD HUNTERS AND A DOG IN TEXAN BOGS. NY: Forest and Stream Publ. Co, 1894. 1st ed. 10 full-pg drwgs. Bound in orig pub's cl. Spine soiled and sl chipped at head and heel, o/w VG. *LAURIE*. $200

Peirce, Augustus Baker. KNOCKING ABOUT. New Haven (etc.), 1924. Mrs. Albert T. Leatherbee (ed). 1st ed. 35 plts. *LEFKOWICZ*. $60

Peirce, Ebeneezer W. INDIAN HISTORY AND GENEALOGY. North Abington: Zerviah Gould Mitchell, 1878. *LOPEZ*. $400

Peirce, Parker I. ANTELOPE BILL. Ross and Haines: Minneapolis, 1962. Ltd ed. #287/550 numbered. About Fine in slipcase. *CONNOLLY & WADE*. $67.50

Peirson, Erma. THE MOHAVE RIVER AND ITS VALLEY...Glendale: Clark, 1970. 1st ed. Dj. *HEINOLDT*. $25

Peirson, Erma. THE MOJAVE RIVER AND ITS VALLEY. A.H. Clark, 1970. 1st ed. Double pp map, fldg map. VF in VF dj. *OREGON*. $25

Peirson, Erma. THE MOJAVE RIVER AND ITS VALLEY. Glendale: Arthur H. Clark, 1970. 1st ed. Fine in Fine dj. *BOOK MARKET*. $35

Peixotto, Ernest. PACIFIC SHORES FROM PANAMA. NY: Scribner's, 1913. 1st ed. Orig cl, heavily gilt w/colored illus laid-on. VG. *CONNOLLY & WADE*. $45

Peixotto. Ernest. THROUGH THE FRENCH PROVINCES. NY: Charles Scribner's Sons, 1909. 1st ed. Inner hinges cracked, o/w VG. *WEBER*. $25

PELAYO. (By William Gilmore Simms.) NY: Harper & Bros, 1838. 2 vols, 1st ed. 19pp ads, 213; 282pp. Orig blue cl w/paper spine labels.

Lib bkpl, blindstamp, some bubbling on one cover, lt scattered foxing, but Nice, VG set. CHAPEL HILL. $400

Pellett, Frank C. A LIVING FROM BEES. Orange Judd, 1944. Fine in VG dj. MAD DOG. $25

Pellett, Frank C. AMERICAN HONEY PLANTS. American Bee Journal, 1930. 3rd rev, enl ed. Fine. MAD DOG. $30

Pelton, John Cotter. LIFE'S SUNBEAMS AND SHADOWS. POEMS AND PROSE. WITH APPENDIX...VOLUME 1, ALL PUBLISHED. SF: Bancroft, 1893. 1st ed. 260pp. Orig dec cl, spine faded, cover lightly faded. Frank M. Pixley (intro). Inscribed, but unsigned, pencil presentation. Howes P185. GINSBERG. $125

Pelzer, Louis. CATTLEMAN'S FRONTIER: A RECORD...1850-1890. Glendale, Clark, 1936. 1st ed. Orig cl. (Bkpl removed, few light white numbers on lower spine; emb lib stamp). Howes P187. GINSBERG. $150

Pelzer, Louis. CATTLEMEN'S FRONTIER: A RECORD...1850-1890. A.H. Clark, 1936. 1st ed. Fine. VARNER. $150

Pemberton, T. Edgar. DICKENS'S LONDON: LONDON IN THE WORKS OF CHARLES DICKENS. London: Samuel Tinsley, 1876. 1st ed. 8vo, 260pp, decorated burgundy cloth, signed presentation copy, cover moderately worn. Good+. GREAT EXPECTATIONS. $30

Pence, Mary Lou. BOSWELL THE STORY OF A FRONTIER LAWMAN. Laramie, WY: the author, 1978. 1st ed, signed and inscribed. Fine in dj. GIBBS. $35

Pendlebury, J.D.S. A HANDBOOK OF THE PALACE OF MINOS AT KNOSSOS. London: Macmillan & Co. 1933. 1st ed. 15 plts, 9 maps (some fldg), plan in rear pocket. KARMIOLE. $40

Pendlebury, J.D.S. A HANDBOOK TO THE PALACE OF MINOS KNOSSOS WITH ITS DEPENDENCIES. London: Max Parrish, (1959). 14 plts, 9 plans. Sig. Good in torn dj. ARCHAEOLOGIA. $25

Pendlebury, J.D.S. THE ARCHAEOLOGY OF CRETE. London: Methuen, (1939). 1st ed. Owner sig. Fine. WEBER. $100

Pendlebury, J.D.S. THE ARCHAEOLOGY OF CRETE. NY, 1963. Glassine dj. O'NEILL. $35

Pendleton, Nathaniel G. MILITARY POSTS--COUNCIL BLUFFS TO THE PACIFIC OCEAN. Wash, HR31, 1843. 1st ed. 78pp. Map. Half morocco. Howes P199. GINSBERG. $250

Pendray, G. Edward. MEN, MIRRORS, AND STARS. NY: Harper, 1946 (1935). Rev ed. VG in clipped dj. KNOLLWOOD. $28

Pendray, G. Edward. THE COMING AGE OF ROCKET POWER. NY: Harper, n.d. (c. 1949) (1945). 4th ed. Corners bumped, moisture stain to bottom margin of plts. Good. KNOLLWOOD. $60

Pendril, Paul. SPORT AND ADVENTURE IN CORSICA. London: Richard Bentley, 1866. 1st hrdcvr ed. Emb blue cl. Some wear to extremities, rear hinge starting, minor tear base of spine, else Good. Rare. OLD LONDON. $100

Penfield, Frederic Courtland. PRESENT-DAY EGYPT. NY: Century Co, 1907. Rev, enl ed. NF. SCHOYER'S. $50

Penfield, Thomas. DIG HERE! San Antonio: Naylor, 1962. 1st ed. VG in NF dj. CONNOLLY & WADE. $30

Penfield, Thomas. WESTERN SHERIFFS AND MARSHALS. NY: Grossett & Dunlap, 1955. VG. BURCHAM. $35

Penfield, Wilder and Herbert Jasper. EPILEPSY AND THE FUNCTIONAL ANATOMY OF THE HUMAN BRAIN. Boston, 1954. 1st ed. FYE. $175

Penfield, Wilder and Lamar Roberts. SPEECH AND BRAIN: MECHANISMS. Princeton, 1959. 1st ed. FYE. $60

Penfield, Wilder and Theodore Erickson. EPILEPSY AND CEREBRAL LOCALIZATION. Springfield, 1941. 1st ed. FYE. $250

Penfield, Wilder and Theodore Rasmussen. THE CEREBRAL CORTEX OF MAN: A CLINICAL STUDY OF LOCALIZATION OF FUNCTION. NY, 1952. 1st ed., 2nd prtg. FYE. $100

Peninou, Ernest P. and Sidney S. Greenleaf. A DIRECTORY OF CALIFORNIA WINE GROWERS AND WINE MAKERS IN 1860. Berkeley: Tamalpais Press, 1967. Ltd ed, one of 450. Frontis; addendum and errata inserted. Grn cl. Fine. WEBER. $100

Penn, John. BARREN REVENGE. London: Collins, 1986. 1st ed. VF in dj. SILVER DOOR. $25

Penn, John. OUTRAGEOUS EXPOSURES. London: Collins, 1988. 1st ed. VF in dj. SILVER DOOR. $25

Pennant, Thomas. ARCTIC ZOOLOGY. London: Robert Faulder, 1792. 2nd ed. 24 plts, 2 fldg maps. Bound in full leather; gilt spine titles; raised bands; eps renewed; offset from plts. Exceptionally nice. 3 vols. PARMER. $1950

Pennell, Elizabeth R. MY COOKERY BOOKS. Boston, 1903. One of 330 large-paper copies. NF. POLYANTHOS. $150

Pennell, Joseph. THE ADVENTURES OF AN ILLUSTRATOR. Boston: LB, 1925. Ltd ed, #59 of unspecified # signed, w/orig signed etching tipped in. 1/2 leather (sl rubbed head of spine), teg. Sl chipped, internally mended dj. CAPTAIN'S BOOKSHELF. $300

Pennell, Joseph. THE GRAPHIC ARTS: MODERNS AND MODERN METHODS. Univ of Chicago Press, 1921. Fine. POLYANTHOS. $75

Pennell-Elmhirst, Capt. FOX-HOUND, FOREST, AND PRAIRIE. London: Routledge, 1892. 1st ed. Half leather, raised bands, orig covers bound in. Fine. OCTOBER FARM. $195

Pennell-Elmhirst, Capt. THE BEST SEASON ON RECORD. London: Routledge, 1885. 2nd ed. Half leather, raised bands, orig. covers bound in. VG. OCTOBER FARM. $175

Penney, F.E. SOUTHERN INDIA. A&C Black, 1914. 1st ed. 20s Series. NF. OLD LONDON. $100

Pennington, C.W. (ed). THE PIMA BAJO OF CENTRAL SONORA, MEXICO. Salt Lake City: Univ of UT, 1979. 1st ed. Both Fine in NF djs. MIKESH. $45

PENNSYLVANIA AT CHICKAMAUGA AND CHATTANOOGA. Harrisburg, 1897. 499pp, half leather, gilt edges. Cover wear o/w VG+. PRATT. $45

Pennypacker, Morton. GENERAL WASHINGTON'S SPIES ON LONG ISLAND AND IN NEW YORK. Brooklyn: Long Island Hist Soc, 1939. 1st ed. Fine in VG dj. CONNOLLY & WADE. $65

Pennypacker, Samuel W. THE AUTOBIOGRAPHY OF A PENNSYLVANIAN. Phila, 1918. HEINOLDT. $15

Penrose, Boies. TRAVEL AND DISCOVERY IN THE RENAISSANCE 1420-1620. Cambridge, MA, 1952. 1st ed. VG in remains of dj. LEFKOWICZ. $55

Penrose, Boies. TRAVEL AND DISCOVERY IN THE RENAISSANCE 1420-1620. Cambridge, 1955. xvi,377pp. O'NEILL. $55

Pentecost, Hugh. CANCELLED IN RED. Dodd, Mead, 1939. 1st ed. Lib label on endpaper, slight edge soil. Dj edgewear & piece missing bottom of spine. BEBBAH. $25

Penzer, N.M. POISON-DAMSELS AND OTHER ESSAYS IN FOLKLORE AND ANTHROPOLOGY. London: Ptd privately for Chas. J. Sawyer, 1952. 1st ed. Red cl. VG. WEBER. $35

Penzer, N.M. THE HAREM. London: Spring Books, (1965, 36). Reprint. VG+ in Good+ dj. AARD. $25

Pepper, J.H. THE PLAYBOOK OF METALS: PERSONAL NARRATIVES....London: Routledge, Warne, 1862. 2nd ed. 504pp. Few dk spots rear cover o/w VG. BOOKCELL. $60

Pepper O.H. Perry. MEDICAL ETYMOLOGY: THE HISTORY AND DERIVATION OF MEDICAL TERMS. Phila, 1949. 1st ed. Extremities rubbed. FYE. $75

Pepper, William. A SYSTEM OF PRACTICAL MEDICINE BY AMERICAN AUTHORS. Phila, 1885. 1st ed. 5 vols. *FYE*. $250

Perceval, Spencer. INQUIRY OR DELICATE INVESTIGATION INTO THE CONDUCT OF HER ROYAL HIGHNESS, THE PRINCESS OF WALES.. IN YEAR 1806. London, 1813. 110pp, errata pg. Light foxing on just a few pp. Rebound in new buckram. *HEINOLDT*. $20

Percival, MacIver. THE FAN BOOK. London: T. Fisher Unwin Ltd, (1920). 1st ed. XXXI plts. Fine in worn dj. *WREDEN*. $75

Percy, Walker. LANCELOT. NY: Farrar, Straus & Giroux, (1977). 1st ed. Fine in dj. *JUVELIS*. $25

Percy, Walker. LANCELOT. NY: FSG (1977). 1st ed. Fine in NF dj (slight fading on spine). Signed. *LOPEZ*. $100

Percy, Walker. LOST IN THE COSMOS. NY: Farrar Straus & Giroux, (1983). One of 350 signed. As New in orig slipcase. *CAPTAIN'S BOOKSHELF*. $175

Percy, Walker. LOST IN THE COSMOS. NY: FSG (1983). 1st ed. Fine in dj. *DORN*. $40

Percy, Walker. LOST IN THE COSMOS. NY: Farrar Straus & Giroux, (1983). Uncorrected proof. Fine in wraps. *CAPTAIN'S BOOK-SHELF*. $175

Percy, Walker. LOVE IN THE RUINS. NY: Farrar, 1971. 1st ed. Fine in Fine dj. *BEASLEY*. $45

Percy, Walker. LOVE IN THE RUINS. NY: Farrar Straus Giroux, (1971). 1st ed. Dj. VF. *JAFFE*. $75

Percy, Walker. LOVE IN THE RUINS. NY: FSG, (1971). 1st ed. NF in NF price-clipped dj w/tiny scratch on front panel. *ROBBINS*. $65

Percy, Walker. LOVE IN THE RUINS. NY: FSG (1971). 1st ed. Top edge sl sunned else Fine in Fine dj. *DORN*. $75

Percy, Walker. NOVEL WRITING IN APOCALYPTIC TIME. New Orleans: Faust Publishing, 1986. 1st ed. 1/300 cl bound, each signed by Eudora Welty and Percy. *JUVELIS*. $250

Percy, Walker. QUESTIONS THEY NEVER ASKED ME. Northridge, CA: Lord John Press, (1979). Orig blue cl backed boards. Fine. 1st ed. #126 of 300 signed. *CHAPEL HILL*. $175

Percy, Walker. QUESTIONS THEY NEVER ASKED ME. Northridge: Lord John Press, 1979. One of 300 signed. Fine in cloth-backed patterned boards. *CAPTAIN'S BOOKSHELF*. $100

Percy, Walker. THE LAST GENTLEMAN. NY: Farrar Straus & Giroux, (1966). 1st ed. Fine in dj (very light edgewear). Inscribed 1982. *CAPTAIN'S BOOKSHELF*. $300

Percy, Walker. THE LAST GENTLEMAN. NY: Farrar, Straus & Giroux, (1966). 1st ed. Orig cl-backed black boards. Top edge of boards sunned, else NF in dj bumped at spine ends. *CHAPEL HILL*. $150

Percy, Walker. THE MESSAGE IN THE BOTTLE. NY: Farrar Straus & Giroux, (1975). 1st ed, 1st issue. Fine in dj. Signed. *CAPTAIN'S BOOKSHELF*. $175

Percy, Walker. THE MESSAGE IN THE BOTTLE. NY: Farrar, Straus & Giroux, (1975). 1st ed. Orig orange cl, top edge stained orange. Fine in dj. *CHAPEL HILL*. $85

Percy, Walker. THE MESSAGE IN THE BOTTLE. NY: Farrar Straus & Giroux, (1975). 1st ed, this being the issue with the top edges unstained. Fine in dj. *CAPTAIN'S BOOKSHELF*. $45

Percy, Walker. THE MOVIEGOER. Franklin Center: Franklin Library, 1980. Ltd ed, bound in full Franklin leather, signed on tipped-in sheet. 2 pp intro by Percy found only in this ed. Eps discoloring around edges, else Fine. *CAPTAIN'S BOOKSHELF*. $200

Percy, Walker. THE MOVIEGOER. London: E & S, 1963. 1st Eng ed. Two short ink marks on ffep, else Fine in dj w/slight wear head of spine. *CAPTAIN'S BOOKSHELF*. $450

Percy, Walker. THE MOVIEGOER. NY: Knopf, 1961. 1st ed. Pub in ed of only 1500. Prev reader's extensive ink annotations 1st 40 pp, o/w NF in dj (lt edgewear; chipping at crown). *LOPEZ*. $450

Percy, Walker. THE MOVIEGOER. NY: Knopf, 1961. 1st ed. Two corners sl bumped, else Fine in dj (very light wear at corners, spinal extremities). *CAPTAIN'S BOOKSHELF*. $1600

Percy, Walker. THE SECOND COMING. NY: Farrar Straus Giroux, (1980). 1st ed. Signed. Dj. VF. *JAFFE*. $85

Percy, Walker. THE SECOND COMING. NY: Farrar, Straus & Giroux, (1980). 1st ed. 1/450 signed. As New pub's box. *JUVELIS*. $100

Percy, Walker. THE SECOND COMING. NY: Farrar, Straus & Giroux, (1980). Uncorrected proof. Fine in ptd wraps. *CAPTAIN'S BOOKSHELF*. $175

Percy, Walker. THE SECOND COMING. NY: Farrar, Straus, Giroux, (1980). 1st, ltd ed. #320 of 450 signed. Orig blue cl. Fine in pub's slipcase. *CHAPEL HILL*. $150

Percy, Walker. THE THANATOS SYNDROME. NY, (1987). 1st ed. Signed, dated presentation. Fine in like dj. *POLYANTHOS*. $50

Percy, Walker. THE THANATOS SYNDROME. NY: Farrar, Straus, Giroux, (1987). 1st ed. One of 250 specially bound, signed. Orig burgundy cl. Unopened, absolutely As New in orig shrinkwrap, pub's slipcase. *CHAPEL HILL*. $150

Percy, Walker. THE THANATOS SYNDROME. NY: Farrar, Straus, Giroux (1987). 1st trade ed. Orig cl-backed boards. Fine in dj. Signed. *CHAPEL HILL*. $85

Pereira, George. PEKING TO LHASA. Boston: Houghton Mifflin Co., 1926. 1st Amer ed. 2 fldg maps. Front cover lightly stained. *KARMIOLE*. $50

Perez Lopez, F. DARK & BLOODY GROUND: A GUERILLA DIARY OF THE SPANISH CIVIL WAR. Boston: Little, Brown, (1972). 1st Amer. ed. 275pp. Dj. *AKA*. $26

Perkin, Robert L. THE FIRST HUNDRED YEARS. AN INFORMAL HISTORY. Doubleday, 1959. 1st ed. Inscribed. VF in VG dj. *CONNOLLY & WADE*. $75

Perkins, C.C. LADY'S BOOK ON ART EMBROIDERY IN SILK. NY: Heminway & Sons, 1886. Rev ed. Chromolitho wraps, sl soiled o/w VG. *SCHOYER'S*. $40

Perkins, D.A.W. HISTORY OF OSCEOLA COUNTY, IOWA. Sioux Falls, SD: Brown & Stenger, 1892. 270, 26pp. Spine extrems, corners frayed. Inner hinges starting. *KARMIOLE*. $45

Perkins, Edna Brush. WHITE HEART OF THE MOHAVE. NY: Boni and Liveright, (1922). 1st ed. VG. *BOOK MARKET*. $30

Perkins, Fred B. THE PICTURE AND THE MEN....NY: A.J. Johnson, 1867. Frontis. Gilt-dec cl, sl spine wear. *SCHOYER'S*. $35

Perkins, J.R. TRAILS, RAILS AND WAR, THE LIFE OF GENERAL G.M. DODGE. Indianapolis, (1929). 1st ed. Dj. Gold worn from spine lettering o/w VG. *PRATT*. $47.50

Perkins, John. TO THE ENDS OF THE EARTH. NY: Pantheon, 1981. 1st ed. VG in dj. *PARMER*. $30

Perkins, Justin. HISTORICAL SKETCH OF THE MISSION TO THE NESTORIANS, AND OF THE ASSYRIA MISSION, BY REV. THOMAS LAURIE. NY, 1862. Pamphlet. 32pp. *O'NEILL*. $50

Perkins, Justin. MISSIONARY LIFE IN PERSIA. Boston, 1861. 255pp. *O'NEILL*. $75

Perkins, Lucy. THE AMERICAN TWINS OF 1812. Houghton Mifflin, (1925). 189pp. Illus by author. Small stain red cloth cvr, else VG+ in Good dj w/triangular piece missing, some chips. *BEBBAH*. $30

PERKY AND HIS PUP. London, (1930s). Moveable bk. *BOOK-FINDERS INTL*. $35

Perlis, Vivian. CHARLES IVES REMEMBERED. Yale Univ Press, 1974. Signed. Fine in dj. *BANCROFT*. $25

Perrault, Charles. CINDERELLA. Scribner's, (1954). 1st ed. Illus and signed by Marcia Brown. Slight edgewear. VG+. *BEBBAH*. $90

Perrin, W. G. BRITISH FLAGS: THEIR EARLY HISTORY, AND THEIR DEVELOPMENT AT SEA. Cambridge, 1922. 1st ed. 14 color plts. Fine. *LEFKOWICZ*. $135

Perrin, William Henry (ed). HISTORY OF SUMMIT COUNTY, WITH AN OUTLINE SKETCH OF OHIO. Chicago: Baskin & Battey, 1881. 25 plts and ports. Rebound in black buckram, aeg. Upper corner first few leaves chipped; hist soc stamp. *BOHLING*. $150

Perrin, William Henry. HISTORY OF STARK COUNTY, WITH AN OUTLINE SKETCH OF OHIO. Chicago: Baskin & Battey, 1881. Some scuffing, front hinge cracked. Good. *BOHLING*. $135.

Perrot, Georges and Charles Chipiez. A HISTORY OF ART IN CHALDAEA & ASSYRIA. London: Chapman and Hall, 1884. 452 engrvs, 15 color plts, teg. Corner bumped, scattered foxing throughout. Good. *ARCHAEOLOGIA*. $175

Perrot, Georges and Charles Chipiez. HISTORY OF ART IN PRIMITIVE GREECE; MYCENIAN ART. 2 vols. London: Chapman and Hall, Ltd., 1894. 54 figs, 21 plts. Good. *ARCHAEOLOGIA*. $95

Perrot, Georges and Charles Chipiez. HISTORY OF ART IN PHRYGIA, LYDIA, CARIA, AND LYCIA. London: Chapman and Hall, 1892. 280 figs. Teg. Bkpl. Good. *ARCHAEOLOGIA*. $125

Perrot, Georges and Charles Chipiez. HISTORY OF ART IN PHOENICIA AND ITS DEPENDENCIES. London: Chapman and Hall, 1885. 2 vols. 10 plts (9 color). Small tears at spine, lightly chipped, stamp at half titles. Good. *ARCHAEOLOGIA*. $150

Perry, Amos. AN OFFICIAL TOUR ALONG THE EASTERN COAST OF THE REGENCY OF TUNIS. Providence: Standard Printing Co., 1891. 1st ed. Signed presentation. Worn, top of spine missing, hinges cracked, internally Good ex-lib. *WORLDWIDE*. $22

Perry, Amos. CARTHAGE AND TUNIS, PAST AND PRESENT. Providence: Providence Press, 1869. 1st ed. viii,560pp. Sl rubbed, o/w VG ex-lib. *WORLDWIDE*. $40

Perry, Anne. BLUEGATE FIELDS. NY: St. Martin's, 1984. 1st Amer ed. Signed. VF in dj. *SILVER DOOR*. $35

Perry, Charles. PORTRAIT OF A YOUNG MAN DROWNING. NY: Simon & Schuster, 1962. 1st ed, 1st bk. As New in dj. *ELSE FINE*. $45

Perry, John. SPINNING TOPS. London, 1901. NF. *POLYANTHOS*. $30

Perry, L.M. MARINE SHELLS OF THE SOUTHWEST COAST OF FLORIDA. Ithaca, 1942 (1940). 40 plts. *SUTTON*. $35

Perry, Richard. CHANGES. Indianapolis: Bobbs-Merrill, (1974). 1st ed. NF in dj. *LOPEZ*. $45

Perry, Richard. CHANGES. Indianapolis: Bobbs-Merrill, 1974. 1st ed. Fine in lightly used dj w/tears. *BEASLEY*. $30

Perry, Thomas. BIG FISH. NY: Charles Scribner's Sons, 1985. 1st ed. Fine in dj. *MORDIDA*. $25

Perry, Thomas. ISLAND. NY: G.P. Putnam's Sons, 1987. 1st ed. VF in dj. *MORDIDA*. $25

Perry, Thomas. METZGER'S DOG. NY: Charles Scribner's Sons, 1983. 1st ed. Spine sl faded o/w Fine in dj. *MORDIDA*. $30

Perry, Thomas. METZGER'S DOG. NY: Scribner's, 1983. 1st ed. VF in dj. *ELSE FINE*. $40

Perry, Thomas. SLEEPING DOGS. NY: Random House, 1992. 1st ed. Advance reading copy. Fine in pict wrappers. *MORDIDA*. $25

Perry, Thomas. THE BUTCHER'S BOY. NY: Charles Scribner's Sons, 1982. 1st ed. Fine in dj, sm scrape front panel. *MORDIDA*. $150

Perse, St. John. ANABASIS. London: Faber & Faber Ltd. 1930. T.S. Eliot (trans, preface). Special ed ltd to 350 numbered, signed by Eliot. *KARMIOLE*. $350

Persico, Joseph E. MY ENEMY, MY BROTHER. MEN AND DAYS OF GETTYSBURG. NY, 1977. 2nd prtg. Fine in dj. *PRATT*. $20

Person, Carl E. LIZARD'S TRAIL: A STORY FROM THE ILLINOIS CENTRAL & HARRIMAN LINES STRIKE OF 1911-1915 INCLUSIVE. Chicago: Lake Pub, 1918. 1st ed. 462pp. Dark blue cloth. Light rubbing to edges, o/w bright copy. *AKA*. $85

Pertchik, Bernard and Harriet. FLOWERING TREES OF THE CARIBBEAN. NY: Rinehart, (1951). 1st ed. 29 full-color plts. Chipped dj. *SILVER*. $30

Perugini, Kate. THE COMEDY OF CHARLES DICKENS. London, 1906. 1st series, 1st ed. Minor cvr staining, o/w VG. *DIAMOND*. $35

PETER RABBIT. London, 1983. Pop-up bk. *BOOKFINDERS INTL*. $25

Peterkin, Julia. BLACK APRIL. Indianapolis: Bobbs-Merrill, 1927. 1st ed, 2nd issue w/Crawford blurb & corrected text. Fine, minor wear at dj spine corners. *ELSE FINE*. $60

Peterkin, Julia. BRIGHT SKIN. Indianapolis: Bobbs-Merrill, (1932). 1st ed. #66 of 250 signed. Orig red cl, teg. NF, lacking slipcase. *CHAPEL HILL*. $175

Peterman, V.M. "Pete". PIONEER DAYS: A HALF-CENTURY OF LIFE. Lubbock, TX: The Author, 1979. Ptd by the Texas Univ Press. 1st ed. Mint. *GIBBS*. $30

Peters, Carl. THE ELDORADO OF THE ANCIENTS. NY: Dutton; London: Pearson, 1902. 1st US ed. 2 fldg maps. Sl rubbed, o/w VG ex-lib. *WORLDWIDE*. $55

Peters, Elizabeth. AMMIE, COME HOME. As Barbara Michaels. NY: Meredith, 1968. 1st ed. VF in dj. *ELSE FINE*. $30

Peters, Elizabeth. CROCODILE ON THE SANDBANK. NY: Dodd Mead, 1975. 1st ed. Fine in price-clipped dj w/minor wear, short closed tear. *MORDIDA*. $85

Peters, Elizabeth. SILHOUETTE IN SCARLET. NY: Congden & Weed, 1983. 1st ed. Remainder dot on top edge, o/w Fine in price-clipped dj. *MORDIDA*. $30

Peters, Elizabeth. STREET OF THE FIVE MOONS. NY: Dodd Mead, 1978. 1st ed. Signed. Crease on feps, o/w Fine in rubbed dj (tiny tears, wear spine ends, at corners). *MORDIDA*. $65

Peters, Elizabeth. SUMMER OF THE DRAGON. NY: Dodd Mead, 1979. 1st ed. Fine in dj. *MORDIDA*. $65

Peters, Elizabeth. THE COPENHAGEN CONNECTION. NY: Congdon & Lattes, 1982. 1st ed. VF in dj. *MORDIDA*. $35

Peters, Elizabeth. THE DEAD SEA CIPHER. NY: Dodd Mead, 1970. 1st ed. Darkened area on fep, o/w Fine in dj w/sl faded spine. *MORDIDA*. $90

Peters, Elizabeth. THE MUMMY CASE. NY: Congden & Weed, 1985. 1st ed. VF in dj. *MORDIDA*. $30

Peters, Elizabeth. THE MURDERS OF RICHARD III. NY: Dodd Mead, 1974. 1st ed. Fine in dj. *MORDIDA*. $85

Peters, Ellis. AN EXCELLENT MYSTERY. London: Macmillan, 1985. 1st ed. Fine in dj. *MORDIDA*. $40

Peters, Ellis. AN EXCELLENT MYSTERY. NY: William Morrow, 1985. 1st Amer ed. Fine in dj. *MORDIDA*. $30

Peters, Ellis. BLACK IS THE COLOUR OF MY TRUE-LOVE'S HEART. NY: William Morrow, 1967. 1st Amer ed. Lt spotting on edges, o/w Fine in dj. *MORDIDA*. $45

Peters, Ellis. CITY OF GOLD AND SHADOWS. London: Macmillan, 1973. 1st ed. Edges spotted o/w Fine in dj. *MORDIDA*. $75

Peters, Ellis. DEAD MAN'S RANSOM. NY: Morrow, 1984. 1st ed. Fine in Fine dj. *BEASLEY*. $25

Peters, Ellis. DEAD MAN'S RANSOM. NY: William Morrow, 1984. 1st Amer ed. VF in dj. *MORDIDA*. $35

Peters, Ellis. FUNERAL OF FIGARO. NY: William Morrow, 1964. 1st Amer ed. Fine in price-clipped dj w/short closed tear. *MORDIDA.* $50

Peters, Ellis. HORTENSUIS: FRIEND OF NERO. NY: Greystone, 1937. 1st ed, 1st bk. VG minor wear at corners and ends of fragile paper-covered boards, spine repaired, light edgewear, chips at corners, spine top of dj. Very scarce. *ELSE FINE.* $75

Peters, Ellis. MONK'S HOOD, THE THIRD CHRONICLE OF BROTHER CADFAEL. Morrow, (1980). 1st Amer ed. Fine in Fine dj. *BEBBAH.* $20

Peters, Ellis. MONK'S HOOD. Morrow, 1980. 1st Amer ed. VF in dj. *STAHR.* $15

Peters, Ellis. THE CONFESSION OF BROTHER HALUIN. NY: Mysterious Press, 1988. 1st Amer. ed. VF in dj. *MORDIDA.* $25

Peters, Ellis. THE CONFESSIONS OF BROTHER HALUIN. London: Headline, (1988). 1st ed. Signed on laid in bkpl. VF in VF dj. *UNGER.* $65

Peters, Ellis. THE DEVIL'S NOVICE. London: Macmillan, 1983. 1st ed. Fine in dj. *MORDIDA.* $45

Peters, Ellis. THE DEVIL'S NOVICE. NY: Morrow, 1984. 1st Amer ed. VF in dj. *SILVER DOOR.* $25

Peters, Ellis. THE GRASS-WIDOW'S TALE. NY: William Morrow, 1968. 1st Amer ed. Name on fep o/w Fine in dj w/tiny wear at top of spine. *MORDIDA.* $75

Peters, Ellis. THE HERETIC'S APPRENTICE. NY: Mysterious Press, 1990. Advance uncorrected proofs. Fine in wraps. *BEASLEY.* $35

Peters, Ellis. THE HERMIT IN EYTON FOREST. London: Stoddart, 1987. 1st ed. Fine in dj. *MORDIDA.* $30

Peters, Ellis. THE HERMIT OF EYTON FOREST. London: Headline, (1987). 1st ed. VF in VF dj. *UNGER.* $40

Peters, Ellis. THE HORN OF ROLAND. London: Macmillan, 1974. 1st ed. Fine in dj. *MORDIDA.* $90

Peters, Ellis. THE KNOCKER ON DEATH'S DOOR. NY: William Morrow, 1971. 1st Amer ed. Inscribed. Pp edges sl darkened o/w Fine in dj w/darkened spine, minor wear at spine ends and darkened back panel. *MORDIDA.* $60

Peters, Ellis. THE LEPER OF ST. GILES. NY: William Morrow, 1982. 1st Amer. ed. VF in dj. *MORDIDA.* $35

Peters, Ellis. THE PILGRIM OF HATE. London: Macmillan, 1984. 1st ed. Fine in dj. *SILVER DOOR.* $30

Peters, Ellis. THE PILGRIM OF HATE. Morrow, 1984. 1st Amer ed. Fine in dj w/small tear. *STAHR.* $15

Peters, Ellis. THE POTTER'S FIELD. London: Headline, 1989. 1st ed. Fine in dj. *MORDIDA.* $35

Peters, Ellis. THE ROSE RENT. NY: William Morrow, 1986. 1st Amer ed. Fine in dj. *MORDIDA.* $25

Peters, Ellis. THE SANCTUARY SPARROW. NY: William Morrow, 1983. 1st Amer ed. VF in dj. *MORDIDA.* $35

Peters, Ellis. THE SUMMER OF THE DANES. London: Headline, 1991. 1st ed. VF in dj. *SILVER DOOR.* $25

Peters, Ellis. THE VIRGIN IN THE ICE. London: Macmillan, 1982. 1st ed. Fine in dj. *MORDIDA.* $50

Peters, Fred J. (comp). RAILROAD—INDIAN AND PIONEER PRINTS BY N. CURRIER AND CURRIER & IVES. NY: Antique Bulletin Pub Co, 1930. Addenda. Sl worn. *WEBER.* $75

Peters, Fred. J. CLIPPER SHIP PRINTS INCLUDING OTHER MERCHANT SAILING SHIPS BY N. CURRIER AND CURRIER & IVES. NY, 1930. Lib Ed. 1st ed. Fine. *LEFKOWICZ.* $100

Peters, Harry T. CALIFORNIA ON STONE. GC, NY: Doubleday Doran. 1935. 112 plts, 3 mounted photogr ports. Ed ltd to 501. Dj. Fine in slipcase. *KARMIOLE.* $500

Peters, Harry T. CURRIER & IVES. PRINTMAKERS TO THE AMERICAN PEOPLE. GC, NY: Doubleday, Doran, 1942. 1st ed. 192 plts. Pict cl, dj sl torn. *HUDSON.* $50

Peters, Hermann. PICTORIAL HISTORY OF ANCIENT PHARMACY. Chicago, 1906. 3rd ed. *FYE.* $60

Peters, John Punnett. NIPPUR, OR EXPLORATIONS AND ADVENTURES ON THE EUPHRATES....NY: G.P. Putnam, 1898-99. 2 vols (complete). Frontis, 2 fldg maps in pocket at rear. Teg. Spines chipped Good. *ARCHAEOLOGIA.* $150

Petersen, Carman. THE MAYA OF GUATEMALA. Seattle: Univ of WA Press, (1976). 1st ed. 73 color plts. Good in dj. *SILVER.* $75

Petersen, Frederick A. MILITARY REVIEW OF THE CAMPAIGN IN VIRGINIA & MARYLAND. New York: Sinclair Tousey. 1862. 56pp. Orig ptd yellow wraps. *KARMIOLE.* $40

Petersen, William J. STEAMBOATING ON THE UPPER MISSISSIPPI, THE WATER WAY TO IOWA. Iowa City, State Hist Soc of Iowa, 1937. 1st ed. Ptd at the Torch Press. Gilt stamped grn cl. VG in Fine dj. Howes P263. *BOHLING.* $85

Petersen, William J. STEAMBOATING ON THE UPPER MISSISSIPPI. 1937, 1st ed. *HEINOLDT.* $85

Petersen, William J. STEAMBOATING ON THE UPPER MISSISSIPPI. Iowa City: State Hist Soc of Iowa, 1968. 2nd ed. Gold-stamped cl in dj. *DAWSON'S.* $40

Petersen, William J. STEAMBOATING ON THE UPPER MISSISSIPPI. Iowa City: Iowa State Hist Soc, 1968. *HEINOLDT.* $25

Petersen, William J. STEAMBOATING ON THE UPPER MISSISSIPPI. Iowa City: State Hist Soc, IA, 1937. 1st ed. VG. Howes P263. *OREGON.* $125

Petersen, William. F. LINCOLN. DOUGLAS. THE WEATHER AS DESTINY. Springfield: Chas. C. Thomas, 1943. 1st ed. About Fine in VG dj. *CONNOLLY & WADE.* $45

Petersen, William. HIPPOCRATIC WISDOM: A MODERN APPRECIATION OF ANCIENT MEDICAL SCIENCE. Springfield, 1946. 1st ed. *FYE.* $50

Petersham, Maud and Miska. THE SILVER MACE. NY: Macmillan, 1956. 1st ed. Spine tips, corners sl bumped, else VG+ in dj, tears. *ACADEMIC LIBRARY.* $25

Peterson, Charles S. LOOK TO THE MOUNTAINS: SOUTHEASTERN UTAH AND THE LA SAL NATIONAL FOREST. Provo, 1975. 1st ed. VF in NF dj. *FIVE QUAIL.* $20

Peterson, Charles S. TAKE UP YOUR MISSION. Tucson, 1973. *FIVE QUAIL.* $20

Peterson, Emil R. and Alfred A. Powers. A CENTURY OF COOS AND CURRY. Portland: Binfords & Mort, 1952. 1st ed. VG in internally repaired, elusive dj. *CONNOLLY & WADE.* $60

Peterson, Fred W. DESERT PIONEER DOCTOR AND EXPERIENCES IN OBSTETRICS. Calexico Chronicle, 1947. 1st ed. Signed. Fine. *BOOK MARKET.* $65

Peterson, Frederick and Walter Haines. A TEXT-BOOK OF LEGAL MEDICINE AND TOXICOLOGY. Phila, 1903. 1st ed. 2 vols. 730, 825pp. Color chromolithographs, plts. *FYE.* $200

Peterson, Keith (pseud of Andrew Klavan). THE SCARRED MAN. NY: Doubleday, 1990. 1st ed. VF in dj. *MORDIDA.* $25

Peterson, R.T. A FIELD GUIDE TO THE BIRDS GIVING FIELD MARKS OF ALL SPECIES FOUND EAST OF THE ROCKIES. Boston, 1947. 2nd rev, enl ed. Wear to extrems; eps browned. Inscribed, signed. *SUTTON.* $30

Peterson, R.T. BIRDS OVER AMERICA. NY, 1948. Spine faded. Inscribed, signed. *SUTTON.* $35

Peterson, Robert C. (ed). THE SCIENCE-FICTIONAL SHER-LOCK HOLMES. Denver, 1960. 1st ed. Signed by Peterson & his collaborator. NF in VG+ dj with few tiny spots, chip. *BEBBAH.* $150

Peterson, Robert. ONLY THE BALL WAS WHITE. Prentice-Hall, 1970. 1st ed. Good+ in VG+ dj. *PLAPINGER.* $125

Peterson, Roger W. ONLY THE BALL WAS WHITE. Englewood Cliffs: Prentice-Hall, (1970). 1st ed. Front hinge neatly repaired, bottom corners little bumped, thus VG in dj w/couple very small chips at extremities. *BETWEEN COVERS.* $100

Petievich, Gerald. MONEY MEN AND ONE SHOT DEAL. 1st ed, 1st bk. VF in dj. *ELSE FINE.* $65

Petievich, Gerald. MONEY-MEN AND ONE-SHOT DEAL. NY: Harcourt, (1981). 1st ed. Fine in Fine dj. *UNGER.* $50

Petievich, Gerald. TO DIE IN BEVERLY HILLS. NY: Arbor House, 1983. 1st ed. VF in dj. *ELSE FINE.* $50

Petievich, Gerald. TO LIVE AND DIE IN L.A. NY: Arbor, 1984. 1st ed. VF in dj. *ELSE FINE.* $50

Petrakis, Harry Mark. CHAPTER SEVEN FROM THE HOUR OF THE BELL. Fldg frontis Warrington Colescott, 1/4 black morocco & marbled boards. Mt. Horeb: Perishable Press, (1976). 1st ed. Ltd to 150 signed by Petrakis; this also signed by Walter Hamady. VF. *JAFFE.* $175

Petrakis, Harry Mark. IN THE LAND OF MORNING. NY: Macmillan, 1973. 1st ed. Signed. VF in dj. *ELSE FINE.* $50

Petrarca Francesco. THE SONNETS OF PETRARCH. Verona: (The Officina Bodoni for) LEC, 1965. Illus by Aldo Salvadori. Ltd to 1500 numbered, signed by the printer, Giovanni Mardersteig and Salvadori. Dj and slipcase. *KARMIOLE.* $150

Petrie, W.M. Flinders. A SEASON IN EGYPT 1887. London: Field & Tuer, "The Leadenhall Press," 1887. 32 plts. Spine and inner joints taped, fep absent. Good. *ARCHAEOLOGIA.* $250

Petrie, W.M. Flinders. ABYDOS. Parts 1-2, 1902-1903. London: Kegan Paul, Trench, Trubner, Quaritch, 1902-1903. (viii),60,viii,56 pp, 145 plts (2 color, 9 fldg). Orig boards w/cl spine, rubbed, spine frayed, o/w VG. Ex-lib w/lib number on spine. *WORLDWIDE.* $175

Petrie, W.M. Flinders. GLASS STAMPS AND WEIGHTS WITH ANCIENT WEIGHTS AND MEASURES. 2 vols in 1. Warminster: Aris & Phillips, (1974). 80 plts. Dj. Good. *ARCHAEOLOGIA.* $125

Petrie, W.M. Flinders. KOPTOS. London: Bernard Quaritch, 1896. 28 plts. Bkpl. Good. *ARCHAEOLOGIA.* $450

Petrie, W.M. Flinders. RELIGIOUS LIFE IN ANCIENT EGYPT. London: Constable, 1924. Signature at flyleaf. Good. *AR-CHAEOLOGIA.* $35

Petrie, W.M. Flinders. RESEARCHES IN SINAI. London: John Murray, 1906. 4 maps (1 fldg). Good. *ARCHAEOLOGIA.* $175

Petrie, W.M. Flinders. ROMAN PORTRAITS AND MEMPHIS (IV). London: School of Archaeology, 1911. Good. *ARCHAEOLOGIA.* $200

Petrie, W.M. Flinders. SCARABS AND CYLINDERS WITH NAMES ILLUSTRATED BY THE EGYPTIAN COLLECTION IN UNIVERSITY COLLEGE, LONDON. London: BSAE, 1917. 74 plts, 3/4 cl. Signature. Good. *ARCHAEOLOGIA.* $175

Petrie, W.M. Flinders. TANIS. 2 Parts. 1. 1883-4; 2. NEBESHEH (A M) AND DEFENNEH (TAHPANHES). London: Kegan Paul, Trench, Trubner, 1889, 1888. Part 1 is 2nd ed.; Part 2 is 1st ed. viii,64,44; viii, 116pp, 81 plts (2 fldg). Orig boards w/cl spines, sl worn, spine frayed, part 2 w/back cover detached, o/w VG. Ex-lib w/number on spine. *WORLDWIDE.* $140

Petrie, W.M. Flinders. TEN YEAR'S DIGGING IN EGYPT (1881-1891). NY: Revell, (c. 1892). Frontis, 115 figs, 1 map. Bkpl, tape on reverse of frontis. Good. *ARCHAEOLOGIA.* $45

Petrie, W.M. Flinders. THE FUNERAL FURNITURE OF EGYPT. x + 30pp. AND STONE AND METAL VASES. vii + 35pp, 45 plts. London: BSAE, 1937. 1st ed. Some lib markings, but Good. *AR-CHAEOLOGIA.* $225

Petrie, W.M. Flinders. THE MAKING OF EGYPT. London: Sheldon Press, (1939). 82 plts. Signature. *ARCHAEOLOGIA.* $85

Petrie, W.M. Flinders. THE ROYAL TOMBS OF THE FIRST DYNASTY. VOLS. I-II (only). London: Egypt Exploration Fund, 1900-01. 130 plts (2 color). Orig boards. Bkpl, embossed stamp. Good. *ARCHAEOLOGIA.* $200

Petrie, W.M. Flinders. TOOLS AND WEAPONS ILLUSTRATED BY THE EGYPTIAN COLLECTION IN UNIVERSITY COL-LEGE, LONDON. Warminster: Aris & Phillips, (1974). 79 plts. Dj. Good. *ARCHAEOLOGIA.* $85

Petrie, W.M. Flinders and F.L.L. Griffith. DESHASHEH. London: Kegan Paul, Trench, Trubner, Quaritch, 1898. 1st ed. 52 pp, folio. Frontis, 37 plts (2 fldg). Orig boards w/cl spine, edges rubbed, o/w VG. Ex-lib w/number on spine. *WORLDWIDE.* $65

Petroff, Ivan. REPORT ON THE POPULATION, INDUSTRIES, AND RESOURCES OF ALASKA. Wash: GPO, 1884. 2 fldg maps, 8 plts. Rebound in cl, sl soiled. Some foxing. *PARMER.* $100

Petry, Ann. COUNTRY PLACE. Boston: Houghton Mifflin, (1947). 1st ed. NF in mildly edgeworn, VG dj. *LOPEZ.* $100

Pettersson, Alan Rune. FRANKENSTEIN'S AUNT. Boston: Little, Brown, 1980. 1st Amer ed. Fine in dj. *MORDIDA.* $30

Pettigrew, Thomas. ON SUPERSTITIONS CONNECTED WITH THE HISTORY AND PRACTICE OF MEDICINE AND SURGERY. London, 1844. 1st ed. 167pp. *FYE.* $200

Pettit, Gaylord Joel. TODAY AND YESTERDAY IN NEW ROCHELLE (NEW YORK). NY: William R. Jenkins Co, 1913. Dec cl, teg. VG. *BURCHAM.* $65

Pettit, Michael. CARDINAL POINT. Iowa City: Univ of Iowa Press, (1988). 1st ed. Signed. Fine in Fine dj. *LOPEZ.* $25

Peugnet, Eugene. THE NATURE OF GUNSHOT WOUNDS OF THE ABDOMEN, AND THEIR TREATMENT: BASED ON A REVIEW OF THE CASE OF THE LATE JAMES FISK, JR., IN ITS MEDICO-LEGAL ASPECTS. NY, 1874. 1st ed. Backstrip worn and partially missing. Contents VG. *FYE.* $175

Peyton, John Lewis. HISTORY OF AUGUSTA COUNTY, VIR-GINIA. Staunton, VA: Yost, 1882. 1st ed. (7),387,(7)pp. Orig cl, inner hinges strengthened, emb lib stamp, paper label on spine. Howes P277. "From the author" on front flyleaf. *GINSBERG.* $150

Peyton, John Lewis. RAMBLING REMINISCENCES...ENGLAND AND GUERNSEY. S.M. Yost & Son, 1888. 298pp. Good+. *BOOK BROKER.* $30

Peyton, John Lewis. THE ADVENTURES OF MY GRANDFATHER. WITH EXTRACTS FROM HIS LET-TERS...BIOGRAPHICAL SKETCHES OF HIMSELF AND HIS SON....NY: Argonaut, 1966. Orig cl. Reprint of rare London 1867 ed. Howes P275. *GINSBERG.* $25

Pfaff, Richard William. MONTAGUE RHODES JAMES. London: Scolar Press, (1980). 1st ed. Dj. *OAK KNOLL.* $45

Pfeiffer, Ida. A JOURNEY TO ICELAND, AND TRAVELS IN SWEDEN AND NORWAY. NY, 1852. 1st ed. Charlotte Cooper (trans). Uniform foxing. VG. *ARTIS.* $75

Pfleuger, Donald H. (ed). CHARLES C. CHAPMAN: THE CAREER OF A CREATIVE CALIFORNIAN, 1853-1944. LA: Anderson, Ritchie & Simon, 1976. Gold-stamped cl. *DAWSON'S.* $50

Pfuhl, Ernst. MASTERPIECES OF GREEK DRAWING AND PAINTING. Trans J.D. Beazley. London: Chatto and Windus, 1926. Good. *ARCHAEOLOGIA.* $65

PHALLIC MISCELLANIES. N.p.: Privately ptd. 1891. (By Hargrave Jennings). viii,102pp. Frontis. Boards somewhat soiled. KARMIOLE. $125

PHANTOM FLOWERS....Boston: Tilton, 1864. 1st ed. Central sig separate, o/w Nice. SECOND LIFE. $45

Phares, Ross. TEXAS TRADITION. NY: Henry Holt & Co, (1954). 1st ed. Boards in dj. DAWSON'S. $40

Phelan, James. HISTORY OF TENNESSEE. Boston/NY: Houghton Mifflin, 1889. Fldg map. Spine faded, inwardly Fine. Ex-lib. HUDSON. $45

Phelps, Capt. William D. FREMONT'S PRIVATE NAVY: THE 1846 JOURNAL OF CAPT. WILLIAM D. PHELPS. Glendale, Clark, 1987. 1st ed. Orig cl. Briton Cooper Busch (ed). One of 500 numbered, signed by Busch. GINSBERG. $40

Phelps, Charles. INJURIES OF THE BRAIN AND ITS MEMBRANES FROM EXTERNAL VIOLENCE WITH A SPECIAL STUDY OF PISTOL-SHOT WOUNDS OF THE HEAD IN THEIR MEDICO-LEGAL AND SURGICAL RELATIONS. NY, 1900. 2nd ed. Scarce. FYE. $200

Phelps, Charles. TRAUMATIC INJURIES OF THE BRAIN AND ITS MEMBRANES. NY, 1897. 1st ed. Full page photo plts. FYE. $250

Phelps, Richard H. NEWGATE OF CONNECTICUT....Hartford: Amer Pub, 1895. Fine. SECOND LIFE. $35

Phelps, S. Dryden. HOLY LAND WITH GLIMPSES OF EUROPE AND EGYPT A YEAR'S TOUR. NY, 1864. 407pp. O'NEILL. $35

Philby, H.St.J.B. A PILGRIM IN ARABIA. London, 1946. 198pp. Dj. 1st trade ed. O'NEILL. $45

Philby, H.St.J.B. SA'UDI ARABIA. London, 1955. Fldg map. xix,393pp. Dj. 1st ed. O'NEILL. $40

Philby, H.St.J.B. THE LAND OF MIDIAN. London, 1957. xi,286pp. 1st ed. O'NEILL. $60

Philip, Alex J. and W. Lawrence Gadd. A DICKENS DICTIONARY. Gravesend: "The Librarian", 1928. 2nd ed, rev, enl. About Fine in like dj (chip, tear). CAPTAIN'S BOOKSHELF. $50

Philippe, Robert. POLITICAL GRAPHICS. NY, 1982. 1st Eng trans. Fine. POLYANTHOS. $60

Philips, Judson and Thomas Johnson. RED WAR. Doubleday, 1936. 1st ed. MADLE. $35

Phillips, Alan. THE LIVING LEGEND. Boston, (1957). 1st ed. NF. DIAMOND. $15

Phillips, C.J. GLASS: THE MIRACLE MAKER. NY (1941). Dj. HEINOLDT. $25

Phillips, Catherine Coffin. JESSIE BENTON FREMONT: A WOMAN WHO MADE HISTORY. SF: John Henry Nash, 1935. 1st ed. Frontis. Untrimmed. Fine in About Fine dj. CONNOLLY & WADE. $175

Phillips, D(avid) L. LETTERS FROM CALIFORNIA: ITS MOUNTAINS, VALLEYS....Springfield, IL State Journal Co, 1877. (4)viii,171pp. Orig cl w/gilt and black stamping. Lt wear and soiling, extrem frayed. Presentation copy. Lib rubberstamps, sm cover label. Howes P312. BOHLING. $125

Phillips, E.D. GREEK MEDICINE. London: Thames and Hudson, (1973). Good in tattered dj. ARCHAEOLOGIA. $65

Phillips, Henry. AN ACCOUNT OF THE CONGO INDEPENDENT STATE. Phila, 1889. Fldg map. Orig cl. Fine. McGOWAN. $85

Phillips, James Duncan. SALEM AND THE INDIES. Boston: Houghton Mifflin Co, 1947. Large paper ed ltd to 225 numbered, signed. Fine. KARMIOLE. $60

Phillips, Jane. MOJO HAND. NY: Trident, 1966. 1st ed. A few spots at lower edge, o/w Fine in bit used dj w/light stains. BEASLEY. $65

Phillips, Jayne Anne. BLACK TICKETS. NY: Delacorte, (1979). Uncorrected proof. Lt spot fore-edge, else Fine in ptd wraps. CAPTAIN'S BOOKSHELF. $200

Phillips, Jayne Anne. FAST LANES. Drawings by Yvonne Jacquette. (NY): Vehicle Editions, (1984). 1st ed. Fine in wrappers. Signed by Phillips and Jacquette. CAPTAIN'S BOOKSHELF. $100

Phillips, Jayne Anne. FAST LANES. NY: Vehicle/Brooke Alexander, 1984. 1/26 lettered bound in paper covered boards. Fine plastic slipcase. BEASLEY. $250

Phillips, Jayne Anne. HOW MICKEY MADE IT. St. Paul: Bookslinger, 1981. Wraps. 1/1000. Fine. BEASLEY. $15

Phillips, Jayne Anne. HOW MICKEY MADE IT. St. Paul: Bookslinger, 1981. 1st ed. 1/150 clothbound numbered, signed. Fine. CAPTAIN'S BOOKSHELF. $100

Phillips, Jayne Anne. HOW MICKEY MADE IT. St. Paul: Bookslinger Editions, 1981. 1st ed. One of 1000 in wrappers. Signed. NF in wrappers. ROBBINS. $75

Phillips, Jayne Anne. MACHINE DREAMS. NY: Dutton, (1984). 1st Amer ed. Inscribed. Fine in dj. DORN. $40

Phillips, Jayne Anne. MACHINE DREAMS. NY: Dutton/Lawrence, (1984). 1st ed. Signed. Fine in Fine dj. LOPEZ. $50

Phillips, Jayne Anne. MACHINE DREAMS. NY: E.P. Dutton, (1984). Uncorrected proof. Fine in wrappers. CAPTAIN'S BOOKSHELF. $75

Phillips, Jayne Anne. SWEETHEARTS. Carrboro: Truck Press, 1976. 1st ed. About Fine in wrappers. CAPTAIN'S BOOKSHELF. $150

Phillips, Jayne Anne. THE SECRET COUNTRY. (Winston-Salem, NC): Palaemon Press, (1982). 1st ed. 1/50 Roman-numeraled copies signed. Fine w/o dj, as issued. CAPTAIN'S BOOKSHELF. $150

Phillips, Lance. YONDER COMES THE TRAINS. NY, 1965, 1st ed. Dj. HEINOLDT. $30

Phillips, M. and W.S. Tomkinson. ENGLISH WOMEN IN LIFE & LETTERS. Oxford Univ Press, 1926. 1st ed. Dj top torn, o/w VG. Scarce. WEBER. $50

Phillips, Montagu L. WORLDS BEYOND THE EARTH. London: Richard Bentley, 1855. Rebound. Old moisture stains on one plt and page margins. KNOLLWOOD. $45

Phillips, Paul. MEDICINE IN THE MAKING OF MONTANA. Missoula: MSU, 1962. 1st ed. Frontis. Fine in VG dj. OREGON. $80

Phillips, Paul. THE FUR TRADE. 2 vols. Norman: Univ of OK, (1967). 2nd ptg. Part of brown portion of label area vol 2 rubbed off. VG in Fine slipcase. OREGON. $100

Phillips, T.E.R. and W.H. Steavenson (eds). SPLENDOUR OF THE HEAVENS, A POPULAR AUTHORITATIVE ASTRONOMY. NY: Robert M. McBride, 1931. Gilt illus blue cl, somewhat spotted & faded, spine darkened. KNOLLWOOD. $200

Phillips, Ulrich Bonnell (ed). NINTH REPORT OF THE HISTORICAL MANUSCRIPT COMMISSION—THE CORRESPONDENCE OF ROBERT TOOMBS, ALEXANDER H. STEPHENS AND HOWELL COBB. Washington, 1913. Ex-lib U.S. Senate. Minor cvr soiling o/w Fine. PRATT. $35

Phillips, William B. IRON MAKING IN ALABAMA. Univ of AL, 1912. 3rd ed. NF. POLYANTHOS. $35

Phillips-Birt, Douglas. THE BUILDING OF BOATS. Partridge Green: Maurice Michael, c. 1979. Some minor flaws, overall VG+ in similar dj. PARMER. $25

Philpotts, Eden. SAURUS. London, 1938. 1st ed. VG. MADLE. $60

Phippen, Francis. AUTHENTIC MEMOIRS OF EDMUND KEAN....London: J.Roach, 1814. 1st (only) ed. Contemp 1/2 calf;

spine ends worn; morocco label; lt dampstaining head of cvrs, text. Rare. *DRAMATIS*. $400

Phisterer, Frederick (comp). NEW YORK IN THE WAR OF THE REBELLION, 1860-1865. 5 vols & index. Albany, 1912. Shelfwear o/w VG+. *PRATT*. $300

Piankoff, Alexander. THE TOMB OF RAMESSES VI. Alexander Piankoff (trans), N. Rambova (ed). Bollingen Series XL. NY: Pantheon Books. (1954). 1st ed. 2 vols (text and plts). Plt portfolio contains 196 loose collotype plts. 2 color facs plts. Separate "lists of plts." Slipcase. *KARMIOLE*. $350

PICASSO 347. NY: Maecenal Press, 1970. 2 octavos in velvet-lined box. Engr. Fine. *POLYANTHOS*. $350

Picasso, Pablo. DESIRE. A PLAY. NY: Philosophical Library, 1948.1st ed. Fine w/owner's name hidden by dj flap, in NF dj w/tiny chip. *BEASLEY*. $45

Picasso, Pablo. HUNK OF SKIN. (SF): City Lights, (1968). 1st US ed. Fine in wraps. *CAPTAIN'S BOOKSHELF*. $30

Picasso, Pablo. SKETCHBOOK. NY: Atlantic Monthly Press, 1986. 1st ed. *SMITH*. $35

Pichon, Baron Jerome. THE LIFE OF CHARLES HENRY COUNT HOYM...1694-1736. NY: The Grolier Club, 1899. Ltd to 303. Orig 1/2 morocco over brocaded cl sides. Some wear to edges of binding and spine ends. *OAK KNOLL*. $100

Pickard, Madge and Carlyle Buley. THE MIDWEST PIONEER: HIS ILLS, CURES, & DOCTORS. NY, 1946. 1st ed. Dj. *FYE*. $40

Pickard, Nancy. MARRIAGE IS MURDER. NY: Scribner, 1987. 1st ed. Review copy, signed. Pub's slip laid in. Fine in dj. *SILVER DOOR*. $35

Pickell, John. A NEW CHAPTER IN THE EARLY LIFE OF WASHINGTON, IN CONNECTION WITH THE NARRATIVE HISTORY....NY: Appleton, 1856. (xii), (17), 178pp. Orig cl. Spine top frayed, upper 1/4 of title pg thinned from erasure, some foxing. Clean & bright. Howes P335. *BOHLING*. $125

Pickell, John. NEW CHAPTER IN THE EARLY LIFE OF WASHINGTON...NARRATIVE HISTORY OF THE POTOMAC COMPANY. NY: Appleton, 1856. 1st ed. 178pp. Orig cl, a few chips on backstrip. Howes P335. *GINSBERG*. $150

Pickering, W.H. THE MOON, A SUMMARY OF THE EXISTING KNOWLEDGE OF OUR SATELLITE, WITH A COMPLETE PHOTOGRAPHIC ATLAS. NY: Doubleday, Page, 1904 (1902). 100 b/w plts. Worn pict cl; corners worn to boards, top & bottom of spine frayed, extrems worn, internally clean & bright. *KNOLLWOOD*. $95

Pickett, A. St. J. THE SUBLIME TRAGEDY OF THE LOST CAUSE. Columbus, 1884. 1st ed. Wear to spine ends, cloth lightly rubbed, else VG. *McGOWAN*. $150

Pickett, George M. SOLDIER OF THE SOUTH. Boston, (1928). Arthur Crew Inman (ed). Rprt of 1913 THE HEART OF A SOLDIER w/add'l material. Fine. *PRATT*. $45

Pickwell, G. AMPHIBIANS AND REPTILES OF THE PACIFIC STATES. Stanford Univ, 1949. 2nd ptg. NF in VG+ dj. *MIKESH*. $37.50

Pickwell, G. AMPHIBIANS AND REPTILES OF THE PACIFIC STATES. Stanford, (1947). 64 plts. Inscrip inked out on ep. *SUTTON*. $27

Pickwell, G. DESERTS. NY: Whittlesey House, 1939. 1st ed. Desert Magazine stamp, bkpl. VG. *CONNOLLY & WADE*. $45

PICTORIAL HUMOR OF THE GOLD RUSH. Bk Club of CA, (1953). 1st ed. 12 repros of drwgs, each in brochure w/text. Cl folder in slipcase, gilt-stamped leather labels on spine. Fine. *AUTHORS OF THE WEST*. $75

PICTORIAL OREGON: THE WONDERLAND. Portland: Portland Press Club, 1915. White-stamped cl, somewhat loose, one leaf detached, wear to binding. *DAWSON'S*. $40

Pienkowski, Jan. HAUNTED HOUSE. London, 1979. Lokvig (eng). Pop-up bk. *BOOKFINDERS INTL*. $60

Pienkowski, Jan. LITTLE MONSTERS. (1981). Pop-up bk. *BOOKFINDERS INTL*. $10

Pienkowski, Jan. ROBOT. London, 1981. James Diaz (eng). Pop-up bk. *BOOKFINDERS INTL*. $50

Pierce, Rev. James W. STORY OF TURKEY AND ARMENIA. Baltimore, 1896. Light cover soil. Orig dec cl. *O'NEILL*. $35

Pierce, Wesley George. GOIN' FISHIN': THE STORY OF THE DEEP-SEA FISHERMEN OF NEW ENGLAND. Salem, 1934. Pub. 26. Fine in worn dj. *LEFKOWICZ*. $75

Piersall, Jim and Al Hirshberg. FEAR STRIKES OUT. Atlantic, Little-Brown, 1955. 1st ed. Good+. *PLAPINGER*. $17.50

Piersol, George (ed). HUMAN ANATOMY INCLUDING STRUCTURE AND DEVELOPMENT. Phila, 1907. 1st ed. 2 vols. 1734 woodcut illus. Backstrips chipped, hinges cracked. *FYE*. $50

Pigman, Walter. THE JOURNAL OF WALTER GRIFFITH PIGMAN. Mexico, MO, 1942. 1st ed, ltd to 200. 82pp. Orig blue paper board w/ptd paper label. Ulla S. Fawkes (ed). Howes P361. *GINSBERG*. $150

Pijl. L. van der and C.H. Dodson. ORCHID FLOWERS, THEIR POLLINATION AND EVOLUTION. Coral Gables, 1966. 12 colored plts. Cl, chipped dj. *SUTTON*. $47

Pike, James. THE SCOUT AND RANGER. Cincinnati, 1865. 1st ed. 394,(395 errata)pp. Frontis. Smooth black cl, emb borders and monograms in blind on sides, title in plain block gilt on backstrip. VG. Rarely found in orig binding. Howes P369. *GINSBERG*. $1250

Pike, James. THE SCOUT AND RANGER. Cincinnati, 1865, 1st ed, 1st issue. 12,19,394pp; 24 plts; errata pg. Bound in 3/4 leather, emb front & back cvrs. Sm hole margin pg 297, no text affected. Sm tear repaired pg 59. Contents VG. *HEINOLDT*. $500

Pike, Zebulon M. THE EXPEDITIONS OF ZEBULON MONTGOMERY PIKE...DURING THE YEARS 1805-6-7. A NEW EDITION...WITH COPIOUS CRITICAL COMMENTARY...BY ELLIOT COUES. NY: Harper, 1895. Best ed. 3 vols. (8,114),356; (6),357-856; (6),857-955pp. 7 maps. Orig cl. Howes P373. *GINSBERG*. $600

Pike, Zebulon M. THE JOURNALS OF ZEBULON MONTGOMERY PIKE, WITH LETTERS. 2 vols. Norman: Univ of OK, (1966). Donald Jackson (ed). 72 plts, 6 fldg maps. 1st ed. VF in VF slipcase. *OREGON*. $120

Pike, Zebulon M. ZEBULON PIKE'S ARKANSAW JOURNAL...HIS NEWLY RECOVERED MAPS. Stephen Hart & Archer B. Hulbert (eds). Colorado Springs: Stewart Comm, (1932). Frontis, 6 plts. VG. Howes H259. *OREGON*. $100

Pilcher, Lewis. A LIST OF BOOKS BY SOME OF THE OLD MASTERS OF MEDICINE AND SURGERY TOGETHER WITH BOOKS ON THE HISTORY OF MEDICINE AND ON MEDICAL BIOGRAPHY...Brooklyn, 1918. Ltd ed of 250. 201pp. VF. *FYE*. $250

Pilcher, Lewis. THE TREATMENT OF WOUNDS, ITS PRINCIPLES AND PRACTICE GENERAL AND SPECIAL. NY, 1883. 1st ed. 116 engrvs. *FYE*. $100

Pinchbeck, Ivy and Margaret Hewitt. CHILDREN IN ENGLISH SOCIETY. London, 1969. 1st ed. 2 vols. Dj. *FYE*. $75

Pinchon, Edgcumb. DAN SICKLES, HERO OF GETTYSBURG AND "YANKEE KING OF SPAIN." GC, 1945. 1st ed. Dj wear and chipping o/w VG+. *PRATT*. $22.50

Pinckney, Charles. THREE LETTERS, WRITTEN, AND ORIGINALLY PUBLISHED, UNDER THE SIGNATURE OF A SOUTH CAROLINA PLANTER. Phila: Aurora Office, 1799. Bound in 3/4 leather with marbled paper over boards. Marbled eps. 8vo, 69pp. Some internal foxing, wear to spine. *PARMER.* $195

Pinckney, James D. REMINISCENCES OF CATSKILL. Catskill: Hall, 1868. 1st ed. 79pp. Orig gold stamped cl, expertly rebacked and recased. Howes P379. *GINSBERG.* $125

Pine, George. BEYOND THE WEST, AN ACCOUNT OF TWO YEARS TRAVEL IN...THE OLD WEST, ON THE PLAINS, IN THE ROCKY MOUNTAINS....Utica, NY: T.J. Griffith, 1871. 2nd ed rev, enl. 19 plts. Orig emb cl edgeworn. Good+. *OREGON.* $95

Pinkerton, Allan. BANK-ROBBERS AND THE DETECTIVES. NY: G.W. Carleton & Co. 1883. 1st ed. 340pp.+8pp ads, frontis. *KARMIOLE.* $45

Pinkerton, Allan. CLAUDE MELNOTTE AS A DETECTIVE AND OTHER STORIES. Chicago, 1875. 1st Amer ed. Woodcut plates. Little corner & spine tip wear. Contents VG. Tipped-in ptd slip: "Compliments of Wm. A. Pinkerton/ Robt. A. Pinkerton." *DIAMOND.* $75

Pinkerton, Allan. MODEL TOWN AND DETECTIVES: BYRON AS A DETECTIVE. NY: G.W. Carlton, 1876. 1st ed. 288, 10pp engr. Grn w/black and gilt. Sl staining and rubbing, else VG. *CONNOLLY & WADE.* $125

Pinkerton, Allan. THE SPY OF THE REBELLION, BEING A TRUE HISTORY OF THE SPY SYSTEM....Carleton, 1983. 1st ed. 23 plts. Some foxing, o/w VG. *OREGON.* $45

PINOCCHIO. London, 1981. Pop-up bk. *BOOKFINDERS INTL.* $30

Pinter, Harold. LANDSCAPE AND SILENCE. London: Methuen, 1969. Uncorrected proof. Tan wrappers. Fine. *JUVELIS.* $60

Pinter, Harold. LANDSCAPE. London: Emanuel Wax for Pendragon Press, 1968. 1st ed. 1/2000 signed. Fine, w/o dj as issued. *JUVELIS.* $75

Pinter, Harold. MONOLOGUE. (London: Covent Garden Press, 1973.) 1st ed. 1/100, signed. Fine in tan calf in slipcase. *JUVELIS.* $150

Pinter, Harold. THE BIRTHDAY PARTY AND OTHER PLAYS. London: Methuen & Co., (1960). 1st ed. Orig black cl. NF in VG dj, minor wear spine ends. *CHAPEL HILL.* $200.

Pinter, Harold. THE DWARFS. London: London Limited Editions, (1990). 1st ed. One of 150. Cl backed marbled boards, tissue dj. Mint. *JAFFE.* $125

Pinter, Harold. THE FRENCH LIEUTENANT'S WOMAN: A SCREENPLAY. Boston: Little Brown, (1981). One of 350 numbered. Signed by Pinter and John Fowles. Fine in cl slipcase. *LOPEZ.* $125

Pinter, Harold. THE FRENCH LIEUTENANT'S WOMAN: A SCREENPLAY. John Fowles (foreword). Boston: Little, Brown, (1981). 1st ed. #16 of specially bound ltd ed, signed by Fowles and Pinter. Mint in slipcase, orig plastic shrinkwrap. *CHAPEL HILL.* $225

Pinter, Howard. THE FRENCH LIEUTENANT'S WOMAN: A SCREENPLAY. Boston: Little, Brown (1981). 1st ed. Fine in dj. *DORN.* $45

Pinto, Edward H. TREEN OR SMALL WOODWARE THROUGHOUT THE AGES. London: B.T. Batsford Ltd. (1949). 1st ed. Spine extrems frayed. Dj spine chipped. *KARMIOLE.* $35

PIONEER WESTERN PLAYBILLS. Bk Club of CA, (1951). 1st ed of 850. 12 tinted playbills each in brochure w/text. Cl folder in slipcase, gilt-stamped leather labels on spine. Fine. *AUTHORS OF THE WEST.* $75

Piozzi, Hester Lynch. ANECDOTES OF THE LATE SAMUEL JOHNSON during the Last Twenty Years of His Life. London: Cadell, 1786. 3rd ed. 307pp. Early calf, nicely rebacked, gilt on red lea label. Bkpl. VG. *HARTFIELD.* $295

Piper, H. Beam. MURDER IN THE GUN ROOM. NY: Knopf, 1953. 1st ed, 1st bk. Name. Fine, minor edgewear to the dj. *ELSE FINE.* $250

Piper, Watty. THE ROAD IN STORYLAND. Platt & Munk, (1952). 4to. Illus by Lucille & H.C. Holling. Abrasion to corner of front fly, else VG in VG dj w/slight wear. *BEBBAH.* $40

PIQUET AND CRIBBAGE. By Aquarius. London: (Allen), 1883. Pub's dk grn cl w/gilt titling, picture; teg. Fine. *BOOK BLOCK.* $45

Pirnie, Miles David. MICHIGAN WATERFOWL MANAGEMENT. Lansing, 1935. 1st ed. Fold-out maps. VG. *ARTIS.* $45

Pitkin, Winifred. HIDDEN CITIES OF MIDDLE AMERICA. THE ARCHAEOLOGICAL ADVENTURES OF A SEPTUAGENARIAN. Glasgow: William Maclellan, (1959). Frontis. Dj. Good. *ARCHAEOLOGIA.* $27.50

Pitman, C.R.S. A GAME WARDEN TAKES STOCK (UGANDA). London: J. Nisbet, (April 1945). Fldg map; 37 full page sepia photos. Good+. *MIKESH.* $45

Pitt, William, Earl of Chatham. ANECDOTES OF THE LIFE OF THE RIGHT HONOURABLE WILLIAM PITT. London: J.S. Jordan, 1793. 3rd ed, corrected. 3 vols. Contemp full flame calf w/morocco spine labels. Couple of joints a little weak, corners bumped on Vol I. VG. *CHAPEL HILL.* $200

Pittman, Capt. Philip. THE PRESENT STATE OF THE EUROPEAN SETTLEMENTS ON THE MISSISSIPPI...ILLUSTRATED BY PLANS AND DRAUGHTS...Cleveland: Clark, 1906. Facs reprint of 1770 London ed. One of 500 numbered. Frank Heywood Hodder (ed). Orig cl, a few spots and speckles. Howes P396. *GINSBERG.* $125

Pitz, Henry. ILLUSTRATING CHILDREN'S BOOKS. NY: Watson-Guptill, (1963). 2nd ed. 19 full color plts. NF in VG dj. *ACADEMIC LIBRARY.* $45

Pitz, Henry. THE PRACTICE OF ILLUSTRATION. NY: Watson-Guptill, (1947). 1st ed. Cloth. *ARTIS.* $37.50

Planche, James Robinson. RECOLLECTIONS AND REFLECTIONS. London: Sampson Low, Marston, 1901. New and rev ed. 8vo, 464pp, illus, red cloth, bkpl laid in. Fine. *GREAT EXPECTATIONS.* $25

Planta, Joseph. THE HISTORY OF THE HELVETIC CONFEDERACY. London, 1807. 2nd ed. 3 vols. 3/4 lea. VG-NF. *POLYANTHOS.* $150

Plante, David. SLIDES. London: MacDonald, (1971). 1st ed. Fine in dj (2 short internally-mended tears). *CAPTAIN'S BOOKSHELF.* $60

Plante, David. THE GHOST OF HENRY JAMES. Boston: Gambit, 1970. 1st US ed. Fine in dj (sl wear at tips). *CAPTAIN'S BOOKSHELF.* $75

Plante, David. THE GHOST OF HENRY JAMES. Boston: Gambit, 1970. 1st US ed, 1st book. Fine in close to Fine dj. *BEASLEY.* $85

Plath, Sylvia. CHILD. (Exeter: Rougemont, 1971). One of 325. Wraps. Fine. *WOOLMER.* $75

Plath, Sylvia. CROSSING THE WATER. NY: Harper & Row, (1971). Uncorrected proof of 1st Amer ed. Spiral-bound ptd wraps. VG. *JAFFE.* $275

Plath, Sylvia. THE BELL JAR. NY, 1971. 1st US ed. NF in dj. *PETTLER.* $75

Plath, Sylvia. THE BELL JAR. NY: Harper, (1971). 1st Amer ed. VF in dj. *CAPTAIN'S BOOKSHELF.* $125

Plath, Sylvia. THE BELL JAR. NY: Harper & Row, 1971. NF in dj (couple of very shallow chips at crown of spine). 1st Amer ed. *CHAPEL HILL.* $125

Plath, Sylvia. WINTER TREES. London: Faber, (1971). 1st ed. Fine in dj. Owner's sig. *CAPTAIN'S BOOKSHELF.* $50

Plath, Sylvia. WINTER TREES. Unbound proof sheets in proof dj. London: Faber, (1971). Uncorrected proof. Fine. *JAFFE.* $125

Plath, Sylvia. WREATH FOR A BRIDAL. Frensham: Sceptre, (1970). One of 100. Wraps. Fine. *WOOLMER.* $90

Plato. THE TRIAL AND DEATH OF SOCRATES. Benjamin Jowett (trans). Verona: At the Stamperia Valdonega for LEC, 1962. One of 1500 illus, signed by Hans Erni and by Giovanni Mardersteig, the ptr. Fine in dj and slipcase, blemish to paper spine label. *CAPTAIN'S BOOKSHELF.* $200

Platon, Nicholas. ZAKROS: THE DISCOVERY OF A LOST PALACE OF ANCIENT CRETE. NY: Charles Scribner, (1971). Dj. Good. *ARCHAEOLOGIA.* $35

Platt, Kin. THE PRINCESS STAKES MURDER. Random House, 1973. 1st ed. Fine in dj. *STAHR.* $25

Platt, Kin. THE SCREWBALL KING MURDER. NY: Random House, 1978. 1st ed. Fine in dj. *MORDIDA.* $30

Platt, Kin. THE SCREWBALL KING MURDER. Random House, 1978. 1st ed. Fine in dj. *STAHR.* $25

Pleasants, J. Hall and Howard Sill. MARYLAND SILVERSMITHS 1715—1830. MD: Lord Baltimore Press, 1930. #254 of 300. 1st ed. Sl shaken, corners bumped. Bkpl. Fine. *BACKROOM.* $425

Pleasonton, A. J. THE INFLUENCE OF THE BLUE RAY....Phila: Claxton, Remsen & Haffelfinger, 1877. VG in blindstamped, gilt titled blue cl; stain, bumping. *KNOLLWOOD.* $40

Plimpton, George. OUT OF MY LEAGUE. Harper, 1961. 1st ed. Good+ in VG dj. *PLAPINGER.* $25

Plimpton, George. THE BEST OF PLIMPTON. NY: Atlantic Monthly, (1990). 1st ed. Signed. VF in VF dj. *UNGER.* $40

Plimpton, George. THE CURIOUS CASE OF SID FINCH. Franklin Center: Franklin Library, 1987. 1st ed. One of unspecified number signed. Fine in full lea. *BETWEEN COVERS.* $45

Plimpton, George. THE CURIOUS CASE OF SIDD FINCH. NY: Macmillan, (1987). 1st ed. Very find in VF dj. *UNGER.* $35

Plomer, Henry R. WILLIAM CAXTON (1424-1491). London: Leonard Parsons, (1925). 1st ed. 195pp. *OAK KNOLL.* $25

Plues, M. RAMBLES IN SEARCH OF WILD FLOWERS, AND HOW TO DISTINGUISH THEM. London, 1863. 1st ed. 12 of 18 hand colored plts. Orig gilt dec cl, wear to extrems, soiled; sm tear. *SUTTON.* $25

Plumb, Charles. JUDGING FARM ANIMALS. NY: Orange Judd, 1937. VG in torn dj. *AMERICAN BOTANIST.* $25

Plummer, Mark, FRONTIER GOVERNOR, SAMUEL J. CRAWFORD OF KANSAS. Univ of Kansas, (1971). 1st ed. 3 maps. VF in VF dj. *OREGON.* $25

Plummer, William. THE HOLY GOOF: A BIOGRAPHY OF NEAL CASSADY. Englewood Cliffs: Prentice Hall, (1981). 1st ed. Fine in Fine dj. *AKA.* $35

Plumpp, Sterling D. PORTABLE SOUL. (Chicago: Third World Press, 1969). 1st ed. White wrappers bit darkened at extremities, else VG. *BETWEEN COVERS.* $50

POCAHONTAS....BY A CITIZEN OF THE WEST. (By Robert Dale Owen.) NY: George Dearborn, 1837. 1st ed. 12mo, 240pp. Recent 1/4 calf and marbled boards. Foxing, else Nice. *CHAPEL HILL.* $175

Podolsky, Edward. ENCYCLOPEDIA OF ABERRATIONS, A PSYCHIATRIC HANDBOOK. NY, 1953. 1st ed. *FYE.* $50

Podwal, Mark. FREUD'S DA VINCI. NY, 1977. 1st ed. Dj. 40 plts. *FYE.* $50

Poe, Edgar Allan. A CHAPTER ON AUTOGRAPHY. Don C. Seitz (ed). NY: Lincoln MacVeagh, The Dial Press, 1926. 1st ed, ltd to 750, this unnumbered. Orig cl-backed paper-covered boards. Fine in NF dj. *CHAPEL HILL.* $75

Poe, Edgar Allan. EUREKA. NY: Geo. P. Putnam, 1848. 1st ed. 143pp,11,(l)pp ads. Orig dk brn cl. Bkpl, corners a trifle rubbed; spine tips expertly repaired, else clean, tight, VG to NF. Custom cl jacket, buckram slipcase. *CHAPEL HILL.* $3,500

Poe, Edgar Allan. TALES OF MYSTERY AND IMAGINATION. NY, 1925. 1st ed. Illus by Harry Clark w/full-page tipped in color plts, and black & white plts. Sunned, extrems and corners little rubbed, bkpl. *POLYANTHOS.* $120

Poe, Edgar Allan. TALES OF MYSTERY AND IMAGINATION. NY: Tudor Pub Co., 1933. Illus by Harry Clarke. Black cl. 8 tipped-in color plts. Fine in orig box (soiled, repaired). Scarce thus. *BLUE MOUNTAIN.* $250

Poe, Edgar Allan. THE POETICAL WORKS OF EDGAR ALLAN POE. Illus Edmund Dulac. NY: Hodder & Stoughton, (ca. 1912). 1st Amer ed. Blue cl dec in black and gilt. 28 full-page plts. Spine a little dull, else NF. *CAPTAIN'S BOOKSHELF.* $175

Poe, Edgar Allan. THE POETICAL WORKS OF EDGAR ALLAN POE...WITH A NOTICE BY JAMES HANNAY. London: W. Kent & Co, (Late D. Bogue), 1859. Early ed. 185,(3)pp,(4)pp ads. Orig gilt dec grn cl, aeg. Rear hinge starting, couple of signatures pulled, but VG. *CHAPEL HILL.* $50

Poe, Edgar Allan. THE RAVEN. Edmund C. Stedman (comment). Illus Gustave Dore. NY: Harper, 1884. 1st ed thus. 26 plts. Pict cl, worn at corners, spinal extrems; aeg. VG. *CAPTAIN'S BOOKSHELF.* $350

Poe, John W. THE DEATH OF BILLY THE KID. Boston, 1933. 1st ed. VG. *VARNER.* $50

Poe, John W. THE DEATH OF BILLY THE KID. Boston: Houghton Mifflin, 1933. 1st ed. VG. *GIBBS.* $50

Poe, Sophie A. BUCKBOARD DAYS. Ed by Eugene Cunningham. Caldwell, 1936. 1st ed. Top backstrip faded where 3/8" of dj missing, o/w Fine in moderately worn, but nearly complete dj. *BAADE.* $95

POEMS ON SEVERAL OCCASIONS. (By Matthew Prior.) London: Tonson, 1709. 1st authorized ed. Neatly rebacked, contemp calf, little rubbed. Nice. *SECOND LIFE.* $175

Pohanka, Brian C. (ed). NELSON A. MILES, A DOCUMENTARY BIOGRAPHY OF HIS MILITARY CAREER. Glendale, (1985). 1st ed. 327pp. VF in dj. *PRATT.* $32.50

Pohl, Frederik (ed). STAR SCIENCE FICTION STORIES. Ballantine, 1953. 1st ed. VG in chipped dj. *MADLE.* $50

Pohl, Frederik and Cyril Kornbluth. THE SPACE MERCHANTS. Ballantine, 1953. 1st ed. Fine in dj. *MADLE.* $250

Pohl, Frederik. BEYOND THE BLUE EVENT HORIZON. Del Rey, 1980. 1st ed. Fine in dj. *MADLE.* $30

Pohl, Frederik. HEECHEE RENDEZVOUS. Del Rey, 1984. 1st ed. Fine in dj. *MADLE.* $30

Pohl, Frederik. MAN PLUS. Random House, 1976. 1st ed. Fine in dj. *MADLE.* $100

Point, Father Nicolas. WILDERNESS KINGDOM. INDIAN LIFE IN ROCKY MOUNTAINS: 1840-1847. Holt, Rinehart, (1967). Joseph Donnelly (trans). 1st ed. VG in Good+ dj. *OREGON.* $45

Point, Father Nicolas. WILDERNESS KINGDOM: INDIAN LIFE IN THE ROCKY MOUNTAINS 1840-1847. THE JOURNALS. NY: Holt, Rinehart, & Winston, 1967. Joseph P. Donnelly (trans). 1st ed. Frontis. Fine in About Fine dj. *CONNOLLY & WADE.* $95

Pointer, Michael. THE PUBLIC LIFE OF SHERLOCK HOLMES. Newton Abbot: David & Charles, 1975. 1st ed. Fine in dj. *SILVER DOOR.* $35

Poland, H. FUR-BEARING ANIMALS IN NATURE AND COMMERCE. Fold-out map and 16 illus. London, 1892. lvi,392pp. Cloth. Pp tanned; eps browned. *SUTTON.* $65

Poli, Francois. GENTLEMAN CONVICTS. London: Hart-Davis, (1960, 59). 1st Eng ed. Fine- in VG dj. *AARD.* $20

Politi, Leo. SONG OF SWALLOWS. NY: Scribner, 1948. Ltr ptg. Signed, dated w/orig drwg by author. Dj, many chips. *SMITH.* $60

Polito, Robert and Michael McCauley (eds). FIREWORKS. NY: Donald I. Fine, 1988. 1st ed. VF in dj. *MORDIDA.* $25

Polito, Robert and Michael McCauley. FIREWORKS. NY: Fine, 1988. 1st ed. Fine in dj. *SILVER DOOR.* $40

Polk, James K. POLK. THE DIARY OF A PRESIDENT, 1845-1849. Allan Nevins (ed). Longman's, 1929. Frontis, 15 plts. 1st ed. VG. *OREGON.* $40

Polk, James K. TREATY OF GUADALUPE HIDALGO. MESSAGE OF THE PRESIDENT OF THE UNITED STATES. Wash, HED50, 1849. 82pp. Cl w/leather label. Howes M565. *GINSBERG.* $100

Pollard, Alfred W. (ed). BOOKS ABOUT BOOKS. London: Kegan Paul, Trench, Trubner, & Co., 1903-1904. 1st eds. 6 vols, complete. Gold-stamped cloth, sunned and scuffed. *DAWSON'S.* $250

Pollard, H.B.C. A HISTORY OF FIREARMS. London: Geoffrey Bles. 1926. 1st ed. 40 plts. Red cl, gilt; small waterstains on spine. *KARMIOLE.* $125

Pollard, Joseph. THE LAND OF THE MONUMENTS. London: Hodder & Stoughton, 1898. 2nd ed. 15 plts. Sl rubbed, front cover soiled by dampness, o/w VG. *WORLDWIDE.* $35

Pollitt, J.J. THE ART OF ROME C. 753 B.C.-A.D. 337: SOURCES AND DOCUMENTS. Cambridge: Cambridge Univ Press, (1983). Dj. Good. *ARCHAEOLOGIA.* $75

Pollock, Channing. HARVEST OF MY YEARS: AN AUTOBIOGRAPHY. Indianapolis, 1943. 1st ed. Signed, dated presentation. Bkpl. NF. *POLYANTHOS.* $65

Pollock, Sir Frederick (ed). MACREADY'S REMINISCENCES, AND SELECTIONS FROM HIS DIARIES AND LETTERS. NY: Macmillan, 1875. 1st Amer ed. 8vo, 750pp, illus, blue pebbled cloth, bkpl, spine and extremities show wear. Good+. *GREAT EXPECTATIONS.* $27.50

Polo, Marco. THE BOOK OF SER MARCO POLO, THE VENETIAN, CONCERNING THE KINGDOMS...Trans, ed by Henry Yule. London: John Murray, 1875. 2 vols. xl,444; xxi,606pp. 2nd ed, revised. Grn cl stamped in gilt, shaken, rubbed, somewhat discolored. Hinges weak on vol 1. Frontis, chromolitho title pgs, 16 color maps, many fldg. Signed by Charles Denby, Jr. *SCHOYER'S.* $175

Pomeranz, Herman. MEDICINE IN THE SHAKESPEAREAN PLAYS AND DICKENS'S DOCTORS. NY, 1936. 1st ed. *FYE.* $100

Pomeroy, Earl. THE PACIFIC SLOPE: A HISTORY OF CALIFORNIA, OREGON...AND NEVADA. NY: Knopf, 1965. 1st ed. VG in dj. *LAURIE.* $27.50

Pomeroy, H.S. THE ETHICS OF MARRIAGE. NY: Funk & Wagnals, 1888. 1st ed. VG. *SECOND LIFE.* $75

Pomfret, John E. (ed). CALIFORNIA GOLD RUSH VOYAGES, 1848-1849....San Marino: Huntington Library, 1954. 1st ed. Fine in dj. *CONNOLLY & WADE.* $45

Ponafidine, Emma Cochran. MY LIFE IN THE MOSLEM EAST. NY, 1932. 1st ed. Dj. *O'NEILL.* $30

Ponafidine, Pierre. LIFE IN THE MOSLEM EAST. NY: Dodd, Mead, 1911. Dec cl, a little rubbed. *SCHOYER'S.* $85

Poncins, Gotran De. THE GHOST VOYAGE OUT OF ESKIMO LAND. GC: Doubleday, 1954. 1st Amer ed. VG with light fading, dj chipped, worn. *PARMER.* $25

Pond, Irving K. BIG TOP RHYTHMS. Chicago & NY: Willatt, Clark, and Co., 1937. NF in Good dj. *BLUE MOUNTAIN.* $75

Ponicsan, Darryl. GOLDENGROVE. NY: Dial Press, 1971. 1st ed, 2nd book. Fine in dj. *BERNARD.* $20

Ponicsan, Darryl. THE LAST DETAIL. NY: Dial Press, 1970. 1st ed, 1st book. Name o/w NF in VG dj which is rubbed at edges. *BERNARD.* $30

Pool, Eugene and Ralph Stillman. SURGERY OF THE SPLEEN. NY, 1923. 1st ed. *FYE.* $50

Pool, Maria Louise. THE RED-BRIDGE NEIGHBORHOOD. NY: Harper & Bros, 1898. 1st ed. Orig pict cl. Name, else NF. *CHAPEL HILL.* $35

Poole, Lynn and Gray. ONE PASSION, TWO LOVES: THE STORY OF HEINRICH AND SOPHIA SCHLIEMANN, DISCOVERERS OF TROY. NY: Thomas Y. Crowell, (1966). Signature at half title. Good in torn dj. *ARCHAEOLOGIA.* $25

Poor, Charles Lane. MEN AGAINST THE RULE. NY: The Derrydale Press, (1937). Ed ltd to 950 numbered. Fine. *KARMIOLE.* $75

Poor, Henry V. THE PACIFIC RAILROADS, AND THE RELATIONS EXISTING BETWEEN THEM AND THE GOVERNMENT OF THE UNITED STATES. NY, 1879. Abridged ed. 16pp. Orig ptd wrappers. Howes P473. *GINSBERG.* $65

POP-UP BOOK OF GNOMES. London, 1979. Pop-up bk. *BOOK-FINDERS INTL.* $40

Popa, Vasko. HOMAGE TO LAME WOLF. SELECTED POEMS 1956-1975. (Oberlin College): Field Translation Series 2, (1979). 1st ed. Fine in dj. *CAPTAIN'S BOOKSHELF.* $35

Pope, Arthur Upham. AN INTRODUCTION TO PERSIAN ART SINCE THE SEVENTH CENTURY A.D. NY: Scribner, 1931. 1st US ed. 103 plts, fldg map. Orig cl, in torn dj. VG. *WORLDWIDE.* $65

Pope, Arthur Upham. MASTERPIECES OF PERSIAN ART. NY: Dryden, 1945. 1st ed. 155 plts. Orig boards w/cl spine, in worn orig cardboard slipcase. VG. *WORLDWIDE.* $70

Pope, Arthur Upham. MAXIM LITVINOFF. NY: L.B. Fischer, 1943. 2nd ed. Hinge starting, but tight. VG. *AKA.* $20

Pope, C.H. SNAKES ALIVE AND HOW THEY LIVE. NY, 1937. Spine ends faded, in chipped dj. *SUTTON.* $30

Pope, C.H. THE GIANT SNAKES, THE NATURAL HISTORY OF THE BOA CONSTRICTOR, THE ANACONDA & THE LARGEST PYTHONS. NY, 1961. 1st ed. VG. *MIKESH.* $30

Pope, Edwin. TED WILLIAMS—THE GOLDEN YEAR 1957. Prentice-Hall, 1970. 1st ed. VG in Fine dj. *PLAPINGER.* $40

Pope-Hennessy, James. SINS OF THE FATHERS. A STUDY OF THE ATLANTIC SLAVE TRADERS. 1441-1807. NY: Alfred A. Knopf, 1968. 1st Amer ed. VG in lt worn dj. *PARMER.* $30

Pope-Hennessy, John. ITALIAN HIGH RENAISSANCE AND BAROQUE SCULPTURE. (London): Phaidon Press, 1963. 1st ed. 3 vols. 168 plts. Orig blue cl, gilt spines. Good in dj's. *KARMIOLE.* $175

POPEYE & OLIVE OYL. London, 1963. 3 pop-ups. Pop-up bk. *BOOK-FINDERS INTL.* $45

Poppoff, Irmis B. GURDJIEFF. NY: Vantage Press, (1969). 1st ed. VG in G+ dj. *BLUE DRAGON.* $27.50

Porter, Arthur A. JOHN PORTER AND HIS DESCENDANTS. Portage, WI, 1933. 1st ed. Orig printed wrappers w/ties. *GINSBERG.* $75

Porter, Burton B. ONE OF THE PEOPLE: HIS OWN STORY. (Colton, CA ?), pub by author, (1907). 1st ed. (7),382pp. Orig cl. *GINSBERG.* $125

Porter, Clyde and Mae Reed Porter. MATT FIELD ON THE SANTA FE TRAIL. Norman: Univ of OK Press, (1960). 1st ed. John E. Sunder (ed). Cl, dj. Fine. *SCHOYER'S.* $40

Porter, Ebenezer. THE RHETORICAL READER. NY: Mark H. Newman & Co., 1851. Full lea, hinges starting, foxing. *OLD LONDON.* $40

Porter, Eliot. ALL UNDER HEAVEN: THE CHINESE WORLD WITH TEXT BY JONATHAN PORTER. NY: Pantheon Books, (1983). 1st ed. Ltd to 250 signed, w/orig signed color photo laid in. Cl, cl fldg box. VF. *JAFFE.* $600

Porter, Eliot. APPALACHIAN WILDERNESS. NY: Dutton, 1970. Fine copy in dj with long but unobtrusive tear on front panel. *LOPEZ.* $135

Porter, Eliot. APPALACHIAN WILDERNESS. NY: Dutton (1970). 1st ed. Fine in dj. *DORN.* $150

Porter, Eliot. DOWN THE COLORADO, JOHN WESLEY POWELL DIARY...FIRST TRIP THROUGH THE GRAND CANYON. ELIOT PORTER PHOTOGRAPHS AND EPILOGUE 1969. Dutton, 1969. 1st ed. VF in Fine dj. *OREGON.* $85

Porter, Eliot. DOWN THE COLORADO. JOHN WESLEY POWELL—DIARY OF THE FIRST TRIP THROUGH THE GRAND CANYON. NY, 1969. 1st ed. Orange cl, 168pp. 1st ed. Fine in VG+ dj. *FIVE QUAIL.* $90

Porter, Eliot. ELIOT PORTER'S SOUTHWEST. NY: Holt, Rinehart and Winston, (1985). 1st ed. Photos, cl w/dj. Fine. *SCHOYER'S.* $45

Porter, Eliot. IN WILDNESS IS THE PRESERVATION OF THE WORLD. Sierra Club, (1962). 1st ed. Exhibit Format Series, #4. VG in VG dj. *OREGON.* $40

Porter, Eliot. THE PLACE NO ONE KNEW, GLEN CANYON ON THE COLORADO. Sierra Club, (1963). 1st ed. Exhibit Format Series, #5. VG in VG dj. *OREGON.* $125

Porter, Eliot. THE PLACE NO ONE KNEW. GLEN CANYON ON THE COLORADO. Ed by David Brower. SF, Sierra Club, 1966. 1st ed. Folio exhibit format, orange cl, heavy glossy stock dj. 159pp. On second blank fly and the half-title page, the owner mounted, in neat triangular corner mounts, 16 color photos taken during a visit to Glen and Rainbow Bridge in 1961. Dj w/chipping along spine head and back edge. Book itself, except for mounted photos, is NF in Good+ dj. *FIVE QUAIL.* $125

Porter, Horace. CAMPAIGNING WITH GRANT. NY: Century, 1897. 1st ptg. Contemp full sheep w/2 red leather spine labels. *SCHOYER'S.* $50

Porter, John B. IF I MAKE MY BED IN HELL. Waco, TX: Word Books, (1969). 1st ed. About Fine in shelfworn dj w/short tear, price clipped. *AKA.* $40

Porter, Joyce. DOVER TWO. London: Cape, 1965. 1st ed. Fine in NF dj. Name. *ELSE FINE.* $30

Porter, Katherine Anne. A CHRISTMAS STORY. Delacorte, (1967). 1st ptg. Illus Ben Shahn. VG+ in VG+ dj w/1 short closed tear. *BEBBAH.* $45

Porter, Katherine Anne. FLOWERING JUDAS AND OTHER STORIES. NY: Harcourt, (1935). 1st augmented ed. Fine in attractive, lightly edgeworn dj. Inscribed. *CAPTAIN'S BOOKSHELF.* $500

Porter, Katherine Anne. FLOWERING JUDAS AND OTHER STORIES. NY: Harcourt, Brace and Co, (c1935). 1st state of copyright pg w/Harcourt Brace copyright. Rev copy, rev info stamped on ffep. Fine in torn jacket missing 1" piece foot of backstrip. *HELLER.* $150

Porter, Katherine Anne. FLOWERING JUDAS AND OTHER STORIES. NY: Harcourt, Brace, (1935). 1st trade ed, 4 stories not in ltd ed of 1930. Orig beige cl. Owner sig under front flap, else Fine in VG dj, couple of tape mends on verso. *CHAPEL HILL.* $125

Porter, Katherine Anne. FRENCH SONG BOOK. (Paris:) Harrison of Paris, (1933). 1st ed. Signed, 1/595 on Van Gelder. Blue boards and maroon cl spine, teg, dj chipped at top, 2" piece missing from bottom edge, bkpl. Fine in Good+ dj. *JUVELIS.* $250

Porter, Katherine Anne. HACIENDA. (NY): Harrison of Paris (1934). 1/895 numbered. VF in orig pub's slipcase. *LOPEZ.* $100

Porter, Katherine Anne. HACIENDA. Harrison of Paris, (1934). 1st ltd numbered ed of 895. Pg 52 corrected. Teg. VG+. *AUTHORS OF THE WEST.* $35

Porter, Katherine Anne. HACIENDA. Paris: Harrison of Paris, 1934. 1st ed. 1/895 signed. Fine in used pub's case. *JUVELIS.* $180

Porter, Katherine Anne. PALE HORSE, PALE RIDER: THREE SHORT NOVELS. London: Cape, (1939). 1st Eng ed. Grn cl stamped in blue. Fine in sl soiled, price clipped, torn dj. *HELLER.* $100

Porter, Katherine Anne. SHIP OF FOOLS. Boston: Atlantic Monthly Press/Little, Brown, (1962). 1st ed. Orig yellow cl. Fine in dj. Signed. *CHAPEL HILL.* $150

Porter, Katherine Anne. SHIP OF FOOLS. Boston: Atlantic-Little Brown, 1962. 1st ed. Fine in Fine dj, short tear rear panel. *BEASLEY.* $50

Porter, Katherine Anne. THE COLLECTED STORIES OF KATHERINE ANNE PORTER. NY: Harcourt Brace & World (1965). 1st ed. Fine in NF dj. *LOPEZ.* $50

Porter, Katherine Anne. THE COLLECTED STORIES OF KATHERINE ANNE PORTER. NY: Harcourt, (1965). 1st ed. Fine in dj (few tiny edge tears). *CAPTAIN'S BOOKSHELF.* $65

Porter, Katherine Anne. THE COLLECTED STORIES. Harcourt, Brace & World, 1965. 1st Amer ed. Fine in price-clipped dj. *STAHR.* $60

Porter, Katherine Anne. THE DAYS BEFORE. Harcourt Brace, (1952). 1st ed. Fine in dj. *AUTHORS OF THE WEST.* $35

Porter, Katherine Anne. THE LEANING TOWER AND OTHER STORIES. NY: Harcourt, Brace, (1944). 1st ed. Orig beige cl. NF in VG dj, few sm chips, tears. *CHAPEL HILL.* $40

Porter, Katherine Anne. THE LEANING TOWER AND OTHER STORIES. Harcourt, Brace, (1944). 1st ed. Fine, name. *AUTHORS OF THE WEST.* $25

Porter, Russell Williams. THE ARCTIC DIARY OF RUSSELL WILLIAMS PORTER. Charlottesville: Univ Press of VA, (1976). Herman Friis (ed). Cl in dj, lt soiling. *DAWSON'S.* $50

PORTLAND CITY DIRECTORY FOR 1872. Portland: S.J. Mc-Cormick, 1872. xxviii,190pp, ads throughout, 8 1/2" x 5 5/8" boards ptd w/adverts. Cl spine, joints frayed, binding starting to detach at rear of book, some light stain. *DAWSON'S.* $200

PORTLAND SOLDIERS AND SAILORS. A BRIEF SKETCH OF THE PART THEY TOOK IN THE WAR OF THE REBELLION. Portland, 1884. 1st ed. Wrappers. Fine. *McGOWAN.* $75

Portoghesi, Paolo. THE ROME OF BORROMINI: ARCHITECTURE AS LANGUAGE. NY: George Braziller, (1968). 1st US ed. Fine (owner sig) in dj w/sm chip; in slipcase. *CAPTAIN'S BOOKSHELF.* $175

PORTRAIT AND BIOGRAPHICAL ALBUM OF PEORIA COUNTY, ILLINOIS. Chicago: Biographical Pub Co., 1890. Leather quite scuffed, front board detached, backstrip torn. Interior clean, tight. *BOHLING.* $110

Posey, Jake. LAST OF THE 40-HORSE DRIVERS. NY: Vantage, 1959. Inscribed. *DAWSON'S.* $35

Post, Marie Caroline. THE LIFE AND MEMOIRS OF COMTE REGIS de TROBRIAND, MAJOR-GENERAL IN THE ARMY OF THE UNITED STATES. NY, 1910. 1st ed. Inscribed by de Trobriand's great-grandson. 5 sm pieces chipped from cvr; minor staining o/w VG+. *PRATT.* $90

Post, Melville D. THE GILDED CHAIR. Toronto, 1910. 1st Canad ed. 4 plates. Several pages badly opened, o/w VG. *DIAMOND.* $45

POSTCRIPTS ON DWIGGINS. 2 vols. Ed by Paul A. Bennett. NY: Typophiles, 1960. One of 600. Fine in glassine djs and slipcase. *DERMONT.* $75

Potok, Chaim. THE GIFT OF ASHER LEV. Franklin Center: Franklin Lib, 1990. Leatherbound ltd ed, signed. Fine. *LOPEZ.* $45

Potous, Paul. MY ENEMY THE CROCODILE. NY: Wilfred Funk, Inc, 1957. 1st Amer. ed. VG in Good+ dj. *BACKMAN.* $25

Potter, Beatrix. WAG-BY-WALL. Horn Book, 1944. 1st ed. 16mo. 1st publication in book form. Woodcut decs. by J.J. Lankes. Tipped-in photo of Miss Potter and girl w/doll. Fine in Fine dj. *BEBBAH.* $70

Potter, Elisha A. THE EARLY HISTORY OF NARRAGANSETT; WITH AN APPENDIX....Providence, (1881). Best ed. (18),423pp. Orig cl, paper spine label defective. Howes P510. *GINSBERG.* $75

Potter, Helen. HELEN POTTER'S IMPERSONATIONS. NY: Edgard S. Werner, 1891. 1st ed. VG. *SECOND LIFE.* $35

Potter, Jack. CATTLE TRAILS OF THE OLD WEST. Clayton, NM: Krehbiel, (1939). 2nd ed. Fldg map at rear. Pict wraps. VF. *OREGON.* $85

Potter, Jean. THE FLYING NORTH. NY: Macmillan, 1947. 1st ed. VG in Fair dj. *AARD.* $25

Potter, John Mason. 13 DESPERATE DAYS. NY, (1964). 1st ed. 200pp. Minor dj wear, o/w VG+. *PRATT.* $37.50

Potter, Stephen. ONE UPMANSHIP. NY: Henry Holt, 1952. 1st ed. Fine in VG dj. *MAD DOG.* $20

Potter, Stephen. ONE-UPMANSHIP. London: Rupert Hart-Davis, 1952. 1st ed. NF, minor chips at dj spine top. *ELSE FINE.* $30

Potter, Stephen. ONE-UPMANSHIP. NY: Holt, (1952). 1st ed. Fine in NF dj. *ELSE FINE.* $30

Potter, Stephen. SUPERMANSHIP. NY: Random House, 1959. 1st ed. Fine in NF dj. *ELSE FINE.* $25

Poulsen, Frederik. GREEK AND ROMAN PORTRAITS IN ENGLISH COUNTRY HOUSES. Oxford: Clarendon Press, 1923. 57 figs, 112 plts. Minor tears at spine. Good. *ARCHAEOLOGIA.* $450

Poulsen, Frederik. TRAVELS & SKETCHES. TRANSLATED FROM THE DANISH OF....London, 1923. 235pp. *O'NEILL.* $35

Pound, Ezra. A DRAFT OF XXX CANTOS. NY, (1933). 1st ed. Port pasted on half title. Fine in dj (spine little sunned). 1000 printed. *POLYANTHOS.* $300

Pound, Ezra. AN AUTOBIOGRAPHICAL OUTLINE. Nadja, (1980). One of 200. Wrappers. Fine. *WOOLMER.* $75

Pound, Ezra. CATHAY. TRANSLATIONS...FOR THE MOST PART FROM THE CHINESE OF RIHAKU. Ptd tan wraps. London: Mathews, 1915. 1st ed. One of 1000. Fine. *JAFFE.* $600

Pound, Ezra. DRAFTS & FRAGMENTS OF CANTOS CX-CXVII. (Iowa City): New Directions & The Stone Wall Press, (1968). 1st ed, unrecorded variant issue: unnumbered, ptd label on slipcase (rust red cl rather than grey cardboards & w/o ptd label). Ltd to 310 signed. Red cl, cl slipcase. VF. *JAFFE.* $650

Pound, Ezra. EZRA POUND: A COLLECTION OF ESSAYS. London: Peter Nevill, (1950). Russell, Peter (ed). 1st ed. Fine in dj. *CAPTAIN'S BOOKSHELF.* $100

Pound, Ezra. FOUR POEMS OF DEPARTURE. London, 1973. One of 200 numbered. Single sheet folded to make four pages. Fine in the orig printed envelope. *WOOLMER.* $48

Pound, Ezra. GAUDIER-BRZESKA. A MEMOIR. London, 1916. 1st ed. 38 illus, 4 port. Uncut. Spine little sunned, extremities rubbed, covers little soiled. NF. *POLYANTHOS.* $300

Pound, Ezra. HOMAGE TO SEXTUS PROPERTIUS. London: Faber, (1934). 1st ed. One of 1000 ptd. Fine in dj (sl worn, torn at top of spine). Boards. *JAFFE.* $250

Pound, Ezra. PAVANNES AND DIVISIONS. NY: Knopf, 1918. Signed. Owner name, address; lettering faded from spine. VG, lacking dj. *LOPEZ.* $850

Pound, Ezra. PERSONAE. THE COLLECTED POEMS. NY: Boni & liveright, 1926. 1st ed. Plates. Spine lettering faded and w/minimal wear to top and bottom of spine. *WOOLMER.* $100

Pound, Ezra. QUIA PAUPER AMAVI. London: The Egoist Press, (1919). 1st ed. Spine label darkened with tiny chip not affecting type; some light foxing, but very nice. The error on page 34 has not been corrected in this copy. Issued w/o dj. *WOOLMER.* $325

Pound, Ezra. RIPOSTES. WHERETO ARE APPENDED THE COMPLETE WORKS OF T.E. HULME WITH PREFATORY NOTE. London: Elkin Matthews, 1915. Fourth issue. 1st ed sheets with new title page on a stub. Wrappers with cubist design by Dorothy S. Pound. Spine worn, some foxing of eps. VG. *WOOLMER.* $250

Pound, Ezra. SECTION: ROCK-DRILL 85-95 DE LOS CAN-TARES. New Directions, (1956). 1st US (offset) ed. Part of bkpl removed from front pastedown. Pencil presentation w/three Chinese characters on title page. Issued in ed of 2081. Fine in excellent dj. *SECOND LIFE.* $450

Pound, Ezra. SEVENTY CANTOS. Cl. London: Faber, (1950). 1st Eng collected ed. One of 1633 ptd. Fine in sl worn dj. *JAFFE.* $110

Pound, Ezra. THE LETTERS OF EZRA POUND, 1907-1941. NY: Harcourt, Brace, (1950). 1st ed. Fine in dj. *CHAPEL HILL.* $75

Pound, Ezra. THE LETTERS OF EZRA POUND. 1907-1941. Ed by D.D. Paige. NY, 1950. 1st ed. NF in dj w/2 short edge tears, sm edge chips; name. *POLYANTHOS.* $45

Pound, Ezra. THE LETTERS OF EZRA POUND. D.D. Paige (ed). London: Faber & Faber, (1951). 1st Eng ed. Fine in dj. *DORN.* $55

Pound, Ezra. THE LITERARY ESSAYS OF EZRA POUND. CT: New Directions, 1954. Ed by T.S. Eliot. 1st US ed. 5000 ptd using English sheets. UK ed preceded this by one month. Name, spine sl rubbed, chip. Dj spine sl sunned; chipped, 2 sm edge tears, rubbed. *POLYANTHOS.* $65

Pound, Ezra. THE SPIRIT OF ROMANCE: AN ATTEMPT TO DEFINE... London: J.M. Dent, nd (1910). 1st ed. 1/950. VG only w/dull spine. *CAPTAIN'S BOOKSHELF.* $150

Pound, Ezra. THRONES 96-109 De Los Cantares. (NY): New Directions, (1959). Some browning at inner gutters, as is common still VG in dj sunned at spine. 1st Amer ed, 1st issue, w/no erratum slip. One of 3000. *CHAPEL HILL.* $55

Pound, Merritt B. BENJAMIN HAWKINS, INDIAN AGENT. Athens, (1951). 1st ed. 270pp. Fine in dj. *PRATT.* $20

Pound, Reginald. SCOTT OF THE ANTARCTIC. NY: Coward-Mc-Cann, 1967. 1st Amer ed, 2nd imp. VG in lightly worn dj. *PARMER.* $35

Pound, Roscoe. CONTEMPORARY JURISTIC THEORY. LA: Ptd at Ward Ritchie Press for Friends of the Colleges at Claremont, CA, 1940. 1st ed. NF in remains of dj. *DIAMOND.* $35

Powell, Aaron Macy. PERSONAL REMINISCENCES OF THE ANTI-SLAVERY AND OTHER REFORMS AND REFORMERS. NY, 1899. 1st ed. Inscribed. Orig cl. Fine. *McGOWAN.* $165

Powell, Adam Clayton, Jr. MARCHING BLACKS. NY, 1945. 1st ed, 1st bk. NF in dj (sl edge rubbed). *POLYANTHOS.* $40

Powell, Addison M. TRAILING AND CAMPING IN ALASKA. NY: A. Wessels, 1909. 1st ed. VG. *BLUE DRAGON.* $70

Powell, Anthony. A QUESTION OF UPBRINGING. NY: Scribner's, 1951. 1st ed. Name. Fine, minor edgewear to dj. *ELSE FINE.* $75

Powell, Anthony. AUTOBIOGRAPHY. London: Heinemann, 1976-1982. 1st eds. Complete in 4 vols. VF in djs and each volume w/the author's presentation inscription. Enclosed in 2 specially made cloth boxes. *WOOLMER.* $300

Powell, Anthony. BOOKS DO FURNISH A ROOM. London: Heinemann, (1971). 1st ed. Dj. Fine. *MUELLER*. $50

Powell, Anthony. HEARING SECRET HARMONIES. Boston: Little, Brown, (1975). 1st US ed. Fine in dj. *WOOLMER*. $25

Powell, Anthony. HEARING SECRET HARMONIES. Little, Brown, 1975. 1st Amer. ed. NF in dj (spine sunned). *STAHR*. $20

Powell, Anthony. JOHN AUBREY AND HIS FRIENDS. NY: Scribners, 1948. 1st US ed. VG in well used dj. *WOOLMER*. $25

Powell, Anthony. NOVELS OF HIGH SOCIETY FROM THE VICTORIAN AGE. London: Pilot Press, 1947. Maroon cl, stamped in black. Text edges browning, o/w Fine. *HELLER*. $50

Powell, Anthony. THE KINDLY ONES. London: Heinemann, (1962). 1st ed. Owner stamp eps, o/w Fine in Fine dj. *LOPEZ*. $65

Powell, Anthony. THE MILITARY PHILOSOPHERS. Boston: Little Brown, 1968. 1st ed. Fine, minor rubs at dj spine ends. *ELSE FINE*. $45

Powell, Anthony. THE SOLDIER'S ART. London: Heinemann, 1966. 1st ed. Fine in dj. *ELSE FINE*. $75

Powell, Donald M. THE PERALTA GRANT. Univ of OK Press, 1960. 1st ed. Fine in sl chipped dj. *VARNER*. $35

Powell, E. Alexander. IN BARBARY: TUNISIA, ALGERIA, MOROCCO AND THE SAHARA. NY & London: Century (1926). 2 fldg maps. Rev slip laid in. Dj sl chipped. Fine. *SCHOYER'S*. $50

Powell, G. Harold. LETTERS FROM THE ORANGE EMPIRE. LA: Hist Soc of Southern CA, 1990. 1st ed, ltd to 100. Signed by L.C. Powell. Fine. *BOOK MARKET*. $50

Powell, H.M.T. THE SANTA FE TRAIL TO CALIFORNIA 1849-1852. THE JOURNAL AND DRAWINGS OF...NY: Lewis, 1981. Reprint of rare 1931 ed. Ltd to 350 numbered. Fldg plts. Leather w/gold lettering, boxed, linen eps. Beautiful facsimile. Howes P525. *GINSBERG*. $250

Powell, John J. THE GOLDEN STATE AND ITS RESOURCES. SF: Bacon, 1874. 1st ed. Cl badly dust soiled. Owner inscrip. *SECOND LIFE*. $75

Powell, John Wesley. EXPLORATION OF THE COLORADO RIVER OF THE WEST AND ITS TRIBUTARIES EXPLORED IN 1869, 1871, AND 1872. Washington, 1875. 80 illus on 68 sheets. xi,291pp. Includes two maps in rear pocket. In orig govt sheepskin or calf, with red and black spine labels. Scuffing, bumping and other external evidence of wear is very moderate. Internally, text is bright, clean, and tight. The two maps inside back cover are sharp, clean. Externally, certainly VG+. Internally, VF. *FIVE QUAIL*. $395

Powell, John Wesley. FIRST THROUGH THE GRAND CANYON. NY, 1915. Ed by Horace Kephart. 1st ed. 320pp. VF. *FIVE QUAIL*. $35

Powell, John Wesley. FOURTH ANNUAL REPORT OF THE UNITED STATES GEOLOGICAL SURVEY. Vol III, 1883. 471pp. Tight, clean. *BOOKCELL*. $40

Powell, John Wesley. REPORT ON THE LANDS OF THE ARID REGION OF THE UNITED STATES. Harvard Univ Press, 1962. Ed by Wallace Stegner. 1st ed thus. 2 fldg maps inside back cover. Fine, in NF dj w/light soil. *FIVE QUAIL*. $35

Powell, John Wesley. SELECTED PROSE OF JOHN WESLEY POWELL. David R. Godine, 1970. George Crossette (ed). 1st ptg of 1,500. Fine in dj. *AUTHORS OF THE WEST*. $40

Powell, John Wesley. THE EXPLORATION OF THE COLORADO RIVER. Univ Chicago, 1967. 1st ed. Brown cloth. xxi,138pp. Illus. One foldout. Fine, in orig 1st ed dj (Good+ to VG, with a bit of staining top edge of back cover of dj). *FIVE QUAIL*. $30

Powell, John Wesley. THIRD ANNUAL REPORT OF THE UNITED STATES GEOLOGICAL SURVEY. Vol III, 1882. 564pp. 3/4 red leather. VG+. *BOOKCELL*. $65

Powell, John. BRING OUT YOUR DEAD: THE GREAT PLAGUE OF YELLOW FEVER IN PHILADELPHIA IN 1793. Phila, 1949. 1st ed. *FYE*. $35

Powell, Lawrence Clark. A PASSION FOR BOOKS. Cleveland, NY: World Pub Co, 1958. 1st trade ed. Inscribed. Fine in dj. *WEBER*. $35

Powell, Lawrence Clark. A SOUTHWESTERN CENTURY: A BIBLIOGRAPHY OF ONE HUNDRED BOOKS....Van Nuys: J.E. Reynolds, Bookseller, (1958). Tom Lea (illus). One of 500 designed by Carl Hertzog. Presentation signed by Hertzog on the colophon. Bound in 1/4 cl and paper boards. Fine in dj. *LAURIE*. $300

Powell, Lawrence Clark. BOOKMAN'S PROGRESS. N.p., 1968. 1st ed. Fine in dj. *BAADE*. $45

Powell, Lawrence Clark. BOOKS IN MY BAGGAGE. Cleveland, NY: World, (1960). 1st ed. Fine in dj. *WEBER*. $25

Powell, Lawrence Clark. CALIFORNIA CLASSICS. LA: Ward Ritchie Press, (1971). 1st ed. Gray cl. Fine in dj. *WEBER*. $45

Powell, Lawrence Clark. EX LIBRIS. Tucson: Press on the Bajada. 1984. Christmas bk for friends. *KARMIOLE*. $35

Powell, Lawrence Clark. FAREWELL TO THE ENCINAL. Tucson: El Signo de los Aboles Caidos. 1982. Powell Christmas book. *KARMIOLE*. $30

Powell, Lawrence Clark. FROM THE HEARTLAND: PROFILES....Flagstaff: Northland, 1976. 1st ed. Presentation label laid on. Fine in Fine dj. *CONNOLLY & WADE*. $45

Powell, Lawrence Clark. FROM THE HEARTLAND: PROFILES....Northland Press, (1976). 1st ed. Review copy, slip glued in. Fine in dj. *AUTHORS OF THE WEST*. $50

Powell, Lawrence Clark. HEART OF THE SOUTHWEST. LA: Dawson's Book Shop, 1955. Dj lightly chipped, 2pp w/newspaper offsetting. Inscribed. Prospectus laid in. *DAWSON'S*. $225

Powell, Lawrence Clark. PHILOSOPHER PICKETT. Berkeley: Univ of CA Press. 1942. 1st ed. Presentation copy, signed by Powell with his initials. *KARMIOLE*. $45

Powell, Lawrence Clark. ROBINSON JEFFERS; THE MAN AND HIS WORK. LA: Primavera Press, 1934. Ltd ed of 750. Inscribed by Powell and Ward Ritchie. Fine. *WEBER*. $400

Powell, Lawrence Clark. ROBINSON JEFFERS; THE MAN AND HIS WORK. Pasadena: San Pasqual Press, 1940. 2nd ed, rev. Inscribed by Powell. VG. *WEBER*. $150

Powell, Michael. 200,000 FEET. THE EDGE OF THE WORLD. NY: Dutton, (1938). 1st ed. Fine in VG dj. *AARD*. $30

Powell, Padgett. EDISTO. NY: Farrar Straus & Giroux, (1984). 1st ed. Fine in dj. Signed. *CAPTAIN'S BOOKSHELF*. $60

Powell, Padgett. TYPICAL. NY: Farrar Straus & Giroux, (1991). 1st ed. As New in dj. Review copy, slip laid in. Signed. *CAPTAIN'S BOOKSHELF*. $40

Powell, Peter John. PEOPLE OF THE SACRED MOUNTAIN. SF: H&R, (1981). 1st ed. 2 vols. Clothbound, in pub's slipcase. Fine. *LOPEZ*. $250

Powell, Richard. FALSE COLORS. NY: Simon & Schuster, 1955. 1st ed. Pp darkened o/w VG in dj, sl faded spine. *MORDIDA*. $25

Powell, Richard. LAY THAT PISTOL DOWN. NY: Simon & Schuster, 1945. 1st ed. Bkseller's stamp fep, light spotting on foreedge o/w VG in dj (sl faded spine; stain back panel). *MORDIDA*. $25

Powell, Richard. SAY IT WITH BULLETS. NY: Simon & Schuster, 1953. 1st ed. Pp sl darkened o/w Fine in dj w/tiny chip at top corner of spine. *MORDIDA*. $35

Powell, Richard. SHOOT IF YOU MUST. NY: Simon & Schuster, 1946. 1st ed. Fine in dj. *MORDIDA*. $40

Powell, Scott. HISTORY OF MARSHAL COUNTY FROM FOREST TO FIELD. Moundsvile, WV, 1925. 1st ed. Orig cl, paper label on spine, bkpl removed. *GINSBERG.* $125

Powell, W.F. TACHY-HIPPODRAMIA. THE NEW SECRET OF TAMING HORSES. Phila, 1872. NF. *POLYANTHOS.* $75

Power, D'Arcy. MEDICINE IN THE BRITISH ISLES. NY, 1930. 1st ed. *FYE.* $45

Power, John. A HANDY-BOOK ABOUT BOOKS. London: John Wilson. 1870. 1st ed. Title, initials and adverts ptd in red and black. Orig mustard cloth over dec boards printed in 6 colors, gilt spine; corners a bit rubbed. *KARMIOLE.* $65

Power, Tyrone. IMPRESSIONS OF AMERICA. London: Richard Bentley, 1836. 1st ed. 2 vols. 8vo; cloth-backed boards, expertly reboarded preserving the orig spines; engr frontis to each vol; paper labels; uncut. VG. *DRAMATIS PERSONAE.* $200

Powers, Alfred (ed). POEMS OF THE COVERED WAGONS. Pacific Pub House, 1947. 1st ed. Boards. Fine w/o dj as issued. *AUTHORS OF THE WEST.* $35

Powers, Edward. WAR AND THE WEATHER. Delavan, WI: Privately published, 1890. 1st rev ed. Fine. *McGOWAN.* $95

Powers, Grant. HISTORICAL SKETCHES...THE COOS COUNTRY AND VICINITY...BETWEEN THE YEARS 1754 AND 1785. Haverhill, NH: Merrill, 1880. 240pp. Faded spine, joint scraped. Howes P535, reprint of rare 1841 ed. *GINSBERG.* $75

Powers, J.F. MORTE D'URBAN. NY: Modern Library, (1966). 1st Modern Library ed. Fine in dj (two short tears). *CAPTAIN'S BOOK-SHELF.* $20

Powers, Richard. PRISONER'S DILEMMA. NY: Beech Tree Books, (1988). 1st ed. Fine in dj. *CAPTAIN'S BOOKSHELF.* $60

Powers, Richard. PRISONER'S DILEMMA. NY: Beech Tree Books, (1988). 1st ed, 2nd book. New in dj. *BERNARD.* $45

Powers, Richard. THREE FARMERS ON THEIR WAY TO A DANCE. NY: Beechtree, (1985). 1st ed. Slight soiling to page edges, else Fine in NF dj with a few tiny nicks. Scarce. *BETWEEN COVERS.* $75

Powers, Richard. THREE FARMERS ON THEIR WAY TO A DANCE. London: W&N, (1988). 1st UK ed. Fine in dj. *CAPTAIN'S BOOKSHELF.* $50

Powers, William Dudley. UNCLE ISAAC: OR OLD DAYS IN THE SOUTH. Richmond, VA, 1899. 1st ed. Orig cl. NF, autographed. *McGOWAN.* $65

Powys, John Cowper. HOMER AND THE AETHER. London: Macdonald, (1959). 1st ed. Inscribed. Fine in chipped dj. *DERMONT.* $200

Powys, John Cowper. HUNTER, REGINALD PORLOCK: A PORTRAIT. Idaho: Caxton Printers, 1940. 1st ed. Uncut. Spine and edges little sunned, traces of removed scotch tape rear ep. Fine. *POLYANTHOS.* $35

Powys, John Cowper. LUCIFER, A POEM. London: Macdonald, (1956). 1/560 numbered/signed. Fine in acetate dj as issued. *DERMONT.* $175

Powys, John Cowper. OWEN GLENDOWER. 2 Vols. NY: Simon & Schuster (1940). 1st Amer ed. VF in pict box (sl worn) which retains orig cellophane window. *DORN.* $125

Powys, John Cowper. SAMPHIRE. NY: T. Seltzer, 1922. 1st ed. Extrems and corners little rubbed. Dj spine little sunned, extrems sl chipped, tiny edge tear. *POLYANTHOS.* $75

Powys, John Cowper. THE PLEASURES OF LITERATURE. London: Cassell and Co, (1938). 1st Eng ed. Cvrs a bit dust marked, rear hinge cracked, o/w VG. *WREDEN.* $25

Powys, Llewelyn. IMPASSIONED CLAY. London, 1931. 1st ed. Woodcut by Lynd Ward. Top spine and edges little rubbed. Fine. *POLYANTHOS.* $35

Powys, Theodore Francis. AN INTERPRETATION OF GENESIS. NY: Viking, 1929. One of 260. Signed. Spine darkened, cvrs a trifle soiled, else Fine. *WREDEN.* $110

Powys, Theodore Francis. FABLES. Gilbert Spencer (illus). London: Chatto & Windus. 1929. Ed ltd to 750 numbered, signed by Powys. Cl bit soiled. *KARMIOLE.* $65

Poyas, Catharine Gendron. YEAR OF GRIEF....Charleston, SC: Walker, Evans & Cogswell, printers, 1869. 1st ed. 244pp. Orig cl. Lib bkpl, blindstamp, lt cover spotting, one signature a little pulled, else VG. *CHAPEL HILL.* $85

Poynter, F.N.L. (ed). MEDICINE AND SCIENCE IN THE 1860'S. London, 1968. *FYE.* $70

Poynter, F.N.L. (ed). THE HISTORY AND PHILOSOPHY OF KNOWLEDGE OF THE BRAIN AND ITS FUNCTIONS. Springfield, 1958. 1st ed. Dj. Scarce. *FYE.* $150

Poynting, F. EGGS OF BRITISH BIRDS, WITH AN ACCOUNT OF THEIR BREEDING-HABITS. (Limicolae). London: R.H. Porter, 1895-6. 54 full pg color plts. 1/2 red leath/cl w/5 spine hubs, t.e.g, marbled eps. 2 author's tls tipped-in. VG+. *MIKESH.* $195

Praed, Mrs. Campbell. FUGITIVE ANNE. Fenno, 1904. 1st ed. VG. *MADLE.* $65

Prager, Hans G. THROUGH ARCTIC HURRICANES. London: Thames and Hudson, c. 1955. Spine lightly faded, else VG. *PARMER.* $22.50

Pragnell, Festus. THE GREEN MAN OF GRAYPEC. Greenberg, 1950. 1st ed. Fine in sl waterstained Bok dj. *MADLE.* $25

Pratt, Ambrose. THE LIVING MUMMY. Stokes, 1910. VG. *MADLE.* $50

Pratt, Fletcher. ALIEN PLANET. NY: Thomas Bouregy, (1962). Rose cl, dj. Fine. *WEBER.* $25

Pratt, John Clark. THE LAOTIAN FRAGMENTS. NY: Viking, (1974). 1st ed, 1st bk. Fine in dj. *HELLER.* $60

Pratt, Julius H. REMINISCENCES PERSONAL AND OTHERWISE. Privately ptd, 1910. 1st ed. (10),287pp. 9 plts. Orig cl. Howes P554. *GINSBERG.* $100

Pratt, Julius H. REMINISCENCES PERSONAL AND OTHERWISE. Privately ptd, 1910. Frontis, plts, double facsim. Orig cl. Spine dull & rubbed, Ownership sig of Pratt, else VG. Howes P554. *BOHLING.* $125

Pratt, W.A. THE YACHTMAN AND COASTER'S BOOK OF REFERENCE, GIVING COURSES AND DISTANCES...FROM CAPE HATTERAS TO ST. JOHN'S, N.B....2nd ed. Hartford: Press of the Case, Lockwood & Brainard Co, 1879. Cvrs rubbed, title pg loose. *LEFKOWICZ.* $75

Pray, Mrs. R.F. DICK DOWLING'S BATTLE. San Antonio, 1936. 1st ed. NF. *McGOWAN.* $95

Pray, Mrs. R.F. DICK DOWLING'S BATTLE, AN ACCOUNT OF THE WAR BETWEEN THE STATES IN THE EASTERN GULF COAST REGION OF TEXAS. San Antonio, 1936. 1st ed. A little cvr wear o/w VG+. *PRATT.* $45

Preble, George H. ORIGIN AND HISTORY OF THE AMERICAN FLAG AND OF THE NAVAL AND YACHT CLUB SIGNALS...WITH A CHRONICLE...Phila.: Brown, 1917. New ed. 2 vols. Orig cl boards, paper labels on spines. Howes P565. *GINSBERG.* $125

Preble, George H. OUR FLAG: ORIGIN AND PROGRESS OF THE FLAG OF THE UNITED STATES OF AMERICA, WITH AN INTRODUCTORY ACCOUNT...ANCIENT AND MODERN NATIONS. Albany: Munsell, 1872. 1st ed. 535pp. Orig cl, hinges mended. Howes P565. *GINSBERG.* $75

Preble, George H. THE CHASE OF THE REBEL STEAMER OF WAR ORETO...INTO THE BAY OF MOBILE, BY THE UNITED STATES STEAM SLOOP ONEIDA...SEPTEMBER 4, 1862. Cambridge, MA, 1862. 1st ed. Ptd for priv circ. Bound in cl, minor dampstain in lower right corner carries through first 18pp, else VG. Howes P-563. *McGOWAN.* $250

Preece, Harold. LONE STAR MAN, IRA ATEN. NY, (1960). 1st ed. 256pp. Tear back of dj o/w VG+. *PRATT.* $20

Preininger, M. JAPANESE FLOWER ARRANGEMENT FOR MODERN HOMES. Boston, 1937 (1936). Hardbound. *SUTTON.* $35

Prenshaw, Peggy Whitman (ed). CONVERSATIONS WITH ELIZABETH SPENCER. Jackson: Univ Press of MS, (1991). 1st ed. VF in dj. Signed. *CAPTAIN'S BOOKSHELF.* $30

Prenshaw, Peggy Whitman (ed). EUDORA WELTY: CRITICAL ESSAYS. Jackson: Univ Press of MS, 1979. 1st ed. Fine in dj. Signed by Welty and Prenshaw. *CAPTAIN'S BOOKSHELF.* $100

Prentice, George D. PRENTICEANA; OR, WIT AND HUMOR....NY: Derby and Jackson, 1860. iv,5-306,(vi)pp. Orig blindstamped cl. Gilt. Ends of spine corners, worn. Lt, early foxing. Owner inscrip. *CONNOLLY & WADE.* $85

Prescott, Philander. THE RECOLLECTIONS OF PHILANDER PRESCOTT...1819-1862. Donald Dean Parker (ed). Lincoln: Univ of NE, 1966. 1st ed. VF in NF dj. *CONNOLLY & WADE.* $37.50

Prescott, William H. BIOGRAPHICAL AND CRITICAL MISCELLANIES. Phila: Lippincott, 1879. New, rev ed. Frontis, vii, 682pp. Orig brn, ornately dec cl, gilt, blindstamped, beveled edges. Inner hinge shows brn ep splitting. Sl edgewear. Sm scuff on spine, else Fine. *CONNOLLY & WADE.* $45

Prescott, William H. BIOGRAPHICAL AND CRITICAL MISCELLANIES. London: Richard Bentley, 1845. 565pp, frontis. 3/4 leather, marbled paper, raised bands, teg. Lightly worn, else VG. *PARMER.* $125

Prescott, William H. HISTORY OF THE CONQUEST OF PERU. 2 vols. Phila: David McKay, 1892. Frontis,459pp; frontis,458pp. NF. *CONNOLLY & WADE.* $45

Prescott, William H. THE LITERARY MEMORANDA OF....C. Harvey Gardiner (ed). Norman: Univ of OK, 1961. 1st ed. 2 vols, slipcased. Grn cl & slipcase. As New. *CONNOLLY & WADE.* $50

Prescott, William H. THE PAPERS OF WILLIAM HICKLING PRESCOTT. Urbana: Univ of IL Press, 1964. C. Harvey Gardiner (ed). Hinge beginning. Blue grn/cl. VG+ in dj. *PARMER.* $40

Prescott, Winward. A BIBLIOGRAPHY OF BOOK-PLATE LITERATURE. Amer Bkplate Soc, P.U.P., 1914. Ltd ed, 250 only. Fine in glassine dj. *POLYANTHOS.* $35

Preston, George R, Jr. THOMAS WOLFE: A BIBLIOGRAPHY. NY: Charles S. Boesen, 1943. 1st ed. Orig tan cl w/paper label. NF. *CHAPEL HILL.* $75

Preston, John (ed). FLESH AND THE WORD. NY: Dutton (1992). Uncorrected proof. NF in wraps. *DORN.* $50

Preston, Paul (pseud). THE FIRESIDE MAGICIAN. NY: Dick & Fitzgerald, (1870). 1st ed. Contemp 1/2 calf; sl inkstaining to fore-edges of couple leaves. VG. *DRAMATIS PERSONAE.* $120

Preuss, Charles. EXPLORING WITH FREMONT. Erwin and Elisabeth Gudde (trans). Norman: Univ of OK Press, 1958. 1st ed. NF in rubbed dj. *PARMER.* $55

Prevost, Renan. SUNDOWN ON THE PACIFIC SHORE. N.p.: Author pub, 1957. 1st ed. Inscribed. Dj, minor chipping, else Fine. *CONNOLLY & WADE.* $65

Price, Anthony. A NEW KIND OF WAR. London: Gollancz, 1987. 1st ed. VF in dj. *MORDIDA.* $30

Price, Anthony. A PROSPECT OF VENGEANCE. London: Gollancz, 1988. 1st ed. Fine in dj. *MORDIDA.* $30

Price, Anthony. OCTOBER MEN. London: Gollancz, 1973. 1st ed. Inscribed. Fine in dj. *MORDIDA.* $185

Price, Anthony. OUR MAN IN CAMELOT. London: Gollancz, 1975. 1st ed. Fine in dj. *MORDIDA.* $125

Price, Anthony. SION CROSSING. London: Gollancz, 1984. 1st ed. Fine in dj. *MORDIDA.* $30

Price, Anthony. SOLDIER NO MORE. London: Gollancz, 1981. 1st ed. Fine in dj. *MORDIDA.* $65

Price, Anthony. THE HOUR OF THE DONKEY. London: Gollancz, 1980. 1st ed. Fine in dj. Not pub in US. *MORDIDA.* $90

Price, Anthony. THE MEMORY TRAP. London: Gollancz, 1989. 1st ed. VF in dj. *MORDIDA.* $30

Price, Anthony. THE OLD VENGEFUL. London: Gollancz, 1982. 1st ed. Edges sl darkened o/w Fine in dj w/crease on back panel. *MORDIDA.* $45

Price, Anthony. TOMORROW'S GHOST. London: Gollancz, 1979. 1st ed. Fine in dj. *MORDIDA.* $85

Price, Con. MEMORIES OF OLD MONTANA. Trail's End, 1945. 7th ptg. Fine in VG dj. *VARNER.* $30

Price, Con. TRAILS I RODE. Pasadena, 1947. 1st ed. NF in dj (sm portion missing top, bottom of backstrip; edgewear). *BAADE.* $90

Price, E. Hoffman, STRANGE GATEWAYS. Arkham House, 1967. 1st ed. VF in dj. *MADLE.* $75

Price, Eugene H. OPEN RANGE RANCHING ON THE SOUTH PLAINS IN THE 1890'S. Clarendon, TX: Clarendon Press, 1971. Fldg map laid-in. 750 copies. Fine. *GIBBS.* $47.50

Price, Harry. THE ROYAL TOUR-1901—OR THE CRUISE OF H.M.S. OPHIR. NY: William Morrow & Co., 1980. Near New in lightly rubbed dj. *PARMER.* $30

Price, J. and Haley, C. S. THE BUYERS' MANUAL AND BUSINESS GUIDE...SF: Francis & Valentine, 1872. 1st ed. 192pp. Faded brn cl that shows wear. Adv, incl 4pp ptd in grn and red. BAL 3348. *SECOND LIFE.* $550

Price, Luxor. THE QUOKS. Stokes, 1924. 1st ed. 64pp. Illus by Price. Cvr has wear, slight edge fraying but VG+ overall. *BEBBAH.* $75

Price, Reynolds (trans). ORACLES. Durham: The Friends of Duke Univ Lib, 1977. 1st ed. Jacob Roquet (illus). #206 of 300 signed by Price and Roquet. 6 etchings. Orig red cl w/13th century Florentine mosaic pattern in gilt on cvrs. Fine. *CHAPEL HILL.* $125

Price, Reynolds, (trans). ORACLES. Etchings by Jacob Roquet. Durham: The Friends of Duke Univ Library, 1977. Fine. 1st ed. #195 of 300 signed by Price and Roquet. Additionally inscribed at colophon. *CHAPEL HILL.* $200

Price, Reynolds. A COMMON ROOM. Essays....NY: Atheneum, 1987. 1st ed. As New in dj. Signed. *CAPTAIN'S BOOKSHELF.* $50

Price, Reynolds. A GENEROUS MAN. NY: Atheneum, (1966). 1st Amer ed. Signed. NF in dj. *DORN.* $75

Price, Reynolds. A GENEROUS MAN. NY: Atheneum, 1966. 1st ed. Bit of fading to edges of cl o/w VF in price-clipped but still Fine dj. *LOPEZ.* $65

Price, Reynolds. A GENEROUS MAN. NY: Atheneum, 1966. 1st ed. Orig grn cl. Sl soiled, but NF in price-clipped dj. *CHAPEL HILL.* $45

Price, Reynolds. A GENEROUS MAN. NY: Atheneum, 1966. Advance copy in pict wrappers and integral dj. One of 500. Fine (sm tear at heel of spine). Signed. *CAPTAIN'S BOOKSHELF.* $125

Price, Reynolds. A LONG AND HAPPY LIFE. London: Chatto & Windus, (1962). 1st Eng ed. Signed. Fine in NF dj w/minor small dampstain bottom of back panel at hinge. *DORN.* $120

Price, Reynolds. A LONG AND HAPPY LIFE. London: Chatto and Windus, 1962. 1st Eng ed, 1st bk. Fine in price clipped dj. *HELLER.* $65

Price, Reynolds. A LONG AND HAPPY LIFE. NY: Atheneum, 1962. 1st ed, 1st book. Signed. NF in bright 1st issue dj w/minimal edgewear. *ROBBINS.* $125

Price, Reynolds. A LONG AND HAPPY LIFE. NY: Atheneum, (1962). 1st Amer ed. Signed. NF in 1st state dj (names in light green on rear panel). *DORN.* $175

Price, Reynolds. A LONG AND HAPPY LIFE. NY: Atheneum, 1962. Adv reading copy of 1st ed. One of 500. Orig ptd yellow wraps w/blurbs by Eudora Welty, Stephen Spender. Wraps soiled, bk sl "bent," thus Good. *CHAPEL HILL.* $200

Price, Reynolds. AN EARLY CHRISTMAS. (Rocky Mount): NC Wesleyan Press, (1992). One of 100 specially bound, signed. As New. *CAPTAIN'S BOOKSHELF.* $75

Price, Reynolds. BACK BEFORE DAY. Rocky Mount, NC: NC Wesleyan College Press, 1989. 1st ed. One of 100 signed. Dj. Mint. *JAFFE.* $50

Price, Reynolds. CHRIST CHILD'S SONG AT THE END OF THE NIGHT. (NY: Albondocani Press, 1978). 1st ed. One of 255 w/o pub's name on 1st pg. Orig illus red wraps. Fine in orig mailing env w/card stiffener. *CHAPEL HILL.* $50

Price, Reynolds. CLEAR PICTURES. NY: Atheneum, 1989. Uncorrected proof. Fine in wrappers, promo material laid in. *LOPEZ.* $40

Price, Reynolds. EARLY DARK: A PLAY. NY: Atheneum, (1977). 1st Amer ed. Signed. Fine in dj. *DORN.* $45

Price, Reynolds. GOOD HEARTS. NY: Atheneum, 1988. 1st ed. As New in dj. Signed. *CAPTAIN'S BOOKSHELF.* $45

Price, Reynolds. GOOD HEARTS. NY: Atheneum, 1988. 1st ed. Signed. Fine in Fine dj. *BEASLEY.* $45

Price, Reynolds. HOME MADE. Photos by Roger Manley. (Rocky Mount, NC): NC Wesleyan College Press, (1990). 1st ed. One of 200 signed by Price & Manley. New. *JAFFE.* $75

Price, Reynolds. KATE VAIDEN. NY: Atheneum, (1986). Uncorrected proof. Signed. Fine in wraps. *DORN.* $85

Price, Reynolds. KATE VAIDEN. NY: Atheneum, 1986. 1st ed. Orig grn cl. Fine in dj. *CHAPEL HILL.* $35

Price, Reynolds. LATE WARNING. NY: Albondocani Press, 1968. 1st ed. One of 150 numbered, signed. Frontis, orig marbled wraps. VF. Scarce. *JAFFE.* $150

Price, Reynolds. LOVE AND WORK. NY: Atheneum, (1968). 1st Amer ed. Signed. Small ink mark ffep else Fine in dj. *DORN.* $65

Price, Reynolds. LOVE AND WORK. NY: Atheneum, 1968. 1st ed. Fine in dj (sun faded). Signed. *CAPTAIN'S BOOKSHELF.* $35

Price, Reynolds. LOVE AND WORK. NY: Atheneum, 1968. 1st ed. Inscribed. Corners bumped, o/w Fine in sl chipped dj. *HELLER.* $55

Price, Reynolds. MUSTIAN. NY: Atheneum, (1983). Signed. Rev copy stamped "Not for resale" bottom edge. Fine in dj. *DORN.* $50

Price, Reynolds. MUSTIAN. NY: Atheneum, 1983. 1st ed. Bottom edges stamped "Not For Sale" else Fine in dj. Inscribed. *CAPTAIN'S BOOKSHELF.* $40

Price, Reynolds. NOON REST, BEST DAY. (NY: Albondocani Press, 1986). Orig mailing env w/card stiffener. 1st ed. One of 350. Rrivately issued. *CHAPEL HILL.* $55

Price, Reynolds. PERMANENT ERRORS. NY: Atheneum, 1970. 1st ed. Owner name fep; stain fore-edge of pgs. Signed. VG in dj. *LOPEZ.* $55

Price, Reynolds. PERMANENT ERRORS. NY: Atheneum, 1970. 1st ed. Fine in dj. Signed. *CAPTAIN'S BOOKSHELF.* $60

Price, Reynolds. PERMANENT ERRORS. NY: Atheneum, 1970. Fine in dj. 1st ed. *CHAPEL HILL.* $50

Price, Reynolds. PRESENCE AND ABSENCE. Bloomfield Hills: Bruccoli Clark, 1973. One of 300 numbered, signed. Loose, unbound signatures laid into fldg clamshell box. VG. *LOPEZ.* $85

Price, Reynolds. PRIVATE CONTENTMENT: A PLAY. NY: Atheneum, 1984. 1st ed. Fine in dj. Signed. *CAPTAIN'S BOOKSHELF.* $50

Price, Reynolds. THE ANNUAL HERON. NY: Albondocani Press, 1980. 1st ed. #207 of 300 signed. Orig French marbled wraps, paper label. Fine. *CHAPEL HILL.* $75

Price, Reynolds. THE FORESEEABLE FUTURE. NY: Atheneum, (1991). 1st Amer ed. Signed. Fine in dj. *DORN.* $35

Price, Reynolds. THE FORESEEABLE FUTURE. NY: Atheneum, 1991. 1st ed. As New in dj. Review copy, slip, promo sheet laid in. Signed. *CAPTAIN'S BOOKSHELF.* $50

Price, Reynolds. THE NAMES AND FACES OF HEROES. NY: Atheneum, (1963). Trade ed. Signed. NF in Fine dj. *DORN.* $140

Price, Reynolds. THE NAMES AND FACES OF HEROES. Stories. NY: Atheneum, 1963. 1st ed. Fine in dj (edge rubbing, short tear). Signed. *CAPTAIN'S BOOKSHELF.* $100

Price, Reynolds. THE SURFACE OF EARTH. NY: Atheneum, (1975). 1st Amer ed. Signed. Fore edge foxing else NF in fragile dj w/few small wrinkles in front flap, small closed tear at head of spine. *DORN.* $60

Price, Reynolds. THE SURFACE OF EARTH. NY: Atheneum, 1975. 1st ed. Fine in dj. Signed. *CAPTAIN'S BOOKSHELF.* $75

Price, Reynolds. THE SURFACE OF EARTH. NY: Atheneum, 1975. 1st ed. Inscribed. NF in dj. *CHAPEL HILL.* $75

Price, Reynolds. THE TONGUES OF ANGELS. NY: Atheneum (and Ultramarine Pub Co), 1990. 1st ed. #35 of 100 numbered, signed. Orig dk blue 1/4 morocco, marbled boards. Fine (issued w/o dj). *CHAPEL HILL.* $150

Price, Reynolds. THE TONGUES OF ANGELS. NY: Atheneum, 1990. 1st ed. As New in dj. Inscribed. *CAPTAIN'S BOOKSHELF.* $35

Price, Reynolds. THE TONGUES OF ANGELS. NY: Atheneum, 1990. Uncorrected proof of 1st ed. Orig ptd red wraps. Pub date on front wrap neatly changed in ink from "April" to "5/16," else Fine. *CHAPEL HILL.* $50

Price, Reynolds. THE TONGUES OF ANGELS. NY: Atheneum, 1990. 1st ed. Orig blue cl. As New in dj. One of unspecified number signed on tipped-in leaf. *CHAPEL HILL.* $45

Price, Reynolds. THE USE OF FIRE. NY: Atheneum, 1990. 1st ed. Fine in dj. Signed. *CAPTAIN'S BOOKSHELF.* $45

Price, Reynolds. THINGS THEMSELVES. NY: Atheneum, (1972). 1st Amer ed. Signed. Fine in dj. *DORN.* $80

Price, Reynolds. THINGS THEMSELVES. NY: Atheneum, 1972. 1st ed. Fine in dj. Signed. *CAPTAIN'S BOOKSHELF.* $75

Price, Richard. BLOODBROTHERS. Boston: Houghton Mifflin, 1976. 1st ed. Signed. Fine in NF dj. *LOPEZ.* $75

Price, Richard. LADIES' MAN. Boston: Houghton Mifflin, 1978. Rev copy, signed. Fine in dj. *LOPEZ.* $65

Price, Richard. THE WANDERERS. Boston: Houghton Mifflin, 1974. 1st ed, 1st book. Bkpl removed from flyleaf o/w Fine in dj. *BERNARD.* $25

Price, Richard. THE WANDERERS. Boston: Houghton Mifflin, 1974. 1st ed. Signed. NF in dj. *LOPEZ.* $100

Price, Richard. THE WANDERERS. Houghton Mifflin, 1974. 1st ed. VF in dj. *STAHR.* $45

Price, Richard. THE WANDERERS. London: Chatto & Windus, 1975. 1st Eng ed. NF in dj. *LOPEZ.* $65

Price, S.F. THE FERN COLLECTOR'S HANDBOOK & HERBARIUM. NY, (1897). 72pp+index. Illus. VG. *MIKESH.* $37.50

Prichard, H. Hesketh. THROUGH THE HEART OF PATAGONIA. NY, 1902. 1st Amer ed. Pict buckram gilt. Name stamp, writing. Sl wear, cvr staining. Inner hinges starting, o/w VG. *DIAMOND.* $75

Prichard, H. Hesketh. THROUGH THE HEART OF PATAGONIA. NY: D. Appleton and Co, 1902. 1st Amer ed. Lg red, gilt dec cl. 6 color illus, 3 fldg maps. Piece of spine cl missing; soiled, foxed. Just Acceptable. *PARMER.* $175

Prichard, James. A TREATISE ON INSANITY AND OTHER DIS-ORDERS AFFECTING THE MIND. Phila, 1837. 1st Amer ed. 1/2 leather, 337pp. *FYE.* $250

Pride, W.F. HISTORY OF...FORT RILEY... Privately ptd, 1926. 1st ed. Fldg maps. Fine. *VARNER.* $60

Pridham, Charles. ENGLAND'S COLONIAL EMPIRE. London: Smith, Elder, 1846. 1st ed. xiii,410pp. Fldg map. Worn. Internally VG; ex-lib. *WORLDWIDE.* $30

Priest, Cecil D. THE BIRDS OF SOUTHERN RHODESIA. London and Beccles, 1933-36. 40 colored plts, fldg map. 4 vols. Orig cl. Some bubbling to cl; spines faded. *SUTTON.* $575

Priestley, J.B. I FOR ONE. London, 1923. 1st ed. Uncut. Offsetting narrow strips front and rear fep. Fine in dj (spine little sunned, extrems sl rubbed). *POLYANTHOS.* $60

Priestley, J.B. THE HAPPY DREAM. Cheltenham, U.K.: The Whittington Press, (1976). 1st ed. Ltd ed, 193/400 signed. Compliments slip, pub leaflet laid in. Teg, uncut. Mint in Mint box. *POLYANTHOS.* $75

Priestley, J.B. THOMAS LOVE PEACOCK. NY: MacMillan, 1927. 1st US ed. Fine in lightly worn, chipped dj. *CAPTAIN'S BOOKSHELF.* $40

Priestley, J.B. THE TOWN MAJOR OF MIRAUCOURT. London: Heinemann, 1930. About Fine in pub slipcase. 1st ed. #259 of 525 signed. *CHAPEL HILL.* $65

Priestley, Raymond. ANTARCTIC RESEARCH. London: Butterworths, 1964. 1st ed. 2 fldg maps, 36 plts. Owner inscrip. Fine. Slipcase faded. Signed. *PARMER.* $125

Priestly, Herbert I. FRANCISCAN EXPLORATIONS IN CALIFORNIA. Glendale: Arthur H. Clark Co, 1946. 1st ed. VG to Fine. *BOOK MARKET.* $150

Priestly, Herbert I. (ed). THE COLORADO RIVER CAMPAIGN 1781-1782: THE DIARY OF PEDRO FAGES. Academy of Pacific Coast History, Vol 3, #2. Berkeley, 1913. Brn wraps. NF. *FIVE QUAIL.* $50

Priestly, Herbert I. TRISTAN DE LUNA. CONQUISTADOR OF THE OLD SOUTH. A.H. Clark, 1936. 1st ed, ltd to 500 numbered. Uncut, mostly unopened, teg. Fine. *OREGON.* $175

Prieto, Guillermo. SAN FRANCISCO IN THE SEVENTIES. SF: John Henry Nash, 1938. 1st ed. Ltd to 650. Edwin S. Morby (ed, trans). Fine in Fine dj. *CONNOLLY & WADE.* $85

Prime, Alfred Coxe. THE ARTS AND CRAFTS OF PHILADEL-PHIA, MARYLAND AND SOUTH CAROLINA 1721-1785, 1786-1800 SERIES I & II. Topsfield, MA: The Walpole Soc, 1929, 1932. 1st eds. Series I ltd to 500. Series II ltd to 400. *BACKROOM.* $250

Prime, E.D.G. AROUND THE WORLD. NY: Harper & Bros, 1872. xvi, 455pp,6pp pub cat. Violet cl stamped in gilt and black, quite faded on spine. *SCHOYER'S.* $50

Prime, William C. BOAT LIFE IN EGYPT AND NUBIA. NY: Harper, 1858. Sl rubbed, spine frayed, o/w VG. *WORLDWIDE.* $28

Prime, William C. BOAT LIFE IN EGYPT AND NUBIA. NY, 1872 (orig 1857). 498pp. 3/4 leather, marbled boards, worn. *HEINOLDT.* $18

Prime, William C. TENT LIFE IN THE HOLY LAND. NY, 1857. Spine rubbed. 497pp. *O'NEILL.* $30

Primm, Sandy. SHORT TIME. St. Louis: Cauldron Press, 1977. 1st ed. Fine in wraps, Signed. *LOPEZ.* $40

Prince, Benjamin F. CENTENNIAL CELEBRATION OF SPRINGFIELD, OHIO, HELD AUGUST 4TH TO 1OTH, 1901. (Springfield, OH, 1901). 1st ed. Orig cl, sm paper label on lower spine. *GINSBERG.* $75

Prince, L. Bradford. HISTORICAL SKETCHES OF NEW MEXICO FROM THE EARLIEST RECORDS TO THE AMERICAN OCCUPATION. Kansas City: Leggat, 1883. 2nd ed. Orig cl. Howes P611. *GINSBERG.* $175

Prince, L. Bradford. SPANISH MISSION CHURCHES OF NEW MEXICO. Cedar Rapids, IA: Torch, 1915. 1st ed. Orig pict cl. Howes P613. *GINSBERG.* $125

PRINCIPAL GAME BIRDS AND MAMMALS OF TEXAS, THEIR DISTRIBUTION AND MANAGEMENT. 21 fold-out range maps (colored). Austin, 1945. Cloth, chipped dj. *SUTTON.* $40

Prinzing, Friedrich. EPIDEMICS RESULTING FROM WARS. Oxford, 1916. 1st ed. Ex-lib. *FYE.* $150

Prioleau, John. THE ADVENTURES OF IMSHI. Boston: Little Brown, 1923. 1st ed. Ex-lib o/w Good. *WORLDWIDE.* $18

Prioleau, John. THE ADVENTURES OF IMSHI. Little Brown, 1923. Faded. *SCHOYER'S.* $25

Prior, Edward S. A HISTORY OF GOTHIC ART IN ENGLAND. London, 1900. Teg. NF. *POLYANTHOS.* $75

Prior, G.T. CATALOGUE OF METEORITES, WITH SPECIAL REFERENCE TO THOSE REPRESENTED IN THE COLLEC-TION OF THE BRITISH MUSEUM. London: British Museum, 1953 (1923). 2nd ed, rev & enl by Max H. Hey. Good. *KNOLLWOOD.* $40

Prior, Margaret. WALKS OF USEFULNESS. 17th ed. NY: Amer Female Guardian Soc, 1850. Blue cl stamped in gilt and blind, sl rubbed. Sl foxing, o/w VG. *SCHOYER'S.* $35

Pritchard, Alan. ALCHEMY: A BIBLIOGRAPHY OF ENGLISH-LANGUAGE WRITINGS. London, 1980. 1st ed. Dj. *FYE.* $100

Pritchard, James A. THE OVERLAND DIARY OF JAMES A. PRITCHARD FROM KENTUCKY TO CALIFORNIA IN 1849. (Denver, CO): Fred A. Rosenstock, 1959. Dale L. Morgan (ed). 1st ed. Frontis, 2 fldg maps, fldg chart in rear pocket. Dj. Fine. *KARMIOLE.* $85

Pritchard, James A. THE OVERLAND DIARY OF JAMES A. PRITCHARD FROM KENTUCKY TO CALIFORNIA IN 1849. WITH A BIOGRAPHY OF CAPTAIN JAMES A PRITCHARD BY HUGH PRITCHARD WILLIAMSON. Denver: Old West Pub, 1959. Dale Morgan (ed).1st ed. Uncut & unopened. VF in VG dj. *OREGON.* $140

Pritchett, V.S. THE SPANISH TEMPER. NY: Knopf, 1954. 1st Amer ed. NF in VG price-clipped dj. *CAPTAIN'S BOOKSHELF.* $40

Pritchett, W. Kendrick. STUDIES IN ANCIENT GREEK TOPOG-RAPHY, PART II (BATTLEFIELDS). Berkeley: Univ of CA Press, 1969. 16 figs. Wraps. Good. *ARCHAEOLOGIA.* $85

Proal, L. PASSION AND CRIMINALITY. Paris, n.d. 679pp. Orig buckram. Spine sl faded. Minor shelfwear, o/w VG+. Privately ptd. Reprint. *DIAMOND.* $35

PROCEEDINGS IN BEHALF OF THE MORTON TES-TIMONIAL. Boston, 1861. 1st ed. 56pp. Wrappers detached. Scarce. *FYE.* $200

PROCEEDINGS IN COMMEMORATION OF THE FIFTIETH ANNIVERSARY OF THE SETTLEMENT OF TALLMADGE. (By Benjamin Tallmadge.) Akron, Ohio: Beebe, 1857. 1st ed. 111,(1)pp. Old cl, emb lib stamp, bkpl removed. Howes T18. *GINSBERG.* $175

PROCEEDINGS OF THE EIGHTEENTH ANNUAL ENCAMP-MENT OF THE DEPARTMENT OF CALIFORNIA, GRAND ARMY OF THE REPUBLIC HELD AT SAN FRANCISCO,

FEBRUARY 18TH, 20TH, AND 21ST, 1885. SF, 1885. VG. *PRATT.* $35

Prochaska, George. A DISSERTATION ON THE FUNCTIONS OF THE NERVOUS SYSTEM. London, 1851. 1st Eng trans. 1463pp. Backstrip lacking. *FYE.* $100

Procter, George H. THE FISHERMEN'S MEMORIAL AND RECORD BOOK.... Gloucester: Procter, 1873. 1st ed. 172pp, ads. Worn. Internally VG. Howes P-626. *SECOND LIFE.* $75

Procton, Mary A. THE INDIANS OF THE WINNIPESAUKEE AND PEMIGEWASSET VALLEYS. Franklin, NH: Towne & Robie, 1930. 1st ed. 17 plts, illus mounted on front cvr. VG. *SCHOYER'S.* $25

Proctor Brothers (eds). THE FISHERIES OF GLOUCESTER FROM 1623 TO 1876, ETC. Gloucester, 1876. 88pp. Illus w/engr and ads. Wraps chipped, else VG. *MIKESH.* $65

Proctor, C.H. THE LIFE OF JAMES WILLIAMS BETTER KNOWN AS PROFESSOR JIM. Hartford, CT: Case, Lockwood & Brainard, 1873. 1st ed. 80pp. Orig grn cl, bit soiled. Scarce. *KAR-MIOLE.* $85

Proctor, Maurice. HIDEAWAY. NY: Harper, 1968. 1st Amer ed. Fine in dj, sl wear. *SILVER DOOR.* $25

Proctor, Richard A. HALF-HOURS WITH THE TELESCOPE. NY: Putnam, 1873. VG. *SECOND LIFE.* $25

Proctor, Richard A. OTHER WORLDS THAN OURS. London: Longmans, Green, 1886 (1870). New ed. Fldg map. Good. *KNOLLWOOD.* $26

Proctor, Richard A. THE SUN: RULER, FIRE, LIGHT AND LIFE OF THE PLANETARY SYSTEM. London: Longmans, Grn, 1872 (1871). 2nd ed. Overall Good. *KNOLLWOOD.* $80

Proctor, Richard A. THE UNIVERSE OF SUNS AND OTHER SCIENCE GLEANINGS. London: Chatto and Windus, 1884. 1st ed. Worn ex-lib. 1 fldg illus. *KNOLLWOOD.* $25

PROGRESSIVE MEN OF THE STATE OF MONTANA. Chicago: Bowen, n.d. (c. 1902). 1st ed. Frontis, 189 plts. Full morocco, blindstamped cover, gilt stamped spine, aeg, dec eps. Tear along spine edge of 2 preliminary leaves and frontis, o/w NF. *OREGON.* $700

Pronzini, Bill. BINDLESTIFF. St. Martin's, (1983). 1st ed. Signed. Fine in NF dj. *BEBBAH.* $30

Pronzini, Bill. BLOWBACK. London: Hale, 1978. 1st British ed. Signed. Fine in dj sl soiled rear panel. *SILVER DOOR.* $35

Pronzini, Bill. BONES. NY: St. Martin's Press, 1985. 1st ed. Fine in dj w/crease on inner front flap and minor wear at spine ends and along edges. *MORDIDA.* $25

Pronzini, Bill. DEADFALL. NY: St. Martin's, 1986. 1st ed. Signed. Fine in dj. *SILVER DOOR.* $35

Pronzini, Bill. DEADFALL. NY: St. Martin's Press, 1986. 1st ed. Fine in dj. *MORDIDA.* $25

Pronzini, Bill. GAMES. NY: Putnam, 1976. 1st ed. Signed. Fine in sl worn dj. *SILVER DOOR.* $35

Pronzini, Bill. GUN IN CHEEK: A STUDY OF "ALTERNATIVE" CRIME FICTION. NY: Coward, McCann & Geoghegan, 1982. 1st ed. Fine in dj. *MORDIDA.* $30

Pronzini, Bill. PANIC! NY: Random House, 1972. 1st ed. Fine in dj w/couple of small pieces missing from back panel and nick at bottom of spine. *MORDIDA.* $25

Pronzini, Bill. SCATTERSHOT. NY: St. Martin's Press, 1982. 1st ed. Fine in dj. *MORDIDA.* $25

Pronzini, Bill. SHACKLES. NY: St. Martin's Press, 1988. 1st ed. Minor wear, o/w Fine in dj. *MORDIDA.* $22.50

Prosch, Charles. REMINISCENCES OF WASHINGTON TERRITORY...OF THE PIONEER PERIOD ON PUGET SOUND. Seattle, WA, 1904. Orig cl. Presentation copy. Howes P633. *GINSBERG.* $125

PROSE AND POETRY OF THE LIVESTOCK INDUSTRY. Antiquarian Press, 1959. Ltd to 550, rpt of 1904 ed. Ex-lib. Rubbed, worn w/usual markings, o/w Fine. *VARNER.* $175

PROSPECTOR, COWHAND, AND SODBUSTER: HISTORIC PLACES. Wash, DC: Dept of Interior, 1967. 1st ed. Nat'l Survey of Hist Sites and Bldgs, Vol XI. Robert G. Ferris (ed). VF. *CONNOLLY & WADE.* $35

Prothero, G.W. A MEMOIR OF HENRY BRADSHAW....London: Kegan Paul, Trench & Co, 1888. 1st ed. Frontis. Orig cl. Fine. *OAK KNOLL.* $85

Prucha, Francis Paul. INDIAN PEACE MEDALS IN AMERICAN HISTORY. WI Hist Soc, 1971. 1st ed. VF in VF dj. *OREGON.* $85

Prudden, T. Mitchell. THE STORY OF THE BACTERIA AND THEIR RELATIONS TO HEALTH AND DISEASE. NY, 1889. 1st ed. *FYE.* $75

Pry, Paul (pseud of William Heath, or John Poole). ODDITIES OF LONDON LIFE. London: Richard Bentley, 1838. 2 vols. 1st ed. 316pp; 234pp. 19th-c 3/4 morocco w/orig grn cl cvrs and spine titles tipped to pastedowns. 22 engr plts. NF, w/bkpl of Lucius Poole, Boston. 1st ed. *CHAPEL HILL.* $275

Puckett, James L. and Ellen. HISTORY OF OKLAHOMA AND INDIAN TERRITORY AND HOMESEEKERS' GUIDE. Vinta, OK: Chieftain Pub Co, 1906. 1st ed. Orig pict wrappers, some chipping to spine. Fine overall. Howes P645. *GINSBERG.* $300

Puckett, R. Campbell. SCIOGRAPHY; OR RADIAL PROJECTION OF SHADOWS. London: Chapman & Hall, 1877 (1868), 3rd ed. Blindstamped maroon cl, stained; spine frayed, worn, hinges repaired, emb mark (ex-lib?). 21 fldg plts. Good. *KNOLLWOOD.* $35

Pugh, Edwin. THE CHARLES DICKENS ORIGINALS. London: T.N. Foulis, 1913. 2nd imprint. Blue cl, spine sl faded. VG. *GREAT EXPECTATIONS.* $35

Pugh, P.D.G. NELSON AND HIS SURGEONS. Edinburgh, 1968. 1st ed. *FYE.* $45

Puharich, Andrija. THE SACRED MUSHROOM. GC: Doubleday, 1959. 1st ed. Pub's promo letter laid in. VG in dj. *LOPEZ.* $45

Puig, Manuel. BETRAYED BY RITA HAYWORTH. NY: Dutton (1971). 1st Amer ed. NF in Fine dj. *DORN.* $175

Puig, Manuel. ETERNAL CURSE ON THE READER OF THESE PAGES. NY: Random House (1982). 1st Amer ed. Fine in dj. *DORN.* $30

Puig, Manuel. HEARTBREAK TANGO. NY: Dutton (1973). 1st Amer ed. Fine in price-clipped dj. *DORN.* $60

Puig, Manuel. KISS OF THE SPIDER WOMAN. NY: Knopf (1979). 1st ed. Lt rmdr mk else Fine in dj. *DORN.* $40

Puig, Manuel. KISS OF THE SPIDER WOMAN. NY: Knopf, 1979. 1st ed. Narrow band of top edge stain on ep, else Fine in dj. *ELSE FINE.* $45

Puig, Manuel. THE BUENOS AIRES AFFAIR. NY: Dutton (1976). 1st ed. Fine in dj. *DORN.* $35

Puig, Manuel. TROPICAL NIGHT FALLING. NY: Simon & Schuster, (1991). Uncorrected proof. Fine in wrappers. *LOPEZ.* $35

Pullein-Thompson, Josephine. HOW HORSES ARE TRAINED. London: Routeledge & Kegan Paul, 1961. 1st ed. VG in VG dj. *OCTOBER FARM.* $15

Pullen, John. A SHOWER OF STARS, THE MEDAL OF HONOR AND THE 27TH MAINE. Phila, (1966). 1st ed. Fine in dj. *PRATT.* $35

Pulszky, Francis. THE TRICOLOR ON THE ATLAS; OR ALGERIA AND THE FRENCH CONQUEST. NY: Nelson, 1855. 1st ed. vi,402pp. 3 tinted fldg plts. Near Good ex-lib. *WORLDWIDE.* $30

Pulteney, Richard. HISTORICAL AND BIOGRAPHICAL SKETCHES OF THE PROGRESS OF BOTANY IN ENGLAND. 2 vols. London, 1790. Pp xvi,(4),360; (8),352,(34). Old half sheep, some edge scuffing. Ffep, vol I title loose. *SUTTON.* $485

Pumpelly, R. MY REMINISCENCES. 2 vols. Holt, 1918. VG+. *BOOKCELL.* $50

Pumpelly, R. TRAVELS & ADVENTURES OF RAPHAEL PUMPELLEY, MINING ENGINEER, GEOLOGIST, ARCHAEOLOGIST & EXPLORER. NY: Holt, 1920. Illus w/frontis. Good+. *MIKESH.* $17.50

Pumpelly, Raphael. ACROSS AMERICA AND ASIA. NY: Leypoldt, 1871. 5th rev ed. 1/4 leather. VG to Fine. *BOOK MARKET.* $40

Purdy, Carol. IVA DUNNIT AND THE BIG WIND. Dial, (1985). 1st ed. Illus and signed w/a drawing by Steven Kellogg. Fine in Fine dj. *BEBBAH.* $25

Purdy, James. 63: DREAM PALACE. NY: The William-Frederick Press, 1956. 1st ed. Orig ptd illus wraps. Fine. Inscription. *CHAPEL HILL.* $300

Purdy, James. CABOT WRIGHT BEGINS. NY: FSG, 1964. 1st ed. Fine in dj. *ELSE FINE.* $30

Purdy, James. COLOR OF DARKNESS. NY: New Directions, 1957. 1st ed. Fine in Fine dj (1" chip at foot of spine). *BEASLEY.* $35

Purdy, James. EUSTACE CHISHOLM AND THE WORKS. Farrar, Straus & Giroux, 1967. 1st ed. Fine in dj. *STAHR.* $20

Purdy, James. MALCOLM. NY: Farrar, 1959. 1st ed. Fine in NF dj. *BEASLEY.* $45

Purdy, James. MOURNERS BELOW. NY: Viking, (1981). Uncorrected proof copy. Inscribed. VG in wrappers. *LOPEZ.* $65

Purdy, James. NARROW ROOMS. Arbor House, 1978. 1st ed. Fine in dj. *STAHR.* $15

Purves-Stewart, J. and Arthur Evans. NERVE INJURIES AND THEIR TREATMENT. London, 1919. 2nd ed. Ex-lib. *FYE.* $50

Pusey, William and Eugene Caldwell. THE PRACTICAL APPLICATION OF THE ROENTGEN RAYS IN THERAPEUTICS AND DIAGNOSIS. Phila, 1904. 2nd ed. 182 illus. *FYE.* $150

Pushkin, Aleksander. EUGENE ONEGIN. Vladimir Nabokov (trans). 4 vols. (NY): Pantheon Books, (1964). 1st ed. Sl dusty, o/w Fine set in price-clipped djs (sl rubbed). Slipcase. *JAFFE.* $350

Pushkin, Alexander. THE GOLDEN COCKEREL. Illus by Edmund Dulac. NY: LEC, N.d. (circa 1949). Ed ltd to 1500 numbered, signed by Dulac. In a folder (spine with a few oil (?) stains) and slipcase (sl faded). *KARMIOLE.* $150

PUSS IN BOOTS. NY: Blue Ribbon Press, (1934). C. Carey Cloud, Harold B. Lentz (illus). 3 colored pop-ups, pict boards. 1st ed. Fine. *JAFFE.* $150

PUSS IN BOOTS. NY, 1977. Nicola Bayley. Pop-up bk. *BOOKFINDERS INTL.* $40

Putnam, Arthur A. SELECTION FROM THE ADDRESSES, LECTURES...WITH A BIOGRAPHIC SKETCH OF ARTHUR A. PUTNAM....Cambridge, Mass, 1910. 1st ed. Orig cl. *GINSBERG.* $75

Putnam, David Binney. DAVID GOES TO GREENLAND. NY/London: G.P. Putnam's Sons, 1926. 4th imp. VG. *PARMER.* $25

Putnam, Frederick W. REPORTS UPON ARCHAEOLOGICAL AND ETHNOLOGICAL COLLECTIONS FORM VICINITY OF SANTA BARBARA, CALIFORNIA, AND FROM RUINED PUEBLOS OF ARIZONA AND NEW MEXICO, AND CERTAIN INTERIOR TRIBES. Washington: GPO, 1879. xxi,497pp. Chromolitho frontis; map; 20 plts. Ex-lib. Minimal marking. Orig cl, scuffed, wear. *SCHOYER'S.* $185

Putnam, G.R. NAUTICAL CHARTS. NY: John Wiley & Sons; London: Chapman & Hall, 1908. 1st ed. 2 plts. VG. Owner stamp. *LEFKOWICZ.* $70

Putnam, George Granville. SALEM VESSELS AND THEIR VOYAGES. Salem, 1924-1930. 1st ed. 4 vols. Attractive set. *LEFKOWICZ.* $200

Putnam, George Haven. A PRISONER OF WAR IN VIRGINIA 1864-64. NY, 1914. Preferred 3rd ed. Spine faded a bit, wear at spine extremities o/w Fine. *PRATT.* $50

Putnam, George Haven. SOME MEMORIES OF THE CIVIL WAR. NY, 1924. 1st ed. 303pp. Minor cover wear, o/w Fine. *PRATT.* $35

Putnam, George Palmer. DEATH VALLEY AND ITS COUNTRY. NY: Duell, Sloan and Pearce, 1946. 1st ed. NF in Good+ dj. *CONNOLLY & WADE.* $35

Putnam, George Palmer. DEATH VALLEY HANDBOOK. NY: Duell, Sloan, Pearce, (1947). 1st ptg. Cl, dj. VG. *SCHOYER'S.* $15

Putnam, George Palmer. DEATH VALLEY HANDBOOK. NY: Duell, Sloan and Pearce, 1947. NF, rubbed dj. *PARMER.* $30

Putnam, James and George Waterman. STUDIES IN NEUROLOGICAL DIAGNOSIS. Boston, 1902. 1st ed. Photo illus. *FYE.* $75

Putnam, James William. ILLINOIS & MICHIGAN CANAL, A STUDY IN ECONOMIC HISTORY. Chicago, 1918. Cl backed boards w/ptd spine labels, glassine wrapper. Fine, unopened. *BOHLING.* $45

PUTNAM POMFRET'S WARD....Beadle's Dime Novels No. 30. Circa August 1862. Last # listed on inside back cvr is No. 42. Cvr is complete. VF, fragile in wraps. *BOOK MARKET.* $65

Putti, Vittorio. HISTORIC ARTIFICIAL LIMBS. NY, 1930. 1st ed. *FYE.* $75

Puzo, Mario. THE DARK ARENA. NY, 1955. 1st ed. Author's 1st bk. Signed, presentation copy. Fine in sl sunned, edge rubbed dj. *POLYANTHOS.* $65

Pycroft, James. THE CRICKET FIELD. London: Longman, Brown, Green and Longmans, 1851.1st ed. Rare. Orig grn cl covered bds rebound in 1/2 maroon dec lea. NF. *OLD LONDON.* $100

Pyle, Howard. BOOK OF PIRATES. Harper, (1921). 209pp. 13 color & b/w illus & decs by Pyle. VG, cvr color pict pastedown w/slight wear, but bright. *BEBBAH.* $55

Pyle, Howard. HOWARD PYLE'S BOOK OF PIRATES. NY & London: Harper and Bros, (1921). Merle Johnson (comp). 1 tipped-in plt, 13 full-page plts. Bumped and rubbed, front hinge starting. NF internally. *BLUE MOUNTAIN.* $95

Pyle, Howard. HOWARD PYLE'S BOOK OF THE AMERICAN SPIRIT. NY: Harper & Row, (1923). Cl w/pict inset, 21 color plts. Corners bumped, 1 long closed tear in dj, else VG. *ACADEMIC LIBRARY.* $75

Pyle, Howard. HOWARD PYLE'S BOOK OF THE AMERICAN SPIRIT. Comp by Merle Johnson; ed by Francis J. Dowd. NY: Harper & Bros. 1923. 1st ed. Dj. Fine. *KARMIOLE.* $275

Pyle, Howard. HOWARD PYLE'S BOOK OF THE AMERICAN SPIRIT. NY, London, 1923. Merle Johnson (comp). 1st ed. 200+ illus, pict cvrs, lea; spine chipped, rubbed; small stain top edge rear cvr. Dj spine chipped, few small stains. *POLYANTHOS.* $300

Pyle, Howard. PEPPER & SALT OR SEASONING FOR YOUNG FOLK. Harper later ptg. 109pp. 74 Pyle illus, full-page plates ptd either in brown or grn. VG. *BEBBAH.* $40

Pyle, Howard. THE MERRY ADVENTURES OF ROBIN HOOD. Scribner's, 1924. 296pp. 23 full-page b/w & numerous decs. by Pyle. Few touches of page soil, else VG w/dec cvr. *BEBBAH.* $55

Pyle, Howard. THE WONDER CLOCK OR FOUR AND TWENTY MARVELOUS TALES, ETC....NY: Harper, 1888. 1st ed. 4to. Modern polished brown morocco spine over the orig grn cl (rubbed). Card bearing Pyle's sig, brief sentiment affixed to front pastedown. *CAPTAIN'S BOOKSHELF.* $375

Pym, Barbara. LESS THAN ANGELS. NY, (1957). 1st US ed. Eps show light foxing, else VG+ in dj. *PETTLER.* $55

Pynchon, Thomas. A JOURNEY INTO THE MIND OF WATTS. (Westminster): (Mouldwarp), (1983). Fine in wraps. *LOPEZ.* $50

Pynchon, Thomas. ENTROPY. Troy Town: Trystero, n.d. Wraps. 1st separate appearance. 2nd ptg (photo collage cover). Fine. *BEASLEY.* $25

Pynchon, Thomas. GRAVITY'S RAINBOW. NY: Viking, (1973). 1st ed. 4,000 hb copies ptd. Tiny flaw in front pastedown else beautiful in NF dj. *ROBBINS.* $425

Pynchon, Thomas. GRAVITY'S RAINBOW. NY: Viking, (1973). 1st ed. Review copy, pub's slip giving details of pub laid in. Cl, dj. VF. *JAFFE.* $750

Pynchon, Thomas. GRAVITY'S RAINBOW. NY: Viking Press, (1973). 1st ed. Fine in dj (four tiny edge tears). *CAPTAIN'S BOOKSHELF.* $450

Pynchon, Thomas. LOW-LANDS. (London): (Aloes) (1978). One of 1500. Fine in wraps. *LOPEZ.* $50

Pynchon, Thomas. LOW-LANDS. London: Aloes, 1978. Wraps. 1st separate appearance. Fine. *BEASLEY.* $40

Pynchon, Thomas. MORTALITY AND MERCY IN VIENNA. London: Aloes, n.d. Wraps. 1st separate appearance, ptg undetermined. Fine *BEASLEY.* $25

Pynchon, Thomas. MORTALITY AND MERCY IN VIENNA. London: Aloes (n.d.) (1976). State (2) of states identified in Mead's bibliography, w/no known priority. Fine. *LOPEZ.* $50

Pynchon, Thomas. THE CRYING OF LOT 49. Lippincott, 1966. 1st ed. About Fine in dj (wear at spine ends, flyleaf folds; missing sm piece foot of spine). Owner name. *STAHR.* $180

Pynchon, Thomas. THE CRYING OF LOT 49. Phila: Lippincott (1966). 1st ed. Fine in NF dj (edgewear at spine extrems). *LOPEZ.* $225

Pynchon, Thomas. THE CRYING OF LOT 49. Phila: Lippincott, (1966). 1st ed. Fine in dj. *CAPTAIN'S BOOKSHELF.* $275

Pynchon, Thomas. THE SECRET INTEGRATION. London, 1980. 1st ed. Ltd ed, to 2500. Pict wraps. Fine. *POLYANTHOS.* $35

Pynchon, Thomas. THE SECRET INTEGRATION. London: Aloes Books, 1980. 1st separate ptg. 1/2500 in wrappers. Fine. *JUVELIS.* $25

Pynchon, Thomas. THE SMALL RAIN. London: Aloes, 1982. Sm bump lower corner. Fine in stapled wraps. *LOPEZ.* $45

Pynchon, Thomas. V. Phila: Lippincott, (1963). 1st ed. Just About Fine in lightly used, internally-mended dj. *CAPTAIN'S BOOKSHELF.* $375

Pynchon. Thomas. V. Phila: Lippincott (1963). 1st ed. NF in very spine-faded, but not rubbed, dj. *LOPEZ.* $650

Pyper, George. THE ROMANCE OF AN OLD PLAYHOUSE. Salt Lake, 1937. 2nd ed. VG. *BENCHMARK.* $25

Q

Quaife, Milo M. (comp). THE DEVELOPMENT OF CHICAGO 1674-1914, SHOWN IN A SERIES OF CONTEMPORARY ORIGINAL NARRATIVES. Chicago: Caxton Club, 1916. 1/175 on Italian hand-made paper. 4 plts. Slight stain base of spine, partially unopened. Very Nice. Howes Q2. *BOHLING.* $350

Quaife, Milo M. CHECAGOU: FROM INDIAN WIGWAM TO MODERN CITY 1673-1835. Chicago: Univ of Chicago, 1933. 1st ed. NF in Good+ dj. *CONNOLLY & WADE.* $30

Quain, Jones and W.J.E. Wilson. A SERIES OF ANATOMICAL PLATES, WITH REFERENCES AND PHYSIOLOGICAL COMMENTS, ILLUSTRATING THE STRUCTURE OF THE DIFFERENT PARTS OF THE HUMAN BODY. Phila, 1846. 3rd ed. 1/2 leather, various paginations, 199 of 200 plts present w/1 duplicate plt. Scattered foxing and staining. Scarce. *FYE.* $500

Quain, Jones. HUMAN ANATOMY. Joseph Leidy, MD (ed). 1st Amer ed. 2 vols. Phila: Lea and Blanchard, 1849. 638; 639, ads. Contemp sheep. VG set. *SECOND LIFE.* $65

Quain, Richard. THE DISEASES OF THE RECTUM. London, 1854. 1st ed. 285pp + 4 hand-colored engrvd plts. Marginal notations and ink underlining on few leaves. Very Scarce. *FYE.* $150

Quarles, Benjamin. THE NEGRO IN THE CIVIL WAR. Boston, (1953). 1st ed. VG. *McGOWAN.* $45

Quarles, Benjamin. THE NEGRO IN THE CIVIL WAR. Boston, (1953). 379pp. Dj wear o/w VG. *PRATT.* $25

QUARTO-MILLENARY. THE FIRST 250 PUBLICATIONS AND THE FIRST 25 YEARS, 1929-1954, OF THE LIMITED EDITIONS CLUB. NY: LEC, 1959. Ed ltd to 2250. Slipcase (w/few small cracks). *KARMIOLE.* $275

Quebbeman, Frances E. MEDICINE IN TERRITORIAL ARIZONA. Phoenix: Arizona Hist Foundation, 1966. 1st ed. Fine in clear plastic cvr. *BOOK MARKET.* $40

Queen, Ellery. A FINE AND PRIVATE PLACE. World, 1971. 1st. Fine in dj. Remainder mark. *STAHR.* $22.50

Queen, Ellery. CALAMITY TOWN. Boston: Little Brown, 1942. 1st ed. Sl worn extrems, couple of closed tears, Fine in dj. *SECOND LIFE.* $125

Queen, Ellery. CALENDAR OF CRIME. Boston: Little Brown, 1952. 1st ed. Fine in dj. *MORDIDA.* $65

Queen, Ellery. ELLERY QUEEN, MASTER DETECTIVE. G&S, (1941). VG but sl cocked in VG dj. *BEBBAH.* $20

Queen, Ellery. FACE TO FACE. NY: NAL, 1967. 1st ed. Bkseller's small label on fep. Fine in dj. *MORDIDA.* $45

Queen, Ellery. IN THE QUEEN'S PARLOR. NY: Simon and Schuster, 1957. 1st ed. Inscribed. Fine in dj. *MORDIDA.* $100

Queen, Ellery. IN THE QUEEN'S PARLOUR AND OTHER LEAVES FROM THE EDITOR'S NOTEBOOK. London, 1957. 1st English ed. *DIAMOND.* $25

Queen, Ellery. INSPECTOR QUEEN'S OWN CASE. NY: Simon & Schuster, 1956. 1st ed. Pp darkened o/w Fine in price-clipped dj. *MORDIDA.* $65

Queen, Ellery. QUEEN'S BUREAU OF INVESTIGATION. Boston: Little Brown, 1954. 1st ed. Fine in price-clipped dj w/sl faded spine. *MORDIDA.* $65

Queen, Ellery. THE CASE BOOK OF ELLERY QUEEN. NY: Lawrence E. Spivak, 1945. 1st ed. Signed by "Ellery Queen" and Frederic Dannay. Pb orig. Bestseller Mystery no. B59. Few tiny nicks along front cover edge, short tear along spine edge and tiny wear at top of spine o/w Fine in wrappers. *MORDIDA.* $100

Queen, Ellery. THE CHINESE ORANGE MYSTERY. NY: Frederick A. Stokes, 1934. 3rd prtg. Inscribed by Queen, signed by both Lee and Dannay. Fine in VG dj w/scraped spine, several short closed tears; chipping top of spine and corners. *MORDIDA.* $125

Queen, Ellery. THE DEVIL TO PAY. NY: Frederick A. Stokes, 1938. 1st ed. Spine and eps darkened o/w VG in dj w/scrape and hole on spine, chipping at top of spine and several short closed tears. *MORDIDA.* $45

Queen, Ellery. THE DRAGON'S TEETH. NY, 1939. 1st Amer ed. Spine darkened. Sl cvr staining and soiling, o/w VG. *DIAMOND.* $45

Queen, Ellery. THE GLASS VILLAGE. Boston: Little Brown, 1954. 1st ed. Fine in price-clipped dj (sl faded spine; creasing front panel; minor wear spine ends, corners). *MORDIDA.* $45

Queen, Ellery. THE KING IS DEAD. Boston: Little Brown, 1952. 1st ed. Fine in dj (sl faded spine; tiny tears). *MORDIDA.* $65

Queen, Ellery. THE ROMAN HAT MYSTERY. Intro Frederic Dannay. NY: Mysterious Press, 1979. Golden Anniversary ed. VF in dj. *MORDIDA.* $40

Queen, Ellery. THE SCARLET LETTERS. Boston: Little Brown, 1953. 1st ed. Fine in dj. *MORDIDA.* $65

Queneau, Raymond. THE BLUE FLOWERS. NY: Atheneum, 1967. 1st ed. Fine in Fine dj. *BEASLEY.* $25

Quennell, Peter. INSCRIPTION ON A FOUNTAIN-HEAD. London: Faber & Faber. Grn paper wraps. VG. *HELLER.* $20

Quentin, Patrick. PUZZLE FOR PUPPETS. NY: Simon and Schuster, 1944. 1st ed. Name fep, o/w Fine in dj with several short closed tears, minor wear. *MORDIDA.* $40

Quentin, Patrick. SUSPICIOUS CIRCUMSTANCES. NY: Simon and Schuster, 1957. 1st ed. Pp darkened, o/w Fine in dj. *MORDIDA.* $45

Quentin, Patrick. THE FOLLOWER. NY: Simon and Schuster, 1950. 1st ed. Top edge sl darkened, o/w Fine in dj. *MORDIDA.* $40

Quentin, Patrick. THE MAN IN THE NET. NY: Simon and Schuster, 1956. 1st ed. Fine in price-clipped dj. *MORDIDA.* $37.50

Quentin, Patrick. THE ORDEAL OF MRS. SNOW. NY: Random House, 1962. 1st Amer ed. Fine in dj w/some slight rubbing. *MORDIDA.* $55

Quevado, Don Francisco de. THE DOG & THE FEVER. Hamded: The Shoe String Press, (1954). 1st ed. Fine in Fine dj. *DORN.* $45

Quick, Herbert. THE INVISIBLE WOMAN. Bobbs-Merrill, (1924). 1st ed. Fine in chipped dj. *AUTHORS OF THE WEST.* $35

Quin, Michael J. A STEAM VOYAGE DOWN THE DANUBE. London, 1836. 3rd ed, w/additions. 2 vols. xv,344pp; vii,340pp. *O'NEILL.* $110

Quin, Mike. THE BIG STRIKE. Olema, CA, 1949. 1st ed. Pict wraps. Fine. *DIAMOND.* $35

Quinby, M. MYSTERIES OF BEE-KEEPING EXPLAINED. NY: Saxton, 1864. 8th ed. VG, tight. *SECOND LIFE.* $45

Quinn, P.T. PEAR CULTURE FOR PROFIT. NY: Orange Judd, 1869. 1st ed. Fine. *BOOK MARKET.* $30

Quinn, Seabury. ROADS. Arkham House, 1948. 1st ed. VF in dj. *MADLE.* $175

Quint, Alonzo H. THE POTOMAC AND THE RAPIDAN. Boston, 1864. 1st ed. 407pp. Cover worn, spine extremities chipped; o/w VG. *PRATT.* $45

Quintanilla, Luis. ALL THE BRAVE. NY: Modern Age Books, (1939). 1st trade ed. Ernest Hemingway (preface). Maroon wraps soiled, rubbed at edges, corners sl creased, front hinge cracked. Very Nice. *BLUE MOUNTAIN.* $50

R

Raban, Jonathan. ARABIA. A JOURNEY THROUGH THE LABYRINTH. NY: Simon & Schuster, 1979. 1st ed. Sl rubbed, o/w VG. *WORLDWIDE.* $18

Rabe, Peter. CODE NAME GIDGET. Greenwich: Fawcett Publications, 1967. 1st ed. Pb orig. Gold Medal no. 1830. Fine, unread, in wrappers. *MORDIDA.* $30

Rackham, Arthur. ARTHUR RACKHAM'S BOOK OF PICTURES. London: William Heinemann, (1913). 44 tipped-in color illus, each w/ptd guard. Gold stamped cloth, light soiling, stain on back cover. One of 1000 signed. *DAWSON'S.* $350

Rackham, Arthur. THE ARTHUR RACKHAM FAIRY BOOK. London: George G. Harrap. (1933). 288pp. With 8 color plts, incl frontis; each pl w/ptd tissue guard. Dec red cl stamped in black and beige, cvr sl soiled. *KARMIOLE.* $150

Rackham, Bernard. THE ANCIENT GLASS OF CANTERBURY CATHEDRAL. London: Lund, Humphries & Co, 1949. Ltd to 960. Gilt lettered blue buckram. 20 full-PG colored plts, 80 monochrome. Boxed. *CULLEN.* $225

Radcliffe, Charles et al. ON DISEASES OF THE SPINE AND NERVES. Phila, 1871. 1st Amer ed. *FYE.* $50

Radcliffe, F.P. Delme. THE NOBLE SCIENCE. London: George Routledge & Sons, 1911. 2 vols. Minor edgewear, else VG-NF. *OLD LONDON.* $225

Rader, Jesse L. SOUTH OF FORTY. Norman: Univ of OK Press, 1947. 1st ed. Cl. VG. *SCHOYER'S.* $90

Radin, Paul. INDIANS OF SOUTH AMERICA. GC: Doubleday, Doran, & Co, 1942. 1st ed. Lt wear, soiling bk and dj. Beige cl; blue/burgundy cover and spine decs. Blue spine titles. Overall VG. *PARMER.* $75

Radin, Paul. THE TRICKSTER. NY: Philosophical Library, (1956). 1st ed. VG in edgeworn dj chipped at spine extrems. *LOPEZ.* $85

Radley, Sheila. BLOOD ON THE HAPPY HIGHWAY. London: Constable, 1983. 1st ed. Fine in dj. *MORDIDA.* $35

Radley, Sheila. DEATH & THE MAIDEN. London: Hamilton, 1978. 1st ed. About Fine in dj. *SILVER DOOR.* $25

Radley, Sheila. FATE WORSE THAN DEATH. NY: Scribner, 1986. 1st Amer ed. Rev copy, pub's slip laid in. VF in dj. *SILVER DOOR.* $25

Larned, W.T. AMERICAN INDIAN FAIRY TALES. Chicago: Volland, (1921). John Rae, illus. 13th ed. Pict boards. General wear; inside VG. *ACADEMIC LIBRARY.* $30

Raemaekers, Louis. KULTUR IN CARTOONS. NY, 1917. 1st ed. Edgewear. Good. *ARTIS.* $30

Raht, Carlysle Graham. THE ROMANCE OF DAVIS MOUNTAINS AND BIG BEND COUNTRY. El Paso: Rahtbooks, (1919). Double pg map, 26 plts. Bright. Howes R16. *KARMIOLE.* $100

Raine, William M. 45-CALIBER LAW. (Evanston, IL, 1941). 1st ed. Pict cl. Ex-lib. VG. *DIAMOND.* $15

Raine, William M. 45-CALIBER LAW. Row, Peterson & Co, (1941). 1st ed. Fine w/o dj as issued. *AUTHORS OF THE WEST.* $17.50

Raine, William M. et al. DENVER MURDERS. NY: Duell, Sloan and Pearce, 1946. 1st ed. NF w/sl soiling, in lightly used dj w/chips. *BEASLEY.* $35

Raine, William M. GUNS OF THE FRONTIER. Houghton Mifflin, 1940. 1st ed. NF in chipped dj. *VARNER.* $45

Raine, William M. IRON HEART. Houghton Mifflin, 1923. 1st ed. Fine. *AUTHORS OF THE WEST.* $25

Rainier, Peter W. PIPELINE TO BATTLE. NY: Random House (1943). 1st Amer ed. Dj chipped. *SCHOYER'S.* $15

Rainwater, Dorothy T. AMERICAN SILVER MANUFACTURERS. Hanover, PA: Everybodys Press, 1966. 1st ed. Good. *BACKROOM.* $25

Raison, Milton. NOBODY LOVES A DEAD MAN. Murray & Gee, 1945. 1st ed. VG in VG dj. *BEBBAH.* $35

Rakosi, Carl. DROLES DE JOURNAL. West Branch, IA: The Toothpaste Press, February, 1981. Fine. 1st ed. #15 of 150 signed. *CHAPEL HILL.* $35

Ralli, Paul. NEVADA LAWYER. Culver City, Ca, (1949). 2nd ed, rev, enl. VG. *DIAMOND*. $25

Ralphson, G. Harvey. BOY SCOUTS BEYOND THE ARCTIC CIRCLE OR THE LOST EXPEDITION. Chicago: M.A. Donahue & Company, c. 1913. Owner's inscrip, else Very Nice in worn dj. *PARMER*. $30

Ralston, Caroline. GRASS HUTS AND WAREHOUSES. Honolulu: Univ of HI, (1978). 1st ed. Fine in Fine dj. *BOOK MARKET*. $25

Rambler, May. LITTLE COMMODORE. NY: Sheldon. Blakeman & Co, 1858. 300pp. Fairly fresh except for corners, head and tail of spine, which are rubbed. Aeg. Lacks ffep. *SCHOYER'S*. $40

Sylvanus (pseud of Robert Colton). RAMBLES IN SWEDEN AND GOTTLAND. London: Richard Bentley. 1847. xviii,360pp. 7 woodcuts, 3 lithos. Cl bit soiled and rubbed. Ffep lacking. Lib label removed from spine. *KARMIOLE*. $65

Ramirez Vazquez, Pedro et al. THE NATIONAL MUSEUM OF ANTHROPOLOGY. MEXICO. NY: Abrams, (1968). 1st ed. 54 color plts tipped-in, 258 b/w plts. Good in dj. *SILVER*. $60

Ramon y Cajal, S. STUDIES ON THE CEREBRAL CORTEX. Springfield, 1955. 1st Eng trans. *FYE*. $100

Ramos, Graciliano. SAO BERNARDO. NY: Taplinger, 1979. 1st ed. Name and date. Fine; 2" tear upper spine fold. 1st US ed. *ELSE FINE*. $25

Rampa, Lobsang. THE THIRD EYE: THE AUTOBIOGRAPHY OF A TIBETAN LAMA. Secker & Warburg, 1956. Later ptg. Fine in lightly worn dj. *STAHR*. $45

Rampling, Anne (pseud of Anne Rice). BELINDA. NY, (1986). 1st ed. Fine in dj. *McCLINTOCK*. $25

Ramsay, David. LIFE OF GEORGE WASHINGTON. NY: Hopkins, 1807. (8),376pp. 1st ed. Contemp full calf, flyleaf clipped. Howes R38. *GINSBERG*. $150

Ramsay, David. THE LIFE OF GEORGE WASHINGTON. London: T. Cadell and W. Davies, 1807. 1st Eng ed. Frontis. Owner sig, lib stamp. Orig boards w/later crude leather reback. *SCHOYER'S*. $45

Ramsay, Robert L. OUR STOREHOUSE OF MISSOURI PLACE NAMES. Columbia: Univ of MO, 1952. Pict wraps. *SCHOYER'S*. $20

Ramsay, W.M. and Gertrude L. Bell. THE THOUSAND AND ONE CHURCHES. London, 1909. 4 maps & plans. xv,580pp. Fine. *O'NEILL*. $175

Ramsey, Frederic and Charles Edward Smith (eds). JAZZMEN. NY: Harcourt, 1939. 1st ed. Signed by Smith. NF in worn dj (darkening). *BEASLEY*. $150

Ramsey, Frederic. BEEN HERE AND GONE. New Brunswick: Rutgers, 1960. 1st ed. Fine in NF dj. *BEASLEY*. $40

Ramsey, Jarold. COYOTE WAS GOING THERE. Seattle: Univ of WA Press, (1977). 1st ed. Fine in NF dj. *LOPEZ*. $35

Ramsey, William. THE GASSES OF THE ATMOSPHERE, THE HISTORY OF THEIR DISCOVERY. London: Macmillan, 1902 (1896). Good in blue cloth prize binding w/bkpl. *KNOLLWOOD*. $80

Rand, A.L. and E.T. Gilliard. HANDBOOK OF NEW GUINEA BIRDS. GC, 1968. 5 colored, 24 plain plts. Some wear. Scarce. *SUTTON*. $365

Rand, Austin L. AMERICAN WATER & GAME BIRDS. NY, 1956. 1st ed. NF in dj. *ARTIS*. $27.50

Rand, Ayn. ATLAS SHRUGGED. NY: Random House, (1957). 1st ed. VG+ in dj sl worn at spine ends. *BERNARD*. $200

Rand, Ayn. ATLAS SHRUGGED. NY: Random House, (1957). 1st ed. Just About Fine in like dj (few tiny chips). *CAPTAIN'S BOOKSHELF*. $250

Rand, Ayn. THE VIRTUE OF SELFISHNESS. (NY): NAL, (1965). 1st ed. VG+ in dj. *BERNARD*. $100

Rand, Carl. THE NEUROSURGICAL PATIENT: HIS PROBLEMS OF DIAGNOSIS AND CARE. Springfield, 1944. 1st ed. 119 illus. *FYE*. $50

Rand, Clayton. SONS OF THE SOUTH. NY: Holt, Rinehart & Winston, 1961. 1st ed. NF in VG dj. *CONNOLLY & WADE*. $35

Rand, Edward Kennard. IN QUEST OF VIRGIL'S BIRTHPLACE. Cambridge, Harvard Univ Press, 1930. Faded spine, stains in text. Fldg map. *SCHOYER'S*. $30

Rand, Edward Kennard. IN QUEST OF VIRGIL'S BIRTHPLACE. Cambridge: Harvard Univ Press, 1930. Fldg map. Fine. *WEBER*. $40

Rand, Edward S. BULBS: HARDY & TENDER BULBS & TUBERS. Boston: Tilton, 1866. 306pp. Nearly New. *AMERICAN BOTANIST*. $50

Randall, David A. DUKEDOM LARGE ENOUGH. NY: Random House, (1969). 1st ed. Inscribed to Jake Zeitlin. Dj. *DAWSON'S*. $50

Randall, E.O. THE MASTERPIECES OF THE OHIO MOUND BUILDERS. Columbus, OH: State Archaeological & Hist Soc, 1908. 1st ed. VG. *OREGON*. $40

Randall, E.O. THE SERPENT MOUND. ADAMS COUNTY, OHIO. Columbus: Ohio State Arch and Hist Soc, 1907. 2nd ed after 1st ed of 1000. Wraps, rebound, retaining title inset. Fine. *CONNOLLY & WADE*. $45

Randall, Isabella. A LADY'S RANCHE LIFE IN MONTANA. London: 1887. (8),170,(2)pp. 1st ed. Orig cl, covers lightly spotted and soiled, as usual. Howes R49. *GINSBERG*. $400

Randall, John H. THE LANDSCAPE AND THE LOOKING GLASS. Boston: Houghton Mifflin, 1960. 1st ed. Fine in sl rubbed dj. *CAPTAIN'S BOOKSHELF*. $30

Randall, Robert (R. Silverberg & R. Garrett). THE SHROUDED PLANET. NY: Gnome Press, 1957. 1st ed. Fine in dj w/trace of wear. *OTHER WORLDS*. $25

Randall, Ruth Painter. MARY LINCOLN, BIOGRAPHY OF A MARRIAGE. Boston, (1953). 1st ed. Cvr wear, o/w VG in dj. *PRATT*. $17.50

Randall-MacIver, David. VILLANOVANS AND EARLY ESTRUSCANS: A STUDY OF THE EARLY IRON AGE IN ITALY AS IT IS SEEN NEAR BOLOGNA, IN ETRURIA AND IN LATIUM. Oxford: Clarendon Press, 1924. 70 figs, 46 plts. Good. *ARCHAEOLOGIA*. $250

Randolph, Edmund. HELL AMONG THE YEARLINGS. NY (1955), 1st ed. James Ryan illus. Dj, small tear. *HEINOLDT*. $15

Randolph, Edmund. HELL AMONG THE YEARLINGS. W.W. Norton, (1955). 1st ed. VG in Good+ dj. *OREGON*. $25

Randolph, Isham. GLEANINGS FROM A HARVEST OF MEMORIES. Columbia, 1937. 1st ed. VG+. *PRATT*. $60

Randolph, Vance. WE ALWAYS LIE TO STRANGERS. Columbia Univ, 1951. 1st ed. Fine in Good+ dj. *OREGON*. $30

Ranjitsinhji, K.S., THE JUBILEE BOOK OF CRICKET. London: William Blackwood and Sons, 1897. 1st ed. Some foxing. VG. *OLD LONDON*. $75

Rank, Otto. ART AND ARTIST. NY: Agathon, 1968. Reprint. Fine. *BEASLEY*. $35

Ranlett, William H. THE ARCHITECT, A Series of Original Designs, for Domestic and Ornamental Cottages and Villas....Vol 1. NY: William H. Graham. 1847. Folio. (2),82pp of text + 60 plts. Old black calf over boards, extrems bit rubbed, but overall exceptional. 1st ed of vol I only. A 2nd vol appeared in 1849, by another pub. *KARMIOLE*. $475

Ranney, Ambrose. LECTURES ON NERVOUS DISEASES FROM THE STANDPOINT OF CEREBRAL AND SPINAL LOCALIZATION, AND THE LATER METHODS EMPLOYED

IN THE DIAGNOSIS AND TREATMENT OF THESE AFFEC-TIONS. Phila, 1890. 1st ed. Color illus. *FYE.* $50

Rannie, David Watson. WORDSWORTH AND HIS CIRCLE. London: Methuen, (1907). 1st ed. NF. *CAPTAIN'S BOOKSHELF.* $45

Ransom, Caroline L. COUCHES AND BEDS OF THE GREEKS, ETRUSCANS AND ROMANS. Chicago: Univ of Chicago Press, 1905. 53 figs, 7 head and tailpieces, 29 plts. Good. *ARCHAEOLOGIA.* $250

Ransom, Jay Ellis. THE GOLD HUNTER'S FIELD BOOK. NY: Harper & Row, 1975. 1st ed. VG in lightly worn dj. *PARMER.* $25

Ransom, John Crowe. CHILLS AND FEVER. NY: Knopf, 1924. 1st ed. Cl-backed dec boards. Stamp, owner pencil sig, corners sl rubbed, o/w Fine in rare dj (sl chipped, closed angular tear at top of spine). *JAFFE.* $350

Ransom, John Crowe. SELECTED POEMS. NY: Knopf, 1945. 1st ed. Fine in dj, couple of tiny nicks. Unusually Nice. *CHAPEL HILL.* $85

Ransom, John L. ANDERSONVILLE DIARY. Auburn, NY: Privately published, 1881. 1st ed. Minor rubbing to spine extremities, else VG to NF. *McGOWAN.* $125

Ransom, M.A. SEA OF THE BEAR. JOURNAL OF A VOYAGE TO ALASKA AND THE ARCTIC, 1921. Annapolis, MD: US Naval Inst. (1964). 1st ed. Signed. Inscrip to prev owner. Dj. *KARMIOLE.* $35

Ransom, Will. PRIVATE PRESSES AND THEIR BOOKS. NY, 1929. Ltd ed, 1200. Spine sunned, little edges rubbed, NF. *POLYANTHOS.* $150

Rao, Raja. KANTHAPURA. NY: New Directions (1963). 1st ed. Fine in dj. *DORN.* $50

Rao, Raja. THE SERPENT AND THE ROPE. NY: Pantheon, (1963). 1st Amer ed. VG+ in lightly used dj. *DORN.* $75

Raper, Arthur. TENANTS OF THE ALMIGHTY. NY: Macmillan. 1943. 1st ed. 80pp photogr plts. Dj. *KARMIOLE.* $40

Raphael, Max. PREHISTORIC CAVE PAINTINGS. (Princeton): Pantheon (1945). NF in like dj. *SCHOYER'S.* $55

Rascoe, Judith. YOURS, AND MINE. Boston: Little Brown, (1973). 1st ed. Fine in NF dj. *LOPEZ.* $45

Raspe, Rudolph Erich. THE TRAVELS AND SURPRISING ADVENTURES OF BARON MUNCHHAUSEN. Five Woodcuts by G. Cruikshank. London: William Tegg. 1869. xxiv,268pp. 23 copper-engr plts, hand-colored frontis. Orig mauve cl, gilt; spine faded. *KARMIOLE.* $125

Raswan, Carl R. BLACK TENTS OF ARABIA. Boston, 1935. *O'NEILL.* $25

Ratcliff, J.D. YELLOW MAGIC, THE STORY OF PENICILLIN. NY, 1945. 1st ed. *FYE.* $30

Rath, Ida Ellen. THE RATH TRAIL. Wichita, (1961). 1st ed. VG in Fine dj. *BOHLING.* $45

Rath, Ida Ellen. THE RATH TRAIL. Wichita: McCormick, (1961). 1st ed. Pict cl. VF in VF dj. *OREGON.* $40

Rathbone, Frederick. WEDGEWOOD. Merion, PA: Buten Museum of Wedgewood, 1968. 1st ed. VG. *BACKROOM.* $30

Rathbun, M.J. THE GRAPSOID CRABS OF AMERICA. Washington, 1918. 161 plts. Binder's buckram (some spotting and discoloration). *SUTTON.* $65

Rathbun, M.J. THE SPIDER CRABS OF AMERICA. Washington, 1925. 283 plts. Binder's buckram (some insect tracings on spine & rear cover, orig wrappers retained). *SUTTON.* $65

Rather, Leland. ADDISON AND THE WHITE CORPUSCLES: AN ASPECT OF NINETEENTH CENTURY BIOLOGY. Berkeley, 1972. 1st ed. Dj. *FYE.* $35

Raumer, Frederick von. AMERICA AND THE AMERICAN PEOPLE. NY, 1846. 512pp. Table. Orig cl (light cover wear). 1st Eng trans. Howes R73. *GINSBERG.* $250

Ravage, Marcus Eli. FIVE MEN OF FRANKFORT. NY: Dial, 1934. 1st ed. Poor dj. *AKA.* $25

Ravenel, Mrs. St. Julien. CHARLESTON. NY: Macmillan, 1916. Good+. *CONNOLLY & WADE.* $35

Ravitch, Mark (ed). THE PAPERS OF ALFRED BLALOCK. Baltimore, 1966. 1st ed. 2 vols. *FYE.* $100

Rawlings, Marjorie Kinnan. CROSS CREEK COOKERY. NY, 1942. 1st ed, 1st issue binding (color illus cl covered boards), drwgs by Robert Camp. VG+ in dj w/a bit of edge chipping. *PETTLER.* $100

Rawlings, Marjorie Kinnan. THE YEARLING. NY: Scribner's, 1938. 1st ed. NF in dj (internally strengthened w/tape but still at least VG). *LOPEZ.* $85

Rawlings, Marjorie Kinnan. THE YEARLING. NY: Scribner's, 1938. 1st ed. Orig tan cl. Owner inscrip. Outer gutters very sl browned as usual, else Fine in Good to VG dj (few chips, tears, long tape repair along front spine edge. *CHAPEL HILL.* $100

Rawlings, Marjorie Kinnan. THE YEARLING. NY: Scribner's, 1938. 1st ed. Orig tan cl. Outer gutters sl browned, though considerably less so than usual, else in VG dj. *CHAPEL HILL.* $150

Rawlings, Marjorie Kinnan. WHEN THE WHIPPOORWILL. NY: Scribner's 1940. 1st ed. Orig grn cl. Bright, VG. *CHAPEL HILL.* $35

Rawlinson, George. THE HISTORY OF ANCIENT EGYPT. 2 vols. NY: Dodd, Mead, 1882. Edges rubbed, spine frayed, o/w Good. *WORLDWIDE.* $45

Rawlinson, George. THE HISTORY OF ANCIENT EGYPT. NY: Nottingham Soc, (1880). Ltd. (1/1000) deluxe subs' ed. 2 vols xiv,312; vii,336pp. 3/4 red morocco over marbled boards. Lt fraying tops of spines, bottom boards, else VG. *BLUE DRAGON.* $45

Rawlinson, Henry. ENGLAND AND RUSSIA IN THE EAST. London, 1875. Fldg map. 393pp. *O'NEILL.* $75

Rawnsley, Mrs. Willingham. THE NEW FOREST. A&C Black, 1904. 1st ed. One of 100, signed. Sl foxing eps, else VG-NF. Rare. *OLD LONDON.* $200

Rawnsley, Mrs. Willingham. THE NEW FOREST. A&C Black, 1915. 1st ed (this series). W/o dj and box, else Good, with extra plt laid in. *OLD LONDON.* $15

Rawson, Kennett Longley. A BOY'S-EYE VIEW OF THE ARCTIC. NY: Macmillan, 1926. Spine darkened, internal wear. *PARMER.* $20

Rawson, W.W. SUCCESS IN MARKET GARDENING: A NEW VEGETABLE GROWERS' MANUAL. Boston: Author, 1892. VG. *AMERICAN BOTANIST.* $35

Rawstorne, Lawrence. GAMONIA: THE ART OF PRESERVING GAME. Phila, 1930. Rprnt of 1837 ed. Dj. NF. *POLYANTHOS.* $45

Ray, Anthony. ENGLISH DELFTWARE POTTERY IN THE ROBERT HALL WARREN COLLECTION. Boston: Boston Book & Art Shop, 1968. 1st Amer ed. VG. *BACKROOM.* $100

Ray, Dorothy Jean. ARTISTS OF THE TUNDRA AND THE SEA. Seattle: Univ of WA Press, 1961. 1st ed. VG in VG- dj. *BLUE DRAGON.* $25

Ray, Gordon N. et al. NINETEENTH-CENTURY ENGLISH BOOKS: SOME PROBLEMS....Urbana: Univ of IL Press, 1952. 1st ed. Cloth. *OAK KNOLL.* $35

Ray, Isaac. MENTAL HYGIENE. Boston, 1863. 1st ed. 338pp. Scarce. *FYE.* $250

Ray, Man. SELF PORTRAIT. Boston: Atlantic Monthly Press, (1963). 1st ed. VF in price-clipped dj. *JAFFE.* $100

Ray, Man. SELF-PORTRAIT. Boston: Little Brown, (1963). 1st ed. About Fine in dj. *KARMIOLE.* $75

Ray, Ophelia. DAUGHTER OF THE TEJAS. Greenwich: NY Graphic Soc (1965). (Reportedly ghostwritten by Larry McMurtry.) 1st ed. Fine in (grey) dj. *LOPEZ.* $150

Raymond, Derek. HE DIED WITH HIS EYES OPEN. London: Alison Press/Secker & Warburg, 1984. 1st ed. Signed. Fine in dj. *MORDIDA.* $35

Raymond, Derek. HOW THE DEAD LIVE. London: Alison Press/Secker & Warburg, 1986. 1st ed. Fine in dj. *MORDIDA.* $30

Raymond, Derek. THE DEVIL'S HOME ON LEAVE. London: Alison Press/Secker & Warburg, 1984. 1st ed. Signed. Fine in dj. *MORDIDA.* $35

Raymond, George. MEMOIRS OF ROBERT WILLIAM ELLISTON, COMEDIAN. Illus by "Phiz." London: John Mortimer, 1845. 2 vols. Contemp half morocco; sporadic light foxing; engr frontis, plts. *DRAMATIS.* $125

Raymond, Rossiter W. CAMP AND CABIN....NY: Fords, Howard & Hulbert, 1880. 342pp. Black stamped cl, fore-edges of boards and tips a bit bumped. *DAWSON'S.* $50

Raynolds, Robert. THOMAS WOLFE: MEMOIR OF A FRIENDSHIP. Austin & London: Univ of TX Press, (1965). 1st ed. Orig blue cl. Fine in NF dj. *CHAPEL HILL.* $30

Read, George. A PIONEER OF 1850, GEORGE WILLIS READ, 1819-1880. Georgia Willis Read (ed). Little Brown, 1927. 1st ed. 15 plts, fldg map at rear. VG. Howes 8420. *OREGON.* $65

Read, Herbert. THE GREEN CHILD. London: E&S, (1947). 1st ed, thus. NF in like dj. *CAPTAIN'S BOOKSHELF.* $35

Read, J. Marion. A HISTORY OF THE CALIFORNIA ACADEMY OF MEDICINE, 1870-1930. SF, 1930. Ltd ed, ptd at Grabhorn Press. 1/4 lea. Ex-lib. *FYE.* $75

Read, John E. NANSEN IN THE FROZEN WORLD. Phila: A. J. Holman & Co, 1897. Obit of Nansen laid in. Pict dec blue cl. VG. *PARMER.* $95

Read, John Meredity. HISTORICAL INQUIRY CONCERNING HENRY HUDSON...Albany, NY, 1866. 209pp. Frontis arms in color. Rebound new buckram. *HEINOLDT.* $25

Read, Opie and Frank Pixley. THE CARPET BAGGER. Chicago: Laird & Lee, 1893. 1st ed. Frontis, tissue guard, 305pp, photo plts. Teg. Untrimmed. Orig pict cl. VG. *CONNOLLY & WADE.* $35

Read, Stanley E. TOMMY BRAYSHAW THE ARDENT ANGLER-ARTIST. Vancouver, 1977. 1st ed. #1106/2000. VF. *ARTIS.* $25

Reade, Charles. THE CLOISTER AND THE HEARTH, A TALE OF THE MIDDLE AGES. Illus by Lynd Ward. 2 vols. NY: LEC, 1932. Ltd to 1500 signed by Ward. Djs and slipcase sl faded. *OAK KNOLL.* $150

Reage, Pauline. THE STORY OF O. Paris: The Olympia Press, (1965). 1st ed. Fine in ptd wraps. *CAPTAIN'S BOOKSHELF.* $100

Reamy, Tom. BLIND VOICES. Berkley, 1978. 1st ed. As New. *MADLE.* $25

RECENT POLAR VOYAGES, A RECORD OF DISCOVERY AND ADVENTURE. London, Edinburgh, and NY: T. Nelson and Sons (c 1877). Red cl bumped, rubbed; owner's name, some foxing. Fldg map. 60 plts. VG. *BLUE MOUNTAIN.* $125

Rechy, John. CITY OF NIGHT. Grove, 1963. 1st ed. Fine in dj w/lightly sunned spine. *STAHR.* $25

Rechy, John. CITY OF NIGHT. NY: Grove, (1963). 1st ed. Fine in Fine dj. *LOPEZ.* $35

Rechy, John. THE SEXUAL OUTLAW. NY: Grove Press, (1977). 1st ed. Fine in dj. Signed. *CAPTAIN'S BOOKSHELF.* $100

Reclus, Elisee. THE OCEAN, ATMOSPHERE, AND LIFE....NY: Harper, Brothers, 1874. Ex-lib, gilt illus worn purple cl; pocket removed, bkpls, spine faded, sl stained, fraying, worn. Internally Good. *KNOLLWOOD.* $36

RECOLLECTIONS OF AN EXCURSION TO THE MONASTERIES OF ALCOBACA AND BATALHA. By the Author of "Vathek". (By William Beckford.) London: R. Bentley, 1835. 1st ed. Tall 8vo w/portrait and half-title. In orig pub's boards, spine renewed, uncut. Early typographic bkpl, contents clean and bright. Fine. *HARTFIELD.* $495

RECONSTRUCTION IN AMERICA. (By Vine W. Kingsley.) NY, 1865. 1st ed. (2),134pp. Orig front ptd wrapper, bound in cl w/leather label. Howes K166. *GINSBERG.* $125

RECORD OF THE SERVICE OF THE FORTY-FOURTH MASSACHUSETTS VOLUNTEER MILITIA IN NORTH CAROLINA AUGUST 1862 TO MAY 1863. Boston: Privately ptd, 1887. 1st ed. Orig 1/2 leather w/marbled boards. Some wear to leather, 1st few leaves show minor staining at fore-edge, else VG Pub's presentation binding. *McGOWAN.* $150

Rector, Frank. HEALTH AND MEDICAL SERVICE IN AMERICAN PRISONS AND REFORMATORIES. NY, 1929. 1st ed. *FYE.* $75

RED AND GOLD STORIES. Whitman, (1927). 1st ed. Illus Frances Kerr Cook. Cvr w/wear, faint stain. Color pict and interior bright. *BEBBAH.* $25

Redding, M. Wolcott. ANTIQUITIES OF THE ORIENT UNVEILED, CONTAINING A CONCISE DESCRIPTION...NY: Redding, 1873. 1st ed. 421pp. 2 color plts (1 fldg); fldg colored map, 90 further plts (3 fldg). Sl rubbed, o/w VG. *WORLDWIDE.* $45

Redfern, Ron. CORRIDORS OF TIME. 1,700,000,000 YEARS OF EARTH AT GRAND CANYON. NY, Times Books, 1980. Large square format (12"x12"), black cl, full-color dj, 198pp. Orig Times ed, not Reader's Digest. Fine in VG+ dj. *FIVE QUAIL.* $75

Redford, A.H. THE HISTORY OF METHODISM IN KENTUCKY (TO 1832). Nashville, 1868-70. 1st ed. 2 vols. Orig cl. Howes R114. *GINSBERG.* $100

Redford, George. A MANUAL OF ANCIENT SCULPTURE. London, 1886. Enlarged ed. NF. *POLYANTHOS.* $45

Redmond, Pat H. HISTORY OF QUINCY AND ITS MEN OF MARK. Quincy, 1869. 1st ed. 302pp. Pp 221-224 in facs. Hinges split and weak. Reading copy. *ARTIS.* $35

Redpath, James. THE PUBLIC LIFE OF CAPT. JOHN BROWN. Boston, 1860. 1st ed. Orig cl. VG. *McGOWAN.* $40

Reed, Alma. THE MEXICAN MURALISTS. NY: Crown, (1960). 1st ed. 16 color plts. Lt edge wear. Good in chipped dj. *SILVER.* $35

Reed and Ronhovde. ARCTIC LABORATORY. Washington, (1971). Wraps. VG. *ARTIS.* $35

Reed, C.K. and C.A. GUIDE TO TAXIDERMY. Worchester, (1908). New ed. Cloth. Lt wear; 1pp w/2" cut. *SUTTON.* $40

Reed, C.K. and C.A. GUIDE TO TAXIDERMY. Worchester, MA: Private Pub, (1914). New, enl ed. Dec cl. VG+. *MIKESH.* $30

Reed, David. UP FRONT IN VIETNAM. NY: Funk & Wagnalls, (1967). Tiny tears, edge wrinkles to dj. *AKA.* $50

Reed, Edwin. FRANCIS BACON OUR SHAKESPEARE. Boston: Charles E. Goodspeed, 1902. Spine sl darkened, o/w VG. *WEBER.* $50

Reed, Ishmael. CATECHISM OF D NEOAMERICAN HOODOO CHURCH. London: Paul Bremen, 1967. 1st ed. Wraps. Volume 11 in the Heritage Series. Fine. *BEASLEY.* $75

Reed, Ishmael. FLIGHT TO CANADA. NY: RH, (1976). 1st ed. Fine in dj. Inscribed. *CAPTAIN'S BOOKSHELF.* $65

Reed, Ishmael. MUMBO JUMBO. GC: Doubleday, 1972. 1st ed. Fine in dj. Review copy, slip laid in. *CAPTAIN'S BOOKSHELF.* $75.

Reed, Ishmael. RECKLESS EYEBALLING. NY: St. Martin's Press, (1986). 1st ed. Fine in dj. Inscribed. *CAPTAIN'S BOOKSHELF.* $35

Reed, Ishmael. SHROVETIDE IN OLD NEW ORLEANS. GC: Doubleday, 1978. 1st ed. NF. *SMITH.* $25

Reed, Ishmael. THE FREE-LANCE PALLBEARERS. GC: Doubleday, 1967. 1st ed. Fine in Fine dj w/one tiny nick and very minor abrasion. *BEASLEY.* $85

Reed, Ishmael. THE FREE-LANCE PALLBEARERS. GC: Doubleday, 1967. 1st ed, 1st bk. Fine in deeply price-dipped dj. *CAPTAIN'S BOOKSHELF.* $100

Reed, Ishmael. THE FREE-LANCE PALLBEARERS. GC: Doubleday, 1967. 1st ed, 1st bk. Dj, sm tear on rear, o/w VF. *SMITH.* $150

Reed, Ishmael. THE LAST DAYS OF LOUISIANA RED. NY: Random House, 1974. 1st ed. Signed in price-clipped dj. *SMITH.* $75

Reed, Ishmael. THE TERRIBLE TWOS. NY: St. Martin's, 1982. 1st ed. Fine. *SMITH.* $40

Reed, Ishmael. THE TERRIBLE TWOS. NY: St. Martin's/Marek, (1982). Fine in dj. *LOPEZ.* $25

Reed, Ishmael. WRITIN' IS FIGHTIN'. NY: Atheneum, 1988. Uncorrected proof. Fine in wraps. *LOPEZ.* $35

Reed, Jeremy. THE LIPSTICK BOYS. London: Enitharmon, 1984. 1st ed. Fine in dj. Signed. *WOOLMER.* $35

Reed, John. INSURGENT MEXICO. NY: D. Appleton, 1914. 1st ed. Very Nice. *SECOND LIFE.* $250

Reed, John. TEN DAYS THAT SHOOK THE WORLD. NY: Boni & Liveright, 1919. 1st ed. Sl stained, front hinge tender as usual. Scarce. *SECOND LIFE.* $75

Reed, John. THE WAR IN EASTERN EUROPE. NY :Scribner, 1916. 1st ed. Stained spine). Lacks fep. Owner sig. *SECOND LIFE.* $125

Reed, John. THE WAR IN EASTERN EUROPE. NY: Scribner's, 1916. 1st ed. Signed on ffep. VF. Very scarce signed. *LOPEZ.* $1750

Reed, Talbot Baines. A HISTORY OF THE OLD ENGLISH LETTER FOUNDRIES....New ed: rev, enl by A.F. Johnson. London: Faber & Faber Ltd. 1952. Fldg frontis. Dj. *KARMIOLE.* $150

Reed, Walt. HAROLD VON SCHMIDT DRAWS AND PAINTS THE OLD WEST. Flagstaff (1972), 1st ed. Dj. *HEINOLDT.* $45

Reed, Walt. HAROLD VON SCHMIDT DRAWS AND PAINTS THE OLD WEST. Northland Press, (1972). 1st ed. VF in Fine dj. *OREGON.* $75

Reed, Walter. THE PROPAGATION OF YELLOW FEVER BASED ON RECENT RESEARCHES. Baltimore, 1901. 1st ed. 31pp. Wraps. *FYE.* $125

Reemelin, Charles. THE VINE-DRESSERS MANUAL. NY: Moore, 1858. 103pp,ads. Pub's cl. Nice, clean. Frontis. *SECOND LIFE.* $150

Reep, Thomas P. LINCOLN AT NEW SALEM. Petersburg, IL, 1927. Rev ed of 1918 ed with sl different title. Minor cvr wear, spine fading o/w Fine. *PRATT.* $25

Rees, John E. IDAHO, CHRONOLOGY, NOMENCLATURE, & BIBLIOGRAPHY. Chicago: W.B. Conkey, 1918. 1st ed. Fine. *OREGON.* $75

Reeves, James J. HISTORY OF THE TWENTY-FOURTH REGIMENT NEW JERSEY VOLUNTEERS. Camden, NJ, 1889. 1st ed. Wrappers. Fine. *McGOWAN.* $150

Reeves, W.P. NEW ZEALAND. A&C Black, 1908. 1st ed. 20s Series. NF. *OLD LONDON.* $175

Reeves, William Pember. NEW ZEALAND. Painted by F. and W. Wright. London: Adam & Charles Black. 1908. 1st ed. 75 color plts, each w/ptd tissue guard, and fldg color map. *KARMIOLE.* $40

REFLEXIONS ON COURTSHIP AND MARRIAGE...WITH TWO DISCOURSES ON JEALOUSY BY...JOSEPH ADDISON. (By Benjamin Franklin?). London: James, 1759. 1st London ed. iv,

60,15pp. Mod half calf, frontis, some foxed, stained. VG. *SECOND LIFE.* $300

Rehder, A. THE BRADLEY BIBLIOGRAPHY, A GUIDE TO THE LITERATURE OF THE WOODY PLANTS OF THE WORLD....5 vols. Cambridge, 1911-18. Black binder's buckram w/lib no on spine, sm lib stamps on pastedown and prelim pp. Prelim pp splitting repaired in vol I, 1 corner bumped, lib pouches removed. *SUTTON.* $650

Reichard, Gladys A. NAVAJO SHEPARD AND WEAVER. Rio Grande: Glorieta, 1968. 1st ed thus. Frontis. Red cl, gilt. Fine. *CONNOLLY & WADE.* $50

Reichard, Gladys A. SPIDER WOMAN: A STORY OF NAVAJO WEAVERS AND CHANTERS. Rio Grande: Glorieta, 1968. 1st ed thus. Frontis, 16 plts. Red cl, gilt. Fine. *CONNOLLY & WADE.* $47.50

Reichenback, William. SIXGUNS AND BULLEYES. Plantersville, SC: Small Arms Technical Pub Co, 1937. VG, dj. *BURCHAM.* $50

Reichler, Joe. INSIDE THE MAJORS. NY: Hart, (1952). VG. *ARTIS.* $25

Reichmann, Felix. SUGAR, GOLD & COFFEE. NY: Cornell Univ Library, 1959. 1st ed. Pict eps. *SILVER.* $25

Reid, Anthony. LAUGHTER IN THE SUN. London: Bles, (1952). Dj chipped, torn. *SCHOYER'S.* $20

Reid, B.L. THE MAN FROM NEW YORK. NY, 1968. Dj. Fine. *POLYANTHOS.* $45

Reid, Hiram A. HISTORY OF PASADENA. Pasadena: Pasadena Hist Co, 1895. Some wear to spine; corners worn; front hinge beginning. Signature (2pp). Black cl w/gilt spine title, cover dec. 675pp. *PARMER.* $350

Reid, Jesse Walton. HISTORY OF THE FOURTH REGIMENT OF S.C. VOLUNTEERS, FROM THE COMMENCEMENT OF THE WAR UNTIL LEE'S SURRENDER. Greenville, SC, 1892. 1st ed. Issued as a pamphlet, now bound in 1/2 lea w/cloth boards, orig ptd wrappers lacking. *McGOWAN.* $850

Reid, Joseph V. YOU CAN MAKE A "STRADIVARIUS" VIOLIN. Popular Mechanics Press, 1950. Fldg pattern sheets. NF. *POLYANTHOS.* $45

Reid, Mayne. THE HUNTERS' FEAST; OR, CONVERSATION AROUND THE CAMP-FIRE. NY: Robert M. Dewitt, (c. 1859). Frontis, 6 plts. Bumped, spine and edges faded. VG. *BLUE MOUNTAIN.* $75

Reid, Sam C., Jr. INTERNATIONAL LAW: THE CASE OF THE PRIVATE ARMED BRIG. OF WAR GEN. ARMSTRONG, CONTAINING LETTERS AND DOCUMENTS...WITH THE DECISION OF THE COURT AND AN APPENDIX...NY: 1857. 1st ed. (23),(9)-240pp. Orig full calf. Presentation. *GINSBERG.* $150

Reid, T. Wemyss. THE LIFE, LETTERS, AND FRIENDSHIPS OF RICHARD MONCKTON MILNES, FIRST LORD HOUGHTON. 2 Vols. NY: Cassell, (1891). 1st ed. 8vo, brown pebbled cloth over bevelled boards, covers stamped in gold. VG+. *GREAT EXPECTATIONS.* $25

Reid, Whitelaw. A RADICAL VIEW: THE "AGATE" DISPATCHES OF WHITELAW REID 1861-1865. James G. Smart (ed). 2 vols. Memphis, (1976). 1st ed. Some dj color rubbed off o/w VG+. *PRATT.* $37.50

Reiger, Barbara and George. THE ZANE GREY COOKBOOK. Prentice Hall, (1976). 1st ed. Pict eps, Fine in dj. *AUTHORS OF THE WEST.* $30

Reik, Theodor. FROM THIRTY YEARS WITH FREUD. Trans Richard Winston. NY: Farrar & Rinehart, Inc. (1940). 1st ed. Presentation, signed. *KARMIOLE.* $75

Reik, Theodor. MASOCHISM IN MODERN MAN. Margaret H. Beigel, Gertrud M. Kurth (trans). NY: Farrar & Rinehart, Inc. (1941). 1st Amer ed. Dj. *KARMIOLE.* $40

Reik, Theodor. THE CREATION OF WOMAN. George Braziller, 1960. 1st ed. NF in dj (tear, sunned spine). *STAHR.* $25

Reilly, Helen. MURDER IN SHINBONE ALLEY. NY: Doubleday Crime Club, 1940. 1st ed. Bkpl. Sm triangular chip at spine head, minor wear to extremities of pict dj. VF. *ELSE FINE.* $50

Rein, David. VARDIS FISHER: CHALLENGE TO EVASION. Normandie House, 1938. 1st ltd ed of 400. Fine, orig glassine tissue dj torn some. *AUTHORS OF THE WEST.* $15

Rein, Mark. THE MISCHIEF OF A POLICE CHIEF. NY, 1921. Signed. NF. *POLYANTHOS.* $30

Reisner, George A. MYCERINUS: THE TEMPLES OF THE THIRD PYRAMID AT GIZA. Cambridge: Harvard Univ Press, 1931. 79 plts, 12 fldg plans. Light shelfwear. Good. *ARCHAEOLOGIA.* $1250

Reisner, George A. THE DEVELOPMENT OF THE EGYPTIAN TOMB DOWN TO THE ACCESSION OF CHEOPS. Cambridge: Harvard Univ Press, 1936. 192 illus, 2 fldg maps at rear. Dj. Good. *ARCHAEOLOGIA.* $1,500

Reiss, Lionel S. MY MODELS WERE JEWS. NY, 1938. Ltd ed, signed. Spine extremities a little rubbed. NF. *POLYANTHOS.* $95

Relander, Click. DRUMMERS AND DREAMERS. Caldwell, 1956. 1st ed. Fine in Fine dj. *OREGON.* $225

Remarque, Erich Maria. A TIME TO LOVE AND A TIME TO DIE. NY: Harcourt-Brace, 1954. 1st ed. VF, minor wear to spine top of dj. *ELSE FINE.* $35

Remarque, Erich Maria. ALL QUIET ON THE WESTERN FRONT. Boston: LB, 1929. 1st US ed. Fine in dj (lightly chipped, few small tears). *CAPTAIN'S BOOKSHELF.* $75

Remarque, Erich Maria. ALL QUIET ON THE WESTERN FRONT. London: Putnam's, (1929). A.W. Wheen (trans). 1st ed in English. Orig tan cl. Faint soiling, else Fine, bright in VG dj (chipping, tears). Scarce in dj. *CHAPEL HILL.* $250

Remarque, Erich Maria. HEAVEN HAS NO FAVORITES. NY: HBW, 1961. 1st ed. Richard & Clara Winston (trans). VF, minor aging to dj spine. *ELSE FINE.* $25

Remarque, Erich Maria. THE BLACK OBELISK. NY: Harcourt-Brace, 1957. 1st ed. Denver Lindley (trans). VF, minor rubs to dj corners. *ELSE FINE.* $30

REMBRANDT ETCHINGS...COLLECTION FORMED BY GORDON W. NOWELL-USTICKE. NY: (Parke-Bernet), 1967-68. 2 vols. Orig grn cl w/gilt titling. Several fold-out illus. Absolutely Fine. *BOOK BLOCK.* $100

Remington, Frederic. CROOKED TRAILS. London & NY: Harper & Bros., 1898. 1st Eng ed. 49 plts. Bumped, sl rubbed. NF in new slipcase. *BLUE MOUNTAIN.* $200

Remington, Frederic. CROOKED TRAILS. NY (Aug 1923). 151pp. Illus author. Dj frayed. Intro Zane Gray. *HEINOLDT.* $25

Remington, Frederic. JOHN ERMINE OF THE YELLOWSTONE. Macmillan, 1902. 1st ed. Teg. Fine. *AUTHORS OF THE WEST.* $150

Remington, Frederic. PONY TRACKS. NY, 1903. 269pp. 70 illus by Remington. *HEINOLDT.* $25

Remington, Frederic. PONY TRACKS. NY: Harper, (1895). 1st ed, 1st bk. Illus. NF, covers bright; a few rubs and bumps to spine ends. *UNGER.* $500

REMINISCENCES OF CHICAGO DURING THE CIVIL WAR. Chicago: Lakeside Press, 1914. Mabel McIlvaine (intro). Bound in orig pub's cl. VG. *LAURIE.* $200

REMINISCENCES OF THE WOMEN OF MISSOURI DURING THE SIXTIES. (Jefferson City, 192?). 1st ed. Soiled, else VG. *McGOWAN.* $125

Remy, Jules and Julius Brenchley. A JOURNEY TO GREAT-SALT-LAKE CITY...London, 1861. 1st Eng ed. 2 vols. 10 illus, fldg map. Orig cl. Howes R210. *GINSBERG.* $750

Remy, Jules. A JOURNEY TO GREAT SALT LAKE CITY...London: W. Jeffs, 1861. 1st Eng ed, orig issued yr before in French. 2 vols. cxxxi,508; vii,605pp. Half titles, 2 engr frontis', engr plts, fldg map. Orig purple emb cl, upper cvr gilt cathedral center vignette, inside joints neatly repaired. Fine. *WEBER.* $900

Renault, Mary. BULL FROM THE SEA. London: Longman's, (1962). 1st ed. Fine in dj. *CAPTAIN'S BOOKSHELF.* $60

Rendell, Ruth. A NEW LEASE OF DEATH. GC: Doubleday Crime Club, 1967. 1st Amer ed. Fine in VG dj (rubbing, wear). *MORDIDA.* $45

Rendell, Ruth. A SLEEPING LIFE. GC: Doubleday, 1978. 1st Amer ed. Fine in dj. *MORDIDA.* $35

Rendell, Ruth. AN UNKINDNESS OF RAVENS. London: Hutchinson, 1985. 1st ed. Signed. VF in dj. *MORDIDA.* $65

Rendell, Ruth. HEARTSTONES. London: Hutchinson, 1987. 1st ed. Signed. VF in dj. *SILVER DOOR.* $35

Rendell, Ruth. HEARTSTONES. NY: Harper & Row, 1987. 1st Amer ed. VF in dj. *MORDIDA.* $25

Rendell, Ruth. LIVE FLESH. London: Hutchinson, 1986. 1st ed. Signed. VF in dj. *MORDIDA.* $65

Rendell, Ruth. MASTER OF THE MOOR. London: Hutchinson, 1982. 1st ed. VF in dj. *MORDIDA.* $65

Rendell, Ruth. MATTERS OF SUSPENSE. Helsinki: Eurographica, 1986. 1st ed. 1/350 numbered, signed. VF in stiff wrappers w/dj. *MORDIDA.* $200

Rendell, Ruth. MATTERS OF SUSPENSE. Ptd Roma wrappers. Helsinki: Eurographica, 1986. 1st ed. Ltd to 350 signed. Mint. *JAFFE.* $175

Rendell, Ruth. MEANS OF EVIL. GC: Doubleday, 1980. 1st Amer ed. Fine in dj, couple short closed tears. *MORDIDA.* $25

Rendell, Ruth. TALKING TO STRANGE MEN. London: Hutchinson, 1987. 1st ed. Review copy, signed. Promo material laid in. VF in dj. *SILVER DOOR.* $45

Rendell, Ruth. TALKING TO STRANGE MEN. London: Hutchinson, 1987. 1st ed. VF in dj. *MORDIDA.* $35

Rendell, Ruth. THE BEST MAN TO DIE. GC: Doubleday Crime Club, 1970. 1st Amer ed. Fine in dj w/tiny wear. *MORDIDA.* $40

Rendell, Ruth. THE BRIDESMAID. London: Hutchinson, 1989. 1st ed. VF in dj. *MORDIDA.* $35

Rendell, Ruth. THE BRIDESMAID. NY: Mysterious Press, (1989). Adv reading copy in ptd wrappers, signed on pub's pasted-in bkpl. Fine. *LOPEZ.* $35

Rendell, Ruth. THE FACE OF TRESPASS. GC: Doubleday Crime Club, 1974. 1st Amer ed. Date stamp, o/w Fine in dj with a short closed tear, wear. *MORDIDA.* $35

Rendell, Ruth. THE FEVER TREE AND OTHER STORIES. London: Hutchinson, 1982. 1st ed. Signed. VF in dj. *MORDIDA.* $75

Rendell, Ruth. THE KILLING DOLL. London: Hutchinson, 1984. 1st ed. Fine in dj. *ELSE FINE.* $40

Rendell, Ruth. THE LAKE OF DARKNESS. London: Hutchinson, 1980. 1st ed. Signed. VF in dj. *SILVER DOOR.* $45

Rendell, Ruth. THE LAKE OF DARKNESS. London: Hutchinson, 1980. 1st ed. Signed. VF in dj. *SILVER DOOR.* $45

Rendell, Ruth. THE SPEAKER OF MANDARIN. London: Hutchinson, 1983. 1st ed. Name. Fine in dj. 35

Rendell, Ruth. THE TREE OF HANDS. London: Hutchinson, 1984. 1st ed. VF in price-clipped dj. *MORDIDA.* $30

Renner, Frederic G. CHARLES M. RUSSELL, GREATEST OF ALL WESTERN ARTISTS. Potomac Corral Westerners, 1968, 1st ed. Wraps. *HEINOLDT*. $25

Rennie, J. INSECT ARCHITECTURE...London, 1857. New ed. *SUTTON*. $45

Rensch, Hero E. and Ethel G. HISTORIC SPOTS IN CALIFORNIA. THE SOUTHERN COUNTIES. Stanford Univ Press, 1938. 2nd ptg. Foxing on fore-edges, o/w VG. *DIAMOND*. $35

Replogle, Charles. AMONG THE INDIANS OF ALASKA. London: Headley Brothers, 1904. 1st ed. Cvrs sl soiled and worn; some interior use. VG-. *PARMER*. $95

REPORT OF COMMISSION TO LOCATE THE SITE OF THE FRONTIER FORTS OF PENNSYLVANIA. 2 vols. PA State, 1896, 1st ed. 627pp; 637pp. Many fldg maps, plans. Color lithos. Professionally rebound in new buckram by hand binder. *HEINOLDT*. $85

REPORT OF COMMITTEE ON DRUG ADDICTION 1929-1941. Washington, DC, 1941. Cloth sl rubbed, o/w VG. *DIAMOND*. $150

REPORT OF EXPLORATIONS FOR A ROUTE FOR THE PACIFIC RAILROAD BY CAPT. J.W. GUNNISON. Washington: A.O.P Nicholson, Printer, 1855. 29 cm. Rebound in black cl, leather spine label w/gilt titles. House of Representatives. 33d Congress, 3d Session. Ex Doc No 91, Vol III. Foxing, crimp affecting approx 100+pp, else VG. Howes B299. *PARMER*. $350

REPORT OF THE COMMISSIONER OF INDIAN AFFAIRS, 1884. (Washington): (GPO), (1884). Front inner hinge separated, title pg missing. *LAURIE*. $75

REPORT OF THE COMMISSIONER OF INDIAN AFFAIRS, 1908. (By Francis E. Leupp.) Washington: GPO, 1909. VG. *LAURIE*. $35

REPORT OF THE COMMISSIONER OF INDIAN AFFAIRS, 1856. Washington, DC, 1857. 1st ed. Cvrs sl worn. Small marginal dampstain. One page repaired, o/w VG. *DIAMOND*. $75

REPORT OF THE COMMISSIONERS ADOPTED IN PURSUANCE OF AN ACT FOR THE AMICABLE SETTLEMENT OF LIMITS WITH THE STATE OF GEORGIA...Wash., 1804. 1st ed. 140pp. Cloth. Howes G119. pp 1-8, Message of the President, are lacking. *GINSBERG*. $125

REPORT OF THE GEOLOGICAL SURVEY OF OHIO. Part I. Geology. 3 vols. Columbus: Nevins & Myers, 1873-1878. 1st ed. Vols. 1 & 2 Good, vol. 3 sunned o/w VG. *ARCHER*. $125

REPORT OF THE GEOLOGICAL SURVEY OF OHIO. Vol. I. Geology and Palaeontology. Part II. Palaeontology. Vol. II. Geology and Palaeontology. Part II. Palaeontology. 2 vols. Columbus, OH: Nevins & Myers, 1873, 1875. 1st eds. 48 plts; 59 plts. Vol. 2, Part 2 rebacked w/new cl; Vol. 1, Part 2 has small lib blind-stamp on title page, bkpl removed. Contents Good in both. *DIAMOND*. $150

REPORT OF THE JOINT COMMITTEE ON THE CONDUCT OF THE WAR. 3 vols. Washington, 1863. Lettering on spine faded o/w unusually well preserved. VG. *PRATT*. $145

REPORT OF THE PROCEEDINGS OF THE SOCIETY OF THE ARMY OF THE TENNESSEE AT THE THIRTY-SECOND MEETING HELD AT DETROIT, MICH., NOVEMBER 14-15, 1900. Cincinnati, 1901. Fep detached o/w VG. *PRATT*. $22.50

REPORT OF THE SELECT COMMITTEE OF THE SENATE OF THE UNITED STATES ON THE SICKNESS AND MORTALITY ONBOARD EMIGRANT SHIPS. Washington, 1854. 1st ed. 147pp. *FYE*. $200

REPORT OF THE SELECT COMMITTEE ON INTERNAL REVENUE FRAUDS TO HOUSE OF REPRESENTATIVES, FEB. 25, 1867. Washington: GPO, 1867. Ex-lib. Cl. Spine tip wear, o/w VG. *DIAMOND*. $35

REPORT OF THE SPECIAL COMMITTEE APPOINTED TO INVESTIGATE THE TROUBLES IN KANSAS; WITH THE VIEWS OF THE MINORITY OF SAID COMMITTEE. House of Representatives, 34th Congress, 1st Session, Report no. 200. Washington: Cornelius Wendell, 1856. Binding worn. *LAURIE*. $60

REPORT OF THE STATE COMMISSIONERS OF FISHERIES FOR THE YEARS 1889-90-91 WITH APPENDIX BY DR. T.H. BEAN....Harrisburg: Edw. Meyers, 1892. 2pp sepia photos, 35 full-pg plts. Cl. Ex-lib. No marks. Good. *ARTIS*. $50

REPORT OF THE SUPERINTENDENT OF THE COAST SURVEY SHOWING THE PROGRESS OF THE SURVEY DURING THE YEAR 1856. House of Representatives, 34th Congress, 3rd Sess. Ex Doc No 18 Washington: Cornelius Wendell. 1856. 67 fldg litho sketches, maps, diagrams. Cvrs faded, eps foxed. *KARMIOLE*. $250

REPORT ON THE PROCEEDINGS OF THE SOCIETY OF THE ARMY OF THE TENNESSEE AT THE THIRTY-SEVENTH MEETING HELD AT VICKSBURG, MISSISSIPPI, NOVEMBER 7-8, 1907. Cincinnati, 1908. Fine. *PRATT*. $22.50

REPORTS OF THE SECRETARY OF WAR, WITH RECONNAISSANCES OF ROUTES FROM SAN ANTONIO TO EL PASO....CAPT. R. B. MARCY'S ROUTES FROM FORT SMITH TO SANTA FE, AND THE REPORT OF LT. J. H. SIMPSON...AND ALSO THE REPORT OF LT. W. H. C. WHITING'S RECONNAISSANCES....(By Joseph E. Johnston et al.) Wash., 1850. 1st ed. 250pp. 2 fldg maps, 72 litho plts, some hand-tinted in color. Some plts w/light staining upper right corner. Rather nice in orig black cl. Howes J170. *GINSBERG*. $850

Repplier, Agnes. AMERICANS AND OTHERS. Boston: Houghton Mifflin/Riverside Press, 1912. 1st ed. Fine. *CONNOLLY & WADE*. $50

Resnicow, Herbert. THE GOLD FRAME. NY: St. Martin's, 1984. 1st ed. Signed. Fine in dj. *SILVER DOOR*. $30

Restle, Marcell. BYZANTINE WALL PAINTING IN ASIA MINOR. Irene R. Gibbons (trans). 3 vols. Greenwich, CT: NY Graphic Society, 1968. 1st ed. 84 color plts, 478 illus, 97 ground plans, drawings, and 6 maps (some fldg). Djs. In slipcover. NF. *WORLDWIDE*. $150

Reston, James, Jr. SHERMAN'S MARCH AND VIETNAM. NY, (1984). 1st ed. Fine in dj. *PRATT*. $25

REVELATIONS: A COMPANION TO THE "NEW GOSPEL OF PEACE." ACCORDING TO ABRAHAM. (By Richard G. White.) NY, 1863. 1st ed. 36pp. Orig bright orange wrappers. Howes W369. *GINSBERG*. $200

Reveles, Efren. INDIAN CAMPFIRE TALES. NY: Exposition, 1954. 1st ed. Fine in VG dj. *CONNOLLY & WADE*. $28.50

Revere, Joseph Warren. NAVAL DUTY IN CALIFORNIA. Oakland, 1947. One of 1000. Howes R222. *GINSBERG*. $30

Revere, Paul. CLEVELAND IN THE WAR WITH SPAIN. Cleveland: n.p., 1900. 1st ed. Spine & edge of boards silverfished, o/w VG. *ARCHER*. $60

Revescz, Geza. THE HUMAN HAND, A PSYCHOLOGICAL STUDY. London, 1958. Dj. *FYE*. $65

Revi, Albert Christian. AMERICAN ART NOUVEAU GLASS. Nashville, TN: Nelsan, 1968. 3rd ptg. VG in dj. *BACKROOM*. $55

Rexford, E.E. AMATEUR GARDENCRAFT. Phila, 1912. Cloth; spotting, soiling front cvr. *SUTTON*. $25

Rexroth, Kenneth. SAUCY LIMERICKS & CHRISTMAS CHEER. Santa Barbara: Bradford Morrow, 1980. Fine in orig mailing env. 1st ed. #111 of 299 signed by Morrow. *CHAPEL HILL*. $40

Rexroth, Kenneth. THE SIGNATURE OF ALL THINGS. NY: New Directions, (1949). 1/1500 unnumbered. Small black star rubber stamped fep. Dj w/tiny chips, light soiling. Overall a nice copy. Scarce. *AKA*. $100

Rey Rosa, Rodrigo. DUST ON HER TONGUE. London: Peter Owen, (1989). Paul Bowles, trans. 1st Eng ed. Fine in dj. *LOPEZ*. $45

Reynolds, Chang. PIONEER CIRCUSES OF THE WEST. LA: Westernlore, 1966. Cl in dj. *DAWSON'S*. $45

Reynolds, Graham. CONSTABLE, The Natural Painter. NY: McGraw-Hill. (1965). 1st ed. 20 mounted color plts. Blue cl. Dj. *KARMIOLE*. $65

Reynolds, J. Russell. A SYSTEM OF MEDICINE. Phila, 1880. 1st Amer ed. 3 vols., full leather, 1127pp. *FYE*. $150

Reynolds, James. GHOSTS IN AMERICAN HOUSES. Farrar, Straus, Cudahy, 1955. Fine in VG dj. *MAD DOG*. $15

Reynolds, John N. A KANSAS HELL, OR LIFE IN THE KANSAS PENITENTIARY. Atchinson: Bee Publishing, 1889. 1st ed. Inner hinges separated. *LAURIE*. $25

Reynolds, John N. THE TWIN HELLS A THRILLING NARRATIVE. Chicago: Bee Publishing Co, 1890. 1st ed. 331pp, Cloth. VG, some wear to cover, but condition is excellent considering cheap paper. *GIBBS*. $35

Reynolds, John. PIONEER HISTORY OF ILLINOIS. Belleville, N.A. Randall, 1852. 1st ed. 348pp. Binding w/light wear, fraying, spotting; rubberstamp on ep; foxing. Good+. *BOHLING*. $550

Reynolds, Quentin. THE FICTION FACTORY. NY, (1955). 1st ed. Fine in dj. *DIAMOND*. $35

Reynolds, William J. MONEY TROUBLE. NY: G.P. Putnam's Sons, 1988. 1st ed. VF in dj. *MORDIDA*. $22.50

Reynolds, William J. MOVING TARGETS. NY: St. Martin's Press, 1986. 1st ed. VF in dj. *MORDIDA*. $25

Reynolds, William J. THE NEBRASKA QUOTIENT. NY: St. Martin's, (1988). 1st ed. Fine in Fine dj. *UNGER*. $30

Reznikoff, Charles. NINE PLAYS. NY: the author, 1927. 1st ed. Fine in Fine dj w/bit soiled front panel. *BEASLEY*. $40

Rhees, William Jones. THE SMITHSONIAN INSTITUTION. 2 vols. Washington: GPO, 1901. 1st ed. 2 fldg maps. Slight cover staining and wear o/w VG. *DIAMOND*. $75

Rhees, William. THE SMITHSONIAN INSTITUTION DOCUMENTS RELATIVE TO ITS ORIGIN AND HISTORY. 1835-1899. 2 vols. Washington, 1901. 1st ed. 1983pp. *FYE*. $100

Rheims, Maurice. THE FLOWERING OF ART NOUVEAU. NY, 1966. Dj. Illus. Some tipped-in color plts, photos. Fine. *POLYANTHOS*. $100

Rhoades, Jeffrey L. SCAPEGOAT GENERAL. THE STORY OF MAJOR GENERAL BENJAMIN HUGER, C.S.A. (Hamden, CT), 1985. 1st ed. Fine in NF dj. *McGOWAN*. $35

Rhoads, S.N. THE MAMMALS OF PENNSYLVANIA AND NEW JERSEY. Phila, 1903. 9 plts, 1 colored map. Cloth, Institutional bkpl, # sticker on spine, pp yellowed. *SUTTON*. $48

Rhode, John. THE VENNER CRIME. London: Odhams, 1933. 1st ed. Cvr, eps lightly foxed, else Fine; minor edgewear, small chip at the lower spine fold of dj. *ELSE FINE*. $85

Rhodes, Dennis E. DENNIS OF ETRURIA: THE LIFE OF GEORGE DENNIS. London: Cecil & Amelia Woolf, (1973). Dj. Good. *ARCHAEOLOGIA*. $45

Rhodes, Eugene Manlove. COPPER STREAK TRAIL. Houghton Mifflin, 1922. 1st ed. Fine. *AUTHORS OF THE WEST*. $60

Rhodes, Eugene Manlove. PASO POR AQUI. Friends of the Alamogordo Public Lib, 1963. 1st thus, ltd ed of 5,000 numbered. Frontis. Softbound. Fine. *AUTHORS OF THE WEST*. $30

Rhodes, Eugene Manlove. THE BEST NOVELS AND STORIES OF EUGENE MANLOVE RHODES. Houghton Mifflin, 1949. 1st ed. Frank V. Dearing (ed). Ep maps. Presentation, ptd plate glued on half-title. Stamp. Fine. *AUTHORS OF THE WEST*. $50

Rhodes, Eugene Manlove. THE LINE OF LEAST RESISTANCE. Chicago: W.H. Hutchinson, 1958. W.H. Hutchinson (ed). One of 500. Ptd wrappers, top of front wrapper sl creased. Inscription from Hutchinson. *DAWSON'S*. $45

Rhodes, Eugene Manlove. THE LITTLE WORLD WADDIES. Carl Hertzog, (1946). 1st ltd ed of 1,000. Frontis, ep maps, biblio. Fine. *AUTHORS OF THE WEST*. $225

Rhodes, Eugene Manlove. THE LITTLE WORLD WADDIES. Chico, CA: Designed and ptd at The Pass on the Rio Bravo by Carl Hertzog for William Hutchinson, 1946. Ltd to 1,000. VG. *GIBBS*. $135

Rhodes, Eugene Manlove. THE RHODES READER. Univ of OK Press, (1960). 2nd prtg. W.H. Hutchinson (ed). Frontis. Inscribed, signed by Hutch. Fine in dj. *AUTHORS OF THE WEST*. $30

Rhodes, Frederick Leland. BEGINNINGS OF TELEPHONY. Harper & Bros., 1929. 1st ed. Fine. *MAD DOG*. $35

Rhodes, H. ALPHONSE BERTILLON. FATHER OF SCIENTIFIC DETECTION. London, 1956. 1st ed. Fore-edges sl foxed, o/w VG. *DIAMOND*. $12.50

Rhodes, James A. and Dean Jauchius. JOHNNY SHILOH. NY, (1959). 1st ed. VG+ in dj. *PRATT*. $17.50

Rhodes, James M. and Dean Jauchius. THE TRIAL OF MARY TODD LINCOLN. Indianapolis, (1950). 1st ed. Dj. VG+. *PRATT*. $20

Rhodes, William Henry. CAXTON'S BOOK: A COLLECTION OF ESSAYS, POEMS, TALES AND SKETCHES. SF: A.L. Bancroft, 1876. Daniel O'Connell (ed). 1st ed. 300pp. Gilt cl. VG. *CONNOLLY & WADE*. $250

Rhys, Horton. A THEATRICAL TRIP FOR A WAGER! Vancouver, 1966. Facs rprt of 1861 London orig ed. One of 500 numbered, signed. Orig cl. Howes R245. *GINSBERG*. $125

Rhys, Jean. WIDE SARGASSO SEA. London, 1966. 1st ed. Intro Francis Wyndham. NF in price clipped dj (extremities, spine minimally rubbed). *POLYANTHOS*. $50

Ribot, Theodule. DISEASES OF MEMORY, DISEASES OF THE WILL, AND DISEASES OF PERSONALITY. NY, c. 1885. 1st Amer ed. *FYE*. $100

Ricci, Franco Maria. TAMARA DE LEMPICKA WITH THE JOURNAL OF GABRIELE D'ANNUNZIO'S HOUSEKEEPER. Parma, Italy, 1977. Chiara & Roncorone (ed). One of 3,000 (#1722). Fine in slipcase. *SMITH*. $250

Ricci, James. THE CYSTOCELE IN AMERICA: A CRITICAL ANALYSIS OF THE AMERICAN LITERATURE ON CYSTOCELE AND PROLAPSE. Phila, 1950. 1st ed. 436pp. Backstrip faded. Scarce. *FYE*. $125

Rice, A.H. and John Baer Stodt. THE SHENANDOAH POTTERY. Strasburg, VA: Shenandoah Pub House, 1929. 1st ed. Good. *BACKROOM*. $80

Rice, Allen. REMINISCENCES OF ABRAHAM LINCOLN BY DISTINGUISHED MEN OF HIS TIME. NY: Harper, 1909. 1st ed. thus. Teg. NF. *ARCHER*. $20

Rice, Anne. CRY TO HEAVEN. Knopf, 1982. 1st ed. Fine in dj, 2 sm tears, few rubbed spots. *STAHR*. $40

Rice, Anne. CRY TO HEAVEN. London: Chatto & Windus, (1990). 1st UK ed. New in dj. *BERNARD*. $35

Rice, Anne. CRY TO HEAVEN. NY: Knopf, 1982. 1st ed. VF in dj. *ELSE FINE*. $60

Rice, Anne. CRY TO HEAVEN. NY: Knopf, 1982. 1st ed. Uncorrected proof copy. Pencil markings front cvr (one partially erased). Fine. *LOPEZ*. $175

Rice, Anne. INTERVIEW WITH A VAMPIRE. NY: Knopf, 1976. 1st ed. Fine in dj. *CAPTAIN'S BOOKSHELF*. $500

Rice, Anne. INTERVIEW WITH THE VAMPIRE. London, 1976. 1st UK ed, rare 1st bk. Fine in price-clipped dj. *PETTLER.* $250

Rice, Anne. INTERVIEW WITH THE VAMPIRE. NY: Knopf, 1976. 1st ed, 1st bk. Lt spot front panel, else just About Fine in Fine dj. Signed. *CAPTAIN'S BOOKSHELF.* $450

Rice, Anne. INTERVIEW WITH THE VAMPIRE. NY: Knopf, 1976. 1st ed, 1st bk. Fine; very minor wear to dj extrems. Signed. *ELSE FINE.* $650

Rice, Anne. INTERVIEW WITH THE VAMPIRE. NY: Knopf, 1976. 1st ed, 1st bk. Fine; minor edgewear to gold foil dj. *ELSE FINE.* $550

Rice, Anne. INTERVIEW WITH THE VAMPIRE. NY: Knopf, 1976. 1st ed. VG+ (slight spine cock) in dj w/two short tears to rear. *OTHER WORLDS.* $395

Rice, Anne. THE FEAST OF ALL SAINTS. NY: S&S, (1979). 1st ed. Rmdr mk bottom edge pp. Fine in dj. *LOPEZ.* $55

Rice, Anne. THE QUEEN OF THE DAMNED. Knopf, 1988. Uncorrected proof. VF in white wraps. Signed. Label pasted towards bottom of cover includes pub date, price, bk club notice and printing figures. *STAHR.* $150

Rice, Anne. THE QUEEN OF THE DAMNED. Knopf, 1988. 1st ed. VF in dj. *STAHR.* $45

Rice, Anne. THE QUEEN OF THE DAMNED. NY, 1988. 1st ed. Signed. VF in dj. *PETTLER.* $45

Rice, Anne. THE QUEEN OF THE DAMNED. NY: Knopf, 1988. 1st ed. VF in dj. Signed. *ELSE FINE.* $60

Rice, Anne. THE QUEEN OF THE DAMNED. NY: Knopf, 1988. 1st ed. Uncorrected proof. Various pub's notations on 1st blank and "PC" on cvr. Fine in wraps. *LOPEZ.* $100

Rice, Anne. THE VAMPIRE LESTAT. NY, 1985. 1st ed. Fine in NF dj. *PETTLER.* $75

Rice, Anne. THE VAMPIRE LESTAT. NY: Knopf, 1985. 1st ed. Fine in dj. *LOPEZ.* $125

Rice, Anne. THE VAMPIRE LESTAT. NY: Knopf, 1985. 1st ed. Fine in dj. Comp copy, slip laid in. *CAPTAIN'S BOOKSHELF.* $150

Rice, Anne. THE WITCHING HOUR. NY: Knopf, 1990. 1st ed. Signed. Fine in Fine dj. *LOPEZ.* $75

Rice, Carew. A SELECTION OF SONGS & SCISSOR-CUT SILHOUETTES. (Charleston: Walker, Evans and Cogswell, 1961). 1st ed. NF in dj. *CAPTAIN'S BOOKSHELF.* $100

Rice, Craig. KNOCKED FOR A LOOP. NY: Simon and Schuster, 1957. 1st ed. Pp darkened, o/w Fine in dj w/some wear. *MORDIDA.* $35

Rice, Craig. MY KINGDOM FOR A HEARSE. NY: Simon and Schuster, 1957. 1st ed. Pp darkened, o/w VG in dj (sm piece missing back panel; short closed tears, wear). *MORDIDA.* $25

Rice, Craig. THE WRONG MURDER. NY: Simon and Schuster, 1940. 1st ed. VG in dj (internal tape mend; wear spine ends, along folds). *MORDIDA.* $75

Rice, David Talbot and Walter Frodl. AUSTRIA MEDIEVAL WALL PAINTINGS. NY: NY Graphic Soc, (1964). 22pp. 32 full-pg color plts. Corners bumped. *ARTIS.* $27.50

Rice, David Talbot. ART OF THE BYZANTINE ERA. NY & Washington: Praeger, 1966. 3rd ptg. Dj. NF. *WORLDWIDE.* $30

Rice, Dennis G. THE ILLUSTRATED GUIDE TO ROCKINGHAM POTTERY AND PORCELAIN. London: Barrie & Jenkins, (1971). Dj. *KARMIOLE.* $30

Rice, Howard and Anne S.K. Brown. AMERICAN CAMPAIGNS OF ROCHAMBEAU'S ARMY 1780, 1781, 1782, 1783. Princeton, NJ, 1972. 1st ed. 2 vols. Orig cl, dj. *GINSBERG.* $150

Rice, Howard. BARTHELEMI TARDIVEAU. A FRENCH TRADER IN THE WEST. Baltimore: Johns Hopkins Press, 1938. 1st ed. Facs (some fldg). *HUDSON.* $60

Rice, Howard. BARTHELEMI TARDIVEAU...BIOGRAPHICAL SKETCH, INCLUDING LETTERS... TO ST. JOHN DE CREVECOEUR (1788-1789). Johns Hopkins, 1938. 1st ed. Frontis, 4 plts, 1 fldg map. VF. *OREGON.* $75

Rice, Josiah M. A CANNONEER IN NAVAJO COUNTRY, JOURNAL OF PRIVATE JOSIAH M. RICE, 1851. Richard Dillon (ed). Denver, 1970. 1st ed ltd to 1,500. Fine in dj. *PRATT.* $50

Rice, Josiah M. A CANNONEER IN NAVAJO COUNTRY. Denver, 1970. Richard H. Dillon (ed). 1st ed. Ltd to 1500. Fine in dj. *BAADE.* $40

Rice, Josiah M. JOURNAL OF JOSIAH M. RICE, 1851. Richard Dillon (ed). Denver: Old West, 1970. 1st ed, ltd to 1500. VF in VF dj. *OREGON.* $25

Rice, Nathan. TRIALS OF A PUBLIC BENEFACTOR, AS ILLUSTRATED IN THE DISCOVERY OF ETHERIZATION. NY, 1859. 1st ed. 460pp. Recent cl, new eps. Very Scarce. *FYE.* $350

Rice, Norman S. ALBANY SILVER 1652—1825. NY: Albany Institute, 1964. 1st ed. VG. Wraps. One of 1000. *BACKROOM.* $12.50

Rich, Claudius James. NARRATIVE OF A JOURNEY TO THE SITE OF BABYLON IN 1811. London: Duncan and Malcolm, 1839. 1st ed. 26 engrvd plts, orig blind-embossed cl. Minor warping to boards, interior Fine. Scarce. *ARCHAEOLOGIA.* $475

Rich, Claudius James. NARRATIVE OF A RESIDENT IN KOORDISTAN. London, 1836. 1st ed. 2 fldg maps, 11 plts (5 double-pg or fldg). 2 vols. Half contemp calf, quite rubbed but sound, internal spotting. xxxii,398pp; viii,410pp. *O'NEILL.* $325

Rich, E.E. (ed). CUMBERLAND HOUSE JOURNALS AND INLAND CORRESPONDENCE 1775-82: SECOND SERIES 1779-82. London: Hudson's Bay Record Soc, 1952. Ltd ed. NF w/light rubbing. Unopened. *PARMER.* $125

Rich, Virginia. THE NANTUCKET DIET MURDERS. NY: Delacorte, 1985. 1st ed. Fine in dj. *SILVER DOOR.* $25

Richard, Rhys. WHALING AND SEALING AT THE CHATHAM ISLANDS. Canberra: J.S. Cumpston, 1982. Near New in rubbed dj. *PARMER.* $35

Richards, Laura E. and Maud Howe Elliot. JULIA WARD HOWE 1819-1910. Boston, 1916. 2 vols. 392; 434pp. 1st ed. *O'NEILL.* $35

Richards, T(homas) Addison. TALLULAH AND JOCASSEE....Charleston: Walker, Richards & Co, 1852. 1st ed, 255pp. Orig brn cl. Lib bkpl, blindstamp, dampstain on rear cover, o/w about VG. *CHAPEL HILL.* $95

Richardson, Albert D. BEYOND THE MISSISSIPPI. Hartford, CT: American Pub Co, c1869. New ed. Cvr somewhat water stained. *HUDSON.* $95

Richardson, Albert D. THE SECRET SERVICE, THE FIELD, THE DUNGEON, AND THE ESCAPE. Hartford, CT: American Pub Co, 1866. Frontis, 11 plts. Cl rubbed, top of spine chipped. VG. *BLUE MOUNTAIN.* $25

Richardson, Benjamin W. BIOLOGICAL EXPERIMENTATION: ITS FUNCTION AND LIMITS. London, 1896. 1st ed. 170pp. *FYE.* $100

Richardson, Charles. TALES OF A WARRIOR. NY & Washington: Neale, 1907. 1st ed. Inscribed. Orig pea grn cl, teg. NF. *CHAPEL HILL.* $75

Richardson, Dorothy. HONEYCOMB. London: Duckworth, (1917). 1st ed. Acidic paper quite browned as usual, endsheets foxed, o/w Fine in scarce dj (sl rubbed, new price sticker on spine). Cl, dj. *JAFFE.* $225

Richardson, Dorothy. JOHN AUSTEN AND THE IN-SEPARABLES. Foreword by John Austen. London: William Jackson, 1930. 1st trade ed. Spinal extrems worn, blue boards sl soiled, VG. *CAPTAIN'S BOOKSHELF.* $40

Richardson, Dorothy. JOHN AUSTEN AND THE IN-SEPARABLES. London: William Jackson Ltd, 1930. John Austen (foreword). 5 wood engr, frontis. Orig wood engr "The Rustic Lovers," ptd on Japanese tissue, signed, dated, numbered by Austen laid in. Cream buckram stamped in gilt on front cover, title in gilt on spine, marbled eps, teg. VG. *HELLER.* $350

Richardson, Frank. FROM SUNRISE TO SUNSET: REMINIS-CENCE. Bristol, TN: 1910. 1st ed. Orig cl. *GINSBERG.* $125

Richardson, Frederick. BOOK FOR CHILDREN. Donohue, (1938). 107pp. Color plates, illus by Richardson. NF in VG+. *BEBBAH.* $65

Richardson, H.E. A SHORT HISTORY OF TIBET. NY: Dutton, 1962. 1st US ed. NF in VG- dj. *BLUE DRAGON.* $37.50

Richardson, John. ARCTIC ORDEAL: THE JOURNAL OF JOHN RICHARDSON. Kingston and Montreal: McGill-Queen's Univ, 1985. NF in VG dj. *PARMER.* $65

Richardson, John. ARCTIC SEARCHING EXPEDITION: A JOUR-NAL OF A BOAT VOYAGE THROUGH RUPERT'S LAND AND THE ARCTIC SEA...NY: Harper & Brothers, 1854. 1 vol ed. xi,516pp, incl 5 appendices. Pp browned, scattered foxing, recently rebound in half lea with marbled paper over boards. Eps renewed with orig eps w/pencilled note bound in. *PARMER.* $195

Richardson, Robert. MURDER IN WAITING. NY: St. Martin's Press, 1991. 1st Amer ed. Fine in dj. *MORDIDA.* $22.50

Richardson, Robert. THE BOOK OF THE DEAD. London: Gollancz, (1989). 1st ed. Signed. Fine in Fine dj. *UNGER.* $75

Richardson, Robert. THE BOOK OF THE DEAD. London: Victor Gollancz, 1989. 1st ed. VF in dj. *MORDIDA.* $40

Richardson, Robert. THE DYING OF THE LIGHT. NY: St. Martin's Press, 1990. 1st Amer ed. Fine in dj. *MORDIDA.* $22.50

Richardson, Rupert and Carl Coke Rister. THE GREATER SOUTHWEST...FROM THE SPANISH CONQUEST TO THE TWENTIETH CENTURY. Glendale: Clark, 1934. 1st ed. 6 maps. Orig cl, spine faded and worn. Howes R261. *GINSBERG.* $100

Richardson, Rupert. THE COMANCHE BARRIER TO SOUTH PLAINS SETTLEMENT. Glendale, 1933. 1st ed. NF. *BAADE.* $350

Richardson, Rupert. THE FRONTIER OF NORTHWEST TEXAS 1846 TO 1876. Glendale: A.H. Clark, 1963. 1st ed. Fine. *OREGON.* $100

Richardson, Samuel. THE CORRESPONDENCE OF SAMUEL RICHARDSON...A BIOGRAPHICAL ACCOUNT OF THAT AUTHOR, AND OBSERVATIONS...BY ANNA LAETITIA BARBAULD. London: Richard Phillips, 1804. 1st ed. 6 vols. Frontis, engr, fldg facs, 2 fldg colorplt frontispieces, contemp black 3/4 calf, marbled eps, gilt ornaments on spines. Owner sig of Lady Wilmot, dated 1836, sm tear at outer edge of p.[iii] of Vol I neatly repaired, sl rubbing to boards & corners, with occasional foxing. Very attractive set. *JAFFE.* $750

Richerand, A. ELEMENTS OF PHYSIOLOGY. Phila: Moore, 1823. 621pp,xvi. Recased in modern brn cl, paper spine label, foxing throughout. Good+. *SMITHFIELD.* $60

Richie, Donald and M. Weatherby (eds). THE MASTERS' BOOK OF IKEBANA. Tokyo, 1966. Kimono-silk floral patterned cl w/cherrywood label, wraparound band. *SUTTON.* $200

Richie, Donald. THE MASTERS' BOOK OF IKEBANA. Tokyo, 1966. Folio in silk. In clear dj w/ptd band. Fine. *POLYANTHOS.* $150

Richler, Mordecai. JACOB TWO-TWO MEETS THE HEADED FANG. NY: Knopf, (1975). 1st ed. Fine in price-clipped dj. *LOPEZ.* $45

Richmond, Ian A. THE CITY WALL OF IMPERIAL ROME: AN ACCOUNT OF ITS ARCHITECTURAL DEVELOPMENT FROM AURELIAN TO NARSES. Oxford: Clarendon Press, 1930. Frontis, 45 figs, 21 plts. Good. *ARCHAEOLOGIA.* $175

Richmond, J.F. NEW YORK AND ITS INSTITUTIONS, 1609-1872. NY, 1872. 16,608pp + ads. Rebound new buckram, erasure on title pg. *HEINOLDT.* $25

Richmond, Mary. SHAKER LITERATURE: A BIBLIOGRAPHY. 2 vols. Hancock, MA: Shaker Comm., 1977. 1st ed. Fine. *ARCHER.* $60

Richter, Conrad. A SIMPLE HONORABLE MAN. Knopf, 1962. 1st ed. Signed. Fine in dj. *AUTHORS OF THE WEST.* $40

Richter, Conrad. A SIMPLE HONORABLE MAN. NY: Knopf, 1962. 1st ed. Fine in dj. *JUVELIS.* $25

Richter, Conrad. TACEY CROMWELL. Knopf, 1942. 1st ed. Fine. *AUTHORS OF THE WEST.* $20

Richter, Conrad. THE AWAKENING LAND: THE TREES, THE FIELDS, THE TOWN. Knopf, 1966. 1st coll ed. Fine in dj. *AUTHORS OF THE WEST.* $30

Richter, Conrad. THE FIELDS. Knopf, 1946. 1st ed. Fine in frayed dj. *AUTHORS OF THE WEST.* $35

Richter, Conrad. THE FREE MAN. Knopf, 1943. 1st ed. Fine in dj. *AUTHORS OF THE WEST.* $35

Richter, Conrad. THE TOWN. Knopf, 1950. 1st ed. Dec cvr. Fine in dj, tiny label. *AUTHORS OF THE WEST.* $35

Richter, Conrad. THE TOWN. NY: Knopf, 1950. 1st ed. VF in Fine dj. *LOPEZ.* $75

Richter, Gisela. GREEK, ETRUSCAN AND ROMAN BRONZES. NY: Metropolitan Museum of Art, 1915. Ltd to 500. Frontis, 1/2 calf, orig wraps bound in. Fine. *ARCHAEOLOGIA.* $950

Richter, Gisela. KOUROI, ARCHAIC GREEK YOUTHS: A STUDY OF THE DEVELOPMENT OF THE KOUROS TYPE IN GREEK SCULPTURE. London: Phaidon, 1970. 3rd ed. Fine in dj. *ARCHAEOLOGIA.* $450

Richter, Gisela. KOUROI...THE GREEK KOUROS FROM THE LATE SEVENTH TO THE EARLY FIFTH CENTURY B.C. NY: Oxford, 1942. 1st ed. About Fine in somewhat worn dj. Inscribed. *CAPTAIN'S BOOKSHELF.* $200

Richter, Gisela. RED-FIGURED ATHENIAN VASES IN THE METROPOLITAN MUSEUM OF ART. 2 vols (complete). New Haven: Yale Univ Press, 1936. Ltd to 500. 34 figs, 181 plts, folio. Corner lightly bumped, o/w Fine. *ARCHAEOLOGIA.* $1,750

Richter, Gisela. THE ARCHAIC GRAVESTONES OF ATTICA. London: Phaidon, 1961. 1st ed. Good in faded dj. *ARCHAEOLOGIA.* $125

Richter, Gisela. THE FURNITURE OF THE GREEKS, ETRUS-CANS AND ROMANS. London: Phaidon Press, (1966). Dj. Several corners lightly bumped. Author's calling card laid in. Good. *ARCHAEOLOGIA.* $500

Richter, Gisela. THE SCULPTURE AND SCULPTORS OF THE GREEKS. New Haven and London: Yale Univ Press, (1962). 2 maps. Signature. Good. *ARCHAEOLOGIA.* $85

Richter, Louise M. CHANTILLY IN HISTORY AND ART. London: John Murray, 1913. 1st ed. Presentation, signed. Frontis, 79 plts. VG. *WREDEN.* $75

Rickard, Mrs. Tex. EVERYTHING HAPPENED TO HIM. London, (1937). 1st Eng ed. VG. *DIAMOND.* $35

Rickenbacker, Eddie. HALL OF FAME OF THE AIR. Racine, WI, (1936). 1st ed. Big Little Book #1159. Little touch of spine end wear, else Very Nice. *McCLINTOCK.* $22.50

Rickenbacker, Edward. RICKENBACKER. AN AUTOBIOG-RAPHY. NJ: Prentice-Hall, (1967). 1st ed. Signed. Fine in Fine dj. *BOOK MARKET.* $75

Ricketts, Benjamin. SURGERY OF THE PROSTATE, PANCREAS, DIAPHRAGM, SPLEEN, THYROID, AND HYDROCEPHALUS. A HISTORICAL REVIEW. Cincinnati, 1904. 1st ed. Inscribed, signed. Ex-lib. Rare. *FYE.* $50

Ricketts, Benjamin. SURGERY OF THE THORAX AND ITS VIS-CERA. Cincinnati, 1918. 1st ed. c. 500pp. Signed. Rare. *FYE.* $275

Ricketts, Benjamin. THE SURGERY OF THE HEART AND LUNGS. NY, 1904. 1st ed. 510pp. 87 plts. Ex-lib, but Fine. Rare. *FYE.* $400

Ricketts, Charles and Jean Paul Raymond. OSCAR WILDE. RECOLLECTIONS. Bloomsbury: Nonesuch Press, 1932. 1st ed. Ltd to 800. Gilt pict cvrs. Fine in internally reinforced dj. *JAFFE.* $175

Rickey, Branch and Robert Riger. THE AMERICAN DIAMOND. Simon & Schuster, 1965. 1st ed. VG in VG dj. *PLAPINGER.* $125

Rickey, Branch and Robert Riger. THE AMERICAN DIAMOND. Simon & Schuster, 1965. 1st ed. Good+ in VG dj. *PLAPINGER.* $100

Rickey, Don. $10 HORSE, $40 SADDLE. COWBOY CLOTHING, ARMS, TOOLS, AND HORSE GEAR OF THE 1880'S. Fort Collins: Old Army Press, (1976). 1st ed. VF in VF dj. *OREGON.* $60

RICKY THE RABBIT. London, 1961. Kubasta. Bright pict cvrs, 4pp story, 2-pg pop-up of Ricky's Easter Egg painting party. *BOOK-FINDERS INTL.* $150

Riddell, John (pseud of Corey Ford). IN THE WORST POSSIBLE TASTE. NY & London: Scribner's, 1932. 1st ed. 14 illus. VG in bright, attractive dj. *BERNARD.* $50

Riddell, Mrs. (Charlotte Elizabeth Lawson). MORTOMLEY'S ES-TATE. London: Tinsley, 1875. New ed. 425pp. Bound in 3/4 calf and paper label. VG, clean. *SECOND LIFE.* $65

Riddle, James. ANIMAL LORE AND DISORDER. NY: Harper, (1950s). A Riddle bk. *BOOKFINDERS INTL.* $45

Rideout, Walter B. THE RADICAL NOVEL IN THE UNITED STATES 1900-1954. Cambridge: Harvard Univ Press, 1956. 1st ed. Fine but for bumped rear corner, in NF dj. *BEASLEY.* $85

Ridge, John Rollin. RIDGE'S POEMS. SF: Henry Payot, 1868. 1st ed. Fine in orig cl, stamped in gilt, w/photo frontis. *LOPEZ.* $650

Ridgely, Mabel Lloyd. THE RIDGELYS OF DELAWARE AND THEIR CIRCLE. Portland, ME (1948), 1st ed. 32 plts. *HEINOLDT.* $35

Ridgway, R. A MANUAL OF NORTH AMERICAN BIRDS. Phila, 1896. 2nd ed. xiii,653pp. 124 plts. Orig gilt-stamped cl. Institutional bkpl, sm sticker on spine; pp yellowed. *SUTTON.* $145

Riding, Laura. DESCRIPTION OF LIFE. NY: Targ Editions, 1980. 1st ed. 1/350 signed. Fine. *JUVELIS.* $75

Riding, Laura. LAURA AND FRANCISCA. Deya: Seizen Press, 1931. 1/200 numbered /signed. Very Nice w/slight wear, fading. *DER-MONT.* $250

Riding, Laura. SOME COMMUNICATIONS OF BROAD REFER-ENCE. Lord John Press, 1983. 1/125 numbered/signed. *DERMONT.* $75

Riding, Laura. THE COLLECTED POEMS OF LAURA RIDING. NY: Random House, (1938). 1st US ed. Fine in lightly soiled, sunned dj. *CAPTAIN'S BOOKSHELF.* $150

Riding, Laura. THE TELLING. NY, 1972. Ltd ed, 74/100 only, signed. Holograph correction on copyright pp. Fine in like dj. *POLYANTHOS.* $75

Ridpath, John Clark and Edward S. Ellis. THE STORY OF SOUTH AFRICA. Chicago: Smith, 1899. ii,652pp. Near VG ex-lib. *WORLDWIDE.* $30

Ridpath, John Clark. BEYOND THE SIERRAS. A TOUR OF SIXTY DAYS. Oakland: Biobooks, (1963). Joseph A. Sullivan (foreword). One of 650. Rprnted from 1888 report of Amer Horticultural Soc. Fine. *LAURIE.* $30

Riedesel, Baroness Von. JOURNAL AND CORRESPONDENCE OF A TOUR OF DUTY 1776-83. Marvin L. Brown (rev, trans). U of NC (1965). *HEINOLDT.* $20

Riefenstahl, Leni. THE LAST OF THE NUBA. NY: Harper & Row, (1974). 1st Amer ed. Owner inscrip. Dj. *KARMIOLE.* $100

Riefenstahl, Leni. THE PEOPLE OF KAU. J. Maxwell Brownjohn (trans). NY: Harper & Row, (1976). 1st Amer ed. *KARMIOLE.* $100

Riegel, Robert E. AMERICA MOVES WEST. NY: Henry Holt, 1937. Good. *LAURIE.* $15

Riese, Walther. A HISTORY OF NEUROLOGY. NY, 1959. 1st ed. Dj. *FYE.* $50

Rigby, Douglas and Elizabeth. LOCK, STOCK, AND BARREL. Phila: Lippincott, 1944. 1st trade ed. NF in frayed dj. *WREDEN.* $28

Rigge, William F. THE GRAPHIC CONSTRUCTION OF ECLIP-SES AND OCCULTATIONS. Chicago: Loyola Univ Press, 1924 (1924). Spine lettering faded, corners & top & bottom of spine a little worn. Good. *KNOLLWOOD.* $45

Riggs, Stephen R. MARY AND I: FORTY YEARS WITH THE SIOUX. Boston, (1887). 2nd ed. 437pp. Frontis. Orig cl. Howes R288. *GINSBERG.* $100

Rignano, Eugenio. UPON THE INHERITANCE OF ACQUIRED CHARACTERS: A HYPOTHESIS OF HEREDITY, DEVELOP-MENT, AND OF SIMILATION. Chicago, 1911. 1st Eng trans. *FYE.* $50

Riis, Jacob A. THE CHILDREN OF THE POOR. NY: Scribner's, 1892. 1st ed. Dec paper-covered boards w/cloth backstrip. Small circular label from lib on spine, "Gift" notation; no other lib marks, and thus, NF. *BEASLEY.* $125

Riis, Jacob A. THEODORE ROOSEVELT, THE CITIZEN. NY: Outlook, 1904. 1st ed. Owner's inscrip. Fine. *BEASLEY.* $65

Riley, Athelstan. ATHOS, OR THE MOUNTAIN OF THE MONKS. London, 1887. Frontis & 7 plts, colored map, illus. Recent cl binding to match orig. Trace of perforation on title. xix,409pp. *O'NEILL.* $175

Riley, C.V. FOURTH REPORT OF THE UNITED STATES EN-TOMOLOGICAL COMMISSION. 64 plts (12 colored), 2 fldg maps. Half morocco, edges rubbed. Ex-lib, Washington, 1885. *SUT-TON.* $45

Riley, James Whitcomb. AN OLD SWEETHEART OF MINE. In-dianapolis, (1902). 1st illus ed and 1st separate ed of the poem. Illus by Howard Chandler Christy. A few small bits of enamel lettering lost on spine, else Fine. *McCLINTOCK.* $40

Riley, James Whitcomb. ARMAZINDY. Indianapolis: Bobbs-Merrill, 1894. Name dated May, 1895. Crown of spine chipped, hairline split along outer joints (with hinges still sound and uncracked internally). Good to VG. 1st ed, 5th ptg (and 1st signed ltd issue). #85 of 100 specially bound, signed. *CHAPEL HILL.* $150

Riley, James Whitcomb. THE BOY LIVES ON OUR FARM. Bobbs-Merrill, (1908). Unpaginated. Illus by Ethel Betts. 5 color plts. Spotting to back cvr, some edgewear, VG w/large bright pict pastedown in color of boy in hayloft. *BEBBAH.* $55

Riley, James Whitcomb. THE RUNAWAY BOY. Bobbs-Merrill, (1906). Unpaginated. 8 color plts. Ethel Betts (illus). Sl edgewear but NF. *BEBBAH.* $50

Riley, James Whitcomb. WHILE THE HEART BEATS YOUNG. Bobbs-Merrill, (1906). 110pp. 16 color plts. Ethel Betts (illus). Cvr edgewear, 2 chips border of pict pastedown not affecting illus. VG+ pictorial endpaper. *BEBBAH.* $60

Riley, James. AN AUTHENTIC NARRATIVE OF THE LOSS OF THE AMERICAN BRIG COMMERCE. Hartford: by the author, 1817. 1st ed. 460,xxxiv pp. Fldg map. 9 full-pg copperpl plts. Full morocco, worn, edges heavily rubbed, spine chipped. Few leaves torn and repaired, foxed throughout, front fly-leaf missing, o/w Good; ex-lib. *WORLDWIDE*. $85

Rilke, Rainer Maria. FROM THE REMAINS OF COUNT C.W. J.B. Leishman (trans). London: The Hogarth Press, 1952. 1st UK ed, 1st ed in Eng. Fine (bkpl) in sl chipped dj. *CAPTAIN'S BOOKSHELF*. $45

Rilke, Ranier Maria. LATER POEMS. London: Hogarth Press, 1938. 1st ed. Woolmer 437, 1/1020. Fine in lightly used dj w/spine chips. *BEASLEY*. $125

Rimbaud, Arthur. A SEASON IN HELL. (LEC, 1986). One of 1000, signed by the translator, Paul Schmidt, and the artist, Robert Mapplethorpe. Mint. *PIRAGES*. $1500

Rimbaud, Arthur. A SEASON IN HELL. (NY): LEC, (1986). One of 1000, leatherbound ed, trans. by Paul Schmidt and illus. w/8 orig photogr by Mappelthorpe. Signed by Mappelthorpe and Schmidt. VF in slipcase. *LOPEZ*. $2500

Rimbaud, Arthur. A SEASON IN HELL. Paul Schmidt (trans). Robert Mapplethorpe (photogravures). (NY): LEC, (1986). 1st ed. One of 1000 signed by Mapplethorpe & Schmidt. Full red morroco, cl slipcase. Mint. *JAFFE*. $2000

Rinehart, F.A. RINEHART'S INDIANS. Omaha: F.A. Rinehart, 1899. 46 half-tone repros of photogr ptd on both sides, and 2 color plts. Bound in pic wrapper. Cover shows wear at spine. Still exceptionally Good very fragile bk, w/one duplicate leaf bound in. *LAURIE*. $200

Rinehart, Mary Roberts. ALIBI FOR ISABEL AND OTHER STORIES. NY & Toronto (1944). 1st ed. VG in worn dj. *McCLINTOCK*. $20

Rinehart, Mary Roberts. CASE OF JENNY BRICE. Indianapolis, (1913). 1st Amer ed. Minor staining of fore-edges. Minor foxing on few pages, o/w VG. *DIAMOND*. $45

Rinehart, Mary Roberts. DANGEROUS DAYS. NY, (1919). 1st Amer ed. Spine sl soiled. Slight cvr staining. Minor silverfishing marks on cvrs. Small tear at fly, o/w VG. *DIAMOND*. $45

Rinehart, Mary Roberts. THE BREAKING POINT. NY, (1922). 1st Amer ed. *DIAMOND*. $35

Rinehart, Mary Roberts. THE CIRCULAR STAIRCASE. Indianapolis, (1908). True 1st ed. with "September" on copyright page. Little shelfwear. Fore-edges sl stained & soiled. Stains and/or slight soiling of few pages, o/w VG. *DIAMOND*. $150

Rinehart, Mary Roberts. THE DOOR. NY: Farrar & Rinehart, 1930. 1st ed. Advance proof copy. Pict wraps, one corner lacking. VG+. *ELSE FINE*. $50

Rinehart, Mary Roberts. THE MAN IN THE LOWER TEN. NY, (1909). 1st Amer ed. Color plates by Howard Chandler Christy. Marginal browning on pages facing plates, o/w VG+. *DIAMOND*. $100

Rinehart, Mary Roberts. THE RED LAMP. NY, (1925). 1st Amer ed. Minor spine tip wear, o/w VG+ in pic. color dj with soiled & defective spine. *DIAMOND*. $125

Rinehart, Mary Roberts. THE WINDOW AT THE WHITE CAT. Indianapolis, (1910). 1st Amer ed. Spine & rear cvr sl faded, o/w VG+. *DIAMOND*. $75

Rinehart, Mary Roberts. THIS STRANGE ADVENTURE. GC, NY: Doubleday, Doran & Co., 1929. Spine ends bumped, bkpl, else NF in lightly worn dj. 1st ed. *CHAPEL HILL*. $65

Rinehart, Mary Roberts. THROUGH GLACIER PARK. Boston: Houghton Mifflin, 1916. 1st ed. 16 plts. Fine. *SECOND LIFE*. $45

Rinehart, Mary Roberts. THROUGH GLACIER PARK. Boston: Houghton Mifflin, 1916. 1st ed. 13 full-pg photos. NF. *LAURIE*. $50

Rinehart, Mary Roberts. WHEN A MAN MARRIES. Toronto, (1909). 1st Canad ed. Color plates by Harrison Fisher. Line drawings by Mayo Bunker. Spine very sl faded. Spine lettering rubbed, o/w VG. *DIAMOND*. $75

Rinehart, Mary Roberts. WHERE THERE'S A WILL. Indianapolis, (1912). 1st Amer ed. Spine sl darkened. Rear cvr & spine sl stained, o/w VG. *DIAMOND*. $75

Ring, Ray. ARIZONA KISS. Boston: Little Brown, 1991. 1st ed. VF in dj. *MORDIDA*. $20

Ring, Ray. PEREGRINE DREAM. NY: St. Martin's Press, 1990. 1st ed. Fine in dj w/couple of closed tears. *MORDIDA*. $25

Ring, Ray. TELLURIDE SMILE. NY: Dodd Mead, 1988. 1st ed. Fine in dj w/minor wear. *MORDIDA*. $35

Rinhart, Floyd and Marion. AMERICAN DAGUERREIAN ART. NY: Potter, (1967). 1st ed. 89 b/w plts. Fine in dj. *CAPTAIN'S BOOKSHELF*. $50

Rink, Henry. DANISH GREENLAND ITS PEOPLE AND ITS PRODUCTS. London: Henry S. King & Co, 1877. Cracked hinges, lt soiling to brds, wear to crnrs. Pict dec red cl. 1 fldg map, 16 engr. Bkpl. *PARMER*. $500

Rinpoche, Rechung. TIBETAN MEDICINE, ILLUSTRATED IN ORIGINAL TEXTS. London, 1973. 1st ed. *FYE*. $60

Rintoul, William. DRILLING AHEAD. Santa Cruz: Valle, 1981. 1st ed. NF in Good+ dj. *CONNOLLY & WADE*. $32.50

Ripley, D. SEARCH FOR THE SPINY BABBLER, BIRD HUNTING IN NEPAL. London, 1953. 1st Eng ed. *SUTTON*. $30

Ripley, D. TRAIL OF THE MONEY BIRD. NY, 1942. Name; some wear, pp yellowed. *SUTTON*. $27

Ripley, Edward Hastings. VERMONT GENERAL, THE UNUSUAL WAR EXPERIENCES OF EDWARD HASTINGS RIPLEY (1862-1865). NY, 1960. Otto Eisenschiml (ed). 1st ed. VG+ in dj. *PRATT*. $55

Ripley, Eliza McHatton. FROM FLAG TO FLAG. NY, 1889. 269pp,8pp ads. 1st ed. Pict cl cvrs sl stained, shelf worn. Sl dampstaining, o/w VG. Howes R307. *DIAMOND*. $50

Ripley, Mary Churchill. THE ORIENTAL RUG BOOK. NY: Stokes, (1904). Sm spot rear cover, o/w tight. 1st ed. Frontis. NF. *CHAPEL HILL*. $150

Ripley, S.D. SEARCH FOR THE SPINY BABBLER. Boston: Houghton Mifflin, 1952. Fine in Good dj. *MIKESH*. $20

Ripley, Thomas. THEY DIED WITH THEIR BOOTS ON. Doubleday, 1935. 1st ed. VG in sl chipped dj. *VARNER*. $22.50

RISE AND PROGRESS OF MINNESOTA TERRITORY. INCLUDING A STATEMENT OF THE BUSINESS PROSPERITY OF SAINT PAUL. (By Charles L. Emerson.) St. Paul, C. L. Emerson, Minnesota Democrat Office, 1855. (vii), 64pp, ads. Orig ptd front wrapper, edge worn, lacking rear wrapper. Rare promotional item. Howes E138 and M649. *GINSBERG*. $1500

Rister, Carl C. BORDER COMMAND. Norman, 1944. 1st ed. 244pp. Lt dj wear o/w Fine. *PRATT*. $55

Rister, Carl C. SOUTHERN PLAINSMEN. Univ of OK Press, 1938. 1st ed. Fine. *VARNER*. $95

Rister, Carl C. THE SOUTHWESTERN FRONTIER, 1865-1881. A.H. Clark, 1928. 1st ed. Fine. *VARNER*. $150

Ritch, Johnny. HORSE FEATHERS. Helena, 1941. 2nd ptg. VG. *VARNER*. $50

Ritch, Johnny. HORSEFEATHERS. Helena, MT: Author, (1941). 95pp, boards. *HEINOLDT*. $25

Ritchie, Anna Cora. FAIRY FINGERS. NY: Carlton, 1865. 1st ed. VG. *SECOND LIFE*. $45

Ritchie, Carson. ROCK ART OF AFRICA. NY: A.S. Barnes, 1979. 1st ed. NF in NF dj. *GREAT EPIC*. $65

Ritchie, G.S. THE ADMIRALTY CHART: BRITISH NAVAL HYDROGRAPHY. NY, 1967. 1st Amer ed. Dj. *LEFKOWICZ*. $55

Ritchie, Lady (Ann Thackeray). BLACKSTICK PAPERS. NY and London: Putnam, Knickerbocker Press, 1908. 1st ed. Orig dj (repaired). NF, largely unopened. *HARTFIELD.* $45

Ritchie, William A. THE ARCHAEOLOGY OF NEW YORK STATE. NY: Natural Hist Press, 1965. 1st ed. Fine in VG+ dj. *AARD.* $40

Ritter, Mary Bennett. MORE THAN GOLD IN CALIFORNIA 1849-1933. Berkeley: Professional Press, 1933. 1st ed. Fine in worn dj. *PARMER.* $95

Ritter, W.E. THE CALIFORNIA WOODPECKER AND I. Berkeley: Univ of CA, 1938. Frontis. Signed. VG. *MIKESH.* $40

Ritz, David. THE MAN WHO BROUGHT THE DODGERS BACK TO BROOKLYN. Simon and Schuster, 1981. 1st ed. About Fine in dj. Remainder mark. *STAHR.* $20

Rivera, Diego with Gladys March. MY ART, MY LIFE. AN AUTOBIOGRAPHY. NY: Citadel Press, (1960). 1st ed. Chipped dj. *SILVER.* $40

Rivera, Diego. THE FRESCOES OF DIEGO RIVERA. NY: Harcourt, Brace. (1929). 1st ed. Edward Weston frontis. *KARMIOLE.* $125

Rives, Hallie Ermine (Mrs. Post Wheeler). THE VALIANTS OF VIRGINIA. Indianapolis: Bobbs-Merrill, (1912). 1st ed. Orig red cl. Spinal extremities and corners a trifle rubbed, owner sig, o/w bright, VG. *CHAPEL HILL.* $30

Rivet, Paul. MAYA CITIES. London: Elek Books, (1962). 2nd impression. 10 color tipped-in plts. Dj. *SILVER.* $45

Rivet, Paul. MAYA CITIES. London: Paul Elek, (1973). 10 color plts, dj. Good. *ARCHAEOLOGIA.* $45

RIVIERA NATURE NOTES, A POPULAR ACCOUNT....(by C. Casey). London, 1903. 2nd ed. 31 plts. Pict cl worn at spine edges, corners. Foxing. Ex-lib. *SUTTON.* $27

Rivoira, G.T. ROMAN ARCHITECTURE AND ITS PRINCIPLES OF CONSTRUCTION UNDER THE EMPIRE. Oxford: Clarendon Press, 1925. Frontis. Good. *ARCHAEOLOGIA.* $250

Rizzuto, Phil and Al Silverman. THE "MIRACLE" NEW YORK YANKEES. Coward McCann, 1962. 1st ed. VG in Fine dj. *PLAPINGER.* $40

Robb, Harry. PODDY. Trail's End, 1947. 1st ed. Fine in VG sl chipped dj. *VARNER.* $50

Robb, Isabel Hampton. NURSING: ITS PRINCIPLES AND PRACTICE FOR HOSPITAL AND PRIVATE USE. Cleveland, 1906. 3rd ed. *FYE.* $125

Robbe-Grillet, Alain. DJINN. NY: Grove (1982). 1st Amer ed. NF in like dj. *DORN.* $35

Robbe-Grillet, Alain. DREAMS OF A YOUNG GIRL. NY: Morrow, 1971. 1st ed. Fine in lightly used price-clipped dj. *CAPTAIN'S BOOKSHELF.* $50

Robbe-Grillet, Alain. LA MAISON DE RENDEZ-VOUS. NY: Grove (1966). 1st Amer ed. Fine in dj. *DORN.* $40

Robbe-Grillet, Alain. RECOLLECTIONS OF THE GOLDEN TRIANGLE. NY: Grove (1986). 1st Amer ed. Rmdr mk else Fine in dj. *DORN.* $25

Robbins, Archibald. A JOURNAL, COMPRISING AN ACCOUNT OF THE LOSS OF THE BRIG COMMERCE. 16th ed. Hartford, CT: Silas Andrews. 1823. 12mo. 276 pp. Fldg map bit soiled. Contemp mottled calf, somewhat scuffed. *KARMIOLE.* $75

Robbins, Guy (ed). THE BREAST. Austin, TX, 1984. 1st ed. Dj. *FYE.* $75

Robbins, Harold. A STONE FOR DANNY FISHER. NY: Knopf, 1952. 1st ed. VF, bright dj has minor rubs at spine ends. *ELSE FINE.* $35

Robbins, Harold. THE CARPETBAGGERS. NY: Simon & Schuster, 1961. 1st ed. As New, dj spine faintly age-darkened. *ELSE FINE.* $35

Robbins, Tod. THE MASTER OF MURDER. London, 1933. 1st ed. Cvr wear, else VG. *MADLE.* $60

Robbins, Tod. THE SPIRIT OF THE TOWN. Ogilvie, 1912. 1st ed. VG. *MADLE.* $100

Robbins, Tom. ANOTHER ROADSIDE ATTRACTION. GC: Doubleday, 1971. 1st ed. Signed, dated 1980. VG+ in VG+ dj. *BEASLEY.* $250

Robbins, Tom. ANOTHER ROADSIDE ATTRACTION. GC: Doubleday, 1971. 1st ed, 1st bk. Edges shelfworn, sm "book sale" stamp marked through w/black marker, else VG+ in dj, worn spine ends. *BERNARD.* $200

Robbins, Tom. ANOTHER ROADSIDE ATTRACTION. London, NY: W.H. Allen, 1973. 1st UK ed, 1st bk. Fine in NF dj. *BERNARD.* $225

Robbins, Tom. EVEN COWGIRLS GET THE BLUES. Boston: Houghton Mifflin, 1976. Uncorrected proof. VG only in powder blue wrappers. *CAPTAIN'S BOOKSHELF.* $125

Robbins, Tom. JITTERBUG PERFUME. NY: Bantam, (1984). 1st ed. NF in NF dj. *AKA.* $35

Robbins, Tom. JITTERBUG PERFUME. NY: Bantam, (1984). Uncorrected proof. 1/4" stain front panel, else Fine in wrappers. *CAPTAIN'S BOOKSHELF.* $50

Robbins, Tom. STILL LIFE WITH WOODPECKER. NY: Bantam Books, (1980). 1st ed. 1st hb ed pub by Bantam (only 2500 hb) issued simultaneously w/softcvr ed. Fine in NF dj (crease). *BERNARD.* $65

ROBERT HELLER, HIS DOINGS. Glasgow: Hay Nisbet, n.d. (1875). 1st ed thus. 12mo; orig orange pict wraps, soiled and creased; covers laid down; sewn; engr portrait to title page; 17 engr illus; small hole to rear wrap and penultimate leaf, affecting two words of text. VG. Scarce. *DRAMATIS PERSONAE.* $250

Robert, Maurice and Frederic Warde. A CODE FOR THE COLLECTOR OF BEAUTIFUL BOOKS. NY: LEC, 1936. Trans by Jacques LeClercq. Light soiling front cover, extremities a bit worn, o/w VG. *WREDEN.* $25

Robert, Maurice. A CODE FOR THE COLLECTOR OF BEAUTIFUL BOOKS. Limited Editions, NY, 1936, 1st ed. Edges rubbed. *HEINOLDT.* $18

Roberts, A. ROBERT'S BIRDS OF SOUTH AFRICA, REVISED BY G.R. MCLACHLAN AND R. LIVERSIDGE. Cape Town, 1957. Rev ed. 56 colored, 8 b/w plts. Dj *SUTTON.* $40

Roberts, Charles G.D. THE HAUNTERS OF THE SILENCES. Boston, 1907. 1st ed. Illus by Charles Livingston Bull. Fine. *McCLINTOCK.* $30

Roberts, Dan W. RANGERS AND SOVEREIGNTY. San Antonio, 1914. 1st ed. Cl cvrs sl spotted, o/w VG+. Howes R339. *DIAMOND.* $60

Roberts, David. DEBORAH: A WILDERNESS NARRATIVE. NY: Vanguard Press, (1970). 1st ed. VG+ in VG dj. *BLUE DRAGON.* $27.50

Roberts, E.M. A FLYING FIGHTER: AN AMERICAN ABOVE THE LINES IN FRANCE. NY: Harper, (1918). 1st ed. Orig cl, spine faded, hinges mended. *GINSBERG.* $100

Roberts, Elizabeth Madox. A BURIED TREASURE. NY: Viking, 1931. 1/200 numbered/signed. Fine in split slipcase. *DERMONT.* $100

Roberts, Gillian. CAUGHT DEAD IN PHILADELPHIA. NY: Charles Scribner's Sons, 1987. 1st ed. VF in dj. *MORDIDA.* $25

Roberts, Gillian. CAUGHT DEAD IN PHILADELPHIA. NY: Scribner, 1987. 1st ed. Review copy, signed. Pub's slip laid in. Fine in dj. *SILVER DOOR.* $35

Roberts, Harry. EUTHANASIA AND OTHER ASPECTS OF LIFE AND DEATH. London, 1936. 1st ed. *FYE.* $40

Roberts, Jack. THE AMAZING ADVENTURES OF LORD GORE. Silverton, Co.: Sundance Books, (1977). Ltd to 2000 numbered & signed. 1st ed. VG. *OREGON.* $40

Roberts, Keith. WINTERWOOD. Morrigan, 1989. 1st ed. Fine in dj. *MADLE.* $35

Roberts, Kenneth. ARUNDEL. GC: Doubleday, Doran & Co., 1936. Reprint. One of special ed signed. Extra page tipped in. Dj art by N.C. Wyeth. VG+ in bright dj sl chipped at spine ends. *BERNARD.* $60

Roberts, Kenneth. LYDIA BAILEY. GC: Doubleday & Company, Inc, 1947. Ltd ed of 1050 signed, w/heavily corrected typed pp of ms laid in (sm piece torn from corner). Frontis. Fine. *BLUE MOUNTAIN.* $100

Roberts, Kenneth. LYDIA BAILEY. GC: Doubleday, 1947. 1st ed. VF, minute edgewear to price clipped dj. *ELSE FINE.* $60

Roberts, Kenneth. NORTHWEST PASSAGE. Cl, dj. GC: Doubleday, Doran, 1937. 1st trade ed. Signed. Mint. *JAFFE.* $200

Roberts, Kenneth. OLIVER WISWELL. GC: Doubleday, Doran, 1940. 1st trade ed. Cl, dj. VF. *JAFFE.* $100

Roberts, Kenneth. RABBLE IN ARMS. GC: Doubleday, Doran & Co., 1938. Reprint. One of special ed signed. Dj art by N.C. Wyeth. VG+ in dj sl chipped at bottom spine edge. *BERNARD.* $60

Roberts, L. RIVERS OF AMERICA: THE MACKENZIE. NY & Toronto: Rinehart, 1949. NF in VG dj. *MIKESH.* $27.50

Roberts, Les. A CARROT FOR THE DONKEY. NY: St. Martin's, 1989. 1st ed. Review copy, signed. Pub's slip laid in. Fine in dj. *SILVER DOOR.* $35

Roberts, Les. AN INFINITE NUMBER OF MONKEYS. NY: St. Martin's Press, 1987. 1st ed. VF in dj. *MORDIDA.* $25

Roberts, Les. NOT ENOUGH HORSES. NY: St. Martin's Press, 1988. 1st ed. VF in dj. *MORDIDA.* $25

Roberts, Millard F. HISTORICAL GAZETTEER, STEUBEN COUNTY, NY, WITH MEMOIRS AND ILLUSTRATIONS. Syracuse, NY, 1891. 592pp + Appendix 18pp. (Business directory in Part Second, bound separately is missing). Fldg map. Rebound. *HEINOLDT.* $25

Roberts, Ned H. THE MUZZLE-LOADING CAP LOCK RIFLE. Harrisburg: Stackpole, (1952). Rev, enl from privately ptd 1940 ed. Fine in Fine dj. *BOOK MARKET.* $35

Roberts, Sydney Castle. A HISTORY OF THE CAMBRIDGE UNIVERSITY PRESS 1521-1921. Cambridge: Univ Press, 1921. Frontis. Lt foxing, 1/4 white and blue cl, Bkpl. VG. *WEBER.* $85

Roberts, T.S. THE BIRDS OF MINNESOTA. Minneapolis, 1932. 1st ed. 92 colored plts. 2 vols. Wear corners, spine ends; lt dampstaining rear cvr Vol II; name on eps. *SUTTON.* $195

Roberts, W. Adolphe. THE FRENCH IN THE WEST INDIES. Indianapolis: Bobbs-Merrill, (1942). 1st ed. Bkpl. VG+ in VG dj. *AARD.* $25

Roberts, W. BOOK-VERSE, AN ANTHOLOGY....London: Elliot Stock, 1896. 1st ed. Orig grn cl, bevelled edges. *OAK KNOLL.* $30

Roberts, Warren. A BIBLIOGRAPHY OF D.H. LAWRENCE. London, 1963. 1st ed. Fine in dj, rubbed, w/rear panel sl soiled. *POLYANTHOS.* $75

Roberts, William F. DIXIE DARKIES. Boston: Bruce Humphries, Inc., (1942). 1st ed. Orig black cl. VG in photogr dj (sm chip head of spine). Signed. *CHAPEL HILL.* $85

Robertson, Archibald. ARCHIBALD ROBERTSON HIS DIARIES AND SKETCHES IN AMERICA, 1762-1780. NY, 1930. 1st ed. One of 200 numbered, signed. H. M. Lydenberg (ed). 1/2 morocco. Howes R350. *GINSBERG.* $175

Robertson, David. REPORTS OF THE TRIALS OF COLONEL AARON BURR (LATE VICE PRESIDENT OF THE U. S.) FOR TREASON...TO WHICH IS ADDED...THE ARGUMENTS AND EVIDENCE...TO COMMIT A. BURR, H.

BLANNERHASSETT, AND I. SMITH...FOR TREASON....Phila, 1808. 2 vols. Orig full calf (joints and hinges expertly reinforced). Howes B1013. *GINSBERG.* $350

Robertson, Don. THE IDEAL, GENUINE MAN. Bangor: Philtrum Press, 1987. Intro by Stephen King. 1st ed. One of 500 numbered, signed by Robertson and King. VF in dj. *MORDIDA.* $100

Robertson, Donald. PRE-COLUMBIAN ARCHITECTURE. NY: George Braziller, 1963. Dj. Good. *ARCHAEOLOGIA.* $35

Robertson, Frank C. and Beth Kay Harris. SOAPY SMITH, KING OF THE FRONTIER CON MEN. NY: Hastings House, 1961. 1st ed. Fine in sl chipped dj. *GIBBS.* $25

Robertson, Fred L. SOLDIERS OF FLORIDA IN THE SEMINOLE, INDIAN - CIVIL AND SPANISH-AMERICAN WARS. (Live Oak), Board of State Institutions, Fl, 1903. 1st ed. Contemp marbled boards, lea spine w/label, lax flyleaf. *GINSBERG.* $300

Robertson, George F. A SMALL BOY'S RECOLLECTIONS OF THE CIVIL WAR. Clover, SC, 1932. 1st ed. Signed. Small piece chipped from cvr o/w VG. *PRATT.* $50

Robertson, John W. FRANCIS DRAKE & OTHER EARLY EXPLORERS ALONG THE PACIFIC COAST. San Marino: Grabhorn, 1927. 1st ed. Ltd to 1000. Fldg map. Bkplt. *CONNOLLY & WADE.* $195

Robertson, John. MICHIGAN IN THE WAR. Lansing, 1882. Rev (i.e. 2nd) ed. 3/4 leather binding. Lib tape on spine, back hinge cracked. VG. *McCLINTOCK.* $65

Robertson, Morgan. DOWN TO THE SEA. Harper, 1905. 1st ed. VG. *MADLE.* $40

Robertson, Morgan. WHERE ANGELS FEAR TO TREAD. Century, 1899. 1st ed. VG. *MADLE.* $65

Robertson, Pauline Durrett and R.L. Robertson. COWMAN'S COUNTRY. Amarillo, TX: Paramount Pub Co, 1981. 1st ed. VF. *GIBBS.* $45

Robertson, Pauline Durrett and R.L. Robertson. PANHANDLE PILGRIMAGE. Canyon, TX: Staked Plains Press, 1976. 1st ed. Fine in dj. *GIBBS.* $40

Robeson, Eslanda Goode. AFRICAN JOURNEY. NY: John Day, (1945). 1st ed. VG in dj chipped at spine extrems. *LOPEZ.* $85

Robeson, Kenneth. THE LAND OF TERROR. Street & Smith, 1933. 1st ed. Unusually Fine. *MADLE.* $200

Robeson, Kenneth. THE MAN OF BRONZE. NY: Street & Smith, (1933). 1st ed. Pp browned, 1st 2 pp chipped; 1" split front cvr, else VG in sl soiled pict paper-cvrd boards, issued w/out dj. *BERNARD.* $100

Robicsek, Francis. THE SMOKING GODS. Norman: Univ of OK Press, (1978). 1st ed. Good in chipped dj. *SILVER.* $75

Robidoux, Orral. MEMORIAL TO THE ROBIDOUX BROTHERS. Kansas City: Smith-Grieves, 1924. 1st ed. Rear cover, eps dampstained. Good+. *OREGON.* $150

Robie, Virginia. HISTORIC STYLES IN FURNITURE. Chicago: Herbert S. Stone. 1905. (12),196pp. Frontis, 114 illus. Paper cvr label. Spine soiled, spine extrems bit rubbed. *KARMIOLE.* $50

Robins, Edward. TWELVE GREAT ACTORS. NY and London: G.P. Putnam's Sons, 1900. 1st ed. *DRAMATIS.* $40

Robinson, Albert G. OLD NEW ENGLAND DOORWAYS. NY: Charles Scribner's Sons. 1920. 1st ed. Frt cvr w/a few small spots. *KARMIOLE*. $40

Robinson, Alfred. LIFE IN CALIFORNIA...CUSTOMS, AND TRADITIONS OF THE INDIANS OF ALTA-CALIFORNIA. Oakland, CA, 1947. Ltd to 750. Orig cl. Howes R363, later ed. *GINSBERG*. $30

Robinson, B.W. A DESCRIPTIVE CATALOGUE OF THE PERSIAN PAINTINGS IN THE BODLEIAN LIBRARY. Oxford: Clarendon Press, 1958. 1st ed. 40 plts. Dj. Fine. *WEBER*. $100

Robinson, Bradley. DARK COMPANION. London: Hodder and Stoughton, 1948. 1st Brit ed. Average used copy. *PARMER*. $35

Robinson, Chandler A. J. EVETTS HALEY: COWMAN-HISTORIAN. El Paso: Carl Hertzog, 1967. One of 600. Designed by Carl Hertzog w/presentation signed by him. Bound in grey heavy weave buckram. Fine. *LAURIE*. $150

Robinson, Charles Alexander, Jr. EPHEMERIDES OF ALEXANDER'S EXPEDITION. Providence: Brown, 1932. Fldg map. Dj chipped. *SCHOYER'S*. $45

Robinson, Charles N. OLD NAVAL PRINTS, THEIR ARTISTS AND ENGRAVERS. London: The Studio, Limited, 1924. One of 1500. 96 plts (24 tipped-in colored plts w/tissue guards). VG w/occasional lt foxing. Gilt dec blue cl. *PARMER*. $650

Robinson, Corinne Roosevelt. MY BROTHER THEODORE ROOSEVELT. NY: Scribner's, 1921. 1st ed. NF. *CONNOLLY & WADE*. $45

Robinson, Edwin Arlington. THE CHILDREN OF THE NIGHT. Boston: Richard G. Badger and Company, 1897. 1st ed, 1/500. Some foxing throughout, else VG. *JUVELIS*. $300

Robinson, Edwin Arlington. THE CHILDREN OF THE NIGHT. Boston: Richard C. Badger, 1897. 1st ed, 1st bk. Rubbed, scattered light foxing, shallow dampstain affecting bottom edges of 1st several pages. Overall, VG. Inscribed. *CAPTAIN'S BOOKSHELF*. $200

Robinson, George. THREE YEARS IN THE EAST: BEING...A JOURNAL WRITTEN DURING A TOUR AND RESIDENCE IN GREECE, EGYPT, PALESTINE, SYRIA AND TURKEY IN 1829-1830, 1831 AND 1832. London, 1837. 5 fldg maps. Full morocco, frt brd loose. viii,416pp. *O'NEILL*. $325

Robinson, J.C. THE TREASURY OF ORNAMENTAL ART....London: Day & Son, (1858). 1st ed. Unpaginated. 71 color litho plts. Orig extra gilt dec cl, aeg. Joints a bit cracked, else Fine. *WREDEN*. $265

Robinson, Jackie with Alfred Duckett. I NEVER HAD IT MADE. Putnam, 1972. 1st ed. VG in Fine dj. *PLAPINGER*. $20

Robinson, Jackie with Alfred Duckett. I NEVER HAD IT MADE. Rachel Robinson, 1987. 1st ptg of reprint ed. Generally, later ptgs or reprints of a title are more plentiful, less expensive, and therefore less desirable than 1st eds, but this is an exception. Fine in Fine dj. *PLAPINGER*. $50

Robinson, John and George Francis Dow. SAILING SHIPS OF NEW ENGLAND 1607-1907. (-Series II. -Series III.) Salem, 1922-1928. Pubs 1, 5, & 18. 3 vols. 606 plts. Fine, attractive set, w/o the djs. *LEFKOWICZ*. $475

Robinson, John and George Francis Dow. THE SAILING SHIPS OF NEW ENGLAND 1607-1907 (Series I) Salem, 1922. Pub. 1. 308 plts. Extremities rubbed. 1st pub of the Society. *LEFKOWICZ*. $150

Robinson, John W. THE SAN GABRIELS. SF: Golden West, 1977. 1st ed. VF. *CONNOLLY & WADE*. $35

Robinson, Mabel. RUNNER OF THE MOUNTAIN TOPS, THE LIFE OF LOUIS AGASSIZ. Random, (1939). Stated 1st ptg. 290pp. Illus by Lynd Ward. 8 color plates. VG+. *BEBBAH*. $40

Robinson, Peter. GALLOWS VIEW. Canada: Viking/Penguin, 1987. 1st ed. Rev copy, signed. Pub's slip laid in. Fine in dj. *SILVER DOOR*. $35

Robinson, Ralph M. THE PENN COUNTRY AND THE CHILTERNS. London: John Lane, and Boston: Dodd, Mead, 1929. Minor bumps, shelfwear, else VG-NF. *OLD LONDON*. $30

Robinson, Selma. CITY CHILD. POEMS. Rockwell Kent (decs). Illus, cl backed dec boards, matching slipcase. NY: The Colophon Ltd, 1931. 1st ed. Ltd to 300 w/orig frontis litho, signed by the poet &, with his heart-shaped mark, by Kent. Fine. *JAFFE*. $150

Robinson, Victor. AN ESSAY ON HASHEESH. NY, 1930. 2nd ed. Dj. Scarce. *FYE*. $75

Robinson, W. THE ENGLISH FLOWER GARDEN AND HOME GROUNDS....London, 1926. 14th ed. 1/2 morocco; lt scuffing, ink name. *SUTTON*. $55

Robinson, W. THE ENGLISH FLOWER GARDEN AND HOME GROUNDS. NY, 1921. 13th ed. Orig cl, upper spine split repaired, spine faded, inner joints open. Ex-lib. *SUTTON*. $40

Robinson, Will H. THE STORY OF ARIZONA. Phoenix: Berryhill Co, (1919). 1st ed. Signed, inscribed. VG. *BOOK MARKET*. $30

Robinson, Will H. THE STORY OF ARIZONA. Phoenix: The Berryhill Company, c1919. 1st ed. Inscribed. Portion of dj preserved on recto of frontis, 2 pict postcards mounted inside back cover. *HUDSON*. $95

Robinson, Will H. THE STORY OF ARIZONA. Phoenix: The Berryhill Co, 1919. 1st ed. Fine, rear hinge cracked. *GIBBS*. $47.50

Robinson, William Morrison, Jr. THE CONFEDERATE PRIVATEERS. New Haven, 1928. 1st ed. Fine in VG dj. *McGOWAN*. $125

Robinson, Zirkle D. THE ROBINSON-ROSENBERGER JOURNEY...1849-50. Francis Coleman Rosenberger (ed). Iowa City: The Prairie Press, (1966). Cl w/dec boards, dj. Mint. *SCHOYER'S*. $40

Robison, Mary. SUBTRACTION. NY: Knopf, 1991. Uncorrected proof. Fine. *CAPTAIN'S BOOKSHELF*. $20

Robsjohn-Gibbings, T.H. and Carlton W. Pullin. FURNITURE OF CLASSICAL GREECE. NY: Alfred A. Knopf, (1963). 4 color illus, Dj. Good. *ARCHAEOLOGIA*. $125

Robson, A.W. Mayo and P.J. Cammidge. THE PANCREAS: ITS SURGERY AND PATHOLOGY. Phila, 1907. 1st Amer ed. *FYE*. $75

Robson, John S. HOW A ONE LEGGED REBEL LIVES. Charlottesville, VA, 1891. 2nd ed. Pamphlet bound in cloth. 2 small lib stamps, else VG. *McGOWAN*. $175

Rocheterie, Maxime de la. THE LIFE OF MARIE ANTOINETTE. Cora H. Bell (trans). 2 vols. NY: Dodd, Mead, 1895. 8vo, xxii,354; xi,377pp. Frontis in each vol. Orig buckram w/gilt crest vignette on front covers. Spines soiled. Little spine tip wear, little cover repair. Two pp badly opened in vol. 2, o/w VG set. *DIAMOND*. $25

Rock, J.F. THE LEGUMINOUS PLANTS OF HAWAII. Honolulu, 1920. 93 plts. Wrappers. Front cvr chipped and reattached at hinge; backstrip, rear cvr missing; some pp chipping, soiling. *SUTTON*. $75

Rockfellow, John A. LOG OF AN ARIZONA TRAIL BLAZER. Tucson: Acme, (1933). 1st ed. Orig dec cl, faded. Inscribed. Howes R392. *GINSBERG*. $100

Rockfellow, John A. LOG OF AN ARIZONA TRAIL BLAZER. Tucson, (1933). 1st ed. Fine. Howes R392. *BOHLING*. $125

Rockne, Bonnie Skiles (ed). THE AUTOBIOGRAPHY OF KNUTE K. ROCKNE. South Bend, Notre Dame Ed (1931). Intro by Fr. John Cavanaugh. Ltd to 2400 signed by Mrs. Knute Rockne and Fr. Cavanaugh. Good. *CULLEN*. $45

Rockwell, A.D. ELECTRO-THERAPEUTICS. 1891, pp. 133-226, IN: H. A. Hare ed. A SYSTEM OF PRACTICAL THERAPEUTICS. VOLUME 1. Phila, 1891. 1st ed. *FYE.* $40

Rockwell, A.D. RAMBLING RECOLLECTIONS, AN AUTOBIOGRAPHY. NY, 1920. 1st ed. 332pp. Front hinges weakened, o/w VG. *PRATT.* $70

Rockwell, Charles. SKETCHES OF FOREIGN TRAVEL AND LIFE AT SEA. Boston, 1842. Frontis. 2 vols in 1. Spine faded, spine ends chipped. xviii,404pp; viii,437pp. 1st ed. *O'NEILL.* $275

Rockwell, Charles. THE CATSKILL MOUNTAINS AND REGION AROUND. NY, 1867. 322pp. Spine rubbed top and bottom. *HEINOLDT.* $20

Rockwell, Robert H. MY WAY OF BECOMING A HUNTER. NY: W.W. Norton & Co, 1955. 1st ed. *BACKMAN.* $25

Rockwood, Roy. THROUGH SPACE TO MARS. Cupples & Leon. VG in chipped dj. *MADLE.* $40

Roda, Joseph. BOWS FOR MUSICAL INSTRUMENTS OF THE VIOLIN FAMILY. Chicago: William Lewis & Son, 1959. Ed ltd to 3000. Scarce. *KARMIOLE.* $175

Roddis, Louis. A SHORT HISTORY OF NAUTICAL MEDICINE. NY, 1941. *FYE.* $80

Rodenbough, Theophilus F. FROM EVERGLADE TO CANON WITH THE SECOND DRAGOONS, AND AUTHENTIC ACCOUNT OF SERVICE IN...THE INDIAN COUNTRY. NY: Van Nostrand, 1875. 1st ed. 561pp. 25 illus and maps, incl 6 in color. Contemp grn cl. Howes R395. *GINSBERG.* $1000

Rodger, Ella. ABERDEEN DOCTORS AT HOME AND ABROAD, THE NARRATIVE OF A MEDICAL SCHOOL. Edinburgh, 1893. 1st ed. Scarce. *FYE.* $75

Rodgers, Charles. "NOBLE FELLOW," WILLIAM STARLING SULLIVANT (BOTANIST) WITH COMPILATION OF NEW SPECIES OF MOSSES....NY, 1940, 1st ed. *HEINOLDT.* $15

Rodin, Alvin. OSLERIAN PATHOLOGY: AN ASSESSMENT AND ANNOTATED ATLAS OF MUSEUM SPECIMENS. Lawrence, KS, 1981. 1st ed. *FYE.* $75

Rodman, Seldon. RENAISSANCE IN HAITI. POPULAR PAINTERS IN THE BLACK REPUBLIC. NY: Pelligrini & Cudahy, 1948. 1st ed. VG, contents Fine. *CONNOLLY & WADE.* $45

Rodney, Janet and Nathaniel Tarn. THE FOREST. Collages by John Digby, wrappers. Mt. Horeb: Perishable Press, 1978. 1st ed. Ltd to 190. VF. *JAFFE.* $150

Roe, Frank. THE NORTH AMERICAN BUFFALO. Univ of Toronto, 1951. 1st ed. VF in VG dj. *OREGON.* $90

Roe, Mrs. Francis M. ARMY LETTERS FROM AN OFFICER'S WIFE, 1871-1888. NY, 1909. 1st ed. Pict cl. Minor cvr wear o/w Fine. *PRATT.* $175

Roe, Mrs. Francis M. ARMY LETTERS FROM AN OFFICER'S WIFE. NY: 1909. 1st ed. 10 plts. Orig cl, sm paper label removed from spine, emb lib stamp. Howes R403. *GINSBERG.* $100

Roehm, Marjorie. THE LETTERS OF GEORGE CATLIN & HIS FAMILY. Univ of CA, 1966. 1st ed. Frontis. VF in Fine dj. *OREGON.* $35

Roerich, Nicholas. ALTAI-HIMALAYA. London: Jarrolds. N.d. (circa 1930). 1st ed. Blue cl. Scarce. *KARMIOLE.* $125

Roethke, Theodore. OPEN HOUSE. NY: Knopf, 1941. 1st ed. VG copy of author's 1st book, but lacking dj. Signed. *WOOLMER.* $350

Roethke, Theodore. THE LOST SON AND OTHER POEMS. London: John Lehmann, (1949). 1st UK. Fine in dj (some light wear to spinal extremities). *CAPTAIN'S BOOKSHELF.* $75

Roethke, Theodore. WORDS FOR THE WIND. GC: Doubleday, 1958. 1st ed. Owner name. VG in very edgeworn dj. *LOPEZ.* $40

Rogers, Fred B. SOLDIERS ON THE OVERLAND, BEING SOME ACCOUNT OF THE SERVICES OF GENERAL PATRICK EDWARD CONNER. SF, 1938. 1st ed ltd to 1000. Fldg map. Minor spotting on the cvr o/w Fine. *PRATT.* $110

Rogers, George. MEMORANDA OF THE EXPERIENCE, LABORS, AND TRAVELS OF A UNIVERSALIST PREACHER. Cincinnati, 1845. 1st ed. 400pp. Contemp full calf, hinges expertly strengthened. Howes R412. *GINSBERG.* $175

Rogers, J.E. THE SHELL BOOK. NY, 1908. 104 plts. Wear to extremities, spine faded, front hinge repaired, rear hinge cracked. *SUTTON.* $50

Rogers, J.M. (ed). THE TOPKAPI MUSEUM. COSTUMES. Boston: Little, Brown/NY Graphic Soc, 1986. 1st US ed. Dj. NF. *WORLDWIDE.* $85

Rogers, J.M. (ed). THE TOPKAPI SARAY MUSEUM. THE ALBUMS AND ILLUSTRATED MANUSCRIPTS. Boston: Little, Brown/NY Graphic Soc, 1986. 1st US ed. 181 color illus, 2 maps. Dj. In slipcase. NF. *WORLDWIDE.* $95

Rogers, J.M. THE TOPKAPI SARAY MUSEUM. CARPETS. Boston: Little, Brown, 1987. 1st ed. 98 color plts. Dj. In slipcase. NF. *WORLDWIDE.* $95

Rogers, J.M. THE TOPKAPI SARAY MUSEUM. THE TREASURY. Boston: Little, Brown, 1987. 1st ed. 124 color plts. Dj. In slipcase. NF. *WORLDWIDE.* $85

Rogers, James E. Thorold. SIX CENTURIES OF WORK & WAGES: THE HISTORY OF ENGLISH LABOUR. NY: Putnam's, 1884. Name. *AKA.* $85

Rogers, Justus H. COLUSA COUNTY: ITS HISTORY...Orland, Ca., 1891. 1st ed. 474pp. Frontis, fldg map, 59 plts. Orig full dec leather. Howes R415. *GINSBERG.* $750

Rogers, Richard and Oscar Hammerstein. THE KING AND I. NY: Random House, (1951). 1st ed. Fine in NF dj, soiled. *UNGER.* $75

Rogers, Rose Annie. THE LONELY ISLAND. Milwaukee: Morehouse Pub Co, 1927. Some spotting, wear esp to head and heel of spine. *PARMER.* $35

Rogers, Samuel. DUSK AT THE GROVE. Boston: Little Brown, 1934. 1st ed. Signed. Fine in NF dj. *LOPEZ.* $35

Rogers, Stanley. FREAK SHIPS. London: Bodley Head, (1936). 1st Eng ed. VG+ in Good dj. *AARD.* $35

Rogers, Thomas. AT THE SHORES. NY: Simon and Schuster, (1980). Adv uncorrected proofs. Title, author in ink on backstrip, o/w Fine in soiled yellow ptd wraps. *HELLER.* $55

Rogers, Thomas. THE PURSUIT OF HAPPINESS. London: The Bodley Head, (1969). 1st Eng ed, 1st bk. Fine in sl soiled white dj, bkseller's stamp, chips. *HELLER.* $50

Rogers, W.E. TREE FLOWERS OF FOREST, PARK, AND STREET. Appleton, 1935. Cl, lt scuffing to edges; minor spotting on spine. *SUTTON.* $75

Rogers, Will. THE AUTOBIOGRAPHY OF WILL ROGERS. Houghton Mifflin/Riverside Press, 1949. Donald Day (ed). 1st ed. VG. *CONNOLLY & WADE.* $20

Rogosin, Donn. INVISIBLE MEN. Atheneum, 1985. 1st ed. VG+ in VG+ dj. *PLAPINGER.* $50

Rohde, Eleanor S. A GARDEN OF HERBS. London: Philip Lee Warner, 1921. 1st ed. VG. *WREDEN.* $22

Rohde, Eleanor S. VEGETABLE CULTIVATION & COOKERY. London: Medici, 1938. Dj worn, w/plastic jacket, contents w/occasional offset from newspaper clipping. *AMERICAN BOTANIST.* $45

Rohmer, Sax. BIMBASHI BARUK OF EGYPT. McBride, 1944. 1st ed. VG. *MADLE.* $50

Rohmer, Sax. BIMBASHI BARUK OF EGYPT. NY: Robert M. McBride, 1944. 1st ed. VG in price clipped dj (chipped, worn, internally mended) attractive pict dj. *BERNARD.* $175

Rohmer, Sax. EGYPTIAN NIGHTS. London: Robert Hale, 1944. 1st ed. Name fep, o/w Fine in dj (short closed tears; couple of nicks base of spine). *MORDIDA.* $350

Rohmer, Sax. EMPEROR FU MANCHU. London: Herbert Jenkins, 1959. 1st ed. Fine in dj w/minor wear at spine ends and short closed tear. *MORDIDA.* $100

Rohmer, Sax. FU MANCHU'S BRIDE. Burt, n.d. Fine in frayed dj. *MADLE.* $30

Rohmer, Sax. HANGOVER HOUSE. NY: Random House, 1949. 1st ed. Fine, dj w/sm chip at spine head, minor edgewear. *ELSE FINE.* $60

Rohmer, Sax. MOON OF MADNESS. Doubleday, 1927. 1st ed. NF in chipped dj. *MADLE.* $135

Rohmer, Sax. PRESIDENT FU MANCHU. GC: Doubleday Crime Club, 1936. 1st ed. Fine in VG dj (dampstain back panel; scrape front panel; nicks at spine ends). *MORDIDA.* $350

Rohmer, Sax. PRESIDENT FU MANCHU. Sun Dial, n.d. Fine. Sl fraying to dj spine. *MADLE.* $35

Rohmer, Sax. RE-ENTER FU MANCHU. Greenwich: Fawcett Pubs, 1957. 1st ed. Pb orig. Gold Medal #684. Faint crease front cvr, o/w Fine in wrappers. *MORDIDA.* $30

Rohmer, Sax. SALUTE TO BAZARADA AND OTHER STORIES. NY, 1971. 1st US ed. Bookfinger imprint. One of 1000. Fine w/dj, as issued. *McCLINTOCK.* $12.50

Rohmer, Sax. SHE WHO SLEEPS. GC: Doubleday Doran, 1928. 1st ed. Sm faded strip at base of spine o/w Fine in dj w/some tiny closed tears and minor wear along top edge. *MORDIDA.* $350

Rohmer, Sax. SINISTER MADONNA. London: Herbert Jenkins, 1956. 1st ed. Corner bumped o/w Fine in dj w/wear at corner and minor wear at spine ends. *MORDIDA.* $75

Rohmer, Sax. SUMURU. NY: Fawcett Pubs, 1951. 1st ed. Pb orig. Gold Medal no. 199. Bkseller's stamp on inside front cover o/w Fine, unread, in wrappers. *MORDIDA.* $45

Rohmer, Sax. TALES OF SECRET EGYPT. A.L. Burt, 1920. Fine in sl frayed dj. *MADLE.* $35

Rohmer, Sax. THE DRUMS OF FU MANCHU. GC: Doubleday Crime Club, 1939. 1st Amer ed. VG in dj (1" piece missing, several closed tears; internal tape repairs, wear). *MORDIDA.* $45

Rohmer, Sax. THE GREEN EYES OF BAST. McBride, 1920. 1st ed. NF in dusty dj. *MADLE.* $350

Rohmer, Sax. THE ISLAND OF FU MANCHU. GC: Doubleday Crime Club, 1941. 1st ed. Fine in dj (minor wear spine ends; couple tiny tears). *MORDIDA.* $450

Rohmer, Sax. THE ISLAND OF FU MANCHU. London: Cassell, 1941. 1st Eng ed. Fine in dj w/closed crease-tear on front panel. This copy was apparently for export as it is labeled "Colonial Edition" on the inner front flap of the dj. *MORDIDA.* $500

Rohmer, Sax. THE MOON IS RED. NY, 1976. 1st US ed. Bookfinger imprint. One of 1000. Fine. *McCLINTOCK.* $12.50

Rohmer, Sax. THE ROMANCE OF SORCERY. London, (1914). 1st ed. Fine. *McCLINTOCK.* $145

Rohmer, Sax. THE SINS OF SEVERAC BABLON. London: Cassell, 1914. 1st ed. Tiny splits upper spine folds; lt foxing to edges, prelim pp, else Fine, bright. *ELSE FINE.* $200

Rohmer, Sax. THE SLAVES OF SUMURU. London: Herbert Jenkins, 1952. 1st hb ed. Inscription, lt spotting on edges o/w VG in dj w/minor wear. *MORDIDA.* $75

Rohmer, Sax. THE TRAIL OF FU MANCHU. NY: The Crime Club, 1934. 1st ed. VG. *POLYANTHOS.* $25

Rohmer, Sax. THE WRATH OF FU MANCHU. NY: Daw Books, 1976. 1st Amer ed. Pb orig. VF, unread, in wrappers. *MORDIDA.* $50

Rohmer, Sax. THE YELLOW CLAW. Burt, n.d. VG in frayed dj, lg chip to rear panel. *MADLE.* $27

Rohmer, Sax. WULFHEIM. NY, 1972. 1st Amer ed. One of 1000. Fine w/o dj as issued. *McCLINTOCK.* $12.50

Rohrer, Joseph. PROF. ROHRER'S ARTISTIC MARCEL, WATER, PERMANENT WAVING AND HAIR BOBBING. NY: 1924. Red and grey cl stamped in gilt. VG. *SCHOYER'S.* $25

Rohrer, Mary. THE HISTORY OF SEATTLE STOCK COMPANIES FROM THEIR BEGINNING TO 1934. Univ of WA, 1945. 1st ed. Fine. *OREGON.* $60

Rojankovsky, Feodor. THE FALCON UNDER THE HAT, RUSSIAN MERRY TALES & FAIRY TALES. Funk & Wagnalls, (1969). 1st ed. 111pp. Illus Rojanovsky. VG+ in Good+ dj w/2 closed tears. *BEBBAH.* $25

Rojankovsky, Feodor. THE TALL BOOK OF MOTHER GOOSE. Harper & Row, (1942). 120pp. Illus by Rajankovsky. NF in VG+ dj. *BEBBAH.* $30

Rojas, Pedro. THE ART & ARCHITECTURE OF MEXICO. London: Hamlyn, (1968). 1st ed. 146 plts. Good in chipped dj. *SILVER.* $25

Rokitansky, Carl. A MANUAL OF PATHOLOGICAL ANATOMY. Phila, 1855. 1st Amer ed. 2 vols. 267, 320pp. VF. *FYE.* $400

Rolfe, Frederick. DON RENATO: AN IDEAL CONTENT. Ed Cecil Woolf. London: Chatto & Windus, 1963. 1st ed. VF in dj. *CAPTAIN'S BOOKSHELF.* $50

Rolfe, Frederick. See also Corvo, Frederick Baron

Rolland, Sandy. RASELYN, HIS SONS AND DAUGHTERS. Sciota, 1980. Ed. ltd to 1000. VG. *OCTOBER FARM.* $65

Rolle, Andrew. THE ROAD TO VIRGINIA CITY. THE DIARY OF JAMES KNOX MILLER. Univ Okla, (1960). 1st prtg of this diary. Signed presentation copy. 1st ed. F in VG dj. *OREGON.* $30

Rolleston, Humphry. SOME MEDICAL ASPECTS OF OLD AGE. London, 1922. Ex-lib. *FYE.* $75

Rolley, Claude. GREEK BRONZES. London: Sotheby's, (1986). 40 color illus, 3 maps. Dj. Good. *ARCHAEOLOGIA.* $95

Rollins, Philip Ashton. JINGLEBOB. NY, 1927. *HEINOLDT.* $12

ROLLS AND LISTS OF CONNECTICUT MEN IN THE REVOLUTION. 1775-1783. Hartford, 1901. 1st ed. Orig cl. Conn Hist Soc Colls V. 8 *GINSBERG.* $75

Rolph, C.H. BOOKS IN THE DOCK. (London): Andre Deutsch, (1969). 1st ed. Dj. VG. *WREDEN.* $20

Rolt-Wheeler, Francis. THE BOY WITH THE U.S. SURVEY. Boston, 1909. 1st ed. 381pp plus adverts. Moderate cover wear, some chaffing spine ends, else VG. *FIVE QUAIL.* $20

Rolvaag, O.E. GIANTS IN THE EARTH. Harper, 1927. 1st ed. Gilt dec cvr. Fine. *AUTHORS OF THE WEST.* $35

Rolvaag, O.E. PURE GOLD. Harper, 1930. 1st ed. English text by Sivert Erdahl and author. Dec eps. Fine, name, date. *AUTHORS OF THE WEST.* $30

Rolvaag, O.E. THE BOAT OF LONGING. Harper, 1933. 1st ed. Nora O. Solum (trans). Dec boards. Fine in clean, frayed dj. *AUTHORS OF THE WEST.* $60

Rolvaag, O.E. THE THIRD LIFE OF PER SMEVIK. Dillon Press, (1971). 1st ed. Ella Valborg Tweet and Solveig Zempel (trans). Fine, nice dj 1/2" tear. *AUTHORS OF THE WEST.* $35

Rolvaag, O.E. THEIR FATHER'S GOD. Harper, 1931. 1st ed. Trygve M. Ager (trans). Dec boards. Fine, clean chipped dj. *AUTHORS OF THE WEST.* $50

Romains, Jules. STEFAN ZWEIG, GREAT EUROPEAN. NY: Viking, 1941. 1/375 for priv distrib. Inscribed. Fine in orig tissue w/few tears. *BEASLEY*. $75

Romains, Jules. THE DEPTHS AND THE HEIGHTS. Trans by Gerard Hopkins. NY: Knopf, 1937. Fine in price-clipped, NF dj w/light edgewear. 1st Amer ed. *CHAPEL HILL*. $40

Romaszkan, Gregor de. EQUITATION IN PICTURES. GC: Doubleday, 1965. 1st U.S. ed. VG+. *OCTOBER FARM*. $20

Rombauer, Irma S. THE JOY OF COOKING: A COMPILATION OF RELIABLE RECIPES WITH A CASUAL CULINARY CHAT. Indianapolis: Bobbs, (1936). 2nd ed, 1st regularly pub ed, 1st issue. NF in somewhat tired, lightly chipped dj. Uncommon, very scarce in dj. *CAPTAIN'S BOOKSHELF*. $450

Romero, George. DAWN OF THE DEAD. St Martins, 1978. 1st ed. NF in dj. *MADLE*. $25

Romero, Pablo Bush. MY ADVENTURES WITH TIGERS AND LIONS: "SHIKAR" IN INDIA, "SAFARI" IN AFRICA. Privately ptd in Mexico by the author, n.d. (1960). Ltd to 1,000. Stated 1st ed. Inscribed. VG in Good+ dj. *BACKMAN*. $175

Ronan, Peter. HISTORICAL SKETCH OF THE FLATHEAD INDIAN NATION FROM THE YEAR 1813 TO 1890. Helena: Journal Pub, (1890). 1st ed. 81 pp. Orig cl, spine lightly discolored, eps worn. Howes R428. Scarce. *GINSBERG*. $250

Ronne, Finn. ANTARCTICA, MY DESTINY. NY: Hastings House, 1979. 1st ed. Review laid in. Fine in Fine dj. *PARMER*. $50

Ronns, Edward. THEY ALL RAN AWAY. NY: Graphic Publishing, 1955. 1st ed. Pb orig. Graphic no. 114. VF, unread, in wrappers. *MORDIDA*. $45

Rooke, Leon. A GOOD BABY. NY: Knopf, (1990). Uncorrected proof. Signed. Fine in wraps. *DORN*. $45

Rooke, Leon. FAT WOMAN. NY: Knopf, (1981). 1st Amer ed. Signed. Fine in dj. *DORN*. $50

Rooke, Leon. LAST ONE HOME SLEEPS IN THE YELLOW BED. Baton Rouge: Louisiana State Univ Press, (1968). 1st ed. 1st bk. Inscribed. Orig grn boards. NF in dj. *CHAPEL HILL*. $45

Rooke, Leon. SHAKESPEARE'S DOG. NY: Knopf, (1983). 1st Amer ed. Signed. Fine in dj. *DORN*. $40

Rooke, Leon. THE BROAD BACK OF THE ANGEL. NY: Fiction Collective, (1977). 1st Amer ed. Signed. Fine in a scuffed else NF dj. *DORN*. $50

Rooney, Pat. WHEN MULDOON IS PRESIDENT SONGSTER. NY: A.J. Fisher, (1879). 60pp, 4pp ads. Color pict wraps, chipped. *SCHOYER'S*. $60

Roosevelt, Franklin D. ON OUR WAY. NY: John Day, 1934. 1st ed. VG in dj. 1st state w/errata slip xi. *SECOND LIFE*. $75

Roosevelt, Franklin D. THE PUBLIC PAPERS AND ADDRESSES OF FRANKLIN D. ROOSEVELT. NY: Random House, 1938. 1st ed. 3 vols. Djs. VG. *WEBER*. $75

Roosevelt, Kermit. THE LONG TRAIL. NY: Review of Reviews. Metropolitan Magazine, 1921. Autographed ed. Free eps browning, minor edgewear. NF. *CONNOLLY & WADE*. $35

Roosevelt, Robert Barnwell. FLORIDA AND GAME WATER BIRDS OF THE ATLANTIC COAST. Orange Judd Co, 1884. 1st ed. Rebound w/lea on boards and leatherette spine. Interior VG. *OREGON*. $30

Roosevelt, T. and K. TRAILING THE GIANT PANDA. NY: Scribners, 1929. Fldg map. VG. *MIKESH*. $40

Roosevelt, T. CALIFORNIA ADDRESSES. SF: CA Promotion Committee, 1903. 1st ed. 20 photos. Bound in 1/4 cl and paper boards. Cvr label sl soiled, o/w NF. *LAURIE*. $75

Roosevelt, T. et al. THE DEER FAMILY. NY, 1903 (1902). 20 plts, 7 range maps. Gilt-dec cl. Some fraying to spine ends; flecking to backstrip; inner joint cracked. *SUTTON*. $40

Roosevelt, Theodore and George Bird Grinnell. HUNTING IN MANY LANDS. NY: Forest & Stream Pub. Co, 1895. 1st ed. Lt fading to spine area but all lettering bright and clean. Review attached to 1st blank pg. VG w/lt wear to spine edges. *BACKMAN*. $325

Roosevelt, Theodore. A BOOK-LOVER'S HOLIDAYS IN THE OPEN. NY, 1920. Black cl. VG+. *FIVE QUAIL*. $35

Roosevelt, Theodore. AFRICAN GAME TRAILS. 2 vols. NY, (1919) Uniform ed. 16 plts, 1 map. Cloth. Spine ends frayed; inner joint cracked; corners worn; sm tear last pg. *SUTTON*. $57

Roosevelt, Theodore. AFRICAN GAME TRAILS. NY & London: Syndicate, (1910). Good+. *MIKESH*. $40

Roosevelt, Theodore. AFRICAN GAME TRAILS. NY: Scribner, 1910. 2nd ed. xxiii,583pp. Near VG ex-lib. *WORLDWIDE*. $30

Roosevelt, Theodore. AFRICAN GAME TRAILS—AN ACCOUNT OF THE AFRICAN WANDERINGS OF AN AMERICAN HUNTER-NATURALIST. NY: Charles Scribner's Sons, 1910. 1st ed. Olive cl. Gilt titles. Minor wear and rubbing extremes. Front and rear internal hinge tape-repaired, else VG. *GREAT EPIC*. $95

Roosevelt, Theodore. HUNTING THE GRISLY & OTHER SKETCHES. NY: Collier, 1893. VG. *MIKESH*. $35

Roosevelt, Theodore. OUTDOOR PASTIMES OF AN AMERICAN HUNTER. NY, 1905. Teg. Gilt pict bds. Fine. *POLYANTHOS*. $100

Roosevelt, Theodore. THE ROUGH RIDERS. NY: Scribner's, 1899. 1st ed. Frontis, xii,298p. Olive drab cl, gilt dec Teg. Spine sl darkened with 1/4" tear at head, else VG. *CONNOLLY & WADE*. $185

Roosevelt, Theodore. THE WORKS OF. NY: Scribners, 1926. 20 vols. Index in last vol. Cl w/paper labels, spines yellowed, else VG. *ARTIS*. $95

Roosevelt, Theodore. THROUGH THE BRAZILIAN WILDERNESS. NY: Scribner's, 1914. 1st ed. 2 fldg maps. Orig brn cl, gilt lettering. Lt fading along spine, rear hinge cracked, edge wear. VG. *SILVER*. $60

Root, A.I. and E.R. Root. THE ABC AND XYZ OF BEE CULTURE. A.I. Root Co., 1940. Fine. *MAD DOG*. $20

Root, Edward W. PHILIP HOOKER: A CONTRIBUTION TO THE STUDY OF THE RENAISSANCE IN AMERICA. NY: Charles Scribner's Sons, 1929. 1st ed. #627 of 750. VG to NF in dj. *BACKROOM*. $350

Root, Frank A. and William E. Connelly. THE OVERLAND STAGE TO CALIFORNIA. Topeka, Kansas, 1901. Rptd by Long's College Book Co, Columbus, OH, 1950. Fldg map tipped to rear cvr. Pict cl, Fine. *SCHOYER'S*. $50

Root, Jonathan. HALLIBURTON THE MAGNIFICENT MYTH. NY: Coward-McCann (1965). 1st ed. Fine in VG dj. *AARD*. $35

Root, L.C. QUINBY'S NEW BEE-KEEPING, THE MYSTERIES OF BEE-KEEPING EXPLAINED. NY, (1913). Rev ed. Illus. VG. *MIKESH*. $15

Rootham, Jasper. MISS FIRE. London, 1946. Fldg map. 224 pp. *O'NEILL*. $32.50

Ropes, John C. THE ARMY UNDER POPE—CAMPAIGNS OF THE CIVIL WAR, Vol IV. NY, 1881. 1st ed. 229pp. Some dj wear, o/w Fine. *PRATT*. $32.50

Ropes, John Codman. THE ARMY UNDER POPE. NY, 1881. 1st ed. VG to NF. *McGOWAN*. $35

Roquelaure, A.N. (pseud of Ann Rice). BEAUTY'S RELEASE. NY: Dutton, 1985. 1st ed. Fine in Fine dj. *BEASLEY*. $150

Roquelaure, A.N. (pseud of Anne Rice). BEAUTY'S PUNISHMENT. (London): Macdonald, (1987). 1st UK ed. Fine in dj. *LOPEZ*. $75

Rosa, Joseph G. COLONEL COLT LONDON. Ontario: Fortress Pub Co, 1976. Stated 1st. Ltd, #494/1,000. Signed. Fine in Fine dj. *BACKMAN.* $150

Rosales, Vicente Perez. CALIFORNIA ADVENTURE. SF: The Bk Club of CA, 1947. Ed ltd to 250. Plain paper dj. Fine. *KARMIOLE.* $75

Roscoe, Thomas. WANDERINGS AND EXCURSIONS IN NORTH WALES. London: C. Tilt, and Simpkin & Co. 1836. xviii,262,(2)pp. 51 engr. Pub's full grn calf, gilt; extrems bit rubbed. Aeg. *KARMIOLE.* $250

Roscoe, Thomas. WANDERINGS AND EXCURSIONS IN SOUTH WALES; INCLUDING THE SCENERY OF THE RIVER WYE. London: C. Tilt, and Simpkin & Co. N.d. (circa 1837). xvi,268,(2)pp. 48 engrs. Pub's full grn calf, gilt; extrems bit rubbed. Aeg. *KARMIOLE.* $250

Rose, Barbara. FRANKENTHALER. NY: Abrams, n.d. 54 color plts. Fine in ptd acetate dj. Inscribed by Frankenthaler & signed Helen. *CAPTAIN'S BOOKSHELF.* $450

Rose, Barbara. FRANKENTHALER. NY: Harry N. Abrams, Inc. (1970). 1st ed. Plastic dj. Fine. *KARMIOLE.* $200

Rose, Elise Whitlock. CATHEDRALS AND CLOISTERS OF THE ISLE DE FRANCE. NY, London: G.P. Putnam's Sons, 1910. 1st Amer ed. 2 vols. Plts. Inner hinges a bit loosened. Mixed set w/different binding treatments, o/w VG. *WEBER.* $35

Rose, Robert R. ADVOCATES AND ADVERSARIES, THE EARLY LIFE AND TIMES OF ROBERT R. ROSE. Gene M. Gressley (ed). Chicago, 1977. 1st ed. Lakeside Classic #75. VG+. *PRATT.* $35

Rose, Victor M. ROSS' TEXAS BRIGADE. BEING A NARRATIVE...IN THE LATE WAR BETWEEN THE STATES. Louisville, 1881. 185pp. 1st ed. Frontis, ports. Orig grn cl, gilt on spine. Howes R444. *GINSBERG.* $1500

Rosen, Edward. THE NAMING OF THE TELESCOPE. NY: Henry Schuman, 1947. Good in dj. *KNOLLWOOD.* $25

Rosen, R.D. STRIKE THREE YOU'RE DEAD. NY: Walker, 1984. 1st ed, 1st bk. VF in dj. *ELSE FINE.* $125

Rosen, R.D. STRIKE THREE YOU'RE DEAD. NY: Walker, 1984. 1st ed. Small stain on fore-edge o/w Fine in dj. *MORDIDA.* $75

Rosenbach, A.S.W. A BOOK HUNTER'S HOLIDAY. Boston, 1936. One of 760. Signed. Uncut. Spine lightly sunned. Boxed. NF. *POLYANTHOS.* $200

Rosenbach, A.S.W. EARLY AMERICAN CHILDREN'S BOOKS. Portland: The Southworth Press, 1933. 1/585 numbered/signed. VF in slipcase. *DERMONT.* $475

Rosenbach, A.S.W. THE UNPUBLISHABLE MEMOIRS. London: Castle, (1924). 1st Eng ed. Fine in somewhat chipped & worn dj. *JAFFE.* $45

Rosenbaum, Elisabeth. A CATALOGUE OF CYRENAICAN PORTRAIT SCULPTURE. London: Oxford Univ Press, 1960. 108 plts. Dj. Good. *ARCHAEOLOGIA.* $150

Rosenberg, Charles. THE CHOLERA YEARS. THE UNITED STATES IN 1832, 1849, AND 1866. Chicago, 1962. 1st ed. Dj. Inscribed, signed. *FYE.* $40

Rosenberg, Harold. SAUL STEINBERG. NY: Alfred A. Knopf in assoc w/Whitney Museum of American Art, 1978. White wraps (sl soiled). NF. *BLUE MOUNTAIN.* $25

Rosenberg, Samuel. NAKED IS THE BEST DISGUISE. Indianapolis: Bobbs-Merrill, 1974. 1st ed. Fine in dj (short closed tears). *MORDIDA.* $25

Rosengarten, Theodore. TOMBEE, PORTRAIT OF A COTTON PLANTER. NY, (1986). 1st ed. VG in dj. *PRATT.* $25

Rosenthal, I. GENERAL PHYSIOLOGY OF MUSCLES AND NERVES. London, 1883. 3rd ed. 74 woodcuts. *FYE.* $50

Rosenthal, M.L. A PRIMER OF EZRA POUND. NY: MacMillan, 1960. 1st ed. Fine in dj. *CAPTAIN'S BOOKSHELF.* $35

Rosett, Joshua. THE MECHANISM OF THOUGHT, IMAGERY, AND HALLUCINATION. NY, 1939. 1st ed. Ex-lib but Fine. *FYE.* $50

Rosevear, D.R. THE CARNIVORES OF WEST AFRICA. London, 1974. 11 colored plts. Cloth, dj. *SUTTON.* $95

Rosevear, D.R. THE RODENTS OF WEST AFRICA. London, 1969. 11 colored plts. Cloth, dj. *SUTTON.* $90

Rosher, Harold. WITH THE FLYING SQUADRON...WITH AN INTRODUCTION BY ARNOLD BENNETT. NY: 1916. 1st Amer ed. Orig dec cl. *GINSBERG.* $75

Roshwald, Mordecai. LEVEL 7. NY, Toronto, London: McGraw-Hill, (1959). 1st ed. Dj. Fine. *WEBER.* $20

Roske, Ralph and Charles van Doren. LINCOLN'S COMMANDO: THE BIOGRAPHY OF COMMANDER W.B. CUSHING, U.S.N. NY: Harper, 1957. 1st ed. VG, bumped. *ARCHER.* $20

Roske, Ralph and Charles Van Doren. LINCOLN'S COMMANDO. NY, (1957). 1st ed. Minor dj chipping, o/w VG. *PRATT.* $37.50

Rosner, Charles. PRINTER'S PROGRESS. A COMPARATIVE SURVEY...1851-1951. Cambridge: Harvard Univ Press, 1951. 1st ed. 3 tipped-in illus. Fine in dj. *WEBER.* $45

Rosner, Fred. MODERN MEDICINE AND JEWISH LAW. NY, 1972. 1st ed. *FYE.* $50

Ross, Alexander. THE FUR HUNTERS OF THE FAR WEST. London, 1855. 1924 Lakeside Classics Reprint (ed by Milo Milton Quaife). 317pp. VG+. *PRATT.* $42.50

Ross, Alexander. THE FUR HUNTERS OF THE FAR WEST; A NARRATIVE OF ADVENTURES IN THE OREGON AND ROCKY MOUNTAINS. London: Smith, Elder & Co, 1855. 1st ed. 2 vols. 3/4 lea and marbled boards. Fldg map repaired. Some dull spots, little rubbing to spines. Nice set. *BOHLING.* $850

Ross, E. Denison. THE ART OF EGYPT THROUGH THE AGES. London: The Studio, 1931. Color frontis, 10 figs, 155 illus, 5 color plts. Tattered dj. Good. *ARCHAEOLOGIA.* $95

Ross, Edmund G. HISTORY OF THE IMPEACHMENT OF ANDREW JOHNSON...(Santa Fe), 1896. 1st ed. (4),180pp. Orig cl. Howes R452. *GINSBERG.* $175

Ross, Frank Jr. SPACE SHIPS AND SPACE TRAVEL. London: Museum Press, 1956. Good in dj; eps lightly foxed. *KNOLLWOOD.* $25

Ross, Ishbel. ANGEL OF THE BATTLEFIELD, THE LIFE OF CLARA BARTON. NY, (1956). 305pp. Dj wear, chipping; o/w VG. *PRATT.* $25

Ross, Ishbel. THE PRESIDENT'S LADY, MARY TODD LINCOLN. NY, (1973). 1st ed. VG+ in dj. *PRATT.* $25

Ross, J.D. A BURNS HANDBOOK. Scotland, 1931. Dj chipped. NF. *POLYANTHOS.* $35

Ross, James. HANDBOOK OF THE DISEASES OF THE NERVOUS SYSTEM. Phila, 1885. 1st Amer ed. Label lacking, corners bumped. *FYE.* $50

Ross, Janet. LAND OF MANFRED...London: Murray, 1889. A little soiled. Fldg map. *SCHOYER'S.* $30

Ross, John. NARRATIVE OF A SECOND VOYAGE IN SEARCH OF A NORTH-WEST PASSAGE AND OF RESIDENCE IN THE ARCTIC REGIONS DURING THE YEARS 1829, 1830, 1831, 1832, 1833. London: A.W. Webster, 1835. xxxiv,740pp. 3 colored plts. 3/4 leather. Bkpl, chipped bottom on back cvr, else VG-. *BLUE DRAGON.* $750

Ross, John. NARRATIVE OF A SECOND VOYAGE IN SEARCH OF A NORTH-WEST PASSAGE AND OF A RESIDENCE IN THE ARCTIC REGIONS DURING THE YEARS 1829, 1830, 1831, 1832, 1833. INCLUDING THE REPORTS ON JAMES

CLARK ROSS AND THE DISCOVERY OF THE NORTHERN MAGNETIC POLE. AND APPENDIX TO THE NARRATIVE OF A SECOND VOYAGE IN SEARCH OF A NORTHWEST PASSAGE...London: A.W. Webster, 1835. 1st ed. Vol 1: (6),errata,(1),xxxiii,pl list,740pp. 31 plts incl 9 colored and 5 charts. Fldg chart bound at front, marginal tear at hinge area. Vol 2: xii,120,cxliv,cii,(1). 20 plts incl 12 colored. (2 plts, 1 text leaf bound out of order). Incl pl list, errata pg and subs's list. *PARMER.* $1450

Ross, Marvin C. RUSSIAN PORCELAINS...MARJORIE MERRIWEATHER POST HILLWOOD. Norman: Univ of OK Press, (1966). 1st ed. 86 color plts. Two-toned cl, teg. Fine in dj, some wear. *CAPTAIN'S BOOKSHELF.* $125

Ross, Marvin C. THE WEST OF ALFRED JACOB MILLER. Norman: Univ of OK Press, (1968). 2nd ed. Cl in dj. *DAWSON'S.* $75

Ross, Marvin C. THE WEST OF ALFRED JACOB MILLER. Univ of OK Press, 1951. 1st ed. Fine in VG dj. *VARNER.* $125

Ross, Marvin. THE WEST OF ALFRED JACOB MILLER. Norman: Univ of OK, (1951). 1st ed. VF in VG dj. *OREGON.* $95

Ross, Nancy Wilson. THE WAVES—THE STORY OF THE GIRLS IN BLUE. NY: Holt, (1943). 1st ed. Inscribed. VG+ in VG dj. *AARD.* $20

Ross, Ronald. STUDIES ON MALARIA. London, 1928. 1st ed. *FYE.* $100

Ross, W. Gillies. ARCTIC WHALERS, ICY SEAS. Toronto, (1985). 1st ed. VF in dj. *ARTIS.* $25

Rossbach, Jeffrey. AMBIVALENT CONSPIRATORS. Phila, 1982. 1st ed. Fine in dj. *PRATT.* $20

Rossetti, W.M. RUSKIN: PRERAPHAELITISM. PAPERS 1854-1862. London: George Allen, 1899. One of 250 numbered. Plates. Spine darkened. Inscription ffep, else very nice. *WOOLMER.* $125

Rossit, Edward A. NORTHWEST MOUNTAINEERING. The Caxton Printers, 1965. 1st ed. NF in dj. *OLD LONDON.* $30

Rossman, Earl. BLACK SUNLIGHT. NY: Oxford Univ Press, 1926. xi, 231pp. Fldg map. General wear. *PARMER.* $35

Rossner, Judith. HIS LITTLE WOMEN. Franklin Center: Franklin Lib, 1990. Fine. Signed. *LOPEZ.* $45

Rossner, Judith. LOOKING FOR MR. GOODBAR. Simon and Schuster, 1975. 1st ed. About Fine in dj. Signed. *STAHR.* $35

Rostand, Edmond. CYRANO DE BERGERAC. Pierre Brissaud (illus). Dec cl w/leather label, slipcase. NY: LEC, 1954. Ltd to 1500 signed by Brissaud. Fine. *JAFFE.* $45

Rostovtzeff, M. THE SOCIAL AND ECONOMIC HISTORY OF THE HELLENISTIC WORLD. Oxford: Clarendon Press, (1967). 3 vols (complete). Frontis, 11 figs, 111 plts. Dj. Good. *ARCHAEOLOGIA.* $150

Roth, Cecil. A HISTORY OF MARRANOS. Phila, 1932. NF. *POLYANTHOS.* $30

Roth, Cecil. JEWISH ART. NYGS, 1971. New, enl ed. Dj. NF. *POLYANTHOS.* $125

Roth, Henry. CALL IT SLEEP. London: Michael Joseph, (1963). 1st Eng ed, 1st bk. Ink name, o/w NF in price clipped dj, chips. *HELLER.* $125

Roth, Henry. CALL IT SLEEP. London: Michael Joseph, (1963). 1st Eng ed, 1st bk. Inscribed. Fine in VG dj. *JUVELIS.* $250

Roth, Henry. CALL IT SLEEP. NY: Robert 0. Ballou, (1935). 2nd ed. Owner sig, spine lettering dulled, trace of soil on binding, few pp w/vague crease, o/w Fine. Signed. *PIRAGES.* $350

Roth, Henry. CALL IT SLEEP. NY: Robert O. Ballou, (1934). 1st ed. Inscribed. Grey cl. Good+ in dj (chipped, torn, w/tape repairs, but almost all there). Scarce in any condition. *JUVELIS.* $2200

Roth, Henry. CALL IT SLEEP. Paterson: Pageant Books, 1960. 2nd ed. Fine in very lightly used dj. *CAPTAIN'S BOOKSHELF.* $50

Roth, Henry. NATURE'S FIRST GREEN. NY: Targ Editions, 1979. 1/350 numbered/signed. Fine in dj. *DERMONT.* $35

Roth, Philip. GOODBYE, COLUMBUS AND OTHER STORIES. Franklin Center: Franklin Library, 1978. Leatherbound ltd ed. reissue, w/special intro by author. Fine. Signed. *LOPEZ.* $100

Roth, Philip. GOODBYE, COLUMBUS. (London): Andre Deutsch, (1959). 1st Eng ed, 1st bk. Fine in dj. *HELLER.* $150

Roth, Philip. GOODBYE, COLUMBUS. Boston: Houghton Mifflin, 1959. 1st ed. NF in sl spine-darkened but still NF dj. Inscribed. *LOPEZ.* $600

Roth, Philip. MY LIFE AS A MAN. NY: HRW, (1974). Uncorrected proof. Sm stain to front wrap. Fine. Inscribed. *LOPEZ.* $200

Roth, Philip. NOVTONY'S PAIN. Hollywood: Sylvester & Orphanos, 1980. 1st ed. Signed. 1/330 on Arches paper. Fine. *JUVELIS.* $75

Roth, Philip. ON THE AIR: A LONG STORY. (NY:) NAL 10, (1970). 1st ed. 1/500. White wrappers. NF. *JUVELIS.* $100

Roth, Philip. READING MYSELF AND OTHERS. NY: FSG, (1975). Uncorrected proof. Fine in tall wraps. Inscribed. *LOPEZ.* $175

Roth, Philip. THE BREAST. NY: HRW, (1972). Uncorrected proof. Inscribed. Fine in wraps. *LOPEZ.* $150

Roth, Philip. THE COUNTERLIFE. Franklin Center: Franklin Lib, 1986. Fine. Signed. *LOPEZ.* $85

Roth, Philip. THE FACTS. A NOVELIST'S AUTOBIOGRAPHY. NY: Farrar Straus Giroux, (1988). 1st ed. One of 250 signed. Mint. Cl, slipcase. *JAFFE.* $75

Roth, Philip. THE GHOST WRITER. NY: Farrar Straus Giroux, (1979). 1st ed. Fine in Fine dj. Inscribed. *LOPEZ.* $100

Roth, Philip. THE GHOST WRITER. NY: FSG, (1979). Uncorrected proof. NF in tall wraps. Inscribed. *LOPEZ.* $150

Roth, Philip. THE GREAT AMERICAN NOVEL. Holt, Rinehart and Winston, 1973. Uncorrected proof. VG+ in wraps. Lower front wrap creased. *STAHR.* $45

Roth, Philip. THE GREAT AMERICAN NOVEL. NY: HRW. (1973). Uncorrected proof. Inscribed. Fine in wraps. *LOPEZ.* $200

Roth, Philip. THE PROFESSOR OF DESIRE. NY: Farrar, Straus & Giroux, (1977). Orig red cl. NF in price-clipped dj. 1st ed. Signed. *CHAPEL HILL.* $75

Roth, Philip. THE PROFESSOR OF DESIRE. NY: FSG, (1977). Uncorrected proof. Fine in tall wraps. *LOPEZ.* $65

Roth, Philip. WHEN SHE WAS GOOD. NY: Random House, (1967). 1st ed. Orig dk blue cl. Fine in NF dj, minor wear top of spine. *CHAPEL HILL.* $75

Roth, Philip. ZUCKERMAN UNBOUND. NY, 1981. Ltd ed, 75/350, signed. Fine in Fine box. *POLYANTHOS.* $60

Roth, Philip. ZUCKERMAN UNBOUND. NY: Farrar Straus Giroux, (1981). 1/350 numbered, signed. *LOPEZ.* $100

Rothenberg, Jerome. BRMTZVH. Mt. Horeb: Perishable Press, (1979). 1st ed. Ltd to 225 signed. Signed by Walter Hamady. Wraps. VF. *JAFFE.* $75

Rothenberg, Jerome. SENECA JOURNAL 1. A POEM OF BEAVERS. Mt. Horeb: Perishable Press, 1973. 1st ed. Ltd to 97 signed by Rothenberg and Walter Hamady. Wraps. VF. *JAFFE.* $150

Rothenstein, William. MEN AND MEMORIES 1972-1900. NY, 1931. 2 vols. F. *POLYANTHOS.* $50

Rouse, Parke Jr. & Kathryn C. Buhler. CHURCH SILVER OF COLONIAL VIRGINIA. Richmond, VA: The VA Museum, 1970. VG. Wraps. *BACKROOM.* $45

Rousselot, Jean. MEDICINE IN ART: A CULTURAL HISTORY. NY, 1966. 1st ed. Dj. Scarce. *FYE.* $175

Rovsing, Thorkild. ABDOMINAL SURGERY. Phila, 1914. 1st Eng trans. 145 illus. *FYE.* $60

Rowan, Carl T. with Jackie Robinson. WAIT TILL NEXT YEAR. Random House, 1960. 1st ed. VG in Good+ dj. *PLAPINGER.* $27.50

Rowan, Carl T. with Jackie Robinson. WAIT TILL NEXT YEAR. Random House, 1960. 1st ed. Fine in price-clipped dj (short tears, rubbing along top edge). Owner inscription. *STAHR.* $45

Rowe, John Howland. MAX UHLE 1856-1944. A MEMOIR OF THE FATHER OF PERUVIAN ARCHAEOLOGY. Berkeley: Univ of CA Press, 1954. 14 plts, wraps. Good. *ARCHAEOLOGIA.* $55

Rowe, Mike. CHICAGO BREAKDOWN. NY: Drake Publishers, (1975). 226pp. 1st ed. Edgetears, chips to dj. *AKA.* $25

Rowe, William Hutchinson. SHIPBUILDING DAYS IN CASCO BAY 1727-1890. Yarmouth, Maine, 1929. 1st ed. Orig cl, worn, ex-lib. *LEFKOWICZ.* $50

Rowland, John. THE DEATH OF NEVILL NORWAY. London: Herbert Jenkins, (1942). 1st ed. VG in dj w/chipped and frayed spine ends, chipped corners, wear along folds and several closed tears. *MORDIDA.* $30

Rowlands, Henry. MONA ANTIQUA RESTAURATA...IN TWO ESSAYS AND AN APPENDIX. 2nd ed, corrected, improved. London: Knox, 1766. 357pp, errata leaf. Later calf backed boards. Map, 12 engr plts. Uncut. Excellent. *SECOND LIFE.* $350

Rowlandson, Mary. THE NARRATIVE OF THE CAPTIVITY AND RESTORATION OF MRS. MARY ROWLANDSON, FIRST PRINTED IN 1682...WHEREUNTO ARE ANNEXED A MAP...AND THE LAST SERMON OF HER HUSBAND....Lancaster, MA, 1903. One of 250 numbered. Orig cl backed boards. "Mrs. Mary Rowlandson's removes" by Henry S. Nourse laid in. 11pp. Orig ptd wrappers. Howes R478. *GINSBERG.* $175

Rowntree, Lester. FLOWERING SHRUBS OF CALIFORNIA AND THEIR VALUE TO THE GARDENER. Stanford Univ Press, (1939). 1st ed. About Fine. *WREDEN.* $25

Rowntree, Lester. RONNIE AND DON. NY: Viking, 1953. 1st ed. Brn ptd cl in dj. *DAWSON'S.* $50

Roy, George. GENERALSHIP, OR HOW I MANAGED MY HUSBAND. Cincinnati: Clarke, 1875. US ed. Some worn pub's cl, else Good. *SECOND LIFE.* $55

Royal Geographical Soc. A SELECTION OF PAPERS ON ARCTIC GEOGRAPHY AND ETHNOLOGY: REPRINTED, AND PRESENTED TO THE ARCTIC EXPEDITION OF 1875....London: John Murray, 1875. 2 fldg maps. VG to Fine, bkpl. *PARMER.* $450

Royall, Anne (Newport), Mrs. THE TENNESSEAN. New-Haven, (CT): Ptd for the Author, 1827. 1st ed. 12mo, 372pp. Orig paper-covered boards, expertly rebacked w/paper spine label nicely restored. Owner inscriptions, scattered foxing, title pg chipped at lower corner affecting no text, o/w VG, untrimmed. *CHAPEL HILL.* $950

Royce, Josiah. THE FEUD OF OAKFIELD CREEK: A NOVEL OF CALIFORNIA LIFE. Houghton Mifflin, 1887. 1st ed. Dec cvr. Fine. *AUTHORS OF THE WEST.* $100

Royce, Josiah. THE LETTERS OF JOSIAH ROYCE. Chicago/London, Univ of Chicago Press, 1970. 1st ed. Blue cl, frontis. John Clendenning (ed). New in New dj. *PARMER.* $35

Royidis, Emmanuel. POPE JOAN. London, 1954. Trans by Lawrence Durrell. Dj. Contemp rev tipped to fep. *O'NEILL.* $22.50

Royko, Mike. I MAY BE WRONG BUT I DOUBT IT. Chicago: Regnery, 1968. 1st ed. Fine but for owner's inscrip, in VG+ dj w/tears. *BEASLEY.* $35

Royle, J.F. AN ESSAY ON THE ANTIQUITY OF HINDOO MEDICINE, INCLUDING AN INTRODUCTORY LECTURE...AT KING'S COLLEGE. London: Allen, 1837. 1st ed.

iv,196pp. Orig cl, orig paper label on backstrip. Good. *BOOKCELL.* $125

Roys, Ralph L. (trans, ed). RITUALS OF THE BACABS. A BOOK OF MAYA INCANTATIONS. Norman: Univ of OK, 1965. 1st ed. 4 plts. Cloth. Fine in NF dj. *CONNOLLY & WADE.* $42.50

Rozmital, Leo of. THE TRAVELS OF LEO OF ROZMITAL THROUGH GERMANY...AND ITALY, 1465-1467. Malcolm Letts (trans, ed). Cambridge: Univ Press for Hakluyt Society, 1957. Hakluyt Society, Second Series, No. CVIII. 5 plts, fldg maps. Orig cl, in sl torn dj, VG. *WORLDWIDE.* $45

Ruark, Robert. THE HONEY BADGER. NY: McGraw-Hill, 1965. 1st ed. Fine+ in Fine+ dj. *GREAT EPIC.* $45

Ruark, Robert. THE OLD MAN AND THE BOY. NY: Holt, (1957). Gift inscript, else Fine in NF dj. 1st ed. *CHAPEL HILL.* $90

Ruark, Robert. THE OLD MAN AND THE BOY. NY: Holt & Co, 1957. Stated 1st ed. VG+ w/2 names. *BACKMAN.* $40

Ruark, Robert. THE OLD MAN AND THE BOY. NY: Holt, (1957). 1st ed. Orig brn cl. Name stamp, else Fine in dj. *CHAPEL HILL.* $100

Ruark, Robert. THE OLD MAN'S BOY GROWS OLDER. NY, (1961). 1st ed. Dj repaired, o/w Fine. *ARTIS.* $40

Ruark, Robert. USE ENOUGH GUN. NY, 1966. 1st ed. Fine in dj. *PETTLER.* $50

Ruark, Robert. USE ENOUGH GUN. NY: NAL, 1966. Stated 1st prtg. VG+ in VG+ dj w/owner inscript. *BACKMAN.* $40

Ruark, Robert. USE ENOUGH GUN. NY: The NAL, 1966. 1st ed. As New in As New dj. *GREAT EPIC.* $75

Rubens, Bernice. MADAME SOUSATZKA. London: Eyre and Spottiswoode, 1962. 1st ed, 2nd book. Fine in lightly used dj. *BEASLEY.* $75

Rubin, Jacob H. I LIVE TO TELL. THE RUSSIAN ADVENTURES OF AN AMERICAN SOCIALIST. Indianapolis: Bobbs-Merrill, 1934. 1st ed. Pencilled quotation on fep, o/w Fine in sl used dj. *BEASLEY.* $35

Rubin, Louis D. THE MOCKINGBIRD IN THE GUM TREE. Baton Rouge: LSU Press (1991). Uncorrected proof. Name, else NF in wraps. *DORN.* $25

Rubin, Louis. THE MOCKINGBIRD IN THE GUM TREE. Baton Rouge: Louisiana State Univ Press, (1991). 1st Amer ed. Inscribed. Fine in dj. *DORN.* $35

Rubin, William (ed). CEZANNE: THE LATE WORK. NY: MOMA. Pict dj (sl chipped). Fine. *BLUE MOUNTAIN.* $45

Rubovits, Frank. DOGGEREL EXCHANGE. Mt. Horeb: Perishable Press, 1978. 1st ed. Ltd to 125. Signed by Walter Hamady. Wraps. VF. *JAFFE.* $75

Ruck, Rob. SANDLOT SEASONS. Univ of Illinois, 1987. 1st ed. Fine in Fine dj. *PLAPINGER.* $50

Rudofsky, Bernard. ARE CLOTHES MODERN? (Chicago): Paul Theobald, 1947. 1st ed. Cloth sl soiled, dj chipped. *KARMIOLE.* $45

Rudolph Franz Karl Joseph, Crown Prince of Austria. TRAVELS IN THE EAST, INCLUDING A VISIT TO EGYPT AND THE HOLY LAND. London: Bentley, 1884. 1st ed. xi,380 pp. 88 plts, 5 illus. Lib buckram, ex-lib; all plts stamped on reverse. *WORLDWIDE.* $145

Ruell, Patrick (pseud of Reginald Hill). THE LONG KILL. London: Methuen, 1987. 1st ed. VF in price clipped dj. *ELSE FINE.* $35

Ruffner, W.H. A REPORT ON WASHINGTON TERRITORY. NY: Seattle, Lake Shore and Eastern RR, 1889, 1st ed. 242pp. 12 plts; 4 maps, very large fldg map Washington Territory in back pocket. Map of US missing. *HEINOLDT.* $60

Ruggles, Eleanor. THE WEST-GOING HEART: A LIFE OF VACHEL LINDSAY. W.W. Norton, (1959). 1st ed. Signed. Fine in dj, chipped. *AUTHORS OF THE WEST.* $20

Ruhen, Olaf. TANGAROA'S GODCHILD—A MEMOIR OF THE SOUTH SEAS. Boston: Little, Brown & Co., 1962. 1st ed. VG in worn dj. *PARMER.* $25

Ruhrah, John. PEDIATRICS OF THE PAST. NY, 1925. 1st ed. 592pp. Rear inner hinge cracked, backstrip dull. Very scarce. *FYE.* $250

Rukeyser, Muriel. BEAST IN VIEW. GC: Doubleday, 1944. 1st ed. Cvrs dampstained; lacking dj. Inscribed. *WOOLMER.* $45

Rukeyser, Muriel. THEORY OF LIGHT. New Haven: Yale Univ Press, 1935. 1st ed, 1st bk. Tan cl in little nicked and some faded red dj. Cl is in excellent condition, dj has bled red to bottom 1/2 inch of spine. Bkpl. Scarce. *SECOND LIFE.* $300

Rukeyser, Muriel. WATERLILY FIRE. NY: Macmillan, 1962. 1st ed. Inscribed. NF in dj. *LOPEZ.* $65

RULES AND ORDERS OF THE COURT OF CHANCERY OF THE STATE OF NEW-YORK, AS REVISED AND ESTABLISHED BY CHANCELLOR WALWORTH. Pub by Wm. & A. Gould & Co. (etc.), Albany, 1834. 2 blanks; title pg; (iii)-(xx),(21)-160 pgs; 2 blanks. Bound in contemp sheep-backed boards. Definitely rubbed and worn; some cracking to joints. Still quite lovely, and well margined. *BOSWELL.* $175

Rumford, Beatrix T. AMERICAN FOLK PAINTINGS...ABBY ALDRICH ROCKEFELLER FOLK ART CENTER. Boston: NY Graphic Soc, 1988. 1st ed. NF in NF dj. *BACKROOM.* $70

Runciman, Steven. BYZANTINE CIVILIZATION. London, 1936. 320 pp. Dj. *O'NEILL.* $30

Runciman, Steven. THE SICILIAN VESPERS. Cambridge, 1958. Fldg map & charts. Dj. 1st ed. *O'NEILL.* $47.50

Runyon, Damon. DAMON RUNYON FAVORITES. Cleveland, NY: World Publishing, (1946). 1st Tower Books ed. NF in dj. *BERNARD.* $25

Runyon, Damon. IN OUR TOWN. NY, (1946). 1st ed. Illus Garth Williams. Sl crease front cover. Fine in dj (extremities, spine and lower edge rear panel little rubbed). *POLYANTHOS.* $40

Runyon, Damon. IN OUR TOWN: TWENTY SEVEN SLICES OF LIFE. NY: Creative Age Press, 1946. 1st ed. Fine, minor chips at dj spine top. *ELSE FINE.* $150

Runyon, Damon. MY OLD MAN. NY, (1939). 1st ed. Complimentary copy from pub, slip laid in. Extremities, spine little sunned. NF in dj (spine little sunned, top little chipped, very small edge tear, little edge rubbed). *POLYANTHOS.* $40

Runyon, Damon. POEMS FOR MEN. NY: Duell, Sloane, Pearce, (1947). 1st ed. Fine in VG+ chipped dj. *BERNARD.* $60

Rupert, Charles. APOSTLE SPOONS. London: Oxford Univ Press, 1929. 1st ed. 23 plts. Fine in sl chipped dj. *CAPTAIN'S BOOKSHELF.* $100

Rusby, Henry. JUNGLE MEMORIES. NY: Whittlesey House, 1933. 1st ed. Pict cl. *SILVER.* $30

Ruscha, Edward. TWENTY-SIX GASOLINE STATIONS. (Alhambra, CA: The Cunningham Press), 1962. One of 400 numbered. Fine in sl bumped slipcase. *CAPTAIN'S BOOKSHELF.* $45

Ruschenberger, W.S.W. A VOYAGE ROUND THE WORLD; INCLUDING AN EMBASSY TO MUSCAT AND SIAM, IN 1835, 1836, AND 1837. Phila: Carey, Lea & Blanchard, 1838. 1st ed. 559,12 ad pp. Orig cl, orig ptd paper spine label, extrems a little rubbed, lt foxing, but VG. *LEFKOWICZ.* $750

Ruschenberger, W.S.W. ELEMENTS OF CONCHOLOGY: PREPARED FOR THE USE OF SCHOOLS & COLLEGES. Phila, (1845). 16mo, 114pp+notices. 1/4 lea, boards. Good+. *MIKESH.* $25

Rush, Benjamin. MEDICAL INQUIRIES AND OBSERVATIONS UPON THE DISEASES OF THE MIND. Phila, 1835. 5th ed. Full leather, 365pp. *FYE.* $200

Rush, Benjamin. MEDICAL INQUIRIES AND OBSERVATIONS: CONTAINING AN ACCOUNT OF THE YELLOW FEVER, AS IT APPEARED IN PHILADELPHIA IN 1797, AND OBSERVATIONS UPON THE NATURE AND CURE OF THE GOUT, AND HYDROPHOBIA. Vol V. Phila, 1798. 1st ed. 8vo. 12,236pp. Contemp calf, scuffed; hinges cracking, but sound. *M & S.* $150

Rush, Benjamin. SIXTEEN INTRODUCTORY LECTURES TO COURSES...PRACTICES OF MEDICINE, WITH A SYLLABUS...TO WHICH ARE ADDED, TWO LECTURES...PLEASURES OF THE SENSES...WITH AN INQUIRY... PROXIMATE CAUSE... Phila: Bradford and Innskeep, 1811. 1st ed. Mod lt brn cl. Lt foxing. Solid. *SMITHFIELD.* $699

Rush, Caroline E. ROBERT MORTON, OR, THE STEPMOTHER...Etc. Phila: Published for the Authoress by Crissy & Marcley, 1850. 1st ed. 191pp. Orig dec red cl. Lt soiling, foxing, spine ends lightly rubbed, but VG. *CHAPEL HILL.* $75

Rush, James. THE PHILOSOPHY OF THE HUMAN VOICE. Phila: Grigg & Elliott, 1833. 2nd ed. Lea, scuffed, foxing, stain lower edge. *OLD LONDON.* $50

Rush, Norman. MATING. NY: Knopf, (1991). 1st ed. VF in VF dj. *UNGER.* $50

Rush, Norman. WHITES. NY: Knopf, 1986. Uncorrected proof. Fine in wraps. *CAPTAIN'S BOOKSHELF.* $100

Rush, Norman. WHITES: STORIES. Knopf, 1986. 1st ed. About Fine in dj w/few chips on edges. *STAHR.* $25

Rushdie, Salman. HAROUN AND THE SEA OF STORIES. (Cambridge): Granta, 1990. Advance proof, letter, compl slip from pub laid in. Ptd wraps. Fine. *JAFFE.* $250

Rushdie, Salman. HAROUN AND THE SEA OF STORIES. London: Granta, (1990). 1st ed. As New in dj. Signed. *CAPTAIN'S BOOKSHELF.* $175

Rushdie, Salman. HAROUN AND THE SEA OF STORIES. London: Granta, (1990). 1st ed. Signed. Fine in Fine dj. *LOPEZ.* $200

Rushdie, Salman. IS NOTHING SACRED? Ptd wrappers. (N.p.): Granta, 1990. 1st (only) ed. Fine. *JAFFE.* $25

Rushdie, Salman. MIDNIGHT'S CHILDREN. NY: Knopf, 1981. 1st ed, preceding Eng. Fine in dj (bit of minor rubbing). *CAPTAIN'S BOOKSHELF.* $175

Rushdie, Salman. MIDNIGHT'S CHILDREN. NY: Knopf, 1981. True 1st ed, preceding Eng ed. Fine in clipped dj, hint of spine fading. *LOPEZ.* $225

Rushdie, Salman. MIDNIGHT'S CHILDREN. NY: Knopf, 1981. True 1st ed. Fine in dj. *LOPEZ.* $225

Rushdie, Salman. SATANIC VERSES. NY: Viking, 1989. 1st ed. VF. *SMITH.* $125

Rushdie, Salman. SHAME. London: Cape, (1983). 1st ed. Signed. Fine. *LOPEZ.* $375

Rushdie, Salman. SHAME. London: Cape, (1983). Uncorrected proof. Rear corner bent, some rubbing to the red wraps. VG. *CAPTAIN'S BOOKSHELF.* $125

Rushdie, Salman. SHAME. London: Cape, (1983). Uncorrected proof. NF. Signed. *LOPEZ.* $450

Rushdie, Salman. THE SATANIC VERSES. (London): Viking, (1988). 1st ed. Signed. Boards, dj. Mint. *JAFFE.* $550

Rushdie, Salman. THE SATANIC VERSES. (London): Viking, (1988). True 1st ed. Fine in dj. *LOPEZ.* $250

Rushdie, Salman. THE SATANIC VERSES. NY, 1989. 1st ed. Fine in like dj. *POLYANTHOS.* $75

Rushdie, Salman. THE SATANIC VERSES. NY, 1989. 1st US ed. VF in dj. *PETTLER.* $60

Rushdie, Salman. THE SATANIC VERSES. NY: Viking, (1989). 1st Amer ptg. Fine in Fine dj. *AKA.* $75

Rushdie, Salman. TWO STORIES. (London): Privately Ptd, 1989. 1st ed. 1/60 (in ed of 72) bound in cl, signed. As New in cl w/leather labels, slipcased. *CAPTAIN'S BOOKSHELF.* $1000

Rushton, Charles. FURNACE FOR A FOE. London, 1957. 1st ed. VG in dj. *MADLE.* $30

Rushton, William. W.G. GRACE'S LAST CASE. London: Methuen, 1984. 1st ed. Fine in dj. *SILVER DOOR.* $25.

Ruskin, John. DAME WIGGINS OF LEE AND HER SEVEN WONDERFUL CATS. Orpington, Kent, George Allen, 1885. Kate Greenaway (illus). 22 woodcuts. Fine w/glassine dj. *ACADEMIC LIBRARY.* $135

Ruskin, John. THE ETHICS OF THE DUST. London: Smith, Elder, 1866. Crack in front hinge, few instances of light foxing, still VG to NF. 1st ed. *CHAPEL HILL.* $75

Ruskin, John. THE KING OF THE GOLDEN RIVER. London: George Harrap, (1932). One of 550 signed by Arthur Rackham (illus). Orig gilt lettered limp vellum, pub's defective slipcase. 4 color plts. Faint circle of darkening at middle of spine (continuing onto covers, about 1 1/2" in diameter), o/w VF. *PIRAGES.* $550

Rusling, James F. ACROSS AMERICA: OR, THE GREAT WEST AND THE PACIFIC COAST. NY: Sheldon & Company, 1874. 1st ed. Fldg map (loose and tape mended), frontis. Foxing. *HUDSON.* $90

Russe, Otto. AN ATLAS OF OPERATIONS FOR TRAUMA. Vienna, 1955. Dj. *FYE.* $50

Russell, A.L.N. WESTMINSTER ABBEY. London: Chatto & Windus, 1934. Patterned boards bound in red half calf. VG. *CULLEN.* $120

Russell, Bertrand. JUSTICE IN WAR TIME. Chicago, 1917. 2nd ed. Ex-lib. Frontis. Cvrs sl stained, o/w VG. *DIAMOND.* $45

Russell, Bertrand. SATAN IN THE SUBURBS AND OTHER STORIES. Simon and Schuster, 1953. 1st ed. NF in price-clipped dj. *STAHR.* $25

Russell, Carl. FIREARMS, TRAPS & TOOLS OF THE MOUNTAIN MEN. Knopf, 1967. 1st ed. VF in VF dj. *OREGON.* $65

Russell, Carl. GUNS ON THE EARLY FRONTIERS. Univ of CA, 1957. 1st ed. Fine in Fine dj. *OREGON.* $70

Russell, Carl. GUNS ON THE EARLY FRONTIERS. Berkeley, 1957. 1st ed. Bkpl. VG in edgetorn dj. *BAADE.* $45

Russell, Carl. GUNS ON THE EARLY FRONTIERS. Berkeley: Univ of CA, 1957. 1st ed. Old vestiges of cello-tape on eps. Brown cl, gilt, damp marks on edges, not affecting internal condition. Good dj, Good+ contents. *CONNOLLY & WADE.* $35

Russell, Charles Edward. FROM SANDY HOOK TO 62.... NY: Century Co, (1929). 1st ed. 18 plts and charts. VG. Front dj tipped in. *LEFKOWICZ.* $55

Russell, Charles M. ACCEPTANCE OF THE STATUE CHARLES M. RUSSELL. Presented by State of Montana. 85th Congress, 2nd Session, Senate Doc 133. GPO, Washington, 1959. *HEINOLDT.* $25

Russell, Charles M. BACK TRAILING ON THE OLD FRONTIERS. Great Falls, MT: Cheely-Raban, 1922. 1st ed. iv,56pp. Pict wraps (red ink w/skull #1 on back). Fine. Howes R526. *OREGON.* $600

Russell, Charles M. GOOD MEDICINE. GC: Doubleday, Doran & Co, 1930. 1st trade ed. Will Rogers intro. Red and gold stamped cl. Spine lightly sunned, bkpl, newspaper stain to one leaf. *DAWSON'S.* $75

Russell, Charles M. STUDIES OF WESTERN LIFE. NY: The Albertype Co, 1890. Cl, three-hole tie, 2nd issue w/letterpress relating to plate #1 added to verso of title pg. 12 plts. 18 x 24.5 cm. Edges sl bumped, else Fine. *VARNER.* $2,000

Russell, Don. THE LIVE AND LEGENDS OF BUFFALO BILL. Norman, (1960). 4th prtg (1973). 514pp. VG+ in dj. *PRATT.* $35

Russell, Eric Frank. DEEP SPACE. Reading, PA: Fantasy Press, (1954). 1st ed. Fine in dj. *McCLINTOCK.* $25

Russell, John Andrew. THE GERMANIC INFLUENCE IN THE MAKING OF MICHIGAN. Univ of Detroit, 1927. 1st ed. Full gilt stamped morocco, raised bands. News clipping tipped in. Fine. *ARTIS.* $75

Russell, Keith C. THE DUCK HUNTINGEST GENTLEMEN. Tulsa: Winchester Press, 1980. 1st trade ed. Fine in VG dj. *BACKMAN.* $30

Russell, Lady Rachel (Wriothesley). LETTERS OF... London: Dilly, 1773. 1st ed. 4to, 216pp. Bound in modern half-calf w/new eps. Some paper restoration to edges of half-title and very tip of title page. VG, clean. *SECOND LIFE.* $250

Russell, Michael. HISTORY AND PRESENT CONDITION OF THE BARBARY STATES. NY: Harper, 1837. Fldg map. Some foxing. *SCHOYER'S.* $35

Russell, Michael. PALESTINE, OR THE HOLY LAND; FROM THE EARLIEST PERIOD TO THE PRESENT TIME. Edinburgh, 1837. Half calf, rubbed. 400 pp. *O'NEILL.* $30

Russell, Michael. VIEW OF ANCIENT AND MODERN EGYPT; WITH AN OUTLINE OF ITS NATURAL HISTORY. NY: J. & J. Harper, 1831. Frontis fold-out map. Full calf rubbed at extremities. Good. *ARCHAEOLOGIA.* $45

Russell, Norman. OPEN THE FLOWER. Mt. Horeb: Perishable Press, 1974. 1st ed. Ltd to 125. Signed by Walter Hamady. Spine sl faded, o/w Fine. Wraps. *JAFFE.* $75

Russell, Osborne. JOURNAL OF A TRAPPER, OR NINE YEARS IN THE ROCKY MOUNTAINS 1834-1843. Boise, Syms York, 1921. 2nd ed. Ltd to 100. VF. *OREGON.* $250

Russell, Osborne. JOURNAL OF A TRAPPER, OR NINE YEARS IN THE ROCKY MOUNTAINS 1834-1843...WITH A BIOGRAPHY OF OSBORNE RUSSELL & MAPS. Portland: Champoeg Press, 1955. Ltd to 750 designed & ptd by Lawton Kennedy. Best ed. 10 maps (2 fldg). Fine. *OREGON.* $100

Russell, Osborne. JOURNAL OF A TRAPPER OR NINE YEARS IN THE ROCKY MOUNTAINS 1834-1843. (Boise, ID), 1921. Spine and top inch of front cover faded, spine lettering dull, indifferent exterior, Fine interior. Howes R537. *BOHLING.* $150

Russell, Peter (ed). AN EXAMINATION OF EZRA POUND. (Norfolk): New Directions, (1950). Rev copy, slip laid in. Fine in dj, sl darkened backstrip. *HELLER.* $50

Russell, Phillips. JOHN PAUL JONES, MAN OF ACTION. Brentano, 1927. 1st ed. 11 plts. VG. *OREGON.* $30

Russell, Phillips. RED TIGER. NY: Brentano, 1929. 1st ed. Spine faded, contents VG. *SILVER.* $25

Russell, Randy. HOT WIRE. NY: Bantam Books, 1989. 1st ed. Pb orig. VF, unread, in wrappers. *MORDIDA.* $20

Russell, Richard. A DISSERTATION CONCERNING THE USE OF SEA WATER IN DISEASES OF THE GLANDS...To Which is Added an Epistolary Dissertation to R. Frewin. Oxford: James Fletcher, 1753. 2nd ed. xv,398pp & corrigenda. Contemp full calf, ribbed spine somewhat dry, sl chipped, joints starting. Copper plate cartouche to title, 7 full-pg plts. Text, plts quite clean. *SMITHFIELD.* $240

Russell, Ruth. LAKE FRONT. Chicago: Rockwell, 1931. 1st ed. Dj. Signed by Russell. Fine, bright. *MUELLER.* $35

Russell, W. Clark. THE FROZEN PIRATE. Hurst, n.d. VG. *MADLE*. $30

Russell, William Howard. A DIARY IN THE EAST DURING THE TOUR OF THE PRINCE AND PRINCESS OF WALES. London: Routledge, 1869. 6 color plts. Bkpl. Good. *ARCHAEOLOGIA*. $75

Russell, William Howard. MY DIARY NORTH AND SOUTH. Boston, 1863. 1st Amer. ed. 602pp. Cover chipped spine extremities; some water staining, o/w VG. *PRATT*. $100

Russo, Richard. THE RISK POOL. NY: RH, (1988). Uncorrected proof. Fine in wraps. *LOPEZ*. $50

Rust, Art Jr. "GET THAT NIGGER OFF THE FIELD!": A SPARKLING INFORMAL HISTORY OF THE BLACK MAN IN BASEBALL. NY: Delacorte, (1976). 1st ed. Fine in Very NF dj w/very short tear; a little rubbing. Adv rev copy w/slip. *BETWEEN COVERS*. $65

Ruth, George Herman. BABE RUTH'S OWN BOOK OF BASEBALL. A.L. Burt, 1928 reprint. Good in Good+ dj. *PLAPINGER*. $85

Ruth, George Herman. BABE RUTH'S OWN BOOK OF BASEBALL. Putnam, 1928. 1st ed. Good in Good+ dj. *PLAPINGER*. $165

Ruthven, A.G. A NATURALIST IN A UNIVERSITY MUSEUM. Ann Arbor, 1931. Ltd ed of 600. Dj. *SUTTON*. $38

Rutledge, Archibald. AN AMERICAN HUNTER. NY: J.B. Lippincott Co, (1937). 5th impression. VG+. Owner blind stamp. *BACKMAN*. $40

Rutledge, Archibald. BRIMMING CHALICE. NY: Henry Harrison (1936). 1st ed. Signed. Orig brn cl. Spine crown chipped, couple of red small marks rear cover. VG. *CHAPEL HILL*. $150

Rutledge, Archibald. DEEP RIVER: THE COMPLETE POEMS OF... Columbia: R.L. Bryan, (1966). 1st rev ed. Fine in dj, some wear. *CAPTAIN'S BOOKSHELF*. $75

Rutledge, Archibald. FROM THE HILLS TO THE SEA. Indianapolis: Bobbs Merrill, (1958). 1st. NF, owner sig; NF price-clipped dj. *CAPTAIN'S BOOKSHELF*. $75

Rutledge, Archibald. HEART OF THE SOUTH. Columbia, SC: The State Co, 1924. 1st ed. Fine, bright. White dj shows minimal spotting. *CHAPEL HILL*. $200

Rutledge, Archibald. HOME BY THE RIVER. Indianapolis & NY: Bobbs-Merrill, (1941). Ltr prtg. Signed. About Fine in price-clipped, VG dj, few tears, internal tape mends. *CHAPEL HILL*. $35

Rutledge, Archibald. HOME BY THE RIVER. Indianapolis/NY: Bobbs-Merrill Co, 1941. 1st ed. Inscribed, signed. VG+. *BACKMAN*. $60

Rutledge, Archibald. HUNTER'S CHOICE. NY: A.S. Barnes & Co, A Countryman Press Book, 1946. 1st trade ed. Ltd to 5,000. VG. *BACKMAN*. $50

Rutledge, Archibald. PLANTATION GAME TRAILS. Boston & NY: Houghton Mifflin, 1921. VG. 1st ed. Signed inscript. Ownshp sig on front pastedown. *CHAPEL HILL*. $135

Rutledge, Archibald. PLANTATION GAME TRAILS. Boston: Houghton Mifflin, 1921. 1st ed. VG. *BOOK BROKER*. $85

Rutledge, Archibald. THE BANNERS OF THE COAST. (Columbia, SC: The State Co), 1908. 1st ed. Orig grey cl stamped in silver. VG. *CHAPEL HILL*. $250

Rutledge, Archibald. THE HEART'S CITADEL AND OTHER POEMS Richmond, VA: The Dietz Press, (1953). 1st ed. Orig grn cl. NF in dj. *CHAPEL HILL*. $55

Rutledge, Archibald. THE SONNETS OF ARCHIBALD RUTLEDGE (Spartanburg, SC: Williams Printing Co), 1938. 1st ed. Signed. Orig brn suede wraps. Bkpl, else VG. *CHAPEL HILL*. $45

Rutledge, Archibald. WILD LIFE OF THE SOUTH. NY: Frederick A. Stokes Co, (1935). 2nd prtg. Inscribed, signed. VG. *BACKMAN*. $75

Ruxton, George Frederick. LIFE IN THE FAR WEST. Ed by LeRoy Hafen. Norman, 1951. 1st ed. Bkpl. Bumped, o/w near VG in sl worn, price-clipped dj. *BAADE*. $50

Ruzicka, Rudolph. STUDIES IN TYPE DESIGN. Hanover: Friends of the Dartmouth Library, (1968). 1st ed. Loose sheets in cl portfolio, slipcase. VF. *JAFFE*. $75

Ryan, Alan (ed). NIGHT VISIONS I. Niles: Dark Harvest, (1984). 1st ed. Trade issue. Almost Fine with 3/4" closed tear. *OTHER WORLDS*. $95

Ryan, Allen. THE BONES WIZARD. Doubleday, 1988. 1st ed. Fine in dj. *MADLE*. $30

Ryan, Cornelius (ed). ACROSS THE SPACE FRONTIER. NY: Viking, 1952. Signed by Willy Ley. Good in chipped & worn dj; top edge of dj spine torn. *KNOLLWOOD*. $75

Ryan, Daniel J. OHIO IN FOUR WARS: A MILITARY HISTORY. Columbus, OH: Heer, 1917. 1st ed. Orig cl. *GINSBERG*. $100

Ryan, Frances Beven. EARLY DAYS IN ESCONDIDO. Escondido: Frances and Lewis Ryan, (1970). Gold-stamped cl in dj w/2 short tears. *DAWSON'S*. $40

Ryan, Frances Beven. YESTERDAYS IN ESCONDIDO. Escondido: Frances and Lewis Ryan, 1973. Gold-stamped cl in dj w/3 short tears. *DAWSON'S*. $40

Ryan, Marah Ellis. FOR THE SOUL OF RAFAEL. Chicago: McClurg, 1906. 1st ed. Tipped-in frontis, 378pp, 18pp tipped-in photos. Untrimmed. Inner hinge paper repair. Ornate pict cl. Edges showing wear, else clean, bright, and VG. *CONNOLLY & WADE*. $40

Ryan, Michael. THE PHILOSOPHY OF MARRIAGE, IN ITS SOCIAL, MORAL, AND PHYSICAL RELATIONS. With an Account....3rd ed, rev, enl. London: H. Bailliere. 1839. viii,388pp. Black morocco over blue pebbled cl, gilt spine. Marbled edges. *KARMIOLE*. $100

Ryan, Richard. DRAMATIC TABLE TALK. London: John Knight and Henry Lacey, 1825 (and 1830). 1st ed. 3 vols. Fldg engr frontispieces; vignette titles, plts; contemp half calf and marbled boards; joints rubbed; gilt to spines; leather labels; marbled edges; cellotape repair one plt; some rubbing to spine ends; internally fresh. *DRAMATIS*. $175

Rycroft, B. KIRSTENBOSCH. Aylesbury, 1980. 135 colored plts. Cl, dj. *SUTTON*. $47.50

Ryder, Jonathan (pseud of Robert Ludlum). THE CRY OF THE HALIDON. NY: Delacorte, 1974. 1st ed. Fine in dj. *MORDIDA*. $40

Ryder, Jonathan (pseud of Robert Ludlum). TREVAYNE. NY: Delacorte, 1973. 1st ed. Front cvr sl discolored near top corner o/w Fine in dj (sl faded spine, sm stain, scratch). *MORDIDA*. $65

Rye, Edgar. THE QUIRT AND THE SPUR. Chicago: W.B. Conkey Co, 1909. 1st ed. VG. Howes R559 *GIBBS*. $275

Rynning, Thomas H. GUN NOTCHES: THE LIFE STORY OF A COWBOY-SOLDIER. NY: F.A. Stokes, 1931. 1st ed. Top of spine softened w/short tear. Internally Fine. Scarce. *CONNOLLY & WADE*. $40

Rynning, Thomas. GUN NOTCHES. Stokes, 1931. 1st ed. Wraps. Some spine end chipping. Good+. *OREGON*. $50

Ryus, W.H. THE SECOND WILLIAM PENN. Kansas City: Frank Riley, (1913). 1st ed. Wraps. Fine. *OREGON*. $30

S

S. WEIR MITCHELL: MEMORIAL ADDRESSES AND RESOLUTIONS. Phila, 1914. 1st ed. 155pp. W/the photographic portrait of Mitchell, often lacking. Fine. Scarce. *FYE.* $100

Sabatini, Rafael. THE CAROLINIAN. London: Hutchinson, (1925). 1st ed. Eps sl darkened o/w Fine in bright dj. *MORDIDA.* $100

Sabatini, Rafael. THE HOUNDS OF GOD. London: Hutchinson, (1928). 1st ed. Eps sl darkened o/w Fine in bright unfaded dj. Almost like New. *MORDIDA.* $100

Sabin, Edwin. KIT CARSON DAYS, 1809-1868. McClurg, 1914. 1st ed. VG. Howes S1. *OREGON.* $150

Sabin, Edwin. KIT CARSON DAYS, 1809-1868. Rev ed. NY: Press of Pioneers, 1935. 2 vols. #96/200 numbered, signed, autographed, slipcased. Vol I has ffep adhered to pastedown, stain on eps to dedication pg. VG in VG slipcase. *OREGON.* $300

Sabin, Edwin. LOST WITH LIEUTENANT PIKE. Phila: J.B. Lippincott, 1919. Map, 6 full-pg illus. Blue-stamped pict cl in chipped dj. *DAWSON'S.* $35

Sabine, Lorenzo. NOTES ON DUELS AND DUELING. Boston: Crosby, Nichols & Co, 1855. 1st ed. Orig cl binding, blind stamped. Ends chipped. Good. Howes S-4. *CULLEN.* $135

Sachs, Ernest. THE DIAGNOSIS AND TREATMENT OF BRAIN TUMORS. St. Louis, 1931. 1st ed. *FYE.* $75

Sachs, Ernest. THE HISTORY AND DEVELOPMENT OF NEUROLOGICAL SURGERY. London, 1952. 1st ed. Ex-lib. *FYE.* $50

Sacks, B. BE IT ENACTED: THE CREATION OF THE TERRITORY OF ARIZONA. Phoenix: AZ Hist Foundation, 1964. 1st ed. 3 fldg maps rear pocket. Fine in Good+ dj. *OREGON.* $45

Sackville-West, Victoria (Vita). CONSTANTINOPLE. EIGHT POEMS. London: Privately Ptd, The Complete Press, 1915. 1st ed. Ptd wraps. Fine. *JAFFE.* $450

Sackville-West, Vita. COUNTRY NOTES. London: Michael Joseph, 1939. 1st ed. Fine but for spot on spine, in used dj. *BEASLEY.* $125

Sackville-West, Vita. GRAND CANYON. NY, 1942. Stated 1st ed. NF in VG jacket. Scarce. *FIVE QUAIL.* $35

Sackville-West, Vita. NO SIGNPOSTS IN THE SEA. GC: Doubleday, 1961. 1st Amer ed. Dj. Fine. *MUELLER.* $15

Sackville-West, Vita. NURSERY RHYMES. London: The Dropmore Press, 1947. 1st ed. One of 550 numbered. Orig gilt dec. cl, inside gilt dentelles, dj, in orig box. VF, partially unopened. *WREDEN.* $165

Sackville-West, Vita. SAINT JOAN OF ARC. London: Cobden-Sanderson, (1936). 1st ed. Total ed of 120, this one of 100 numbered, signed. Fine in sl soiled white cl. *SECOND LIFE.* $350

Sadler, Barry (with Tom Mahoney). I'M A LUCKY ONE. NY: Macmillan, (1967). 1st ed. Dj edgeworn. *AKA.* $35

Sadler, Bay. THE MOI. Nashville: Aurora, (1977). 1st ed. Fine in lightly used dj. *AKA.* $50

Sadler, Mark. DEADLY INNOCENTS. NY: Walker, 1986. 1st ed. Signed. VF in dj. *SILVER DOOR.* $35

Sadlier, Michael. BLESSINGTON-D'ORSAY, A MASQUERADE. London: Constable & Co, Ltd, (1933). 1st ed. Inscribed. Tls laid in. VG. *HELLER.* $50

Sadoul, Georges. FRENCH FILM. London: Falcon Press, 1953. 1st ed. Fine in lightly used dj w/sticker tear on front panel and small chip on rear panel. *BEASLEY.* $75

Saffell, W.T.R. RECORDS OF THE REVOLUTIONARY WAR: CONTAINING THE MILITARY AND FINANCIAL CORRESPONDENCE...GENERAL ORDERS OF WASHINGTON, LEE...VALLEY FORGE. NY: Pudney, 1858. 1st ed. 554,(12 ads)pp. Orig cl, lax flyleaf, a few signatures sprung. Howes S10. *GINSBERG.* $125

Safford, J.M. and J.B. Killebrew. THE ELEMENTARY GEOLOGY OF TENNESSEE. Nashville: Albert B. Tavel, 1888. Maps. Orig printed bds. *HUDSON.* $40

Safford, James M. GEOLOGY OF TENNESSEE. Nashville: S.C. Mercer, 1869. Fldg litho view (sl torn), 7 litho plts, hand colored map (removed, encapsulated). Hinges weak. Ex-lib. *HUDSON.* $295

Safford, William H. THE LIFE OF HARMAN BLENNERHASSETT. COMPRISING AN AUTHENTIC NARRATIVE...Chillicothe, Ohio, 1850. 1st ed. 239pp. Frontis. Orig gold stamped cl. Howes S13. *GINSBERG.* $200

Safrastian, Arshak. KURDS AND KURDISTAN. London, 1948. *O'NEILL.* $30

Safroni-Middleton. A VAGABOND'S ODYSSEY: London: Grant Richards. 1896. (328)pp. Red cl stamped in gilt, a little soiled. Frontis. *SCHOYER'S.* $30

Safroni-Middleton, A(rnold). SAILOR AND BEACHCOMBER CONFESSIONS OF A LIFE AT SEA....NY: Charles Scribner's Sons, 1915. 1st Amer ed, ptd from Eng sheets, w/cancel title. 24 plts from photos. Lt foxing. *LEFKOWICZ.* $65

Sagan, Francoise. BONJOUR TRISTESSE. NY: Dutton, 1955. 1st US ed. NF. VG dj. *CAPTAIN'S BOOKSHELF.* $35

Sage, Dean et al. SALMON AND TROUT. NY: Macmillan, 1904. Gilt dec cl. Good. *CULLEN.* $60

Sage, J.H. and L.B. Bishop. THE BIRDS OF CONNECTICUT. Hartford, 1913. Wrappers chipped, spotted; ink name. *SUTTON.* $30

Sage, J.H. and L.B. Bishop. THE BIRDS OF CONNECTICUT. Hartford, 1913. VG. *MIKESH.* $32.50

Sage, Lee. THE LAST RUSTLER. Little Brown, 1930. 1st ed. VG in sl chipped dj. *VARNER.* $35

Sagendorph, Robb. AMERICA AND HER ALMANACS...1639-1970. Dublin, NH & Boston: Little Brown, 1970. Fine in Good+ dj. *CONNOLLY & WADE.* $35

Saggs, H.W.F. EVERYDAY LIFE IN BABYLONIA AND ASSYRIA. London: Batsford; NY: Putnam, 1965. 1st ed. Dj. Ex-lib, o/w VG. *WORLDWIDE.* $16

Saign, Ray S, Richard Donaldson and Fred Fiet (eds). THE STAGECOACH MUSEUM GUN COLLECTION. Minneapolis, (1978). 1st ed. Fine in dj. *LAURIE.* $30

Saint-Exupery, Antoine de. NIGHT FLIGHT. NY: Century, 1932. 1st ed. Fine but for bkpl and small sunned spot. In lightly chipped dj. *BEASLEY.* $45

Saint-Exupery, Antoine de. THE LITTLE PRINCE. NY: Reynal & Hitchcock, (1943). Katherine Woods (trans). 1st trade ed. Pict cl. Fine in price-clipped dj. *JAFFE.* $350

Saint-Gaudens, Augustus. THE REMINISCENCES OF AUGUSTUS SAINT-GAUDENS. Saint-Gaudens (ed). NY: Century Co. 1913. 1st ed. 2 vols. 89 photogr plts. Grn cl over gilt boards. Teg. *KARMIOLE.* $60

Saintsbury, George. A CONSIDERATION OF THACKERAY. London: OUP, 1931. NF, lacking dj. *CAPTAIN'S BOOKSHELF.* $40

Sajous, Charles. THE INTERNAL SECRETIONS AND THE PRINCIPLES OF MEDICINE. Phila, 1911. 4th ed. 2 vols. *FYE.* $50

Sakaki, Nanao. BELLYFULLS. Eugene: Toad Press, (1966). Trans by Neale Hunter. 1st ed. Fine in wrappers. *CAPTAIN'S BOOKSHELF.* $20

Sala, George Augustus. BREAKFAST IN BED: OR, PHILOSOPHY BETWEEN THE SHEETS. Boston: Redpath, 1863. 1st Amer ed. Fine, tight. *MUELLER.* $40

Salamanca, J.R. THE LOST COUNTRY. NY: Simon & Schuster, 1958. 1st ed. 1st bk. Orig black boards w/yellow cl spine. Acidic pgs browning as usual, else Fine in modestly used dj. *CHAPEL HILL.* $40

Salas, Floyd. TATTOO THE WICKED CROSS. NY: Grove Press, (1967). 1st ed, 1st book. Fine in dj. *BERNARD.* $25

Saldern, Axel Von. ANCIENT GLASS IN THE MUSEUM OF FINE ARTS, BOSTON. Boston: Museum of Fine Arts, (1968). 70 plts (4 color). Dj. Good. *ARCHAEOLOGIA.* $65

Sale, Medora. MURDER IN A GOOD CAUSE. NY: Scribner, 1990. 1st Amer ed. Review copy, signed. Pub's slip laid in. VF in dj. *SILVER DOOR.* $35

Saleeby, C. SURGERY AND SOCIETY, A TRIBUTE TO LISTERISM. NY, 1912. *FYE.* $50

Salinger, J.D. FRANNY AND ZOOEY. Boston & Toronto: Little, Brown & Co., (1961). 1st ed. Name & address stamped on flyleaf o/w NF in dj. *BERNARD.* $85

Salinger, J.D. FRANNY AND ZOOEY. Boston: Little, Brown, (1961). Owner's sig, else NF in lightly soiled dj (couple of closed tears). 1st ed. *CHAPEL HILL.* $65

Salinger, J.D. NINE STORIES. Boston: Little Brown, (1953). Owner name fep. NF dj (moderately spine-faded). *LOPEZ.* $500

Salinger, J.D. NINE STORIES. Boston: Little, Brown, 1953. 1st ed. Close to Fine but w/spine gilt flaked away; in somewhat sunned and rubbed dj w/short tears, small chip rear panel, sl wear spine ends. *BEASLEY.* $450

Salinger, J.D. RAISE HIGH THE ROOF BEAM, CARPENTERS And SEYMOUR AN INTRODUCTION. Boston: Little, Brown, (1963). 1st ed, 1st issue, no dedication pg. Orig grey cl. "1963" inked ffep, some dampstaining to eps but none visible in text, thus VG copy in Fine dj. *CHAPEL HILL.* $250

Salinger, J.D. THE CATCHER IN THE RYE. Boston: LB, 1951. 1st ed, 1st bk. Spine lettering a bit dull, else About Fine in splendid dj. *CAPTAIN'S BOOKSHELF.* $1750

Salinger, J.D. THE CATCHER IN THE RYE. Boston: LB, 1951. 1st ed. Spine gilt faded, o/w NF in supplied NF dj. *LOPEZ.* $750

Salinger, J.D. THE CATCHER IN THE RYE. Boston: Little, Brown, 1951. 1st ed, 1st bk. Orig black cl. Fine in NF dj. Quite Nice, gilt spine lettering bright, unrubbed. *CHAPEL HILL.* $1750

Salinger, J.D. THE CATCHER IN THE RYE. London: Hamish, (1951). 1st English ed. Fine in dj that is sl rubbed along edges. *UNGER.* $800

Salinger, J.D. THE CATCHER IN THE RYE. London: Hamish Hamilton, (1951). VG in somewhat tired pict dj (few tears and wrinkles). 1st Eng ed. *CHAPEL HILL.* $275

Salinger, J.D. THE CATCHER IN THE RYE. London: Hamish Hamilton, (1951). Blue cl, silver stamping. 1st Eng ed, 1st bk. NF in sl chipped dj. *HELLER.* $250

Salinger, J.D. THE COMPLETE UNCOLLECTED SHORT STORIES OF J.D. SALINGER. 2 vols. N.p., n.p., (1974). 1st ed, 2nd issue perfect bound in glossy ppwrps. Fine pict ppwrps. *BERNARD.* $350

Salinger, J.D. THE COMPLETE UNCOLLECTED SHORT STORIES. (N.p.; n.d., but 1974). 1st ed, 1st issue. 2 vols. Spine and edges of Vol 1 sl sunned, else Fine in wrappers. *CAPTAIN'S BOOKSHELF.* $600

Salinger, J.D. THE COMPLETE UNCOLLECTED SHORT STORIES. (n.p.): (n.p.), (1967). 2nd ed. Suppressed. 2 vols. Fine in wrappers. *LOPEZ.* $350

Salinger, J.D. THE COMPLETE UNCOLLECTED SHORT STORIES. N.p., n.d. 2 vols. Wraps. 2nd ed, w/pict wraps. Fine. *BEASLEY.* $200

Salinger, M. FLOWERS. THE FLOWER PIECE IN EUROPEAN PAINTING. NY: Harper & Brothers, (1949). 1st Amer. ed. Corners bumped, shaken, else Good. *WREDEN.* $30

Salisbury, Albert and Jane. TWO CAPTAINS WEST. Seattle, (1950). 1st ed. Dj has minor chipping and small tear on back, o/w Fine. *PRATT.* $35

Salisbury, Harrison. THE LONG MARCH. Franklin Center: Franklin Library, 1985. 1st ed. One of unspecified number signed. Fine in full lea. *BETWEEN COVERS.* $45

SALMONIA...BY AN ANGLER. (By Humphry Davy.) London: John Murray, 1828. 1st ed. viii,273pp. 2 fldg plts. Uncut in orig boards (paper torn off along spine edge affecting edge of label, etc). Minor foxing, but excellent, tight. *SECOND LIFE.* $350

Salomons, David. PHOTOGRAPHIC NOTES AND FORMULAE. Turbridge Wells: A.K. Baldwin, Grosvenor Printing Works. 1890. 1st ed. 54pp. Orig. red cl, gilt. Fine. *KARMIOLE.* $100

Salomonsen, Finn and Gitz-Johansen. GRONLANDS FUGLE. THE BIRDS OF GREENLAND. Kobenhavn: Ejnar Munksgaard, 1950. 3 vols. Fldg colored map inserted loosely. 52 color plts (superb cond). Orig ptd wraps sl age darkened, chipped; owner inscrip. Sm tape mark spine of vol III; interiors Fine. *PARMER.* $550

SALT LAKE CITY, AND THE WAY THITHER. London: T. Nelson & Sons, (c. 1890). 31pp ptd in blue ink, panoramic color print, 10 full-pg color prints from photos. Blind, black and gold stamped cl, 2 small ink chips on the panorama. *DAWSON'S.* $75

Salten, Felix. BAMBI, A LIFE IN THE WOODS. Simon & Schuster, 1928. 1st Amer ed. Illus by Kurt Wiese. Whittaker Chambers (trans). Some cvr wear, VG+. *BEBBAH.* $40

Salter, James. DUSK & OTHER STORIES. Cl, dj. SF: North Point, 1988. 1st ed, hb issue. Mint. *JAFFE.* $25

Salter, James. THE ARM OF FLESH. NY: Harper, (1961). 1st ed. NF in dj missing a horizontal piece about 2" long and 1/2" wide from lower edge of front panel, o/w VG. *LOPEZ.* $100

Salter, James. THE ARM OF FLESH. NY: Harper, (1961). 1st ed. Fine in NF dj. *LOPEZ.* $175

Saltiel, E. H. and George Barnett. HISTORY AND BUSINESS DIRECTORY OF CHEYENNE...REGIONS OF THE ROCKY MOUNTAINS. New Haven, 1975. Facs reprint of 1866 orig ed. Archibald Hanna (intro). One of 400 numbered. *GINSBERG.* $25

Salvator, Ludwig Louis. LOS ANGELES IN THE SUNNY SEVENTIES. Marguerite Eyer Wilbur (trans). LA: Jake Zeitlin, 1929. One of 900 ptd by Bruce McCallister. Marbled boards w/cl spine and leather spine label, edges of boards and label lightly rubbed, front inner hinge starting. *DAWSON'S.* $100

Sampson, Ezra. THE BRIEF REMARKER ON THE WAYS OF MAN. Canandaigua, NY: J.D. Bemis. 1823. 264pp. Orig calf, extrems bit rubbed. *KARMIOLE.* $50

Sams, Ferrol. THE WIDOW'S MITE & OTHER STORIES. Atlanta: Peachtree, (1987). 1st Amer ed. Signed. Fine in dj. *DORN.* $30

Samson, Jack (ed). THE BEST OF COREY FORD. NY: Holt, Rinehart and Winston, 1975. Stated 1st ed. Fine in Fine dj. *BACKMAN.* $45

Samuelson, James. BULGARIA, PAST AND PRESENT. London, 1888. xiv,247pp. Spine label, light shelfwear. *O'NEILL.* $45

SAN FRANCISCO: A GUIDE TO THE BAY AND ITS CITIES. NY: Hastings House, 1940. 1st ed. Amer Guide series. WPA guide. VG in Good dj. *CONNOLLY & WADE.* $45

SAN FRANCISCO: A GUIDE...NY, 1940. American Guide Series. WPA guide. 1st ed. No dj. *SCHOYER'S.* $30

SAN JOAQUIN COUNTY, CALIFORNIA: ITS FAVORABLE LOCATION...CITY OF STOCKTON: ITS INDUSTRIES....Stockton, CA: Orr and Ruggles, 1887. 130pp. Map, woodcuts in text, ads. Old cl w/orig ptd wrappers bound in at rear, leather label on spine, emb lib stamp, bkpl removed. Howes S75. *GINSBERG.* $150

Sanborn, F.B. (ed). MEMOIRS OF PLINY EARLE, M.D., WITH EXTRACTS FROM HIS DIARY AND LETTERS (1830-1892) AND SELECTIONS FROM HIS PROFESSIONAL WRITINGS (1839-1891). Boston, 1898. 1st ed. 409pp. Ex-lib but Fine. *FYE.* $75

Sanborn, F.B. (ed). THE FIRST & LAST JOURNEYS OF THOREAU. Boston: Biblio Soc, 1905. Ltd ed. 1/489. Moderate foxing, else VG+; uncut in worn, complete slipcase. *MIKESH.* $75

Sanborn, Kate. OLD TIME WALL PAPERS. NY: Literary Collector Press, 1905. 1st ed. VG. *BACKROOM.* $300

Sanchez Salazar, Gustavo A. THE GREAT REBEL: CHE GUEVARA IN BOLIVIA. NY: Grove, (1969). 1st ed. Dj w/short mended tear. *AKA.* $26

Sanchez, Sonia. WE A BADDDDD PEOPLE. Detroit: Broadside Press, (1970). 1st ed. About Fine in lightly rubbed wrappers. Inscribed. *BETWEEN COVERS.* $85

Sanchez-Saavedra, E.M. A DESCRIPTION OF THE COUNTRY: VIRGINIA'S CARTOGRAPHERS AND THEIR MAPS, 1607-1881. V.S.L, 1975. Bklet, portfolio of 9 facs maps. VG. *BOOK BROKER.* $100

Sand, Algo. SENOR BUM IN THE JUNGLE. NY: National Travel Club, 1932. 1st ed. *SILVER.* $25

Sandburg, Carl. ABRAHAM LINCOLN, THE PRAIRIE YEARS. 1 vol abridged ed. NY, (1929). VG+ in dj. *PRATT.* $20

Sandburg, Carl. ABRAHAM LINCOLN, THE PRAIRIE YEARS. 2 vols. NY, (1926). 1st ed. Fine. *PRATT.* $60

Sandburg, Carl. ABRAHAM LINCOLN, THE WAR YEARS. 4 vols. NY, 1939. 1st ed after ptg of 525 deluxe copies. Sm chip from vol II, minor waterstain back of Vol. III o/w VG+. *PRATT.* $90

Sandburg, Carl. ADDRESS BEFORE A JOINT SESSION OF CONGRESS. NY: Harcourt, Brace, (1959). 1/750 numbered, signed. Sl spine faded, o/w Fine w/o dj (as issued?). *LOPEZ.* $65

Sandburg, Carl. LINCOLN COLLECTOR. NY: Bonanza Books, 1960. Rprt of 1st trade ed. Ink name, dj worn. *OAK KNOLL.* $20

Sandburg, Carl. POTATO FACE. Harcourt, Brace, (1930). 1st ed. 96pp. Sl fraying to top, bottom of spine. VG. *BEBBAH.* $60

Sandburg, Carl. REMEMBRANCE ROCK. NY, (1948). 2 vols. Ltd ed, 693/975 (of 1000) on all rag paper, signed. Fine in glassine djs (vol 1 torn). Aug, 1948 issue of Southern Packet w/essay laid in. *POLYANTHOS.* $150

Sandburg, Carl. ROOTABAGA STORIES. Harcourt, Brace, (1922). 1st ed. 230pp. Illus by Maud & Miska Petersham. Color frontis. Some edgewear, VG+. *BEBBAH.* $75

Sandburg, Carl. THE AMERICAN SONGBAG. NY,(1927). Orig ed. Orig red cl. Few pp margins sl torn, o/w VG. Sandburg sig attached to fly. *DIAMOND.* $75

Sandburg, Carl. THE PAMPHLET POETS. NY: Simon and Schuster, 1926. 1st ed. Wraps. Very close to Fine. *BEASLEY.* $60

Sandburg, Carl. THE SANDBURG RANGE. NY: Harcourt, Brace, 1957. 1st ed. Blue cl, Fine in About Fine dj. *CONNOLLY & WADE.* $35

Sandby, George. MESMERISM AND ITS OPPONENTS...NY: Benjamin & Young, 1844. 1st Amer ed. 8vo. 8, 135pp. Contemp cloth backed marbled boards. Lib stamp & label on title. *M & S.* $85

Sandeman, Christopher. A WANDERER IN INCA LAND. NY: Charles Scribner's Sons, (1949). 1st ed. Fldg map. *KARMIOLE.* $45

SANDER'S COMPLETE LIST OF ORCHID HYBRIDS...TO JANUARY 1ST, 1946. St. Albans, (1947). 2 supplements of corrections. 1 pl. Buckram. *SUTTON.* $45

Sanders, Alvin H. (ed). THE STORY OF THE HEREFORDS. Chicago: Breeder's Gazette, 1914. 1st ed. Ex-lib. *DIAMOND.* $50

Sanders, Alvin H. AT THE SIGN OF THE STOCKYARD INN. Chicago: Breeder's Gazette, 1915. 1st ed. 32 plts. 3/4 morocco. Front hinge cracking, spine edge worn. Good+. *OREGON.* $55

Sanders, Alvin H. RED WHITE AND ROAN: STORIES RELATING TO THE SHORTHORN BREED. Chicago: American Shorthorn Breeders Assn, 1936. 1st ed. Orange cl, blue lettering. VF. *CONNOLLY & WADE.* $80

Sanders, Dori. CLOVER. Chapel Hill: Algonquin, (1990). 1st Amer ed. Signed. Fine in dj. *DORN.* $35

Sanders, F.C.S. CALIFORNIA AS A HEALTH RESORT. SF: Bolte & Braden Co, 1916. 1st ed. Minor cover wear, else VG. *PARMER.* $75

Sanders, J.H. HORSE-BREEDING. Chicago, 1893. About VG. *OCTOBER FARM.* $25

Sanders, J.H. THE BREEDS OF LIVESTOCK AND THE PRINCIPLES OF HEREDITY. Illus. Chicago: Sanders, 1887. 4to, 480pp. Good. *OCTOBER FARM.* $125

Sanders, T.W. POPULAR HARDY PERENNIALS....London, (c. 1928). Rev ed. 15 colored plts. Cl, some spotting on spine; dj, pieces missing. *SUTTON.* $27

Sanders, Wiley Britton (ed). NEGRO CHILD WELFARE IN NORTH CAROLINA: A ROSENWALD STUDY. Chapel Hill, 1933. 1st ed. Orig cl. VG. *McGOWAN.* $45

Sanderson, James Monroe. MY RECORD IN REBELDOM, AS WRITTEN BY FRIEND AND FOE...NY, 1865. 1st ed. Wrappers, rear wrap lacking, front wrap partially detached. Good. *McGOWAN.* $150

Sandford, John. RULES OF PREY. NY: Putnam, 1989. 1st ed, 1st bk. VF in dj. *ELSE FINE.* $25

Sandlin, Tim. SEX AND SUNSETS. NY: Henry Holt & Co., 1987. 1st ed, 1st bk. NF. *SMITH.* $30

Sando, Joe S. THE PUEBLO INDIANS. (SF): (Indian Historian Press), (1982). 2nd ed. Illus. VG in dj w/faint staining along bottom portion. *LOPEZ.* $45

Sandoz, Mari. CAPITAL CITY. Little, Brown & Co, 1939. 1st ed. Fine in dj. *AUTHORS OF THE WEST.* $50

Sandoz, Mari. HOSTILES AND FRIENDLIES: SELECTED SHORT WRITINGS. Lincoln: Univ of NE Press, 1959. 1st ed. Fine in Fine dj. *BOOK MARKET.* $50

Sandoz, Mari. OLD JULES COUNTRY. NY: Hastings House, 1965. 1st ed. VF in VG dj. *CONNOLLY & WADE.* $27.50

Sandoz, Mari. OLD JULES. Little, Brown, 1935. 1st issue, w/o cvr sketch. Fine. *AUTHORS OF THE WEST.* $35

Sandoz, Mari. SON OF THE GAMBLIN' MAN: THE YOUTH OF AN ARTIST. Clarkson N. Potter, (1960). 1st ed. Fine in dj. *AUTHORS OF THE WEST.* $30

Sandoz, Mari. THE BUFFALO HUNTERS. Hastings, 1954. 1st ed. Tape repaired dj. Adv Presentation Issue stated on extra bound-in leaf. Signed. VG in Good+ dj. *OREGON.* $95

Sandoz, Mari. THE BUFFALO HUNTERS. Hastings, 1954. 1st trade ed. Some color pencil underlining, chipped dj. *OREGON.* $15

Sandoz, Mari. THE BUFFALO HUNTERS. Hastings House, 1954. 1st ed. Fine in dj w/sunned spine. *STAHR.* $45

Sandoz, Mari. THE BUFFALO HUNTERS: THE STORY OF THE HIDE MEN. Hastings House, (1954). 1st issue, w/"Bismarck" misspelled and placed across the line in Minnesota on fep map. Signed. Fine, clean sl chipped dj. *AUTHORS OF THE WEST.* $150

Sandoz, Mari. THE CATTLEMEN: FROM THE RIO GRANDE ACROSS THE FAR MARIAS. Hastings, (1958). 1st ed. Fine in Good+ dj. *OREGON.* $35

Sandoz, Mari. THE CATTLEMEN: FROM THE RIO GRANDE ACROSS THE FAR MARIAS. NY: Hastings House, (1958). 1st ed. Adv presentation copy from the American Procession Series, signed. Pub's letter laid in. Fine in NF dj with short closed tear. *UNGER.* $175

Sandoz, Mari. THE CATTLEMEN: FROM THE RIO GRANDE ACROSS THE FAR MARIAS. NY: Hastings House, 1958. 1st ed, one of an advance presentation ed. Signed. Fine in dj. *ELSE FINE.* $150

Sandoz, Mari. WINTER THUNDER. Phila: Westminster, 1954. 1st ed. Fine, minor rub at dj spine head. *ELSE FINE.* $45

Sandoz, Mari. WINTER THUNDER. Phila: Westminster Press, (1954). 1st ed. Foxing to a few pages, particularly eps, else VG in VG dj w/foxing, small hole rear panel. *BETWEEN COVERS.* $35

Sandoz, Maurice. THE MAZE. Doubleday, 1945. Fine in dj. *MADLE.* $40

Sands, Ledyard. THE BIRD, THE GUN AND THE DOG. NY, 1939. 1st ed. VF. *BOND.* $55

Sands, Oliver Jackson. THE DEEP RUN HUNT CLUB...(Whittet & Shepperson), 1977. Signed, ltd ed of 750. Inscribed. VG. *BOOK BROKER.* $75

Sandstrom, Alan and Pamela. TRADITIONAL PAPERMAKING AND PAPER CULT FIGURES OF MEXICO. Norman: Univ of OK Press, (1986). 1st ed. 8 color plts. Dj. *SILVER.* $25

Sandstrom, Eve K. DEATH DOWN HOME. NY: Scribner, 1990. 1st ed, 1st bk. Review copy, signed. Pub's slip laid in. Fine in dj. *SILVER DOOR.* $35

Sandys, W. and S.A. Forster. THE HISTORY OF THE VIOLIN. London: J.R. Smith, 1864. 390pp. Color frontis. *CULLEN.* $80

Sanford, Herb. TOMMY AND JIMMY: THE DORSEY YEARS. New Rochelle: Arlington House, 1972. 1st ed. Fine in Fine dj. *BEASLEY.* $45

Sanford, L.C. et al. THE WATER-FOWL FAMILY. NY, 1903. 20 plts. Institutional bkpl; call numbers on spine. *SUTTON.* $45

Sanford, Mollie Dorsey. MOLLIE: THE JOURNAL OF... IN NEBRASKA AND COLORADO TERRITORIES 1857-1866. (Omaha): Univ of NE Press, 1959. 1st ed. Fine in dj. *SCHOYER'S.* $25

Sanford, Paul. SIOUX ARROWS AND BULLETS. San Antonio, (1969). 1st ed. Dj. Fine. *PRATT.* $22.50

Sanford, Trent Elwood. THE STORY OF ARCHITECTURE IN MEXICO. NY: W.W. Norton, (1947). 64 plts. Good in tattered dj. *ARCHAEOLOGIA.* $45

Sanford, Trent. THE STORY OF ARCHITECTURE IN MEXICO. NY: Norton, (1947). 1st ed. Chipped dj. *SILVER.* $40

Sanger, William. THE HISTORY OF PROSTITUTION. NY, 1939. Facs of 1859 ed. *FYE.* $40

Sansom, Arthur. CHLOROFORM, ITS ACTION AND AD-MINISTRATION. Phila, (1865). 1st Amer ed. *FYE.* $200

Sansom, Joseph. TRAVELS IN LOWER CANADA, WITH THE AUTHOR'S RECOLLECTIONS....London: Sir Richard Phillips and Co, 1820. 2nd ed. Wear to binding. 3/4 leather, marbled paper. Eps renewed. Plt sl foxed, else VG. *PARMER.* $225

SANTA BARBARA: A GUIDE. NY, 1941. American Guide Series. WPA guide. 1st ed. Torn dj. *SCHOYER'S.* $40

SANTA BARBARA: A GUIDE. NY: Hastings House, 1941. 1st ed American Guide series. WPA guide. VF in Good+ dj. *CONNOLLY & WADE.* $45

Santa Maria, Father Vicente. THE FIRST SPANISH ENTRY INTO SAN FRANCISCO BAY 1775: THE ORIGINAL NARRA-TIVE....John Galvin (ed). SF: Howell, 1971. 1st ed. Ltd to 5000. Fldg map. Fine in About Fine dj. *CONNOLLY & WADE.* $75

Santee, Ross. APACHE LAND. Scribner, 1947. 1st ed. Owner name and address, o/w VG in Good+ dj. *OREGON.* $45

Santee, Ross. COWBOY. NY: Cosmopolitan, 1928. 1st ed. VG. *CONNOLLY & WADE.* $65

Santee, Ross. LOST PONY TRACKS. NY, 1953. Dj, some frayed. *HEINOLDT.* $25

Santee, Ross. THE POOCH. Cosmopolitan Bk Corporation, 1931. 1st ed. VG, dj panels tipped in, bkpl. *AUTHORS OF THE WEST.* $25

Santee, Ross. THE POOCH. NY: Cosmopolitan, 1931. 1st ed. Dampstain to lower spine corner of front cover. Good+ in Good+ dj. *OREGON.* $35

Santini, Piero. THE FOREWORD IMPULSE. NY: Huntington, 1936. #259/950. VG. *OCTOBER FARM.* $65

Santmyer, Helen Hooven. ...AND LADIES OF THE CLUB. NY: Putnam (1984). Adv review copy of 1st Putnam ed. NF in wraps. *DORN.* $30

Santmyer, Helen Hoover. OHIO TOWN. n.p.: Ohio State Univ Press, (1962). 1st ed. Sm, lt erasure title pg, else Fine in dj. *CAPTAIN'S BOOK-SHELF.* $60

Sappington, John. THE THEORY AND TREATMENT OF FEVERS. Arrow Rock, MO, 1844. 1st ed. Full lea, 216pp. Head of spine chipped. *FYE.* $250

Sargeant, Winthrop. JAZZ, HOT AND HYBRID. NY: Dutton, 1946. New and enl ed. Fine but for sunned spots and bkpl, in used dj. *BEAS-LEY.* $35

Sargent, F.W. ON BANDAGING AND OTHER OPERATIONS OF MINOR SURGERY. Phila, 1867. 3rd ed. 187 woodcut illus. 383pp. *FYE.* $350

Sargent, F.W. ON BANDAGING, AND OTHER OPERATIONS OF MINOR SURGERY. Phila, 1848. 1st ed. 128 Fine woodcut illus. Full leather, 379pp. Scattered foxing, o/w VF. Scarce. *FYE.* $300

Sargent, F.W. ON BANDAGING AND OTHER OPERATIONS OF MINOR SURGERY. Phila: Blanchard & Lea, 1862. 1st ed thus. New ed. Full calf, outer hinges split but still holding. Good. *ARTIS.* $35

Sargent, Shirley. RANGER IN SKIRTS. Nashville: Abingdon Press, (1966). Brn stamped cl in dj, 3 short tears. Signed. *DAWSON'S.* $30

Saroyan, William. A TOOTH AND MY FATHER. NY: Doubleday, (1974). 1st ed. NF in VG dj. *ACADEMIC LIBRARY.* $25

Saroyan, William. THE ADVENTURES OF WESLEY JACKSON. Harcourt, Brace, (1946). 1st ed. Fine, nice chipped dj. *AUTHORS OF THE WEST.* $30

Saroyan, William. THE ASSYRIAN AND OTHER STORIES. Harcourt Brace, (1950). 1st ed. Names, else Fine, clean chipped dj. *AUTHORS OF THE WEST.* $25

Saroyan, William. THE BEAUTIFUL PEOPLE. Harcourt, Brace, (1941). 1st ed. Bkpl, else Fine, nice frayed dj. *AUTHORS OF THE WEST.* $30

Saroyan, William. THE BICYCLE RIDER IN BEVERLY HILLS. Charles Scribner's Sons, 1952. 1st ed. Fine, nice chipped dj. *AUTHORS OF THE WEST.* $25

Saroyan, William. THE HUMAN COMEDY. Illus Don Freeman. NY: Harcourt, (1943). 1st ed (stated), 1st novel. NF (embossed owner sig on 1st 2 pgs) in lightly used dj (few small tears). *CAPTAIN'S BOOKSHELF.* $75

Saroyan, William. THE TIME OF YOUR LIFE. Harcourt, Brace, (1939). 1st ed. VG+. *AUTHORS OF THE WEST.* $30

Saroyan, William. THE WILLIAM SAROYAN READER. George Braziller, Inc, 1958. 1st ed. Boards. Fine in sl chipped dj. *AUTHORS OF THE WEST.* $25

Sarton, May. A PRIVATE MYTHOLOGY. NY: Norton, (1966). 1st ed. Fine in sl rippled, corner torn dj. SECOND LIFE. $45

Sarton, May. A RECKONING. NY: Norton, (1978). 1st ed. Inscribed. NF in dj. LOPEZ. $65

Sarton, May. CRUCIAL CONVERSATIONS. NY: Norton, (1975). 1st ed. Inscribed. NF in dj. LOPEZ. $65

Sarton, May. FAITHFUL ARE THE WOUNDS. NY: Rinehart, (1955). Later prtg. Customs sticker on fep, o/w VG in dj. Inscribed. LOPEZ. $45

Sarton, May. I KNEW A PHOENIX. Rinehart, 1959. 1st ed. Fine in dj. Signed, inscribed. STAHR. $45

Sarton, May. PLANT DREAMING DEEP. NY: Norton, (1968). 1st ed. Price-clipped dj, VG. SCHOYER'S. $25

Sarton, May. THE MAGNIFICENT SPINSTER. NY: Norton, (1985). 1st ed. Fine in dj. SECOND LIFE. $25

Sarton, May. THE WRITING OF A POEM. Claremont: Scripps College, 1957. Wraps, close to Fine. Issued as Scripps College Bulletin XXXI:2 (February 1957). BEASLEY. $65

Sartre, Jean-Paul. NAUSEA. Lloyd Alexander (trans). (Norfolk, CT): New Directions, (1949). Fine in VG dj (few small edge chips). 1st Amer ed. CHAPEL HILL. $60

Sartre, Jean-Paul. THE WALL AND OTHER STORIES. Norfolk: New Directions, (1948). 1st Amer ed. Publisher's review slip inserted. Fine. MUELLER. $50

Sass, H.R. and A.R. Smith. ADVENTURES IN GREEN PLACES. NY, 1935. Illus. Fine. MIKESH. $20

Sassoon, Philip. THIRD ROUTE. GC. NY: Doubleday, Doran, 1929. 1st Amer ed. Dj chipped, spine-darkened. SCHOYER'S. $35

Sassoon, Siegfried. MEMOIRS OF A FOX-HUNTING MAN. NY: Coward McCann. N.d. (circa 1929). 7 plts, each w/tissue guard. White cl. Dj. In pub's slipcase. KARMIOLE. $75

Sassoon, Siegfried. NATIVITY. London: Faber & Faber. Purple paper wraps. Fine. HELLER. $40

Sassoon, Siegfried. THE HEART'S JOURNEY. NY/London: Crosby Gaige/Heinemann, 1927. 1/590, of 599 total. Signed. VG. LOPEZ. $75

Sassoon, Siegfried. TO MY MOTHER. London: Faber and Gwyer, n.d. NF w/sunning, wraps. BEASLEY. $25

Sassoon, Siegfried. TO THE RED ROSE. London: Faber and Faber, n.d. Wraps, Fine. BEASLEY. $25

Sato, Shozo. ART OF ARRANGING FLOWERS. NY: Abrams, n.d. (1965). 366pp. Glassine wrapper. Institutional ownership stamps. Many tipped-on color photos. SCHOYER'S. $75

Satterfield, Archie. ALASKA BUSH PILOTS IN THE FLOAT COUNTRY. Seattle: Superior, 1969. 1st ed. VG in worn dj. PARMER. $35

Satterlee, Marion P. A DETAILED ACCOUNT OF THE MASSACRE BY THE DETROIT INDIANS OF MINNESOTA IN 1862. Minneapolis: priv ptd, n.d. (1923). 1st ed. New wrappers. Damp mark at rear, not beyond 10 pp, not affecting text. Photo attached to wrapper front. CONNOLLY & WADE. $85

Satterthwait, Walter. AT EASE WITH THE DEAD. NY: St. Martin's, (1990). 1st ed. Fine in Fine dj. UNGER. $65

Satterthwait, Walter. WALL OF GLASS. NY: St. Martin's, (1987). 1st ed. Fine in Fine dj. UNGER. $125

Satterthwait, Walter. WALL OF GLASS. St. Martin's, 1987. 1st ed. Fine in dj. VF but for very small rubbed spot at flyleaf fold. STAHR. $60

Saucier, Ted. BOTTOMS UP. NY: Greystone, (1951). Pict cl. Fine. ARTIS. $19.50

Saulmon, Frederick. A PRACTICAL ESSAY ON STRICTURE OF THE RECTUM. London, 1833. 1/4 leather, 317pp. FYE. $125

Saum, Lewis. THE FUR TRADER AND THE INDIAN. Seattle: Univ of WA, (1965). 1st ed. Frontis. VF in VF dj. OREGON. $40

Saunders, C.F. WESTERN WILD FLOWERS AND THEIR STORIES. GC, 1933. Cl, worn dj. Signed inscrip tipped on. SUTTON. $50

Saunders, Charles Francis. THE INDIANS OF THE TERRACED HOUSES. NY, 1912. 1st ed. Cl cvrs sl stained, shelfworn. Inner hinges repaired. Little soiling few pp, o/w VG. DIAMOND. $50

Saunders, Charles Francis. THE SOUTHERN SIERRAS OF CALIFORNIA. Boston: Houghton Mifflin, 1923. 1st ed. 32 full-pg photo illus. Gold-stamped pict cl. DAWSON'S. $50

Saunders, Edward. THE HYMENOPTERA ACULEATA OF THE BRITISH ISLANDS. London, 1896. viii, 391 pp. Contemp half morocco w/marbled eps, aeg. Spine darkened, scuffed. SUTTON. $585

Saunders, J.B. de C.M. and C.D. O'Malley. THE ILLUSTRATIONS FROM THE WORKS OF ANDREAS VESALIUS OF BRUSSELS. Cleveland, 1950. 1st ed. Dj. 96 full-page plts. FYE. $100

Saunders, Lyle. A GUIDE TO MATERIALS BEARING ON CULTURAL RELATIONS IN NEW MEXICO. Albuquerque, NM: Univ of NM Press, 1944. 1st ed. Lib. bkpl and spine number, o/w VG. GIBBS. $75

Saunders, Lyle. A GUIDE TO MATERIALS BEARING ON CULTURAL RELATIONS IN NEW MEXICO. Albuquerque: Univ of NM Press, 1944. 1st ed. Fine in Fine dj. BOOK MARKET. $150

Saunders, William. A TREATISE ON THE STRUCTURE, ECONOMY, AND DISEASES OF THE LIVER, TOGETHER WITH AN INQUIRY INTO THE PROPERTIES AND COMPONENT PARTS OF THE BILE AND BILIARY CONCRETIONS. London, 1793. 1st ed. 232pp. Recent 1/4 leather and marbled boards. Worm hole affecting margin of 25 leaves, o/w Fine. FYE. $350

Savage, Edward N. A CHRONOLOGICAL HISTORY OF THE BOSTON WATCH AND POLICE, FROM 1631-1865. 2nd ed, revised. Boston: By the Author. 1865. 408pp. Frontis. Orig brn textured cl, gilt. KARMIOLE. $75

Savage, Elizabeth. A GOOD CONFESSION. Boston: Little Brown, (1975). Inscribed. NF in dj. LOPEZ. $30

Savage, James Woodruff. HISTORY OF THE CITY OF OMAHA, NEBRASKA...AND SOUTH OMAHA. NY & Chicago: Munsell & Co, 1894. xvi, 699pp. Frontis, 24 plts, 53 ports, index. Recased, retaining orig cl gilt title boards & leather corners, new backstrip, aeg. Clean. Howes S124. BOHLING. $200

Savage, James. A GENEALOGICAL DICTIONARY OF THE FIRST SETTLERS OF NEW ENGLAND. Boston, 1860-1862. 1st ed. 4 vols. (16),516; (4),599; (4),664; (6),714pp. Contemp half morocco, raised bands on spine, spines flecking, bkpls, emb lib stamps, hinges mended. Howes S123. Also incl "Genealogical notes and errata to Savage.. by C. H. Dall (Lowell, MA, n.d. 8pp). GINSBERG. $150

Savage, Richard Henry. THE LITTLE LADY OF LAGUNITAS. NY: American News Co, 1892. 1st ed. 482pp. Pgs fragile and browning, as usual. Chip at edge of intro pg, not affecting text. VG. CONNOLLY & WADE. $75

Savage, William W., Jr. COWBOY LIFE: RECONSTRUCTING AN AMERICAN MYTH. Univ of OK Press, (1975). 1st ed. Fine, Nice sl chipped dj. AUTHORS OF THE WEST. $25

Savage, William W., Jr. THE COWBOY HERO. Univ of OK Press, (1979). 1st ed. Fine in dj. AUTHORS OF THE WEST. $25

Savage-Landor, A. Henry. ACROSS UNKNOWN SOUTH AMERICA. London: Hodder and Stoughton, 1913. 2 vols. Some edgewear. Covers bright. Blue cl w/gilt spine, cover titles; gilt cover decs. 2 maps, 7 colored plts (lacking plt at pg 238 of vol I). VG+. PARMER. $165

Savage-Landor, A. Henry. EVERYWHERE THE MEMOIRS OF AN EXPLORER. NY: Stokes, 1924. 1st US ed. 2 vols. Bkpl. Fine. *AARD*. $85

Savory, T.H. THE ARACHNIDA. London, 1935. 8 plts. *SUTTON*. $65

Savoy, Gene. ON THE TRAIL OF THE FEATHERED SERPENT. Indianapolis: Bobbs-Merrill, 1974. 1st prtg. NF in VG dj. *PARMER*. $25

Sawtell, Clement Cleveland. CAPTAIN NASH DECOST AND THE LIVERPOOL PACKETS. Mystic: The Marine Hist Assoc, Inc., 1955. Orig grn ptd wraps. Cvr faded; remnants of bkpl, else VG. *PARMER*. $20

Sawyer, Alan. ANCIENT PERUVIAN CERAMICS. NY: MMA, (1966). 1st ed, ltd. Good. *SILVER*. $30

Sawyer, Eugene T. THE LIFE AND CAREER OF TIBURCIO VASQUEZ. Oakland: (Grabhorn), 1944. 1st ptg. Ltd to 500. Fine. *VARNER*. $75

Saxe, John G(odfrey). THE MONKEY KING. Boston: Ticknor & Field, 1860. 1st ed. (182)pp. 1st state of binding w/o gilt on cover, issued w/o the adv in some copies. Brown cl, VG. BAL 17291. *SECOND LIFE*. $45

Saxon, A.H. ENTER FOOT AND HORSE. New Haven: Yale Univ Press, 1968. 1st ed. Fine in dj. *DRAMATIS PERSONAE*. $40

Saxon, Lyle et al. GUMBO YA-YA: A COLLECTION OF LOUISIANA FOLK TALES. HMCO/Louisiana Writers Project, 1945. Fine in G+ dj. *MAD DOG*. $30

Saxton, et al. FESSENDEN, AMERICAN KITCHEN GARDEN, 1854. RICHARDSON, THE HOG, ORIGIN & VARIETIES, 1855. MILBURN, M. THE COW, 1856. STEVENS, PESTS OF THE FARM, 1855. NY: Saxton, 1856. 428pp. 3/4 leather, spine worn. Contents VG. *AMERICAN BOTANIST*. $100

Say, Thomas. THE COMPLETE WRITINGS OF THOMAS SAY ON THE ENTOMOLOGY OF NORTH AMERICA. Ed J.L. Le Conte. Memoir of author by G. Ord. NY, 1859. 2 vols. Engr frontis, 54 hand-colored plts. 8vo, pp. xxiv, 412; iv, 814. Half morocco (rubbed & with some scuffing, rear inner hinge of Vol. 1 separated, slight marginal dampstaining at bottom of text pp. in Vol. 1, stickers removed from front pastedowns; plts very bright and clean except for 3 w/minor smudges). *SUTTON*. $1,500

Sayers, Dorothy L. (ed). GREAT SHORT STORIES OF DETECTION, MYSTERY AND HORROR. London: Victor Gollancz, 1928. 1st ed. Fine in dj, sl faded spine. *MORDIDA*. $350

Sayers, Dorothy L. (ed). THE OMNIBUS OF CRIME. Payson & Clark, 1929. 2nd prtg. VG with cvr wear, abrasion to two corners. *BEBBAH*. $15

Sayers, Dorothy L. (ed). THE OMNIBUS OF CRIME. Payson and Clark, 1929. 1st. NF. *STAHR*. $20

Sayers, Dorothy L. and St. Clare Byrne. BUSMAN'S HONEYMOON. London: Gollancz, 1937. 1st ed. Grey wrappers, some soiling to spine, generally VG. *JUVELIS*. $550

Sayers, Dorothy L. BUSMAN'S HONEYMOON. NY: Harcourt Brace, 1937. 1st Amer ed. Fine in dj. *MORDIDA*. $250

Sayers, Dorothy L. IN THE TEETH OF THE EVIDENCE AND OTHER STORIES. NY, 1940. 1st ed. Fine in price-clipped dj (little edge rubbed). *POLYANTHOS*. $35

Sayers, Dorothy L. IN THE TEETH OF THE EVIDENCE. London: Gollancz, 1939. 1st ed. NF, no dj. *ELSE FINE*. $100

Sayers, Dorothy L. STRONG POISON. NY: Brewer & Warren, (1930). 1st US ed. Attractive, NF in pict cl lacking dj. *CAPTAIN'S BOOKSHELF*. $100

Sayers, Dorothy L. THE NINE TAILORS. NY: Harcourt, Brace and Company, (1934). 1st Amer ed. Spine cocked, somewhat dimmed. Dj w/several internal tape repairs. *JUVELIS*. $175

Sayers, Edward. THE AMERICAN FLOWER GARDEN COMPANION. Boston: Weeks, Jordan, 1839. 2nd ed. 175pp. VG w/foxing. *SECOND LIFE*. $125

Sayles, John. LOS GUSANOS. (NY): Harper Collins, (1991). Signed. Fine in dj. *LOPEZ*. $50

Sayles, John. PRIDE OF THE BIMBOS. Boston: LB, (1975). 1st ed. NF in NF dj. *LOPEZ*. $150

Sayles, John. PRIDE OF THE BIMBOS. Little, Brown, 1975. Ex libris. 1st ed. VG in a dj (sunned spine; sm chip, closed tear rear panel). Bk has tape on boards and pocket removed from the rfep. *STAHR*. $45

Sayles, Ted & Mary Stevens. THROW STONE, THE FIRST AMERICAN BOY. Reilly & Lee, 1960. 1st ed. 142pp. Illus by Barton Wright. VG in dj w/chips and pen mark, trimmed at top edge. *BEBBAH*. $25

Saylor, Henry H. ARCHITECTURAL STYLES FOR COUNTRY HOUSES. NY: McBride, Nast & Co., 1912. 1st ed. Owner sig, bkpl. *CAPTAIN'S BOOKSHELF*. $75

Scammon, Charles M. THE MARINE MAMMALS OF THE NORTH-WESTERN COAST OF NORTH AMERICA...WITH AN ACCOUNT OF THE AMERICAN WHALE-FISHERY. Riverside, CA, (1969). (Facs of orig ed of 1874, w/new intro.). 3 charts on 2 sheets in pocket. *LEFKOWICZ*. $100

Scarborough, Dorothy. FROM A SOUTHERN PORCH. G.P. Putnam, 1919 1st ed. Dec cvr. VG+, lt foxing throughout. *AUTHORS OF THE WEST*. $50

Scarborough, Elizabeth Ann. THE HEALER'S WAR. NY: Doubleday, (1988). Uncorrected proof. 1st state of proof, w/pgs shot from ms rather than typeset. *LOPEZ*. $200

Scarpa, Antonio. A TREATISE ON HERNIA. Edinburgh, 1814. 1st Eng trans. 548pp. 14 Fine engrvd plts. 1/2 leather, skillfully rebacked preserving orig marbled boards. VF. Scarce. *FYE*. $1,250

Scearce, Stanley. NORTHERN LIGHTS TO FIELDS OF GOLD. Caldwell, 1939. 1st ed. Ex-lib w/no external marks and no rear pocket. Good. *ARTIS*. $17.50

Scearce, Stanley. NORTHERN LIGHTS TO FIELDS OF GOLD. Caldwell: Caxton Printers, 1939. VG in chipped dj. *PARMER*. $70

Scearce, Stanley. NORTHERN LIGHTS TO THE FIELDS OF GOLD. Caldwell: Caxton, 1943. 2nd prtg. VG in VG- dj. *BLUE DRAGON*. $30

Schacht, Al. CLOWNING THROUGH BASEBALL. NY: A. S. Barnes & Co, 1941. VG. *BURCHAM*. $20

Schacht, Al. MY OWN PARTICULAR SCREWBALL. Doubleday, 1955. Ed Keyes (ed). Inscribed and dated by Schacht. VG+ in VG dj. *PLAPINGER*. $55

Schack, William. AND HE SAT AMONG THE ASHES. NY: American Artists Group, (1939). 1st ed. Dj. *KARMIOLE*. $30

Schaefer, Jack. THE PIONEERS. Houghton Mifflin, 1954. 1st ed. Fine, clean chipped dj. *AUTHORS OF THE WEST*. $50

Schaeffer, Luther M. SKETCHES OF TRAVELS IN SOUTH AMERICA, MEXICO AND CALIFORNIA. NY: James Egbert, 1860. Emb boards, lt wear. 247pp. VG. *CULLEN*. $100

Schaeffer, Susan Fromberg. ANYA. NY: Macmillan, (1974). 1st ed. Signed. VG in dj. *LOPEZ*. $25

Schaeffer, Susan Fromberg. BUFFALO AFTERNOON. NY: Knopf, 1989. 1st ed. Signed. Fine in NF dj. *AKA*. $35

Schaff, Philip. AMERICA. A Sketch of the Political, Social and Religious Character of the United States....Trans from the German. NY: C. Scribner. 1855. 1st Amer ed. xxiv, 292,(8)pp. Orig. black cloth, gilt spine; small chip bottom of spine, tear to ffep. *KARMIOLE*. $45

Schaff, Philip. THROUGH BIBLE LANDS. NY, (1878). 413 pp. 1st ed. *O'NEILL*. $65

Schaldach, William J. COVERTS & CASTS. NY: A.S. Barnes & Co, 1943. Stated 1st prtg. VG. *BACKMAN*. $40

Schaller, George B. GOLDEN SHADOWS, FLYING HOOVES. NY: Knopf, 1973. 1st ed. Ownership stamp of US Navy bottom edge of pages, o/w NF in price-clipped dj. *LOPEZ*. $55

Schaller, George B. THE YEAR OF THE GORILLA. (Chicago): Univ of Chicago Press, (1964). 1st ed. Fine in NF dj. *LOPEZ*. $50

Schama, Simon. DEAD CERTAINTIES. Knopf, 1991. 1st ed. VF in dj. Signed. *STAHR*. $35

Schappes, Morris (ed). DOCUMENTARY HISTORY OF JEWS IN THE U. S. 1654-1875. Presentation copy. NY, 1950. 1st ed. *HEINOLDT*. $25

Scharf, J. Thomas. CHRONICLES OF BALTIMORE BEING A COMPLETE HISTORY OF "BALTIMORE TOWN" AND BALTIMORE CITY. Baltimore, 1874, 1st ed. 8, 756pp. Hinges reinforced, wear top & bottom of spine. *HEINOLDT*. $45

Scharff, R.F. EUROPEAN ANIMALS: THEIR GEOLOGICAL HISTORY AND GEOGRAPHICAL DISTRIBUTION. London, 1907. Frontis. Gilt stamped cl. Institutional bkpl; # sticker on spine. *SUTTON*. $40

Schele, Linda & Mary Ellen Miller. THE BLOOD OF KINGS. Fort Worth: Kimball Art Museum, (1986). 1st ed rptd w/corrections. 123 color plts. Signed by Miller. Good in dj. *SILVER*. $60

Schell, Jonathan. THE VILLAGE OF BEN SUC. NY: Knopf, 1968. 1st ed. Price clipped, 2" closed, tape mended tear. *AKA*. $50

Schenck, John S. HISTORY OF IONIA AND MONTCALM COUNTIES, MICHIGAN. Phila: D.W. Ensign, 1881. 2 color maps, 94 plts and ports (4 double). Moderate wear, foot of spine chipped, still VG. *BOHLING*. $150

Schenk, Peter A. THE GARDENER'S TEXT BOOK. NY: Orange Judd, 1865?. 306pp. Cloth worn, contents w/tape repair to bottom corner. Orig pub by Jewett in 1851. Scarce. *AMERICAN BOTANIST*. $75

Schiff, Stuart (ed). WHISPERS II. Doubleday, 1979. 1st ed. Fine in dj. Signed. *MADLE*. $25

Schillings, C.G. FLASHLIGHTS IN THE JUNGLE. NY: Doubleday, Page, 1905. Near VG ex-lib. *WORLDWIDE*. $35

Schillings, C.G. FLASHLIGHTS IN THE JUNGLE. NY, 1906. NF. *POLYANTHOS*. $100

Schillings, C.G. IN WILDEST AFRICA. Frederick Whyte (trans). NY: Harper, 1907. 1st ed. Bkpl. Sl rubbed, o/w VG. *WORLDWIDE*. $25

Schillings, C.G. WITH FLASH-LIGHT AND RIFLE—PHOTOGRAPHING BY FLASH-LIGHT. NY: Harper & Brothers, 1905. 1st ed. Lion photo pasted down front cvr. Wear extremes. Front and back internal hinges starting, else VG. *GREAT EPIC*. $45

Schlebecker, John T. CATTLE RAISING ON THE PLAINS 1900-1961. Univ of NE, 1963. 1st. ed. Fine in Fine dj. *VARNER*. $50

Schlegel, H. and Wolverhorst, J.A. Verster. THE WORLD OF FALCONRY. NY, Paris, Lausanne: The Vendome Press, 1979. 1st ed. NF in dj. *OLD LONDON*. $85

Schleiden, Jacob Mathias. PRINCIPLES OF SCIENTIFIC BOTANY. London: Ptd for Longman et al, 1849. 1st Eng ed. 616pp, 6 plts. Blindstamped gilt grn cl, worn. Ex-lib, spine ends torn, ink on fore-edge, sl marginal waterstaining rear pp else contents VG. *SMITHFIELD*. $113

Schley, Frank. AMERICAN PARTRIDGE AND PHEASANT SHOOTING. Frederick, MO: Baughman Bros., 1877. 1st ed. Good. *BLUE MOUNTAIN*. $125

Schley, Winfield S. REPORT OF, COMMANDING GREELY RELIEF EXPEDITION OF 1884. Washington, 1887. 1st ed. 75pp + numerous full-page engr, photos, etc. 4 full-pg maps in back. 4to. New backstrip. Orig leather label chipped. *ARTIS*. $100

Schley, Winfield S. REPORT OF WINFIELD S. SCHLEY...GREELY RELIEF EXPEDITION OF 1884. Wash: GPO, 1887. 1st ed. 32 plts, 3 maps. Cl worn, soiled; some internal foxing. *PARMER*. $95

Schliemann, Heinrich. ILIOS: THE CITY AND COUNTRY OF THE TROJANS. London: John Murray, 1880. 1st Eng ed. Frontis, 6 fldg plans, 1 fldg map. Orig blue pict cl, teg. Signature at flyleaf, o/w Fine. *ARCHAEOLOGIA*. $450

Schliemann, Henry. MYCENAE; A NARRATIVE OF RESEARCHES AND DISCOVERIES AT MYCENAE AND TIRYNS. London: John Murray, 1878. 1st Eng ed. 549 figs, 25 plts (4 color), 8 plans. Orig gilt pict cl, teg. Minor shelfwear, interior Fine. Scarce in this condition. *ARCHAEOLOGIA*. $350

Schlissel, Lillian, Vicki L. Ruiz and Janice Monk. WESTERN WOMEN, THEIR LAND, THEIR LIFE. Albuquerque, (1988). 1st ed. 354pp. Fine in dj. *PRATT*. $27.50

Schmidt, Rudolph. PAIN, ITS CAUSATION AND DIAGNOSTIC SIGNIFICANCE IN INTERNAL DISEASES. London, 1908. 1st Eng trans. *FYE*. $50

Schmitt, Jo Ann. FIGHTING EDITORS. Naylor, (1958). 1st ed. VF in VF dj. *OREGON*. $25

Schmitt, Martin F. and Dee Brown. FIGHTING INDIANS OF THE WEST. NY: Scribner's, 1948. 1st ed. 272 photos. NF in dj. *LAURIE*. $60

Schmitt, Martin F. and Dee Brown. THE SETTLERS' WEST. NY: Scribner's, c1955. Dj. *HUDSON*. $35

Schmitz, James. A NICE DAY FOR SCREAMING. Chilton, 1965. 1st ed. NF in sl wrinkled dj. *MADLE*. $250

Schmitz, James. THE WITCHES OF KARRES. Chilton, 1968. Fine in dj. *MADLE*. $35

Schmitz, Joseph William. THUS THEY LIVED. SOCIAL LIFE IN THE REPUBLIC OF TEXAS. San Antonio: The Naylor Co, 1936. Fine in dj. *GIBBS*. $55

Schneider, Isadore. THE TEMPTATION OF ANTHONY AND OTHER POEMS. NY: Boni and Liveright, 1928. 1st ed. Lightly worn w/small wrinkle in dulled spine, in very lightly used dj w/few small chips. *BEASLEY*. $100

Schoenberger, Dale T. THE GUNFIGHTERS. Caxton, 1971. 1st ptg. Fine in sl rubbed dj. *VARNER*. $35

Schofield, John M. FORTY SIX YEARS IN THE ARMY. NY: Century, 1897. (16),577pp. 1st ed. Orig cl. *GINSBERG*. $150

Scholefield, E.O.S. and R.E. Gosnell. A HISTORY OF BRITISH COLUMBIA. PART I and PART II. Vancouver and Victoria, BC: British Columbia Hist Assoc, 1913. Ltd ed of 350, signed by Gosnell. 210,226,vipp. Orig full suede leather binding. VG. *WEBER*. $350

Scholes, William Arthur. FOURTEEN MEN. Melbourne and London: F.W. Cheshire, c. 1949. Dj trimmed, tipped in on rfep, wear. *PARMER*. $20

Scholl, William. THE HUMAN FOOT: ANATOMY, DEFORMITIES AND TREATMENT. Chicago, 1920. 271 illus. *FYE*. $75

Scholz, Friderich. SLEEP AND DREAMS WITH THE ANALOGY OF INSANITY TO SLEEP AND DREAMS BY MILO JEWETT. NY, 1893. 1st ed. *FYE*. $50

Scholz, Janos (ed). BAROQUE AND ROMANTIC STAGE DESIGN. NY: A Bittner Art Book, Beechurst Press, (1955). New ed. Dj. *KARMIOLE*. $50

Schoolcraft, Henry. A VIEW OF THE LEAD MINES OF MISSOURI: INCLUDING SOME OBSERVATIONS...OF MISSOURI AND ARKANSAW AND OTHER SECTIONS....NY, 1819. 1st ed. 299pp. 3 plts. Full calf, leather label on spine, top of backstrip expertly mended. Howes S194. *GINSBERG*. $650

Schoolcraft, Henry. INFORMATION, RESPECTING THE HISTORY, CONDITION AND PROSPECTS OF THE INDIAN TRIBES OF THE UNITED STATES: COLLECTED AND PREPARED....Part 1. Phila: Lippincott, Grambo & Co, 1853. 76 full-pg litho plts (complete). Bound in orig pub's cl, blind and gilt stamped, skillfully rebacked and restored. VG. *LAURIE.* $500

Schoolcraft, Henry. INQUIRIES RESPECTING THE HISTORY, PRESENT CONDITION, AND FUTURE PROSPECTS OF THE INDIAN TRIBES OF THE UNITED STATES. N.p. (Washington), n.d. (1847). 1st ed. ii,55pp. Orig ptd wraps chipped, detached; ink stain in margin (not affecting text) of last few pp. Howes S184. *OREGON.* $650

Schoolcraft, Henry. NARRATIVE OF AN EXPEDITION THROUGH THE UPPER MISSISSIPPI TO ITASCA LAKE...THROUGH ST. CROIX AND BURNTWOOD (BROULE) RIVERS; IN 1832. Harpers, 1834. 1st ed. 308pp, 5 maps, 2 fldg. Errata. Ex-lib, no markings except for sm worn, faded paper spine label, remnants of label. Lacks rear eps. Dampspot lower edge 1st few leaves. Internally VG. Howes S187. *OREGON.* $400

Schoonover, T.J. THE LIFE AND TIMES OF GEN. JOHN A. SUTTER. Sacramento: Bullock-Carpenter Ptg Co, 1907. 2nd ed. Black stamped cl, top tips bumped. *DAWSON'S.* $30

Schorger, A.W. THE PASSENGER PIGEON, ITS NATURAL HISTORY AND EXTINCTION. Madison, 1955. Some cvr spotting; inch slit to outer hinge. *SUTTON.* $57

Schorr, Mark. ACE OF DIAMONDS. NY: St. Martin's, 1984. 1st ed. Signed. Fine in dj. *SILVER DOOR.* $35

Schouten, J. THE ROD AND SERPENT OF ASKLEPIOS. Amsterdam, 1967. 1st Eng trans. Dj. *FYE.* $90

Schreiber, Hermann and Georg. VANISHED CITIES. Richard and Clara Winston (trans). NY: Knopf, 1957. 1st ed. Ex-lib. Dj. Good. *WORLDWIDE.* $16

Schreiber, Ron (ed). 31 NEW AMERICAN POETS. (NY: Hill & Wang, 1969). 1st ed. Fine in dj. *CAPTAIN'S BOOKSHELF.* $50

Schreiner, Olive. STORY OF AN AFRICAN FARM. LEC, 1961. One of 1500. Illus and signed by Paul Hogarth. X-lib, but marked only with bookplate ffep verso. *SCHOYER'S.* $65

Schreiner, Olive. UNDINE. NY: Harper, 1928. 1st Amer ed. Dj flaws. Fine. *MUELLER.* $25

Schreiner, Samuel A., Jr. THE TRIALS OF MRS. LINCOLN. NY, (1987). 1st ed. 333pp. Fine in dj. *PRATT.* $20

Schrenck-Notzing, A. von. THERAPEUTIC SUGGESTION IN PSYCHOPATHIA SEXUAL (PATHOLOGICAL MANIFESTATIONS OF THE SEXUAL SENSE), WITH ESPECIAL REFERENCE TO CONTRARY SEXUAL INSTINCT. Phila, 1898. 1st Eng trans. Ex-lib. *FYE.* $75

Schriber, Fritz. THE COMPLETE WAGON AND CARRIAGE PAINTER. NY: M.T. Richardson, 1885. 182pp. Illus. Orig pict cl. VG. *OREGON.* $60

Schroeder van der Kolk, J.L.C. ON THE MINUTE STRUCTURE AND FUNCTIONS OF THE SPINAL CORD AND MEDULLA OBLONGATA, AND ON THE PROXIMATE CAUSE AND RATIONAL TREATMENT OF EPILEPSY. London, 1859. 1st Eng trans. *FYE.* $75

Schuckers, J.W. THE LIFE AND PUBLIC SERVICES OF SALMON PORTLAND CHASE. NY, 1874. 1st ed. 659pp & ads. A little cover wear, o/w VG+. *PRATT.* $45

Schulberg, Budd. THE HARDER THEY FALL. NY: Random House, 1947. 1st ed. Fine in sl worn dj. *ELSE FINE.* $50

Schulberg, Budd. THE HARDER THEY FALL. NY: Random House, (1947). 1st ed. Dj. Fine. *WEBER.* $25

Schullian, Dorothy and Francis Sommer. A CATALOGUE OF INCUNABULA AND MANUSCRIPTS IN THE ARMY MEDICAL LIBRARY. NY, 1950. 1st ed. *FYE.* $90

Schultes, R.E. and A.S. Pease. GENERIC NAMES OF ORCHIDS....NY, 1963. Cl, chipped dj. *SUTTON.* $50

Schulthess, Emil. ANTARCTICA. NY: Simon & Schuster, 1960. 1st ed. VG. *BLUE DRAGON.* $45

Schultz, James Willard. BEAR CHIEF'S WAR SHIRT. Mountain Press, 1984. 1st ed. Wilbur Ward Betts (ed). Title pg inserted, as pub. Fine in dj. *AUTHORS OF THE WEST.* $20

Schultz, James Willard. ON THE WARPATH. Boston, 1914. 1st ed. 245pp. Illus by George Varian. Cover wear but VG. *PRATT.* $75

Schultz, James Willard. WILLIAM JACKSON, INDIAN SCOUT. Boston: Houghton Mifflin, 1926. 1st ed. 4 plts. Pict cl, VG. *SCHOYER'S.* $75

Schultze, David. THE JOURNALS AND PAPERS OF DAVID SCHULTZE. Pennsburg Schwenkfelde, 1952. Ed by Andrew Berky. 2 vols. 1st eds. 2 fldg maps, 6 plts. VF. *OREGON.* $45

Schultze, Oskar. ATLAS AND TEXT-BOOK OF TOPOGRAPHIC AND APPLIED ANATOMY. Phila, 1905. 1st Eng trans. 22 color lithographic plts, color illus. *FYE.* $50

Schurmann, Ulrich. ORIENTAL CARPETS. London: Paul Hamlyn, 1968. 2nd ed. VG in Good dj. *BACKROOM.* $20

Schutz, Benjamin M. ALL THE OLD BARGAINS. NY: Bluejay Books, 1985. 1st ed. VF in dj. *MORDIDA.* $25

Schutz, Benjamin M. EMBRACE THE WOLF. NY: Bluejay Books, 1985. 1st ed. VF in dj. *MORDIDA.* $25

Schuyler, Eugene. TURKISTAN. NOTES OF A JOURNEY IN RUSSIAN TURKISTAN, KHOKAND, BUKHARA, AND KULDJA. London, 1876. 3 maps. 2 vols. Spine ends chipped. xii,411pp; viii,463pp. Nice. *O'NEILL.* $300

Schuyler, George S. BLACK AND CONSERVATIVE. New Rochelle: Arlington House, (1966). 1st ed. VG in dj chipped at spine crown w/several other modest chips. *LOPEZ.* $45

Schwartz, Delmore. "I AM CHERRY ALIVE," THE LITTLE GIRL SANG. Harper & Row, (1979). 1st ed. Unpaginated. Illus by Barbara Cooney. Fine in Fine dj. *BEBBAH.* $30

Schwartz, Delmore. SHENANDOAH. Connecticut: New Directions, The Poet of the Month, (1941). 1st ed. Wraps, in pict dj. Fine. *POLYANTHOS.* $75

Schwartz, Delmore. SUCCESSFUL LOVE AND OTHER STORIES. NY: Corinth, 1961. 1st ed. Uncommon hardcvr issue of collection issued simultaneously in wraps. Rev copy w/slip laid in. Fine in dj. *LAME DUCK.* $150

Schwartz, Delmore. THE WORLD IS A WEDDING. (Norfolk): New Directions, (1948). 1st ed. Fine in dj (trifle of rubbing). *CAPTAIN'S BOOKSHELF.* $125

Schwarz-Bart, Andre. THE LAST OF THE JUST. NY: Atheneum (1960). 1st Amer ed. Brief inscrip. Fine in Fine price clipped dj. *DORN.* $85

Schwatka, Frederick. A SUMMER IN ALASKA. St Louis, 1892. 2nd ed. 418pp. Pict cl, inner hinges weak, Good. *ARTIS.* $37.50

Schwatka, Frederick. A SUMMER IN ALASKA. St Louis, 1893. 418pp. Inner hinges weak, Near VG. *ARTIS.* $40

Schwatka, Frederick. A SUMMER IN ALASKA. St. Louis: J.W. Henry, 1894. Good. *BLUE DRAGON.* $30

Schwatka, Frederick. ALONG ALASKA'S GREAT RIVER. NY: Cassell, c. 1855. Fldg maps (1 in pocket). Ex-lib. *HUDSON.* $75

Schwatka, Frederick. NIMROD IN THE NORTH. Boston: Educational Pub Co, (c. 1892). 198pp. Good+. *BLUE DRAGON.* $25

Schwatka, Frederick. THE CHILDREN OF THE COLD. NY, 1899. 212pp. Illus. VG w/edgewear; cvr and spine pics. in silver, black, & gilt fairly bright. Scarce. *BEBBAH.* $50

Schweidler, Mary. THE AMBER WITCH. London: Hacon & Ricketts, Vale Press, 1903. Lady Duff Gordon (trans). Boards as issued, paper label, quarto. Sl soil. Ltd to 300. VG. *CULLEN.* $275

Schwerner, Armand. THE TABLETS I-VIII. West Branch, IA: Cummington Press, 1968. 1st ed. Ltd to 320, this being one of 150 unsigned. Fine in dec wraps. *JAFFE.* $65

Schwiebert, Ernest. REMEMBRANCES OF RIVERS PAST. NY: Macmillan Co, 1972. Stated 1st prtg. VG+ in VG dj. *BACKMAN.* $30

Sciaky, Leon. FAREWELL TO SALONICA. NY, 1946. *O'NEILL.* $40

Scobee, Barry. FORT DAVIS TEXAS: 1583-1960. TX: (Pub by author), (1963). 1st ed. Fine. *BOOK MARKET.* $40

Scobee, Barry. THE STEER BRANDED MURDER. Houston: The Frontier Press, 1952. 1st ed. VG in wraps. *GIBBS.* $30

Scoresby, Captain (William). THE ARCTIC REGIONS; THEIR SITUATION, APPEARANCES, CLIMATE, AND ZOOLOGY. London: The Religious Tract Soc, (1849). Lea spine, marbled paper over boards. Rubbed, worn. *PARMER.* $75

Scot, Reginald. THE DISCOVERIE OF WITCHCRAFT. (Bungay): John Rodker, 1930. One of 1275. Orig Morocco-backed buckram, teg, other edges untrimmed. Minor abrasions, fading o/w Fine. *PIRAGES.* $275

Scott, Charles F(elton). LETTERS. Iola, Kansas: Iola Register Print, 1892. iv,219pp. Orig cl, presentation copy. Binding worn. Quite scarce. *BOHLING.* $60

Scott, Edwin J. RANDOM RECOLLECTIONS OF A LONG LIFE 1806-1876. Columbia, 1884. 1st ed. VG. Howes S-220. *McGOWAN.* $125

Scott, Edwin J. RANDOM RECOLLECTIONS OF A LONG LIFE: 1806 TO 1876. Columbia, SC: Calvo, 1884. 1st ed. (6),216pp. Orig cl. Howes S220. *GINSBERG.* $175

Scott, Evelyn. A CALENDAR OF SIN. American Melodramas. NY: Jonathan Cape & Harrison Smith, (1931). 2 vols, 1st ed. Fine in djs (couple of nicks at spine crowns, some soiling). *CHAPEL HILL.* $150

Scott, Evelyn. THE WAVE. NY: Jonathan Cape and Harrison Smith, (1929). 1st ed. Orig blue cl. Offsetting to front ep, else Fine in VG dj, some chipping top edge. *CHAPEL HILL.* $50

Scott, Frank J. ART OF BEAUTIFYING SUBURBAN HOME GROUNDS. NY: Appleton, 1870. 618pp. Cloth worn; rear boards and a few inner pages waterstained. Contents sound and tight. *AMERICAN BOTANIST.* $75

Scott, G.C. FISHING IN AMERICAN WATERS. NY, 1869. 1st ed. VG. *MIKESH.* $60

Scott, Hugh Lenox. SOME MEMORIES OF A SOLDIER. NY: 1928. 673pp. 1st ed. Orig cl, top of spine faded. *GINSBERG.* $150

Scott, Hugh. IN THE HIGH YEMEN. London, 1942. *O'NEILL.* $45

Scott, J.M. ICEBOUND. London: Gordon & Cremonesi, 1977. 1st ed. Fine in sl soiled dj. *PARMER.* $40

Scott, James K.P. THE STORY OF THE BATTLES AT GETTYSBURG. Harrisburg, 1927. 1st ed. 301pp + ads. Dj wear o/w VG+. *PRATT.* $50

Scott, John. PARTISAN LIFE WITH COL. JOHN S. MOSBY. NY, 1867. 1st ed. Minor wear to spine extremities, corners scuffed, else VG to NF. H.G. Gowen's copy, signed by him. *McGOWAN.* $285

Scott, Jonathan M. BLUE LIGHTS; OR, THE CONVENTION. A POEM IN FOUR CANTOS. NY: Baldwin, 1817. 1st ed. 150pp. Orig printed pict blue boards wear to hinges, a few holes in spine. *GINSBERG.* $175

Scott, Lord George. GROUSE LAND AND THE FRINGE OF THE MOOR. London: Witherby, London, 1937. 1st ed. Minor soiling. Good+. *OLD LONDON.* $20

Scott, Mary Hurlburt. THE OREGON TRAIL THROUGH WYOMING. A CENTURY OF HISTORY 1812-1912. Aurora, CO: Powder River, 1958. 1st ed, #21/750. 2 fldg maps laid in. Signed. VF. *OREGON.* $150

Scott, P. THE EYE OF THE WIND: AN AUTOBIOGRAPHY. London: H & S, (1968). Fine in NF dj. *MIKESH.* $25

Scott, P. THE SWANS. Boston, 1972. Worn dj. *SUTTON.* $60

Scott, P. WILD CHORUS. London, 1938. 1st, ltd ed. Only 1250 ptd, 250 reserved for US. 24 colored plts. Orig blue buckram. Spine faded. Signed. Very scarce. *SUTTON.* $395

Scott, Paul. A MALE CHILD. NY: Dutton (1957). 1st Amer ed. Lt damp stain bottom of spine else VG in VG dj missing 1". *DORN.* $45

Scott, Paul. A MALE CHILD. NY: Dutton, 1957. 1st US ed. Slight rubbing bottom of boards, else Fine in NF dj w/small tape shadow rear panel. *BETWEEN COVERS.* $65

Scott, Paul. SIX DAYS IN MARAPORE. GC: Doubleday, 1953. 1st US ed. VG+ in VG+ dj. *AARD.* $60

Scott, Paul. THE BIRDS OF PARADISE. London: Eyre & Spottiswoode (1962). 1st Eng ed. Fine in sl used NF dj. *DORN.* $70

Scott, Paul. THE JEWEL IN THE CROWN. Morrow, 1966. 1st Amer ed. About Fine in dj (lt wear). *STAHR.* $45

Scott, Paul. THE MARK OF THE WARRIOR. London: Eyre & Spottiswoode (1958). 1st Eng ed. Inscribed, signed. NF in Fine dj. *DORN.* $225

Scott, Paul. THE MARK OF THE WARRIOR. NY: Morrow (1958). 1st Amer ed. Fine in NF dj. *DORN.* $85

Scott, Robert F. SCOTT'S LAST EXPEDITION. VOL. I. BEING THE JOURNALS...VOL II. BEING THE REPORTS...ARRANGED BY LEONARD HUXLEY. NY: Dodd, Mead & Co, 1913. 1st Amer ed. 2 vols. 7 photo, 10 color plts, 2 panorama (vol 1); 7 colored plts, 3 double-pg, 7 maps (vol 2). Foxing to fore-edges, shelfwear, else VG. *PARMER.* $245

Scott, Robert F. THE VOYAGE OF THE 'DISCOVERY'. London: Smith, Elder & Co, 1905. 2 vols. 2nd impression. 2 fldg maps. Rubbing, wear to blue cl cvrs; lt foxing, internal spotting. Good. *PARMER.* $400

Scott, Robert Garth. INTO THE WILDERNESS WITH THE ARMY OF THE POTOMAC. Bloomington, (1985). 1st ed. VG+ in dj. *PRATT.* $27.50

Scott, Samuel W. and Samuel P. Angel. HISTORY OF THE THIRTEENTH REGIMENT TENNESSEE VOLUNTEER CAVALRY U.S.A. Phila, (1903). 1st ed. Bound in 1/4 leather w/marbled boards. *McGOWAN.* $175

Scott, Sir Walter. KENILWORTH: A ROMANCE. Edinburgh, 1821. 1st ed. 3 vols. Contemp 1/2 lea, gilt spines. Bkpls, sl rubbed. NF. *POLYANTHOS.* $200

Scott, Sir Walter. LETTERS ON DEMONOLOGY AND WITCHCRAFT, ADDRESSED TO J.G. LOCKHART, ESQ. London: Murray, 1830. 1st ed. George Cruikshank (illus). Full brn crushed morocco, gilt, by Wallis. Owner sig, catalogue entry on front flyleaves, o/w Fine. *JAFFE.* $350

Scott, Sir Walter. THE LADY OF THE LAKE. Bobbs-Merrill, (1910). 1st ed. Plts by Howard Chandler Christy. Gilt pict boards, Dj has 3 pieces missing, edge tears, spine detached, piece mended. *POLYANTHOS.* $95

Scott, William B. ANTIQUARIAN GLEANINGS IN THE NORTH OF ENGLAND. Being Examples of....London: George Bell. N.d. (circa 1851). 18pp text + 38 hand-colored plts of antiquities. Orig grn cl, spine extrems bit frayed. Some plts w/marginal tears (not affecting the images). Some lt foxing. All plts present, but some out-of-sequence. *KARMIOLE.* $175

Scott, Winfield Townley. "A DIRTY HAND": THE LITERARY NOTEBOOKS OF W.T.S. Univ of TX Press, (1969). 1st ed. Frontis. Fine in dj. *AUTHORS OF THE WEST.* $20

Scott-Mitchell, Fredk. PRACTICAL GILDING, BRONZING, LACQUERING AND GLASS EMBOSSING. London, 1915. 2nd ed w/add'l chapters and illus. Pub's dk grn cl w/gilt lettering. Part of "The Decorator" Series of Practical Handbooks by A. S. Jennings (ed). *BOOK BLOCK.* $250

Scoyen, Eivind T. and Frank J. Taylor. RAINBOW CANYONS. Stanford Univ Press, 1931. 1st ed. VG+. *FIVE QUAIL.* $25

Scribner, Harry. MY MYSTERIOUS CLIENTS. Cincinnati: Robert Clarke, 1900. 1st ed. Just About Fine w/very small tear on front fly. Painted pict front board bright and unrubbed. *BETWEEN COVERS.* $85

Scrope, William. DAYS OF DEER STALKING IN THE SCOTTISH HIGHLANDS. London: Hamilton, Adams & Co. and Glasgow: Thomas D. Morison, 1883. 1st ed. Some wear to extremities, altogether quite good. Rare. *OLD LONDON.* $150

Scudder, John. ON THE USE OF MEDICATED INHALATIONS...Cincinnati, 1874. 3rd ed. Woodcut illus. Scarce. *FYE.* $40

Scudder, Ralph E. CUSTER COUNTRY. Portland: Binford, (1963). 1st ed. Fine. *BOOK MARKET.* $15

Scudder, Vida D. A LISTENER IN BABEL. Boston: Houghton Mifflin, 1903. 1st ed. Fine w/light rubbing at foot of spine. *BEASLEY.* $75

Scull, E. Marshall. HUNTING IN THE ARCTIC AND ALASKA. London: Duckworth & Co, 1914. Crnrs, edges bumped, o/w VG. Bkpl. *PARMER.* $125

Scully, Vincent. PUEBLO ARCHITECTURE OF THE SOUTHWEST: A PHOTOGRAPHIC ESSAY. Fort Worth: Amon Carter Museum, (1971). 1st ed. Fine in very sl used dj. *CAPTAIN'S BOOKSHELF.* $50

Seabrook, William. THE WHITE MONK OF TIMBUCTOO. NY: Harcourt, Brace and Co., (1934). Silverfish nibbling on cvrs, else Fine. *WREDEN.* $25

Seabrook, William. THE WHITE MONK OF TIMBUCTOO. NY: Harcourt, Brace, 1934. 2nd ptg. Sl rubbed, o/w VG. *WORLDWIDE.* $16

Seabury, Samuel. LETTERS OF A WESTCHESTER FARMER (1774-1775). White Plains, NY, 1930. Orig cl. *GINSBERG.* $35

Seale, A. QUEST FOR THE GOLDEN CLOAK. SF, 1946. Ink inscrip, photo address card and sig of author taped to pastedown. Dj worn. *SUTTON.* $35

Seale, Bobby. SEIZE THE TIME: THE STORY OF THE BLACK PANTHER PARTY & HUEY P. NEWTON. NY: Random House, (1968). 1st ed. Name fep, couple tiny dj tears. *AKA.* $35

Searight, Frank Thompson. SWEPT BY FLAMES. A THRILLING TALE. Chicago: Laird & Lee, 1906. Orig color ptd wraps quite soiled, interior VG. *PARMER.* $65

Searight, Thomas B. THE OLD PIKE: A HISTORY OF THE NATIONAL ROAD. Uniontown, PA: the author, 1894. 1st ed. 384pp. Orig cl. Howes S257. *GINSBERG.* $125

Searle, Ronald. FORTY DRAWINGS. Cambridge: Univ Press, 1946. 1st ed. Some foxing to eps, o/w Fine. Inscribed. *DERMONT.* $350

Sears, John Van Der Zee. MY FRIENDS AT BROOK FARM. NY: Desmond FitzGerald, 1912. 1st ed. Owner's inscrip, bad crease on front board, lesser crease on rear board. *BEASLEY.* $40

Sears, Stephen W. LANDSCAPE TURNED RED, THE BATTLE OF ANTIETAM. New Haven, 1983. 1st ed. 431pp. Fine in dj. *PRATT.* $25

Seaver, George. EDWARD WILSON OF THE ANTARCTIC. NY: Dutton, 1937. 1st US ed. VG. *AARD.* $30

Seaver, George. SCOTT OF THE ANTARCTIC. London: John Murray, 1940. Light edgewear, some offsetting to endpapers, overall VG. *PARMER.* $35

Sechenov, Ivan. SELECTED WORKS. Moscow, 1935. 1st ed. Dj. Exlib. Scarce. *FYE.* $150

SECOND BRIGADE OF THE PENNSYLVANIA RESERVES AT ANTIETAM. Harrisburg, 1908. Fldg map. Fine. *PRATT.* $40

Secoy, Frank Raymond. CHANGING MILITARY PATTERNS OF THE GREAT PLAINS, 17TH CENTURY THROUGH EARLY 19TH CENTURY. Locust Valley, NY, (1953). 112pp. Spine faded o/w Fine. *PRATT.* $22.50

Sedding, J.D. GARDEN-CRAFT, OLD AND NEW. London, 1892, 2nd ed. 16 plts. Faded cl. *SUTTON.* $65

Sedelmayr, Jacobo. JACOBO SEDELMAYR, MISSIONARY, FRONTIERSMAN, EXPLORER IN ARIZONA AND SONORA. Four Original Manuscript Narratives, 1744-1751. Trans and annotated by Peter Masten Dunne. AZ Pioneers' Hist Soc, 1955. Ltd ed of 600. Deluxe ed, descriptive flyer laid in. NF. *FIVE QUAIL.* $85

Sedgwick, Catharine Maria. LETTERS FROM ABROAD TO KINDRED AT HOME. 2 vols. NY: Harper, 1841. 1st ed. 8vo, 275pp,adv, 297. Vol 1 is state B (no priority), w/p 276 "Catalogue of books"; The catalogue is of the 2nd ptg (no sequence noted). Vol 2 is 1st ptg, collated as 1st w/adv pp 1-2. This is in a brown cl. Pub's cl (some bumped and worn). VG. BAL 17384. *SECOND LIFE.* $125

Sedgwick, Catharine Maria. MEMOIR OF JOSEPH CURTIS. NY: Harper, 1858. 1st ed. Orig cl, rebacked. VG. BAL 17421. *SECOND LIFE.* $45

Seebohm, H. THE BIRDS OF SIBERIA, A RECORD OF A NATURALIST'S VISITS TO THE VALLEYS OF THE PETCHORA AND YENESEI. London, 1901. 1 fldg map. Some edgewear; cvrs soiled; no. sticker on spine; ex-lib. *SUTTON.* $88

Seely, J.E.B. ADVENTURE—THE AUTOBIOGRAPHY OF MAJOR-GENERAL THE RT. HON. J. B. SEELY. NY: Stokes, 1930. 1st US ed. VG in VG dj. *AARD.* $25

Seemann, Berthold. VITI: AN ACCOUNT OF A GOVERNMENT MISSION TO THE VITIAN OR FIJAN ISLANDS. London: Macmillan, 1862. 1st ed. 8vo, 447pp, with frontis, fldg map, and 3 color plts bound in nicely repaired leather. Sl foxing to ep; faint dampstain to bottom edge. Fine. *PARMER.* $260

Segal, Lore. ALL THE WAY HOME. NY: Farrar Straus Giroux, (1973). 1st ed. Fine in NF spine-faded dj. *BETWEEN COVERS.* $45

Seguin, E.C. MEDICAL THERMOMETRY AND HUMAN TEMPERATURE. NY, 1876. 1st ed. 446pp. *FYE.* $200

Seguin, Edward. IDIOCY: AND ITS TREATMENT BY THE PHYSIOLOGICAL METHOD. NY, 1866. 1st ed. 457pp. *FYE.* $350

Seitz, Don C. PAUL JONES: HIS EXPLOITS IN ENGLISH SEAS DURING 1778-1780. 1st ed. NY: (1917). Inner hinges cracked, covers rubbed. *LEFKOWICZ.* $35

Selby, Hubert. LAST EXIT TO BROOKLYN. London: Calder & Boyars, 1968. 1st ed, 2nd ptg. NF. *SMITH.* $25

Selby, Hubert. LAST EXIT TO BROOKLYN. NY: Grove Press, (c1964). 1st ed, 1st bk. Fine in dj. *HELLER.* $50

SELECT EXAMPLES OF ARCHITECTURAL GRANDEUR IN BELGIUM, GERMANY, AND FRANCE. 2 vols in one. London: Henry G. Bohn, 1837. 2 sets 12 mounted black and white etchings, each w/8pp intro text. Thick paper. Hunter grn cl, maroon morocco backstrip. Gilt stamped morocco label in center of front cvr. Single-ruled backstrip gilt border edge, spine lettered in gilt. Sl markings on covers, discoloration on edges. Some foxing, front hinge starting to crack. Some rubbing on spine. O/w VG, large-margined vol. *CULLEN.* $250

SELECT FABLES WITH CUTS DESIGNED AND ENGRAVED BY THOMAS AND JOHN BEWICK. Together with a Memoir and a Descriptive Catalogue of the Messrs Bewick. Printed by S. Hodgson, for Emerson Charnley et al. London: 1820. 1st ed. Tall 4to; pp (2) xl, 332. Engr frontis port. 3/4 brown morocco and linen, gilt extra, raised bands, spine gilt in panels, marbled eps, aeg. Front cover sl darkened, else lovely book, engravings in Fine state. *HARTFIELD.* $695

SELECTIONS FROM THE COLLECTION OF FRANCIS P. GAR-VAN. NY: William Bradford Press, 1931. Exceptionally clean. VG. Wraps. *BACKROOM.* $120

Self-Margaret Cabell. RED CLAY COUNTRY. NY: Harper, 1936. 1st ed. VG. *OCTOBER FARM.* $18

Seligman, Adrian. NO STARS TO GUIDE. London: Hodder & Stoughton, (1947). 6 fldg maps. In chipped dj. *SCHOYER'S.* $35

Seligman, C.G. and Brenda Z. Seligman. PAGAN TRIBES OF THE NILOTIC SUDAN. NY: Humanities Press, 1950. New imp. Spine tips worn, o/w Good+. *ACADEMIC.* $47

Sell, Henry Blackman and Victory Weybright. BUFFALO BILL AND THE WILD WEST. NY: Oxford Univ, 1955. 1st ed. NF in NF dj. *CONNOLLY & WADE.* $57.50

Sellers, C.C. CHARLES WILLSON PEALE. VOL I: EARLY LIFE (1741-1790). Vol II: LATER LIFE (1790-1827). Phila, 1947. 1st ed thus. Some rubbing; backstrips dulled. *SUTTON.* $200

Selway, N.C. THE REGENCY ROAD...JAMES POLLARD. London: Faber & Faber, (1957). 1st ed. 66 color plts. Fine in spine-faded dj, sm chip. *CAPTAIN'S BOOKSHELF.* $75

Selwyn, Cecil E. PRAIRIE PATCHWORK OR WESTERN POEMS FOR WESTERN PEOPLE. Winnipeg, 1910. 1st ed. Pict cl. Good. *ARTIS.* $35

Selwyn-Brown, A. THE PHYSICIAN THROUGHOUT THE AGES. 2 vols. Capehart-Brown, 1928. Dec cvrs. VG. *BOOKCELL.* $70

Sendak, Maurice. HIGGLETY PIGGLETY POP! Or There Must Be More To Life. NY: Harper, (1967). 1st ed. Fine in dj (price-clipped on lower front flap, leaving the $4.95 price at the top). Signed. *CAPTAIN'S BOOKSHELF.* $90

Sendak, Maurice. OUTSIDE OVER THERE. Harper & Row, (1981). Unpaginated. NF in NF dj w/sl edgewear, tiny closed edge tear. *BEBBAH.* $30

Sendak, Philip. IN GRANDPA'S HOUSE. Harper & Row, (1985). 1st ed. 42pp. Illus by Maurice Sendak. Fine in Fine dj. *BEBBAH.* $30

Senkewicz, Robert. VIGILANTES IN GOLD RUSH SAN FRAN-CISCO. Stanford Univ, 1985. 1st ed. VF in VF dj. *OREGON.* $25

Senn, Nicholas. IN THE HEART OF THE ARCTICS. Chicago, (1907). 336pp. Gilt cl. VG. *ARTIS.* $45

Senn, Nicholas. IN THE HEART OF THE ARCTICS. Chicago: W.B. Conkey Co., (1907). Cover cloth wrinkled, marginal dampstaining, well-used. *PARMER.* $100

Senn, Nicholas. INTESTINAL SURGERY. Chicago, 1889. 1st ed. 269pp. *FYE.* $250

Senn, Nicholas. PRINCIPLES OF SURGERY. Phila, 1891. 1st ed. 611pp. Ads wrinkled, covers spotted. *FYE.* $150

Senn, Nicholas. SURGICAL BACTERIOLOGY. Phila, 1891. 2nd ed. *FYE.* $75

Senzel, Howard. BASEBALL AND THE COLD WAR. Harcourt, Brace and Jovanovich, 1977. 1st ed. VG in Fine dj. *PLAPINGER.* $35

Seredy, Kate. A TREE FOR PETER. Viking, 1941. 1st ed. 102pp. Illus by Seredy. 6pp have soil; tiny blue spots to cvr, else VG. *BEBBAH.* $25

Seredy, Kate. THE GOOD MASTER. Viking, 1935. 1st ed. 211pp. Illus by author. VG in VG dj w/edgewear, small chipping top, bottom of spine, short closed tear rear panel. *BEBBAH.* $45

Seredy, Kate. THE OPEN GATE. Viking, 1943. 1st ed. 281pp. Illus by Seredy. VG w/slight wear to top, bottom of spine. *BEBBAH.* $25

Seredy, Kate. THE OPEN GATE. Viking, 1943. 1st ed. 281pp. Illus by author. VG+ in VG dj w/few chips, skinned patch at spine. *BEBBAH.* $45

Serling, Rod. PATTERNS. NY: S&S, (1957). 1st ed. NF, some foxing, in a VG dj darkened at spine. *UNGER.* $75

Serling, Rod. PATTERNS. NY: Simon & Schuster, 1957. 1st ed, 1st book. Photo illus. NF in price clipped dj. *BERNARD.* $60

Serulan (pseud of Henry Laurens?). POEMS, ORIGINAL AND TRANSLATED. Charleston: John Russell, 1854. 1st ed. 136pp. Orig blue cl. Lib bkpl, blindstamp, some rubbing, darkening to binding, o/w VG. *CHAPEL HILL.* $75

SERVICE AT THE UNVEILING AND DEDICATION OF A MEMORIAL TO WYSTAN HUGH AUDEN. 2 October 1974. Wrappers. *WOOLMER.* $25

Service, Robert W. RHYMES OF A ROLLING STONE. Toronto: William Briggs, 1912. 1st ed. Rebound in 1/4 grn calf over grn cl w/gilt. Extrems of spine rubbed, still attractive. *CAPTAIN'S BOOKSHELF.* $100

Servin, James. COLT FIREARMS FROM 1836. Harrisburg: Stack-pole Books, (1954). April 1981, enl, updated 7th ed. Fine in Fine dj. *BACKMAN.* $30

Serviss, Garrett P. EDISON'S CONQUEST OF MARS. LA: Carcosa House, 1947. #355/1,500. Good. *KNOLLWOOD.* $45

Seton, Ernest Thompson. LIFE HISTORIES OF NORTHERN ANIMALS, AN ACCOUNT OF THE MAMMALS OF MANITOBA. Vol. 1-Grass-Eaters. Vol. 2-Flesh-eaters. 100 plts and 266 text-figures plus 68 range maps. 2 vols. NY, 1909. Orig tan gilt-stamped buckram w/leather spine labels. Cvrs soiled, label on Vol. 1 splitting & perishing; label on Vol. 2 scraped, tears to heel of spine; Bkpls, # sticker on spines. Internally clean and solid. Vol. 1 contains tipped in T.L.S. from author. *SUTTON.* $400

Seton, Ernest Thompson. MONARCH THE BIG BEAR OF TAL-LAC. NY, 1904. 1st ed. 8 plts. Unpaginated, cloth. Wear at extrems, spotting on rear cover, hinges cracked, ink inscription & name stamps. *SUTTON.* $55

Seton, Ernest Thompson. THE ARCTIC PRAIRIES: A CANOE JOURNEY OF 2,000 MILES IN SEARCH OF THE CARIBOU, ETC. NY: Int'l Univ, (1943). VG+ in VG dj. *MIKESH.* $45

Seton, Ernest Thompson. THE ARCTIC PRAIRIES. London: Constable & Co. Ltd, 1920. New Rev Ed. Pict cvr. VG. *AUTHORS OF THE WEST.* $30

Seton, Ernest Thompson. THE BIG BEAR OF TALLAC. Charles Scribner's Sons, 1904. 1st ed. Title pg in color, pict cvr. VG+. *AUTHORS OF THE WEST.* $75

Seton, Ernest Thompson. THE BIOGRAPHY OF A GRIZZLY. NY: Century, (1907). 75 drawings. VG+. *MIKESH.* $30

Seton, Ernest Thompson. THE BIOGRAPHY OF A SILVER FOX. Century, 1909. 1st ed. Illus by Seton. Wear, corner stain to rear cvr, smudging to some pp. *BEBBAH.* $30

Seton, Ernest Thompson. THE TRAIL OF THE SANDHILL STAG. NY: Charles Scribner's Sons. 1899. Sm 8vo. 94pp. Frontis, 7 plts, many sm drwgs. Title page ptd in grn and black. Orig grn dec cl, gilt, w/overlapping edges. Scarce. *KARMIOLE.* $100

Seton, Ernest Thompson. TRAIL OF AN ARTIST-NATURALIST, THE AUTOBIOGRAPHY OF E.T. SETON. NY, 1940. VG+. *MIKESH.* $95

Seton, Ernest Thompson. TWO LITTLE SAVAGES. Toronto: William Briggs, 1903. Pict eps, cvr. VG, spine rubbed top and bottom. *AUTHORS OF THE WEST.* $40

Seton, Ernest Thompson. TWO LITTLE SAVAGES. NY: Doubleday, 1903. 1st ed. Uncut. VG. *SECOND LIFE.* $45

Seton, Grace Thompson. YES, LADY SAHEB. NY & London: Harper & Bros, 1925. Purple dec cl, stamped in gilt. Spine and upper edges faded. Stated 1st ed. *SCHOYER'S.* $22.50

Seton, Julia M. THE PULSE OF THE PUEBLO. Santa Fe: Seton Village Press, 1939. 1st ed, adv rev material laid in. Edgewear, else Good+. *CONNOLLY & WADE.* $32.50

Seton-Thompson, Ernest. THE BIOGRAPHY OF A GRIZZLY. NY: Scribner's, Apr. 1900. VG. *MIKESH.* $35

Seton-Thompson, Grace Gallatin. A WOMAN TENDERFOOT. NY: Doubleday Page, 1900. Ernest Seton-Thompson, G. Wright, E.M. Ashe (illus). 1st ed. Presentation, signed. VG. *LAURIE.* $75

Settle, Mary Lee. BLOOD TIE. Boston: Houghton Mifflin, 1977. 1st ed. VF in dj. Signed. *CAPTAIN'S BOOKSHELF.* $50

Settle, Mary Lee. CELEBRATION. Franklin Center: Franklin Library, 1986. Ltd ed. Fine in Franklin leather. Signed. *CAPTAIN'S BOOKSHELF.* $50

Settle, Mary Lee. CHARLEY BLAND. Franklin Center: Franklin Library, 1989. Ltd ed. Fine in Franklin leather. Signed. *CAPTAIN'S BOOKSHELF.* $50

Settle, Mary Lee. CHARLEY BLAND. Franklin Center: Franklin Library, 1989. 1st ed. One of unspecified number signed. Fine in full lea. *BETWEEN COVERS.* $65

Settle, Mary Lee. THE KILLING GROUND. NY: Farrar Straus Giroux, (1982). Adv reading copy w/an autograph letter laid in. Fine in wrappers. *LOPEZ.* $65

Settle, Mary Lee. THE KILLING GROUND. NY: Farrar Straus Giroux (1982). 1/150 numbered, signed. *LOPEZ.* $85

Settle, Mary Lee. THE LOVE EATERS. London: Heinemann, (1954). 1st ed, preceding the Amer. Foxing, else About Fine in like dj. Inscribed. *CAPTAIN'S BOOKSHELF.* $250

Settle, Mary Lee. THE LOVE EATERS. NY: Harper & Bros, (1954). 1st Amer ed. 1st bk. Orig cl-backed yellow boards. Top edge soiled, thus VG in lightly soiled dj, lower corner clipped from front flap. *CHAPEL HILL.* $225

Settle, Mary Lund and Raymond W. SADDLES AND SPURS. Harrisburg, (1955). 1st ed. Dj. VG. *PRATT.* $35

Settle, Mary Lund and Raymond W. SADDLES AND SPURS. Harrisburg, PA: Stackpole, (1955). Pict cl, dj. VG. *SCHOYER'S.* $30

Seuss, Dr. (pseud of Theodore Geisel). BONERS. Viking, 1931. 4th ptg. 102pp. Illus by Dr. Seuss, his first book. VG+ in Good dj w/chips, piece missing lower spine. *BEBBAH.* $30

Seuss, Dr. (pseud of Theodore Geisel). THE 500 HATS OF BARTHOLOMEW CUBBINS. NY: Vanguard Press, (1938). 1st ed. Orig cl-backed boards. Bkpl, else VG in dj (edgewear, 1 1/2" closed tear bottom spine). Inscribed. *CHAPEL HILL.* $550

Seuss, Dr. (pseud of Theodore Geisel). THE SEVEN LADY GODIVAS. NY: Random House, (1939). 1st ed. Orig salmon cl. VG in sl rubbed dj (couple of nicks, wear to spine ends). Promo "Godiva Book Mark" laid in. Inscribed. *CHAPEL HILL.* $650

Seuss, Dr. (pseud of Theodore Geisel). THE SEVEN LADY GODIVAS. Random, (1939). 1st ptg. Unpaginated. Illus in 2-colors by Seuss. NF. *BEBBAH.* $65

Sevareid, Eric. NOT SO WILD A DREAM. NY: Knopf, 1946. 1st ed, 1st book. VG in dj. *BERNARD.* $20

SEVEN AND NINE YEARS AMONG THE COMANCHES AND APACHES. Jersey City, NJ: Clark Johnson, M.D, 1879. 8 plts, dec orange cl. VG. *SCHOYER'S.* $45

Severin, Mark F. YOUR WOOD-ENGRAVING. (London): Sylvan Press. (1953). 1st ed. Presentation, inscribed. Dj. *KARMIOLE.* $40

Sevey, Glenn. BEAN CULTURE. NY: Orange Judd, 1920. VG ex-lib. *AMERICAN BOTANIST.* $25

Sevey, Glenn. PEAS AND PEA CULTURE. NY: Orange Judd, 1919. VG. *AMERICAN BOTANIST.* $25

Sevigne, Marie de Rabutin-Chantal, Marquise de. THE LETTERS OF MADAME DE SEVIGNE. Phila: J.P. Horn & Co. 1927. 7 vols. Ed ltd to 1550 numbered sets. "The Carnavalet Edition", Djs. Fine. *KARMIOLE.* $125

Seward, Anna. MEMOIRS OF THE LIFE OF DR. DARWIN. London, 1804. 1st ed. Pp xiv,430. Contemp calf, red label. Backstrip darkened; joints, extrems scuffed; ink name. *SUTTON.* $350

Seward, Anna. MEMOIRS OF THE LIFE OF DR. DARWIN. London: J. Johnson, 1804. 1st ed. Tall 8vo; pp 430. Final leaf of errata and adverts present. Contemp calf, rebacked. Nice. *HARTFIELD.* $395

Seward, Olive Risley. WILLIAM H. SEWARD'S TRAVELS AROUND THE WORLD. NY: D. Appleton, 1873. Fldg map. Rebacked w/spine laid down. *HUDSON.* $45

Seward, William H. AUTOBIOGRAPHY OF WILLIAM H. SEWARD, FROM 1801 TO 1834. NY: D. Appleton and Co, 1877. 1st ed. 9 tissue guard ports. Ffep detached but present, card pocket removed, some scuffing. *PARMER.* $75

Sewel, William. THE HISTORY OF THE RISE, INCREASE AND PROGRESS OF THE CHRISTIAN PEOPLE CALLED QUAKERS. Burlington, NJ, 1774. 12, 812pp + index. Some foxing. Rebound in new buckram. Folio. *HEINOLDT.* $225

Sewell, Anna. BLACK BEAUTY. Boston: American Humane Society, n.d. Early prtg. Pb. Front cover edge shows wear, still VG. *OCTOBER FARM.* $25

Sexton, Anne. THE BOOK OF FOLLY. Boston: Houghton Mifflin, 1972. One of 500 specially bound, signed. Fine in slipcase. *CAPTAIN'S BOOKSHELF.* $75

Sexton, Anne. THE BOOK OF FOLLY. Boston: Houghton Mifflin, 1972. 1/500 numbered, signed. Fine in pub's tissue dj w/light wear, in slipcase. *LOPEZ.* $85

Sexton, Anne. THE BOOK OF FOLLY. Boston: Houghton Mifflin, 1972. 1st ed. One of 500 signed. Orig cl-backed red boards, aeg. Copy number evidently erased from colophon, else Fine in pub's slipcase, paper label. *CHAPEL HILL.* $75

Sexton, Anne. TO BEDLAM AND PART WAY BACK. Boston, 1960. 1st ed, 1st bk. Fine in NF price clipped dj. *POLYANTHOS.* $100

Sexton, Anne. TRANSFORMATIONS. Boston: Houghton Mifflin, 1971. Fine in orig tissue jacket and publisher's slipcase w/paper label. 1st ed. One of 500 signed. *CHAPEL HILL.* $100

Sexton, R.W. INTERIOR ARCHITECTURE, THE DESIGN OF INTERIORS OF MODERN AMERICAN HOUSES. NY: Architectural Book, Paul Wenzel & Maurice Krakow, (1927). Dj worn, o/w Fine. *WEBER.* $75

Seymour, Flora Warren. THE INDIANS TODAY. Chicago: Benj. H. Sanborn, 1926. 1st ed. Signed. VG. *LAURIE.* $25

Seymour, Harold. BASEBALL. Oxford, 1960, 1971. 2 vol set. Vol 1 ltr ptg, VG+; vol 2 1st ed, VG+. *PLAPINGER.* $75

Seymour, Harold. BASEBALL—THE EARLY YEARS. Oxford, 1960. Good+ without dj. *PLAPINGER.* $45

Seymour, John. THE FAT OF THE LAND. NY: Taplinger, 1962. 1st US ed. VG in worn dj-portion taped. *SECOND LIFE.* $25

Seymour. 101 PHOTOGRAPHS. Chicago: Pellegrini & Cudahy, 1947. Photos. Spine sl discolored. VG. *BANCROFT.* $35

Shaara, Michael. THE KILLER ANGELS. David McKay, 1974. Advance reading copy. NF in red wraps. Owner's name marked out on ffep, light wear. *STAHR.* $100

Shaara, Michael. THE KILLER ANGELS. NY, (1974). 2nd prtg. Light dj wear o/w Fine. *PRATT.* $22.50

Shaara, Michael. THE KILLER ANGELS. NY: David McKay, (1974). 1st ed. Fine in Fine dj. *LOPEZ*. $250

Shackelford, George Green. GEORGE WYTHE RANDOLPH AND THE CONFEDERATE ELITE. Athens, GA, (1988). 1st ed. Fine in dj. *PRATT*. $22.50

Shackleford, William Yancy. BELLE STARR, THE BANDIT QUEEN. Girard, KS: Haldemann Julius, (1943). 1st ed. Wraps. VG. *OREGON*. $25

Shackleford, William Yancy. GUN-FIGHTERS OF THE OLD WEST. Girard, KS: Haldeman-Julius, 1943. 1st ed. Fine. Silver ptd wraps. *CONNOLLY & WADE*. $25

Shackleton, Edward A. ARCTIC JOURNEYS. London: Hodder and Stoughton, 1937. 1st ed. Spine faded, else NF. Dj worn. Owner inscrip. *PARMER*. $65

Shackleton, Ernest H. HEART OF THE ANTARCTIC. London: Wm. Heinemann, 1909. 1st ed. 2 vols. xlviii,372pp; xv,419pp. 3 fldg maps & panorama in pocket, frontis, 12 colored, 257 b/w plts, illus and diagrams. Orig blue cl (sun faded spine) blocked in silver, gilt top edge. VG set. *BLUE DRAGON*. $375

Shackleton, Ernest H. SOUTH. NY: Macmillan, 1920. 1st Amer ed. Fldg map. Some wear, marks on cover. Title page perforated with "Advance Reading Copy Not for Sale." *PARMER*. $195

Shackleton, Ernest H. SOUTH. NY: Macmillan, 1926. 1 vol reprint ed. VG. *BLUE DRAGON*. $40

Shackleton, Robert. BOOK OF CHICAGO. Phila, 1920. 1st ed. Dec cover. Boxed. *HEINOLDT*. $15

Shacochis, Bob. EASY IN THE ISLANDS. NY: Crown, 1985. 1st ed, 1st bk. Fine in dj. with pub. promo. wrap-around band. *ELSE FINE*. $45

Shafer, Henry. THE AMERICAN MEDICAL PROFESSION, 1783-1850. NY, 1936. 1st ed. *FYE*. $75

Shaffer, E.T.H. CAROLINA GARDENS. Garden Club Ed. (Chapel Hill): Univ of North Carolina Press. 1939. "2nd Edition." Dj. *KARMIOLE*. $30

Shahn, Bernarda Bryson. BEN SHAHN. NY: Harry N. Abrams, (1972). 1st ed. Red linen. Fine in color dj. *KARMIOLE*. $300

Shairp, John Campbell et al. LIFE AND LETTERS OF JAMES DAVID FORBES. London: Macmillan & Co. 1873. 1st ed. xiv,578pp+(2)pp of ads. Fldg map. Frt cvr sl creased 2 places, extrems bit frayed. *KARMIOLE*. $125

Shakespeare, William. HAMLET. (LEC, 1933). One of 1500 signed by the illustrator, Eric Gill. Spine darkened, o/w fine in sl rubbed slipcase. *PIRAGES*. $300

Shakespeare, William. ROMEO AND JULIET. With Designs by Oliver Messel. NY: Charles Scribner's Sons. (1936). 40 plts, (8 being mounted color). Purple cl, sl soiled. Dj. Presentation inscrip from Messel ffep. *KARMIOLE*. $100

Shakespeare. THE TEMPEST. London: Chapman & Hall, 1908. 1st ed. Near 4to. 130pp. 20 color plates by Paul Woodroffe. Small amount of foxing to prelims. Ornate gilt spine and cvr w/rubbing, small spot. VG. *BEBBAH*. $50

Shakleton, Elizabeth. TOURING THROUGH FRANCE. Phila: PN Pub Co, 1925. Dark blue dec cl. VG. *SCHOYER'S*. $30

Shaler, William. JOURNAL OF A VOYAGE BETWEEN CHINA AND THE NORTH-WESTERN COAST OF AMERICA MADE IN 1804 BY...Claremont, CA, 1935. 700 numbered ptd. Orig cl backed boards. George Lindsley Burr's copy, bkpls, sig on ffep. *GINSBERG*. $150

Shambaugh, Bertha M.H. AMANA: THE COMMUNITY OF TRUE INSPIRATION. Iowa City: State Hist Soc of Iowa, 1908. 1st ed. VG+ w/rear hinge weakening. *BEASLEY*. $100

Shane, Susannah. LADY IN LILAC. NY: Dodd, Mead, 1941. 1st ed, 1st bk. Advance prepub in stiff wraps w/dj attached to spine by pub. Spine bowed & edges worn. VG. *BERNARD*. $45

Shange, Ntozake. FOR COLORED GIRLS WHO HAVE CONSIDERED SUICIDE WHEN THE RAINBOW IS ENUF. NY, 1977. 1st hb ed, 1st bk. Fine in dj. *PETTLER*. $45

Shange, Ntozake. SASSAFRASS, CYPRESS & INDIGO. (London): Methuen, (1983). 1st Eng ed. Fine in Fine dj. *LOPEZ*. $20

Shange, Ntozake. SASSAFRASS, CYPRESS & INDIGO. NY: St. Martin's Press, (1982). 1st ed, 1st novel. Signed and dated 1988. Fine in NF dj. *ROBBINS*. $40

Shange, Ntozake. SASSAFRASS, CYPRESS & INDIGO. St. Martin's, 1982. Uncorrected proof. Fine in wraps. *STAHR*. $60

Shange, Ntozake. SASSAFRASS. (Berkeley): (Shameless Hussy Press), (1977). 1st ed. Orig wrappers, sl soiled. VG. *LOPEZ*. $65

Shange, Ntozake. SASSAFRASS. Berkeley: Shameless Hussy Press, (1977). 1st ed. Fine in pict wraps. *CAPTAIN'S BOOKSHELF*. $35

Shannon, Bill and George Kalinsky. THE BALL PARKS. Hawthorn, 1975. 1st ed. VG+ in VG+ dj. *PLAPINGER*. $175

Shannon, Eliza Roe. A MINISTER'S LIFE: MEMOIRS OF CHARLES HILL ROSE. Chicago, Lakeside Press, privately printed, 1900. 1st ed. Orig cl. *GINSBERG*. $100

Shannon, Fred A. THE ORGANIZATION AND ADMINISTRATION OF THE UNION ARMY 1861-1865. Cleveland, Clark, 1928. 1st ed. 2 vols. Orig cl. Bkpls removed, lib labels removed from lower spines. Howes S327. *GINSBERG*. $125

Shapiro, H. and Z. Miller (eds). PHYSICIAN TO THE WEST: SELECTED WRITINGS OF DANIEL DRAKE ON SCIENCE & SOCIETY. Lexington, 1970. 1st ed. Dj. *FYE*. $50

Shapiro, Karl (ed). AMERICAN POETRY. NY: Crowell (1960). 1st ed. Inscribed. VG in wraps. *DORN*. $45

Shapiro, Karl. ADULT BOOKSTORE. NY: Random House (1976). Uncorrected proof. Signed. Fine in wraps. *DORN*. $65

Shapiro, Karl. POEMS OF A JEW. NY: Random House, (1958). 1st ed. Presentation, inscribed. Fine in sl chipped dj. *JAFFE*. $125

Shapiro, Karl. TRIAL OF A POET. NY: Reynal & Hitchcock (1957). 1st ed. Inscribed. VG in chipped dj. *DORN*. $55

Shapiro, Karl. WHITE-HAIRED LOVER. NY: Random House (1968). 1st ed. Inscribed. Fine in NF dj. *DORN*. $40

Shapiro, Milton. THE ROY CAMPANELLA STORY. Messner, 1958. 1st ed. VG in Good+ dj. *PLAPINGER*. $40

Shapley, Harlow and Helen E. Howarth. A SOURCE BOOK IN ASTRONOMY. NY: McGraw-Hill, 1929, 1st ed, 2nd impression. Corners bumped, o/w VG in maroon cl. *KNOLLWOOD*. $60

Sharp, Cecil. ENGLISH FOLK SONGS FROM THE SOUTHERN APPALACHIANS. Oxford Univ Press, 1952. *BANCROFT*. $22

Sharp, Paul F. WHOOP-UP COUNTRY: THE CANADIAN-AMERICAN WEST, 1865-1885. Hist Soc of Montana, 1960. 2nd ed. Fine in Good, rubbed dj. *VARNER*. $25

Sharp, Samuel. A TREATISE ON THE OPERATIONS OF SURGERY, WITH A DESCRIPTION AND REPRESENTATION OF THE INSTRUMENTS USED IN PERFORMING THEM. London, 1772. 19th ed. 14 Fine engrvd plts. Recent 1/4 leather, 247pp. Faint lib stamps, else VF. *FYE*. $375

Sharp, Samuel. A TREATISE ON THE OPERATIONS OF SURGERY, WITH A DESCRIPTION AND REPRESENTATION OF THE INSTRUMENTS USED IN PERFORMING THEM. London, 1761. 8th ed. Full leather, 234pp. Engrvd plts. *FYE*. $350

Sharpe, Reginald R. LONDON AND THE KINGDOM: A HISTORY. London, 1894. 3 vols. Fold-out frontis facsimiles. Gilt-pict bds. NF. *POLYANTHOS.* $65

Sharpe, Samuel. THE HISTORY OF EGYPT FROM THE EARLIEST TIMES TILL THE CONQUEST OF THE ARABS. 2 vols. (complete). London: Bell & Daldy, 1870. 5th ed. Frontis map, 404 figs. Spotting to boards, small tears at top and bottom of spine, hinges reinforced w/tape, signatures. Good. *ARCHAEOLOGIA.* $85

Sharpe, Samuel. THE HISTORY OF EGYPT FROM THE EARLIEST TIMES TILL THE CONQUEST BY THE ARABS A.D. 640. 2 vols. London: Moxon, 1859. 4th ed. xxxii,407; xx,8pp. Orig cl, crudely rebacked, rubbed, o/w Good. Ex-lib w/number on spine. *WORLDWIDE.* $85

Sharpe, W.C. HISTORY OF SEYMOUR, CONNECTICUT, With

Biographies and Genealogies. Seymour: Author, 1879. 1st ed. *HEINOLDT.* $30

Sharpe, William. DIAGNOSIS AND TREATMENT OF BRAIN INJURIES. Phila, 1920. 1st ed. *FYE.* $75

Shaw, Albert. ABRAHAM LINCOLN: A CARTOON HISTORY. 2 vols. NY: Review of Reviews, 1929. 1st ed. Blue cl, gilt pict covers. NF. *CONNOLLY & WADE.* $75

Shaw, Anna Howard. THE STORY OF A PIONEER. NY: (1915) 1st ed. Red cl. VG in dj. Fine. *SECOND LIFE.* $75

Shaw, Archer. THE PLAIN DEALER: ONE HUNDRED YEARS IN CLEVELAND. NY: Knopf, 1942. 1st ed. Fine in VG torn & rubbed dj. *ARCHER.* $20

Shaw, C.E. and S. Campbell. SNAKES OF THE AMERICAN WEST. NY, 1974. Illus. VG+. *MIKESH.* $22.50

Shaw, G. GENERAL ZOOLOGY OR SYSTEMATIC NATURAL HISTORY, Vol 1, Parts 1 and 2; Vol 2, Parts 1 and 2, Mammalia. 2 vols in 4. 235 engr plts. London, 1800-01. ix,1112pp. Half morocco w/gilt dec spines; marbled boards, eps, pp edges. Worn & rubbed at edges; some spine end chipping, 1 hinge tender, some scattered foxing & offsetting from plts. 1 plate loose, emb stamps on plts. Ex-lib. *SUTTON.* $385

Shaw, G(eorge) Bernard (ed). FABIAN ESSAYS IN SOCIALISM. London: The Fabian Society, 1889. 1st ed. Orig grn cl. Sl bubbling to cvrs, owner sig, else nice, VG. *CHAPEL HILL.* $150

Shaw, George A. MADAGASCAR AND FRANCE, WITH SOME ACCOUNT...NY: American Tract Society, n.d. (ca. 1890). 438pp. Fldg map. Near Good ex-lib. *WORLDWIDE.* $30

Shaw, George Bernard. AN INTELLIGENT WOMAN'S GUIDE TO SOCIALISM AND CAPITALISM. NY: Brentano's, 1928. 1st US ed. Fine, lacking dj. *WOOLMER.* $35

Shaw, George Bernard. BACK TO METHUSELAH. NY: LEC, 1939. John Farleigh (illus). Cl w/leather labels, slipcase. Ltd to 1500 signed by Farleigh. Fine. *JAFFE.* $75

Shaw, George Bernard. LONDON MUSIC IN 1888-89 AS HEARD BY CORNO DI BASSETTO (LATER KNOWN AS BERNARD SHAW) WITH SOME FURTHER AUTOBIOGRAPHICAL PARTICULARS. NY: Dodd, Mead, 1937. 1st US Ed. About Fine. *WOOLMER.* $45

Shaw, George Bernard. PASSION PLAY. Iowa City: Windhover Press, 1971. 1st ed. Ltd to 350. Linen-backed dec boards, linen slipcase. VF. *JAFFE.* $225

Shaw, George Bernard. THE QUINTESSENCE OF IBSENISM. London: Walter Scott, 1891. 1st ed, 1st issue. 161 pp,6 ads. Blue cl bumped, sl stained. Lettered in gilt. Teg. VG. *BLUE MOUNTAIN.* $125

Shaw, Irwin. IN THE COMPANY OF DOLPHINS. (NY): Bernard Geis, (1964). 154pp. 1st ed. Dj worn, yellowed. *SCHOYER'S.* $20

Shaw, Irwin. LUCY CROWN. NY: Random House, (1956). 1st ed. VG+ in dj. *BERNARD.* $20

Shaw, Irwin. SAILOR OFF THE BREMEN & OTHER STORIES. NY: Random House, (1939). 1st ed, 2nd book. NF in very attractive dj which is soiled on rear panel. *BERNARD.* $125

Shaw, Irwin. THE TROUBLED AIR. NY: Random House, (1951). VG in price-clipped dj. 1st ed. *CHAPEL HILL.* $40

Shaw, Joseph T. (ed). THE HARD-BOILED OMNIBUS. EARLY STORIES FROM BLACK MASK. NY: Simon and Schuster, 1946. 1st ed. Fine in Fine dj but for short tear on rear panel, smaller tear at rear spine fold. *BEASLEY.* $100

Shaw, Lloyd. COWBOY DANCES. Caxton, 1939. 1st ed. Pict cvrs, eps. Signed. Fine. *AUTHORS OF THE WEST.* $50

Shaw, Thomas. CLOVERS AND HOW TO GROW THEM. NY: Orange Judd, 1906. VG. *AMERICAN BOTANIST.* $28

Shaw, Thomas. TRAVELS, OR OBSERVATIONS RELATING TO SEVERAL PARTS OF BARBARY AND THE LEVANT. Oxford: Ptd at the Theatre, 1738. 1st ed. (8),xviii,44,68pp. Eng title-page, 33 maps, plts (7 fldg). Contemp calf, very worn, both covers detached, slight tears in a few fldg plts, but no loss, last few leaves w/marginal smudge, o/w VG. *WORLDWIDE.* $325

Shawn, Wallace. OUR LATE NIGHT. NY: Targ Editions, 1984. 1st ed. One of 150 signed. Cl backed pict boards, glassine dj. Mint. *JAFFE.* $125

Shay, John C. TWENTY YEARS IN THE BACKWOODS OF CALIFORNIA. Boston: The Roxburgh Pub Co, (1923). Gold stamped cl. Inscribed. *DAWSON'S.* $40

Shea, John G. (ed). THE FALLEN BRAVE, A BIOGRAPHICAL MEMORIAL OF THE AMERICAN OFFICERS WHO HAVE GIVEN THEIR LIVES FOR THE PRESERVATION OF THE UNION. NY, 1861. 1st ed. 224pp, 8 portraits on steel by J.A. O'-Neill. Ex-lib but the only indication is a bookplate. A little cover wear o/w VG. *PRATT.* $75

Shea, John G. DANIEL HYACINTH MARY LIENHARD DE BEAUJEU, COMMANDANT OF FORT DU QUESNE AND OF THE FRENCH FORCES IN THE BATTLE OF JULY 9, 1755. N.p., n.d., ca. 1880. 8pp. Only 100 pub. Orig plain wrappers. *GINSBERG.* $50

Shea, John G. DISCOVERY AND EXPLORATION OF THE MISSISSIPPI VALLEY. Clinton Hall, NY: Redfield, 1852. lxxx,268pp, fldg facs map, 8 pgs of ads, 8 7/8" x 5 3/4". Blind-stamped cl, wear to spine and tips, title-leaf detaching, tape repair to map, bkpls removed. *DAWSON'S.* $300

Sheahan, James W. THE LIFE OF STEPHEN A. DOUGLAS. NY: Harper, 1860. Frontis. Lacks ffep. *SCHOYER'S.* $40

Shearman, Montague et al. ATHLETICS AND FOOTBALL (BADMINTON LIBRARY). Boston: Little, Brown, & Co., and London: Longmans, Green, & Co., 1887. 1st Amer ed. Minor shelfwear, else NF. *OLD LONDON.* $85

Sheean, Vincent. AN AMERICAN AMONG THE RIFFI. NY & London: Century, (1926). *SCHOYER'S.* $20

Sheed, Wilfrid. JOSEPH: A PATRON SAINT BOOK. NY: Sheed & Ward, (c1958). 1st ed, 1st bk. Fine in dj. *HELLER.* $60

Sheehan, J. Eastman. GENERAL AND PLASTIC SURGERY WITH EMPHASIS ON WAR INJURIES. NY, 1945. 496 figures. *FYE.* $100

Sheehan, Patty. KYLIE'S SONG. Santa Barbara: (1988). Illus by Itoko Maeno. Fine in Fine dj. *BEBBAH.* $30

Sheehan, Perley Poore. THE ABYSS OF WONDERS. Reading: Polaris Press, 1953. One of 1500 numbered. Slip case. Fine. *WEBER.* $20

Sheehan, Susan. TEN VIETNAMESE. NY: Knopf, 1967. 1st ed. Sl cocked, chip crown of dj, price clipped. *AKA.* $40

Sheeran, Rev. James B. CONFEDERATE CHAPLAIN: A WAR JOURNAL OF REV. JAMES B. SHEERAN, 14TH LOUISIANA, CSA. Milwaukee, 1960. 1st ed. Orig cl, dj. *GINSBERG.* $25

Sheffield, Charles. EARTH WATCH, A SURVEY. London: Sidgwick & Jackson, 1981. VG in dj. *KNOLLWOOD.* $40

Sheffy, L.F. THE LIFE AND TIMES OF TIMOTHY DWIGHT HOBART, 1855-1935. Canyon, TX: Panhandle Plains Historical Society, 1950. 1st ed. 7 plts. VG. *OREGON.* $80

Sheldon, Charles. THE WILDERNESS OF DENALI. NY: Scribner's, (1930) 1960. "New ed." VG+ in VG dj. *BACKMAN.* $40

Sheldon, Charles. THE WILDERNESS OF DENALI. NY: Scribners, (1960). Pvt lib label taped to spine of dj, o/w VG. *ARTIS.* $32.50

Sheldon, Charles. THE WILDERNESS OF THE NORTH PACIFIC COAST ISLANDS, ETC. NY, 1912. 1st ed. NF. *MIKESH.* $235

Sheldon, Charles. THE WILDERNESS OF THE NORTH PACIFIC COAST ISLANDS. Scribners, 1912. 1st ed. xvi,246pp + frontis, 44 plts, 1 fldg map. Fine. *OREGON.* $150

Sheldon, Charles. THE WILDERNESS OF THE UPPER YUKON. A HUNTER'S EXPLORATIONS FOR WILD SHEEP IN SUB-ARCTIC MOUNTAINS. NY: Scribner's, 1919. 2nd ed, rev. Fldg map. Fine. *PARMER.* $275

Sheldon, Charles. THE WILDERNESS OF THE UPPER YUKON. Camden: Premier Press, 1987. Ltd ed, 427/3000. Full dec leather (blue), aeg. As New. *BLUE DRAGON.* $55

Sheller, Roscoe. BLOWSAND. Portland, OR: Metropolitan, 1963. 1st ed. Signed. Fine in Good+ dj. *CONNOLLY & WADE.* $35

Shelley, Mary. FRANKENSTEIN; or THE MODERN PROMETHEUS. Univ of CA, 1984. 1st trade ed. W/52 woodcuts by Barry Moser. Fine in Fine dj. *BEBBAH.* $40

Shelton, L. BEAUTIFUL GARDENS IN AMERICA. NY, 1915. 1st ed. 8 colored, 176 monochrome plts. Gilt dec cl w/lt wear at corners, speckling on cvrs. *SUTTON.* $65

Shelton, William Henry. THE JUMEL MANSION: BEING A FULL HISTORY. Boston: Houghton Mifflin, 1916. 1st ed. 1/750. Pict grn cl in blue, red, white and gilt, teg. Fine. Howes S-382. *CAPTAIN'S BOOKSHELF.* $175

Shepard, A.K. THE LAND OF THE AZTECS; OR, TWO YEARS IN MEXICO. Albany: Weed, Parsons & Company, 1859. 1st ed. 209pp, dark brn emb cl, gilt spine titles. Chip head of spine; else VG. Howes S385. *PARMER.* $195

Shepard, Elihu H. THE EARLY HISTORY OF ST. LOUIS AND MISSOURI FROM ITS FIRST EXPLORATION BY WHITE MEN IN 1673 TO 1843. St. Louis, 1870. 1st ed. Cvrs sl stained. Bottom 1/4 of cvrs & text damp-stained, o/w text VG & tight. Inscribed. Howes S387. *DIAMOND.* $75

Shepard, Odell. THE HARVEST OF A QUIET EYE. Boston/NY: Houghton Mifflin Co, 1927. 1st ed. VG+ in Good+ dj. Name, label. *BACKMAN.* $25

Shepard, Sam. OPERATION SIDEWINDER. Indianapolis: Bobbs-Merrill, (1970). 1st ed. VG in VG dj. *DRAMATIS PERSONAE.* $90

Shepard, Sam. THE UNSEEN HAND AND OTHER PLAYS. Indianapolis: Bobbs-Merrill, 1972. 1st ed. Very small mark to front of dj, else VG. *DRAMATIS PERSONAE.* $80

Shepherd, Henry Elliott. NARRATIVE OF PRISON LIFE AT BALTIMORE AND JOHNSON'S ISLAND, OHIO. Baltimore: Privately published. 1917. 1st ed. Orig 1/2 leather with marbled boards. NF. Scarce. *McGOWAN.* $750

Shepherd, Thos. H. METROPOLITAN IMPROVEMENTS; OR, LONDON, IN THE NINETEENTH CENTURY. London: Jones, 1847. 8vo. xlii,316pp. Engr title-pg, 44 plts. Orig cl, spine tears, sl foxed and spotted, o/w VG; aeg. *WORLDWIDE.* $95

Sheppard, Edgar. LECTURES ON MADNESS IN ITS MEDICAL, LEGAL, AND SOCIAL ASPECTS. London, 1873. 1st ed. Front inner hinge cracked. *FYE.* $150

Sheppard, William Arthur. RED SHIRTS REMEMBERED, SOUTHERN BRIGADIERS OF THE RECONSTRUCTION PERIOD. Atlanta, 1940. 1st ed. Inscribed. VG+ in dj. *PRATT.* $95

Shepperson, Archibald B. JOHN PARADISE AND LUCY LUDWELL—OF LONDON AND WILLIAMSBURG. Richmond: Dietz Press, 1942. 1st ed. Almost Fine in Fine dj. *AARD.* $25

Sherer, John. RURAL LIFE. London: The London Printing and Pub Co., Ltd. N.d. (circa 1868). xvi,1016pp. Index. Frontis w/tissue guard. Orig 1/2 brown calf over marbled boards, gilt. Edges marbled. *KARMIOLE.* $250

Sheridan, Clare. MY AMERICAN DIARY. NY: Boni & Liveright (1922). 1st US ed. Cvrs warped, sl stained. Lib bkpl. VG. *SECOND LIFE.* $35

Sheridan, Clare. TURKISH KALEIDOSCOPE. NY: Dodd, Mead., 1926. Few pencil notes, o/w fresh. *SCHOYER'S.* $25

Sheridan, Philip H. INDIAN FIGHTING IN THE FIFTIES IN OREGON AND WASHINGTON TERRITORIES. Fairfield, WA, (1987). 92pp. VF. *PRATT.* $15

Sheridan, Philip H. OUTLINE DESCRIPTIONS OF THE POSTS IN THE MILITARY DIVISION OF THE MISSOURI. Fort Collins: Old Army Press, (1972). Reprints 1876 ed. Howes S394. VG in VG dj. *OREGON.* $60

Sheridan, Richard Brinsley. THE RIVALS. Illus Rene Ben Sussan. Cl, glassine dj, slipcase. London: LEC, 1953. Ltd to 1500 ptd at The Curwen Press, illus handcolored in Paris, signed by Ben Sussan. Fine. *JAFFE.* $150

Sherman, Harold M. BASES FULL! Grosset & Dunlap, 1928. VG in dj. Evidence of dampstain to both book and jacket. *STAHR.* $25

Sherman, John. RECOLLECTIONS OF FORTY YEARS IN THE HOUSE, SENATE AND CABINET. Chicago: Werner, 1895, 1896. Ltr 1 vol ptg. VG+. *ARCHER.* $45

Sherman, Mandel and Thomas R. Henry. HOLLOW FOLK. NY, (1933). Sl wear. *NUTMEG.* $20

Sherman, William Tecumseh. HOME LETTERS OF GENERAL SHERMAN. NY, 1909. Ed by M.A. DeWolfe Howe. 1st ed. Spine faded a little o/w VG+. *PRATT.* $40

Sherman, William Tecumseh. HOME LETTERS OF GENERAL SHERMAN. NY, 1909. 1st ed. NF. *McGOWAN.* $55

Sherman, William Tecumseh. MEMOIRS OF GENERAL W.T. SHERMAN. 2 vols. NY, 1875. 405 & 409pp & ads. Cvrs badly worn, spine and back of one volume separated from text, however still attached. Hinges firm and o/w VG. *PRATT.* $60

Sherren, James. INJURIES OF NERVES AND THEIR TREATMENT. NY, 1908. 1st Amer ed. *FYE.* $75

Sherrill, Charles Hitchcock. STAINED GLASS TOURS IN FRANCE. NY & London: John Lane, 1908. *CULLEN.* $20

Sherrington, Charles. MAN ON HIS NATURE. Cambridge, 1951. 2nd ed. *FYE.* $50

Sherrington, Charles. SELECTED WRITINGS OF SIR CHARLES SHERRINGTON. Ed by D. Denny-Brown. NY, 1940. 1st Amer ed. Ex-lib. Scarce. *FYE.* $200

Sherrington, Charles. THE ENDEAVOUR OF JEAN FERNEL. Cambridge, 1946. 1st ed. Dj. *FYE.* $60

Sherrington, Charles. THE INTEGRATIVE ACTION OF THE NERVOUS SYSTEM. New Haven, 1948. 2nd ed. *FYE.* $50

Sherwin, Oscar. PROPHET OF LIBERTY, THE LIFE AND TIMES OF WENDELL PHILLIPS. NY, (1958). 1st ed. 814pp. A little dj wear, chipping; o/w VG+. *PRATT.* $30

Sherwood, Midge. DAYS OF VINTAGE, YEARS OF VISION. Vol. I. San Marino: Orizaba Pubs, 1982. Gold-stamped cl in dj. Inscribed. *DAWSON'S.* $125

Sherwood, Robert Emmet. THE QUEEN'S HUSBAND. NY: Scribner's, 1928. Fine in NF dj. 1st ed. TLS from Sherwood laid in. *CHAPEL HILL.* $45

Sherwood, Robert Emmet. WATERLOO BRIDGE. NY & London: Scribner's, 1930. NF in dj (sl chipping). 1st ed. *CHAPEL HILL.* $35

Sherwood-Dunn, B. REGIONAL ANESTHESIA (VICTOR PAUCHET'S TECHNIQUE). Phila, 1922. 1st ed. *FYE.* $50

Shiel, M.P. THE INVISIBLE VOICES. NY: Vanguard Press, 1936. 1st US ed. VG in soiled dj which is rubbed at edges. *BERNARD.* $125

Shiel, M.P. XELUCHA AND OTHERS. Sauk City, WI: Arkham House, 1975. One of 4,283. This was 1st US collection of Shiel's supernatural tales. New in dj. *BERNARD.* $25

Shields, G.O. (Coquina). HUNTING IN THE GREAT WEST (RUSTLINGS IN THE ROCKIES.) Chicago: Belford, Clarke, (1883). Some signatures loose, o/w Good. *LAURIE.* $45

Shields, G.O. THE BIG GAME OF NORTH AMERICA. Chicago/NY: Rand, McNally, 1980. Pp 184-85 stained. *HUDSON.* $80

Shimer, R.H. SQUAW POINT. NY: Harper & Row, 1972. 1st ed. Tiny spotting top edge, o/w Fine in dj, sl fading. *MORDIDA.* $35

Shimer, R.H. THE CRICKET CAGE. NY: Harper & Row, 1975. 1st ed. VF in dj. *MORDIDA.* $30

Shine, Walter and Jean. A MACDONALD POTPOURRI. Gainesville, FL: Univ of FL, 1988. 1st ed. VF w/o dj as issued. *MORDIDA.* $60

Shingleton, Royce Garden. JOHN TAYLOR WOOD, SEA GHOST OF THE CONFEDERACY. Athens, (1982). Light dj wear o/w Fine. *PRATT.* $27.50

Shinkle, James. ROBERT CASEY AND THE RANCH ON THE RIO HONDO. Roswell, NM: Hall-Poorbaugh Press, (1970). 1st ed. Fine. *OREGON.* $40

Shinn, G. Hazen. SHOSHONEAN DAYS: RECOLLECTIONS OF A RESIDENCE OF FIVE YEARS AMONG THE INDIANS...1885-1889. Glendale: Arthur H. Clark, privately ptd for author, 1941. 1st ed, ltd to 250. Fine. *BOOK MARKET.* $325

Shipp, Barnard. HISTORY OF HERNANDO DE SOTO AND FLORIDA...FROM 1512 TO 1568. Phila., 1881. 1st ed. (12),689pp, untrimmed. 2 fldg maps. Orig cl, a little light staining on covers, hinges mended. Howes S423. *GINSBERG.* $300

Shippey, Lee. THE LOS ANGELES BOOK. Boston: Houghton Mifflin, 1950. 1st ed. Fine in NF dj. *CONNOLLY & WADE.* $35

Shippey, Lee. THE LUCKIEST MAN ALIVE. LA: Westernlore, 1959 1st ed. Inscribed. Dj, minor chipping, else Fine. Blue cl, gilt. VF. *CONNOLLY & WADE.* $40

Shiras, George. HUNTING WILD LIFE WITH CAMERA AND FLASHLIGHT. 2 vols. Washington, 1935. VG. *ARTIS.* $35

Shirley, Evelyn Philip. SOME ACCOUNT OF ENGLISH DEER PARKS. London: John Murray, 1867. 1st ed. G+. *OLD LONDON.* $125

Shirley, Glenn. BUCKSKIN AND SPURS. A GALLERY....NY: Hastings, 1958. 1st ed. VF in Fine dj. *CONNOLLY & WADE.* $35

Shirley, Glenn. SIX-GUN AND SILVER STAR. Albuquerque: Univ of NM Press, 1955. 1st ed. Cl, dj. VG. *SCHOYER'S.* $30

Shirley, Glenn. TOUGHEST OF THEM ALL. Univ of NM, 1953. 1st ed. Fine in Fine dj. *VARNER.* $25

SHIRLEY TEMPLE IN "DIMPLES". Akron, OH & NY, 1936. 1st ed. Saalfield Pub Co imprint. Stapled wraps. VG. *McCLINTOCK.* $35

SHIRLEY TEMPLE IN "HEIDI". Akron, 1937. Edgewear. Good. *ARTIS.* $22.50

SHIRLEY TEMPLE IN "POOR LITTLE RICH GIRL". Akron, OH & NY, (1936). 1st ed. Saalfield Pub Co. Stapled wraps. VG. *McCLINTOCK.* $35

SHIRLEY TEMPLE IN "STOWAWAY". Akron, OH & NY, 1937. 1st ed. Saalfield imprint. Stapled wraps. VG. *McCLINTOCK.* $35

Shishido, Misako. THE FOLK TOYS OF JAPAN. Rutland, VT: Japan Pub Trading Co, (1963). 1st ed. Fine in VG dj. *WREDEN.* $35

Shivers, Louise. HERE TO GET MY BABY OUT OF JAIL. NY: Random House, (1983). 1st ed, 3rd prtg. Inscribed. Orig cl-backed boards. Fine in dj. *CHAPEL HILL.* $30

Shklovsky, I.S. COSMIC RADIO WAVES. Cambridge: Harvard Univ Press, 1960. VG in plastic covered dj. *KNOLLWOOD.* $35

Shock, Nathan. A CLASSIFIED BIBLIOGRAPHY OF GERONTOLOGY AND GERIATRICS. Stanford, 1951. 1st ed. Dj. *FYE.* $125

Shoemaker, Len. ROARING FORK VALLEY: AN ACCOUNT OF ITS SETTLEMENT AND DEVELOPMENT. Denver: Sage, Alan Swallow, 1958. 1st ed. NF in Good dj. *CONNOLLY & WADE.* $65

Sholes, A.E. VOLUME IX. SHOLE'S DIRECTORY OF THE CITY OF SAVANNAH, 1888. Savannah, 1888. Shaken w/loose pp. Ex-lib. *HUDSON.* $95

Sholokhov, Mikhail. AND QUIET FLOWS THE DON. Trans Stephen Garry. London: Putnam, (1934). 1st ed in Eng, 1st bk. Offsetting to eps, else Fine in dj (sunned and lightly chipped). *CAPTAIN'S BOOKSHELF.* $150

SHOOTING THE LONG BOW—A SHORT LESSON IN ARCHERY. LA: National Archery Tackle Co., n.d. (20s?) Probably 1st ed. Small 4to, red paper stapled pamphlet. Scarce. In custom case. *OLD LONDON.* $20

Shore, Teignmouth. CANTERBURY. A&C Black, 1907. 1st ed. 7s 6d Series. Minor tear top spine, else VG-NF. *OLD LONDON.* $40

Short, Ernest H. THE HOUSE OF GOD. NY: Macmillan, 1926. 97 plts. VG+. *BLUE DRAGON.* $50

Short, Nicholas M. et al. MISSION TO EARTH....NASA SP-360, Washington, DC, 1976. VG in pict grey cl. *KNOLLWOOD.* $55

Shortridge, G.C. THE MAMMALS OF SOUTH WEST AFRICA, A BIOLOGICAL ACCOUNT OF THE FORMS OCCURRING IN THAT REGION. 18 plts and 12 maps. 2 vols. London, 1934. Gilt-dec cl. Spines faded; corners bumped; pp yellowed. *SUTTON.* $215

SHREWBETTINA GOES TO WORK. NY, 1981. John Goodall. Pop-up bk. *BOOKFINDERS INTL.* $30

Shriner, C.A. THE BIRDS OF NEW JERSEY. N.p., 1896. 31 plts. Ep partially split; occasional pg soiling; pp yellowed; ex-lib. *SUTTON.* $40

Shriner, C.A. THE BIRDS OF NEW JERSEY. N.p.: NJ Fish and Game Commission, 1896. 212pp; plts. Good+. *SMITHFIELD.* $27

Shternfeld, A. SOVIET SPACE SCIENCE. NY: Basic Books, 1959. 2nd rev ed. Good in worn dj. *KNOLLWOOD.* $34

Shuckard, W.E. BRITISH BEES. London, 1866. 16 hand colored plts. Wear at extremities, hinges reinforced. Pres copy w/inscrip. *SUTTON.* $135

Shuler, Marjorie. A PASSENGER TO ADVENTURE. NY: Appleton Century, 1939. 1st ed. VG in Good dj. *AARD.* $25

Shulman, Alix. TO THE BARRICADES. NY: Crowell, (1971). 1st ed. Dj rubbed, short tear, price-clipped. *AKA.* $22

Shulman, H.M. SLUMS OF NEW YORK. NY, 1938. 1st ed. Top fore-edge sl stained, o/w VG in sl soiled, repaired dj. *DIAMOND.* $25

Shulman, Irving. THE AMBOY DUKES. GC: Doubleday, 1947. 1st ed, 1st bk. Fine in dj (chipped, torn, o/w VG+). *ARCHER.* $30

Shulman, Max. THE MANY LOVES OF DOBIE GILLIS. Doubleday, 1951. 1st ed. VG in chipped and worn dj. *STAHR.* $15

Shumway, Nina. YOUR DESERT AND MINE. LA: Westernlore, 1960. 1st ed. Fine in Fine dj. *OREGON.* $30

Shurcliff, Sidney Nichols. JUNGLE ISLANDS. NY: G.P. Putnam's Sons, 1930. 1st ed. Hinge weak, small dampstain at heel. *PARMER.* $75

Shurcliff, Sidney Nichols. JUNGLE ISLANDS. THE "ILLYRIA" IN THE SOUTH SEAS. THE RECORD OF THE CRANE PACIFIC EXPEDITION. NY: G.P. Putnam's Sons, 1930. 1st ed. Orig gilt dec black cl. Gilt titles. Very minor spots else Fine. *GREAT EPIC.* $95

Shurtleff, Harold R. THE LOG CABIN MYTH: A STUDY OF THE EARLY DWELLINGS. Harvard Univ Press, 1939. 1st ed. Samuel Eliot Morison (ed). VG, name. *AUTHORS OF THE WEST.* $30

Shute, Henry. THE REAL DIARY OF A REAL BOY. Smith, (1967). 194pp. Illus by Tasha Tudor. VG in VG dj. *BEBBAH.* $30

Shute, Nevil. BEYOND THE BLACK STUMP. London: Heinemann, 1956. 1st ed. Fine in dj w/minor wear. *ELSE FINE.* $50

Shute, Nevil. MOST SECRET. NY: Morrow, 1945. Fine in dj w/two small chips, minor edgewear. *ELSE FINE.* $25

Shute, Nevil. ON THE BEACH. NY: Morrow, 1957. 1st ed. Fine in dj w/light wear. *ELSE FINE.* $40

Shutes, Milton H. LINCOLN AND CALIFORNIA. Stanford, (1943). 1st ed. Fine in dj. *PRATT.* $25

Shutes, Milton H. LINCOLN AND CALIFORNIA. Stanford Univ.: Stanford Univ Press, (1943). Dj. Fine. *SCHOYER'S.* $25

Siberrad, Una and Sophie Lyall. DUTCH BULBS AND GARDENS. A&C Black, 1909. 1st ed. 7s 6d Series. Some edgewear, front cover dogeared, few pages loose, but easily VG. *OLD LONDON.* $40

Sibley, Henry H. IRON FACE: THE ADVENTURES OF JACK FRAZER. Chicago: Caxton Club, 1950. T. Blegen and S. Davidson (eds). Ltd to 500, 1st thus. Red and gilt cl. Fine. *CONNOLLY & WADE.* $150

Sibley, Henry H. THE UNFINISHED AUTOBIOGRAPHY OF...TOGETHER WITH...LETTERS FROM THE THIRTIES. Theodore Blegen (ed), Minneapolis: Voyageur Press, 1932. 1st ed, #11/200, slipcased. 1/4 leather, cl. Fine in Good+ slipcase. Howes S445. *OREGON.* $150

Sibley, Henry Hastings. IRON FACE, THE ADVENTURES OF JACK FRAZER, FRONTIER WARRIOR, SCOUT AND HUNTER. Ed by Theodore C. Blegen & Sarah A. Davidson. Chicago, 1950. 1st ed in book form; ltd to 500. 206pp. Fine. *PRATT.* $110

Sibree, James. MADAGASCAR BEFORE THE CONQUEST. NY: Macmillan; London: Fisher Unwin, 1896. 1st ed. xii,382pp. Fldg map. Near VG ex-lib. *WORLDWIDE.* $40

Sickler, Joseph S. TEA BURNING TOWN. NY: Author, (1950). *HEINOLDT.* $35

Siddons, Anne Rivers. COLONY. NY: Harper Collins (1992). Adv rev copy from uncorrected proofs. Signed. Fine in wraps. *DORN.* $45

Siddons, Anne Rivers. HEARTBREAK HOTEL. NY: S&S, (1976). 1st ed. Just about Fine (rmdr mk) in like dj. Inscribed by Siddons. *CAPTAIN'S BOOKSHELF.* $60

Siddons, Anne Rivers. HEARTBREAK HOTEL. NY: Simon & Schuster (1976). 1st ed. Inscribed. Fine in dj. *DORN.* $75

Siddons, Anne Rivers. HOMEPLACE. NY: Harpers, (1987). 1st ed. Fine in dj. Briefly inscribed by Siddons. *CAPTAIN'S BOOKSHELF.* $45

Siddons, Anne Rivers. OUTER BANKS. NY: Harper Collins, (1991). 1st ed. As new in dj. Briefly inscribed by Siddons. *CAPTAIN'S BOOKSHELF.* $40

Siddons, Anne Rivers. OUTER BANKS. NY: Harper Collins (1991). Adv rev copy from uncorrected proofs. Signed. Fine in wraps. *DORN.* $45

Siddons, Anne Rivers. PEACHTREE ROAD. NY: Harper, (1988). 1st ed. Fine in dj. Briefly inscribed by Siddons. *CAPTAIN'S BOOKSHELF.* $50

Sidebottom, John K. OVERLAND MAIL. (London): Postal History Society, (1948). Cl a little soiled and scraped. *SCHOYER'S.* $45

Sidemann, Belle Becker and Lillian Friedman (eds). EUROPE LOOKS AT THE CIVIL WAR. NY, (1960). 1st ed. 323pp. Light dj wear, line of staining on upper corner; o/w Fine. *PRATT.* $30

Siebenheller, Norma. P.D. JAMES. NY: Ungar, 1983. 1st ed. VF in dj. *ELSE FINE.* $20

Siedentopf, A.R. THE LAST STRONGHOLD OF BIG GAME. NY: McBride, 1946. VG+. *MIKESH.* $20

Siegel, Rudolph. GALEN ON SENSE PERCEPTION. Basel, 1970. 1st ed. Dj. *FYE.* $75

Sienkiewicz, Henry. PORTRAIT OF AMERICA. LETTERS OF HENRY SIENKIEWICZ. Charles Morley (ed, trans). NY: Columbia Univ, 1959. 1st ed. Fine in VG dj. *CONNOLLY & WADE.* $40

Sienkiewicz, Henryk. QUO VADIS? Verona: Printed at the Officina Bodoni for LEC, 1959. 1/1500 illus, signed by Salvatore Fiume and Giovanni Mardersteig, the printer. Fine in spine sunned dj and slipcase. *CAPTAIN'S BOOKSHELF.* $125

Sierksma, F. TIBET'S TERRIFYING DEITIES. Rutland: Chas. Tuttle, (1966). 42 plts. 1st ed. VG. *BLUE DRAGON.* $85

Sigal, Clancy. ZONE OF THE INTERIOR. NY: Crowell, (1976). 1st ed. Signed. Fine in Fine dj. *LOPEZ.* $35

Sigaud, Louis A. BELLE BOYD, CONFEDERATE SPY. Richmond, (1944). 2nd ed, (1945). 254pp. Ex-lib. Ffep torn out. VG in dj. *PRATT.* $35

Sigerist, Henry (ed). AMERICAN REVIEW OF SOVIET MEDICINE. VOLUMES 1-5. 1943-1947. Scarce. *FYE.* $200

Sigerist, Henry. AMERICAN MEDICINE. NY, 1934. 1st Eng trans. Spine faded w/small tear at head of spine. *FYE.* $95

Sigerist, Henry. MAN AND MEDICINE: AN INTRODUCTION TO MEDICAL KNOWLEDGE. NY, 1932. 1st Eng trans. *FYE.* $75

Sigerist, Henry. ON THE HISTORY OF MEDICINE. Ed. by Felix Marti-Ibanez. NY, 1960. 1st ed. *FYE.* $50

Sigerist, Henry. ON THE SOCIOLOGY OF MEDICINE. NY, 1960. 1st ed. *FYE.* $50

Sigerist, Henry. THE GREAT DOCTORS. NY, 1933. 1st Eng trans. 436pp. *FYE.* $100

Sigler, W.F. and J.W. FISHES OF THE GREAT BASIN, A NATURAL HISTORY. Reno: Univ of NV, 1987. 1st ed. NF in Fine dj. *MIKESH.* $30

Sigmund, Jay G. WAPSIPINICON TALES. Cedar Rapids: IA, (1927). 1st ed. Fine in Good dj. *DIAMOND.* $25

SIGNS BEFORE DEATH. A RECORD OF STRANGE APPARITIONS. London: (Wm. Tegg), 1875. New, enl ed. Pub's brn grained cl over beveled boards. 32-pg catalogue of bks of William Tegg & Co. after last pg of text (foxed; the book is not foxed). *BOOK BLOCK.* $50

Sigourney, Mrs. L(ydia) H(untley). LETTERS OF LIFE. NY: Appleton, 1866. 1st ed. 414pp. Ptg B (no priority) on sheets that bulk 7/8". VG. BAL 17960. *SECOND LIFE.* $50

Siguenza y Gongora, Carlos de. THE MERCURIO VOLANTE...FIRST EXPEDITION OF DON DIEGO DE VARGAS INTO NEW MEXICO IN 1692. LA, Quivira Society, 1932. 1st Eng trans. Ltd to 655 numbered. Orig cl over boards. Fine. Howes S455. *GINSBERG.* $125

Silberrad, U. and S. Lyall. DUTCH BULBS AND GARDENS. London, 1909. 24 colored plts. Cloth. Front hinge cracked, spine ends chipped; ep browning, lt foxing. *SUTTON.* $50

Silko, Leslie Marmon. ALMANAC OF THE DEAD. NY: S&S, (1991). 1st ed. Fine in Fine dj. Signed. *LOPEZ*. $45

Silko, Leslie Marmon. CEREMONY. NY: Viking, (1977). 1st ed. Fine in dj with small spot of rubbing at top of spine but o/w Fine, virtually unfaded, a rarity with the first issue jacket on this title. *LOPEZ*. $250

Silko, Leslie Marmon. CEREMONY. NY: Viking, (1977). 1st ed. Fine in dj (spine faded). *CAPTAIN'S BOOKSHELF*. $100

Silko, Leslie Marmon. STORYTELLER. NY: Seaver Books, (1981). 1st ed. Uncommon hardcover ed. Fine in Fine dj. *LOPEZ*. $150

Sillar, Frederick Cameron and Ruth Mary Meyler. THE SYMBOLIC PIG. Edinburgh.: Oliver & Boyd. (1961). 1st ed. 8 color plts. Gray cl in dj. Scarce. *KARMIOLE*. $50

Sillitoe, Alan. SATURDAY NIGHT AND SUNDAY MORNING. NY: Alfred A. Knopf, 1959. 1st Amer ed. Orig cl-backed boards. Fine in excellent dj (sl fraying; soil, rubbing). *PIRAGES*. $125

Sillitoe, Alan. SATURDAY NIGHT AND SUNDAY MORNING. NY: Knopf, (1959). 1st US ed, 1st bk. Fine in NF dj. *UNGER*. $75

Sillitoe, Alan. THE LOST FLYING BOAT. Boston: LB, (1983). 1st US ed. Fine in dj. Inscribed. *CAPTAIN'S BOOKSHELF*. $75

Sills, Beverly. BUBBLES—A SELF PORTRAIT. Indianapolis: Bobbs-Merrill, (1976). 1st ed. Bkpl. Fine- in Fine- dj. *AARD*. $25

Silva, Rev. Owen da (ed). MISSION MUSIC OF CALIFORNIA: A COLLECTION...MISSION HYMNS AND MASSES. (LA): (Warren F. Lewis), (1941). 1st ed. Signed. One of 975 numbered. NF in chipped dj. *LAURIE*. $100

Silver, H. HISTORY OF NEW HAMPSHIRE GAME & FUR-BEARERS. Concord: F. & G. Dept, May 1957. Ex-libris. VG+. *MIKESH*. $20

Silverberg, Robert. LORD VALENTINE'S CASTLE. Harper, 1980. One of 250 numbered, signed. As New in slipcase. *MADLE*. $100

Silverberg, Robert. SAILING TO BYZANTIUM. SF: Underwood-Miller, 1985. Signed, ltd ed. One of 250. 1st ed. VF in dj, slipcase. *ELSE FINE*. $65

Silverman, Al. JOE DIMAGGIO—THE GOLDEN YEAR 1941. Prentice-Hall, 1969. 1st ed. VG+ in Fine dj. *PLAPINGER*. $45

Simak, Clifford D. COSMIC ENGINEERS. (London): Severn House, (1985). 1st thus. Fine in Fine dj. *OTHER WORLDS*. $25

Simak, Clifford. RING AROUND THE SUN. Simon & Schuster, 1953. 1st ed. NF in dj. *MADLE*. $65

Simenon, Georges. AFRICAN TRIO. NY: HBJ, 1979. 1st ed. VF in dj. *ELSE FINE*. $25

Simenon, Georges. BETTY. NY: Harcourt Brace Jovanovich, 1975. 1st Amer ed. Fine in dj. *MORDIDA*. $25

Simenon, Georges. DESTINATIONS. GC: Doubleday, 1955. 1st ed. Name. Fine; very narrow chip at spine heel, light edgewear to dj. *ELSE FINE*. $30

Simenon, Georges. FOUR DAYS IN A LIFETIME. London: Hamish Hamilton, 1977. 1st Eng ed. Fine in dj. *MORDIDA*. $30

Simenon, Georges. INSPECTOR MAIGRET AND THE KILLERS. Doubleday, 1954. 1st Amer ed. VG in dj with edgewear, chips, piece missing spine. *BEBBAH*. $22

Simenon, Georges. INTIMATE MEMOIRS. London: Hamilton, 1984. 1st Brit. ed. NF in dj with minimal wear. *SILVER DOOR*. $25

Simenon, Georges. MAGNET OF DOOM. London: Routledge, 1948. 1st ed. Fine in Fine dj. *BEASLEY*. $40

Simenon, Georges. MAIGRET AND THE TOY VILLAGE. NY: Harcourt, 1979. 1st Amer ed. Fine in dj. *SILVER DOOR*. $22.50

Simenon, Georges. MAIGRET AND M. LABBE. Harcourt, Brace, (1942). 1st Amer ed. Corner bump, wear, Good+. *BEBBAH*. $18

Simenon, Georges. MAIGRET AND THE APPARITION. NY: HBJ, 1976. 1st ed. VF in dj. *ELSE FINE*. $20

Simenon, Georges. MAIGRET AND THE BUM. Harcourt Brace Jovanovich, (1973). 1st Amer ed. VG in VG dj. *BEBBAH*. $15

Simenon, Georges. MAIGRET AND THE BURGLAR'S WIFE. Garden City: Doubleday Crime Club, 1956. 1st Amer ed. Fine in dj w/wear, couple closed tears. *MORDIDA*. $35

Simenon, Georges. MAIGRET AND THE BURGLAR'S WIFE. London: Hamilton, (1955). 1st Eng ed. Signed on bkpl. NF in NF dj. *UNGER*. $75

Simenon, Georges. MAIGRET AND THE BURGLAR'S WIFE. London: Hamish Hamilton, 1953. 1st Eng ed. Eps darkened, o/w Fine in dj. *MORDIDA*. $32.50

Simenon, Georges. MAIGRET AND THE KILLER. Harcourt Brace Jovanovich, (1971). 1st Amer ed. VG in dj with few tiny chips else VG. *BEBBAH*. $15

Simenon, Georges. MAIGRET AND THE LONER. Harcourt Brace Jovanovich, (1975). 1st Amer ed. VG in VG dj with touch of soil to top edge. *BEBBAH*. $15

Simenon, Georges. MAIGRET AND THE LONER. London: Hamish Hamilton, 1975. 1st Eng ed. VF in dj. *MORDIDA*. $45

Simenon, Georges. MAIGRET AND THE MINISTER. London: Hamish Hamilton, 1969. 1st Eng ed. Edges slightly darkened o/w VG in dj w/darkened spine. *MORDIDA*. $35

Simenon, Georges. MAIGRET AND THE NAHOUR CASE. NY: Harcourt Brace Jovanovich, 1982. 1st Amer ed. Fine in dj. *MORDIDA*. $25

Simenon, Georges. MAIGRET AND THE SATURDAY CALLER. London: Hamish Hamilton, 1964. 1st ed. Fine in NF dj (bit of darkening and small chip at head of spine). *BEASLEY*. $30

Simenon, Georges. MAIGRET AND THE SPINSTER. NY: HBJ, 1977. 1st ed. VF in dj. *ELSE FINE*. $20

Simenon, Georges. MAIGRET AND THE WINE MERCHANT. NY: Harcourt Brace Jovanovich, 1971. 1st Amer ed. Fine in dj w/tiny wear. *MORDIDA*. $25

Simenon, Georges. MAIGRET IN EXILE. Harcourt Brace Jovanovich, 1979. 1st Amer ed. VG in VG dj. *BEBBAH*. $15

Simenon, Georges. MAIGRET KEEPS A RENDEZVOUS. NY: Harcourt Brace, 1941. 1st Amer ed. VG in dj w/internal tape stains, chipped corners, and frayed spine ends. *MORDIDA*. $65

Simenon, Georges. MAIGRET'S FIRST CASE. London: Hamish Hamilton, 1958. 1st ed. Fine in Fine dj. *BEASLEY*. $40

Simenon, Georges. MAIGRET'S CHRISTMAS. NY: HBJ, 1977. 1st ed. VF in dj. *ELSE FINE*. $25

Simenon, Georges. MAIGRET'S FIRST CASE. London: Hamish Hamilton, 1958. 1st ed. Fine in Fine dj. *BEASLEY*. $40

Simenon, Georges. MAIGRET'S FIRST CASE. London: Hamish Hamilton, 1958. 1st Eng ed. Fine in dj w/tiny wear at top of spine and at corners. *MORDIDA*. $45

Simenon, Georges. MAIGRET'S PIPE. London: Hamish Hamilton, 1977. 1st Eng ed. Fine in dj. *MORDIDA*. $45

Simenon, Georges. MAIGRET'S SPECIAL MURDER. London: Hamish Hamilton, 1964. 1st Eng ed. Edges sl spotted, o/w Fine in dj w/wear. *MORDIDA*. $45

Simenon, Georges. MONSIEUR MONDE VANISHES. NY: HBJ, 1977. 1st ed. VF in dj. *ELSE FINE*. $25

Simenon, Georges. SUNDAY AND THE LITTLE MAN FROM ARCHANGEL. NY: HB&W, 1966. 1st ed. Fine in dj. *ELSE FINE*. $30

Simenon, Georges. TEDDY BEAR. NY: Harcourt Brace Jovanovich, 1972. 1st Amer ed. Fine in dj. *MORDIDA*. $30

Simenon, Georges. THE BLUE ROOM AND THE AC-COMPLICES. NY: HB & W, 1964. 1st ed. Fine. Minor rubs dj spine ends. *ELSE FINE.* $35

Simenon, Georges. THE BLUE ROOM. London: Hamish Hamilton, 1965. 1st ed. Fine in Fine dj. *BEASLEY.* $30

Simenon, Georges. THE DISAPPEARANCE OF ODILE. NY: Harcourt, 1972. 1st Amer ed. VF in dj. *SILVER DOOR.* $30

Simenon, Georges. THE FAMILY LIE. London: Hamish Hamilton, 1978. Fine in Fine dj. *BEASLEY.* $30

Simenon, Georges. THE FAMILY LIE. NY: HBJ, 1978. 1st ed. VF in dj. *ELSE FINE.* $25

Simenon, Georges. THE GIRL IN HIS PAST. Prentice-Hall, (1952). 1st Amer ed. VG in VG dj with edgewear, dampstain to bottom of rear panel. *BEBBAH.* $20

Simenon, Georges. THE HATTER'S PHANTOMS. NY: HBJ, 1976. 1st ed. VF in dj. *ELSE FINE.* $25

Simenon, Georges. THE IRON STAIRCASE. London: Hamish Hamilton, 1963. 1st Eng ed. Fine in dj w/minor wear, couple short closed tears. *MORDIDA.* $45

Simenon, Georges. THE IRON STAIRCASE. NY: HBJ, 1977. 1st ed. VF in dj. *ELSE FINE.* $25

Simenon, Georges. THE NOVEL OF MAN. NY: Harcourt, Brace, & World, 1964. 1st Amer ed. Ltd ed pub as New Year's greeting to friends. VF w/o dj as issued. *MORDIDA.* $25

Simenon, Georges. THE OLD MAN DIES. London: Hamish Hamilton, 1968. 1st ed. Fine in worn dj. *BEASLEY.* $25

Simenon, Georges. THE PATIENCE OF MAIGRET. London: Hamish Hamilton, 1966. 1st Eng ed. Fine in dj (sl darkened spine; rubbing along folds). *MORDIDA.* $30

Simenon, Georges. THE PREMIER. London: Hamish Hamilton, 1961. 1st Eng ed. Fine in dj. *MORDIDA.* $45

Simenon, Georges. THE RICH MAN. Harcourt Brace Jovanovich, (1971). 1st Amer ed. VG in VG dj. *BEBBAH.* $15

Simenon, Georges. THE SECOND MAIGRET OMNIBUS. London: Hamish Hamilton, 1964. Omnibus ed. Fine in dj w/minor wear at spine ends. *MORDIDA.* $45

Simenon, Georges. THE SHADOW FALLS. NY: Harcourt Brace, 1945. 1st Amer ed. VG in dj. *MORDIDA.* $45

Simenon, Georges. THE SHORT CASES OF INSPECTOR MAIGRET. Doubleday, 1959. 1st Amer ed. VG with edgewear in Good dj with few chips, tape repair on reverse. *BEBBAH.* $15

Simenon, Georges. THE SHORT CASES OF INSPECTOR MAIGRET. GC: Doubleday Crime Club, 1959. 1st ed. Lt ring stain on back cover o/w Fine in dj. Queen's Quorum title #118. *MORDIDA.* $100

Simenon, Georges. THE SNOW WAS BLACK. Prentice-Hall, (1950). 1st Amer ed. VG in Good dj. *BEBBAH.* $30

Simenon, Georges. THE WIDOWER. London: Hamish Hamilton, 1961. 1st Eng ed. Fine in dj. *MORDIDA.* $35

Simenon, Georges. THE WITNESSES & THE WATCHMAKER. GC: Doubleday, 1956. 1st ed. Fine. Minor wear to dj corners. *ELSE FINE.* $35

Simenon, Georges. THREE BEDS IN MANHATTAN. London: Hamish Hamilton, 1976. 1st Eng ed. Fine in price-clipped dj. *MORDIDA.* $30

Simenon, Georges. TIDAL WAVE. GC: Doubleday, 1954. 1st ed. Fine; lt edgewear, small chips at dj spine corners. *ELSE FINE.* $40

Simic, Charles and Mark Strand (eds). ANOTHER REPUBLIC: 17 EUROPEAN AND SOUTH AMERICAN WRITERS. NY: Ecco Press, 1976. 1st ed. Fine in dj. *CAPTAIN'S BOOKSHELF.* $35

Simic, Charles. AUSTERITIES. Poems. NY: Braziller, (1982). 1st ed. Fine in dj. *CAPTAIN'S BOOKSHELF.* $40

Simic, Charles. BIOGRAPHY AND A LAMENT. Hartford: Bartholomew's Cobble, (1976). 2nd ed. 1/200 signed. Fine in wrappers. *CAPTAIN'S BOOKSHELF.* $35

Simic, Charles. BIOGRAPHY AND A LAMENT. Poems 1961-1967. Hartford: Bartholomew's Cobble, (1976). 1st ed. Fine in wrappers. *CAPTAIN'S BOOKSHELF.* $40

Simic, Charles. CHARON'S COSMOLOGY. Poems. NY: Braziller, (1977). 1st ed. Fine in dj. *CAPTAIN'S BOOKSHELF.* $45

Simic, Charles. CLASSIC BALLROOM DANCES. POEMS. NY: Braziller, (1980). 1st ed. Fine in dj. *CAPTAIN'S BOOKSHELF.* $40

Simic, Charles. RETURN TO A PLACE LIT BY A GLASS OF MILK. NY: George, (1974). 1st ed. Fine in dj. *CAPTAIN'S BOOKSHELF.* $45

Simic, Charles. SCHOOL FOR DARK THOUGHTS. Pawlet: Banyan Press, 1978. 1st ed. 1/235 signed. Fine in wrappers w/paper label. *CAPTAIN'S BOOKSHELF.* $75

Simic, Charles. SHAVING AT NIGHT. POEMS. Woodcuts by Helen Siegal. SF: Meadow Press, 1982. 1st ed. 1/200 signed by Simic and Siegal. Fine. *CAPTAIN'S BOOKSHELF.* $100

Simic, Charles. SOMEWHERE AMOUNG US A STONE IS THINKING NOTES. (SF: Kayak, 1969). Fine in wrappers. Inscribed. *CAPTAIN'S BOOKSHELF.* $100

Simic, Charles. THE CHICKEN WITHOUT A HEAD: A NEW VERSION. Portland: Trace Editions, 1983. 1st ed. 1/75 numbered, signed. Inscribed. Fine in wrappers. *CAPTAIN'S BOOKSHELF.* $75

Simic, Charles. WHAT THE GRASS SAYS. (SF: Kayak), n.d. 1st ed. Fine in wraps. Inscribed. *CAPTAIN'S BOOKSHELF.* $125

Simmons, Charles. THE OLD-FASHIONED DARLING. NY: Coward, McCann & Geoghegan, (1971). 1st ed. Inscribed. VG in dj. *LOPEZ.* $45

Simmons, Dan. PHASES OF GRAVITY. London: Headline, 1989. 1st hardcover ed. Signed, ltd. #31 of 250. Leather binding, aeg. Fine in slipcase. *ELSE FINE.* $200

Simmons, Dan. SONG OF KALI. NY: Bluejay Books, 1987. 1st ed. As New in dj. *ELSE FINE.* $150

Simmons, Dan. THE FALL OF HYPERION. Doubleday, 1990. Uncorrected proof. VF in royal blue wraps. *STAHR.* $60

Simmons, Herbert A. CORNER BOY. Boston: Houghton Mifflin, 1957. 1st ed, 1st bk. Name. Fine, minor rubbing at dj corner. *ELSE FINE.* $45

Simmons, Marc. THE LITTLE LION OF THE SOUTHWEST, A LIFE OF MANUEL ANTONIO CHAVES. Chicago, (1973). 1st ed. 263pp. Minor dj chipping, marks left on title page when bkpl removed o/w VG+. *PRATT.* $35

Simms, W. Gilmore. EUTAW. A SEQUEL TO THE FORAYERS, OR THE RAID OF THE DOG-DAYS. NY: Redfield, 1856. 1st ed. Ad leaf inserted at front. (2)pp ads, 582pp,4pp ads. Orig olive grn cl. Sm morocco bkpl but handsome showing little wear. Custom grn cl chemise, 1/4 morocco slipcase. *CHAPEL HILL.* $425

Simms, W. Gilmore. MELLICHAMPE. NY: Redfield, 1854. 1st rev ed. 431pp,(16)pp ads. Orig cl. Lt spotting on cover, traces of lt foxing, but VG. Frontis, engr, ptd title pgs. *CHAPEL HILL.* $75

Simms, W. Gilmore. POEMS, DESCRIPTIVE, DRAMATIC, LEGENDARY AND CONTEMPLATIVE. NY: Redfield, 1853. 2 vols, 1st ed. Issue A, w/NY, Redfield imprint (later Charleston, John Russell imprint). 348; 360pp,(12)pp ads. Orig grn cl. Lib bkpl, blindstamp, spine ends lightly rubbed, neat bkpl, blindstamp of non-circulating lib, else VG+ set. BAL 18144. Comma after "Descriptive" lacking on title pg. *CHAPEL HILL.* $350

Simms, W. Gilmore. THE LIFE OF FRANCIS MARION. NY, Geo. F. Coolidge, (1844). 347pp + frontis & 10 plts. Orig embossed cl w/pict glt stamped spine. 10th ed (ca 1850). VG. *OREGON.* $45

Simms, W. Gilmore. THE WIGWAM AND THE CABIN...FIRST SERIES. NY: Wiley and Putnam, 1845. 1st ed, 1st ptg. [4](ads),233,10pp(ads). Orig ptd wrappers. Lacking rear cover; lower corner front cvr chipped; repair to spine, some occasional foxing, withal Good. *WREDEN.* $350

Simon, Edith. THE PIEBALD STANDARD. Boston: Little, Brown, & Co, (1959). 1st ed. VG in G dj. *BLUE DRAGON.* $27.50

Simon, John. GENERAL PATHOLOGY, AS CONDUCIVE TO THE ESTABLISHMENT OF RATIONAL PRINCIPLES FOR THE DIAGNOSIS AND TREATMENT OF DISEASE. Phila, 1852. 1st Amer ed. *FYE.* $100

Simon, Roger L. HEIR. Macmillan, 1968. 1st ed. Fine, dj. Signed, inscribed. *STAHR.* $25

Simon, Roger L. THE BIG FIX. (London): Deutsch, (1974). 1st Eng ed. Signed. Fine in laminated boards. *LOPEZ.* $50

Simon, Roger L. THE BIG FIX. Straight Arrow, 1973. 1st ed. VG or better in wraps. Signed & inscribed. Reading crease near spine. *STAHR.* $20

Simon, Roger L. THE MAMA TASS MANIFESTO. Holt, 1970. 1st ed. NF in dj. Signed & inscribed. Dj spine lightly faded. *STAHR.* $20

Simon, Roger L. THE STRAIGHT MAN. NY: Villard, 1986. 1st ed. Signed. VF in dj. *SILVER DOOR.* $35

Simon, Roger L. WILD TURKEY. Straight Arrow, 1974. 1st. NF in dj. Small chip head of spine. *STAHR.* $20

SIMPLE STORIES FOR LITTLE READERS. Phila: Fithian, 1841. 1st ed. 72pp. 5 hand-colored illus. VG to Fine. *BOOK MARKET.* $50

Simpson, Charles. LIFE IN THE MINES. Chicago: Rhodes & McClure, (1898). Cover shows some wear, else clean. *LAURIE.* $30

Simpson, Dorothy. CLOSE HER EYES. London: Joseph, 1984. 1st ed. NF in Fine dj. *SILVER DOOR.* $25

Simpson, Dorothy. DOOMED TO DIE. NY: Charles Scribner's Sons, 1991. 1st Amer ed. VF in dj. *MORDIDA.* $22.50

Simpson, Dorothy. SUSPICIOUS DEATH. London: Joseph, 1988. 1st ed. About Fine in dj. *SILVER DOOR.* $25

Simpson, Evan John. ATLANTIC IMPACT 1861. Melbourne, (1952). 1st ed. Fine in VG dj. *McGOWAN.* $45

Simpson, George Gaylord. ATTENDING MARVELS—A PATAGONIAN JOURNAL. (Argentina). NY: Macmillan, 1934. Fldg map. 1st ed. Fine in Near VG dj. *GREAT EPIC.* $45

Simpson, George. AN OVERLAND JOURNEY ROUND THE WORLD DURING THE YEARS 1841 AND 1842. Phila: Lea, 1847. 1st Amer ed. 2 vols bound in one: 273, 230pp. Orig cl. Howes S495. *GINSBERG.* $300

Simpson, George. LONDON CORRESPONDENCE INWARD FROM SIR GEORGE SIMPSON 1841-42. London: Hudson's Bay Record Soc, 1973. Frontis, 3 fldg maps (1 dampstained). Mark on back cvr. VG. *PARMER.* $40

Simpson, James H. NAVAHO EXPEDITION. Ed by Frank McNitt. Norman, (1964). 1st ed. 296pp. VG+ in dj. *PRATT.* $40

Simpson, James. REPORT AND MAP OF THE ROUTE FROM FORT SMITH, ARKANSAS, TO SANTA FE, NEW MEXICO, MADE BY...Wash., SED12, 1850. 1st ed. 25pp., foxed. 4 fldg maps. Half morocco. Howes S500. *GINSBERG.* $300

Simpson, John. GAME AND GAME COVERTS. Sheffield and London, 1907. 1st ed. Some wear to extremities, some foxing, else VG+. *OLD LONDON.* $40

Simpson, Louis. A REVOLUTION IN TASTE. NY: Macmillan (1978). Uncorrected proof. Signed. NF in wraps. *DORN.* $60

Simpson, Louis. AT THE END OF THE OPEN ROAD. Middletown: Weslyan, (1963). 1st ed. Fine in dj (slight wear). Inscribed. *CAPTAIN'S BOOKSHELF.* $45

Simpson, Louis. COLLECTED POEMS. NY: Paragon House (1988). Review copy w/materials. Fine in dj. *DORN.* $30

Simpson, Louis. RIVERSIDE DRIVE. NY: Atheneum (1962). 1st ed. Inscribed. NF in sl used dj. *DORN.* $60

Simpson, Louis. SELECTED POEMS. NY: Harcourt, Brace & World, (1965). Fine in dj w/minimal soiling. 1st ed. *CHAPEL HILL.* $35

Simpson, Louis. SELECTED POEMS. NY: HBW (1965). 1st ed. Fine in dj. *DORN.* $30

Simpson, Louis. THE ARRIVISTES. NY: Fine Editions Press, (1949). 1/500 in pb of 1st bk. Top right spine edge split 1"; right spine corner chipped, cvr soiled, else VG. *BERNARD.* $150

Simpson, Louis. THE BEST HOUR OF THE NIGHT. New Haven: Ticknor & Fields (1983). Uncorrected proof. Signed. Fine in wraps. *DORN.* $50

Simpson, Mona. THE LOST FATHER. NY: Knopf, 1992. Uncorrected proof. Fine in ptd wraps. *CAPTAIN'S BOOKSHELF.* $75

Simpson, R. Hope and J.F. Lazenby. THE CATALOGUE OF THE SHIPS IN HOMER'S ILIAD. Oxford: Clarendon Press, 1970. 12 plts, 7 maps. Dj. Signature at flyleaf. Good. *ARCHAEOLOGIA.* $125

Sims, Orland L. GUN-TOTERS I HAVE KNOWN. Austin: Encino Press, 1967. One of 750 numbered, signed. Fine. *LAURIE.* $75

Sims, Richard. HANDBOOK TO THE LIBRARY OF THE BRITISH MUSEUM: CONTAINING A BRIEF HISTORY.... London: John Russell Smith, 1854. Extrems rubbed, nick in spine, o/w VG, tight. *WREDEN.* $50

SINBAD THE SAILOR. Barcelona, 1984. 4 double pg pop-ups. Pop-up bk. *BOOKFINDERS INTL.* $15

Sinclair, Andrew. GOG. London: Weidenfeld & Nicholson, (1967). 1st ed. Slight bump to bottom edge near gutter, else Fine in dj w/small closed tear. *CAPTAIN'S BOOKSHELF.* $65

Sinclair, Archibald, and Henry, William. SWIMMING (BADMINTON LIBRARY). London: Longmans, Green, 1893. 1st ed. Wear to extremities, else G+. *OLD LONDON.* $50

Sinclair, Upton. 100% THE STORY OF A PATRIOT. Pasadena: the author, 1920. 1st ed. Fine in VG rubbed dj w/chips. *BEASLEY.* $50

Sinclair, Upton. AUTOBIOGRAPHY OF UPTON SINCLAIR. NY: Harcourt, 1962. 1st ed. About Fine in lightly worn dj. *AKA.* $25

Sinclair, Upton. DRAGON'S TEETH. NY: Viking, 1942. 1st ed. VG in dj (edgewear, stains, internal strengthening at edges). *LOPEZ.* $40

Sinclair, Upton. EPIC ANSWERS. LA: End Poverty League, n.d., (1934). 3rd ed in wraps. VG. *AKA.* $20

Sinclair, Upton. FASTING CURE. NY: Mitchell Kennerly, 1911. Brn cloth. Owner's odd mark fep, lt cover wear, sm minor stain top edge. *AKA.* $50

Sinclair, Upton. OIL! A NOVEL. NY: Boni, 1927. 1st ed. Pict black cl printed in yellow. Little shelfwear. Several page margins creased, o/w VG. *DIAMOND.* $35

Sinclair, Upton. OUR LADY. Emmaus: Rodale Press, 1938. 1st ed. VG w/spine wear. Adv rev, slip pasted in. *BEASLEY.* $35

Sinclair, Upton. THE GNOMOBILE. NY: Farrar, 1936. 1st ed. Fine in lightly used dj w/small chips at foot of bit sunned spine. *BEASLEY.* $75

Sinclair, Upton. THE GOOSE-STEP. Rev Ed. Pasadena, CA: Pub by Author. (1924). x,488pp,(7)pp ads. Signed. Maroon cl stamped in black; spine soiled and faded. *KARMIOLE.* $40

Sinclair, Upton. THE JUNGLE. (Pasadena, CA): Upton Sinclair. 1920. New ed. Signed. Dec maroon cl, spine faded. *KARMIOLE.* $40

Sinclair, Upton. THE JUNGLE. Illus Fletcher Martin. Baltimore: LEC. 1965. Ed ltd to 1500 numbered, signed by Upton Sinclair and Fletcher Martin. Tan pigskin over boards. Slipcase. *KARMIOLE.* $85

Sinclair, Upton. THE JUNGLE. London, 1906. 1st Eng ed. Pict orange cvrs sl soiled & stained. Text sl shaken, o/w VG. *DIAMOND.* $75

Sinclair, Upton. THE JUNGLE. NY, 1906. 1st ed. Extremities, spine and corners minimally rubbed, white lettering on spine faded, tiny name. Fine. *POLYANTHOS.* $100

Sinclair, Upton. THE JUNGLE. NY, 1906. 1st ed. Pict green cl lettered in white. Spine lettering rubbed off, o/w VG. *DIAMOND.* $75

Sinclair, Upton. THE JUNGLE. NY: Jungle Publishing, 1904. The most desirable form of this book, w/Jungle Publishing imprint, Socialist Party seal on front board, and Sustainer's Edition label on front pastedown. NF w/only light spine flaking. *BEASLEY.* $175

Sinclair, Upton. THE MONEY CHANGERS. NY: Dodge, 1908. 1st ed. Lightly soiled, NF. *CAPTAIN'S BOOKSHELF.* $50

Sinclair, Upton. WORLD'S END. NY & Pasadena, CA: Pub by the Author, (1940). Bkpl, else NF in VG dj (some creases and tears). 1st ed. Signed. One of an unspecified number issued to Sinclair by the Viking Press for presentation; w/Viking Press logo on title page. *CHAPEL HILL.* $95

Singer, Charles (ed). A HISTORY OF TECHNOLOGY, VOLUME I (only): FROM EARLY TIMES TO FALL OF ANCIENT EMPIRES. Oxford: Clarendon Press, (1958). Frontis, 570 figs, 36 plts, 8 maps, 10 tables. Good. *ARCHAEOLOGIA.* $125

Singer, Charles. A SHORT HISTORY OF MEDICINE. NY, 1928. 1st ed. *FYE.* $50

Singer, Charles. FROM MAGIC TO SCIENCE: ESSAYS ON THE SCIENTIFIC TWILIGHT. London, 1928. 1st ed. *FYE.* $100

Singer, Charles. GREEK BIOLOGY & MEDICINE. Oxford, 1922. 1st ed. *FYE.* $50

Singer, Dorothea. CATALOGUE OF LATIN AND VERNACULAR ALCHEMICAL MANUSCRIPTS IN GREAT BRITAIN AND IRELAND DATING FROM BEFORE THE XVI CENTURY. Brussels 1928-31. 1st ed. Wrappers. *FYE.* $150

Singer, Dorothea. SELECTIONS FROM THE WORKS OF AMBROISE PARE WITH SHORT BIOGRAPHICAL AND EXPLANATORY AND BIBLIOGRAPHICAL NOTES. London, 1924. 1st ed. *FYE.* $75

Singer, I.J. THE SINNER. NY: Liveright Inc. (1933). Trans by Maurice Samuel. 1st Amer ed. (4),314pp. Tan cloth, spine a bit soiled. Dj. *KARMIOLE.* $50

Singer, Isaac Bashevis. A FRIEND OF KAFKA. NY: Farrar, 1970. 1st ed. Fine in Fine dj (little creasing at corner). *BEASLEY.* $35

Singer, Isaac Bashevis. A YOUNG MAN IN SEARCH OF LOVE. GC: Doubleday, (1978). 1st ed. Illus by Raphael Soyer. Inscribed by Singer; also inscribed by Soyer. NF in NF, edge rubbed dj. *UNGER.* $175

Singer, Isaac Bashevis. ALONE IN THE WILD FOREST. Trans by Author and Elizabeth Shub. NY: Farrar, Straus & Giroux, (1971). Gilt lettering on spine misprinted (ptd only on extreme edge of spine), else Fine in lightly sunned dj. 1st ed. *CHAPEL HILL.* $35

Singer, Isaac Bashevis. LOST IN AMERICA. GC: Doubleday, 1981. Raphael Soyer (illus). 1st ed. Ltd to 500 signed, w/separate print, signed, laid in. Cl, slipcase. VF. *JAFFE.* $350

Singer, Isaac Bashevis. OLD LOVE. NY: Farrar, Straus, Giroux, (1979). Fine in price-clipped dj. 1st ed. *CHAPEL HILL.* $35

Singer, Isaac Bashevis. ONE DAY OF HAPPINESS. NY: Red Ozier Press, 1982. Richard Callner (illus). 1st ed. Ltd to 155 (entire ed) signed by Singer & Callner. 1/4 purple morocco, paste-paper boards, cl slipcase. Spine sl faded, o/w Fine. *JAFFE.* $375

Singer, Isaac Bashevis. PASSIONS. NY: Farrar, Straus, (1975). 1st ed. Inscribed. Fine in Fine dj. *UNGER.* $75

Singer, Isaac Bashevis. THE COLLECTED STORIES OF ISAAC BASHEVIS SINGER. NY: Farrar, Straus, Giroux, (1982). 1st ed. Orig grn cl. Fine in dj. 1st ed. Inscribed. *CHAPEL HILL.* $125

Singer, Isaac Bashevis. THE FAMILY MOSKAT. NY, 1950. 1st ed. Offsetting inside front cover and ffep, extremities, spine minimally rubbed. Fine in dj (spine sl sunned, extremities few very small chips, little rubbed). *POLYANTHOS.* $75

Singer, Isaac Bashevis. THE FAMILY MOSKAT. NY: Knopf, 1950. 1st ed, 1st bk. Fine Minor rubbing spine ends of bright dj. *ELSE FINE.* $125

Singer, Isaac Bashevis. THE SPINOZA OF MARKET STREET. NY: Farrar, 1961. 1st ed. Fine in Fine dj (sun darkening to spine and top edge). *BEASLEY.* $75

Singer, Kurt. DISEASES OF THE MUSICAL PROFESSION: A SYSTEMATIC PRESENTATION OF THEIR CAUSES, SYMPTOMS AND METHODS OF TREATMENT. NY, 1932. 1st Eng trans. Scarce. *FYE.* $150

Singh, Khushwant. THE SIKHS. London: Allen & Unwin, (1953). 1st Eng ed. Fine- in VG+ dj. *AARD.* $25

Singh, Mandajeet. HIMALAYAN ART. Greenwich: NY Graphic Society, 1968. 1st ed. 151 color plts (some double pg.), 28 b/w color maps. VG. *BLUE DRAGON.* $145

Singleton, E. THE SHAKESPEARE GARDEN. NY, 1931. Cloth. Ink inscrip. Dj faded, chipped. *SUTTON.* $45

Singleton, Esther (ed, trans). ROMANTIC CASTLES AND PALACES AS SEEN AND DESCRIBED BY FAMOUS WRITERS. NY: Dodd, Mead, 1905. 48 plts. Orig richly gilt cl, sl rubbed, 1 pl frayed, o/w VG; teg. *WORLDWIDE.* $18

Singleton, Esther. SOCIAL NEW YORK UNDER THE GEORGES 1714 -1776. NY: Appleton, 1902. 1st ed. VG. *BACKROOM.* $40

Singleton, Esther. SOCIAL NEW YORK UNDER THE GEORGES. NY: 1902. 1st ed. Auto-pres. *HEINOLDT.* $30

Singleton, William Henry. CONTRABAND OF WAR. NY, (1970). Ed by Laurel F. and Joel A. Vlock. 1st ed. A little dj wear o/w Fine. *PRATT.* $30

Sipes, William B. THE PENNSYLVANIA RAILROAD...EMBRACING HISTORICAL...OF INTEREST ON ITS VARIOUS LINES IN PENNSYLVANIA AND NEW JERSEY. Phila., 1875. 1st ed. (4),281pp. 3 plts. Contemp half mo, front cover has a light milklike stain, inner hinges mended. Howes S513. *GINSBERG.* $100

Siringo, Charles A. RIATA AND SPURS. Boston: Houghton Mifflin, 1927. 1st ed, 1st ptg. VG. Facs dj. *OUTPOST.* $100

Siskind, Aaron. PHOTOGRAPHS. Intro Harold Rosenberg. NY: Horizon, (1959). 1st ed. 50 plts. Fine in dj sl faded at spine. Signed. *CAPTAIN'S BOOKSHELF.* $225

Siskind, Aaron. PLACES. NY: Light Gallery/ Farrar Straus & Giroux, (1976). 1st ed. Fine in sl used, price-clipped dj. Inscribed. *CAPTAIN'S BOOKSHELF.* $200

Sitwell, Edith. I LIVE UNDER A BLACK SUN. London: Victor Gollancz, 1937. 1st ed. Black cl stamped in gold on backstrip. VG in soiled, chipped, torn dj. *HELLER.* $75

Sitwell, Edith. MUSIC AND CEREMONIES. NY: Vanguard Press, (1963). 1st Amer ed, 1st thus. VG in dj. *SCHOYER'S.* $20

Sitwell, Edith. POOR MEN'S MUSIC. London: Fore Publications, 1950. Light soiling, else NF. 1st ed. Signed. *CHAPEL HILL.* $150

Sitwell, Edith. THE COLLECTED POEMS OF EDITH SITWELL. NY: Vanguard, (1954). 1st Amer ed. Orig black cl. Fine in price-clipped dj. Inscribed. *CHAPEL HILL.* $125

Sitwell, Edith. THE SONG OF THE COLD. NY: Vanguard, (1948). One of 2650. 1st ed. Fine in sl chipped price clipped dj. *SECOND LIFE.* $35

Sitwell, N.H.H. ROMAN ROADS OF EUROPE. London: Cassell, (1981). Dj. Good. *ARCHAEOLOGIA.* $65

Sitwell, Osbert. BEFORE THE BOMBARDMENT. London: Duckworth, 1926. 1st ed. Presentation, signed. Considerable grease stain several pp. Fair. *WREDEN.* $125

Sitwell, Osbert. COLLECTED STORIES. London, 1953. 1st ed. Signed presentation. Spine very sl sunned. Fine in dj (spine very sl sunned). *POLYANTHOS.* $85

Sitwell, Osbert. DUMB-ANIMAL AND OTHER STORIES. London: Duckworth, 1930. 1st ed, ltd to 110. Signed. NF. *WREDEN.* $120

Sitwell, Osbert. ESCAPE WITH ME—AN ORIENTAL SKETCHBOOK. NY: Harrison-Hilton, 1940. 1st US ed. Fine in VG dj. *AARD.* $35

Sitwell, Sacheverell and Wilfred Blunt. GREAT FLOWER BOOKS 1700-1900, A BIBLIOGRAPHICAL RECORD....London, 1956. 20 colored, 16 plain plts. 1/2 cl (corners sl bumped, head of spine bumped, lower edges scuffed). Dj chipped, sm tears. *SUTTON.* $775

Sitwell, Sacheverell and Wilfrid Blunt. GREAT FLOWER BOOKS, 1700-1900. A BIBLIOGRAPHICAL RECORD....London: Collins, 1956. 1st ed. Orig green cl over marbled boards. 36 plts. Good in dj, tears. Scarce. *KARMIOLE.* $750

Sitwell, Sacheverell. SPAIN. London: B.T. Batsford, 1951. 2nd ed. Dj. *SCHOYER'S.* $15

SIX CALIFORNIA TALES. Bk Club of CA, (1939). 1st ed of 650. Printed in chapbks by six printers. Cl folder in slipcase, leather shelfback and gilt-stamped labels. Fine. *AUTHORS OF THE WEST.* $100

SIX MONTHS IN KANSAS. BY A LADY. (By Hannah Anderson Ropes). Boston: Jewett, 1856. 4th thousand. 1st ed. Piece cut from top of front fly leaf. *SECOND LIFE.* $75

Sizer, Nelson and H.S. Drayton. HEADS AND FACES, AND HOW TO STUDY THEM, A MANUAL OF PHRENOLOGY AND PHYSIOGNOMY FOR THE PEOPLE. NY, 1896. 264 woodcut illus. *FYE.* $50

Sizer, Nelson. FORTY YEARS IN PHRENOLOGY. NY, 1882. Gilt-pict cover. NF. *POLYANTHOS.* $45

Sizer, Nelson. FORTY YEARS IN PHRENOLOGY. NY: Fowler and Wells, 1892. Dec grn gilt cl. Sl worn, stained, corners bumped. Good+. *SMITHFIELD.* $33

Sjowall, Maj and Per Wahloo. MURDER AT THE SAVOY. NY: Pantheon Books, 1971. 1st Amer ed. VF in dj. *MORDIDA.* $35

Sjowall, Maj and Per Wahloo. THE FIRE ENGINE THAT DISAPPEARED. NY: Pantheon Books, 1970. 1st Amer ed. Fine in dj. *MORDIDA.* $40

Sjowall, Maj and Per Wahloo. THE LAUGHING POLICEMAN. NY: Pantheon Books, 1970. 1st Amer ed. Fine in dj. *MORDIDA.* $45

Sjowall, Maj and Per Wahloo. THE MAN WHO WENT UP IN SMOKE. NY: Pantheon Books, 1969. 1st ed. Fine in price-clipped dj. *MORDIDA.* $50

Sjowall, Maj and Per Wahloo. THE TERRORISTS. NY: Pantheon Books, 1976. 1st Amer ed. VF in dj. *MORDIDA.* $25

Skaggs, Jimmy M. THE CATTLE-TRAILING INDUSTRY BETWEEN SUPPLY AND DEMAND, 1866-1890. Lawrence, KS: Univ Press of KS, 1973. 1st ed. VF in dj. 17.50

Skaife, S.H. AFRICAN INSECT LIFE. London, (1954). 75 plts. Ex-lib. *SUTTON.* $43

Skarsten, M.O. GEORGE DROUILLARD, HUNTER & INTERPRETER, 1807-1810. A.H. Clark, 1964. Uncut, unopened. 1st ed. VF. *OREGON.* $100

Skelding, S.B. FLOWERS FROM HILL AND DALE, POEMS. NY, 1883. 12 chromolithos. Ornamental cl, some wear at corners. Lt spotting, some tissue guards loose, some browning, foxing pp edges, affecting several plts. *SUTTON.* $57

Sketch, Alexander. BIRDS OF TROPICAL AMERICA. Austin: Univ of TX Press, (1983). 1st ed. Dj. *SILVER.* $25

SKETCHES OF MR. MATHEWS CELEBRATED TRIP TO PARIS. London, n.d. 24pp, paper covered blue boards, lt foxing. Detached from boards. Fold out engrs by Robert Cruikshank. Good. *CULLEN.* $125

SKETCHES OF SWITZERLAND. BY AN AMERICAN. (By James Fenimore Cooper.) Part second. Phila: Carey, Lea & Blanchard, 1836. 2 vols. 12mo. 219; 226pp. Purple muslin cl, ptd paper spine label; sm tear head of top hinge of vol 1. BAL 3874. *WEBER.* $150

Skey, F.C. HYSTERIA. REMOTE CAUSES OF DISEASE IN GENERAL. TREATMENT OF DISEASE BY TONIC AGENCY. LOCAL OR SURGICAL FORMS OF HYSTERIA, ETC. NY, 1868. 2nd Amer ed. *FYE.* $40

Skilton, C.P. BRITISH WINDMILLS AND WATERMILLS. London: Collins, 1947. 1st ed. Owner name, address, dj flap copy taped to ffep. VG+. *AARD.* $12.50

Skinner, Otis. FOOTLIGHTS AND SPOTLIGHTS. Indianapolis: Bobbs Merrill, (1924). #27/500, signed and inscribed. Newsclips and flyer laid in. Fine- in Good+ dj. *AARD.* $50

Skinner, Robert P. ABYSSINIA OF TO-DAY. London: Arnold; NY: Longmans, Green, 1906. 1st US ed. 1 map. Sl rubbed and faded, o/w VG ex-lib. *WORLDWIDE.* $25

Skinner, Thomas. ADVENTURES DURING A JOURNEY OVER LAND TO INDIA. Phila: A. Waldie, and Boston: Weeks, Jordan, 1837. (vi),359pp. 1st Amer ed. 12mo. Brown cl, quite worn and unattractive but sturdy and readable. Foxed. 1st pub in London in 1836. *SCHOYER'S.* $60

Skrebneski, Victor. A MATTER OF RECORD. PORTRAITS. GC: Doubleday, 1978. 1st ed. Signed by author year of pub. Fine in Fine dj. *BEASLEY.* $85

Skvoresky, Josef. THE ENGINEER OF HUMAN SOULS. NY: Knopf, 1984. 1st ed. Signed. NF in dj. *LAME DUCK.* $85

SKY-HI, A TRIP INTO SPACE WITH TERRY. (1952). Measures 8" x 10.5", comb-bound, rear cvr larger than front cvr w/shaped top. Moveable color cardboard figure of Terry fastened to front cvr; moveable wheel showing solar system fastened to inside of rear cvr. 2 pop-ups w/other illus pp in bright color. Slight edgewear but NF, pop-ups Fine. *BEBBAH.* $25

Slade, Adolphus. RECORDS OF TRAVELS IN TURKEY, GREECE & C... WITH THE CAPTAIN PASHA IN THE YEARS 1829, 1830, AND 1831. Phila: Carey & Hart, 1833. Half calf, marbled boards. 262 and 259pp, plus ads. 1st Amer ed. *O'NEILL.* $185

Sladek, John. BUGS. London: Macmillan, (1989). 1st ed. Signed. Fine in dj. *OTHER WORLDS.* $35

Sladen, Douglas. CARTHAGE AND TUNIS: THE OLD AND NEW GATES OF THE ORIENT. Phila: Jacobs, 1906. 2 vols. 1st ed. Sl rubbed, o/w VG ex-lib. *WORLDWIDE.* $75

Sladen, Douglas. ORIENTAL CAIRO. London: Hurst & Blackett, n.d. (1911). Lacks ffep, some foxing. Fldg map. *SCHOYER'S.* $40

Slater, Elsie McElroy. EL PASO BIRDS. El Paso: (Carl Hertzog), 1945. One of 1,000, designed by Hertzog. Presentation signed by him. Bound in double-fold paper covers, w/square back, hand sewn. VG. *LAURIE.* $50

Slater, John M. EL MORRO: INSCRIPTION ROCK, NEW MEXICO. LA: The Plantin Press, 1961. One of 500. Cl in dj. *DAWSON'S.* $75

Slater, John M. EL MORRO; INSCRIPTION ROCK, NEW MEXICO. LA: The Plantin Press, 1961. Ltd ed of 500. Color frontis. Grn cl. Fine in dj. *WEBER.* $45

Slesinger, Tess. THE UNPOSSESSED. NY: Simon and Schuster, 1934. 1st ed, 1st bk. Corner sl bumped, o/w Fine in sl soiled dj. *HELLER.* $100

Slijper, E.J. WHALES. London: Hutchinson, 1962. 8vo, 475pp, 1st English ed. Fine in NF dj. *GREAT EPIC.* $75

Slim, Iceberg. PIMP: THE STORY OF MY LIFE. LA: Holloway House, 1967. 1st ed. VG in wraps. Scarce. *LAME DUCK.* $75

Slingerland, M.V. & C.R. Crosby. MANUAL OF FRUIT INSECTS, NY 1941. 1st ed. Ex-lib. *SUTTON.* $38

Slipher, Earl C. THE PHOTOGRAPHIC STORY OF MARS. Cambridge, MA: Sky Publishing & Flagstaff, AZ: Northland Press, 1962. Fldg map, 48 plts. VG. *KNOLLWOOD.* $60

Sloan, E.L. THE SALT LAKE CITY DIRECTORY AND BUSINESS GUIDE FOR 1869. Salt Lake City: Author, 1869. 1st ed. (v),57-219,(2)pp. Index, adverts. Has uncommon tipped-in folded frontis, though half is lacking at fold line. Boards show extensive wear, else NF. Rare. Howes S-555. *CONNOLLY & WADE.* $975

Sloan, E.L. THE SALT LAKE CITY DIRECTORY AND BUSINESS GUIDE FOR 1869. Salt Lake City: E.L. Sloan, 1869 (Probably ptd in Chicago -Howes). 1st ed. Adv ep. Tipped-in fldg frontis (usually not present) though half is lacking at the fold. (5),57-219,(2)pp., illus, index. Grn pebbled cl spine w/title, pub in gilt. Black boards, quite worn, w/adv in gilt on both covers. Although a fragile bk, hinges strong, internal condition is NF. Rare. Howes S-555 *CONNOLLY & WADE.* $1425

Sloan, E.P. THE THYROID: SURGERY, SYNDROMES, TREATMENT. Springfield, 1936. 1st ed. *FYE.* $50

Sloan, John Alexander. NORTH CAROLINA IN THE WAR BETWEEN THE STATES. Washington, DC, 1883. 2 vols (2 parts, all published). 1st ed. Wrappers bound in 1/2 leather w/marbled boards. Tear in wrap on part 1 repaired, bookseller's label on part 2. VG. *McGOWAN.* $650

Sloan, John. JOHN SLOAN'S NEW YORK SCENE. NY: Harper & Row, 1965. 1st ed. NF in NF dj (tear to price-clipped dj). *AKA.* $40

Sloan, W.B. THE COMPLETE FARRIER OR HORSE DOCTOR. Chicago: Eastman & McClellan, 1849. 3rd ed, enrlgd and improved. Frontis woodcut. Orig pict printed brds, browned, roan spine. Few leaves dogeared. *HUDSON.* $450

Sloane, Mary. STRONG CABLES RISING. NY: Dutton, 1942. Fine in VG dj (few internal tape reinforcements). 1st ed. #204 of 391 , signed. Additional signed inscript from Robert P. Tristram Coffin, who contributes the preface. Bkpl. *CHAPEL HILL.* $35

Slocum, Charles E. THE LIFE AND SERVICES OF MAJOR-GENERAL HENRY WARNER SLOCUM...IN DIFFERENT MILITARY CAMPAIGNS...Toledo, 1913. (11). 1st ed. 391pp. Orig cl. *GINSBERG.* $100

Slovo, Gillian. MORBID SYMPTOMS. London: Pluto, 1984. 1st ed. Fine in dj. *STAHR.* $20

Small, A.E. MANUAL OF HOMEOPATHIC PRACTICE. NY: Boericke & Tafel, 1876. 15th enl ed. xxi,826pp. Half leather. Missing a few pp in back from index. G+ *BLUE DRAGON.* $45

Small, Albert E. CAPE COD AND RETURN. Boston: House of Edinboro, 1953. 1st ed. VG in VG dj. *CONNOLLY & WADE.* $25

Small, Tunstall and Christopher Woodbridge. MOULDINGS OF THE WREN & GEORGIAN PERIODS. A Portfolio of full-size Sections. London: The Architectural Press/NY: William Helburn, Inc, (c. 1920s). 20 plts laid loose, w/15 pp of text (soiled, slight wear to edges) in gray paper over boards portfolio (rubbed, chipped at joints) titled in grayish blue w/gray silk-ties. VG. *BLUE MOUNTAIN.* $45

Smalley, Eugene V(irgil). HISTORY OF THE NORTHERN PACIFIC RAILROAD. NY: 1883. xxiv, 437pp. Engr illus., maps, folded profile. Orig gilt stamped cl. Light shelf wear, spine ends lightly frayed. VG. Howes S561. *BOHLING.* $200

Smalley, Henry. AN ANALYSIS OF HORSEMANSHIP. Washington: Amer Remount Assoc, 1932. 1st ed. VG. *OCTOBER FARM.* $45

Smedley, Harold Hinsdill. PRESENTING FLY PATTERNS AND THEIR ORIGINS. Muskegon: Westshore Publications, 1943. 1st ed. Errata slip tipped in. VG in Good+ dj. *BACKMAN.* $100

Smee, Alfred. MY GARDEN, ITS PLAN AND CULTURE. London: Bell and Daldy and NY: Scribner, 1872. 1st ed. 1250 engrs. Grn cl stamped in gold, dust rubbed, foxed. VG. *SECOND LIFE.* $165

Smellie, William. ANATOMICAL TABLES, WITH EXPLANATIONS, AND AN ABRIDGEMENT OF THE PRACTICE OF MIDWIFERY. A New Edition, with Notes and Illustrations by A. Hamilton. Edinburgh: William Creech, 1787. Folio. 40 full page engr plts. Orig marbled boards & lea label. New lea back & corners. Progressively lighter staining to first five leaves; single tear through most plates skillfully repaired w/o loss. *M & S.* $1250

Smellie, William. THE PHILOSOPHY OF NATURAL HISTORY. Boston: Hillyard, Gray, Little and Wilkins, 1827. 2nd ed. 322pp,24pp cat. Heavy foxing; 2" piece missing from ep w/no loss; boards, spine worn. Good+. *SMITHFIELD.* $73

Smialowski, Arthur and Donald Currie. PHOTOGRAPHY IN MEDICINE. Springfield, 1960. 1st ed. Dj. 282 illus. *FYE.* $100

Smiles, Samuel. LIFE OF A SCOTCH NATURALIST, THOMAS EDWARD. London: John Murray, 1893. New ed. Rebacked w/orig backstrip. Contents Good. *DIAMOND.* $25

Smiles, Samuel. ROBERT DICK: BAKER OF THURSO, GEOLOGIST AND BOTANIST. NY: Harper and Bros., n.d. (1878). 436pp. Brn cl worn, corners bumped, contents VG. *SMITHFIELD.* $28

Smiley, Jane. A THOUSAND ACRES. NY: Knopf, 1991. 1st ed. As New in dj. *CAPTAIN'S BOOKSHELF.* $50

Smiley, Jane. THE GREENLANDERS. NY: Knopf (1988). Adv rev copy in wraps. Lt use on cvrs, else VG. *DORN.* $40

Smith, A. Merwyn. SPORT AND ADVENTURE IN THE INDIAN JUNGLE. London: Hurst & Blackett. 1904. 1st ed. (12),308pp. 19 illus. Orig dec grn cl, gilt spine. *KARMIOLE.* $75

Smith, Adam. AN INQUIRY INTO THE NATURE AND CAUSES OF THE WEALTH OF NATIONS. London: Strahan, 1799. 9th ed. 3 vols. 499; 527; 465pp. 3/4 leather, marbled boards. Sl foxing. VG. *SMITHFIELD.* $235

Smith, Adolphe. MONACO AND MONTE CARLO. Phila: Lippincott, 1912. Rubbed, silver-fished. 8 color plts. Pale pencil notes. *SCHOYER'S.* $25

Smith, Albert. THE NATURAL HISTORY OF THE GENT. London: David Bogue. 1847. 1st ed. This copy w/o ads at back. viii,104pp. 19th-century grn calf over grn cl, gilt spine; spine extrems sl rubbed. *KARMIOLE.* $85

Smith, Alson. A VIEW OF THE SPREE. NY: John Day, (1962). 1st ed. Fine- in VG price-clipped dj. *AARD.* $15

Smith, Alson. MEN AGAINST THE MOUNTAINS....NY: John Day, (1965). 1st ed. Some edge soiling o/w Fine in Fine dj. *OREGON.* $40

Smith, Amanda. AN AUTOBIOGRAPHY OF MRS. AMANDA SMITH, THE COLORED EVANGELIST. Chicago: Meyer & Bro., 1893. 1st ed. Front few pp dampstained in couple places, boards bit rubbed, corners bumped. VG-. Very Scarce. *BETWEEN COVERS.* $175

Smith, Anthony. MATO GROSSO. LAST VIRGIN LAND. NY: Dutton, 1971. 1st US ed. Fine in Fine dj. *CONNOLLY & WADE.* $40

Smith, C. Alphonso. O. HENRY: A BIOGRAPHY. London: Hodder & Stoughton, 1916. 1st British ed. Front cvr spotted, else Fine. *AUTHORS OF THE WEST.* $17.50

Smith, C. Henry. THE MENNONITES. Berne, IN: Mennonite Book Concern, 1920. 1st ed. *KARMIOLE.* $35

Smith, Caroline L. THE AMERICAN HOME BOOK OF IN-DOOR GAMES, AMUSEMENTS, AND OCCUPATIONS. Illus. Boston: Lee and Shepard, 1873. Orig pict cloth, gilt; dec gilt spine; light soiling and rubbing; engr frontis, title, and plts. VG. *DRAMATIS PERSONAE.* $100

Smith, Charles R. MARINES IN THE REVOLUTION. Washington: GPO, 1975. 1st ed. VG. *ARTIS.* $25

Smith, Charlie. CANAAN. London: HH, (1985). 1st UK. Fine in pict dj which differs from the US ed. Inscribed. *CAPTAIN'S BOOKSHELF.* $75

Smith, Charlie. CANAAN. NY: Simon & Schuster, (1984). 1st Amer ed. Signed. Rem mark bottom edge else Fine in dj. *DORN.* $50

Smith, Charlie. RED ROADS. NY: Dutton, (1987). 1st ed. As New in dj. Scarce. Signed. *CAPTAIN'S BOOKSHELF.* $125

Smith, Charlie. SHINE HAWK. Latham: Paris Review Editions, (1988). 1st Amer ed. Signed. Fine in NF dj. *DORN.* $40

Smith, Clark Ashton. GENIUS LOCI AND OTHER TALES. Sauk City: Arkham House, 1948. 1st ed. Fine in NF dj. *BEASLEY.* $175

Smith, Clark Ashton. GENIUS LOCI. Arkham House, 1948. 1st ed. Fine in dj. *MADLE.* $175

Smith, Clark Ashton. LOST WORLDS. Arkham House, 1944. 1st ed. Fine in dj. *MADLE.* $400

Smith, Clark Ashton. OTHER DIMENSIONS. Arkham House, 1970. 1st ed. Fine in dj. *MADLE.* $85

Smith, Clark Ashton. OUT OF TIME & SPACE. Jersey: Spearman, 1971. 1st ed. Fine in dj w/light edgewear. *ELSE FINE.* $45

Smith, Clark Ashton. POEMS IN PROSE. Arkham House, 1965. 1st ed. Fine in Mint dj. *MADLE.* $200

Smith, Clark Ashton. SELECTED POEMS. Arkham House, 1971. 1st ed. VF in dj. *MADLE.* $95

Smith, Clark Ashton. SPELLS AND PHILTRES. Arkham House, 1958. 1st ed. Fine in dj. *MADLE.* $450

Smith, Clark Ashton. TALES OF SCIENCE AND SORCERY. Arkham House, 1964. 1st ed. Fine in dj. *MADLE.* $125

Smith, Clark Ashton. TALES OF SCIENCE AND SORCERY. Sauk City: Arkham House, 1964. 1st ed. 2482 copies. Fine in NF dj. *ROBBINS.* $95

Smith, Clark Ashton. THE ABOMINATIONS OF YONDO. Arkham House, 1960. 1st ed. VF in dj. *MADLE.* $175

Smith, Clark Ashton. THE ABOMINATIONS OF YONDO. Sauk City: Arkham House, 1960. 1st ed. Fine in NF dj. *OTHER WORLDS.* $125

Smith, Clark Ashton. THE BLACK BOOK OF CLARK ASHTON SMITH. Sauk City: Arkham House, (1979). 1st ed. Fine in wraps. *OTHER WORLDS.* $45

Smith, Clark Ashton. THE DARK CHATEAU. Arkham House, 1951. 1st ed. Fine in dj. *MADLE.* $650

Smith, Cornelius C. EMILIO KOSTERLITZKY, EAGLE OF SONORA AND THE SOUTHWEST BORDER. Glendale, 1970. 1st ed. 344pp. VG+. *PRATT.* $50

Smith, Cornelius C. WILLIAM SANDERS OURY: HISTORY-MAKER OF THE SOUTHWEST. Tucson: Univ of AZ, 1967. 1st ed. Fine in Fine dj. *CONNOLLY & WADE.* $42.50

Smith, Dama M. I MARRIED A RANGER. Stanford, 1931. Orange cloth, 179pp. Signed. Clean, tight in Good+ dj. *FIVE QUAIL.* $30

Smith, Dama M. I MARRIED A RANGER. Stanford Univ Press, (1930). 1st ed. Spine faded. Small stain on rear cvr, o/w VG. Inscribed by author & signed by her husband. *DIAMOND.* $45

Smith, DeCost. MARTYRS OF THE OBLONG AND LITTLE NINE. Caldwell: Caxton Printers, 1948. 1st ed. Fine in dj. *LAURIE.* $30

Smith, DeCost. MARTYRS OF THE OBLONG AND LITTLE NINE. Caldwell, ID: Caxton Printers, 1948. 13 plts. 2 djs (one ptd, one pict) as issued. Top edge soiled, nick upper edge of outer dj. NF. *BOHLING.* $45

Smith, DeCost. MARTYRS OF THE OBLONG AND LITTLE NINE. Caldwell, 1948. #113 of a ltd 1st ed of 1,000. A little dj wear o/w Fine. *PRATT.* $35

Smith, Donald L. THE TWENTY-FOURTH MICHIGAN OF THE IRON BRIGADE. Harrisburg, PA, 1962. 1st ed. Fine in dj. *McCLINTOCK.* $50

Smith, E. Kirby. TO MEXICO WITH SCOTT. Harvard Univ Press, 1917. 1st ed. Inscribed by grandson. VG. *DIAMOND.* $35

Smith, E.F. JAMES WOODHOUSE: A PIONEER IN CHEMISTRY 1717-1809. Winston, 1918. VG+. *BOOKCELL.* $40

Smith, Earl. THE WESTFALL COUNTRY. Exposition, (1963). 1st ed. Fine in Good+ dj. Scarce. Full pp signed presentation inscription. *OREGON.* $50

Smith, Edgar C. A SHORT HISTORY OF NAVAL AND MARINE ENGINEERING. Cambridge: Babcock and Wilcox, Ltd., 1937. Some wear and fading, small spot on spine, else VG. *PARMER.* $75

Smith, Edmund B. GOVERNORS ISLAND, ITS MILITARY HISTORY UNDER THREE FLAGS, 1637-1922. Valentine's Manual, 1923. NY, 1st ed. Rebound. *HEINOLDT.* $25

Smith, Edward C. A HISTORY OF LEWIS COUNTY, WEST VIRGINIA. Weston, WV, 1920. 1st ed. Orig cl, sm paper label on spine, bkpl removed. *GINSBERG.* $125

Smith, Edward E. GALACTIC PATROL. Reading: Fantasy Press, 1950. 1st ed. Bkpl. Fine; dj w/minor edgewear. *ELSE FINE.* $45

Smith, Edward E. GREY LENSMAN. Reading: Fantasy Press, 1951. 1st ed. Fine but for sunned spot on spine, in lightly used dj w/spine chips. *BEASLEY.* $75

Smith, Edward E. MONA LISA OVERDRIVE. London, (1988). 1st ed. Preceded Amer ed. Fine in dj. *McCLINTOCK.* $45

Smith, Edward E. SKYLARK THREE. Reading: Fantasy Press, 1948. 1st ed. Bkpl. NF; dj rear panel lightly foxed. *ELSE FINE.* $40

Smith, Edward E. SPACEHOUNDS OF IPC. Reading: Fantasy Press, 1949. 2nd ed. Bkpl. NF in dj. *ELSE FINE.* $50

Smith, Edward E. THE SKYLARK OF SPACE. Hadley, 1947. 2nd ed. NF in dj. Inscribed. *MADLE.* $125

Smith, Edward E. TRIPLANETARY. Reading, PA: Fantasy Press, (1948). 1st ed. Fine in VG dj (light rub spots). *McCLINTOCK.* $35

Smith, Edward E. TRIPLANETARY. Reading: Fantasy Press, 1948. 1st ed. 1/500 signed, numbered, this copy with variant non-numbered/limitation nebula plate. Cl defaced by drwgs else VG in 2nd state dj. *OTHER WORLDS.* $40

Smith, Edward H. MYSTERIES OF THE MISSING. Lincoln McVeagh/The Dial Press, 1927. Fine. *MAD DOG.* $15

Smith, Edward. FOREIGN VISITORS IN ENGLAND....London: Elliot Stock, 1889. 1st ed. Orig grn cl, beveled edges. Bkpl. *OAK KNOLL.* $30

Smith, Eliza. THE COMPLEAT HOUSEWIFE: OR, ACCOMPLISH'D GENTLEWOMAN'S COMPANION. London: Pemberton, 1737. 8th ed, w/additions. xvi,354,xv,3pp ads. Frontis, 6 fold-out plts (corner of one lacking). Bound in contemp stamped calf, rebacked w/new eps. Pasted to the verso of title page is recipe for cure for bite of a mad dog, that is sometimes seen. Foxing to title page o/w nice, clean. *SECOND LIFE*. $750

Smith, F. Dumont. SUMMIT OF THE WORLD. Chicago: Rand MacNally, 1909. 4th ed. Shelfwear, generally G+. *OLD LONDON*. $35

Smith, F. Hopkinson and F. Berkeley Smith. ENOCH CRANE. NY: Scribner's, 1916. 1st ed. Orig grn cl. NF in VG dj (some edge-chipping, few closed tears). *CHAPEL HILL*. $55

Smith, F. Hopkinson. A WHITE UMBRELLA IN MEXICO. Boston: Houghton Mifflin, 1889. 1st ed. Eps lightly foxed, else VG+. *CONNOLLY & WADE*. $30

Smith, F. Hopkinson. COLONEL CARTER'S CHRISTMAS. NY, 1903. 1st ed. Orig cl. VG. *McGOWAN*. $37.50

Smith, F. Hopkinson. COLONEL CARTER'S CHRISTMAS. NY: Scribner's, 1903. 1st ed, special ltd issue. #231 of 500 signed. Frontis, 3 plts not found in regular trade ed. Orig dec gilt-stamped vellum w/wallet fore edge, teg. Bkpl, sm holes on ffep, spine a trifle darkened, but VG. *CHAPEL HILL*. $85

Smith, F. Hopkinson. COLONEL CARTER'S CHRISTMAS. NY: Scribner's, 1903. 1st trade ed. Orig dec grn cl, teg. Lettering a bit rubbed on front, else bright, VG. *CHAPEL HILL*. $45

Smith, F. Hopkinson. IN THACKERAY'S LONDON. NY, 1914. Teg. 20+ tipped-in plts. NF. *POLYANTHOS*. $35

Smith, F. Hopkinson. THE ROMANCE OF AN OLD-FASHIONED GENTLEMAN. NY: Scribner's, 1907. 1st ed, lg paper issue. Orig olive-grn cl w/paper spine label. Spine lightly faded, couple of tiny pieces missing from spine label, but NF. *CHAPEL HILL*. $55

Smith, Fay Jackson et al. FATHER KINO IN ARIZONA. Phoenix: Arizona Hist Foundation, 1966. 1st ed. Presentation signed by Smith and Fox. Fine. *LAURIE*. $40

Smith, G. Elliot and T.H. Pear. SHELL SHOCK AND ITS LESSONS. Manchester, 1917. 1st ed. *FYE*. $50

Smith, G. Elliot. EGYPTIAN MUMMIES. NY, 1925. Teg. NF. *POLYANTHOS*. $125

Smith, G.M. MARINE ALGAE OF THE MONTEREY PENINSULA (CALIFORNIA). Stanford, CA: Stanford Univ, (1964). NF in VG+ dj. *MIKESH*. $30

Smith, Gene. HIGH CRIMES AND MISDEMEANORS. NY, 1977. 1st ed. 320pp. Fine in dj. *PRATT*. $22.50

Smith, George A. THE RISE, PROGRESS AND TRAVELS OF THE CHURCH OF JESUS CHRIST OF LATTER DAY SAINTS,...AND BRIEF ACCOUNT OF THE SETTLEMENT OF SALT LAKE VALLEY...Salt Lake City: Deseret, 1869. 1st ed. 49pp. Orig ptd wrappers. Howes S595. *GINSBERG*. $200

Smith, Gerald A. and Wilson G. Turner. INDIAN ROCK ART OF SOUTHERN CALIFORNIA WITH SELECTED PETROGLYPH CATALOG. Redlands: San Berardino County Museum Assoc, (1975). Black-ptd cl in dj. *DAWSON'S*. $100

Smith, Graham. KING'S CUTTERS. London: Conway Maritime Press, 1983. VG in similar dj. *PARMER*. $20

Smith, H.M. HANDBOOK OF LIZARDS. Ithaca, (1946). 126 text figures. 135 photos, 41 maps. Some pencil underlining in intro, dj chipped. *SUTTON*. $60

Smith, Harry B. (ed). THE DICKENS-KOLLE LETTERS. Boston: Bibliophile Society, 1910. 1st ltd ed. Spine and rear board show staining, marginal dampstaining throughout, one of 483. Good. *GREAT EXPECTATIONS*. $35

Smith, Henry. ANATOMICAL ATLAS, ILLUSTRATIVE OF THE STRUCTURE OF THE HUMAN BODY. Phila, 1859. 634 woodcuts. 3/4" cut from top of title page, front hinge cracked. Contents Fine. *FYE*. $100

Smith, Herndon. CENTRALIA, THE FIRST FIFTY YEARS 1845-1900. Centralia: Daily Chronicle, (1942). 1st ed. Fldg map. VF in Fine dj. *OREGON*. $75

Smith, Ira. BASEBALL'S FAMOUS OUTFIELDERS. Barnes, 1954. 1st ed. VG in VG+ dj. *PLAPINGER*. $35

Smith, Isaac. CRIME OF THE STATE: DETAILING THE REMARKABLE EXPERIENCES OF ISAAC SMITH. Columbus: Author pub, 1897. 1st ed. 156pp. Fine in pict wraps. Rare. *CONNOLLY & WADE*. $110

Smith, J. Greig. ABDOMINAL SURGERY. Phila, 1887. 1st Amer ed. *FYE*. $175

Smith, J. Thorne. BILTMORE OSWALD. THE DIARY OF A HAPLESS RECRUIT. NY, (1918). 1st ed. Author's 1st bk. Pict cvrs. NF. *POLYANTHOS*. $45

Smith, J(erome) V(an) C(rowninshield). PILGRIMAGE TO EGYPT...Boston: Gould & Lincoln, 1852. (xiv),383pp,6pp pub ads. 1st ed. Brn blind-stamped cl, faded, somewhat worn. Foxing, old marginal waterstains, several signatures pulled. *SCHOYER'S*. $45

Smith, James E. AN INTRODUCTION TO THE STUDY OF BOTANY. London: Longman, 1833. 7th ed. Rebound in 1908. Grn cl, leather spine label. Near VG. *SMITHFIELD*. $50

Smith, James Power. GENERAL LEE AT GETTYSBURG. Richmond, n.d. 1st ed. Wrappers. Minor chipping, else VG. *McGOWAN*. $85

Smith, Jedediah. THE CALIFORNIOS VERSUS JEDIDIAH SMITH 1826-27. Spokane: Arthur Clark Co, 1990. 1st ed, ltd to 950. Fine. *BOOK MARKET*. $35

Smith, Jesse Guy. HEROES OF THE SADDLE BAGS. San Antonio: The Naylor Co, 1951. 1st ed. VG. *GIBBS*. $30

Smith, John Calvin. THE ILLUSTRATED HAND-BOOK, A NEW GUIDE FOR TRAVELERS THROUGH THE UNITED STATES OF AMERICA, ETC. NY: Sherman & Smith, 1851. Fldg map in back (upper half torn away). *HUDSON*. $95

Smith, John Calvin. THE ILLUSTRATED HANDBOOK, A NEW GUIDE FOR TRAVELERS. NY: Sherman & Smith, 1847. 24 mo, 233pp. Fldg color outline map. Brown cl w/gilt stamped spine & front cover, blindstamped rear cover. Nice w/light fraying of extremities, lacks frontis. Howes S614 (2nd ed). *BOHLING*. $250

Smith, John Chabot. ALGER HISS: THE TRUE STORY. NY: Holt Rinehart, 1976. 1st ed. NF in dj. *AKA*. $23

Smith, John Jay and John F. Watson. AMERICAN HISTORICAL AND LITERARY CURIOSITIES. 6th ed. Phila: W. Brotherhead, 1861. later spine repair, edges worn, stamp. *WEBER*. $50

Smith, Joseph. OLD REDSTONE; OR, HISTORICAL SKETCHES OF WESTERN PRESBYTERIANISM. Phila, 1854. 1st ed. 459pp. Orig cl, gold tooling on spine. Howes S621. *GINSBERG*. $175

Smith, Joseph. THE BOOK OF MORMON: AN ACCOUNT WRITTEN BY THE HAND OF MORMON...(IN MORMON CHARACTERS). NY, 1869. 1st ed in Mormon characters. 116pp. Orig pict boards. Part one of the Book of Mormon. Howes S623. *GINSBERG*. $75

Smith, Julie. NEW ORLEANS MOURNING. NY: St. Martin's Press, 1990. 1st ed. VF in dj. *MORDIDA*. $35

Smith, Julie. TRUE-LIFE ADVENTURE. NY: Mysterious, (1985). 1st ed. Signed. Fine in Fine dj. *UNGER*. $35

Smith, Ken. ELEVEN POEMS. Leeds: School of English, Univ of Leeds, 1964. Northern House Pamphlet Poets. 1st ed, 1st book. Inscribed by author. Wraps. Close to Fine. *BEASLEY*. $150

Smith, Lady Eleanor and John Hinde. BRITISH CIRCUS LIFE. London: Harrap, 1948. 1st ed. VG in Good dj. *OCTOBER FARM*. $45

Smith, Lee S. ROUND THE WORLD TOWARD THE WESTER-ING SUN. Chicago et al: Revell, 1904. Red cl stamped in gilt, a little rubbed and shaken. Presentation inscrip. SCHOYER'S. $25

Smith, Lee. BLACK MOUNTAIN BREAKDOWN. NY, 1980. 1st ed. Fine in dj. PETTLER. $35

Smith, Lee. BLACK MOUNTAIN BREAKDOWN. NY: Putnam, (1980). 1st ed. Fine (light rmdr mk "P" on bottom edges) in dj. Signed. CAPTAIN'S BOOKSHELF. $60

Smith, Lee. CAKEWALK. NY: Putnam, (1981). 1st ed. Fine in dj. Signed. CAPTAIN'S BOOKSHELF. $45

Smith, Lee. CAKEWALK. NY: Putnam, (1981). 1st ed. Signed. Fine in dj. LOPEZ. $85

Smith, Lee. CAKEWALK. NY: Putnam, 1981. 1st ed. Fine in Fine dj. BEASLEY. $30

Smith, Lee. FAIR AND TENDER LADIES. NY: Putnam's, (1988). Uncorrected proof of 1st ed. Orig ptd orange wraps. Fine. CHAPEL HILL. $75

Smith, Lee. FAMILY LINEN. NY: Putnam, (1985). 1st ed. Signed. Fine in Fine dj. LOPEZ. $75

Smith, Lee. FAMILY LINEN. NY: Putnam's, (1985). 1st ed. Inscribed. Orig blue boards. Fine in dj. CHAPEL HILL. $50

Smith, Lee. FAMILY LINEN. Putnam, 1985. 1st ed. About Fine in dj. STAHR. $15

Smith, Lee. FANCY STRUT. NY: Harper, (1973). 1st ed. Bit cocked but VG in like dj. Signed. CAPTAIN'S BOOKSHELF. $60

Smith, Lee. ME AND MY BABY VIEW THE ECLIPSE. Stories. NY: Putnam's, (1990). 1st ed. Signed. Orig two-toned boards. As New in dj. CHAPEL HILL. $35

Smith, Lee. ORAL HISTORY. NY: Putnam, (1983). 1st ed. Fine in dj w/sm tear. Signed. CAPTAIN'S BOOKSHELF. $45

Smith, Lee. SOMETHING IN THE WIND. Harper & Row, 1971. 1st ed. Fine in dj w/wear at edges. STAHR. $45

Smith, Lee. SOMETHING IN THE WIND. NY: H&R, (1971). 1st ed. Owner name fep, o/w Fine in dj. Signed. LOPEZ. $150

Smith, Lee. SOMETHING IN THE WIND. NY: Harper, (1971). 1st ed. Label removed from ffep, else Fine in like dj. Signed. CAPTAIN'S BOOKSHELF. $100

Smith, Lee. SOMETHING IN THE WIND. NY: Harper & Row, (1971). 1st ed. Signed, dated. Orig cl-backed blue boards. Fine in dj, two short, closed tears. CHAPEL HILL. $175

Smith, Lou. EWELL BLACKWELL. Barnes, 1951. 1st ed. VG+ without dj. PLAPINGER. $50

Smith, Lucy. BIOGRAPHICAL SKETCHES OF JOSEPH SMITH THE PROPHET, AND HIS PROGENITORS FOR MANY GENERATIONS. Liverpool & London, 1853. 1st ed. 297pp, full brown lea somewhat worn; hinges, and spine cracked, lacks ffep, one leaf loose and miscropped, title page sl stained, corner torn from leaf 275-6 affecting 3 or 4 words of text, o/w interior tight and clean. BENCHMARK. $750

Smith, M. EAST COAST MARINE SHELLS. Ann Arbor, 1937. 1st ed. 74 plts. Ex-lib. SUTTON. $35

Smith, M. TRITON HELMET AND HARP SHELLS. Winter Park, 1948. 16 plts. Dj chipped. SUTTON. $35

Smith, M. WORLD-WIDE SEA SHELLS. Lantana, 1940. Signed. Dj (some wear). SUTTON. $45

Smith, Mark. THE DEATH OF THE DETECTIVE. NY: Knopf, 1974. 1st ed. VF in dj. ELSE FINE. $35

Smith, Martin Cruz. NIGHTWING. NY: Norton, (1977). 1st ed. Fine in dj w/tiny wrinkle at crown. LOPEZ. $50

Smith, Martin Cruz. POLAR STAR. Franklin Center: Franklin Lib, 1989. Fine. Signed. LOPEZ. $65

Smith, Martin Cruz. STALLION GATE. NY: Random House, (1986). 1st ed. Fine in dj. LOPEZ. $25

Smith, Martin. CANTO FOR A GYPSY. NY: Putnam, (1972). 1st ed. Fine in NF dj (short tear upper edge rear panel, bit of creasing there). LOPEZ. $65

Smith, Matthew Hale. SUNSHINE AND SHADOW IN NEW YORK. Hartford: J.B. Burr, 1868. 1st ed. Spine sl faded, shelfwear, cvr staining. Contents VG. DIAMOND. $75

Smith, Meredith J. and Rosemary W. Ganf. MARSUPIALS OF AUSTRALIA. VOLUME I. POSSUMS, THE KOALA AND WOMBATS. 24 colored and 4 tinted plts. Melbourne, 1980. Ltd ed of 1000, signed by author and artist. Full canvas, dec, blind-stamped leather panel w/gilt edge inlaid on front cvr and spine. Fine, as issued. SUTTON. $550

Smith, Mrs. A. Murray. WESTMINSTER ABBEY. A&C Black, 1904. 1st ed. 7s 6d Series. Minor spot front cover, else VG-NF. OLD LONDON. $40

Smith, Mrs. Amanda. AN AUTOBIOGRAPHY. Chicago: Meyer & Brother, 1893. Fresh brick cl stamped in gilt and blind. VG. SCHOYER'S. $75

Smith, Nathan. MEDICAL AND SURGICAL MEMOIRS. Baltimore, 1831. 1st ed. Recent 1/2 leather, 374pp. FYE. $250

Smith, Nathan. SURGICAL ANATOMY OF THE ARTERIES. Baltimore, 1835. 2nd ed. Recent 1/4 leather, 132pp + 17 (of 20) hand colored plts. Foxed and browned as usual, inner margin of 1 leaf torn w/loss of part of text. Plts 14, 18, and 19 are missing. FYE. $150

Smith, Nathan. SURGICAL ANATOMY OF THE ARTERIES. Baltimore: J.N. Toy & W.R. Lucas. 1830. 1st ed. 104,(8)pp. + 18 hand-colored lithographs drawn by J. Swett of Baltimore (lithographed by Endicott & Swett). With a number of added ptd text "slips." Orig marbled boards, rebacked (20th c) in calf w/renewed calf corners. Some browning and foxing. With the 19th c Amer bkpl of Beverly R. Wellford. KARMIOLE. $850

Smith, P.W. THE AMPHIBIANS AND REPTILES OF ILLINOIS. Urbana, (1961). Wrappers. Spine chipped, some fading and spotting, ink inscrip. SUTTON. $27

Smith, Page. JOHN ADAMS. NY, 1962. 1st ed. 2 vols. Dj. HEINOLDT. $15

Smith, Paul Jordan. ON STRANGE ALTARS: A BOOK OF ENTHUSIASMS. NY: Albert & Charles Boni, 1924. 1st ed. Spine a bit faded, else VG. WREDEN. $20

Smith, Private Benjamin T. PRIVATE SMITH'S JOURNAL. Ed by Clyde C. Walton. Chicago, 1963. 1st ed. Lakeside Classic #61. Dj wear, o/w VG. PRATT. $35

Smith, R. Bosworth. LIFE OF LORD LAWRENCE. NY: Scribner's, 1883. 2 vols. xiv,484pp,4pp pub ads; xix,567pp. Olive cl stamped in red and gilt. Frontis. Fldg map, color plan. SCHOYER'S. $75

Smith, R.A. A HISTORY OF DICKINSON COUNTY, IOWA, TOGETHER WITH AN ACCOUNT OF THE SPIRIT LAKE MASSACRE. Des Moines: Kenyon, 1902. 1st ed. Frontis. Red blind stamped cloth w/gilt. VG. Howes 659. CONNOLLY & WADE. $150

Smith, R.R.R. HELLENISTIC ROYAL PORTRAITS. Oxford: Clarendon Press, 1988. 80 plts. Dj. Good. ARCHAEOLOGIA. $125

Smith, Richard C. A SECRET SINGING. NY: NAL, 1988. 1st ed. Signed. VF in dj. MORDIDA. $20

Smith, Richard C. WILD JUSTICE. NY: St. Martin's Press, 1990. 1st ed. Signed. VF in dj. MORDIDA. $20

Smith, Richard Gordon. ANCIENT TALES AND FOLKLORE OF JAPAN. A&C Black, 1908. 1st ed. 20s Series. Front cover sl loose, else VG. OLD LONDON. $125

Smith, Robert. THE WAR IN THE PACIFIC: THE APPROACH TO THE PHILLIPINES. Washington: Dept Army/USGPO, 1953. 1st ed. Spine a bit sunned, o/w NF. *ARCHER*. $25

Smith, Ross Jr. 14,000 MILES THROUGH THE AIR. NY, 1922. NF. *POLYANTHOS*. $75

Smith, Ross. 14,000 MILES THROUGH THE AIR. NY: The Macmillan Co. 1922. 1st ed. *KARMIOLE*. $50

Smith, S. Compton. CHILE CON CARNE; OR, THE CAMP AND THE FIELD. NY: Miller, 1857. 1st ed. (16),404,(12),(4)pp. Spine frayed and worn at lower spine and lower joints. *GINSBERG*. $150

Smith, Stevie. THE BEST BEASTS. NY: Knopf, 1969. 1st ed. Fine in VG dj (2" tear in rear, sunned). *ARCHER*. $20

Smith, Theodore C. THE LIFE AND LETTERS OF JAMES ABRAM GARFIELD. New Haven, 1925. 1st ed. 2 vols. Orig cl. *GINSBERG*. $75

Smith, Thomas and John O. Choules. THE ORIGIN & HISTORY OF MISSIONS. Boston, 1838. 2 vols. 5th ed. 1/2 calf, rubbed. 622;610pp. *O'NEILL*. $225

Smith, Thorne. THE PASSIONATE WITCH. GC: Doubleday, 1941. 1st ed. Eps foxed and darkened, else NF in sl spine-darkened NF dj. *BETWEEN COVERS*. $125

Smith, Thorne. THE PASSIONATE WITCH. GC: Doubleday-Doran, 1941. 1st ed. Illus by Herbert Roese. Fine in illus cvr, internal mending. Lt edgewear to dj. *ELSE FINE*. $160

Smith, Truman. SPEECH OF TRUMAN SMITH ON THE PHYSICAL CHARTER OF THE NORTHERN STATES OF MEXICO. Wash, 1848. 1st ed. 31pp. Cl w/morocco spine label. Howes S680. *GINSBERG*. $225

Smith, W.D.A. UNDER THE INFLUENCE: A HISTORY OF NITROUS OXIDE AND OXYGEN ANAESTHESIA. London, 1982. 1st ed. Dj. *FYE*. $75

Smith, W.H.B. PISTOLS & REVOLVERS, VOLUME ONE OF THE N.R.A. BOOK OF SMALL ARMS. Wash. DC/The Military Service Pub. Co. Harrisburg: N.R.A. of America, 1946. 1st ed. VG in ragged edge-torn dj. *BACKMAN*. $25

Smith, Wallace. BESSIE COTTER. Paris: The Obelisk Press, (c1946). VG in orig ptd wraps. *HELLER*. $75

Smith, Wallace. OREGON SKETCHES. Putnam, 1925. 1st ed. 19 plts. Lrg bkpl, o/w VG in Good+ spine faded dj. *OREGON*. $35

Smith, Wilbur A. CRY WOLF. GC: Doubleday, 1977. 1st ed. Fine; tiny edge tear to dj. *ELSE FINE*. $25

Smith, Wilbur A. HUNGRY AS THE SEA. GC: Doubleday, 1978. 1st ed. Name. VF in dj. *ELSE FINE*. $25

Smith, Wilbur A. HUNGRY AS THE SEA. London: Heinemann, 1978. 1st ed. Fine; minor wear at dj spine ends. *ELSE FINE*. $40

Smith, Wilbur A. THE EYE OF THE TIGER. London: Heinemann, 1975. 1st ed. Fine; minor edgewear to dj. *ELSE FINE*. $40

Smith, Wilbur A. THE TRAIN FROM KATANGA. NY: Viking, 1965. 1st ed. Fine; minor wear to dj. *ELSE FINE*. $40

Smith, Wilbur A. WHEN THE LION FEEDS. NY: Viking Press, (1964). 1st ed, 1st book. NF in dj. *BERNARD*. $65

Smith, William (ed). DICTIONARY OF GREEK AND ROMAN ANTIQUITIES. London: John Murray, 1849. 2nd enrlgd ed. Full calf w/5 raised bands, red leather label, gilt-extra (rubbed). Good. *ARCHAEOLOGIA*. $125

Smith, William Fielding. DIAMOND SIX. GC, 1958. 1st ed. Dj. VG+. *PRATT*. $20

Smith, William Gardner. SOUTH STREET. NY, 1954. 1st ed. Fine in dj, sl sunned, rubbed, a few nicks. Fine. *POLYANTHOS*. $75

Smith, William Henry. THE ST. CLAIR PAPERS: THE LIFE AND PUBLIC SERVICES OF ARTHUR ST. CLAIR...Cincinnati:

Clarke, 1882. 2 vols. 1st ed. Map, 2 ports. Orig cl. Howes S26. *GINSBERG*. $200

Smith, William Stevenson. A HISTORY OF EGYPTIAN SCULPTURE AND PAINTING IN THE OLD KINGDOM. Oxford: Oxford Univ Press, 1946. Color frontis, 239 figs, 62 plts (2 color). Good. *ARCHAEOLOGIA*. $475

Smith, William Stevenson. INTERCONNECTIONS IN THE ANCIENT NEAR EAST. New Haven & London: Yale Univ Press, 1965. 221 figs. Spine faded. Good. *ARCHAEOLOGIA*. $175

Smith, William. A BRIEF STATE OF THE PROVINCE OF PENNSYLVANIA. NY: Sabin, 1865. One of 200. 44pp. Orig ptd wrappers. Howes S686. *GINSBERG*. $45

Smith, Winifred. ITALIAN ACTORS OF THE RENAISSANCE. NY: Coward, McCann, 1930. Dj torn, chipped. *SCHOYER'S*. $35

Smith, Winifred. THE COMMEDIA DELL'ARTE. NY: Columbia Univ Press, 1912. 1st ed. Orig cloth; bkpl and stamp of priv circulating lib; illus; head of spine worn. With presentation inscrip. VG. *DRAMATIS PERSONAE*. $35

SMITHSONIAN INSTITUTION, ANNUAL REPORT FOR 1854. 269pp. Minor dampstains, sl foxing. Ex-lib. Good+. *BOOKCELL*. $30

SMITHSONIAN INSTITUTION, ANNUAL REPORT FOR 1863. 446pp. Good+. End leaves heavily foxed. *BOOKCELL*. $27

SMITHSONIAN INSTITUTION, ANNUAL REPORT FOR 1864. End leaf foxing. VG. *BOOKCELL*. $27

SMITHSONIAN INSTITUTION, ANNUAL REPORT FOR 1870. 494pp. Good. *BOOKCELL*. $27

SMITHSONIAN INSTITUTION, ANNUAL REPORT FOR 1883. 959pp. Cvr chipping, wear on backstrip. Good+. *BOOKCELL*. $27

SMITHSONIAN INSTITUTION, ANNUAL REPORT FOR 1906. Ex-lib. VG. *BOOKCELL*. $27

SMITHSONIAN INSTITUTION, ANNUAL REPORT FOR 1909. Good+. *BOOKCELL*. $30

SMITHSONIAN INSTITUTION, ANNUAL REPORT FOR 1917. VG. *BOOKCELL*. $15

SMITHSONIAN INSTITUTION. ANNUAL REPORT FOR 1884. Washington, DC: 1885. Engr. VG+. *MIKESH*. $15

SMITHSONIAN INSTITUTION, ANNUAL REPORT FOR 1916. Washington, DC: 1917. Illus. VG. *MIKESH*. $12.50

SMITHSONIAN INSTITUTION, ANNUAL REPORT FOR 1936. Washington, DC: 1937. Illus. VG. *MIKESH*. $12.50

SMITHSONIAN INSTITUTION, PROCEEDINGS, VOLUME 29. Washington, DC: 1906. Good+. *MIKESH*. $20

Smollett, Tobias. THE MISCELLANEOUS WORKS...Edinburgh: Ptd for Silvester Doig & Andrew Stirling...1817. 5th ed. 6 vols. 3/4 brn calf, tan cl w/minor wear to corners. Sl occasional foxing on Vol 1. NF. *BLUE MOUNTAIN*. $275

Smyth, C. Piazzi. LIFE AND WORK AT THE GREAT PYRAMID DURING THE MONTHS OF JANUARY, FEBRUARY, MARCH, AND APRIL, A.D. 1865. 3 vols. Edinburgh: Edmonston & Douglas, 1867. Frontis each vol. Orig cl, spines very worn, sl foxed, o/w VG. Teg. *WORLDWIDE*. $300

Smyth, C. Piazzi. OUR INHERITANCE IN THE GREAT PYRAMID. London: Isbiter, 1880. 4th enl ed. Frontis, 24 plts (11 color). Loosely inserted are (2) 4-pg letters from Smyth, signed by him, and copies of 4 letters sent to Smyth by A.B. Redfield. *WORLDWIDE*. $140

Smyth, H. D. ATOMIC ENERGY FOR MILITARY PURPOSES. Princeton: Princeton Univ Press, 1945. Orange cl. VG. *SMITHFIELD*. $55

Smyth, H.D. A GENERAL ACCOUNT OF THE DEVELOPMENT OF METHODS OF USING ATOMIC ENERGY FOR

MILITARY PURPOSES. (Washington: War Department), 1945. First pub ed (preceded by mimeographed version for the press). Upper portion wrappers and spine sunned, owner's sig. *DAWSON'S.* $400

Smyth, Henry D. ATOMIC ENERGY FOR MILITARY PURPOSES. Princeton: Princeton Univ Press, 1945. 1st commercial ed. Dj w/small chip out at head and tail, small tear at middle of spine. Bright, NF. *BLUE MOUNTAIN.* $125

Smyth, Henry D. ATOMIC ENERGY FOR MILITARY PURPOSES. THE OFFICIAL REPORT ON THE DEVELOPMENT OF THE ATOMIC BOMB. Princeton, 1945. 1st ed. *FYE.* $50

Smyth, William Henry. A CYCLE OF CELESTIAL OBJECTS, OBSERVED, REDUCED, AND DISCUSSED. Oxford: Clarendon Press, 1881 (1844). Rev by George F. Chambers. Good. *KNOLLWOOD.* $400

Smythe, F.S. BRITISH MOUNTAINEERS. (Britain in Pictures). London: Collins, 1946. 2nd imp. NF in dj. *OLD LONDON.* $12.50

Smythe, F.S. THE MOUNTAIN SCENE. London: Adam & Charles Black, 1938. 2nd ed. Spine badly faded, some wear. *PARMER.* $40

Smythe, Gonzalvo. MEDICAL HERESIES HISTORICALLY CONSIDERED. Phila, 1880. 1st ed. 228pp. *FYE.* $100

Snell, Henry James. PRACTICAL INSTRUCTIONS IN ENAMEL PAINTING...FULL INSTRUCTIONS FOR THE MANUFACTURE OF THE VITREOUS PIGMENTS REQUIRED. London: (Brodie & Middleton/Simkin, Marshall), n.d. (ca. 1890). Pub's blue cl w/dec in gilt and black ink. VF. 12 color plts. 32-pg catalogue at rear of text. *BOOK BLOCK.* $225

Snellgrove, David. HIMALAYAN PILGRIMAGE. Oxford: Bruno Cassirer, (1961). 44 plts, maps, color frontis. 1st ed. VG in VG- dj. *BLUE DRAGON.* $65

Snelling, O.F. DOUBLE O SEVEN JAMES BOND: A REPORT. (London): Neville Spearman/Holland Press, (1964). 1st ed. Fine in dj. *JUVELIS.* $50

Snelling, William. TALES OF THE NORTHWEST. Univ of MN, 1936. Ltd to 1000 numbered. Reprint of 1830 ed. VG. *OREGON.* $35

Snider, Denton J. A WALK IN HELLAS OR THE OLD IN THE NEW. St. Louis, 1892. 525 pp. Spine ends chipped, else sound. *O'NEILL.* $40

Snodgrass, A.M. ARMS AND ARMOUR OF THE GREEKS. London: Thames and Hudson, (1982). *ARCHAEOLOGIA.* $50

Snodgrass, R.E. PRINCIPLES OF INSECT MORPHOLOGY. NY, (1935). Cloth. *SUTTON.* $45

Snodgrass, W.C. HEART'S NEEDLE. NY: Knopf, 1959. 1st ed. Ltd to 1500. Fine in dj. *JAFFE.* $175

Snodgrass, W.C. REMAINS. POEMS BY S.S. GARDONS. Mt. Horeb, WI: Perishable Press, 1970. 1st ed. One of 200 ptd. 1/4 morocco, marbled boards. VF. *JAFFE.* $275

Snodgrass, W.D. AFTER EXPERIENCE: POEMS. NY: Harper, (1968). 1st ed. Fine in dj. Signed. *CAPTAIN'S BOOKSHELF.* $45

Snodgrass, W.D. ANTONIO VIVALDI: THE FOUR SEASONS. NY: Targ Editions, 1984. 1st ed. 1/150 signed. *JUVELIS.* $90

Snow, C.P. THE AFFAIR. Franklin Center: Franklin Library, 1981. Leatherbound ltd ed reissue. Signed. Fine. *LOPEZ.* $60

Snow, Charles E. EARLY HAWAIIANS: AN INITIAL STUDY OF SKELETAL REMAINS FROM MOKAPU, OAHU. Lexington: Univ of KY Press, 1974. Fine. *PARMER.* $35

Snow, Edward Rowe. PIRATES AND BUCCANEERS OF THE ATLANTIC COAST. Boston: The Yankee Pub Co, 1944. 1st ed. Bit of wear to head and heel, spine faded, else VG in lightly worn dj. *PARMER.* $45

Snow, Edward Rowe. PIRATES AND BUCCANEERS OF THE ATLANTIC COAST. Boston: The Yankee Pub Co, 1944. Signed "Edward Rowe Snow" and "Anna Myrle Snow." VG. *PARMER.* $70

Snow, Elliot. THE SEA, THE SHIP AND THE SAILOR: TALES OF ADVENTURE FROM LOG BOOKS AND ORIGINAL NARRATIVES. Salem, 1925. Pub. 7. Fine. Worn dj. *LEFKOWICZ.* $85

Snow, John. ON CHLOROFORM AND OTHER ANAESTHETICS: THEIR ACTION AND ADMINISTRATION. Birmingham, 1989. Facs of 1858 ed. 1st ed. Full lea. *FYE.* $50

SNOW WHITE & THE SEVEN DWARFS. London, 1979. Shook and Halley (illus). Tor Lokvig (eng). Pop-up bk. *BOOKFINDERS INTL.* $40

SNOW WHITE. (1971). 6 double pg pop-ups. Pop-up bk. *BOOKFINDERS INTL.* $30

Snyder, Don J. VETERANS PARK. Watts, 1987. 1st ed. Fine in dj w/short tear, chip on front panel. *STAHR.* $20

Snyder, Gary. A CURSE ON THE MAN IN WASHINGTON, PENTAGON. Unicorn Broadsheet One, 1968. Broadside. 1st issue with "Buddah" on line 16. Limitation not stated. *WOOLMER.* $45

Snyder, Gary. A RANGE OF POEMS. London: Fulcrum, (1966). 1st ed. Fine in dj. *CAPTAIN'S BOOKSHELF.* $125

Snyder, Gary. A RANGE OF POEMS. London: Fulcrum Press, (1966). 1st British ed. Fine, frayed dj, 1/2" tape mark on ep. *AUTHORS OF THE WEST.* $40

Snyder, Gary. EARTH HOUSE HOLD: TECHNICAL NOTES...(NY): New Directions, (1969). 1st ed. Fine in dj. *CAPTAIN'S BOOKSHELF.* $125

Snyder, Gary. MANZANITA. Kent State Univ, 1971. 1st ed. Fld broadside. NF w/few minor creases. *BEASLEY.* $30

Snyder, Gary. MYTHS AND TEXTS. NY: Totem/Corinth, (1960). 1st ed. Fine in wrappers. *CAPTAIN'S BOOKSHELF.* $100

Snyder, Gary. MYTHS AND TEXTS. NY: Totem Press (1960). 1st ed. Dec wraps. Signed. Cvrs sl used; sm red stain front cvr. Still VG. *DORN.* $150

Snyder, Gary. REGARDING WAVE. London: Fulcrum, (1970). 1st ed. Fine in dj. *CAPTAIN'S BOOKSHELF.* $50

Snyder, Gary. RIPRAP & COLD MOUNTAIN POEMS. (SF: Four Seasons Foundation, 1965). 1st ed, 1st issue, w/no price on rear panel. Pub as Writing 7. Fine in wrappers. *CAPTAIN'S BOOKSHELF.* $25

Snyder, Gary. RIPRAP. (Ashland, MA): Origin Press, 1959. 1st ed, 1st bk. 1/500. Owner's sig. Fine in wrappers w/ptd label. *CAPTAIN'S BOOKSHELF.* $500

Snyder, Gary. RIPRAP. (Ashland): Origin Press, 1959. 2nd ed., one of 1,000 in wrappers. Inscribed. Front cover faded at edges. VG. *LOPEZ.* $100

Snyder, Gary. SIX SECTIONS FROM MOUNTAINS AND RIVERS WITHOUT END. SF: Four Seasons Foundation, 1965. 1st ed. Pub as Writing 9. Fine in wrappers. *CAPTAIN'S BOOKSHELF.* $25

Snyder, Gary. SIX SECTIONS FROM MOUNTAINS AND RIVERS WITHOUT END. London: Fulcrum Press, (1967). 1st ed. 1/100 ptd on Glastonbury paper and signed. Fine in dj. *CAPTAIN'S BOOKSHELF.* $150

Snyder, Gary. SIX SECTIONS FROM MOUNTAINS AND RIVERS WITHOUT END. London: Fulcrum Press, (1967). 1st ed. Fine in dj. *CAPTAIN'S BOOKSHELF.* $75

Snyder, Gary. THE BACK COUNTRY. London: Fulcrum Press, (1967). 1st ed. 1/100 on Glastonbury paper signed. Fine in dj. *CAPTAIN'S BOOKSHELF.* $200

Snyder, Gary. THE BACK COUNTRY. London: Fulcrum Press, (1967). 1st ed. Fine in dj. *CAPTAIN'S BOOKSHELF.* $75

Snyder, L.L. ARCTIC BIRDS OF CANADA. Toronto, 1957. Cl (scuffed on one edge of cvr), dj (chipped; worn). *SUTTON.* $85

Soane, E.B. TO MESOPOTAMIA AND KURDISTAN IN DISGUISE. WITH HISTORICAL NOTICES...London, 1912. *O'NEILL.* $110

Sobotta, Johannes. ATLAS AND TEXT-BOOK OF HUMAN ANATOMY. Phila, 1909. 1st Eng trans, 2nd prtg. 3 vols. 1/2 leather, 258, 194, 342pp + 831 illus. Some rubbing of hinges and spines. Overall, VG. Scarce. *FYE.* $250

SOLD AMERICAN!--THE FIRST FIFTY YEARS. THE AMERICAN TOBACCO COMPANY. 1954. 1st ed. VG. *CONNOLLY & WADE.* $35

Solier, Charles (ed). CHAGALL'S POSTERS: A CATALOGUE RAISONNE. NY: Crown, (1975). 1st US ed. Fine in dj and cardboard slipcase. *CAPTAIN'S BOOKSHELF.* $100

Sollers, Phillippe. THE PARK. NY: Red Dust, 1969. 1st ed. Fine in Fine dj. *BEASLEY.* $25

Solly, Samuel. SURGICAL EXPERIENCES: THE SUBSTANCE OF CLINICAL LECTURES. London, 1865. 1st ed. Skillfully recased. *FYE.* $175

Solomita, Stephen. A TWIST OF THE KNIFE. NY: G.P. Putnam's Sons, 1988. 1st ed. VF in dj. *MORDIDA.* $35

Solomita, Stephen. BAD TO THE BONE. NY: G.P. Putnam's Sons, 1991. 1st ed. Fine in dj. *MORDIDA.* $20

Solomita, Stephen. FORCE OF NATURE. NY: G.P. Putnam's Sons, 1989. 1st ed. Fine in dj. *MORDIDA.* $25

Solomon, Carl. MISHAPS, PERHAPS. SF: Beach Books, 1966. 1st ed. Signed. Pict wraps little sunned and edge rubbed. Fine. *POLYANTHOS.* $40

Solomon, David (ed). LSD: THE CONSCIOUSNESS EXPANDING DRUG. NY: Putnam, (1964). Intro Timothy Leary. Fine in VG dj. *LOPEZ.* $40

Solzhenitsyn, Aleksandr. AUGUST 1914: THE RED WHEEL/KNOT 1. NY: Farrar Straus & Giroux, (1989). One of 200 specially bound, signed. Fine in slipcase. *CAPTAIN'S BOOKSHELF.* $300

Solzhenitsyn, Aleksandr. AUGUST 1914. THE RED WHEEL/KNOT I. H.T. Willetts (trans). NY: Farrar Straus & Giroux, (1989). 1st ed. One of 200 numbered, signed. Red cl, black cl slipcase. Mint. *JAFFE.* $350

Solzhenitsyn, Aleksandr. GULAG ARCHIPELAGO. NY: Harper, 1973. 1st ed. Owner inscrip, o/w NF in NF dj. *AKA.* $30

Solzhenitsyn, Aleksandr. THE FIRST CIRCLE. NY: Harper, (1968). 1st US. Some foxing to fore-edges, else About Fine in like dj. Review copy: slip, newsletter laid in. *CAPTAIN'S BOOKSHELF.* $60

Solzhenitsyn, Alexander. ONE DAY IN THE LIFE OF IVAN DENISOVICH. NY: Dutton, (1963). 1st ed. Fine in NF dj with a couple nicks. *UNGER.* $65

Solzhenitsyn, Alexander. ONE DAY IN THE LIFE OF IVAN DENISOVICH. NY: Praeger, 1963. 1st ed. 1st work into English. NF in VG+ dj. *LAME DUCK.* $35

Solzhenitsyn, Alexander. ONE DAY IN THE LIFE OF IVAN DENISOVICH. Praeger, 1963. 1st Amer ed. NF, dj (three very small chips). *STAHR.* $25

SOME OF AESOP'S FABLES WITH MODERN INSTANCES. Macmillan, 1883. 1st Amer ed. 4to. 79pp. Illus by Randolph Caldecott. Interior Fine, wear to dec cvrs, severe cvr bump. *BEBBAH.* $90

Somers, Jane (pseud of Doris Lessing). IF THE OLD COULD...Knopf, 1984. 1st Amer. ed. NF in dj (chip foot of spine). Review copy. *STAHR.* $25

Somers, Richard J. RICHMOND REDEEMED, THE SIEGE OF PETERSBURG. GC, 1981. 670pp. Ex-lib, but evidenced only by two unobtrusive markings. Light dj wear o/w Fine. *PRATT.* $27.50

Somerville and Ross. "HAPPY DAYS!". London: Longmans, Green, 1946. 1st prtg. Endpapers lightly foxed, ow VG. *OCTOBER FARM.* $45

Somerville and Ross. THE SWEET CRY OF HOUNDS. Boston: Houghton Mifflin, 1937. 1st U.S. ed. Spine label chipped, o/w VG. *OCTOBER FARM.* $45

Somerville and Ross. WHEEL-TRACKS. London: Longmans, Green, 1923. 1st ed. Good+. *OCTOBER FARM.* $40

Somerville, J. Alexander. MAN OF COLOR, AN AUTOBIOGRAPHY. LA: Lorrin L. Morrison, (1949). Signed, prospectus laid in. Gold-stamped cl in dj. *DAWSON'S.* $40

Somerville, Martha (ed, comp). PERSONAL RECOLLECTIONS, FROM EARLY LIFE TO OLD AGE, OF MARY SOMERVILLE..London: John Murray, 1873. 3rd thousand. VG in black 1/2 leather. *KNOLLWOOD.* $110

Somerville, Mary. PHYSICAL GEOGRAPHY. NY: Sheldon, 1867. New Amer ed from rev 3rd London ed. Contemp cl worn at top of spine. VG. *SECOND LIFE.* $45

Somerville, Mary. PHYSICAL GEOGRAPHY. Phila: Lea & Blanchard, 1848. 1st US ed. Foxing, o/w Good. *KNOLLWOOD.* $65

Somerville. THE STATES THROUGH IRISH EYES. Boston: Houghton Mifflin, 1930. 1st trade ed. Spine faded. VG. *OCTOBER FARM.* $40

Sommer, F. MAN & BEAST IN AFRICA. NY: Citadel, 1954. 1st US ed. VG+ in Fair dj. *MIKESH.* $37.50

Sommer, Scott. LAST RESORT. NY: Random House, (1982). 1st ed. Signed. Fine in Fine dj. *LOPEZ.* $35

Sommer, Scott. LIFETIME. NY: Random House, (1981). 1st ed. Signed. Fine in Fine dj. *LOPEZ.* $45

Sommer, Scott. NEARING'S GRACE. NY: Taplinger, (1979). 1st ed. Signed. Fine in Fine dj. *LOPEZ.* $85

Sommerfield, John. VOLUNTEER IN SPAIN. NY: Knopf, 1937. 1st US ed. VG in bright, NF dj. *BERNARD.* $25

SONG OF ROLAND. NY: LEC, 1938. Trans by Charles Scott Moncreiff. 1/1500. Fine in faded pub's box. *JUVELIS.* $50

Sonn, Albert. EARLY AMERICAN WROUGHT IRON. 3 VOLS. NY: Scribner's, 1928. 1st ed. Few plts loose but complete. Contents VG. *BACKROOM.* $400

Sonne, Conway B. WORLD OF WAKARA. San Antonio, n.d. 1st ed. 235pp. Fine in dj w/light wear, large chips. *PRATT.* $20

Sonnichsen, C.L. BILLY KING'S TOMBSTONE. Caxton, 1951. 3rd ptg. Fine in Fine dj. *VARNER.* $25

Sonnichsen, C.L. COWBOYS AND CATTLE KINGS. Norman, 1951. 2nd ptg. Fine in very chipped dj. *VARNER.* $25

Sonnichsen, C.L. COWBOYS AND CATTLE KINGS. Norman: Univ of OK, 1950. 1st ed. Fine in Good+ dj. *CONNOLLY & WADE.* $65

Sonnichsen, C.L. OUTLAW: BILL MITCHELL ALIAS BALDY RUSSELL. Sage, 1965. 1st ptg. Fine in NF dj. *VARNER.* $35

Sonnichsen, C.L. PASS OF THE NORTH. El Paso, 1969. 2nd prtg. VG in chipped dj. *BAADE.* $52.50

Sonnichsen, C.L. TEN TEXAS FEUDS. Univ of NM, 1957. 1st ed. Fine in NF dj. *VARNER.* $45

Sonnichsen, C.L. THE GRAVE OF JOHN WESLEY HARDIN. College Station, TX, (1979). 1st ed. 90pp. Three small pieces torn from dj o/w Fine. *PRATT.* $22.50

Sontag, Susan. A SUSAN SONTAG READER. NY: Farrar Straus Giroux, (1982). 1/350 numbered, in pub's slipcase. Signed. *LOPEZ.* $65

Sophian, Abraham. EPIDEMIC CEREBROSPINAL MENINGITIS. St. Louis, 1913. 1st ed. *FYE.* $50

Sorenson, A.L. HANDS UP! THE HISTORY OF A CRIME. College Station, TX: Early West, (1982). 1st ed. Leather. Rprnt from 1877 ed. Ltd to 1,000. Fine. *BOOK MARKET.* $38

Sorenson, Alfred. HISTORY OF OMAHA FROM THE PIONEER DAYS TO THE PRESENT TIME. Omaha: Gibson, Miller & Richardson, 1889. (2nd ed c. 1876). 342pp. Ads, double view, orig cl. Some wear and rubbing. Howes S765. *BOHLING.* $150

Sorrentino, Gilbert. CORROSIVE SUBLIMATE. LA: Black Sparrow, 1971. 1/200 numbered, signed. NF. *LOPEZ.* $35

Sorrentino, Gilbert. STEELWORK. NY, 1970. 1st ed. Signed. Fine in Fine dj. *POLYANTHOS.* $30

Sorrentino, Gilbert. THE DARKNESS SURROUNDS US. Highlands, (NC): Jonathan Williams, Publisher, 1960. 1st ed. Orig ptd photogr wraps. Fine. *CHAPEL HILL.* $150

Sorrentino, Gilbert. THE SKY CHANGES. NY: Hill and Wang, (1966). 1st ed. Signed. Fine in Fine dj. *LOPEZ.* $75

Sotbene, Oswold. THE SHRINE OF AESCULAPIUS. Cleveland, 1905. 277pp. 4 Fine illus. Scarce. *FYE.* $100

Soustelle, Jacques. THE DAILY LIFE OF THE AZTECS ON THE EVE OF THE SPANISH CONQUEST. London: Weidenfeld & Nicolson, (1961). 2 maps. Good. *ARCHAEOLOGIA.* $25

SOUTH CAROLINA. YEAR BOOK-1880. CITY OF CHARLESTON, SO. CA. Charleston, SC: The News and Courier Book Presses, 1880. Fldg map, 5 facs fldg maps. Ex-lib. *HUDSON.* $95

SOUTH DAKOTA: A GUIDE TO THE STATE. NY: Hastings House, (1952). 2nd ed. Compiled by the Federal Writers' Project. Cl in dj (3 chips, foxing). *DAWSON'S.* $40

Southard, E.E. and H.C. Solomon. NEUROSYPHILIS, MODERN SYSTEMATIC DIAGNOSIS AND TREATMENT. Boston, 1917. 1st ed. *FYE.* $50

SOUTHERN CALIFORNIA CHAPTER AMERICAN INSTITUTE OF ARCHITECTS AND LOS ANGELES ARCHITECTURAL CLUB. LA: Young & McCallister, 1923. Black and gold stamped boards w/cl spine, top tips bumped. *DAWSON'S.* $75

SOUTHERN CALIFORNIA TOURISTS' GUIDE BOOK, EMBRACING...LOS ANGELES, SAN BERARDINO...COUNTIES, ALSO A CONDENSED GUIDE TO SAN FRANCISCO. LA: George E. Place & Co, 1888-89. 3rd ed. 2 full-pg illus, ads, pict wrappers. Stain to latter part of bk, chips to lower corners or wrappers. *DAWSON'S.* $150

SOUTHERN SILVER. Houston, TX: Museum of Fine Arts, 1968. 1st ed. VG. Wraps. *BACKROOM.* $30

Southern, Terry and Mason Hoffenberg. CANDY. NY, 1964. 1st US ed. Fine in NF dj. *PETTLER.* $25

Southern, Terry. FLASH AND FILIGREE. (London): Andre Deutsch, (1958). One of 160. Fine in sl soiled ptd wraps. Unopened. *HELLER.* $100

Southern, Terry. FLASH AND FILIGREE. NY: Coward-McCann, (1958). 1st Amer ed. Inscribed. Uncommon 1st issue, in grey cl, in 1st issue dj, w/no mention of Dr. Strangelove. Very scarce thus. VG in edgeworn dj. *LOPEZ.* $150

Southesk, The Earl of. SASKATCHEWAN AND THE ROCKY MOUNTAINS. Edinburgh: Edmonston and Douglas, 1875. 1st ed. Blue cl, gilt titles; xxx,448pp. 2 fldg maps. Partially unopened. Sl fading of spine, else NF. *PARMER.* $250

Southwell, Thomas. THE SEALS AND WHALES OF THE BRITISH SEAS. London, 1881. 1st ed. (viii), 128, (2 ads) pp. 29 illus, 2 tables. Orig dec cl, gilt, covers a little rubbed. Better than average, scarce. *LEFKOWICZ.* $300

Southwick, Marcia. BUILD WITH ADOBE. Denver: Sage Books, 1965. 1st ed. Fine in Good+ dj. *CONNOLLY & WADE.* $35

Souvielle, E.M. THE ULYSSIAD. Jacksonville, FL: Dacosta Printing & Pub. House, 1896. 1st ed. 53pp. Orig blue cl. Lt wear, few sm spots, front cover sl bowed, but VG. *CHAPEL HILL.* $75

Sowell, Andrew J. EARLY SETTLERS AND INDIAN FIGHTERS OF SOUTHWEST TEXAS. Austin, 1900. 1st ed. 844pp. Orig red gold stamped cl. Very nice. Usually found rebound. Howes S797. *GINSBERG.* $1500

Sowell, Andrew J. EARLY SETTLERS AND INDIAN FIGHTERS OF SOUTHWEST TEXAS. NY: Argosy-Antiquarian Ltd, 1964. 2 vols. Ltd to 750. Fine in slipcase. *GIBBS.* $125

Sowell, Andrew J. LIFE OF BIG-FOOT WALLACE. Bandera, TX: Frontier Times, 1934. Small piece missing from title page, no effect, and binding loose. Very scarce, partly due to cheap and fragile paper. Wraps, frontis. *GIBBS.* $50

Soyinka, Wole. MADMEN AND SPECIALISTS. NY: Hill & Wang, (1971). 1st ed. NF in dj. *LOPEZ.* $45

Soyinka, Wole. MADMEN AND SPECIALISTS. NY: Hill & Wang, (1971). 1st ed. Fine in dj. *BETWEEN COVERS.* $50

Soyinka, Wole. SEASON OF ANOMY. NY: Third Press, (1974). 1st ed. Rmdr stamp bottom edge of pages, o/w Fine in NF dj. *LOPEZ.* $75

Soyinka, Wole. THE MAN DIED. NY: Harper, (1972). 1st ed. Fine in dj. *BETWEEN COVERS.* $50

Spalding, A.G. AMERICA'S NATIONAL GAME. NY: American Sports Pub Co, 1911. 1st ed. 2 double side fold-outs (fold of 1 pl repaired w/tape, sm tear w/wear at another fold of that pl). Pict blue cl bumped, tail of spine sl chipped, hinges cracked. VG, bright. *BLUE MOUNTAIN.* $500

Spalding, A.G. BASEBALL—AMERICA'S NATIONAL GAME. American Sports, 1911. 1st ed. VG. *PLAPINGER.* $450

Spalding, Charles C. ANNALS OF THE CITY OF KANSAS: EMBRACING FULL DETAILS OF THE TRADE AND COMMERCE...TOGETHER WITH STATISTICS OF THE AGRICULTURAL...EMBRACING WESTERN MISSOURI, KANSAS, THE INDIAN COUNTRY, AND NEW MEXICO. Kansas City, 1858. 1st ed. 111pp. Frontis, 6 plts. Orig gold stamped cl. Howes S805. *GINSBERG.* $3500

Spalding, Rev. J.L. SOCIALISM AND LABOR AND OTHER ARGUMENTS. Chicago: McClurg, 1902. 1st ed. Fine but for light penciling & offsetting on pastedown. *BEASLEY.* $35

Spalteholz, Werner. HAND ATLAS OF HUMAN ANATOMY. Trans. by Lewellys Barker. Phila, c. 1930. 7th ed. 3 vols. VF. *FYE.* $75

Sparhawk, Frances Campbell. SENATOR INTRIGUE AND INSPECTOR NOSEBY. Boston: Red-Letter, 1895. 1st ed. NF. *LOPEZ.* $85

Spark, Muriel. A FAR CRY FROM KENSINGTON. London: London Limited Editions, (1988). 1st ed. Ltd to 150 signed. Cl backed marbled boards, glassine dj. VF. *JAFFE.* $125

Spark, Muriel. CHILD OF LIGHT. Hadleigh: Tower Bridge (1951). 1st Eng ed. Fine in sl dusty Fine dj. *DORN.* $175

Spark, Muriel. JOHN MASEFIELD. London: Peter Nevill (1953). 1st Eng ed. NF in Fine dj. *DORN.* $125

Spark, Muriel. THE BALLAD OF PECKHAM RYE. Phila: Lippincott 1960. 1st ed. Fine in dj. *ELSE FINE.* $60

Spark, Muriel. THE FANFARLO AND OTHER VERSE. Aldington: Hand & Flower Press, 1952. 1st ed. Fine in wraps. *BEASLEY.* $85

Spark, Muriel. THE GIRLS OF SLENDOR MEANS. London: Mac-Millan, 1963. 1st ed. One corner sl bumped, else Fine in dj. *CAPTAIN'S BOOKSHELF.* $60

Sparks, Jared. THE LIFE OF JOHN LEDYARD, THE AMERICAN TRAVELLER. Cambridge: Hilliard and Brown, 1828. 1st ed. Orig boards, ptd paper spine label, uncut, extrems rubbed, some internal foxing, but remarkably close to orig state. *LEFKOWICZ.* $550

Sparks, W.H. THE MEMORIES OF FIFTY YEARS...CHIEFLY SPENT IN THE SOUTHWEST. Phila., 1870. 1st ed. 489pp. Orig cl. Howes S819. *GINSBERG.* $125

Sparling, H. Halliday. THE KELMSCOTT PRESS AND WILLIAM MORRIS, MASTER-CRAFTSMAN. London: Macmillan. 1924. 1st ed. 16 plts, frontis. Fine in sl soiled dj. *KARMIOLE.* $125

Sparrow, Walter Shaw. BRITISH SPORTING ARTISTS FROM BARLOW TO HERRING. London: Spring Books, 1965. Reprint. VG. *OCTOBER FARM.* $58

Sparrow, Walter Shaw. BRITISH SPORTING ARTISTS FROM BARLOW TO HERRING. London, 1922. 27 full-pg color illus, 76 b/w. VG-NF. *POLYANTHOS.* $200

Sparrow, Walter Shaw. HENRY ALKEN. Vol. I of The Sport of Our Fathers. London & NY: Williams and Norgate & Scribner, 1927. 1st US ed. VG in Fair dj. *OCTOBER FARM.* $165

Sparrow, Walter Shaw. WOMEN PAINTERS OF THE WORLD. F. Stokes, (1905). Gilt dec pict boards, some sun fading. VG. *CULLEN.* $65

Spaulding, Edward S. THE QUAILS. NY: Macmillan Co, 1949. 1st ed. VG. *BACKMAN.* $50

Spearman, Frank. WHISPERING SMITH. NY: Scribner's, 1906. VG. 1st ed. *CHAPEL HILL.* $65

Spears, John R. ILLUSTRATED SKETCHES OF DEATH VALLEY AND OTHER BORAX DESERTS. Chicago: Rand McNally, 1892. 1st ed. Hardbound. 226pp. Fine. *BOOK MARKET.* $250

Spears, John. THE STORY OF THE NEW ENGLAND WHALERS. NY: Macmillan, 1908. 1st ed. Rear board a bit rubbed, o/w Fine. *ARCHER.* $45

Speck, Gordon. BREEDS & HALF BREEDS. C.N. Potter, (1969). 1st ed. VG in VG dj. *OREGON.* $45

Speck, Gordon. BREEDS AND HALF-BREEDS. NY, (1969). 1st ed. Dj. VG+. *PRATT.* $30

Speck, Gordon. BREEDS AND HALF-BREEDS. NY: Clarkson N. Potter, (1969). 1st ed. Cl, dj. Fine. *SCHOYER'S.* $30

Speck, Gordon. SAMUEL HEARNE AND THE NORTHWEST PASSAGE. Caldwell: Caxton, 1963. 1st ed. VG in VG dj. *PARMER.* $35

Spector, Benjamin. A HISTORY OF TUFTS COLLEGE MEDICAL SCHOOL. Boston, 1943. *FYE.* $45

Spectorsky, A.C. (ed). THE BOOK OF THE SEA. NY: Appleton-Century-Crofts, (1954). 1st ed. VG+ in acetate dj. *BERNARD.* $125

Speer, John W. A HISTORY OF BLANCO COUNTY. Austin: The Pemberton Press, 1965. 1st ed. Henry C. Armbruster (ed). Signed by editor. Fine in chipped dj. *GIBBS.* $35

Speer, John. LIFE OF GEN. JAMES H. LANE. Garden City, KS: John Speer, 1897. 2nd ed. 352pp + 4pp railroad ads. Dec cl, pamphlet laid in. *SCHOYER'S.* $85

Speir, Jerry. ROSS MACDONALD. NY: Fredrick Ungar, 1978. 1st ed. VF in dj. *MORDIDA.* $30

Speke, John Hanning. JOURNAL OF THE DISCOVERY OF THE SOURCE OF THE NILE. NY: Harper, 1864. 1st ed. 599pp. Fldg maps. Rubbed and faded, spine chipped w/sl tears; sl foxing, o/w VG ex-lib. *WORLDWIDE.* $75

Spelman, Edward (trans). Dionysus Halicarnassus. ROMAN ANTIQUITIES...trans into English..London: Ptd and sold by the Booksellers in London and Westminster, 1758. 1st ed in Eng. 4 vols. (58), 456pp, lp errata; 439pp, lp errata; 438pp, lp errata; 516pp, lp errata.

Later 3/4 calf and marbled boards. Rubbed on edges. Dec gilt spine panels. Labels missing from some vols. Cracked front inner hinge of vol. 1. Ex-lib w/collection bkpls. Only intermittent foxing. *SCHOYER'S.* $400

Spelman, Henry. RELATION OF VIRGINIA. London: Chiswick Press, published by James Hunnewell, 1872. 1st ed. One of 100 ptd. 58,(1)pp, extra title leaf photogr facs. Orig plain wrappers, several emb lib stamps. Howes S829. *GINSBERG.* $300

Speltz, Alexander. STYLES OF ORNAMENT, EXHIBITED IN DESIGNS AND ARRANGED IN HISTORICAL ORDER....Chicago, 1928. Dj. *HEINOLDT.* $20

Spence, Edward F. THE PIKE FISHER. London: A. & C. Black, Ltd. 1928. 1st ed. *KARMIOLE.* $35

Spence, W. Jerome D. and David L. Spence. A HISTORY OF HICKMAN COUNTY, TENNESSEE. Nashville, 1900. 1st ed. Port. Orig cl, sm paper label on spine, bkpl removed. *GINSBERG.* $125

Spencer, Baldwin & F.J. Gillen. THE NATIVE TRIBES OF CENTRAL AUSTRALIA. London, 1899. 2 fldg maps, 4 fldg plts. 3/4 maroon crushed levant, new hand-marbled eps, silk thread headbands, title label in gilt. xx,671pp. Uncut. Dup of Smithsonian Institution. *O'NEILL.* $350

Spencer, Charles L. KNOTS, SPLICES AND FANCY WORK. Glasgow: Brown, Son & Ferguson, 1942. Reprint (with Supplement). VG-NF. Scarce. *OLD LONDON.* $20

Spencer, Elizabeth. JACK OF DIAMONDS. (NY: Viking, (1988). 1st ed. Signed inscription. Orig cl-backed boards. Fine in dj. *CHAPEL HILL.* $35

Spencer, Elizabeth. JACK OF DIAMONDS. NY: Viking, (1988). 1st ed. VF in dj. Signed. *CAPTAIN'S BOOKSHELF.* $35

Spencer, Elizabeth. KNIGHTS AND DRAGONS. NY: McGraw-Hill, (1965). 1st Amer ed. Signed. NF in dj. *DORN.* $70

Spencer, Elizabeth. NO PLACE FOR AN ANGEL. NY: McGraw Hill, (1967). 1st ed. Fine in dj w/sm rubbed spot at spine head. Signed. *CAPTAIN'S BOOKSHELF.* $75

Spencer, Elizabeth. NO PLACE FOR AN ANGEL. NY: McGraw-Hill, (1967). 1st ed. Orig dk blue cl. NF in dj. *CHAPEL HILL.* $45

Spencer, Elizabeth. SHIP ISLAND AND OTHER STORIES. NY: McGraw Hill, (1968). 1st ed. Fine in dj sl spine darkened. Inscribed. *CAPTAIN'S BOOKSHELF.* $200

Spencer, Elizabeth. THE LIGHT IN THE PIAZZA. NY: McGraw Hill, (1960). 1st ed. Fine in price clipped dj. Signed by Spencer. *CAPTAIN'S BOOKSHELF.* $100

Spencer, Elizabeth. THE LIGHT IN THE PIAZZA. NY: McGraw-Hill, (1960). 1st ed. Adv rev copy, slip laid in. Orig cl-backed boards. One corner Very lightly bumped, o/w Fine in dj. *CHAPEL HILL.* $45

Spencer, Elizabeth. THE MULES. (N.p.): Palaemon Press, (1982). 1/150 numbered, in wrappers, signed. Fine. *LOPEZ.* $35

Spencer, Elizabeth. THE NIGHT TRAVELERS. NY: Viking, (1991). 1st Amer ed. Signed. Fine in dj. *DORN.* $35

Spencer, Elizabeth. THE NIGHT TRAVELLERS. NY: Viking, (1991). 1st ed. As New in dj. Signed. *CAPTAIN'S BOOKSHELF.* $30

Spencer, Elizabeth. THE SALT LINE. NY: Doubleday, (1984). Uncorrected proof. Signed. Also laid in is a TLS requesting a quote. Top of spine badly bumped, tape reinforcement at base of spine. *DORN.* $65

Spencer, Elizabeth. THE SALT LINE. NY: Doubleday, (1984). Signed. Rmdr spray bottom edge, else NF in Fine dj. *DORN.* $40

Spencer, Elizabeth. THE SNARE. NY: McGraw Hill, (1972). 1st ed. Fine in dj w/sm chips. Signed. *CAPTAIN'S BOOKSHELF.* $45

Spencer, Elizabeth. THE SNARE. NY: McGraw-Hill (1972). 1st ed. Lt spotting top edge else VG in NF dj. *DORN.* $50

Spencer, Elizabeth. THE VOICE AT THE BACK DOOR. NY: McGraw-Hill, (1956). 1st Amer ed. Signed. Some minor wear to extremities, else VG+ in VG+ dj with some shallow chipping at top of spine else bright and unsoiled. *DORN.* $125

Spencer, Elizabeth. THE VOICE AT THE BACK DOOR. NY: McGraw-Hill, (1956). 1st ed. Orig cl-backed boards. Fine in NF dj. *CHAPEL HILL.* $125

Spencer, Elizabeth. THIS CROOKED WAY. NY: Dodd, Mead, (1952). 1st ed. Sl offsetting from clipping on front eps, else Fine in sl worn dj w/blurb from Eudora Welty on front flap. Signed. *CAPTAIN'S BOOKSHELF.* $175

Spencer, Elizabeth. THIS CROOKED WAY. NY: Dodd Mead, (1952). 1st Amer ed. Signed. Fine in VG+ dj. *DORN.* $200

Spencer, Elizabeth. THIS CROOKED WAY. NY: Dodd, Mead & Co., (1952). 1st ed, 2nd book. Name & date on flyleaf o/w NF in dj which has one very tiny chip at bottom edge of front panel, rear panel lightly soiled. *BERNARD.* $125

Spencer, Elizabeth. THIS CROOKED WAY. NY: McGraw Hill, (1968). 1st ed, thus. Fine in price clipped dj. Signed. *CAPTAIN'S BOOKSHELF.* $40

Spencer, J.A. THE EAST: SKETCHES OF TRAVEL IN EGYPT AND THE HOLY LAND. NY: Putnam; London: Murray, 1850. 1st ed. 7 (of 8) tinted plts, 4 more plts (1 fldg). Orig cl, edges rubbed, spine chipped & torn, sl foxed, o/w Good. *WORLDWIDE.* $75

Spencer, Orson. LETTERS EXHIBITING THE MOST PROMINENT DOCTRINES OF THE CHURCH OF JESUS CHRIST OF LATTER-DAY SAINTS. Liverpool, 1848. 1st ed in book form, 244pp; rebound; ex-lib with perforated stamp on title page, final leaf of text, and one interior leaf; page ends brittle, a few cracked, o/w interior tight and clean. *BENCHMARK.* $400

Spencer, Robert F. THE NORTH ALASKAN ESKIMO. Washington, DC: GPO, 1959. VG. *BLUE DRAGON.* $45

Spencer, Scott. ENDLESS LOVE. NY: Knopf, 1979. 1st ed. Inscribed. NF in price-clipped dj. *LOPEZ.* $45

Spencer, Scott. LAST NIGHT AT THE BRAIN THIEVES BALL. Boston: HM, 1973. 1st ed. Bkpl, o/w Fine in dj. *LOPEZ.* $45

Spencer, Scott. WAKING THE DEAD. NY: Knopf, 1986. 1st ed. Inscribed. Fine in dj. *LOPEZ.* $45

Spender, Harold. IN PRAISE OF SWITZERLAND. London: Constable, 1912. 1st ed. Spine faded, minor shelfwear, else VG. *OLD LONDON.* $50

Spender, Stephen. JOURNALS, 1939-1983. Franklin Center: Franklin Lib, 1985. Leatherbound ltd ed. Signed. *LOPEZ.* $45

Spender, Stephen. POEMS. London: Faber, (1933). 1st ed. Fine in sl soiled dj, 1 short closed tear. *JAFFE.* $225

Spender, Stephen. TWENTY-FIVE POEMS. Helsinki: Eurographica, 1988. 1st of this ed. Ltd to 350 signed. Ptd wraps. Mint. *JAFFE.* $150

Spenser, Edmund. THE FAERIE QUEENE. Agnes Miller Parker (illus). 2 vols. Oxford: The LEC, 1953. Ltd to 1500 signed by Parker. Djs lightly foxed, o/w Fine set. Slipcase. *JAFFE.* $225

Spenser, Edmund. THE WORKS OF SPENSER. Oxford: Shakespeare Head Press, 1930. Ltd to 375 on handmade paper. 8 vols. Hilda Quick (decs), Joscelyne Gaskin (engr initials). 1/4 grn calf, marbled boards. Fine set. *JAFFE.* $1000

Sperlich, Norbert and Elizabeth. GUATEMALA BACKSTRAP WEAVING. Norman: Univ of OK Press, (1980). 1st ed. Good in dj. *SILVER.* $35

Spewack, Samuel and Bella. KISS ME KATE: A MUSICAL PLAY. Lyrics by Cole Porter. NY: Knopf, 1953. 1st ed. Fine, minor wear to dj. *ELSE FINE.* $125

Speyer, Leonora (ed). AMERICAN POETS: AN ANTHOLOGY OF CONTEMPORARY VERSE. Munich: Kurt Wolff Verlag, (1925).

1st ed. Publ's 3/4 lea over marbled boards. Endsheets sl foxed, else Fine. *CAPTAIN'S BOOKSHELF.* $175

Spicer, Bart. BROTHER TO THE ENEMY. NY: Dodd-Mead, 1958. 1st ed. Fine in dj. *ELSE FINE.* $25

Spicer, Jack. LAMENT FOR THE MAKERS. Oakland: White Rabbit Press, 1962. Wraps. 1/100. Variant issue w/cover printed in brown (not brown and black) and w/acknowledgements facing title page (rather than on its verso). Fine. *BEASLEY.* $200

Spiegelberg, Flora. PRINCESS GOLDENHAIR AND THE WONDERFUL FLOWER. Illus by Milo Winter. Chicago: Rand McNally & Co. (1915). 2 color plts. Brown cloth, stamped in white, w/mounted color plate. *KARMIOLE.* $100

Spielberg, Stephen. CLOSE ENCOUNTERS OF THE THIRD KIND. NY: Delacorte, 1977. 1st ed. Adv rev copy, slip and promo laid in. Fine in Fine dj. *BEASLEY.* $50

Spielmann, M.H. and G.S. Layard. KATE GREENAWAY. London: Adam and Charles Black, 1905. xx,301pp. 1st ed. Color frontis, 53 color plts. Orig dec cl, teg. Spine faded, head of spine chipped, shaky, else internally VG. *WREDEN.* $165

Spier, Peter. WE THE PEOPLE, THE CONSTITUTION OF THE UNITED STATES OF AMERICA. Doubleday, (1987). 1st ed. Illus by author. Fine in Fine dj. *BEBBAH.* $25

Spilbergen, Joris van. THE EAST AND WEST INDIAN MIRROR. BEING AN ACCOUNT OF JORIS VAN SPEILBERGEN'S VOYAGE....J.A.J. de Villiers (trans). London, 1906. Hakluyt Society Series II:18. Best ed. 1st reliable ed after 1st of 1619. 25 fldg plts and maps, some w/accompanying leaves of facs text. Orig cl, front inner hinge neatly repaired, spine faded, still VG. *LEFKOWICZ.* $100

Spillane, Mickey. DAY OF THE GUNS. Dutton, 1964. 1st ed. NF in VG+ dj with rubs. *BEBBAH.* $25

Spillane, Mickey. KISS ME, DEADLY. Dutton, 1952. 1st ed. VG in dj split at edge, wear, chips, piece missing spine bottom, short closed tear, tape repairs. *BEBBAH.* $45

Spillane, Mickey. KISS ME, DEADLY. NY: Dutton, (1952). 1st ed. VG in VG dj. *UNGER.* $75

Spillane, Mickey. KISS ME, DEADLY. NY: E.P. Dutton, 1952. 1st ed. VG in dj (chipped spine ends, corners; staining back panel). *MORDIDA.* $35

Spillane, Mickey. MY GUN IS QUICK. NY: Dutton, 1950. 1st ed. Spine heel fading, else Fine in bright dj w/sm tears. *CAPTAIN'S BOOKSHELF.* $250

Spillane, Mickey. THE KILLING MAN. London: Heinemann, 1990. 1st Brit ed. Fine in dj. *SILVER DOOR.* $22.50

Spillane, Mickey. THE KILLING MAN. NY: Dutton, (1989). 1st ed. Signed. VF in VF dj. *UNGER.* $45

Spillane, Mickey. THE KILLING MAN. NY: Dutton, 1989. 1st ed. Signed. Fine in Fine dj. *BEASLEY.* $60

Spillane, Mickey. VENGEANCE IS MINE! NY: Dutton, 1950. 1st ed. 3 sm indentations several pp, else VG in dj (chipped, soiled). *BERNARD.* $225

Spiller, Burton L. GROUSE FEATHERS. NY: Derrydale Press, 1935. 1st ed. Ltd ed, #128/950. Lynn Bogue Hunt (illus). Fine, not pub w/dj. Name, gift inscrip. *BACKMAN.* $260

Spiller, Burton L. GROUSE FEATHERS. NY: Macmillan Co, 1947. 1st trade ed. VG. *BACKMAN.* $32

Spindler, Will H. TRAGEDY STRIKES AT WOUNDED KNEE. Rushville, NE, 1955. 1st ed. Signed. 80pp. Pict wraps. Fine. *PRATT.* $35

Spitta, Phillip. JOHANN SEBASTIAN BACH. London, 1899. 3 vols. NF. *POLYANTHOS.* $125

Spivak, John. THE MEDICAL TRUST UNMASKED. NY, 1929. 1st ed. *FYE.* $75

Splawn, A.J. KA-MI-AKIN. LAST HERO OF THE YAKIMAS. Portland: Binfords & Mort, 1944. 2nd ed. Fine in VG dj. *OREGON.* $45

Spokesfield, Walter E(arnest). HISTORY OF WELLS COUNTY, NORTH DAKOTA & ITS PIONEERS....Jamestown, ND, (1928, altered to read 1929 in forward). Pict red cl. Lib rubberstamps, ms addition to map on pg 8, inscription on ep. Scarce. *BOHLING.* $250

SPORTMAN'S DICTIONARY, or the Gentleman's Companion for Town and Country...London: Robinson, 1792. Unpaginated. Recent fine rebinding in 3/4 polished morocco, raised bands, gilt and blind decorations, gilt on black lea title, marbled boards. Frontis, 12 full-page engr. Light uniform foxing, else text Fine. *HARTFIELD.* $385

Sprague, J. T. THE TREACHERY IN TEXAS. NY: NY Hist Soc, 1862. 34pp. Wraps. *HEINOLDT.* $18

Sprague, Marshall. MASSACRE, THE TRAGEDY OF WHITE RIVER. Boston, (1957). 1st ed. 364pp. Dj wear o/w VG+. *PRATT.* $25

Spratling, William. FILE ON SPRATLING. Boston: Little Brown, (1967). 1st ed. Good in chipped dj. *SILVER.* $35

Spratt, G. OBSTETRIC TABLES COMPRISING GRAPHIC ILLUSTRATIONS...PRACTICAL REMARKS EXHIBITING ON DISSECTED PLATES...IN MIDWIFERY. Phila: Thomas, Cowperthwaite, 1848. 1st Amer after 4th London ed. Full calf, blind tooled Amer binding, rebacked quarto, some foxing throughout. List of British subscribers present. 7 plts in tint, numerous overlays, all Good. *CULLEN.* $750

Spring, A.W. THE CHEYENNE AND BLACK HILLS STAGE AND EXPRESS ROUTES. A.H. Clark, 1949. 1st ed. Fine. *VARNER.* $150

Spring, Agnes Wright. CASPER COLLINS, THE LIFE AND EXPLOITS OF AN INDIAN FIGHTER IN THE SIXTIES. NY, 1927. 1st ed. 187pp. Light dj wear, o/w Fine. *PRATT.* $75

Springer, Lieutenant Charles H. SOLDIERING IN SIOUX COUNTRY: 1865. San Diego, 1971. Ed by Benjamin Franklin Cooling III. 1st ed. Plain plastic dj. VG+. *PRATT.* $35

Springs, Elliott White. THE RISE AND FALL OF CAROL BANKS. GC: Doubleday, 1931. 1st ed. (12),307pp. Orig cl. Ltd to 200 numbered, signed. Pages are made of cloth. *GINSBERG.* $150

Sproston, John Glendy, U.S.N. A PRIVATE JOURNAL. Tokyo: Sophia Univ, 1940. xii, 122pp. Red cl, a little faded. *SCHOYER'S.* $40

Sprunt, A. FLORIDA BIRD LIFE, BASED UPON AND SUPPLEMENTARY TO "FLORIDA BIRD LIFE" by A.H. Howell (1932). NY, 1954. 40 colored plts. Lt scuffing. *SUTTON.* $85

Sprunt, Alexander, Jr., NORTH AMERICAN BIRDS OF PREY. NY: Harper & Bros., 1955. 1st ed. Signed by author. Dj only fair, else NF. *OLD LONDON.* $20

Sprunt, James. DERELICTS. Wilmington, NC, 1920. 1st ed. . Fine. *McGOWAN.* $550

Sprunt, James. TALES OF CAPE FEAR BLOCKADE. Wilmington, NC, 1960. 388 of ltd ed of 500. Fldg map. NF in dj. *McGOWAN.* $45

Spurling, J. and Basil Lubbock. SAIL: THE ROMANCE OF THE CLIPPER SHIPS. London, (1927-1936). 3 vols. 1st ed of each vol (2nd prtg of 1st vol), each one of 1000 ptd. Orig cl (vol 1 sl different in color from 2 and 3). Fine set, very scarce, very attractive. *LEFKOWICZ.* $1,250

Spurlock, Pearl. OVER THE OLD OZARK TRAILS IN THE SHEPHERD OF THE HILLS COUNTRY. Branson, MO: White River Leader, (1942). 3rd ed. Inscribed. VG in VG+ dj. *BOHLING.* $27

Spurzheim, J.G. OBSERVATIONS ON THE DERANGED MANIFESTATIONS OF THE HUMAN MIND--OR, INSANITY. Boston, 1836. 3rd Amer ed. 272pp + 4 plts. Exceptionally Fine. *FYE.* $250

Spyri, Johanna. GRITLI'S CHILDREN, A STORY OF SWITZERLAND. Lippincott, (1924). 265pp. Dec in grn. 14 color illus by Maria Kirk. VG w/dec cvr & pict pastedown. *BEBBAH.* $45

Squier, E. George. PERU. NY, 1877. 1st ed. xx, 599pp. Pict and dec cl gilt, teg. Sl cvr wear, staining. VG. Sig of E. Roberts. Lib stamp. *DIAMOND.* $125

Squire, J.C. A LONDON REVERIE. London, 1928. Teg. NF. *POLYANTHOS.* $75

Squire, John (ed). CHEDDAR GORGE: A BOOK OF ENGLISH CHEESE. London: Collins, (1937). 1st ed. NF in trifle soiled else VG dj. *WREDEN.* $45

St. Clair, Arthur. THE ST. CLAIR PAPERS. Cincinnati: R. Clarke, 1882. 2 vols. Fldg map. Very Nice w/light foxing. *BOHLING.* $250

St. Clair, Daniel. FROM BEWILDERNESS BACK TO WILDERNESS. Alaska: Magpie Press, 1970. 1st ed. Oblong octavo in stapled wrappers, Illus. Fine. *LOPEZ.* $85

St. Clair, William. LORD ELGIN AND THE MARBLES. London, 1967. *O'NEILL.* $40

St. Clair, William. LORD ELGIN AND THE MARBLES. London: Oxford. 1967. Priv lib stamps. Dj chipped. *SCHOYER'S.* $18.50

St. George, Eleanor. DOLLS OF THREE CENTURIES. NY, 1951. NF. *POLYANTHOS.* $35

St. John, Bayle. ADVENTURES IN THE LIBYAN DESERT AND THE OASIS OF JUPITER AMMON. NY: Putnam; London: Murray, 1849. 244pp,4pp pub ads. Frontis. 1st ed. Cl rubbed, stained, small holes in backstrip, foxed. *SCHOYER'S.* $65

St. John, Charles. NATURAL HISTORY AND SPORT IN MORAY. Edinburgh: David Douglas, 1882. 1st ed. Minor bumps, tears, wear at extremities, spine fading, thus VG. *OLD LONDON.* $175

St. John, Charles. WILD SPORTS AND NATURAL HISTORY OF THE HIGHLANDS. London and Edinburgh: Foulis, 1919. 1st ed. Minor shelfwear. VG-NF. *OLD LONDON.* $85

St. John, J.A. EGYPT AND NUBIA, THEIR SCENERY AND THEIR PEOPLE. London: Chapman and Hall, (c. 1845). 125 figures, aeg. Bkpl, inscription, worn at extrems, sm tears at spine. Good. *ARCHAEOLOGIA.* $85

St. John, J.A. EGYPT AND NUBIA. London: Chapman and Hall, 1845. viii,472pp,16pp. Pub catalogue dated July 1845. Orig brn blind-stamped cl, rubbed; lacking head of spine; 1 signature pulled, musty. Good only. *SCHOYER'S.* $85

ST. LOUIS CITY GUIDE. 1909. 12mo, 87pp, red pict wraps. *HUDSON.* $20

St. Paul, Henry. OUR HOME AND FOREIGN POLICY. (Mobile), 1863. 1st ed. 23pp. disbound as issued, in half morocco slipcase. Howes S36. *GINSBERG.* $600

Stables, Gordon. O'ER MANY LANDS, ON MANY SEAS. London: Cassell (n.d.). 176pp. VG w/gilt and black dec on brown cl of sailing ship and jungle scene. *BEBBAH.* $45

Stables, Gordon. OFF TO KLONDYKE OR A COWBOY'S RUSH TO THE GOLD FIELDS. London: John Nisbet & Co., 1898. Shelfwear, mark on front cover, prize bkpl. *PARMER.* $95

Stackpole, Edouard A. CAPTAIN PRESCOTT AND THE OPIUM SMUGGLERS. Mystic: The Marine Hist Assoc, Inc., 1954. Wraps soiled, sm marginal dampstain to prelims, else VG. *PARMER.* $12.50

Stackpole, Edouard A. SCRIMSHAW AT MYSTIC SEAPORT. Mystic: Marine Hist Assoc, 1958. Wraps lightly soiled and faded, else VG. 1st ed was issued in wraps. *PARMER.* $35

Stackpole, Edouard. THE WRECK OF THE STEAMER SAN FRANCISCO. Mystic, CT: Marine Hist Assoc, December, 1954. #27. 1st ed. Blue stiff wraps, faded on borders, else VG. *CONNOLLY & WADE.* $35

Stackpole, Edward J. and Wilbur S. Nye. THE BATTLE OF GETTYSBURG, A GUIDED TOUR. Harrisburg, 1963. 96pp. Wraps. VG+. *PRATT.* $30

Stackpole, Edward J. FROM CEDAR MOUNTAIN TO ANTIETAM AUGUST-SEPTEMBER, 1862. Harrisburg: Stackpole, 1959. 1st ed. Occasional neat, scholarly, elucidating marginal notes. Pict cl. VG. *CONNOLLY & WADE.* $35

Stackpole, Edward L. THEY MET AT GETTYSBURG. Harrisburg, (1956). 1st ed. 342pp. Dj chipped, o/w Fine. *PRATT.* $35

Stacy-Judd, Robert. THE ANCIENT MAYAS. ADVENTURES IN THE JUNGLES OF YUCATAN. LA: Haskell-Travers, Inc., (1934). 1st ed. Bound in orange buckram, ptd on grn paper. VG in Good+ dj. *OREGON.* $65

Staender, Gilbert and Vivian. ADVENTURES WITH ARCTIC WILDLIFE. Caldwell: Caxton Printers, 1970. NF in lightly worn dj. *PARMER.* $40

STAFFA & IONA DESCRIBED AND ILLUSTRATED. (By William Keddie.). Glasgow: Blackie & Son, n.d. (c. 1850). 160pp,16pp ads. 8 full page plts. Fldg map. Limp brn cl, extrems fraying. *KARMIOLE.* $40

Stafford and Marvin Bell. SEGUES: A CORRESPONDENCE IN POETRY. David R. Godine, (1983). 1st ed. Fine. *AUTHORS OF THE WEST.* $25

Stafford, David. THE SILENT GAME—THE REAL WORLD OF IMAGINARY SPIES. London: Viking, 1989. 1st British ed. Fine in dj. *SILVER DOOR.* $25

Stafford, Jean. BOSTON ADVENTURE. NY: Harcourt, Brace, (1944). Orig ptd tan wraps. Some soiling, but VG. Advance proof copy of author's 1st bk. Stamped "Review Copy" on front wrap, giving pub date of Sep. 21, 1944, price of $2.75. Rare wartime production. *CHAPEL HILL.* $175

Stafford, Jean. THE COLLECTED STORIES OF JEAN STAFFORD. NY: Farrar Straus Giroux, (1969). 1st ed. NF in internally strengthened dj. *LOPEZ.* $45

Stafford, Kim Robert and William. BRAIDED APART. Confluence Press, (1976). 1st ed. Softbound. Fine. *AUTHORS OF THE WEST.* $25

Stafford, Kim Robert and William. IN THE CLOCK OF REASON. Victoria, B.C.: Soft Press. 1st Canadian ltd ed of 300 numbered, signed by author and Nancy S. Craig (illus). Pict cvr. Softbound. Fine. *AUTHORS OF THE WEST.* $35

Stafford, Muriel. X MARKS THE SPOT. NY: Duell, Sloan and Pearce, 1943. 1st ed. Fine in dj w/internal tape mend, nicks at top of spine and couple of short closed tears. *MORDIDA.* $40

Stafford, William. ALLEGIANCES. NY: Harper, (1970). 1st ed. Signed. Boards, dj. VF. *JAFFE.* $50

Stafford, William. ELEVEN UNTITLED POEMS. Mt. Horeb, WI: Perishable Press, (1968). 1st ed. One of 250. Spine sl faded, o/w Fine. Wraps. *JAFFE.* $150

Stafford, William. GOING PLACES. Reno: WCPR, (1974). 1st ed. Wrappers faded at edges, else Fine. *WOOLMER.* $40

Stafford, William. SOMEDAY, MAYBE. NY: Harper (1973). 1st ed. Uncorrected proof. Signed. Fine in wraps. *DORN.* $75

Stafford, William. SOMEDAY, MAYBE. NY: Harper, 1973. 1st ed. Inscribed. Cl backed boards, dj. Fine. *JAFFE.* $50

Stafford, William. STORIES THAT COULD BE TRUE: NEW AND COLLECTED POEMS. Harper & Row, (1977). 1st ed. Signed. Fine in dj. *AUTHORS OF THE WEST.* $60

Stafford, William. THE QUIET OF THE LAND. NY: Nadja, (1979). 1/200 numbered/signed. Wrappers. Fine. *DERMONT.* $60

Stafford, William. THE RESCUED YEAR. NY: Harper (1966). 1st ed. Signed. Fine in dj. *DORN.* $50

Stafford, William. THE RESCUED YEAR. NY: Harper, (1966). 1st ed. Signed. Dec boards, dj. VF. *JAFFE.* $75

Stafford, William. THINGS THAT HAPPEN WHERE THERE AREN'T ANY PEOPLE. POEMS. Brockport, NY: BOA Editions, 1980. 1st ed. Signed. Fine in dj w/small tear. *DERMONT.* $25

Stafford, William. TRAVELING THROUGH THE DARK. NY: Harper, (1962). 1st ed. Dec boards, dj. VF. *JAFFE.* $175

Stafford, William. TUFT BY PUFF. Mt. Horeb, WI: Perishable Press, 1978. 1st ed. One of 240. Fine. *JAFFE.* $125

Stafford, William. WEATHER. POEMS. Mt. Horeb, WI: Perishable Press, (1969). 1st ed. One of 207. Wraps. Fine. *JAFFE.* $150

Stafford, William. WEST OF YOUR CITY. POEMS. Los Gatos, CA: Talisman Press, 1960. 1st ed. Presentation inscrip. Rare in ptd dj. *DERMONT.* $850

Stafford, William. WYOMING CIRCUIT. Accordion-fold in two-toned emb boards. (N.p.): Tideline Press, 1980. 1st ed. Ltd to 125 signed. VF. *JAFFE.* $150

Stagg, Amos Alonzo. TOUCHDOWN! NY: Longmans, Green, 1927. 1st ed. VG w/priv lib stamp inside. *BEASLEY.* $35

Stagge, Jonathan. THE DOGS DO BARK. GC: Doubleday Crime Club, 1937. 1st ed. VF; minor wear dj spine ends. *ELSE FINE.* $75

Stanard, Mary Newton. RICHMOND, ITS PEOPLE AND ITS STORY. Phila, 1923. 1st ed. Presentation, signed. VG+. *PRATT.* $55

Stanard, Mary Newton. THE STORY OF BACON'S REBELLION. Neale, 1907. 1st ed. VG. *BOOK BROKER.* $35

Stanard, Mary Newton. THE STORY OF VIRGINIA'S FIRST CENTURY. Phila, 1928. 1st ed. Gilt cl, VG. *ARTIS.* $25

STANDARD ATLAS OF WALWORTH COUNTY, SOUTH DAKOTA. Chicago: Geo. A. Ogle & Co, 1911. Blind and gold stamped cl w/leather spine and tips, leather worn and chipped, fep creased. *DAWSON'S.* $200

Standlee, Mary. THE GREAT PULSE: JAPANESE MIDWIFERY AND OBSTETRICS THROUGH THE AGES. Rutland, VT, 1959. 1st ed. *FYE.* $60

Stanger, Frank M. and Alan K. Brown. WHO DISCOVERED THE GOLDEN GATE? (San Mateo): San Mateo County Hist Assoc, 1969. Ed ltd to 1500 numbered. *KARMIOLE.* $35

Stanley, F. (pseud of Father Stanley Crocchiola). FORT BASCOM, COMANCHE-KIOWA BARRIER. N.p., (1961). 1st ed. Signed. Dj spine faded a little o/w Fine. *PRATT.* $105

Stanley, F. (pseud of Father Stanley Crocchiola). FORT STANTON. N.p., (1964). 1st ed ltd to 500. Signed. Dj spine faded a little o/w Fine. *PRATT.* $105

Stanley, F. (pseud of Father Stanley Crocchiola). JIM COURTRIGHT, TWO GUN MARSHALL OF FORT WORTH. Denver: World Press, (1957). 2nd ptg. Fine in VG dj. *OREGON.* $17.50

Stanley, F. (pseud of Father Stanley Crocchiola). RAILROADS OF THE TEXAS PANHANDLE. 1976. 1st ed. Fine in Fine dj. *VARNER.* $60

Stanley, F. (pseud of Father Stanley Crocchiola). RAILROADS OF THE TEXAS PANHANDLE. Borger, TX: Hess Publishing Co, 1976. 1st ed. VF in dj. Very scarce. *GIBBS.* $90

Stanley, F. (pseud of Father Stanley Crocchiola). THE TEXAS PANHANDLE FROM CATTLEMEN TO FEED LOTS (1880-1970). 1971. 1st ed. Signed presentation. Ltd to 500. Fine in faded dj. *VARNER.* $65

Stanley, Henry M. IN DARKEST AFRICA; OR THE QUEST, RES-CUE, AND RETREAT OF EMIN GOVERNOR OF EQUATORIA. NY: Scribner, 1890. 2 vols. 1st ed. xiv,547; xvi,540pp. 2 steel-engr plts. 3 fldg maps in back pockets. Sl rubbed, o/w VG ex-lib. *WORLDWIDE.* $70

Stanley, Henry M. THE AUTOBIOGRAPHY OF SIR HENRY MORTON STANLEY. Boston & NY: Houghton Mifflin (River-side), 1937. 1st ed. Dorothy Stanley (ed). Fldg map. Sl rubbed, frayed, o/w VG. *WORLDWIDE.* $25

Stanley, Henry M. THE CONGO AND THE FOUNDING OF ITS FREE STATE. London: Low, Marston, Searle, 1885. 2 vols. 1st ed. xxvii,528pp; x,483pp. 2 fldg maps. Recent buckram, title page in vol 1 supplied in facs. Book affected by dampness, o/w Good. *WORLDWIDE.* $60

Stanley, Reva. A BIOGRAPHY OF PARLEY P. PRATT. Caxton, 1937. NF. *POLYANTHOS.* $45

Stanley, Reva. A BIOGRAPHY OF PARLEY P. PRATT. Caldwell, 1937 (Caxton Press). 1st ed. Bkpl, some wear on spine, o/w VG. *BENCHMARK.* $40

Stansbury, Howard. EXPLORATION AND SURVEY OF THE VALLEY OF THE GREAT SALT LAKE OF UTAH, INCLUD-ING A RECONNAISSANCE....Phila, 1852. 2nd ed, 487pp. Orig cl. Exterior wear, sunned spine, bkpl, private lib stamps. Interior tight and clean, all plts present, no map vol. *BENCHMARK.* $125

Stanton, Elizabeth Cady. EIGHTY YEARS AND MORE, REMINIS-CENCES OF...1815-1897. NY, 1898. 1st ed. 474pp. Unsigned presentation. Nice, tight. *SECOND LIFE.* $300

Stanton, Frank L. COMES ONE WITH A SONG. Indianapolis & Kansas City: The Bowen-Merrill Co, 1899. 2nd ed. Signed inscrip. 200pp. Orig dec cl, teg. Sm bkseller's label, but VG. *CHAPEL HILL.* $35

Stanton, Frank L. UP FROM GEORGIA. NY: Appleton, 1902. 1st ed. Orig dec violet cl. NF. *CHAPEL HILL.* $35

Stanton, Robert Brewster. DOWN THE COLORADO. Norman, OK, 1965. 1st ed. Fine in Fine dj. *FIVE QUAIL.* $75

Stapfer, Edmond. PALESTINE IN THE TIME OF CHRIST. Annie Harwood Holmden (trans). NY: Armstrong, 1885. 3rd ed. 3 plts (2 fldg), 2 fldg tables. Sl rubbed, spine frayed, o/w VG. *WORLDWIDE.* $28

Stapledon, Olaf. LAST AND FIRST MEN. Cape & Smith, 1931. 1st US ed, 2nd binding. VG. *MADLE.* $25

Stapledon, Olaf. LAST AND FIRST MEN. Cape & Smith, 1931. 1st US ed, 1st binding, spine faded, else VG. *MADLE.* $75

Stapledon, Olaf. LAST MEN IN LONDON. London, 1934. Fine in NF in dj. *MADLE.* $125

Stapledon, Olaf. ODD JOHN. Dutton, 1936. 1st US ed. Fine in NF dj. *MADLE.* $250

Stapledon, Olaf. PHILOSOPHY AND LIVING. Harmondsworth, Middlesex, (1939). 2 vols. 1st ed. Pelican Books A53 and A54. Fine set. *McCLINTOCK.* $45

Stapledon, Olaf. THE FLAMES. London, 1947. 1st ed. VG in chipped dj. *MADLE.* $35

Stapledon, Olaf. TO THE END OF TIME: THE BEST OF...NY: Funk & Wagnalls, (1953). 1st thus. VG+ in sl edgeworn dj. *OTHER WORLDS.* $35

STAR TREK. Random House, 1977. 4 double-pg pop-ups. Pop-up bk. *BOOKFINDERS INTL.* $60

STAR WARS, THE EMPIRE STRIKES BACK. Random, (1980). 1st ed. Measures 9" x 6.75" closed. 2 pop-ups & 11 push/pull tabs operating moveable parts. NF. *BEBBAH.* $20

Starbuck, Alexander. HISTORY OF THE AMERICAN WHALE FISHERY FROM ITS INCEPTION TO THE YEAR

1876. Wash., SMD107, 1878. 1st ed. (9),768pp. 6 plts. Orig cl. Howes S892. *GINSBERG.* $600

Stark, Freya. ALEXANDER'S PATH FROM CARIA TO CICILIA. London: Murray, 1958. 1st ed. Fldg map. Dj torn. VG. *WORLDWIDE.* $18

Stark, Freya. DUST IN THE LION'S PAW. AUTOBIOGRAPHY 1939-1946. NY: Harcourt, Brace & World, 1961. 1st ed. Sl rubbed, o/w VG. *WORLDWIDE.* $20

Stark, Freya. EAST IN WEST. London: Murray, 1945. 2nd ptg. Dj. NF. *WORLDWIDE.* $18

Stark, Freya. GATEWAYS AND CARAVANS. A PORTRAIT OF TURKEY. NY: Macmillan, 1971. 1st US ed. 168 plts. Double-pg map. Sl rubbed, o/w VG. *WORLDWIDE.* $55

Stark, Freya. TRAVELLER'S PRELUDE. London: Murray, 1951. 2nd ed. Dj torn. VG. *WORLDWIDE.* $18

Stark, Richard (pseud of Donald Westlake). BUTCHER'S MOON. NY: Random House, 1974. 1st ed. Fine in dj. *MORDIDA.* $55

Stark, Richard (pseud of Donald Westlake). DEADLY EDGE. NY: Random House, 1971. 1st ed. Few small spots on bottom edge o/w Fine in dj. *MORDIDA.* $45

Stark, Richard (pseud of Donald Westlake). SLAYGROUND. Lon-don: Allison, 1984. 1st British hardcover ed. Signed by author as Donald Westlake. Fine in dj. *SILVER DOOR.* $37.50

Stark, Richard (pseud of Donald Westlake). SLAYGROUND. NY: Random House, 1971. 1st ed. Name and address on front pas-tedown o/w Fine in dj w/lamination streak on back panel. *MORDIDA.* $25

Stark, Richard (pseud of Donald Westlake). THE DAMSEL. Lon-don: Hodder, 1968. 1st British ed. Signed by author as Donald Westlake. About Fine in dj, lt wear, soiling. *SILVER DOOR.* $35

Starke, Barbara. BORN IN CAPTIVITY: THE STORY OF A GIRL'S ESCAPE. Indianapolis: Bobbs-Merrill, (1931). Stated 1st ed. Somewhat soiled yellow cl, dampstains top edge, spine some-what cocked. VG. *SCHOYER'S.* $20

Starkey, Marion. THE CHEROKEE NATION. Knopf, 1946. 1st ed. Fine in very chipped dj. *VARNER.* $35

Starkie, Walter. DON GYPSY. NY: E.P. Dutton & Co, Inc, (1937). 1st ed. Cl bit soiled, spine faded. *KARMIOLE.* $30

Starr, Frederick. IN INDIAN MEXICO. Chicago: Forbes & Co, 1908. 1st ed. Ex-lib. Reading copy. Some photos have sm tears at edges. Good. *SILVER.* $35

Starr, Frederick. LIBERIA: DESCRIPTION, HISTORY, PROBLEMS. Chicago: by the author, 1913. 1st ed. Fldg map. Very sl rubbed, o/w VG ex-lib. *WORLDWIDE.* $22

Starr, Frederick. THE TRUTH ABOUT THE CONGO. Chicago: Forbes, 1907. 1st ed. Sl rubbed, o/w VG ex-lib. *WORLDWIDE.* $25

Starr, M. Allen. ORGANIC NERVOUS DISEASES. Phila, 1903. 1st ed. *FYE.* $125

Starr, Stephen Z. COLONEL GRENFELL'S WAR, THE LIFE OF A SOLDIER OF FORTUNE. Baton Rouge, (1971). 1st ed. Light dj wear o/w Fine. *PRATT.* $32.50

Starr, Tramp. POP. 359. Terre Haute: the author, 1941. Inscribed by the author. Fine w/o dj (if there ever was one.) *BEASLEY.* $45

Starrett, Vincent. STEPHEN CRANE. A BIBLIOGRAPHY. Phila: The Centaur Book Shop, 1923. Ltd ed 66/335. Frontis. Extremities, spine minimally rubbed. Fine. *POLYANTHOS.* $75

Starrett, Vincent. AUTOLYCUS IN LIMBO. NY: Dutton, 1943. Former owner's name stamp, else Fine in VG dj (small chip at head of spine). 1st ed. One of 1500. *CHAPEL HILL.* $45

Starrett, Vincent. BOOKMAN'S HOLIDAY. NY: Random House, (1942). 1st ed. Fine in sl chipped dj. *WREDEN.* $35

Starrett, Vincent. BOOKS ALIVE. NY: Random House, 1940. Cvrs a bit soiled, front hinge cracked, withal Good. *WREDEN.* $15

Starrett, Vincent. THE PRIVATE LIFE OF SHERLOCK HOLMES. Chicago: Univ of Chicago, 1960. Rev, enl ed. Fine in dj with sl faded spine; wear at spine ends, corners. *MORDIDA.* $75

Starrett, Vincent. THE QUICK AND THE DEAD. Arkham House, 1965. 1st ed. VF in dj. *MADLE.* $60

Starrs, Frank. SCOUTING DAVE OR, THE WINNEBAGO RENEGADE. No. 151. Circa march 1876. Last # listed on back cvr is No. 191. Cvr complete w/some tape on spine, sl damage, o/w VF. Fragile. Wraps. *BOOK MARKET.* $55

STATE OF NEBRASKA OFFICIAL BRAND BOOK FOR 1953. VG. Red buckram cl. *BURCHAM.* $85

Statham, F. Reginald. PAUL KRUGER AND HIS TIMES. Boston: Page; London: Fisher Unwin, 1898. vii,312pp. Fldg map. Sl rubbed, soiled, o/w VG ex-lib. *WORLDWIDE.* $35

STATUTES OF THE STATES OF NEW YORK RELATING TO COMMON SCHOOLS. Albany. 1841. 1/2 lea, orig ptd boards. NF. *POLYANTHOS.* $60

Staveley, Gaylord. BROKEN WATERS SING. Boston, 1971. 1st ed. Signed by author in two places. Fine in VG+ dj. *FIVE QUAIL.* $25

Steadman, Ralph. SIGMUND FREUD. NY and London: Paddington, 1979. 1st ed. Fine. *SMITH.* $100

Stearns, W.A. and E. Coues. NEW ENGLAND BIRD LIFE, BEING A MANUAL....2 vols. Boston, 1883. Vol I is 4th ed. Spines darkened, institutional bkpls, no. sticker on spines. *SUTTON.* $75

Stebbing, E.P. STALKS IN THE MIMALYAS—JOTTINGS OF A SPORTSMAN-NATURALIST. London: Bodley Head, 1912. 1st ed. Almost Fine. *AARD.* $100

Stebbing, T.R.R. THE NATURALIST OF LINNAEUS. London, 1891. Light soiling. *SUTTON.* $45

Stebbins, N.L. THE ILLUSTRATED COAST PILOT. WITH SAILING DIRECTIONS. Boston, (1902). Orig limp sailcl, cvrs a bit dampstained, but internally clean. 1st pub in 1891, showing only the coast from NY to Eastport. Quite scarce. *LEFKOWICZ.* $195

Steckmesser, Kent. THE WESTERN HERO IN HISTORY AND LEGEND. Norman: Univ of OK, (1965). 1st ed. VF in VF dj. *OREGON.* $40

Stedman, Charles Ellery. THE CIVIL WAR SKETCHBOOK OF CHARLES ELLERY STEDMAN, SURGEON, UNITED STATES NAVY. San Rafael, CA, 1976. 1st ed. 218pp. Some dj wear, o/w Fine. *PRATT.* $35

Stedman, E.C. EDGAR ALLAN POE. Boston: Houghton, Mifflin, 1881. 1st ed. 12mo. Orig ptd vellum wraps. Very slight soiling on cover, but Nice. *CHAPEL HILL.* $60

Stedman, E.C. EDGAR ALLAN POE. Boston: Houghton Mifflin, 1881. 1st ed. One of 750 ptd. Presentation, inscribed. Orig pict parchment. Cvrs worn, soiled. *JAFFE.* $375

Stedman, E.C. POETS OF AMERICA. Boston: Houghton Mifflin, 1885. 1st (trade) ed, 1st state. One of approx 1732. Contemp gift in-scrip, cvrs bit rubbed. Blue cl. VG. *JAFFE.* $125

Steed, Neville. TINPLATE. London: Weidenfeld, 1986. 1st ed, 1st book. Signed. *SILVER DOOR.* $37.50

Steed, Neville. TINPLATE. London: Weidenfeld, 1986. 1st ed. Signed. *SILVER DOOR.* $37.50

Steedman, Amy. LEGENDS AND STORIES OF ITALY FOR CHILDREN....NY: G.P. Putnam's Sons, (1909). Rear cover shelf-faded, lt scattered foxing not affecting plts, else About Fine. *WREDEN.* $40

Steel, A.G. and R.H. Lyttelton. CRICKET. London and Bombay: Longmans, Green & Co., 1904. 7th ed. 3/4 lea. VG. *OLD LONDON.* $60

Steel, A.G. and R.H. Lyttelton. CRICKET. London: Longmans, Green & Co., 1888. From The Badminton Lib of Sports and Pastimes. 1st ed. NF. *OLD LONDON.* $100

Steel, A.G. and R.H. Lyttelton. CRICKET. London: Longmans Green/The Badminton Library, 1904. 7th ed, rev. VG. *OCTOBER FARM.* $45

Steel, Flora Annie. ENGLISH FAIRY TALES. Macmillan, 1918. 1st Amer ed. 363pp. 16 full-page color plates by Arthur Rackham, illus. Only slight edgewear, tear to rear endpaper. VG+. With bright gilt dec front cvr, spine. *BEBBAH.* $190

Steel, Flora Annie. INDIA. A&C Black. 1912 reprint. 20s Series. Ffep excised, minor foxing, a couple of stains, generally VG. *OLD LONDON.* $35

Steele, Ashbel. CHIEF OF THE PILGRIMS; OR, THE LIFE AND TIMES OF WILLIAM BREWSTER....Phila., 1857. 1st ed. 416pp. 9 engr plts, some light foxing. Orig cl, a few chips to front joint. Howes S918. *GINSBERG.* $125

Steele, H. Rooksby and F.R. Yerbury. THE OLD BANK OF ENGLAND, LONDON. London: Ernest Benn, Ltd. 1930. 1st ed. 16 fldg plans. Dj (w/mounted photo). *KARMIOLE.* $65

Steele, James W. FRONTIER ARMY SKETCHES. Chicago, 1883. 2nd ed. 329pp,ads. Spine worn top, bottom. Dec cvr. *HEINOLDT.* $35

Steele, John. IN CAMP AND CABIN. MINING LIFE AND ADVENTURE, IN CALIFORNIA DURING 1850 AND LATER. Lodi, WI: Steele, 1901. 1st ed. 81pp. Orig prey ptd wrappers, double columns. T. W. Streeter's copy w/bkpl. Howes S924. *GINSBERG.* $1250

Steele, Max. WHERE SHE BRUSHED HER HAIR AND OTHER STORIES NY: Harper & Row, (1968). 1st ed. Inscribed. Orig cl-backed boards. Fine in price-clipped dj. *CHAPEL HILL.* $40

Steele, Richard. THE CONSCIOUS LOVERS. London: for J. Tonson, 1723. 1st ed. Large 8vo; later half calf; joints worn, spine chipped, internally Fine. *DRAMATIS PERSONAE.* $100

Steele, Rufus. SCAR NECK. THE ADVENTUROUS STORY OF A GREAT NEVADA MUSTANG. NY: Harper, 1930. 1st ed. Eps foxed, o/w VG in Fair dj. *OCTOBER FARM.* $20

Steele, Zulma. ANGEL IN TOP HAT. NY: Harper, (1942). 1st ed. Prev owner's name blacked out ffep. VG+ in VG dj. *AARD.* $25

Stefansson, Vilhjalmur. ARCTIC MANUAL. NY: Macmillan, 1944. 1st trade ed. VG. *BLUE DRAGON.* $27.50

Stefansson, Vilhjalmur. DISCOVERY. NY: McGraw-Hill, 1964. Stated 1st. VG in similar dj. *PARMER.* $35

Stefansson, Vilhjalmur. DISCOVERY. NY: McGraw-Hill, (1964). 1st ed. VG+ in VG- dj. *BLUE DRAGON.* $30

Stefansson, Vilhjalmur. HUNTERS OF THE GREAT NORTH. NY, (1922). Inscribed. Cl dusty. Some lettering flaked. Good. *ARTIS.* $37.50

Stefansson, Vilhjalmur. HUNTERS OF THE GREAT NORTH. NY: Harcourt, Brace & Co, (1922). 1st ed. Good. *BLUE DRAGON.* $30

Stefansson, Vilhjalmur. HUNTERS OF THE GREAT NORTH. NY: Harcourt, Brace, (1922). 1st ed. Inscribed. 2 fldg maps. VG. *WEBER.* $50

Stefansson, Vilhjalmur. MY LIFE WITH THE ESKIMO. NY: Macmillan Co, 1921. Autographed. Good+. *BLUE DRAGON.* $60

Stefansson, Vilhjalmur. MY LIFE WITH THE ESKIMO. NY: Macmillan, 1913. 1st ed. 2 fldg maps. Slightest shelfwear, mark on front pastedown, else NF. *PARMER.* $195

Stefansson, Vilhjalmur. NORTH WEST TO FORTUNE. NY: Duell, Sloan and Pearce, 1958. 1st ed. NF in lightly rubbed dj. *PARMER.* $45

Stefansson, Vilhjalmur. THE ADVENTURE OF WRANGEL ISLAND. NY: Macmillan, 1925. 1st ed. Inscribed. VG. *BLUE DRAGON.* $75

Stefansson, Vilhjalmur. THE ADVENTURE OF WRANGEL IS-LAND. NY: Macmillan, 1925. 1st ed. Good+. *BLUE DRAGON.* $45

Stefansson, Vilhjalmur. THE FRIENDLY ARCTIC, THE STORY OF FIVE YEARS IN POLAR REGIONS. NY, 1939. Later prtg. Map in rear pocket. Fine. *ARTIS.* $45

Stefansson, Vilhjalmur. THE STANDARDIZATION OF ERROR. NY: W.W. Norton & Co, Inc, 1927. VG. Inscription. *PARMER.* $110

Stefansson, Vilhjalmur. UNSOLVED MYSTERIES OF THE ARCTIC. NY, 1939. 2nd ed. Part of dj tipped onto back ep. Lib stamp. Spine sl sunned. *ARTIS.* $18.50

Steffens, Lincoln. THE LETTERS OF LINCOLN STEFFENS, 1889-1936. NY: Harcourt, Brace, (1938). 1st ed. 2 vols. Ella Winter, Granville Hicks (eds). VG+ in dj (top edges tattered). Moderate shelfwear to slipcase. *AKA.* $65

Steffens, Lincoln. THE SHAME OF THE CITIES. NY: McClure, Philips, 1904. 1st ed. 306,[6]pp (ads). Spine faded, o/w Fine. *WREDEN.* $110

Steggall, John. AN ESSAY ON MINERAL, VEGETABLE, ANIMAL, AND AERIAL POISONS. London S. Highley, 1833. 2nd ed. Orig cl and paper spine label (now sl eroded). 12 hand colored plts (incl frontis). Offsetting from plts, pp bit browned at edges, few minor spots, o/w excellent internally in well preserved sl worn binding. *PIRAGES.* $275

Stegner, Wallace. A SHOOTING STAR. Viking, 1961. 1st ed. About Fine. Dj lightly soiled on rear panel. *STAHR.* $45

Stegner, Wallace. A SHOOTING STAR. Viking, 1961. 1st ed. Fine in dj. *AUTHORS OF THE WEST.* $20

Stegner, Wallace. ALL THE LITTLE LIVE THINGS. Viking, 1967. 1st ed. Fine in dj lightly chipped and torn along top edge, critter marks near spine. *STAHR.* $30

Stegner, Wallace. ANGLE OF REPOSE. GC: Doubleday, 1971. 1st ed. Fine in VG dj (internally strengthened w/tape at extrems). Inscribed. *LOPEZ.* $100

Stegner, Wallace. BEYOND THE HUNDREDTH MERIDIAN. Boston, 1954. Brown cloth. xiii,438pp; fldg frontis. 1st ed. Fine in VG+ dj. *FIVE QUAIL.* $65

Stegner, Wallace. BEYOND THE HUNDREDTH MERIDIAN. Boston: Houghton Mifflin, 1954. 1st ed. VG in lightly edgeworn dj. *LOPEZ.* $125

Stegner, Wallace. CROSSING TO SAFETY. NY: Random House, 1987. 1st ed. Fine. *SMITH.* $30

Stegner, Wallace. CROSSING TO SAFETY. NY: RH, (1987). Uncorrected proof. Sm smudges on wraps, o/w Fine, promo sheet laid in. *LOPEZ.* $50

Stegner, Wallace. CROSSING TO SAFETY. Random House, (1987). 1st ed. Review copy, slip laid in. Fine in dj. *AUTHORS OF THE WEST.* $40

Stegner, Wallace. MORMON COUNTRY. Duell, Sloan & Pearce, (1942). 1st ed. Unobtrusive internal erasures. *AUTHORS OF THE WEST.* $30

Stegner, Wallace. MORMON COUNTRY. NY: Duell, Sloan & Pearce, 1942. 1st ed. Fine in Fine dj. *GIBBS.* $37.50

Stegner, Wallace. ON A DARKLING PLAIN. NY: Harcourt, (1940). 1st ed. VG in VG edge-chipped dj. *UNGER.* $225

Stegner, Wallace. ON THE TEACHING OF CREATIVE WRITING. (Hanover): Dartmouth, (1988). Signed. Fine w/o dj (as issued?). *LOPEZ.* $85

Stegner, Wallace. RECAPITULATION. Doubleday & Co, 1979. 1st ed. Boards. Fine in dj. *AUTHORS OF THE WEST.* $20

Stegner, Wallace. RECAPITULATION. Franklin Center: Franklin Library, 1979. Ltd ed. Fine in Franklin leather. *CAPTAIN'S BOOKSHELF.* $60

Stegner, Wallace. REMEMBERING LAUGHTER. Boston: Little, Brown, 1937. 1st ed, 1st book. Very sunned, a few pages soiled; o/w Nice in lightly used dj. *BEASLEY.* $50

Stegner, Wallace. SECOND COMING. Houghton Mifflin, 1947. 1st ed. About Fine in worn dj w/chips. *STAHR.* $150

Stegner, Wallace. THE BIG ROCK CANDY MOUNTAIN. Franklin Center: Franklin Library, 1978. Ltd ed reissue. Leatherbound, aeg, silk eps. Signed. Fine. *LOPEZ.* $100

Stegner, Wallace. THE GATHERING OF ZION. NY, 1964. 1st ed, 4th ptg. VF in Fine dj. *FIVE QUAIL.* $25

Stegner, Wallace. THE GATHERING OF ZION. NY: McGraw-Hill, (1964). 1st ed. Signed. NF in sl spine-darkened dj. *LOPEZ.* $150

Stegner, Wallace. THE GATHERING OF ZION. NY: McGraw-Hill, (1964). 1st ed. VG in price-clipped dj. *LOPEZ.* $85

Stegner, Wallace. THE GATHERING OF ZION—THE STORY OF THE MORMON TRAIL. NY: 1964. 1st ed. VG+ in sl worn dj. *BENCHMARK.* $32.50

Stegner, Wallace. THE POTTER'S HOUSE. The Prairie Press, 1938. 1st ltd ed of 490 copies. Fine. *AUTHORS OF THE WEST.* $300

Stegner, Wallace. THE SOUND OF MOUNTAIN WATER. Doubleday & Co, 1969. 1st ed. Fine, bkpl. *AUTHORS OF THE WEST.* $20

Stegner, Wallace. THE SOUND OF MOUNTAIN WATER: THE CHANGING AMERICAN WEST. Doubleday, 1969. 1st ed. VG or better in dj. Owner's sig. *STAHR.* $40

Stegner, Wallace. THE SPECTATOR BIRD. Franklin Center: Franklin Library, 1976. Ltd ed. Fine in Franklin leather. *CAPTAIN'S BOOKSHELF.* $60

Stegner, Wallace. THE SPECTATOR BIRD. Franklin Library, First Edition Society, 1976. 1st "limited" deluxe ed. Bound in full, gilt dec, ribbed, grn leather, w/silk eps, bkmark. Aeg. FES pamphlet laid in. New. *AUTHORS OF THE WEST.* $50

Stegner, Wallace. THE SPECTATOR BIRD. GC: Doubleday, 1976. 1st ed. Signed. Fine in NF, price-clipped dj. *LOPEZ.* $135

Stegner, Wallace. THE UNEASY CHAIR. GC: Doubleday, 1974. Stated 1st ed. Dj worn. VG. *AKA.* $20

Stegner, Wallace. THE UNEASY CHAIR. GC: Doubleday, 1974. 1st ed. Fine in lightly rubbed, black dj w/sl sunned spine. Inscribed, 10-line quotation in holograph. *CAPTAIN'S BOOKSHELF.* $175

Stegner, Wallace. THE WOMEN ON THE WALL. Boston: Houghton Mifflin, (1950). 1st ed. Signed. Small printing; hard to find. VG in VG dj with shallow chipping to edges. *UNGER.* $225

Stegner, Wallace. THIS IS DINOSAUR. NY, 1955. 1st ed. Covers worn, bkseller's ticket. About Good+ externally, VG inside. *FIVE QUAIL.* $25

Steig, William. THE AGONY IN THE KINDERGARTEN. NY: Duell, Sloan & Pearce. (1950). 1st ed. Dj. *KARMIOLE.* $30

Stein, Gertrude. AN ACQUAINTANCE WITH DESCRIPTION. London: Seizen Press, 1929. 1/225 numbered/signed. Fine. *DERMONT.* $400

Stein, Gertrude. BREWSIE AND WILLIE. NY: Random House, (1946). Slight darkening along front gutter from binder's glue, else Fine in lightly used dj. 1st ed. One of 6000. *CHAPEL HILL.* $75

Stein, Gertrude. FOUR SAINTS IN THREE ACTS: AN OPERA TO BE SUNG. NY: Random House, 1934. Stated 1st ed. Black cl, spine faded, rubbed at corners. *SCHOYER'S.* $35

Stein, Gertrude. GEOGRAPHY AND PLAYS. Boston: Four Seas, (1922). 1st ed. 8vo, 419pp. Bound in blue cl backed grey boards, Wilson's 2nd binding. Fine in little chipped grey dj. 2500 copies ptd in 1922, the sheets were issued over a number of years in diverse bindings. *SECOND LIFE.* $375

Stein, Gertrude. LECTURES IN AMERICA. NY: Random House (1935). 1st ed. VG in VG edge-chipped dj. *DORN.* $100

Stein, Gertrude. LECTURES IN AMERICA. NY: Random House, (1935). 1st ed. Cl bumped, eps darkened at hinges, dj. Frontis. NF. *BLUE MOUNTAIN.* $125

Stein, Gertrude. PORTRAITS AND PRAYERS. NY: Random House, (1934). 1st ed. Orig cl, photo port front cvr. Clear double-layer cellophane dw ptd in red w/grey paper flaps (one folds partly over onto front board). Signed and inscribed. VF in Mint orig cellophane dw (sl chipped; long closed tear in one layer of cellophane on back panel). *PIRAGES.* $850

Stein, Gertrude. PORTRAITS AND PRAYERS. NY: Random House, (1934). Rear cvr a little soiled, name on front pastedown, else NF. 1st ed. One of 1800. *CHAPEL HILL.* $175

Stein, Gertrude. WHAT ARE MASTERPIECES? LA: Conference Press, (1940). 1st ed. Dj flaws. Fine. *MUELLER.* $65

Stein, Harry. HOOPLA. Knopf, 1983. 1st ed. Fine in dj. *STAHR.* $30

Stein, Leo. THE A-B-C OF AESTHETICS. NY: Boni & Liveright, 1927. 1st ed. Sl cocked, corners frayed o/w Good. *ARCHER.* $15

Stein, William. HUALCAN: LIFE IN THE HIGHLANDS OF PERU. Ithaca: Cornell Univ Press, (1961). 1st ed. *SILVER.* $25

Steinach, Eugen. SEX AND LIFE. NY: Viking Press, 1940. 1st ed. About Fine in Good dj. *WREDEN.* $35

Steinbeck, John. A RUSSIAN JOURNAL. NY: Viking, 1948. 1st ed. Fine; minor chipping at dj corners. *ELSE FINE.* $125

Steinbeck, John. A RUSSIAN JOURNAL. NY: Viking, 1948. Fine in NF dj. 1st ed. *CHAPEL HILL.* $150

Steinbeck, John. A RUSSIAN JOURNAL. NY: Viking Press, 1948. 1st ed. Illus. w/photos by Robert Capa. VG+ in dj sl chipped at top of spine. *BERNARD.* $100

Steinbeck, John. AMERICA AND AMERICANS. NY: Viking Press, (1966). 1st ed. Illus. 1st binding w/spine lettering reading from top to bottom. Fine. *BERNARD.* $25

Steinbeck, John. BURNING BRIGHT. NY: Viking, 1950. 1st ed. NF. *SMITH.* $175

Steinbeck, John. BURNING BRIGHT. NY: Viking Press, 1950. 1st ed. NF in VG dj which is lightly soiled & with one Very tiny chip at top right spine corner. *BERNARD.* $100

Steinbeck, John. CANNERY ROW. London: William Heinemann, (1945). 1st British ed. VG+. *AUTHORS OF THE WEST.* $20

Steinbeck, John. CANNERY ROW. NY: Viking, 1945. 1st ed. Small amount of discoloration in the front gutter else VF. Minor wear dj spine ends. Yellow binding. *ELSE FINE.* $125

Steinbeck, John. CUP OF GOLD. NY: Covici Friede, (1936). 2nd ed, 1st book. VG+ in bright, attractive, price clipped dj sl worn at spine ends. *BERNARD.* $125

Steinbeck, John. CUP OF GOLD. NY: Covici-Friede (1936). 2nd issue, 2nd ptg in blue cl. Fine in dj. *DORN.* $135

Steinbeck, John. EAST OF EDEN. NY: (Viking), n.d. (1952). 1st ed. Pub's grn cl in VG dj (owner name free endleaf). *BOOK BLOCK.* $165

Steinbeck, John. HOW EDITH MCGILLGUDDY MET R.L.S. Cleveland: The Rowfant Club, 1943. 1st ed. #110 of 152 ptd at the Grabhorn Press in SF. Orig 1/4 cl, floral striped boards, paper labels. Both boards bumped at top, but VG. Scarce. *CHAPEL HILL.* $1,500

Steinbeck, John. JOHN STEINBECK: A COLLECTION...BY HARRY VALENTINE....Foreword by John R. Payne. Santa Barbara: Bradford Morrow Bkseller, (1980). 1st ed. One of 2500 in wraps. Morrow Catalogue 8. Spine a bit faded, else Fine. *CAPTAIN'S BOOKSHELF.* $20

Steinbeck, John. JOURNAL OF A NOVEL: THE EAST OF EDEN LETTERS. NY: Viking Press, (1969). One of ltd ed of 600. Color frontispiece & 7 facsimile pp from the manuscript. Top corner tips sl frayed, red line on bottom page edges o/w VG+ but lacking orig glassine dj & slipcase. *BERNARD.* $175

Steinbeck, John. JOURNAL OF A NOVEL: THE EAST OF EDEN LETTERS. NY: Viking, (1969). 1st ed. One of 600. NF in pub's slipcase, mild wear. *UNGER.* $200

Steinbeck, John. LETTERS TO ELIZABETH: A SELECTION OF LETTERS FROM JOHN STEINBECK TO ELIZABETH OTIS. SF: Bk Club of CA, 1978. One of 500. Dj. *DAWSON'S.* $125

Steinbeck, John. NOTHING SO MONSTROUS. (NY: The Pynson Printers), 1936. One of 150. Orig orange cl-backed marbled boards. Fine. *WEBER.* $850

Steinbeck, John. OF MICE AND MEN. NY: Covici Friede, (1937). 1st ed. Fine in NF dj (uniformly tanned on spine). Bkpl. *LOPEZ.* $550

Steinbeck, John. OF MICE AND MEN. NY: Covici-Friede, (1937). Couple of tiny spots on cl at spine ends, o/w Fine in fresh pict dj (unobtrusive closed tear, small abrasion on rear panel). 1st ed, 1st state, w/bullet between the 8s on p. 88, and w/"and only moved because the heavy hands were pendula" on p. 9, lines 2-3 up. Very scarce in this cond. *CHAPEL HILL.* $600

Steinbeck, John. OF MICE AND MEN. NY: LEC, 1970. 1/1500 illus, signed by Fletcher Martin. Fine in slipcase. *CAPTAIN'S BOOKSHELF.* $200

Steinbeck, John. OF MICE AND MEN. NY: Viking, (1937). 1st ed, 1st issue. Some soiling, else VG in a VG, lightly soiled dj. *UNGER.* $350

Steinbeck, John. ONCE THERE WAS A WAR. NY: Viking, 1958. 1st ed. Sl water stains back of dj and binding. VG+. *SMITH.* $125

Steinbeck, John. SWEET THURSDAY. NY: (Viking), 1954. 1st ed. Pub's mustard cl in orig dj (sl wear top of spine). *BOOK BLOCK.* $50

Steinbeck, John. SWEET THURSDAY. NY: Viking (1954). 1st ed. Spine sl sunned else VG in price-clipped VG dj. *DORN.* $50

Steinbeck, John. SWEET THURSDAY. NY: Viking, 1954. 1st ed. Fine; minor wear to spine ends of bright dj. *ELSE FINE.* $75

Steinbeck, John. SWEET THURSDAY. NY: Viking Press, 1954. 1st ed. VG+ in dj which is about 1/8" shorter than the book. *BERNARD.* $60

Steinbeck, John. THE FORGOTTEN VILLAGE. NY: Viking, 1941. 1st ed. Illus. Spine lightly tanned, some browning to inner hinges due to poor binding glue o/w VG+ in VG dj which has 2 small chips at top edge of front panel & externally reinforced with tape at spine ends. *BERNARD.* $100

Steinbeck, John. THE GRAPES OF WRATH. NY: Viking, (1939). 1st ed. Fine in VG 1st issue dj (internally strengthened along top edge, mildly spine faded). *LOPEZ.* $650

Steinbeck, John. THE GRAPES OF WRATH. NY: Viking, (1939). 1st ed. Cl, dj. Fine. *JAFFE.* $1100

Steinbeck, John. THE GRAPES OF WRATH. NY: Viking, (1939). 1st ed, 1st ptg, top edge stained yellow, "First Published in April 1939" and no notice of later ptg on copyright pg, and "First Edition" on front flap of jacket. Orig pict beige cl. Very Nearly Fine in pict dj, only a couple of tiny nicks. *CHAPEL HILL.* $1100

Steinbeck, John. THE LONG VALLEY. NY: Viking, 1938. Bkseller's label on rear pastedown, soiling along bottom half of front gutter, but VG in dj (sl browned at edges and w/light wear to spine ends). 1st ed. *CHAPEL HILL.* $225

Steinbeck, John. THE LONG VALLEY. NY: Viking Press, 1938. 1st ed. NF in dj which is very sl worn at spine ends. *BERNARD.* $325

Steinbeck, John. THE MOON IS DOWN. London & Toronto: Wm. Heinemann Ltd., (1942). 1st UK ed. Spine sl ridged o/w bright, VG+ copy in dj which is lightly soiled on rear panel. *BERNARD*. $85

Steinbeck, John. THE MOON IS DOWN. London: William Heinemann, (1942). 1st ed. VG+. *AUTHORS OF THE WEST*. $25

Steinbeck, John. THE RED PONY. NY, Viking. 1st illus ed. VG in slipcase. *OCTOBER FARM*. $25

Steinbeck, John. THE RED PONY. Viking, (1945). 1st illus ed. Fine in VG slipcase. *OREGON*. $60

Steinbeck, John. THE SHORT REIGN OF PIPPIN IV. NY: Viking Press, 1957. 1st ed. VG+ in dj which has one very tiny chip at top right spine corner. *BERNARD*. $50

Steinbeck, John. THE SHORT REIGN OF PIPPIN IV. NY: Viking, 1957. 1st ed. NF. *SMITH*. $75

Steinbeck, John. THE STEINBECK OMNIBUS. London: William Heinemann, (1950). 1st British ed. Fine. *AUTHORS OF THE WEST*. $25

Steinbeck, John. THE STEINBECK POCKET BOOK. Phila: The Blakiston Co., (1943). 1st ed. Distributed by Pocket Books. VG+ ppwrps (edges rubbed). *BERNARD*. $30

Steinbeck, John. THE WAYWARD BUS. NY: Viking, 1947. 1st ed. Fine in VG dj (price-clipped, torn, lightly chipped). *ARCHER*. $40

Steinbeck, John. THE WINTER OF OUR DISCONTENT. London: Heinemann, (1961). 1st Eng. ed. Owner name, address. VG+ in VG dj. *AARD*. $25

Steinbeck, John. THE WINTER OF OUR DISCONTENT. NY: Viking, 1961. 1st ed. NF. *SMITH*. $100

Steinbeck, John. THE WINTER OF OUR DISCONTENT. NY: Viking, 1961. 1st ed. Fine in dj (three tiny tears, touch of sunning to spine). *CAPTAIN'S BOOKSHELF*. $75

Steinbeck, John. THE WINTER OF OUR DISCONTENT. NY: Viking, 1961. 1st ed. Cl, dj. Fine. *JAFFE*. $100

Steinbeck, John. TORTILLA FLAT. Viking, 1947. 1st ed. with these illus. 17 color illus. by Peggy Worthington. NF with minor scuff to cvr in G+ dj with 2 closed tears top of spine repaired internally with tape, series of tiny holes along dj spine. *BEBBAH*. $100

Steinbock, R. Ted. PALEOPATHOLOGICAL DIAGNOSIS AND INTERPRETATION: BONE DISEASES IN ANCIENT HUMAN POPULATIONS. Springfield, 1976. *FYE*. $75

Steinbrunner, Chris and Otto Penzler (eds.). DETECTIONARY. Lock Haven, PA: Hammermill Paper, 1972. Ltd ed. Fine in wrappers. *MORDIDA*. $150

Steindler, Arthur. MECHANICS OF NORMAL AND PATHOLOGICAL LOCOMOTION IN MAN. Springfield, 1935. 1st ed. *FYE*. $150

Steindler, Arthur. ORTHOPEDIC OPERATIONS: INDICATIONS, TECHNIQUE, AND END RESULTS. Springfield, 1940. 1st ed. *FYE*. $150

Steiner, Edward A. ON THE TRAIL OF THE IMMIGRANT. NY, 1906. 375 pp. *O'NEILL*. $30

Steiner, Rudolf. THE STORY OF MY LIFE. London, 1928. Dj w/lt rubbing. NF. *POLYANTHOS*. $35

Steininger, G. Russell and Paul Von de Velde. THREE DOLLARS A YEAR. NY: Delphic Studios, (1935). 1st ed. Chipped dj. *SILVER*. $25

Steinmetz, Rollin C. VANISHING CRAFTS AND THEIR CRAFTSMEN. Rutgers U, 1959. 1st ed. D/w some frayed. *HEINOLDT*. $12

Stejneger, Leonhard. GEORG WILHELM STELLER, THE PIONEER OF ALASKAN NATURAL HISTORY. Cambridge: Harvard Univ, 1936. 28 plts, fldg map. VG+. *MIKESH*. $75

Stejneger, Leonhard. GEORG WILHELM STELLER: THE PIONEER OF ALASKAN NATURAL HISTORY. Cambridge:

Harvard Univ Press, 1936. 1st ed. Worn spine lettering, else VG+. *BLUE DRAGON*. $45

Stekel, Wilhelm. IMPOTENCE IN THE MALE. NY: Liveright, (1939). Authorized Eng version by Oswald H. Boltz. 2 vols. Fine in VG djs. *WREDEN*. $40

Stekloff, G.M. HISTORY OF THE FIRST INTERNATIONAL. NY: International, 1928. 1st ed. Name fep. 2pp sm edge pieces missing, not affecting text. VG. *AKA*. $45

Stellman, Louis J. PORT O' GOLD. Boston, (1922). 1st ed. 16 plts. One corner sl bumped, o/w NF. Bkpl of Robert Ernest Cowan. Newspaper review laid in. *DIAMOND*. $35

Stenhouse, Mrs T.B.H. TELL IT ALL: THE STORY OF A LIFE'S EXPERIENCE IN MORMONISM. Hartford: A.D. Worthington, 1876. 623pp + frontis, 18 plts. Edgeworn. G+. *OREGON*. $45

Stenhouse, Mrs. T.B.H. "TELL IT ALL". Hartford; Worthington, 1875. Rprnt. Port. External wear, VG. BAL 1948. *SECOND LIFE*. $65

Stenhouse, T.B.H. ROCKY MOUNTAIN SAINTS....London, n.d. 761pp, ads, frontis. Orig grn dec cl, hinges cracked. Near VG. *BENCHMARK*. $150

Stephens, Anne S. FASHION AND FAMINE. NY: Bunce & Brother, 1854. 1st ed, 1st bk. VG in pub's cl. *SECOND LIFE*. $75

Stephens, James. THE CROCK OF GOLD. London: Macmillan, 1912. Gift inscript, but VG to NF. 1st ed, 1st issue binding, w/gilt fleur-de-lis penetrating oval on front cvr. *CHAPEL HILL*. $95

Stephens, James. THE CROCK OF GOLD. London: MacMillan, 1912. 1st ed, 1st binding. Fine (discreet bkpl) in VG later issue ptd dj. Half morocco slipcase. *CAPTAIN'S BOOKSHELF*. $400

Stephens, James. THE DEMI-GODS. London: Macmillan, 1914. VG. 1st ed, 1st issue, w/half-title present. *CHAPEL HILL*. $50

Stephens, John L. INCIDENTS OF TRAVEL IN EGYPT, ARABIA....NY: Harper & Brothers, 1845 (1837). 10th ed. 2 vols, 240pp; 286pp. Lacks map. Edges worn, foxing. *SILVER*. $100 UTAH—A GUIDE TO THE STATE. NY, 1945. 2nd ed. VG+. Comp by Dale Morgan. *BENCHMARK*. $20

Stephens, John L. INCIDENTS OF TRAVEL IN EGYPT, ARABIA PETRAEA....2 vols. NY: Harper, 1841. 10th ed, enl. 240; 286pp. 18 plts, 1 fldg map. Orig cl, rubbed, faded and soiled, spine frayed, sl foxing, sl dampstained, o/w Good. *WORLDWIDE*. $65

Stephens, John L. INCIDENTS OF TRAVEL IN YUCATAN. 2 vols (complete). NY: Harper & Brothers, 1843. 1st ed. 124 illus (74 full pp, 2 fldg), 1 fldg map, mid-19th century 3/4 morocco. Spines heavily chipped and faded, corners rubbed, scattered foxing, corner of 1 text pp chipped in margin only, most plts clean. *ARCHAEOLOGIA*. $450

Stephens, Robert Neilson. THE MYSTERY OF MURRAY DAVENPORT. Boston: L.C. Page, 1903. 1st ed. Fine in blue cloth-covered boards w/gold-stamped titles. *MORDIDA*. $50

Stephens, Robert W. AUGUST BUCHEL TEXAN SOLDIER OF FORTUNE. (Dallas, 1970). 1st ed. Ltd to 200. Fine. *McGOWAN*. $37.50

Stephenson, L.W. THE CRETACEOUS FORMATIONS OF NORTH CAROLINA. Part 1. Raleigh, 1923. 102 plts (incl fldg map). Light wear. *SUTTON*. $75

Stephenson, Terry E. THE SHADOWS OF OLD SADDLEBACK: FROM THE DAYS....The Fine Arts Press: 1948. 1st ed after ltd ed of 500. Gilt sl worn on spine, else VG. *CONNOLLY & WADE*. $65

Stepniak (pseud of S.M. Kravchinskii). THE RUSSIAN STORMCLOUD. London, 1886. NF. *POLYANTHOS*. $50

Stepniak. (pseud of S.M. Kravchinskii). UNDERGROUND RUSSIA. NY, 1883. VG-NF. *POLYANTHOS*. $35

Stepp, John W. and William I. Hill (comp and eds.). MIRROR OF THE WAR, THE WASHINGTON STAR REPORTS THE CIVIL WAR. Englewood Cliffs, 1961. 1st ed. VG+ in dj. *PRATT*. $25

Steptoe, John. DADDY IS A MONSTER SOMETIMES. NY: Lippincott, 1980. 1st ed. Fine in dj w/couple short tears. Signed. *BETWEEN COVERS.* $85

Sterling, George. 35 SONNETS. Bk Club of CA, 1917, ltd 300. 54pp. Boards. Red stain along edge cover. *HEINOLDT.* $35

Sterling, George. ROBINSON JEFFERS. NY: Boni & Liveright, 1926. 1st ed. VF in price-clipped dj. *JAFFE.* $125

Sterling, George. ROBINSON JEFFERS: THE MAN AND THE ARTIST. NY: Boni & Liveright, 1926. 1st ed. 3 silverfish holes bottom of spine, o/w Fine. *WEBER.* $100

Sterling, George. SONNETS TO CRAIG. Upton Sinclair, (1928). 1st ed. Fine in dj. *AUTHORS OF THE WEST.* $25

Sterling, George. THE BINDING OF THE BEAST AND OTHER WAR VERSE. A.M. Robertson, 1917. 1st ed. Fine, name. *AUTHORS OF THE WEST.* $20

Stern, Madeleine. THE LIFE OF MARGARET FULLER. NY: E.P. Dutton, 1942. 1st ed. Stain on ffeps from newspaper reviews laid in, else Fine. *WREDEN.* $45

Stern, Philip Van Doren. AN END TO VALOR: THE LAST DAYS OF THE CONFEDERACY. Boston, 1958. 1st ed. Signed. Dj chipped o/w VG. *PRATT.* $47.50

Stern, Philip Van Doren. AN END TO VALOR: THE LAST DAYS OF THE CIVIL WAR. Boston: Houghton Mifflin, 1958. 1st ed. VG in parchment dj. Spine darkened on dj, else Fine. *CONNOLLY & WADE.* $42.50

Stern, Philip Van Doren. ROBERT E. LEE: THE MAN AND THE SOLDIER. NY: Bonanza, 1963. VG in Good+ dj. *CONNOLLY & WADE.* $25

Stern, Philip Van Doren. THEY WERE THERE. NY, (1959). 1st ed. 166pp. Minor cover wear, o/w Fine. *PRATT.* $40

Stern, Steve. THE MOON & RUBEN SHEIN. (Little Rock: August House, 1984). 1st ed. Fine in dj, tiny tear. Inscribed. *CAPTAIN'S BOOKSHELF.* $35

Sternberg, Maximilian. ACROMEGALY. London, 1899. 1st Eng trans. 138pp. Photo illus. *FYE.* $200

Sterne, Laurence. THE LIFE AND OPINIONS OF TRISTAM SHANDY, GENTLEMAN. Waltham Saint Lawrence: Golden Cockerel Press, 1929. 3 vols. One of 500 numbered. 15 Labourer copper engrs. Gill text. Fine. *MUELLER.* $100

Stetson (Gilman), Charlotte Perkins. THE YELLOW WALL PAPER. Boston: Small, Maynard, 1899. 1st ed. First few leaves detached, but present (including title page), tiny spine chip. Nice. *BEASLEY.* $400

Steuart, Sir Henry. THE PLANTER'S GUIDE....Edinburgh & London: Murray, 1828. 2nd ed, enl. 527pp. Uncut in orig paper boards, w/skillful rebacking and orig label. 6 engr plts. Excellent. *SECOND LIFE.* $275

Steven, John. THE PATHOLOGY OF MEDIASTINAL TUMOURS WITH SPECIAL REFERENCE TO DIAGNOSIS. London, 1892. 1st ed. *FYE.* $75

Stevens, C.A. BERDAN'S UNITED STATES SHARPSHOOTERS IN THE ARMY OF THE POTOMAC, 1861-1865. St. Paul, 1892.. 1st ed. (23),555pp. Orig pict cl, faded as usual, a few leaves lightly rippled. Howes S957. Rare. *GINSBERG.* $300

Stevens, Francis. THE HEAD OF CERBERUS. Reading: Polaris Press, 1952. One of 1,500 numbered. Slipcase. Fine. *WEBER.* $20

Stevens, George Alexander. A LECTURE ON HEADS. London: T. Bensley, 1799. Small 8vo; contemp full tree calf; gilt-dec. spine, frontis vignettes; morocco label. VG. *DRAMATIS PERSONAE.* $225

Stevens, George Thomas. THREE YEARS IN THE SIXTH CORPS. Albany, 1866. 1st ed. Orig full morocco w/gilt-tooled Greek cross on covers, aeg. Pub's presentation copy. *McGOWAN.* $250

Stevens, Henry. CATALOGUE OF MY ENGLISH LIBRARY. COLLECTED AND DESCRIBED BY HENRY STEVENS...FOR PRIVATE DISTRIBUTION. London: Ptd by C. Whittingham, 1853. 1st ed. One of 1000. xi,107pp. Orig blind dec. cl, t.e.g, stamped in gilt on front cover "My English Library" with Stevens' initials below and "H. Stephani et amicorum" below that. Presentation copy, signed. Dewitt Miller's copy, w/his signature. Head and toe of spine a trifle worn, bottom corner of cl on front cover damaged, else VG. *WREDEN.* $140

Stevens, Henry. RECOLLECTIONS OF MR. JAMES LENOX OF NEW YORK, AND THE FORMATION OF HIS LIBRARY. BY HENRY STEVENS OF VERMONT....London: Henry Stevens & Son, 1886. 1st ed. ix,211pp. Frontis port, pl. Orig 3/4 cl, marbled boards, eps; leather label on spine. Label cracked, sm chip head of spine, spine soiled, else VG. *WREDEN.* $70

Stevens, Henry. RECOLLECTIONS OF MR. JAMES LENOX OF NEW YORK AND THE FORMATION OF HIS LIBRARY. London: Henry Stevens, 1887. 1st ed. ix, 211pp. Plts, tissue guards, guards causing offsetting. Orig 1/4 white cl, marbled boards, cl corners, dark grn morocco spine label. Fine. *WEBER.* $45

Stevens, John H. PERSONAL RECOLLECTIONS. Minneapolis: Pub by author, 1890. 1st ed. Top, bottom spine, corners rubbed. *HEINOLDT.* $35

Stevens, Lt. Col. Phillip, U.S.A. SEARCH OUT THE LAND. Chicago, (1969). 1st ed. 192pp. Dj w/light wear and small tears o/w Fine. *PRATT.* $27.50

Stevens, R.O. TALK ABOUT WILDLIFE FOR HUNTERS, FISHERMEN, AND NATURE LOVERS. Raleigh, 1944. Cloth, frontis. Some spotting & smudging to cvrs. Inscribed. *SUTTON.* $37

Stevens, Shane. BY REASON OF INSANITY. NY: Simon & Schuster, 1979. 1st ed. Remainder stamp on bottom edge o/w Fine in price-clipped dj. *MORDIDA.* $35

Stevens, Shane. GO DOWN DEAD. NY: Morrow, (1966). 1st ed, 1st bk. Fine; scrape on front of dj. Inscribed. *ELSE FINE.* $95

Stevens, W.C. KANSAS WILD FLOWERS. Lawrence, 1948. 1st ed. Cl w/lt wear. *SUTTON.* $48

Stevens, Wallace. OPUS POSTHUMOUS. REVISED, ENLARGED, & CORRECTED EDITION. Milton J. Bates (ed). NY: Knopf, 1989. Uncorrected proof. Ptd wraps. Mint. *JAFFE.* $50

Stevens, Wallace. OPUS POSTHUMOUS. Samuel French Morse (ed). NY: Knopf, 1957. 1st ed. Fine in sl worn, price-clipped dj. *JAFFE.* $125

Stevens, Wallace. THE AURORAS OF AUTUMN. NY: Knopf, (1950). 1st ed. Dj. VF. *JAFFE.* $250

Stevens, Wallace. THE COLLECTED POEMS. NY: Knopf, 1954. 1st ed. Ltd to 2500 numbered. Frontis. Faint annotations, o/w VG in edgeworn dj. *JAFFE.* $225

Stevens, Wallace. THE NECESSARY ANGEL. NY, 1951. 1st ed. Fine in dj w/extrems little rubbed, price clipped. *POLYANTHOS.* $150

Stevenson, Adlai. THE SPEECHES OF ADLAI STEVENSON. NY: Random House, (1952). 1st ed. Foreword by John Steinbeck. Ppwrps. Edges sl worn & rear cover lightly soiled o/w VG+. *BERNARD.* $40

Stevenson, Matilda Coxe. THE ZUNI INDIANS. BAE Annual Report #23. Washington: GPO. Facsimile reprint by Rio Grande Press: Glorieta, 1985. 139 plts. NF, no dj, as issued. *CONNOLLY & WADE.* $52.50

Stevenson, Mrs. Robert Louis. CRUISE OF THE "JANET NICHOL" AMONG THE SOUTH SEA ISLANDS: A DIARY. NY: Scribner's, 1914. 1st ed. Dk red buckram stamped in gilt, soiled, faded on spine. VG. *SCHOYER'S.* $35

Stevenson, Rev. THE GENTLEMAN GARDENER...WORK TO BE DONE EVERY MONTH. London, 1766. Rev 7th ed. Contemp calf, rubbed. NF. *POLYANTHOS.* $60

Stevenson, Robert Louis. A CHILD'S GARDEN OF VERSES. Limited Editions, 1944. #326 of 1100 numbered, signed illus, Roger Duvoisin. 4to. 112pp. Scuffing to spine ends, slight cvr edgewear but VG+ bright volume. *BEBBAH.* $115

Stevenson, Robert Louis. A CHILD'S GARDEN OF VERSES. Platt & Munk, (1961). Illus by Eulalie. VG in Good dj w/chips, short closed edge tears. *BEBBAH.* $25

Stevenson, Robert Louis. A CHILD'S GARDEN OF VERSES. Walck, (1947). 118pp. Illus by Tasha Tudor. Illus endpaper. VG+. *BEBBAH.* $25

Stevenson, Robert Louis. A LODGING FOR THE NIGHT. London: Chatto & Windus, 1914. 1st separate ed. Brown morocco, gilt stamped, teg. Tissue dj, spine and top edge sl sunned, else Fine. *JUVELIS.* $75

Stevenson, Robert Louis. ACROSS THE PLAINS WITH OTHER MEMORIES & ESSAYS. London: Chatto & Windus, 1892. 1st ed. Cvrs sl marked, teg. Small marginal tear on title-page, o/w NF. *DIAMOND.* $75

Stevenson, Robert Louis. AN INLAND VOYAGE. Boston: Roberts, 1883. 1st US ed. Dec grn cl. Short tear in ffep, owner sig, else NF. *CAPTAIN'S BOOKSHELF.* $125

Stevenson, Robert Louis. ISLAND NIGHTS' ENTERTAINMENTS. London, 1893. 1st ed, 1st issue. Pict cvrs gilt. Illus by Gordon Browne and W. Hatherell. Spine sunned, extrems and lower edges rubbed. NF. *POLYANTHOS.* $125

Stevenson, Robert Louis. KIDNAPPED. Being Memoirs of the Adventures of David Balfour in the Year 1751. (London): Cassell & Co., 1886. 311pp, (17)pp ads. Orig brown cl. Early bkseller's blindstamp, bkpl of former owner, hinges cracked. VG 1st ed, 1st issue, w/"business" rather than "pleasure" on p. 40, line 11; ad for illus Treasure Island on p. (312); and 16 unnumbered pages of publisher's ads. *CHAPEL HILL.* $950

Stevenson, Robert Louis. LETTERS...TO HIS FAMILY AND FRIENDS. Sidney Colvin (ed). NY: Scribners, 1899. Two vols. xliii,443; xiv,461pp. Red cl stamped in gilt. Hinges reinforced, in slipcase and with oilcloth djs. Spines a little faded. Teg. Bkpls, owner marks, not unattractive. *SCHOYER'S.* $65

Stevenson, Robert Louis. PRAYERS WRITTEN AT VAILIMA. London: Chatto & Windus, 1922. 3rd imp. Alberto Sangorski (illuminations). Bkpl of Estelle Doheny. *WEBER.* $100

Stevenson, Robert Louis. PRINCE OTTO. Boston, 1886. 1st ed. Spine sunned, extrems and corners little rubbed, name. NF. *POLYANTHOS.* $75

Stevenson, Robert Louis. ROBERT LOUIS STEVENSON'S STORY OF MONTEREY. SF: Colt Press, 1944. Ltd ed of 500. VG. *WEBER.* $50

Stevenson, Robert Louis. SONGS OF TRAVEL AND OTHER VERSES. London: Chatto & Windus, 1896. Eps tanned, some soiling and foxing, still VG. Inscribed. 1st ed. *CHAPEL HILL.* $50

Stevenson, Robert Louis. THE AMATEUR EMIGRANT & THE SILVERADO SQUATTERS. London: Folio Society, 1991. 1st folio ed. Frontis. Pict cvr. New in slipcase. *AUTHORS OF THE WEST.* $35

Stevenson, Robert Louis. THE MASTER OF BALLANTRAE. London: Cassell, 1889. 1st ed. One corner sl bumped else Fine in pict red cl. *CAPTAIN'S BOOKSHELF.* $250

Stevenson, Robert Louis. THE STRANGE CASE OF DR. JEKYLL AND MR. HYDE. Illus Edward A. Wilson. 1/4 leather & marbled boards, slipcase. NY: LEC, 1952. Ltd to 1500 signed by Wilson. Fine. *JAFFE.* $75

Stevenson, Robert Louis. THE STRANGE CASE OF DR. JEKYLL AND MR. HYDE. Illus by S.G. Hulme Beaman. London: The Bodley Head. (1930). 1st ed with Beaman illus. 7 full-page plts, frontis. Dj. Fine. *KARMIOLE.* $75

Stevenson, Robert Louis. VAILIMA LETTERS: BEING CORRESPONDENCE ADDRESSED BY ROBERT LOUIS STEVENSON TO SIDNEY COLVIN. 2 vols. Chicago: Stone and Kimball, 1895. 281, 275pp. 12mo. 1st Amer ed. Grn cl stamped in gilt, a little faded. Teg. Several bkpls. Frontis. *SCHOYER'S.* $75

Stevenson, W.F. WOUNDS IN WAR: THE MECHANISM OF THEIR PRODUCTION AND THEIR TREATMENT. London, 1897. 1st ed. Ex-lib. 86 illus. Scarce. *FYE.* $100

Stevenson, W.F. WOUNDS IN WAR: THE MECHANISM OF THEIR PRODUCTION AND THEIR TREATMENT. NY, 1898. 1st Amer ed. 437pp. 86 illus. Scarce. *FYE.* $200

STEVENSON'S BABY BOOK. SF: (John Howell), #114 of 500 ptd in black and blue (title in red) on Italian (Etruria) deckle edge handmade paper. Pub's cl back w/paper label over patterned paper boards. *BOOK BLOCK.* $65

Steward, Don M. FRONTIER PORT. A CHAPTER IN SAN DIEGO HISTORY. LA: Ward Ritchie Press, 1965. 1st ed. Signed. Cloth, paper illus laid-on cover. Fine in Good gilt cl slipcase. *CONNOLLY & WADE.* $65

Steward, Julian (ed). HANDBOOK OF SOUTH AMERICAN INDIANS. 7 vols. Washington, 1946-59, BAE Bulletin 143. 1st ed. Plts, fldg maps. Orig cl. VG. *SILVER.* $340

Stewart, Alvan. WRITINGS AND SPEECHES OF ALVAN STEWART, ON SLAVERY. Ed by Luther Rawson Marsh. NY: A.B. Burdick. 1860. 1st ed. 426pp+(2)pp of ads. Frontis and title sl foxed. *KARMIOLE.* $75

Stewart, Edgar L. CUSTER'S LUCK. Norman, (1955). 3rd prtg., (1957). Laid in is map of "The Crazy Horse Country 1842-1877". A little dj chipping o/w VG. *PRATT.* $50

Stewart, George L. PICKETT'S CHARGE, A MICROHISTORY OF THE FINAL ATTACK AT GETTYSBURG. Boston, 1959. 1st ed. 354pp. Light dj wear, o/w VG. *PRATT.* $55

Stewart, George R. DOCTOR'S ORAL. Random House, (1939). 1st ed. Dec cvr, pict eps. Fine in dj. *AUTHORS OF THE WEST.* $60

Stewart, George R. JOHN PHOENIX, ESQ. THE VERITABLE SQUIBOB. A LIFE OF CAPT. GEORGE H. DERBY U.S.A. NY, 1937. Fine in VG dj. *FIVE QUAIL.* $40

Stewart, George R. JOHN PHOENIX, ESQ. THE VERITABLE SQUIBOB. NY: Henry Holt, 1937. 1st ed. VG in VG dj. *CONNOLLY & WADE.* $55

Stewart, George R. NAMES ON THE LAND. NY: Random House, 1945. 1st ed. VG in pict dj some chipping on spine. *CONNOLLY & WADE.* $30

Stewart, George R. ORDEAL BY HUNGER: THE STORY OF THE DONNER PARTY. Boston: Houghton Mifflin, 1960. New ed. NF in VG dj. *CONNOLLY & WADE.* $17.50

Stewart, George R. THE CALIFORNIA TRAIL: AN EPIC WITH MANY HEROES. McGraw-Hill, (1962). 1st ed. Fine in dj. *AUTHORS OF THE WEST.* $35

Stewart, George R. THE OPENING OF THE CALIFORNIA TRAIL. Berkeley: Univ of CA, 1953. 1st ed. Ltd to 350. NF in VG dj. *CONNOLLY & WADE.* $42.50

Stewart, George R. THE YEARS OF THE CITY. Houghton Mifflin, 1955. 1st ed. Fine in dj. *AUTHORS OF THE WEST.* $20

Stewart, Henry. IRRIGATION FOR THE FARM, GARDEN, & ORCHARD. NY: Orange Judd, 1877. 264pp. Nearly new. *AMERICAN BOTANIST.* $20

Stewart, J.I.M. (pseud of Michael Innes). MY AUNT CHRISTINA AND OTHER STORIES. NY: W.W. Norton, 1983. 1st Amer ed. Advance review copy, slip laid in. VF in dj. *MORDIDA.* $25

Stewart, J.I.M. (pseud of Michael Innes). THE MAN WHO WROTE DETECTIVE STORIES. London: Victor Gollancz, 1959. 1st ed. VG in dj (minor wear spine ends; chip; couple short closed tears). *MORDIDA.* $40

Stewart, James Hervey. RECOLLECTIONS OF THE EARLY SETTLEMENT OF CARROLL COUNTY, INDIANA. Cincinnati: Ptd by Hitchcock & Walden for the author, 1872. 2 plts. Orig brown cloth w/gilt title and black ruling. Binding soiled, extremities lightly frayed. Good+. *BOHLING.* $150

Stewart, John D. GIBRALTAR. Boston: Houghton-Mifflin, 1967. 1st ed. Fine- in VG dj. *AARD.* $15

Stewart, Lucy S. THE REWARD OF PATRIOTISM: A REFUTATION...OF THE DEFENDERS...AN EXPOSITION OF THE CAUSE WHICH THEY OVERCAME. NY: Neale, 1930. 1st ed. 484pp. Orig cl. *GINSBERG.* $75

Stewart, Ora Pate. BUTTERMILK AND BRAN. San Antonio: Naylor, 1964. 1st ed. Inscribed. Fine in NF dj. *CONNOLLY & WADE.* $27.50

Stewart, Rev. K.J. GEOGRAPHY FOR BEGINNERS. Richmond, VA: J.W. Randolph, 1864. Palmetto series. Sun stained board, wear at hinges. *CULLEN.* $120

Stewart, Robert E. and M.F. ADOLPH SUTRO. A BIOGRAPHY. Berkeley: Howell-North, 1962. 1st ed. Fine in NF dj. *CONNOLLY & WADE.* $47.50

Stewart, Robert. THE AMERICAN FARMER'S HORSE BOOK. Cincinnati: Vent, 1867. 1st ed. 600pp. Gold stamped calf. *SECOND LIFE.* $150

Stewart, Will. SEE TEE SHOCK. Simon & Schuster, 1950. 1st ed. Fine in dj. *MADLE.* $65

Stickney, F.L. THE RUBBER MASK. NY: Chelsea House, 1937. 1st ed. Stamp, o/w VG in dj, wear along folds. *MORDIDA.* $25

Stierlin, Henri. ART OF THE AZTECS AND ITS ORIGINS. NY: Rizzoli, 1982. 1st Amer ed. NF in VG dj. *PARMER.* $90

Stiles, Henry Reed. BUNDLING: ITS ORIGIN, PROGRESS AND DECLINE IN AMERICA. Albany: Knickerbocker, 1871. 1st ed. Orig brown pebbled cl w/gilt. VG. *CONNOLLY & WADE.* $65

Still, Alfred. SOUL OF LODESTONE. Murray Hill Books, 1946. Fine. *MAD DOG.* $15

Still, James. HOUNDS ON THE MOUNTAIN. Lexington: The Anvil Press, 1965. 1/250 numbered. Binding loose, else NF in grn cl w/paper spine label. Signed. *CAPTAIN'S BOOKSHELF.* $50

Still, James. ON TROUBLESOME CREEK. NY: Viking, (1941). 1st Amer ed. Signed. VG in VG dj w/small stain bottom of back panel. *DORN.* $100

Still, James. ON TROUBLESOME CREEK. NY: Viking, 1941. 1st ed. Fine in sl used dj, no spine darkening. Signed. *CAPTAIN'S BOOKSHELF.* $125

Still, James. RIVER OF EARTH. NY: Viking, 1940. 1st ed. Offsetting to fep and front dj flap, NF in VG+ w/tiny hole to spine panel. *LAME DUCK.* $85

Still, James. RUSTIES AND RIDDLES & GEE-HAW WHIMMY—DIDDLES. (Lexington): The Univ Press of Kentucky, (1989). 1st combined ed. As New in dj. Signed. *CAPTAIN'S BOOKSHELF.* $35

Still, James. RUSTIES AND RIDDLES & GEE-HAW WHIMMY-DIDDLES. Lexington: Univ of KY Press, (1989). 1st Amer ed. Signed. Fine in dj. *DORN.* $35

Still, James. SPORTY CREEK. NY: Putnam, (1977). 1st ed. Fine in price clipped dj. Signed. *CAPTAIN'S BOOKSHELF.* $50

Still, James. SPORTY CREEK. NY: Putnam, (1977). 1st Amer ed. Signed. Paper clip indentation top of first 4 pages else Fine in VG dj missing a 1/4" chip from bottom of front panel. *DORN.* $125

Still, James. THE RUN FOR THE ELBERTAS. Lexington: Univ of KY Press, (1980). 1st Amer ed. Signed. Fine in dj. *DORN.* $50

Still, James. THE WOLFPEN NOTEBOOKS. (Lexington): Univ of Kentucky Press, (1991). 1st ed. As New in dj. Signed. *CAPTAIN'S BOOKSHELF.* $30

Stillman, J.D.B. AROUND THE HORN TO CALIFORNIA IN 1849. Lewis Osborne, 1967. 1st ltd, numbered ed of 1950. Fine. *AUTHORS OF THE WEST.* $40

Stillman, J.D.B. THE GOLD RUSH LETTERS OF J.D.B. STILLMAN. Palo Alto: Lewis Osborne, 1967. Ltd to 2350. 1st thus. VF. *OREGON.* $40

Stillman, J.D.B. THE GOLD RUSH LETTERS OF J.D.B. STILLMAN. Palo Alto: Lewis Osborne, 1967. One of 2350. Fine. *LAURIE.* $50

Stillwell, Margaret Bingham. NOAH'S ARK IN EARLY WOODCUTS AND MODERN RHYMES. NY: Edmond Byrne Hackett, The Brick Row Bookshop, (1942). 1st ed, ltd to 300. Fine in chipped glassine wrapper. *WREDEN.* $50

Stillwell, Margaret. THE AWAKENING INTEREST IN SCIENCE DURING THE FIRST CENTURY OF PRINTING 1450-1550. NY, 1970. Ltd ed. *FYE.* $150

Stirling, James. JAMES STIRLING BUILDINGS AND PROJECTS. London: Architectural Press, (1984). 1st ed. Dj. VG. *WEBER.* $25

STIRLINGSHIRE, AN INVENTORY OF THE ANCIENT MONUMENTS. (Edinburgh: HMSO). 1963. 1st ed. 2 vols. 4 fldg plans. Lg color fldg plan, color fldg map, lg color fldg map laid in. Djs sl worn. *KARMIOLE.* $150

Stix, H. et al. THE SHELL. 203 illus incl 82 tipped-in, colored plts. Cloth (slight dampstaining to lower edge of front cover, rear corner bumped), d.f. (rubbed), NY 1968. *SUTTON.* $65

Stockham, Alice B. TOKOLOGY, A BOOK FOR EVERY WOMAN, ILLUSTRATED. Chicago: Stockham, 1901. Rev ed. Pamphlet in rear pocket. *SECOND LIFE.* $50

Stocking, Charles Francis. LUCILE CRANDEN AND THE NEW DEAL. Chicago: Maestro, 1934. 1st ed. Fine but for sunning, in NF dj. *BEASLEY.* $40

Stockton, Ernest L. HISTORY EXCURSIONS INTO TENNESSEE-ITS EARLY HERITAGE. (Exton, PA): The Newcomen Society American Branch, 1941. 2nd ptg. Wraps. *HUDSON.* $30

Stockton, Frank. THE CASTING AWAY OF MRS. LECKS AND MRS. ALESHINE. NY: The Century Co., 1892. 1st combined ed. Olive grn cl. NF. Signed. *CAPTAIN'S BOOKSHELF.* $50

Stockton, Frank. THE GIRL AT COBHURST. NY: Scribner's, 1898. VG. 1st ed, state A, w/imprint date on title page set 1/4" wide. BAL 19452. *CHAPEL HILL.* $50

Stockton, Frank. THE GREAT STONE OF SARDIS. Harper, 1898. 1st ed. VG. *MADLE.* $37

Stockton, Frank. THE VIZIER OF THE TWO-HORNED ALEXANDER. Century, 1899. 1st ed. VG. *MADLE.* $40

Stoddard, H.L. THE BOBWHITE QUAIL, ETC. NY: Scribners, (1946). Plts, figures. Fine. *MIKESH.* $100

Stoddard, H.L. THE BOBWHITE QUAIL. NY: Scribners, (1941). 69 plts. NF. *MIKESH.* $100

Stoddard, James & Elliot Cutler. TORULA INFECTION IN MAN. NY, 1916. 1st ed. 98pp + plts. Wrappers. Inscribed. *FYE.* $150

Stoddard, John L. FAMOUS PARKS AND PUBLIC BUILDINGS IN AMERICA. NY, 1902. Fine. *POLYANTHOS.* $85

Stoddard, William Osborn. THE ROYAL DECREES OF SCANDEROON. NY: Russells' American Steam Ptg House, 1869. 1st ed. 45pp, frontis, 4 plts. Orig cl w/gilt. Little spine tip & corner wear. Stain at bottom pp margins, o/w VG. *DIAMOND*. $75

Stoker, Bram. DRACULA. Leonard Wolf (intro, notes, bib). Art by Saty. NY: Potter, (1975). 1st ed thus. NF in price-clipped dj (several sm tears, chips). *CAPTAIN'S BOOKSHELF*. $75

Stoker, Bram. PERSONAL REMINISCENCES OF HENRY IRVING. NY: Macmillan, 1906. 1st US ed. 2 vols. Bkpls. Fine-. *AARD*. $65

Stoker, Bram. THE GATES OF LIFE. NY: Cupples & Leon, (1908). 1st US ed. Olive cl stained rear board. Good, tight. *SECOND LIFE*. $35

Stoker, Bram. THE LAIR OF THE WHITE WORM. London: Rider, (1911). 1st ed, but later issue/prtg. (Front cvr lettered in blind and no ads at rear.) 6 color plts. Name stamp else Good in VG dj. *OTHER WORLDS*. $95

Stokes, William, Henry Ackland, George Rolleston, W.W. Gull & J. Hughes Bennett. MEDICINE IN MODERN TIMES OR DISCOURSES DELIVERED AT A MEETING OF THE BRITISH MEDICAL ASSOCIATION AT OXFORD. London, 1869. 1st ed. 255pp. Ex-lib. Outer hinges torn. *FYE*. $100

Stokes, William. LECTURES ON THE THEORY AND PRACTICE OF PHYSIC. Phila, 1837. 1st Amer ed. 1/2 leather, 408pp. Ex-lib. Front hinge cracked. *FYE*. $100

Stone, Edward L. (comp). A BOOK-LOVER'S BOUQUET. NY: William Edwin Rudge, 1931. One of 525 numbered. A. Gaylord Beaman's copy, w/his bkpl. Spine faded, else VG. *WREDEN*. $20

Stone, Edwin Martin. THE INVASION OF CANADA IN 1775....Providence, 1867. 1241,380pp. 1st ed. Old cl. Howes S1031. *GINSBERG*. $100

Stone, Harry (ed). CHARLES DICKENS' UNCOLLECTED WRITINGS FROM "HOUSEHOLD WORDS" 1850-1859. Indiana Univ Press, (1968). 2 vols. Fine in djs. *DIAMOND*. $45

Stone, I.F. UNDERGROUND TO PALESTINE. NY: Boni & Gaer, 1946. 1st ed. NF in VG+ dj w two short tears. Laid in is reader's response postcard w/quotation from Einstein regarding the book. *LAME DUCK*. $85

Stone, Irving. ADVERSARY IN THE HOUSE. GC, NY: Doubleday & Co, 1947. 1st ed. Spine, rear cvr a bit soiled, else VG in sl worn dj. *WREDEN*. $30

Stone, Irving. DEPTHS OF GLORY. Franklin Center: Franklin Library, 1985. Leatherbound ltd 1st ed. Fine. Signed. *LOPEZ*. $45

Stone, Irving. EARL WARREN: A GREAT AMERICAN STORY. NY: Prentice Hall, (1948). 1st ed. NF in VG dj, 2 sm tears. *WREDEN*. $35

Stone, Irving. FALSE WITNESS. A NOVEL. NY: Doubleday, Doran and Co, 1940. 1st ed. VG in sl chipped dj (sm hole rear flap). *WREDEN*. $35

Stone, Irving. IMMORTAL WIFE. GC, NY: Doubleday, Doran & Co, 1944. 1st ed. Sl silverfish nibbling rear cover, else Fine in worn dj. *WREDEN*. $35

Stone, Irving. LOVE IS ETERNAL: A NOVEL ABOUT MARY TODD AND ABRAHAM LINCOLN. GC, NY: Doubleday & Co., 1954. 1st ed. Fine in sl worn dj. *WREDEN*. $40

Stone, Irving. LUST FOR LIFE. London, NY, Toronto: Longmans, Green and Co, 1934. 1st ed. Cvrs dust-marked, else VG in chipped dj. *WREDEN*. $65

Stone, Irving. MEN TO MATCH MY MOUNTAINS. GC, NY: Doubleday & Co., 1956. 1st ed. The "Special Far West Edition, limited in number." Signed. VF. *WREDEN*. $100

Stone, Irving. THE PASSIONATE JOURNEY. GC, NY: Doubleday & Co, 1949. 1st ed. Top of spine bumped, else Fine in Good dj. *WREDEN*. $35

Stone, Irving. THE PASSIONS OF THE MIND. GC, NY: Doubleday, 1971. Former owner's emb stamp, but About Fine in pub's slipcase w/paper label. 1st ed. #312 of 500 signed. *CHAPEL HILL*. $45

Stone, Irving. THE PASSIONS OF THE MIND. NY, 1971. Dj. Signed. NF. *POLYANTHOS*. $35

Stone, Irving. THE PRESIDENT'S LADY. GC, NY: Doubleday & Co., 1951. 1st ed. Fine in very sl worn dj. *WREDEN*. $35

Stone, Irving. THEY ALSO RAN. GC, NY: Doubleday, Doran and Co., 1943. 1st ed. Fine in VG dj despite inside repair. *WREDEN*. $40

Stone, Reynolds. THE TURN OF THE YEARS. THE SEASONS' COURSE. Engrs by Reynolds Stone. As Old As the Century by V.S. Pritchett. Intro Paul Theroux. (London): Michael Russell, (1982). 1st ed. 1/150 signed by Pritchett and Theroux. Fine in cloth w/wood-engr label and glassine dj. *CAPTAIN'S BOOKSHELF*. $150

Stone, Robert. A FLAG FOR SUNRISE. London: Secker & Warburg, (1981). 1st Eng ed. Fine in Fine dj. Signed. *LOPEZ*. $125

Stone, Robert. A FLAG FOR SUNRISE. NY: Knopf (1981). 1st ed. Signed. Fine in price-clipped dj. *DORN*. $65

Stone, Robert. A FLAG FOR SUNRISE. NY: Knopf, 1981. 1st ed. Inscribed, dated yr of pub. Fine in NF dj. *JUVELIS*. $80

Stone, Robert. A FLAG FOR SUNRISE. NY: Knopf, 1981. Uncorrected proof. Fine in yellow wrappers. *CAPTAIN'S BOOKSHELF*. $125

Stone, Robert. A FLAG FOR SUNRISE. NY: Knopf, 1981. 1st ed. Fine in dj. Signed. *CAPTAIN'S BOOKSHELF*. $85

Stone, Robert. A HALL OF MIRRORS. Boston: HMCo. (1974). 1st ed, 1st bk. VG in VG price clipped dj. *DORN*. $200

Stone, Robert. A HALL OF MIRRORS. Boston: Houghton Mifflin, 1967. 1st ed, 1st bk. Lt shelfwear, signed. VG in VG dj. *LOPEZ*. $300

Stone, Robert. A HALL OF MIRRORS. Boston: Houghton Mifflin, 1968. 1st ed. Fine in dj. *CAPTAIN'S BOOKSHELF*. $275

Stone, Robert. A HALL OF MIRRORS. Boston: Houghton Mifflin, 1967. 1st ed. Fine in dj. Inscribed. *CAPTAIN'S BOOKSHELF*. $375

Stone, Robert. A HALL OF MIRRORS. London: Bodley Head, (1968). 1st Eng ed. Light soiling to page edges; NF in NF dj. Signed. *LOPEZ*. $350

Stone, Robert. CHILDREN OF LIGHT. (London): Deutsch, (1986). Correct 1st ed, published in England a week earlier than in the US. Fine in Fine dj. *LOPEZ*. $75

Stone, Robert. CHILDREN OF LIGHT. Knopf, 1986. 1st ed. NF. dj. Signed. *STAHR*. $40

Stone, Robert. CHILDREN OF LIGHT. NY: Knopf, 1986. 1st ed. Fine in Fine dj. Signed. *LOPEZ*. $65

Stone, Robert. DOG SOLDIERS Houghton Mifflin, 1974. 1st ed. VF in price-clipped dj. *STAHR*. $60

Stone, Robert. DOG SOLDIERS. Boston: Houghton Mifflin, 1974. Stain on rear cover, o/w VG in moderately worn dj, also stained on rear. Inscribed. *LOPEZ*. $45

Stone, Robert. DOG SOLDIERS. Boston: Houghton Mifflin, 1974. 1st ed. NF in VG dj. Signed. *CHAPEL HILL*. $150

Stone, Robert. DOG SOLDIERS. Houghton Mifflin, 1974. Adv reading copy. VF, wraps. *STAHR*. $150

Stone, Robert. DOG SOLDIERS. London: Secker & Warburg (sic), 1975. Variant ed in binding similar to pub's binding, w/British title pg and variant dj, unlaminated, lacking price, date codes but o/w resembling US jacket. Signed. *LOPEZ*. $150

Stone, Robert. DOG SOLDIERS. London: Secker & Warburg, 1975. 1st Eng ed. Very scarce ed, ptd in US and w/similar binding to US ed, but a completely different dj design. NF in VG dj (spine-faded). Signed. *LOPEZ.* $250

Stone, Robert. OUTERBRIDGE REACH. Boston: Houghton Mifflin, 1992. Advance reading copy. Fine in wraps. *BEASLEY.* $65

Stone, Robert. OUTERBRIDGE REACH. NY: Ticknor, (1992). 1st ed. One of 300 numbered, signed. VF in pub's slipcase. *UNGER.* $125

Stone, Robert. OUTERBRIDGE REACH. NY: Ticknor & Fields, 1992. Uncorrected proof. Fine in pict wrappers. *CAPTAIN'S BOOK-SHELF.* $75

Stone, Robert. OUTERBRIDGE REACH. NY: Ticknor and Fields, 1992. 1st ed. Signed. Fine in Fine dj. *BEASLEY.* $45

Stone, Robert. OUTERBRIDGE REACH. NY: Ticknor and Fields, 1992. Signed. Wraps. Adv reading copy. Fine. *BEASLEY.* $100

Stone, Rufus Barrett. MCKEAN, THE GOVERNOR'S COUNTY (PA). NY, 1926, 1st ed. Frontis. Dj torn & frayed. *HEINOLDT.* $15

Stone, Willard (ed). CONTRIBUTIONS TO MEDICAL SCIENCE DEDICATED TO ALDRED SCOTT WARTHIN. Ann Arbor, 1927. 1st ed. *FYE.* $50

Stoneman, Vernon. JOHN AND THOMAS SEYMOUR: CABINET-MAKERS IN BOSTON 1794—1816. Boston: Special Pubs, 1959. Only ed. NF. *BACKROOM.* $185

Stoney, Samuel Gaillard. PLANTATIONS OF THE CAROLINA LOW COUNTRY. Charleston, SC: Carolina Art Assoc, (1939). 2nd ed, ltd to 1,500. Fine. *WEBER.* $85

Stong, Phil. HORSES AND AMERICANS. NY, 1939. 1st ed. Tipped in frontis. Orig buckram, teg. Bkpl removed from half-title page, o/w NF. Author's Autograph Edition ltd to 500 (#343). *DIAMOND.* $85

Stong, Phil. POSITIVE PETE. Dodd, Mead, 1947. 1st ed. 64pp. Illus by Kurt Wiese. Edgewear. VG+ in VG dj w/wear, short edge tears repaired w/tape. *BEBBAH.* $30

Stookey, Byron. SURGICAL AND MECHANICAL TREATMENT OF PERIPHERAL NERVES. Phila, 1922. 1st ed. *FYE.* $175

Stopes, Marie. A BANNED PLAY AND A PREFACE ON CENSORSHIP. London: Bale, Sons & Danielsson, 1926. 1st ed. Sl soiled orig cl. Good, tight. *SECOND LIFE.* $75

Stopes, Marie. CONTRACEPTION (BIRTH CONTROL). ITS THEORY, HISTORY AND PRACTICE. A MANUAL FOR THE MEDICAL AND LEGAL PROFESSIONS. London, 1924. 1st ed, 3rd ptg. *FYE.* $100

Stopes, Marie. WISE PARENTHOOD, THE TREATISE ON BIRTH CONTROL FOR MARRIED PEOPLE....London: Putnam, (1925). 12th ed. rev. 385th thousand. *SECOND LIFE.* $25

Stoppard, Tom. LORD MALQUIST & MR MOON. (London): Anthony Blond, (1966). 1st ed. Orig orange boards. Fine in NF dj, 3/4" chip top of rear panel. *CHAPEL HILL.* $225

Stoppard, Tom. LORD MALQUIST & MR. MOON. NY: Knopf (1968). 1st ed. NF in dj (fold tear, lt damp stain). *DORN.* $35

Storer, Horatio. THE CAUSATION, COURSE, AND TREATMENT OF REFLEX INSANITY IN WOMEN. Boston, 1871. 1st ed. *FYE.* $150

Storer, Tracy and Lloyd P. Tevis. CALIFORNIA GRIZZLY. Berkeley/LA: Univ of CA Press, 1955. 1st ed. VG+ in Good+ dj. *BACKMAN.* $75

Storey, David. THIS SPORTING LIFE. Macmillan, 1960. 1st Amer ed. NF in dj. Browning to pp. *STAHR.* $45

STORIES FROM THE CHAP-BOOK....Chicago, 1896. Turn-of-the-century pub's binding (one of the 1st bks w/cloth cvrs pict illus w/lithography); pink cl w/pict design stamped on sides in blue, yellow, and grn; lettering in blue. Ptd by Lakeside Press in Caslon type on laid paper (w/watermark four). Some minimal spotting on cover, but altogether Very Nice. *BOOK BLOCK.* $175

Storm, Colton. CATALOGUE OF THE EVERETT D. GRAFF COLLECTION OF WESTERN AMERICANA. Chicago, 1968. 1st ed. Fine in dj. *McCLINTOCK.* $65

Storm, Colton. CATALOGUE OF THE EVERETT D. GRAFF COLLECTION OF WESTERN AMERICANA. Univ Chicago, (1968). 864pp. 1st ed. F in F dj. *OREGON.* $50

Storm, Hyemeyohsts. SEVEN ARROWS. NY: H&R, (1972). 1st ed. NF in dj. *LOPEZ.* $100

Storm, Hyemeyohsts. SONG OF HEYOEHKAH. NY: Harper, (1981). 1st ed. Rmdr mk, owner sig, else Fine in sl used price clipped dj. *CAPTAIN'S BOOKSHELF.* $50

Storrs and Wetmore. SANTA FE TRAIL, FIRST REPORTS: 1825. Houston: Stagecoach Press, 1960. 1st ed, ltd to 550. Paper label on cover. VF in VF dj. *OREGON.* $45

STORY OF MANITOU. Denver & Rio Grand RR, 1881. 64pp. Dec. cover (chipped, repaired). Contents VG. Wraps. *HEINOLDT.* $20

Story, William W. CASTLE ST. ANGELO AND THE EVIL EYE. London: Chapman & Hall, 1877. Somewhat rubbed, soiled. *SCHOYER'S.* $25

Stotsenburg, John H. AN IMPARTIAL STUDY OF THE SHAKESPEARE TITLE. Louisville, KY: John P. Morton, 1904. Navy blue cl, teg. Dj. VG. *WEBER.* $50

Stotz, Charles Morse. THE EARLY ARCHITECTURE OF WESTERN PENNSYLVANIA. NY: William Helburn, Inc, 1936. 1st ed. #449 of 1000. VG. *BACKROOM.* $200

Stotz, Charles Morse. THE EARLY ARCHITECTURE OF WESTERN PENNSYLVANIA. NY: William Helburn, 1936. 2nd prtg of 470. Fldg map. Dj. *WEBER.* $300

Stout, James W. THE AUTOGIOGRAPHY OF JAMES W. STOUT. Stickney, SD, 1947. 1st ed. Stapled wraps. Fair. *ARTIS.* $20

Stout, Rex. A FAMILY AFFAIR. Viking, 1975. 1st ed. VG+ with slight fading of cvr edges in VG+ dj. *BEBBAH.* $18

Stout, Rex. AND BE A VILLAIN. Viking, 1948. 1st ed. Edgewear, 2 small skinned patches on ffep. Good+ in Fair dj. *BEBBAH.* $40

Stout, Rex. BAD FOR BUSINESS. NY: Farrar & Rinehart, n.d. (1940). 1st ed. Fine, dj worn at folds, chipped on top edge. *ELSE FINE.* $110

Stout, Rex. DEATH OF A DOXY. NY: Viking Press, 1966. 1st ed. Sm stain fore-edge, o/w Fine in dj, tiny corner wear. *MORDIDA.* $65

Stout, Rex. DEATH OF A DOXY. Viking, 1966. 1st ed. VG+ with slight edgewear in dj with edgewear, creases, slight soil rear panel, Good+. *BEBBAH.* $30

Stout, Rex. DEATH OF A DUDE. NY: Viking, (1969). 1st ed. VG+ in dj. *BERNARD.* $50

Stout, Rex. DOUBLE FOR DEATH: A TECUSMEH FOX MYSTERY. NY: Farrar & Rinehart, 1939. 1st ed. Fine; light edgewear to dj. *ELSE FINE.* $450

Stout, Rex. GAMBIT. NY: Viking, (1962). 1st ed. NF in sl spine-faded dj with bit of edgewear. *LOPEZ.* $50

Stout, Rex. IN THE BEST FAMILIES. NY: Viking, 1950. 1st ed. Fine; minor wear to extrems; lt spine fade to dj. *ELSE FINE.* $175

Stout, Rex. JUSTICE ENDS AT HOME AND OTHER STORIES. Viking, 1977. 1st ed. NF in NF dj. *BEBBAH.* $25

Stout, Rex. JUSTICE ENDS AT HOME AND OTHER STORIES. NY: Viking, 1977. 1st ed. John McAleer (ed). VF in dj. *SILVER DOOR.* $35

Stout, Rex. PLEASE PASS THE GUILT. NY: Viking, 1973. 1st ed. VF in dj. *ELSE FINE.* $35

Stout, Rex. PLOT IT YOURSELF. Viking, 1959. 1st ed. About Fine in dj (lightly worn at head of spine and at corner of front flyleaf fold). Signed & inscribed. *STAHR.* $600

Stout, Rex. THE DOORBELL RANG. NY: Viking, (1965). 1st ed. Inscribed and signed in year of pub. Fine in NF dj. *LOPEZ*. $500

Stout, Rex. THE DOORBELL RANG. NY: Viking Press, 1965. 1st ed. Fine in dj (short closed tear, nicks, tiny tears, minor wear). *MORDIDA*. $35

Stout, Rex. THE DOORBELL RANGE. Viking, 1965. 1st ed. VG+ in VG dj with edgewear, tiny chip. *BEBBAH*. $40

Stout, Rex. THE FATHER HUNT. Viking, 1968. 1st ed. VG+ with narrow fading top of front board in VG dj with edgewear, 3 short closed edge tears. *BEBBAH*. $35

Stout, Rex. THE MOTHER HUNT. NY: Viking Press, 1963. 1st ed. Fine in dj. *MORDIDA*. $110

Stout, Rex. THE NERO WOLFE COOK BOOK. NY: Viking Press, 1973. 1st ed. Fine in dj. *MORDIDA*. $85

Stout, Rex. THE RED BOX. NY: Farrar & Rinehart, 1937. 1st ed. Edges sl darkened, o/w NF w/o dj. *MORDIDA*. $45

Stout, Rex. TOO MANY CLIENTS. NY: Viking, 1960. 1st ed. VG+ in (internally mended; faded) dj. *BERNARD*. $60

Stout, Rex. TROUBLE IN TRIPLICATE. Viking, 1949. 1st ed. VG in dj with small skinned patch to rear panel, sunned spine but VG jacket. *BEBBAH*. $70

Stout, Wesley W. THE GREAT DETECTIVE. Detroit, 1946. NF. *POLYANTHOS*. $35

Stout, William Bushnell. SO AWAY I WENT. Indianapolis: Bobbs Merrill, (1951). 1st ed. Signed. *ARTIS*. $22.50

Stowe, Harriet Beecher. DRED: A TALE OF THE GREAT DISMAL SWAMP. Boston: Phillips, Sampson, 1856. 1st ed. 2 vols. 329, 370pp. State 1 of vol 1 p88, but w/damage to the type on p209, lines 2-3 up. State 1 of vol II, p370. Binding A, w/holly like blind stamping and yellow eps. VG set. BAL 19389. *SECOND LIFE*. $125

Stowe, Harriet Beecher. DRED; A TALE OF THE GREAT DISMAL SWAMP. Boston, 1856. 2 vols. 1st ed. Orig cl, slight wear to spine extremities, corners scuffed, else VG. *McGOWAN*. $150

Stowe, Harriet Beecher. LIFE OF HARRIET BEECHER STOWE. Compiled from her Letters...by her Son, Charles Edward Stowe. London: Sampson & Low, 1889. Somewhat soiled, spine a little loose, but VG. 1st Eng ed. *CHAPEL HILL*. $65

Stowe, Harriet Beecher. PALMETTO-LEAVES. Boston: James R. Osgood & Co, 1873. 1st ed. 12mo, 321pp. Orig dec dk grn cl w/bevelled edges. Pgs heavily browned at edges, o/w bright, VG. *CHAPEL HILL*. $120

Stowe, Harriet Beecher. SUNNY MEMORIES OF FOREIGN LANDS. Boston: Phillips, Sampson, 1854. 1st ed. 2 vols. Brn cl, eps foxed. VG set. *SECOND LIFE*. $75

Stowe, Harriet Beecher. SUNNY MEMORIES OF FOREIGN LANDS. Boston: Phillips, Sampson, 1854. 1st ed. Lacks half front fly leaf, eps foxed, wear at extrems of spine. Good. BAL 19375. *SECOND LIFE*. $45

Stowe, Harriet Beecher. THE KEY TO UNCLE TOM'S CABIN. London: Clarke, Beeton, and Thomas Bosworth, (1853). 2nd Eng ed.? Complete ed, 2nd issue w/appendix added, in binding A. Dk blue grn cl. Fine. BAL 19357. *SECOND LIFE*. $150

Stowe, Harriet Beecher. UNCLE TOM'S CABIN. NY: LEC, 1938. 1/1500 illus, signed by Miguel Covarrubias. 1/2 leather over marbled boards. Fine in slipcase w/wear at top of opening. *CAPTAIN'S BOOKSHELF*. $300

Stowe, Harriet Beecher. UNCLE TOM'S CABIN. With 27 Illus on Wood by George Cruikshank. London: John Cassell. 1852. 1st Eng ed. xxiv, 391pp+(l)pp of ads. Frontis port, title-page illus and 27 plts. Finely bound by Riviere & Son in full tan polished calf. Aeg. Bkpl. *KARMIOLE*. $400

Stowe, Harriet Beecher. UNCLE TOM'S CABIN. With Twenty-seven illus on wood by George Cruikshank. London: John Cassell, 1852. 1st illus Eng ed and 1st ed containing Cruikshank illus. Full polished tan calf by Riviere, extra gilt tooled spine, dentelles, teg. Trace of rubbing to the corners, bottom edges and front panel, but beautiful. *CAPTAIN'S BOOKSHELF*. $750

Stowe, Harriet Beecher. UNCLE TOM'S CABIN; OR, NEGRO LIFE IN THE SLAVE STATES OF AMERICA. Reprinted verbatim from the 10th Amer. ed. London: Clarke, 1852. 1st UK ed. Pp x,329. Bound in little shabby pub's cl, lacks rear fep, hinge little loose. Cut sig of author laid in. VG. BAL 19518. Rare. *SECOND LIFE*. $800

Stowe, Harriet Beecher. WE AND OUR NEIGHBORS. NY: Ford, (1875). 1st ed. VG. *SECOND LIFE*. $45

Strachey, Lytton. ELIZABETH AND ESSEX. London: Chatto & Windus, 1928. 1st trade ed. Clippings pasted inside front cover, else Fine. *WOOLMER*. $35

Strahan, S.A.K. MARRIAGE AND DISEASE. A STUDY OF HEREDITY AND THE MORE IMPORTANT FAMILY DEGENERATIONS. NY, 1892. 1st ed. *FYE*. $75

Strahorn, Carrie. FIFTEEN THOUSAND MILES BY STAGE, A WOMAN'S UNIQUE EXPERIENCE DURING THIRTY YEARS. NY: Putnam, 1911. 1st ed. xxv, 673pp. Frontis, 4 color plts. Exceptionally Fine. Howes S1054. *OREGON*. $450

Strahorn, Robert E. TO THE ROCKIES AND BEYOND; OR, A SUMMER ON THE UNION PACIFIC RAILROAD AND BRANCHES...WITH COMPLETE DESCRIPTIONS...AND SAN JUAN REGIONS...Omaha, 1879. 2nd ed, rev, enl. 216pp. Map and plts, lg fldg map mended. Orig ptd wrappers. Howes S1058. *GINSBERG*. $300

Straight, Michael. CARRINGTON: A NOVEL OF THE WEST. Knopf, 1960. 1st ed. Inscribed, signed. Fine, nice dj, chipped. *AUTHORS OF THE WEST*. $50

Strakacz, Aniela. PADEREWSKI AS I KNEW HIM. New Brunswick, NJ: Rutgers Univ Press, (1949). 1st ed. Fine- in VG+ dj. *AARD*. $25

Strand, Mark. 18 POEMS FROM THE QUECHUA. Cambridge: Halty Ferguson, 1971. 1st ed. One of 1000. Fine. Inscribed. *CAPTAIN'S BOOKSHELF*. $45

Strand, Mark. PROSE, FOUR POEMS. Portland: Charles Seluzicki, 1987. Printed by Barbara Cash at the Ives Street Press, Sweden, Maine. Wraps, 1/187, numbered and signed. Fine. *BEASLEY*. $125

Strand, Mark. PROSE. Portland: Seluzicki, 1987. 1st ed. 1/187 signed. Fine in wrappers. *CAPTAIN'S BOOKSHELF*. $125

Strand, Mark. REASONS FOR MOVING. NY: Atheneum, 1968. 1st ed. Fine in dj with sl darkened spine. *CAPTAIN'S BOOKSHELF*. $75

Strand, Mark. SELECTED POEMS. NY: Knopf, (1990). Uncorrected proof. Ptd wraps. VF. *JAFFE*. $50

Strand, Mark. THE LATE HOUR. NY: Atheneum, 1978. 1st ed. Review copy, pub's slip laid in. VF. *JAFFE*. $65

Strand, Mark. THE LATE HOUR. NY: Atheneum, 1978. 1st ed. Fine in dj. Inscribed. *CAPTAIN'S BOOKSHELF*. $40

Strand, Mark. THE MONUMENT. NY: Ecco Press, (1978). 1st ed. Fine in dj. *CAPTAIN'S BOOKSHELF*. $30

Strand, Mark. THE SARGEANTVILLE NOTEBOOK. Providence: Burning Deck, 1973. 1st ed. 1/400. Fine in wrappers. *CAPTAIN'S BOOKSHELF*. $150

Strange, John Stephen. THE CLUE OF THE SECOND MURDER. GC: Doubleday Crime Club, 1929. 1st ed. Names, o/w NF in VG dj (internal tape repairs; 3/4" piece missing; streak-tear; wear). *MORDIDA*. $32.50

Strange, John Stephen. THE MAN WHO KILLED FORTESCUE. GC: Doubleday Crime Club, 1928. 1st ed, 1st bk. VF w/only sl spine fade to orange dj. *ELSE FINE.* $75

Stratton, Arthur. THE GREAT RED ISLAND. NY: Scribners, (1964). 1st US ed. Fine- in Fine- dj. *AARD.* $25

Stratton, Clarence. SWORDS AND STATUES, A TALE OF 16TH CENTURY ITALY. Winston, 1937. 254pp. Color frontis, 7 full-pg b/w illus by Robert Lawson. Minor page soil, some cvr wear but Good+. *BEBBAH.* $30

Stratton, Florence. THE STORY OF BEAUMONT. (Houston: Hercules Ptg and Bk Co, c.1925). 31 plts. Spine sunned. *SCHOYER'S.* $65

Stratton, Royal B. CAPTIVITY OF THE OATMAN GIRLS. Time-Life Classics of the Old West, 1982. Facs rprnt of 1857 ed pub by author. Frontis. Ribbon marker. Emb lea, gilt. Fine. *CONNOLLY & WADE.* $25

Stratton, William Avery. WHEN WM. AVERY STRATTON OWNED THE MISSISSIPPI RIVER 1871. (Oxford, NY, 1935). VG. Scarce. *BOHLING.* $40

Stratton-Porter, Gene. A GIRL OF THE LIMBERLOST. Nelson Doubleday, (1909). Color frontis & pict cvr pastedown. Light edgewear. VG+. *BEBBAH.* $60

Stratton-Porter, Gene. AT THE FOOT OF THE RAINBOW. Grosset & Dunlap, (1907). 3 color plates. Some slight page soil, 1 leaf crinkled, cvr wear but color pict pastedown bright. Overall Good+. *BEBBAH.* $22

Stratton-Porter, Gene. LADDIE. A TRUE BLUE STORY. NY, 1913. 1st ed. Illus by Herman Pfeifer. Spine sl sunned, extrems little rubbed, name, bkpl. NF. *POLYANTHOS.* $125

Stratton-Porter, Gene. LADDIE: A TRUE BLUE STORY. GC: Doubleday Page, 1913. 1st ed. VF, minor wear to dj spine ends. 4 color plts. Binding variant B. Scarce in dj. *ELSE FINE.* $325

Straub, Peter. GHOST STORY. London: Cape, 1979. 1st ed. Fine in dj. *ELSE FINE.* $45

Straub, Peter. GHOST STORY. NY: Coward, 1979. 1st ed. Fine in close to Fine dj w/light wear at spine head. *BEASLEY.* $35

Straub, Peter. IF YOU COULD SEE ME KNOW. NY: CMG, 1977. 1st ed. Tiny date stamp, else VF in dj. *ELSE FINE.* $85

Straub, Peter. JULIA. NY, 1975. 1st US ed. 1 small chip at dj spine, bk is sl cocked, else VG+. *PETTLER.* $60

Straub, Peter. KOKO. Dutton, 1988. 1st ed. As New. *MADLE.* $30

Straub, Peter. MARRIAGES. NY, 1973. 1st US ed. NF in bit worn dj. *PETTLER.* $65

Straub, Peter. MYSTERY. NY: Dutton, 1990. 1st ed. Signed. Fine in Fine dj. *BEASLEY.* $45

Straub, Peter. SHADOW LAND. Coward-McCann, 1980. 1st ed. Fine in dj. *MADLE.* $25

Straus, Ralph. CARRIAGES AND COACHES: THEIR HISTORY AND THEIR EVOLUTION. Phila: Lippincott, 1912. 1st U.S. ed. VG. *OCTOBER FARM.* $295

Strawberry, Darryl. DARRYL. Bantam, 1992. Later ptg. VF in dj. Signed. *STAHR.* $35

Street, C.J.C. IRELAND IN 1921. London, 1922. VG-NF. *POLYANTHOS.* $35

Street, John. THE COMPOSITION OF CERTAIN PATENT AND PROPRIETARY MEDICINES. Chicago, 1917. 1st ed. Scarce. *FYE.* $50

STREET-WALKER. NY: Viking, 1960. 1st Amer ed. VG in dj. *SCHOYER'S.* $15

Streeter, Daniel W. CAMELS!! NY/London: G.P. Putnam's Sons, 1927. Stated 1st ed. VG w/owner inscrip. *BACKMAN.* $25

Streeter, Floyd B. PRAIRIE TRAILS & COW TOWNS. Boston, 1936. 1st ed. Fine. *VARNER.* $150

Streeter, Floyd B. THE COMPLETE AND AUTHENTIC LIFE OF BEN THOMPSON. F. Fell, 1957. 1st ed. (?). Fine in VG dj. *VARNER.* $30

Streeter, Floyd B. THE COMPLETE AND AUTHENTIC LIFE OF BEN THOMPSON, MAN WITH A GUN. NY, (1957). 1st ed. 217pp. Dj wear o/w VG. *PRATT.* $22.50

Streeter, Thomas W. THE CELEBRATED COLLECTION OF AMERICANA FORMED BY THE LATE THOMAS W. STREETER. 8 vols. NY, 1966-1969. 1st ed. 1st state (bound in boards). 3 vols show marginal pencil notes; spine of index vol uniformly faded. Orig prices realized lists laid-in, except for vols 2,7. This info all ptd in index vol 8. VG+. *McCLINTOCK.* $850

Streeter, Thomas W. THE CELEBRATED COLLECTION OF AMERICANA FORMED BY THE LATE THOMAS WINTHROP STREETER. Morristown, NJ: Sold by Order of the Trustees. NY: Parke-Bernet Galleries, Inc. 1966-1970. 8 vols, incl Index vol. 2-pg color plt. Excellent set. *KARMIOLE.* $600

Strete, Craig. IF ALL ELSE FAILS. GC: Doubleday, 1980. 1st ed. Fine in NF dj. *LOPEZ.* $75

Strete, Craig. PAINT YOUR FACE ON A DROWNING IN THE RIVER. NY: Greenwillow, (1978). 1st ed. Fine in NF dj. *LOPEZ.* $75

Stribling, T.S. THE STORE. GC: Doubleday Doran, 1932. 1st ed. VG, lacking dj. *LOPEZ.* $25

Stribling, T.S. UNFINISHED CATHEDRAL. GC: Doubleday, Doran, 1934. 1st ed. Tape marks front, rear eps, else Fine in dj. Inscribed. *CAPTAIN'S BOOKSHELF.* $60

Stricker, Salomon. MANUAL OF HUMAN AND COMPARATIVE HISTOLOGY. London, 1870. 1st Eng trans. 3 vols. Outer hinges weak, part of backstrip of Vol. 1 missing. Contents Fine. *FYE.* $100

Strieber, Whitley. BILLY. Putnam, 1990. Uncorrected proof. Fine in blue wraps. Pub date written on front cover and spine. Label on front cover. *STAHR.* $35

Strieber, Whitley. BLACK MAGIC. NY: Morrow, 1982. 1st ed. NF in dj. *OTHER WORLDS.* $25

Strieber, Whitley. THE HUNGER. Morrow, 1981. 1st ed. NF. Very lt wear to dj. *STAHR.* $20

Strieber, Whitley. THE HUNGER. NY: Morrow, 1981. 1st ed. NF in dj, tiny tears, chipping. *OTHER WORLDS.* $30

Strieber, Whitley. THE NIGHT CHURCH. Simon and Schuster, 1983. 1st ed. Fine in dj (sm rubbed spots). *STAHR.* $25

Strieber, Whitley. THE WOLFEN. Bantam, 1979. 1st ed. Sl dampened, else NF. *MADLE.* $30

Strieber, Whitley. THE WOLFEN. NY: Morrow, 1978. 1st ed. Fine in Fine dj. *OTHER WORLDS.* $50

Strieber, Whitley. UNHOLY FIRE. Dutton, 1992. Advance reading copy. VF in dec wraps. *STAHR.* $25

Strieder, Peter. ALBRECHT DURER: PAINTINGS, PRINTS, DRAWINGS. Nancy M. Gordon, Walter L. Strauss (trans). NY: Abraris Books, (1982). Dj. Fine. *WEBER.* $85

Stringfellow, Thornton. SLAVERY: ITS ORIGIN, NATURE, AND HISTORY, CONSIDERED IN THE LIGHT OF BIBLE TEACHINGS, MORAL JUSTICE AND POLITICAL WISDOM. NY, 1861. 2nd ed. Orig cl, rubbed, else VG. *McGOWAN.* $275

Strohbach, G. QUACKS AND GRAFTERS BY EX-OSTEOPATH. Cincinnati, 1908. 1st ed. *FYE.* $45

Strommenger, Eva. 5000 YEARS OF THE ART OF MESOPOTAMIA. NY: Harry N. Abrams, (1964). 70 figs, 324 plts (44 color). Dj. Good. *ARCHAEOLOGIA.* $250

Strong, D.E. GREEK AND ROMAN GOLD AND SILVER PLATE. London: Methuen, (1966). 40 figs, 68 plts. Good in tattered dj. *ARCHAEOLOGIA*. $45

Strong, Donald and David Brown (eds). ROMAN CRAFTS. London: Duckworth, (1976). 18 color plts. Dj. Good. *ARCHAEOLOGIA*. $65

Strong, Donald. THE EARLY ETRUSCANS. NY: Putnam, 1968. 1st ed. VG. *WORLDWIDE*. $22

Strong, James Clark. BIOGRAPHICAL SKETCH OF JAMES CLARK STRONG. Los Gatos, Ca., 1910. 1st ed. Orig gilt stamped cl, presentation inscrip. Howes S 1080. *GINSBERG*. $300

Stroud, Robert. DISEASES OF CANARIES. Ed by Herbert Sanborn. Kansas City, MO, 1933. 1st ed. *DIAMOND*. $45

Strumpell, Adolf von. A TEXT-BOOK OF MEDICINE. NY, 1911. 2 vols. 4th Amer ed. *FYE*. $50

Struve, Otto & Velta Zebergs. ASTRONOMY OF THE 20TH CENTURY. NY: Macmillan, 1962. 1st prtg. VG in sl worn dj. *KNOLLWOOD*. $30

Stuart, Charles B. THE NAVAL DRY DOCKS OF THE UNITED STATES. NY, 1852. 1st ed. (41,126,94)pp. Orig folio full old tooled morocco. Howes S1095. *GINSBERG*. $750

Stuart, Granville. FORTY YEARS ON THE FRONTIER AS SEEN IN THE JOURNALS & REMINISCENCES OF GRANVILLE STUART. Glendale: A.H. Clark, 1957. 2nd ed. 2 vols. in 1. 9 plts. Fine. Incl 2 Charles M. Russell illus not in 1st ed. Prospectus leaf laid in. Howes S1096. *OREGON*. $125

Stuart, Granville. FORTY YEARS ON THE FRONTIER....A.H. Clark, 1925. 2 vols. 1st ed. Fine. Edges sl bumped, still bright, clean set. *VARNER*. $400

Stuart, Jesse. FORETASTE OF GLORY. NY, 1946. 1st ed. Inscribed, signed, dated. Fine in VG dj, nicked at spine ends. *McCLINTOCK*. $125

Stuart, Jesse. HEAD O' W-HOLLOW. NY, 1936. 1st ed. VG+ in dj which has chipping at its edges and front fold. *PETTLER*. $115

Stuart, Jesse. KENTUCKY WAS MY LAND. NY: Dutton, 1952. 1st ed. Owner's sig, address. NF in a like, lightly soiled dj. Contemp presentation inscrip. *CAPTAIN'S BOOKSHELF*. $100

Stuart, Jesse. MONGREL METTLE. Dutton, 1944. 1st ed. Illus. Dusty top edge but VG in dj with skinned patch, piece missing spine top, edge wear, split at flap fold. *BEBBAH*. $75

Stuart, Jesse. MONGREL METTLE. NY, 1944. 1st ed. Good in worn dj. *McCLINTOCK*. $25

Stuart, Jesse. SAVE EVERY LAMB. NY, Toronto & London, (1964). 1st ed. Fine in NF dj (lt shelfwear). Nice. *McCLINTOCK*. $25

Stuart, Jesse. SAVE EVERY LAMB. NY: McGraw-Hill, 1964. 1st ed. Fine in dj. *ELSE FINE*. $35

Stuart, Jesse. TAPS FOR PRIVATE TUSSIE. NY, 1943. 1st ed. VG in edge chipped dj which has internal clear tape repairs. *PETTLER*. $45

Stuart, Jesse. TAPS FOR PRIVATE TUSSIE. NY: Dutton, 1943. 1st ed, lib variant in reddish cl. VF in dj. Signed. *CAPTAIN'S BOOKSHELF*. $175

Stuart, Jesse. THE THREAD THAT RUNS SO TRUE. NY: Scribner's, (1959). Ltr. prtg. Inscribed. Orig grn cl. Fine in NF pict dj. *CHAPEL HILL*. $45

Stuart, Lady Louisa. NOTES BY...ON GEORGE SELWYN AND HIS CONTEMPORARIES BY JOHN HENEAGE JESSE. W.S. Lewis (ed). NY: Oxford Univ, 1928. 1st ed thus. One of 500 numbered. Uncut, unopened. Port. Fine. *SECOND LIFE*. $85

Stuart, Reginald. CALVIN B. WEST OF THE UMPQUA. Stockton, CA: History Foundation, 1956. 1st ed, ltd to 250. 3 plts. VF. *OREGON*. $50

Stuart, Ruth McEnery. AUNT AMITY'S SILVER WEDDING. NY, 1909. 1st ed. Orig cl. VG. *McGOWAN*. $37.50

Stuart, Ruth McEnery. DADDY DO-FUNNY'S WISDOM JINGLES. NY: The Century Co, 1913. 1st ed. Orig pict orange cl. Inscription, some soiling, but VG. *CHAPEL HILL*. $65

Stuart, Ruth McEnery. GEORGE WASHINGTON JONES. Phila: Henry Altemus Co, (1903). 1st ed. Orig dec blue cl. VG. *CHAPEL HILL*. $25

Stuart, Ruth McEnery. IN SIMKINSVILLE. NY & London: Harper & Bros. 1904. 1st ed. Orig pinkish brn cl stamped in silver. VG. *CHAPEL HILL*. $25.

Stuart, Ruth McEnery. NAPOLEAN JACKSON: THE GENTLEMAN OF THE PLUSH ROCKER. NY, 1916. 1st ed. Orig cl. VG. *McGOWAN*. $27.50

Stuart, Ruth McEnery. THE WOMAN'S EXCHANGE OF SIMPKINSVILLE. NY & London: Harper & Bros, (1893). 1st separate ed. Frontis, plt. Owner inscrip, few small spots corner of rear cvr, but bright, VG. *CHAPEL HILL*. $20

Stuart-Wortley, Lady Emmeline. TRAVELS IN THE UNITED STATES. NY: Harper & Brothers, 1851. 1st Amer. ed. 12mo, 463pp + 10pp pub. ads. Contemp. 3/4 leather & boards (worn). Little wear and repair to spine using matching cl. Some age-staining to contents, little fore-edge staining. Bkplt removed, o/w Good. *DIAMOND*. $75

Stubbings, Frank H. PREHISTORIC GREECE. NY: Day, 1973. 1st US ed. Dj. NF. *WORLDWIDE*. $16

Stuck, Hudson. VOYAGES ON THE YUKON AND ITS TRIBUTARIES. NY: Scribner's, 1917. 1st ed. Light soil. VG. *BLUE DRAGON*. $95

STUDIES ON EPIDEMIC INFLUENZA. Pittsburgh, 1919. 1st ed. 294pp + plts. *FYE*. $50

Sturge, Joseph. A VISIT TO THE UNITED STATES IN 1841. London, 1842. 1st ed. Orig cl, spine extremities chipped, else VG. *McGOWAN*. $165

Sturgeon, Theodore. A TOUCH OF STRANGE. GC: Doubleday, 1958. 1st ed. Fine, dj has the usual dust soiling. *ELSE FINE*. $80

Sturgeon, Theodore. MORE THAN HUMAN. Farrar, 1953. 1st ed. VG. *MADLE*. $40

Sturgeon, Theodore. MORE THAN HUMAN. Farrar, 1953. 1st ed. Fine in dj. *MADLE*. $325

Sturgeon, Theodore. THE DREAMING JEWELS. Greenberg, 1950. 1st ed. VG in chipped dj. *MADLE*. $30

Sturgeon, Theodore. THUNDER AND ROSES. London, 1957. 1st ed. VF in dj. *MADLE*. $50

Sturgeon, Theodore. WITHOUT SORCERY. (Phila): Prime Press, 1948. 1st ed, trade issue. Signed. Owner name, date else solid VG to VG+ in worn, sl chipped dj. *OTHER WORLDS*. $85

Sturgis, R. Clipston, Jr. BOOK-PLATES BY FREDERICK GARRISON HALL. Boston: The Troutsdale Press, 1905. Orig 1/4 parchment, boards w/paper cover label. Dust soiled, o/w VG. *WEBER*. $50

Sturt, Charles. JOURNAL OF THE CENTRAL AUSTRALIAN EXPEDITION 1844-1845. London: Calaban, 1984. 1st ed. New in similar dj. *PARMER*. $40

Stutler, Boyd B. GLORY, GLORY HALLELUJAH! THE STORY OF "JOHN BROWN'S BODY" AND "BATTLE HYMN OF THE REPUBLIC." Cincinnati, (1960). 1st ed. Plain plastic dj. Dj wear o/w Fine. *PRATT*. $45

Stylianou, A. & J. THE HISTORY OF THE CARTOGRAPHY OF CYRPUS. Nicosia, 1980. Fldg map. Dj. *O'NEILL*. $110

Styron, Arthur. THE LAST OF THE COCKED HATS. Norman: Univ of OK Press, 1945. Stated 1st ed. 12 plts. Dj. *SCHOYER'S*. $25

Styron, William. ADMIRAL ROBERT PENN WARREN AND THE SNOWS OF WINTER. Winston-Salem, NC: Palaemon Press, (1978). 1st ed. #39 of 250 numbered, signed. Orig lt blue wraps, with paper label. Fine. *CHAPEL HILL.* $75

Styron, William. AGAINST FEAR. Palaemon Press, (1981). Ltd ed, 300 only, signed. Printed wraps. Fine. *POLYANTHOS.* $65

Styron, William. AS HE LAY DEAD, A BITTER GRIEF. NY: Albondocani Press, 1981. 1st ed. #75 of 300 numbered, signed. Orig French marbled wraps, paper label. Fine. *CHAPEL HILL.* $75

Styron, William. BLANKENSHIP. (State College, PA): Press de la Warr, 1988. 1st ed. #81 of only 100 signed. Orig French marbled wraps, paper label. Fine. Colophon states "This limited signed edition of 'Blankenship' has been published for the friends of William Styron, Christmas 1988." *CHAPEL HILL.* $90

Styron, William. IN THE CLAP SHACK. NY: Random House, (1973). 1st ed. Orig cl-backed boards. Virtually As New in price-clipped dj. *CHAPEL HILL.* $55

Styron, William. IN THE CLAP SHACK. NY: Random House, (1973). 1st ed. Signed. Orig cl-backed boards. Fine in price-clipped dj. *CHAPEL HILL.* $75

Styron, William. IN THE CLAP SHACK. NY: Random House, (1973). 1st ed. Fine in Fine, price-slipped dj. Signed. *LOPEZ.* $100

Styron, William. LIE DOWN IN DARKNESS. Franklin Center: Franklin Library, 1982. Ltd ed. Fine in Franklin leather. Signed. *CAPTAIN'S BOOKSHELF.* $100

Styron, William. LIE DOWN IN DARKNESS. Indianapolis & NY: BobbsMerrill, (1951). 1st ed. Orig olive brn cl. Fine, bright in pict dj, modest wear. *CHAPEL HILL.* $175

Styron, William. LIE DOWN IN DARKNESS. Indianapolis: Bobbs Merrill (1951). 1st ed. Top edge sl sunned else Fine in Fine dj. *DORN.* $200

Styron, William. LIE DOWN IN DARKNESS. Indianapolis: Bobbs-Merrill, (1951). Fine in price-clipped dj showing minimal wear. Custom slipcase. 1st ed. Inscribed. *CHAPEL HILL.* $250

Styron, William. SET THIS HOUSE ON FIRE. NY: Random House (1960). 1st ed. Fine in NF dj. *DORN.* $60

Styron, William. SET THIS HOUSE ON FIRE. NY: Random House, 1960. 1st ed. Fine, minor rubs at dj corners. *ELSE FINE.* $65

Styron, William. SET THIS HOUSE ON FIRE. NY: Random House, (1960). 1st ed. Orig black cl. Rear hinge tender, else Fine in dj. Unusually bright, crisp. *CHAPEL HILL.* $50

Styron, William. SHADRACH. LA, CA: Sylvester & Orphanos, 1979. 1st ed. #203 of 300 numbered, signed. Orig beige cl stamped in black and gilt, leather spine label. Fine. *CHAPEL HILL.* $125

Styron, William. SOPHIE'S CHOICE. NY: Random House, (1979). 1st ed. Fine in dj. Signed. *CAPTAIN'S BOOKSHELF.* $100

Styron, William. SOPHIE'S CHOICE. NY: Random House, (1979). 1st trade ed. Inscribed. Fine in dj. *JUVELIS.* $60

Styron, William. SOPHIE'S CHOICE. NY: Random House, (1979). 1st ed. One of an unspecified number specially bound for presentation. Orig lt blue cl. Fine in tissue jacket, few short tears. *CHAPEL HILL.* $95

Styron, William. SOPHIE'S CHOICE. NY: Random House, (1979). 1st signed, ltd ed. One of 500 specially bound. Orig dk blue cl. Mint in pub's slipcase, orig plastic shrinkwrap. *CHAPEL HILL.* $250

Styron, William. SOPHIE'S CHOICE. NY: Random House, (1979). 1st trade ed. Orig burgundy cl. Fine in NF dj. Advance reading copy, slip laid in. *CHAPEL HILL.* $55

Styron, William. SOPHIE'S CHOICE. NY: Random House, (1979). 1st trade ed. Orig burgundy cl. Sl soiled, sm abrasion front panel, else NF in dj. *CHAPEL HILL.* $40

Styron, William. THE CONFESSIONS OF NAT TURNER. London: Jonathan Cape, (1968). 1st Eng ed. Orig brn boards. Owner sig, sm label under flap, else Fine in dj. *CHAPEL HILL.* $45

Styron, William. THE CONFESSIONS OF NAT TURNER. NY: Modern Library, (1970). 1st Modern Library ed. Fine in sl used dj w/tiny tears. *CAPTAIN'S BOOKSHELF.* $30

Styron, William. THE CONFESSIONS OF NAT TURNER. NY: Random House (1967). 1st ed. Fine in Fine dj, no fading. *DORN.* $50

Styron, William. THE CONFESSIONS OF NAT TURNER. NY: Random House, (1967). 1st ed. #234 of 500 specially bound, signed. Orig red cl. VG in pub's slipcase. *CHAPEL HILL.* $250

Styron, William. THE CONFESSIONS OF NAT TURNER. NY: Random House, (1967). 1st ed. One of unspecified number signed. Orig black cl. Fine in dj. *CHAPEL HILL.* $175

Styron, William. THE CONFESSIONS OF NAT TURNER. Pirated Taiwanese ed. Fine in NF dj. *DORN.* $65

Styron, William. THE LONG MARCH. NY: Random House/Modern Library, (1952). Correct 1st ed, a Modern Library pb. VG only in pict wraps. *CAPTAIN'S BOOKSHELF.* $75

Styron, William. THE MESSAGE OF AUSCHWITZ. (Blacksburg, VA): Press de la Warr, 1979. 1st ed. #167 of 200 numbered, signed. Orig unptd stiff wraps. Fine in NF dj. *CHAPEL HILL.* $95

Styron, William. THE MESSAGE OF AUSCHWITZ. Virginia: Press de la Warr, 1979. 1st separate ed. Ltd ed, 169/226 signed. Wraps, dj w/tiny crease lower spine. Fine. *POLYANTHOS.* $75

Styron, William. THIS QUIET DUST & OTHER WRITINGS. London: Cape, (1982). 1st Eng ed. VF in dj. *CAPTAIN'S BOOKSHELF.* $25

Styron, William. THIS QUIET DUST & OTHER WRITINGS. London: Cape, (1983). 1st Eng ed. Fine in dj. Signed. *LOPEZ.* $100

Styron, William. THIS QUIET DUST & OTHER WRITINGS. NY, 1982. 1st ed. Signed. Fine in like dj. *POLYANTHOS.* $30

Styron, William. THIS QUIET DUST & OTHER WRITINGS. NY: Random House, (1982). 1st ed. #131 of 250 specially bound, signed. Orig burgundy cl. As new in pub's slipcase w/paper label. *CHAPEL HILL.* $150

Styron, William. THIS QUIET DUST & OTHER WRITINGS. NY: Random House (1982). 1st ed. Fine in dj. *DORN.* $35

Sublett, Jesse. TOUGH BABY. NY: Viking, 1990. 1st ed. Review copy, signed. Promo material, photo laid in. VF in dj. *SILVER DOOR.* $35

Suckling, Sir John. THE POEMS. Ballantyne Press (for Vale Press), 1896. One of 300 for sale (310 total). Dk brn crushed levant morocco, marbled eps, teg, other edges untrimmed. Sm cracks at ends of joints, o/w minor soiling. VF internally. *PIRAGES.* $300

Suckow, Ruth. THE FOLKS. Farrar & Rinehart, (1934). 1st ltd ed of 175 two-vol sets, numbered, signed. Fine. *AUTHORS OF THE WEST.* $75

Sudsbury, Elretta. JACKRABBITS TO JETS. San Diego: Neyenesch, 1967. 1st ed. Fine. *CONNOLLY & WADE.* $65

Sue, Eugene. THE WANDERING JEW. London, 1844-45. 1st ed. Cl rebound. VG. *MADLE.* $350

Suetonius. THE LIVES OF THE TWELVE CAESARS. Rev, w/intro by Moses Hadas. Verona: Printed at the Stamperia Valdonega for The LEC, 1963. 1/1500 illus, signed by Salvatore Fiume and Giovanni Mardersteig. Fine in dj, slipcase. *CAPTAIN'S BOOKSHELF.* $200

SUFFOLK COUNTY, PORTRAIT AND BIOGRAPHICAL RECORD. NY, 1896. Teg. Gilt pict full lea boards. NF. *POLYANTHOS.* $125

Sugranes, Eugene. THE OLD SAN GABRIEL MISSION. San Gabriel, (1909). Wraps little edge worn. VG. *BOHLING.* $30

Sullivan, Dulcie. THE LS BRAND. THE STORY OF A TEXAS PANHANDLE RANCH. Austin: Univ of Texas Press, 1968. VG, dj. *BURCHAM.* $35

Sullivan, Edward. CHAPLIN VS. CHAPLIN. Hollywood, CA 1965. 1st ed. Pict wraps. Pg margins browning, o/w VG. *DIAMOND.* $25

Sullivan, Eleanor. WHODUNIT: A BIBLIO-BIO-ANECDOTAL MEMOIR OF FREDERIC DANNAY. "ELLERY QUEEN." NY: Targ Editions. 1984. Ed ltd to 150 signed. Fine. *KARMIOLE.* $100

Sullivan, Eleanor. WHODUNIT: A BIBLIO-BIO-ANECDOTAL MEMOIR OF FREDERIC DANNAY. NY: Targ Editions, 1984. 1st ed. Pub in ed of 150 signed by Sullivan and artist John Groth. VF in plain frosted dj. *MORDIDA.* $125

Sullivan, Frank S. A HISTORY OF MEADE COUNTY, KANSAS. Topeka, 1916. 1st ed. VG. *VARNER.* $45

Sullivan, John. LETTERS AND PAPERS OF MAJOR-GENERAL JOHN SULLIVAN CONTINENTAL ARMY. Otis G. Hammond (ed). Concord, NH, 1930-1939. 1st ed. 3 vols. Orig cl. New Hampshire Hist Soc Colls. V. 13-Vol. 1: 1771-1777; Vol. 2: 1778-1779; Vol. 3: 1779-1795. *GINSBERG.* $125

Sullivan, Louis H. KINDERGARTEN CHATS ON ARCHITEC-TURE, EDUCATION AND DEMOCRACY. Claude F. Bragdon (ed). NP: Scarab Fraternity Press, 1934. 1st ed. Fine in worn, rubbed dj. *CAPTAIN'S BOOKSHELF.* $275

Sullivan, Maurice. JEDEDIAH SMITH, TRADER AND TRAIL BREAKER. Press of the Pioneers, 1936. 1st ed. Frontis. VG in VG dj. *OREGON.* $150

Sullivan, Maurice. THE TRAVELS OF JEDEDIAH SMITH. A DOCUMENTARY OUTLINE INCLUDING THE JOURNAL OF THE GREAT AMERICAN PATHFINDER. Santa Ana: Fine Arts Press, 1934. 1st ed. Frontis, 12 plts (fldg map). Orig pict cl, gilt stamped spine. VG. Howes S1127. *OREGON.* $450

Sullivan, May Kellogg. A WOMAN WHO WENT TO ALASKA. Boston, (1915). Pict cl. Minor stain at edges of first few pages. Good, sound. *ARTIS.* $24.50

Sullivan, Walter. QUEST FOR A CONTINENT. NY: McGraw-Hill, 1957. 1st Amer ed. VG (bumped bottom edge, worn dj). *PARMER.* $35

Sullivant, W.S. ICONES MUSCORUM...AND SUPPLEMENT. 210 copper-engr plts. Cambridge, MA, & London, 1864; 1874. 2 vols. 19th cent cl rebacked, retaining orig backstrip; eps renewed. *SUTTON.* $1,150.

Sully, Langdon. NO TEARS FOR THE GENERAL, THE LIFE OF ALFRED SULLY, 1821-1879. Palo Alto, (1974). 1st ed. Fine in dj. *PRATT.* $25

Sully, Langdon. NO TEARS FOR THE GENERAL. Palo Alto: Amer West, 1974. 1st ed. Fine in Fine dj. *CONNOLLY & WADE.* $37.50

Summers, Hollis. SIT OPPOSITE EACH OTHER. New Brunswick, NJ: Rutgers Univ Press, (1970). 1st ed. Signed. Orig grn cl. Fine in NF dj. *CHAPEL HILL.* $25

Summers, Hollis. THE WEATHER OF FEBRUARY. NY: Harper & Bros. (1957). 1st ed. Inscribed. Orig cl-backed grn boards. NF in VG dj. *CHAPEL HILL.* $30

Summers, James. WHO WON? THE OFFICIAL AMERICAN YACHT RECORD FOR 1893. NY: "Who Won?" Pub Co., 1898. Fldg plt, tables, charts, color plts. Stains. Internally Fine. *HUDSON.* $150

Summers, Montague (ed). THE SUPERNATURAL OMNIBUS. GC: Doubleday, 1932. 1st US ed. Fine in NF, internally reinforced dj. Contents differ from UK edition. *BEASLEY.* $45

Summers, Montague. THE GEOGRAPHY OF WITCHCRAFT. NY: Knopf, 1927. 1st US ed. NF. *BEASLEY.* $65

Summers, Montague. THE VAMPIRE IN EUROPE. Dutton, 1929. 1st US ed. VG. *MADLE.* $50

Summerson, John. JOHN NASH. ARCHITECT TO KING GEORGE IV. London: George Allen & Unwin Ltd. (1935). 1st ed. Fldg map. Dj sl chipped, soiled. *KARMIOLE.* $30

Sumner, Charles. SPEECH OF HON. CHARLES SUMNER, OF MASSACHUSETTS, ON THE CESSION OF RUSSIAN AMERICAN TO THE UNITED STATES. Wash., 1867. 1st ed. 48pp. Fldg litho map, partly colored. Orig ptd wrappers. The map, first to use the name "Alaskan," is usually wanting. It has a minor 1 1/4" tear. Howes S1134. *GINSBERG.* $1500

Sumner, Charles. WHITE SLAVERY IN THE BARBARY STATES. Boston: Jewett, 1853. 1st ed. Cl chipped at extrems of spine, o/w VG *SECOND LIFE.* $40

Sumner, Charles. WHITE SLAVERY IN THE BARBARY STATES. Boston: Jewett; Cleveland: Jewett, Proctor & Worthington; London: Low, 1853. 1st ed. 135 pp. 37 engrs in text. Orig cl, rubbed and worn, edges frayed, sl smudged and spotted. Ex-lib, o/w Good. *WORLDWIDE.* $95

Sumner, Lowell and Joseph Dixon. BIRDS AND MAMMALS OF THE SIERRA NEVADA. Univ Calif, 1953. 1st ed. 2 fldg maps. Fine in VG dj. *OREGON.* $100

Sunder, John E. BILL SUBLETTE, MOUNTAIN MAN. Norman: Univ of OK, (1959). 1st ed. VF in VF dj. *OREGON.* $50

Sunder, John E. BILL SUBLETTE, MOUNTAIN MAN. Univ of OK Press, 1959. 1st ed. Fine in Fine dj. Scarce. *VARNER.* $50

Sunder, John E. THE FUR TRADE ON THE UPPER MISSISSIP-PI, 1840-1865. Norman: Univ of OK Press, (1965). 1st ed. Cl, dj. Fine. *SCHOYER'S.* $35

Sunder, John E. THE FUR TRADE ON THE UPPER MISSOURI: 1840-1865. Norman: Univ of OK, (1965). 1st ed. Fine in Fine dj. *OREGON.* $45

Sunter, G.H. ADVENTURES OF A TREPANG FISHER. London: Hurst & Blackett, 1937. Illus. VG. *MIKESH.* $55

Supf, Peter. AIRMAN'S WORLD. NY: Wm. Morrow. 1933. Dj (top edge sl chipped). *KARMIOLE.* $30

Supree, Burton. BEAR'S HEART. Phila: Lippincott, (1977). 1st ed. NF in edgeworn dj. *LOPEZ.* $60

Surface, Frank M. THE GRAIN TRADE DURING THE WORLD WAR. NY: Macmillan, 1928. Fold out forms. Pocket of forms in back. Cl. VG in chipped dj. *BURCHAM.* $45

Surtees, R.S. HANDLEY CROSS. London: Bradbury, Agnew, & Co, n.d. viii, 550pp. Illus John Leech. Hand colored frontis and plts. Orig gilt pict red cl. Unusually Fine, bright. *WREDEN.* $160

Surtees, R.S. HANDLEY-CROSS OR MR. JORRICK'S HUNT. London: Edward Arnold, n.d. (18-?). 2 vols. Probable 1st ed. Minor marks and shelfwear, thus VG-NF. *OLD LONDON.* $150

Surtees, R.S. MR. SPONGE'S SPORTING TOUR. London: Bradbury, Agnew, & Co, n.d. Illus John Leech. Hand colored frontis and plts. Orig gilt pict red cl. Cvrs sl soiled, some creasing affecting a few plts, o/w Fine. *WREDEN.* $120

Surtees, R.S. PLAIN OR RINGLETS. London: Bradbury, Agnew & Co., n.d.(1884?). Reprint. Bright with only minor edgewear. VG-NF. *OLD LONDON.* $50

Surtees, R.S. THE NOVELS OF R.S. SURTEES. John Leech (illus). London & NY: Eyre & Spottiswoode & Charles Scribner's Sons, 1929. 10 vols. Ltd to 976 numbered sets. Orig red cl w/paper labels on spines, tissue djs, individual red cardboard slipcases w/ptd labels. Fine set in djs & slipcases. *JAFFE.* $750

Susanne (pseud of E.E. Scharf). FAMOUS SADDLE HORSES. Louisville, KY, 1932. 1st ed. VG. *BOND.* $65

Suskind, Patrick. PERFUME: THE STORY OF A MURDERER. NY: Knopf, 1986. 1st US ed. New in dj. *BERNARD.* $45

Sutcliffe, Halliwell. THE STRIDING DALES. London and NY: Warne, 1929. 1st ed. Some edgewear, generally tight, thus VG. *OLD LONDON*. $95

Sutherland, Scott. BLOOD IN THEIR INK: THE MARCH OF THE MODERN MYSTERY NOVEL. London: Stanley Paul, 1953. 1st ed. Fine in dj. *MORDIDA*. $50

Sutter, J.A. NEW HELVETIA DIARY, A RECORD OF EVENTS KEPT BY JOHN A SUTTER...FROM SEPTEMBER 9, 1845, TO MAY 25, 1848. SF: Grabhorn, 1939. Ltd ed of 950. Cl backed paper over boards. Charles Cushing (preface), H. B. Van Sicklen (intro). Howes S1155. *GINSBERG*. $175

Sutter, J.A. NEW HELVETIA DIARY. SF: Grabhorn Press in arrangement with The Soc of CA Pioneers, 1939. Ltd ed of 950. Color frontis. Fine. *WEBER*. $155

Sutter, J.A. THE DIARY OF JOHANN AUGUST SUTTER. SF: Grabhorn Press, 1932. Ltd ed. Fldg plt. VG. *WEBER*. $50

Sutter, Johann. THE DIARY OF JOHANN AUGUST SUTTER. SF: Grabhorn Press, 1932. Fldg color plate. Spine ends somewhat chipped, spine label chipped with loss of 'August Sutter' o/w VG. Publication notice laid in. *OREGON*. $65

Sutton, Ernest V. A LIFE WORTH LIVING. Pasadena: Trail's End, 1948. 1st ed, ltd to 2000. Presentation, signed and dated. First blank page opened roughly. Light edgewear, else Fine. Scarce. *CONNOLLY & WADE*. $60

Sutton, George Miksch. AT THE BEND IN A MEXICAN RIVER. NY: Paul Eriksson, (1972). 1st ed. 12 color plts. *SILVER*. $30

Sutton, Richard L. AN ARCTIC SAFARI. St. Louis: The C.V. Mosby Co. 1932. 1st ed. Inscribed. Blue cl, faded. Lib # (faded) on spine; removed bkpl. *KARMIOLE*. $50

Sutton, Richard L. and Richard L. Sutton, Jr. THE LONG TREK. St. Louis: The C.V. Mosby Co. 1930. 1st ed. 348pp. Inscribed by Richard L. Sutton, Jr. in 1975. *KARMIOLE*. $75

Sutton, Richard L. TIGER TRAILS IN SOUTHERN ASIA. St. Louis: The C.V. Mosby Co. 1926. 1st ed. Red gilt cloth. *KARMIOLE*. $60

Sverdrup, Otto. SVERDRUP'S ARCTIC ADVENTURES. London: Longmans, (1959). VG in VG- dj. *BLUE DRAGON*. $27.50

Svevo, Italo. CONFESSIONS OF ZENO. London: Putnam, 1930. 1st ed, 1st cheap ed. Sl foxing and offsetting, else VG+ in marbled cl boards and spine tanned VG+ dj w/small water spot to center of front panel. *LAME DUCK*. $85

Swainson, W. ON THE NATURAL HISTORY & CLASSIFICATION OF QUADRUPEDS. London: Longman, Rees, 1835. 397pp. Recased w/orig backstrip (minor chipping), external joint reinforced. Good. *BOOKCELL*. $45

Swainson, W. THE CABINET OF NATURAL HISTORY CONDUCTED BY THE REV. D. LARDNER, ETC. London: Longman, Orme, etc., 1840. 1st ed. VG+. *MIKESH*. $100

Swainson, W. THE NATURAL HISTORY OF FISHES, AMPHIBIANS, AND REPTILES. London, 1838-39. 2 vols. pp vi,368,ads; vi,452,ads. Orig cl w/paper labels. Very worn, some cover spotting, 1 cover loose, covers reattached on vol 2, pieces of backstrips missing, pp browned, ex-lib. *SUTTON*. $95

Swallow, Alan (ed). ANCHOR IN THE SEA: AN ANTHOLOGY OF PSYCHOLOGICAL FICTION. Swallow, 1947. 1st ed. Fine, name. *AUTHORS OF THE WEST*. $20

Swallow, Alan. XI POEMS. The Prairie Press, 1943. Softbound pamphlet, very nicely designed and ptd, signed. Fine. *AUTHORS OF THE WEST*. $35

Swallow, George Clinton. GEOLOGICAL REPORT...ALONG THE LINE OF THE SOUTH-WESTERN BRANCH...STATE OF MISSOURI. St. Louis: George Knapp & Co, 1859. 93pp, errata, 2 plts,

fldg color map. Orig cl (faded). Paper a little darkened & w/offsetting from 1st plt. VG. *BOHLING*. $225

Swan, Charles. JOURNAL OF A VOYAGE UP THE MEDITERRANEAN; PRINCIPALLY AMONG THE ISLANDS OF THE ARCHIPELAGO....London, 1826. 2 vols. Modern 1/4 calf. xv,366pp; 423pp. Uncut. *O'NEILL*. $450

Swan, Howard. MUSIC IN THE SOUTHWEST 1825-1950. San Marino: Huntington Library, 1952. 1st ed. Gilt worn on spine, else Fine. *CONNOLLY & WADE*. $35

Swan, James G. THE NORTHWEST COAST; OR, THREE YEARS RESIDENCE IN WASHINGTON TERRITORY. NY, 1857. 1st ed. (15),(4)pp. Map, plts. Orig cl. Howes S1164. *GINSBERG*. $175

Swan, Joseph. A DEMONSTRATION OF THE NERVES OF THE HUMAN BODY. London, 1834. 1st quarto ed. 4to, 1/2 leather, rebacked. 98, 83pp + 25 plts. New eps. *FYE*. $500

Swan, Oliver G. (ed.) FRONTIER DAYS. NY: Grosset & Dunlap, 1928. Pict eps, colored frontis. Tan cl, colored pict inset on cover. About Fine. *CONNOLLY & WADE*. $35

Swanberg, W.A. FIRST BLOOD, THE STORY OF FORT SUMTER. NY, (1957). 1st ed. VG+ in dj. *PRATT*. $20

Swanberg, W.A. FIRST BLOOD. THE STORY OF FORT SUMTER. Scribner's, (1957). 1st ed. Special ed, signed 1st ptg. VF in VF dj. *OREGON*. $30

Swanberg, W.A. SICKLES THE INCREDIBLE. NY, 1956. 1st ed. 433pp. Minor chipping, o/w VG in dj. *PRATT*. $50

Swann, Peter C. CHINESE PAINTING. NY, 1958. NF. *POLYANTHOS*. $50

Swanton, E.W. A HISTORY OF CRICKET. Vol II. London: George Allen & Unwin, 1962. 1st ed thus. Fine in VG dj. *OLD LONDON*. $25

Swanton, John. INDIAN TRIBES OF THE LOWER MISSISSIPPI VALLEY AND ADJACENT COAST OF GULF OF MEXICO. BAE Bull 43. 1911. 1st ed. Frontis-fldg map, 31 plts. Rubber stamp number on ep, title page; o/w VG. *OREGON*. $45

Swanton, John. TLINGET MYTHS AND TEXTS. Wash, DC: GPO, 1909. 1st ed. BAE Bull 39. Orig cl. VF in orig mailing wrapper. *CONNOLLY & WADE*. $125

Swarth, Harry S. BIRDS AND MAMMALS OF THE 1909 ALEXANDER ALASKA EXPEDITION. Berkeley: Univ of CA, 1911. Light wear to wraps. Signed. *PARMER*. $75

Swedenborg, E. SOME SPECIMENS OF A WORK ON THE PRINCIPLES OF CHEMISTRY. London: Newbery, 1847. xlii,253pp. 20 plts. Minor wear rear external joint o/w VG. *BOOKCELL*. $125

Sweeney, Z.T. BIENNIAL REPORT OF THE COMMISSIONER OF FISHERIES AND GAME FOR INDIANA. Indianapolis, 1908. Good. *ARTIS*. $39.50

Sweeney, Z.T. UNDER TEN FLAGS. AN HISTORICAL PILGRIMAGE. Cincinnati, 1889. Half calf, rubbed. xvi,508pp. Pres. *O'NEILL*. $45

Sweet, A.E. and J. Armoy Knox. ON A MEXICAN MUSTANG THROUGH TEXAS, FROM THE GULF TO THE RIO GRANDE. London: Chatto & Windus, 1884. 1st ed. 265 drwg, engrs. Bound in full cl, skillfully rebacked and restored. Slight wear to extremities, o/w VG. *LAURIE*. $100

Sweet, A.E. and J. Armoy Knox. ON A MEXICAN MUSTANG, THROUGH TEXAS, FROM THE GULF TO THE RIO GRANDE. Hartford: S.S. Scranton & Co, 1883. 1st ed. Reinforced w/new eps. Clean, tight. *LAURIE*. $75

Sweet, A.E. and J. Armoy Knox. ON A MEXICAN MUSTANG, THROUGH TEXAS....Hartford: S.S. Scranton, 1883. 1st ed, 1st state w/"000" on chapter headings on pp 10-14 of Contents. 672pp. Ex-lib in orig red pict cl. VG. *SCHOYER'S*. $80

Sweet, A.E. and J. Armoy Knox. ON A MEXICAN MUSTANG THROUGH TEXAS, FROM THE GULF TO THE RIO GRANDE. Hartford, CT, 1883. 672pp. Rebound new buckram. *HEINOLDT.* $20

Sweet, A.E. and J. Armoy Knox. SKETCHES FROM "TEXAS SIFTINGS." NY: Texas Sifting Pub Co, 1882. 1st ed. Bright pict cl. VG. *SCHOYER'S.* $80

Sweetman, Luke. BACK TRAILING ON OPEN RANGE. Caldwell: Caxton, 1951. 1st ed. 18 full pp illus. Pict cloth. VF in VG dj. *OREGON.* $60

Swem, E.G. BROTHERS OF THE SPADE....Amer Antiquarian Soc, rptd from the Proceedings for April, 1948. 2 plts w/marginal dampstaining not affecting ports. 1 map. Buckram. Lt pp yellowing. Inscribed. *SUTTON.* $275

Swift, Frank and Marvin R. Clark. THE SKATERS TEXT BOOK. NY: John A. Gray & Green, Printers, (1868). 1st and only ed. 115pp, 2 ads. Cl bumped, soiled, pp sl soiled, few pp corners creases, lacks 1 ad leaf. VG. Scarce. *BLUE MOUNTAIN.* $150

Swift, Graham. EVER AFTER. NY: Knopf, 1992. Uncorrected proof. Fine in wrappers. *LOPEZ.* $35

Swift, Graham. OUT OF THIS WORLD. NY, (1988). 1st ed. Signed. Fine in like dj. *POLYANTHOS.* $30

Swift, Graham. OUT OF THIS WORLD. NY: Poseidon, (1988). 1st Amer ed. Fine in dj. *LOPEZ.* $20

Swift, Hildegarde Hoyt. NORTH STAR SHINING. NY: Morrow, 1947. Drwgs by Lynd Ward. 1st ed. Cl. Full color painting by Ward on paper title label on cover. VF in VG dj. *CONNOLLY & WADE.* $125

Swift, Jonathan. GULLIVER'S TRAVELS. Rand McNally, 1939. Windemere Series. 344pp. 5 color plts by Milo Winter. Fine w/color pict pastedown in VG+ dj (short closed tear, minor chips at spine ends, spot of soil to rear panel). *BEBBAH.* $65

Swift, Lindsay. BROOK FARM. ITS MEMBERS, SCHOLARS, AND VISITORS. NY: Macmillan, 1900. 1st ed. Bkpl, a few minor spots, o/w NF. *BEASLEY.* $100

Swift, Louis F. THE YANKEE OF THE YARDS. Chicago: Shaw, 1927. 13 plts. *SCHOYER'S.* $30

Swiggert, Howard. MARCH OR DIE. NY: Putnam, 1953. Dj torn, covers sl silverfished, o/w VG. *WORLDWIDE.* $18

Swiggett, Capt S. A. THE BRIGHT SIDE OF PRISON LIFE. Baltimore, (1897). 254pp. Orig cl. *GINSBERG.* $75

Swinburne, Algernon Charles. A CENTURY OF ROUNDELS AND OTHER POEMS. NY: R. Worthington, 1883. VG. 1st Amer ed. *CHAPEL HILL.* $50

Swinburne, Algernon Charles. A STUDY OF BEN JONSON. NY: Worthington, 1889. 1st Amer ed. 181pp. Bkpl. Excellent. *HARTFIELD.* $45

Swinburne, Algernon Charles. BOTHWELL: A TRAGEDY. London: Chatto and Windus, 1874. 1st ed. 3/4 black lea and blue cl. Rebound w/o the ads; occas foxing. NF. *BLUE MOUNTAIN.* $135

Swinburne, Algernon Charles. LOVE'S CROSS CURRENTS. NY and London: Harper, 1905. 1st this ed. *HARTFIELD.* $85

Swinburne, Algernon Charles. SELECTED POEMS OF CHARLES ALGERNON SWINBURNE. London & NY, 1928. 1st ed. Amer issue. Illus by Harry Clarke. Gold and black binding quite bright. Fine. *McCLINTOCK.* $125

Swinburne, Algernon Charles. THE SPRINGTIDE OF LIFE. London: William Heinemann, (1918). 1st trade ed. Green cl rubbed, bumped. 8 color plts by Arthur Rackham. VG. *BLUE MOUNTAIN.* $150

Swinburne, Algernon Charles. WILLIAM BLAKE. A CRITICAL ESSAY. London: John Camden, 1868. iv,304,ads. 16pp Illus. Blue gilt-lined cl; spine and corners sl rubbed, inner hinges cracked. Bkpl of Estelle Doheny. *WEBER.* $700

Swinfen, David B. RUGGLES' REGIMENT. Hanover, NH, (1982). 1st ed. Fine in dj. *PRATT.* $30

Swinton, William. CAMPAIGNS OF THE ARMY OF THE POTOMAC. NY, 1866. 1st ed. 640pp, illus, maps, index. A little cvr fading and soiling o/w VG. *PRATT.* $75

Sword, Wiley. SHILOH, BLOODY APRIL. NY, (1974). 1st ed. VG+ in dj. *PRATT.* $45

Sydenham, Thomas. THE WORKS OF THOMAS SYDENHAM, M.D. WITH A LIFE OF THE AUTHOR BY R.G. LATHAM. London, 1848-1850. 1st ed. 2 vols. Recent buckram, 276, 394pp. *FYE.* $200

Sykes, Ella C. PERSIA AND ITS PEOPLE. NY: Macmillan, 1910. 1st ed. 20 plts, 1 fldg map. Orig gilt cl, edges rubbed, spine sl frayed, eps foxed, o/w VG. *WORLDWIDE.* $55

Sykes, Ella C. THROUGH PERSIA ON A SIDE-SADDLE. Phila: Lippincott, 1898. 1st ed. 29 (of 32) plts, fldg map. Ex-lib. Good. *WORLDWIDE.* $35

Sykes, Godfrey. A WESTERLY TREND...BEING A VERACIOUS CHRONICLE....Tucson: Arizona Pioneers Hist Soc, 1944. Adv rev copy. Tan textured stiff wraps. VF. *CONNOLLY & WADE.* $50

Sykes, Godfrey. A WESTERLY TREND. Tucson: Pioneer's Hist Soc, 1944. 1st ed. 1/2000. 325pp. Orange cloth. NF in lightly chipped dj. *FIVE QUAIL.* $35

Sykes, Godfrey. THE COLORADO DELTA. Amer Geog Soc Special Pub No 19. Spine a bit sunburned, light cover soil, else VG+. *FIVE QUAIL.* $65

Sykes, Godfrey. THE COLORADO DELTA. Carnegie Institute of Washington and Amer Geogr Soc of NY, 1937. 1st ed. Carnegie Institute Pub No. 460. Colored, fldg map at rear. Grn cl, gilt. VF. *CONNOLLY & WADE.* $95

Sykes, Major Percy Molesworth. TEN THOUSAND MILES IN PERSIA OR EIGHT YEARS IN IRAN. London, 1902. Lib buckram, call numbers on spine, thumb soil. xv,481pp. *O'NEILL.* $75

Sykes, Percy Molesworth. TEN THOUSAND MILES IN PERSIA; OR, EIGHT YEARS IN IRAN. London: Murray, 1902. 1st ed. Fldg map. Cl sl rubbed and soiled. Ex-lib, o/w VG. *WORLDWIDE.* $145

Sylvia, Stephen W. and Michael J. O'Donnell. CIVIL WAR CANTEENS. Orange, VA, 1983. 1st ed. Wraps. VG+. *PRATT.* $27.50

Syme, James. OBSERVATIONS IN CLINICAL SURGERY. Edinburgh, 1862. 2nd ed. 217pp. Scarce. *FYE.* $250

Syme, James. PRINCIPLES OF SURGERY. Edinburgh, 1842. 3rd ed. 508pp. Lithographs. Orig cloth, rebacked. Fine. *FYE.* $250

Symonds, John Addington. MANY MOODS: A VOLUME OF VERSE. London: Smith, Elder, 1878. 1st ed. Fine. *MUELLER.* $37.50

Symonds, R.W. ENGLISH FURNITURE FROM CHARLES II TO GEORGE II. London: Bemrose & Sons Ltd, 1929. #637/1000. Front cvr, spine water damaged, not affecting contents. *BACKROOM.* $160

Symonds, R.W. ENGLISH FURNITURE FROM CHARLES II TO GEORGE II. London: The Connoisseur, 1929. 1st ed. Ltd to 1,000. Lightly dampstained; bumped, rubbed. VG. *BLUE MOUNTAIN.* $285

Symonds, R.W. THOMAS TOMPION: HIS LIFE AND WORK. NY: Spring Books, 1969. 2nd ed. VG in VG dj. *BACKROOM.* $80

Symons, A.J.A. THE QUEST FOR CORVO. London, 1934. 1st ed. Fine in VG dj. *POLYANTHOS.* $100

Symons, Arthur. JEZEBEL MORT AND OTHER POEMS. London: William Heinemann, (1951). 1st ed. Edges bit foxed, else Fine in foxed dj. *WREDEN.* $65

Symons, Arthur. NOTES ON JOSEPH CONRAD. London: Myers, 1925. Boards, scarce dj (defective). Few hinges cracked. *MUELLER.* $30

Symons, Arthur. THE FOOL OF THE WORLD AND OTHER POEMS. London, 1906. 1st ed. Bkpl, spine little creased, few tiny white spots; uncut. Fine. *POLYANTHOS*. $35

Symons, Julian. BLOODY MURDER. London: Viking, 1985. 1st prtg of author's rev ed. Fine in dj. *SILVER DOOR*. $35

Symons, Julian. THE MAN WHOSE DREAMS CAME TRUE. London: Collins, 1968. 1st ed. Fine in dj. *SILVER DOOR*. $25

Symons, Julian. THE MODERN CRIME STORY. Helsinki: Eurographica, 1986. 1st of this ed. Ltd to 350 signed. Ptd wrappers. Mint. *JAFFE*. $125

Symons, Julian. THE NAME OF ANNABEL LEE. London: Macmillan, 1983. 1st ed. VF in dj. *MORDIDA*. $35

Symons, Julian. THE PLOT AGAINST ROGER RIDER. London: Collins Crime Club, 1973. 1st ed. Fine in Fine dj. *BEASLEY*. $35

Symons, Thomas W. REPORT OF AN EXAMINATION OF THE UPPER COLUMBIA RIVER...IN SEPTEMBER AND OC-TOBER, 1881, TO DETERMINE...ADAPTABILITY TO STEAMBOAT TRANSPORTATION. Washington: GPO, 1882. Detailed maps. J.P. Lesley's copy. VG. *LAURIE*. $100

Synge, J.M. RIDERS TO THE SEA. Boston, 1911. 1st ed. NF. *POLYANTHOS*. $30

Synge, J.M. THE ARAN ISLANDS. Boston: John W. Luce & Company, 1911. 1st Amer ed. Jack B. Yeats (illus). Parchment-backed dec boards. Faint offsetting, spine label nicked, o/w Fine. *JAFFE*. $75

Synge, J.M. THE SHADOW OF THE GLEN AND RIDERS TO THE SEA. London: Elkin Mathews, 1905. 1st Eng ed. Fine in dec grn wrappers. Custom fldg cl slipcase. *CAPTAIN'S BOOKSHELF*. $350

SYRIA AND ASIA MINOR. (By Josiah Conder.) London: For James Duncan, 1824. 2 vols. 3/4 lea, a little rubbed. 2 fldg maps, 6 plts. Bkpls. *SCHOYER'S*. $75

Szalet, Leon. EXPERIMENT "E": A REPORT FROM AN EXTER-MINATION LABORATORY. NY, 1945. NF. *POLYANTHOS*. $30

Szasz, Kathleen. PETISHISM: PET CULTS OF THE WESTERN WORLD. London: Hutchinson, (1968). 1st ed. Dj price clipped. *AKA*. $20

Szebenyei, Joseph. REPORTERS, KINGS AND OTHER VAGABONDS. Caldwell, ID: Caxton, 1951. 1st ed. *HEINOLDT*. $10

T

Tabeau, Pierre. TABEAU'S NARRATIVE OF LOISEL'S EXPEDI-TION TO THE UPPER MISSOURI. Annie Heloise Abel (ed). Norman: Univ of OK, 1939. 1st ed. Fldg chart. VF in VG dj. *OREGON*. $65

Taber, Gladys. ONE DOZEN AND ONE. Lippincott, (1966). 1st ed. VG in VG dj. *BEBBAH*. $30

Taber, Gladys. THE EVERGREEN TREE. Phila, 1937. 1st ed. Lib rebound. VG. *NUTMEG*. $22.50

Taber, M.J. THE CATHEDRALS OF ENGLAND. Boston: L.C. Page, 1905. 1st Amer ed. VG. *WEBER*. $45

Tabor, G. THE LANDSCAPE GARDENING BOOK....NY, 1916. Rev ed. Cl. *SUTTON*. $35

Tabouis, G.R. THE PRIVATE LIFE OF TUTANKHAMEN. NY: McBride, 1929. 1st ed. Sl rubbed, spine faded, o/w VG. *WORLDWIDE*. $28

Taft, L.R. GREENHOUSE CONSTRUCTION, A COMPLETE MANUAL. NY: Orange Judd, 1926. Cloth marked w/dents on front. *AMERICAN BOTANIST*. $20

Taggard, Genevieve (ed). CIRCUMFERENCE: VARIETIES OF METAPHYSICAL VERSE, 1456-1928. 1st ltd ed of 1,050 num-

bered, signed. Fancy boards, vellum backstrip. Fine in dj, bkpls. *AUTHORS OF THE WEST*. $40

Taggard, Genevieve. TRAVELLING STANDING STILL: POEMS, 1918-1928. Knopf, 1928. 1st ed. Fine. *AUTHORS OF THE WEST*. $25

Taine, John. GREEN FIRE. Dutton, 1928. 1st ed. Near VG. *MADLE*. $40

Taine, John. QUAYLE'S INVENTION. Dutton, 1927. 1st ed. Near VG. *MADLE*. $40

Taine, John. SEEDS OF LIFE. Reading: Fantasy Press, 1951. 1st ed. Owner's inscrip, o/w Fine in Fine dj but for a few tears. *BEASLEY*. $35

Talbot, Clare Ryan. HISTORIC CALIFORNIA BOOKPLATES. LA: Graphic Press, 1936. 1st ed. 1/4 cl and paper boards. Spine label chipped, o/w NF. *LAURIE*. $75

Talbot, Clare Ryan. HISTORIC CALIFORNIA IN BOOKPLATES. LA: Graphic Press, 1936. 1st ed. Unopened. VG. *WEBER*. $100

Talbot, Theodore. THE JOURNALS OF THEODORE TALBOT 1843 AND 1849-1852. Portland, 1931. Charles H. Carey (ed). 1st ed. VG. *OREGON*. $75

Talbot, Theodore. THE JOURNALS OF THEODORE TAL-BOT...WITH THE FREMONT EXPEDITION...Portland, Oregon, 1931. 1st ed. Orig cl. Howes T13. *GINSBERG*. $125

Talboys, W.P. WEST INDIA PICKLES. NY: Carleton, 1876. 1st ed. 16mo, 209pp. Sl cover wear, fly detached, o/w Good. *DIAMOND*. $25

Talcott, Dudley Vaill. REPORT OF THE COMPANY. NY: Harrison Smith and Robert Haas, 1936. 1st ptg. Dj worn, chipped; offsetting to eps; mild foxing, else VG. *PARMER*. $65

Tallent, Annie D. THE BLACK HILLS: OR, THE LAST HUNT-ING GROUND OF THE DAKOTAHS...St.Louis: Nixon-Jones, 1899. 1st ed. Minor shelfwear & cvr staining. Recased, new eps. Plate facing p.1 replaced by facs copy. One page margin repaired; 1 page margin torn, not affecting letterpress, o/w VG. Howes T214. *DIAMOND*. $125

Tallent, Elizabeth. IN CONSTANT FLIGHT. NY: Knopf, 1983. 1st ed. Signed. Fine in NF, price-clipped dj. *LOPEZ*. $45

Tallmadge, Benjamin. MEMOIR OF COLONEL BENJAMIN TALLMADGE. NY: Gilliss, 1904. Orig vellum backed boards. Pub of Soc of the Sons of the Revolution in the State of NY: Vol 1. One of 350. Reprint of rare 1858 orig ed. Howes T17. *GINSBERG*. $150

Tan, Amy. THE JOY LUCK CLUB. NY: Putnam, (1989). 1st ed, 1st bk. Fine in dj w/tiny tear. *CAPTAIN'S BOOKSHELF*. $200

Tan, Amy. THE JOY LUCK CLUB. NY: Putnam, 1989. 1st ed. NF in price clipped dj. *ELSE FINE*. $90

Tan, Amy. THE JOY LUCK CLUB. Putnam, 1989. 1st ed. Fine in dj. One short, closed tear on rear panel. 1st novel. *STAHR*. $100

Tan, Amy. THE KITCHEN GOD'S WIFE. NY: Putnam, (1991). 1st ed. As New in dj. Signed. *CAPTAIN'S BOOKSHELF*. $50

Tan, Amy. THE KITCHEN GOD'S WIFE. NY: Putnam, (1991). 1st ed. Signed. VF in VF dj. *UNGER*. $50

Tan, Amy. THE KITCHEN GOD'S WIFE. Putnam, 1991. Advance reading copy. Fine in blue dec wraps. *STAHR*. $45

Tan, Amy. THE KITCHEN GOD'S WIFE. Putnam, 1991. Uncor-rected proof. Fine in red wraps. Not the more common advanced reading copy in blue dec wraps. *STAHR*. $100

Tannehill, Ivan Ray. HURRICANES. Princeton Univ Press, 1938. VG in grey cl, bright gilt titling. *KNOLLWOOD*. $38

Tannen, Mary. EASY KEEPER. Farrar Straus Grioux, 1991. Uncor-rected proof. VG or better in wraps. Cover crease *STAHR*. $15

Tanner, Henry Schenk. THE CENTRAL TRAVELLER, OR TOURIST'S GUIDE THROUGH THE STATES....NY: T.R. Tan-ner, 1844. 2nd ed. Fldg maps. Rear hinge worn, lacks fep. Few maps frayed, else Superior. *HUDSON*. $295

Tanner, Mary J. A BOOK OF FUGITIVE POEMS. Salt Lake City: Ptd by J. C. Graham & Co., 1880. viii, 128pp. Orig black lea, worn, inner hinges cracked, lacks rep. Former owner's ink stamp. *WEBER.* $45

Tanner, Robert G. STONEWALL IN THE VALLEY. GC, (1976). Dj wear, o/w Fine. *PRATT.* $25

Tanner, Robert G. STONEWALL IN THE VALLEY...SPRING 1862. GC: Doubleday, 1976. 1st ed. VG in VG dj. *CONNOLLY & WADE.* $17.50

Tanquerel des Planches, Louis. LEAD DISEASES: A TREATISE WITH NOTES AND ADDITIONS ON THE USE OF LEAD PIPE AND ITS SUBSTITUTES BY SAMUEL L. DANA. Lowell, 1848. 1st Eng trans. Recent cloth, 443pp. Perforation stamp on title, scattered foxing. Ex-lib. *FYE.* $300

Tapie, Michel and Tore Haga. AVANT-GARDE ART IN JAPAN. NY: Harry N. Abrams, Inc., (1962). 34 tipped-in color plts. Color pict dj soiled, sl chipped top edge. NF. *BLUE MOUNTAIN.* $125

Tapley, William, et al. VEGETABLES OF NY: CUCURBITS. Albany: Lyon, 1937. Stiff boards in orig mailer. As New. *AMERICAN BOTANIST.* $40

Tapley, William, et al. VEGETABLES OF NY: SWEET CORN. Albany: Lyon, 1934. Stiff paper covers, in orig mailer. As New. *AMERICAN BOTANIST.* $40

Tapply, William G. A VOID IN HEARTS. NY: Charles Scribner's Sons, 1988. 1st ed. VF in dj. *MORDIDA.* $25

Tapply, William G. CLIENT PRIVILEGE. (NY): Delacorte (1990). 1st ed. Signed. Fine in Fine dj. *LOPEZ.* $40

Tapply, William G. DEAD WINTER. NY: Delacorte Press, 1989. 1st ed. Adv rev copy w/sheet and photo laid in. VF in dj. *MORDIDA.* $25

Tapply, William G. DEATH AT CHARITY'S POINT. NY: Charles Scribner's Sons, 1984. 1st ed. VF in dj. *MORDIDA.* $125

Tapply, William G. DEATH AT CHARITY'S POINT. NY: Scribners, 1984. 1st ed. VF in dj. *ELSE FINE.* $150

Tapply, William G. FOLLOW THE SHARKS. NY: Charles Scribner's Sons, 1985. 1st ed. Adv rev copy w/slip and flyer laid in. VF in dj. *MORDIDA.* $30

Tapply, William G. FOLLOW THE SHARKS. NY: Scribner's, (1985). 1st ed. *UNGER.* $30

Tapply, William G. FOLLOW THE SHARKS. Scribners, 1985. 1st ed. Fine in price clipped dj. *STAHR.* $20

Tapply, William G. THE DUTCH BLUE ERROR. NY: Charles Scribner's Sons, 1984. 1st ed. VF in dj. *MORDIDA.* $165

Tapply, William G. THE DUTCH BLUE ERROR. NY: Scribner's, (1984). 1st ed. VF in VF dj. *UNGER.* $150

Tapply, William G. THE DUTCH BLUE ERROR. NY: Scribners, 1984. 1st ed. VF in dj. *ELSE FINE.* $250

Tapply, William G. THE MARINE CORPSE. NY: Scribner, 1986. 1st ed. Signed. VF in dj. *SILVER DOOR.* $35

Tapply, William G. THE VULGAR BOATMAN. NY: Charles Scribner's Sons, 1987. 1st ed. VF in dj. *MORDIDA.* $20

Taracouzio, T.A. SOVIETS IN THE ARCTIC. NY: Macmillan, 1938. 7 maps (1 fldg in pocket). Some offsetting, light soil, else VG. *PARMER.* $65

Tarbell, Ida M. A REPORTER FOR LINCOLN, STORY OF HENRY E. WING, SOLDIER AND NEWSPAPERMAN. NY, 1927. 1st ed. 78pp. A little dj wear, chipping; o/w Fine. *PRATT.* $20

Tarbell, Ida M. HE KNEW LINCOLN. NY, 1909. Minor cover wear o/w Fine. *PRATT.* $12.50

Tarbell, John A. HOMEOPATHY SIMPLIFIED. Boston: Otis Clapp & Sons, 1874. Rev ed. G. *BLUE DRAGON.* $40

Targ, William (ed). BIBLIOPHILE IN THE NURSERY. Cleveland and NY: World Publishing Co, (1957). 1st ed. Fldg frontis. Dj. VF. *WREDEN.* $75

Targ, William (ed). BIBLIOPHILE IN THE NURSERY. Cleveland, 1957. 1st ed. Fine. *POLYANTHOS.* $60

Targ, William (ed). BOUILLABAISSE FOR BIBLIOPHILES. Cleveland, 1955. 1st ed. Signed presentation. Fine. *POLYANTHOS.* $75

Targ, William. INDECENT PLEASURES. NY: Macmillan, (1975). Fine in NF dj. 1st ed. *CHAPEL HILL.* $35

Targ, William. LAFCADIO HEARN: FIRST EDITIONS AND VALUES. Chicago: The Black Archer Press. 1935. Ed ltd to 550. Extrems bit rubbed. *KARMIOLE.* $60

TARGET: GERMANY. NY: Simon & Schuster, in cooperation w/Life Magazine. 1943. 1st ed. Dj. *KARMIOLE.* $35

Tarkington, Booth. ALICE ADAMS. GC: Doubleday Page, 1921. 1st ed. VG in 2nd state dj (reviews on rear panel). *LOPEZ.* $50

Tarkington, Booth. CLAIRE AMBLER. GC, NY: Doubleday, Doran, 1928. NF in price-clipped dj (sl darkened spine). 1st ed. *CHAPEL HILL.* $45

Tarkington, Booth. PRESENTING LILY MARS. GC, 1933. 1st ed. Sl mottled black cl. Inscribed. VG. *NUTMEG.* $35

Tarkington, Booth. RUMBIN GALLERIES. GC, NY Doubleday, Doran & Co, 1937. NF in dj (some Very shallow edge chips). 1st ed. *CHAPEL HILL.* $50

Tarkington, Booth. THE FASCINATING STRANGER AND OTHER STORIES. GC, NY: Doubleday, Page, 1923. Fine, unopened in lightly sunned dj and worn pub's slipcase. 1st ed. #234 of 377 signed. *CHAPEL HILL.* $150

Tarkington, Booth. THE GENTLEMAN FROM INDIANA. NY: Doubleday & McClure Co., 1899. Owner's name, hinges starting, else VG. 1st ed, 1st state, w/"so pretty" on p. 245, line 16. 2nd issue binding, w/corncob pointing down. *CHAPEL HILL.* $125

Tarkington, Booth. THE GENTLEMAN FROM INDIANA. NY: Doubleday & McClure, 1899. 1st ed, 1st issue w/pict cl, top edge stained grn. On p245, "eye" as last word on line 12 and "so pretty" on line 16. 1st bk. *CULLEN.* $125

Tarkington, Booth. THE MAGNIFICENT AMBERSONS. GC: Doubleday Page, 1918. 1st ed. VG, lacking dj. *LOPEZ.* $40

Tarkington, Booth. THE TWO VAN REVELS. NY: McClure, Phillips & Co., 1902. Bkpl, else Fine in NF dj (few nicks and edge tears). 1st ed, 2nd state, w/1st pg of ads listing two titles (including Monsieur Beaucaire as 80th Thousand) and 2nd pg of ads listing four titles (including Monsieur Beaucaire as 70th Thousand). Rare in dj. *CHAPEL HILL.* $350

Tarpley, Fred. FROM BLINKY TO BLUE-JOHN: A WORD ATLAS OF NORTHEAST TEXAS. Wolf City, TX: Univ Press, 1970. 1st ed. VF, pict cl in Fine dj. *CONNOLLY & WADE.* $37.50

Tassin, Ray. STANLEY VESTAL, CHAMPION OF THE OLD WEST. Glendale: Arthur H. Clark, 1973. Near New, worn dj. *PARMER.* $18

Tate, Allen (ed). A SOUTHERN VANGUARD. NY: Prentice-Hall, (1947). 1st ed. Fine in well-used dj. Signed by Andrew Lytle. *CAPTAIN'S BOOKSHELF.* $50

Tate, Allen (ed). A SOUTHERN VANGUARD. NY: Prentice-Hall, (1947). 1st ed. Orig brn cl. Owner name, else NF in VG dj. *CHAPEL HILL.* $50

Tate, Allen and Ridley Wills. THE GOLDEN MEAN AND OTHER POEMS. (Nashville): (The authors, 1923). 1/200 numbered. Sl foxing, outer ptd wraps sl browned. Tate's 1st bk. Signed by both. VG. Rare. *CAPTAIN'S BOOKSHELF.* $3000

Tate, Allen. ALL IS BRILLIG (OR OUGHT TO BE). Preface by James Dickey. (Winston Salem) : Palaemon Press, (1979). 1/50 in

Roman numerals (from total ed of 200). Fine in ptd wraps. Inscribed by pub and Dickey. *CAPTAIN'S BOOKSHELF.* $65

Tate, Allen. MR. POPE AND OTHER POEMS. NY: Minton, Balch & Co, 1928. 1st ed. Orig black cl w/olive grn paper labels. Some offsetting to front ep, front jacket flap, but NF in dj (shallow chip top of rear panel, couple of tiny nicks). Unusually Nice. *CHAPEL HILL.* $700

Tate, Allen. POEMS 1922-1947. NY: Scribners, 1948. 1st ed. Fine chipped, sl used dj. *CAPTAIN'S BOOKSHELF.* $40

Tate, Allen. SELECTED POEMS. NY: Scribner's, (1937). 1st Amer ed. Inscribed to Minnie Mite Moody. Light foxing and yellowing of eps else VG+ in sl soiled dj w/chipping top and bottom of spine else VG. Included also is Moody's TOWERS OF IVORY, signed by Moody. *DORN.* $300

Tate, Allen. STONEWALL JACKSON: A NARRATIVE. Minton, Balch, 1928. 3rd ptg. Fair. *BOOK BROKER.* $38

Tate, Allen. THE FATHERS. NY: Putnam (1938). 1st ed. Sl used, VG in VG dj. *DORN.* $110

Tate, Allen. THE FORLORN DEMON. Chicago: Regnery, 1953. 1st ed. Inscribed. Orig burgundy cl. NF in modestly rubbed dj (shallow chipping at spine ends affecting no lettering). *CHAPEL HILL.* $150

Tate, James and Bill Knott. ARE YOU READY MARY BAKER EDDY??? (Berkeley): (Cloud Marauder), (1970). One of 700 in wrappers. Fine. *LOPEZ.* $35

Tate, James. AMNESIA PEOPLE. Girard: Little Balkans Press, 1970. 1/150, each numbered and signed. Very minor damping, else NF. *BEASLEY.* $65

Tate, James. NOTES OF WOE. Iowa City: Stone Wall Press, 1968. 1st ed. Ltd to 230. Boards. Fine. *JAFFE.* $225

Tate, James. SHEPHERDS OF THE MIST. LA: Black Sparrow Press, 1969. NF in acetate jacket. 1st ed. #82 of 150 hb, signed. *CHAPEL HILL.* $35

Tate, James. THE TORCHES. Santa Barbara: Unicorn, (1968). One of 250 hb of a total ed of 1300 (there were also 30 signed). Fine. *LOPEZ.* $50

Taton, Rene (ed). THE BEGINNINGS OF MODERN SCIENCE FROM 1450 TO 1800. NY: Basic Books, 1964 (France 1958). VG in beige cl. *KNOLLWOOD.* $55

Tauber, Peter. THE LAST BEST HOPE. NY: Harcourt Brace Jovanovich, (1977). 1st ed. Signed. NF in dj. *LOPEZ.* $45

Tavener, P.A. BIRDS OF CANADA. National Museum of Canada Bulletin #72. Ottowa, 1934. 1st ed. 87 color plts. VG. *OREGON.* $40

Tavernier, A. ELEMENTS OF OPERATIVE SURGERY WITH COPIOUS NOTES AND ADDITIONS BY S.D. GROSS. Phila, 1829. 1st Eng trans. Full leather, 448pp. Inscribed and signed in initials. Name to whom inscribed has been cut away. *FYE.* $300

Taylor, A. Elizabeth. THE WOMAN SUFFRAGE MOVEMENT IN TENNESSEE. NY: Bookman, (1957). 1st ed. VG in dj. *SECOND LIFE.* $35

Taylor, Bayard (ed). CYCLOPAEDIA OF MODERN TRAVEL: A RECORD.... Cincinnati: Moore, Wilstach, Keys; NY: Law, 1856. 1st ed. Generally Good. *WORLDWIDE.* $25

Taylor, Bayard (ed). PICTURESQUE EUROPE...GREAT BRITAIN AND THE CONTINENT. NY: D. Appleton, (1875-78). 1st ed. 2 vols. Orig morocco w/raised bands, gilt-dec spine panels, aeg. Minor wear. BAL 19754. *CHAPEL HILL.* $250

Taylor, Bayard (ed). PICTURESQUE EUROPE: GREAT BRITAIN AND THE CONTINENT. NY, 1875. 4 vols. Illus. NF. *POLYANTHOS.* $350

Taylor, Bayard. A JOURNEY TO CENTRAL AFRICA, OR LIFE AND LANDSCAPES...NY: Putnam, 1859. 10th ed. Fldg map. Rubbed, spine frayed and faded, o/w VG ex-lib. *WORLDWIDE.* $30

Taylor, Bayard. ELDORADO; OR, ADVENTURES IN THE PATH OF EMPIRE; COMPRISING A VOYAGE TO CALIFORNIA...AND EXPERIENCES OF MEXICAN TRAVEL. NY: Putnam, 1850. 1st ed. 2 vols. (12),251; 247,(23)pp. 8 colored plts. Orig cl. Often rebound and trimmed, title pg of vol 1 has irregular cut at crown, light foxing. Howes 743. *GINSBERG.* $750

Taylor, Bayard. THE LANDS OF THE SARACEN. NY: Putnam, 1855. 1st ed. 451pp. Tinted frontis, engr title-pg, fldg map. Orig cl, sl rubbed and soiled, slight foxing, o/w VG. *WORLDWIDE.* $35

Taylor, Benjamin C. ANNALS OF THE CLASSIS OF BERGEN OF REFORMED DUTCH CHURCH..CIVIL HISTORY OF THE ANCIENT TOWNSHIP OF BERGEN IN NJ. NY: Reformed Protestant Dutch Church, (1857). 479pp. 21 full-pg engrs. Cover some rubbed & worn. Contents VG. *HEINOLDT.* $25

Taylor, Benjamin F. BETWEEN THE GATES. Chicago: S.C. Griggs, 1878. 1st ed. Frontis, 8pp ads. Cvrs sl worn, o/w VG. *DIAMOND.* $25

Taylor, Benjamin F. BETWEEN THE GATES. Chicago: Griggs, 1878. 1st ed. 292pp + 8pp book ads. Frontis. Orig dec cl. VG. *CONNOLLY & WADE.* $67.50

Taylor, C.W. (comp). MASTERS AND MASTERPIECES OF THE SCREEN. NY: F.F. Collier & Son, (1927). Orig pict self-wrappers. A few stains on wrappers, else Fine. *WREDEN.* $65

Taylor, Coley B. MARK TWAIN'S MARGINS ON THACKERAY'S "SWIFT." NY: Gotham House, 1935. Ed ltd to 1000 numbered. Dj. Small lib rubber stamp on half-title, verso of title, o/w Fine. *KARMIOLE.* $45

Taylor, Elizabeth. AT MRS. LIPPINCOTE'S. NY: Knopf, 1945. 1st US ed of 1st book. Fine in lightly used dj. *BEASLEY.* $30

Taylor, Elizabeth. IN A SUMMER SEASON. London: Davies, 1961. 1st ed. Fine; lt wear dj extrems. *ELSE FINE.* $30

Taylor, Elizabeth. THE BLUSH. NY: Viking, 1959. 1st ed. Fine in dj. *ELSE FINE.* $45

Taylor, Elizabeth. THE WEDDING GROUP. NY: Viking, 1968. 1st ed. Bkpl. VF in dj. *ELSE FINE.* $30

Taylor, Eva G.R. THE HAVEN-FINDING ART: A HISTORY OF NAVIGATION. NY, (1957). 1st Amer ed, pub simultaneously w/Eng ed. Dj repaired. *LEFKOWICZ.* $50

Taylor, Frederick W. THE PRINCIPLES OF SCIENTIFIC MANAGEMENT. NY, 1913. NF. *POLYANTHOS.* $45

Taylor, Hannis. THE SCIENCE OF JURISPRUDENCE....NY, 1908. 1st ed. Teg. Minor shelf wear. Inner hinges starting. Ink marks, o/w VG. *DIAMOND.* $50

Taylor, J. Traill. THE OPTICS OF PHOTOGRAPHY AND PHOTOGRAPHIC LENSES. London: Whittaker & Co. 1892. 1st ed. (2),viii,244pp. 1/2 red calf over maroon cl, dec gilt spine, grn leather spine label; spine a bit faded. *KARMIOLE.* $100

Taylor, J.M. BENCH SHOW AND FIELD TRIAL RECORDS AND STANDARDS OF DOGS IN AMERICA AND VALUABLE STATISTICS 1874-1892. Vol. I. NY: Rogers & Sherwood, 1892. 4to, grn cl (rubbed & soiled) w/title dec & 2 vignettes on front cover. 519pp. (hinges cracked; occasional light foxing; sl shaken). Clippings tipped-in. VG. *BLUE MOUNTAIN.* $275

Taylor, James W. RELATIONS BETWEEN THE U.S. AND NORTHWEST BRITISH AMERICA. LETTER FROM...CENTRAL DISTRICTS OF THE RED RIVER OF THE NORTH AND THE SASKATCHEWAN. Wash., HD146, 1862. 85pp. Fldg map. Half morocco. Howes T56. *GINSBERG.* $150

Taylor, John. PONDORO—LAST OF THE IVORY HUNTERS. NY: Simon & Schuster, 1955. 1st ed. Original green cl backed grey boards. Gilt titles. Dj with minor chips, else NF. *GREAT EPIC.* $95

Taylor, John. PONDORO—LAST OF THE IVORY HUNTERS. NY: Simon & Schuster, 1955. Stated 1st prtg. VG+ in VG+ dj. *BACKMAN.* $65

Taylor, Joseph Henry. BEAVERS, THEIR WAYS AND OTHER SKETCHES. Privately ptd, n.d. 1st ed. Frontis, 18 plts. No plt p19 (nor sign of having been one) as called for in illus list. VG. Howes T66. *OREGON.* $275

Taylor, Joshua N. SEA YARNS...REMINISCENCES OF CAPT. JOSHUA N. TAYLOR. Np, nd (c1915). 1st ed. Orig ptd wraps, sl soiled. *LEFKOWICZ.* $200

Taylor, Mart. THE GOLD DIGGER'S SONG BOOK. SF: The Bk Club of CA, 1975. Ed ltd to 450 numbered. Fine. *KARMIOLE.* $45

Taylor, Mrs. B. (Harriet Osgood). JAPANESE GARDENS. NY, 1912. 28 tipped-in colored plts. Dec boards, cl spine. Worn at corners and edges. Soiled, lt foxing, o/w nice internally. *SUTTON.* $85

Taylor, Oliver. HISTORIC SULLIVAN: A HISTORY OF SULLIVAN COUNTY, TENNESSEE. Bristol, TN: King, 1909. 1st ed. 31 plts. Orig cl, sm paper label on spine, bkpl removed. *GINSBERG.* $125

Taylor, P. Walker. MURDER IN THE FLAGSHIP. NY: M.S. Mill, 1937. 1st Amer ed. VG in dj (sl faded spine; corner wear; short closed tears). *MORDIDA.* $30

Taylor, Peter. A LONG FOURTH AND OTHER STORIES. NY: Harcourt, Brace, (1948). 1st ed. Fine in dj (sl faded at spine, missing 1" piece top of back panel. *JAFFE.* $175

Taylor, Peter. A SUMMONS TO MEMPHIS. London: Chatto & Windus, 1987. 1st UK ed. NF in dj. *LAME DUCK.* $30

Taylor, Peter. A SUMMONS TO MEMPHIS. NY: Knopf, (1986). 1st Amer ed. Signed. Very small rem dot bottom edge else Fine in dj. *DORN.* $85

Taylor, Peter. A SUMMONS TO MEMPHIS. NY: Knopf, 1986. Uncorrected proof. Fine in ptd wraps. Signed. *CAPTAIN'S BOOKSHELF.* $175

Taylor, Peter. A SUMMONS TO MEMPHIS. NY: Knopf, 1986. 1st ed. Orig cl-backed boards. Fine in dj. *CHAPEL HILL.* $35

Taylor, Peter. A WOMAN OF MEANS. NY: Harcourt, Brace and Co. (1950). 1st ed. Signed. VG in edgeworn VG dj. *DORN.* $250

Taylor, Peter. A WOMAN OF MEANS. NY: Harcourt, (1950). 1st ed. Fine in sl edgeworn dj sl faded spine. Signed. *CAPTAIN'S BOOKSHELF.* $200

Taylor, Peter. HAPPY FAMILIES ARE ALL ALIKE. NY: McDowell-Obolensky, (1959). 1st ed. Fine in sl rubbed dj. *JAFFE.* $125

Taylor, Peter. IN THE MIRO DISTRICT AND OTHER STORIES. NY: Knopf, 1977. 1st ed. Fine in dj. Inscribed. *CAPTAIN'S BOOKSHELF.* $100

Taylor, Peter. IN THE MIRO DISTRICT AND OTHER STORIES. NY: Knopf, 1977. 1st ed. Dj. VF. *JAFFE.* $45

Taylor, Peter. IN THE MIRO DISTRICT AND OTHER STORIES. London: Chatto & Windus, 1977. 1st Eng ed. One of 1,750. Inscribed. Orig black cl. As New in dj. *CHAPEL HILL.* $85

Taylor, Peter. IN THE MIRO DISTRICT AND OTHER STORIES. NY: Knopf (1977). 1st ed. Signed. NF in price-clipped Fine dj. *DORN.* $90

Taylor, Peter. MISS LEONORA WHEN LAST SEEN AND FIFTEEN OTHER STORIES. NY: Obolensky, (1963). 1st ed. Fine in dj w/sl darkened spine. Signed. *CAPTAIN'S BOOKSHELF.* $200

Taylor, Peter. MISS LEONORA WHEN LAST SEEN AND FIFTEEN OTHER STORIES. NY: Obolensky, (1963). Fine in a very lightly used price-clipped dj. *CAPTAIN'S BOOKSHELF.* $150

Taylor, Peter. MISS LEONORA WHEN LAST SEEN. NY: Ivan Obolensky, (1963). 1st ed. Orig yellow cl. VG in dj. 1st ed. *CHAPEL HILL.* $75

Taylor, Peter. MISS LEONORA WHEN LAST SEEN. NY: Obolensky (1963). 1st ed. NF in NF dj. *DORN.* $125

Taylor, Peter. TENNESSEE DAY IN ST. LOUIS. NY: Random House, (1957). 1st ed. Cl-backed boards, dj. NF. *JAFFE.* $100

Taylor, Peter. TENNESSEE DAY IN ST. LOUIS. NY: Random House, (1957). 1st ed. A few spots of foxing on front fly and front flap, else Fine in bright, NF dj. Scarce. *BETWEEN COVERS.* $100

Taylor, Peter. TENNESSEE DAY IN ST. LOUIS. NY: RH, (1957). 1st ed. Fourth bk, 1st play. Inscribed in 1968. NF in dj. *LOPEZ.* $225

Taylor, Peter. TENNESSEE DAY IN ST. LOUIS: A PLAY. NY: Random House, (1957). 1st ed. Fine in sl used dj. Signed. *CAPTAIN'S BOOKSHELF.* $125

Taylor, Peter. THE COLLECTED STORIES OF PETER TAYLOR. NY: Farrar, Straus & Giroux, (1969). 1st ed. Orig black cl. VG in dj. *CHAPEL HILL.* $45

Taylor, Peter. THE COLLECTED STORIES OF PETER TAYLOR. NY: FSG, (1969). 1st ed. Signed. VF in Fine dj. *LOPEZ.* $150

Taylor, Peter. THE COLLECTED STORIES. NY: FSG, (1969). 1st ed. Signed. Fine in lightly soiled dj. *ROBBINS.* $85

Taylor, Peter. THE EARLY GUEST. (n.p.): Palaemon Press, (1982). One of 140 numbered, of which 100 were for sale. NF in wrappers and signed. *LOPEZ.* $75

Taylor, Peter. THE OLD FOREST AND OTHER STORIES. NY: Dial, (1985). 1st Amer ed. Signed. Faint rem mark bottom edge else Fine in dj. *DORN.* $90

Taylor, Peter. THE WIDOWS OF THORNTON. NY: Harcourt, (1954). 1st ed. Fine in sl rubbed dj w/wear to spine extrems. Signed. *CAPTAIN'S BOOKSHELF.* $200

Taylor, Peter. THE WIDOWS OF THORNTON. NY: Harcourt, Brace and Co., (1954). 1st Amer ed. Signed. VG in scuffed dj with two 1" closed fold tears bottom of front panel. About VG. *DORN.* $185

Taylor, Peter. THE WIDOWS OF THORNTON. NY: Harcourt Brace, (1954). 1st ed. Signed. Fine in NF dj. *LOPEZ.* $300

Taylor, Robert Lewis. A JOURNEY TO MATECUMBE. NY: McGraw-Hill, 1961. 1st ed. As New in dj. *ELSE FINE.* $50

Taylor, Robert Lewis. THE TRAVELS OF JAIMIE McPHEETERS. Doubleday & Co, 1958. 1st ed. Fine in dj. *AUTHORS OF THE WEST.* $25

Taylor, Robert Lewis. THE TRAVELS OF JAIMIE MCPHEETERS. GC: Doubleday, 1958. 1st ed. VG in internally strengthened dj. *LOPEZ.* $40

Taylor, W.P. (ed). THE DEER OF NORTH AMERICA. 2 colored and 39 b/w plts. Harrisburg, 1961 (1956). Cloth. *SUTTON.* $55

Taylor, W.P. (ed). THE DEER OF NORTH AMERICA. Harrisburg & Washington, DC: Stackpole, (1961). 2nd ed. Plts, figures, maps. Fine in Fair dj. *MIKESH.* $35

Taylor, William. OUR SOUTH AMERICAN COUSINS. NY, 1879. 1st ed. 318pp, frontis port. Some cover wear, inner hinges cracking, o/w Good. *DIAMOND.* $25

Taylor, William. STORY OF MY LIFE. NY: Hunt & Eaton, 1895. Ed by John Clark Ridpath. 1st ed. 76 plts. Rubbed, soiled; spine frayed, sl torn, o/w VG. *WORLDWIDE.* $20

Teale, E.W. THE GOLDEN THRONG. NY, 1940. 1st ed. Dj chipped. *SUTTON.* $35

Teale, Edwin Way. THE GOLDEN THRONG. Dodd, Mead, 1940. 1st ed. VG in dj. *MAD DOG.* $30

Teaque, Charles Collins. FIFTY YEARS A RANCHER. N.p.: CA Walnut Growers Assoc, 1944. 2nd ed. NF. *CONNOLLY & WADE.* $35

Teasdale, Sara. DARK OF THE MOON. NY: The Macmillan Co, 1926. 1st ed. Presentation, inscribed. Cl bumped, sl rubbed at edges in chipped dj. NF. *BLUE MOUNTAIN.* $95

Teasdale, Sara. STRANGE VICTORY. NY, 1933. 1st ed. Portrait, poem in facsimile. Fine in dj (spine sl sunned tiny chip top). *POLYANTHOS*. $50

Teasdale, Sara. STRANGE VICTORY. NY: Macmillan, 1933. Fine in dj (small chip at head of spine). 1st ed. *CHAPEL HILL*. $45

Tebbel, John and Keith Jennison. THE AMERICAN INDIAN WARS. Harper, (1960). 1st ed. Fldg map. VG in VG dj. *OREGON*. $25

Teed, G.H. FIVE IN FEAR. London: Stanley Smith, 1936. 1st ed. Edges sl spotted and bkpl on fep o/w VG in dj w/wear along folds. *MORDIDA*. $45

Teichmann, Emil. A JOURNEY TO ALASKA IN THE YEAR 1868: BEING A DIARY OF THE LATE...NY, 1963. One of 97 specially bound, numbered. Orig cl w/vellum spine, boxed. Howes T88. *GINSBERG*. $75

Teilhard de Chardin, Pierre. THE MAKING OF A MIND: LETTERS FROM A SOLDIER-PRIEST (1914-1919). NY: Harper, (1965). 1st ed. VF in dj. *ELSE FINE*. $40

Telushkin, Joseph. THE UNORTHODOX MURDER OF RABBI MOSS. London: Collins, 1986. 1st ed. VF in dj. *SILVER DOOR*. $22.50

Temkin, Owsei and C.L. (eds). ANCIENT MEDICINE: SELECTED PAPERS OF LUDWIG EDELSTEIN. Baltimore, 1967. 1st ed. *FYE*. $75

Temple, Mrs. Gertrude. HOW I RAISED SHIRLEY TEMPLE. BY HER MOTHER...AS TOLD TO MARY SHARON. Akron, OH & NY, 1935. 1st ed. Stapled pict wraps. Saalfield Pub Co, imprint. VG. *McCLINTOCK*. $35

Temple, Shirley. SHIRLEY TEMPLE'S STORYBOOK. NY: Random. 1st ed. Cl, boards. Signed. NF in chipped dj. *ACADEMIC LIBRARY*. $40

Templeton, Sardis W. THE LAME CAPTAIN: THE LIFE AND ADVENTURES OF PEGLEG SMITH. LA: Westernlore, 1965. Fabricoid dj. *DAWSON'S*. $35

Templeton, Sardis. THE LAME CAPTAIN. LA: Westernlore, 1965. 1st ed. VF in VF dj. *OREGON*. $45

TEN ACRES ENOUGH. (By Edmund Morris.) NY: Miller, 1864. 255pp. Cl and contents VG. *AMERICAN BOTANIST*. $35

TEN THOUSAND A-YEAR. (By Samuel Warren.) Phila: Carey & Hart, 1840-41. 6 vols. 1st US ed, 1st state (w/o vol number and rule on the title page of vol 1). 12mo. Orig boards, paper spine, some foxing and soiling, else VG set in orig pub's binding. Flyleaf mounted in vol 1. Scarce. *SECOND LIFE*. $325

Tenggren, Gustav. MOTHER GOOSE. Boston: Little Brown, 1940. 1st ed. Color pict cl. VG. *ARTIS*. $25

Tennyson, Alfred, Lord. ENOCH ARDEN. Boston, 1865. 78pp. Many engraved illus. Leather rubbed. *HEINOLDT*. $12

Tennyson, Alfred Lord. IDYLLS OF THE KING. NY: LEC, 1952. Illus Lynd Ward. Red leather & cl, marbled board slipcase. One of 1500 ptd at Yale Univ Press & signed by Ward. Fine. *JAFFE*. $100

Tennyson, Alfred Lord. IN MEMORIUM. Boston: Ticknor, Reed and Fields, 1850. 1st US ed. Orig brown ribbed cloth, tooled in blind. Slight wear to head of spine, else NF (neat, contemp owner sig). *CAPTAIN'S BOOKSHELF*. $125

Tennyson, Alfred Lord. LOCKSLEY HALL SIXTY YEARS AFTER Etc. London: Macmillan, 1886. 1st ed. Lt foxing to eps, else NF; sl dulled. *CHAPEL HILL*. $45

TENTH REPORT OF THE BUREAU OF AGRICULTURE, LABOR AND INDUSTRY OF THE STATE OF MONTANA FOR THE YEAR ENDING NOVEMBER 30, 1906. Helena: Independent Pub. Co. 1st ed. 28 plts (6 fldg). Wraps. Fine. *OREGON*. $60

Teonge, Henry. THE DIARY OF HENRY TEONGE, CHAPLAIN ON BOARD H.M.'S SHIPS...NY & London: Harper & Bros (1927). Dj. *SCHOYER'S*. $16.50

Teonge, Henry. THE DIARY OF HENRY TEONGE, CHAPLAIN ON BOARD HIS MAJESTY'S SHIPS...London: Charles Knight, 1825. 1st ed. 8vo, fldg facsimile, 2 title pp, xviii, half-title, 327pp, index, list of the Royal Navy, 1675. Modern 3/4 maroon goat and marbled paper over boards, marbled eps. Repair verso of title page. Marginal staining through p. vii of preface. *PARMER*. $200

Teonge, Henry. THE DIARY OF...CHAPLAIN ON BOARD H.M.'S SHIPS ASSISTANCE, BRISTOL, AND ROYAL OAK, 1675-1679. NY, 1927. x,318pp. Unopened. *O'NEILL*. $30

Terhost, Bernd. WITH THE RIFF KABYLES. NY: Stokes, (n.d.) (ca 1926). Corners bumped, spine ends rubbed. *SCHOYER'S*. $20

TERRA COTTA OF THE ITALIAN RENAISSANCE. NY: National Terra Cotta Society, (1925). 1st ed. Owner sig. Fine. *CAPTAIN'S BOOKSHELF*. $60

Terrace, Edward L.B. EGYPTIAN PAINTINGS OF THE MIDDLE KINGDOM. London: George Allan and Unwin, 1968. 57 color plts, 13 figs. Dj. Good. *ARCHAEOLOGIA*. $95

Terrell, John Upton and Colonel George Walton. FAINT THE TRUMPET SOUNDS. NY, (1966). 1st ed. Repaired dj o/w VG+. *PRATT*. $40

Terrell, John Upton and Donna M. INDIAN WOMEN OF THE WESTERN MORNING....NY: Dial, 1974. 1st ed. Cloth. VG in VG dj. *CONNOLLY & WADE*. $30

Terrell, John Upton. BUNKHOUSE PAPERS. NY: Dial, 1971. 1st ed. Inscr. VF in VG dj. *CONNOLLY & WADE*. $47.50

Terrell, John Upton. SIOUX TRAIL. NY, (1974). 1st ed. 213pp. Fine in dj. *PRATT*. $25

Terrell, John Upton. THE ARROW AND THE CROSS. Santa Barbara, 1979. 1st ed. VG+ in dj. *PRATT*. $25

Terrell, John Upton. WAR FOR THE COLORADO RIVER. Clark, 1958. Two vols. VF in VG+ djs. *FIVE QUAIL*. $55.

Terrell, John Upton. WAR FOR THE COLORADO RIVER. Glendale: Arthur H. Clark Co, 1965. 2 vols. 1st ed. Fine. *BOOK MARKET*. $40

Terrell, John. WAR FOR THE COLORADO RIVER. A.H. Clark, 1965. 2 vols. 1st ed. Both vols signed. VF in VF dj. *OREGON*. $70

Terry, T. Philip. TERRY'S GUIDE TO MEXICO. Boston, 1938, rev. ed. Orig cl. 34 maps and plans. Light wear, large map improperly folded and protrudes a little. *BOHLING*. $45

Terry, Wallace. BLOODS. NY: Random House, (1984). 1st ed. NF in lightly worn dj, chips. VG. *AKA*. $35

Tessier, Thomas. THE NIGHTWALKER. Atheneum, 1979. 1st Amer ed. Fine in dj. *STAHR*. $100

TESTIMONY OF CHRIST'S SECOND APPEARING, EXEMPLIFIED BY THE PRINCIPLES & PRACTICE OF THE TRUE CHURCH OF CHRIST. (By Benjamin Seth Youngs.) (Albany, 1856). 4th ed. Modern 3/4 lea, gilt stamped morocco spine labels. Text w/foxing, pencilled inscription on ep. *BOHLING*. $200

Thackeray, William Makepeace. THE NEWCOMES. Illus Edward Ardizzone. 2 vols. Glassine djs, slipcase. Cambridge: LEC, 1954. Ltd to 1500 ptd at Cambridge Univ Press & signed by Ardizzone. Fine. *JAFFE*. $150

Thackeray, William Makepeace. NOVELS BY EMINENT HANDS, AND CHARACTER SKETCHES. London: Bradbury and Evans, 1856. 1st book ed. 8vo, 75pp w/orig yellow printed wrappers bound in. Full maroon morocco covers, elaborately gilt dec, uncut, all edges gilt. Very Nice. *HARTFIELD*. $295

Thackeray, William Makepeace. THE ORPHAN OF PIMLICO, AND OTHER SKETCHES, FRAGMENTS AND DRAWINGS.

London: Smith, Elder, & Co, 1876. 1st ed. 4 to. Orig grn leather backed gray boards. Spine sl rubbed, boards soiled. Title & rules in gilt on spine and title in red within a dec red frame. 100 leaves, incl eps. VG. *BLUE MOUNTAIN.* $150

Thane, Eric. HIGH BORDER COUNTRY. NY, 1942. 1st ed. 335pp. Fine in VG dj. *VARNER.* $25

Thatcher, B.B. INDIAN BIOGRAPHY, OR, AN HISTORICAL AC-COUNT....2 vols. NY: Harper & Brothers, 1843. Some foxing and dampstain, o/w tight set. *LAURIE.* $45

Thayer, Alexander Wheelock. LIFE OF LUDWIG VAN BEETHOVEN. NY: Beethoven Society, 1921. 3 vols. boxed. NF. Fragile. *BANCROFT.* $60

Thayer, Eli. A HISTORY OF THE KANSAS CRUSADE ITS FRIENDS AND FOES. NY, 1889. 1st ed. Orig cl. VG. *McGOWAN.* $125

Thayer, James Bradley. A WESTERN JOURNEY WITH MR. EMERSON. Boston: Little, Brown, & Co, 1884. 1st ed. Orig vellum wrappers; orig ptd dj only lightly used. *JUVELIS.* $600

Thayer, William M. FROM TANNERY TO THE WHITE HOUSE. Providence, RI: Buker Pub Co, 1885. Engr port, 11 plts; aeg. Bright pict cl. *SCHOYER'S.* $25

Thayer, William M. MARVELS OF THE NEW WEST. Norwich, CT, 1888. 1st ed. 715pp. Damp-staining on bottom & part of outer page margins. Inner hinges starting, o/w VG. *DIAMOND.* $45

THE "POP-UP" MOTHER GOOSE. Chicago, (1934). Measures 9" x 8" closed. Three pop-ups. 13pp. Illus. Color pop-ups by Harold Lentz as well as pict cvrs. Cvrs have edgewear, some soil to pp, but pop-ups bright and nice, Overall book VG, pop-ups VG+. *BEBBAH.* $75

THE 32ND DIVISION IN THE WORLD WAR. Milwaukee, (1920). Issued by the Joint War History Commission of Michigan and Wisconsin. Cloth. *ARTIS.* $35

THE ADMINISTRATIVE HISTORY OF THE OPERATIONS OF THE (BRITISH) 21 ARMY GROUP ON THE CONTINENT OF EUROPE. Germany, 1945. No author. 151pp, 48 fldg maps. Worn boards. *CULLEN.* $150

THE ADVENTURES OF DAVID SIMPLE: Containing An Account of His Travels Through London And Westminster In The Search of a REAL FRIEND. By a Lady. (By Sarah Fielding.) London: A. Millar, 1774. 2nd ed, same year as the 1st, but Revised, Corrected and With A Preface By Henry Fielding. 2 vols. Large 12mo, w/final ad leaf present. Full early polished calf, nicely rebacked; w/double lea labels, and spares laid in. Pretty set, scarce. *HARTFIELD.* $595

THE ADVENTURES OF PEREGRINE PICKLE. (By Tobias Smollett.) London: Strahan, Rivington, etc., 1784. 7th ed. 4 vols. (xii),268; 298; 282; 304pp. Full contemp calf, gilt on back labels. Engr frontis. Attractive. *HARTFIELD.* $395

THE ALASKA BOOK. THE STORY OF OUR NORTHERN TREASURELAND. Chicago: Ferguson Publishing Co, (1960). Leatherbound. Wear on bottom fore-edge corners, else Good+. *BLUE DRAGON.* $25

THE ALLIES FAIRY BOOK. Phila: J.B. Lippincott Co./London: William Heinemann, (1916). 1st Amer ed. Blue cl titled in white; pictorial eps. xxii,121,(1)pp. Prelims foxed. 12 color plts by Arthur Rackham. NF. *BLUE MOUNTAIN.* $225

THE ALLIES' FAIRY BOOK. Edmund Grosse (intro); Arthur Rackham (illus). London: William Heinemann. (1916). 12 color plts, incl frontis; each pl w/ptd tissue guard. Orig dec blue cl stamped in black and gold, spine a bit faded. Scarce. *KARMIOLE.* $125

THE AMATEUR PHOTOGRAPHERS ANNUAL, 1891. London: Hazell, Watson & Viney, Ltd. 1891. 1st ed. (42),166pp, (12)pp ads.

Indices. 1/2 maroon calf over blue cl, dec gilt spine, grn leather spine label. *KARMIOLE.* $100

THE AMERICAN ANTI-SLAVERY ALMANAC FOR 1839. NY: American Anti-Slave Soc, 1839. Yellow ptd self wraps, 48pp (little soiled). 13 woodcuts. Sewn. *SECOND LIFE.* $45

THE AMERICAN CRUISER; OR, THE TWO MESSMATES. A TALE OF THE LAST WAR. Boston: Waite, Peirce and Co, 1846. (By George Little.) 1st ed. Frontis, plts. Orig cl, binding dampstained, sl foxing within. *LEFKOWICZ.* $80

THE AMERICAN MANUAL OF TYPOGRAPHY. NY, 1903. 2nd ed. 3/4 lea worn and rubbed. NF. *POLYANTHOS.* $85

THE AMERICANS IN THE GREAT WAR. VOLUME I. France: Michelin & Cie, Clermont-Ferrand, c1920. Maps, plans in text. *HUDSON.* $35

THE AMERICANS IN THE GREAT WAR. VOLUME II. France: Michelin & Cie, Clermont-Ferrand, c1920. Maps, plans in text. *HUDSON.* $35

THE ANATOMICAL REMEMBRANCER; OR COMPLETE POCKET ANATOMIST. NY, 1845. 1st Amer ed. 245pp. *FYE.* $60

THE ARABIAN NIGHTS ENTERTAINMENTS...THE DEFINITIVE AND ALL-INCLUSIVE BURTON TRANSLATION. Illus by Arthur Szyk. 4 vols, in 2 slipcases. Ipswich: LEC, 1954. Ltd to 1500. Fine set. *JAFFE.* $200

THE ARABIAN NIGHTS. Winston, (1924). 1st ed. 257pp. Illus by Adelaide Bolton. Sl wear, VG. *BEBBAH.* $25

THE ART OF COOKERY MADE PLAIN AND EASY...(by Hannah Glasse). London: Millar and Tonson, 1760. 7th ed. Pp xxxii,384,xxiv. Contemp calf, rebacked w/new spine and eps. Ink scribbling in some margins, couple of stains on title pg. VG, clean. *SECOND LIFE.* $750

THE ASSASSINATION OF ABRAHAM LINCOLN...AND THE ATTEMPTED ASSASSINATION OF WILLIAM H. SEWARD....AND FREDERICK W. SEWARD...Washington, DC: GPO, 1867. xxx,930pp. Engr frontis. Orig cl. Rebacked w/new cl, spine label. Marbled fore-edges, eps. Sl corner, shelf wear. Cvrs stained, faded. Minor staining few pp. VG. *DIAMOND.* $85

THE ASSOCIATION OF RAILWAY SURGEONS. OFFICIAL REPORT OF THE SIXTH ANNUAL MEETING. Chicago, 1893. 1st ed. Scarce. *FYE.* $75

THE ATTACHE; OR, SAM SLICK IN ENGLAND. (By Thomas Chandler Haliburton.) In 2 vols. London: Richard Bentley, 1843. 1st ed. viii, 278; vi, 290pp. Orig purple cl faded, spine extrems bit chipped. *KARMIOLE.* $150

THE AUTOBIOGRAPHY OF BENVENUTO CELLINI. Doubleday, 1946. Illus by Salvador Dali. 1/1000 numbered, signed by Dali. Very lt wear to spine cl, o/w About Fine in worn pub's slipcase. *DERMONT.* $200

THE AUTOMOBILE CLUB OF SOUTHERN CALIFORNIA TOUR BOOK... COVERING THE PRINCIPAL TOURS OF CALIFORNIA FROM SAN FRANCISCO ON THE NORTH TO TIA JUANA, MEXICO, ON THE SOUTH. LA: G.F. Beck, (1911). Maps, ads. Recent leather, w/dec gold-stamped sections of orig binding laid down. Corners of prelim leaves frayed, tape repairs to 4 leaves. *DAWSON'S.* $350

THE BERKSHIRE HILLS. NY: Funk & Wagnalls. 1939. 1st ed. WPA American Guide Series. Dj lightly chipped. *KARMIOLE.* $45

THE BIOGRAPHY OF THE BRITISH STAGE. (By Sarah Bartley (?)). London: for Sherwood, Jones & Co, 1824. 1st ed. Later 1/2 roan, spine ends worn; uncut; sm tear half title; lacking frontis. *DRAMATIS.* $585

THE BLACK BOOK OF POLAND. NY, 1942. Illus. NF. *POLYANTHOS.* $100

THE BLACK HOLE. Walt Disney Prod, 1979. 4 double-pg pop-ups. Pop-up bk. *BOOKFINDERS INTL.* $35

THE BLUE BOOK OF THE STATE OF WISCONSIN. Milwaukee: Milwaukee Litho and Engr. Co, 1883. Fldg maps. Hinges weak. *HUDSON.* $50

THE BOLD LITTLE COWBOY. London, 1960. 3 pop-ups. Pop-up bk. *BOOKFINDERS INTL.* $45

THE BOOK OF AMERICAN NEGRO POETRY. Chosen and ed by James Weldon Johnson. NY: Harcourt Brace & Co., (1922). 1st ed. Owner's name, couple of pp carelessly opened, foxing to eps, some chips at extremities of spine label, else VG. Lacking dj. *BETWEEN COVERS.* $125

THE BOSTON ALMANAC FOR THE YEAR 1865. No. 30. Boston/NY: American News Co, 1865. Fldg plan, tables, ads. *HUDSON.* $25

THE BOTANIST'S CALENDAR, AND POCKET FLORA: ARRANGED ACCORDING TO THE LINNAEAN SYSTEM....Oval vignette half-title. 2 vols. London, 1797. Pp vi(1),396,(92). Contemp, gilt-dec, tree sheep (lt rubbing of edges, some weakness of hinges), o/w Very Nice, clean. *SUTTON.* $285

THE BOY'S OWN BOOK. Chicago, 1883. 354pp. Illus. Cvr & spine dec in gilt & black on grey-grn cloth. VG w/slight edgewear. *BEBBAH.* $35

THE BRAVO: A TALE. (By James Fenimore Cooper.) Phila: Carey & Lea, 1831. 1st ed, 1st issue. 2 vols. viii,240,ads(36); 236pp. Blue paper boards, white shelfback, ptd paper spine label; p.11 corner torn (w/loss of letters from text), spine worn, flyleaf 2/3 missing. Red cl slipcase, red leather spine label. BAL 3852. *WEBER.* $450

THE BRIGAND CAPTAIN. Beadle's New Dime Novels No. 328. Circa 1880. Last # listed on inside back cvr is No. 382. Chips, 2 pieces cut out of cvr, not affecting picture. VG, fragile in wraps. *BOOK MARKET.* $50

THE CALIFORNIA LITERARY PAMPHLETS. Grabhorn Press, (1936). 1st ed of 500 distributed by Bk Club of CA. Cl folder in slipcase w/leather labels on spine, stamped in gold. VG+. *AUTHORS OF THE WEST.* $125

THE CASE FOR THE SHORTER WORK DAY. Supreme Court of the US, October Term, 1915. 1st ed. 2 vols. Reprinted by the National Consumer's League, NY City, no date. Orig wraps sl chipped, repaired, o/w VG. *DIAMOND.* $150

THE CATTLE BARONS' REBELLION AGAINST THE LAW AND ORDER. FIRST EYEWITNESS ACCOUNTS OF THE JOHNSON COUNTY WAR IN WYOMING, 1892. Evanston: Branding Iron Press, 1955. Reprint of rare 1st ed. Ltd. to 1000 numbered. Signed, dated by pub Herbert Brayer. In stiff paper folder. VG. *OREGON.* $60

THE CENTRAL VALLEY PROJECT. Sacramento, 1942. American Guide Series. WPA guide. 1st ed. *SCHOYER'S.* $35

THE CHICAGO ANTHOLOGY. A COLLECTION OF VERSE FROM THE WORK OF CHICAGO POETS. Selected and arranged by Charles G. Blanden and Minna Mathison. Chicago: The Roadside Press, 1916. 1st ed. Presentation, inscribed, signed, dated by Blanden. Protected in mylar. NF. *CONNOLLY & WADE.* $150

THE CHINESE MASSACRE AT ROCK SPRINGS, WYOMING TERRITORY, Sept., 1885. Boston: Franklin Press, 1886. 1st ed. Chipped lib boards. Orig repaired wraps bound in. Text VG. *DIAMOND.* $75

THE CITY PARK. London, 1982. Repro of Lother Meggendorfer's stand up bk. *BOOKFINDERS INTL.* $55

THE COLD-WATER-MAN; OR, A POCKET COMPANION FOR THE TEMPERATE. By Doctor Springwater, of North America. (By James Quaw.) Albany: Ptd by Packard and Van Benthuysen, 1832. 1st ed. 216pp. Orig brown cl rubbed w/orange paper label on spine. Some foxing. NF. *BLUE MOUNTAIN.* $45

THE COMPLETE STORY OF THE GALVESTON HORROR. WRITTEN BY THE SURVIVORS. N.p.: United Pubs, 1900. 1st ed. Frontis. Orig cl. Pict inset, gilt. Rubbed, Good+. *CONNOLLY & WADE.* $30

THE CORONATION OF THE QUEEN. London, 1953. Stand-up bk. *BOOKFINDERS INTL.* $60

THE CREEPS OMNIBUS. London, 1935. 1st ed. Good+. *MADLE.* $25

THE DAILY NEWS' HISTORY OF BUCHANAN COUNTY & ST. JOSEPH, MO. By the St. Joseph Pub Co., Press of Lon. Hardman, (c. 1898). 13 plts. Light etching of cloth, else VG. *BOHLING.* $125

THE DALTON BROTHERS AND THEIR ASTOUNDING CAREER OF CRIME BY AN EYE WITNESS. NY: Frederick Fell, 1954. 1st ed thus. Fine in VG dj. Reprint 1892 1st ed. Issued in wrappers. *CONNOLLY & WADE.* $30

THE DALTON BROTHERS. BY AN EYEWITNESS. F. Fell, 1954. 1st ed. Fine in Fine dj. *VARNER.* $30

THE DAMSEL OF DARIEN. (By William Gilmore Simms.) Phila: Lea and Blanchard, Successors to Carey and Co, 1839. 2 vols, 1st ed. 2pp ads, 308pp; 281pp,2pp ads. Orig grn muslin w/paper spine labels. Owner sig, author's name written on title pg both vols in unknown hand o/w exceptionally Nice set. Text clean, spine labels unchipped. Custom red cl chemises, 1/4 morocco double slipcase. Bkpl on protective chemises. *CHAPEL HILL.* $750

THE DAVENPORT BROTHERS. Boston: William White and Company, 1869. 1st ed. Orig cloth; rear hinge pulling at ends; embossed stamp to title and another leaf, private ownership stamp to title, presentation book mark; illus. VG. *DRAMATIS PERSONAE.* $150

THE DAYS OF OLD AND DAYS OF GOLD IN BRITISH COLUMBIA. (Victoria: William H. Cullin, 1912). Gold-ptd wraps bit chipped; front cvr almost detached. *DAWSON'S.* $75

THE DESCENDANT. (By Ellen Glasgow.) NY: Harper, 1897. Anonymously published. 1st ed, author's 1st bk. Owner's sig ffep. NF. Bkpl of H. Bradley Martin. *LAME DUCK.* $200

THE DIARY OF A PUBLIC MAN. New Brunswick, 1946. 1st ed, thus. VG+. *PRATT.* $20

THE DR. WILLIAM H. CRIM COLLECTION OF ANTIQUES. Baltimore, April 22, 1903. VG to NF. Orig blue wraps. *BACKROOM.* $175

THE DRAMATIC WORKS OF JOHN LILLY. London: John Russell Smith, 1858. 1st Collected Edition. 2 vols. Small 8vo; contemp tree calf; spine joints a bit dry; morocco labels; gilt dec gilt borders and dentelles; aeg. Internally Fine. *DRAMATIS PERSONAE.* $125

THE DWINDLING PARTY. London, 1982. Edward Gorey. Pop-up bk. *BOOKFINDERS INTL.* $50

THE EDUCATION OF A FRENCH MODEL, KIKI'S MEMOIRS. Intro by Ernest Hemingway. NY: Pub at the sign of the Boar's Head, 1950. Trans by Samuel Putnam. VG in yellow cl and torn and soiled dj. *SECOND LIFE.* $45

THE EDUCATION OF HENRY ADAMS: AN AUTOBIOGRAPHY. Henry S. Canby (intro). Boston: LEC, 1944. One of 1500 illus, signed by Samuel Chamberlain. Fine in lightly soiled slipcase. *CAPTAIN'S BOOKSHELF.* $100

THE EXPLOITS AND TRIUMPHS, IN EUROPE, OF PAUL MORPHY, THE CHESS CHAMPION. (By Frederick Milnes Edge.) NY: D. Appleton and Company, 1859. 1st ed. Brn cl rubbed, bumped & stained, chipped at spine & joints. viii,203pp,4pp pub's catalog. Front hinge starting; one page corner creased; owner stamp, names. Frontis, 3 plts. *BLUE MOUNTAIN.* $275

THE EXTERMINATION OF 500,000 JEWS IN THE WARSAW GHETTO. NY, (1944). NF. *POLYANTHOS.* $35

THE FACTS OF LIFE. London, 1984. Jonathan Miller and David Pelham. Pop-up bk. *BOOKFINDERS INTL.* $40

THE FAMOUS PARKS AND GARDENS OF THE WORLD. London: T. Nelson, 1880. Small hole in front joint, hinges cracking, o/w VG. *WREDEN.* $70

THE FARMER'S GUIDE IN HIRING AND STOCKING FARMS....(By Arthur Young.) Dublin: Exshaw et al, 1771. 1st Dublin ed. 2 vols. 336; 380pp. 4 figures (2 full-pg), 8 engr plts (2 fldg). Contemp calf, hinge little tender. VG. *SECOND LIFE.* $425

THE FIRST SETTLERS OF NEW-ENGLAND. (By Lydia Maria Child.) Boston: Munroe and Francis, and Charles S. Francis, New-York: (1829) 1st ed. 1st issue w/imprint as noted. 283pp,adv. Uncut, bound in orig (repaired) linen backed boards w/paper label. Water stain through leaves. Sticker. Tight. BAL 3100. *SECOND LIFE.* $65

THE FIRST SETTLERS OF VIRGINIA. (By John Davis). NY: Ptd for I. Riley & Co, 1806. 2nd ed, enl. 284pp. Newly rebound in 1/4 calf and marbled boards. NF. *CHAPEL HILL.* $250

THE FLATEY BOOK AND RECENTLY DISCOVERED VATICAN MANUSCRIPTS CONCERNING AMERICA. London: Norroena Society, 1906. Grn cl w/silver/brn cover illus. Some wear, overall VG. *PARMER.* $95

THE FOUR GOSPELS OF THE LORD JESUS CHRIST, ACCORDING TO THE AUTHORIZED VERSION OF KING JAMES I. Waltham St. Lawrence, 1931. One of 500. 65 wood engr by Eric Gill. Linen boards, pigskin spine and tips, raised bands, teg; sm area of sl discoloration on front cover, which is usually the case with this book. *DAWSON'S.* $7500

THE FOUR HUNDREDTH ANNIVERSARY CELEBRATION OF THE DE HUMANI CORPORIS FABRICA OF ANDREAS VESALIUS. New Haven, 1943. 1st ed. Scarce. *FYE.* $75

THE FURNITURE OF THOMAS CHIPPENDALE. (Added title: SPECIMENS OF OLD ENGLISH FURNITURE IN THE POSSESSION OF PARTRIDGE, LEWIS AND SIMMONS). London: (Geo. Pulman & Sons). N.d. (circa 1925). 34 photogr plts. Spine a bit darkened. *KARMIOLE.* $75

THE GENERAL: OR, TWELVE NIGHTS IN THE HUNTERS CAMP: A NARRATIVE OF REAL LIFE. (By William Barrows.) Boston: Lee and Shepard, 1869. 1st ed. Author's name spelled "Barrow" on spine. Good. Howes B188. *LAURIE.* $100

THE GENIUS OF ERIN, COLUMBIA'S FREEDOM, FLIGHTS OF FANCY, LUCINDA, &c. Being, Part 1. of a Series of Poems, by a Citizen of South Carolina. (By Alexander Garden.). Charleston, (SC): D.J. Dowling, printer, 1836. 1st ed. 190pp. Orig cl-backed boards. Lib bkpl, blindstamp; lt shelfwear, dampstaining on covers, lt internal dampstaining at rear, but generally VG. *CHAPEL HILL.* $200

The GENIUS OF LOTHAR MEGGENDORFER. NY, 1985. Appreciation by Maurice Sendak. Tor Lokvig (eng). Moveable bk. *BOOKFINDERS INTL.* $30

THE GENTLEMAN FARMER....(By Henry Home, Lord Kames.) Edinburgh: John Bell, 1779. 2nd ed, w/additions. 438pp. Later calf backed boards, owner sigs little trimmed, some minor foxing. 3 plts. VG. *SECOND LIFE.* $325

THE GEORGIA BEQUEST. MANOLIA; OR, THE VALE OF TALLULAH. By W.R. Rembert.) Augusta: McKinne & Hall, 1854. 1st ed. 12mo, 192pp. Orig purple cl. Lib bkpl, blindstamp, spine and corners a bit faded, but VG. *CHAPEL HILL.* $95

THE GOLDEN SIXPENCE. London: Nelson, (n.d., c. 1910). Near 4to. Unpaginated. 4 full-page color plates + numerous b/w illus. Corners bumped else VG w/bright pict cvr of tiny snow shovelers. Red cloth binding has bled to rear cvr in two places. *BEBBAH.* $38

THE GREAT DINOSAUR POP-UP BOOK. London, 1986. Illus Karen Johnson. Pop-up bk. *BOOKFINDERS INTL.* $18

THE GREAT INDUSTRIES OF THE UNITED STATES. Hartford: J.B. Burr & Hyde, 1872. xx,1,304pp, index, 73 full pg illus. Orig dec cl. Some wear on spine, else NF. *CONNOLLY & WADE.* $225

THE HAND-BOOK OF WHIST. Phila: George S. Appleton. 1849. 1st ed. 63pp+(l)pp ads. Fine. *KARMIOLE.* $35

THE HASHEESH EATER: BEING THE LIFE OF A PYTHAGOREAN. (By Fitz-Hugh Ludlow.) NY: Harper & Brothers, 1857. 1st ed, 1st bk. 371pp. Textured brn cl rubbed & bumped, head & tail of spine & rear joint worn. Dec blind frame gilt title. Scattered foxing. VG. *BLUE MOUNTAIN.* $125

THE HEADSMAN; OR, THE ABBAYE DES VIGNERONS. (By James Fenimore Cooper.) Phila: Carey, Lea & Blanchard, 1833. 2 vols. 263,(1),ads(24); 262,(3),ads(36)pp. Blue-gray paper boards, tan paper shelfback, ptd paper label on spine; spine worn, label lacking from 2nd vol. BAL 3862. Not all copies have the ads. *WEBER.* $300

THE HIBERNIAN PATRIOT...(By Jonathan Swift.) Printed at Dublin. London Reprinted: A. Moor, 1730. 1st London ed. Tall 8vo, 264pp. Contemp speckled calf, gilt rules, lea label. Top inch of front hinge starting, else bright, well-margined. *HARTFIELD.* $485

THE HISTORY OF INOCULATION AND VACCINATION FOR THE PREVENTION AND TREATMENT OF DISEASE. London, 1913. 1st ed. *FYE.* $45

THE HISTORY OF JACKSON COUNTY, IOWA. Chicago: Western Historical Company, 1879. 2pp map. Brown 1/2 morocco, broken, needing rebinding. *HUDSON.* $50

THE HISTORY OF THE REBELLION, 1745 AND 1746....(By Andrew Henderson.) London: rprtd from the Edinburgh ed: Griffiths, 1748. viii,126pp. Contemp calf, some worn contemp calf. VG, hinges little tender. *SECOND LIFE.* $245

THE HISTORY OF THE WAR, BETWEEN THE UNITED STATES AND GREAT-BRITAIN, WHICH COMMENCED IN JUNE, 1812...CORRESPONDENCE WHICH PASSED BETWEEN THE TWO GOVERNMENTS...TO WHICH IS ADDED, THE TREATY OF PEACE, AND A LIST OF VESSELS.... Hartford: William S. Marsh, 1815. (By John Russell, Jr.) 1st ed. 472pp. Contemp calf, cvrs worn, foxing throughout. Scarce. *LEFKOWICZ.* $175

THE HISTORY OF TOM THUMB. NY: McLoughlin Brothers, n.d. Part of the "Aunt Louisa's Big Picture Series." Pict wrappers worn at spine, few closed tears, 1 corner chipped, but still VG. *JAFFE.* $125

THE HUDSON—FULTON CELEBRATION MCMIX. THE METROPOLITAN MUSEUM OF ART EXHIBITION VOL. 1 AND 2. NY: MET, 1909. 1st ed. VG. *BACKROOM.* $150

THE HUMAN BODY. London, 1983. Jonathan Miller and David Pelham. Pop-up bk. *BOOKFINDERS INTL.* $45

THE IDENTITY OF JUNIUS. (By John Taylor.) 1st Amer ed, from 2nd Eng ed. Corrected, enl. NY: Kirk & Mercein, 1818. 300pp, 6fldg facs plts. Contemp full calf worn. Outer hinges cracking, front cover loose. Age-staining, damp-staining (mostly marginal) in text, o/w VG. *DIAMOND.* $150

THE INFINITE BEYOND. London, 1989. Pop-up bk. *BOOKFINDERS INTL.* $10

THE INSURANCE LIBRARY ASSOCIATION, BOSTON. Boston, MA, 1901. 1st ed. VG. Rebound. *BACKROOM.* $50

THE JAMES CURRAN COLLECTION OF RARE EIGHTEENTH CENTURY AMERICAN FURNITURE. March 1940. Wraps soiled, label attached. Good+, priced. *BACKROOM.* $40

THE JOURNAL OF HEALTH CONDUCTED BY AN ASSOCIATION OF PHYSICIANS. VOLUMES 1-4. Phila, 1830-1833. 1st ed. 4 vols. 1/4 lea. Title page of Vol. 1 torn w/o loss of text, eps lacking, scattered foxing. Scarce. *FYE.* $200

THE LEATHER BOTTEL. (Concord, MA: Sign of the Vine. N.d. circa 1902). 24mo. (4),10pp. Frontis. Ptd in red and black. Designed by Will Bradley. Boards, paper cvr label. *KARMIOLE.* $100

THE LETTERS OF JUNIUS....(By William R. Dickerson.) Phila: Pub anonymously, 1848. 1st ed. New wraps. Orig wraps not bound in. Title-pg sl browned, chipped. Corners sl chipped, o/w VG. *DIAMOND.* $45

THE LIBRARY OF JEROME KERN. NY: The Anderson Galleries, 1929. 2 vols. 1st ed. Orig ptd wraps. VG set (prices realized pencilled in). *CHAPEL HILL.* $200

THE LIFE AND ADVENTURES OF MRS. CHRISTIAN DAVIES. (By Daniel DeFoe?). London: Montagu, 1741. 2nd ed, to which is added an appendix. iv,87,104,xvi,20pp. Frontis (lacking top margin), Bound in rebacked contemp calf w/new eps, Nice. *SECOND LIFE.* $450

THE LIFE AND ADVENTURES OF PETER WILKINS....By R.S. (pseud), a Passenger in the Hector. Improved Edition. (By Robert Paltock.) Boston: Charles Gaylord. 1832. 12mo. 186 pp. Frontis. Contemp calf over ptd boards. Extrems rubbed. *KARMIOLE.* $75

THE LIFE AND WRITINGS OF MAJOR JACK DOWNING...Boston: Lilly, Wait, Colman, & Holden, 1834. 3rd ed. 11 plts. Orig cl, boards; pict gilt spine. *SCHOYER'S.* $45

THE LIFE, CAMPAIGNS, AND PUBLIC SERVICES OF GENERAL McCLELLAN. Phila: T.B. Peterson & Brothers, (1864). 17-18pp, 24pp pub's ads. Frontis. Orig cl. *SCHOYER'S.* $40

THE LIFE OF EDMUND KEAN. (By Bryan W. Procter.) NY: Harper & Brothers, 1835. 1st Amer ed. Orig patterned cl; edges soiled; spine faded; paper label, worn; scattered foxing. *DRAMATIS.* $60

THE LIFE OF EDMUND KEAN. (By Bryan W. Procter.) London: Edward Moxon, 1835. 1st ed. 2 vols. Later full calf, gilt, engr frontis port to 1st vol. Leather label; gilt dentelles; residue of removed bkpl to paste-down of Vol I; faint staining to cvrs of 1st vol; else Fine. *DRAMATIS.* $175

THE LIFE OF NAPOLEON BONAPARTE....(By Sir Walter Scott.) Phila: Carey, Lea & Carey, 1827. 1st US ed. 3 vols. Orig boards, uncut (cvr of vol 1 & 2, separate). Generally VG, clean set. Frontis. Bound w/ads, errata. *SECOND LIFE.* $125

THE LIFE OF P.T. BARNUM. Written by himself, Author's Edition. London: Sampson Low, Son & Co., 1855. 1st Eng ed, 3rd state. Small 8vo, contemp half roan; extremities rubbed; illus. VG. *DRAMATIS PERSONAE.* $80

THE LILY AND THE TOTEM....(By William Gilmore Simms.) NY: Baker & Scribner, 1850. 1st ed. 470pp. Orig blue-grn cl. Few spots of marginal foxing, but superb. Nice. *CHAPEL HILL.* $500

THE LITTLE GUIDE AROUND NEW YORK, WITH A MAP, FOR THE MILLION. NY: H.H. Lloyd and Co, 1858. Part of rear wrapper gone, no loss of text. Double pp city plan. *HUDSON.* $50

THE LITTLEST ANGEL. 1964. Illus Borge Svennson. Dick Dudley (eng). Pop-up bk. *BOOKFINDERS INTL.* $35

THE LIVES OF GENERAL U.S. GRANT, AND SCHUYLER COLFAX. Phila: T.B. Peterson and Brothers, (1868). 362pp,16pp pub's ads. 2 ports, 4 plts. Spine ends chipped. *SCHOYER'S.* $35

THE LOOKING-GLASS FOR THE MIND, or The Juvenile Friend....(By Arnaud Berquin). Phila: John Bioren. 1819. iv,272pp. Copper-engr frontis and text woodcuts, many somewhat crudely (by a child) hand-colored. Contemp mottled calf, worn, spine extrems repaired, outer hinges cracked but holding sound. Occasional text soiling, a few minor tears. Still, a complete copy of a scarce American juvenile. *KARMIOLE.* $150

THE LUCKY COIN. NY, 1989. Marget Greaves (story), Liz Underhill (illus). Flaps every page, lucky coin on back. Moveable bk. *BOOKFINDERS INTL.* $15

THE MANNERS, CUSTOMS, AND ANTIQUITIES OF THE INDIANS OF NORTH AND SOUTH AMERICA. (By Samuel Griswold Goodrich.) Phila: Thomas, Cowperthwait & Co, 1846. Calf, rear hinge cracked, one sig pulled. *HUDSON.* $85

THE MARINER'S CHRONICLE: CONTAINING NARRATIVES OF THE MOST REMARKABLE DISASTERS AT SEA....New Haven: Durrie and Peck, 1834. 1st ed. Frontis, 12 woodcut plts, each w/2 images. Foxed, but Good. Modern plain buckram. *LEFKOWICZ.* $125

THE MARKET. London, 1987 (Hong Kong). Pop-up bk. *BOOKFINDERS INTL.* $18

THE MARTYRDOM OF LOVEJOY. (by Henry Tanner). Chicago: Fergus Ptg Co, 1881. 1st ed. 233,(1)pp, ivpp ads. Orig cl. Spine sl faded. Remains of cover label. Spine tips, bottom corners worn, else VG. Ex-libris. Howes T22. *DIAMOND.* $85

THE MASSACRE OF GLENCO...13th OF FEB. 1692. Edinburgh: (Rptd for D. Webster from ed of 1704),1818. 1st ed. Modern marbled wrappers. Sm repair, mostly marginal, has been made in one leaf, o/w very fresh. *BOOK BLOCK.* $75

THE MASSACRE OF LIEUTENANT GRATTAN & HIS COMMAND BY INDIANS. A.H.Clark, 1983. 1st ed. 5 color plts tipped in. Only 250 hand ptd. Prospectus laid in. 1st ed. VF. *OREGON.* $150

THE MEDICAL & SURGICAL REGISTER: CONSISTING CHIEFLY OF CASES IN THE NEW-YORK HOSPITAL BY JOHN WATTS, JUN., VALENTINE MOTT, AND ALEXANDER H. STEVENS. NY, 1818. 1st ed. Full leather, 406pp. Fine engrvd plts. Fine. Rare. *FYE.* $800

THE MIDDLE STATES: A HANDBOOK FOR TRAVELLERS. Boston: Houghton, Osgood and Company, 1879. 3rd ed. 21 (of 22) maps and plans. Cl somewhat water spotted. *HUDSON.* $125

THE MIGHTY GIANTS. London, 1988. 4 double pg pop-ups. Pop-up bk. *BOOKFINDERS INTL.* $10

THE MILITARY HISTORY OF OHIO. NY: Hardesty, 1889. 316pp. 1/2 leather, no spine, cvrs loose but holding. Good. *ARTIS.* $75

THE MONIKINS. A TALE. (By James Fenimore Cooper). London: Richard Bentley, 1835. 1st ed. 3 vols. 12mo. xii,300;300; 318pp. Orig brn calf-backed marbled boards. Vol 1 w/lt worming at inner corners; occasional foxing, stains; corner showing, sides sl rubbed. BAL 3867. *WEBER.* $400

THE MOTHER'S MANUAL....(by Frances Trollope). London: Treuttel and Wurtz, 1833. 2nd ed. 82pp. 20 plts. Full calf, hinges tender, wear along hinges, extrems of spine. Very clean. *SECOND LIFE.* $325

THE NATURAL HISTORY OF INSECTS. NY, 1855. Ltr prtg. 2 vols. Call number sticker on spine, bkpls. *SUTTON.* $35

THE NAVAL TEMPLE: CONTAINING A COMPLETE HISTORY OF THE BATTLES FOUGHT BY THE NAVY OF THE UNITED STATES...1794, TO THE PRESENT TIME....Boston: Barber Badger, 1816. (By Horace Kimball.) 1st ed. Engr title, 19 plts. Antique-style modern calf, dampstains to 1st few leaves foxing, but Good. *LEFKOWICZ.* $275

THE NAVIGATOR: CONTAINING DIRECTIONS FOR NAVIGATING THE MONONGAHELA, ALLEGHENY, OHIO, AND MISSISSIPPI RIVERS. (By Zadok Cramer.) Pittsburgh: Cramer, Spear, & Eichbaum, 1811. 7th ed. Orig unlettered calf-backed boards. Very Nice, but incomplete, lacking pp 253-264 or Sig. X, which comprises 4 maps. W/rubber stamped cipher and coronet on title. *HUDSON.* $250

THE NEGROES OF NEBRASKA. Lincoln, NE, 1940. WPA. 1st ed. Orig stiff ptd wrappers. Fine. *McGOWAN.* $75

THE NEGROES OF NEBRASKA. Omaha Urban League Comunity Center, 1940. 1st ed. Fine in wraps. *BEASLEY.* $40

THE NEW ENGLAND FARRIER. (By Paul Jewett.) Boston: Gaylord, 1840. 22nd ed. 2 plts. 214pp. Worn paper covered boards w/paper label. VG. *SECOND LIFE.* $85

THE NORTH GEORGIA GAZETTE, AND WINTER CHRONICLE. London: John Murray, 1821. 1st ed. Modern cl spine and brds; eps renewed. Sm flaw in paper of half-title; else very nice. *PARMER.* $500

THE OBSTETRICAL JOURNAL OF GREAT BRITAIN AND IRELAND INCLUDING MIDWIFERY AND THE DISEASES OF WOMEN AND CHILDREN. VOLUMES 1-7. Ed. by J.H. Aveling. London, 1873-1879. One backstrip missing w/spine broken on that vol. Other vols. VG. *FYE.* $300

THE OFFICIAL GUIDE TO THE KLONDYKE COUNTRY AND THE GOLD FIELDS OF ALASKA. With Official Maps. Chicago: W.B. Conkey Co, 1897. 1st ed. 295pp. Fldg map. Dec red cover w/gilt w/overall spot discoloration, o/w VG. *BLUE DRAGON.* $150

THE OFFICIAL HISTORY OF THE STRIKE OF 1886 ON THE SOUTHWESTERN RAILWAY. Jefferson City: Tribune State Printer, 1887. 1st ed. NF but possibly missing a prelim between title page and intro. Comp slip. *BEASLEY.* $85

THE OLD TESTAMENT. (By Marguerite DeAngeli.) Doubleday, (1960). Stated 1st ed. Illus by author. VG in VG dj w/chips, 2 scratches to rear panel. *BEBBAH.* $32

THE OREGON TRAIL, THE MISSOURI RIVER TO THE PACIFIC OCEAN. NY: Hastings, (1939). 1st ed. American Guide Series. Color fldg map tipped to rear. VG. *OREGON.* $60

THE ORIGINAL LIFE AND ADVENTURES OF TOM QUICK, THE INDIAN SLAYER, AS PUBLISHED AT MONTICELLO IN 1851. (By James E. Quinlan.) Deposit, NY: Deposit Journal, 1894. Cloth w/gilt title. Pulp paper darkened, hinges weak, bkpl. VG. Howes Q21. *BOHLING.* $75

THE ORIGINAL MR. JACOBS: A STARTLING EXPOSE. Telemachus Thomas Timayenis (attributed to). NY: The Minerva Pub Co (Press of J.J. Little & Co), (1888). 1st ed. Orig orange cl rubbed, bumped, bkpl removed from front pastedown, w/gilt title on spine. Dec eps. vi,308pp. Ink inscrip title pg. VG. *BLUE MOUNTAIN.* $375

THE PARLIAMENTS AND COUNCILS OF ENGLAND. (By Charles Henry Parry.) London: John Murray, 1839. 1st ed. Rebound in buckram. Fine. *DIAMOND.* $150

THE PATHFINDER; OR, THE INLAND SEA. (By James Fenimore Cooper.) Phila: Lea & Blanchard, 1840. 1st Amer ed, state 1, w/imprints of J. Fagan and T.K. & P.G. Collins at center of verso of title (unpaginated). 2 vols. 12mo. i-vi, (13)-240; 233pp. Purple cl, ptd paper spine label. Foxing, but VG. BAL 3892. *WEBER.* $500

THE PATHFINDER; OR THE INLAND SEA. (By James Fenimore Cooper.) London: Richard Bentley, 1840. 1st ed. 3 vols. 12mo. viii,320; 348; 339pp. Muslin purple cl backed boards, ptd paper spine label. Sig of Rev. H. Percival. Bkpl. BAL 3891. *WEBER.* $1,000

THE PENINSULAR CAMPAIGN OF GENERAL MCCLELLAN IN 1862. Boston, 1881. 249pp. Fldg map. A little dj wear o/w VG+. *PRATT.* $135

THE PETER RABBIT STORY BOOK. Platt & Munk, (1935). Illus Bess Goe Willis, color frontis. VG+. *BEBBAH.* $30

THE PHARMACOPOEIA OF THE UNITED STATES OF AMERICA. NY: Published by S. Converse, November, 1830. 2nd ed. 176pp. Rebound in cl. Ink name,number on title page, little age staining in text, ex-lib w/lib blind-stamp bottom of title page. *DIAMOND.* $150

THE PHYSIOGRAPHY OF THE RIO GRANDE VALLEY, NEW MEXICO. Washington, DC: GPO, 1913. 1 fldg map, plts. Orig grn cl. *HUDSON.* $40

THE PILOT; A TALE OF THE SEA. (By James Fenimore Cooper.) London: G. Cowie & Co, 1826. 2 vols. viii,288, 313pp. Purple calf-backed marbled boards; a few signatures loose in vol 1, o/w Good. *WEBER.* $150

THE PIRATES OWN BOOK, OR AUTHENTIC NARRATIVES. (Ellms, Charles, comp). Salem, 1924. Pub. 4. Facs of orig ed of 1837. Fine. *LEFKOWICZ.* $125

THE PLAY BOOK OF ROBIN HOOD. NY: Harper Bros, 1927. Front and rear both have fold out flaps, and all 4 "pages" open up to depict Sherwood Forest and Nottingham. The bk itself comes out and after the story there are 8pp cut-outs, each w/stand to glue on back. Some browning of pp overall, all illus, cut-outs are Fine. Pop-up bk. *BOOKFINDERS INTL.* $250

THE POP UP KAMA SUTRA. NY: Bonanza, 1984. 1st ed. 4 pop ups. VF. *MAD DOG.* $35

THE POP-UP MOTHER GOOSE. With "Pop-up" Illustrations in Full Color by Harold B. Lentz. 3 colored pop-ups, pict boards. NY: Blue Ribbon Press, (1934). 1st ed. Owner inscrip, o/w Fine. *JAFFE.* $150

THE POP-UP PUSS IN-BOOTS. Blue Ribbon, (1934). Measures 9" x 8" closed. 3 pop-ups, 13pp text. Illus Carey Cloud & Harold Lentz. Some wear to cvr but VG+ and interior and pop-up Fine. *BEBBAH.* $75

THE PRAIRIE: A TALE. By the Author of the "Pioneers and the Last of the Mohicans." Phila: Carey, Lea & Carey, 1827. 2 vols. 1st Amer ed w/copyright notice corrected by slip pasted in. 1/2 leather, fancy boards. One spine eroded at top. Texts foxed, edges stained yellow. VG. *AUTHORS OF THE WEST.* $350

THE PRAIRIE; A TALE. (By James Fenimore Cooper.) Phila: Carey, Lea & Carey, 1827. 2 vols. 12mo. ads. 12,(v)-xii,13-252; 1-276pp. Ads dated April 1827, and not present in all copies. Mounted slip verso of title-pg, revising copyright notice. Later brn paper shelf-back, w/orig blue-gray paper over boards, ptd paper label. Owner sig. Foxed and browned but generally well-preserved. *WEBER.* $750

THE PRESERVATION OF OUR TREES. Kent: Davey Tree Expert Co., 1912. 1st ed. 60pp, wraps. VG. *ARCHER.* $20

THE PROCEEDINGS AT LARGE ON THE TRIAL OF JOHN DONELLAN, ESQ. FOR THE WILLFUL MURDER (BY POISON) OF SIR THE. EDWARD ALLESLEY BOUGHTON...TRIED BEFORE MR. JUSTIC BULLER. London 1781. 1/2 lea, 152pp. *FYE.* $250

THE PROCEEDINGS OF THE CHARAKA CLUB. Vol 4. NY, 1916. Ltd ed. *FYE.* $100

THE PROCEEDINGS OF THE CHARAKA CLUB. Vol 5. NY, 1919. Ltd ed. Scarce. *FYE.* $150

THE PROCEEDINGS OF THE CHARAKA CLUB. Vol 7. NY, 1931. Ltd ed. *FYE.* $75

THE REAL GHOSTBUSTERS. US, 1987. 3 double-pg pop-ups. Pop-up bk. *BOOKFINDERS INTL.* $20

THE REGISTER OF THE AMERICAN SADDLE HORSE BREEDERS' ASSOCIATION. Vol. IX. Louisville, 1929. Quarter leather. Spine worn. *OCTOBER FARM.* $95

THE REGISTER OF THE AMERICAN SADDLE HORSE BREEDERS' ASSOCIATION. Vol. X. Louisville, 1931. Spine ends worn. *OCTOBER FARM.* $95

THE REGISTER OF THE AMERICAN SADDLE HORSE BREEDERS' ASSOCIATION. Vol. XI. Louisville, 1932. Spine ends worn. *OCTOBER FARM.* $95

THE REGISTER OF THE NATIONAL SADDLE HORSE BREEDERS' ASSOCIATION. Vol. 1. Louisville, 1892. VG. *OCTOBER FARM.* $325

THE ROARING TWENTIES. London, 1984. Pop-up bk. *BOOKFINDERS INTL.* $20

THE ROMANCE OF BALLOONING. NY: The Viking Press, (1971). 1st ed. Mounted color plts, fldg map. Illus color dj. *KARMIOLE.* $40

THE ROMANCE OF KING ARTHUR AND HIS KNIGHTS OF THE ROUND TABLE. Macmillan, 1917. 1st Amer trade ed. 517pp. 16 color plates & 7 b/w plates by Arthur Rackham. Color plates w/titled slip sheets. Gilt dec spine, cvr. VG+ w/one color plate w/1.25" mended tear. *BEBBAH.* $160

THE ROYAL DECREES OF SCANDEROON. (By William Osborn Stoddard). NY: Russells' American Steam Printing House, 1869. 1st ed. Frontis, 4plts. Orig cl w/gilt vignette & ptg. Spine tip, corner wear. Stain at bottom pp margins, o/w VG. *DIAMOND.* $75

THE SCHOOLHOUSE FARTHEST WEST: ST. LAWRENCE ISLAND, ALASKA. By V.C. Gambell.) NY: Woman's Board of Home Missions of the Presbyterian Church, (1910). 2nd ed. Light wear, wraps split at spine ends. *BOHLING.* $45

THE SEA, THE SHIP AND THE SAILOR. Salem: Marine Research Society, 1925. VG in dj. *PARMER.* $85

THE SECRET MUSEUM OF ANTHROPOLOGY. Privately issued by the Amer Anthropological Soc, NY, 1935. 1st ed. VG. *CONNOLLY & WADE.* $25

THE SHERLOCK HOLMES. Northumberland Street. London. W.C.2. Catalogue of the Collection in the Bars and the Grill Room and in the Reconstruction of Part of the Living Room at 221B Baker Street....London, (1959). 4th impression. Wraps. *DIAMOND.* $25

THE SIEGE OF DETROIT IN 1763. N.p., 1912. 1958 reprint. Lakeside Classic #56. Gift card laid in. Fine. *PRATT.* $35

THE SLANG DICTIONARY. London, 1864. 2nd ed. Rubbing to spine extremities. *POLYANTHOS.* $60

THE SLAVE: OR MEMOIRS OF ARCHY MOORE. (By Richard Hildreth.) 2nd ed. 2 vols in 1. Boston: Whipple and Damrell, 1840. 8vo. 123;115pp. Orig cloth backed boards, front cover nearly detached. Binding soiled, light waterstaining throughout text. *M & S.* $500

THE SLEEPY LAGOON CASE. Orson Welles (foreword). LA: The Citizens' Committee for the Defense of Mexican-American Youth. 1942. Orig ptd tan wrappers. *KARMIOLE.* $30

THE SOCIAL EVIL IN CHICAGO, A STUDY OF EXISTING CONDITIONS....Chicago: Gunthorpe-Warren, (1911). 3rd ed. Hinges loose. VG. *SECOND LIFE.* $45

THE SPINNER'S BOOK OF FICTION. SF: Paul Elder, 1903. 1st ed. Frontis, 5 inserted full color plts. Teg, untrimmed. Fine. *CONNOLLY & WADE.* $80

THE SPORTSMAN IN IRELAND...London: Henry Colburn, 1840. 1st ed. Minor chipping top and base of spine, some shelfwear, overall remarkably Good. Rare. *OLD LONDON.* $85

THE SPY; A TALE OF THE NEUTRAL GROUND....London: G. and W.B. Whittaker, 1823. 2nd ed. xii, 318; 314; 301pp. Orig boards, ptd paper spine label; spines worn, covers off, label browned and chipped, but present. *WEBER.* $200

THE STATUTE LAWS OF THE TERRITORY OF IOWA, Enacted at the First Session of the Legislative Assembly of Said Territory, Held at Burlington, A.D. 1839-'39. Published by Authority. Dubuque: Russell & Reeves, Printers. 1839. (2),596pp. Orig calf-backed boards, somewhat rubbed. Some internal stains and foxing, but overall decent. Rare. *KARMIOLE.* $350

THE STORM. (By Daniel Defoe). London: Sawbridge, 1704. 1st ed. 272pp. Sm hole title pg (not affecting text, some repair, some worming affecting couple of letters.) Rebacked. VG. *SECOND LIFE.* $300

THE STORY OF AMERICAN HEROISM, THRILLING NARRATIVES OF PERSONAL ADVENTURE DURING THE GREAT CIVIL WAR AS TOLD BY MEDAL WINNERS AND ROLL OF HONOR MEN. Chicago, 1896. 1st ed. 798pp. Light cover wear o/w Fine. *PRATT.* $110

THE STORY OF DR. SCORESBY THE ARCTIC NAVIGATOR. London: T. Nelson and Sons, 1880. Frontis. Rubbed, series title on spine. *LEFKOWICZ.* $45

THE SURGEON'S VADE-MECUM: CONTAINING THE SYMPTOMS CAUSES, DIAGNOSIS, PROGNOSIS, AND TREATMENT OF SURGICAL DISEASES....Albany, (1813). (By Robert Hooper.) 1st Amer ed. Full leather, 275pp. *FYE.* $200

THE TALES OF THE GENII; OR, THE DELIGHTFUL LESSONS OF HORAM....Sir Charles Morell (trans). 2 vols. London: For James Wallis, 1805. 1st ed. xliv,368pp; 432pp. 14 plts. 1/2 morocco, gilt spine, edges sl rubbed, hinges tender, sl foxed, o/w VG. *WORLDWIDE.* $125

THE THINGS IN MOLDY MANOR. NY, 1988. Illus Andy Everitt-Stewart. Keith Moseley (eng). Pop-up bk. *BOOKFINDERS INTL.* $15

THE THOUSAND AND ONE NIGHTS COMMONLY CALLED, IN ENGLAND, THE ARABIAN NIGHTS' ENTERTAINMENTS. A New Translation...by Edward William Lane. 1st ed of the Lane trans. 3 vols. London: Charles Knight. 1839-1841. xxxiv,618; xii,644; xii,764pp. 19th-c full maroon pebbled calf, gilt; extrems bit rubbed. Very nice. *KARMIOLE.* $275

THE THREE KITTENS. London: George Routledge, n.d. Dec wrappers worn at spine & splitting, some foxing, o/w VG. *JAFFE.* $125

THE TOUR OF DOCTOR SYNTAX THROUGH LONDON, OR THE PLEASURES AND MISERIES OF THE METROPOLIS. London, 1820. 20 hand colored plts, incl title pg; 3/4 lea. NF. *POLYANTHOS.* $300

THE TOURIST, OR POCKET MANUAL FOR TRAVELLERS...AND STAGE ROAD. (By Robert J. Vandewater.) NY: J. & J. Harper, 1830. 1st ed. 59pp. Fold-out frontis map. Orig cl backed boards w/ptd label. Binding spotted & w/some wear, tight, foxing. Howes V28. *BOHLING.* $225

THE TOURIST, OR POCKET MANUAL FOR TRAVELLERS...AND STAGE ROAD. (by Robert J. Vandewater) NY: Harper & Bros., 1835. 4th ed, enl, improved. 106pp. Fold out frontis, map. Orig cl w/ptd label. Light wear, some foxing, map w/tear on half of one fold (3"). VG. *BOHLING.* $175

THE TOWN MOUSE AND THE COUNTRY MOUSE. Saalfield, (1942). 12pp. Illus Ethel Hays. Combbound thick cardboard pict boards. Corner wear, VG+ w/extremely scarce dj (narrow piece missing at spine; other short tears, but Good+). *BEBBAH.* $35

THE VINTER'S, BREWERS, SPIRIT MERCHANT'S AND LICENSED VICTUALLER'S GUIDE. By a practical man. London: Sherwood, Gilbert & Piper, 1838. 5th ed. Cover staining, recased w/new eps; slight staining, foxing some pp, o/w Good. *DIAMOND.* $60

THE WAR OF THE REBELLION: A COMPILATION OF THE OFFICIAL RECORDS OF THE UNION AND CONFEDERATE ARMIES. Orig issue in red leather with gold lettering. All volumes with a little cover wear o/w VG+.

SERIES I, VOLUME XI, PART II. Reports, etc. The Peninsular Campaign; March 17-September 2, 1862. *PRATT.* $20

SERIES I, VOLUME XVI, PART I. Reports. Operations in Kentucky, Middle and East Tennessee, North Alabama, and Southwest Virginia; June 10-October 31, 1862. *PRATT.* $20

SERIES I, VOLUME XVI, PART II. Correspondence, etc. Operations in Kentucky, Middle and East Tennessee, and North Alabama, and Southwest Virginia; June 10-October 31, 1862. *PRATT.* $20

SERIES I, VOLUME XVII, PART II. Correspondence, etc. Operations in West Tennessee and Northern Mississippi; June 10, 1862-January 20, 1863. *PRATT.* $20

SERIES I, VOLUME XX, PART II. Correspondence, etc. Operations in Kentucky, Middle and East Tennessee, North Alabama, and

Southwest Virginia; November 1, 1862-January 20, 1863. Front cover detached but present. *PRATT.* $12.50

SERIES I, VOLUME XXII, PART II. Correspondence-Operations in Missouri, Arkansas, Kansas, the Indian Territory, and the Department of the Northwest; January 1-December 31, 1863. *PRATT.* $20

SERIES I, VOLUME XXIII, PART I. Reports-Operations in Missouri, Arkansas, Kansas, the Indian Territory, and Department of the Northwest; November 20, 1862-December 31, 1863. *PRATT.* $20

SERIES I, VOLUME XXX, PART IV. Correspondence, Union and Confederate-Operations in Kentucky, Southwest Virginia, Tennessee, Mississippi, North Alabama, and North Georgia; August 11, 1863-October 19, 1863. *PRATT.* $20

SERIES I, VOLUME XXXIV, PART III. Correspondence, etc. Operations in Louisiana and the Trans-Mississippi States and Territories, April 1-June 30, 1864. *PRATT.* $20

SERIES I, VOLUME XXXVI, PART I. Reports. Operations in Southeastern Virginia and North Carolina; May 1-June 12, 1864. *PRATT.* $20

SERIES I, VOLUME XXXVI, PART III. Correspondence, etc. Operations in Southwest Virginia and North Carolina; May 20-June 12, 1864.; *PRATT.* $20

SERIES I, VOLUME XL, PART III. Correspondence, etc. Operations in Southeastern Virginia and North Carolina; August 1-December 31, 1864. *PRATT.* $20

SERIES I, VOLUME XLII, PART I. Reports. Operations in North Carolina and Southeastern Virginia; October 1-December 31, 1864. *PRATT.* $20

SERIES I, VOLUME XLIII, PART I. Reports, Correspondence, etc. Operations in Northern Virginia, West Virginia, Maryland, and Pennsylvania; August 4-December 31, 1864. *PRATT.* $20

SERIES I, VOLUME XLV, PART I. Reports, Correspondence, etc. Operations in Kentucky, Southwest Virginia, Tennessee, Mississippi, Alabama, and North Georgia; November 14, 1864-January 23, 1865. *PRATT.* $20

SERIES I, VOLUME XLV, PART II. Correspondence, etc. Operations in Kentucky, Southwest Virginia, Tennessee, Mississippi, Alabama, and North Georgia; December 1, 1864-January 23, 1865. *PRATT.* $20

SERIES I, VOLUME XLIX, PART I. Reports, Correspondence, etc. Operations in Kentucky, Southwestern Virginia, Tennessee, North and Central Georgia, Mississippi, Alabama, and West Florida; January 1-June 30, 1865. *PRATT.* $20

SERIES I, VOLUME LII, PART I. Reports, Correspondence, etc. Operations in Southwestern Virginia, Kentucky, Tennessee, Mississippi, Alabama, West Florida, Northern Georgia. Supplement; January 1, 1861-June 30, 1865. *PRATT.* $20

SERIES I, VOLUME LII, PART II. Reports, Correspondence, etc. Operations in Southwestern Virginia, Kentucky, Tennessee, Mississippi, Alabama, West Florida, Northern Georgia. Supplement; January 1, 1861-June 30, 1865. *PRATT.* $20

THE WEPT OF WISH TON-WISH: A TALE....(by James Fenimore Cooper.) Phila: Carey, Lea & Carey, 1829. 1st Amer ed. 2 vols. 251; 234, (ads) 6pp. Blue-gray paper boards, white paper shelfback; pp (11)-12 w/marginal tear into text; foxed; lacks front boards to both vols; vol II w/spine label worn. Slipcase, leather spine label. BAL 3844. *WEBER.* $350

THE WESTERN SANITARY COMMISSION, A SKETCH OF ITS ORIGIN, HISTORY, LABORS FOR THE SICK AND WOUNDED OF THE WESTERN ARMIES, AND AID GIVEN TO FREEDMEN AND UNION REFUGEES, WITH INCIDENTS OF HOSPITAL LIFE. St. Louis, 1864. 1st ed. 144pp. Head and tail of spine chipped. Contents Fine. *FYE.* $300

THE WESTERNERS' BRAND BOOK 1944: BEING A COLLECTION...MARCH 1944 TO MARCH 1945....Unopened. Grey, gilt dec cl. Fine. *CONNOLLY & WADE.* $150

THE WESTERNERS' BRAND BOOK LOS ANGELES CORRAL, 1947. LA, 1948. Ltd to 600. About Fine. *CONNOLLY & WADE.* $145

THE WESTERNERS BRAND BOOK, 1947. (LA): LA Corral of the Westerners, 1947. Two-tone cl in moderately chipped dj. *DAWSON'S.* $100

THE WESTERNERS' BRAND BOOK LOS ANGELES CORRAL, 1948. LA, 1949. Ltd to 400. Tri-fold colored map, fldg colored map. Full-color center painting by Charles Russell. Pict bevelled boards. About Fine. *CONNOLLY & WADE.* $95

THE WESTERNERS' BRAND BOOK LOS ANGELES CORRAL, BOOK 6. LA, 1956. Ltd to 400. Fine. *CONNOLLY & WADE.* $95

THE WESTERNERS' BRAND BOOK LOS ANGELES CORRAL, BOOK SEVEN. LA, 1957. Ltd to 475. Fine. *CONNOLLY & WADE.* $115

THE WESTERNERS BRAND BOOK: BOOK EIGHT. (LA): LA Corral of the Westerners, (1959). Two-tone fabricoid in dj. *DAWSON'S.* $75

THE WESTERNERS' BRAND BOOKS. LOS ANGELES CORRAL, BOOK EIGHT. LA, 1959. Ltd to 525. Bkpl, sm inscription, else Fine. *CONNOLLY & WADE.* $95

THE WESTERNERS BRAND BOOKS. LOS ANGELES CORRAL. BRAND BOOK #9, (1961). Ltd to 550. Fine. *BOOK MARKET.* $35

THE WESTERNERS' BRAND BOOK LOS ANGELES CORRAL, BOOK NINE. LA, 1961. Ltd to 550. Lower corner lightly bumped, else Fine. *CONNOLLY & WADE.* $90

THE WESTERNERS' BRAND BOOK LOS ANGELES CORRAL, BOOK TEN. LA, 1963. Ltd to 525. Fold-out, colored print by Clarence Ellsworth. Gilt on spine sl darkened, else Fine. *CONNOLLY & WADE.* $95

THE WESTERNERS BRAND BOOKS. LOS ANGELES CORRAL. BRAND BOOK #11, 1964. Ltd to 525 numbered. Fine in Fine dj. *BOOK MARKET.* $125

THE WESTERNERS' BRAND BOOK LOS ANGELES CORRAL, BOOK NUMBER 11: THE CALIFORNIA DESERTS. L.A. 1964. Ltd to 525, this being #108. Orange lettering on spine sl faded, else Fine. *CONNOLLY & WADE.* $95

THE WESTERNERS' BRAND BOOK LOS ANGELES CORRAL, BOOK XII. LA, 1966. Ltd to 500. Gilt sl faded on spine, else Fine. *CONNOLLY & WADE.* $70

THE WESTERNERS BRAND BOOK NO. 13 L.A. CORRAL. 1969. Fine in NF dj. *VARNER.* $45

THE WESTERNERS' BRAND BOOK LOS ANGELES CORRAL, NUMBER 13. LA, 1969. Ltd to 750. Fine. *CONNOLLY & WADE.* $75

THE WESTERNERS BRAND BOOKS. LOS ANGELES CORRAL. BRAND BOOK #14. Ed by Doyce Nunis, (1974). Ltd to 500. Fine in Fine dj. *BOOK MARKET.* $45

THE WESTERNERS' BRAND BOOK LOS ANGELES CORRAL, NUMBER 14. LA, 1974. Ltd to 500. VF in Fine dj. *CONNOLLY & WADE.* $75

THE WESTERNERS' BRAND BOOK LOS ANGELES CORRAL. NUMBER 16. LA, 1982. As New in as New dj. *CONNOLLY & WADE.* $65

THE WESTERNERS BRAND BOOKS. LOS ANGELES CORRAL. BRAND BOOK #17, (1986). Ltd to 500. Fine in Fine dj. *BOOK MARKET.* $25

THE WESTERNERS' BRAND BOOK LOS ANGELES CORRAL, BOOK SEVENTEEN. LA, 1986. As New in New dj. *CONNOLLY & WADE.* $50

THE WESTERNERS BRAND BOOKS. LOS ANGELES CORRAL. BRAND BOOK #18. Doyce Nunis (ed). (1841). 1st ed. Specially bound w/title pg bound in and issued in ltd ed of 300 (though not stated). Fine in Fine dj. *BOOK MARKET.* $50

THE WESTERNERS BRAND BOOK II. (San Diego: San Diego Corral of the Westerners, 1971). Laid-in map, illus, gold-stamped fabricoid. *DAWSON'S.* $50

THE WESTERNERS BRAND BOOKS. SAN DIEGO CORRAL. BRAND BOOK #1, (1968). Ltd to 500 numbered. Fine. *BOOK MARKET.* $60

THE WINTER TOURIST'S GUIDE BOOK TO CHEAP AND PLEASANT WINTER HOMES. 1881-82. Fernandina, FL: Florida Mirror Steam Printing, 1881. Orig wraps. VG. *SECOND LIFE.* $35

THE WOODLAND COMPANION....(by J. Aikin). London, 1802. 1st ed. Pp (3),92. Contemp 1/4 calf worn, scuffed; some spine splitting, brn spots affecting 1 pl; name. Bk solid. *SUTTON.* $285

THE WORKS OF WILLIAM HARVEY, M.D....TRANSLATED FROM THE LATIN WITH A LIFE OF THE AUTHOR BY ROBERT WILLIS. London, 1847. 1st ed. 624pp. *FYE.* $300

Theiner, George. A DAY AT THE FARM. London, 1964. Illus Rudolph Lukes. VG *BOOKFINDERS INTL.* $65

Theobald, F.V. AN ACCOUNT OF BRITISH FLIES. (Diptera). London, 1892. 4 plts. Vol. 1 (all published). Ex-lib. *SUTTON.* $28

Theodoric. THE SURGERY OF THEODORIC ca. A.D. 1267. 2 vols. NY, 1955-1960. 1st Eng trans. 223, 233pp. Binding of vol. I darkened. *FYE.* $100

Theroux, Alexander. DARCONVILLE'S CAT. GC: Doubleday, 1981. 1st ed. VF, minute rub to dj flap fold. *ELSE FINE.* $60

Theroux, Alexander. MASTER SNICKUP'S CLOAK. NY: Harper & Row, (1979). 1st Harper ed. Fine in dj (sm wrinkle). Signed. *CAPTAIN'S BOOKSHELF.* $100

Theroux, Alexander. THREE WOGS. Boston: Gambit, 1972. 1st ed. Fine in NF, price-clipped dj and inscribed. *LOPEZ.* $225

Theroux, Paul and Bruce Chatwin. PATAGONIA REVISITED. Boston, Houghton Mifflin, 1986. Adv copy, stamped "Not for Resale" on title page, signed. Fine in dj. *LOPEZ.* $45

Theroux, Paul. A CHRISTMAS CARD. Illus John Lawrence. London: Hamilton, (1978). 1st ed. Fine in dj. *CAPTAIN'S BOOKSHELF.* $40

Theroux, Paul. CHICAGO LOOP. London: Hamilton, (1990). 1st ed. Dj. Mint. *JAFFE.* $45

Theroux, Paul. CHICAGO LOOP. London: Hamish Hamilton, (1990). 1st Eng ed. Signed. Spine sl rolled, o/w Fine in Fine dj. *LOPEZ.* $60

Theroux, Paul. FONG AND THE INDIANS. Boston: Houghton Mifflin, 1968. 1st ed. NF in sl soiled white dj, short tears. *HELLER.* $75

Theroux, Paul. FONG AND THE INDIANS. Boston: Houghton Mifflin, 1968. 1st ed. NF in like dj (one tear on front panel). *LOPEZ.* $125

Theroux, Paul. FONG AND THE INDIANS. Boston: Houghton Mifflin, 1969. 1st ed. Fine in dj (touch of edge wear). *CAPTAIN'S BOOKSHELF.* $175

Theroux, Paul. JUNGLE LOVERS. Boston: Houghton Mifflin, 1971. 1st ed. Fine in Fine dj but for a few small wrinkles foot of spine. *BEASLEY.* $75

Theroux, Paul. JUNGLE LOVERS. Boston: Houghton Mifflin, 1971. 1st ed. Fine (owner sig) in lightly used dj (short tear). *CAPTAIN'S BOOKSHELF.* $50

Theroux, Paul. LONDON SNOW. Houghton, 1980. 1st Amer trade ed. VF in dj. *STAHR.* $15

Theroux, Paul. LONDON SNOW: A CHRISTMAS STORY. Wood engrs by John Lawrence. (Salisbury): Michael Russell, (1979). 1st ed. 1/450 signed. Fine in glassine dj. *CAPTAIN'S BOOKSHELF.* $125

Theroux, Paul. MY SECRET HISTORY. London: Hamish Hamilton, (London Limited Editions), 1989. 1st ed. Ltd to 150 signed. Cl backed marbled boards, glassine dj. Mint. *JAFFE.* $150

Theroux, Paul. PICTURE PALACE. Boston: Houghton Mifflin, 1978. 1st ed. Fine in black on silver dj. Signed. *CAPTAIN'S BOOKSHELF.* $75

Theroux, Paul. PICTURE PALACE. Boston: Houghton Mifflin, 1978. 1st ed. Signed. Fine in NF dj. *LOPEZ.* $75

Theroux, Paul. PICTURE PALACE. Boston: Houghton Mifflin, 1978. Uncorrected proof. Ink initial on front panel else Fine in wrappers. *CAPTAIN'S BOOKSHELF.* $125

Theroux, Paul. PICTURE PALACE. Houghton Mifflin, 1978. 1st trade ed. VG+ in dj. Signed. Dj rubbed: light wear at head & foot of spine. Magic marker on bottom edge. *STAHR.* $45

Theroux, Paul. SAILING THROUGH CHINA. Boston, Houghton Mifflin, 1984. 1st ed. Signed. Fine in price-clipped dj. *LOPEZ.* $60

Theroux, Paul. SAILING THROUGH CHINA. (Salisbury): Michael Russell, (1983). Illus by Patrick Procktor. 1st ed. 1/150 numbered, signed by Theroux and Procktor. Fine in glassine dj. *CAPTAIN'S BOOKSHELF.* $125

Theroux, Paul. SAINT JACK. Boston: Houghton Mifflin, 1973. 1st ed. Signed. Fine in NF price-clipped dj. *LOPEZ.* $100

Theroux, Paul. SAINT JACK. Boston: Houghton Mifflin, 1973. NF in lightly soiled dj. 1st ed. *CHAPEL HILL.* $40

Theroux, Paul. SUNRISE WITH SEAMONSTERS. Houghton Mifflin, 1985. 1st ed. VF in dj. *STAHR.* $25

Theroux, Paul. THE BLACK HOUSE. Boston: Houghton Mifflin, 1974. 1st ed. Fine in lightly rubbed dj, sl faded spine. *CAPTAIN'S BOOKSHELF.* $30

Theroux, Paul. THE CONSUL'S FILE. Boston: Houghton Mifflin, 1977. 1st Amer ed. Fine in dj. Signed. *CAPTAIN'S BOOKSHELF.* $85

Theroux, Paul. THE CONSUL'S FILE. Boston: Houghton Mifflin, 1977. Uncorrected proof. VG in wrappers. *CAPTAIN'S BOOKSHELF.* $100

Theroux, Paul. THE CONSUL'S FILE. Boston: Houghton Mifflin, 1977. 1st ed. As New in dj. *ELSE FINE.* $35

Theroux, Paul. THE CONSUL'S FILE. London: Hamish Hamilton, (1977). 1st ed. Fine in dj. *CAPTAIN'S BOOKSHELF.* $75

Theroux, Paul. THE GREAT RAILWAY BAZAAR. BY TRAIN THROUGH ASIA. Boston: Houghton Mifflin, 1975. 1st ed. Fine in sl rubbed dj. *HELLER.* $60

Theroux, Paul. THE GREAT RAILWAY BAZAAR. Boston: Houghton Mifflin, 1975. 1st ed, 1st issue. Fine in dj (lightly rubbed at spinal extremities, small internal mend). Signed. *CAPTAIN'S BOOKSHELF.* $75

Theroux, Paul. THE KINGDOM BY THE SEA. Boston: Houghton Mifflin, 1983. 1st ed. 1/250 specially bound, numbered, signed. Fine in slipcase. *CAPTAIN'S BOOKSHELF.* $125

Theroux, Paul. THE MOSQUITO COAST. (Boston: Houghton Mifflin, 1982). 1st ed. One of 340 of special ed signed. Orig cl, pub's slipcase. Mint. *PIRAGES.* $125

Theroux, Paul. THE MOSQUITO COAST. Boston: Houghton Mifflin, 1982. 1/325 numbered, specially bound, signed. Fine in slipcase. *CAPTAIN'S BOOKSHELF.* $75

Theroux, Paul. THE MOSQUITO COAST. Boston: Houghton Mifflin, 1982. 1st Amer ed. Fine in dj. Signed. *CAPTAIN'S BOOKSHELF.* $75

Theroux, Paul. THE MOSQUITO COAST. Houghton Mifflin, 1982. Advance reading copy. VF in dec wraps. *STAHR.* $25

Theroux, Paul. V.S. NAIPAUL. (London): Deutsch, (1972). 1st ed. Fine in price-clipped dj. *LOPEZ.* $1000

Theroux, Paul. WALDO. Boston: Houghton Mifflin, 1967. 1st ed, 1st bk. Fine in dj (trace of rubbing). *CAPTAIN'S BOOKSHELF.* $175

Theroux, Paul. WALDO. Boston: Houghton Mifflin, 1967. 1st ed, 1st bk. VG+ in dj (sl rubbed edges). *BERNARD.* $150

Theroux, Paul. WORLD'S END AND OTHER STORIES. Boston: Houghton Mifflin, 1980. 1st ed. Fine in dj. Signed. *CAPTAIN'S BOOK-SHELF.* $75

Thesing, Curt. GENEALOGY OF LOVE. London: George Rout-ledge and Sons, 1933. 1st ed in Eng. Trans by Eden and Cedar Paul. Spine faded, cvrs a bit dust-marked, else VG. *WREDEN.* $40

THEY BUILT A CITY. 150 YEARS OF INDUSTRIAL CINCIN-NATI. Cincinnati, 1938. 1st ed. WPA. VG. *ARTIS.* $15

Thiel, Albert W.R. CHINESE POTTERY AND STONEWARE. NY, (1953). 24 color plts. Dj rubbed at extremities. Fine. *POLYAN-THOS.* $45

THIRD ANNUAL REPORT OF THE REGENTS OF THE UNIVERSITY ON THE CONDITION OF THE STATE CABINET OF NATURAL HISTORY...ANTIQUARIAN COL-LECTION, ANNEXED THERETO. Albany, 1850. Rev ed. 183pp, 24 plts, 17 in full color. Some foxing. Rebound in lea. Good to VG. *CONNOLLY & WADE.* $150

Thom, Adam. THE CLAIMS TO THE OREGON TERRITORY CONSIDERED. London: Smith, Elder & Co, 1844. Stitched as is-sued. Howes T-161. Pristine. *PIRAGES.* $150

Thomas, Alfred B. AFTER CORONADO. SPANISH EXPLORA-TION NORTHEAST OF NEW MEXICO, 1696-1727...Norman: Univ of OK, 1935. 1st ed. Fine in VG dj. *OREGON.* $65

Thomas, Alfred B. FORGOTTEN FRONTIERS. A STUDY OF THE SPANISH INDIAN POLICY OF DON JUAN BAUTISTA DE ANZA. Norman: Univ of OK, 1932. 1st ed. 2 facs, 4 maps (3 fldg). Signed presentation. VG in VG dj. *OREGON.* $120

Thomas, Alfred Barneby. TEODORO DE CROIX AND THE NORTHERN FRONTIER OF NEW SPAIN, 1776-1783. Univ of OK, 1941. 1st ed. Vol 5 in Amer Expl & Travel Series. 4 plts, fldg map. VG. *OREGON.* $30

Thomas, Benjamin P. PORTRAIT FOR POSTERITY. N.p. (1947). 1st ed. Minor dj wear o/w Fine. *PRATT.* $25

Thomas, Bertram. ARABIA FELIX. ACROSS THE "EMPTY QUARTER" OF ARABIA. NY: Scribner, 1932. 1st ed. 58 plts, 1 chart, 2 maps (1 fldg). Orig cl, sl rubbed. Ex-lib w/lib number on spine, o/w VG. *WORLDWIDE.* $45

Thomas, Bob. WALT DISNEY, THE ART OF ANIMATION. Simon & Schuster, (1958). Corner bumps. VG in Fair dj w/chips (1 lg); plastic coating separating. *BEBBAH.* $35

Thomas, Charles W. ICE IS WHERE YOU FIND IT. Indianapolis, (1951). 1st ed. VG. *ARTIS.* $15

Thomas, Craig. FIREFOX. Holt Rinehart Winston, 1977. Advanced Reading Copy. VF, wraps. *STAHR.* $15

Thomas, Craig. SEA LEOPARD. London: Michael Joseph, 1981. 1st ed. Signed bkpl. Sl bumped lower corners, date, o/w Fine in price-clipped dj w/scratch. *MORDIDA.* $35

Thomas, Craig. SNOW FALCON. London: Michael Joseph, 1979. 1st ed. Fine in dj. *MORDIDA.* $40

Thomas, Craig. SNOW FALCON. NY: Holt, Rinehart and Winston, 1979. 1st ed. Signed. Corners bumped o/w Fine in dj. *MORDIDA.* $40

Thomas, Craig. THE LAST RAVEN. London: Collins, 1990. 1st ed. Inscribed. Corners bumped o/w Fine in dj. *MORDIDA.* $50

Thomas, Cyrus. CATALOGUE OF PREHISTORIC WORKS EAST OF THE ROCKY MOUNTAINS. Washington: GPO, 1891. 17 maps (1 fldg). Orig ptd wraps soiled, worn w/few small chips to edges of title and few leaves, repaired at inner edge, bound in new

red leather w/gilt-lettered black spine. VG, unopened (few chips edges title, few leaves). *BLUE MOUNTAIN.* $125

Thomas, D.M. SPHINX. Viking, 1987. Uncorrected proof of 1st Amer ed. VF in wraps. *STAHR.* $20

Thomas, D.M. THE FLUTE-PLAYER. London, 1979. 1st ed. Rev copy w/slip laid in. Fine in Fine dj. *POLYANTHOS.* $45

Thomas, D.M. THE WHITE HOTEL. NY: Viking, 1981. Uncor-rected proof. About Fine in dj. Lt wear to front cover. *STAHR.* $40

Thomas, D.M. THE WHITE HOTEL. Viking, 1981. 1st Amer ed. VF in dj. *STAHR.* $25

Thomas, Dorothy Swaine and Richard S. Nishimoto. THE SPOILAGE: JAPANESE-AMERICAN EVACUATION AND RESETTLEMENT. Berkeley, LA: Univ of CA Press, 1946. Gold-stamped cl in dj. *DAWSON'S.* $75

Thomas, Dorothy Swaine. THE SALVAGE. Berkeley and LA: Univ of CA Press, 1952. Cl in dj. *DAWSON'S.* $45

Thomas, Dylan. 18 POEMS. London: The Fortune Press, (ca. 1942). 3rd ed. Rebound. Contemp black cl, blue paper-covered boards. Half-title wanting, but about VG. *CHAPEL HILL.* $75

Thomas, Dylan. A CHILD'S WALES IN CHRISTMAS. Norfolk: New Directions, (1954). 1st separate ed. Fine in NF dj. Very Nice. *LOPEZ.* $75

Thomas, Dylan. ADVENTURES IN THE SKIN TRADE. London: Putnam, (1955). 1st ed. Fine in NF dj w/two small edge tears. *UNGER.* $85

Thomas, Dylan. ADVENTURES IN THE SKIN TRADE. NY: n.d., 1955. 1st ed. VG. *SMITH.* $65

Thomas, Dylan. COLLECTED POEMS. (NY): New Directions Books, (1953). 1st Amer ed, 1st issue. Orig cl. Crease back cvr; cl just sl spotted, o/w Fine in dj (frayed, sl faded; chip, o/w excellent). *PIRAGES.* $75

Thomas, Dylan. DEATHS AND ENTRANCES. London: J.M. Dent & Sons, (1946). 1st ed. Orig orange cl. Owner sig, else NF in dj. *CHAPEL HILL.* $200

Thomas, Dylan. IN COUNTRY SLEEP. NY, 1952. 1st ed. Fine in dj (2 tiny tears). *POLYANTHOS.* $120

Thomas, Dylan. LETTERS TO VERNON WATKINS. London: J.M. Dent & Sons Ltd, (1957). Sl chipped dj. *KARMIOLE.* $30

Thomas, Dylan. QUITE EARLY ONE MORNING. NY: New Direc-tions, (1954). 1st US ed. Fine in dj w/scarce wraparound band which notes that this collection includes "A Child's Christmas in Wales." *CAPTAIN'S BOOKSHELF.* $60

Thomas, Dylan. THE MAP OF LOVE. London: J.M. Dent & Sons, (1939). 1st ed, 1st issue. Orig mauve cl. Spine sl faded, else NF in dj, sl sunned spine. Handsome. *CHAPEL HILL.* $450

Thomas, Dylan. THE POEMS. Daniel Jones (ed). London: J.M. Dent, (1971). 1st ed. Dj. VF. *JAFFE.* $45

Thomas, Dylan. UNDER MILK WOOD. (NY): New Directions, (1954) 1st Amer ed. Orig cl. Frontis photo. VF in Very Nice dj (bit rubbed, creased; tiny tears, chips). *PIRAGES.* $100

Thomas, Edward J. MEMOIRS OF A SOUTHERNER 1840-1923. Savannah, GA, 1923. 1st ed. Ffep lacking, minor spotting on spine, yet VG. *McGOWAN.* $95

Thomas, Edward. BEAUTIFUL WALES. A&C Black, 1905. 1st ed. 20s Series. Ffep loose, some edgeware, else Good. *OLD LONDON.* $50

Thomas, Edward. GEORGE BORROW: THE MAN AND HIS BOOKS. NY, 1912. Teg. Light sunning. NF. *POLYANTHOS.* $35

Thomas, Edward. OXFORD. A&C Black, 1903. 1st ed. 20s Series. Small tear top of spine, yellowing feps, else NF. *OLD LONDON.* $65

Thomas, Edward. OXFORD. A&C Black, 1922. 1st ed (this series). Dj poor, else VG indeed. *OLD LONDON.* $25

Thomas, Frank. SHERLOCK HOLMES: BRIDGE DETECTIVE RETURNS. LA: Frank Thomas, 1975. 1st ed. Initials on bottom edge o/w Fine in stiff wrappers. *MORDIDA.* $45

Thomas, G. Holt. AERIAL TRANSPORT. London: Hodder, (1920). 1st ed. Fldg map at rear, frontis, plts. Orig pict cl, bkpl removed, emb lib stamp, a few small numbers on spine. *GINSBERG.* $125

Thomas, Gabriel. HISTORICAL AND GEOGRAPHICAL ACCOUNT OF PROVINCE AND COUNTRY OF PENNSYLVANIA AND OF WEST NEW JERSEY IN AMERICA. London, 1698 reprinted NY 1848. 34pp. U/c. Bound in new buckram. *HEINOLDT.* $40

Thomas, George C., Jr. and George C. Thomas III. GAME FISH OF THE PACIFIC. Phila and London: Lippincott, 1930. 1st ed. Minor edgewear, foxing on a few pages, else VG. *OLD LONDON.* $40

Thomas, George. THE PRACTICAL BOOK OF OUTDOOR ROSE GROWING. Phila, 1914. 1st ed. 96 color plts, charts, halftones. Nice, tight. *SECOND LIFE.* $25

Thomas, Ianthe. WALK HOME TIRED, BILLY JENKINS. NY: Harper, (1974). 1st ed. Fine in sl soiled dj. *BETWEEN COVERS.* $85

Thomas, Isaiah. THE HISTORY OF PRINTING IN AMERICA. Edited by Marcus A. McCorison from the Second Edition. Barre, MA: Imprint Society. 1970. Frontis. Leaf from the orig ed (1810) tipped-in. Ed ltd to 1,950 ptd at the Stinehour Press. Blue cl, slipcase with paper label. *KARMIOLE.* $100

Thomas, J.C. CHASIN' THE TRANE: THE MUSIC AND MYSTIQUE OF JOHN COLTRANE. Doubleday, 1975. 1st ed. About Fine in lightly scuffed & darkened dj. Signed & inscribed by Thomas. *STAHR.* $60

Thomas, J.J. THE AMERICAN FRUIT CULTURIST....NY, 1856 (1852). Grn cl, binding rubbed. *SUTTON.* $40

Thomas, John. PRACTICAL OBSERVATIONS ON CHRONIC AFFECTIONS OF THE DIGESTIVE ORGANS, AND ON BILIOUS AND NERVOUS DISORDERS. Cheltenham, 1821. 2nd ed. Paper backed boards, 168pp. Paper backstrip chipped w/pieces missing, o/w VG. *FYE.* $100

Thomas, Lately. A DEBONAIR SCOUNDREL. SF, (1962). 1st ed. Cl. NF in dj. *DIAMOND.* $15

Thomas, Lately. THE VANISHING EVANGELIST. NY: Viking, 1959. 2nd prtg. Cl in torn dj. *DAWSON'S.* $25

Thomas, Lewis. THE LIVES OF A CELL. NY: Viking, (1974). 1st ed. Fine in dj. *CAPTAIN'S BOOKSHELF.* $35

Thomas, Lowell, Jr. OUT OF THIS WORLD: ACROSS THE HIMALAYAS TO FORBIDDEN TIBET. Greystone, 1950. 1st ed. Fine in sl soiled dj w/sunned spine. *STAHR.* $35

Thomas, Lowell. MAGIC DIALS, THE STORY OF RADIO AND TELEVISION. (NY): Polygraphic Company of America. 1939. 1st ed. Color photo front cvr. Dj little worn. *KARMIOLE.* $75

Thomas, Lowell. THE BOYS' LIFE OF COLONEL LAWRENCE. NY: Century, 1927. 1st ed. Inscribed, signed. Worn extremes. *GREAT EPIC.* $45

Thomas, Lowell. WITH LAWRENCE IN ARABIA. NY & London: Century, 1924. 1st ed. 64 plts. Sl rubbed, spine sunned, o/w VG. *WORLDWIDE.* $18

Thomas, Northcote W. CRYSTAL GAZING. NY, 1905. NF. *POLYANTHOS.* $35

Thomas, Piri. DOWN THESE MEAN STREETS. NY: Knopf, 1967. Stated 1st ed. NF in lightly worn dj. *AKA.* $50

Thomas, Ross. BRIARPATCH. NY: Simon and Schuster, 1984. 1st ed. VF in dj. *MORDIDA.* $35

Thomas, Ross. CAST A YELLOW SHADOW. NY: Morrow, 1967. 1st ed. Few very small spots on the yellow boards, else NF in dj. Signed. *CAPTAIN'S BOOKSHELF.* $150

Thomas, Ross. CAST A YELLOW SHADOW. NY: William Morrow, 1967. 1st ed. Bkseller's sm label front pastedown, sl darkening along top edges of cvrs, o/w Fine in dj. *MORDIDA.* $200

Thomas, Ross. CAST A YELLOW SHADOW. NY: Wm Morrow, 1967. 1st ed. VG+ in price clipped dj (chip; 1" internally mended tear). *BERNARD.* $100

Thomas, Ross. CHINAMAN'S CHANCE. NY: S&S, (1978). 1st ed. Signed. Rmdr mk, else Fine in sl soiled dj. *UNGER.* $60

Thomas, Ross. CHINAMAN'S CHANCE. NY: Simon & Schuster, 1979. 1st ed. Adv rev copy w/slip laid in. Fine in dj. *MORDIDA.* $100

Thomas, Ross. CHINAMAN'S CHANCE. NY: Simon and Schuster, 1978. 1st ed. Rmdr stamp bottom edge, o/w Fine in price-clipped dj. *MORDIDA.* $30

Thomas, Ross. MISSIONARY STEW. NY: Simon & Schuster, 1983. 1st ed. Fine in dj w/rubbing along front flap fold. *MORDIDA.* $35

Thomas, Ross. OUT ON THE RIM. London: Century, 1988. 1st Eng ed. VF in dj. *MORDIDA.* $35

Thomas, Ross. OUT ON THE RIM. NY: Mysterious Press, 1987. 1st ed. VF in dj. *MORDIDA.* $25

Thomas, Ross. OUT ON THE RIM. NY: Mysterious Press, 1987. 1st ed. Signed. VF in dj. *SILVER DOOR.* $35

Thomas, Ross. SPIES, THUMBSUCKERS, ETC. Northridge: Lord John Press, 1989. 1st ed. One of 50 deluxe numbered, signed. VF w/o dj as issued. *MORDIDA.* $150

Thomas, Ross. SPY IN THE VODKA. London: Hodder & Stoughton, 1967. 1st Eng ed. Pub in US as The Cold War Swap. Edges spotted o/w Fine in dj w/couple of closed tears and minor wear at top of spine. *MORDIDA.* $100

Thomas, Ross. THE BACKUP MEN. Morrow, 1971. 1st ed. Fine in rudely price-clipped dj, lt crease bottom of front panel. *STAHR.* $90

Thomas, Ross. THE BACKUP MEN. NY: Morrow, 1971. 1st ed. Fine in dj. *ELSE FINE.* $100

Thomas, Ross. THE BACKUP MEN. NY: William Morrow, 1971. 1st ed. VF in dj. *MORDIDA.* $175

Thomas, Ross. THE COLD WAR SWAP. NY: William Morrow, 1966. 1st ed. Fine in dj (sl faded spine; short closed tear; tiny wear spine ends). *MORDIDA.* $650

Thomas, Ross. THE EIGHTH DWARF. Simon and Schuster, 1979. 1st ed. Fine in dj. Bkpl. *STAHR.* $35

Thomas, Ross. THE FOOLS IN TOWN ARE ON OUR SIDE. London: Hodder & Stoughton, 1970. 1st ed. Precedes Amer ed. Fine in dj w/crease-tear on back panel, several short closed tears and small scrape on front panel. *MORDIDA.* $175

Thomas, Ross. THE FOOLS IN TOWN ARE ON OUR SIDE. NY: William Morrow, 1971. 1st Amer ed. Fine, tight, in price-clipped dj. *MORDIDA.* $125

Thomas, Ross. THE FOURTH DURANGO. NY: Mysterious Press, 1989. 1st ed. VF in dj. *MORDIDA.* $25

Thomas, Ross. THE MONEY HARVEST. London: Hamish Hamilton, 1975. 1st Eng ed. Fine in dj. *MORDIDA.* $45

Thomas, Ross. THE MORDIDA MAN. NY: Simon & Schuster, 1981. 1st ed. VF in dj. *ELSE FINE.* $50

Thomas, Ross. THE PORKCHOPPERS. Morrow, 1972. 1st ed. Fine in dj. *STAHR.* $45

Thomas, Ross. THE PORKCHOPPERS. NY: Morrow, (1972). 1st ed. NF in NF dj. *UNGER.* $75

Thomas, Ross. THE PORKCHOPPERS. NY: Morrow, 1972. 1st ed. Fine in NF dj. *ELSE FINE.* $70

Thomas, Ross. THE SEERSUCKER WHIPSAW. NY: William Morrow, 1967. 1st ed. Inscribed. Fine in dj. *MORDIDA.* $600

Thomas, Ross. THE SEERSUCKER WHIPSAW. William Morrow & Co, Inc, 1967. 1st ed. Inscribed. NF in sl soiled, chipped dj. *HELLER.* $150

Thomas, Ross. TWILIGHT AT MAC'S PLACE. NY: Mysterious Press, 1990. 1st ed. VF in dj. *MORDIDA.* $22.50

Thomas, Ross. YELLOW-DOG CONTRACT. London: Hamish Hamilton, 1977. 1st ed. VF in dj. *MORDIDA.* $35

Thomas, Ross. YELLOW-DOG CONTRACT. Morrow, 1976. 1st ed. VG or better in dj (short tear, sm abrasion top front flyleaf fold). Bk sl cocked. *STAHR.* $35

Thomas, Ross. YELLOW-DOG CONTRACT. NY: Morrow, (1977). 1st ed. Inscribed. Fine in dj, a touch rubbed. *UNGER.* $75

Thomas, Ross. YELLOW-DOG CONTRACT. NY: Morrow, 1977. 1st ed. Fine in dj. *ELSE FINE.* $75

Thomas, Stephen D. THE LAST NAVIGATOR. London: Hutchinson, 1987. As New in dj. *PARMER.* $25

Thomas, T. Gaillard. ABORTION AND ITS TREATMENT...PRACTICAL EXPERIENCE. NY: Appleton, 1897. Rpt of 1890 ed. VG. *SECOND LIFE.* $85

Thomas, Verlin. THE SUCCESSFUL PHYSICIAN. 1923. 1st ed. *FYE.* $75

Thomason, J.W., Jr. GONE TO TEXAS. NY, 1937. 1st ed. Good, binding sunned, spotted. *VARNER.* $20

Thomes, William H. THE GOLD HUNTER'S ADVENTURES OR, LIFE IN AUSTRALIA. Chicago: Donnelley, Loyd & Co., 1883. Shelfwear; spine splitting, front hinge weak. *PARMER.* $55

Thomes, William H. THE WHALEMAN'S ADVENTURES IN THE SANDWICH ISLANDS AND CALIFORNIA. Boston: Lee & Shepard, 1872. 1st ed. Spine tips repaired, little corner wear, o/w VG. *DIAMOND.* $75

Thompson, C.J.S. MYSTERIES OF SEX. London: Hutchinson & Co, (1938). 1st ed. Color frontis, plts. Cvrs a bit soiled, top edges foxed, small stains on title, else VG. *WREDEN.* $40

Thompson, C.J.S. THE MYSTERY AND ART OF THE APOTHECARY. London, 1929. 1st ed. *FYE.* $60

Thompson, David G. THE MOHAVE DESERT REGION CALIFORNIA: A GEOGRAPHIC...HYDROLOGIC RECONNAISSANCE. Washington: GPO, 1929. Water Supply Paper 578. 1st ed. Fine in wraps. Extra env of "pocket" maps not incl. *BOOK MARKET.* $65

Thompson, Dorothy Burr. TROY: THE TERRACOTTA FIGURINES OF THE HELLENISTIC PERIOD. Princeton: Princeton Univ Press for the Univ of Cincinnati, 1963. 63 plts. Good in tattered dj. *ARCHAEOLOGIA.* $85

Thompson, Dunstan. THE PHOENIX IN THE DESERT. London: Lehman, 1951. 1st ed. 16 plts. Dj. Title-page very sl foxed, o/w VG. *WORLDWIDE.* $35

Thompson, Edward Herbert. PEOPLE OF THE SERPENT: LIFE AND ADVENTURE AMONG THE MAYAS. Boston: Houghton Mifflin, 1932. Frontis. Spine faded. Good. *ARCHAEOLOGIA.* $35

Thompson, Edward. PEOPLE OF THE SERPENT. Boston: Houghton Mifflin, 1932. 1st ed. *SILVER.* $30

Thompson, Edwin Porter. HISTORY OF THE FIRST KENTUCKY BRIGADE. Cincinnati, 1868. 1st ed. Bound in 1/2 leather w/marbled boards. Beautiful. *McGOWAN.* $450

Thompson, Gerald. EDWARD F. BEALE AND THE AMERICAN WEST. Univ of NM Press, 1983. 1st ed. VF in Fine dj. *FIVE QUAIL.* $25

Thompson, Henry T. OUSTING THE CARPETBAGGERS FROM SOUTH CAROLINA. Columbia, SC, (1926). 2nd ed., (1927). Dj. VG+. *PRATT.* $80

Thompson, Henry Yates. AN ENGLISHMAN IN THE AMERICAN CIVIL WAR. Ed by Sir Christopher Chancellor. NY, (1971). 5 plts, fldg map. Fine in dj. *BOHLING.* $35

Thompson, Hunter S. FEAR AND LOATHING IN LAS VEGAS. NY: Random House, (1971). 1st ed. Fine in Fine dj. *UNGER.* $200

Thompson, Hunter S. FEAR AND LOATHING IN LAS VEGAS. Random House, 1972. 1st ed. About Fine in dj. Bk is lightly sunned along top edge. Dj has two small scrapes, very light wear. *STAHR.* $175

Thompson, Hunter S. FEAR AND LOATHING IN LAS VEGAS. NY: Random House, 1971. 1st ed. VF, minor fading to dj spine lettering. *ELSE FINE.* $200

Thompson, Hunter S. FEAR AND LOATHING IN LAS VEGAS. NY: Random House, (1971). 1st ed. Light sunning to top edges of boards, else Fine in price-clipped dj. *CAPTAIN'S BOOKSHELF.* $125

Thompson, Hunter S. FEAR AND LOATHING ON THE CAMPAIGN TRAIL '72. SF: Straight Arrow, (1973). 1st ed. Nicks to cover, musty. Good in Poor dj. *AKA.* $35

Thompson, Hunter S. FEAR AND LOATHING: ON THE CAMPAIGN TRAIL '72. SF: Straight Arrow, (1973). 1st ed. Fine in price-clipped dj. *UNGER.* $125

Thompson, Hunter S. THE CURSE OF LONO. NY: Bantam, (1983). Uncorrected proof of this bk which was only issued in wrappers. Quarto sheets bound with threaded screws; NF. *LOPEZ.* $375

Thompson, Hunter S. THE GREAT SHARK HUNT. NY: Summit, (1979). 1st ed. Fine in Fine dj. *UNGER.* $75

Thompson, J. Eric (intro). ANCIENT MAYA RELIEF SCULPTURE. Merle Greene (rubbings). NY: Museum of Primitive Art, 1967. 1st ed. Ltd. to 4000. 60 b/w rubbings. Boxed. Fine. *SILVER.* $40

Thompson, J. Eric. MAYA ARCHAEOLOGIST. London: Robert Hale, (1963). 22 figs, 1 map. Corners bumped. Good in torn dj. *ARCHAEOLOGIA.* $35

Thompson, J. Eric. MAYA ARCHAEOLOGIST. Norman: Univ of OK Press, (1963). 1st ed. Good in chipped dj. *SILVER.* $30

Thompson, James Westfall. ANCIENT LIBRARIES. Berkeley: Univ of CA Press, 1940. 1st ed. Fine in sl soiled dj. *WREDEN.* $15

Thompson, Jerry. HENRY HOPKINS SIBLEY, CONFEDERATE GENERAL OF THE WEST. Natchitoches, LA, 1987. 1st ed. Fine in dj. *PRATT.* $27.50

Thompson, Jerry. MY LIFE IN THE KLAN. NY: Putnam, (1982). 1st ed. Fine in NF dj. *AKA.* $17

Thompson, Jim. HARD CORE. NY: Donald I. Fine, 1986. Omnibus ed. VF in dj. *MORDIDA.* $30

Thompson, Jim. MORE HARD CORE. NY: Donald I. Fine, 1986. Omnibus ed. VF in dj. *MORDIDA.* $25

Thompson, Jim. NOTHING MORE THAN MURDER. NY: Harper & Brothers, 1949. 1st ed. Covers stained along front edges o/w VG in dj (sl faded spine; chipped, frayed spine ends; creasing front panel; closed tears, wear). *MORDIDA.* $250

Thompson, Jim. NOW AND ON EARTH. Belen, NM: Dennis McMillan, 1986. Appreciation by Stephen King. Ltd ed. One of 400 numbered. VF in dj. *MORDIDA.* $135

Thompson, Jim. POP. 1280. Greenwich: Gold Medal, 1964. 1st ed. Pb orig. Fine in wraps. *BEASLEY.* $100

Thompson, Jim. THE KILL-OFF. NY: Lion Books, (1957). Pb orig. Good. *LOPEZ.* $175

Thompson, Jim. THE KILLER INSIDE ME. LA: Blood and Guts Press, 1989. Intro by Stephen King. Ltd ed. One of 350 numbered, signed by King. As New in dj w/slipcase. *MORDIDA.* $150

Thompson, John R. POEMS OF JOHN R. THOMPSON. John S. Patton (ed). NY: Scribner's, 1920. 1st ed. Orig grn cl. Bright, NF in

VG dj (very lt dampstain on front, some edge-chipping, sm piece missing from top rear panel). *CHAPEL HILL.* $75

Thompson, Kay. ELOISE IN MOSCOW. Simon & Schuster, (1959). Stated 1st ptg. Illus by Hilary Knight. Two double-fold pp. Fine in VG+ dj. *BEBBAH.* $150

Thompson, Kay. ELOISE. London: Reinhardt, 1958. 2nd reprtg. 4to. Unpaginated. Illus by Hilary Knight. NF in VG+ dj w/light soil to rear panel, edgewear. *BEBBAH.* $30

Thompson, L. and R.H. Winnick. ROBERT FROST: THE LATER YEARS, 1938-1963. NY: Holt, Rinehart & Winston, (1976). 1st ed. 468pp. Edges lightly rubbed o/w Fine in NF dj. *AKA.* $60

Thompson, Lawrance. ROBERT FROST: THE YEARS OF TRIUMPH, 1915-1938. NY: Holt, Rinehart & Winston, (1970). 1st ed. 743pp. Fine in NF dj. *AKA.* $60

Thompson, Leslie P. FISHING IN NEW ENGLAND. NY: D. Van Nostrand Co. (1955). Color frontis, 9 plts (7 in color). Ltd to 1200 numbered. Grn gilt cl in faded dj. *KARMIOLE.* $75

Thompson, Margaret J. CAPT. NATHANIEL L. THOMPSON OF KENNEBUNK & THE SHIPS HE BUILT, 1811-89. Boston: Lauriat, 1937. 1st trade ed of 1,000. Almost Fine. *AARD.* $50

Thompson, Maurice. ALICE OF OLD VINCENNES. Indianapolis: The Bowen Merrill Co, (1900). 1st ed, 1st prtg. Running heads ptd in boldface capital letters, pg 1 numbered, pg (420) blank, and frontis ptd in colors. Orig pict grn cl. VG+. *CHAPEL HILL.* $50

Thompson, Maurice. MY WINTER GARDEN. NY: The Century Co, 1900. 1st ed. Orig grey cl, teg. Bkpl, NF. *CHAPEL HILL.* $45

Thompson, Maurice. STORIES OF THE CHEROKEE HILLS. Boston & NY, 1898. 1st ed. Orig dec cl. NF. *McGOWAN.* $45

Thompson, R. Lowe. THE HISTORY OF THE DEVIL. NY: Harcourt, Brace, 1929. Rear cover sl stained, else VG. *WREDEN.* $25

Thompson, R.A. CONQUEST OF CALIFORNIA....Santa Rosa, 1896. 33pp. 1st ed. Orig ptd wrappers. Howes T119. *GINSBERG.* $75

Thompson, R.L. GLIMPSES OF MEDICAL EUROPE. Phila, 1908. 1st ed. Scarce. *FYE.* $75

Thompson, R.W. WILD ANIMAL MAN. NY: Morrow, 1934. VG in Fair dj. *MIKESH.* $20

Thompson, Rev. Joseph P(arrish). PHOTOGRAPHIC VIEWS OF EGYPT, PAST AND PRESENT. Glasgow: William Collins, n.d. (ca. 1854). Spine faded, torn ffep. Circulating lib bkpl. *SCHOYER'S.* $45

Thompson, Ruth Plumly. KABUMPO IN OZ. Reilly & Lee, (1922) c. 1930 w/Dorothy portrait following ownership page (which has penciled names) & half title at end of book. 12 color illus (coated one side) & b/w by John Neill. 297pp. Some page soil, pencil drawing rear endpaper, cvr pict abraded. 2nd Thompson Oz, but first title completely credited to her. *BEBBAH.* $65

Thompson, Ruth Plumly. THE GIANT HORSE OF OZ. Chicago: The Reilly & Lee Co, (1928). 1st ed. John R. Neill (illus). Pict eps, color plts, tipped in. One of the earliest copies with the "r" in "morning" undamaged, on page 116, line 1. Sl browning to margins of the title pg, cut to cl on heel, else Nice, bright. *SECOND LIFE.* $225

Thompson, Ruth Plumly. THE GNOME KING OF OZ. Chicago, 1927. 1st ed. Illus by John R. Neill. Spine, illus front cvr sl rubbed. NF. *POLYANTHOS.* $125

Thompson, Silvanus. THE ELECTROMAGNET AND ELECTRO MAGNETIC...London & NY: Spon, 1891. 1st US ed. Sl wear at spine ends o/w VG. *MAD DOG.* $27.50

Thompson, Theophilus. ANNALS OF INFLUENZA OR EPIDEMIC CATARRHAL FEVER IN GREAT BRITAIN FROM 1510 TO 1837. London, 1852. 1st ed. 406pp. *FYE.* $150

Thompson, W. Ernest. FROM THE GRASS ROOTS A LAND MAN'S STORY. Austin: Steck-Warlick Co, 1969. 1st ed, inscribed, signed w/T.L.S. laid-in. Fine in VG dj. *GIBBS.* $30

Thompson, Winfield M, William P. Stephens, and William U. Swann. THE YACHT "AMERICA." Boston, 1925. 1st ed. One of 375 lg paper copies, signed by all 3 authors. Color frontis this issue only. Orig half cl, boards a little soiled. *LEFKOWICZ.* $150

Thomson, Alexis. ON NEUROMA AND NEUROFIBROMATOSIS. Edinburgh, 1900. 1st ed. Author's ptd presentation slip laid in. Photo illus. *FYE.* $100

Thomson, Anthony. THE DOMESTIC MANAGEMENT OF THE SICK-ROOM, NECESSARY IN AID OF MEDICAL TREATMENT, FOR THE CURE OF DISEASES. Phila, 1845. 353pp. *FYE.* $100

Thomson, Arthur. A HANDBOOK OF ANATOMY FOR ART STUDENTS. Oxford, 1915. 4th ed. Small portion of front cover stained. Earlier owner has embellished few photo illus w/colored pencil. *FYE.* $100

Thomson, C. Wyville. THE ATLANTIC. A PRELIMINARY ACCOUNT OF THE GENERAL RESULTS OF THE EXPLORING VOYAGE OF HMS "CHALLENGER" DURING THE YEAR 1873 AND THE EARLY PART OF THE YEAR 1876. NY: Harper & Brother, 1878. 2 vols. set in gilt dec. green cloth over 8vo boards. 391pp; 340pp + ads, /106 & 62 woodcuts; 4 & 4 vignettes; and 42 plates under tissue. Appendices & index. Fldg maps. VG with light rubbing. *PARMER.* $285

Thomson, D. HANDY BOOK OF FRUIT CULTURE UNDER GLASS. Edinburgh & London, 1873. 1st ed. Orig dec cl worn at edges and corners; spine ends frayed, partially missing; some spine splitting, front hinge cracked. 3 lib stamps in text. *SUTTON.* $75

Thomson, Elizabeth. HARVEY CUSHING: SURGEON, AUTHOR, ARTIST. NY, 1950. 1st ed. *FYE.* $30

Thomson, H. C. OUTGOING TURK. NY: Appleton & Co., 1897. Fairly soiled, backstrip worn, loose; lacks ffep, shaken. W.a.f. *SCHOYER'S.* $25

Thomson, J.J. and G.P. CONDUCTION OF GASES THROUGH ELECTRICITY. 2 vol. Cambridge: Univ Press, 1928. 3rd ed. VG. *BOOKCELL.* $95

Thomson, James. THE SEASONS. London: Nonesuch Press, 1927. Ltd ed, 1350/1500 for sale in Eng and America. 5 illus. John Beresford (intro). Uncut, marbled covers. Spine sunned, tiny nick top. Fine. *POLYANTHOS.* $75

Thomson, June. NO FLOWERS BY REQUEST. London: Constable, 1987. 1st ed. Signed. NF in dj. *SILVER DOOR.* $35

Thomson, June. TO MAKE A KILLING. London: Constable, 1982. 1st ed. Inscribed. Edges sl darkened o/w Fine in dj w/small scrape on front fold. *MORDIDA.* $35

Thomson, Robert Dundas. EXPERIMENTAL RESEARCHES ON THE FOOD OF ANIMALS....NY: Saxton, 1856. 1st ed. Lib stamp, pocket removed. VG. *SECOND LIFE.* $45

Thomson, W. GREAT CATS I HAVE MET. Boston, 1896. 8vo, 179pp. Drawings, dec cl. VG. *MIKESH.* $35

Thorburn, Grant. LIFE AND WRITINGS OF GRANT THORBURN. NY: Walker, 1852. 276pp. Cloth worn, contents foxed. *AMERICAN BOTANIST.* $65

Thorburn, Grant. MEN AND MANNERS IN BRITAIN. NY: Wiley & Long, 1834. 1st US ed. 187pp. Name, foxing. VG. *SECOND LIFE.* $75

Thorburn, W. Stewan. A GUIDE TO THE COINS OF GREAT BRITAIN & IRELAND. London: Gill, 1888. 2nd ed. 29 full-pg plts. Incl 8 emb plts. Excellent. *SECOND LIFE.* $145

Thoreau, H.D. NOTES ON NEW ENGLAND BIRDS. F.A. Allen (ed). Boston, 1910. 9 plts, fldg map. Institutional bkpl, sticker on spine, o/w nice. *SUTTON.* $40

Thoreau, Henry David. A WEEK ON THE CONCORD AND MERRIMACK RIVERS. (Lunenburg): LEC, 1975. 1/2000 illus, signed by Raymond J. Holden. Fine in slipcase. *CAPTAIN'S BOOKSHELF.* $75

Thoreau, Henry David. CAPE COD. Boston: Ticknor and Fields, 1865. 1st ed. 12mo. 252pp. Orig gilt stamped cloth, a few spots, but VG. A superior copy. BAL 20115, binding D. With the December 1864 catalogue. *M & S.* $750

Thoreau, Henry David. CAPE COD. Portland: LEC, 1968. 1/1500 illus, signed by Raymond J. Holden. Fine in slipcase. *CAPTAIN'S BOOKSHELF.* $100

Thoreau, Henry David. CIVIL DISOBEDIENCE. Boston: (David R. Godine), 1969. One of 650 ptd on Eng hand-made paper in black and red at the Gehenna Press. Grn cl spine over brn paper-covered boards, ptd paper spine label; in matching protective slipcase. Absolutely Fine. *BOOK BLOCK.* $200

Thoreau, Henry David. EXCURSIONS. R.W. Emerson (ed). Boston: Ticknor and Fields, 1863. 1558 printed, 1500 bound. 1st ed. 8vo. 319pp. Frontis port. Orig blue green cloth, light rubbing, tips of spine worn. Sl browning & foxing, but sound & crisp. VG. BAL 20111, 5238. *M & S.* $450

Thoreau, Henry David. LETTERS TO VARIOUS PERSONS. R.W. Emerson (ed). Boston, 1865. 1st ed. 229pp. Binding variant B. Owner sig, photo of owner (Mary A. Fuller) tipped in. Nick to top of spine, o/w Fine. BAL 5246. *SECOND LIFE.* $350

Thoreau, Henry David. WALDEN. Boston: Ticknor and Fields, 1864. 4th ptg, one of 280 printed. 12mo. 357pp. Orig cloth, ends of spine chipped, otherwise Fine. *M & S.* $325

Thorek, Max. MODERN SURGICAL TECHNIC. Phila, 1939. 1st ed., 2nd prtg. 3 vols. 2045pp. 2174 illus. *FYE.* $175

Thorek, Max. THE HUMAN TESTIS: ITS GROSS ANATOMY, HISTOLOGY, PHYSIOLOGY, PATHOLOGY....Phila, 1924. 1st ed. 308 illus. Ex-lib. *FYE.* $150

Thorndike, Ashley H. SHAKESPEARE'S THEATER. NY: Macmillan, 1916. 1st ed. VG. *DRAMATIS PERSONAE.* $35

Thorndike, Rachel Sherman. THE SHERMAN LETTERS. NY, 1894. 1st ed. Cover chipped at spine extremities, about 1/3 of front waterstained o/w VG. *PRATT.* $35

Thorne, Edward and Henry W. Frohne. DECORATIVE DRAPERIES & UPHOLSTERY. GC, NY: Garden City Pub Co, Inc. (1937). 1st ed. Dj. *KARMIOLE.* $45

Thorne, Narcissa Niblack. MINIATURE ROOMS DESIGNED AND ARRANGED BY MRS. JAMES WARD THORNE. Chicago: Privately printed, 1933. Gray wrappers, shaken and foxed in part. *HUDSON.* $75

Thorne, Samuel. 1848, THE JOURNAL OF A BOY'S TRIP ON HORSEBACK. NY: Privately Ptd, 1936. Ed ltd to 500 numbered. Fldg map. Fine. *KARMIOLE.* $50

Thornson, J.J. CONDUCTION OF ELECTRICITY THROUGH GASES. Cambridge Univ Press, 1900 (1903). 2nd ed. Top & bottom of spine fraying, back top edge of spine torn, corners bumped & a bit worn, o/w Good. *KNOLLWOOD.* $110

Thornton, J. Quinn. THE CALIFORNIA TRAGEDY. Oakland: Biobooks, (1945). One of 1,500. Fine in dj. *LAURIE.* $45

Thornton, Philip. DEAD PUPPETS DANCE. London: Collins, 1937. Backstrip chipped, pencil notations. *SCHOYER'S.* $20

Thornton, Philip. THE VOICE OF ATLAS. London: Maclehose, 1936. 1st ed. 24 plts. Tattered dj. VG. *WORLDWIDE.* $30

Thornton, Philip. THE VOICE OF ATLAS: IN SEARCH OF MUSIC IN MOROCCO, London: Maclehose, 1936. Spotted. *SCHOYER'S.* $25

Thorp, N. Howard (Jack). PARDNER OF THE WIND. Caxton, 1945. 1st ed. Spine sunned, tiny nicks at top, but Fine. *AUTHORS OF THE WEST.* $60

Thorp, Raymond and Robert Bunker. CROW KILLER, THE SAGA OF LIVER-EATING JOHNSON. Bloomington, (1958). 2nd prtg, (1969). A little dj wear o/w Fine. *PRATT.* $25

Thorp, Raymond and Robert Bunker. CROW KILLER, THE SAGA OF LIVER-EATING JOHNSON. IN Univ, (1958). 1st ed. Fine in Fine dj. *OREGON.* $35

Thorp, Raymond. VIPER. THE CONFESSIONS OF A DRUG ADDICT. London: Robert Hale, 1956. 1st ed. Boards springing sl as is common, label on pastedown, o/w Fine in lightly used dj w/tears. *BEASLEY.* $45

Thorpe, Edward. CHANDLERTOWN. NY: St. Martin's, 1984. 1st Amer ed. One sl bumped cvr tip o/w VF in dj. *SILVER DOOR.* $30

Thorson, Alice Otillia. THE TRIBE OF THE PEZHEKEE: A LEGEND OF MINNESOTA. Minneapolis: Heywood Manufacturing Co, 1901. 1st ed. VG. *LAURIE.* $15

Thorwald, Jurgen. SCIENCE AND SECRETS OF EARLY MEDICINE. NY, 1963. *FYE.* $50

Thorwald, Jurgen. THE TRIUMPH OF SURGERY. NY, 1960. 1st ed. 454pp. *FYE.* $100

THOSE FABULOUS FLYING MACHINES. NY. 3-D bk. *BOOKFINDERS INTL.* $24

Thrapp, Dan L. THE CONQUEST OF APACHERIA. Norman: Univ of Oklahoma, 1967. 1st ed. Cl. VG in chipped dj. *BURCHAM.* $45

Thrapp, Dan. VICTORIO AND THE MIMBRES APACHES. Univ of OK, (1974). 1st ed. F in VG dj. *OREGON.* $45

Thrift, Minton. MEMOIR OF THE REV. JESSE LEE. WITH EXTRACTS FROM HIS JOURNALS. NY, 1823. 1st ed. (8),360pp. Full contemp 12mo calf, hinges weak. *GINSBERG.* $75

THRILLS. London, 1935. 1st ed. Spine faded, else VG. *MADLE.* $35

Thrum, Thos. G. HAWAIIAN ALMANAC AND ANNUAL FOR 1921. Honolulu: Thos. G. Thrum, 1920. Ex-lib. Soiled, paper browned. *PARMER.* $60

Thurber, F.B. COFFEE: FROM PLANTATION TO CUP, A BRIEF HISTORY....NY, 1883 (1881). 3rd ed. 2 plts. Orig cl, lt scuffing, sm spine end tear, front hinge cracked. Inscribed. *SUTTON.* $95

Thurber, James. ALARMS & DIVERSIONS. Harper, (1957). Stated 1st ed. VG+ in VG dj with few chips. *BEBBAH.* $27

Thurber, James. ALARMS & DIVERSIONS. NY, 1957. 1st ed. Fine in price-clipped Fine bright dj but for some slight spine sunning. *PETTLER.* $22.50

Thurber, James. FURTHER FABLES FOR OUR TIME. NY: S & S (1956). 1st ed. VG in chipped dj. *DORN.* $20

Thurber, James. FURTHER FABLES FOR OUR TIME. NY: Simon & Schuster, 1956. 1st ed. NF. *SMITH.* $35

Thurber, James. FURTHER FABLES FOR OUR TIME. NY: Simon & Schuster, 1956. 1st ed. Fine- in VG price-clipped dj. *AARD.* $25

Thurber, James. FURTHER FABLES OF OUR TIME. Simon & Schuster, 1956. 1st prtg. VG+ in VG+ dj. *BEBBAH.* $40

Thurber, James. LANTERNS & LANCES. NY, 1961. 1st ed. NF in VG+ dj. *PETTLER.* $20

Thurber, James. THE GREAT QUILLOW. Illus Doris Lee. NY: Harcourt, Brace, (1944). 1st ed. Light spotting to the eps, else NF in lightly soiled dj (short edge tears). *CAPTAIN'S BOOKSHELF.* $75

Thurber, James. THE THURBER CARNIVAL. NY: Modern Library, (1957). 1st ML ed. Fine in lightly rubbed price-clipped dj. *CAPTAIN'S BOOKSHELF.* $25

Thurber, James. THE WHITE DEER. NY: Harcourt, Brace (1945). 1st ed. Fine in sl soiled dj. *DORN.* $85

Thurber, James. THE WONDERFUL O. NY: S & S (1957). 1st ed. VG in VG edgeworn dj. *DORN.* $30

Thurber, James. THE WONDERFUL O. NY: Simon & Schuster, 1957. 1st ed. NF. *SMITH.* $40

Thurber, James. THURBER COUNTRY. NY: Simon & Schuster, 1953. 1st ed. VG+. *SMITH.* $40

Thurman, Violet Bierman. "OLD TOWN" INDIANOLA CATTLE FOLKS IN TEXAS. San Antonio: Standard Printing Co, 1952. 1st ed, signed. Soiled cover, o/w VG. *GIBBS.* $35

Thurman, Wallace. NEGRO LIFE IN NEW YORK'S HARLEM. A LIVELY PICTURE OF A POPULAR AND INTERESTING SECTION. Little Blue Book No. 494. Ed by Haldeman-Julius. Girard, KS. 1st ed. Ptd wraps, rear wrapper little creased. Fine. *POLYANTHOS.* $110

Thurston, C. WILDFLOWERS OF SOUTHERN CALIFORNIA. Pasadena, 1936. Limp cl, worn dj. *SUTTON.* $35

Thurston, George H. PITTSBURGH AS IT IS. Pittsburgh: W.S. Haven, 1857. 1st ed. Fine fldg map. Gray printed wrappers. Light foxing, faint writing couple pp, extremely well-preserved. *HUDSON.* $180

Thurston, Lucy. LIFE AND TIMES OF MRS. LUCY G. THURSTON...FROM LETTERS. Ann Arbor, MI: S.C. Andrews, (1882). 1st ed. Good+. *OREGON.* $70

Thwaites, R.G. (ed). FRONTIER DEFENSE ON THE UPPER OHIO, 1777-1778. Madison: Wisconsin Historical Soc, 1912. Fldg frontis map, 9 plts, gilt spine title. Light soiling, weak hinges. Nice. Howes T256. *BOHLING.* $75

Thwaites, R.G. (ed). ORIGINAL JOURNALS OF LEWIS AND CLARK EXPEDITION 1804-1806...TOGETHER WITH MANUSCRIPT MATERIAL...FROM OTHER SOURCES. 8 vols. NY: Antiquarian, 1959. Ltd to 750 (700 numbered for sale). 7 frontispieces, 38 plts. VF. Howes L320. *OREGON.* $550

Tibbles, Thomas Henry. BUCKSKIN AND BLANKET DAYS. GC, 1957 (1985 reprint). Lakeside Classic #83. 466pp. Fine. *PRATT.* $25

Tibbles, Thomas Henry. BUCKSKIN AND BLANKET DAYS. NY, 1957. 1st ed. VG in dj. *ARTIS.* $17.50

Tibbles, Thomas Henry. BUCKSKIN AND BLANKET DAYS: MEMOIRS OF A FRIEND OF THE INDIANS. GC: Doubleday, 1957. Theodore Bates Cogswell (ed). 1st ed, from ms written in 1905. Fine in dj. *LAURIE.* $20

Tibbles, Thomas Henry. BUCKSKINS AND BLANKET DAYS, MEMOIRS....Chicago: Lakeside Classic, 1985. VF. *OREGON.* $25

Tice, John H. OVER THE PLAINS, ON THE MOUNTAINS; OR KANSAS.... St. Louis, 1872. iv, 262pp & 2pp ads. Orig cl, 2 title pgs, the 2nd transcribed here. Should be recased, clean & tight, backstrip torn & chipped, w/middle portion missing, title remains, front hinge weak. Scarce, and except for spine, Nice. *BOHLING.* $300

Ticehurst, N.F. THE MUTE SWAN IN ENGLAND, ITS HISTORY. London, 1957. 31 plts. Ink notes front pastedown; bkpl. *SUTTON.* $50

Ticknor, George. LIFE OF WILLIAM HICKLING PRESCOTT. London: Routledge, Warne, and Routledge, 1864. 1st Eng ed. xiii, 511pp. 3/4 leather, raised spine bands, gilt titles, teg, marbled paper over boards, eps. Modest shelfwear, overall VG+. *PARMER.* $125

Tidcombe, Marianne. THE BOOKBINDINGS OF T. J. COBDEN-SANDERSON. (London: The British Library, 1984). 1st ed. Original cloth (issued w/o dj). Pub's slipcase. Mint. *PIRAGES.* $150

Tidswell, Herbert. THE TOBACCO HABIT. ITS HISTORY AND PATHOLOGY. London, 1912. 1st ed. Inscribed. *FYE.* $75

Tierney, Kevin. DARROW: A BIOGRAPHY. NY: Thomas Y. Crowell, (1979). 1st ed. NF in NF dj. *AKA.* $25

Tierney, Richard L. COLLECTED POEMS: NIGHTMARES AND REVISIONS. (Sauk City): Arkham House, 1981. 1st ed. Fine in wrappers. *OTHER WORLDS.* $35

Tietze, Hans. MASTERPIECES OF EUROPEAN PAINTING IN AMERICA. NY: Oxford Univ Press, (1939). 304 plts. Dj. Fine. *WEBER.* $75

Tiffany, Louis. THE TIFFANY STUDIOS COLLECTION OF NOTABLE ORIENTAL RUGS. NY: Tiffany Studios, 1906, 1907. Ltd to 500, signed by T.F. Cole. 2 vols. Bkpl. Spine sl rubbed, some leaves roughly opened, o/w VG. *WEBER.* $225

Tilden, Freeman. FOLLOWING THE FRONTIER, WITH F. JAY HAYNES. PIONEER PHOTOGRAPHER OF THE OLD WEST. NY: Knopf, 1964. 1st ed. VG. *OREGON.* $55

Tilgham, Tench Francis. THE CONFEDERATE BAGGAGE AND TREASURE TRAIN ENDS ITS FLIGHT IN FLORIDA. N.p., 1939. Wrappers, little loose w/foxing and small tears about edges. Good+. *McGOWAN.* $37.50

Tilghman, Christopher. IN A FATHER'S PLACE. NY: FSG, (1990). 1st ed. Author's 1st bk. Signed. *LOPEZ.* $65

Tilley, John Shipley. LINCOLN TAKES COMMAND. Chapel Hill: Univ of North Carolina, 1941. 1st ed. Fine in Good+ dj. *CONNOLLY & WADE.* $55

Tillinghast, Pardon Elisha. HISTORY OF THE TWELFTH REGIMENT RHODE ISLAND VOLUNTEERS IN THE CIVIL WAR, 1862-1863. Providence, 1904. 1st ed. A little cvr wear and soiling o/w VG+. *PRATT.* $85

Tillotson, M.R. and Frank J. Taylor. GRAND CANYON COUNTRY. Stanford, 1929. 1st ed. Light shelfwear, else VG+ to Fine. *FIVE QUAIL.* $30

Tillotson, M.R. and Frank J. Taylor. GRAND CANYON COUNTRY. Stanford Univ: Stanford Univ Press, 1935. 2nd ed. Extensive inscrip. Spine faded; else VG+. *PARMER.* $30

Tilney, Frederick and Hubert Howe. EPIDEMIC ENCEPHALITIS. NY, 1920. 1st ed. Photo illus. Scarce. *FYE.* $50

Timbs, John. CURIOSITIES OF LONDON. London: Virtue, (1867). New ed, corrected, enl. 7 engr plts. 3/4 contemp grn leather, emb cl. Shelfwear, cvr staining, o/w VG. *DIAMOND.* $75

Timbs, John. ENGLISH ECCENTRICS AND ECCENTRICITIES. London: Chatto and Windus, 1875 (1874). Joints, headpiece and corners worn; color frontispiece; illus. *DRAMATIS.* $70

Timmons, Wilbert H. MORELOS OF MEXICO; PRIEST, SOLDIER, STATESMAN. El Paso: Texas Western College Press, 1963. 1st ed. One of 500, trade ed. Designed by Carl Hertzog. Fine in dj. *LAURIE.* $150

TIMOTHY LEARY, APPELLANT, V. STATE OF CALIFORNIA, APPELLEE. SF: City Lights, 1970. 1st ed. Wraps. NF w/two sticker stains. *BEASLEY.* $35

Tin Yin. WILD ANIMALS OF BURMA. 88 plts. Rangoon, 1967. Cl-covered boards. *SUTTON.* $75

Tinkel, Lon. MR. DE, A BIOGRAPHY OF EVERETTE LEE DEGOLYER. Boston: Little, Brown, 1970. 1st ed. VG in VG dj. *CONNOLLY & WADE.* $25

Tinker, Edward Larocque. NEW YORKER UNLIMITED: THE MEMOIRS OF EDWARD LAROCQUE TINKER. Austin: Encino Press & Univ of Texas, 1970. Fine. *LAURIE.* $20

Tinker, Edward Larocque. THE HORSEMEN OF THE AMERICAS. Hastings House, 1953. 1st Amer. ed. Ltd ed of 1575 numbered (this not numbered). 7 color plts. VG in VG dj. *OREGON.* $65

Tinker, Edward Larocque. THE SPLENDID SPECTACLE OF POR-TUGESE BULLFIGHTING. Austin: Encino Press, 1967. One of 300 for general distribution, of a total ed of 600. Fine. *LAURIE.* $40

Tinker, George H. NORTHERN ARIZONA AND FLAGSTAFF IN 1887. Glendale: Arthur H. Clark, 1969. 1st ed thus. Front ptd wrapper of orig ptg reproduced on front cover cl binding. Bkpl removed, else Fine. Uncut. *CONNOLLY & WADE.* $45

Tinkham, George H. A HISTORY OF STOCKTON FROM ITS OR-GANIZATION UP TO THE PRESENT TIME INCLUDING A SKETCH OF SAN JOAQUIN COUNTY. SF: Hinton, 1880. 1st ed. (16),397pp. 2 orig albumen mounted photos, 4 ports, a little stained. Orig full calf, spine and front hinge expertly mended, bkpl removed, some staining to rear. Howes T273. *GINSBERG.* $500

Tinkle, Lon. AN AMERICAN ORIGINAL: THE LIFE OF J. FRANK DOBIE. Boston, (1978). 1st ed. Signed. Fine in dj. *ARTIS.* $20

Tinkle, Lon. AN AMERICAN ORIGINAL: THE LIFE OF J. FRANK DOBIE. Little, Brown & Co, (1978). 1st ed. Fine in dj. *AUTHORS OF THE WEST.* $20

Titley, Norah M. MINIATURES FROM PERSIAN MANUSCRIPTS. London: British Museum, 1977. 1st ed. 41 plts. Dj. NF. *WORLDWIDE.* $125

Titley, Norah M. PERSIAN MINIATURE PAINTING AND ITS IN-FLUENCE....Austin, TX: Univ of Texas Press, 1984. 1st ed. Dj. NF. *WORLDWIDE.* $35

Titmarsh, M.A. (pseud of William Makepeace Thackeray). THE IRISH SKETCH BOOK. London: Chapman & Hall, 1843. 1st ed. 2 vols. Orig emb grn cl. Bindings sl cocked, minute wear at extrems of spines, o/w exceptionally Fine, bright set, encl in 2 separate 1/2 morocco slipcases. *JAFFE.* $1250

Titmarsh, Mr. M.A. (pseud of William Makepeace Thackeray). DOC-TOR BIRCH AND HIS YOUNG FRIENDS. London: Chapman and Hall, 1849. 49pp,(1)p ads. Orig ptd pink wraps bound in full dark grn levant morocco, w/raised bands, gilt-tooled spine panels, gilt inner dentelles, aeg. Catalog descrip taped to front flyleaf, else excellent. 1st ed. *CHAPEL HILL.* $275

Tixier, Victor. TIXIER'S TRAVELS ON THE OSAGE PRAIRIES. John F. McDermott (ed). Norman: Univ of OK, 1940. 1st trans into English. Frontis, 8 plts, 2 fldg maps. Fine in Fine dj. Howes T276. *OREGON.* $50

Tizard, W.L. THE THEORY AND PRACTICE OF BREWING. London: Sold by all Booksellers, 1850. 3rd ed. Mod blue cl. VG. *WEBER.* $100

TOBACCO TALK BY AN OLD SMOKER. Phila: The Nicot Publishing Co., 1894. 1st ed. *KARMIOLE.* $40

TOBY CLAYPOT SOLVES A PROBLEM. London, (1980's). John Patience. 1/4" tear on 1st pop-up—does not detract, better off not mended. Pop-up bk. *BOOKFINDERS INTL.* $15

Todd, Edgeley. A DOCTOR ON THE CALIFORNIA TRAIL. Denver: Old West, (1971). 1st ed, ltd to 1500. 2 maps (1 fldg). Prospectus laid in. VF. *OREGON.* $25

Todd, Edwin. THE NEUROANATOMY OF LEONARDO DA VINCI. Santa Barbara, 1983. 1st ed. *FYE.* $60

Todd, Frederick. SOLDIERS OF THE AMERICAN ARMY, 1775-1954. Chicago: Regnery, (1954). 1st thus. Fine in Good+ dj. *OREGON.* $45

Todd, Helen. A MAN NAMED GRANT. Boston: Houghton Mifflin, 1940. 1st ed. Fine. *CONNOLLY & WADE.* $30

Todd, Helen. A MAN NAMED GRANT. Boston: Houghton Mifflin, 1940. 1st ptg. Dj. *SCHOYER'S.* $15

Todd, Mabel Loomis. TRIPOLI THE MYSTERIOUS. Bostom: Small, Maynard, 1912. 1st ed. 61 plts. Sl rubbed, o/w VG. *WORLDWIDE.* $20

Todd, Richard Cecil. CONFEDERATE FINANCE. Athens, GA, (1954). 1st ed. Fine in NF dj. *McGOWAN.* $65

Todd, Ruthven. TRACKS IN THE SNOW. London: Grey Walls, 1946. 1st ed. One page improperly trimmed, else VG in dj. Inscribed. *LAME DUCK.* $50

Todd, W.E.C. BIRDS OF THE LABRADOR PENINSULA AND ADJACENT AREAS, A DISTRIBUTIONAL LIST. Pittsburgh, 1963. 9 colored plts. Dj, lt chipping; sm piece missing. *SUTTON.* $185

Todd, W.E.C. BIRDS OF WESTERN PENNSYLVANIA. Pittsburgh, 1940. 22 colored plts, fldg map. Spine, front cvr darkened or discolored, edges scuffed, ink inscrip covering most of blank pg; bkpl. *SUTTON.* $95

Tofsrud, O.T. A HISTORY OF PIERCE COUNTY. Rugby, ND, (1936). 1st ed. 3 plts. Fine. *OREGON.* $45

Tolbert, Frank X. DICK DOWLING AT SABINE PASS. NY, (1962). 1st ed. Page sl toned, else NF in NF dj. *McGOWAN.* $75

Tolkien, J.R.R. and E.V. Gordon. SIR GAWAIN AND THE GREEN KNIGHT. Oxford, 1925. 1st ed. 1st issue w/4pp of ads insert. Spine sunstruck, else Fine. *McCLINTOCK.* $350

Tolkien, J.R.R. FARMER GILES OF HAM. Boston: Houghton Mifflin, 1950. Cl a little mottled at edges, thus VG in bright pict dj. 1st Amer ed. *CHAPEL HILL.* $175

Tolkien, J.R.R. SMITH OF WOOTON MAJOR. Boston, 1967. 1st Amer ed. Fine in dj. *McCLINTOCK.* $35

Tolkien, J.R.R. THE ADVENTURES OF TOM BOMBADIL AND OTHER VERSE FROM THE RED BOOK. London: Allen & Unwin, (1962). 1st ed. Fine in dj. *WOOLMER.* $75

Tolkien, J.R.R. THE LETTERS OF J.R.R. TOLKIEN. Boston: Houghton Mifflin, 1981. 1st US ed. Fine in dj (sm scrape on front panel). *CAPTAIN'S BOOKSHELF.* $25

Tolkien, J.R.R. THE RETURN OF THE KING. London, 1955. 1st ed. Lt discoloration to dj spine, else Fine in dj. *McCLINTOCK.* $450

Tolkien, J.R.R. THE ROAD GOES EVER ON. A SONG CYCLE. Boston, 1967. 1st ed. Decs by Tolkien. Music by Donald Swann. Fine in NF price clipped dj. *POLYANTHOS.* $95

TOLKIEN, J.R.R. THE SILMARILLION. George Allen & Unwin, 1977. 1st ed. Fine in dj. *STAHR.* $35

Tollemache, Lionel. STONES OF STUMBLING. London, 1891. 1st ed. Scarce. *FYE.* $75

Toller, Jane. PRISONERS-OF-WAR WORK 1756-1815. Cambridge: Golden Head Press, 1965. 1st ed. Orig 1/4 cl, dj. VF. Scarce. *LEFKOWICZ.* $75

Tolson, M.B. LIBRETTO FOR THE REPUBLIC OF LIBERIA. NY: Twayne, 1953. 1st ed. Fine in NF dj but for short tears and quarter-size chip on front panel. *BEASLEY.* $100

Tolstoy, Alexandra. TOLSTOY: A LIFE OF MY FATHER. NY: Harper, (1953). 1st ed. 543pp. Dj. *AKA.* $30

Tolstoy, Leo. 'THE KINGDOM OF GOD IS WITHIN YOU' CHRISTIANITY NOT AS A MYSTIC RELIGION BUT AS A NEW THEORY OF LIFE. Trans by Constance Garnett. London: Heinemann, 1894. 1st Eng ed. 2 vols. Sl foxing, else NF w/sunned spines. *CAPTAIN'S BOOKSHELF.* $300

Tolstoy, Leo. ANNA KARENINA. Cambridge: LEC, 1951. Illus by Barnett Freedman. 2 vols. One of 1500 ptd at the Univ Press & signed by Freedman. Pict cl. Ptd label on slipcase sl soiled, worn, o/w Fine set. *JAFFE.* $150

Tolstoy, Leo. TOLSTOY'S LETTERS. R.F. Christian (ed, trans). NY: Charles Scribner's Sons, (1978). 2 vols. Djs. VG. *WEBER.* $25

Tolstoy, Leo. WAR AND PEACE. Louise and Aylmer Maude (trans), Aylmer Maude (intro). 6 vols. Glasgow: Ptd for members of LEC at The University Press, 1938. Ltd to 1500, this one #1229, signed by Barnett Freedman (illus) w/fingerprint in red ink. Color plts, line drawings, color pict eps, pict cl. Spines very sl rubbed, o/w NF set in sl worn & repaired boxes. *DIAMOND.* $100

TOM AND JERRY. London, 1972. 3 pop-ups. Pop-up bk. *BOOK-FINDERS INTL.* $25

Tomlinson, Charles. A PEOPLED LANDSCAPE. London: Oxford Univ Press, 1963. 1st ed. Dj sunned at spine, o/w Fine. *JAFFE.* $65

Tomlinson, Charles. SEEING IS BELIEVING. London: Oxford Univ Press, 1960. 1st Eng ed, enl. Orig pub in America in 1958; this ed drops 1 poem, adds 15. Dj. Fine. *JAFFE.* $75

Tomlinson, H.M. A BROWN OWL. GC: Henry & Longwell, 1928. 1st ed. One of 107 signed by Tomlinson, Christopher Morley, Frank Henry & Dan Longwell. Dec boards w/ptd label, glassine dj. VF in cl slipcase. *JAFFE.* $250

Tomlinson, H.M. ALL OUR YESTERDAYS. London: Heinemann, (1930). Fine in dj. 1st Eng trade ed, 1st issue, w/"Our All Yesterdays" in running head on page 67. *CHAPEL HILL.* $50

Tomlinson, H.M. OUT OF SOUNDINGS. London: William Heinemann, Ltd, 1931. Illus by H. Charles Tomlinson. 1st ed. 1/275 signed by author, artist. Few bubbles on spine, else Fine, unopened in lightly used slipcase. *JUVELIS.* $75

Tomlinson, H.M. THE SEA AND THE JUNGLE. London: Duckworth & Co, (1912). Few dots of foxing to prelims; emb seal title pg, but Fine. 1st ed, 1st issue. *CHAPEL HILL.* $95

Tomlinson, Rev. Lewis. RECREATIONS IN ASTRONOMY. London: John W. Parker, 1840. 1st ed. Corners bumped, worn; boards waterstained; old moisture staining some pages, else Good. *KNOLLWOOD.* $110

Tompkins, C.B. et al. HIGH SPEED COMPUTING DEVICES. McGraw Hill, 1950. 1st ed. Owner's name, o/w Fine. *MAD DOG.* $75

Tompkins, Col. Frank. CHASING VILLA...PERSHING'S EXPEDITION INTO MEXICO. Harrisburg: The Military Service Pub Co, 1934. Owner stamp. Corner wear. Gold cl w/grn titles. VG. *PARMER.* $125

Tompkins, E.P. and J. Lee Davis. THE NATURAL BRIDGE AND ITS HISTORICAL SURROUNDINGS. Natural Bridge of VA, 1939. 1st ed. Fine in NF dj. *CONNOLLY & WADE.* $45

Tompkins, Peter. MYSTERIES OF THE MEXICAN PYRAMIDS. NY: Harper, (1976). 1st ed. Good in dj. *SILVER.* $25

Tooker, Richard. THE DAY OF THE BROWN HORDE. Payson & Clarke, 1931. 1st ed. VG in frayed dj. *MADLE.* $100

Toole, John Kennedy. A CONFEDERACY OF DUNCES. Baton Rouge: Louisiana State Univ, (1982). 1st ed. Fine in NF dj (internally strengthened). *LOPEZ.* $350

Toole, John Kennedy. A CONFEDERACY OF DUNCES. Baton Rouge: Louisiana State Univ Press, (1982). 1st ed. Fine in dj (tiny bit of rubbing but Fine). *LOPEZ.* $450

Toole, John Kennedy. A CONFEDERACY OF DUNCES. Baton Rouge: Louisiana State Univ Press, 1980. Walker Percy (foreword). Fine in dj. Signed by Percy. *CAPTAIN'S BOOKSHELF.* $500

Toole, John Kennedy. A CONFEDERACY OF DUNCES. Walker Percy (foreword). Baton Rouge & London: Louisiana State Univ Press, 1980. 1st ed. Orig tan cl. VG in dj. *CHAPEL HILL.* $350

Toole, John Kennedy. THE NEON BIBLE. NY: Grove Press, (1989). As New in dj. 1st ed. Adv rev copy w/pub's slip and flyer laid in. *CHAPEL HILL.* $35

Toole, T.R. ILLUSTRATED AND DESCRIPTIVE HISTORY OF THE ANIMALS. NY: Martin B. Brown, 1876. 1st ed. 4to, color-pict wraps, sewn; gilt border to cover; light soiling and wear to edges; 25 engr illus to text, seven full page, engraving to rear wrap. *DRAMATIS PERSONAE.* $70

Toombs, Samuel. NEW JERSEY TROOPS IN THE GETTYSBURG CAMPAIGN FROM JUNE 5 TO JULY 32, 1863. Orange, NJ, 1888. 1st ed. 406pp. VG. *PRATT.* $75

Topolski, Feliks. PORTRAIT OF G.B.S. NY: Oxford Univ Press, 1947. Ltd ed of 1,000. Dj. Fine. *WEBER.* $25

Toponce, Alexander. REMINISCENCES OF ALEXANDER TOPONCE. Norman: Univ of OK, 1971. 1st ed. VF in NF dj. Howes T299 *CONNOLLY & WADE.* $27.50

Torosian, Michael (ed). THE SISKIND VARIATIONS. (Toronto): Lumiere Press, 1990. 1st ed. Ltd to 190 numbered. Signed by Siskind & Harry Callahan. Cl backed boards. Mint. *JAFFE.* $350

Torosian, Michael (ed). THE SISKIND VARIATIONS. Toronto: Lumiere Press, 1990. 1st ed. 1/190 in linen backed grey boards and paper label. 6 gelatin-silver prints, incl 1 by Harry Callahan. Fine. Signed by Siskind and Callahan. *CAPTAIN'S BOOKSHELF.* $275

Torrey, B. and F.H. Allen (eds). THE JOURNAL OF HENRY DAVID THOREAU. Salt Lake City, (1984). 15 vols. with box. Fine in VG djs. *MIKESH.* $65

Torrey, J. A COMPENDIUM OF THE FLORA OF THE NORTHERN AND MIDDLE STATES...NY, 1826. 403pp. Contemp sheep very scuffed, outer hinges repaired w/cl taped on to spine; worn leather spine label retained, foxed. Ex-lib. *SUTTON.* $200

Torrey, J. and A. Gray. A FLORA OF NORTH AMERICA: CONTAINING ABRIDGED DESCRIPTIONS....Vol I. NY, 1838-40. Pp xiv,(1),711. Recent buckram w/foxing; lower corners pp in back contain dampstain rings. Institutional bkpl. *SUTTON.* $225

Tose, Frank. TRAPPING. TANNING. TAXIDERMY. Winnepeg: Grain Grower's Guide, 1921. 1st ed. Brown dec cl. VG. Scarce. *CONNOLLY & WADE.* $45

Tottenham, K. BIRD DOCTOR. Edinburgh, 1961. *SUTTON.* $23

TOULOUSE-LAUTREC. CATALOGUE OF THE COLLECTION OF FINE LITHOGRAPHS AND DRAWINGS. London: (Sotheby), 1966. Ptd boards w/pict dj. Fine, scarce. *BOOK BLOCK.* $50

Tourgee, Albion W. A FOOL'S ERRAND. BY ONE OF THE FOOLS. NY: Fords, Howard & Hulbert, 1880. (viii),361,(4)pp. Book adverts. 12mo. Pict red cl. NF. *CONNOLLY & WADE.* $65

Tourgee, Albion W. A FOOL'S ERRAND. NY, (1879). 1st ed. A little cover wear, o/w Fine. *PRATT.* $40

Tourgee, Albion W. THE STORY OF A THOUSAND. (105TH O.V.I.) Buffalo, NY, 1896. 1st ed. Ex-lib, minimal marks, front hinge cracking. VG. *McCLINTOCK.* $95

Town, Salem. AN ANALYSIS OF THE DERIVATIVE WORDS IN TBE ENGLISH LANGUAGE. 3rd ed, rev, enl. NY: (Harper & Bros), 1836. Dusky grn ribbon-stamped cl. Spine has paper title label (sl chipped, w/loss of 1 letter). Particularly well preserved. Quite nice, lt overall foxing. *BOOK BLOCK.* $120

Towne, C.W. and E.N. Wentworth. CATTLE AND MEN. Norman: Univ of OK, (1955). 1st ed. VF in VG dj. *OREGON.* $30

Towne, C.W. and E.N. Wentworth. SHEPHERD'S EMPIRE. Norman: Univ of OK, 1945. 1st ed. 10 maps (3 dbl page). Inscribed presentation. VG in VG dj. *OREGON.* $45

Towne, C.W. and E.N. Wentworth. SHEPHERD'S EMPIRE. Univ of OK Press, 1945. 1st ed. Fine in Fine dj. *VARNER.* $45

Townsend, Alexander. THE WOODEN WOMAN. Doubleday-Doran, 1930. 1st ed. Fine in dj. *MADLE.* $50

Townsend, Belton O'Neall. PLANTATION LAYS AND OTHER POEMS. Columbia, SC: Charles A. Calvo, Jr, 1884. 1st ed. Inscribed. 106,(1),(1)pp. Orig brn cl. Lib bkpl, blindstamp, lt spotting to cover, top of spine rubbed, else VG. *CHAPEL HILL.* $85

Townsend, C.W. THE BIRDS OF ESSEX COUNTY, MAS-SACHUSETTS ALONG WITH SUPPLEMENT. Cambridge, 1905 & 1920. 2 plts. Some pg yellowing. *SUTTON.* $125

Townsend, Francis E. NEW HORIZONS: (AN AUTOBIOG-RAPHY). Chicago: J.L. Stewart Pub Co, 1943. Pict fabricoid, some lt wear and a spotting, small stamp on front ep. *DAWSON'S.* $30

Townsend, General E.D. THE CALIFORNIA DIARY OF GENERAL E.D. TOWNSEND. Malcolm Edwards (ed). LA: Ward Ritchie Press, (1970). 1st ed. VF in Fine slipcase. *OREGON.* $50

Townsend, William H. LINCOLN THE LITIGANT. Boston, 1925. 1st ed. Ltd to 1,050. VG+. *PRATT.* $30

Townshead, R.B. THE TENDERFOOT IN NEW MEXICO. NY, 1924. 1st ed. Tear top spine repaired. *HEINOLDT.* $25Corle, Edwin. DEATH VALLEY AND THE CREEK CALLED FURNACE... WITH PHOTOGRAPHS BY ANSEL ADAMS. LA: The Ward Ritchie Press, 1962. 1st ed. Grey cl. Fine in dj. *WEBER.* $145

Townshend, F. Trench. A CRUISE IN GREEK WATERS, WITH A HUNTING EXCURSION IN TUNIS. London, 1870. New cl. xv,286pp. Light stain on corner 1st few pgs. Scarce. Fresh, tight. *O'NEILL.* $75

Toynbee, Jocelyn M.C. ANIMALS IN ROMAN LIFE AND ART. (London): Thames and Hudson, (1973). Dj. Good. *ARCHAEOLOGIA.* $50

Toynbee, Jocelyn M.C. ART IN ROMAN BRITAIN. London: Phaidon, (1962). Stain at flyleaf. Dj. Good. *ARCHAEOLOGIA.* $85

Toynbee, Jocelyn M.C. DEATH AND BURIAL IN THE ROMAN WORLD. London: Thames and Hudson, (1971). 30 figs. Dj. Good. *ARCHAEOLOGIA.* $45

Tozer, Rev. Henry F. THE ISLANDS OF THE AEGEAN. Oxford, 1890. Fldg map as frontis, sm tear in fold. *O'NEILL.* $125

TRACES OF THE ROMAN AND MOOR; OR, TWICE TROD-DEN TRACKS....NY: Lamport, Blakeman & Law, 1853. 450pp. Frontis. Generally Good. *WORLDWIDE.* $28

Tracy, Jack and Jim Berkey. SUBCUTANEOUSLY, MY DEAR WATSON: SHERLOCK HOLMES AND THE COCAINE HABIT. Bloomington, IN: James A. Rock, 1978. 1st ed. Pb ed pub simultaneously w/hb ed. Sm spot front cvr o/w Fine in stiff wraps. *MORDIDA.* $45

Train, Arthur and Robert Williams Wood. THE MAN WHO ROCK-ED THE EARTH. Doubleday, 1915. 1st ed. VG. *MADLE.* $50

Train, Arthur. MR. TUTT FINDS A WAY. NY: Charles Scribner's Sons, 1945. 1st ed. VG in dj w/several short closed tears and minor wear at spine ends. *MORDIDA.* $35

Train, Arthur. NO MATTER WHERE. NY: Scribner's, 1933. 1st ed. Inscribed. Fine, lacking dj. *LOPEZ.* $45

Train, Arthur. THE CONFESSIONS OF ARTEMAS QUIBBLE. Scribner's, 1911. 1st ed. Remains of bookplate on front endpaper, stain to rear cvr, bump to front cvr edge, overall VG. *BEBBAH.* $15

TRANSACTIONS OF THE NEW JERSEY STATE MEDICAL SOCIETY 1859-1865. 6 vols. bound in 1. 95, 103, 115, 116, 113, 172, 174pp. Ex-lib. *FYE.* $150

TRANSACTIONS OF THE OHIO STATE MEDICAL SOCIETY. 6 VOLUMES. (1884, 1886, 1888, 1890, 1895, 1896). Ex-lib. Scarce. *FYE.* $75

Tranter, G.J. PLOWING THE ARCTIC. Toronto, (1945). 1st ed. Dj worn. *ARTIS.* $17.50

Tranter, G.J. PLOWING THE ARCTIC. Toronto: Longmans, Green & Co, 1945. 1st Canadian ed. VG+ in Good dj. *BLUE DRAGON.* $25

Traub, H.P. THE AMARYLLIS MANUAL. NY, 1958. Cl. Upper pp smudged. Dj, some soiling, sm tear. *SUTTON.* $35

TRAVELS OF AN IRISH GENTLEMAN. IN SEARCH OF A RELIGION. By the Editor of "Captain Rock's Memoirs." (By Thomas Moore.) In Two Vols. London: Longman, Rees, Orme, Brown, Green & Longman. 1833. 1st ed. 2 vols. xii,336; viii,354pp. Contemp maroon calf over marbled boards, spines bit rubbed. *KAR-MIOLE.* $100

TRAVELS THROUGH THE INTERIOR PARTS OF AMERICA. (By Thomas Anburey.) London: William Lane, 1789. 1st ed. 2 vols. Fldg map, 7 plts (4 fldg). Grn 1/2 morocco, rebacked w/orig spines preserved. Lacks half titles, some foxing. *HUDSON.* $900

Traven, Ben. GENERAL FROM THE JUNGLE. NY: Hill and Wang (1972). 1st Amer ed. Fine in dj. *DORN.* $50

Traven, Ben. THE DEATH SHIP. Knopf, 1934. 1st Amer ed. Very slight wear, slight fraying at spine bottom, bottom corners else VG. *BEBBAH.* $90

Traven, Ben. THE DEATH SHIP. NY: Knopf (1934). 1st Amer ed. Cvrs scuffed, name, or About VG in VG dj. *DORN.* $275

Traven, Ben. THE NIGHT VISITOR AND OTHER STORIES. NY: Hill and Wang (1966). 1st Amer ed. Small bkstore label, name else NF in VG dj. *DORN.* $40

Traven, Ben. THE WHITE ROSE. Westport: Lawrence Hill (1979). 1st Amer ed. Fine in sl used dj, sm edge tear. *DORN.* $35

Traven, Ben. TO THE HONORABLE MISS S....Westport: Lawrence Hill (1981). 1st Amer ed. Fine in dj. *DORN.* $25

Traver, Robert (pseud of John D. Voelker). SMALL TOWN D.A. NY, 1954. 1st ed. Boards. Sm wear spots spine tip, o/w NF in sl chipped dj. Inscribed. *DIAMOND.* $75

Traver, Robert (pseud of John D. Voelker). ANATOMY OF A FISHERMAN. NY, (1964). 1st ed. VF in a chipped dj. *BOND.* $90

Traver, Robert (pseud of John D. Voelker). ANATOMY OF A FISHERMAN. NY: McGraw Hill, (1964). 1st ed. Fine in chipped dj. *ARTIS.* $100

Traver, Robert (pseud of John D. Voelker). HORNSTEIN'S BOY. NY: St. Martin's, (1962). 1st ed. Fine in frayed dj. *ARTIS.* $22.50

Traver, Robert (pseud of John D. Voelker). SMALL DOWN D.A. NY, 1954. 1st ed. Small wear spots at one spine tip, o/w NF in sl chipped dj. Inscribed. *DIAMOND.* $75

Traver, Robert (pseud of John D. Voelker). THE JEALOUS MISTRESS. Boston: Little Brown, (1967). 2nd ptg. Fine in dj. *ARTIS.* $35

Traver, Robert (pseud of John D. Voelker). TROUBLESHOOTER. NY: Viking, 1943. 1st ed. Author's 1st bk. VG+ in dj w/chipping to spine extrems and wear along folds. *LAME DUCK.* $60

Traver, Robert (pseud of John D. Voelker). TROUT MADNESS. NY: St. Martin's, (1960). 1st ed. Fine. *ARTIS.* $25

Traver, Robert (pseud of John D. Voelker). TROUT MADNESS. NY: St. Martin's Press, 1960. 1st ed. Name. *BACKMAN.* $28

Travis, Helga. THE UMATILLA TRAIL, PIONEER DAYS IN THE WASHINGTON TERRITORY. NY: Exposition, (1951). 1st ed. VG in VG dj. *OREGON.* $45

Traylor, Samuel W. Sr. OUT OF THE SOUTHWEST: A TEXAS BOY. Allentown: Ptd for the author by Geo. P. Schlicher, 1936. 1st ed. Signed presentation. Frontis. 17 plts. Dec cl, gilt. VG. Scarce. *CONNOLLY & WADE.* $50

Treadwell, E.F. THE CATTLE KING. Fresno, 1966. 2nd ptg of 2nd ed. Fine in Fine dj. *VARNER.* $20

Treadwell, Edward F. THE CATTLE KING: A DRAMATIZED BIOGRAPHY. NY, 1931. 1st ed. Orig cl. Signed. Howes T336. *GINSBERG.* $85

TREASURE ISLAND. London, 1975. 6 pop-ups. Pop-up bk. *BOOK-FINDERS INTL.* $25

TREASURE ISLAND. London, 1979. Illus Pavlin and Seda. 6 double-pg pop-ups. Pop-up bk. *BOOKFINDERS INTL.* $20

TREASURY OF TRAVEL AND ADVENTURE, IN NORTH AND SOUTH AMERICA, EUROPE....NY: Appleton, 1865. 456pp. Generally Good. *WORLDWIDE*. $35

Treat, A. E. MITES OF MOTHS AND BUTTERFLIES. Ithaca, 1975. Dj w/light wear. *SUTTON*. $40

Treat, Lawrence. BIG SHOT. NY: Harper & Brothers, (1951). 1st ed. Inscribed, signed in March, 1951. VG in edgeworn dj. *LOPEZ*. $25

Treat, Lawrence. D AS IN DEAD. NY: Duell, Sloan & Pearce, 1941. 1st ed. Some fading on cvrs, o/w VG in dj (nicks, wear). *MORDIDA*. $30

Treat, Lawrence. T AS IN TRAPPED. Morrow, 1947. 1st ed. VG+ with spot lower edge of cvr in VG dj. *BEBBAH*. $20

Treat, Mary. INJURIOUS INSECTS OF FARM & GARDEN. NY: Orange Judd, 1908. *AMERICAN BOTANIST*. $25

Treat, Roger. WALTER JOHNSON. Messner, 1948. 1st ed. Good+ in VG+ dj. *PLAPINGER*. $150

Tree, Herbert Beerbohm. NOTHING MATTERS AND OTHER STORIES. Boston: Houghton Mifflin, 1917. 1st US ed. VG. Signed, dated 1917. *CAPTAIN'S BOOKSHELF*. $100

Trefousse, Hans. BEN BUTLER: THE SOUTH CALLED HIM BEAST! NY: Twayne, 1957. 1st ed. VG, bumped. *ARCHER*. $25

Tregenza, L.A. RED SEA MOUNTAINS OF EGYPT. London: Oxford Univ Press, 1955. Dj chipped. *SCHOYER'S*. $16.50

Trent, W.P. (ed). THE JOURNALS OF WASHINGTON IRVING. Boston: Bibliophile Soc, 1919. 3 vols. 430 copies. NF. *POLYANTHOS*. $75

Tresunngar, Hugo. DARK JUSTICE. LA: Sutton House, (1938). 1st ed. Prev owner's name. VG in VG- dj. *AARD*. $20

Trevanian. THE EIGER SANCTION. NY: Crown, 1972. 1st ed, 1st bk. NF in dj. *ELSE FINE*. $85

Trevanian. THE LOO SANCTION. NY: Crown Publishers, 1973. 1st ed. VF in price-clipped dj. *MORDIDA*. $30

Treves, Frederick. THE ELEPHANT MAN AND OTHER REMINISCENCES. London, 1924. 222pp. *FYE*. $50

Treves, Frederick. THE RIVIERA OF THE CORNICHE ROAD. NY, 1921. 1st Amer ed. Cloth. Pict. spine gilt. Very slight silverfishing on covers, o/w VG. *DIAMOND*. $25

Treves, Frederick. THE TALE OF A FIELD HOSPITAL. London: Cassell, 1900. vii + 109pp + ads. 1st ed. Orig morocco. Spine rebacked. Some foxing else NF. Very scarce. *GREAT EPIC*. $245

Trevisan, A.F. MEN AND JACKASSES. NY: Pilgrim Press, 1938. 1st ed. 11 plts. Fine in Good+ dj. *OREGON*. $17.50

Trevor, William. BEYOND THE PALE. Viking, 1982. 1st Amer ed. VF in dj. *STAHR*. $15

Trevor, William. MISS GOMEZ AND THE BRETHREN. London: Bodley Head, 1971. 1st ed. Minor bump at spine heel, else Fine in dj. *ELSE FINE*. $125

Trevor, William. MRS. ECKDORF IN O'NEILL'S HOTEL. London: Bodley Head, 1969. 1st ed. VF, minor rubbing at dj extrems. *ELSE FINE*. $90

Trevor, William. THE BOARDING-HOUSE. Viking, 1965. 1st Amer ed. VF in dj. *STAHR*. $90

Trevor, William. THE OLD BOYS. NY: Viking, 1964. 1st ed, 1st novel. VF, dj sl aged darkened on the spine. *ELSE FINE*. $100

Trevor, William. THE OLD BOYS. Viking, 1964. 1st Amer ed. Fine in dj (darkened spine). *STAHR*. $110

Trevor-Battye, Aubyn. ICE-BOUND ON KOLGUEV. Westminster: Archibald Constable, 1895. 3rd ed. 453pp. Lt soiling to grn cl, sm tear. Interior clean, tight. Bkpl. *PARMER*. $150

TRIAL OF ANDREW JOHNSON. Washington: GPO, 1868. 3 vols. (in 2). xxii,741; xxii,498,401pp. Orig black cl. *SCHOYER'S*. $125

Trigoboff, Joseph. THE BONE ORCHARD. NY: Walker, 1990. 1st ed. Review copy, signed. Pub's slip laid in. VF in dj. *SILVER DOOR*. $30

Trillin, Calvin. AN EDUCATION IN GEORGIA. NY: Viking, (1964). 1st ed. VG in dj. *LOPEZ*. $85

Trilling, Lionel. E. M. FORSTER. Norfolk: New Directions, 1943. 1st ed. Inscribed by author. Fine in lightly worn dj w/a few small chips. *BEASLEY*. $75

Trilling, Lionel. THE MIDDLE OF THE JOURNEY. NY: Viking, 1947. 1st ed. Inscribed by author. A little sunning and corner bumping, o/w NF in VG+ dj. *BEASLEY*. $75

Trimble, Joe. PHIL RIZZUTO. Barnes, 1951. 1st ed. Good+ in VG dj. *PLAPINGER*. $27.50

Triplett, Frank. CONQUERING THE WILDERNESS OR NEW PICTORIAL HISTORY....Chicago: Werner, 1895. Frontis, xxxix, 742pp. Orig pict cl. Front inner hinge repaired, else VG. Scarce. *CONNOLLY & WADE*. $85

Triplett, Frank. THE LIFE, TIMES, & TREACHEROUS DEATH OF JESSE JAMES. Chicago: Sage Books, 1970. Rprt of rare 1882 ed. Fine in VG dj. *OREGON*. $30

Trippensee, R.E. WILDLIFE MANAGEMENT. 2 vols. NY, 1948-53. 1st eds. Cloth. Some rubbing; flecking to backstrip vol 2. *SUTTON*. $65

Tristram, E.W. ENGLISH WALL PAINTING OF THE 14TH CENTURY. London, 1955. NF. *POLYANTHOS*. $60

Tristram, H.B. THE GREAT SAHARA: WANDERING SOUTH OF THE ATLAS MOUNTAINS. London: Murray, 1860. 1st ed. xv,435pp. 2 fldg maps. Rubbed & faded, spine frayed & chipped, 1st and few last leaves foxed, o/w Good ex-lib. *WORLDWIDE*. $40

Tristram, H.B. THE LAND OF ISRAEL; A JOURNAL OF TRAVELS IN PALESTINE, UNDERTAKEN WITH SPECIAL REFERENCE TO ITS PHYSICAL CHARACTER. London, 1866. 2nd ed. Frontis in color, 2 fldg maps. xx,656pp. NF. *O'NEILL*. $150

Tristram, H.B. THE LAND OF MOAB. TRAVELS AND DISCOVERIES....NY, 1873. 416 pp, trace of lib label. *O'NEILL* . $45

Tristram, H.B. THE LAND OF MOAB: TRAVELS AND DISCOVERIES....NY: Harper, 1873. 1st ed. 416pp. Fldg color map. Orig cl, edges sl rubbed, spine frayed, sl foxed. Ex-lib w/spine sticker, o/w VG. *WORLDWIDE*. $60

Trollope, Anthony. A LETTER FROM ANTHONY TROLLOPE DESCRIBING A VISIT TO CALIFORNIA IN 1875. SF: Colt Press, 1946. 1st ed, ltd to 500. VG. *OREGON*. $50

Trollope, Anthony. NORTH AMERICA. 2 vols. London: Chapman & Hall, 1862. 1st ed. Fldg map in vol 1. Old lib 1/4 cl, spines laid down. Ads lacking. Old labels and stamps of Eng circulating lib. *HUDSON*. $125

Trollope, Anthony. THE LAST CHRONICLE OF BARSET. 32 illus by George H. Thomas. London: Smith & Elder, 1867. 1st ed. 2 vols. Later 3/4 calf and cl w/red spine labels. Some scuffing to the corners, but attractive. *CAPTAIN'S BOOKSHELF*. $600

Trollope, Anthony. THE LAST CHRONICLE OF BARSET. London: Smith, Elder & Co, 1867. 2 vols. 1st ed. Crushed levant, raised bands, gilt spine, marbled eps. Felt-lined cl slipcase. 32 full-pg engr plts. Lt foxing. Lovely, exceptionally clean. *PIRAGES*. $750

Trollope, Anthony. THE LAST CHRONICLE OF BARSET. NY: Harper & Brothers, 1867. 1st Amer ed. Split at top of joint, bumped, sl worn head, tail of spine, some foxing, front edge fep dampstained. VG. *BLUE MOUNTAIN*. $125

Trollope, Anthony. THE VICAR OF BULLHAMPTON. London, 1870. 1st ed. 30 illus by H. Woods. Full calf, gilt spine, leather label, sl rubbed. NF. *POLYANTHOS*. $250

Trollope, Anthony. THE WEST INDIES AND THE SPANISH MAIN. London: Chapman and Hall, 1859. 1st ed. 395pp. 3/4 red pebbled morocco, marbled boards, raised bands, spine gilt in panels. Fine color map frontispiece. Lib bkpl front pastedown, contents Fine. *HARTFIELD.* $495

Trollope, Frances. DOMESTIC MANNERS OF THE AMERICANS. NY: Dodd, Mead, 1927. Reprint from 5th London ed. Spine gilt sl dulled, else VG. *HARTFIELD.* $65

Trollope, Frances. PARIS AND PARISIANS IN 1835. London: Richard Bentley, 1836. 2 vols. 1st ed. 418,412pp. Bound in contemp full calf w/raised bands nicely stamped on spine. (Rebacked w/orig spines laid down). Bound w/half titles and engr pieces. 12 full-pg engrs by A. Hervieu. Nice, Clean set. rare. *SECOND LIFE.* $375

Trollope, Mrs. (Francis M.). DOMESTIC MANNERS OF THE AMERICANS. London: Whittaker, Treacher, 1832. 2nd ed. (stated). 2 vols. xii,304; viii,304pp + 23 lithos (24 called for). Ribbon markers. Orig 1/2 calf w/marbled boards. Spine blocked in gilt. Black labels. 12mo. Eps replaced. Vol II has small chip at head and heel of spine; hinges reinforced w/glue. Else, with defects noted, VG. Scarce. Howes T357. *CONNOLLY & WADE.* $110

Trotsky, Leon. THE HISTORY OF THE RUSSIAN REVOLUTION. Trans by Max Eastman. London: Victor Gollancz, 1932. 3 vols. 1st Eng ed. Djs. Fine. Rare in this condition. *WEBER.* $500

Troughton, E. FURRED ANIMALS OF AUSTRALIA. 25 colored plts. NY, 1947. 1st Amer ed. Cloth. *SUTTON.* $55

Troughton, Ellis. FURRED ANIMALS OF AUSTRALIA. NY: Angus and Roberston, 1947. 1st Amer ed. Some shelfwear, else VG in worn dj. *PARMER.* $40

TROUT FISHING. NY: Outdoor Life/Harper & Row, 1972. 1st ed. VG+ in Good dj. *BACKMAN.* $25

Trout, Kilgore (pseud of Philip Jose Farmer). VENUS ON THE HALF-SHELL. NY: Dell, 1975. 1st ed. Pb orig. Fine in wraps. *ELSE FINE.* $20

Trovillion, Violet and Hall W. THE PRIVATE PRESS AS A DIVERSION. Herrin, IL: Trovillion Private Press. 1937. Ltd to 147 numbered, signed by the Trovillions. Christmas greetings for 1937 (4 pp) laid in. *KARMIOLE.* $75

Trow, M.J. LESTRADE & THE LEVIATHAN. London: Macmillan, 1987. 1st ed. Review copy, pub's slip laid in. Fine in dj. *SILVER DOOR.* $27.50

Trow, M.J. THE ADVENTURES OF INSPECTOR LESTRADE. London: Macmillan, 1985. 1st ed. Fine in dj. *SILVER DOOR.* $25

Trowbridge, Bertha Chadwick (ed). OLD HOUSES OF CONNECTICUT. Bertha Chadwick Trowbridge, Charles McLean Andrews (eds). New Haven: Yale Univ Press. 1923. Ltd to 1000 numbered, signed by president of the Yale Univ Press. Slipcase (rubbed). *KARMIOLE.* $150

Trowbridge, M.E.D. PIONEER DAYS. THE LIFE-STORY OF GERSHOM AND ELIZABETH DAY. Amer Baptist Pub Soc, 1895. 1st ed. VG. Howes T359. *OREGON.* $100

Troyer, Howard William. NED WARD OF GRUBSTREET. Cambridge: Harvard Univ Press, 1946. VG. *NUTMEG.* $15

Truesdale, Captain John. THE BLUE COATS AND HOW THEY LIVED. Phila, (1867). 1st ed. 510pp. Rebound. VG. *PRATT.* $32.50

Truman, Benjamin Cummings. OBSERVATIONS OF BENJAMIN CUMMINGS TRUMAN ON EL CAMINO ROAD. Msgr. Francis J. Weber (ed). LA: Dawson's, 1978. 1st ed, ltd to 400. LA Miscellany #9. VG. *CONNOLLY & WADE.* $50

Truman, Harry S. MR. CITIZEN. NY, 1960. Ltd ed, 701/1000 signed. Fine w/o dj as issued in NF box. *POLYANTHOS.* $500

Truman, Harry S. PUBLIC PAPERS OF THE PRESIDENTS OF THE UNITED STATES: HARRY S. TRUMAN, CONTAINING THE PUBLIC MESSAGES, SPEECHES, AND STATEMENTS OF THE PRESIDENT. Washington: USGPO, 1961-6. 8 vols. Ex-lib. NF. *ARCHER.* $100

Truman, Harry S. THE FREE WORLD AND FREE TRADE. The Jno. E. Owens Memorial Lecture, 1957. Dallas: Southern Methodist Univ Press, 1963. One of 1000. Fine in slipcase. *LAURIE.* $40

Trumbo, Dalton. ADDITIONAL DIALOGUE. LETTERS OF DALTON TRUMBO, 1942-1962. NY: Evans, 1970. 1st ed. Close to Fine w/owner's name, in lightly used dj. *BEASLEY.* $25

Trumbo, Dalton. ECLIPSE. London: Lovat Dickson & Thompson, 1935. 1st ed. Shabby copy of author's 1st bk, lacks dj. *LAME DUCK.* $175

Trumbo, Dalton. WASHINGTON JITTERS. NY: Knopf, 1936. 1st ed. VG in dj w/wear to edges and folds. *LAME DUCK.* $125

Trumbull, G. NAMES & PORTRAITS OF BIRDS WHICH INTEREST GUNNERS. NY, 1888. Engr. Gilt dec cl. VG. *MIKESH.* $55

Trumbull, J. Hammond (ed). THE TRUE-BLUE LAWS OF CONNECTICUT AND NEW HAVEN...Hartford, CT: American Pub Co, 1876. 1st ed. Dec title-pg in lt blue. Orig dec blind-stamped lt blue cl w/gilt seal of Connecticut. Sm stain bottom of spine, o/w NF. *DIAMOND.* $85

Trumbull, J. Hammond. THE TRUE-BLUE LAWS OF CONNECTICUT AND NEW HAVEN AND THE FALSE BLUE LAWS. Hartford: Amer Pub Co. 1876. 1st ed. 360pp. *KARMIOLE.* $35

Trumbull, James H. NATICK DICTIONARY. Wash, DC: GPO, 1903. 1st ed. Smithsonian Inst: B.A.E. Bull #25. Orig cl. About Fine. *CONNOLLY & WADE.* $135

Trumbull, James H. NATICK DICTIONARY. Wash: GPO, 1903. Issued as BAE Bull 25. VG+ w/some wear to boards. *BEASLEY.* $40

Trumbull, James Hammond. NATICK DICTIONARY. BAE, Bulletin 25. Wash: GPO, 1903. Ex-lib, some pencil notes, still VG. *LAURIE.* $60

Trump, David. CENTRAL AND SOUTHERN ITALY BEFORE ROME. London: Thames and Hudson, (1966). Dj. Signature. Good. *ARCHAEOLOGIA.* $25

Trusler, John. HOGARTH MORALIZED; A COMPLETE EDITION OF ALL...ADMIRED WORKS OF WILLIAM HOGARTH....London: John Major. 1831. xxvi,294pp. + 54 proof plts (containing 56 engrs), 12 text woodcuts, and a copper-engr frontis. 19th c full gilt calf w/black leather spine label; spine sl rubbed. *KARMIOLE.* $175

Truss, Seldon. NUMBER NAUGHT. Dodd, Mead, 1930. 1st Amer ed. Good in Good dj with piece missing top of spine, small chips & tiny hole back panel. *BEBBAH.* $25

Trypanis, C.A. THE ELEGIES OF A GLASS ADONIS. NY: Chilmark Press, 1967. 1/450, numbered, signed w/lengthy Typographical Note by Will Carter. NF. *BEASLEY.* $75

Tubby, A.H. and Robert Jones. MODERN METHODS IN THE SURGERY OF PARALYSES WITH SPECIAL REFERENCE TO MUSCLE-GRAFTING, TENDON TRANSPLANTATION & ARTHRODESIS. London, 1903. 1st ed. 1/4 leather, 311pp. *FYE.* $250

Tucci, Giuseppe. NEPAL. NY: Dutton, (1962). 1st US ed. 60 photo ptls. NF in VG- dj. *BLUE DRAGON.* $45

Tuchman, Barbara. A DISTANT MIRROR. NY: Knopf, 1978. 1st ed. One of an unspecified number, signed on tipped-in leaf. Fine in close to Fine dj w/rough top edge. *BEASLEY.* $75

Tucker, Glenn. HANCOCK THE SUPERB. Indianapolis: Bobbs-Merrill, 1960. 1st ed. NF in torn dj, rubbed, good. *ARCHER.* $50

Tucker, Glenn. LEE AND LONGSTREET AT GETTYSBURG. Indianapolis, (1968). 1st ed. 286pp. Light dj wear, o/w Fine. *PRATT.* $40

Tucker, Glenn. ZEB VANCE, CHAMPION OF PERSONAL FREEDOM. Indianapolis, (1965). 1st ed. VG+ in dj. *PRATT.* $30

Tucker, M.A.R. CAMBRIDGE. A&C Black, 1907. 1st ed. VG-NF. *OLD LONDON.* $100

Tucker, Marcia. JAMES ROSENQUIST. APRIL 12-MAY 29, 1972. NY: Whitney Museum of Art, (1972). Wraps (soiled). 4pp "Lenders" index laid in. NF. *BLUE MOUNTAIN.* $35

Tucker, Mary. ITINERANT PREACHING UN THE EARLY DAYS OF METHODISM. Boston: Russell, 1872. Thomas W. Tucker (ed). 1st ed. Faded. Inscribed by ed. VG. *SECOND LIFE.* $65

Tucker, Patrick T. RIDING THE HIGH COUNTRY. Ed by Grace Stone Coates. Caldwell: ID, 1933. 1st ed. Fine in dj. Howes T395. *DIAMOND.* $100

Tucker, Robert C. STALIN AS REVOLUTIONARY: 1879-1929. NY: Norton, (1973). 1st ed. 519pp. Dj price clipped w/edgetears. *AKA.* $25

Tucker, Wilson. RED HERRING. Rinehart, 1951. 1st ed. Ex-lib. Near VG. Inscribed. *MADLE.* $35

Tucker, Wilson. THE CHINESE DOLL. Rinehart, 1946. 1st ed, 1st bk. Chip from spine of dj & bk, else VG in dj. *MADLE.* $60

Tucker, Wilson. THE CITY IN THE SEA. Rinehart, 1951. 1st ed. VF in dj. Inscribed. *MADLE.* $150

Tucker, Wilson. THE TIME MASTERS. Rinehart, 1953. 1st ed. Fine in dj. *MADLE.* $85

Tuckerman, Charles K. THE GREEKS OF TODAY. NY, 1872. Spine ends frayed. 366 pp. *O'NEILL.* $75

Tuckerman, Henry T. SICILY: A PILGRIMAGE. NY: Putnam, 1852. 1st ed. 187pp. Good. *WORLDWIDE.* $25

Tuckerman, Henry T. THE LIFE OF SILAS TALBOT, A COMMODORE IN THE NAVY OF THE UNITED STATES. NY: J.C. Riker, 1850. 1st ed. Lacking ffep, but attractive withal. Scarce. *LEFKOWICZ.* $150

Tudor, Tasha. TAKE JOY! THE TASHA TUDOR CHRISTMAS BOOK. World, (1966). 157pp. Illus by Tasha Tudor. Fine in VG+ dj w/light edgewear. *BEBBAH.* $30

Tudor, Tasha. WINGS FROM THE WIND, AN ANTHOLOGY OF POEMS. Lippincott, (1964). 1st ed. Illus by Tasha Tudor. Browning of paper-covered boards, else NF in VG+ dj w/few small closed edge tears. *BEBBAH.* $50

Tuer, Andrew W. (ed). STORIES FROM OLD-FASHIONED CHILDREN'S BOOKS. London: Leadenhall Press, 1899-1900. 1st ed. Frontis. Illus. VG. *WREDEN.* $70

Tuer, Andrew W. HISTORY OF THE HORN-BOOK. London: The Leadenhall Press, Ltd. 1897. 1st ed. xviii,486pp+a page of ads. 3 facs horn-books in rear pocket. Lea spine label sl rubbed; front outer hinge w/minor crack. Overall VG. *KARMIOLE.* $350

Tuer, Andrew W. PAGES AND PICTURES FROM FORGOTTEN CHILDREN'S BOOKS. London: Leadenhall Pr., 1898-99. 1st ed. Cl, gold lettering. Teg. Spine tips worn, else VG. *ACADEMIC LIBRARY.* $45

Tuer, Andrew W. STORIES FROM OLD-FASHIONED CHILDREN'S BOOKS. London: Leadenhall Pr, 1899-1900. 1st ed. 250 cuts. (1 b/w illus neatly colored). Teg, spine tips worn, corners bumped. Good+. *ACADEMIC LIBRARY.* $45

Tuer, Andrew W. THE FOLLIES & FASHIONS OF OUR GRANDFATHERS (1807)....London: Field & Tuer, The Leadenhall Press, 1886/7. 1st ed. One of 250 numbered on lg paper. Signed. Grease stains spine, rear cvr, likewise at tail end of signet, eps foxed, o/w Fine. *WREDEN.* $130

Tuggle, W.O. SHEM, HAM, & JAPHETH: THE PAPERS OF W.O. TUGGLE. Eugene Current-Garcia (ed). Athens: Univ of Georgia, 1973. 1st ed. 4pp paper laid in containing two maps. Fine in NF dj. *CONNOLLY & WADE.* $40

Tuke, D. Hack. ILLUSTRATIONS OF THE INFLUENCE OF THE MIND UPON THE BODY IN HEALTH AND DISEASE. Phila, 1873. 1st ed. Front inner hinge weak, head of spine torn. *FYE.* $75

Tuke, D. Hack. ILLUSTRATIONS OF THE INFLUENCE OF THE MIND UPON THE BODY IN HEALTH AND DISEASE. London, 1872. 1st ed. 444pp. Inscribed. Head and tail of spine worn, backstrip faded. *FYE.* $250

Tuke, D. Hack. SLEEP-WALKING AND HYPNOTISM. London, 1884. 1st ed. 120pp. Scarce. *FYE.* $200

Tuker. M.A.R. CAMBRIDGE. A&C Black, 1922. 1st ed (this series). 1 plt detached, dj only fair else VG-NF. *OLD LONDON.* $30

Tull, Jethro. THE HORSE-HOEING HUSBANDRY. London: Cobben, 1829, Later ptg of collected ed. VG. *SECOND LIFE.* $175

Tullidge, Edward. LIFE OF BRIGHAM YOUNG. NY, 1876. 1st ed., 458 pp (+81pp supp), port, owner's name, re-backed with spine laid down; interior tight and clean. Acceptable. *BENCHMARK.* $95

Tullis Russell, Ltd. CHARLES DICKENS, 1812-1870. A BIOGRAPHY, WITH EXAMPLES OF THE WORK OF HIS FINEST ILLUSTRATORS. Tullis Russell (London), n/d. c. 1962. 27pp. Portrait, 8 color plts by Sam Kyd; 13 short leaves. *HEINOLDT.* $40

Tully, Andrew. THE TIME OF THE HAWK. NY: Morrow, 1967. 1st ed. NF in dj. *LOPEZ.* $45

Tully, Jim. BIDDY BROGAN'S BOY. NY: Scribner's, 1942. 1st ed. Fine, minor rubs at spine ends of dj. *ELSE FINE.* $50

Tumblety, Frances. A FEW PASSAGES IN THE LIFE OF DR. FRANCES TUMBLETY...Cincinnati: Pub by author, 1866. 82pp. Wraps. Some cvr wear, edges frayed. In specially designed box. *HEINOLDT.* $40

Tunstall, John Henry. THE LIFE AND DEATH OF JOHN HENRY TUNSTALL: THE LETTERS, DIARIES....Frederick W. Nolan (ed). Albuquerque: Univ of NM, 1965. 1st ed. Fine in Fine dj. *CONNOLLY & WADE.* $45

Tupper, Harmon. TO THE GREAT OCEAN. SIBERIA AND THE TRANS-SIBERIA RAILWAY. Boston: Little Brown, (1965). 1st ed. VG. *ARTIS.* $25

Turberville, A.S. (ed). JOHNSON'S ENGLAND. 2 vols. Oxford Univ Press, 1933. 1st ed. Dec cl gilt. Foxing top fore-edges, o/w NF in djs. *DIAMOND.* $75

Turberville, A.S. ENGLISH MEN AND MANNERS IN THE EIGHTEENTH CENTURY. Oxford: Clarendon Press, 1926. 1st ed. *HARTFIELD.* $135

Turbeville, Deborah. WALLFLOWER. NY: Congreve, 1978. 1st ed. VG. *SMITH.* $60

Turgenieff, Ivan. DIMITRI ROUDINE: A NOVEL. NY: Holt & Williams, 1873. 1st Amer ed, 1st ed in English. Cover soil. *MUELLER.* $35

Turnbull, Andrew. THOMAS WOLFE. NY: Scribner's, (1967). 1st ed. One of an unspecified number signed. Spine lettering rubbed, else NF, lacking dj. Custom slipcase. *CHAPEL HILL.* $45

Turnbull, Colin M. WAYWARD SERVANTS: THE TWO WORLDS OF THE AFRICAN PYGMIES. London: Eyre & Spottiswoode, (1966). 1st ed. NF in VG dj. *ACADEMIC.* $40

Turnbull, W.P. THE BIRDS OF EAST PENNSYLVANIA AND NEW JERSEY. Phila, 1869. Binder's buckram. Institutional bkpl; orig wrappers retained; ex-lib, scarce. *SUTTON.* $115

Turner, D.C. THE VAMPIRE BAT, A FIELD STUDY IN BEHAVIOR AND ECOLOGY. 15 photo plts. Baltimore, 1975. Cloth, dj. *SUTTON.* $20

Turner, Don. KIRIAKOS. A BRITISH PARTISAN IN WARTIME GREECE. London, 1982. Dj. *O'NEILL.* $25

Turner, Frank M. THE GREEK HERITAGE IN VICTORIAN BRITAIN. New Haven: Yale Univ Press, (1981). Dj. Good. *ARCHAEOLGIA.* $65

Turner, Frederick Jackson. THE SIGNIFICANCE OF SECTIONS IN AMERICAN HISTORY. NY: Henry Holt & Co, (1932). 1st ed. 10 maps. Bound in orig pub's cl. Unopened. NF. *LAURIE.* $50

Turner, G.L. (ed). NINETEENTH-CENTURY SCIENTIFIC IN-
STRUMENTS. Univ of CA Press, 1983. Near New w/dj. *BOOKCELL*.
$100

Turner, Henry Smith. THE JOURNALS OF HENRY SMITH
TURNER, WITH STEPHEN WATTS KEARNY TO NEW
MEXICO AND CALIFORNIA. Norman, (1966). Ed by Dwight L.
Clarke. 1st ed. 156pp. Dj. Fine. *PRATT*. $32.50

Turner, John. PIONEERS OF THE WEST: A TRUE NARRA-
TIVE. Cincinnati: Jennings, 1903. Orig cl. 1st ed. Howes T424.
GINSBERG. $150

Turner, L.M. CONTRIBUTIONS TO THE NATURAL HISTORY
OF ALASKA, RESULTS OF INVESTIGATIONS
MADE...FROM MAY, 1874, TO AUGUST, 1881. 11 colored plts,
15 plain plts. Washington, 1886. 226pp. Half morocco. Front cvr
detached; extrems scuffed; spotting of cloth, lt foxing; emb stamp on
plts. Bkpl. *SUTTON*. $115

Turner, Timothy G. TURN OFF THE SUNSHINE: TALES OF LOS
ANGELES....Caldwell: The Caxton Printers, 1942. 1st ed. Black ptd
cl in worn, tape repaired dj. *DAWSON'S*. $50

Turner-Turner, J. THREE YEARS HUNTING & TRAPPING IN
AMERICA & THE GREAT NORTHWEST. NY: Arno Press,
1967. Abercrombie & Fitch Co. Reprint of 1888 ed. VG+ in
Good+ dj. *BACKMAN*. $35

Turney, Ida Virginia. PAUL BUNYON, THE WORK GIANT.
Portland: Binfords and Mort, 1941. Ltd 1st ed, #3/500. Fine in VG
dj. *CONNOLLY & WADE*. $45

Turnor, Reginald. THE SPOTTED DOG: A BOOK OF ENGLISH
INN SIGNS. London, 1948. VG-NF. *POLYANTHOS*. $30

Turow, Scott. ONE L. NY: Putnam, (1977). 1st ed. NF in like dj (few
small tears). Contemp presentation inscription. *CAPTAIN'S BOOK-
SHELF*. $250

Turow, Scott. ONE L. NY: Putnam, 1977. 1st ed. Very NF in dj.
Scarce in 1st ed. *LAME DUCK*. $200

Turow, Scott. PRESUMED INNOCENT. NY: Farrar Straus Giroux,
1987. 1st ed. Fine in dj. *MORDIDA*. $45

Turow, Scott. PRESUMED INNOCENT. NY: FSG, 1987. 1st ed. VF
in dj. *ELSE FINE*. $60

Turow, Scott. THE BURDEN OF PROOF. Franklin Center:
Franklin Library, 1990. Second novel, this being the true 1st ed,
leatherbound and signed. Fine. *LOPEZ*. $100

Turrill, Gardner Stilson. A TALE OF THE YELLOWSTONE, OR,
IN A WAGON THROUGH WESTERN WYOMING AND
WONDERLAND. Jefferson: G.S. Turrill, 1901. 1st ed. VG. *LAURIE*.
$200

Tuson, Edward. SPINAL DEBILITY: ITS PREVENTION,
PATHOLOGY AND CURE, IN RELATION TO CURVA-
TURES, PARALYSIS, EPILEPSY, AND VARIOUS DEFORM-
ITIES. London, 1861. 1st ed. 155pp. Title page chipped and
detached, fep lacking, paper brittle, spine very worn. Rare. *FYE*. $150

Tuten, Frederic. THE ADVENTURES OF MAO ON THE LONG
MARCH. (NY): Citadel Press, (1971). 1st ed, scarce 1st book. Fine
in dj. *BERNARD*. $75

Tuten, Frederic. THE ADVENTURES OF MAO ON THE LONG
MARCH. (NY): Citadel Press, (1971). 1st ed, inscribed. 1st bk. NF
in dj. *LOPEZ*. $65

Tuthill, Franklin. HISTORY OF CALIFORNIA. SF: H.H. Bancroft,
1866, 1st ed. 16, 657pp. Rebound in buckram by hand binder. Lt
foxing. *HEINOLDT*. $50

Tuthill, Franklin. THE HISTORY OF CALIFORNIA. SF: H.H.
Bancroft & Company, 1866. xvi,657pp. Cl, rebacked, foxing, flower
stains to some leaves at end. *DAWSON'S*. $75

Tutt, J.W. A NATURAL HISTORY OF THE BRITISH LEPIDOP-
TERA. Vol. 2. London, 1900. w/7 plts. Ex-lib. *SUTTON*. $45

Tutt, J.W. A NATURAL HISTORY OF THE BRITISH LEPIDOP-
TERA. Vol 3. London, 1902. Spine faded, ends chipped, eps
browned. *SUTTON*. $45

Tutt, J.W. A NATURAL HISTORY OF THE BRITISH LEPIDOP-
TERA. Vol 8. London, 1905-6. Numerous plts (bound out of sequence). Spine faded, ends chipped, light foxing. *SUTTON*. $45

Tutuola, Amos. MY LIFE IN THE BUSH OF GHOSTS. London:
Faber, (1954). 1st ed. Fine in NF dj. *LOPEZ*. $65

Tutuola, Amos. THE PALM-WINE DRINKARD. NY: Grove,
(1953). 1st Amer ed. NF in dj. *LOPEZ*. $50

Tutuola, Amos. THE WITCH HERBALIST OF THE REMOTE
TOWN. London: Faber, (1981). 1st Eng ed. Issue in wrappers.
Fine. *LOPEZ*. $20

Twain, Mark and Charles Dudley Warner. THE GILDED AGE, A
TALE OF TODAY. Hartford: American Pub Co, 1874. 1st ed, a
later state, w/o the repeated lines on pp 351, 352,353, and title page
dated 1874. Nice in sl scuffed pub's 1/2 morocco. BAL 3357.
SECOND LIFE. $200

Twain, Mark and Charles Dudley Warner. THE GILDED AGE, A
TALE OF TODAY. Hartford: American Pub Co, 1873. 1st ed, 1st
state w/repeated lines on pp 351, 352, 353. Recased and placed back
in the orig sl repaired pub's sheep. This has all the 1st issue points,
issued w/out the ads. Has genuine title page, w/imprint of Wm. H.
Lockwood and copyright notice on verso of the title pg. P. (vii), the
reading under the Chapter V is: Eschol Sellers (later changed to
Beriah). P. xvi final illus is numbered 211; p. 246 line 5 from the bottom: ...Halleluja/ (later a comma was added at the end of the line).
P. 280, line 18 with a period after Dr. Jackson. With the repeated
lines on pp351,352,353; p. 403, no illus. Nice, Rare. *SECOND LIFE*.
$3000

Twain, Mark, William Dean Howells (et al). THE NIAGRA BOOK.
NY: Doubleday Page, 1901. 1st new, revised ed w/photos. Neat contemp owner's name, date, etc. on ffep, else beautiful w/delicate
white lettering still bright and fresh. *CAPTAIN'S BOOKSHELF*. $100

Twain, Mark. A DOG'S TALE. London: Anti-Vivisection Society,
1903. Orig wraps. 1st separate ed. Fine. BAL 3479. *SECOND LIFE*.
$200

Twain, Mark. A DOUBLE BARRELLED DETECTIVE STORY.
NY: Harper, 1902. 1st ed. Red cl gilt, teg. Illus Lucius Hitchcock. Lt
erasure on 2nd fep, some smudging to gilt title piece on front panel,
else bright, NF. *CAPTAIN'S BOOKSHELF*. $125

Twain, Mark. A TRAMP ABROAD. Hartford, CT & London, 1880.
1st ed. Pub's cl. Blanck's state B of the blind stamped border and
#1 deeply stamped on back cvr, interiorly state B of both pict fron-
tis and frontis port of Twain. Back hinge separating, some wear top
edge of spine, minor wear to cvr corners. Fine. *McCLINTOCK*. $75

Twain, Mark. A TRAMP ABROAD. Hartford: American Publishing
Co, 1880. 1st ed. 631pp. 328 illus. Lt brn cl. Frontis is state B, frontis captioned "Titian's Moses." Sheets bulks 1 5/8", binding stamping definitely curved at inner corners. Sm tear to flyleaf (news clipping pasted on). News clipping tipped to flyleaf. Flyleaves loose, but
VG, tight. *SECOND LIFE*. $250

Twain, Mark. A TRAMP ABROAD. Illus by David Knight.
(Hartford, CT): LEC, (1966). Ed ltd to 1500 numbered, signed by
Knight. Slipcase. *KARMIOLE*. $85

Twain, Mark. ADVENTURES OF HUCKLEBERRY FINN. Grn cl.
1st state for clothbound copies. Spine ends sl frayed, gilt stamping
on spine somewhat darkened. Bkpl, name stamps on feps. Sl
shelfwear bottom edge of boards. Overall VG. *LOPEZ*. $1500

Twain, Mark. ADVENTURES OF HUCKLEBERRY FINN. NY:
Webster, 1885. 1st ed. W/earliest states for cl copies, pp 13 and 57
uncorrected, title page and 283 are cancels, page 155 lacking second

5, and frontis in state 2 of 3. Bound in blue cloth which is distinctly less common than the green. Spine ends repaired. Short tear to one page, tiny nick to ffep. VG. *LAME DUCK.* $2650

Twain, Mark. AN UNEXPECTED ACQUAINTANCE. NY: Harper & Bros. 1904. 1st ed thus. Ptd wraps. Dust soil. Evidence of previous tape along spine edge. Strip of tape on inner edge of inside front cover. Covers detached. Label removed from cover long before, thinning paper and tearing it in one place. Internally VG. *CONNOLLY & WADE.* $50

Twain, Mark. CHRISTIAN SCIENCE. NY: Harper, 1907. 1st ed, mixed state. Red cl, hinge tender. (The boxed statement of Twain's work has 18 titles, the later state, while the frontis carries the date "1906," the earliest state. Illus are set in 6 lines—latest state). VG. BAL 3497. *SECOND LIFE.* $50

Twain, Mark. CLEMENS OF THE CALL: MARK TWAIN IN SAN FRANCISCO. Univ of CA Press, 1969. 1st ed. Edgar M. Branch (ed). New in dj. *AUTHORS OF THE WEST.* $25

Twain, Mark. COMPLETE ESSAYS OF MARK TWAIN. NY, (1963). Charles Neider (ed). Dj. *HEINOLDT.* $15

Twain, Mark. CONCERNING CATS. TWO TALES BY MARK TWAIN. SF: The Bk Club of CA, 1959. Ltd ed of 450. Prospectus. Dj. Fine. *WEBER.* $200

Twain, Mark. EDITORIAL WILD OATS. NY: Harper, 1905. 1st ed. Spine somewhat dull, but letters visible. NF. *CAPTAIN'S BOOKSHELF.* $60

Twain, Mark. ENGLISH AS SHE IS TAUGHT. With Biographical Sketch of Author by Matthew Irving Lans. Boston: Mutual Book Co., (1900). 28pp, (l)p ads. Orig ptd grey wraps 1" chip at foot of spine, but generally NF of a fragile item. 1st Amer ed (and first separate ed), 2nd state, w/"The five" on p. 16, line 5. *CHAPEL HILL.* $175

Twain, Mark. EUROPE AND ELSEWHERE. Brander Matthews (appreciation), A.B. Paine (intro). NY: Harper, (1923). 1st ed. 8vo, 406pp. Some light dust wear to cover, else Fine in near perfect dj (couple of very minor chips). Rare thus. 1st appearance of most of the material. BAL 3536. *SECOND LIFE.* $950

Twain, Mark. EXTRACT FROM CAPTAIN STORMFIELD'S VISIT TO HEAVEN. NY: Harpers, 1909. 1st ed. Minor bumping to edges, else Fine in pict covers. Frontis, cover illus. by Albert Levering. *ELSE FINE.* $110

Twain, Mark. FOLLOWING THE EQUATOR. A JOURNEY AROUND THE WORLD. Hartford: Amer Pub Co, 1897. 1st ed, 1st issue w/Hartford only on title pg. 712pp. Frontis. Blue pict cl. BAL 3451. Owner name ffeps, o/w VG. *OREGON.* $175

Twain, Mark. FOLLOWING THE EQUATOR. Hartford: Amer Pub Co, 1897. 1st ed, 1st state (single imprint). 712pp. Blue cl, some external wear, lib stamp ep (almost separate). BAL 3451. *SECOND LIFE.* $75

Twain, Mark. LETTERS FROM HONOLULU. Honolulu, 1939. 1st ed. Intro John W. Vandercook. Uncut. Spine little sunned. Fine in glassine dj. *POLYANTHOS.* $75

Twain, Mark. LIFE ON THE MISSISSIPPI. Boston: James R. Osgood, 1883. 1st US ed, 1st issue w/all points. One sig. sprung, else very attractive, NF in the pub's 3/4 leather binding. *CAPTAIN'S BOOKSHELF.* $1250

Twain, Mark. LIFE ON THE MISSISSIPPI. Boston: James R. Osgood & Co, 1883. 1st Amer ed, 1st state. Vignette of Twain in flames on p. 441 and caption reading "The St. Louis Hotel" on p. 443. 1st state is scarce. 624pp. Orig dec brn cl w/pict gilt-stamping. Owner's name stamp, spine extremities rubbed, but Nice, bright. VG or better. *CHAPEL HILL.* $550

Twain, Mark. LIFE ON THE MISSISSIPPI. Boston: Osgood, 1883. 1st ed. Brown cloth stamped in gilt and black, all first state points.

Handsome w/tender hinges and little wear to spine ends. BAL 3411. *BEASLEY.* $400

Twain, Mark. LIFE ON THE MISSISSIPPI. Edward Wagenknecht (intro). NY: LEC, 1944. One of 1500 illus, signed by Thomas Hart Benton. Fine lacking slipcase. *CAPTAIN'S BOOKSHELF.* $250

Twain, Mark. MARK TWAIN'S SAN FRANCISCO. McGraw-Hill, (1963). 1st ed. Bernard Taper (ed). Frontis. Fine in dj. *AUTHORS OF THE WEST.* $35

Twain, Mark. MARK TWAIN'S SCRAPBOOK. NY: Daniel Slote & Co, 1878. 6 1/2 x 9 1/4 inches. Brn cl, front hinge tender. Unpaginated. VG. See BAL 3614. *SECOND LIFE.* $75

Twain, Mark. MARK TWAIN'S SKETCHES, NEW AND OLD. Hartford, CT & Chicago, IL, 1875. 1st ed. 1st state, one of the earliest distributed copies (lacking inserted slip facing p.299). Spine ends and cover tips show usual shelfwear, front interior hinge cracking, o/w very clean interior, nice bright dec front cvr. *McCLINTOCK.* $200

Twain, Mark. PERSONAL RECOLLECTIONS OF JOAN OF ARC. NY, 1896. 1st ed. 2nd state of ad leaf in back. Twain's name appears on the binding. Buckram on spine dulled w/age, lt rub touches, cvrs Fine, interior superb. *McCLINTOCK.* $65

Twain, Mark. PUDD'NHEAD WILSON. Together with Pudd'nhead Wilson's Calendar. Avon, CT: LEC, 1974. 1/2000. Illus, signed by John Groth. Fine in slipcase. *CAPTAIN'S BOOKSHELF.* $125

Twain, Mark. REPORT FROM PARADISE. NY, 1952. 1st ed. Rev copy, slip laid in. VG in dj. BAL 3581. *SECOND LIFE.* $45

Twain, Mark. ROUGHING IT. NY: LEC, 1972. Illus by Noel Sickles. Ed ltd to 1500 numbered, signed by Sickles. Slipcase. *KARMIOLE.* $85

Twain, Mark. ROUGHING IT. NY: LEC, 1972. 1/1500 illus, signed by Noel Sickles. Fine in slipcase. *CAPTAIN'S BOOKSHELF.* $125

Twain, Mark. SAINT JOAN OF ARC. Harper, 1919. 1st ed, 1st issue. 32pp. Partially unopened. Color illus by Howard Pyle, dec in tint by Wilfred J. Jones. Color pict pastedown on cvr bordered by gilt on black cl. NF in dec grey paper dj has few chips, 2 small closed tears, short separation at front flap but bright, VG+. *BEBBAH.* $175

Twain, Mark. SAINT JOAN OF ARC. NY & London, 1919. 1st ed, 1st state w/pict eps. New color plts by Howard Pyle. Owner blind stamp, else unusually Fine. Front cvr pastepl. *McCLINTOCK.* $75

Twain, Mark. SAINT JOAN OF ARC. NY: Harpers, 1919. 1st separate ed, 2nd state. Illus by Howard Pyle. Eps unptd, marginal dec on p18 inverted. VF in rare pub's dj (couple chips top of spine). BAL 3683. *SECOND LIFE.* $200

Twain, Mark. THE £1,000,000 BANK NOTE. NY: Webster, 1893. 1st ed. 260pp. Some minor external wear, else VG, tight. BAL 3436. *SECOND LIFE.* $150

Twain, Mark. THE ADVENTURES OF HUCKLEBERRY FINN (TOM SAWYER'S COMRADE). NY, 1885. 1st Amer ed. Early mixed state (not earliest issue) in orig pub's pict cl. 1st state grn cl, pale peach eps, non-gilded edges. State 2 of title leaf (a cancel), only known state 1 of title is in prospecti and one set of advance sheets. State 1 of p.(13) and of line 11, bottom of p.57. State 3 of p.283, cancel leaf to censor. State 3 of p. 155. Usual state of p. 161. State 3 in blackish brn port of Twain. Back hinge cracked, moderately shaken, moderate wear to spine ends, corners. *McCLINTOCK.* $275

Twain, Mark. THE ADVENTURES OF THOMAS JEFFERSON SNODGRASS. Charles Honce (ed). Chicago: Pascal Covici, 1928. #1 of 375 numbered. Cloth-backed brn boards, paper labels. NF in defective dj. BAL 3544. *CAPTAIN'S BOOKSHELF.* $200

Twain, Mark. THE ADVENTURES OF TOM SAWYER BY MARK TWAIN. Hartford, Conn.: American Publishing Company, 1876. 1st Amer ed. Sq 8vo. (12),(17)-(280)pp. Illus. Orig dec blue cloth. VF, with merest traces of shelfwear to corners & tips of spine.

A bright, near brilliant copy. Copy very tight, text immaculate. BAL 3369, Second Issue, Printing A (on laid paper). *M & S.* $2000

Twain, Mark. THE ADVENTURES OF TOM SAWYER. Hartford: The American Publishing Co., 1876. 1st ed, 2nd ptg, issue A, with mispagination. "THE" on half-title is 1/16". 274, (1)pp + (4)pp of ads. Illus. 8vo. Rebound in black lea, lea label, raised bands. New eps. Internally Very Nice. *BOOKMINE.* $1250

Twain, Mark. THE ADVENTURES OF TOM SAWYER. Heritage, (1937). 284pp. 8 tipped-in color plts by Norman Rockwell. Fine in Fine slipcase. *BEBBAH.* $30

Twain, Mark. THE ADVENTURES OF TOM SAWYER. NY: Harpers, (1903). Part of the uniform ed. NF in red cl w/Mark Twain's sig. tipped in at front. *CAPTAIN'S BOOKSHELF.* $450

Twain, Mark. THE AMERICAN CLAIMANT. NY: Webster, 1892. 1st ed. 277pp, ad. Grey-grn cl (sl rubbing). Repair to front hinge, NF. BAL 3434. *SECOND LIFE.* $150

Twain, Mark. THE CHOICE HUMOROUS WORKS OF...rev, corrected by author. London: Chatto and Windus, 1881. 563pp, 32pp ads. Red cl, some worn. Rprt of 1873 issue (BAL 3551). Foxing. *SECOND LIFE.* $45

Twain, Mark. THE INNOCENTS ABROAD. NY: LEC, 1962. 1/1500. Illus, signed by Fritz Kredel. Fine in slipcase. *CAPTAIN'S BOOKSHELF.* $150

Twain, Mark. THE INNOCENTS ABROAD...Fritz Kredel (illus). NY: LEC, at the Thistle Press. 1962. Ed ltd to 1500 numbered, signed by Kredel. Slipcase. *KARMIOLE.* $100

Twain, Mark. THE INNOCENTS ABROAD; or, The New Pilgrim's Progress. In Two Volumes. With Illustrations. Boston: Joseph Knight Co. 1895. Deluxe reprint with illus (photogravures) used for 1st time. About Fine in orig red linen djs. *KARMIOLE.* $200

Twain, Mark. THE MAN THAT CORRUPTED HADLEYBURG AND OTHER STORIES AND SKETCHES. London: Chatto & Windus, 1900. 1st UK ed. (8), 414 (2)pp + 32 pp of ads. Frontis. 8vo. Orange cl over boards, pict front cover stamped in black and yellow, spine stamped in gold, dec eps, teg. *BOOKMINE.* $150

Twain, Mark. THE NOTORIOUS JUMPING FROG & OTHER STORIES. Illus by Joseph Low. NY: LEC, 1970. Ed ltd to 1500 numbered, signed by Joseph Low. Slipcase. *KARMIOLE.* $85

Twain, Mark. THE PRINCE AND THE PAUPER. Illus by Clarke Hutton. Westerham, England: LEC, 1964. Signed by Clarke Hutton. Slipcase. *KARMIOLE.* $85

Twain, Mark. THE PRIVATE LIFE OF ADAM AND EVE: BEING EXTRACTS FROM THEIR DIARIES. NY: Harper, (1931). 1st ed thus w/100 drawings by F. Strothmann and Lester Ralph. Top front corner bumped, else Fine in lightly used, lightly sunned pict dj. Uncommon. *CAPTAIN'S BOOKSHELF.* $200

Twain, Mark. THE TRAGEDY OF PUDD'NHEAD WILSON AND THE COMEDY OF THOSE EXTRAORDINARY TWINS. Hartford: American Publishing Co, 1894. 1st ed, 1st state w/sheets bulking 1 1/8" w/facs sig on frontis 1 7/16" wide. 8vo, 432pp. Reddish brn cl, stamped in gold, w/just minimal wear, NF. BAL 3442. *SECOND LIFE.* $650

Tweed, T.F. GABRIEL OVER THE WHITE HOUSE. Farrar, 1933. VG in sl frayed dj. *MADLE.* $25

TWELVE STARS OF OUR REPUBLIC. (By Edwin Williams). NY, 1850, 1st ed. 364pp. 4 plts in color, steel engr plts. Bright heavily embossed in gold front & back covers and spine. New eps. *HEINOLDT.* $20

TWENTY-SEVENTH ANNUAL REPORT OF THE ATCHISON, TOPEKA & SANTA FE RAILWAY COMPANY. NY: Montross & Clarke Co Press, 1921. Fldg map, tables. Gray wraps, loose. Exlib. *HUDSON.* $60

Twiford, William Richard. SOWN IN THE DARKNESS. Tremayne, 1940. 1st ed. Fine in sl frayed dj. *MADLE.* $75

Twist, Ananias. SNIDE LIGHTS ON TEXAS HISTORY. San Antonio: Naylor, 1959. 1st ed. Fine in VG dj. *CONNOLLY & WADE.* $25

Twitchell, Ralph Emerson. THE LEADING FACTS OF NEW MEXICAN HISTORY. Albuquerque: Horn & Wallace, 1963. Facs of 1911 ed. 2 vols. Red cl, gilt spine titles. Fine. *PARMER.* $300

Twitchell, Ralph Emerson. THE SPANISH ARCHIVES OF NEW MEXICO. 2 vols. (Cedar Rapids): Torch Press, 1914. 1st ed. Cloth, teg, unopened, bkpl. Howes T445. *DAWSON'S.* $500

TWO MONTHS ABROAD....(By Elias Hasket Derby). Boston, 1844. 64pp, ptd wrapper w/ads. Front wrap loose & quite chipped. *BOHLING.* $45

Twombly, George F. ALL-AMERICAN DROPOUT. Self-pub, 1967. 1st ed. VG in Fine dj. *PLAPINGER.* $35

Tylecote, R.F. METALLURGY IN ARCHAEOLOGY. A PREHISTORY OF METALLURGY IN THE BRITISH ISLES. London: Edward Arnold, (1962). 74 figs, 28 plts. Good. *ARCHAEOLOGIA.* $50

Tyler, Anne. A SLIPPING-DOWN LIFE. Knopf, 1970. 1st ed. Fine in price-clipped dj (very lt wear to spine ends, front flyleaf fold). Rmdr mark; sticker shadow ffep. *STAHR.* $225

Tyler, Anne. A SLIPPING-DOWN LIFE. NY: Knopf, 1970. 1st ed. Orig beige cl, yellow boards. Faint tape mark, inked "R" (probably a remainder mark) on ffep, o/w NF in price-clipped dj, tiny chip top front panel. *CHAPEL HILL.* $350

Tyler, Anne. A SLIPPING-DOWN LIFE. NY: Knopf, 1970. 1st ed. Inscribed. Cl-backed boards. Rmdr mk ffep, crease in flap of dj, o/w Fine. *JAFFE.* $185

Tyler, Anne. BREATHING LESSONS. Knopf, 1988. Uncorrected proof. VF in grey wraps in cardboard folder. Signed. *STAHR.* $125

Tyler, Anne. BREATHING LESSONS. NY: Knopf, 1988. 1st ed. Fine (rem mk top edges) in price-clipped dj. Signed. *CAPTAIN'S BOOKSHELF.* $50

Tyler, Anne. BREATHING LESSONS. NY: Knopf, 1988. 1st ed. Fine in dj. *LOPEZ.* $35

Tyler, Anne. BREATHING LESSONS. NY: Knopf, 1988. 1st trade ed. Orig grn cl, tan boards. About Fine in price-clipped dj. *CHAPEL HILL.* $25

Tyler, Anne. CELESTIAL NAVIGATION. Knopf, 1974. 1st ed. Fine in dj (rubbed at spine ends and flyleaf folds). *STAHR.* $150

Tyler, Anne. CELESTIAL NAVIGATION. NY: Knopf (1974). 1st ed. Rmdr stamp else NF in dj. *DORN.* $125

Tyler, Anne. CELESTIAL NAVIGATION. NY: Knopf, 1974. 1st ed. Orig gold cl. Fine in dj. *CHAPEL HILL.* $225

Tyler, Anne. DINNER AT THE HOMESICK RESTAURANT. Knopf, 1982. 1st ed. Fine in dj (tear lower front flyleaf corner; 2 sm rubbed spots). *STAHR.* $45

Tyler, Anne. DINNER AT THE HOMESICK RESTAURANT. NY: Knopf, 1982. Wraps. Uncorrected proofs. VG+ w/some dog-eared pages. *BEASLEY.* $150

Tyler, Anne. DINNER AT THE HOMESICK RESTAURANT. NY: Knopf, (1982). 1st ed. Inscribed. Cl-backed boards, dj. VF. *JAFFE.* $225

Tyler, Anne. EARTHLY POSSESSIONS. Knopf, 1977. 1st ed. Fine in lightly worn dj (small chip). *STAHR.* $60

Tyler, Anne. EARTHLY POSSESSIONS. NY: Knopf, 1977. 1st ed. Sm erasure on ffep, bottom corners sl bumped, else Fine in dj. Signed. *CAPTAIN'S BOOKSHELF.* $175

Tyler, Anne. EARTHLY POSSESSIONS. NY: Knopf, 1977. 1st ed. Inscribed. Cl-backed boards, dj. VF. *JAFFE.* $225

Tyler, Anne. IF MORNING EVER COMES. London: Chatto & Windus, 1965. 1st UK. Sticker removed from ffep, else Fine in lightly rubbed price-clipped dj (few tiny nicks). Signed. *CAPTAIN'S BOOKSHELF.* $450

Tyler, Anne. MORGAN'S PASSING. Knopf, 1980. 1st ed. Fine in price-clipped dj. *STAHR.* $45

Tyler, Anne. MORGAN'S PASSING. London: Chatto & Windus, 1980. 1st ed. Fine in dj. *ELSE FINE.* $75

Tyler, Anne. MORGAN'S PASSING. NY: Knopf, 1980. 1st ed. Inscribed. Cl-backed boards, dj. VF. *JAFFE.* $225

Tyler, Anne. MORGAN'S PASSING. NY: Knopf, 1980. Rmdr mk, o/w NF in dj. Inscribed. *LOPEZ.* $200

Tyler, Anne. SAINT MAYBE. NY: Knopf, 1991. One of an unspecified number (probably around 500) w/extra leaf tipped in and signed. Fine in Fine dj. *LOPEZ.* $100

Tyler, Anne. SAINT MAYBE. NY: Knopf, 1991. Signed on tipped-in sheet. Fine in Fine dj. *DERMONT.* $65

Tyler, Anne. SAINT MAYBE. NY: Knopf, 1991. Uncorrected proof. Slight bump at bottom of spine, else Fine in wrappers. *CAPTAIN'S BOOKSHELF.* $125

Tyler, Anne. SEARCHING FOR CALEB. NY: Knopf, 1976. 1st ed. Tiny pen mark (not a remainder mark) on top edge near gutter, else Fine in dj. *CAPTAIN'S BOOKSHELF.* $300

Tyler, Anne. THE ACCIDENTAL TOURIST. NY: Knopf, (1985). 1st ed. One of an unspecified number signed on a tipped in page. Fine in Fine dj. *UNGER.* $125

Tyler, Anne. THE ACCIDENTAL TOURIST. NY: Knopf, 1985. 1st ed. Orig cl-backed tan boards. Red mark top edge, else fresh, virtually As New in dj. *CHAPEL HILL.* $45

Tyler, Anne. THE ACCIDENTAL TOURIST. NY: Knopf, 1985. 1st ed. Signed on tipped-in leaf, one of an unspecified number so prepared (probably around 700). Fine in Fine dj. *LOPEZ.* $100

Tyler, Anne. THE TIN CAN TREE. NY: Knopf, 1965. Fine in VG dj w/some soiling on spine and rear panel. 1st ed. *CHAPEL HILL.* $500

Tyler, Comrade William N. THE DISPATCH CARRIER...INDIVIDUAL EXPERIENCE IN THE CIVIL WAR, FROM 1861 TO 1865...Port Byron, Ill: Globe, 1892 2nd ed. 89,61pp. Orig printed wrappers. *GINSBERG.* $150

Tyler, Daniel. A CONCISE HISTORY OF THE MORMON BATTALION IN THE MEXICAN WAR 1846-1847. Salt Lake, 1881. 1st ed. 376pp, 3/4 leather worn and cracking, crown of spine soft; interior tight and clean. *BENCHMARK.* $160

Tyler, Mason Whiting. RECOLLECTIONS OF THE CIVIL WAR. NY, 1912. 1st ed. 379pp, illus., fldg map. A little cvr wear o/w VG+. *PRATT.* $70

Tyler, Ron (ed). ALFRED JACOB MILLER, ARTIST ON OREGON TRAIL. Fort Worth: Amon Carter Museum, 1982. 1st ed. Fldg map. VF in VF dj. *OREGON.* $50

Tyndall, John. LECTURES ON LIGHT. NY, 1873. 1st ed. *FYE.* $75

Tyson, Edward. A PHILOLOGICAL ESSAY CONCERNING THE PYGMIES OF THE ANCIENTS... NOW EDITED...BY BERTRAM C.A. WINDLE. London: David Nutt, 1894. Facsimile of 1699 title pg. Cvrs soiled, else About Fine. *WREDEN.* $50

U

Udall, David King. ARIZONA PIONEER MORMON. DAVID KING UDALL. Tucson: Arizona Silhouettes, 1959. 1st ed. VG in somewhat worn dj. *CONNOLLY & WADE.* $35

Udell, John. JOURNAL OF JOHN UDELL KEPT DURING A TRIP ACROSS THE PLAINS. LA: N.A. Kovach, 1946. CA Centennial Series #3. Fine in VG dj. Orig pub in 1868 in pamphlet form. Reprint, 1st trade ed in hb after ltd ed of 35 signed, numbered. Howes U4. *CONNOLLY & WADE.* $45

Ukiyo-E Hanga. MASTER PRINTS OF JAPAN. Abrams, (1969). NF. *POLYANTHOS.* $60

Ullman, James Ramsey. KINGDOM OF ADVENTURE: EVEREST. NY: William Sloane Assoc, 1947. 1st ed. VG in well worn dj. *PARMER.* $25

Ulmann, Doris. A BOOK OF PORTRAITS OF THE FACULTY OF THE MEDICAL DEPARTMENT OF THE JOHNS HOPKINS UNIVERSITY BALTIMORE. Baltimore, 1922. 1st ed. Folio (26 1/2 cms x 39 1/2 cms), untrimmed. Fine. Very Rare. *FYE.* $750

UNCLE PEASLY & THE PEA POD KIDS. 1986. Illus Milkie. Costello (eng). Missing the 3 dolls. Pop-up bk. *BOOKFINDERS INTL.* $15

Underhill, Francis T. DRIVING FOR PLEASURE. NY: Appleton, 1897. 2nd ed. 158pp, 124 full pg photogr plts. Bound in rubbed 3/4 calf and suede. Front hinge tender, internal staining, name, o/w VG. *SECOND LIFE.* $250

Underhill, Harold A. MASTING AND RIGGING. THE CLIPPER SHIP & OCEAN CARRIER....Glasgow: Brown, Son and Ferguson Ltd, 1953. Rprt. Grn cl, gilt spine titles. 51 plts (some fldg). NF. *PARMER.* $75

Underwood, Arthur. NOTES ON ANAESTHETICS, WITH AN APPENDIX CONTAINING ILLUSTRATIVE CASES AND ENGRAVINGS OF ANAESTHETIC APPARATUS. London, 1885. 1st ed. Woodcut illus. Scarce. *FYE.* $150

Underwood, John J. ALASKA—AN EMPIRE IN THE MAKING. NY: Dodd, Mead, 1913. 440pp + fldg map. 1st ed. Orig grey dec cl. Very minor wear extremes else NF. *GREAT EPIC.* $95

Underwood, Michael. ANYTHING BUT THE TRUTH. London: Macmillan, 1978. 1st ed. Presentation copy, signed. Fine in dj. *SILVER DOOR.* $30

Underwood, Thomas Bryan. CHEROKEE LEGENDS AND THE TRAIL OF TEARS. Knoxville: S.B. Newman, 1956. 1st ed. Wraps. NF. *CONNOLLY & WADE.* $25

UNITED STATES COAST AND GEODETIC SURVEY REPORT, 1887. Washington: GPO, 1889. Fold-out maps, 42 fold-out survey maps following text. Binding worn, interior Fine. *VARNER.* $115

UNITED STATES COAST PILOT. ALASKA PART 2, YAKUTAT BAY TO ARCTIC OCEAN. Washington, 1938. 4th ed. Fold-out color maps. VG. *ARTIS.* $17.50

UNITED STATES COAST PILOT. PACIFIC COAST. CALIFORNIA, OREGON, AND WASHINGTON. Washington, DC: GPO, 1943. 6th ed. Covers lightly soiled and worn, else VG. Printer's flaw pp. 323-324. *PARMER.* $25

UNIVERSAL SONGSTER OR MUSEUM OF MIRTH.... 3 vols. London, 1834. 446; 448; 448pp, Frontis, title pg, 27 other illus by George Cruikshank. Rebound in new buckram by hand binder w/slipcase to match. *HEINOLDT.* $50

Unruh, John D. THE PLAINS ACROSS. Univ of IL, (1979). 1st ed. 9 maps. VF in VF dj. Scarce. *OREGON.* $75

Unsal, Behcet. TURKISH ISLAMIC ARCHITECTURE IN SELJUK AND OTTOMAN TIMES. London: Alec Tiranti. 1970. 1st ed. Dj. *KARMIOLE.* $65

Up De Graff, F.W. HEAD-HUNTERS OF THE AMAZON. London: H. Jenkins, 1923. Fldg map. VG+. *MIKESH.* $37.50

UP TO THE CLOUDS ON MULEBACK. (By Charles W. Kellogg.) Worcester: (Charles W. Kellogg), 1938. Pict boards in moderately worn dj. *DAWSON'S.* $40

Updike, John. A CHILD'S CALENDAR. NY: Knopf, (1965). 1st ed. A bit cocked, else Fine in VG dj w/small snag tear, little wrinkling on front panel, and little wear at extremities. Scarce. *BETWEEN COVERS*. $125

Updike, John. A GOOD PLACE. (n.p.): Aloe Editions, 1973. One of 100 numbered, signed. Very lt crease, o/w Fine in saddlestiched wrappers. *LOPEZ*. $375

Updike, John. A MONTH OF SUNDAYS. NY, 1975. Ltd ed, 27/450 printed on special paper and specially bound. Signed. Mint in Mint dj and box. *POLYANTHOS*. $150

Updike, John. A MONTH OF SUNDAYS. NY: Knopf, 1975. One of ltd ed of 450 signed. New in dj in slipcase. *BERNARD*. $125

Updike, John. A SOFT SPRING NIGHT IN SHILLINGTON. Northridge: Lord John, 1986. 1/50 deluxe copies, 1/4 bound in leather, numbered and signed. Fine in slipcase. *LOPEZ*. $175

Updike, John. A&P: LUST IN THE AISLES. (Minneapolis): Redpath Press, (1986). With a card laid in inscribed. Fine in wrappers with orig mailing envelope. *LOPEZ*. $45

Updike, John. ASSORTED PROSE. NY: Knopf, 1965. 1st ed. One of sm # issued w/tipped-in leaf signed, for members of The First Edition Circle of Kroch's & Brentano's. Dj. Fine. *JAFFE*. $250

Updike, John. BATH AFTER SAILING. (Stevenson): (Country Squire), (1968). One of 125 numbered, signed. Fine in stiff wrappers. *LOPEZ*. $750

Updike, John. BECH IS BACK. NY: Knopf, 1982. 1st ed. Ltd to 500 signed. Dj. Mint. *JAFFE*. $150

Updike, John. BECH IS BACK. NY: Knopf, 1982. 1st ed. Signed. Fine in Fine dj. *LOPEZ*. $75

Updike, John. BECH IS BACK. NY: Knopf, 1982. 1st ed. #92 of 500 specially bound, signed. Orig black buckram. Fine in dj, sl soiled pub's pict slipcase. *CHAPEL HILL*. $150

Updike, John. BECH: A BOOK. NY: Knopf, 1970. 1st ed. VF in dj. *ELSE FINE*. $40

Updike, John. BECH: A BOOK. NY: Knopf, 1970. One of ltd ed of 500 signed by author. New in dj in slipcase. *BERNARD*. $125

Updike, John. BOTTOM'S DREAM. NY: Knopf, (1969). 1st ed. Issue in pic cloth, issued w/o dj. Inscribed. Light overall wear; VG. *LOPEZ*. $125

Updike, John. BOTTOM'S DREAM. NY: Knopf, (1969). 1st ed. NF in dj (sm hole rear panel). *LOPEZ*. $100

Updike, John. BOTTOM'S DREAM. Warren Chappell (illus). NY: Knopf, (1969). 1st ed. Orig blue cl. NF in dj. *CHAPEL HILL*. $125

Updike, John. BROTHER GRASSHOPPER. Worcester, MA: Metacom Press, 1990. 1st ed. Signed. Ltd to 176, numbered. Fine in dj. *JUVELIS*. $125

Updike, John. BROTHER GRASSHOPPER. Worcester: Metacom, 1990. One of 150 numbered, signed. 1/4 bound in cl, marbled paper boards. Fine in dj. *LOPEZ*. $175

Updike, John. BUCHANAN DYING. NY: Knopf, 1974. 1st ed. Orig plum cl. Fine in dj. *CHAPEL HILL*. $50

Updike, John. COUPLES: A SHORT STORY. Cambridge: Halty Ferguson, 1976. One of 250 numbered, signed. Fine in wrappers. *LOPEZ*. $285

Updike, John. CUNTS. NY: Frank Hallman, (1974). 1/250 numbered, signed. Fine w/o dj as issued. *LOPEZ*. $250

Updike, John. CUNTS. NY: Frank Hallman, (1974). One of ltd ed of 276. Signed by author. New, issued w/out dj. *BERNARD*. $300

Updike, John. EGO AND ART IN WALT WHITMAN. NY: Targ, 1980. 1/350 signed. Fine in plain tan dj. *LOPEZ*. $85

Updike, John. EMERSONIANISM. Cleveland: Bits Press, (1984). 1/200 signed. Fine w/o dj as issued. *LOPEZ*. $85

Updike, John. FACING NATURE. NY: Knopf, 1985. 1st ed. Orig tan cl. Fine in dj, couple short scratches on front panel. *CHAPEL HILL*. $35

Updike, John. FIVE POEMS. (Cleveland): Bits Press, (1980). One of 50 numbered copies on handmade paper, signed. *LOPEZ*. $400

Updike, John. FROM THE JOURNAL OF A LEPER. Northridge: Lord John, 1978. One of 300 numbered, signed. Fine w/o dj as issued. *LOPEZ*. $100

Updike, John. GETTING OLDER. Helsinki: Eurographica, (1986). 1st ed. 1/350 signed. Fine in wrappers. *JUVELIS*. $250

Updike, John. GETTING OLDER. Helsinki: Eurographica, 1986. 1st ed. Ltd to 350 signed. Ptd wraps. Mint. *JAFFE*. $250

Updike, John. GETTING THE WORDS OUT. Northridge: Lord John, 1988. One of 50 deluxe copies bound in 1/4 leather, signed. Fine w/o dj as issued. *LOPEZ*. $125

Updike, John. GOING ABROAD. Helsinki: Eurographica, 1988. 1st ed. Ltd to 350 signed. Ptd wraps. Mint. *JAFFE*. $250

Updike, John. GOING ABROAD. Helsinki: Eurographica, 1988. Ltd ed. 1/350 signed, dated. Fine in wrappers and dj. *JUVELIS*. $150

Updike, John. HAWTHORNE'S CREED. NY: Targ, (1981). One of 250, signed. Fine in plain grey-grn dj. *LOPEZ*. $100

Updike, John. HUB FANS BID KID ADIEU. Northridge: Lord John, 1977. One of 26 lettered copies. Signed. Fine in slipcase. *LOPEZ*. $650

Updike, John. HUB FANS BID KID ADIEU. Northridge: Lord John, 1977. One of 300 numbered, signed. Fine w/o dj as issued. *LOPEZ*. $125

Updike, John. HUGGING THE SHORE. NY: Knopf, 1983. Uncorrected proof. *LOPEZ*. $200

Updike, John. IMPRESSIONS. Hollywood: Sylvester & Orphanos, 1985. 1st ed. 1/330 signed on Arches paper. 14 color plts. Fine in slipcase. *JUVELIS*. $300

Updike, John. IN MEMORIAM FELIS FELIS. One of 200 unnumbered & unsigned out of a total ed of 238. Mint. *JAFFE*. $100

Updike, John. IN MEMORIAM. FELIS FELIS. A POEM. U.K., (1989). Pictures by R.B. Kitaj. 1st ed. 200 unnumbered. This copy specially signed. Pict boards in orig. glassine dj. Mint. *POLYANTHOS*. $75

Updike, John. IOWA. A BROADSIDE. Portland: Press-22, (1980). Ltd ed, 24/200 (of 226) only. Signed. Etching by Liza Jones. Fine. *POLYANTHOS*. $60

Updike, John. JESTER'S DOZEN. Northridge: Lord John, 1984. One of 150 specially bound, numbered and signed. Fine w/o dj as issued. *LOPEZ*. $150

Updike, John. MARRY ME. A ROMANCE. NY: Knopf, 1976. 1st ed. Ltd to 300 signed. Cl, dj, slipcase. Fine. *JAFFE*. $175

Updike, John. MARRY ME. London, 1977. 1st ed. Signed presentation. Tiny nick lower spine. Fine in like dj. *POLYANTHOS*. $55

Updike, John. MARRY ME. NY: Knopf, 1976. 1st ed. As New in dj. *ELSE FINE*. $40

Updike, John. MARRY ME. NY: Knopf, 1976. 1st trade ed, signed. NF in dj. *LOPEZ*. $45

Updike, John. MARRY ME. NY: Knopf, 1976. True 1st ed. A "limited" leatherbound ed from the Franklin Library (Franklin Center: Franklin Library, 1976). Although not called for, this is signed. *LOPEZ*. $125

Updike, John. MIDPOINT AND OTHER POEMS. NY, 1969. 1st ed. Signed. Tiny stain lower front cover. Fine in dj (spine little rubbed tiny edge tear). *POLYANTHOS*. $50

Updike, John. MIDPOINT AND OTHER POEMS. NY: Knopf (1969). 1st ed. Fine in dj. *DORN*. $40

Updike, John. MIDPOINT AND OTHER POEMS. NY: Knopf, 1969. 1st ed. Ltd to 350 signed. Cl, dj, slipcase. Fine. *JAFFE.* $175

Updike, John. MITES & OTHER POEMS IN MINIATURE. Northridge: Lord John Press, 1990. 1st ed. Ltd to 200 numbered signed. 3 x 2 1/4", dec boards. Mint. *JAFFE.* $50

Updike, John. MITES & OTHER POEMS IN MINIATURE. Northridge: Lord John, 1990. Miniature bk, measuring approximately 3" x 2". One of 200 numbered, signed. Fine. *LOPEZ.* $75

Updike, John. MORE STATELY MANSIONS. Jackson: Nouveau Press, 1987. One of 300 numbered, signed. Fine w/o dj as issued. *LOPEZ.* $85

Updike, John. MUSEUMS & WOMEN. NY: Knopf, 1972. 1st ed. Fine in price-clipped dj. *LOPEZ.* $30

Updike, John. ODD JOBS: ESSAYS AND CRITICISM. Knopf, 1991. Uncorrected proof. VF in gold wraps. *STAHR.* $90

Updike, John. OF THE FARM. (London): Deutsch, (1966). 1st Eng ed. Fine in NF dj. *LOPEZ.* $100

Updike, John. OF THE FARM. NY: Knopf, 1965. 1st ed. Fine in lightly used dj. *JUVELIS.* $55

Updike, John. OF THE FARM. NY: Knopf, 1965. 1st ed. Fine in price-clipped dj. *ELSE FINE.* $65

Updike, John. OLINGER STORIES. NY: Vintage, 1964. 1st ed. Paperback orig. Fine. *BEASLEY.* $25

Updike, John. OLINGER STORIES. NY: Vintage Books, (1964). 1st ed. Orig pict wraps. VG. *CHAPEL HILL.* $40

Updike, John. ON THE MOVE. Cleveland: Bits Press, (1988). One of 120 signed. VF in oversize wrappers as issued. *BETWEEN COVERS.* $85

Updike, John. PEOPLE ONE KNOWS. Northridge: Lord John, 1980. 1/300 numbered signed. Fine in slipcase. *LOPEZ.* $85

Updike, John. PICKED-UP PIECES. NY: Alfred A. Knopf, 1975. One of ltd ed of 250 signed. New in dj in slipcase. *BERNARD.* $250

Updike, John. PICKED-UP PIECES. NY: Knopf, 1975. 1st ed. One of 250 signed. Cl, dj, slipcase. Fine. *JAFFE.* $250

Updike, John. PIGEON FEATHERS AND OTHER STORIES. Knopf, 1962. 1st ed. VG in dj with few chips, edge soil & staining to spine. *BEBBAH.* $75

Updike, John. PIGEON FEATHERS AND OTHER STORIES. NY: Knopf, 1962. 1st ed. Orig red cl, greenish grey boards. Fine in price-clipped dj, lt soiling, a few short tears. Signed. *CHAPEL HILL.* $200

Updike, John. RABBIT AT REST. Knopf, 1990. Uncorrected proof. Fine in yellow wraps. *STAHR.* $90

Updike, John. RABBIT AT REST. NY, 1990. 1st ed. Signed presentation. Fine in like dj. *POLYANTHOS.* $75

Updike, John. RABBIT AT REST. NY: Knopf, (1990). 1st trade ed. Signed. VF in VF dj. *UNGER.* $75

Updike, John. RABBIT AT REST. NY: Knopf, 1990. 1st ed. Ltd to 350 signed. Cl-backed marbled boards, acetate dj, slipcase. Mint. *JAFFE.* $275

Updike, John. RABBIT AT REST. NY: Knopf, 1990. 1st trade ed. Fine in Fine dj. *LOPEZ.* $30

Updike, John. RABBIT AT REST. NY: Knopf, 1990. Adv uncorrected proofs in yellow wraps. Fine. *BEASLEY.* $125

Updike, John. RABBIT IS RICH. NY: Knopf, 1981. 1st ed. One of 350, signed. Mint in dj, pub's slipcase, orig plastic shrinkwrap. *CHAPEL HILL.* $225

Updike, John. RABBIT IS RICH. NY: Knopf, 1981. 1st ed. Of a 1st ptg of 100,000, this of an unspecified number w/extra leaf tipped in, signed. Fine in dj. *LOPEZ.* $100

Updike, John. RABBIT IS RICH. NY: Knopf, 1981. 1st ed. Fine in Fine dj. *LOPEZ.* $35

Updike, John. RABBIT REDUX. Franklin Center: Franklin Library, 1981. Ltd ed leatherbound reissue. Signed. Fine. *LOPEZ.* $75

Updike, John. RABBIT REDUX. NY: Knopf, (1971). 1st ed. Inscribed. Fine in dj, soiling to rear panel. *UNGER.* $125

Updike, John. RABBIT REDUX. NY: Knopf, 1971. 1st ed. Ltd to 350 signed. Dec cl, acetate dj, slipcase. VF. *JAFFE.* $350

Updike, John. RABBIT REDUX. NY: Knopf, 1971. 1st ed. Orig red cl. Fine in dj. *CHAPEL HILL.* $50

Updike, John. RABBIT REDUX. NY: Knopf, 1971. 1st ed. As New in dj. *ELSE FINE.* $65

Updike, John. RABBIT, RUN. Franklin Center: Franklin Library, 1977. Leatherbound "limited" reissue. Silk eps, gilt pg edges, etc. Fine, signed. *LOPEZ.* $75

Updike, John. RABBIT RUN. NY: Alfred Knopf, 1960. 1st ed. Fine in dj (light wear to head of spine, light rubbing to corners, tiny tear). Signed. *CAPTAIN'S BOOKSHELF.* $600

Updike, John. RABBIT, RUN. NY: Knopf, 1960. 1st ed. NF in sl soiled dj, minor rubbing at spine. *CHAPEL HILL.* $350

Updike, John. RABBIT, RUN. NY: Knopf, 1960. 1st ed. Cl-backed boards. Fine in sl rubbed dj. *JAFFE.* $400

Updike, John. ROGER'S VERSION. Franklin Center: Franklin Library, 1986. True 1st ed. Leatherbound ltd ed. Marbled endpapers, gilt pages edges, silk ribbon marker. Fine. *LOPEZ.* $85

Updike, John. ROGER'S VERSION. Knopf, 1986. 1st trade ed. Fine in dj. Signed. *STAHR.* $45

Updike, John. ROGER'S VERSION. NY: Knopf, 1986. 1st ed. Ltd to 350 signed. Cl-backed dec boards, dj, slipcase. Mint. *JAFFE.* $150

Updike, John. ROGER'S VERSION. NY: Knopf, 1986. 1st trade ed. Orig grey cl. Fine in dj. *CHAPEL HILL.* $25

Updike, John. ROGER'S VERSION. NY: Knopf, 1986. One of 350 numbered, specially bound, signed. Fine in pub's acetate dj and slipcase. Unopened, in the pub's orig shrinkwrap. *LOPEZ.* $125

Updike, John. S. (London): Deutsch, (1988). 1st English ed. One of 85 numbered signed. 1/4 grn calf, marbled boards, marbled board slipcase. Mint. *JAFFE.* $225

Updike, John. S. (London): Deutsch, (1988). One of 75 numbered, in 1/4 leather and marbled paper boards, signed. Fine in marbled slipcase. *LOPEZ.* $250

Updike, John. S. NY: Knopf, 1988. 1st ed. Ltd to 350 signed. Cl, acetate dj, slipcase. Mint. *JAFFE.* $150

Updike, John. S. NY: Knopf, 1988. Wraps. Adv uncorrected proofs. Fine. *BEASLEY.* $125

Updike, John. SELF-CONSCIOUSNESS. NY: Knopf, 1989. 1st trade ed. Signed. Fine in Fine dj. *LOPEZ.* $65

Updike, John. SIXTEEN SONNETS. Cambridge: Halty Ferguson, 1979. 1/250 numbered signed by the author. Fine in wrappers. *LOPEZ.* $85

Updike, John. SPRING TRIO. (n.p.): Palaemon Press, (1982). 1/150 numbered signed. Total ed was 176. Fine in wrappers. *LOPEZ.* $150

Updike, John. SUNDAY IN BOSTON. (n.p.). Rook Broadsides, 1975. Of 300 copies total, this is one of 100 numbered, signed but not illus. Fine. *LOPEZ.* $125

Updike, John. SUNDAY IN BOSTON. Rook Broadsides 5. Pennsylvania, (1975). Ltd ed, 280/300 signed. Fine. *POLYANTHOS.* $60

Updike, John. TALK FROM THE FIFTIES. One of 300 numbered, signed. *LOPEZ.* $85

Updike, John. TELEPHONE POLES. NY: Knopf, 1963. 1st ed. Signed. Fine in sl age-darkened, NF dj. *LOPEZ.* $150

Updike, John. THE AFTERLIFE. (Warwickshire): Sixth Chamber Press, 1987. One of 175 numbered in full cl, signed. Fine w/o dj as issued. *LOPEZ.* $175

Updike, John. THE BELOVED. 1/300 numbered, signed. Fine. *LOPEZ*. $100

Updike, John. THE CARPENTERED HEN AND OTHER TAME CREATURES. NY: Harper & Bros, (1958). 1st ed. Orig black cl, grey boards. Faintest hint of soiling, but Fine in 1st state dj, w/"two small children" in biographical blurb rear flap. *CHAPEL HILL*. $850

Updike, John. THE CARPENTERED HEN AND OTHER TAME CREATURES. NY: Harper, (1958). 1st ed, 1st state dj. Cl-backed boards. Fine. *JAFFE*. $450

Updike, John. THE CARPENTERED HEN AND OTHER TAME CREATURES: POEMS. NY: Harper, (1958). 1st ed. Binding flaw causes a sl "over-opened" appearance at title pg, else Fine in dj (tiny tear). Dj (price-clipped, $3 price stamped diagonally on flap). *CAPTAIN'S BOOKSHELF*. $350

Updike, John. THE CARPENTERED HEN. NY: Harper, (1958). 1st ed, 1st bk. VG in lightly soiled, VG, first issue dj. *LOPEZ*. $500

Updike, John. THE CENTAUR. NY: Knopf, 1963. 1st ed. Fine, sm chip to upper corner of dj spine. *ELSE FINE*. $45

Updike, John. THE CENTAUR. NY: Knopf, 1963. 1st ed. Orig cl backed boards. NF in sl soiled dj, couple of sm closed tears along top edge. *CHAPEL HILL*. $200

Updike, John. THE CENTAUR. NY: Knopf, 1963. 1st ed. Cl-backed boards, dj. Fine. *JAFFE*. $100

Updike, John. THE CHASTE PLANET. Worcester: Metacom Press, 1980. 1/300 numbered copies in wrappers, a total ed of 326 signed. Fine. *LOPEZ*. $85

Updike, John. THE CHASTE PLANET. Worcester: Metacom Press, 1980. French marbled blue paper wraps, w/title in black on white paper label. Total ed of 326; this 1/300 numbered, signed. Fine. *BLUE MOUNTAIN*. $95

Updike, John. THE COUP. NY: Knopf, 1978. 1st ed, 1st state. Top edges stained yellow. As New in dj. *ELSE FINE*. $45

Updike, John. THE COUP. NY: Knopf, 1978. 1st ed. Ltd to 350 signed. Cl, dj, slipcase. VF. *JAFFE*. $250

Updike, John. THE POORHOUSE FAIR (TOGETHER WITH) RABBIT RUN. NY: Modern Library, (1965). 1st ML ed. Fine in dj (touch of rubbing to spine). *CAPTAIN'S BOOKSHELF*. $30

Updike, John. THE POORHOUSE FAIR. NY: Knopf, 1959. 1st ed. Orig brn cl, grey boards. Top edge sl bumped, couple of spots on cvrs, else NF in dj, chipping top of spine. *CHAPEL HILL*. $250

Updike, John. THE POORHOUSE FAIR. NY: Knopf, 1959. 1st ed. Signed. VG in dj with several short tears internally repaired and bit of chipping at crown of spine. *LOPEZ*. $375

Updike, John. THE POORHOUSE FAIR. NY: Knopf, 1959. 1st ed. Cl-backed boards. Superb, virtually As New save for 1/2" closed tear in dj. *JAFFE*. $400

Updike, John. THE SAME DOOR. NY: Knopf, 1959. 1st ed. VG in dj with modest chipping. Inscribed. *LOPEZ*. $250

Updike, John. THE WITCHES OF EASTWICK. Franklin Center: Franklin Lib, 1984. Leatherbound ltd. 1st ed. Signed. *LOPEZ*. $85

Updike, John. THE WITCHES OF EASTWICK. NY: Knopf, 1984. 1st signed, ltd ed, specially bound. Mint in acetate jacket, pub's slipcase, orig plastic shrinkwrap. *CHAPEL HILL*. $225

Updike, John. THE WITCHES OF EASTWICK. NY: Knopf, 1984. 1st trade ed. Orig purple cl. Fine in dj. *CHAPEL HILL*. $35

Updike, John. THREE ILLUMINATIONS IN THE LIFE OF AN AMERICAN AUTHOR. NY: Targ Editions, 1979. 1/350 numbered signed. Fine in plain white tissue dj. *LOPEZ*. $100

Updike, John. THREE ILLUMINATIONS IN THE LIFE OF AN AMERICAN AUTHOR. NY: Targ Editions, 1979. 1st ed. #68 of 350, signed. Orig tan cl, marbled boards. Fine in unptd white tissue jacket. *CHAPEL HILL*. $125

Updike, John. THREE TEXTS FROM EARLY IPSWICH. (Ipswich): (The 17th Century Day Committee), (1968). One of 50 numbered, signed. Fine in stapled wrappers. *LOPEZ*. $375

Updike, John. THREE TEXTS FROM EARLY IPSWICH. One of 950 unnumbered copies, this specially signed. Fine in wrappers. *LOPEZ*. $150

Updike, John. TOO FAR TO GO. NY: Fawcett Crest, (1979). 1st ed. Orig ptd wraps. VG. *CHAPEL HILL*. $25

Updike, John. TRUST ME. Knopf, 1987. 1st ed. Fine in dj. Signed. *STAHR*. $45

Updike, John. TRUST ME. NY: Knopf, 1987. 1st ed. Ltd to 350 signed. Cl-backed dec boards, dj, slipcase. Mint. *JAFFE*. $150

Updike, John. TRUST ME. NY: Knopf, 1987. 1st ed. Orig cl-backed boards. Fine in dj. Advance reading copy, slip laid in. *CHAPEL HILL*. $40

Updike, John. WARM WINE. NY: Albondocani Press, 1973. 1/250 numbered signed of ed of 276. Fine in wrappers. *LOPEZ*. $85

Upfield, Arthur W. GRIPPED BY DROUGHT. Missoula: Dennis McMillan, 1990. 1st Amer ed. VF in dj. *MORDIDA*. $35

Upfield, Arthur W. ROYAL ABDUCTION. Dennis McMillan, 1984. 1st Amer ed. VF in dj. *MORDIDA*. $45

Upfield, Arthur W. THE BUSHMAN WHO CAME BACK. Doubleday, 1957. 1st Amer ed. Ex lib. VG in dj. *STAHR*. $25

Upfield, Arthur W. THE MURCHISON MURDERS. Miami Beach: Dennis McMillan, 1987. 1st Amer ed. As New in dj. *MORDIDA*. $35

Upfield, Arthur W. THE MYSTERY OF SWORDFISH REEF. Sydney: Angus & Robertson, 1939. 1st ed. Partial ring-stain on front cover and light spotting on edges o/w Fine in dj w/short closed tear. *MORDIDA*. $450

Upfield, Arthur W. THE SANDS OF WINDEE. (Sydney): Angus & Robertson, (1958). 1st ed. Fine in lightly used price-clipped dj (sm tear). *CAPTAIN'S BOOKSHELF*. $75

Upham, Charles W. LIFE, EXPLORATIONS AND PUBLIC SERVICE OF JOHN CHARLES FREMONT. Boston, 1856. VG\NF. *POLYANTHOS*. $35

Upham, Charles W. LIFE EXPLORATIONS AND PUBLIC SERVICE OF JOHN CHARLES FREMONT. Boston: Ticknor and Fields, 1856. 12mo, 13 plts, frontis. Worn, bumped, bkpl, foxing. Good. *PARMER*. $40

Upham, Charles W. LIFE, EXPLORATIONS AND PUBLIC SERVICES OF JOHN CHARLES FREMONT. Boston: Ticknor and Fields, 1856. 1st ed. 14 plts. Orig cl. *SCHOYER'S*. $40

Upshur, George Lyttleton. AS I RECALL THEM: MEMORIES OF CROWDED YEARS. NY: Wilson-Erickson, 1936. 1st ed. Signed and ltd to 750. Fep has shadow from old news clipping. Gilt on spine darkened. All else Fine. Scarce. *CONNOLLY & WADE*. $75

Upson, William Hazlett. NO REST FOR BOTTS. NY: Rinehart, 1952. 1st ed. Fine; lt wear to dj extrems. *ELSE FINE*. $40

Upton, Harriet Taylor. A TWENTIETH CENTURY HISTORY OF TRUMBULL COUNTY OHIO. Vol. I (only) of 2. Chicago: Lewis Pub., 1909. 1st ed. 643pp, half-leather. *ARCHER*. $45

Upton, Winslow. STAR ATLAS CONTAINING STARS VISIBLE TO THE NAKED EYE AND CLUSTERS, NEBULAE...Boston: Ginn, 1896. Minor stains, dents; extremity wear, scattered light foxing to prelims, but Nice. *KNOLLWOOD*. $80

Urban, John W. BATTLE FIELD AND PRISON PEN, OR THROUGH THE WAR, AND A THRICE A PRISONER. Phila, (1882). 1st ed. Cvr wear o/w VG. *PRATT*. $60

Urbanek, Mae. WYOMING PLACE NAMES. Boulder: Johnson Pub, (1967). 1st ed. Ltd to 500 numbered. Signed. VF in VG dj. *OREGON*. $75

Uris, Leon. ARMAGEDDON. GC: Doubleday, 1964. 1st ed. Fine, minor edgewear to dj. *ELSE FINE.* $35

Uris, Leon. MILA 18. GC: Doubleday, 1961. 1st ed. Fine in dj. *ELSE FINE.* $35

Urquart, F.A. THE MONARCH BUTTERFLY. Toronto, 1960. 12 colored plts. Dj w/small tears. *SUTTON.* $60

Urquhart, B.L. (ed). THE RHODODENDRON. 36 colored plts. 2 vols. Sharpthorne, 1958-62. Cl, djs. Few tears to dj of Vol I. *SUTTON.* $385

URSULA: A TALE OF COUNTRY LIFE. (By Elizabeth Missing Sewell.) 2 vols. NY: Appleton, 1858. 1st US ed. 312pp,314,adv. Pub's cl. VG set. *SECOND LIFE.* $75

Urwin, Gregory J.W. CUSTER VICTORIOUS. Rutherford, (1983). 1st ed. Light dj wear o/w Fine. *PRATT.* $30

US Bureau of Navigation. FIFTY-FIRST ANNUAL LIST OF MER-CHANT VESSELS OF THE UNITED STATES... FOR THE YEAR ENDED JUNE 30,1919. Washington: GPO, 1920. *LEF-KOWICZ.* $70

US Bureau of Navigation. FORTY-SEVENTH ANNUAL LIST OF MERCHANT VESSELS OF THE UNITED STATES ... FOR THE YEAR ENDED JUNE 30, 1915. Washington: GPO, 1915. Top part of front inner hinge chewed, but sound, VG. *LEFKOWICZ.* $70

US Bureau of Navigation. MERCHANT VESSELS OF THE UNITED STATES...JUNE 30, 1931. Washington: GPO, 1931. Orig cl, cvrs stained, inner hinges tender. *LEFKOWICZ.* $50

US Bureau of Navigation. TWENTY-FIFTH ANNUAL LIST OF MERCHANT VESSELS OF THE UNITED STATES,... FOR THE YEAR ENDED JUNE 30, 1893. Washington: GPO, 1893. 2 color plts. Cl rubbed. *LEFKOWICZ.* $100

US Bureau of Navigation. TWENTY-SEVENTH ANNUAL LIST OF MERCHANT VESSELS OF THE UNITED STATES, FOR THE YEAR ENDED JUNE 30, 1895. Washington: GPO, 1895. vi,407pp. Orig cl, inner hinges tender. *LEFKOWICZ.* $100

US Dept of State. THE BIENNIAL REGISTER OF ALL OF-FICERS AND AGENTS....Washington: Blair & Rives, 1838. viii,208,325pp. Orig full dk-blue leather. *SCHOYER'S.* $85

US Light-House Board. LIST OF LIGHTS AND FOG SIGNALS ON THE ATLANTIC....Washington: GPO, 1908. 25 plts, fldg map. Wrappers. *LEFKOWICZ.* $65

US ONE. MAINE TO FLORIDA. NY: Modern Age Books, (1938). 1st ed. WPA guide. xxviii,344pp + (4)pp ads. Fldg map tipped-in at back. Dj. *KARMIOLE.* $45

Usamah Ibn Munqidh. AN ARAB-SYRIAN GENTLEMAN AND WARRIOR IN THE PERIOD OF THE CRUSADES. MEMOIRS....Philip K. Hitti (trans). NY: Columbia Univ Press, 1929. 1st ed. 4 plts, 1 map. Worn, spine chipped, corners frayed, some marginal notes. Ex-lib w/sticker on spine, o/w Good. *WORLDWIDE.* $75

Ussher, Clarence. AN AMERICAN PHYSICIAN IN TURKEY: A NARRATIVE OF ADVENTURES IN PEACE AND IN WAR. Boston, 1917. 1st ed. *FYE.* $40

UTAH. A GUIDE TO THE STATE. NY, (1941). 1st ed. NF in sl chipped dj. *DIAMOND.* $60

Utley, Cutcheon and Burton. MICHIGAN AS A PROVINCE, TER-RITORY AND STATE. 4 vols. Publishing Soc of Michigan, 1906. 1st ed. Gilt-stamped cl. Fine. *ARTIS.* $100

Utley, Robert M. (ed). LIFE IN CUSTER'S CAVALRY. New Haven: Yale Univ, 1977. 1st ed. Fine in Good+ dj. *CONNOLLY & WADE.* $37.50

Utley, Robert M. BILLY THE KID: A SHORT AND VIOLENT LIFE. Lincoln: Univ of NE Press, (1989). 1st ed. Signed. NF in dj. *OUTPOST.* $35

Utley, Robert M. CAVALIER IN BUCKSKIN, GEORGE ARMSTRONG CUSTER AND THE WESTERN MILITARY FRONTIER. Norman, (1988). 1st ed. 226pp. Fine in dj. *PRATT.* $22.50

Utley, Robert M. FOUR FIGHTERS OF LINCOLN COUNTY. Al-buquerque: Univ of NM Press, (1986) Deluxe 1st ed, ltd to 150, signed. Fine. *BOOK MARKET.* $38

Utley, Robert M. FRONTIER REGULARS, THE UNITED STATES ARMY AND THE INDIANS, 1866-1890. NY, (1973). 1st ed. Inscribed. Light dj wear o/w Fine. *PRATT.* $75

Uzanne, Octave. THE BOOK-HUNTER IN PARIS. London: Elliot Stock, 1893. 1st ed in Eng. Spine faded, cvrs sl soiled, small damp-stain rear cover, withal Good. *WREDEN.* $50

V

Vachell, Horace Annesley. SPORT AND LIFE ON THE PACIFIC SLOPE. London: Eveleigh Nash, 1908. 1st ed. Minor shelfwear, else VG-NF. *OLD LONDON.* $85

Vachss, Andrew. BLUE BELLE. NY, 1988. 1st ed. Signed. Pub photo laid in. Fine in Fine dj. *POLYANTHOS.* $30

Vachss, Andrew. BLUE BELLE. NY: Knopf, 1988. 1st ed. VF in dj. *MORDIDA.* $25

Vachss, Andrew. FLOOD. NY: Donald I. Fine, 1985. 1st ed, 1st novel. VF in dj. Ptd on dj is "Special Advance Reader's Edition—Not For Sale." *MORDIDA.* $35

Vachss, Andrew. STREGA. NY: Knopf, 1987. 1st ed. Signed. VF in dj. *SILVER DOOR.* $35

Vachss, Andrew. STREGA. NY: Knopf, 1987. 1st ed. VF in dj. *MOR-DIDA.* $25

Vaeth, J. Gordon. 200 MILES UP, THE CONQUEST OF THE UPPER AIR. NY: Ronald Press, 1951. VG. *KNOLLWOOD.* $35

Vail, Gilbert. A HISTORY OF COSMETICS IN AMERICA. NY: Toilet Goods Assoc, 1947. 1st ed. 139pp. Gray paper over boards, maroon and gold stamped letters on spine and front cover. *BOOK-MINE.* $45

Vaka, Demetra (Mrs. Kenneth Brown). HAREMLIK. Boston & NY: Houghton Mifflin, 1909. 1st ed. Edges a little rubbed, o/w VG. *WORLDWIDE.* $18

Vaka, Demetra. CONSTANTINE: KING AND TRAITOR. London, 1918. *O'NEILL.* $45

Vaka, Demetra. HEART OF THE BALKANS. Boston & NY: Houghton Mifflin, 1917. *SCHOYER'S.* $20

Valentia, George Viscount. VOYAGES AND TRAVELS TO INDIA, CEYLON, THE RED SEA...YEARS 1802, 1803, 1804, 1805 AND 1806. 4 vols. London: Rivington, 1811. 2nd ed. xi,439; iv,499; vi,495. 8vo, 1pp, 4to. Present copy consists of 3 vols text and atlas vol of French ed. The latter is complete w/28 plts, maps (6 fldg). Text vols in marbled boards, rebacked in cl, edges heavily rubbed, ex-lib, internally Good. Atlas vol recently rebound to match others. *WORLDWIDE.* $450

Valin, Jonathan. FINAL NOTICE. NY: Dodd Mead, 1980. 1st ed. VF in dj. *MORDIDA.* $125

Valin, Jonathan. LIFE'S WORK. London: Mysterious Press/Century, 1988. 1st British ed. Review copy, pub's slip laid in. Fine in dj. *SIL-VER DOOR.* $25

Valin, Jonathan. LIFE'S WORK. NY: Doubleday, (1986). 1st ed. Signed. VF in VF dj. *UNGER.* $35

Valin, Jonathan. THE LIME PIT. NY: Dodd, Mead, (1980). 1st ed. Fine in Fine dj. *UNGER.* $45

Vallejo, Cesar. COMPLETE POSTHUMOUS POETRY. Univ of CA, 1978. 1st ed. Inscribed by Eshleman (trans). VF. *SMITH.* $60

Van Allsburg, Chris. JUST A DREAM. Boston: Houghton Mifflin, 1990. 1st ed. Signed in 1990. Fine in dj. *LOPEZ.* $50

Van Allsburg, Chris. THE WRETCHED STONE. Boston: Houghton Mifflin, 1991. 1st ed. Signed. *LOPEZ.* $65

Van Allsburg, Chris. THE Z WAS ZAPPED. Boston: Houghton Mifflin, 1987. 1st ed. Signed. VF in VF dj. *ACADEMIC LIBRARY.* $38

Van Allsburg, Chris. THE Z WAS ZAPPED. Boston: Houghton Mifflin, 1987. 1st ed. Signed. Fine in Fine dj. *LOPEZ.* $50

Van Allsburg, Chris. TWO BAD ANTS. Boston: Houghton, Mifflin, 1988. 1st ed. Cloth. Signed. VF in VF dj. *ACADEMIC LIBRARY.* $45

Van Ash, Cay and Elizabeth Rohmer. MASTER OF VILLAINY: A BIOGRAPHY OF SAX ROHMER. London: Tom Stacey, 1972. 1st Eng ed. Fine in dj w/some tiny closed tears and minor wear at corners. *MORDIDA.* $85

Van Ash, Cay. TEN YEARS BEYOND BAKER STREET. NY: Harper & Row, 1984. 1st ed. Fine in dj. *MORDIDA.* $45

Van Buren, Martin. GOROSTIZA PAMPHLET. MESSAGE FROM THE PRESIDENT OF THE UNITED STATES TRANSMITTING A COPY AND TRANSLATION OF A PAMPHLET...PRINTED AND CIRCULATED BY THE LATE MINISTER FROM MEXICO BEFORE HIS DEPARTURE FROM THE UNITED STATES, ETC....Wash, 1838. 1st ed in English. 120pp. Map. Modern half morocco. Howes G6. *GINSBERG.* $400

Van Cleve, Charlotte O. "THREE SCORE YEARS AND TEN." LIFE LONG MEMORIES....(Minneapolis), 1888. 1st ed, 1st issue, copyright notice on slip. 176pp. Orig grn cl. Howes V21. *GINSBERG.* $125

Van de Water, Frederic F. GLORY-HUNTER, A LIFE OF GENERAL CUSTER. Indianapolis: Bobbs-Merrill, 1934. 1st ed. Backstrip sl darkened. VG. *CONNOLLY & WADE.* $42.50

Van de Water, Frederick F. GLORY HUNTER, THE LIFE OF GENERAL CUSTER. Indianapolis, 1934. 1st ed. Pasted to the fep is a letter signed by author. Minor cvr wear o/w Fine. *PRATT.* $100

Van de Wetering, Janwillem. INSPECTOR SAITO'S SMALL SATORI. NY: Putnam, (1985). 1st ed. Inscribed yr of pub. Fine in dj. *LOPEZ.* $45

Van de Wetering, Janwillem. OUTSIDER IN AMSTERDAM. Boston: Houghton Mifflin, 1975. 1st Amer ed. Fine in dj w/minor wear. *MORDIDA.* $25

Van de Wetering, Janwillem. ROBERT VAN GULIK: HIS LIFE HIS WORK. Miami Beach: Dennis McMillan, 1987. 1st ed. One of 350 numbered, signed. VF in dj. *MORDIDA.* $65

Van de Wetering, Janwillem. THE EMPTY MIRROR. Boston: Houghton Mifflin, 1974. 1st ed. VG in VG dj. *BLUE DRAGON.* $25

Van de Wetering, Janwillem. THE JAPANESE CORPSE. Boston: Houghton Mifflin, 1977. 1st Amer ed. Fine in dj. *MORDIDA.* $25

Van de Wetering, Janwillem. TUMBLEWEED. Boston: H-M, 1976. 1st ed. VF in dj. *ELSE FINE.* $30

van der Heyden, A. A. M. and H. H. Scullard (eds). ATLAS OF THE CLASSICAL WORLD. (London & Edinburgh): Nelson, 1960. 2nd prtg. *SCHOYER'S.* $20

Van der Meulen, D. FACES IN SHEM. London: Murray, 1961. 1st ed. 16 plts, double-pg map. Dj. NF. *WORLDWIDE.* $35

Van der Post, Laurens. VENTURE TO THE INTERIOR. London: The Hogarth Press, 1952. 1st ed. First state Zebra dj. Very minor foxing, small spot front cvr. NF in VG dj. *GREAT EPIC.* $95

Van der Post, Laurens. VENTURE TO THE INTERIOR. NY: Morrow, 1951. 1st US ed. Fine in lightly used dj. Rev copy, slip laid in. *CAPTAIN'S BOOKSHELF.* $45

Van der Veer, Judy. NOVEMBER GRASS. NY: Longmans, Green and Co, 1940. 1st ed. Cl in moderately chipped dj, sl cocked, light newspaper stain to flyleaf and front ep. Inscribed. *DAWSON'S.* $45

Van Devier, Roy. A SON OF MICHIGAN OR A SHORT BIOGRAPHY OF BYRON A. DUNN. Akron: The author, 1949. 1st ed. 27pp, blue wraps. NF. *ARCHER.* $25

Van Dine, S.S. THE BENSON MURDER CASE. NY: Scribner's, 1926. 1st ed, 1st bk. Minor shelf wear, VG, no dj. *ELSE FINE.* $200

Van Dine, S.S. THE CASINO MURDER CASE. NY: Scribner's, 1934. 1st ed. Fine in dj w/minor wear. *MORDIDA.* $175

Van Dine, S.S. THE DRAGON MURDER CASE. NY: Scribner's, 1933. 1st ed. VG in dj (1/4" strip missing top of spine; chipping base of spine, corners; wear along folds; nicks). *MORDIDA.* $100

Van Dine, S.S. THE GRACIE ALLEN MURDER CASE. NY, 1938. 1st ed. VG in edgeworn dj, shallowly chipped at spine ends. *McCLINTOCK.* $35

Van Dine, S.S. THE GREENE MURDER CASE. G&D, (1928). 1st movie ed. VG+. *BEBBAH.* $15

Van Dine, S.S. THE GREENE MURDER CASE. Scribners, 1928. 1st ed. Fine. Bkpl. Emb lettering on boards clean & bright. *STAHR.* $20

Van Dine, S.S. THE JOHN RIDDELL MURDER CASE. By Corey Ford as John Riddell. NY: Scribner's, 1930. 1st ed. NF, publisher's seal opened, but present, chip in rear panel, light soil & minor edgewear to pict jacket. *ELSE FINE.* $150

Van Dine, S.S. THE KENNEL MURDER CASE. NY: Charles Scribner's Sons, 1933. 1st ed. VG w/bright unfaded, unchipped lettering on cvrs in dj w/wear. *MORDIDA.* $125

Van Dine, S.S. THE SCARAB MURDER CASE. NY, 1930. 1st ed. VG in price-clipped bit chipped dj w/internal clear tape reinforcement. *PETTLER.* $100

Van Dine, S.S. THE SCARAB MURDER CASE. NY: Scribner's, 1930. 1st ed. Fine, dj lightly worn at extremities, narrow chip at spine top, not affecting title lettering. *ELSE FINE.* $135

Van Dine, S.S. THE SCARAB MURDER CASE. Scribners. 1930. 1st ed. About Fine. Dj has darkened spine and is chipped at head of spine. Bkpl. *STAHR.* $150

Van Dine, S.S. THE WINTER MURDER CASE. NY: Charles Scribner's Sons, 1939. 1st ed. Fine in dj (minor rubbing on spine; nicks top of spine; minor corner wear). *MORDIDA.* $300

Van Doren, Carl. THE SECRET HISTORY OF THE AMERICAN REVOLUTION. NY: Viking, 1941. 2nd ptg. VG in chipped dj. *SECOND LIFE.* $35

Van Doren, Mark (ed). CORRESPONDENCE OF AARON BURR AND HIS DAUGHTER THEODOSIA. NY, 1929. One of 500. NF. *POLYANTHOS.* $60

Van Dyke, Harry. THE PHYSIOLOGY AND PHARMACOLOGY OF THE PITUITARY BODY. Chicago, 1936-1939. 1st ed. 2 vols. Vol. 1 ex- lib in buckram. *FYE.* $100

Van Dyke, Henry et al (eds). A BOOK OF PRINCETON VERSE II, 1919. Princeton: Princeton Univ Press, (1919). 1st ed. Contains 3 poems by F. Scott Fitzgerald. Orig pea grn cl, teg. Owner sigs, sm marginal chip one leaf, but Nice, VG. *CHAPEL HILL.* $150

Van Dyke, Henry. A PRAYER FOR CHRISTMAS MORNING. NY: Dutton, (1900?). Ptd in Bavaria. 7 tipped in leaves. Cl backed vellum boards, Excellent. *SECOND LIFE.* $45

Van Dyke, Henry. DAYS OFF. Scribner's, 1907. 1st ed. Margaret Armstrong signed dec cvr in blue, grn, white & gilt w/some rubbing of white pigment. Color illus by Frank Schoonover. VG w/gilt dec spine. *BEBBAH.* $25

Van Dyke, Henry. LADIES OF THE RACHMANINOFF EYES. NY: FSG, 1965. 1st ed. Fine; minor fade dj spine. *ELSE FINE.* $65

Van Dyke, Henry. OUT-OF-DOORS IN THE HOLY LAND. NY, 1908. xiii,325pp. Uncut. Fine. *O'NEILL.* $25

Van Dyke, Henry. THE GRAND CANYON AND OTHER POEMS. NY, 1914. 1st ed. Light cover wear, sunfade to spine, else VG. *FIVE QUAIL.* $20

Van Dyke, John C. THE GRAND CANYON OF THE COLORADO. RECURRENT STUDIES IN IMPRESSIONS AND APPEARANCES. NY, 1920. Red cloth, xii, 218pp. Fldg map. NF. *FIVE QUAIL.* $35

Van Dyne, Edith (pseud of L. Frank Baum). AUNT JANE'S NIECES AND UNCLE JOHN. Chicago, (1911). Later ptg. (Reilly & Lee) on spine. Plainer binding. Light soil, lower edge front cover, else VG. *McCLINTOCK.* $17.50

Van Every, Edward. SINS OF NEW YORK. NY, 1930. Cl sl faded, stained. Sl spine tip, cover wear. *DIAMOND.* $25

Van Gieson, Judith. NORTH OF THE BORDER. NY: Walker, 1988. 1st ed. VF in dj. *MORDIDA.* $30

Van Gulik, Robert. CHINESE NAIL MURDERS: JUDGE DEE'S LAST THREE CASES. NY: Harper & Row, (1961). 1st Amer ed. NF in dj just sl chipped, and sl browned on spine. *SCHOYER'S.* $60

Van Gulik, Robert. FANTOOM IN FOE-LAI (THE CHINESE GOLD MURDERS). The Hague: W. Van Hoeve, 1958. 1st ed. Fine in stiff pict wrappers. *MORDIDA.* $125

Van Gulik, Robert. HET CHINESE LAKSCHERM (THE LAC-QUER SCREEN). The Hague: W. Van Hoeve, 1962. 1st Dutch ed. Fine in stiff pict wrappers. *MORDIDA.* $125

Van Gulik, Robert. MEER VAN MIEN-YUAN (THE CHINESE LAKE MURDERS). The Hague: W. Van Hoeve, 1959. 1st ed. Fine in stiff pict wrappers. *MORDIDA.* $125

Van Gulik, Robert. MURDER IN CANTON. NY: Scribner's, 1967. 1st Amer ed. Some staining on pages o/w Fine in dj. *MORDIDA.* $30

Van Gulik, Robert. NECKLACE AND CALABASH. NY: Charles Scribner's Sons, 1971. 1st Amer ed. Fine in dj w/slight spine fading. *MORDIDA.* $35

Van Gulik, Robert. NECKLACE AND CALABASH. NY: Scribners, 1971. 1st ed. VF in bright dj. *ELSE FINE.* $35

Van Gulik, Robert. THE CHINESE BELL MURDERS. London: Michael Joseph, (1958). 1st Eng ed. 1st Eng language pub of a Judge Dee mystery. NF in NF dj with a soil spot to rear panel. *UNGER.* $200

Van Gulik, Robert. THE CHINESE GOLD MURDERS. NY: Harper, (1959). 1st US ed. Name, VG+ in dj (sl wear, soil). *BERNARD.* $75

Van Gulik, Robert. THE CHINESE GOLD MURDERS. NY: Harper, 1961. 1st ed. VF in dj. *ELSE FINE.* $65

Van Gulik, Robert. THE HAUNTED MONASTERY. NY: Charles Scribner's Sons, 1968. 1st Amer ed. Fine in dj. *MORDIDA.* $50

Van Gulik, Robert. THE LACQUER SCREEN. NY: Scribners, 1969. 1st ed. VF in dj. *ELSE FINE.* $35

Van Gulik, Robert. THE MONKEY AND THE TIGER. NY: Scribners, 1966. 1st ed. VF in dj. *ELSE FINE.* $35

Van Gulik, Robert. THE MONKEY AND THE TIGER. NY: Charles Scribner's Sons, (1966). 1st Amer ed. Fine in price clipped dj, sm internal stain. *HELLER.* $50

Van Gulik, Robert. THE RED PAVILION. Scribner's, 1968. 1st Amer ed. About Fine in dj lightly chipped at spine ends. *STAHR.* $40

Van Lennep, Henry J. BIBLE LANDS: THEIR MODERN CUS-TOMERS & MANNERS ILLUSTRATIVE OF SCRIPTURE. NY, 1875. 832 pp. Nice. *O'NEILL.* $110

Van Lennep, Henry J. THE ORIENTAL ALBUM: TWENTY IL-LUSTRATIONS IN OIL COLORS, OF THE PEOPLE AND SCENERY OF TURKEY, WITH AN EXPLANATORY AND DESCRIPTIVE TEXT. NY, 1862. 20 full-pg color lithographs. Qtr lea, orig gilt pict front cover. 48pp. Light cover wear, hinges tender, else Fine. *O'NEILL.* $2850

Van Lennep, Henry. TRAVELS IN LITTLE-KNOWN PARTS OF ASIA MINOR. London, 1870. 2 vols. x,343; x,330pp. *O'NEILL.* $375

Van Loon, Hendrik W. SHIPS AND HOW THEY SAILED THE SEVEN SEAS. London: George G. Harrap, 1935. VG with light wear in worn dj. *PARMER.* $65

Van Loon, Hendrik W. THE STORY OF WILBUR THE HAT. Liveright, (1925). 1st ed. 110pp. Color plts by author. Edgewear. VG+ w/color pict pastedown front cvr, dec rear cvr. *BEBBAH.* $40

Van Milligen, Alexander. CONSTANTINOPLE. A&C Black, 1906. 1st ed. 20s Series. NF. *OLD LONDON.* $160

Van Ness, Wm. P. AN EXAMINATION OF THE VARIOUS CHARGES EXHIBITED AGAINST AARON BURR, ESQ...BY ARISTEDES. NY, 1803. 1st ed. 118,(1)pp. Half morocco. Howes V37. *GINSBERG.* $150

Van Noppen, Ina Woestemeyer. STONEMAN'S LAST RAID. (Raleigh, 1961). 2nd prtg. Fine. *McGOWAN.* $45

Van Offelin, Marion and Carol Beckwith. NOMADS OF NIGER. NY: Abrams, 1983. Sl rubbed, o/w VG ex-lib. *WORLDWIDE.* $35

Van Peebles, Melvin. A BEAR FOR THE F.B.I. NY: Trident, (1968). 1st ed. VG in dj. *LOPEZ.* $30

Van Peebles, Melvin. THE TRUE AMERICAN. GC: Doubleday, 1976. 1st ed. Fine in NF dj. *LOPEZ.* $30

Van Rensselaer, Schuyler. ENGLISH CATHEDRALS. NY: The Century Co, 1892. Spec ed. 2 vols. 1/4 bound in grn leather. Lt wear, overall very clean. NF. *BACKROOM.* $325

Van Rensselaer, Schuyler. ENGLISH CATHEDRALS. NY: The Century Co, 1892. Trade ed. One of 250. Boards sl soiled. *BACKROOM.* $180

Van Rensselaer, Stephen. CHECK LIST OF EARLY AMERICAN BOTTLES AND FLASKS. NY: The author, 1921. Special ed. NF. *BACKROOM.* $50

Van Sickle, V.A. THE WRONG BODY. NY: Alfred A. Knopf, 1937. 1st ed. Inscribed. Fine in VG dj (nicks and wear; internal tape mend; sl soiled back panel). *MORDIDA.* $40

Van Tassel, Charles Sumner. STORY OF THE MAUMEE VAL-LEY, TOLEDO & THE SANDUSKY REGION. Chicago: S.J. Clarke Company, 1929. 2 vols. Vols 1 & 2 of 4, lacking vols of biography. VG+. *BOHLING.* $125

Van Tramp, John C. PRAIRIE AND ROCKY MOUNTAIN AD-VENTURES. Columbus, 1866. 685pp; 61 plts. Rebound new buckram, leather labels, hand binder. Foxing. *HEINOLDT.* $25

Van Urk, J. Blan. LITTLE CHARLIE THE FOX. Wilmington: Serendipity, 1977. VG+ in VG+ dj. *OCTOBER FARM.* $25

Van Vechten, Carl. PARTIES. SCENES FROM CONTEM-PORARY NEW YORK LIFE. NY: Knopf, 1930. One of 250 numbered, signed. Fine in dj w/few small edge tears and sl used slipcase. *DERMONT.* $125

Van Vogt, A.E. and E. Mayne Hull. OUT OF THE UNKNOWN. LA: Fantasy Publishing, (1948). 1st ed. Inscribed by both authors and dated in yr of pub. VG in edgeworn dj. *LOPEZ.* $85

Van Vogt, A.E. MASTERS OF TIME. Fantasy Press, 1950. One of 500 numbered, signed. Fine in sl frayed dj. *MADLE.* $150

Van Vogt, A.E. SLAN. Arkham House, 1946. 1st ed. Fine in dj. *MADLE.* $250

Van Vogt, A.E. SLAN. NY: Simon & Schuster, 1951. 1st ed w/revised text of 1st book. Orig published by Arkham House in 1946, Van Vogt rev. part of the text for 1951 ed. (1st thus). VG in dj sl chipped at top of spine & moderately worn at edges. *BERNARD.* $35

Van Vogt, A.E. THE BOOK OF PTATH. Fantasy Press, 1947. One of 500 numbered, signed. Fine in sl nicked dj. *MADLE.* $150

Van Vogt, A.E. THE WEAPON SHOPS OF ISHER. Greenberg, 1952. 1st ed. Fine in sl soiled dj. *MADLE.* $75

Van Vogt, A.E. THE WORLD OF A. NY: Simon & Schuster, 1948. 1st ed. VG+ in dj sl rubbed at edges. *BERNARD.* $75

Van Walleghen, Michael. THE WICHITA POEMS. William Kough (illus). Iowa City: Stone Wall Press, 1973. 1st ed. Ltd to 250. Boards w/ptd label on spine. Fine. *JAFFE.* $150

Van Wormer, J. THE WORLD OF THE BLACK BEAR. Phila, 1966. Cloth w/light fading, worn dj. *SUTTON.* $24

Van Wormer, J. THE WORLD OF THE COYOTE. Phila, (1964). Cloth, dj. *SUTTON.* $25

Van Wormer, J. THE WORLD OF THE MOOSE. Phila, 1972. Half cloth, dj. *SUTTON.* $25

Vance, Jack. BIG PLANET. Avalon, 1957. 1st ed. Ex-lib in NF in dj. *MADLE.* $100

Vance, Jack. THE HOUSES OF ISZM. NY: Ace Double, 1964. 1st ed. Close to Fine in wraps. *BEASLEY.* $25

Vance, Jack. VANDALS OF THE VOID. Phila: Winston, 1953. 1st ed. Fine, tiny chips upper dj extrems. *ELSE FINE.* $125

Vance, Joel. FATS WALLER: HIS LIFE AND TIMES. Chicago: Contemporary, 1977. 1st ed. Fine in Fine dj. *BEASLEY.* $35

Vance, John Holbrook. THE PLEASANT GROVE MURDERS. Indianapolis: Bobbs-Merrill, 1967. 1st ed. Lt staining top edge, o/w Fine in dj (several short closed tears; sl faded spine). *MORDIDA.* $85

Vance, Louis Joseph. ENCORE THE LONE WOLF. Phila: J.B. Lippincott, 1933. NF in VF bright like-new dj. *MORDIDA.* $65

Vance, Louis Joseph. THE LONE WOLF. Boston, 1914. 1st Amer ed. Spine lettering rubbed. Minor cvr staining, o/w VG. *DIAMOND.* $75

Vance, Louis Joseph. THE STREET OF STRANGE FACES. Phila: J.B. Lippincott, 1934. 1st ed. File copy w/stamps. Fine in VG dj (chipping). *MORDIDA.* $35

Vance, Louis Joseph. THE TREMBLING FLAME. Phila: J.B. Lippincott, 1931. 1st ed. File copy w/stamps. Fine in VG dj w/darkened spine, chipping, wear. *MORDIDA.* $35

VanCleve, Spike. 40 YEARS GATHERIN'S. Lowell Press, 1977. 1st ed. Inscribed. Fine in Fine dj. *VARNER.* $25

Vandenhoff, George. LEAVES FROM AN ACTOR'S NOTE-BOOK. NY: D. Appleton and Company, 1860. 1st ed. Shelfworn; corners bumped; foxed. *DRAMATIS.* $70

Vandercook, John W. KING CANE: AN EPIC OF SUGAR IN HAWAII. NY: Harper, 1939. 1st ed. 14 photo plts. Grn cl over cane dec boards. About Fine in Good+, scarce dj. *CONNOLLY & WADE.* $45

Vanderlip, Washington B. (as narrated by) and set forth by Homer B. Hulbert. IN SEARCH OF A SIBERIAN KLONDIKE. NY: Century Co, 1903. VG. *BLUE DRAGON.* $37.50

Vanderwood, Paul. NIGHT RIDERS OF REELFOOT LAKE. Memphis State Univ, (1969). 1st ed. Fine in VG dj. *OREGON.* $25

Vandiveer, Clarence. FUR-TRADE AND EARLY WESTERN EXPLORATION. A.H. Clark, 1929. 1st ed. 5 plts. Sm stamp ffep, title page; o/w VF. *OREGON.* $95

Vandiver, Frank. JUBAL'S RAID. NY, (1960). 1st ed. 198pp. Little dj wear, o/w VG+. *PRATT.* $45

Vandiver, Frank. THEIR TATTERED FLAGS, THE EPIC OF THE CONFEDERACY. NY, (1970). 1st ed. VG in dj. *PRATT.* $35

Vandyke, Theodore S. MILLIONAIRES OF A DAY. NY: Fords, Howard & Hulbert, 1892. 208pp, 12pp ads. Ptd wrappers, stamps on upper wrapper and title pg rubbed out, with that on the title pg affecting 3 words of the title, sl wear and soiling. *DAWSON'S.* $40

Varagnac, Andre. FRENCH COSTUMES. Paris/London: Hyperion, 1939. 1st ed. 40 color plts. Fine in VG+ dj. *AARD.* $95

Vargas Llosa, Mario. CAPTAIN PANTOJA AND THE SPECIAL SERVICE. NY: Harper & Row et al, (1978). 1st US ed. Fine in dj. *BERNARD.* $40

Vargas Llosa, Mario. CAPTAIN PANTOJA AND THE SPECIAL SERVICE. London: Cape, (1978). 1st UK ed. Fine in dj. *BETWEEN COVERS.* $35

Vargas Llosa, Mario. CONVERSATION IN THE CATHEDRAL. NY: H&R, (1975). 1st ed. NF in dj with edge tears at spine crown. *LOPEZ.* $125

Vargas Llosa, Mario. CONVERSATION IN THE CATHEDRAL. Trans Gregory Rabassa. NY: Harper, (1975). 1st US ed. Fine in dj. *CAPTAIN'S BOOKSHELF.* $100

Vargas Llosa, Mario. THE CUBS AND OTHER STORIES. NY: Harper, (1979). 1st ed. Fine in dj w/tiny tear rear panel. *BETWEEN COVERS.* $30

Vargas Llosa, Mario. THE CUBS AND OTHER STORIES. NY: Harper, 1979. 1st ed. Wraps. Adv uncorrected proofs. *BEASLEY.* $35

Vargas Llosa, Mario. THE GREEN HOUSE. NY & Evanston: Harper & Row, (1968). 1st ed, 2nd book. NF in dj. *BERNARD.* $40

Vargas Llosa, Mario. THE GREEN HOUSE. NY, 1968. 1st US ed. Fine in NF dj. *PETTLER.* $40

Vargas Llosa, Mario. THE TIME OF THE HERO. Grove, (1966). 1st Amer ed. Short narrow stain to front edge, else VG in VG dj with slight soil to rear panel. *BEBBAH.* $40

Vargas Llosa, Mario. THE TIME OF THE HERO. NY, 1966. 1st US ed, 1st bk. Fine in dj. *PETTLER.* $30

Vargas Llosa, Mario. THE TIME OF THE HERO. NY: Grove, 1966. 1st ed. Fine in very close to Fine dj w/a few nicks. *BEASLEY.* $50

Vargas Llosa, Mario. THE WAR OF THE END OF THE WORLD. NY: Farrar, Straus & Giroux, (1984). 1st ed. Signed. New in dj. *BERNARD.* $65

Vargas Llosa, Mario. THE WAR OF THE END OF THE WORLD. Farrar Straus Giroux, (1984). Uncorrected advance proofs. Sl wrinkling first few pp. Fine, wraps. *BEBBAH.* $50

Vargas Llosa, Mario. THE WAR OF THE END OF THE WORLD. NY: Farrar, 1984. Wraps. Adv uncorrected proofs. *BEASLEY.* $35

Varner, John and Jeanette Varner. DOGS OF THE CONQUEST. Univ of OK Press, 1983. 1st ed. Fine in Fine dj. *MAD DOG.* $20

Varner, John Grier and Jeannette Johnson Varner. THE FLORIDA OF THE INCA. Austin: Univ of TX Press, 1951. VG. *NUTMEG.* $40

Varnum, William H. INDUSTRIAL ARTS DESIGN. Chicago & NY: Scott, Foresman, (1916). Sm dampstain along top edge at rear, hut o/w VG. Scarce. *WEBER.* $75

Vasari, Giorgio. LIVES OF THE MOST EMINENT PAINTERS, SCULPTORS, & ARCHITECTS. London: Macmillan and The Medici Society, 1912-14. 10 vols. Gaston Du C. De Vere (trans). Orig cl, teg, other edges untrimmed. 500 plts. Bkpl removal each vol; tops of 2 spines sl damaged; few tears internally, o/w Fine. *PIRAGES.* $350

Vassiliev, M. SPUTNIK INTO SPACE. Dial, NY, 1958. Good in red cl; eps discolored. *KNOLLWOOD.* $28

Vassilikos, Vassilis. Z. NY: FSG, (1968). 1st Amer ed. Fine in NF dj. *DORN.* $30

Vassos, John and Ruth Vassos. CONTEMPO. NY: E.P. Dutton & Co., 1929. 1st ed. Frontis, 22 plts. Orig blue cloth stamped in silver; spine extrems lightly rubbed. Signed. *KARMIOLE*. $150

Vassos, John. DOGS ARE LIKE THAT. NY: E.P. Dutton & Co. (1941). 1st ed. Presentation inscrip, signed, and with 4 orig ink drwgs of dogs. *KARMIOLE*. $150

Vaughan, H.W. TYPES AND MARKET CLASSES OF LIVESTOCK. Columbus: Adams, 1930. 3rd rev, ltr prtg. Good+. *OCTOBER FARM*. $35

Vaughan, Ruben V. THE PRINT OF MY REMEMBRANCE: THE AUTOBIOGRAPHY. Hollywood: Limb, 1955. 1st ed. Inscribed, signed. Fine in fair dj. *CONNOLLY & WADE*. $35

Vaughn, J.W. THE BATTLE OF PLATTE BRIDGE. Norman, (1963). 1st ed. 132pp. Dj spine faded, o/w Fine. *PRATT*. $40

Vaughn, J.W. WITH CROOK AT THE ROSEBUD. Harrisburg, (1956). 1st ed. 245pp. Fine in dj. *PRATT*. $45

Vaux, W.S.W. NINEVEH AND PERSEPOLIS: AN HISTORICAL SKETCH. London: Hall, Virtue, 1851. 12 plts, 1 fldg map. Orig cl, spine chipped & torn, Ex-lib w/lib number on spine, o/w Good. *WORLDWIDE*. $45

Veblen, Thorstein. IMPERIAL GERMANY & THE INDUSTRIAL EVOLUTION. NY: Macmillan, 1915. 1st ed. Spine a bit darkened, about VG+. *AKA*. $45

Vecki, Victor. THE PATHOLOGY AND TREATMENT OF SEXUAL IMPOTENCE. Phila, 1899. 1st Eng trans. *FYE*. $75

Veeck, Bill with Ed Linn. THE HUSTLER'S HANDBOOK. Putnam, 1965. 1st ed. Good in VG dj. *PLAPINGER*. $45

Veeck, Bill with Ed Linn. THIRTY TONS A DAY. Viking, 1972. 1st ed. Fine in dj w/light wear. *STAHR*. $35

Veeck, Bill with Ed Linn. VEECK AS IN WRECK. Putnam, 1962. 1st ed. Good in VG dj. *PLAPINGER*. $35

Velazquez, Loreta Janeta. THE WOMAN IN BATTLE...Hartford: T. Belknap. N.d. (circa 1876). Reprint ed. 606pp. Frontis. Spine extremities sl frayed. *KARMIOLE*. $50

Velikovsky, Immanuel. OEDIPUS AND AKHNATON. GC: Doubleday & Co, 1960. 1st ed. VG in VG- dj. *BLUE DRAGON*. $35

Velikovsky, Immanuel. PEOPLES OF THE SEA. GC: Doubleday, 1977. 1st ed. 16 illus, ep maps. VG in VG- dj. *BLUE DRAGON*. $25

Velikovsky, Immanuel. RAMSES II AND HIS TIME. GC: Doubleday, 1978. 1st ed. VG in VG dj. *BLUE DRAGON*. $20

Velikovsky, Immanuel. STARGAZER AND GRAVEDIGGERS. NY: Wm. Morrow & Co, 1983. 1st ed. VG+ in VG dj. *BLUE DRAGON*. $20

Velikovsky, Immanuel. WORLDS IN COLLISION. NY: Macmillan, 1950. 1st ed. VG. *BLUE DRAGON*. $25,

Venables, Rev. Hubert. THE FRANKENSTEIN DIARIES. NY: Viking Press, (1980). 1st ed. Illus. w/drawings, many from orig by Frankenstein. Fine green leatherette in NF dj which is lightly stained on inside. *BERNARD*. $25

Veney, Bethany. NARRATIVE OF BETHANY VENNEY, A SLAVE WOMAN. Worchester, MA, 1889. Wraps, sl soiled. Staples rusting. VG. *SCHOYER'S*. $40

Vennor, Henry G. OUR BIRDS OF PREY, OR THE EAGLES, HAWKS, AND OWLS OF CANADA. Montreal, 1876. viii,154pp. 30 mounted albumen photogr plts. Orig gilt-dec cl. Lt scuffing; some wear to corners and spine ends; lt browning to pp; waving to pl pgs; rear hinge cracked; remnant of sm number sticker on spine; some soiling to 1 pl pg, not affecting photo. Bkpl. *SUTTON*. $650

Vermeule, Cornelius C. ROMAN IMPERIAL ART IN GREECE AND ASIA MINOR. Cambridge: Harvard Univ Press, 1968. 184 figs, 3 plans. Dj. Good. *ARCHAEOLOGIA*. $95

Vernam, Glenn R. THE RAWHIDE YEARS. Doubleday, 1976. 1st ed. Fine in Fine dj. *VARNER*. $17.50

Verne, Jules. EIGHT HUNDRED LEAGUES UNDER THE AMAZON. PART I & PART II. NY, n.d. Burt reprint. Contemp pencilled ep inscrip reads "1908". VG. *McCLINTOCK*. $15

Verne, Jules. THE ANNOTATED JULES VERNE. NY: Crowell, (1978). Ed by Walter James Miller. 1st ed. Illus. Fine in dj. *CAPTAIN'S BOOKSHELF*. $35

Verne, Jules. THE DESERT OF ICE; OR, THE FURTHER ADVENTURES OF CAPTAIN HATTERAS. Phila: Alta Edition, Porter & Coates, (c.1874). Some wear, soiling; age-darkening to pgs. Overall VG. *PARMER*. $65

Verne, Jules. THE MYSTERIOUS ISLAND. Baltimore: LEC, 1959. 1/1500. Illus, signed by Edward A. Wilson. Fine in slipcase. *CAPTAIN'S BOOKSHELF*. $125

Verne, Jules. THE TOUR OF THE WORLD IN EIGHTY DAYS. Boston: James R. Osgood and Co, 1873. 1st Amer ed. Orig blue cl. Frontis. Binding cocked, tiny punctures front cvr, sl fading to backstrip; bumped and rubbed, but still Excellent. Bkpl. *PIRAGES*. $275

Verner, Elizabeth O'Neill. PRINTS AND IMPRESSIONS OF CHARLESTON. Columbia: Bostick & Thornley, 1939. 1st ed. One of 1500 signed. 48 etchings. Just About Fine in a worn, cracked slipcase. *CAPTAIN'S BOOKSHELF*. $175.

Verner, Gerald. THE GHOST MAN. NY: Macaulay, 1936. 1st Amer ed. VG in dj w/1" piece missing at corner of front panel and several short closed tears. *MORDIDA*. $30

Vernon, Arthur. THE HISTORY AND ROMANCE OF THE HORSE. Boston, (1939). 1st ed. Rear cvr sl stained, o/w NF. *DIAMOND*. $45

Vernon, Paul E. MOROCCO FROM A MOTOR. London: Black, 1927. 1st ed. 48 color plts, fldg map. Presentation copy, signed. Sl rubbed and soiled, o/w VG. *WORLDWIDE*. $28

Verrill, A. Hyatt. IN THE WAKE OF THE BUCCANEERS. NY: Century, 1923. 1st ed. Some light foxing. Pict cl, gilt. VG. Protected by the scarce dj. *CONNOLLY & WADE*. $45

Vervliet, Hendrik D.L. (ed). THE BOOK THROUGH FIVE THOUSAND YEARS. London: Phaidon. (1972). 1st ed. 254 illus (112 in color, 7 of which are tipped-in). Red cl, gilt spine. Dj. *KARMIOLE*. $150

Vestal, Stanley. BIGFOOT WALLACE. Houghton Mifflin, 1942. 1st ed. Fine. *VARNER*. $50

Vestal, Stanley. BIGFOOT WALLACE: TEXAN FRONTIER FIGHTER, A BIOGRAPHY. Boston: Houghton Mifflin, 1942. Riverside Press. 1st ed. Red cl, worn on edges, faded area on spine else tight, clean, VG. *CONNOLLY & WADE*. $65

Vestal, Stanley. HAPPY HUNTING GROUNDS. Chicago: Lyons and Carnahan, 1928. 1st ed. 4 colored plts. Pict label inset on front cvr. NF. *CONNOLLY & WADE*. $40

Vestal, Stanley. JIM BRIDGER, MOUNTAIN MAN. Morrow, 1946. 1st ed. NF in chipped dj. *VARNER*. $35

Vestal, Stanley. JIM BRIDGER, MOUNTAIN MAN. NY, 1946. 1st ed. VG. *DIAMOND*. $25

Vestal, Stanley. JIM BRIDGER, MOUNTAIN MAN. NY: Morrow, 1946. 1st ed. VG in chipped dj. *CONNOLLY & WADE*. $45

Vestal, Stanley. JOE MEEK, THE MERRY MOUNTAIN MAN. Caldwell, ID, 1952. 1st ed. VG. *PRATT*. $75

Vestal, Stanley. JOE MEEK, THE MERRY MOUNTAIN MAN. Caxton, 1952. 2nd ptg. VG. *OREGON*. $40

Vestal, Stanley. KING OF THE FUR TRADERS....PIERRE ESPIRIT RADISSON. Houghton Mifflin, 1940. 1st ed. Fine in NF dj. *VARNER*. $75

Vestal, Stanley. KIT CARSON, THE HAPPY WARRIOR OF THE OLD WEST. Boston, 1928. 1st ed. Faded spine o/w VG. *PRATT.* $40

Vestal, Stanley. THE MISSOURI. Farrar & Rinehart, (1945). 1st ed. VG in Fine dj. *OREGON.* $35

Vestal, Stanley. THE MISSOURI. NY: Farrar & Rinehart, 1945. 1st ed. VG in chipped dj. *CONNOLLY & WADE.* $35

Vestal, Stanley. WARPATH AND COUNCIL FIRE. Random, 1948. 1st ed. Fine in Fine dj. *VARNER.* $65

VESTIGES OF THE NATURAL HISTORY OF CREATION. Wiley & Putnam, 1845. 291pp. Head of backstrip repaired, clean tight internally. Good. *BOOKCELL.* $95

Veth, Cornelis. COMIC ART IN ENGLAND. London, 1929. Illus. NF. *POLYANTHOS.* $95

Viardot, Louis. WONDERS OF ITALIAN ART. London: Sampson Low, Son & Marston, 1870. 1st ed. viii,61pp. 9 tipped in actual albumen photos and other illus, one of which is missing. Orig cl, sl rubbed, top and bottom of spine sl frayed, o/w VG. aeg. *WORLDWIDE.* $45

Vickers, Roy. A MURDER FOR A MILLION. London: Herbert Jenkins, 1924. 1st ed. NF w/sunned spine. Not pub in US. *BEASLEY.* $40

Vickers, Roy. THE DEPARTMENT OF DEAD ENDS. NY: Spivak, 1947. 1st ed. Wraps, VG, browning and fragile. *BEASLEY.* $75

Vidal, Gore. A THIRSTY EVIL. NY, 1956. 1st ed. Fine- in same dj. *McCLINTOCK.* $40

Vidal, Gore. EMPIRE. Franklin Center: Franklin Lib, 1987. Leatherbound ltd ed. Signed. *LOPEZ.* $65

Vidal, Gore. HOLLYWOOD. NY: Random House, (1990). 1st ed. Signed. VF in VF dj. *UNGER.* $45

Vidal, Gore. HOLLYWOOD. NY: Random House, (1990). Uncorrected proof. Ptd wraps. VF. *JAFFE.* $65

Vidal, Gore. IN A YELLOW WOOD. NY: Dutton, (1947). 1st ed. Author's second book. NF in NF bright dj, some edge nicks and rubbing. *UNGER.* $225

Vidal, Gore. IN A YELLOW WOOD. NY: Dutton, 1947. trifle dusty, else NF in dj (small chip at foot of spine affecting no lettering). 1st ed. *CHAPEL HILL.* $250

Vidal, Gore. IN A YELLOW WOOD. NY: Dutton, 1947. 1st ed. Heavily foxed on 1st few pages, o/w VG in dj. Signed and dated 1981. *LOPEZ.* $125

Vidal, Gore. ROCKING THE BOAT. Boston: Little Brown, 1962. 1st ed. VG+ in dj w/couple of tiny scrape holes to front panel. Rev copy w/slip laid in. *LAME DUCK.* $75

Vidal, Gore. ROCKING THE BOAT. Little, Brown, 1962. 1st ed. Fine in dj. Signed. *STAHR.* $75

Vidal, Gore. THE CITY AND THE PILLAR. Dutton, 1948. 1st ed. Fine in VG+ dj missing 1/4" strip head of spine. Signed. *STAHR.* $150

Vidal, Gore. THE CITY AND THE PILLAR. NY, 1948. Name. Fine in dj (spine very sl sunned, extremities sl rubbed). *POLYANTHOS.* $150

Vidal, Gore. THE JUDGMENT OF PARIS. Dutton, 1952. 1st ed. NF in a dj rubbed and chipped; internally reinforced. Signed. *STAHR.* $100

Vidal, Gore. THE JUDGMENT OF PARIS. NY: Dutton, 1952. 1st ed. Bookplate on pastedown. Fine, minor rubbing at dj corners. *ELSE FINE.* $150

Vidal, Gore. THE LADIES IN THE LIBRARY AND OTHER STORIES. Helsinki: Eurographica, (1985). 1st ed. Ltd to 350 signed. Ptd wraps. Mint. *JAFFE.* $175

Vidal, Gore. WILLIWAW. NY: Dutton, (1946). 1st ed. Author's first book. Inscribed. VG+ in a VG complete dj with minor nicks and soiling. *UNGER.* $400

Vidal, Gore. WILLIWAW. NY: Dutton, 1946. 1st ed, signed. Orig black cl. Fine in price-clipped dj, sl rubbing. Superb. *CHAPEL HILL.* $600

Viele, Teresa. FOLLOWING THE DRUM. A GLIMPSE OF FRONTIER LIFE. NY, 1858. 1st ed, 1st issue. 256,(7),(1)-4pp. Orig cl, wear to joints, chipped at crown of spine. Howes V92. *GINSBERG.* $250

Viereck, H.L. et al. THE HYRNENOPTERA OR WASP-LIKE INSECTS OF CONNECTICUT. Hartford, 1916. 10 plts. Wrappers chipped, rear wrapper missing, name on cover & title page. *SUTTON.* $65

Viertel, Peter. WHITE HUNTER, BLACK HEART. GC: Doubleday, 1953. 1st ed. VG+ in VG dj. *BERNARD.* $65

Viets, Henry. A BRIEF HISTORY OF MEDICINE IN MASSACHUSETTS. Boston, 1930. *FYE.* $50

Vilimkova, Milada. EGYPTIAN JEWELLERY. London: Paul Hamlyn, (1969). 94 color illus. Dj. Good. *ARCHAEOLOGIA.* $95

Villa, Jose Garcia. FOOTNOTE TO YOUTH. NY: Scribners, 1933. 1st ed. Fine in lightly used dj. 1st book. *BEASLEY.* $150

Villa, Jose Garcia. VOLUME TWO. NY : New Directions, 1949. 1st ed. Inscribed. Fine in lightly used dj. Villa inscriptions uncommon. *BEASLEY.* $125

Villard, Henry. THE PAST AND PRESENT OF THE PIKE'S PEAK GOLD REGIONS. Princeton Univ Press, 1932. 1st prtg. Foldout map. Fine. *AUTHORS OF THE WEST.* $40

Villarejo, Oscar M. DR. KANE'S VOYAGE TO THE POLAR LANDS. Phila: Univ of Pennsylvania, 1965. NF in lightly rubbed dj. *PARMER.* $35

Villiers, A.J. WHALING IN THE FROZEN SOUTH. Indianapolis, (1925). 1st ed, 292pp. VG. *ARTIS.* $27.50

Villiers, A.J. WHALING IN THE FROZEN SOUTH. Indianapolis: Bobbs-Merrill Company, c. 1925. Covers faded and showing wear, some very light foxing. *PARMER.* $50

Villiers, A.J. WHALING IN THE FROZEN SOUTH. Indianapolis: The Bobbs-Merrill Co. (1925). 1st ed. Frontis portrait, 42 plts. Grn cloth, gilt. Dj chipped in a few places. *KARMIOLE.* $75

Villiers, Alan. WHALERS OF THE MIDNIGHT SUN. NY, 1934. 1st ed. VG. *ARTIS.* $17.50

Vince, S. THE ELEMENTS OF ASTRONOMY. Phila: Kimber & Conrad, 1811, 1st US ed, corrected, enl. Rebound in modern leather, red spine label, new eps; some spotting, browning pgs, pencil notes. 1 fldg plt. *KNOLLWOOD.* $150

Vincent, Frank. ACTUAL AFRICA, OR THE COMING CONTINENT. NY: Appleton, 1895. 1st ed. xxiii,541pp. Near Good ex-lib. *WORLDWIDE.* $28

Vincent, Frank. THROUGH AND THROUGH THE TROPICS. NY: Harper & Brothers, 1876. 304pp, 2pp ads, 4pp pub cat. 1st ed. Grn cl stamped in black, somewhat worn. Some internal stains. *SCHOYER'S.* $30

Vincenz, Stanislaw. ON THE HIGH UPLANDS. NY: Roy, (1955). Trans H.C. Stevens. 1st US ed. VG+ in VG- dj. *AARD.* $25

Vine, Barbara (pseud of Ruth Rendell). A DARK-ADAPTED EYE. Author's 1st book as Barbara Vine. London: Viking, 1986. 1st ed. Remainder mark on pastedown endpaper, else Fine, tiny tear at dj corner. *ELSE FINE.* $35

Vinge, Joan. SNOW QUEEN. Dial, 1980. 1st ed. VG in dj. *MADLE.* $65

Viola, Herman J. THE INDIAN LEGACY OF CHARLES BIRD KING. Washington: Smithsonian, 1976. 1st ed. 152pp. About Fine in NF dj. *CONNOLLY & WADE.* $45

Viola, Herman J. THE NATIONAL ARCHIVES OF THE UNITED STATES. NY: Abrams, (1984). 1st (?) ed. Fine in Fine dj. *AARD.* $30

Viola, Herman J. THOMAS L. MCKENNEY...Chicago: Sage-Swallow, (1974). 1st ed. VF in VF dj. *OREGON.* $35

Virchow, Rudolf. COLLECTED ESSAYS ON PUBLIC HEALTH AND EPIDEMIOLOGY. Canton, MA, 1985. 1st Eng trans. 2 vols. 619, 614pp. Djs. *FYE.* $100

VIRGINIA: A GUIDE TO THE OLD DOMINION. Oxford Univ Press, (1940). 1st ed. WPA guide. Map in end pocket. VG. *BOOK BROKER.* $35

VISIT TO THE CIRCUS. NY: McLoughlin Bros, n.d. (c. 1890). Large 8vo; orig chromolitho covers; spine worn and stitched; 14 chromolitho pages. VG. *DRAMATIS PERSONAE.* $100

VISIT TO THE CIRCUS. NY: McLoughlin Bros. n.d. Color pict self-wraps (creased, 2 sm tears, spine re-stitched). 8 leaves sl creased. VG. *BLUE MOUNTAIN.* $100

Visscher, William L. A THRILLING AND TRUTHFUL HISTORY OF THE PONY EXPRESS. Chicago: Rand McNally, (1908). 1st ed. Pict cl, spine type rubbed, some soiling. *SCHOYER'S.* $40

Visscher, William L. A THRILLING AND TRUTHFUL HISTORY OF THE PONY EXPRESS...Chicago: Chas. Powner, 1946. 2nd ed. Fine in G+ dj. *OREGON.* $35

Vittorini, Elio. IN SICILY. Norwalk, CT, (1949). Stated 1st ed. Fine in VG dj. *BOND.* $18.50

Vittorini, Elio. IN SICILY. NY: New Directions, 1949. 1st ed. In dj. Traces of removed tape inside cvrs and dj flap edges. *POLYANTHOS.* $25

Vivian, Herbert. TUNISIA AND THE MODERN BARBARY PIRATES. NY: Longman, Green & Co., 1899. xvi+341pp. Fldg map. Sl rubbed & soiled, o/w VG ex-lib. *WORLDWIDE.* $25

Vivian, Herbert. TUNISIA AND THE MODERN BARBARY PIRATES. NY: Longmans, Green, 1899. Fldg map. Faded. Ex-lib. *SCHOYER'S.* $20

Vizenor, Gerald Robert. SUMMER IN THE SPRING. (Minneapolis): Nodin Press, (1965). 1st ed. *LOPEZ.* $150

Vizenor, Gerald. EARTHDIVERS. Minneapolis: Univ of MN Press, (1981). 1st ed. Fine in VG dj. *LOPEZ.* $45

Vizenor, Gerald. THE EVERLASTING SKY. NY: Crowell-Collier, (1972). Fine in NF, price-clipped dj. *LOPEZ.* $35

Vizenor, Gerald. THE HEIRS OF COLUMBUS. Hanover: Wesleyan Univ Press, (1991). Adv rev copy. Fine in Fine dj. *LOPEZ.* $35

Vizenor, Gerald. THE TRICKSTER OF LIBERTY. TRIBAL HEIRS TO A WILD BARONAGE. Minneapolis: Univ of MN Press, (1981). Adv rev copy. Fine in wrappers. *LOPEZ.* $35

Vizetelly, Henry. A HISTORY OF CHAMPAGNE WITH NOTES ON THE OTHER SPARKLING WINES OF FRANCE. London: H. Sotheran & Co, 1882. 263pp,index,ads. 350 engrs. Worn at ends; fep, frontis loose. Shaken, Good. *CULLEN.* $185

Vliet, R.G. THE MAN WITH THE BLACK MOUTH. (Santa Cruz: Kayak, 1970). 1st ed. One of 1000. Faint crease on rear wrap, else Fine in very sl soiled wrappers. Scarce. *BETWEEN COVERS.* $100

Vogel, Joseph. AT MADAME BONNARD'S. NY: Knopf, 1935. 1st ed. Fine in worn dj w/small chips and tears. *BEASLEY.* $50

Vogel, Joseph. MAN'S COURAGE. NY: Knopf, 1938. 1st ed. Close to Fine in NF dj w/a few short tears. Uncommon. *BEASLEY.* $125

Vogel, Julius. THE PATHOLOGICAL ANATOMY OF THE HUMAN BODY. London: H. Balliere, 1847. Trans by George E. Day and L.M. Cantab. Full lea prize binding, marbled edges. Extrems worn, bkpl. Good. *KNOLLWOOD.* $150

Vogel, Virgil. AMERICAN INDIAN MEDICINE. Norman, 1977. 1st ed. Dj. *FYE.* $90

Vogel, Virgil. AMERICAN INDIAN MEDICINE. Univ of OK, (1970). 1st ed. VF in VG dj. *OREGON.* $45

Voight, David Quentin. AMERICAN BASEBALL. Univ of OK Press, 1968 & 1970. 2 vols.: Vol. 1, 2nd prtg; vol. 2, 1st ed. Fine in Fine dj. 2 vol. set. *PLAPINGER.* $75

Voigt, Charles A. FAMOUS GENTLEMEN RIDERS. London: Hutchinson, n.d. (1930). Minor shelfwear, else VG. *OLD LONDON.* $50

Volavkova, Hana. ...I NEVER SAW ANOTHER BUTTERFLY, CHILDREN'S DRAWINGS & POEMS FROM THE THERESIENSTADT CONCENTRATION CAMP 1942-1944. McGraw-Hill, 1962. 2nd ed. VG+. Browning to cvr lower edge. Dj (edgewear, corner chip, skinned patch, but VG). *BEBBAH.* $25

Vollmann, William T. YOU BRIGHT AND RISEN ANGELS. (London): Andre Deutsch, (1987). 1st ed, 1st book. NF in Fine dj. *ROBBINS.* $65

Vollmann, William T. YOU BRIGHT AND RISEN ANGELS. Deutsch, 1987. 1st Eng ed. Eng ed precedes Amer ed. Fine in dj. *LAME DUCK.* $75

Volonakis, Michael D. THE ISLAND OF ROSES AND HER ELEVEN SISTERS....London, 1922. Uncut. *O'NEILL.* $60

Volpe, Edmond. A READER'S GUIDE TO WILLIAM FAULKNER. NY: FS&Co, (1964). 1st ed. Pgs browning, else Fine (owner sig) in dj. *CAPTAIN'S BOOKSHELF.* $40

Voltaire. THE HISTORY OF ZADIG, OR, DESTINY. Gilt-decorated cl, tissue dj, slipcase. Paris: LEC, 1952. One of 1500 ptd by Priester Freres, illus by Duval, hand-coloring by Girardot. Fine. *JAFFE.* $100

Von Bothmer, Dietrich. THE AMASIS PAINTER AND HIS WORLD. NY: Thames and Hudson, (1985). 8 color plts. *ARCHAEOLOGIA.* $85

von Braun, Werner & Frederick I. Ordway III. NEW WORLDS...OUR SOLAR SYSTEM. GC, NY: Anchor Press/Doubleday, 1979, 1st ed. VG in maroon cl; scuff marks. *KNOLLWOOD.* $35

von Braun, Wernher et al. MOON, MAN'S GREATEST ADVENTURE. NY: Harry N. Abrams, n.d. but 1970. VG in sl worn & chipped dj. Small waterstain on dj. *KNOLLWOOD.* $200

Von Hagen, Victor W. FREDERICK CATHERWOOD ARCH. NY: Oxford Univ Press, 1950. 1st ed. Color frontis. Chipped dj. *SILVER.* $30

Von Hagen, Victor W. HIGHWAY OF THE SUN. A SEARCH FOR THE ROYAL ROADS OF THE INCAS. NY: Duell, Sloan and Pearce, (1955). 1st ed. 4 maps. Dj. Good. *ARCHAEOLOGIA.* $25

Von Hagen, Victor W. ROADS THAT LED TO ROME. Cleveland and NY: World Pub Co., (1967). Dj. *SCHOYER'S.* $20

Von Hagen, Victor W. THE AZTEC AND MAYA PAPERMAKERS. NY: J.J. Augustin, (1944). 1st trade ed. Dard Hunter (intro). Frontis, 39 photo plts in back. 1st trade ed. Fine in dj. *CULLEN.* $125

Von Hagen, Victor W. THE DESERT KINGDOMS OF PERU. Greenwich, CT: NY Graphic Soc. (1964). 1st ed. Dj. Fine. *KARMIOLE.* $45

Von Hagen, Victor W. THE GOLDEN MAN: A QUEST FOR EL DORADO. London: Book Club, (1974). 12 color illus. Inscription. Dj. Good. *ARCHAEOLOGIA.* $25

von Harbou, Thea. ROCKET TO THE MOON. World-Wide, 1930. 1st US ed. VG. *MADLE.* $60

Von Keith, J.H. VON KEITH'S WESTWARD OR 1000 ITEMS ON THE WONDERS AND CURIOSITIES OF SOUTHERN CALIFORNIA. LA: J.W. Grn & Co, (1887). xiv,100pp, 6 5/8" x 4 3/8". Ptd wraps, tail of spine cracked. *DAWSON'S.* $600

von Nebesky-Wojkowitz, Rene. WHERE THE GODS ARE MOUNTAINS. NY: Reynal & Co, (1956 or 57). VG in G dj. *BLUE DRAGON.* $35

Von Rosentiel, Helen. AMERICAN RUGS AND CARPETS. NY: William Morrow & Co, Inc, 1978. Corners bumped. VG in dj. BACKROOM. $35

Von Winning, Hasso. PRE-COLUMBIAN ART OF MEXICO AND CENTRAL AMERICA. NY: Harry N. Abrams. (1968). 1st ed. Dj. Fine. KARMIOLE. $275

Von Winning, Hasso. PRE-COLUMBIAN ART OF MEXICO AND CENTRAL AMERICA. NY: Abrams. (1968). 590 photogr plts, 5 maps, 1 table. Ltd to 1800 numbered, this being one of 100 Roman numeral copies reserved for bksellers, and signed. Full grn morocco, gilt. Fine in pub slipcase. KARMIOLE. $500

von Wuthenau, Alexander. TERRACOTTA POTTERY IN PRE-COLUMBIAN CENTRAL AND SOUTH AMERICA. NY: Greystone, 1965. 1st ed. NF in NF dj. CONNOLLY & WADE. $35

von Ziemssen, H. (ed). DISEASES OF THE BRAIN AND ITS MEMBRANES. NY, 1877. 1st Eng trans. FYE. $65

Vonnegut, Kurt. BETWEEN TIME AND TIMBUKTU. (NY): Delacorte, (1972). 1st ed. Fine in price clipped dj. Signed by Vonnegut. CAPTAIN'S BOOKSHELF. $200

Vonnegut, Kurt. BLUEBEARD. Delacorte, 1987. 1st ed. One of 500 numbered, signed. As New in slipcase. MADLE. $100

Vonnegut, Kurt. BLUEBEARD. Delacorte, 1987. Uncorrected proof. VF, wraps. STAHR. $50

Vonnegut, Kurt. BLUEBEARD. NY, (1987). 1st ed. Fine in dj. Signed. CAPTAIN'S BOOKSHELF. $60

Vonnegut, Kurt. BREAKFAST OF CHAMPIONS. (NY): Delacorte, 1973. 1st ed. Sl bumped o/w Fine in NF dj. ARCHER. $45

Vonnegut, Kurt. GALAPAGOS. Franklin Center: Franklin Library, 1985. Ltd ed. Fine in Franklin leather. Signed. CAPTAIN'S BOOKSHELF. $50

Vonnegut, Kurt. HOCUS POCUS. Franklin Center: Franklin Lib, 1990. Leatherbound ltd 1st ed. Signed. Fine. LOPEZ. $100

Vonnegut, Kurt. HOCUS POCUS. Putnam's, 1990. Uncorrected proof. VF in gold wraps. STAHR. $50

Vonnegut, Kurt. JAILBIRD. NY: Delacorte, (1979). 1st trade ed. Fine in price clipped dj. Signed. CAPTAIN'S BOOKSHELF. $75

Vonnegut, Kurt. MOTHER NIGHT. Greenwich, CT, 1962. 1st ed, pb orig. Gold Medal s1191. Price on ep, some spine slant, else VG in bit worn wrappers. PETTLER. $30

Vonnegut, Kurt. MOTHER NIGHT. NY: Harper, (1966). 1st hardcvr ed w/new intro by Vonnegut. Owner sig. Fine in dj w/sm tear. CAPTAIN'S BOOKSHELF. $125

Vonnegut, Kurt. PALM SUNDAY. NY: Delacorte, (1981). 1st ed. Fine in dj. Signed. CAPTAIN'S BOOKSHELF. $75

Vonnegut, Kurt. PLAYER PIANO. Scribner's, 1952. 1st ed. About Fine in dj (sl chipped; browned on spine). STAHR. $300

Vonnegut, Kurt. SLAPSTICK. Delacorte, 1976. One of 250, signed & numbered. VF in slipcase. STAHR. $125

Vonnegut, Kurt. SLAUGHTERHOUSE FIVE OR THE CHILDREN'S CRUSADE. NY: Delacorte, (1969). 1st ed. Attractive, NF in like dj. CAPTAIN'S BOOKSHELF. $150

Vonnegut, Kurt. SLAUGHTERHOUSE-FIVE. (NY): SL/Delacorte, (1969). 1st ed. NF in sl spine-darkened but still NF dj. LOPEZ. $300

Vonnegut, Kurt. THE SIRENS OF TITAN. NY: Dell, (1959). 1st ed, pb orig. Orig pict wraps. VG to NF showing only lt expected wear. CHAPEL HILL. $75

Vonnegut, Kurt. THE SIRENS OF TITAN. Dell, 1959. 1st ed. VG in wraps. MADLE. $50

Vonnegut, Kurt. THE SIRENS OF TITAN. NY: Dell First Edition, 1959. Paperback orig. Wraps. Fine but for few light rubs to spine. BEASLEY. $50

Vonnegut, Kurt. WAMPETERS, FOMA & GRANFALLOONS. NY, 1974. 1st ed. Fine in dj. PETTLER. $35

Vonnegut, Kurt. WAMPETERS FOMA & GRANFALLOONS. NY: Delacorte, (1974). 1st ed. Fine in sl edge rubbed dj. Signed. CAPTAIN'S BOOKSHELF. $100

Voplcka, Charles J. SECRETS OF THE BALKANS. Chicago: Rand McNally, 1921. SCHOYER'S. $25.

Vorpahl, Ben Merchant. MY DEAR WISTER...Palo Alto: American West Pub Co, 1973. 2nd prtg. NF in VG dj. PARMER. $30

Vorse, Mary Heaton. I'VE COME TO STAY. NY: Century, 1918. 1st ed. Spine sl cocked and sunned, o/w NF. BEASLEY. $60

Vorse, Mary Heaton. STRIKE! NY: Liveright, 1930. 1st ed. Owner's name. NF in bit used dj w/creases. BEASLEY. $185

Vorse, Mary Heaton. TIME AND THE TOWN, A PROVINCETOWN CHRONICLE. NY: Dial, 1942. 1st ed. Inscribed. Fine but for sl cocked spine, in sl chipped, sl torn dj. BEASLEY. $150

Vought, John G. TREATISE ON BOWEL COMPLAINTS. Rochester, NY: Ptd for the author by E. Peck & Co., 1828. 1st ed. 216pp. Contemp calf covers worn, outer hinge cracked, interior foxed. Tight. DIAMOND. $75

Vyner, Robert T. (revised by William Blew). NOTITIA VENATICA. London: John C. Nimmo, 1892. A "New" ed, complete in one vol. Rebacked with orig spine strip laid down, corners with recent reinforcement, 12 hand colored illustrations, some small tears, chips and edgewear, but still G+. OLD LONDON. $150

W

Waber, Bernard. IRA SLEEPS OVER. Houghton Mifflin, (1972). Near 4to. 48pp. Illus by author. Fine in Fine dj. Inscribed. BEBBAH. $25

Wace, Alan J.B. and Frank H. Stubbings. A COMPANION TO HOMER. London: Macmillan, (1970). 69 figs, 40 plts. Signature at flyleaf. Dj. Good. ARCHAEOLOGIA. $125

Wace, Alan J.B. MYCENAE. AN ARCHAEOLOGICAL HISTORY AND GUIDE. Princeton: Princeton Univ Press. 1949. 1st ed. 2 fldg plans. Cloth bit soiled. KARMIOLE. $45

Waddell, Joseph A. ANNALS OF AUGUSTA COUNTY, VIRGINIA, WITH REMINISCENCES...A DIARY OF THE WAR...A CHAPTER ON RECONSTRUCTION. Richmond: Jones, 1886. 1st ed. (8),374pp. 2 maps, 1 fldg. Orig cl, paper label on spine, bkpl removed, inner hinges strengthened. Howes W2. With the supplement, Richmond, 1888. (2),381-492pp. Old cl, small paper label on spine, bkpl removed. GINSBERG. $200

Waddell, L.A. THE INDO-SUMERIAN SEALS DECIPHERED. London: Luzac & Co. 1925. 1st ed. Dj sl torn. KARMIOLE. $50

Waddington, C.H. BEHIND APPEARANCES—A STUDY OF THE RELATIONS BETWEEN PAINTING AND THE NATURAL SCIENCES. Cambridge, MA: MIT Press, (1970,69). 1st US ed. 71 tipped color plts. AARD. $60

Wade, Blanche. ANT VENTURES. Rand McNally, (1924). 1st ed. 246pp. Illus Harrison Cady. Slight wear to color cvr pict & edgewear but VG. BEBBAH. $40

Wade, Henry. GOLD WAS OUR GRAVE. London: Constable, 1954. 1st ed. Review clipping on fep o/w VG in dj w/3/4" missing at top of front panel, internal tape repairs and several closed tears. MORDIDA. $25

Waer, Jack. 17 AND BLACK. Viking, 1954. 1st ed. VG or better in lightly worn dj. STAHR. $20

Wafer, Lionel. A NEW VOYAGE AND DESCRIPTION OF THE ISTHMUS OF AMERICA. Rprtd from orig ed of 1699. George Parker Winship (ed). Cleveland: The Burrows Brothers Co. 1902. 2 fldg maps; 3 fldg plts. Ltd to 500 numbered. *KARMIOLE.* $75

Wafer, Lionel. A NEW VOYAGE AND DESCRIPTION OF THE ISTHMUS OF AMERICA. Cleveland: The Burrows Brothers Co, 1903. 1/500. George Parker Winship (ed). Spotted cvrs, interior foxing. Rprnt from orig 1699 ed. Black cl. 3 fldg plts, 2 fldg maps. *PARMER.* $95

Wagenheim, Kal. BABE RUTH—HIS LIFE AND LEGEND. Praeger, 1974. 1st ed. Fine in VG dj. *PLAPINGER.* $35

Wagenknecht, Edward. MARK TWAIN: THE MAN AND HIS WORK. Norman: Univ of OK, (1961). 1st rev, enl ed. NF in dj. *CAPTAIN'S BOOKSHELF.* $25

Wager, Richard. GOLDEN WHEELS. Cleveland: Western Reserve Hist Soc, 1975. 1st ed. NF in VG dj. *ARCHER.* $40

Wager, Walter. VIPER THREE. NY: Macmillan, 1971. 1st ed. NF. *SMITH.* $20

WAGGLES. A Nodding Head Book. Holland, (1950s). 4 illus, each w/spring mounted head. Moveable bk. *BOOKFINDERS INTL.* $90

Wagner, F. Hol, Jr. "THE COLORADO ROAD," HISTORY, MOTIVE POWER & EQUIPMENT OF...AND DENVER RAILWAYS. (Denver: Intermountain Chapter, National Railway Hist Soc, 1970.) Cl, dj. Slipcased, 11.5 X 9". #216 of 1000, signed. Fine. *BOHLING.* $85

Wagner, Henry R. BULLION TO BOOKS. LA: The Zamorano Club, 1942. 1st ed. One of 300. Frontis portrait, plts. Fine. *WREDEN.* $325

Wagner, Henry R. JUAN RODRIGUEZ CABRILLO: DISCOVERER OF THE COAST OF CALIFORNIA. SF: CA Hist Soc, 1941. One of 750 ptd by Lawton Kennedy. Dec boards w/linen spine, paper spine label, tips sl bumped. *DAWSON'S.* $90

Wagner, Henry R. SPANISH EXPLORATIONS IN THE STRAIT OF JUAN DE FUCA. Santa Ana: Fine Arts Press, 1933. 1st ed. Maps and plans (some fldg). VG. *PARMER.* $600

Wagner, Henry R. with Helen Rand Parish. THE LIFE AND WRITINGS OF BARTOLOME DE LAS CASAS. Albuquerque: Univ of NM Press, 1967. 1st ed. Purple cl. VG in rubbed dj. *PARMER.* $75

Wagner, Jack R. SHORT LINE JUNCTION, A COLLECTION OF CALIFORNIA- NEVADA RAILROADS. Fresno: Academy Library Guild, 1956. Sm chip in jacket along fore-edge. Fine in leatherette dj. *BOHLING.* $60

Wagner, Karl Edward. WHY NOT YOU AND I? Arlington Heights: Dark Harvest, 1987. 1st ed, trade issue. Fine in Fine dj. *OTHER WORLDS.* $35

Wagner, Richard. THE RING OF THE NIBELUNG. NY: GC, (1939). Rprt. 24 color plts by Arthur Rackham. Cl dusty, sl soiled, o/w Good, sound. *ARTIS.* $45

Wagner, Richard. THE STORY OF BAYREUTH AS TOLD IN THE LETTERS OF RICHARD WAGNER. Boston, 1912. Ed by C.V.Kerr.NF.*POLYANTHOS.* $60

Wagoner, David. A PLACE TO STAND. Bloomington: Indiana Univ Press, 1958. 1st ed. NF in like dj. *CAPTAIN'S BOOKSHELF.* $100

Wagoner, David. NEW AND SELECTED POEMS. Bloomington: Indiana Univ Press, 1969. 1st ed. Pub's comp card laid in. Fine in Fine dj but for 1" tear front panel. *BEASLEY.* $35

Wagoner, David. SLEEPING IN THE WOODS. Bloomington: Indiana Univ Press, 1974. 1st ed. Pub's comp card laid in. Fine in Fine dj. *BEASLEY.* $35

Wagoner, David. STAYING ALIVE. 1st ed. Bloomington: Indiana Univ Press, 1966. Fine in Fine dj. *BEASLEY.* $35

Wainwright, John. DEATH IN A SLEEPING CITY. London: Collins Crime Club, 1965. 1st ed, 1st book. Fine in dj. *MORDIDA.* $35

Wainwright, Nicholas. PAINTINGS AND MINIATURES AT THE HISTORICAL SOCIETY OF PENNSYLVANIA. Phila: Hist Soc of PA, 1974. 1st ed. NF in NF dj. *BACKROOM.* $40

Waite, Arthur (ed). THE WORKS OF THOMAS VAUGHN: EUGENIUS PHILALETHES. London: Theosophical Pub House, 1919. 1st ed. Frontis. Gilt top edge, raised bands, spine label. VG. Rare. *BLUE DRAGON.* $250

Wakefield, Dan. ISLAND IN THE CITY. THE WORLD OF SPANISH HARLEM. Boston: Houghton Mifflin, 1959. 1st ed, 1st book. Fine in NF dj. *ROBBINS.* $35

Wakefield, Edward. NEW ZEALAND AFTER FIFTY YEARS. London: Cassell & Co., 1889. Fldg map. Some wear edges of spine, minimal foxing at preliminaries, overall VG. *PARMER.* $125

Wakefield, H.R. THE CLOCK STRIKES TWELVE. Sauk City: Arkham House, 1946. 1st ed, ltd to 4040. Fine in NF dj with sunning to rear panel. *ROBBINS.* $45

Wakefield, John A. HISTORY OF THE WAR BETWEEN THE UNITED STATES AND THE SAC AND FOX NATIONS OF INDIANS. Jacksonville, IL: ptd by Calvin Goudy, 1834. x,142pp. Contemp, later owner inscrips on front pastedown and ep; some underlining on title pg. Orig 3/4 leather w/marbled boards; marbling cracked and very worn in places, some old tape repairs evident; rear board cracked. Foxing. Good, scarce. Howes W-19. *SCHOYER'S.* $600

Wakefield, John A. WAKEFIELD'S HISTORY OF THE BLACK HAWK WAR: A REPRINT OF THE FIRST EDITION...PREFACE AND NOTES BY FRANK E. STEVENS. Chicago: Caxton, 1908. One of 200 ptd. 13 photogr plts. Orig vellum backed blue boards. Howes W19. Contains facs reprt of 1834 orig. *GINSBERG.* $250

Wakefield, Priscilla. EXCURSIONS IN NORTH AMERICA....London: Darton & Harvey, 1806. 1st ed. (xii),420,(iv). Contemp calf, hinge little worn. Fldg map. VG. Howes W-21. *SECOND LIFE.* $425

Wakefield, Priscilla. INSTINCT DISPLAYED....London: Darton and Harvey, 1814. 2nd ed. Modern boards w/paper label, new eps. *SECOND LIFE.* $85

Wakeman, Edgar. THE LOG OF AN ANCIENT MARINER. BEING THE LIFE AND ADVENTURES OF CAPTAIN EDGAR WAREMAN. SF: Bancroft, 1878. 378pp + frontis port, 4pp ads. Orig pict gilt stamped cloth. Howes W23. 1st ed. Fine. *OREGON.* $225

Wakoski, Diane. COINS AND COFFINS. (NY): Hawk's Well, (1962). 1st ed of author's 1st bk. Contemp presentation inscrip from author. VG in wrappers. *LOPEZ.* $125

Wakoski, Diane. COINS AND COFFINS. NY: Hawk's Well Press, 1962. 1st ed. Wraps. Fine w/only minor rubs. *BEASLEY.* $85

Wakoski, Diane. MAKING A SACHER TORTE. 1/4 leather & boards. Mt. Horeb: Perishable Press, 1981. 1st ed. Ltd to 225. VF. *JAFFE.* $250

Wakoski, Diane. ON BARBARA'S SHORE. LA: Black Sparrow, 1971. 1/404 sewn in wraps. Fine. *BEASLEY.* $25

Wakoski, Diane. SATURN'S RINGS. NY: Targ Editions, (1982). 1st ed. 1/250 signed. Fine. *JUVELIS.* $75

Wakoski, Diane. THE MOTORCYCLE BETRAYAL POEMS. NY: S&S, (1971). 1st ed. Fine in dj. *CAPTAIN'S BOOKSHELF.* $50

Wakoski, Diane. THE MOTORCYCLE BETRAYAL POEMS. NY: Simon & Schuster, 1971. 1st ed. Fine; crease at dj front flap. *ELSE FINE.* $40

Walcot, W. ARCHITECTURAL WATER-COLOURS & ETCHINGS OF W. WALCOT. NY, London: H.C. Dickins and Technical Journals, 1919. 1st ed. Bkpl. VG. *WEBER.* $75

Walcott, Derek. DREAM ON MONKEY MOUNTAIN. NY: Farrar Straus Giroux, (1970). Fine in NF dj. *LOPEZ.* $35

Walcott, Derek. DREAM ON MONKEY MOUNTAIN. NY: Farrar Straus Giroux, (1970). 1st ed. NF in dj. Inscribed. *LOPEZ.* $100

Walcott, Derek. POEMS OF THE CARIBBEAN. (NY): (LEC), (1983). One of 2000 numbered, signed by author and Romare Bearden, the artist, w/orig litho by him. Sl dust soiling, o/w NF in slipcase. *LOPEZ.* $400

Walcott, Derek. SELECTED POEMS. NY: Farrar Straus, (1964). 1st ed. Signed in 1978. Prev owner name on front pastedown, o/w Fine in NF, price-clipped dj. *LOPEZ.* $125

Walcott, Derek. SELECTED POEMS. NY: Farrar, Straus & Co., (1964). 1st ed. Fine in dj w/negligible wear. Inscribed. *BETWEEN COVERS.* $275

Walcott, Derek. SELECTED POEMS. NY: Farrar Straus & Giroux, (1964). 1st ed. Fine in very lightly used dj. Signed. *CAPTAIN'S BOOKSHELF.* $150

Walcott, Derek. THE FORTUNATE TRAVELLER. Poems. NY: FS&G, (1981). 1st ed. Fine in dj. Review copy, slip promo material laid in. Inscribed. *CAPTAIN'S BOOKSHELF.* $100

Walcott, Derek. THE GULF. London: Cape, (1969). 1st ed. Fine in NF dj. *LOPEZ.* $85

Walden, Arthur T. A DOG-PUNCHER ON THE YUKON. Boston, 1931. Not 1st ed. VG. *ARTIS.* $20

Waldman, Anne and Ted Berrigan. MEMORIAL DAY. NY: Poetry Project, 1971. 1st ed. Fine in wraps. *BEASLEY.* $30

Waldman, Frank. THE RETURN OF THE PINK PANTHER. London: Barker, 1977. 1st Brit hardcover ed. Fine in dj. *SILVER DOOR.* $22.50

Waldman, Milton. AMERICANA. NY, 1925. NF. *POLYANTHOS.* $75

Waldo, Anna Lee. SACAJAWEA. (NY): Avon, (1979). Pb orig. NF in wrappers. *LOPEZ.* $40

Waldo, Frank. MODERN METEOROLOGY. London: Walter Scott, 1893. Good in maroon cl, bright gilt titling; corners bumped, worn, extremity wear, pencil marks, bkpl. Nice. *KNOLLWOOD.* $40

Waldo, Fullerton. THE SAGA OF A SUPER CARGO. THE RECORD OF A VOYAGE TO GREENLAND. Phila, (1926). Dj edgeworn. *ARTIS.* $17.50

Waldschmidt, Ernst and Rose Leonore. NEPAL. NY: Universe Books, (1970). 1st Amer ed. 82 plts. Light sun fading on cover edges, else VG+ in VG dj. *BLUE DRAGON.* $55

Wales, Philip. REPORT ON YELLOW FEVER IN THE U.S.S. PLYMOUTH IN 1878-9. Washington, 1880. 1st ed. 6 heliotype photo plts. Scarce. *FYE.* $150

Waley, Arthur (trans). A HUNDRED AND SEVENTY CHINESE POEMS. London: Constable, 1918. 1st ed. Signed. Cl-backed boards. Sm stain front cvr, o/w Fine. *JAFFE.* $250

Waley, Arthur. THE POETRY AND CAREER OF LI PO. London: Allen & Unwin, (1950). 1st ed. VG in G dj. *BLUE DRAGON.* $17.50

Walker, A. Earl (ed). THE LATE EFFECTS OF HEAD INJURY. Springfield, 1969. Dj. *FYE.* $100

Walker, A. Earl. POSTTRAUMATIC EPILEPSY. Springfield, 1949. 1st ed. Dj. Very Scarce. *FYE.* $100

Walker, A. Earle. PENICILLIN IN NEUROLOGY. Springfield, 1946. 1st ed. Dj. *FYE.* $125

Walker, Alexander. INTERMARRIAGE: OR THE MODE IN WHICH, AND THE CAUSES WHY BEAUTY, HEALTH, AND INTELLECT, RESULT FROM CERTAIN UNIONS, AND DEFORMITY DISEASE AND INSANITY, FROM OTHERS. NY, 1839. 1st Amer ed. 384pp. *FYE.* $75

Walker, Alice. GOOD NIGHT, WILLIE LEE, I'LL SEE YOU IN THE MORNING. (NY): (Dial), (1979). Uncorrected proof. Bound w/black tape spine (generally an indication that not many copies were done). Fine in wraps. *LOPEZ.* $950

Walker, Alice. GOOD NIGHT, WILLIE LEE, I'LL SEE YOU IN THE MORNING. (London): Women's Press, (1987). 1st UK ed. Fine in wrappers. *ROBBINS.* $25

Walker, Alice. GOOD NIGHT WILLIE LEE, I'LL SEE YOU IN THE MORNING. NY: Dial, (1979). 1st trade ed, this being the issue in wrappers. Fine. *LOPEZ.* $50

Walker, Alice. GOODNIGHT, WILLIE LEE, I'LL SEE YOU IN THE MORNING: POEMS. NY: Dial, (1979). 1st ed. Fine in dj. *CAPTAIN'S BOOKSHELF.* $375

Walker, Alice. HER BLUE BODY EVERYTHING WE KNOW. Harcourt Brace Jovanovich, (1991). 1st ed. Signed. Fine in Fine dj. *BEBBAH.* $40

Walker, Alice. HORSES MAKE A LANDSCAPE LOOK MORE BEAUTIFUL. NY: HBJ, 1984. 1st ed. VF in dj. *ELSE FINE.* $40

Walker, Alice. IN LOVE & IN TROUBLE. STORIES OF BLACK WOMEN. NY: Harcourt Brace & Jovanovich, (1973). 1st ed. Fine in dj. *CAPTAIN'S BOOKSHELF.* $500

Walker, Alice. IN LOVE AND TROUBLE. STORIES OF BLACK WOMEN. NY: Harcourt, Brace Jovanovich, (1973). 1st ed. Fine in Fine dj. *LOPEZ.* $500

Walker, Alice. IN SEARCH OF OUR MOTHER'S GARDENS. NY: Harcourt, (1983). 1st ed. Signed. Fine in Fine dj. *UNGER.* $100

Walker, Alice. IN SEARCH OF OUR MOTHERS' GARDENS. San Diego: Harcourt Brace & Jovanovich, (1983). Uncorrected proof, Fine in wraps. *CAPTAIN'S BOOKSHELF.* $200

Walker, Alice. LANGSTON HUGHES, AMERICAN POET. NY: Crowell, 1974. 1st ed. Rmdr mark bottom edge. Fine in dj. Scarce. *LAME DUCK.* $850

Walker, Alice. LANGSTON HUGHES, AMERICAN POET. NY: Crowell, (1974). Don Miller (illus). NF (tiny scrape on front board and bit of rippling to rear board; sm red spot on bottom pp edges), o/w Fine in Fine dj. *LOPEZ.* $850

Walker, Alice. MERIDIAN. NY: Harcourt, (1976). 1st ed. Fine in dj. *CAPTAIN'S BOOKSHELF.* $175

Walker, Alice. MERIDIAN. NY: Harcourt Brace Jovanovich, (1976). Adv rev copy. Cheap paper pages and dj browning; couple of tiny spots to top pp edges, o/w Fine in Fine dj w/minute wear at crown. *LOPEZ.* $275

Walker, Alice. ONCE. NY: Harcourt, Brace & World, (1968). 1st ed. Orig cl-backed boards. VG in dj. Signed on half-title. *CHAPEL HILL.* $1000

Walker, Alice. ONCE: POEMS. NY: HB&W, (1968). 1st ed, 1st bk. Fine in dj (trace of rubbing, tiny tear). Superior copy. *CAPTAIN'S BOOKSHELF.* $750

Walker, Alice. REVOLUTIONARY PETUNIAS & OTHER POEMS. NY: Harcourt Brace & Jovanovich, (1973). 1st ed. Fine in dj. *CAPTAIN'S BOOKSHELF.* $500

Walker, Alice. THE COLOR PURPLE. (London): Women's Press, (1986). 1st UK hardcover ed. NF in like dj. *ROBBINS.* $65

Walker, Alice. THE COLOR PURPLE. (London): Women's Press, (1986). 1st Eng hb ed. Fine in Fine dj. *LOPEZ.* $75

Walker, Alice. The COLOR PURPLE. NY: Harcourt, (1982). 1st ed. Fine in dj, tiny tear. Walker's clipped sig tipped in. *CAPTAIN'S BOOKSHELF.* $450

Walker, Alice. THE COLOR PURPLE. NY: HBJ, (1982). 1st ed. VF in dj. *LOPEZ.* $450

Walker, Alice. THE TEMPLE OF MY FAMILIAR. Harcourt Brace Jovanovich, 1989. Advance reading copy. Fine in dec wraps. *STAHR.* $35

Walker, Alice. THE TEMPLE OF MY FAMILIAR. San Diego & NY: Harcourt Brace Jovanovich, (1989). 1st ed. Inscribed. Orig cl-backed boards. As New in dj. *CHAPEL HILL.* $50

Walker, Alice. THE TEMPLE OF MY FAMILIAR. San Diego: HBJ, 1989. 1st trade ed. Fine in Fine dj and signed. *LOPEZ.* $45

Walker, Alice. THE THIRD LIFE OF GRANGE COPELAND. (London): Women's Press, (1985). 1st UK ed. Fine in NF dj. *ROBBINS.* $50

Walker, Alice. THE THIRD LIFE OF GRANGE COPELAND. NY: Harcourt Brace Jovanovich, (1970). 1st, 1st novel. Orig red cl, grey boards. About Fine in dj (short clean tear rear panel). Signed on half-title. *CHAPEL HILL.* $350

Walker, Alice. THE THIRD LIFE OF GRANGE COPELAND. NY: Harcourt Brace Jovanovich, (1970). 1st ed, 1st novel. Orig cl-backed boards. Fine in dj. *CHAPEL HILL.* $275

Walker, Alice. THIRD LIFE OF GRANGE COPELAND. NY, 1970. 1st ed. Owner name, else NF in dj (2 ink prices on front flap, overall light soil). Rare early title. *PETTLER.* $150

Walker, Alice. TO HELL WITH DYING. San Diego: Harcourt Brace Jovanovich, (1988). 1st ed. Fine in NF dj. *BETWEEN COVERS.* $65

Walker, Alice. TO HELL WITH DYING. San Diego: Harcourt, Brace, (1988). 1st ed. Signed. Cloth, boards, 12 full pg color illus. Fine in Fine dj. *ACADEMIC LIBRARY.* $30

Walker, Alice. YOU CAN'T KEEP A GOOD WOMAN DOWN: STORIES. NY: Harcourt Brace & Jovanovich, (1981). 1st ed. Fine in dj. *CAPTAIN'S BOOKSHELF.* $300

Walker, Alice. YOU CAN'T KEEP A GOOD WOMAN DOWN: STORIES. NY: Harcourt, (1981). Uncorrected proof. Fine in wraps. *CAPTAIN'S BOOKSHELF.* $450

Walker, C.B. THE MISSISSIPPI VALLEY, AND PREHISTORIC EVENTS. Burlington, IA: R.T. Root, 1879. 1st ed. 4 color plts. Cvrs sl worn & stained. Inner hinges cracking, o/w VG. *DIAMOND.* $70

Walker, Charles S. SAMUEL MINOT JONES: THE STORY OF AN AMHERST BOY. Amherst, 1922. 1st ed. Orig cl. *GINSBERG.* $60

Walker, Dale L. (ed). WILL HENRY'S WEST. Texas Western Press, 1984. 1st ed. Signed. New in dj. *AUTHORS OF THE WEST.* $25

Walker, Don D. CLIO'S COWBOYS. Univ of NE Press, (1981). 1st ed. New in dj. *AUTHORS OF THE WEST.* $25

Walker, Elizabeth. HAWAII AND THE SOUTH SEAS—A GUIDE BOOK. NY: Coward-McCann, 1931. 1st ed. NF dj. *GREAT EPIC.* $95

Walker, Eric. TREETOPS HOTEL. London: Robert Hale, 1966. 6th prtg. Fine in dj. *GREAT EPIC.* $35

WALKER EVANS: AMERICAN PHOTOGRAPHS. NY: Museum of Modern Art, 1938. Black cl over boards, small ptd paper label on spine. Ed of 5000. Fine. *BOOKMINE.* $125

Walker, Franklin. A LITERARY HISTORY OF SOUTHERN CALIFORNIA. Univ of CA Press, 1950. 1st ed. Fine in dj. *AUTHORS OF THE WEST.* $30

Walker, Franklin. JACK LONDON AND THE KLONDIKE: THE GENESIS OF AN AMERICAN WRITER. London: The Bodley Head, (1966). 1st British ed. Fine in dj. *AUTHORS OF THE WEST.* $40

Walker, Fred. DESTINATION UNKNOWN—RUNNING AWAY TO DANGER. Phila: Lippincott, 1935. 1st ed. Almost Fine in VG dj. *AARD.* $35

Walker, Harry with Tom Meany. HOW TO BAT. McGraw Hill, 1963. 2nd prtg. B/w dwgs. Inscribed by Walker. VG in Good+ dj. *PLAPINGER.* $50

Walker, Henry J. JESSE JAMES "THE OUTLAW." Des Moines, IA: Wallace-Homestead Co, 1961. 1st ed. VF. *GIBBS.* $25

Walker, James P. BOOK OF RAPHAEL'S MADONNAS. NY: Leavitt & Allen, 1860. 1st ed. 104pp. 14 tipped in actual albumen photos. Orig morocco, rubbed and scuffed, top and bottom of spine and lower corners chipped, o/w VG; aeg. *WORLDWIDE.* $95

Walker, John. FOLK MEDICINE IN MODERN EGYPT. London: Luzac, 1934. 4 plts. Good. *ARCHAEOLOGIA.* $75

Walker, Margaret. HOW I WROTE JUBILEE. Chicago: Third World, 1972. 1st ed. Wraps. Fine. *BEASLEY.* $45

Walker, Margaret. OCTOBER JOURNEY. Broadside Press, 1973. 1st ed. About Fine in dec wraps. Small water discoloration on front cover. *STAHR.* $35

WALKER PERCY: 1916-1990. (NY): Farrar Straus & Giroux, (1991). 1st ed. Fine in ptd wrappers, as issued. Not formally offered for sale. Fine. *CAPTAIN'S BOOKSHELF.* $60

Walker, Peter F. VICKSBURG, A PEOPLE AT WAR, 1860-1865. Chapel Hill, (1960). 2nd prtg. VG+ in dj. *PRATT.* $30

Walker, Sir Hovenden. THE WALKER EXPEDITION TO QUEBEC, 1771. Toronto, Champlain Soc, 1953. Gerald S. Graham (ed). Orig cl. Publications of the Champlain Soc. V. 32. One of 550 numbered. Howes W39. *GINSBERG.* $275

Walker, William. THE WAR IN NICARAGUA. Mobile: Goetzel, 1860. 1st ed. 431,(1)pp. Port, colored fldg map, mended twice w/scotch tape. Orig cl. *GINSBERG.* $300

Walker, William. THE WAR IN NICARAGUA. Mobile: S.H. Goetzel. 1860. 1st ed. 432pp. Frontis. Fldg map. Spine soiled. Very scarce. *KARMIOLE.* $300

Walkinshaw, Lawrence. THE SANDHILL CRANES. Bloomfield Hill: Cranbrook Institute of Science, 1949. 1st ed. VG. *BACKMAN.* $25

Wall, Bernhardt. FOLLOWING GENERAL SAM HOUSTON, FROM 1793-1863. Austin: The Steck Co, 1935. 1st ed. VG. *GIBBS.* $75

Wall, Bernhardt. FOLLOWING ABRAHAM LINCOLN 1809-1865. NY, (1943). Dj. VG. *PRATT.* $32.50

Wallace, A.R. DARWINISM: AN EXPOSITION OF THE THEORY OF NATURAL SELECTION. London: Macmillan, 1889. 494pp. Minor cvr scuffing, orig cl. Good+ to VG. *BOOKCELL.* $75

Wallace, A.R. THE GEOGRAPHICAL DISTRIBUTION OF ANIMALS WITH A STUDY OF THE RELATIONS OF LIVING AND EXTINCT FAUNASNY, 1876. 1st Amer ed. 7 colored maps (some fldg), 20 plts. 2 vols. xxiii,503pp; ix,607pp. Orig gilt-dec cl. Minor cvr spotting; edges sl darkened; 1 hinge cracked; # sticker on spines; bkpls. *SUTTON.* $400

Wallace, A.R. THE MALAY ARCHIPELAGO, THE LAND OF THE ORAN-UTAN & BIRD OF PARADISE, ETC. London & NY, (1902). VG. *MIKESH.* $37.50

Wallace, A.R. THE MALAY ARCHIPELAGO. Harper, 1869. 1st Amer ed. 638pp. Minor head, backstrip wear. VG. *BOOKCELL.* $80

Wallace, Alexander. THE DESERT AND THE HOLY LAND. Glasgow, 1882. 2nd ed. 328 pp. *O'NEILL.* $75

Wallace, Alfred R. DARWINISM, AN EXPOSITION OF THE THEORY OF NATURAL SELECTION WITH SOME OF ITS APPLICATIONS. London, 1889. 1st ed. 494pp. *FYE.* $250

Wallace, Edgar. THE GOVERNOR OF CHI-FOO. Cleveland: World Syndicate Publishing, 1933. 1st Amer ed. Pp and eps darkened o/w VG in dj w/crease-tear on front panel, several short closed tears, and minor wear at spine ends and at corners. *MORDIDA.* $30

Wallace, Edgar. THE THIEF IN THE NIGHT. NY: World Wide Pub, n.d. 1st Amer ed. Ptd from 1928 English Reader's Library plts. Pp darkened, o/w VG in dj w/chips, several tears). *MORDIDA*. $65

Wallace, Edgar. WHITE FACE. GC: Doubleday, Doran. (1931). 1st ed. VG in dj, worn, attractive pict dj. *BERNARD*. $50

Wallace, Ernest and E. Adamson Hoebel. THE COMANCHES....Univ of OK Press, 1952. 1st ed. Fine in Fine dj. *VARNER*. $40

Wallace, Frederick William. WOODEN SHIPS AND IRON MEN. NY: George Sully, (1937). Reset from the orig ed pub by Lauriat. *LEFKOWICZ*. $50

Wallace, Isabel. LIFE AND LETTERS OF GENERAL W. H. L. WALLACE. Chicago: Donnelley, 1909. 1st ed. Orig cl. *GINSBERG*. $125

Wallace, John. CARPETBAG RULE IN FLORIDA: THE INSIDE WORKINGS. Jacksonville, FL: Da Costa, 1888. 1st ed. 444pp. Port. New half morocco. Howes W53. *GINSBERG*. $750

Wallace, Lew. LIFE OF GEN. BEN HARRISON. Phila et al: Hubbard Brothers, (1888). Frontis, 7 plts. *SCHOYER'S*. $20

Wallace, Philip. COLONIAL IRONWORK IN OLD PHILADELPHIA. NY: Architectural Bk Pub Co, 1930. VG. *BACKROOM*. $95

Wallace, Phillip. COLONIAL HOUSES. NY: Architectural Book Publ. Co, 1931. 1st ed. VG. 248pp. *BACKROOM*. $120

Wallace, Susan E. THE LAND OF THE PUEBLOS. NY: Alden, 1888. 12 plts. Owner inscrip ffep, small name stamp on title page. Nice. *BOHLING*. $65

Wallace, Willard M. SOUL OF THE LION, A BIOGRAPHY OF GENERAL JOSHUA L. CHAMBERLAIN. NY, (1960). 1st ed. 357pp. Dj wear, chipping; o/w VG+. *PRATT*. $50

Wallace, Wm. Swilling. ANTOINE ROBIDOUX, 1794-1860. LA: Dawson, 1953. 1st ed, ltd to 450. Frontis. VF. *OREGON*. $65

Wallant, Edward Lewis. THE PAWNBROKER. NY: HBW, 1961. Fine; short tear dj spine fold. *ELSE FINE*. $35

Wallant, Edward Lewis. THE TENANTS OF MOONBLOOM. NY, 1963. 1st ed. NF in dj. *PETTLER*. $25

Wallen, Henry D....REPORT OF THE SECRETARY OF WAR, COMMUNICATING...THE REPORT OF CAPTAIN...OF HIS EXPEDITION, IN 1859, FROM DALLES CITY TO GREAT SALT LAKE, AND BACK....(Wash.. SD34, 1860). 1st ed. 51pp. Fldg map. Half morocco. Howes W57. *GINSBERG*. $200

Waller, Augustus D. LECTURES ON PHYSIOLOGY. FIRST SERIES: ON ANIMAL ELECTRICITY. London, 1897. 1st ed. 144pp. *FYE*. $300

Waller, Brown. LAST OF THE GREAT TRAIN ROBBERS. South Brunswick, NY: Barnes, (1968). 1st ed. Dj. Fine. *SCHOYER'S*. $25

Waller, Fats. FATS WALLER'S ORIGINAL PIANO CONCEPTIONS. NY: Mills Music, 1932? 1st ed. Separating wraps neatly tape mended, o/w VG. *BEASLEY*. $35

Waller, John L. COLOSSAL HAMILTON OF TEXAS: A BIOGRAPHY OF ANDREW JACKSON HAMILTON. El Paso: Texas Western Press, 1968. Designed by Carl Hertzog, w/presentation signed by him. Fine in sunned dj. *LAURIE*. $50

Walles, B.L.C. REPORT ON THE AGRICULTURE & GEOLOGY OF MISSISSIPPI. E. Barksdale, 1854. 17 plts, fldg map. Extremities chipped, little shaken, extensive pencil notes on ep and a couple of places within, bottom inch of flyleaf removed. *BOHLING*. $200

Wallihan, A.G. Mr. and Mrs. CAMERA SHOTS AT BIG GAME. NY: Doubleday, 1904. 1st US ed. VG+. *MIKESH*. $100

Walling, Emory A. MEMOIRS OF THE ERIE COUNTY, PENNSYLVANIA, BENCH AND BAR. Erie Printing Company, 1928. Inscribed. Very Nice. *BOHLING*. $50

Wallmo, O.C. (ed). MULE & BLACK-TAILED DEER OF NORTH AMERICA. Lincoln & London: Univ of Nebraska, 1981. Fine in VG+ dj. *MIKESH*. $30

Walpole, Horace. LETTERS OF HORACE WALPOLE...TO SIR HORACE MANN....Ed by Lord Dover. With an Original Memoir of the Author, by the Editor. Third Edition. In Three Volumes. London: Richard Bentley. 1834. 3 vols. iii,380; (2),420; (2),408pp. Index. 19th century blue-green calf over patterned purple cl, gilt spines with maroon lea spine labels. Bkpls. *KARMIOLE*. $100

Walpole, Horace. MEMOIRS OF THE REIGN OF KING GEORGE THE THIRD. First Published by Sir Denis Le Marchant Bart. And Now Reedited by C.F. Russell Barker. With Sixteen Portraits. London: Lawrence & Bullen. 1894. 4 vols. Index. Ed ltd to 740. Spine faded. Teg. *KARMIOLE*. $75

Walpole, Hugh. ROGUE HERRIES. London: Macmillan, 1930. 1st ed. VG, lacking dj. Inscribed in 1933. *LOPEZ*. $30

Walpole, Hugh. THE SILVER THORN. London: Macmillan, 1928. 1st ed. Inscribed in year of pub. In custom quarter leather slipcase and folding chemise. Fine in VG (fragile) dj. *LOPEZ*. $85

Walser, Richard (ed). THE ENIGMA OF THOMAS WOLFE. Cambridge: Harvard Univ Press, 1953. 1st ed. Orig two-toned red cl. Faint tape marks on eps, else Fine in NF dj (couple of tears near head of spine). *CHAPEL HILL*. $30

Walsh, James. PSYCHOTHERAPY INCLUDING THE HISTORY OF THE USE OF MENTAL INFLUENCE, DIRECTLY AND INDIRECTLY, IN HEALING AND THE PRINCIPLES FOR THE APPLICATION OF ENERGIES DERIVED FROM THE MIND TO THE TREATMENT OF DISEASE. NY, 1912. 1st ed. *FYE*. $75

Walsh, Marie. THE MISSION BELLS OF CALIFORNIA. SF, Harr Wagner, (1934). 1st ed. Fine. *OREGON*. $45

Walsh, Ray. THE MYCROFT MEMORANDA. London: Deutsch, 1984. 1st ed. Fine in NF dj. *SILVER DOOR*. $25

Walsh, Rev. R. A RESIDENCE AT CONSTANTINOPLE, DURING A PERIOD INCLUDING THE COMMENCEMENT...GREEK & TURKISH REVOLUTIONS. London, 1836. 1st ed. Port, fldg map, all plts called for. 2 vols. New 1/2 calf. xv,412pp; viii,542pp. 6pp inscrip. Very handsome set. *O'NEILL*. $350

Walsh, Rev. R. NARRATIVE OF A JOURNEY FROM CONSTANTINOPLE TO ENGLAND. Phila, 1828. Orig calf, worn, hinges split. *O'NEILL*. $125

Walsh, Roy E. GUNNING THE CHESAPEAKE—DUCK AND GOOSE SHOOTING ON THE EASTERN SHORE. Cambridge: Tidewater Pub, 1960. 1st ed. VG+ in VG dj. *BACKMAN*. $38

Walshe, W.H. A PRACTICAL TREATISE ON DISEASES OF THE LUNGS. Phila: Blanchard and Lee, 1860. New Amer ed. Blindstamped brn cl, edge-worn, rebacked, pencilling on end matter, contents VG. *SMITHFIELD*. $30

Walsingham, Lord, and Payne-Gallwey, Sir Ralph. SHOOTING (BADMINTON LIBRARY). London and Bombay: Longmans, Green, 1902. New Imp. Minor wear to extremities, else VG+. *OLD LONDON*. $65

WALT DISNEY WORLD. Hallmark, 1972. Pop-up bk. *BOOKFINDERS INTL*. $45

Walter, Norman. THE SEXUAL CYCLE OF HUMAN WARFARE. London: Mitre Press, 1950. 1st ed. Color plts (1 fldg). Sl wrinkle in cl on front cover, else VG in chipped dj. *WREDEN*. $40

Walton, Eda Lou. DAWN BOY. NY: Dutton, (1926). One of 750. VG, lacking dj. *LOPEZ*. $65

Walton, Eda Lou. DAWN BOY: BLACKFOOT AND NAVAJO SONGS. NY: Dutton, 1926. 1st ed. Cl, paper label front cvr, spine. NF. *CONNOLLY & WADE*. $52.50

Walton, Evangeline. WITCH HOUSE. Sauk City: Arkham House, 1945. Ltd to 3000. Mint in Mint dj. *CULLEN.* $60

Walton, George. SENTINEL OF THE PLAINS, FORT LEAVEN-WORTH AND THE AMERICAN WEST. Englewood Cliffs, NJ, (1973). 1st ed. Fine in dj. *PRATT.* $32.50

Walton, George. SENTINEL OF THE PLAINS. Englewood Cliffs: Prentice-Hall, (1973). 1st ptg. Cl, dj. Fine. *SCHOYER'S.* $20

Walton, Isaac and Cotton, Charles. THE COMPLETE ANGLER; OR CONTEMPLATIVE MAN'S RECREATION...London: Printed for Samuel Bagster, 1808. 1st Bagster ed. 8vo; vi,512pp. 14 full-page engr plates, text illus. Handsomely rebound in full chestnut calf, gilt extra, dec borders tooled in blind, lea label, all edges gilt, silk ribbon markers. Beautiful, scarce. *HARTFIELD.* $485

Walton, Isaak. THE COMPLEAT ANGLER. London: J.M. Dent and Company, 1896. Ed w/intro by Andrew Lang. 1st ed thus. Illus by Edmund Joseph Sullivan. Bkpl, scattered penciled annotations, some fading to edges. *BOOKMINE.* $95

Walton, Ortiz M. MUSIC: BLACK, WHITE AND BLUE. NY: Morrow, 1972. 1st ed. Fine w/bkplt, in NF dj but for tear. *BEASLEY.* $25

Walton, Wm. M. LIFE AND ADVENTURES OF BEN THOMPSON. Frontier Press, 1954. Ltd to 1000. Rpt of 1884 ed. Cvr sl foxed, o/w Fine. *VARNER.* $40

Walworth, Arthur. BLACK SHIPS OFF JAPAN. NY: Alfred A. Knopf, 1946. 1st ed. Covers soiled and show wear. *PARMER.* $25

Wambaugh, Joseph. THE CHOIRBOYS. Delacorte, 1975. 1st ed. NF in dj. *STAHR.* $15

Wambaugh, Joseph. THE GOLDEN ORANGE. Morrow, 1990. 1st ed. Fine in dj. Signed & inscribed. *STAHR.* $35

Wambaugh, Joseph. THE SECRETS OF HARRY BRIGHT. Morrow, 1985. Uncorrected proof. Fine in white wraps w/black and white image of the dj. *STAHR.* $20

Wampler, Joseph. HAVASU CANYON—GEM OF THE GRAND CANYON. Berkeley, 1959. Stiff pict paper wraps. VG. *FIVE QUAIL.* $15

Wandrei, Donald. POEMS FOR MIDNIGHT. Arkham House, 1964. 1st ed. VF in Mint dj. *MADLE.* $175

Wandrei, Donald. STRANGE HARVEST. Sauk City: Arkham House, 1965. 1st ed. NF in Almost Fine dj. *OTHER WORLDS.* $60

Wandrei, Donald. THE EYE AND THE FINGER. Arkham House, 1944. 1st ed. Fine in dj. *MADLE.* $250

Wandrei, Donald. THE WEB OF EASTER ISLAND. Sauk City: Arkham House, 1948. 1st ed. Name, else solid VG+ in dj. *OTHER WORLDS.* $50

Wandrei, Donald. THE WEB OF EASTER ISLAND. Sauk City: Arkham House, 1948. 1st ed, ltd to 3068 . Fine in Fine dj. *ROBBINS.* $55

Wangensteen, Owen and Sarah. THE RISE OF SURGERY FROM EMPIRIC CRAFT TO SCIENTIFIC DISCIPLINE. Minneapolis, 1978. 1st ed. *FYE.* $75

Wantling, William. THE AWAKENING. (London): Turret Books, (1967). 1/200 numbered signed. Fine in dj. *LOPEZ.* $45

Warburton, Eliot. THE CRESCENT AND THE CROSS; OR ROMANCE AND REALITIES OF EASTERN TRAVEL. London, 1855. ix,380pp. Attractive early ed. *O'NEILL.* $37.50

Warburton, R.E. Egerton. HUNTING SONGS. NY: Scribner's, 1925. 1st US ed. VG in Fair dj. *OCTOBER FARM.* $65

Ward, Charles Willis. THE AMERICAN CARNATION. HOW TO GROW IT. NY: De La Mere, 1903. 1st ed. Rubbed cl. Good. *SECOND LIFE.* $40

Ward, Grace E. IN THE MIZ. With Eight Full-Page Plates in Color....by Clara E. Atwood. Boston: Little, Brown. 1904. Blue cl

w/color illus pasted on front cvr; portion of back cvr stained, cl somewhat soiled. *KARMIOLE.* $75

Ward, H.W. THE BOOK OF THE PEACH. A PRACTICAL HANDBOOK. London: Scott, 1903. Worn cl, contents VG. *AMERICAN BOTANIST.* $22

Ward, John. OUR SUDAN: ITS PYRAMIDS AND PROGRESS. London: Murray, 1905. 1st ed. Fldg map. Sl rubbed & soiled, spine frayed, o/w VG ex-lib. *WORLDWIDE.* $50

Ward, L.F. GUIDE TO THE FLORA OF WASHINGTON AND VICINITY. Washington, 1881. 1 fold-out map, tears repaired w/tape. Orig cl worn, rubbed. *SUTTON.* $50

Ward, Lester. YOUNG WARD'S DIARY. NY, (1935). 1st ed. 321pp. Spine faded o/w VG. *PRATT.* $60

Ward, Lynd. GOD'S MAN, A NOVEL IN WOODCUTS. NY: Cape & Smith, 1929. One of 409 signed. Bound in black cl over boards, illus on front cvr, paper title label on spine. Slipcase. Spine faded, sig. Fine. *HELLER.* $500

Ward, Lynd. MADMAN'S DRUM: A NOVEL IN WOODCUTS. NY: Cape & Smith, 1930. 1st ed. Edges & corners sl worn. Lacks dj. *AKA.* $75

Ward, Lynd. MADMAN'S DRUM: A NOVEL IN WOODCUTS. NY: Cape, (1930). 1st ed. Unopened. Some pages with shallow margin tears and soiling, dj soiled and worn at edges, else Fine. *MUELLER.* $200

Ward, Lynd. THE SILVER PONY. Houghton Mifflin, 1973. 1st ptg. 175pp. Ward full-page drawings. NF in VG+ dj w/2 chips tape repaired. *BEBBAH.* $75

Ward, Maria. FEMALE LIFE AMONG THE MORMONS. Phila, J. Potter, 1863. 40th thousand. Fair. *OREGON.* $35

Ward, Marion. BOAT CHILDREN OF CANTON. McKay, (1944). 1st ed. 92pp. Illus by Helen Sewell. Small spot to cvr, forward edge. VG+ in dj w/few closed edge tears, chips. VG and bright. *BEBBAH.* $25

Ward, R. THE SPORTSMAN'S HANDBOOK TO PRACTICAL COLLECTING, PRESERVING & ARTISTIC SETTING UP OF TROPHIES, SPECIMENS, ETC. London: R. Ward, (1891). 6th ed. 145pp+ads. Gilt dec, full lea. VG. *MIKESH.* $95

Ward, Ralph T. PIRATES IN HISTORY. Baltimore: York Press, 1974. Small spot at base of spine, else NF. *PARMER.* $30

Ward, Sam. SAM WARD IN THE GOLD RUSH. Carvel Collins (ed). Stanford: Stanford Univ, 1949. 1st ed. Fine. *CONNOLLY & WADE.* $37.50

Ward, Samuel. SAM WARD IN THE GOLD RUSH. Stanford Univ, 1949. 1st ed. Ed by Carvel Collins. Fine in VG dj. *CONNOLLY & WADE.* $50

Ward, Thomas and Paul Fountain. RAMBLES OF AN AUSTRALIAN NATURALIST. London: John Murray, 1907. 1st ed. Offset to eps, wear to head and heel of spine, else Very nice. *PARMER.* $60

Ward-Perkins, J.B. CITIES OF ANCIENT GREECE AND ITALY: PLANNING IN CLASSICAL ANTIQUITY. NY: George Braziller, (1974). Corner bumped. Good. *ARCHAEOLOGIA.* $45

Warden, Ernest. THRILLING TALES OF KANSAS. Wichita: Author pub, n.d. (1932). Ptd by the Wichita Eagle Press. Ptd wrapper. Private lib stamp, sig, date on inner front cover. NF. *CONNOLLY & WADE.* $45

Warden, William. LETTERS WRITTEN ON BOARD HMS THE NORTHUMBERLAND. Albany: Websters, 1817. 1st US ed. Contemp calf. VG. *SECOND LIFE.* $75

Wardlaw, Charles. FUNDAMENTALS OF BASEBALL. Scribners, 1924. Ltr ptg (1925). VG. *PLAPINGER.* $40

Wardrop, A.E. MODERN PIG STICKING. London: Macmillan, (1930). 2nd ed. Photos. Dec cl. VG+. *MIKESH.* $60

Ware, Capt. Eugene F. THE INDIAN WARS OF 1864. Topeka, 1911. 1960 reprint. 1st ed. Dj has faded spine o/w VG. *PRATT.* $40

Ware, Francis. DRIVING. NY: Doubleday, Page, 1903. 1st ed. VG. *OCTOBER FARM.* $295

Ware, James Redding. PASSING ENGLISH OF THE VICTORIAN ERA. London: George Routledge & Sons, Ltd. N.d. (circa 1909). 1st ed. Double column text. Two-tone red cloth. Teg. *KARMIOLE.* $30

Warfield, William. THE GATE OF ASIA. A JOURNEY....NY & London: Putnam, 1916. 1st ed. 48 plts. Ex-lib w/number on spine, o/w VG. *WORLDWIDE.* $18

Warga, Wayne. HARDCOVER. NY: Arbor, (1985). 1st ed. Inscribed. VF in VF dj. *UNGER.* $30

Warga, Wayne. HARDCOVER. NY: Arbor House, 1985. 1st ed. Inscribed. VF in dj. *MORDIDA.* $25

Warhol, Andy. a. NY, 1968. 1st ed. Fine in dj. *PETTLER.* $90

Warhol, Andy. AMERICA. NY: Harper & Row. (1985). 1st ed. Gray linen stamped in black. Dj. The scarce clothbound ed. Fine. *KARMIOLE.* $60

Warhol, Andy. ANDY WARHOL'S EXPOSURES. NY, 1979. 1st ed. Signed. Fine in like dj. *POLYANTHOS.* $250

Warhol, Andy. ANDY WARHOL'S INDEX (BOOK). NY: Random House, 1967. Unpaginated. Photos, graphic art. Complete w/10 inserted devices including 3 pop-ups, the photo illus record, mobile, and balloon (as usual disintegrated and cementing 2 pp together). One leaf w/small portion torn away at top margin, tab carelessly removed, Overall Very Nice. *KARMIOLE.* $650

Warhol, Andy. BLUE MOVIE. NY: Grove, 1970. 1st ed. Wraps. Fine. *BEASLEY.* $25

Warhol, Andy. BLUE MOVIE: A FILM. NY: Grove, (1970). 1st ed. NF in wrappers. *CAPTAIN'S BOOKSHELF.* $60

Warhol, Andy. PORTRAITS OF THE 70s. David Whitney (ed). NY: Random House in association w/Whitney Museum of American Art, (1979). 1st ed. #73 of 200, signed. Orig black cl. Fine in sl rubbed pub's slipcase. *CHAPEL HILL.* $450

Warhol, Andy. THE PHILOSOPHY OF ANDY WARHOL (FROM A TO B AND BACK AGAIN). NY & London: Harcourt Brace Jovanovich, (1975). 1st ed. Orig orange cl, yellow boards. Fine in dj, crease on front flap. Signed, initialled w/orig drwg. *CHAPEL HILL.* $375

Waring, Edward. PHARMACOPOEIA OF INDIA. London 1868. 1st ed. 1/4 lea, 503pp. Skillfully rebacked preserving orig spine. Rare. *FYE.* $250

Waring, Guy. MY PIONEER PAST. Boston, (1936). 1st ed. NF. *DIAMOND.* $45

Waring, Guy. MY PIONEER PAST. Boston: B. Humphries, (1936). 1st ed. 31 plts. VF in VG dj. Presentation card of E. Waring tipped in. *OREGON.* $65

Waring, Guy. MY PIONEER PAST. Boston: Bruce Humpheries, (1936). 1st ed. 256pp. Stain affecting dj, cover, and numerous pages (not affecting text). *AKA.* $40

Waring, Janet. EARLY AMERICAN WALL STENCILS. NY: William R. Scott, Inc, 1937. 1st ed. One of 800. VG in dj torn, chipped. *BACKROOM.* $150

Waring, Ruth Ann and Helen Wells. SU-LIN—THE REAL STORY. Chicago: Rand McNally, 1937. 1st ed. Fine- in VG+ dj. *AARD.* $25

Warkworth, Lord. NOTES FROM A DIARY IN ASIATIC TURKEY. London, 1898. Fldg map. *O'NEILL.* $175

Warmington, G.R. KING OF DREAMS. Doran, 1926. 1st ed. Fine in dj. *MADLE.* $75

Warner, C.A. TEXAS OIL AND GAS SINCE 1543. Houston: Gulf Publishing Co, 1939. 1st ed. VF, tight ed. *GIBBS.* $275

Warner, Charles Dudley. IN THE LEVANT. Boston: Houghton Mifflin, 1881. 9th ed. Sl rubbed, o/w VG. *WORLDWIDE.* $18

Warner, Charles Dudley. IN THE LEVANT. Boston: Riverside Press, 1893. 2 vols. 1st illus ed. Teg. NF. *POLYANTHOS.* $75

Warner, Charles Dudley. MY SUMMER IN A GARDEN. Boston, 1892 (1885). Cl, spine ends worn. Bkpl. *SUTTON.* $25

Warner, Charles Dudley. MY SUMMER IN A GARDEN. Boston: Fields, Osgood, & Co, 1871. 183pp. Orig grn cl. Early name, spine extremities rubbed, else NF. 1st ed. In the scarcer of two bindings (priority not determined), w/triple rule frame on cvr and no filigree medallion at center. *CHAPEL HILL.* $75

Warner, Charles Dudley. ON HORSEBACK IN VIRGINIA. Boston: Houghton Mifflin, 1889. 1st ed. Inscribed. (8),331,15pp adv. 12mo. Grn pict cl. VG+. *CONNOLLY & WADE.* $65

Warner, J.J. et al. AN HISTORICAL SKETCH OF LOS ANGELES COUNTY...9-8-1771 TO 7-4-1876. LA: O.W. Smith, 1936. Rprt of rare 1876 ed. Corner wear, lt soiling; o/w Fine. Howes W110. *OREGON.* $45

Warner, J.J. et al. AN HISTORICAL SKETCH OF LOS ANGELES COUNTY...TO JULY 4, 1876. LA: Lewin & Co, 1876. 1st ed. Orig ptd wraps. VF, encl in slipcase. *BOOK MARKET.* $285

Warner, Langdon. THE CRAFT OF THE JAPANESE SCULPTOR. NY: Morill Press. 1936. 1st ed. 85pp plts, each w/accompanying pg text. Rubbed. Edgewear. Good. *ARTIS.* $45

Warner, Louis H. ARCHBISHOP LAMAY AN EPOCH MAKER. Santa Fe, NM: Santa Fe New Mexican Publishing Corp, 1936. 1st ed. VG. *GIBBS.* $45

Warner, Matt and Murray E. King. THE LAST OF THE BANDIT RIDERS. Caxton, 1940. 1st ed. Fine in sl chipped dj. *VARNER.* $110

Warner, Matt and Murray E. King. THE LAST OF THE BANDIT RIDERS. NY: Bonanza, (1940). VF in Good+ dj. *CONNOLLY & WADE.* $32.50

Warner, P.F. THE FIGHT FOR THE ASHES IN 1926. London: Harrap, 1926. 1st ed. Scarce. Fine. *OLD LONDON.* $45

Warner, Slyvia Townsend. MR. FORTUNE'S MAGGOT. London: Chatto & Windus, 1927. 1st ed. Dj evenly tanned, but VG. *JAFFE.* $100

Warner, Sylvia Townsend. SOME WORLD FAR FROM OURS and 'STAY, CORYDON, THOU SWAIN'. London: Elkin Mathews & Marrot, 1929. One of 530 numbered, signed. Fine in NF dj. *DERMONT.* $65

Warner, Sylvia Townsend. THE ESPALIER. London: Chatto & Windus, 1925. 1st ed. Cl w/ptd label. Faint creases in dj, o/w Fine. *JAFFE.* $225

Warner, Ted (ed). THE DOMINGUEZ-ESCALANTE JOURNAL. Trans by Fray Angelico Chavez. Provo, 1976. Text in English and Spanish. Corners bumped, else a VG+. *FIVE QUAIL.* $25

Warre, Capt. Henry. SKETCHES IN NORTH AMERICAN AND THE OREGON TERRITORY....Barre, MA, 1970. Ltd to 950 numbered. 71 full pg plts, many colored. Archibald Hanna (intro). Orig cl, boxed. *GINSBERG.* $100

Warren, Benjamin Harry. REPORT ON THE BIRDS OF PENNSYLVANIA. Harrisburg, PA: E.K. Meyers, 1888. 1st ed. 50 plts (49 color). Inscribed. Covers sl soiled, o/w Nice. *DIAMOND.* $125

Warren, Benjamin Harry. REPORT ON THE BIRDS OF PENNSYLVANIA WITH SPECIAL REFERENCE TO THE FOOD-HABITS....Harrisburg, 1890. 2nd ed. 100 plts (99 colored; 1 pl loose & chipped). 1/2 leather. Very worn; backstrip missing; shaken; bkpl; tears to index pg. *SUTTON.* $56

Warren, Benjamin Harry. REPORT ON THE BIRDS OF PEN-NSYLVANIA. Harrisburg, (1890). 2nd ed. 100 full page color plts. Cl boards. Rebacked, else VG. *MIKESH.* $85

Warren, David B. et al. MARKS OF ACHIEVEMENT. NY: Abrams, 1987. 1st ed. VG. *BACKROOM.* $45

Warren, J. Mason. SURGICAL OBSERVATIONS, WITH CASES AND OPERATIONS. NY, 1867. 1st ed. Fine lithographic illus. 630pp. Exceptionally Fine. Scarce. *FYE.* $700

Warren, John Byrne Leicester (Lord De Tabley). A GUIDE TO THE STUDY OF BOOK-PLATES (EX LIBRIS). NY, London: John Lane, The Bodley Head, 1900. 2nd ed. Fine. *WEBER.* $50

Warren, John C. ETHERIZATION; WITH SURGICAL REMARKS. Boston, 1848. 1st ed. 100pp. Backstrip missing, ex-lib w/small impression stamp on title and bkpl. Contents Fine. Scarce. *FYE.* $500

Warren, John C. PHYSICAL EDUCATION AND THE PRESER-VATION OF HEALTH. Boston, 1846. 1st ed. 90pp. Scarce. *FYE.* $200

Warren, John C. SURGICAL PATHOLOGY AND THERAPEUTICS. Phila, 1895. 1st ed. Inner hinges cracked. *FYE.* $100

Warren, John. THE MATADORS: 1879-1951. Privately ptd, 1952. Pb. Fine. *VARNER.* $85

Warren, Peter. MINOAN STONE VASES. Cambridge: Cambridge Univ Press, 1969. 8 figs. Dj. Good. *ARCHAEOLOGIA.* $85

Warren, Raymond. THE PRAIRIE PRESIDENT: LIVING THROUGH THE YEARS WITH LINCOLN 1809-1861. Chicago: Reilly & Lee, 1930. 1st ed. Largely unopened. Cloth. Fine in VG dj. *CONNOLLY & WADE.* $40

Warren, Robert Penn (ed). A SOUTHERN HARVEST. SHORT STORIES BY SOUTHERN WRITERS. Boston: Houghton Mif-flin, 1937. 1st ed. Orig blue cl. Some offsetting to eps, but NF in VG pict dj (lt rubbing, edgewear, couple short tears). *CHAPEL HILL.* $275

Warren, Robert Penn. A PLACE TO COME TO. NY: Random House, (1977). 1st Amer ed. Signed inscription. Orig cl-backed boards. Rmdr mk bottom edge, else Fine in dj. *CHAPEL HILL.* $85

Warren, Robert Penn. A PLACE TO COME TO. NY: Random House, (1977). Front pastedown stained, spine rubbed and a little cocked, thus Good to VG in NF pub's slipcase. 1st Amer ed. #305 of 350 signed. *CHAPEL HILL.* $75

Warren, Robert Penn. A PLACE TO COME TO. NY: Random House, 1977. 1st ed. As New in dj. *ELSE FINE.* $30

Warren, Robert Penn. ALL THE KING'S MEN. London: E&S, 1960. 2nd Eng ed (reset). Fine in very lightly soiled dj. *CAPTAIN'S BOOK-SHELF.* $60

Warren, Robert Penn. ALL THE KING'S MEN. London: Eyre, (1948). 1st English ed. NF in lightly soiled dj. *UNGER.* $275

Warren, Robert Penn. ALL THE KING'S MEN. NY: Harcourt Brace, (1946). 1st ed. VG in 1st issue dj (moderate edgewear). About VG. *LOPEZ.* $675

Warren, Robert Penn. ALL THE KING'S MEN. NY: Harcourt, Brace, (1946). 1st ed. Orig dk red cl. Fine in price-clipped, NF dj (lt edgewear, dampstain on verso at bottom of spine). 1st issue dj w/Sinclair Lewis blurb on rear panel. Inscribed. *CHAPEL HILL.* $2,600

Warren, Robert Penn. ALL THE KINGS MEN. Franklin Center: Franklin Library, 1977. Ltd ed. Illus. Fine in leather. Signed. *CAPTAIN'S BOOKSHELF.* $200

Warren, Robert Penn. AT HEAVEN'S GATE. NY: Harcourt, (1943). 1st ed. NF in worn dj w/1.5" chip. *CAPTAIN'S BOOKSHELF.* $150

Warren, Robert Penn. AT HEAVEN'S GATE. NY: Harcourt Brace & Co., (1943). 1st ed. Fine in bright NF dj w/small chip head of spine, touch of rubbing to spinal extremities. *BETWEEN COVERS.* $350

Warren, Robert Penn. AT HEAVEN'S GATE. NY: Harcourt, Brace, (1943). 1st ed. Orig blue cl. Fine in VG to NF dj sl chipped at spine ends (affecting no lettering). *CHAPEL HILL.* $450

Warren, Robert Penn. BALLAD OF A SWEET DREAM OF PEACE: A CHARADE FOR EASTER. Dallas: Pressworks, (1980). 1/350, this unnumbered, signed by author and illustrator. Fine w/o dj, as issued. *LOPEZ.* $50

Warren, Robert Penn. BAND OF ANGELS. NY: Random House, 1955. 1st ed. Fine in NF dj. *ELSE FINE.* $40

Warren, Robert Penn. BAND OF ANGELS. NY: Random House, (1955). 1st ed. Inscribed one month after pub. Orig beige cl. VG in rubbed dj, some abrasion on rear panel. *CHAPEL HILL.* $200

Warren, Robert Penn. BAND OF ANGELS. NY: Random House, (1955). 1st ed. Orig beige cl. NF in VG to NF dj. *CHAPEL HILL.* $40

Warren, Robert Penn. BEING HERE. POETRY 1977-1980. NY: Random House, (1980). 1st ed. Fine in price clipped dj. Signed. *CAPTAIN'S BOOKSHELF.* $65

Warren, Robert Penn. BEING HERE. Poetry 1977-1980. NY: Ran-dom House (1980). 1st ed. Signed. Orig cl-backed white boards. Fine in price-clipped dj. *CHAPEL HILL.* $85

Warren, Robert Penn. BEING HERE. POETRY 1977-1980. NY: RH, (1980). 1st ed. Signed. Fine in Fine, price-clipped dj. *LOPEZ.* $75

Warren, Robert Penn. BROTHER TO DRAGONS. A Tale in Verse and Voices. (NY: Random House, (1953). 1st ed. Fine in lightly spine-darkened dj, sl rubbing top of spine. *CHAPEL HILL.* $95

Warren, Robert Penn. CHIEF JOSEPH OF THE NEZ PERCE. NY: Random House, (1983). 1st ed. #5 of 250 numbered, signed. Fine in pub's slipcase. *UNGER.* $200

Warren, Robert Penn. DEMOCRACY & POETRY. Cambridge: Harvard Univ Press, (1975). 2nd ptg. Fine in dj. Signed. *CAPTAIN'S BOOKSHELF.* $25

Warren, Robert Penn. HOMAGE TO THEODORE DREISER. NY: Random House, (1971). 1st ed. Fine in price clipped dj. Signed. *CAPTAIN'S BOOKSHELF.* $60

Warren, Robert Penn. HOW TEXAS WON HER FREEDOM. San Jacinto Monument, TX: San Jacinto Museum of History, 1959. Scarce hb issue, 1 of 512. Trace of rubbing to bottom of boards, else Fine w/o dj as issued. *BETWEEN COVERS.* $500

Warren, Robert Penn. INCARNATIONS. POEMS 1966-1968. NY: RH, (1968). 1/250 numbered signed. Fine in dj, in NF slipcase. *LOPEZ.* $125

Warren, Robert Penn. INCARNATIONS: POEMS 1966-1968. NY: Random House, (1968). 1st ed. Fine in price clipped dj. Signed. *CAPTAIN'S BOOKSHELF.* $75

Warren, Robert Penn. JEFFERSON DAVIS GETS HIS CITIZEN-SHIP BACK. (Lexington): The Univ Press of Kentucky, (1980). 1st ed. Fine in dj. Signed. *CAPTAIN'S BOOKSHELF.* $60

Warren, Robert Penn. JEFFERSON DAVIS GETS HIS CITIZEN-SHIP BACK. (Lexington): Univ Press of Kentucky, (1980). 1st ed. Signed. VF in dj. *LOPEZ.* $85

Warren, Robert Penn. JOHN BROWN. THE MAKING OF A MAR-TYR. NY: Payson & Clarke, 1929. 1st ed, 1st bk, inscribed. Orig maroon cl. NF in price-clipped pict dj, several archival tape reinfor-cements on verso. *CHAPEL HILL.* $1500

Warren, Robert Penn. JOHN GREENLEAF WHITTIER'S POETRY. Minneapolis: Univ of Minnesota Press, (1971). VF in fine dj. Signed. *LOPEZ.* $85

Warren, Robert Penn. MEET ME IN THE GREEN GLEN. NY: Random House, 1971. 1st ed. As New in dj. *ELSE FINE.* $35

Warren, Robert Penn. MEET ME IN THE GREEN GLEN. NY: Random House, (1971). 1st ed. #150 of 300 specially bound.

Signed. Orig beige, brown cl. Fine in orig acetate jacket (sm corner chip), pub's slipcase. *CHAPEL HILL.* $225

Warren, Robert Penn. OR ELSE. Poem/Poems 1968-1974. NY: Random House (1974). 1st ed. Signed. Orig black cl. Fine in dj. *CHAPEL HILL.* $85

Warren, Robert Penn. OR ELSE—POEM/POEMS 1968-1974. NY: RH, (1974). 1/300 specially-bound numbered, signed. Fine in slipcase. *CAPTAIN'S BOOKSHELF.* $125

Warren, Robert Penn. PROMISES. POEMS 1954-1956. London, 1959. 1st ed. Fine in dj (tiny tear side lower spine). *POLYANTHOS.* $50

Warren, Robert Penn. RUMOR VERIFIED. POEMS 1979-1980. London, 1982. 1st ed. Review copy, slip laid in. Signed presentation. Fine in dj (corners minimally rubbed). *POLYANTHOS.* $60

Warren, Robert Penn. RUMOR VERIFIED. Poems 1979-1980. NY: Random House, (1981). 1st trade ed. Signed. Orig beige cl. Fine in dj. *CHAPEL HILL.* $75

Warren, Robert Penn. RUMOR VERIFIED. Poems 1979-1980. NY: Random House, (1981). 1st ed. #224 of 250 signed. Orig blue cl. About Fine in pub's slipcase. *CHAPEL HILL.* $125

Warren, Robert Penn. SELECTED ESSAYS. NY: Random House, 1958. 1st ed. Fine in Fine dj (lightly sunned spine). *BEASLEY.* $40

Warren, Robert Penn. SELECTED POEMS 1923-1943. London: Fortune Press, nd (1951). 1st ed. Fine; minor edgewear, small chips at dj spine ends. *ELSE FINE.* $125

Warren, Robert Penn. SELECTED POEMS 1923-1943. NY: Harcourt, Brace, (1944). 1st ed. One of 1,500. Orig grey cl. Fine in lightly chipped and browned dj, tape reinforcement on verso. *CHAPEL HILL.* $175

Warren, Robert Penn. SELECTED POEMS, 1923-1975. Franklin Center: Franklin Library, 1981. 1st ed of this collection, leatherbound. Signed. Fine. *LOPEZ.* $100

Warren, Robert Penn. SELECTED POEMS 1923-1975. NY: Random House, (1976). 1st ed. Fine in dj. *CAPTAIN'S BOOKSHELF.* $45

Warren, Robert Penn. SELECTED POEMS 1923-1975. NY: Random House (1976). 1st signed ltd ed. #138 of 250 specially bound. Orig black cl. Fine in pub's slipcase. *CHAPEL HILL.* $175

Warren, Robert Penn. SELECTED POEMS 1923-1976. Franklin Center: Franklin Library, 1976. Illus. Ltd ed. Fine in leather. *CAPTAIN'S BOOKSHELF.* $75

Warren, Robert Penn. THE CAVE. London, 1959. 1st ed. Fine in price clipped dj (few small edge tears). *POLYANTHOS.* $45

Warren, Robert Penn. THE CAVE. NY: Random House, 1959. 1st ed. Fine in dj w/minor edgewear. *ELSE FINE.* $30

Warren, Robert Penn. THE CAVE. NY: Random House. (1959). 1st ed. Signed by Warren ffep. Dj. *KARMIOLE.* $60

Warren, Robert Penn. THE CIRCUS IN THE ATTIC AND OTHER STORIES. NY: Harcourt, (1947). 1st ed. One of 3500 ptd. Fine in sl used price clipped dj w/sm rubbed spot affecting some spine lettering. Inscribed. *CAPTAIN'S BOOKSHELF.* $200

Warren, Robert Penn. THE GODS OF MOUNT OLYMPUS. NY: Random House, (1959). Fine in lightly used dj. *DERMONT.* $125

Warren, Robert Penn. THE LEGACY OF THE CIVIL WAR: MEDITATIONS ON THE CENTENNIAL. NY: Random House, (1961). 1st ed. Fine in price clipped dj. Inscribed. *CAPTAIN'S BOOKSHELF.* $100

Warren, Robert Penn. TWO POEMS. (Winston Salem): Palaemon Press, (1979). 1/200 numbered, signed by Warren. Fine in marbled paper boards. *CAPTAIN'S BOOKSHELF.* $100

Warren, Robert Penn. WHO SPEAKS FOR THE NEGRO?. NY: Random House, (1965). 1st ed. Fine in dj. Signed. *CAPTAIN'S BOOKSHELF.* $100

Warren, Robert Penn. WILDERNESS. NY: Random House, (1961). 1st ed. Inscribed a week before official pub date. Orig reddish orange cl. Fine in NF dj. *CHAPEL HILL.* $175

Warren, Robert Penn. WORLD ENOUGH AND TIME. NY: RH, (1950). #456 of unknown number of special ltd ed for bksellers. Fine in sl chipped acetate dj, as issued. Signed. *CAPTAIN'S BOOKSHELF.* $200

Warren, Robert Penn. WORLD ENOUGH AND TIME. NY: RH, (1950). Inscribed in year of pub. VG, lacking dj. *LOPEZ.* $100

Warriner, Francis. CRUISE OF THE UNITED STATES FRIGATE POTOMAC ROUND THE WORLD...1831-1834.... NY: Leavitt, 1835. 366pp. Worn orig, cl chipped on spine. Good. *SECOND LIFE.* $150

Warthin, Aldred. OLD AGE THE MAJOR INVOLUTION. THE PHYSIOLOGY AND PATHOLOGY OF THE AGING PROCESS. NY, 1929. Ltd ed. Signed. *FYE.* $50

Warthin, Aldred. THE PHYSICIAN OF THE DANCE OF DEATH. NY, 1931. Ltd ed. 142pp. 92 Fine illus. *FYE.* $100

Washburn, George. FIFTY YEARS IN CONSTANTINOPLE, AND RECOLLECTIONS OF ROBERT COLLEGE. Boston, 1909. xxxi,317pp. Uncut. Nice. *O'NEILL.* $65

Washburn, Wilcomb E. RED MAN'S LAND—WHITE MAN'S LAW. NY: Scribner's, (1971). 1st ed. Fine in dj. *LAURIE.* $27.50

Washburne, Elihu Benjamin. SKETCH OF EDWARD COLES, SECOND GOVERNOR OF ILLINOIS, AND OF THE SLAVERY STRUGGLE OF 1823-24. Chicago, 1882. 1st ed. Orig cl. NF w/presentation. *McGOWAN.* $125

Washington, Booker T. UP FROM SLAVERY. NY: Doubleday, Page, & Co, 1909. Orig red cl (spine extrems worn), frontis port. Inscribed. *MOTT.* $350

WASHINGTON, CITY AND CAPITAL. Washington, 1937. 1st ed. Cover dull, contents clean, tight. *HEINOLDT.* $35

WASHINGTON, CITY AND CAPITAL. Washington, 1937. 1st ed. WPA guide. Fldg map in rear pocket. Corner of 1/2 title chipped. Cl dull but overall Good, sound. *ARTIS.* $35

Washington, George. LETTERS AND RECOLLECTIONS OF...NY: Doubleday, 1906. 8 plts. Deluxe ed, teg, dec cl. Largely unopened. *SCHOYER'S.* $25

Washington, George. THE DIARIES OF GEORGE WASHINGTON, 1748-1799. John C. Fitzpatrick (ed). Boston: Houghton, (1925). 4 vols. Orig cl. Vol 1 has a few scratches on spine. *GINSBERG.* $100

Washington, George. WASHINGTON AND THE WEST. Cleveland: Arthur H. Clark, 1911. Frontis, 5 maps (2 fldg). Cloth soiled. *SCHOYER'S.* $25

Washington, George. WASHINGTON'S POLITICAL LEGACIES. NY: George Forman, 1800. Subscriber sig front flyleaf, rear ep. Emb stamp, bkpl. Orig full tree calf w/dec gilt-stamped spine, red leather spine label. Howes W-149. *SCHOYER'S.* $150

Washington, George. WRITINGS. Wash, 1931-44. J.C. Fitzpatrick, (ed). 1st ed. 39 vols. Orig cl, ex-lib. *GINSBERG.* $1000

WASHINGTON: A GUIDE TO THE EVERGREEN STATE. Portland: Binfords & Mort, 1941. WPA guide. 1st ed. Fldg map in rear pocket. VG in fair dj. *CONNOLLY & WADE.* $55

Wasson, George S., and Lincoln Colcord. SAILING DAYS ON THE PENOBSCOT. Salem, 1932. Pub 24. Worn dj. *LEFKOWICZ.* $150

Waterfield, Gordon. LAYARD OF NINEVEH. London: John Murray, (1963). Small stain at top board. Good. *ARCHAEOLOGIA.* $45

Waterfield. Gordon. LUCIE DUFF GORDON IN ENGLAND, SOUTH AFRICA AND EGYPT. NY: Dutton, (1937). 1st ed. VG. *SCHOYER'S.* $30

Waterhouse, Charles. VIETNAM WAR SKETCHES FROM THE AIR, LAND, AND SEA. 1st ed. Rutland: Tuttle, 1970. Wraps, Fine. *BEASLEY*. $45

Waterhouse, Sylvester. THE RESOURCES OF MISSOURI. Edition... 20,000 Copies. St. Louis, MO: Aug. Wiebusch & Son. 1867. 96pp. Orig ptd wrappers, sl worn. *KARMIOLE*. $30

Waterloo, Stanley. THE STORY OF AB. Doubleday, 1925. VG in dj. *MADLE*. $50

Waterman, C.H. FLORA'S LEXICON....Phila, (1839). 4 hand-colored plts w/browned pp. 252pp. Orig gilt dec cl worn at extrems, some spine edge splitting. Scattered foxing. Ex-lib. *SUTTON*. $95

Waterman, Charles F. THE PRACTICAL BOOK OF TROUT FISHING. NY: Simon & Schuster, 1977. 1st ed. Fine in VG+ dj. *BACKMAN*. $30

Waterman, Thomas Tileston and John A. Barrows. DOMESTIC COLONIAL ARCHITECTURE OF TIDEWATER VIRGINIA. Chapel Hill, NC: Univ of NC Press. (1947). Rprnt of orig 1932 Scribner's ed. Grn cl, gilt. In pub's slipcase (extrems sl worn). *KARMIOLE*. $100

Waterman, Thomas Tileston. THE MANSIONS OF VIRGINIA, 1706-1776. Chapel Hill: Univ of NC Press. (1945). 1st ed. Slipcase. *KARMIOLE*. $35

Waters, David Watkins. THE ART OF NAVIGATION IN ENGLAND IN ELIZABETHAN AND EARLY STUART TIMES. New Haven: Yale Univ Press, 1958. 1st ed. Dk blue cl, gilt spine. Fine, scarce. *WEBER*. $150

Waters, Frank. MASKED GODS: NAVAHO AND PUEBLO CEREMONIALISM. Univ of New Mexico Press, (1950). 1st ed. Fine in dj w/few small tears, chips. *DERMONT*. $125

Waters, Frank. MASKED GODS: NAVAHO AND PUEBLO CEREMONIALISM. Albuquerque: Univ of NM, 1950. 1st trade ed. Fine in VG dj. *CONNOLLY & WADE*. $75

Waters, Frank. PUMPKIN SEED POINT. Chicago, 1969. 1st ed. Former owner sig. Fine in tear repaired, moderately worn, price-clipped dj. *BAADE*. $50

Waters, Frank. THE COLORADO. NY, 1946. 1st ed. Rivers of America Series. 8vo. Red cloth, xii,400pp; VG+ in VG+ dj (light chips). *FIVE QUAIL*. $35

Waters, Frank. THE COLORADO. NY: Rinehart, (1946). 1st ed. Fine in Fine dj. *BOOK MARKET*. $75

Waters, Frank. THE EARP BROTHERS OF TOMBSTONE. THE STORY OF VIRGIL EARP. NY: Clarkson N. Potter, 1960. 1st ed. Evidence of dj having once been attached lightly to the eps, else VG in VG dj. *CONNOLLY & WADE*. $25

Waters, Frank. THE MAN WHO KILLED THE DEER. Flagstaff: Northland Press, 1965. Ltd ed of 1250, numbered, signed. Fine in slipcase. *WEBER*. $65

Waters, Frank. THE MAN WHO KILLED THE DEER. Flagstaff: Northland Press, (1965). Ltd ed of 1250 numbered, signed. VF in VF slipcase. *OREGON*. $120

Waters, Frank. THE MAN WHO KILLED THE DEER. NY: Farrar, Rinehart, (1942). 1st ed. Fine in chipped, internally and externally mended dj. Inscribed. *CAPTAIN'S BOOKSHELF*. $150

Waters, Frank. TO POSSESS THE LAND: A BIOGRAPHY OF ARTHUR ROCHFORD MANBY. Chicago: Swallow Press. (1973). 1st ed. Signed by Waters. Fine in fine dj. *DERMONT*. $40

Waterton, Charles. ESSAYS ON NATURAL HISTORY, CHIEFLY ORNITHOLOGY WITH AN AUTOBIOGRAPHY...AND A VIEW OF WALTON HALL. London: Longman et al, 1844. 5th ed. 334pp, cat; engr frontis. Blindstamped gilt purple cl cvr moderately rippled, stained, ex-lib; contents very clean. Good+. *SMITHFIELD*. $33

Waterton, Charles. WANDERINGS IN SOUTH AMERICA, THE NORTH-WEST OF THE UNITED STATES...1812, 1816, 1820, AND 1824....London, 1839. 4th ed. Frontis. iv,307pp. Orig gilt-stamped cl. Wear and splitting around spine ends; corners bumped, front joint cracked. *SUTTON*. $95

Waterton, Charles. WANDERINGS IN SOUTH AMERICA. London, 1879. New ed, Rev. J.G. Wood (ed). 100 illus. Gilt pict cl. Hinges broken; wear, spotting; water spot 12 pp. Contents VG. Howes W 158. *SILVER*. $75

Waterton, Charles. WANDERINGS IN SOUTH AMERICA...AND THE ANTILLES, IN THE YEARS 1812, 1816, 18 20, & 1824. London: B. Fellowes, 1828. 2nd ed. Frontis, (viii),341pp. Figures, untrimmed. Orig boards, worn on extremities. Vertical split on backstrip w/orig binding string still holding securely. Most of orig paper title label on backstrip still present. VG. Howes W158 *CONNOLLY & WADE*. $150

Waterton, Charles. WANDERINGS IN SOUTH AMERICA...THE UNITED STATES...ANTILLES...1812, 1816, 1820, AND 1824....London: J. Mawman, 1825. 1st ed. 4to, 27cm, vii, 326pp, frontis. Some wear boards, spine, lt foxing; overall VG. Howes W158. *PARMER*. $850

Watkins, Floyd C. and John T. Hiers, eds. ROBERT PENN WARREN TALKING: INTERVIEWS 1950-1978. NY: Random House, (1980). 1st ed. Fine in dj. Inscribed. *CAPTAIN'S BOOKSHELF*. $60

Watkins, John. CHARACTERISTIC ANECDOTES...GREAT-BRITAIN AND IRELAND...THREE LAST CENTURIES....London: Albion Press, ptd for James Cundee, 1808. 1st ed. (4),552,(6). Modern brn backed paper, blue boards. 4 stains title-pg (one effecting 1st word of title), foxing, uncut. Bkpls. *WEBER*. $250

Watkins, T.H. GOLD AND SILVER IN THE WEST. Palo Alto: American West, 1971. 1st ed. Fine in NF dj. *CONNOLLY & WADE*. $45

Watkins, T.H. THE GRAND COLORADO. (Palo Alto): American West, (1969). 1st ed. Fine in Fine dj. *BOOK MARKET*. $50

Watkins, T.H. THE GRAND COLORADO. (Palo Alto): American West Pub, (1969). 1st ed. NF in dj. *LOPEZ*. $65

Watkins, T.H. THE GRAND COLORADO. N.p., 1969, 4to., 310pp, illus, map eps. Fine in NF dj. *FIVE QUAIL*. $25

Watkins, Vernon. ELEGY FOR THE LATEST DEAD. Privately ptd, 1977. 1st ed, one of 120 numbered. Fine. *BEASLEY*. $50

Watson, Alfred E.T. KING EDWARD VII AS A SPORTSMAN. London: Longmans, Green, 1911. 1st ed. VG. *OCTOBER FARM*. $65

Watson, Colin. BROOMSTICKS OVER FLAXBOROUGH. London: Eyre Methuen, 1972. 1st ed. Fine in dj. *MORDIDA*. $65

Watson, Colin. HOPJOY WAS HERE. NY: Walker, 1963. 1st Amer ed. Fine in dj. *MORDIDA*. $35

Watson, Colin. KISSING COVENS. NY: G.P. Putnam's Sons, 1972. 1st Amer ed. Fine in dj. *MORDIDA*. $35

Watson, Colin. LONELYHEART 4122. London: Eyre & Spottiswoode, 1967. 1st ed. Fine in dj (couple closed tears; sl darkening along edges). *MORDIDA*. $65

Watson, Colin. PLASTER SINNERS. London: Eyre Methuen, 1980. 1st ed. Fine in dj. *MORDIDA*. $45

Watson, Colin. WHATEVER'S BEEN GOING ON AT MUMBLESBY? London: Methuen, 1982. 1st ed. Fine in dj. *MORDIDA*. $45

Watson, Douglas. WEST WIND. THE LIFE STORY OF JOSEPH REDDEFORD WALKER....LA: Percy Booth, 1934. 1st ed, ltd to 100. Frontis, fldg map. 1/2 morocco w/gilt lettered spine. Corner bumped; light edgewear o/w VG. Howes W165. *OREGON*. $500

Watson, Elmo Scott. THE PROFESSOR GOES WEST. Illinois Wesleyan, 1954. 1st ed. VF. *FIVE QUAIL*. $35

Watson, Frederick. HUNTING PIE. THE WHOLE ART AND CRAFT OF FOXHUNTING. NY: Derrydale, 1931. Ltd. ed. of 750 unnumbered. About VG. *OCTOBER FARM.* $135

Watson, James & John Tooze. THE DNA STORY, A DOCUMENTARY HISTORY OF GENE CLONING. SF, 1981. 1st ed. *FYE.* $75

Watson, James. THE DOUBLE HELIX: A PERSONAL ACCOUNT OF THE DISCOVERY OF THE STRUCTURE OF DNA. NY, 1968. 1st ed. *FYE.* $22.50

Watson, May & Alex Lillico. TAFT RANCH. A HISTORY OF THE FIFTY YEARS OF DEVELOPMENT....N.p., n.d. (c. 1936). 1st ed. 39pp + 16pp ads. Wraps. VG. Howes W172. *OREGON.* $85

Watson, Richard. BITTERS BOTTLES. NY, 1965. 1st ed. Dj. *FYE.* $75

Watson, Rowland. A SCRAPBOOK OF INNS. NY: Medill McBride & Co. (1950). 1st ed. Grn cl, gilt. Dj. *KARMIOLE.* $30

Watson, Thomas A. EXPLORING LIFE: THE AUTOBIOGRAPHY OF... NY: D. Appleton, 1926. 1st ed. Grn cl cvr worn; contents Near VG. Presentation copy. *SMITHFIELD.* $50

Watson, Thomas H. NAVAL ARCHITECTURE: A MANUAL. 3rd ed. London (etc.) 1903. 57 fldg plans. Attractive. *LEFKOWICZ.* $100

Watson, W. THE FORESTER'S MANUAL. Edinburgh: Stirling, Kenney, 1837. 1st ed. Cl w/worn paper label. Sl foxed. VG. *SECOND LIFE.* $75

Watson, Wilbur J. and Sara Ruth Watson. BRIDGES IN HISTORY AND LEGEND. Cleveland: J.H. Jansen. 1937. 1st ed. *KARMIOLE.* $75

Watson, William. SCULPTURE OF JAPAN FROM THE 5TH TO THE 15TH CENTURY. London: The Studio, (1959). VG. *ARTIS.* $27.50

Watson, William. THE ELOPING ANGELS. A Caprice. London: Elkin Mathews & John Lane, 1893. 29, (2)pp, 7pp ads. Orig dk blue cl, teg. Ffep cracking, but VG. 1st trade ed. *CHAPEL HILL.* $75

Watson, William. THE HOPE OF THE WORD AND OTHER POEMS. London: Bodley Head, 1898. One of 125 large paper copies. Presentation, inscribed, signed by pub, John Lane. Ep offsetting. Fine. *MUELLER.* $100

Watson, William. THE POEMS OF WILLIAM WATSON. NY: Lane, 1905. 2 vols. 1st ed. Cvrs silverfished at extrems. Fine. *MUELLER.* $45

Watterson, Henry. HISTORY OF THE SPANISH-AMERICAN WAR. NY (1938). 4 colored lithos, double pg plts. Dec cover. Some spine wear. *HEINOLDT.* $25

Wattles, Gurdon Wallace. AUTOBIOGRAPHY OF GURDON WALLACE WATTLES: GENEALOGY. (NY): Pub by author, 1922. 1st ed. VG. *LAURIE.* $100

Watts, Alan. IN MY OWN WAY: AN AUTOBIOGRAPHY. Pantheon, 1972. 1st ed. Fine in dj sunned on spine. *STAHR.* $35

Watts, Ralph. VEGETABLE FORCING. NY: Orange Judd, 1917. VG. *AMERICAN BOTANIST.* $25

Watts, Ralph. VEGETABLE GARDENING. NY: Orange Judd, 1924. Rev ed. VG. *AMERICAN BOTANIST.* $18

Watts, W.W. OLD ENGLISH SILVER. NY: Scribner's, 1924. 1st ed. VG. *BACKROOM.* $200

Waugh, Alec. THE EARLY YEARS OF ALEC WAUGH. NY: Farrar Straus, (1963). Inscribed "with best wishes" at Christmas, 1963. Fine in NF, price-clipped dj. *LOPEZ.* $45

Waugh, Evelyn. A LITTLE LEARNING. Boston: Little-Brown, 1964. 1st ed. Fine; dj sunned at extrems. *ELSE FINE.* $25

Waugh, Evelyn. BASIL SEAL RIDES AGAIN, Or, The Rake's Regress. Boston: Little, Brown, (1963). Top third of rear cvr spotted, o/w About Fine. 1st Amer ed. #238 of 1000 signed. *CHAPEL HILL.* $135

Waugh, Evelyn. BASIL SEAL RIDES AGAIN. Boston: Little Brown & Co., (1963). 1st US ed. One of 1000 numbered, signed. Fine, issued without dj. *UNGER.* $225

Waugh, Evelyn. BLACK MISCHIEF. London: Chapman & Hall, (1932). 1st ed. Sl cocked, else NF lacking the dj. *CAPTAIN'S BOOKSHELF.* $75

Waugh, Evelyn. BRIDESHEAD REVISITED. Boston: (Little Brown), 1945. 1st Amer ed. Pub's red cl, in orig sl chipped dj. Fine. *BOOK BLOCK.* $35

Waugh, Evelyn. CHARLES RYDER'S SCHOOLDAYS. NY: Little Brown, 1982. 1st ed. Uncorrected proof. Fine in wraps. *SMITH.* $35

Waugh, Evelyn. LABELS. (London): Duckworth, 1930. 1st ed. Spine very sl faded, else Very NF, lacking dj. Inscribed. Bkpl on front pastedown. *BETWEEN COVERS.* $1250

Waugh, Evelyn. LABELS. (London): Duckworth, 1930. One of 110 numbered and signed, with a page of manuscript laid in that is closely handwritten, numbered 18 at top. Corners very lightly bumped, small, neat bkpl on front pastedown. Fine w/o dj as issued. *BETWEEN COVERS.* $1500

Waugh, Evelyn. OFFICERS AND GENTLEMEN. London: Chapman & Hall, (1955). 1st ed. Fine; minor rubs to dj corners. *ELSE FINE.* $145

Waugh, Evelyn. PUT OUT MORE FLAGS. Boston: Little-Brown, 1942. 1st ed. VF; minor wear extrems of unfaded dj. *ELSE FINE.* $350

Waugh, Evelyn. ROSSETTI: HIS LIFE AND WORK. London: Duckworth, 1928. 1st ed. Small spots of foxing to page edges, else Fine in white dj. *BETWEEN COVERS.* $3750

Waugh, Evelyn. SCOOP: A NOVEL ABOUT JOURNALISTS. London: Chapman & Hall, (1933). 1st ed. Sl cocked, else NF lacking dj. *CAPTAIN'S BOOKSHELF.* $75

Waugh, Evelyn. THE HOLY PLACES. London and NY: Queen Anne & BBC, 1953. One of 1000 numbered for the US. Fine in stained and torn dj. *BEASLEY.* $125

Waugh, Evelyn. THE LETTERS OF EVELYN WAUGH AND DIANA COOPER. NY: T & F, 1992. Uncorrected proof. Fine in wrappers. *LOPEZ.* $45

Waugh, Evelyn. THE LOVED ONE. (London): Chapman & Hall, n.d. (1948). One of 250 numbered large paper copies signed by Waugh and illus Stuart Boyle. Sl bumped at corners, else Fine w/o dj as issued. *BETWEEN COVERS.* $1250

Waugh, Evelyn. THE LOVED ONE. Boston: Little, Brown, 1948. 1st US ed. Fine in very sl worn dj. *CAPTAIN'S BOOKSHELF.* $75

Waugh, Evelyn. THE ORDEAL OF GILBERT PINFOLD. London, 1957. 1st ed. Tiny bkshop label. NF in dj w/edge chips, closed short tears. *POLYANTHOS.* $25

Waugh, Hilary. THE ODDS RUN OUT. NY: Coward, 1949. 1st ed. Glue residue rear pastedown, light wear spine ends, o/w NF in lightly used dj. *BEASLEY.* $25

Waugh, Hillary. THE NERISSA CLAIRE CASE. London: Gollancz, 1983. 1st ed. VF in dj. *SILVER DOOR.* $22.50

Waugh, Lorenzo. AUTOBIOGRAPHY OF...Oakland, 1883. 1st ed. 311pp. Orig cl. Howes W181. *GINSBERG.* $75

Waugh, Norah. CORSETS AND CRINOLINES. London: B.T. Batsford. (1954). 1st ed. Dj. *KARMIOLE.* $75

Wavy Gravy. SOMETHING GOOD FOR A CHANGE. NY: St. Martins, 1992. Wraps. Adv uncorrected proofs, Fine. *BEASLEY.* $25

Waxell, Sven. THE AMERICAN EXPEDITION. London: William Hodge, 1952. ix + 236pp + 7 fldg maps + 1 fldg illus. 1st ed. Fine in NF dj. *GREAT EPIC.* $55

Way, Isabel Stewart. SEED OF THE LAND. NY: Appleton, 1935. 1st ed. NF w/a little spine wear in bit worn, sl chipped dj. *BEASLEY.* $45

Way, Thomas E. SGT. FRED PLATTEN'S TEN YEARS ON THE TRAIL OF THE REDSKINS. Williams, AZ, 1963. 2nd ed. VG+. *PRATT.* $37.50

Wayland, Francis. MEMOIR OF THE LIFE AND LABORS OF THE REV. ADONIRAM JUDSON, D.D. Boston: Phillips, Sampson and Co, 1853. 2 vols. 544, 522pp. 1st ed. Brown cl stamped in blind and gilt, somewhat shaken and w/some rubbing and stains. Some foxing. Frontis. *SCHOYER'S.* $40

Wayland, John W. A HISTORY OF ROCKINGHAM COUNTY, VIRGINIA. Dayton, Ruebush, 1912. 1st ed. Orig pict cloth, paper label on spine, bkpl removed. *GINSBERG.* $100

Wayland, John Walter. BATTLE OF NEW MARKET. New Market, VA: Henkel Press, 1926. 1st ed. NF. *McGOWAN.* $125

Wayland, John Walter. JOHN KAGI AND JOHN BROWN. Strasburg, VA, 1961. 1st ed. Orig cl. F. *McGOWAN.* $75

Weadock, Jack. DUST OF THE DESERT. NY: Appleton, 1936. 1st ed. Signed, inscribed. Fine in VG to Fine dj. *BOOK MARKET.* $60

Weadock, Jack. DUST OF THE DESERT. Tucson: Arizona Silhouettes, 1963. Fine in Fine dj. *CONNOLLY & WADE.* $40

Weatherly, F.E. LITTLE PICKLE. Illus by Jane M. Dealy. NY: E.P. Dutton & Co. N.d. (circa 1890). (24)pp. 8 color plts. *KARMIOLE.* $50

Weathers, J. (ed). COMMERCIAL GARDENING....London, 1913. 4 vols. 64 plts (16 colored). Dec cl, some wear, soiling, occasional foxing. Sm name stamp front of vols. *SUTTON.* $125

Weathers, J. A PRACTICAL GUIDE TO GARDEN PLANTS...ALSO THE BEST KINDS OF FRUITS AND VEGETABLES...London, 1901. Orig cl (lt soiling, splitting to head of spine, 2" spine edge split), o/w Nice ex-lib. *SUTTON.* $43

Weaver, John D. WIND BEFORE RAIN. NY: Macmillan, 1942. 1st ed. 1st bk. Signed. Orig beige cl. Bkpl, offsetting right, dedication pgs from newspaper clipping (no longer present), o/w NF in VG dj, sunned spine. *CHAPEL HILL.* $35

Webb, Beatrice. HEALTH OF WORKING GIRLS, A HAND-BOOK. London: Blackie, 1917. 1st ed. VG. *SECOND LIFE.* $85

Webb, Beatrice. MY APPRENTICESHIP. NY & London: Longmans, 1923. 1st ed. 7 plts. Nice in dj. *SECOND LIFE.* $45

Webb, James Josiah. ADVENTURES IN THE SANTA FE TRADE 1844-1847. Ralph Bieber (ed). Vol 1 in SW Series. A.H. Clark, 1931. 1st ed. Frontis, 7 plts, fldg map. Fine. *OREGON.* $150

Webb, James. A SENSE OF HONOR. Englewood Cliffs: Prentice-Hall, (1981). 1st ed. VG+ in lightly worn dj. *AKA.* $35

Webb, James. FIELDS OF FIRE. Englewood Cliffs: Prentice Hall, Inc, (c1978). Uncorrected proof. Fine in ptd wraps. *HELLER.* $100

Webb, James. FIELDS OF FIRE. Englewood Cliffs: Prentice Hall, (1978). 1st ed. Fine in NF dj. *LOPEZ.* $75

Webb, James. FIELDS OF FIRE. Prentice-Hall, 1978. Uncorrected proof. Fine in orange wraps. *STAHR.* $60

Webb, Joe. THE CARE AND TRAINING OF THE TENNESSEE WALKING HORSE. Searcy, 1962. 1st ed. VG in Fair dj. *OCTOBER FARM.* $38

Webb, Kate. ON THE OTHER SIDE. (NY): Quadrangle, (1972). 1st ed. Dust top edges, o/w Fine in VG dj. *AKA.* $40

Webb, W.E. BUFFALO LAND. Cincinnati: E. Hannaford and Co, 1873. xxiii,503pp. Black and gold stamped dec cl, edges and spine worn. *DAWSON'S.* $50

Webb, W.E. BUFFALO LAND: AN ACCOUNT OF THE DISCOVERIES, ADVENTURES & MISHAPS OF A SCIENTIFIC & SPORTING PARTY IN THE WILD WEST, ETC. Cincinnati, Chicago, SF: Hannaford, 1872. Engr; gilt dec cl. VG. *MIKESH.* $100

Webb, Walter Prescott. THE TEXAS RANGERS, A CENTURY OF FRONTIER DEFENSE. Austin, 1935. 2nd ed, (1965). VG+ in dj. *PRATT.* $32.50

Webb, William. HENRY AND FRIENDS: THE CALIFORNIA YEARS, 1946-1977. Santa Barbara: Capra Press, (1991). 1st ed. One of 100 numbered, hardbound, signed by Webb, w/orig photo of Miller laid in. As New, w/o dj, as issued. *SMITH.* $75

Webber, Charles W. OLD HICKS THE GUIDE; OR, ADVENTURES IN THE CAMANCHE COUNTRY....NY, 1848. 1st ed. 356pp. Orig cl, inner hinge expertly strengthened, spine a little faded. Howes W198. *GINSBERG.* $300

Webber, Elsie. THE SAVING RAIN. Boston: Branden, (1989). Fine in dj. *LOPEZ.* $60

Weber, Bruce. BEAR POND. N.p.: Bullfinch Press and Little, Brown, (1990). 1st ed. Fine in dj. *CAPTAIN'S BOOKSHELF.* $60

Weber, Bruce. O RIO DE JANEIRO: A PHOTOGRAPHIC JOURNAL. NY: Knopf, 1986. 1st ed. Fine in pict wraps. Signed. *CAPTAIN'S BOOKSHELF.* $175

Weber, Carl J. THOMAS HARDY IN MAINE. Portland, ME: Southworth-Anthoensen Press, 1942. 2 plts. Ed ltd to 425. *KARMIOLE.* $40

Weber, David J. THE TAOS TRAPPERS. Norman: Univ of OK, (1971). 1st ed. VF in VF dj. *OREGON.* $50

Weber, David J. THE TAOS TRAPPERS: THE FUR TRADE IN THE FAR SOUTHWEST, 1540-1846. Norman: Univ of Oklahoma Press, 1971. 1st prtg stated. Faded spine. VG. *BURCHAM.* $45

Webster, Daniel. SPEECH OF HON. DANIEL WEBSTER ON MR. CLAY'S RESOLUTIONS IN THE SENATE OF THE U.S. MARCH 7, 1850. Boston: Redding & Co., 1850. Rebound 1st ed. Fine. *OREGON.* $32.50

Webster, E.B. THE KING OF THE OLYMPICS. Port Angeles, WA: Priv Pub, 1920. VG+. *MIKESH.* $45

Webster, J. Vinson. TWO TRUE CALIFORNIA STORIES. AUGUSTA DANE; OR, THE INFLUENCE OF CIRCUMSTANCES. MARY MORTON; OR, THE RESULT OF A FASHIONABLE EDUCATION. SF: P.J. Thomas, 1883. 1st ed. VG. *CONNOLLY & WADE.* $75

Webster, Noah. A DICTIONARY FOR PRIMARY SCHOOLS. NY & New Haven 1833. 1st ed. Sq 16mo. 341,(2)pp. Contemp calf, rebacked, new endpapers. *M & S.* $400

Webster, Noah. THE ELEMENTARY SPELLING BOOK. NY, (1829). NF. *POLYANTHOS.* $60

Webster, Samuel Charles (ed). MARK TWAIN, BUSINESS MAN. Boston: Little Brown, 1946. xii,409pp. Dj. *BOOKMINE.* $25

Wechsberg, Joseph. THE LOST WORLD OF THE GREAT SPAS. NY, 1979. Dj. *FYE.* $45

Wechsler, Herman J. GREAT PRINTS & PRINTMAKERS. NY: Abrams, (1967). 100 plts. Dk gray cl, orig glassine wrapper. VG. *WEBER.* $85

Wecter, Dixon (ed). MARK TWAIN TO MRS. FAIRBANKS. San Marino: Huntington Library, 1949. 1st ed. Cloth. VF. *CONNOLLY & WADE.* $85

Wedeck, Harry. DICTIONARY OF APHRODISIACS. NY, 1961. 1st ed. *FYE.* $50

Weed, C.M. LIFE HISTORIES OF AMERICAN INSECTS. NY, 1897. 1st ed. Nice ex-lib copy. *SUTTON.* $37

Weeden, Howard (Miss). SHADOWS ON THE WALL. Huntsville, AL: Howard Weeden, 1899. 1st ed. 1st bk. Small 4to, (27)pp. Orig white cl. Lightly soiled, ink stamp, but VG. *CHAPEL HILL.* $200

Weedon, Lucy. CHILD CHARACTERS FROM DICKENS. RETOLD BY LUCY L. WEEDON. London: Ernest Nistar; NY: Dutton, (1905). Plts, half tones, gray cl over boards, pict cvrs and spine in gold, green, red, yellow, and black, pict eps, aeg. Illus by Arthur A. Dixon. VG. *BOOKMINE.* $65

Weegee (pseud of Arthur Fellig). NAKED CITY. NY: Essential Books, (1945). 1st ed. Fine lacking dj. *CAPTAIN'S BOOKSHELF.* $75

Weegee (pseud of Arthur Fellig). NAKED CITY. NY, (1945). 1st ed. Orig buckram. Spine very sl darkened, o/w NF. *DIAMOND.* $100

Weegee (pseud of Arthur Fellig). WEEGEE'S PEOPLE. NY: Essential Books; Duell, Sloan & Pearce, (1946). 1st ed, 2nd book. Photo illus. VG+ in dj sl worn at spine bottom. *BERNARD.* $100

Weegee (pseud of Arthur Fellig). WEEGEE'S PEOPLE. Essential Books. NY: Duell, Sloan & Pearce. (1946). 1st ed. Unpaginated. Brown cloth stamped in brown and gold. *KARMIOLE.* $60

Weeks, Alvin G. MASSASOIT OF THE WAMPANOAGS WITH A BRIEF COMMENTARY ON INDIAN CHARACTER; AND SKETCHES....Fall River, Mass.: Privately ptd, 1920. 1st ed. Frontis. xvi,270pp. Orig emb cl, gilt. VG. Scarce. *CONNOLLY & WADE.* $75

Weeks, Alvin G. MASSASOIT OF THE WAMPANOAGS...AND SKETCHES OF OTHER GREAT CHIEFS, TRIBES AND NATIONS... (Norwood): Pub by author, 1919. 1st ed. NF. *LAURIE.* $20

Weeks, Edward. THE OPEN HEART. Boston: LB, (1955). 1st ed. One of an unspecified number with signed leaf tipped in. NF in dj. *LOPEZ.* $35

Weeks, Edwin Lord. FROM THE BLACK SEA THROUGH PERSIA AND INDIA. NY: Harper & Bros. 1896. 1st ed. xii,(2),438pp. + (2)pp. of ads. Cloth lightly soiled. *KARMIOLE.* $75

Weeks, Edwin Lord. FROM THE BLACK SEA THROUGH PERSIA AND INDIA. NY: Harper, 1896. 1st ed. Worn, rubbed, back cover detached, title page soiled, o/w Good ex-lib. *WORLDWIDE.* $25

Weeks, George F. CALIFORNIA COPY. Washington, D.C.: Washington College Press, 1928. 1st ed. 11pp photos. Tiny nibble at top edge of spine and top edge of rear board, else VF. Scarce. *CONNOLLY & WADE.* $65

Weeks, Jeanne G. and Donald Treganowan. RUGS AND CARPETS OF EUROPE. NY: Weathervane Bks, 1969. VG in Good dj, edges brn. *BACKROOM.* $30

Weems, John Edward. DEATH SONG, THE LAST OF THE INDIAN WARS. GC, 1976. 1st ed. 311pp. VG+ in dj. *PRATT.* $22.50

Wehde, A. FINGER-PRINTS CAN BE FORGED. Chicago, 1924. 1st ed. 12mo, 134, (10)pp, frontis. Lacks front free fly. Bkpl removed, o/w VG. *DIAMOND.* $12.50

Wehr, Julian. ANIMATED MOTHER GOOSE. NY: Grosset and Dunlap, 1942. 1st ed. A mechanical Mother Goose w/all moving tabs in working order. Spiral-bound. Fine in lightly used dj. *BEASLEY.* $125

Weichmann, Louis. A TRUE HISTORY OF THE ASSASSINATION OF ABRAHAM LINCOLN AND OF THE CONSPIRACY OF 1865. NY, 1975. Ed by Floyd E. Risvold. 1st ed. Dj. VG+. *PRATT.* $32.50

Weichmann, Louis. A TRUE HISTORY OF THE ASSASSINATION OF ABRAHAM LINCOLN AND OF THE CONSPIRACY OF 1865. Ed by Floyd Risvold. NY: Knopf, 1975. 1st ed. Signed by ed. Fine in NF dj a bit rubbed. *ARCHER.* $30

Weider, Ben and David Hapgood. THE MURDER OF NAPOLEON. NY: Congdon & Lattes, 1982. 1st ed. VF in dj. *MORDIDA.* $30

Weidman, Jerome. I CAN GET IT FOR YOU WHOLESALE. NY, 1937. 1st ed. Signed, presentation copy. Offsetting ffep, spine sl sunned. Dj w/spine little rubbed, 2 tiny chips. Author's 1st bk. Scarce. *POLYANTHOS.* $250

Weidman, Jerome. WHAT'S IN IT FOR ME? NY, 1938. 1st ed. Signed, presentation copy. Fine in dj w/spine and edges rubbed, 2

sm edge chips lower edge front panel, piece missing top edge rear panel, small chip lower edge. *POLYANTHOS.* $65

Weigall, Arthur. A HISTORY OF THE PHARAOHS. 2 vols. NY: E.P. Dutton, (1925). 2 maps. Signature. Good. *ARCHAEOLOGIA.* $85

Weigall, Arthur. NERO, THE SINGING EMPEROR OF ROME. GC: Garden City Press, (1930). Frontis. Bkpl. Good in tattered dj. *ARCHAEOLOGIA.* $35

Weigall, Arthur. THE GLORY OF THE PHARAOHS. London: Butterworth, 1923. 2nd ed. Good ex-lib w/number on spine. *WORLDWIDE.* $28

Weigall, Arthur. THE LIFE AND TIMES OF AKHNATON. Edinburgh: Wm. Blackwood, 1910. 1st ed. Plts. Cracked outer hinges. Good. *BLUE DRAGON.* $30

Weigley, Russell F. QUARTERMASTER GENERAL OF THE UNION ARMY, A BIOGRAPHY OF M.C. MEIGS. NY, 1959. VG+ in dj. *PRATT.* $50

Weil, Gunther et al (eds). THE PSYCHEDELIC READER. New Hyde Park: University Books, (1965). 1st ed. NF in dj. *LOPEZ.* $45

Weil, Simone. THE ILIAD OR THE POEM OF FORCE. Mary McCarthy (trans). Iowa City: Stone Wall Press, 1973. 1st ed. Ltd to 150. Red cl w/ptd label on spine. Fine. *JAFFE.* $350

Weiler, Milton C. THE CLASSIC DECOY SERIES. A PORTFOLIO OF PAINTINGS. NY: Winchester Press, 1969. One of 1,000, this copy out of series, a salesman's sample. 24 color plts. Wrappers, gilt titles, brown linen spine ties, slipcase. Fine. *WEBER.* $400

Weill, Gus. THE BONNET MAN. NY: Macmillan, 1978. 1st ed. VF in dj. *MORDIDA.* $25

Weinbaum, Stanley. A MARTIAN ODYSSEY. Fantasy Press, 1949. One of 500 numbered, plated. NF in sl frayed dj. *MADLE.* $175

Weinbaum, Stanley. THE BLACK FLAME. Fantasy Press, 1948. One of 500 numbered, plated. Fine in dj. *MADLE.* $200

Weinbaum, Stanley. THE BLACK FLAME. Reading: Fantasy, 1948. 1st ed. Fine in lightly used dj w/chips. *BEASLEY.* $50

Weir, Capt. Robert, et al. RIDING/POLO (BADMINTON LIBRARY). Boston: Little, Brown, and London: Longmans, Green, 1891. 1st Amer ed. Minor edgewear and foxing, thus VG-NF. *OLD LONDON.* $85

Weir, Irene. THE GREEK PAINTER'S ART. Boston: Ginn, (1905). Light chipping at spine. Good. *ARCHAEOLOGIA.* $35

Weir, L.H. (ed). PARKS. 2 vols. NY, 1928. Cl, some wear at corners and spine ends. Overall soiling, lt signs of dampness index pp. *SUTTON.* $150

Weis, Norman D. GHOST TOWNS OF THE NORTHWEST. KNOWN AND UNKNOWN. Caldwell: Caxton, 1971. 1st ed. NF in VG dj. *CONNOLLY & WADE.* $30

Weiser, Frederick S. and Howell J. Heaney. THE PENNSYLVANIA GERMAN FRAKTUR OF THE FREE LIBRARY OF PHILADELPHIA: AN ILLUSTRATED CATALOG. Phila: The PA German Soc, 1976. 1st ed. As New. *BACKROOM.* $75

Weiss, H.B. and G.M. Ziegler. THOMAS SAY, EARLY AMERICAN NATURALIST. Springfield, 1931. Notes on eps. *SUTTON.* $50

Weisse, Franz. THE ART OF MARBLING. North Hills, PA: Bird & Bull Press, 1980. 1st ed. Ltd to 300. Illus w/samples, 1/4 morocco & boards. Mint. *JAFFE.* $375

Welch, James. FOOL'S CROW. (NY): Viking, (1986). 1st ed. Remainder mark, o/w Fine in Fine dj and inscribed. *LOPEZ.* $85

Welch, James. FOOL'S CROW. NY: Viking, (1986). 1st ed. Fine in dj. *CAPTAIN'S BOOKSHELF.* $35

Welch, James. FOOL'S CROW. Viking, 1986. Advance reading copy. Fine in wraps. *STAHR.* $35

Welch, James. RIDING THE EARTHBOY 40. NY: Harper, 1976. Rev and expanded ed. Fine w/owner's stamp in NF dj. *BEASLEY.* $45

Welch, James. RIDING THE EARTHBOY 40. NY: World, (1971). 1st ed. Fine in Fine dj. *UNGER.* $175

Welch, James. RIDING THE EARTHBOY 40. NY: World, (1971). 1st ed. Fine in NF dj. *LOPEZ.* $125

Welch, James. RIDING THE EARTHBOY 40. NY: World, (1971). 1st ed, 1st bk. Fine in NF dj. *LOPEZ.* $125

Welch, James. THE DEATH OF JIM LONEY. London: Gollancz, 1980. 1st Brit ed. Fine in dj. *LOPEZ.* $50

Welch, James. THE DEATH OF JIM LONEY. NY: Harper, (1979). 1st ed. Fine in NF price-clipped dj. *UNGER.* $65

Welch, James. WINTER IN THE BLOOD. NY: Harper & Row et al, (1974). 1st ed, 1st novel. Fine in dj. *BERNARD.* $75

Welch, W.M. HOW TO ORGANIZE, CLASSIFY AND TEACH A COUNTRY SCHOOL. W.M. Welch Pub., 1886. 2nd ed. VG+. *MAD DOG.* $15

Welch, William. PATHOLOGY AND PREVENTIVE MEDICINE. Baltimore, 1920. 1st ed. *FYE.* $75

Weld, Stephen Minton Weld. WAR DIARY AND LETTERS OF STEPHEN MINOT WELD 1861-1865. Cambridge, 1912. 2nd ed, (1979) ltd to 850. Minor shelf wear o/w Fine. *PRATT.* $60

Weller, Earle V. (comp). BALLADS OF ELDORADO. SF, 1940. 1st ed, ltd to 300. Fine. *OREGON.* $50

Welles, C.M. THREE YEARS WANDERINGS OF A CONNECTICUT YANKEE. NY: American Subscription Pub House, 1859. 358pp, 10 engr plts. Orig dec cl, faded, lt tidemarks throughout, presentable. *LEFKOWICZ.* $125

Wellman, Manly Wade. GIANT IN GRAY, A BIOGRAPHY OF WADE HAMPTON OF SOUTH CAROLINA. NY, (1949). 1st ed. 387pp, illus., notes, biblio., index. VG. *PRATT.* $60

Wellman, Manly Wade. SHERLOCK HOLMES'S WAR OF THE WORLDS. NY: Warner Books, 1975. 1st ed. Pb orig. Name on 1st pp o/w Fine, unread, in wrappers. *MORDIDA.* $45

Wellman, Manly Wade. THEY TOOK THEIR STAND, THE FOUNDERS OF THE CONFEDERACY. NY, (1959). 1st ed. Minor dj wear o/w VG+. *PRATT.* $37.50

Wellman, Manly Wade. WHO FEARS THE DEVIL. Sauk City: Arkham House, 1963. 1st ed. Fine but for signs of partial cocktail ring on front board, in lightly used and lightly rubbed dj. *BEASLEY.* $100

Wellman, Manly Wade. WHO FEARS THE DEVIL? Arkham House, 1963. 1st ed. Fine in dj. *MADLE.* $200

Wellman, Paul I. A DYNASTY OF WESTERN OUTLAWS. GC: Doubleday, 1961. 1st ed. NF, chipped dj. *PARMER.* $50

Wellman, Paul I. SPAWN OF EVIL: THE INVISIBLE EMPIRE. Doubleday, 1964. 1st ed. Name, else Fine in Good dj. *CONNOLLY & WADE.* $25

Wellman, Paul I. THE COMMANCHEROS. GC: Doubleday, (1952). 1st ed. Inscribed. NF in dj with a few scattered nicks and chips to spine ends. *UNGER.* $75

Wellman, Paul I. THE TRAMPLING HERD, THE STORY OF THE CATTLE RANGE IN AMERICA. Carrick & Evans, (1939). 1st ed. VG. *OREGON.* $45

Wellman, Paul I. THE TRAMPLING HERD. Doubleday, 1951. Rpt. Fine in chipped dj. *VARNER.* $30

Wellmann, Walter. THE AERIAL AGE...NY: A.R. Keller, 1911. 448pp. 1st ed. Orig. gilt dec blue cvr. Gilt titles. Minor wear, one

corner slight bump. Front interior hinge starting. Owner's signature else VG. *GREAT EPIC.* $95

Wells, Carolyn. THE DIAMOND PIN. Phila: Lippincott, 1919. 1st ed. Color frontispiece by Gayle Hoskins. VG+, a sound, attractive copy. *ELSE FINE.* $45

Wells, Charles Wesley. FRONTIER LIFE: BEING A DESCRIPTION OF MY EXPERIENCE...WITH SKETCHES...AND MY EARLY WORK IN THE MINISTRY. Cincinnati, 1902. 1st ed. 313pp. Orig cl, spine lightly faded. Howes W244. *GINSBERG.* $175

Wells, Emma M. THE HISTORY OF ROANE COUNTY, TENNESSEE, 1801-1870. Chattanooga, TN, (1927). 1st ed. Orig cl, sm paper label on spine, bkpl removed. *GINSBERG.* $75

Wells, Evelyn. CHAMPAGNE DAYS OF SAN FRANCISCO. NY: Appleton-Century, 1939. 1st ed. Inscribed, signed, dated. Frontis. 30 plts. Cloth, gilt. Fine in chipped, scarce dj. *CONNOLLY & WADE.* $45

Wells, H.G, Julian S. Huxley, and C.P. Wells. THE SCIENCE OF LIFE. GC, NY: Doubleday, Doran & Co, 1931. 4 vols. 1st ed. Color frontis. Ltd to 750 numbered sets, signed by all 3 authors. Orig blue cl over boards, paper spine labels, spines faded, sl rubbed. Good. *KARMIOLE.* $225

Wells, H.G. CHRISTINA ALBERTA'S FATHER. NY, 1925. 1st ed. Little edge crease front cover. Fine in scarce price clipped dj (lower spine sl chipped, little edge rubbed, small tear side spine rear panel, also little soiled). *POLYANTHOS.* $55

Wells, H.G. FLOOR GAMES. London: Frank Palmer, (1911). 1st ed. Slight foxing to page edges and first and last pages, else NF w/pict front cover and unrubbed painted lettering. *BETWEEN COVERS.* $225

Wells, H.G. IN THE DAYS OF THE COMET. London, 1906. 1st ed. (Currey binding B). VG. *MADLE.* $125

Wells, H.G., Julian S. Huxley and C.P. Wells. THE SCIENCE OF LIFE. GC: Doubleday, Doran & Co. 1931. 4 vols. Ed ltd to 750 numbered sets, signed by all 3 authors. Spines faded, bit rubbed. *KARMIOLE.* $225

Wells, H.G. MANKIND IN THE MAKING. NY, 1904. 1st Amer ed. VG+. *McCLINTOCK.* $45

Wells, H.G. TALES OF SPACE AND TIME. Doubleday-McClure, 1899. 1st ed. Spine frayed. VG. *MADLE.* $150

Wells, H.G. THE ADVENTURES OF TOMMY. Stokes, 1929. 1st Amer ed. 4to. Color illus by author. 2 leaves have a short closed tear, spine edges & cvr corners frayed, cvr pict pastedown has tiny spotting. Interior VG+, cvr Good+. *BEBBAH.* $40

Wells, H.G. THE ANATOMY OF FRUSTRATION. A MODERN SYNTHESIS. London: Cresset Press, 1936. 1st ed. Spine little sunned, extremities and edges little rubbed. NF. *POLYANTHOS.* $25

Wells, H.G. THE CROQUET PLAYER. London: Chatto & Windus, 1936. Neat owner emb stamp, else NF in lightly used dj. 1st ed. *CHAPEL HILL.* $65

Wells, H.G. THE FATE OF MAN. NY, (1939). 1st ed. NF in dj w/extrems sl rubbed. *POLYANTHOS.* $25

Wells, H.G. THE FIRST MEN IN THE MOON. Bowen-Merrill, 1901. 1st US ed pp in Grosset binding. Good+. *MADLE.* $75

Wells, H.G. THE FIRST MEN IN THE MOON. London, 1901. 1st ed. (Currey binding D). Good+. *MADLE.* $200

Wells, H.G. THE FUTURE IN AMERICA. NY & London, 1906. 1st Amer ed. Fine. *McCLINTOCK.* $45

Wells, H.G. THE HOLY TERROR. NY, (1939). 1st Amer ed. Fine in dj w/light edgewear. *McCLINTOCK.* $50

Wells, H.G. THE INVISIBLE MAN. Harper, 1898. VG. *MADLE.* $95

Wells, H.G. THE NEW AMERICA: THE NEW WORLD. London: Cresset Press, 1935. 1st ed. Bkpl. Fine in dj (spine little sunned). *POLYANTHOS.* $60

Wells, H.G. THE RIGHTS OF MAN. Middlesex, U.K. and NY: Penguin Books, (1940). 1st ed. Browned in orig wrappers, w/ptd dj. VG. *SECOND LIFE.* $35

Wells, H.G. THE SEA LADY. Appleton, 1902. 1st US ed. VG. *MADLE.* $250

Wells, H.G. THE WAR IN THE AIR. London, 1908. 1st ed. (Currey binding C). Good. *MADLE.* $100

Wells, H.G. THE WAY THE WORLD IS GOING. GUESSES AND FORECASTS OF THE NEXT FEW YEARS. London, 1928. 1st ed. Bkpl. Fine in dj (spine little sunned, extremities minimally rubbed). *POLYANTHOS.* $75

Wells, H.G. THE WORLD SET FREE, A STORY OF MANKIND. NY: Dutton, (c1914). 1st Amer ed. VG in orig brn cl stamped in gold, backstrip and front cvr. *HELLER.* $75

Wells, H.G. YOU CAN'T BE TOO CAREFUL. Putnam, 1942. 1st Amer. ed. VG. Dj is chipped at spine ends, has edge wear & is sunned on spine. *STAHR.* $15

Wells, James M. THE CHISOLM MASSACRE. Chisolm Monument Assoc, 1878. 3rd ed. 331pp, port. Good+. *BOOK BROKER.* $60

Wells, John G. WELLS POCKET HAND-BOOK OF NEBRASKA: PAST, PRESENT, AND PROSPECTIVE...COMPRISING A CONCISE DELINEATION...WITH AMPLE DESCRIPTIONS...TO WHICH IS PREFIXED PREEMPTION LAWS RELATING TO THE PUBLIC LANDS...NY, 1857. 1st ed. 90,(10)pp. 2 fldg maps at rear. Orig cl, a few light stains. Howes W251. *GINSBERG.* $750

Wells, Linton. AROUND THE WORLD IN TWENTY-EIGHT DAYS. Boston & NY: Houghton Mifflin Co, 1926. Ltd ed of 350 numbered, signed. Spine soiled, cl and leather label rubbed, paper clip stain front pastedown. NF. *BLUE MOUNTAIN.* $75

Wells, Polk. LIFE & ADVENTURES OF POLK WELLS...G.A. Warnica, n.d. (ca 1907). 1st ed. VF. *OREGON.* $200

Wells, Rolla. EPISODES OF MY LIFE. St. Louis, 1933. 1st ed. Orig boards w/blue leather spine. Inscribed presentation. Howes W254. *GINSBERG.* $125

Wells, Samuel. NEW PHYSIOGNOMY, OR, SIGNS OF CHARACTER, AS MANIFESTED THROUGH TEMPERAMENT AND EXTERNAL FORMS, AND ESPECIALLY IN "THE HUMAN FACE DIVINE." NY, 1871. 1st ed. 1000+ woodcuts. *FYE.* $75

Welty, Eudora. A CURTAIN OF GREEN. Katherine Anne Porter intro. London: John Lane The Bodley Head, (1943). Couple of ink numerals on fep, else Fine in lightly rubbed dj. 1st Eng ed. *CHAPEL HILL.* $450

Welty, Eudora. A FLOCK OF GUINEA HENS SEEN FROM A CAR. Albondocani Press, 1970. Wraps. Issued in an ed of 300 as holiday greeting. 1/110 where 1st page bears imprint of press. This copy signed by publisher. Fine. *BEASLEY.* $125

Welty, Eudora. A PAGEANT OF BIRDS. NY: Albondocani, 1974. 1/300 numbered in wrappers, signed. *LOPEZ.* $275

Welty, Eudora. A PAGEANT OF BIRDS. NY: Albondocani Press, 1974. 1/26 lettered (from ed of 326) signed. Fine in pict wraps. *CAPTAIN'S BOOKSHELF.* $450

Welty, Eudora. A PAGEANT OF BIRDS. NY: Albondocani Press, 1974. 1/300 numbered, signed. Fine in pict wraps. *CAPTAIN'S BOOKSHELF.* $175

Welty, Eudora. DELTA WEDDING. NY: Harcourt, Brace, (1946). Fine in dj (minimal rubbing). 1st ed. *CHAPEL HILL.* $300

Welty, Eudora. DELTA WEDDING. NY: Harcourt, Brace, (1946). Gift inscript, else NF in price-clipped, VG dj (some soiling and rubbing). 1st ed. *CHAPEL HILL.* $200

Welty, Eudora. DELTA WEDDING. NY: Harcourt, Brace & Company, (1946). 1st ed. Signed. VG in dj. *JUVELIS.* $250

Welty, Eudora. EUDORA. Jackson: Mississippi Dept. of Archives and History, 1984. 1st ed. Pict wrappers. Fine. *SMITH.* $35

Welty, Eudora. LOSING BATTLES. NY: Random House, (1970). Harmless remainder mark on top edge, else Fine in dj. 1st ed. Inscribed. *CHAPEL HILL.* $125

Welty, Eudora. LOSING BATTLES. NY: Random House, (1970). 1st ed, ltd issue. 1/300 specially bound, numbered, signed. Fine in sl worn slipcase. *CAPTAIN'S BOOKSHELF.* $325

Welty, Eudora. LOSING BATTLES. NY: Random House, (1970). Fine in dj. 1st ed. *CHAPEL HILL.* $45

Welty, Eudora. MORGANA. Jackson: Univ Press of Mississippi, (1988). 1/250 numbered, signed by author and illustrator. Fine in slipcase. *LOPEZ.* $250

Welty, Eudora. MUSIC FROM SPAIN. Greenville, MS: The Levee Press, 1948. Boards a little spotted and soiled, thus VG. 1st ed. #428 of 775 signed. *CHAPEL HILL.* $550

Welty, Eudora. MUSIC FROM SPAIN. Greenville, MS: The Levee Press, 1948. Label chipped, affecting 1st letter of author's name, boards soiled, thus Good to VG only. 1st ed. #633 of 775 signed. *CHAPEL HILL.* $250

Welty, Eudora. MUSIC FROM SPAIN. Greenville, MS: The Levee Press, 1948. 1st signed ltd ed. #52 of 775 signed. Orig salmon boards w/paper spine label. Innocuous bump at head of spine, hint of darkening to edges, else Fine, unusually Nice. *CHAPEL HILL.* $750

Welty, Eudora. MUSIC FROM SPAIN. Greenville: The Levee Press, 1948. 1/775 signed. Fragile paper boards extensively rubbed on front and rear panels, thus just Good. *CAPTAIN'S BOOKSHELF.* $450

Welty, Eudora. ONE TIME, ONE PLACE. MISSISSIPPI IN THE DEPRESSION/ A SNAPSHOT ALBUM. NY: Random House, (1971). 1st ed. Illus. Fine in price clipped dj. Signed. *CAPTAIN'S BOOKSHELF.* $200

Welty, Eudora. ONE WRITER'S BEGINNING. Cambridge: Harvard Univ Press (1984). 1st ed. VF in dj. *DORN.* $45

Welty, Eudora. ONE WRITER'S BEGINNINGS. Cambridge, MA: Harvard Univ Press, 1984. 1st ed. Fine in sl chipped dj. *SCHOYER'S.* $20

Welty, Eudora. ONE WRITER'S BEGINNINGS. Cambridge, Mass. & London: Harvard Univ. Press, 1984. 1st ed. #30 of 350 specially bound, signed. Photo of Welty w/grandmother, not present in trade ed. Orig beige and tan cl. Virtually as New in pub's slipcase. *CHAPEL HILL.* $250

Welty, Eudora. ONE WRITER'S BEGINNINGS. Cambridge: Harvard Univ Press, 1984. 1st ed. Adv rev copy, dated slip laid in. As New. *SMITH.* $75

Welty, Eudora. PHOTOGRAPHS. Jackson & London: Univ Press of Mississippi, (1989). Foreword by Reynolds Price. Fine in pub's matching slipcase. 1st ed. #154 of 375 numbered, signed. *CHAPEL HILL.* $350

Welty, Eudora. PHOTOGRAPHS. Jackson: Univ Press of Mississippi, (1989). 1/375 numbered signed. Additionally signed by Reynolds Price, who wrote intro. Fine in Fine dj. *LOPEZ.* $375

Welty, Eudora. PHOTOGRAPHS. Jackson: Univ Press of MS, (1989). 1st ed, 1/375 numbered, signed. Foreword by Reynolds Price and signed by him. VF in slipcase. *ROBBINS.* $350

Welty, Eudora. PHOTOGRAPHS. Jackson: Univ Press of Mississippi, 1989. 1st ed. Reynolds Price (intro). One of 250 signed. Slipcase. Mint. *JAFFE.* $250

Welty, Eudora. PLACE IN FICTION. NY: House of Books, 1957. 1st ed. #189 of 300. Prospectus laid in. Orig brn cl. Fine in tissue jacket. *CHAPEL HILL.* $550

Welty, Eudora. RETREAT. (Winston Salem): Palaemon Press, (1981). 1/150 numbered, signed. Fine in cloth-backed patterned boards. Inscribed. *CAPTAIN'S BOOKSHELF.* $150

Welty, Eudora. SHORT STORIES. NY: Harcourt, Brace, (1949). 1st ed. One of 1,500 privately ptd, not issued for sale. Signed. Orig rose boards. VG. *CHAPEL HILL.* $250

Welty, Eudora. THE BRIDE OF THE INNISFALLEN And Other Stories. NY: Harcourt, Brace, (1955). Fine in Nearly Fine dj. 1st ed, 2nd issue w/multiple copyright dates. *CHAPEL HILL.* $200

Welty, Eudora. THE COLLECTED STORIES OF EUDORA WELTY. London: Marion Boyars, (1981). 1st Eng ed. Orig cl-backed boards. Fine in dj. *CHAPEL HILL.* $60

Welty, Eudora. THE COLLECTED STORIES OF EUDORA WELTY. NY & London: Harcourt Brace Jovanovich, (1980). 1st signed, ltd ed. #304 of 500 specially bound. Orig maroon cl. Mint in pub's slipcase, orig plastic shrinkwrap. *CHAPEL HILL.* $350

Welty, Eudora. THE COLLECTED STORIES OF EUDORA WELTY. NY & London: Harcourt Brace Jovanovich, (1980). 1st trade ed. Orig cl-backed boards. Fine in dj, sl sunned top edge. Inscribed. *CHAPEL HILL.* $200

Welty, Eudora. THE EYE OF THE STORY. NY: Random House, (1978). Fine in dj. 1st ed. *CHAPEL HILL.* $45

Welty, Eudora. THE EYE OF THE STORY. NY: Random House, (1978). 1st ed. One of 300 specially bound signed. Orig cl-backed boards. NF in pub's slipcase. *CHAPEL HILL.* $250

Welty, Eudora. THE EYE OF THE STORY. NY: RH, (1978). 1/300 numbered signed. Fine in NF slipcase. *LOPEZ.* $300

Welty, Eudora. THE EYE OF THE STORY. Selected Essays and Reviews. NY: Random House, (1978). 1st trade ed. Signed. Orig grn cl-backed boards. Fine in dj. *CHAPEL HILL.* $150

Welty, Eudora. THE EYE OF THE STORY: SELECTED ESSAYS AND REVIEWS. NY: Random House, (1978). 1st ed. Rmdr mk. Fine in dj. Signed. *CAPTAIN'S BOOKSHELF.* $75

Welty, Eudora. THE GOLDEN APPLES. NY, 1949. 1st ed. Signed. Bk spine has light sunning, else NF, bright in dj. *PETTLER.* $200

Welty, Eudora. THE GOLDEN APPLES. NY: Harcourt, (1949). 1st ed. Fine in dj, sl sunned spine. *CAPTAIN'S BOOKSHELF.* $175

Welty, Eudora. THE GOLDEN APPLES. NY: Harcourt, Brace (1949). 1st ed. Lt edgewear else VG+ in VG+ dj, chips. *DORN.* $140

Welty, Eudora. THE GOLDEN APPLES. NY: Harcourt, Brace, (1949). NF in bright dj (small hole at top of spine (affecting no lettering). 1st ed. Signed. *CHAPEL HILL.* $300

Welty, Eudora. THE OPTIMIST'S DAUGHTER. (London:) Deutsch (1973). 1st Eng ed. VG. *JUVELIS.* $45

Welty, Eudora. THE OPTIMIST'S DAUGHTER. Franklin Center: Franklin Library, 1978. Ltd ed. Fine in maroon Franklin leather. Signed. *CAPTAIN'S BOOKSHELF.* $75

Welty, Eudora. THE OPTIMIST'S DAUGHTER. NY: Random House, (1972). Bkpl, cl soiled, thus VG in bright, NF dj. 1st ed. *CHAPEL HILL.* $40

Welty, Eudora. THE OPTIMIST'S DAUGHTER. NY: Rinehart & Holt, (1972). One of approx 225 numbered, signed. Colophon states the limitation as 300, but about 75 were destroyed. Fine in NF slipcase. *LOPEZ.* $400

Welty, Eudora. THE OPTIMIST'S DAUGHTER. Trade ed. NF in price-clipped dj. *LOPEZ.* $45

Welty, Eudora. THE PONDER HEART. NY: Harcourt, Brace, (1954). 1st ed. Adv rev copy, pub slip tipped in. Orig cl-backed dec boards. NF in dj. *CHAPEL HILL.* $250

Welty, Eudora. THE ROBBER BRIDEGROOM. GC: Doubleday, Doran, 1942. 1st ed. Orig blue cl. Some offsetting to fep, else NF in dj (spine sl faded, worn at ends). *CHAPEL HILL.* $400

Welty, Eudora. THE ROBBER BRIDEGROOM. GC: Doubleday, Doran, 1942. 1st ed. Orig blue cl. Fine in pict dj (hint of rubbing top of spine). Nice. *CHAPEL HILL.* $600

Welty, Eudora. THE ROBBER BRIDEGROOM. GC: Doubleday, 1942. NF in bright NF dj. Inscribed in year of pub. *LOPEZ.* $750

Welty, Eudora. THE ROBBER BRIDEGROOM. GC: Doubleday, Doran, 1942. 1st ed. Fine in price clipped dj w/sl rubbing and sm tear at spine heel. Signed. *CAPTAIN'S BOOKSHELF.* $850

Welty, Eudora. THE SHOE BIRD. NY: Harcourt, Brace & World, (1964). 1st ed. Illus. Fine in dj. *BERNARD.* $150

Welty, Eudora. THE WIDE NET AND OTHER STORIES. London: John Lane The Bodley Head, (1945). 1st Eng ed. Hint of foxing to fore-edge, but Fine in dj ptd on both sides. *CHAPEL HILL.* $600

Welty, Eudora. THE WIDE NET AND OTHER STORIES. NY: Harcourt, Brace & Co, (1943). 1st ed. Orig blue cl. Fine in lightly soiled dj (pink spine lettering faded as usual). *CHAPEL HILL.* $550

Welty, Eudora. THE WIDE NET AND OTHER STORIES. NY: Harcourt, Brace & Co, (1943). 1st ed. Orig blue cl. Owner name, else Fine in VG dj (few edge tears, couple of sm chips affecting no lettering, sm abrasion front panel affecting couple of letters). *CHAPEL HILL.* $400

Welty, Eudora. THE WIDE NET AND OTHER STORIES. NY: Harcourt, (1943). 1st ed. Fine, lacking dj. *CAPTAIN'S BOOKSHELF.* $100

Welty, Eudora. WOMEN! MAKE TURBAN IN OWN HOME! (Winston Salem): Palaemon Press, (1979). 1/200 numbered, signed. Fine in grn boards w/o dj, as issued. Signed. *CAPTAIN'S BOOKSHELF.* $125

Welty, Eudora. WOMEN! MAKE TURBAN IN OWN HOME! N.p.: Palaemon Press, (1979). 1st ed, 1/200 numbered, signed. Tiny faint smudge on cover else Fine w/o dj as issued. *ROBBINS.* $125

Wendover, R. Y. R. H. WENDOVER'S VIEWS ON THE MONROE DOCTRINE...RAILROADS...AND UNION AND FRATERNITY, WITH PRACTICAL STRICTURES...ALSO, A SUPPLEMENT OF ORIGINAL ITEMS OF INTEREST. St. Louis, 1867. 1st ed. 40pp. Orig printed front wrapper. Rubber lib stamp. *GINSBERG.* $75

Wendt, Edmund. A TREATISE ON ASIATIC CHOLERA. NY, 1885. 1st ed. *FYE.* $50

Wengenroth, Stow. MAKING A LITHOGRAPH. London: The Studio, 1936. 1st ed. Dj. *KARMIOLE.* $45

Wenham, Edward. OLD FURNITURE FOR MODERN ROOMS. London: G. Bell & Sons. 1939. 1st ed. 1/2 blue morocco over blue cl, gilt spine. Teg. *KARMIOLE.* $35

Wenkham, Robert. MAUI—THE LAST HAWAIIAN PLACE. SF: Friends of the Earth, (1970). Later ptg. 61 color plts. Fine- in Fine- dj. *AARD.* $30

Wensley, F. FORTY YEARS OF SCOTLAND YARD. NY, 1931. 312pp. Slight cvr staining and rubbing. Pencil marks on few pages, o/w VG. *DIAMOND.* $20

Wentworth, Frank L. ASPEN ON THE ROARING FORK. Lakewood, CO; Rizzari, 1950. 1st ed thus. Ltd to 600. Fldg map in rear pocket. Ptd in dark brown ink, uncut. Red cl, gilt. NF. *CONNOLLY & WADE.* $95

Wentworth, Lady. ARAB HORSE NONSENSE. Oxford: Ronald, 1950. 1st ed. VG in VG dj. *OCTOBER FARM.* $35

Wentworth, Patricia. FEAR BY NIGHT. Phila: Lippincott, 1934. 1st ed. VF; minor wear dj spine ends. *ELSE FINE.* $125

Wentworth, Patricia. POISON IN THE PEN. Phila: J.B. Lippincott, 1954. 1st ed. Fine in dj. *MORDIDA.* $30

Wentworth, Patricia. SHE CAME BACK. Phila: Lippincott, 1945. 1st ed. Fine in Good+ dj a bit rubbed. *ARCHER.* $25

Wentworth, Patricia. THE ALINGTON INHERITANCE. Phila: J.B. Lippincott, 1958. 1st ed. Fine in dj. *MORDIDA.* $25

Wentworth, Patricia. THE CATHERINE-WHEEL. Phila: J.B. Lippincott, 1949. 1st ed. Fine in dj w/dampstain on back panel, rubbing on front panel and small chip and minor wear at top of spine. *MORDIDA.* $25

Wentworth, Patricia. THE FINGERPRINT. Phila: J.B. Lippincott, 1956. 1st ed. Fine in dj. *MORDIDA.* $30

Wentworth, Patricia. THE WATERSPLASH. London: Hodder & Stoughton 1953. 1st ed. Fine; light edgewear to dj. *ELSE FINE.* $35

Wentworth, Patricia. THROUGH THE WALL. Phila: Lippincott, 1950. 1st ed. Fine; minor rubs at dj corners. *ELSE FINE.* $30

Wenzell, A.B. THE PASSING SHOW. NY: P. F. Collier & Son, 1903. A.B. Wenzell (illus). 2 color (1 double pg) and 42 monochrome plts (incl 12 double-pg plts). Modern brn cl-backed pict paper over boards. Edges scuffed, new endleaves. Handsome. *WEBER.* $200

Werner, Jane. A CHILD'S BOOK OF BIBLE STORIES. NY, (1944). 1st ed. Masha (illus). VG in dj. *ARTIS.* $19.50

Werner, M.R. BRIGHAM YOUNG. NY, Harcourt, Brace & Co. (1925). 1st ed. VG. *OREGON.* $40

Werner, M.R. BRIGHAM YOUNG. NY: Harcourt, Brace & Co., (1925). 1st ed. 15 plts. Good+. *OREGON.* $20

Werner, M.R. BRIGHAM YOUNG. NY: Harcourt, Brace and Company, 1925. 2nd prtg. Smudge pp 88, front hinge weak, else VG. *PARMER.* $35

Werth, John J. A DISSERTATION ON THE RESOURCES AND POLICY OF CALIFORNIA: MINERAL, AGRICULTURAL AND COMMERCIAL, INCLUDING A PLAN FOR THE DISPOSAL OF THE MINERAL LANDS.. Benica, CA, 1851. 1st ed. 87pp. Half calf w/marbled boards, title in gilt on spine, minor paper restoration, o/w VG. Historical ex libris stamp. Graff calls for the errata list to be at foot of page viii but actually it is vii. On page 84 there is a ptd note pasted in stating: "Note.-This comparative statement refers to dutiable goods only." This is not noted by either Howes, Cowan, Graff, but the Streeter copy so notes. Howes W262. Cowan p. 675. *GINSBERG.* $1500

Wertham, Fredric. SEDUCTION OF THE INNOCENT. NY, (1954). NF. *POLYANTHOS.* $50

Wescott, Glenway. TWELVE FABLES OF AESOP. (NY: Museum of Modern Art, 1954). 1st this ed. #269 of 975. Orig cl-backed patterned boards. NF in remnants of orig glassine jacket, sl used pub's slipcase. Signed by Wescott, illus Antonio Frasconi, printer Joseph Blumenthal. *CHAPEL HILL.* $150

West, Anthony C. REBEL TO JUDGMENT. NY: Oblensky, 1962. 1st ed. VF; minor age darkening to dj spine. *ELSE FINE.* $20

West, Anthony C. RIVER'S END AND OTHER STORIES. NY: McDowell Oblensky, 1958. 1st ed. VF; minute edgewear to dj. *ELSE FINE.* $35

West, Anthony C. THE FERRET FANCIER. NY: Simon & Schuster, 1963. 1st ed. As New in dj. *ELSE FINE.* $25

West, Herbert Faulkner. "SUNNY INTERVALS." Hanover, NH: Westholm Publications, 1972. #324/400, signed. Slight dusting, nick to dj. *NUTMEG.* $22.50

West, Herbert Faulkner. NOTES FROM A BOOKMAN. N.p.: Westholm Publications, 1968. Ltd to 399 numbered, signed. Dj. *KARMIOLE.* $50

West, Jessamyn. THE FRIENDLY PERSUASION. NY: Harcourt, Brace, (1945). NF in VG dj. 1st ed. *CHAPEL HILL.* $150

West, L.S. THE HOUSEFLY. NY, 1951. Some wear extremities. Name stamp. *SUTTON.* $47

West, Nathanael. THE COMPLETE WORKS OF NATHANAEL WEST. NY, (1957). 1st collected ed. Lt shelfwear dj, else Fine. Bk is VF. *McCLINTOCK.* $35

West, Nathanael. THE DAY OF THE LOCUST. NY: Random House, (1939). 1st ed. Rebound in full modern red morocco w/marbled eps. *CAPTAIN'S BOOKSHELF.* $400

West, Nathaniel. THE ANCESTRY, LIFE, AND TIMES OF HON. HENRY HASTINGS SIBLEY. St. Paul: Pioneer Press, 1889. 1st ed. x,596pp. Frontis. Fine. *OREGON.* $75

West, Nathaniel. THE ANCESTRY, LIFE AND TIMES OF HON. HENRY HASTINGS SIBLEY, LL.D. Saint Paul, 1889. 1st ed. Cvr has minor wear and a little staining o/w VG+. *PRATT.* $75

West, Paul. ALLEY JAGGERS. NY: Harper & Row, (1966). 1st ed. Signed. Fine in dj. *BERNARD.* $75

West, Paul. ALLEY JAGGERS. NY: Harper & Row, 1966. 1st ed. VF in dj. *ELSE FINE.* $50

West, Paul. BELA LUGOSI'S WHITE CHRISTMAS. NY: Harper & Row, 1972. 1st ed. VF in dj. *ELSE FINE.* $40

West, Paul. BELA LUGOSI'S WHITE CHRISTMAS. NY: Harper & Row, (1972). 1st ed. Signed. Fine in dj. *BERNARD.* $50

West, Paul. GALA. NY: Harper & Row, (1976). 1st ed. Signed. Fine in dj. *BERNARD.* $50

West, Paul. I'M EXPECTING TO LIVE QUITE SOON. London: Victor Gollancz, 1971. 1st UK ed. Signed. Price sticker removed from front pastedown o/w Fine in price clipped dj. *BERNARD.* $50

West, Paul. I'M EXPECTING TO LIVE QUITE SOON. NY: Harper & Row, 1970. 1st ed. VF in dj. *ELSE FINE.* $40

West, Paul. I'M EXPECTING TO LIVE QUITE SOON. NY: Harper & Row, (1970). 1st ed. Signed. Fine in dj. *BERNARD.* $65

West, Ray B., Jr. KINGDOM OF THE SAINTS. NY, 1957. 1st ed. 389pp. Dj has a little wear o/w VG+. *PRATT.* $32.50

West, Ray B., Jr. KINGDOM OF THE SAINTS: THE STORY OF BRIGHAM YOUNG AND THE MORMONS. NY: Viking, 1957. 1st ed. Fine in VG dj. *CONNOLLY & WADE.* $35

West, Ray, Jr. KINGDOM OF THE SAINTS. NY: Viking, 1957. 1st ed. Fine in Good dj w/chips, sunning. *ARCHER.* $25

West, Rebecca. BLACK LAMB AND GREY FALCON. NY: Viking, 1943. 1 vol ed. Dj yellowed, chipped. *SCHOYER'S.* $20

West, Rebecca. D.H. LAWRENCE. London: Martin Secker, 1930. 1st ed. Orig brown cl, teg. Fine in lightly used and chipped dj. *CAPTAIN'S BOOKSHELF.* $50

West, Rebecca. ST. AUGUSTINE. NY: Appleton, 1933. 1st US ed. Fine in lightly used dj. *CAPTAIN'S BOOKSHELF.* $50

West, Richard S., Jr. GIDEON WELLES, LINCOLN'S NAVY DEPARTMENT. Indianapolis, 1945. 1st ed. Signed. Dj worn and chipped o/w VG. *PRATT.* $42.50

West, Richard S., Jr. GIDEON WELLES, LINCOLN'S NAVY DEPARTMENT. Indianapolis, 1945. 1st ed. Dj worn and chipped o/w VG. *PRATT.* $35

West, Richard S., Jr. THE SECOND ADMIRAL, A LIFE OF DAVID DIXON PORTER, 1813-1891. NY, 1937. 1st ed. Dj wear and chipping o/w VG+. *PRATT.* $45

Westcott, Edward Noyes. DAVID HARUM: A STORY OF AMERICAN LIFE. NY: D. Appleton, 1898. 1st. Later state (?) with imperfect "J" on p 40. Lakeside Press cl fldg box. Fine. *MUELLER.* $100

Westendorf, Wolfhart. PAINTING, SCULPTURE, AND ARCHITECTURE OF ANCIENT EGYPT. NY: Harry N. Abrams, (1968). Bkpl, embossed stamp, corner bumped. Dj. Good. *ARCHAEOLOGIA.* $65

Westermann, William L. THE SLAVE SYSTEMS OF GREEK AND ROMAN ANTIQUITY. Phila: The Amer Philosophical Soc, 1955. 1st ed. Dj a bit soiled. *KARMIOLE.* $30

Westermarck, Edward. MEMOIRS OF MY LIFE. NY: Macualey (1929, 27). 1st US ed. VG. *AARD.* $30

Westermarck, Edward. THE HISTORY OF HUMAN MARRIAGE. London, 1894. 2nd ed. 644pp. *FYE.* $100

Westermeier, Clifford. TRAILING THE COWBOY. HIS LIFE AND LORE AND TOLD BY FRONTIER JOURNALISTS. Caldwell: Caxton, 1955. 1st ed. VF in VF dj. *OREGON.* $45

WESTERN BORDER LIFE; OR, WHAT FANNY HUNTER SAW AND HEARD IN KANSAS AND MISSOURI. NY: Derby & Jackson, 1857. 408pp. Cloth, hand-colored frontis. VG. *GIBBS.* $30

WESTERNERS BRAND BOOKS. See THE WESTERNERS BRAND BOOKS.

Westing, Fred. PENNSY STEAM AND SEMAPHORES. Superior, 1974. 1st ed. Fine in Fine dj. *VARNER.* $30

Westlake, Donald E. A LIKELY STORY. NY: Penzler Books, 1984. 1st ed. One of 250 numbered, signed. VF in slipcase w/o dj as issued. *MORDIDA.* $45

Westlake, Donald E. COPS AND ROBBERS. London: Hodder, 1973. 1st Brit ed. Signed. NF in dj. *SILVER DOOR.* $35

Westlake, Donald E. ENOUGH. NY: Evans, 1977. 1st ed. Fine in dj. *ELSE FINE.* $25

Westlake, Donald E. ENOUGH. NY: Evans, 1977. 1st ed. Signed. Fine in dj. *SILVER DOOR.* $35

Westlake, Donald E. EX OFFICIO. NY: Evans, 1970. 1st ed. Fine in dj. *ELSE FINE.* $60

Westlake, Donald E. GOD SAVE THE MARK. NY: Random House, 1967. 1st ed. Fine in VG dj w/small stain on front cover. *MORDIDA.* $25

Westlake, Donald E. HIGH ADVENTURE. NY: Mysterious, (1985). 1st ed. Signed. VF in VF dj. *UNGER.* $45

Westlake, Donald E. KAHAWA. NY: Viking, (1982). 1st ed. Fine in dj and signed. *LOPEZ.* $45

Westlake, Donald E. SACRED MONSTER. NY: Mysterious Press, 1989. 1st ed. VF in dj. *MORDIDA.* $20

Westlake, Donald E. SOMEBODY OWES ME MONEY. NY: Random House, 1969. 1st ed. Fine in dj w/crease inner front flap. *MORDIDA.* $40

Westlake, Donald E. THE BLACKBIRD. As Richard Stark. NY: Simon & Schuster, 1969. 1st ed. NF in dj. *ELSE FINE.* $40

Westlake, Donald E. TWO MUCH! NY: Evans, 1975. 1st ed. As New, minor edgerubs to dj. *ELSE FINE.* $30

Weston, Edward. MY CAMERA ON POINT LOBOS. Boston: Virginia Adams, Yosemite National Park, and Houghton Mifflin Co. 1950. 1st ed. 80,(2)pp. 30 glossy photo plts. Spiral-bound ptd boards. Fine in rare photo illus dj (spine sl worn). *KARMIOLE.* $350

Weston, Garnett. THE MAN WITH THE MONOCLE. GC: Doubleday Crime Club, 1943. 1st ed. VG in dj w/wear, sm tear. *MORDIDA.* $25

Weston, Mildred. VACHEL LINDSAY: POET IN EXILE. Ye Galleon Press, (1987). 1st ed. Frontis. New w/o dj as issued. *AUTHORS OF THE WEST.* $15

Weston, Otheto. MOTHER LODE ALBUM. Stanford: Stanford Univ, 1948. 1st ed. VF in VG dj. *CONNOLLY & WADE.* $60

Weston, Walter. JAPAN. A&C Black, 1926. 1st ed (this series). W/o dj, else VG-NF. *OLD LONDON.* $30

Westphal, William. TEN YEARS IN SOUTH AFRICA. (Chicago: B.S. Wasson & Co, Prntrs, 1892). 1st ed. Fldg map, 8 plts. Orig. grn gilt cl, faded. *KARMIOLE.* $50

Wetherell, W.D. SOUVENIRS. Random House, 1981. 1st ed. About Fine in dj. Remainder mark on bottom. *STAHR.* $35

Wetmore, A. and B.H. Swales. THE BIRDS OF HAITI AND THE DOMINICAN REPUBLIC. Washington, 1931. 10 plts, 1 fldg map. Wrappers w/lt chipping, smudging. *SUTTON.* $60

Wetmore, Helen Cody and Zane Grey. LAST OF THE GREAT SCOUTS (BUFFALO BILL). NY, (1918). 1st ed thus. Lt cvr wear. VG. *McCLINTOCK.* $8.50

Wetmore, Helen Cody and Zane Grey. LAST OF THE GREAT SCOUTS (BUFFALO BILL). NY: Grosset & Dunlap, 1918. 1st ed thus: pp 321 to 333 by Zane Grey. Inscribed by author's daughter. Pict tan and wine cl. Very Nearly Fine. Howes W297. *CONNOLLY & WADE.* $40

Wetmore, Helen Cody. LAST OF THE GREAT SCOUTS...(Duluth, MN, 1899). 1st ed. 19 plts. Cvrs sl soiled, worn, stained. Pages browning. Little staining some pp, o/w VG. Howes W297. *DIAMOND.* $60

Wexley, John. JUDGMENT OF JULIUS & ETHEL ROSENBERG. NY: Cameron & Kahn, 1955. 3rd ptg. Edgeworn, price-clipped dj. VG. *AKA.* $25

Weyer, Montana Helena. TRAILING THE TEPEES. NY, (1968). 1st ed. 197pp. Small piece torn from dj o/w VG. *PRATT.* $15

Whalen, Philip. SCENES OF LIFE AT THE CAPITAL. Bolinas: Grey Fox, 1971. Expanded version, cloth ed. Fine. *BEASLEY.* $35

Whanslaw, H.W. and Victor Hotchkiss. SPECIALIZED PUPPETRY. Redhill, Surry, (1948). VG. *NUTMEG.* $22.50

Wharfield, H.B. WITH SCOUT AND CAVALRY AT FORT APACHE. Tucson, 1965. Ed by John Alexander Carrol. 1st ed. Minor shelf wear o/w Fine. *PRATT.* $32.50

Wharton, Edith and Ogden Codman, Jr. THE DECORATION OF HOUSES. NY: Scribners, 1897. 1st ed. Marbled paper over boards w/ptd label on spine. Photo. Some foxing, portion of label missing from spine, binding worn especially at spine and tips. Good+. *JUVELIS.* $450

Wharton, Edith. A MOTOR-FLIGHT THROUGH FRANCE. NY: Scribners, 1908. 1st ed. Grn gilt stamped cl, teg, some wear to edges, pp somewhat sunned at edges, cream dj ptd in grn repeating cover design, sl chipped at top and bottom of spine and along hinges and corners, but still complete and generally Nice. *JUVELIS.* $600

Wharton, Edith. A SON AT THE FRONT. NY: Scribner's, 1923. 1st ed. Fine in scarce dj, lightly chipped, worn, w/internal archival tape mends. *JAFFE.* $125

Wharton, Edith. A SON AT THE FRONT. NY: Scribners, 1923. 1st ed. Red gilt stamped cl, gilt a shade dimmer on spine. Rare dj has some chips to top and bottom of spine. Generally VG. *JUVELIS.* $250

Wharton, Edith. AN EDITH WHARTON TREASURY. NY: Appleton-Century-Crofts, 1950. Quinn, Arthur Hobson (ed). Review copy. Fine in NF dj. *JUVELIS.* $50

Wharton, Edith. AND BEYOND. NY: D. Appleton and Company, 1926. 1st ed. Black moire cl, gilt stamped, ptd purple dj, dec eps. Some soiling to spine, corners bumped, spine dull and gilt faded. Dj lightly used. Good to VG only. *JUVELIS.* $150

Wharton, Edith. ETHAN FROME. (Portland): LEC, 1939. One of 1500 numbered. Signed by illus, Henry Varnum Poor. VG in slipcase. *LOPEZ.* $85

Wharton, Edith. ETHAN FROME. London: Eveleigh Nash & Grayson Ltd, 1924. 1st Eng ed. Sl cocked, else VG in orig cl. *HELLER.* $100

Wharton, Edith. ETHAN FROME. NY: (Scribner's), 1911. 1st ed, 1st issue w/last line of type on p. 135 in perfect condition. Pub's burgundy cl w/gilt titling; spine sunned, teg. *BOOK BLOCK.* $165

Wharton, Edith. ETHAN FROME. NY: Scribner's, 1911. 1st issue, Fine but for lightly sunned spine. *BEASLEY.* $150

Wharton, Edith. ETHAN FROME. NY: Scribners, 1922. 1st ed thus. 1/2,000 designed by Bruce Rogers for William Rudge. Tan boards, brown cl spine. VG except for 4" white mark on spine. Pub's box present but broken. *JUVELIS.* $125

Wharton, Edith. FIGHTING FRANCE FORM DUNKERQUE TO BELFORT. NY: Scribners, 1925. 1st ed. Red cl, sl soiled, in very rare white dj ptd in black w/picture of soldiers. Dj badly darkened on spine and parts of front cover, but complete. *JUVELIS.* $250

Wharton, Edith. FIGHTING FRANCE FROM DUNKERQUE TO BELFORT. NY: Scribners, 1925. 1st ed. Red cl. Good. *JUVELIS.* $30

Wharton, Edith. FIGHTING FRANCE. FROM DUNKERQUE TO BELFORT. NY: Scribner's, 1915. 1st ed. Red cl. Fine. *JAFFE.* $125

Wharton, Edith. FRENCH WAYS AND THEIR MEANING. NY: Appleton, 1919. 1st. NF in pict grn cl. *CAPTAIN'S BOOKSHELF.* $75

Wharton, Edith. FRENCH WAYS AND THEIR MEANING. NY: Appleton, 1919. 1st ed. Pencil owner's name and date; spine gilt faded, o/w VG. *LOPEZ.* $100

Wharton, Edith. MADAME DE TREYMES. NY: Scribner, 1907. 1st ed. Elaborate gilt floral design on front panel. One corner sl bumped, a little rubbing at spinal extremities, else attractive, NF. *CAPTAIN'S BOOKSHELF.* $100

Wharton, Edith. MADAME DE TREYMES. NY: Scribners, 1907. 1st ed. NF w/light rubbing to spine ends. *BEASLEY.* $75

Wharton, Edith. TALES OF MEN AND GHOSTS. NY: Scribners, 1914. 1st ed. Slight offsetting to eps, bkpl, spine lettering somewhat faded, thus VG. Scarce. *BETWEEN COVERS.* $150

Wharton, Edith. THE CUSTOM OF THE COUNTRY. NY: Scribners, 1913. 1st ed. Bkpl, very slight wear at extremities, else NF. Lacking rare dj. *BETWEEN COVERS.* $125

Wharton, Edith. THE CUSTOM OF THE COUNTRY. NY: Scribners, 1913. 1st ed. Fading to spine, sl cocked, else Good. *JUVELIS.* $75

Wharton, Edith. THE FRUIT OF THE TREE. NY: Scribners, 1907. 1st ed. NF, w/only one bit of spotting. *JUVELIS.* $175

Wharton, Edith. THE FRUIT OF THE TREE. NY: Scribners, 1907. 1st ed, 2nd state with Grosset and Dunlap binding. VG. *JUVELIS.* $40

Wharton, Edith. THE GLIMPSES OF THE MOON. NY: Appleton, 1922. Close to Fine in lightly used dj. *BEASLEY.* $125

Wharton, Edith. THE GODS ARRIVE. NY: D. Appleton, 1932. 1st ed. NF in dj. *LOPEZ.* $125

Wharton, Edith. THE GODS ARRIVE. NY: D. Appleton and Company, 1932. 1st ed. VG in dj. *JUVELIS.* $75

Wharton, Edith. THE GREAT INCLINATION. NY: Scribner, 1899. 1st ed, 2nd ptg. 254pp. Grey boards stamped in gold. This is Johnson's 2nd state binding w/"Edith Wharton" on the spine and the later ptg w/the Merrymount Press slug on (p.255). Sl rubbed, else Fine, uncut. *SECOND LIFE.* $300

Wharton, Edith. THE HERMIT AND THE WILD WOMAN, AND OTHER STORIES. NY: Scribners, 1908. 1st ed. Spine sunned and sl cocked. Ex-libris. *JUVELIS.* $40

Wharton, Edith. THE MARNE. NY: Appleton, 1918. 1st ed. Fine in NF dj, a bit tanned on spine and w/some slight offsetting to rear panel. Very Scarce in dj. *BETWEEN COVERS.* $400

Wharton, Edith. THE VALLEY OF DECISION. NY: Scribners, 1902. 2 vols. 1st ed. Dark red cl stamped in gold on the spine. Wear to edges of spine and tips, ink stains front cover vol 1. Good. *JUVELIS.* $100

Wharton, Edith. XINGU AND OTHER STORIES. NY: Scribners, 1916. 1st ed. Red cl, spine faded and gilt dimmed, interior sound. *JUVELIS.* $75

Wharton, Francis. THE REVOLUTIONARY DIPLOMATIC CORRESPONDENCE OF THE UNITED STATES...Wash, 1889. 1st ed. 6 vols. Orig cl. *GINSBERG.* $150

Wharton, H.M. A PICNIC IN PALESTINE. Baltimore, MD: Wharton & Barron. 1892. 1st ed. Orig dec blue cl, sl soiled. *KARMIOLE.* $45

Wharton, William H. THRILLING TALES OF THE FROZEN NORTH. Phila: John Potter, 1894. Good. *BLUE DRAGON.* $25

Wharton, William. BIRDY. NY: Knopf, 1979. 1st ed, 1st bk. Fine in Fine dj (2 short internally mended tears at spine folds). *BEASLEY.* $35

Wharton, William. BIRDY. NY: Knopf, 1979. 1st ed. Fine in dj. *LAME DUCK.* $45

Wharton, William. BIRDY. NY: Knopf, 1979. 1st ed. Signed. Fine in NF dj (short tear bottom edge front panel near spine). *LOPEZ.* $100

WHAT AMERICA THINKS: EDITORIALS AND CARTOONS. Chicago, 1941. NF. *POLYANTHOS.* $100

WHAT TO OBSERVE AT THE BED-SIDE AND AFTER DEATH IN MEDICAL CASES. Phila, 1855. 2nd Amer ed. *FYE.* $100

Whately, Richard. HISTORIC DOUBTS RELATIVE TO NAPOLEON BUONAPARTE. London: John W. Parker & Son, 1860. Lea, bkpl, normal wear. *OLD LONDON.* $75

Wheat, Carl I. MAPPING THE TRANSMISSISSIPPI WEST, 1540-1861. 5 vols in 6. SF: The Institute of Hist Cartography, 1957-1963. One of 1000 sets. Two-tone cl. Set incl prospectuses for all 5 vols, w/that for Vol I being ptd at the Grabhorn Press, as is that vol itself. Tipped to the fep of Vol I, leaving a small stain, is a note from Wheat to a customer for the series. *DAWSON'S.* $3250

Wheatley, Dennis. THE SULTAN'S DAUGHTER. London: Hutchinson, (1963). 1st ed. Fine in NF dj. *UNGER.* $40

Wheatley, H.B. HOW TO FORM A LIBRARY. London: Elliot Stock, 1886. Cvrs trifle soiled, bit shaky, else Good. *WREDEN.* $12

Wheatley, H.B. LITERARY BLUNDERS. London: Elliot Stock, 1905. Bumped, small stain front cover, else VG. *WREDEN.* $15

Wheatley, H.B. LITERARY BLUNDERS. London: Elliot Stock, 1893. 1st ed. Orig brn cl backed boards. One of a smaller number bound thus and ptd on better paper. *OAK KNOLL.* $40

Wheatley, H.B. PRICES OF BOOKS. London: George Allen, 1898. 1st ed. Half-title creased, fore-edge of a few pp stained, o/w VG. *WREDEN.* $35

Wheeler, C.H. TEN YEARS ON THE EUPHRATES. Boston, 1868. *O'NEILL.* $47.50

Wheeler, Edward S. SCHEYICHBI AND THE STRAND, or EARLY DAYS ALONG THE DELAWARE. Phila, 1876. 1st ed. 6, 116pp. Rebound new buckram. *HEINOLDT.* $18

Wheeler, Harold. THE STORY OF THE BRITISH NAVY. London: George G. Harrap & Co., 1922. 1st ed. Foxing to fore-edge, slight wear to edges, else VG. *PARMER.* $40

Wheeler, Homer. BUFFALO DAYS, FORTY YEARS IN THE OLD WEST. Indianapolis: Bobbs-Merril, (1925). 1st ed. 15 plts. Lower corner wear, o/w VG in Good+ dj. *OREGON.* $50

Wheeler, Monroe (ed). BRITAIN AT WAR. Text by T.S. Eliot, Herbert Read, E.J. Carter and Carlos Dyer. NY: MOMA, (1941). 1st ed. VG. *SECOND LIFE.* $15

Wheeler, Richard. WITNESS TO GETTYSBURG. NY, (1987). 1st ed. 273pp, illus., index, dj. Fine. *PRATT.* $20

Wheeler, Sessions S. PAIUTE. Caldwell, ID, 1965. 1st ed. 231pp. Light dj wear o/w Fine. *PRATT.* $17.50

Wheeler, W.H. THE DRAINAGE OF FENS AND LOW LANDS BY GRAVITATION AND STEAMPOWER. London: E. & F.N. Spon, 1888. 1st ed. 175pp + 48pp pub's catalogue dated Nov. 1912 + 18 illus on 7 plts. Small tear spine tip, inner hinges starting, o/w Good. *DIAMOND.* $45

Wheeler, W.M. ANTS...NY, 1926 (1910). Worn at corners, spine ends frayed. *SUTTON.* $55

Wheeler, William. THE LETTERS OF...EDITED AND WITH A FOREWORD BY CAPTAIN B.H. LIDDELL HART. Boston, 1951. Dj. 1st ed. *O'NEILL.* $45

Wheelock, Eleazer. A CONTINUATION OF THE NARRATIVE OF THE INDIAN CHARITY-SCHOOL...WITH DARTMOUTH-COLLEGE...IN HANOVER...NEW-HAMPSHIRE, 1771. (Hartford), 1771. 61 pp. 1st ed, 1st issue. Half morocco. Howes W330. *GINSBERG.* $150

Wheelock, Julia. THE BOYS IN WHITE, THE EXPERIENCE OF A HOSPITAL AGENT IN AND AROUND WASHINGTON. NY, 1870. 1st ed. 268pp. Water stain affecting the 1st few leaves. *FYE.* $300

Whelen, Townsend. THE HUNTING RIFLE....Harrisburg: Stackpole Sons, 1940. 1st ed. VG. *BACKMAN.* $45

Whelen, Townsend. WILDERNESS HUNTING AND WILDCRAFT. Marshallton, DE: Small Arms Technical Pub Co., 1927. 1st ed. Blue cl, blind and gilt-stamped. *KARMIOLE.* $40

WHEN YOU COME WEST...YOU WILL SEE MOUNTAINS...Chavre Chamber of Commerce (c. 1940-50). 114pp. Ring binder, boards (little worn). Contents VG. *HEINOLDT.* $15

WHERE THE TWO CAME TO THEIR FATHER. A NAVAHO WAR CEREMONIAL. NY: Pantheon, (1943). 1st ed. Vol published in the Bollingen series, a portfolio of 18 plts of Navajo ceremonial sand paintings, each plt measuring 18" x 24", with a booklet of commentary by Joseph Campbell, Maud Oakes and Jeff King. In cloth folio sl age-darkened and spotted, o/w VG. Plts and booklet complete and Fine. *LOPEZ.* $850

WHERE TO HUNT AMERICAN GAME. Lowell: United States Cartridge Co., 1898. 1st ed. Some wear to extremities. else VG. *OLD LONDON.* $40

Whipple, A.B.C. YANKEE WHALERS IN THE SOUTH SEAS. NY 1954. *HEINOLDT.* $10

Whipple, A.W. REPORT OF THE SECRETARY OF WAR, COMMUNICATING IN ANSWER TO A RESOLUTION OF THE SENATE, THE REPORT OF THE LIEUTENANT WHIPPLE'S EXPEDITION FROM SAN DIEGO TO THE COLORADO. Washington: 1851. 1st ed. 28pp. Fine. Senate Ex Doc 19. *BOOK MARKET.* $150

Whipple, George M. HISTORY OF THE SALEM LIGHT INFANTRY FROM 1805 TO 1890. Salem, MA, 1890. 1st ed. Ex-lib. A little cvr wear o/w Fine. *PRATT.* $40

Whistler, James Abbot McNeil. THE GENTLE ART OF MAKING ENEMIES. NY: Lovell, 1890. 1st authorized ed. Little worn and stained cl backed boards, uncut, little foxed. VG. *SECOND LIFE.* $45

Whitaker, Arthur P. SPANISH-AMERICAN FRONTIER: 1783-1795: THE WESTWARD MOVEMENT. Boston, 1927. 1st ed. 3 maps. Orig cl, paper label removed from spine; emb lib stamp, bkpl removed. Howes W345. Samuel E. Morison (intro). *GINSBERG.* $75

Whitaker, Charles Harris (ed). BERTRAM GROSVENOR GOODHUE, ARCHITECT AND MASTER OF MANY ARTS. NY: Press of the American Inst of Architects, 1925. 1st ed. 273 plts, 5 color plts. Orig beige and blue cl. Fine in dj, chips. *KARMIOLE.* $200

Whitaker, Irwin and Emily. A POTTER'S MEXICO. Albuquerque: Univ of Mexico, 1978. 1st ed. Fine in NF dj. *CONNOLLY & WADE.* $42.50

Whitaker, Mary Scrimzeour. POEMS. Charleston: John B. Nixon, 1850. 1st ed. 12mo. Contemp half morocco. Lib bkpl, blindstamp, some rubbing, small bump on fore-edge of cvrs, scattered lt foxing, else VG. *CHAPEL HILL.* $125

White, Annie Randall. TWENTIETH CENTURY ETIQUETTE. Chicago: Imperial Publishing, (1900). Cloth w/pict illus laid down. Front hinge weak, wear to tips & spine extremities. *DAWSON'S.* $60

White, Ared. SEVEN TICKETS TO SINGAPORE. Boston: Houghton Mifflin, 1939. 1st ed. VG in dj (sl faded spine; chipping; tiny closed tears). *MORDIDA.* $25

White, Ared. THE SPY NET. Boston: Houghton Mifflin, 1931. 1st ed. Edges foxed, o/w VG in dj, couple tiny tears; sm chip. *MORDIDA.* $30

White, Arthur Silva. EXPANSION OF EGYPT UNDER ANGLO-EGYPTIAN CONDOMINIUM. NY: New Amsterdam Bk Co., 1900. Spotted on front. 4 fldg maps. Top 2" of ffep removed. *SCHOYER'S.* $50

White, Dale and Larry Florek. TALL TIMBER PILOTS. NY, 1953. 1st ed. VG in chipped dj. *ARTIS.* $16.50

White, E.B. CHARLOTTE'S WEBB. Garth Williams (illus). NY: Harper, (1952). 1st ed. Mariana Thurber's sig on ffep, o/w VF. Dj. *JAFFE.* $450

White, E.B. LETTERS OF E.B. WHITE. NY: H&R, (1976). 1st ed. One of an unspecified number signed on tipped-in leaf. NF in dj. *LOPEZ.* $150

White, E.B. STUART LITTLE. NY, 1945. 1st ed. Illus by Garth Williams. Pict cvrs, spine and corners sl rubbed. NF. *POLYANTHOS.* $50

White, E.B. THE POINTS OF MY COMPASS. NY: Harper & Row, 1962. 1st ed. Fine, lt wear at dj corners & spine ends. *ELSE FINE.* $40

White, E.B. THE SECOND TREE FROM THE CORNER. NY: Harper, (1954). One of 500 for presentation to friends; signed "EBW" on tipped in leaf. VG in dj spine-darkened, chipped at extrems of spine. *LOPEZ.* $135

White, E.W. CAMEOS FROM THE SILVERLAND. London, 1881-82. 2 vols. Fldg map. Ink inscrip on eps, pp yellowed. *SUTTON.* $145

White, Edmund. NOCTURNES FOR THE KING OF NAPLES. NY: St. Martins Press, (1978). 1st ed. Fine in dj. Signed. *CAPTAIN'S BOOKSHELF.* $125

White, Edmund. STATES OF DESIRE: TRAVELS IN GAY AMERICA. NY, 1980. 1st ed. Inscribed, signed. Fine. *POLYANTHOS.* $50

White, Edward Lucas. LUKUNDOO & OTHER STORIES. NY: Doran, (1927). 1st ed. NF in bright pict dj. *BERNARD.* $225

White, Emil (ed). HENRY MILLER: BETWEEN HEAVEN & HELL; A SYMPOSIUM. Big Sur: Emil White, 1961. Blue cloth binding with cloth label on spine. Covers a bit sprung. Light wear at extremities with 1" long indent to front cover. *AKA.* $60

White, Fred M. THE MYSTERY OF THE FOUR FINGERS. NY: W.J. Watt, 1908. 1st ed. Precedes the Eng ed, pub as The Four Fingers. Fine w/o dj. *MORDIDA.* $50

White, George Starr. MY BIOGRAFY. LA: Privately ptd by author, 1936. Signed, dated. Photo laid in. 1st ed. Front inner hinge cracked, repaired. About Fine. *CONNOLLY & WADE.* $50

White, Gilbert. NATURAL HISTORY AND ANTIQUITIES OF SELBORNE. London, 1875. Thoroughly rev w/add notes. Teg, 3/4 lea, w/engr. NF. *POLYANTHOS.* $150

White, Gilbert. THE NATURAL HISTORY OF SELBORNE. Ipswich: Ptd by W.S. Cowell Ltd. for the Members of the LEC, 1972. John Nash (illus). Ed ltd to 1500 numbered, signed by Nash. Slipcase. *KARMIOLE.* $85

White, Gleeson. BOOK-SONG, AN ANTHOLOGY....London: Elliot Stock, 1893. 1st ed. Orig grn cl, beveled edges. *OAK KNOLL.* $25

White, Henry Kirke. HISTORY OF THE UNION PACIFIC RAILWAY. Chicago: UC Press, 1895. 111, 129pp. 14 charts (2 fldg). Grn cl w/gilt title. Rubbed. VG. *BOHLING.* $125

White, J.H. CINCINNATI LOCOMOTIVE BUILDERS 1845-1868. Washington, 1965. Fine. *VARNER.* $20

White, James and William Sweet. PAIN: ITS MECHANISMS AND NEUROSURGICAL CONTROL. Springfield, 1955. 1st ed. *FYE.* $75

White, James. THE AUTONOMIC NERVOUS SYSTEM: ANATOMY, PHYSIOLOGY, AND SURGICAL TREATMENT. NY, 1935. 1st ed. 96 illus. *FYE.* $50

White, Kent Jr. PRAIRIE FIRE. Canton: Daring Books, (1983). 1st ed. Apparently only issued in dj. NF. *LOPEZ.* $65

White, Lionel. BIG STEAL. Greenwich: Fawcett Pubs, 1960. 1st ed. Pb orig. Gold Medal #998. Short crease back cvr corner, o/w Fine in wrappers. *MORDIDA.* $25

White, Margaret. HAND-WOVEN COVERLETS. Newark, NJ: Newark, Museum, 1947. NF. *BACKROOM.* $25

White, Margaret. QUILTS AND COUNTERPANES. Newark, NJ: Newark Museum, 1948. VG. Wraps. *BACKROOM.* $50

White, Minor. MINOR WHITE: RITES & PASSAGES. (Millerton, NY): Aperture, 1978. 1st ed. Dj. *KARMIOLE.* $60

White, Owen P. LEAD AND LIKKER. NY, 1932. VG. *VARNER.* $40

White, Owen P. LEAD AND LIKKER. NY: Minton, Balch, 1932. 1st ed. About Fine, scarce. *CONNOLLY & WADE.* $50

White, Patrick. RIDERS IN THE CHARIOT. NY: Viking (1961). 1st Amer ed. NF in VG dj w/few edge chips. *DORN.* $35

White, Patrick. RIDERS IN THE CHARIOT. NY: Viking, 1961. 1st ed. VF in dj. *ELSE FINE.* $50

White, Patrick. THE LIVING AND THE DEAD. NY: Viking, 1941. 1st ed., 2nd book. Fine, minor edgewear to the dj. *ELSE FINE.* $350

White, Patrick. THE TREE OF MAN. NY: Viking, (1955). 1st Amer ed. Light damp stain bottom else VG in dj. *DORN.* $35

White, Patrick. THE TWYBORN AFFAIR. London: Jonathan Cape, 1979. 1st ed. Fine in dj. *ELSE FINE.* $55

White, Patrick. VIVISECTOR. NY: Viking (1970). 1st ed. Paper label else NF in dj. *DORN.* $35

White, Philo. PHILO WHITE'S NARRATIVE OF A CRUIZE IN THE PACIFIC. Ed by Charles L. Camp. Denver, CO: Old West Pub Co, (1965). Ed ltd to 1000. *KARMIOLE.* $35

White, Philo. PHILO WHITE'S NARRATIVE OF A CRUIZE...ON THE U. S. SLOOP OF WAR "DALE", 1841-1843. Charles L. Camp (ed). Denver, (1965). 1st ed. Ltd to 1000. Orig sm folio cl. *GINSBERG.* $50

White, Robert. MADEIRA: ITS CLIMATE AND SCENERY. London: Cradock, 1851. 1st ed. Small 8vo, viii, 203pp + fldg map, title-page vignette. Dec. cl gilt. Slight cover wear and soiling, else Good. *DIAMOND.* $50

White, Sol. SOL WHITE'S OFFICIAL BASE-BALL GUIDE. Camden House, 1984. Rpt of 1907 ed. Fine. *PLAPINGER.* $150

White, Stewart Edward. AFRICAN CAMP FIRES. GC: Doubleday, Page & Co, (1913). Later ptg. VG. *BACKMAN.* $30

White, Stewart Edward. BLAZED TRAIL STORIES, AND, STORIES OF THE WILD LIFE. NY, 1904. 1st ed. Minor foxing, 2 small holes rear cvr, o/w VG. *DIAMOND.* $25

White, Stewart Edward. THE GRAY DAWN. Doubleday Pg, (1915). 1st ed. Frontis. VG+. *AUTHORS OF THE WEST.* $20

White, Stewart Edward. THE HOLD-UP. SF: Book Club of CA, 1937. 1/600. Contemp calf. VG. *BOHLING.* $30

White, Stewart Edward. THE MOUNTAINS. NY, 1904. 1st ed. 16 plts (color). Few small cvr stains, erasure on fly, o/w VG. *DIAMOND.* $25

White, Stewart Edward. THE MOUNTAINS. NY: Doubleday, Page & Co., 1910. Reprint. Small spot, shelfwear, else VG+. *OLD LONDON.* $30

White, Stewart Edward. THE MOUNTAINS. NY: McClure, Phillips, 1904. 2nd impression. Inner hinge repaired. NF. *CONNOLLY & WADE.* $30

White, Stewart Edward. THE MYSTERY. With Samuel Hopkins Adams. Chicago: McClure-Phillips, 1907. 1st ed, 1st mystery. NF, top edge dusty, beginning to wear at corners. 16 plts. *ELSE FINE.* $65

White, Stewart Edward. THE RULES OF THE GAME. Doubleday, Pg, 1910. 1st ed. VG+. *AUTHORS OF THE WEST.* $20

White, Stewart Edward. THE RULES OF THE GAME. NY, 1911. 1st ed. 4 color plts. Small stain on spine, one page margin repaired, o/w VG. *DIAMOND.* $25

White, Stewart Edward. THE SILENT PLACES. NY, 1904. 1st ed. 7 color plts. Cvrs sl shelfworn, stained, o/w VG. *DIAMOND.* $25

White, T. H. THE BOOK OF BEASTS. NY: G.P. Putnam's Sons, (1954). Dj. Fine. *WEBER.* $20

White, T.H. FAREWELL VICTORIA. NY: Harrison Smith & Robert Haas, 1934. 1st ed. Fine in sl used dj. *DERMONT.* $150

White, T.H. THE BOOK OF MERLYN. Univ of Texas, (1977). 1st trade ed. 137pp. Illus by Trevor Stubley. Fine in VG+ dj. *BEBBAH.* $30

White, T.H. THE GOSHAWK. NY: Putnam, 1951. 1st US ed. Fine in Fine dj. *BEASLEY.* $35

White, T.H. THE ONCE AND FUTURE KING. NY: Putnam, (1958). 1st US ed. NF in lightly soiled dj. *CAPTAIN'S BOOKSHELF.* $75

White, Teri. BLEEDING HEARTS. NY: Mysterious Press, 1984. 1st ed. Signed. VF in dj. *SILVER DOOR.* $35

White, Trumbull. COMPLETE STORY OF THE SAN FRANCIS-CO HORROR. N.p.: n.p. 1906. 1st ed. Some fade and edgewear. Contents Fine. *CONNOLLY & WADE.* $32.50

White, Trumbull. OUR NEW POSSESSIONS...FOUR BOOKS IN ONE. N.p.: Author published, 1898. 1st ed. VG. *CONNOLLY & WADE.* $35

White, W.H. A MANUAL OF NAVAL ARCHITECTURE. FOR THE USE OF OFFICERS....AND YACHTSMEN. 2nd ed, rev, enl. London: John Murray, 1889. Cvrs rubbed, bit foxed. *LEFKOWICZ.* $95

White, William. CANCER OF THE BREAST. NY, 1930. *FYE.* $50

Whitehead, Alfred North and Bertrand Russell. PRINCIPIA MATH-EMATICA. Cambridge: (Univ Press), 1950. 2nd ed, 3rd ptg. 3 vols. Pub's blue cl, in the djs. Fine set. *BOOK BLOCK.* $150

Whitehead, Charles. A MAN AND HIS DIAMONDS. Vantage Press, 1980. 1st ed. Good in Fine dj. *PLAPINGER.* $85

Whitehead, Henry. WEST INDIA LIGHTS. Sauk City, WI: Arkham House, 1946. 1/3037. VG+ in dj, sl tanned spine. *BERNARD.* $65

Whitehead, Henry. JUMBEE AND OTHER UNCANNY TALES. Arkham House, 1944. 1st ed. Fine in dj. *MADLE.* $300

Whitehead, Henry. WEST INDIA LIGHTS. Arkham House, 1946. 1st ed. Fine in Mint dj. *MADLE.* $125

Whitehead, James. JOINER. NY: Knopf, 1971. 1st ed. About Fine in like dj w/short tear. Signed. *CAPTAIN'S BOOKSHELF.* $50

Whitehead, Thomas. VIRGINIA: A HANDBOOK GIVING ITS HIS-TORY.... Everett Waddey, 1893. Paper cvr, some tear & soil. Good+. *BOOK BROKER.* $45

Whiteman, Robin. THE CADFAEL COMPANION: THE WORLD OF BROTHER CADFAEL. Ellis Peters intro. London: Macdonald, 1991. 1st ed. Signed by Peters and Whiteman. VF in dj. *MORDIDA.* $65

Whitfield, Raoul. GREEN ICE. England: No Exit Press, 1988. 1st British ed. Fine in dj. *SILVER DOOR.* $35

Whitfield, Raoul. GREEN ICE. NY: Knopf, 1930. 1st ed. Unevenly sunned, VG. *ARCHER.* $35

Whitfield, Raoul. THE VIRGIN KILLS. England: No Exit Press, 1988. 1st British ed. Fine in dj. *SILVER DOOR.* $35

Whitford, William Clarke. COLORADO VOLUNTEERS IN THE CIVIL WAR, THE NEW MEXICO CAMPAIGN IN 1861. Denver, 1906. 1st ed. 159pp. Pict wraps. Small repaired tear on front cover o/w VG. *PRATT.* $160

Whiting, Henry. REVOLUTIONARY ORDERS OF GENERAL WASHINGTON, ISSUED DURING THE YEARS 1778, '80, '81, AND '82, SELECTED FROM THE MSS. OF JOHN WHITING...AND EDITED BY HIS SON. NY: Wiley, 1844. 1st ed. 255pp. Orig cl. Laid in 2 page ALS. Presentation inscrip. on inside front cover. *GINSBERG.* $125

Whiting, Lilian. KATE FIELD. A RECORD. Boston, 1899. 1st ed. Spine sl faded. Little shelfwear, foxing, o/w VG. *DIAMOND.* $25

Whiting, Lilian. THE LAND OF ENCHANTMENT: FROM PIKE'S PEAK TO THE PACIFIC. Boston: Little, Brown, 1906. 1st ed. Fine. *CONNOLLY & WADE.* $45

Whiting, Perry. AUTOBIOGRAPHY OF PERRY WHITING, PIONEER BUILDING MATERIAL MERCHANT OF LOS ANGELES. LA: Smith Barnes, (1930). 1st ed. VG. *OREGON.* $45

Whiting, Perry. AUTOBIOGRAPHY OF PERRY WHITING....LA: Privately ptd, 1930. 1st ed. Frontis. Lea textured fabricoid, gilt dec. NF. Scarce. *CONNOLLY & WADE.* $50

Whiting, Robert. THE CHRYSANTHEMUM AND THE BAT: BASEBALL SAMURAI STYLE. NY: Dodd, (1977). 1st ed. Fine in dj. *CAPTAIN'S BOOKSHELF.* $65

Whitlock, Herbert P. THE STORY OF JADE. NY, 1949. Dj rubbed, chip bottom panel. Fine. *POLYANTHOS.* $40

Whitman, Walt. LEAVES OF GRASS COMPRISING ALL THE POEMS WRITTEN BY WALT WHITMAN FOLLOWING THE ARRANGEMENT OF THE EDITION OF 1891-2. NY: Random House, 1930. Ltd ed of 400 numbered. Orig rustic red goatskin backed wooden boards; hinges a bit stressed and weakened. bkpl. VG. *WEBER.* $1750

Whitman, Walt. POEMS FROM LEAVES OF GRASS. London: J.M. Dent & Sons, Ltd.; NY: E.P. Dutton & Co, 1913. 1st ed. (Wells 2nd issue binding; Bradley 1st issue binding). Pict grn cl sl rubbed, stamped in black w/title in gilt on spine. xii,260pp. 24 tipped-in color plts by Margaret Cook (3 corners creased). NF. *BLUE MOUNTAIN.* $350

Whitman, Walt. THE CORRESPONDENCE OF WALT WHITMAN. Vol. V. 1890-1892. E. Miller (ed). NY: NY Univ Press, 1969. 1st ed. Bumped o/w Fine in NF dj. *ARCHER.* $25

Whitmarsh, Samuel. EIGHT YEARS EXPERIENCE AND OBSERVATION IN THE CULTURE OF THE MULBERRY TREE, AND IN THE CARE OF THE SILK WORM. Northhampton, MA: Butler, 1839. 1st ed. Fold-out frontis, bound in pub's cl (worn), leaves browned. Good. *SECOND LIFE.* $135

Whitney, Carrie Westlake. KANSAS CITY, MISSOURI; ITS HISTORY AND ITS PEOPLE 1808-1908. Chicago: S.J. Clarke Pub Co., 1908. Vols. 1 & 2 (of 3). Rebound in black buckram, aeg. Vol 1 fore-edge stained throughout, early leaves w/chipping, short tears, seminary stamp. Vol 2 VG. *BOHLING.* $125

Whitney, Caspar. CHARLES ADELBERT CANFIELD. NY: privately ptd, 1930. 1st ed. Full brown morocco w/red and black morocco spine labels, light wear, t.e.g. Fine. Produced in ed of 175, only 25 were bound in full morocco, designed and ptd by D. B. Updike at the Merrymount Press. Howes W384. *GINSBERG.* $750

Whitney, Caspar. JUNGLE TRAILS AND JUNGLE PEOPLE. NY: Scribner's, 1905. 4 pp pub ads. Some wear, hinges repaired, some internal stains. *SCHOYER'S.* $45

Whitney, Helen Hay. THE PUNCH & JUDY BOOK. NY: Duffield & Co., (1906). Pictures by Charlotte Harding. 1st ed. Pict endpapers. VG. *DRAMATIS PERSONAE.* $100

Whitney, Joel P. SILVER MINING REGIONS OF COLORADO. SOME ACCOUNT OF THE DIFFERENT PROCESSES...FOR WORKING THE GOLD ORES OF THAT TERRITORY. NY: Van Nostrand, 1865. 1st ed. 107pp. Orig ptd front wrappers only ("editor of the Herald" in ink on front wrapper), rubber lib stamp. Howes W388. *GINSBERG.* $750

Whitney, Orson. SATURDAY NIGHT THOUGHTS. Salt Lake, 1921. 1st ed. VG+. *BENCHMARK.* $25

Whittaker, Frederick. A COMPLETE LIFE OF GEN. GEORGE A. CUSTER. NY, (1876). 1st ed. 648pp. Pict cloth. Usual cvr wear o/w VG+. *PRATT.* $200

Whittaker, Frederick. A POPULAR LIFE OF GEN. GEORGE A. CUSTER. NY: Sheldon & Co, 1876. 1st ed. 648pp. VG. *BOOK MARKET.* $80

Whittemore, Edward. JERICHO MOSAIC. W. W. Norton, 1987. 1st ed. Fine in dj. *STAHR.* $30

Whittemore, Reed. HEROES & HEROINES. NY: Reynal & Hitchcock, 1946. 1st ed. Covers faded. Lacking dj. Inscribed. Author's 1st book. *WOOLMER.* $50

Whittemore, Thomas. THE MOSAICS OF ST. SOPHIA AT ISTANBUL. SECOND PRELIMINARY REPORT. Oxford, 1936. 20 plts, plan. *O'NEILL.* $35

Whittemore, Thomas. THE MOSAICS OF ST. SOPHIA AT ISTANBUL. PRELIMINARY REPORT. Oxford, 1933. 21 plts, plan. *O'NEILL.* $37.50

Whittier, John Greenleaf. AMONG THE HILLS, AND OTHER POEMS. Boston: Fields, Osgood, & Co., 1869. 100pp, 4pp ads. Orig terra-cotta cl. Spine ends worn, else VG (very early pencilled initials). 1st ed, w/no publisher's monogram on spine. *CHAPEL HILL.* $40

Whittier, John Greenleaf. BALLADS OF NEW ENGLAND. Boston, 1870. 1st ed. Aeg. Spine sunned, extremities little rubbed. Fine. *POLYANTHOS.* $45

Whittier, John Greenleaf. HOME BALLADS AND POEMS. Boston, 1860. 1st ed. Correct 1st state of ads bound in (16pp, dated "July, 1860). Sl spine end wear, else VG. *McCLINTOCK.* $20

Whitting, P.D. BYZANTINE COINS. NY: Putnam, 1973. 1st ed. Dj. VG. *WORLDWIDE.* $60

Whittington, Harry. BURDEN'S MISSION. NY: Avon, (1968). Pb orig. Crease one corner of front wrap, o/w About Fine & unread. *AKA.* $30

Whittington, Harry. DOOMSDAY MISSION. (NY): Banner, (1967). Pb orig. Unread copy, About Fine. *AKA.* $45

Whitwell, J.R. HISTORICAL NOTES ON PSYCHIATRY (EARLY TIMES—END OF 16TH CENTURY). London, 1936. 1st ed. Backstrip dull. *FYE.* $75

Whyte, Frederick. ACTORS OF THE CENTURY. London: Bell, 1898. Bit scuffed, dusty; contents fine. *DRAMATIS.* $45

Whyte-Melville, G.J. SONGS AND VERSES. NY: Scribner's, 1924. 1st US ed. Good. *OCTOBER FARM.* $35

Wickersham, James. OLD YUKON. TALES-TRAILS-AND TRIALS. Washington: Washington Law Book Lib, 1938. 1st ed. VG. *BLUE DRAGON.* $40

Wickersham, James. "OLD YUKON" TALES-TRAILS-TRIALS. Washington, D.C.: Washington Law Book Co, 1938. 1st ed. Owner inscrip. VG. *PARMER.* $55

Wickersham, James. OLD YUKON TALES-TRAILS-TRIALS. Washington, DC, 1938. 1st ed. Map frontis. Shelfwear. Good, sound. *ARTIS.* $35

Wickes, Stephen. HISTORY OF THE ORANGES IN ESSEX COUNTY, NJ FROM 1666 TO 1806. Newark, NJ: 1892. 1st ed. 26 plts & illus. Orig binding, worn top & bottom spine. *HEINOLDT.* $60

Wickhoff, Franz. ROMAN ART: SOME OF ITS PRINCIPLES AND THEIR APPLICATION TO EARLY CHRISTIAN PAINTING. London: William Heinemann, 1900. Frontis, 31 figs, 13 plts. Good. *ARCHAEOLOGIA.* $150

Wicks, Mark. ORGAN BUILDING FOR AMATEURS. London & NY: Ward, Lock and Co, 1887. 1st ed. 287pp,(xvi)ads. Pict grn cl Sm stain top front cvr; back cvr bubbled. Color illus of organ. Title in gilt w/color vignettes on spine. Hinges reinforced w/linen tape, shaken. Color fldg frontis, 14 fldg plts (sm piece torn from bottom of 1 plt; few short tears to others) 6 full-pg plts B/w organ photo laid in. VG. *BLUE MOUNTAIN.* $125

Wickson, Edward J. RURAL CALIFORNIA. NY: Macmillan, 1923. 1st ed. Vol 3 in the Rural State and Province Series. Fine. *CONNOLLY & WADE.* $45

Wickson, Edward J. THE CALIFORNIA FRUITS AND HOW TO GROW THEM....SF: Dewey, 1891. 2nd ed, rev, enl. Front hinge tender. VG. *SECOND LIFE.* $45

Wickson, Edward J. THE CALIFORNIA FRUITS AND HOW TO GROW THEM. SF: Pacific Rural Press, 1910. 5th ed, rev. Good. *PARMER.* $20

Wideman, John Edgar. A GLANCE AWAY. NY: Harcourt, Brace, World, Inc, (c1967). 1st ed, 1st bk. Inscribed. NF. *HELLER.* $55

Wideman, John Edgar. PHILADELPHIA FIRE. NY: Holt, (1990). Uncorrected proof. Fine in wraps, in proof dj. *LOPEZ.* $45

Wideman, John Edgar. REUBEN. NY: Holt, (1987). Fine in dj. *LOPEZ.* $25

Wideman, John Edgar. SENT FOR YOU YESTERDAY. (London: Allison & Busby, 1984). 1st Eng ed and 1st hb. Adv review copy, slip laid in. Fine in Fine dj. *LOPEZ.* $45

Wideman, John Edgar. SENT FOR YOU YESTERDAY. (NY): Avon, (1983). Pb orig. Pages browning slightly w/age, o/w Fine. Signed. *LOPEZ.* $75

Widney, J.P. THE LURE AND THE LAND: AN IDYL OF THE PACIFIC. LA: Pacific: Times-Mirror, 1932. 1st ed. Inscribed. Ltd to 1000. Fine. Scarce. *CONNOLLY & WADE.* $45

Wiebe, Rudy. PEACE SHALL DESTROY MANY. McClelland & Stewart, (1962). 1st Canadian ed, 1st novel. Signed. Fine in dj. *AUTHORS OF THE WEST.* $75

Wiebe, Rudy. THE BLUE MOUNTAINS OF CHINA. Erdman's, (1970). 1st ed. New in dj. *AUTHORS OF THE WEST.* $25

Wiebe, Rudy. THE SCORCHED-WOOD PEOPLE. McClelland & Stewart, (1977). 1st Canadian ed. Signed. Fine in dj. *AUTHORS OF THE WEST.* $30

Wiebe, Rudy. THE TEMPTATIONS OF BIG BEAR. Toronto: McClelland & Stewart, (1973). 1st Canadian ed. Ep maps. Fine in dj. *AUTHORS OF THE WEST.* $25

Wiedeman, Mary (ed). BENCHMARK PAPERS IN HUMAN PHYSIOLOGY: MICROCIRCULATION. Stroudshurg, PA, 1974. 1st ed. *FYE.* $50

Wiedersheim, R. THE STRUCTURE OF MAN: AN INDEX TO HIS PAST HISTORY. London, 1895. 1st Eng trans. *FYE.* $50

WIELAND, OR THE TRANSFORMATION. AN AMERICAN TALE. (By Charles Brockden Brown.) NY, 1798. 1st ed. 12mo. (3),298pp. Full contemp tree calf, lea label on spine (Hinges cracked but sound). BAL 1496. *M & S.* $950

Wiener, Norbert. CYBERNETICS OR CONTROL AND COMMUNICATION IN THE ANIMAL AND THE MACHINE. NY: The Technology Press, (1948). 1st ed. Author's 1st bk. Fine. *POLYANTHOS.* $200

Wiener, Norbert. THE TEMPTER. NY: Random House (1959). 1st ed. Fine in bright dj (fold tear). *DORN.* $75

Wieners, John. A LETTER TO CHARLES OLSON. Brooklyn: Charters/Portents 11, 1968. 1st ed. One of 300. Fldg broadside, sealed w/sticker and strip of tissue. Fine. *BEASLEY.* $25

Wieners, John. ACE OF PENTACLES. NY: Carr and Wilson, 1964. 1st ed. NF, issued in an unptd tissue jacket, lacking here. *BEASLEY.* $35

Wieners, John. ACE OF PENTACLES. NY: James F. Carr and Robert A. Wilson, 1964. 1st ed, regular issue. Fine in sl worn glassine dj. *CAPTAIN'S BOOKSHELF.* $35

Wieners, John. ACE OF PENTACLES. Poems. NY: James F. Carr and Robert A. Wilson, 1964. 1st ed. 1/75 in cloth w/orig ms pg tipped in and signed. Fine in sl nicked glassine dj. *CAPTAIN'S BOOKSHELF.* $150

Wieners, John. ACE OF PENTACLES. NY: James F. Carr and Robert A. Wilson, 1964. 1st ed, wrappered issue. Fine in pict wraps. *CAPTAIN'S BOOKSHELF.* $15

Wieners, John. BEHIND THE STATE CAPITOL OR CINCINNATI PIKE. (Boston): The Good Gay Poets (1975). 1st ed. 1/100 in cloth, signed. Fine w/o dj, as issued. *CAPTAIN'S BOOKSHELF.* $75

Wieners, John. HOTELS. (NY): Angel Hair Books, (1974). 1st ed. 1/500. Fine in wraps. *CAPTAIN'S BOOKSHELF.* $35

Wieners, John. INVITATION. (Santa Barbara: Unicorn Press, 1970). 1st ed. 1/200 signed. Fine in boards w/paper label. *CAPTAIN'S BOOKSHELF.* $60

Wieners, John. NERVES. (London): Cape Goliard Press, (1970). 1st ed. 1/100 signed. Fine in dj. *CAPTAIN'S BOOKSHELF.* $60

Wieners, John. PLAYBOY, also known as WE WERE THERE. (Boston: Good Gay Poets, 1972). 1st ed, w/grn and red stock covers. NF in pict stapled wrappers. Signed and hand-corrected by Wieners. *CAPTAIN'S BOOKSHELF.* $60

Wieners, John. PRESSED WAFER. (Buffalo: The Gallery Upstairs Press, 1967). 1st ed, wrappered issue. Fine. *CAPTAIN'S BOOKSHELF.* $20

Wieners, John. SELECTED POEMS. NY: Grossman, 1972. 1st ed. Fine in Fine dj. *BEASLEY.* $50

Wieners, John. SELECTED POEMS. NY: Grossman, 1972. 1st ed. Fine in dj. *CAPTAIN'S BOOKSHELF.* $35

Wieners, John. THE HOTEL WENTLEY POEMS. (SF: Auerhahn Press), 1958. 1st ed, 1st (expurgated) issue, but w/expurgated works written in by hand. Inscribed. White rear cvr faintly tanned & soiled, o/w Fine. Pict wraps. *JAFFE.* $275

Wieners, John. THE HOTEL WENTLY POEMS. (SF: Auerhahn Press), 1958. NF in wrappers. *CAPTAIN'S BOOKSHELF.* $75

Wieners, John. THE HOTEL WENTLY POEMS. SF: Dave Haselwood, 1965. 2nd ed rev. Fine in wrappers. *CAPTAIN'S BOOKSHELF.* $30

Wieners, John. UNHIRED. Mt. Horeb: Perishable Press, 1968. Wraps, 1/250. Fine. *BEASLEY.* $175

Wieners, John. UNHIRED. Wrappers. (Mt. Horeb): Perishable Press, (1968). 1st ed. Ltd to 250. Spine sl faded, o/w Fine. *JAFFE.* $75

Wieners, John. YOUTH. NY: Phoenix Book Shop, 1970. 1st ed. 1/100 signed. Fine in wrappers. *CAPTAIN'S BOOKSHELF.* $75

Wiese, Kurt. YOU CAN WRITE CHINESE. NY: Viking, 1945. 1st ed. Cloth/pict boards. Illus in three colors. NF in VG+ dj. *ACADEMIC LIBRARY.* $40

Wiesel, Elie. THE FIFTH SON. Franklin Center: Franklin Lib, 1985. Leatherbound ltd 1st ed. Signed. *LOPEZ.* $50

Wiggin, Kate Douglas. MARM LISA. Boston, 1896. 1st ed. Pict cvrs. NF. *POLYANTHOS.* $35

Wiggin, Kate Douglas. MOTHER CAREY'S CHICKENS. Boston & NY: Houghton Mifflin, 1911. NF. 1st ed. *CHAPEL HILL.* $50

Wiggin, Kate Douglas. ROSE O' THE RIVER. Houghton Mifflin, 1905. 1st ed. Slight edgewear. VG+. *BEBBAH*. $20

Wiggin, Kate Douglas. THE DIARY OF A GOOSE GIRL. Boston, 1902. 1st ed. Illus by Claude A. Shepperson. Pict cvrs, spine sl rubbed. Fine. *POLYANTHOS*. $35

Wiggin, Kate Douglas. THE ROMANCE OF A CHRISTMAS CARD. NY: A.L. Burt, (1916). Rprt ed, inscribed in 1918. VG in pict boards, lacking dj. *LOPEZ*. $85

Wiggin, Kate Douglas. THE ROMANCE OF A CHRISTMAS CARD. Houghton Mifflin, 1916. 1st ed. 4 color plts; pict pastedown by Alice Hunt. VG w/some edge chipping of cvr pastedown. *BEBBAH*. $30

Wightman, Edith Mary. ROMAN TRIER AND THE TREVERI. NY & Washington: Praeger (1971). Dj. *SCHOYER'S*. $35

Wigston, W.F.C. HERMES STELLA OR NOTES AND JOTTINGS UPON THE BACON CIPHER. London, 1890. NF. *POLYANTHOS*. $60

Wilbur, Marguerite. JOHN SUTTER, RASCAL AND ADVEN-TURER. NY: Liveright, (1949). 1st ed. 9 plts. Fine in Fine dj. *OREGON*. $30

Wilbur, Richard. ADVICE TO A PROPHET. NY: Harcourt, (1961). Inscribed. Adv rev copy. NF in sl worn dj. *DORN*. $75

Wilbur, Richard. POEMS 1943-1956. London: Faber, (1957). 1st Eng ed. Signed by author and Donald Davie. Fine in sl frayed dj missing piece. *DORN*. $120

Wilbur, Richard. WALKING TO SLEEP. London: Faber, (1971). 1st Eng ed. Bound proof in wraps. Signed. *DORN*. $75

Wilcox, Collin. DOCTOR, LAWYER. London: Hale, 1978. 1st British ed. Signed. Fine in NF dj. sl soiled. *SILVER DOOR*. $35

Wilcox, Don. JOE SUNPOOL. Boston: Little Brown, (1956). 1st ed. VG in edgeworn dj. *LOPEZ*. $75

Wilcox, Henry S. THE TRIALS OF A STUMP-SPEAKER. NY: J.S. Ogilvie, 1906. Pict cl. *SCHOYER'S*. $35

Wilcox, Mary Emily Donelson. CHRISTMAS UNDER THREE FLAGS. Washington: Neale Company, 1900. 13 plts. Pict cl, some soiling, 2 holes in backstrip, shaken text. *SCHOYER'S*. $35

Wilcox, Rhoda Davis. THE MAN ON THE IRON HORSE. Colorado Springs: Dentan Printing Co, 1959. Cl. VG. *BURCHAM*. $45

WILD ANIMAL STORIES. NY, 1988. Repro of Ernest Nister movable bk. Orig pub 1867. *BOOKFINDERS INTL*. $15

Wild, H. (ed). COMMUNICATIONS FROM THE INTERNATION-AL POLAR COMMISSION. IN 6 PARTS. St. Petersburg, 1882. Together 334pp. 4to. Orig. wraps fragile, chipped at edges. Mostly uncut. Very scarce. *ARTIS*. $275

Wilde, Oscar. A WOMAN OF NO IMPORTANCE. London: John Lane, 1894. 1st ed. Slight foxing to eps, cloth boards a bit soiled. VG. *BETWEEN COVERS*. $350

Wilde, Oscar. DE PROFUNDIS. Putnam, (1909). Stated 2nd ed with added matter. Frontis portrait. Some edgewear to paper-covered boards, sunning to spine else VG+. *BEBBAH*. $25

Wilde, Oscar. DE PROFUNDIS. Robert Ross (ed). NY: Modern Library, (1926). 1st ML ed. Light wear to spinal extremities, else NF in leatherette binding. Morse Peckham's bkpl. *CAPTAIN'S BOOK-SHELF*. $30.

Wilde, Oscar. FOR LOVE OF THE KING. A Burmese Masque. London: Methuen & Co. (1922). 1st ed. Ed ltd to 1000. Dj. *KARMIOLE*. $200

Wilde, Oscar. LADY WINDEMERE'S FAN. London: Elkin Mathews and John Lane, 1893. 1st ed. VG w/scattered light foxing, 2 consecutive pages w/short tears on edges, some modest bubbling to cloth boards, overall light soiling. *BETWEEN COVERS*. $600

Wilde, Oscar. RAVENNA. Oxford: Thos. Shrimpton & Son, 1878. 1st ed. 16pp. Orig ptd pale blue-grn wraps. Front wrap expertly repaired, minor wear to foreedge, o/w NF. Custom blue cl chemise, 1/4 morocco slipcase. *CHAPEL HILL*. $750

Wilde, Oscar. SALOME. NY: E.P. Dutton & Co. (1927). Inventions by John Vassos. Ed ltd to 500 numbered, signed. Spine sl faded, o/w Fine. *KARMIOLE*. $175

Wilde, Oscar. SALOME. London: LEC, 1938. Illus by Aubrey Beardsley. 14 plts. Gilt purple cl. Volume II: Wilde, Oscar. SALOME. Illus par Andre Derain. Paris: LEC, 1938. 10 color drwgs by Derain. Ed ltd to 1500 numbered, signed by Derain. Stiff black ptd wrappers. Both vols in slipcase (a bit worn). Bkplt. *KAR-MIOLE*. $350

Wilde, Oscar. SOME LETTERS FROM OSCAR WILDE TO ALFRED DOUGLAS, 1892-1897. SF: Ptd for William Andrews Clark, Jr. By John Henry Nash, 1924. Ed ltd to 225 numbered ptd for private distribution. Frontis. Ptd slip tipped-in, inscribed by William Andrew Clark, Jr. Owner inscrip, boards bit soiled, corners sl rubbed. *KARMIOLE*. $375

Wilde, Oscar. THE HAPPY PRINCE AND OTHER TALES. Stamford, CT: The Overbrook Press, 1936. Illus Rudolph Ruzicka. Cl-backed parchment-tipped paste-paper boards, cl & board slipcase. 1st ed. Ltd to 250. Fine. *JAFFE*. $150

Wilde, Oscar. THE HAPPY PRINCE AND OTHER TALES. Boston: Roberts Brothers, 1888. Walter Crane, Jacomb Hood (illus). 1st Amer ed. Orig pict mustard cl. Inscrip, cvrs rubbed at extrems of spine & corners, o/w Good. *JAFFE*. $75

Wilde, Oscar. THE HAPPY PRINCE. Boston: Roberts Bros., 1888. Illus by Walter Crane and Jacomb Hood. 1st Amer ed. (10),116pp. Orig gray cloth stamped in red, with illus in brown, gilt spine. Very nice, bright. Amer ed was pub same yr as British. *KARMIOLE*. $500

Wilde, Oscar. THE PICTURE OF DORIAN GRAY. NY: Ivers, 1890. 1st ed. Lovely unrestored 1st Amer ed, which preceded Brit ed by one yr. Very fragile in wraps w/short split along one fold. VG+. In a custom quarter lea box. *LAME DUCK*. $1850

Wilde, Oscar. THE POEMS OF OSCAR WILDE. NY: Boni & Liveright. 1927. Illus Jean de Bosschere. Blue cl, gilt. *KARMIOLE*. $65

Wilde, Percival. DESIGN FOR MURDER. NY: Random House, 1941. 1st ed. VG in dj w/internal tape mends. *MORDIDA*. $45

Wilde, Percival. THE DEVIL'S BOOTH. NY: Harcourt Brace, 1930. 1st ed. VG in sl soiled dj (internal tape mends; wear; several short tears). *MORDIDA*. $30

Wilde, Percival. TINSLEY'S BONES. NY: Random House, 1942. 1st ed. VG in dj. *MORDIDA*. $45

Wilde, W.R. NARRATIVE OF A VOYAGE TO MADEIRA, TENERIFFE, AND ALONG THE SHORES OF THE MEDITERRANEAN, INCLUDING A VISIT TO ALGIERS, EGYPT, PALESTINE, TYRE, RHODES, TELEMESSUS, CYPRUS, AND GREECE. Dublin, 1840. 2 charts, 2 plts of skulls, numerous engravings. 2 vols. Recased. xiv,464pp; viii,495pp. 1st ed. Trace of lib markings. *O'NEILL*. $325

Wilder, Thornton. HEAVEN'S MY DESTINATION. NY: Harper, 1935. 1st ed. Fine in white dj w/few tiny edge tears. *CAPTAIN'S BOOK-SHELF*. $100

Wilder, Thornton. OUR CENTURY. (NY:) The Century Association, 1947. 1st ed, 1/1000. Fine in lightly used dj. *JUVELIS*. $50

Wilder, Thornton. OUR TOWN. NY: Coward McCann, (1938). 1st ed. Cvrs sl sun faded else NF in VG dj, missing chips. *DORN*. $145

Wilder, Thornton. OUR TOWN. NY: Coward McCann Inc, (1938). 1st ed. VG in VG dj. *JUVELIS*. $200

Wilder, Thornton. THE BRIDGE OF SAN LUIS REY. NY: Albert & Charles Boni, 1927. 1st Amer ed. Orig brownish grey cl. NF in

VG dj (several chips and tears, incl lg chip head of spine affecting first couple of words in title). Inscribed. *CHAPEL HILL*. $375

Wilder, Thornton. THE EIGHTH DAY. NY: Harper, (1967). 1st ed. Ltd to 500 specially ptd, bound, signed. Cl, acetate dj, slipcase. VF. *JAFFE*. $125

Wilder, Thornton. THE EIGHTH DAY. NY: Harper & Row, (1967). 1st ed. 1/500 signed. Fine in VG slipcase. *JUVELIS*. $90

Wilder, Thornton. THE EIGHTH DAY. NY: Harper & Row, (1967). 1st ed. Presentation, inscribed. Cl backed boards. Fine in price-clipped dj. *JAFFE*. $175

Wilder, Thornton. THE LONG CHRISTMAS DINNER. NY, 1931. 1st ed. VG in bit chipped price-clipped dj. *PETTLER*. $50

Wilder, Thornton. THE WOMAN OF ANDROS. London & NY: Longmans Green, 1930. One of 230 signed. Spine little faded, else fine. *WOOLMER*. $400

Wilder, Thornton. THEOPHILUS NORTH. NY: Harper & Row, Publs, (1973). 1st ed. Fine in dj. *JUVELIS*. $40

Wilding, Michael. SCENIC DRIVE. Sydney: Wild & Woolley, (1976). 1st ed. Inscribed. Fine in wrappers. *LOPEZ*. $25

Wilenski, R.H. FLEMISH PAINTERS 1430-1830. NY, 1960. 2 vols. Fine. *POLYANTHOS*. $150

Wiley, Bell Irvin and Hirst D. Milhollen. THEY WHO FOUGHT HERE. NY: Macmillan, 1959. 1st ed. Fine in VG dj. *CONNOLLY & WADE*. $42.50

Wiley, Bell Irvin and Hirst D. Milhollen. THEY WHO FOUGHT HERE. NY, 1959. 1st ed. VG in dj. *PRATT*. $35

Wiley, Bell Irvin. THE COMMON SOLDIER IN THE CIVIL WAR. 2 vols. in one. (THE LIFE OF BILLY YANK & THE LIFE OF JOHNNY REB). NY, (1958). 454 & 444pp. Dj wear o/w VG+. *PRATT*. $40

Wiley, Bell Irvin. THE ROAD TO APPOMATTOX. Memphis, 1956. 1st ed. Gift copy, "Compliments of Memphis State College", signed by the President of that institution, the publishers. 121pp. Illus. Dj chipping o/w VG. *PRATT*. $50

Wiley, Hugh. FO' MEALS A DAY. NY: Knopf, 1927. 1st ed. Orig cl-backed patterned boards. NF in VG dj (1" piece lacking top of spine, sm hole in pub's imprint at bottom). *CHAPEL HILL*. $75

Wilhelm, H.R.H. EARLY SACRAMENTO. Sacramento, 1973. Ltd to 400. Fine in glassine dj. *BAADE*. $95

Wilhelm, Kate. MORE BITTER THAN DEATH. Simon & Schuster, 1963. 1st ed, 1st bk. Chip in dj, else NF. *MADLE*. $65

Wilkerson, Don. THE POST WAR COLT SINGLE-ACTION RE-VOLVER. Dallas: Taylor Pub. Co, 1978. 1st ed. Ltd to 3,000, signed. Leather w/raised gilt lettering on spine and cvr. Raised gilt Colt revolver on cvr. Fine. *BACKMAN*. $150

Wilkerson, Don. THE POST WAR COLT SINGLE-ACTION RE-VOLVER. Dallas: Taylor Pub Co, 1980. Expanded 2nd ed. Signed. Bound in simulated leather but also in pict dj. Fine in Fine dj. *BACK-MAN*. $75

Wilkes, George. MCCLELLAN: FROM BALL'S BLUFF TO AN-TIETAM. NY, 1863. 2nd ed, enlarged. Wrappers. Good. *McGOWAN*. $37.50

Wilkes, Rear Admiral Charles. AUTOBIOGRAPHY OF REAR AD-MIRAL CHARLES WILKES, U.S. NAVY. 1798-1877. Wash, DC: Dept of the Navy, 1978. Spine fading, bumping to crnrs, else Fine. *PARMER*. $75

Wilkin, R. Apiarian, Cadiz, Ohio. HAND-BOOK OF BEE-CUL-TURE. Pittsburgh: Haven, 1871. 1st ed. 96pp. Frontis. Bumped cl. Good. *SECOND LIFE*. $125

Wilkins, George H. FLYING THE ARCTIC. NY: Putnam's, 1928. 2nd prtg. VG. *BLUE DRAGON*. $30

Wilkins, George H. FLYING THE ARCTIC. NY: Putnam's Sons, 1928. 1st ed. Unobtrusive damp spots on cvr and spine else VG. *GREAT EPIC*. $45

Wilkins, George H. FLYING THE ARCTIC. NY/London: G.P. Putnam's Sons, 1928. 1st ptg. Bkpl. VG+. *PARMER*. $65

Wilkins, George H. UNDER THE NORTH POLE. N.p.: Brewer, Warren & Putnam, (1931). Inscribed. VG. *BLUE DRAGON*. $65

Wilkins, H. Percy and Patrick Moore. THE MOON, A COMPLETE DESCRIPTION OF THE SURFACE OF THE MOON, CON-TAINING THE 300-INCH WILKINS LUNAR MAP. London: Faber & Faber, 1955. Corners bumped. Good. *KNOLLWOOD*. $45

Wilkins, John H. ELEMENTS OF ASTRONOMY, ILLUSTRATED WITH PLATES, FOR THE USE OF SCHOOLS. Boston: Hilliard, Gray, Little & Wilkins, 1828 (1822). 5th ed. 1/4 leather w/marbled boards. Corners worn, extremities worn. Internally a few spots, tear to one pg, else Nice. *KNOLLWOOD*. $45

Wilkins, Mary E. A NEW ENGLAND NUN AND OTHER STORIES. NY: Harper & Bros, 1891. VG or better. 1st ed. *CHAPEL HILL*. $50

Wilkins, Thurman. CHEROKEE TRAGEDY. NY: The Macmillan Co, 1970. 1st prtg. VG in dj. *PARMER*. $35

Wilkins, W. Glyde. CHARLES DICKENS IN AMERICA. NY: Scribner's, 1912. 1st Amer ed. 8vo, 318pp, illus, bkpl, spine lightly faded. VG+. *GREAT EXPECTATIONS*. $35

Wilkinson, Alix. ANCIENT EGYPTIAN JEWELLERY. London: Methuen, (1971). 77 figs, 64 plts. Good. *ARCHAEOLOGIA*. $125

Wilkinson, Gardner. MODERN EGYPT AND THEBES. London: John Murray, 1843. 2 vols (complete). 1 fldg map, orig cl boards. Bkpl, signature, slight discoloration to small area of spine of vol 1. Good. *ARCHAEOLOGIA*. $650

Wilkinson, J. Gardner. THE MANNERS AND CUSTOMS OF THE ANCIENT EGYPTIANS. New ed, rev and corrected by Samuel Birch. 3 vols (complete). London: John Murray, 1878. 643 figs, 72 plts. Bkpl, several corners lightly bumped. Good. *ARCHAEOLOGIA*. $375

Wilkinson, J.G. ON COLOR AND THE NECESSITY FOR A GENERAL DIFFUSION OF TASTE. London, 1858. 1st ed. 8 chromolitho plts. Orig cl soiled, worn. Rebacked while retaining orig backstrip. Plts, title bit soiled, some wear to fore-edges. *SUTTON*. $335

Wilkinson, J.V.S. THE LIGHTS OF CANOPUS (ANVAR I SUB-AILI). London: The Studio, n.d. (ca. 1930). 1st ed. Orig cl, sl faded; bkpl, o/w VG. *WORLDWIDE*. $95

Wilkinson, Sylvia. MOSS ON THE NORTH SIDE. Boston: Houghton Mifflin, 1966. 1st ed. As New in pict dj. *CHAPEL HILL*. $50

Willard, Berton C. RUSSELL W. PORTER. Freeport, ME: Bond Wheelwright, 1976. 1st prtg. VG. *KNOLLWOOD*. $26

Willard, Berton C. RUSSELL W. PORTER. Freeport: Bond Wheelwright Company, 1976. 1st prtg. NF in VG dj. *PARMER*. $35

Willard, Charles Dwight. THE HERALD'S HISTORY OF LOS AN-GELES CITY. LA: Kingsley-Barnes & Neuner Co, 1901. 54 full-pg illus. Later cl, some leaves creased. *DAWSON'S*. $60

Willard, Frances E. A WHEEL WITHIN A WHEEL. Chicago: Woman's Temperance Pub. Co, (1898). 1st ed. Sl soiled cl. VG, tight. *SECOND LIFE*. $125

Willard, Frances E. HOW TO WIN. A BOOK FOR GIRLS. NY: Funk & Wagnalls, 1887. 4th ed. VG, tight. *SECOND LIFE*. $75

Willard, Frances. WOMAN AND TEMPERANCE: OR, THE WORK AND WORKERS OF THE WOMAN'S CHRISTIAN TEMPERANCE UNION. Hartford, 1884. 4th ed. Engrvd portrait. *FYE*. $75

Willard, Nancy. EAST OF THE SUN AND WEST OF THE MOON. HBJ, (1989). 1st ed. Illus, signed by Barry Moser. Fine in Fine dj. *BEBBAH.* $30

Willard, Nancy. SAILING TO CYTHERA AND OTHER ANATOLE STORIES. David McPhail, illus. NY: Harcourt, Brace, (1974). 1st ed. Light soiling, else Fine in dj. *CAPTAIN'S BOOKSHELF.* $50

Willard, Theodore A. BRIDE OF THE RAIN GOD. Cleveland, (1930). 1st ed. 11 plts. Fine in sl worn silver pict. dj. *DIAMOND.* $35

Willard, Theodore A. THE CITY OF THE SACRED WELL. NY: Grosset & Dunlap, (1926). 7 plts. Signature. Good. *ARCHAEOLOGIA.* $25

Willard, Theodore A. THE CITY OF THE SACRED WELL. London, (1926). 1st Eng. ed. Shelf wear, cvr staining. Name on fly, o/w VG. *DIAMOND.* $35

Willard, X.A. WILLARD'S PRACTICAL DAIRY HUSBANDRY: A COMPLETE TREATISE....NY: Moore, 1872. 1st ed. 546pp,ads. Private lib label, removed from ep. Fine. *SECOND LIFE.* $75

Willcocks, W. THE NILE RESERVOIR DAM AT ASSUAN AND AFTER. London: Spon; NY: Spon & Chamberlain, 1901. 1st ed. Fldg frontis, 12 fldg plts. Edges rubbed; sl foxed and spotted, o/w VG. *WORLDWIDE.* $65

Willeford, Charles. A GUIDE FOR THE UNDEHEMOR-RHOIDED. Miami: Pub by author, 1977. 1st ed. Signed. VF in dj. *MORDIDA.* $165

Willeford, Charles. COCKFIGHTER JOURNAL. Santa Barbara: Neville, 1989. 1st ed. Foreword by James Lee Burke. One of 300 numbered, signed by Burke. VF w/o dj as issued. *MORDIDA.* $100

Willeford, Charles. EVERYBODY'S METAMORPHOSIS. Missoula: Dennis McMillan, 1988. 1st ed. 1/400 numbered, signed. VF in dj. *MORDIDA.* $100

Willeford, Charles. HIGH PRIEST OF CALIFORNIA & WILD WIVES. SF: Re/Search Pubs, 1987. 1st ed. One of 250 numbered, signed. VF in dj. *MORDIDA.* $85

Willeford, Charles. I WAS LOOKING FOR A STREET. Woodstock, VT: Countryman Press, 1988. 1st ed. VF in dj. *MORDIDA.* $30

Willeford, Charles. I WAS LOOKING FOR A STREET. Woodstock, VT, 1988. 1st ed. NF in dj. *PETTLER.* $20

Willeford, Charles. KISS YOUR ASS GOOD-BYE. London: Gollancz, 1989. 1st Eng ed. VF in dj. *MORDIDA.* $45

Willeford, Charles. KISS YOUR ASS GOODBYE. London: Victor Gollancz, 1989. 1st UK ed. Fine in dj. *BERNARD.* $40

Willeford, Charles. KISS YOUR ASS GOODBYE. Miami Beach: Dennis McMillan, 1987. 1/400 numbered/signed. Fine in Fine dj. *DERMONT.* $75

Willeford, Charles. MIAMI BLUES. NY: St. Martin's Press, 1984. 1st ed. VF in dj, tiny rubbed spots back panel. *MORDIDA.* $100

Willeford, Charles. MIAMI BLUES. NY: St. Martins, 1984. 1st ed. VF in dj. *ELSE FINE.* $125

Willeford, Charles. NEW FORMS OF UGLY. Miami Beach: Dennis McMillan, 1987. 1st ed. One of 350 numbered, signed. VF in dj. *MORDIDA.* $90

Willeford, Charles. NEW HOPE FOR THE DEAD. NY: St. Martins, 1985. 1st ed. VF in price clipped dj. *ELSE FINE.* $75

Willeford, Charles. NEW HOPE FOR THE DEAD. NY: St. Martin's Press, 1985. 1st ed. Signed. Fine in dj. *MORDIDA.* $125

Willeford, Charles. OFF THE WALL. Montclair: Pegasus Rex Press, 1980. 1st ed. VF in dj. *MORDIDA.* $75

Willeford, Charles. PROLETARIAN LAUGHTER. Yonkers: Alicat Bookshop Press, 1948. 1st ed, 1st bk. Pub in ed of 1000. Pp somewhat darkened, o/w Fine in wrappers. *MORDIDA.* $125

Willeford, Charles. PROLETARIAN LAUGHTER: POEMS. Yonkers: The Alicat Bookshop Press, 1948. One of 1000. Fine in ptd wraps. *HELLER.* $100

Willeford, Charles. SIDESWIPE. London: Gollancz, 1988. 1st Eng. ed. VF in dj. *MORDIDA.* $25

Willeford, Charles. SIDESWIPE. NY: St. Martin's, (1987). 1st ed. Signed. Fine in Fine dj. *UNGER.* $100

Willeford, Charles. SIDESWIPE. St. Martin's Press, 1987. 1st ed. Fine in dj. *STAHR.* $25

Willeford, Charles. SOMETHING ABOUT A SOLDIER. NY: Random House, 1986. 1st ed. VF in dj. *MORDIDA.* $30

Willeford, Charles. THE BURNT ORANGE HERESY. NY: Crown, 1971. 1st ed. NF; minor wear at spine ends, very small chip on dj edge. *ELSE FINE.* $85

Willeford, Charles. THE BURNT ORANGE HERESY: NY: Crown Publishers, 1971. 1st ed. Some light stains on fore-edge o/w Fine in dj w/wrinkling on back panel. *MORDIDA.* $125

Willeford, Charles. THE OUTCAST POETS. Yonkers: Alicat Bookshop, 1947. 1st ed. Ptd envelope containing loose sheets of poetry by P.K. Thomajan, Miriam Allna deFord, Robert Anthony, F.H. Kaler and Willeford. VF. *MORDIDA.* $100

Willeford, Charles. THE WAY WE DIE NOW. Hastings-on-Hudson: Ultramarine Press, 1988. 1st ed. One of 99 numbered, bound in 1/2 leather, signed. VF w/o dj as issued. *MORDIDA.* $150

Willeford, Charles. THE WAY WE DIE NOW. London: Gollancz, 1989. 1st ed. Fine. *SMITH.* $20

Willeford, Charles. THE WAY WE DIE NOW. NY: Random House, 1988. 1st ed. VF in dj. *MORDIDA.* $25

Willeford, Charles. THE WOMAN CHASER. Chicago: Newsstand Library, 1960. 1st ed. Pb orig. Magenta Book #U137. VF, unread, in wrappers. *MORDIDA.* $165

Willeford, Charles. UNDERSTUDY FOR LOVE. Chicago: Newsstand Library, 1961. 1st ed. Pb orig. Newsstand Library Magenta Book U170. Fine, unread in wraps. *MORDIDA.* $200

Willet, J.E. WONDERS OF INSECT LIFE. Boston, 1880. Ex-lib. *SUTTON.* $65

Willett, Edward. CAT'S CRADLE. RHYMES FOR CHILDREN. Illus by Charles Kendrick. NY: R. Worthington. 1881. 60pp, each w/color ptd illus. Corners worn. *KARMIOLE.* $75

Willey, Gordon. AN INTRODUCTION TO AMERICAN ARCHAEOLOGY. Vol I: NORTH AND MIDDLE AMERICA. New Jersey, Prentice Hall, 1966. Chipped dj. Vol II: SOUTH AMERICA. NJ: Prentice Hall, (1971). 1st ed. Chipped dj. *SILVER.* $75

WILLIAM BAILEY: RECENT PAINTINGS. JANUARY 6 - FEBRUARY 10, 1979. Intro Mark Strand. NY: Robert Schoelkopf Gallery, 1979. 1st ed. Inscribed. *CAPTAIN'S BOOKSHELF.* $30

Williams, A. Bryan. GAME TRAILS IN BRITISH COLUMBIA. NY: Scribner's, 1925. 1st US ed. VG. *OCTOBER FARM.* $65

Williams, Alfred. NEWHOUSE BEAR TRAPS. Salem: Pub by author, 1985. 1st (and probably only) ed, stated 1st prtg. Signed. 44pp. Fine. *BACKMAN.* $30

Williams, B.S. CHOICE STOVE AND GREENHOUSE FLOWERING PLANTS....Fold-out, hand colored frontis (sm tear at fold), 2 plans. London, 1869. Gilt dec cl, faded spine, edges darkened; lt foxing. *SUTTON.* $65

Williams, Beryl and Samuel Epstein. THE ROCKET PIONEERS. London: Lutterworth Press, 1957. Good in worn & chipped dj; pp edges spotted. *KNOLLWOOD.* $36

Williams, Cecil B. PARADISE PRAIRIE. NY, (1953). 1st ed. 372pp. VG+ in dj. *PRATT.* $25

Williams, Charles H. LAST TOUR OF DUTY AT THE SIEGE OF CHARLESTON. Providence, 1882. 1st ed, ltd to 250. Wrappers. NF. *McGOWAN.* $45

Williams, Charles. A MYTH OF SHAKESPEARE. London: OUP, 1928. 1st ed. Rev copy w/slip pasted in. Clippings pasted inside front cover. Spine faded. *WOOLMER.* $75

Williams, Charles. AGROUND. NY: Viking Press, 1960. 1st ed. VG in dj w/minor wear at spine ends and at corners. *MORDIDA.* $45

Williams, Charles. DEAD CALM. NY: Viking Press, 1963. 1st ed. Fine in price-clipped dj. *MORDIDA.* $50

Williams, Charles. MAN ON A LEASH. London: Cassell, 1974. 1st Eng ed. Fine in dj w/lt dampstain base of spine. *MORDIDA.* $27.50

Williams, Charles. SCORPION REEF. NY: Macmillan, 1955. 1st ed. Fine in dj w/tiny wear at base of spine. *MORDIDA.* $75

Williams, Charles. THE FIGURE OF BEATRICE: A STUDY IN DANTE. London: Faber & Faber, (1943). 1st ed. Just about Fine in VG dj chipped at spine extrems. *CAPTAIN'S BOOKSHELF.* $100

Williams, Charles. THE LONG SATURDAY NIGHT. Greenwich: Fawcett Pubs, 1962. 1st ed. Pb orig. Gold Medal #1200. Name, o/w Fine in wrappers. *MORDIDA.* $35

Williams, Chauncey. LONE ELK. THE LIFE STORY OF BILL WILLIAMS TRAPPER. Denver: John Van Male, 1935-6. 2 vols. 1st ed, ltd to 500. Wraps. VG in custom-made box. Howes W449. *OREGON.* $175

Williams, Edgar. ILLUSTRATED HISTORICAL ATLAS MAP OF MARION AND LINN COUNTIES, OREGON. SF: Edgar Williams, 1878. 1st ed. 19 double pp, 1 single pp map. Rebound in brn cl w/large section of orig cl w/title, pub, and date laid on. VG. *OREGON.* $600

Williams, Edward H. OPIATE ADDICTION. ITS HANDLING AND ITS TREATMENT. NY, 1922. 1st ed. Slight cvr staining. Some marginal damp-staining, o/w VG. Inscribed. *DIAMOND.* $50

Williams, Elizabeth Whitney. A CHILD OF THE SEA. Harbor Springs, 1905. 1st ed. Gilt cl, rear corners of spine headpiece chewed, Good. *ARTIS.* $50

Williams, Frederick Benton (pseud of Herbert Elliot Hamblen). ON MANY SEAS. NY: 1897. William Stone Booth (ed). x,417 pp. Orig cl, rubbed. 1st pub in 1896; this is the 2nd prtg. *LEFKOWICZ.* $65

Williams, Gaar. AMONG THE FOLKS IN HISTORY. Winnetka: The Book & Print Guild, (1935). Frontis. Velvet red binding, metallic clasp, gilt edges. One fly leaf loose, lt wear. VG. *CULLEN.* $75

Williams, George Washington. A HISTORY OF THE NEGRO TROOPS IN THE WAR OF THE REBELLION 1861-1865. NY, 1888. 1st ed. Ex-lib with bkpl, small label removed from spine, no other markings, rear inner hinge cracking, else VG. *McGOWAN.* $285

Williams, Gomer. HISTORY OF THE LIVERPOOL PRIVATEERS AND LETTERS...LIVERPOOL SLAVE TRADE. London and Liverpool, 1897. 1st ed. Ink note, else VG. *McCLINTOCK.* $55

Williams, H. Noel. MADAME DE MONTESPAN. NY: Scribner's, 1903. 1st ed. 16 photogravures. Uncut. Stamped pub's cl. *SECOND LIFE.* $65

Williams, H.T. (ed). WINDOW GARDENING DEVOTED SPECIALLY TO THE CULTURE OF FLOWERS AND ORNAMENTAL PLANTS. NY, 1872. 4th ed. Orig cl worn at extrems, sl cracking of front hinge. *SUTTON.* $65

Williams, H.W. TRAVELS IN ITALY, GREECE, AND THE IONIAN ISLANDS IN A SERIES OF LETTERS, DESCRIPTIONS OF MANNERS, SCENERY, AND THE FINE ARTS. Edinburgh, 1820. 20 plts (2 fldg). 2 vols. Contemp paneled calf gilt, handsomely rebacked, red lettering pieces. xxii,399pp; xiv,437pp. Attractive. *O'NEILL.* $550

Williams, Helen Maria. A NARRATIVE OF THE EVENTS WHICH HAVE TAKEN PLACE IN FRANCE...1815, TILL THE RESTORATION OF LOUIS XVIII. London: Murray, 1815. 1st ed. 389pp. Contemp calf, spine gilt (sl wear to joints). Very Nice. *SECOND LIFE.* $300

Williams, Henry T. (ed). THE PACIFIC TOURIST. NY: Henry T. Williams, 1876. 1st ed. Lacks fldg map. *SECOND LIFE.* $50

Williams, Henry T. (ed). THE PACIFIC TOURIST: WILLIAMS' ILLUSTRATED TRANS-CONTINENTAL GUIDE OF TRAVEL. NY: Henry T. Williams, 1877. 309,(14)pp. Blind and gold stamped cl, spine sunned, light wear to tips and head and tail of spine, front hinge split, light stain to top margin of some leaves. *DAWSON'S.* $125

Williams, Henry T. (ed). THE PACIFIC TOURIST; WILLIAMS' ILLUSTRATED TRANS-CONTINENTAL GUIDE OF TRAVEL. NY: Henry T. Williams, 1879. Rebound in cl. VG. *LAURIE.* $100

Williams, Henry. A PRACTICAL GUIDE TO THE STUDY OF THE DISEASES OF THE EYE: THEIR MEDICAL AND SURGICAL TREATMENT. Boston, 1869. 3rd ed. 422pp + 7 engrvd plts (1 fldg).

Williams, Howell (ed). LANDSCAPES OF ALASKA. Berkeley: Univ of Calfornia Press, 1958. 1st ed. VG in VG- dj. *BLUE DRAGON.* $35

Williams, Joan. OLD POWDER MAN. NY: HBW, (1966). 1st ed. Inscribed yr of pub. NF in dj. *LOPEZ.* $85

Williams, John A. CAPTAIN BLACKMAN. GC: Doubleday, 1972. 1st ed. Fine; minor edgewear to price clipped dj. *ELSE FINE.* $30

Williams, John A. CAPTAIN BLACKMAN. GC: Doubleday, 1972. 1st ed. Rmdr speckling bottom edge pp, o/w VF in dj. *LOPEZ.* $45

Williams, John A. CAPTAIN BLACKMAN. GC: Doubleday, 1972. 1st ed. 336pp. Pub's comp stamp front pastedown. VG+ to NF- in price-clipped, shelf-worn dj. *AKA.* $35

Williams, John A. FLASHBACKS. GC: Anchor/Doubleday, 1973. 1st ed. NF in dj. *LOPEZ.* $50

Williams, John A. NIGHT SONG. (London: Collins, 1962). 1st Eng ed. Bkstore stamp front pastedown o/w Fine in NF dj. *LOPEZ.* $55

Williams, John A. NIGHT SONG. NY: Farrar Straus and Cudahy, (1961). 1st ed. Fine in VG dj. *LOPEZ.* $100

Williams, John A. NIGHT SONG. NY: FSC, 1961. 1st ed., 1st novel. VF, minute edgewear to dj. *ELSE FINE.* $125

Williams, John A. THE ANGRY ONES. NY: Ace, (1960). 1st book, pb orig. Cheap paper browning, o/w VG in wrappers. *LOPEZ.* $75

Williams, John A. THE BERHAMA ACCOUNT. Far Hills: New Horizon, (1985). 1st ed. Fine in NF dj. *LOPEZ.* $45

Williams, John A. THE MOST NATIVE OF SONS. GC: Doubleday, 1970. 1st ed. Fine in price-clipped but o/w Fine dj. *LOPEZ.* $65

Williams, John A. THIS IS MY COUNTRY TOO. (NY): NAL, (1965). 1st ed. Fine in NF dj. *LOPEZ.* $65

Williams, John H. THE MOUNTAIN THAT WAS GOD. NY, Tacoma: Putnam/Williams, 1911 (10,11). 2nd rev ed. Almost Fine in wraps. *AARD.* $75

Williams, John H. THE MOUNTAIN THAT WAS GOD. Tacoma: Williams, and NY and London: Putnam's, 1911. 2nd ed. Chipping, minor tape reinforcement top and base of spine, else VG. Scarce. In custom case. *OLD LONDON.* $20

Williams, John Jay. THE ISTHMUS OF TEHUANTEPEC. NY: Appleton, 1852. 1st ed, errata tipped. 14 color lithos, 2 b/w plts, fldg map. Orig blind-stamped dec cl, spine gilt. Ex-lib, pin-perforate stamp at bottom of title-page, bkpl. Lt foxing, age-staining, o/w Nice. *DIAMOND.* $150

Williams, Jonathan and Fielding Dawson. THE EMPIRE FINALS AT VERONA. Highlands: Jargon, 1959. 1/1000. Wraps in dj. Fine but for sticker tear on copyright page, in dj w/tears, chip. *BEASLEY.* $45

Williams, Jonathan. DEAR WORLD, FORGET IT! LOVE, MNEMOSYNE: A RANGE OF LETTERS, 1984-85, etc. Roswell/Denver: DBA/JCA Editions, 1985. 1st ed. 1/175 issued as Christmas greeting. Acetate wrappers in velo binder. Fine, signed. *CAPTAIN'S BOOKSHELF.* $75

Williams, Jonathan. IN THE FIELD AT THE SOLSTICE. Champaign: Alvin Doyle Moore, 1976. 1st ed. 1/103. Loose sheets laid into unptd red cover. Fine. *CAPTAIN'S BOOKSHELF.* $250

Williams, Jonathan. QUOTE, UNQUOTE. Berkeley: Ten Speed Press, (1989). 1st ed. Signed. Fine in wrappers. *LOPEZ.* $35

Williams, Jonathan. THE FIFTY-TWO CLERIHEWS OF CLARA HUGHES. Atlanta: Pynyon Press, (1983). 1st Amer ed. Signed. Fine in wraps. *DORN.* $20

Williams, Jonathan. UNTINEARS AND ANTENNAE FOR MAURICE RAVEL. St. Paul: Truck Press, (1977). 1st Amer ed. Signed. Fine in wraps. *DORN.* $20

Williams, Joseph Vincent. JAMES TATE WILLIAMS, HIS FAMILY AND RECOLLECTIONS. Kingsport, TN: Kingsport Press, 1938. Leather spine. Rubbed edges. Signed. VG. *BURCHAM.* $45

Williams, Mary (ed). CHRONOLOGY 1941-1945. Washington: Dept. Army/USGPO, 1960. 1st ed. NF. *ARCHER.* $25

Williams, Mary Floyd. HISTORY OF THE SAN FRANCISCO COMMITTEE OF VIGILANCE OF 1851. Berkeley: Univ of Calif. 1921. 1st ed. Ex-lib. *OREGON.* $45

Williams, Mentor L. (ed). SCHOOLCRAFT'S INDIAN LEGENDS. East Lansing: Michigan State Univ Press, 1956. 1st ed. Fine in dj. *LAURIE.* $40

Williams, Mrs. (Catharine Reed). BIOGRAPHY OF REVOLUTIONARY HEROES. Providence: by the author, 1839. 1st ed. Orig cl w/later lea label. Nice. Engr frontis. Howes W-448. *SECOND LIFE.* $85

Williams, Philip Lee. ALL THE WESTERN STARS. Atlanta: Peachtree, (1988). 1st Amer ed. Signed. Fine in dj. *DORN.* $35

Williams, Philip Lee. THE SONG OF DANIEL. Atlanta: Peachtree Publishers, (1989). 1st Amer ed. Signed. Fine in dj. *DORN.* $30

Williams, R. and R.E. Bishop. THE WAYS OF WILDFOWL. Chicago, 1971. Dj w/sm tears. *SUTTON.* $65

Williams Robert and Tom Spies. VITAMIN B1 (THIAMIN) AND ITS USE IN MEDICINE. NY, 1938. 1st ed. *FYE.* $100

Williams, Roswell (pseud of Frank Owen). LOVES OF LO FOH. Macaulay, 1936. 1st ed. VG in NF dj. *MADLE.* $75

Williams, Samuel H. VOODOO ROADS. Wien (Vienna): Verlag Fur Jugend Und Volk, 1949. 1st ed. Dj Good only. VG. *CONNOLLY & WADE.* $35

Williams, Stephen. A CATECHISM OF MEDICAL JURISPRUDENCE, BEING PRINCIPALLY A COMPENDIUM OF THE OPINIONS OF THE BEST WRITERS UPON THE SUBJECT. WITH A PRELIMINARY DISCOURSE UPON THE IMPORTANCE UPON THE STUDY OF FORENSIC MEDICINE. Northampton, 1835. 1st ed. 205pp. Cloth backed boards. Last index leaf missing, lib bkpl. *FYE.* $100

Williams, T. Harry. LINCOLN AND HIS GENERALS. NY, (1952). 1st ed. 370pp. Dj wear, o/w VG+. *PRATT.* $22.50

Williams, Tennessee. 27 WAGONS FULL OF COTTON AND OTHER ONE-ACT PLAYS. Norfolk, CT: New Directions, (1953). 3rd ed, enl. Orig yellow boards. VG in dj (closed tear, crease on rear panel). *CHAPEL HILL.* $40

Williams, Tennessee. 27 WAGONS FULL OF COTTON AND OTHER ONE-ACT PLAYS. Norfolk, CT: New Directions, (1945 stated, but actually 1948). 2nd ed, enl. Orig cl-backed yellow boards. Fine in lightly used dj. *CHAPEL HILL.* $50

Williams, Tennessee. ANDROGYNE, MON AMOUR. (NY): New Directions, (1977). 1st ed. Ltd to 200 signed. Laid-in frontis, slipcase. VF. *JAFFE.* $275

Williams, Tennessee. BATTLE OF ANGELS. Murray, Utah: Pharos, Spring 1945. 1st ed, pub as a double issue (Nos 1 & 2) of Pharos. Orig ptd wraps. Dampstain lower corner rear wrap, last few pgs (not affecting text), yapp edges of wraps bit faded, worn as usual, still Good. *CHAPEL HILL.* $375

Williams, Tennessee. CAT ON A HOT TIN ROOF. NY: New Directions, 1955. 1st ed. Fine in very close to Fine dj. *BEASLEY.* $75

Williams, Tennessee. CAT ON A HOT TIN ROOF. NY: New Directions, 1955. 1st ed. Fine, sm chip in bottom edge of dj. *ELSE FINE.* $125

Williams, Tennessee. EIGHT MORTAL LADIES POSSESSED. NY: New Directions, 1973. 1st ed. Bkpl. Light damp marks to lower cover & dj interior, else Fine. *ELSE FINE.* $25

Williams, Tennessee. GARDEN DISTRICT, TWO PLAYS: SOMETHING UNSPOKEN, SUDDENLY LAST SUMMER. London: Secker & Warburg, 1959. Rev copy, slip laid in. Fore edge sl foxed, o/w Fine in dj. *HELLER.* $100

Williams, Tennessee. GRAND. NY: House of Books, 1964. 1/300 numbered, signed. Fine in orig glassine sl chipped dj. *CAPTAIN'S BOOKSHELF.* $300

Williams, Tennessee. GRAND. NY: House of Books, 1964. 1st ed. Ltd to 300 signed. Yellow cl. Fine in sl torn glassine dj. *JAFFE.* $275

Williams, Tennessee. HARD CANDY: A BOOK OF STORIES. NY, 1954. "Limited Edition." Patterned boards. Fine in slipcase (bit of wear at corners). *PETTLER.* $85

Williams, Tennessee. IN THE WINTER OF CITIES. (Norfolk, CT): New Directions, (1956). 1st ed. Orig cl-backed boards. NF in lightly soiled dj, sm chips at spine ends. *CHAPEL HILL.* $150

Williams, Tennessee. MEMOIRS. GC, NY: Doubleday, 1975. 1st ed. Orig black cl, orange boards. NF in dj. Inscribed. *CHAPEL HILL.* $350

Williams, Tennessee. MOISE AND THE WORLD OF REASON. NY: Simon & Schuster, 1975. 1st ed. As New in dj. *ELSE FINE.* $45

Williams, Tennessee. ONE ARM AND OTHER STORIES. NY: New Directions, 1954. 1st ed. Fine in very close to Fine in dj w/few sm tears. *BEASLEY.* $60

Williams, Tennessee. STEPS MUST BE GENTLE. A Dramatic Reading for Two Performers. NY: Targ Editions, (1980). 1st ed. One of 350 signed. Orig cl-backed marbled boards. Fine in unptd white tissue jacket. *CHAPEL HILL.* $200

Williams, Tennessee. STEPS MUST BE GENTLE. NY: Targ, (1980). One of 350 signed. Fine in plain white dj. *LOPEZ.* $175

Williams, Tennessee. SUDDENLY LAST SUMMER. (NY): New Directions, 1958. 1st ed. Review copy, slip laid in. Fine in dj. *JUVELIS.* $175

Williams, Tennessee. SUMMER AND SMOKE. London: John Lehmann, (1952). 1st Eng ed. Orig orange cl. Fine in price-clipped dj. *CHAPEL HILL.* $80

Williams, Tennessee. THE KNIGHTLY QUEST AND OTHER STORIES. NY: New Directions, 1966. 1st ed. Fine in dj. *ELSE FINE.* $60

Williams, Tennessee. THE NIGHT OF THE IGUANA. (NY): New Directions, 1962. 1st ed. NF in dj. *CHAPEL HILL.* $125

Williams, Tennessee. THE NIGHT OF THE IGUANA. Dramatists Play Service, 1963. About Fine in lavender wraps. *STAHR.* $25

Williams, Tennessee. THE REMARKABLE ROOMING-HOUSE OF MME. LE MONDE. NY: Albondocani, 1984. 1st ed. Ltd to 175 ptd. Marbled wraps. VF. *JAFFE.* $150

Williams, Tennessee. THE ROMAN SPRING OF MRS. STONE. (NY: New Directions, (1950). 1st ed. Orig black cl. NF in lightly soiled dj. *CHAPEL HILL.* $55

Williams, Tennessee. THE ROMAN SPRING OF MRS. STONE. (NY): New Directions, (1950). 1st ed. Dj. Fine. *JAFFE.* $85

Williams, Tennessee. THE ROMAN SPRING OF MRS. STONE. NY: New Directions, 1950. 1st ed. Fine in NF dj. *BEASLEY.* $45

Williams, Tennessee. THE ROMAN SPRING OF MRS. STONE. NY: New Directions, 1950. 1st ed. Fine, minor edgewear to the dj. *ELSE FINE.* $65

Williams, Tennessee. THE ROSE TATTOO. (NY: New Directions, (1951). 1st ed, 1st binding. Orig rose cl. Fine in lightly used dj. *CHAPEL HILL.* $125

Williams, Tennessee. THE ROSE TATTOO. NY: New Directions, 1951. 1st ed. Spine sunned o/w Fine. *ARCHER.* $35

Williams, Thomas A. ELIPHAS LEVI: MASTER OF OCCULTISM. Univ of Alabama Press, (1975). 1st ed. NF in VG dj. *BLUE DRAGON.* $35

Williams, Thomas. A HIGH NEW HOUSE. NY: Dial, 1963. 1st ed. Fine in NF dj. Signed. *LOPEZ.* $75

Williams, Thomas. LEAH, NEW HAMPSHIRE. NY: Morrow, (1992). 1st ed. As New in dj. Rev copy, slip, promo sheet laid in. *CAPTAIN'S BOOKSHELF.* $25

Williams, Thomas. THE FOLLOWED MAN. NY: Marek, 1978. 1st ed. VF in dj. *ELSE FINE.* $25

Williams, Thomas. THE NIGHT OF TREES. NY: Macmillan, 1961. 1st ed. Fine in Fine dj. Signed. *LOPEZ.* $85

Williams, Thomas. TOWN BURNING. NY: Macmillan, 1959. 1st ed. Fine in NF, price-clipped dj. Signed. *LOPEZ.* $65

Williams, Thomas. WHIPPLE'S CASTLE. NY: Random House, (1968). 1st ed. NF in dj. Signed. *LOPEZ.* $40

Williams, Valentine. THE FOX PROWLS. Boston: Houghton Mifflin, 1939. 1st ed. VF, minor wear to extremities of pict dj. *ELSE FINE.* $40

Williams, W. Mattieu. THE FUEL OF THE SUN. London: Simpkin Marshall, 1870. 1 plt. Some pencil underlining, else Good. *KNOLLWOOD.* $95

Williams, W.L. THE DISEASES OF THE GENITAL ORGANS OF DOMESTIC ANIMALS. Ithaca, 1921. 1st ed. Good+. *OCTOBER FARM.* $25

Williams, Walter (ed). A HISTORY OF NORTHEAST MISSOURI. Chicago: Lewis Publishing Company, 1913. 3 vols. Leather portions scuffed and peeling; tight. *BOHLING.* $160

Williams, William Carlos. I WANTED TO WRITE A POEM, THE AUTOBIOGRAPHY OF THE WORKS OF A POET. Boston: Beacon Press, (c1958). 1st ed. Edith Heal (ed). Fine in bright dj, sm chips. *HELLER.* $75

Williams, William Carlos. JOURNEY TO LOVE. NY: Random House, (1955). Advance review copy, slip laid in. Fine in VG dj w/sm bit of soiling, couple of edge tears rear cover. *LOPEZ.* $85

Williams, William Carlos. PATERSON (BOOK I). (NY): New Directions, (1946). 1st ed. NF in dj (some edgewear, sm internally repaired tear). *LOPEZ.* $65

Williams, William Carlos. PATERSON (BOOK I). New Directions, (1946). 1st ed. One of 1000. VG. *SECOND LIFE.* $75

Williams, William Carlos. PATERSON (BOOK III). New Directions, (1949). 1st ed. One of 1000. VG uncut. *SECOND LIFE.* $75

Williams, William Carlos. PATERSON. BOOK I (—BOOK V). (NY): New Directions, (1946-1958). 5 vols. 1st eds. Bound in eds of 1063, 1009, 999, 995 & 3000 respectively. Lt foxing to cvrs of 1st 2 vols, o/w unusually Fine set w/no wear to djs. *JAFFE.* $1750

Williams, William Carlos. PATERSON. BOOKS I-V. (NY): New Directions, (1946-1958). 1st ed. 5 vols. Vols 1-4. NF in dj w/sunning to spines, Vol I internally mended, Vol 2 w/two small chips, Vol 5 just About Fine in dj. *CAPTAIN'S BOOKSHELF.* $750

Williams, William Carlos. SELECTED ESSAYS OF WILLIAM CARLOS WILLIAMS. NY: Random House, (1954). 1st ed. Fine (owner sig, address) in very lightly soiled dj. *CAPTAIN'S BOOKSHELF.* $40

Williams, William Carlos. THE COLLECTED LATER POEMS. (Norfolk): New Directions, (1950). 1st ed. 1st binding of trade ed, w/"The Rose" loosely laid in. NF in edgeworn dj. *LOPEZ.* $75

Williams, William Carlos. THE COMPLETE COLLECTED POEMS 1906-1938. Norfolk, CT: New Directions, (1938). 1st ed, 1st binding: One of 506 out of total ed of 1500. Grn cl, dj (sm piece torn from top of spine & internally repaired), o/w Fine. *JAFFE.* $650

Williams, William Carlos. THE SELECTED LETTERS OF WILLIAM CARLOS WILLIAMS. John C. Thirlwall (ed). NY: McDowell, Obolensky, (1957). 1st ed. One of 75 signed. Bkpl, o/w Fine. Slipcase. *JAFFE.* $650

Williams, William Carlos. THE SELECTED LETTERS OF WILLIAM CARLOS WILLIAMS. NY: McDowell, Obolensky, (1957). Title rubbed from spine. Tan veined cream board slipcase w/ptd paper label. Ltd ed of 75 numbered, signed. NF. *BLUE MOUNTAIN.* $850

Williams, William Carlos. THE WILLIAM CARLOS WILLIAMS READER. NY: New Directions, 1966. 1st ed. VF, minor rubs at dj corners. *ELSE FINE.* $75

Williamson, (Peter). FRENCH AND INDIAN CRUELTY EXEMPLIFIED , IN THE LIFE,...OF PETER WILLIAMSON...Edinburgh: J.Stewart, 1787. Later ed. Contemp full calf cvrs worn & stained. Lacks frontis. Pp 73/74 w/sl loss of text. Little of pp 71/72 torn w/no loss of text. Side margins of pp 3-10 worn w/loss of few letters & page numbers, o/w text VG. Front cvr reattached. Rebacked w/orig backstrip. Howes W500. *DIAMOND.* $125

Williamson, Hamilton. A MONKEY TALE. Doubleday, (1929). 1st ed. Illus by Berta & Elmer Hader. VG in Good dj w/tape remains at 2 short closed tears. *BEBBAH.* $35

Williamson, Henry. DANDELION DAYS. London, 1930. Rev ed. This ed printed on Eng hand-made paper. 160/200 signed. Teg, uncut. Spine little sunned, covers little dust soiled. Fine. *POLYANTHOS.* $100

Williamson, Henry. THE LABOURING LIFE. London: Cape, 1932. 1/122 numbered. Signed, specially bound w/vellum backstrip. Fine. *BEASLEY.* $300

Williamson, Henry. THE VILLAGE BOOK. London, 1930. Special ed. ltd, 144/504 signed. Teg, uncut. Vellum spine and edges little sunned, crease lower corner front cover, bkpl. Fine. *POLYANTHOS.* $150

Williamson, Jack. DARKER THAN YOU THINK. Fantasy Press, 1948. One of 500 numbered, signed. Fine in dj. *MADLE.* $200

Williamson, Jack. LEGION OF SPACE. Fantasy Press, 1947. One of 500 numbered, signed. Fine in dj. *MADLE.* $200

Williamson, Jack. THE LEGION OF SPACE. Reading, PA: Fantasy Press, 1947. 1st ed. VF in VG dj. *BOND.* $50

Williamson, Jack. THE LEGION OF TIME. Fantasy Press, 1952. One of 350 numbered, signed plated copies. Fine in Mint dj. *MADLE.* $200

Williamson, John P. AN ENGLISH DAKOTA DICTIONARY. WASICUN KA DAKOTA IESKA WOWAPI. NY: American Tract Society, 1938. Fine. *LAURIE.* $45

Williamson, R.T. DISEASES OF THE SPINAL CORD. London, 1911. 1st ed. *FYE.* $100

Williamson, Samuel T. IMPRINT OF A PUBLISHER, THE STORY OF FRANK GANNETT AND HIS INDEPENDENT NEWSPAPERS..N.p.: Robert M. McBride & Co., (1948). 1st ed. Dj spine faded. *OAK KNOLL.* $30

Williamson, Thames. HUNKY. NY: Coward McCann, 1929. 1st ed. Fine in VG+ dj. *AARD.* $25

Williamson. Jack. THE COMETEERS. Fantasy Press, 1950. One of 500 numbered, signed. Fine in dj. *MADLE.* $200

Williford, Charles. HIGH PRIEST OF CALIFORNIA. N.p.: Beacon, (1953). Pb orig. Beacon B130. Spine crease w/crack; chipping; interior spine crack. *AKA.* $75

Willingham, Calder. END AS A MAN. NY: Vanguard Press, (1947). 1st ed, 1st book in 1st issue dj. Signed on special printed label pasted to flyleaf. Eps sl soiled o/w bright & NF in VG dj sl worn at edges. *BERNARD.* $100

Willingham, Calder. PROVIDENCE ISLAND. NY: Vanguard, (1969). Adv reading copy. About VG in wraps. *DORN.* $40

Willingham, Calder. REACH TO THE STARS. NY: Vanguard Press, (1951). 1st ed. Signed on special printed label pasted to flyleaf. VG in price clipped dj which is edge-worn and a bit chipped at spine ends. *BERNARD.* $40

Willis, Bailey. A YANQUI IN PATAGONIA. Stanford: Stanford Univ Press, 1947. 1st ed, 2nd prtg. VG in well-worn dj. *PARMER.* $30

Willis, N. Parker. SUMMER CRUISE IN THE MEDITERRANEAN, ON BOARD AN AMERICAN FRIGATE. Auburn, 1853. 396 pp. Sound. *O'NEILL.* $50

Willis, Robert. WILLIAM HARVEY: A HISTORY OF THE DISCOVERY OF THE CIRCULATION OF THE BLOOD. London, 1878. 1st ed. 350pp. Signed by author's granddaughter. Minor tear to head of spine, o/w VG. Lacks portrait. *FYE.* $250

Willius, Fredrick and Thomas Dry. A HISTORY OF THE HEART AND CIRCULATION. 1948. 1st ed. 456pp. *FYE.* $150

Willius, Fredrick and Thomas Keys. CARDIAC CLASSICS. St. Louis, 1941. 1st ed. 858pp. Scarce. *FYE.* $100

Willock, Colin. THE GUN-PUNT ADVENTURE. London: Faber & Faber, 1958. 1st ed. VG+ in VG dj. *BACKMAN.* $25

Willock, John. VOYAGES AND ADVENTURES OF JOHN WILLOCK, MARINER. INTERSPERSED WITH REMARKS...Phila: Hogan & M'Elroy, 1798. 1st Amer ed. (vii)-238,(1 blank),8 subscribers pp. Engr frontis. Contemp calf, covers a bit worn. Howes W508. *GINSBERG.* $850

Willox, D. WITH THE BRITISH BOWLERS IN CANADA—1906. Glasgow: D. Gilfillan & Co., n.d. (1907?). Some edgewear, else VG. *OLD LONDON.* $50

Wills, Geoffrey. CANDLESTICKS. NY: Clarkson N. Potter, 1974. 1st Amer ed. VG in dj. *BACKROOM.* $35

Willson, Roscoe G. NO PLACE FOR ANGELS. The Arizona Republic, 1958. 1st ed. Inscribed. Fine in chipped dj. *VARNER.* $35

Willson, Roscoe G. NO PLACE FOR ANGELS...STORIES OF OLD ARIZONA DAYS. Phoenix: Arizona Republic, 1958. 1st ed. Inscribed. Fine. *CONNOLLY & WADE.* $30

Wilmerding, John. FITZ HUGH LANE. NY (etc.), (1971). 1st ed. 203 pp. 10 color plts. About Fine, dj. *LEFKOWICZ.* $80

Wilmot, Mrs. Frank (comp). OREGON BOYS IN THE WAR. Portland: Glass & Prudhomme, 1918. 1st ed. Stiff pict wraps. VG. *CONNOLLY & WADE.* $30

Wilson, A.N. SCANDAL. London: Hamish Hamilton, (1983). 1st ed. Fine in dj. *CAPTAIN'S BOOKSHELF.* $75

Wilson, A.N. THE LIFE OF JOHN MILTON. Oxford: Oxford Univ Press, 1983. 1st ed, Amer issue w/sticker in dollars over ptd price in pounds on front flap of dj. VF. Boards, dj. *JAFFE.* $50

Wilson, A.N. TOLSTOY. London: Hamilton, (1988). 1st ed. Boards, dj. VF. *JAFFE.* $50

Wilson, A.N. WISE VIRGIN. London: Secker & Warburg, (1982). 1st ed. Fine in dj. *CAPTAIN'S BOOKSHELF.* $75

Wilson, Albert. RAMBLES IN NORTH AFRICA. Boston: Little, Brown & Co. 1926. 1st ed. Dj. *KARMIOLE.* $40

Wilson, Angus. ANGLO-SAXON ATTITUDES. London: Secker & Warburg, 1956. 1st ed. Fine in dj w/few sm tears. *CAPTAIN'S BOOKSHELF.* $75

Wilson, Angus. THE OLD MEN AT THE ZOO. London: Secker & Warburg, (1961). 1st ed. Fine in dj (trifle darkened at spine). *CAPTAIN'S BOOKSHELF.* $60

Wilson, Arnold. A DICTIONARY OF BRITISH MARINE PAINTERS. (3rd prtg, w/additions.) Leigh-on Sea, (1980). 48 plts. Dj. *LEFKOWICZ.* $50

Wilson, Augusta Evans. DEVOTA, "J'Y SUIS, J'Y RESTE." NY: G.W. Dillingham Co, (1907). 1st ed. Orig red cl w/color pict label, teg. Slight darkening at bottom of spine, but NF. *CHAPEL HILL.* $30

Wilson, B.R. and K. Gillett. AUSTRALIAN SHELLS...Rutland, VT & Tokyo, (1972). Fine in Fine dj in VG+ slipcase. *MIKESH.* $40

Wilson, C.B. THE COPEPODS OF THE WOODS HOLE REGION, MASSACHUSETTS. Washington, 1932. 41 plts. Wrappers (backstrip & rear wrapper missing.) Ex-lib. *SUTTON.* $55

Wilson, Colin. BEYOND THE OUTSIDER. Boston/Cambridge: Houghton Mifflin Co/Riverside Press, 1965. 1st US ed. VG+ in price clipped dj. *BERNARD.* $50

Wilson, Colin. CHORDS AND DISCORDS. NY, (1966). 1st ed. Fine in NF dj. *POLYANTHOS.* $35

Wilson, Colin. HERMANN HESSE. London: Village Press, 1974. 1st ed. Fine in wraps. *BEASLEY.* $25

Wilson, Colin. NECESSARY DOUBT. NY: Trident, 1964. 1st ed. Fine; dj lightly worn at spine corners. *ELSE FINE.* $40

Wilson, Colin. RITUAL IN THE DARK. London: Gollancz, 1960. 1st ed. Edges and pages darkened o/w Fine in dj w/wraparound. *MORDIDA.* $100

Wilson, Colin. THE MIND PARASITES. Sauk City: Arkham House, 1967. 1st ed. Bottom corners sl bumped, else Fine in sl rubbed dj. *CAPTAIN'S BOOKSHELF.* $75

Wilson, Colin. THE OUTSIDER. Houghton Mifflin, 1956. True 1st Amer ed. VG in dj with light soil to rear panel, small chips, light edgewear but Good. *BEBBAH.* $45

Wilson, Colin. THE SCHOOLGIRL MURDER CASE. Crown, 1974. 1st Amer ed. Fine in price-clipped dj (short, closed tear at head of spine). *STAHR.* $20

Wilson, Colin. THE SCHOOLGIRL MURDER CASE. London: Hart Davis McGibbon, 1974. 1st ed. Fine in dj. *ELSE FINE.* $50

Wilson, Colin. THE SEX DIARY OF GERARD SORME. Dial, 1963. 1st Amer ed. Fine in VG dj (bruised & torn at head of spine; two small chips). *STAHR.* $35

Wilson, Colin. THE SPACE VAMPIRES. NY: Random House, 1976. 1st ed. Fine in dj. *ELSE FINE.* $35

Wilson, Colin. THE VIOLENT WORLD OF HUGH GREENE. Boston: Houghton Mifflin, 1963. VG. *SMITH.* $25

Wilson, Colin. THE WORLD OF VIOLENCE. London: Gollancz, 1963. 1st ed. VF in dj. *ELSE FINE.* $50

Wilson, Daniel Munn. WHERE AMERICAN INDEPENDENCE BEGAN, QUINCY....Boston, 1902. 1st ed. *HEINOLDT.* $15

Wilson, Dick. THE LONG MARCH 1935. NY: Viking, (1971). 2nd ptg. Dj price-clipped, edgewear, flap crease. VG. *AKA.* $18

Wilson, E.B. THE CELL IN DEVELOPMENT & INHERITANCE. Macmillan, 1906. 2nd ed. VG. *BOOKCELL.* $75

Wilson, Edmund. AXEL'S CASTLE. NY: Scribner's, 1931. 1st ed. Cl w/paper label on spine, dj. Aside from sl fading top edge of dj, flawless. Rare. *JAFFE*. $750

Wilson, Edmund. LETTERS ON LITERATURE AND POLITICS, 1912-1972. NY: FSG, (1977). Uncorrected proof. Fine in wrappers. *LOPEZ*. $40

Wilson, Edmund. PATRIOTIC GORE, STUDIES IN THE LITERATURE OF THE AMERICAN CIVIL WAR. NY, 1962. 1st ed. A little dj wear o/w Fine. *PRATT*. $50

Wilson, Edmund. THE AMERICAN EARTHQUAKE. NY, 1958. 1st ed, dj. *HEINOLDT*. $15

Wilson, Edmund. THE BOYS IN THE BACK ROOM. NOTES ON CALIFORNIA NOVELISTS. SF: The Colt Press, 1941. 1st ed, ltd to 1500. Fine. *OREGON*. $75

Wilson, Edmund. THE BOYS IN THE BACK ROOM. SF: Colt Press, 1941. Ltd ed, 1500. Bkpl, little soiled inside covers and 1st front and last rear ep, covers little soiled, edge rubbed. NF in dj (sunned, few small edge tears and edge chips, lib stamps). *POLYANTHOS*. $100

Wilson, Edmund. THE BOYS IN THE BACK ROOM. SF: Colt Press, 1941. 1st ed. One of 100 (not numbered, out of sequence?) signed. Some pencil marks, o/w VG+. *SMITH*. $600

Wilson, Edmund. THE WOUND AND THE BOW. Boston: Houghton Mifflin, 1941. 1st ed. NF in VG+ dj. *LAME DUCK*. $200

Wilson, Edmund. THE WOUND AND THE BOW: SEVEN STUDIES IN LITERATURE. Boston: Houghton Mifflin Co., 1941. 1st ed. Fine in NF dj w/minor nick, touch of rubbing to spine extremities. *BETWEEN COVERS*. $225

Wilson, Edmund. TO THE FINLAND STATION. NY: Harcourt, (1940). 1st ed. Fine in sl spine-faded price-clipped dj w/few short closed tears. *CAPTAIN'S BOOKSHELF*. $300

Wilson, Edward. DIARY OF THE "TERRA NOVA" EXPEDITION. NY: Humanities Press, 1972. VG in VG dj. *BLUE DRAGON*. $45

Wilson, Erasmus. A SYSTEM OF HUMAN ANATOMY, GENERAL AND SPECIAL. Phila, 1854. 4th Amer ed. 251 Fine woodcut illus. *FYE*. $75

Wilson, Erasmus. THE DISSECTOR'S MANUAL OF PRACTICAL AND SURGICAL ANATOMY. Ed. by William Hunt. Phila, 1856. 3rd Amer. ed. Full leather, 583pp. 154 woodcuts. *FYE*. $50

Wilson, Ernest H. ARISTOCRATS OF THE GARDEN. Boston: The Stratford Co. (1932). 1st 2 vol ed. 70 leaves of plts. Grn cl; djs. Fine set. *KARMIOLE*. $85

Wilson, Ernest H. IF I WERE TO MAKE A GARDEN. Boston: The Stratford Co. (1931). 1st ed. 37 plts. Dj. Fine. *KARMIOLE*. $75

Wilson, Ernest H. PLANT HUNTING. Boston: The Stratford Co. 1927. 2 vols. 128 plts. Djs. Fine set. *KARMIOLE*. $125

Wilson, Francis. JOHN WILKES BOOTH, FACT AND FICTION OF LINCOLN'S ASSASSINATION. Boston, (1929). 1st trade ed. VG. *PRATT*. $40

Wilson, Francis. THE WEATHER. London, 1987. Illus Philip Jacobs. Paul Wilgress (eng). Pop-up bk. *BOOKFINDERS INTL*. $35

Wilson, Goodridge. SMYTH COUNTY HISTORY AND TRADITIONS. (Kingsport, TN), 1932. 1st ed. Orig cl. *GINSBERG*. $75

Wilson, Herbert Earl. THE LORE AND THE LURE OF THE YOSEMITE. SF, (1923). 2nd ptg. Pict boards worn, sl stained. Lacks spine tip. Text VG. Inscribed. *DIAMOND*. $25

Wilson, Iris Higbie. WILLIAM WOLFSKILL 1798-1866, FRONTIER TRAPPER TO CALIFORNIA RANCHERO. A.H. Clark, 1965. 1st ed. Frontis. VG. *OREGON*. $65

Wilson, Iris Higbie. WILLIAM WOLFSKILL 1798-1866. Glendale, 1965. 1st ed. Fine; sm bump center cvr edge. *VARNER*. $45

Wilson, John A. ADVENTURES OF ALF. WILSON. A THRILLING EPISODE....Toledo: Blade, 1880. 1st ed. 237pp. Orig gold stamped cl. *GINSBERG*. $350

Wilson, John S. JAZZ. THE TRANSITION YEARS, 1940-1960. NY: Appleton, 1966. 1st ed. NF in bit rubbed and sl used dj. *BEASLEY*. $40

Wilson, Joseph T. THE BLACK PHALANX...Hartford: American Publishing Company, 1888. 1st ed. Pencil name, corners sl bumped, else Fine, unrubbed w/gilt lettering on spine and front panel bright. *BETWEEN COVERS*. $225

Wilson, Joyce. THE ARK OF NOAH. SF: The Press in Tuscany Alley, (1975). One of 300 numbered, signed. Unpaginated. Pict title, full-pg color illus. Orig wrappers, pict label on front cvr. Fine. *WREDEN*. $85

Wilson, Joyce. THE FOUR KINGS OF THE FOREST. A FABLE. SF: The Press in Tuscany Alley, (1973). One of 275, numbered, signed by Wilson. Orig pict wrappers. As New. *WREDEN*. $75

Wilson, Joyce. THE SWING. POEMS AND ILLUSTRATIONS....SF: The Press in Tuscany Alley, (1981). One of an ed of 300, signed by Wilson and printer, Adrian Wilson. Unpaginated. Full-pg color illus. Orig pict wrappers. As New. *WREDEN*. $65

Wilson, Mona. THE LIFE OF WILLIAM BLAKE. Frontispiece. London: Peter Davies, Ltd. 1932. 1st ed. Frontis. Light blue-grn cl. Dj. *KARMIOLE*. $40

Wilson, Neill C. and Frank J. Taylor. THE BUILDING OF TRANS MOUNTAIN. Vancouver: Trans Mountain Oil Pipe Line Co, 1954. 1st ed, numbered. Fine. *BLUE DRAGON*. $60

Wilson, Neill C. SILVER STAMPEDE...OLD PANAMINT. NY: Macmillan, 1937. 1st ed. VF in VF, Mint dj. *BOOK MARKET*. $75

Wilson, Neill C. TREASURE EXPRESS. Macmillan, 1938. 4th ptg. Fine in chipped dj. *VARNER*. $20

Wilson, R.L. COLT. AN AMERICAN LEGEND. NY, (1985). Special 4th prtg "Collector's Edition" bound in lea and signed by Wilson on pub's bkpl. Fine in orig shipping box. *BAADE*. $175

Wilson, Raymond. OHIYESA. Urbana: Univ of IL Press, (1983). 1st ed. Fine in VG dj. *LOPEZ*. $30

Wilson, Rufus. OUT OF THE WEST. NY: Press of the Pioneers, 1933. 1st ed. VF in Good dj. *OREGON*. $55

Wilson, Rufus. OUT OF THE WEST. NY: Press of the Pioneers, 1933. 1st ed. VG. *LAURIE*. $40

Wilson, S.A. Kinnier. NEUROLOGY. Baltimore, 1955. 2nd ed. 3 vols, 2160pp. *FYE*. $200

Wilson, Samuel. CHICAGO AND ITS CESS-POOLS OF INFAMY. Chicago: the author, n.d. Ltr ed. 223pp, brown cloth. VG. *ARCHER*. $17.50

Wilson, Warren, et al. THE RECOVERY OF JERUSALEM....NY: Appleton, 1871. 1st ed. 22 plts, 7 fldg. Orig cl, edges rubbed, 1 plt torn along fold, o/w Good. Ex-lib w/number on spine. Very scarce. *WORLDWIDE*. $60

Wilson, William L. A BORDERLAND CONFEDERATE. (Pittsburgh, 1962). 1st ed. Fine. *McGOWAN*. $25

Wilson, William L. A BORDERLAND CONFEDERATE. Pittsburg, (1962). 1st ed. Light dj wear o/w Fine. *PRATT*. $35

Wilson, William. DETOUR. NY: Berkley, (1974). 1st ed. NF in a dj with lt stain, o/w VG. *LOPEZ*. $35

Wilson, Woodrow. A HISTORY OF THE AMERICAN PEOPLE. NY: Harper, 1902. 5 vols. Dampstain vol I; minor stain vol IV. Teg, red cl. *SCHOYER'S*. $40

Wilson. Robert Thomas. HISTORY OF THE BRITISH EXPEDITION TO EGYPT. Phila: Conrad & Co., 1803. 1st Amer ed. xxvi,317,315pp plus 1 p. ad. Engr frontis, 1 fldg map, 2 fldg charts. With half-title. Newly rebound. Some foxing. *SCHOYER'S*. $150

Wilton, George Wilton. FINGERPRINTS: HISTORY, LAW AND ROMANCE. London, 1938. 1st ed. 9 plts. NF. *DIAMOND.* $75

Wiltsee, Ernest. THE PIONEER MINER AND THE PACK MULE EXPRESS. SF: CA Hist Soc, 1931. 1st ed. 10 plts, fldg map. VF in Good+ dj. *OREGON.* $200

Wimsatt, William K., Jr. and Fred A. Pottle (eds). BOSWELL FOR THE DEFENCE 1769-1774. London, (1960). 1st Eng ed. 2 fldg plts. NF in dj. *DIAMOND.* $35

Winchell, Alexander. WALKS AND TALKS IN THE GEOLOGICAL FIELD. NY: Chautauqua Press, 1886. Good. *KNOLLWOOD.* $25

Wind, Herbert Warren. THE STORY OF AMERICAN GOLF. NY: Simon & Schuster, 1956. 1st ptg of rev ed. Fine- in VG-. *AARD.* $30

Wind, Herbert Warren. THE WORLD OF P.G. WODEHOUSE. NY: Praeger, 1971. 1st ed. Fine in dj. *ELSE FINE.* $45

Windeler, Adolphus. THE CALIFORNIA GOLD RUSH DIARY OF A GERMAN SAILOR. Illus. Ed by W.T. Jackson. Berkeley: Howell North, (1969). 1st ed. VF in VF dj. *OREGON.* $40

Windham, Donald. THE HITCHHIKER. Florence: (n.p.), (1950). One of 250 numbered, signed. Fine in wrappers. *LOPEZ.* $150

Windle, Mary J. LIFE IN WASHINGTON, AND LIFE HERE AND THERE. Phila: J.B. Lippincott, 1859. 1st ed. Blind-stamped brown cloth w/gilt. Rare, sporadic light foxing, else VG. Scarce. Howes W559. *CONNOLLY & WADE.* $195

Windt, H. de. FROM PEKIN TO CALAIS BY LAND. London: Chapman & Hall, 1892. 365pp. 2nd ed. Fairly shaken and worn cl. Map. *SCHOYER'S.* $35

Winfield, Marshall. A HISTORY OF CAROLINE COUNTY VIRGINIA FROM ITS FORMATION IN 1727 TO 1924...TO WHICH IS APPENDED "A DISCOURSE OF VIRGINIA" BY EDWARD M. WINGFIELD. Richmond, Trevvet, 1924. 1st ed. (13),528pp. Orig cl, paper label on spine, bkpl removed. Howes W566. *GINSBERG.* $100

Wing, Samuel B. THE SOLDIER'S STORY, A PERSONAL NARRATIVE OF THE LIFE, ARMY EXPERIENCES AND MARVELOUS SUFFERINGS SINCE THE WAR. Phillips, 1898. 1st ed. 118pp, illus, pict cloth. VG. *PRATT.* $65

Wingard, E.A. ECHOES AND OTHER POEMS. Newberry, SC: Lutheran Pub. Board, 1899. 1st ed. 169, (3)pp. Orig grn cl. Owner inscrip, slight spotting on cvr, but VG. *CHAPEL HILL.* $35

Wingfield, R.D. FROST AT CHRISTMAS. London: Constable, 1989. 1st hardcover ed. Signed. VF in dj. *MORDIDA.* $45

Winkler, J.R. A BOOK OF BEETLES. London, 1964. Dj chipped. *SUTTON.* $36

Winks, Robin W. (ed). COLLOQUIUM ON CRIME. NY: Charles Scribner's Sons, 1986. 1st ed. Adv rev copy, slip and flyer laid in. VF in dj. *MORDIDA.* $45

Winks, Robin W. MODUS OPERANDI...DETECTIVE FICTION. Boston: Godine, 1982. 1st ed. Fine in dj. *SILVER DOOR.* $25

Winn, Mary Day. THE MACADAM TRAIL. TEN THOUSAND MILES BY MOTOR COACH. NY: Alfred Knopf, 1931. 1st ed. Minor corner fray, else VG. *BURCHAM.* $50

WINNIE—THE—POOH AND THE BIRTHDAY BURGLAR. London, 1979. Pooh glove puppet at rear which comes through hole each pg. A Puppet Book. *BOOKFINDERS INTL.* $40

WINNIE—THE—POOH. London, 1984. Reprint. Tabs reglued pg 4. A Moveable bk. *BOOKFINDERS INTL.* $28

Winning, Hasso von. PRE-COLUMBIAN ART OF MEXICO AND CENTRAL AMERICA. NY: Abrams, n.d. (1968). 1st ed. 1/100 bound in full lea for subscribers, signed. Fine. *CAPTAIN'S BOOKSHELF.* $500

Winningham, Geoff. GOING TEXAN: THE DAYS OF THE HOUSTON LIVESTOCK SHOW AND RODEO. Houston: Mavis P. Kelsey, 1972. 1st ed. Fine in VG dj. *CONNOLLY & WADE.* $45

Winship, George Parker. THE CORONADO EXPEDITION 1540--1542. Rio Grande Press, 1964. NF. *FIVE QUAIL.* $75

Winslow, Arthur. FRANCIS WINSLOW: HIS FORBEARS AND LIFE...DURING XXX YEARS. Norwood, MA: Privately ptd, 1935. 1st ed. One of 300. (xvi),352pp. 15 plts, 1 plt incl in pagination. Quite scarce. *LEFKOWICZ.* $125

Winslow, Forbes. ON OBSCURE DISEASES OF THE BRAIN, AND DISORDERS OF THE MIND: THEIR INCIPIENT SYMPTOMS, PATHOLOGY, DIAGNOSIS, TREATMENT AND PROPHYLAXIS. Phila, 1860. 1st Amer ed. 576pp. Exceptionally Fine. *FYE.* $250

Winslow, Kathryn. BIG PAN-OUT: THE STORY OF THE KLONDIKE GOLD RUSH. NY: Norton, 1951. 1st ed. NF in Good+ dj. *CONNOLLY & WADE.* $30

Winslow, Richard Elliott III. GENERAL JOHN SEDGWICK, THE STORY OF A UNION CORPS COMMANDER. Novato, (1982). 1st ed. 205pp. VG+. *PRATT.* $25

Winsor, Justin (ed). NARRATIVE AND CRITICAL HISTORY OF AMERICA. Boston, NY: Houghton, Mifflin, 1884-89. 8 vols. 1st ed. Orig dk brn 3/4 morocco; marbled sides, eps, raised bands, teg. 19 inserted plts and maps. Lea sl marked, worn; binding excellent. Short closed marginal tear, but Fine internally. Howes W-578. *PIRAGES.* $450

Winston, Robert W. ROBERT E. LEE, A BIOGRAPHY. NY, 1934, 1st ed. Cover dull, contents VG. *HEINOLDT.* $12

Winter, Elise (with Frank E. Smith). DINNER AT THE MANSION. Oxford: Yoknapatawpha Press, 1st ed. (1982). Fine in dj. *CAPTAIN'S BOOKSHELF.* $30

Winterich, John T. AN AMERICAN FRIEND OF DICKENS. NY: Thomas F. Madigan, 1933. 1st ltd ed. 8vo, 14pp, 3 facs letters, #135 of 150, pict paper covered boards. Fine. *GREAT EXPECTATIONS.* $65

Winterich, John T. BOOKS AND THE MAN. NY: Greenberg, 1929. 1st ed. Fine. *WREDEN.* $25

Winterson, Jeanette. SEXING THE CHERRY. (London): Bloomsbury, (1989). 1st ed. Signed. Lt crease fep; name & date on half-title, o/w Fine in Fine dj. *LOPEZ.* $75

Winthrop, Theodore. THE CANOE AND THE SADDLE. Boston, 1863. Shelfwear. *ARTIS.* $25

Winthrop, Theodore. THE CANOE AND THE SADDLE. Boston, 1863. 1st ed. 375pp,18pp ads. Rebacked w/part of orig backstrip. Little corner wear, o/w VG. Ex-lib. Howes W584. *DIAMOND.* $75

Wintringham, T.H. THE COMING WORLD WAR. NY: Thomas Seltzer, (1935). 1st US ed. Top edges bit dusty, browning to pastedowns & eps o/w Fine in lightly worn dj with wrap-around band. *AKA.* $35

Wintrobe, Maxwell (ed). BLOOD PURE AND ELOQUENT: A STORY OF DISCOVERY, OF PEOPLE, AND OF IDEAS. NY, 1980. 1st ed. *FYE.* $100

Wirt, William. TWO PRINCIPAL ARGUMENTS OF WILLIAM WIRT ESQUIRE, ON THE TRIAL OF AARON BURR FOR HIGH TREASON....Richmond, 1808. 1st ed. (2),221 pp. Orig 12mo full calf w/leather label. Howes W587. *GINSBERG.* $1250

WISCONSIN HISTORICAL COLLECTIONS. Madison. Vol III, 3rd Annual, 1857, 547pp, light foxing & cover wear. Vol IV, 4th Annual, 1859, reprint 1906, 495pp. Vol VII, years 1873, 1874, 1875, 1876, 1876, 495pp, blind stamp. Vol VIII, years 1877, 1878, 1879, 1879, 511pp, cover soil. Vol XII, years 1891-92, 1892, 498pp. $15 each or the lot. *HEINOLDT.* $60

Wise, H.C. COLONIAL ARCHITECTURE FOR THOSE ABOUT TO BUILD. Phila, 1913. NF. *POLYANTHOS.* $75

Wise, Jennings Cropper. THE LONG ARM OF LEE; OR, THE HISTORY OF THE ARTILLERY...OF NORTHERN VIRGINIA WITH A BRIEF ACCOUNT...CONFEDERATE BUREAU OF ORDNANCE. Lynchburg, VA, 1915. 1st ed. 2 vols. New cl. *GINSBERG.* $125

Wise, Jennings Cropper. THE MILITARY HISTORY OF THE VIRGINIA MILITARY INSTITUTE. Lynchburg, VA, 1915. 1st ed. Custom bound in full cloth from orig untrimmed sheets. Fine. *McGOWAN.* $125

Wise, Thomas James. A SHELLEY LIBRARY. London: Ptd for Priv Circulation Only. 1924. Ed ltd to 160. Fine. *KARMIOLE.* $250

Wise, William. MASSACRE AT MOUNTAIN MEADOWS. NY, (1976). 1st ed. 317pp. Dj worn o/w Fine. *PRATT.* $37.50

Wiseman, C.M.L. CENTENNIAL HISTORY OF LANCASTER, OHIO AND LANCASTER PEOPLE: 1898. Lancaster: C.M.L. Wiseman, 1898. 1st ed. Index. Orig blue cloth w/gold teg. VF. Scarce. *CONNOLLY & WADE.* $95

Wiseman, Richard. SEVERALL CHIRURGICALL TREATISES. London, 1686. 2nd ed. Folio, recent 1/2 morocco w/raised bands and marbled boards, new eps. Title page and dedication leaf have been remargined (inner margin), o/w Fine. *FYE.* $1000

Wislizenus, F.A. A JOURNEY TO THE ROCKY MOUNTAINS IN THE YEAR 1839. St Louis: Missour Hist Soc, 1912. Ltd to 500 numbered. Fldg map. Howes W596. *OREGON.* $250

Wislizenus, F.A. MEMOIR OF A TOUR TO NORTHERN MEXICO....Glorieta: Rio Grande, (1969). 3 fldg maps rear pocket. Fine. Howes W597. *OREGON.* $30

Wislizenus, F.A. MEMOIR OF A TOUR TO NORTHERN MEXICO....Wash., 1848. 1st ed. 141 pp. 3 fldg maps. Sewn, laid in l/2 morocco box. Howes W597. *GINSBERG.* $350

Wistar, Isaac Jones. AUTOBIOGRAPHY, 1827-1905. Phila: Wistar Institute, (1937). Lg paper ed, 1st ed. Fine in Fine dj. *BOOK MARKET.* $40

Wistar, Isaac Jones. AUTOBIOGRAPHY OF ISAAC JONES WISTAR, 1827-1905. Phila: Wistar Institute, 1937. Dj faded, else VG. Howes W-598. *LAURIE.* $60

Wistar, Isaac Jones. AUTOBIOGRAPHY OF ISAAC JONES WISTAR. NY, 1937. 1st ed after private publication. 528pp. Fldg map. Minor dj chipping o/w Fine. *PRATT.* $47.50

Wistar,Isaac J. AUTOBIOGRAPHY OF ISAAC J. WISTAR. Phila: 1914. 1st ed. 2 vols. Map, plts. Orig cl w/lea labels on spine, light staining on front cover of vol 1. One of 250 numbered sets. Howes W 598. *GINSBERG.* $375

Wister, Fanny Kemble (ed). OWEN WISTER OUT WEST: HIS JOURNALS AND LETTERS. Chicago: Univ of Chicago, 1958. 1st ed. 4 plts photos. Name, else NF in NF dj. *CONNOLLY & WADE.* $40

Wister, J. LILAC CULTURE, ITS HISTORY, GROWTH AND PROPAGATION. NY, 1936. New ed. 11 plts. Cloth. Inscription, name stamp. Chipped dj. *SUTTON.* $35

Wister, Jones A. "BAWL" FOR AMERICAN CRICKET. Phila: Priv ptd, 1893. 1st ed. Gray cl over bds. Scarce. VG. *OLD LONDON.* $40

Wister, Owen. LADY BALTIMORE. NY: MacMillan, 1906. 1st ed. NF in dec grn cl. *CAPTAIN'S BOOKSHELF.* $45

Wister, Owen. THE VIRGINIAN. LA: LEC, 1951. Illus William Moyers. Cl, glassine dj, slipcase. Ltd to 1500 ptd at The Plantin Press & signed by Moyers. Fine. *JAFFE.* $75

Wister, Owen. THE VIRGINIAN. NY: Macmillan, (1902). 1st ed. Bound in red lea and cl, raised bands and lea inserts for author and title. Orig cover tipped in. VG. *UNGER.* $200

Wister, Owen. WATCH YOUR THIRST. NY, 1923. Ltd ed, 760/1000, signed. Uncut. Extremities, spine minimally rubbed. Fine in dj (few small edge chips, few short edge tears). *POLYANTHOS.* $75

Wither, George. A LOVE SONG. (Concord, MA: Sign of the Vine. 1903.) 24mo. 16pp. Ptd in red and black. Designed by Will Bradley. Boards, paper cvr label. *KARMIOLE.* $100

Withers, Alexander S. CHRONICLES OF BORDER WARFARE OR A HISTORY OF THE SETTLEMENT BY THE WHITES OF NORTHWESTERN VIRGINIA, AND THAT OF THE INDIAN WARS AND MASSACRES IN THAT SECTION OF THE STATE. Cincinnati: Chase, 1908. Reuben G. Thwaites (ed). NF. Howes W601. *CONNOLLY & WADE.* $65

Withers, Alexander S. CHRONICLES OF BORDER WARFARE: OR, A HISTORY...INDIAN WARS AND MASSACRES IN THE STATE...Clarkesburg, VA, 1831. 1st ed. 319,(1)pp. Full calf. Howes W601. Few copies are complete or in good condition. *GINSBERG.* $375

Withington, Antoinette. THE GOLDEN CLOAK. AN INFORMAL HISTORY OF HAWAIIAN ROYALTY....Honolulu: Hawaiiana Press, (1953). 1st ed. 33 plts. VF in Good+ dj. *OREGON.* $45

Witt, C. THE RETREAT OF THE TEN THOUSAND. Frances Younghusband (trans). London & NY: Longmans, Green, 1892. 1st Eng ed. Sl rubbed, soiled; ffep missing, o/w VG. *WORLDWIDE.* $18

Wittemann, A. SAN ANTONIO ILLUSTRATED. NY: A. Wittemann, 1892. 1st ed. 42 photos. Fine. Scarce. *GIBBS.* $75

Witter, Dean. MEANDERINGS OF A FISHERMAN. Privately ptd, n.d. (ca 1955). Ptd by James H. Barry Co of SF: 1955. Fine. *CONNOLLY & WADE.* $65

Wittingham, Richard. THE DIMAGGIO ALBUMS. Intro, commentaries by Joe Dimaggio. NY: Putnam, 1989. 1st ed. 2 vols. One of 700 leatherbound sets, signed. Fine in Fine slipcase w/cl Yankee uniform inset. *BEASLEY.* $500

Wittke, Carl. REFUGEE OF REVOLUTION: THE GERMAN FORTY-EIGHTERS IN AMERICA. Phila: Univ of Pennsylvania, 1952. 1st ed. About Fine. *CONNOLLY & WADE.* $45

Wodehouse, P.G. ANGEL CAKE. GC: Doubleday, 1952. 1st ed. Fine; minor wear at spine ends of price clipped dj. *ELSE FINE.* $125

Wodehouse, P.G. AUTHOR! AUTHOR! NY, 1962. 1st ed. Fine in VG dj. *McCLINTOCK.* $25

Wodehouse, P.G. COCKTAIL TIME. NY: Simon & Schuster, 1958. 1st ed. Brief inscription. Fine, light edgewear to dj. *ELSE FINE.* $50

Wodehouse, P.G. EGGS, BEANS AND CRUMPETS. NY: Doubleday Doran, 1940. 1st Amer. ed. VG in dj with extensive internal tape reinforcing, external tape mends at spine ends, chipping at top of spine, wear along folds and sl faded spine. *MORDIDA.* $150

Wodehouse, P.G. FULL MOON. Herbert Jenkins, 1947. 1st Eng. ed. VG to VG+. Ffep has been removed. Wear at spine; also small stains. *STAHR.* $15

Wodehouse, P.G. GOLF WITHOUT TEARS. NY: George H. Doran Company, (1924). 1st Amer ed of "The Clicking of Cuthbert." Bumped, sl soiled, stained, owner name. NF. Scarce. *BLUE MOUNTAIN.* $225

Wodehouse, P.G. HEAVY WEATHER. Toronto: McClelland & Stewart, 1933. 1st ed. Fine; minor wear to dj. *ELSE FINE.* $200

Wodehouse, P.G. JEEVES AND THE TIE THAT BINDS. NY, (1971). 1st ed. Fine in VG dj. *McCLINTOCK.* $20

Wodehouse, P.G. MIKE AT WRYKYN. NY: Simon & Schuster, 1963. 1st ed. Fine; minor wear at dj extrems. *ELSE FINE.* $50

Wodehouse, P.G. MONEY FOR NOTHING. GC: Doubleday, 1928. 1st US ed. VG. *BEASLEY.* $40

Wodehouse, P.G. MONEY IN THE BANK. (London): Herbert Jenkins, (1946). 1st UK ed. Front board bowed & a trifle soiled, o/w Near VG. *ARCHER.* $30

Wodehouse, P.G. MULLINER OMNIBUS. London: Jenkins, 1935. 1st ed. Name. Fine. *ELSE FINE.* $85

Wodehouse, P.G. PEARLS, GIRLS AND MONTY BODKIN. London: Barrie & Jenkins, 1972. 1st ed. Fine in price clipped dj. *ELSE FINE.* $60

Wodehouse, P.G. QUICK SERVICE. Toronto: Longmans Green, 1941. 1st ed. Fine; lt edgewear to pict dj. *ELSE FINE.* $150

Wodehouse, P.G. SIR AGRAVAINE. London: Blandford, 1984. 1st ed. As new in jacket. 21 full- pg color illus. *ELSE FINE.* $50

Wodehouse, P.G. STIFF UPPER LIP, JEEVES. NY, 1963. 1st ed. Fine in NF dj. *McCLINTOCK.* $35

Wodehouse, P.G. SUMMER LIGHTNING. London: Jenkins, 1929. 1st ed. Slight spine fade, beginning to wear at the extrems. NF. *ELSE FINE.* $150

Wodehouse, P.G. SUMMER MOONSHINE. NY: Doubleday Doran, 1937. 1st ed. NF; 2nd state pict dj has some spine fade, minor wear. *ELSE FINE.* $135

Wodehouse, P.G. SUNSET AT BLANDINGS. London: Chatto & Windus, 1977. 1st ed. Tiny edgetear in ep repaired, else Fine in dj. *ELSE FINE.* $35

Wodehouse, P.G. THANK YOU, JEEVES. Boston: Little Brown, 1934. 1st US ed of 1st Jeeves novel. Minor fading to cl, else VG+ in dj w/substantial chipping. *LAME DUCK.* $85

Wodehouse, P.G. THE HEART OF A GOOF. London: Jenkins, 1926. 1st ed. Beginning to wear at extrems, VG+. (Pub in US as DIVOTS.) *ELSE FINE.* $225

Wodehouse, P.G. THE INTRUSION OF JIMMY. NY, (1910). Pre-WWII G&D rpt. VG. *McCLINTOCK.* $10

Wodehouse, P.G. THE LUCK OF THE BODKINS. Little, Brown, 1935. 1st Amer ed. Sunning of spine. VG+. *BEBBAH.* $50

Wodehouse, P.G. THE MOST OF P.G. WODEHOUSE. NY: Simon & Schuster, 1960. 1st ed. Fine; minor wear at dj spine corners. *ELSE FINE.* $50

Wodehouse, P.G. THE PLOT THAT THICKENED. NY: Simon & Schuster, (1973). 221pp. Orig brown cl. Remainder mark, else Fine in dj. 1st Amer ed. *CHAPEL HILL.* $35

Wodehouse, P.G. THE PLOT THAT THICKENED. NY: Simon & Schuster, 1973. 1st ed. Inscription under dj flap. Fine in dj. *ELSE FINE.* $50

Wodehouse, P.G. THE PRINCE AND BETTY. NY: Watt, (1912). Early reissue ("Popular Edition" on spine). Pict label front cvr. Spine dull, corner tips sl frayed, front inner hinge cracked at pastedown, else VG. *BERNARD.* $75

Wodehouse, P.G. THE RETURN OF JEEVES. NY: S&S, 1954. 1st US ed, rev from English. NF in sl rubbed price clipped dj w/chips. *CAPTAIN'S BOOKSHELF.* $90

Wodehouse, P.G. THE WORLD OF WODEHOUSE CLERGY. London, etc, (1984). 1st ed. Fine in dj. *McCLINTOCK.* $25

Wodehouse, P.G. VERY GOOD, JEEVES. GC, 1930. 1st ed. VG. *McCLINTOCK.* $20

Woglum, Gilbert Totten. PARAKITES. A TREATISE ON THE MAKING AND FLYING OF TAILESS KITES. NY & London, 1896. 1st ed. Pale yellow binding w/finger soil, interior Fine, still unopened. *McCLINTOCK.* $55

Woiwode, Larry. INDIAN AFFAIRS. Atheneum, 1992. Uncorrected proof. Fine in red wraps. *STAHR.* $25

Woiwode, Larry. POPPA JOHN. NY: FSG, (1981). 1st ed. Inscribed in 1981. Fine in Fine dj. *LOPEZ.* $40

Woiwode, Larry. WHAT I'M GOING TO DO, I THINK. Farrar, Straus & Giroux, 1969. 1st ed. Fine in dj that has a tear at the head of spine. Ffep corner clipped. *STAHR.* $35

Wolberg, Lewis R. MICRO-ART—ART IMAGES IN A HIDDEN WORLD. NY: Abrams, (1978?). 93 tipped-in plts. Prev owner's name. Fine in Fine- dj. *AARD.* $75

Wolcott, Walter. THE MILITARY HISTORY OF YATES COUNTY, N.Y. Penn Yan, NY, 1895. 1st ed. NF. *McGOWAN.* $150

Wolf, Edwin and John Fleming. ROSENBACH: A BIOGRAPHY. Cleveland and NY: World Pub, (1960). 1st ed. Dj. *DAWSON'S.* $75

Wolf, Gary. WHO CENSORED ROGER RABBIT? NY: St. Martin's, 1981. 1st ed. VF, a few small rubs at dj extremities. *ELSE FINE.* $125

Wolf, Sara. LONG CHAIN OF DEATH. NY: Walker, 1987. 1st ed. VF in dj. *MORDIDA.* $20

Wolfe, Aaron (pseud of Dean R. Koontz). INVASION. NY: Laser, 1975. 1st ed. Paperback orig. VG in wraps. *ELSE FINE.* $15

Wolfe, Bernard. THE GREAT PRINCE DIED. NY: Scribners, 1959. 1st ed. Close to Fine in lightly used dj w/small chip. *BEASLEY.* $35

Wolfe, Bertram D. A LIFE IN TWO CENTURIES: AN AUTOBIOGRAPHY. Intro Leonard Shapiro. NY: Stein & Day, (1981). 1st ed. 2 corners lightly bumped, else Fine in dj (few short tears). *CAPTAIN'S BOOKSHELF.* $40

Wolfe, Bertram. THE FABULOUS LIFE OF DIEGO RIVERA. NY: Stein & Day, (1963). 1st ed. Fine in dj w/sl sunned spine. *CAPTAIN'S BOOKSHELF.* $45

Wolfe, Gene. CLAW OF THE CONCILLIATOR. Timescape, 1981. 1st ed. Fine in dj. *MADLE.* $60

Wolfe, Gene. THE FIFTH HEAD OF CERBERUS. NY: Scribner, (1972). 1st ed. Fine in dj. *CAPTAIN'S BOOKSHELF.* $35.

Wolfe, Gene. THE SWORD OF THE LICTOR. Timescape, 1982. 1st ed. Fine in dj. *MADLE.* $60

Wolfe, Humbert. CURSORY RHYMES. London: Ernest Benn, 1927. VG w/extra spine label tipped in at rear. 1st ed. One of 500 signed. *CHAPEL HILL.* $65

Wolfe, Linnie Marsh (ed). JOHN OF THE MOUNTAINS: UNPUBLISHED JOURNALS OF JOHN MUIR. Boston: Houghton Mifflin, 1938. 1st ed. 459pp. Fine in VG dj. *BOOK MARKET.* $95

Wolfe, Thomas. A WESTERN JOURNAL. Pittsburgh: Univ of Pittsburgh Press. 1951. 1st ed. Dj sl chipped. *KARMIOLE.* $30

Wolfe, Thomas. AMERICA. FROM OF TIME AND THE RIVER. Chicago: Privately Ptd (at the Norman Press), 1942. 1st separate ed. Fine in dj (sm chip top corner front panel, affecting no lettering; short tear top rear panel). *CHAPEL HILL.* $300

Wolfe, Thomas. FROM DEATH TO MORNING. NY: Scribner's, 1935. 1st ed. Orig brownish maroon cl. Fine in price-clipped dj with minimal rubbing. *CHAPEL HILL.* $225

Wolfe, Thomas. FROM DEATH TO MORNING. NY: Scribner's, 1935. 1st ed. Orig browning maroon cl. Owner sig, faint tape marks on eps, gilt spine lettering dulled, thus VG in worn, price-clipped dj, some chipping, tears. *CHAPEL HILL.* $150

Wolfe, Thomas. LOOK HOMEWARD, ANGEL. London: Heinemann, (1930). 1st Eng ed. One of 3,000. Orig blue cl. Fine, bright in dj. *CHAPEL HILL.* $1750

Wolfe, Thomas. LOOK HOMEWARD, ANGEL. NY: Scribner's, 1929. 1st ed. Inscribed, bkpl. Orig dk blue cl. Fine in NF dj (few sm clean edge tears mended on verso). 1st issue jacket (one of 3500 thus), with Doris Ulmann's photo of Wolfe on rear panel. *CHAPEL HILL.* $6000

Wolfe, Thomas. LOOK HOMEWARD, ANGEL. NY: Scribner's, 1929. 1st ed. Orig dk blue cl. Fine in lightly used 1st issue dj (few sm chips top edge not affecting lettering). Jacket is backed w/stiff paper on verso. *CHAPEL HILL.* $1300

Wolfe, Thomas. MANNERHOUSE. NY, 1948. Ltd ed. 491/500. Portrait, 12pp page facsimile of holograph letter. Fine in dj (spine sunned w/2-1/2" tear top sides, top spine little sunned, little rubbed, small tear top edge). *POLYANTHOS*. $150

Wolfe, Thomas. OF TIME AND THE RIVER. NY: Scribner's, 1935. Spine dulled, owner's sig, tape marks on eps, thus VG in creased dj. 1st ed. *CHAPEL HILL*. $150

Wolfe, Thomas. OF TIME AND THE RIVER. NY: Scribner's 1935. 1st ed. Orig black cl. Owner sig, w/o dj, else VG. *CHAPEL HILL*. $40

Wolfe, Thomas. OF TIME AND THE RIVER. NY: Scribner's, 1935. 1st ed, 6th prtg. Orig black cl. Spine dulled, but VG in bright dj, couple of creases. *CHAPEL HILL*. $850

Wolfe, Thomas. OF TIME AND THE RIVER: A LEGEND OF MAN'S HUNGER IN HIS YOUTH. NY: Scribners, 1935. 1st ed. VG lacking dj. Inscribed. *CAPTAIN'S BOOKSHELF*. $1000

Wolfe, Thomas. SELECTIONS FROM THE WORKS OF THOMAS WOLFE. London: Heinemann, (1952). Maxwell Geismar (ed). 1st Eng ed, and 1st ed under this title. Orig grn cl. Bkpl, else Fine in NF dj (sm closed tear between spine, rear panel). *CHAPEL HILL*. $40

Wolfe, Thomas. THE HILLS BEYOND. With a Note on Thomas Wolfe by Edward C. Aswell. NY & London: Harper & Bros, (1941). 1st ed. Orig dk blue cl. VG to NF in dj. *CHAPEL HILL*. $125

Wolfe, Thomas. THE HOUND OF DARKNESS. John L. Idol, Jr. (ed). (N.p.): The Thomas Wolfe Society, 1986. 1st ed. #37 of 600. Inscribed. Orig black cl. Fine. *CHAPEL HILL*. $95

Wolfe, Thomas. THE LETTERS OF THOMAS WOLFE TO HIS MOTHER. C. Hugh Holman, Sue Ross Fields (eds). Chapel Hill: Univ. of NC Press, 1968. 1st ed. Orig blue cl. Tape marks on eps, else Fine in price-clipped dj. *CHAPEL HILL*. $25

Wolfe, Thomas. THE STORY OF A NOVEL. NY: Scribner's, 1936. 1st ed. Fine, bright in dj, some soiling. *CHAPEL HILL*. $125

Wolfe, Thomas. THE WEB AND THE ROCK. London: Heinemann, (1947). 1st Eng ed. Orig black cl. Offsetting to ffep, else Fine in minimally rubbed dj. *CHAPEL HILL*. $150

Wolfe, Thomas. THOMAS WOLFE'S LETTERS TO HIS MOTHER, JULIA ELIZABETH WOLFE. John Skally Terry (ed). NY: Scribner's, 1943. 1st ed. Orig black cl. VG in price-clipped dj, moderate edgewear, several chips. *CHAPEL HILL*. $45

Wolfe, Thomas. THOMAS WOLFE'S PURDUE SPEECH "WRITING AND LIVING." W. Lafayette: Purdue Univ Studios, 1964. 1st ed. Fine in lightly rubbed dj. *BEASLEY*. $45

Wolfe, Thomas. WELCOME TO OUR CITY. Richard S. Kennedy (ed). Baton Rouge & London: Louisiana State Univ. Press, (1983). 1st ed. Inscribed by ed. 2500 ptd. Virtually as New in dj. *CHAPEL HILL*. $45

Wolfe, Thomas. YOU CAN'T GO HOME AGAIN. NY, 1940. 1st ed. Traces of removed tape inside cvrs and feps. Dj w/traces of tape inside flaps, strengthened internally, sl chipped, small edge tear, little edge rubbed. VG. *POLYANTHOS*. $45

Wolfe, Thomas. YOU CAN'T GO HOME AGAIN. NY, 1940. 1st ed. Extremities spine very sl bumped. Fine in dj (extremities, spine and corners chipped. Two 1" chips top edge front cover sides spine. Edge rubbed). *POLYANTHOS*. $75

Wolfe, Tom. FROM BAUHAUS TO OUR HOUSE. NY: Farrar Straus & Giroux, (1981). 1st ed. 1/350 specially bound, numbered, signed. Fine in slipcase. *CAPTAIN'S BOOKSHELF*. $125

Wolfe, Tom. MAUVE GLOVES & MADMEN, CLUTTER & VINE. NY: FSG, 1976. 1st ed. Fine in dj. *ELSE FINE*. $30

Wolfe, Tom. RADICAL CHIC AND MAU-MAUING THE FLAK CATCHERS. NY: Farrar, Straus, (1970). 1st ed. Fine in dw. *CAPTAIN'S BOOKSHELF*. $50

Wolfe, Tom. THE BONFIRE OF THE VANITIES. NY: Farrar Straus Giroux, (1987). 1st ed. Ltd to 250 signed. Slipcase. Mint. *JAFFE*. $350

Wolfe, Tom. THE BONFIRE OF THE VANITIES. NY: Farrar, Straus, Giroux, (1987). 1st ed. #92 of 250 signed. Orig grey cl. As New in pub's slipcase. Accompanied by 18pp advance promo pamphlet, containing 1st chapter of the novel. Fine in pict wraps. *CHAPEL HILL*. $250

Wolfe, Tom. THE BONFIRE OF THE VANITIES. NY: Farrar, Straus & Giroux, (1987). Uncorrected proof. Fine in ptd wraps. *CAPTAIN'S BOOKSHELF*. $100

Wolfe, Tom. THE BONFIRE OF THE VANITIES. NY: FSG, (1987). 1st ed. VF in VF dj. *UNGER*. $60

Wolfe, Tom. THE ELECTRIC KOOL-AID ACID TEST. NY: Farrar Straus Giroux, (1968). 1st ed. VG in price-clipped dj. *LOPEZ*. $85

Wolfe, Tom. THE KANDY-KOLORED TANGERINE FLAKE STREAMLINE BABY. NY: FSG, (1965). 1st ed, 1st ed. NF in VG dj. *UNGER*. $100

Wolfe, Tom. THE PAINTED WORD. NY, (1975). 1st ed. Fine in lightly used price-clipped dj. *CAPTAIN'S BOOKSHELF*. $45

Wolfe, Tom. THE PUMP HOUSE GANG. NY: Farrar, 1968. 1st ed. Fine but for initials fep, in Fine dj but for slight wear head of spine. *BEASLEY*. $35

Wolfe, Tom. THE PUMP HOUSE GANG. NY: FS&G, (1968). 1st ed. Fine in dw. *CAPTAIN'S BOOKSHELF*. $50

Wolfe, Tom. THE PUMP HOUSE GANG. NY: FSG, 1968. 1st ed. Fine in dj. *ELSE FINE*. $50

Wolfe, Tom. THE RIGHT STUFF. NY: Farrar Straus & Giroux, (1979). Uncorrected proof. Corner clipped from ffep, else NF in lightly spotted wrappers. *CAPTAIN'S BOOKSHELF*. $75

Wolfe, Tom. THE RIGHT STUFF. NY: FSG, (1979). 1st ed. Fine in NF dj. *UNGER*. $35

Wolff, Geoffrey. PROVIDENCE. NY: Viking, (1986). 1st ed. Fine in Fine dj. Signed. *LOPEZ*. $30

Wolff, John E. ROUTE OF THE MANLY PARTY OF 1849-50 IN LEAVING DEATH VALLEY FOR THE COAST. N.p, n.d, (1931?). 1st ed. 29pp. More than one type of binding used. Fine. *BOOK MARKET*. $150

Wolff, Tobias. BACK IN THE WORLD. Boston: Houghton Mifflin, 1985. 1st ed. Fine in Fine dj. Signed. Pub's promo postcard laid in. *LOPEZ*. $85

Wolff, Tobias. BACK IN THE WORLD. Houghton, 1985. 1st ed. VF in dj. Complimentary copy with "bookcard.". *STAHR*. $35

Wolff, Tobias. BACK IN THE WORLD. Houghton Mifflin, 1985. 1st ed. Fine in NF dj. *BEBBAH*. $30

Wolff, Tobias. BACK IN THE WORLD. Uncorrected proof, signed. Fine in dj. *LOPEZ*. $100

Wolff, Tobias. IN THE GARDEN OF NORTH AMERICAN MARTYRS. NY: Ecco Press, (1981). Fine in dj. *LOPEZ*. $75

Wolff, Tobias. IN THE GARDEN OF THE NORTH AMERICAN MARTYRS. Ecco, 1981. 1st ed. Fine in Fine dj. *BEBBAH*. $60

Wolff, Tobias. THE BARRACKS THIEF. NY: Ecco Press, (1984). 1st ed. Fine in Fine dj and signed. *LOPEZ*. $100

Wolff, Tobias. THE BARRACKS THIEF. NY: Ecco Press, (1984). 1st ed. Orig cl-backed boards. Fine in dj. Signed. *CHAPEL HILL*. $125

Wolff, Tobias. THE BARRACKS THIEF. NY: Ecco Press, 1984. 1st ed. Fine in dj. *ELSE FINE*. $40

Wolff, Tobias. THE LIAR (Vineburg): (Engdahl Typography), 1989. Of 200, this one of 50 signed. Fine in Fine dj. *LOPEZ*. $175

Wolff, Tobias. THE OTHER MILLER. Derry & Ridgewood: Babcock & Koontz, (1986). 1/40 Roman numeral copies signed by Wolff and the artist, Gaylord Schanilec. Fine. *LOPEZ.* $225

Wolff, Tobias. THE OTHER MILLER. Derry/Ridgewood: Babcock & Koontz, (1986). 1/200 numbered, of 240 total, signed. Fine w/o dj, as issued. *LOPEZ.* $125

Wolff, Tobias. THIS BOY'S LIFE. NY: Atlantic Monthly, (1989). 1st ed. Signed month after pub. Fine in Fine dj. *LOPEZ.* $85

Wolff, Tobias. THIS BOY'S LIFE. Uncorrected proof. Signed. *LOPEZ.* $150

Wolff, Tobias. THIS BOY'S LIFE: A MEMOIR. Atlantic Monthly, 1989. Uncorrected proof. About Fine in baby-blue wraps. *STAHR.* $45

Wolff, Tobias. UGLY RUMORS. London: Allen & Unwin, 1975. 1st ed. Author's little-known 1st bk. Published only in England. NF in VG+ dj. *LAME DUCK.* $650

Wolff, Tobias. UGLY RUMOURS. London: Allen & Unwin, (1975). 1st ed. Fine in dj. Scarce. *BETWEEN COVERS.* $750

Wolff, Tobias. UGLY RUMOURS. London: George Allen & Unwin, (1975). 1st ed. Scarce and "suppressed" 1st bk, never pub in US. Fine in dj. *LOPEZ.* $750

Wolff, Werner. ISLAND OF DEATH (EASTER ISLAND). NY: J.J. Augustin, 1948. Inscribed. VG in worn dj. *PARMER.* $100

Wolff, Werner. ISLAND OF DEATH: A KEY TO EASTER ISLAND'S CULTURE. NY, 1948. NF. *POLYANTHOS.* $100

Wolhuter, Harry. MEMORIES OF A GAME RANGER. N.p.: Wildlife Protection Soc of South Africa, (1948), 1965. 8th ed. VG+ in VG+ dj. *BACKMAN.* $32

Wolhuter, Harry. MEMORIES OF A GAME-RANGER. Pretorius: (Apr. 1958). Fine in VG+ dj. *MIKESH.* $45

Wolle, Muriel S. MONTANA PAY DIRT. A GUIDE TO THE MINING CAMPS. Denver: Sage Books, (1963). 1st ed. VG in VG dj. *OREGON.* $100

Wolle, Muriel S. STAMPEDE TO TIMBERLINE. Chicago: The Swallow Press, Inc, 1974. 2nd ed. Grey cl. VG in sl worn dj. *PARMER.* $40

Wolle, Muriel S. STAMPEDE TO TIMBERLINE: THE GHOST TOWNS AND MINING CAMPS OF COLORADO. Denver: Sage, 1965. VF. *CONNOLLY & WADE.* $35

Wolle, Muriel S. STAMPEDE TO TIMBERLINE: THE GHOST TOWNS AND MINING CAMPS OF COLORADO. Chicago: Swallow Press, 1949. VG in tattered dj. *BURCHAM.* $25

Wolle, Muriel S. THE BONANZA TRAIL. Univ of IN, 1953. 1st ptg. Fine in Fine dj. *VARNER.* $35

Wolle, Muriel S. THE BONANZA TRAIL. Bloomington: IN Univ Press, 1953. 1st ed. Fine in Fine dj. *BOOK MARKET.* $50

Wollheim, Donald. THE SECRET OF SATURN'S RINGS. Phila: Winston, 1954. 1st ed. Fine in colorful pict dj. *ELSE FINE.* $75

Wollheim, Donald. THE SECRET OF SATURN'S RINGS. Winston, 1954. 1st ed. VG in sl frayed dj. *MADLE.* $60

WOMEN TORCH-BEARERS, THE STORY OF THE WOMAN'S CHRISTIAN TEMPERANCE UNION. Evanston, IL, 1924. 2nd ed. 320pp. Scarce. Photo illus. *FYE.* $75

Wood, Albert. IN A SPERM WHALE'S JAWS...George C. Wood (ed). Hanover, NH, 1954. One of 1000 ptd by Friends of the Dartmouth Lib. 1st ed. (18)pp. Wraps, Fine. *LEFKOWICZ.* $60

Wood, Benjamin. FORT LAFAYETTE; OR, LOVE AND SECESSION. A NOVEL. NY: Carleton, 1862. 1st ed. 300,(8)pp. Orig cl. *GINSBERG.* $75

Wood, C.F. A YACHTING CRUISE IN THE SOUTH SEAS. London: Henry S. King and Co, 1875. 1st ed. (6),221,(1 blank, 2 ads). Orig cl. Old lib blindstamp, and remains of pocket inside back cvr. *LEFKOWICZ.* $200

Wood, Casey and F.M. Fyfe. (trans and eds). THE ART OF FALCONRY. Stanford Univ Press, 1943. 1st ed (this translation). W/o dj (as issued). Minor shelfwear, else NF. *OLD LONDON.* $150

Wood, Casey and F.M. Fyfe. THE ART OF FALCONRY, ETC. Stanford Univ, (1961). Fine. *MIKESH.* $60

Wood, Charles. LINES WEST...1887 TO 1967. Superior, 1967. 2nd ed. Fine in Fine dj. *VARNER.* $25

Wood, Don. I REMEMBER PENSY. NY, 1973. 1st ed. Fine in Fine dj. *VARNER.* $30

Wood, George & Franklin Bache. THE DISPENSATORY OF THE UNITED STATES OF AMERICA. Phila, 1849. 8th ed. Full leather, 1380pp. *FYE.* $125

Wood, J.G. INSECTS AT HOME. Phila, 1873. 20 plts. Ex-lib. *SUTTON.* $35

Wood, J.W. PASADENA, CALIFORNIA HISTORICAL AND PERSONAL. (Pasadena): J.W. Wood, 1917. Black-stamped cl, inscribed. *DAWSON'S.* $50

Wood, John E. SUN, MOON AND STANDING STONES. UK: Oxford Univ Press, 1978. VG in dj. *KNOLLWOOD.* $28

Wood, John Sumner. THE VIRGINIA BISHOP, A YANKEE HERO OF THE CONFEDERACY. Richmond, 1961. 1st ed. Dj torn with small piece missing from back o/w VG+. *PRATT.* $32.50

Wood, Richard G. STEPHEN HARRIMAN LONG, 1784-1864, ARMY ENGINEER, EXPLORER, INVENTOR. Glendale, 1966. 1st ed. 292pp. Fine. *PRATT.* $40

Wood, Richard G. STEPHEN HARRIMAN LONG, 1784-1864. Glendale: Arthur H. Clark, 1966. 1st ed. Fine. *BOOK MARKET.* $40

Wood, Richard G. STEPHEN HARRIMAN LONG, 1784-1864. Glendale, 1966. 1st ed. *GINSBERG.* $25

Wood, Stanley. OVER THE RANGE TO THE GOLDEN GATE. Chicago: R.R. Donnelley & Sons Co, 1901. Maps in text, tables. Small stamp on title. *HUDSON.* $35

Wood, Stanley. OVER THE RANGE TO THE GOLDEN GATE: A COMPLETE TOURIST'S GUIDE. Chicago: Donnelly, 1904. 1st ed thus: revised and updated from the 1894 ed by C.E. Hooper. Riverside Press. VG. *CONNOLLY & WADE.* $45

Wood, Sumner G. ULSTER SCOTS AND BLANFORD SCOUTS. Medway, MA, 1928. 1st ed. Errata slip. Auto-presentation. *HEINOLDT.* $20

Wood, Ted. LIVE BAIT. NY: Charles Scribner's Sons, 1985. 1st ed. VF in dj. *MORDIDA.* $37.50

Wood, Ted. MURDER ON ICE. NY: Charles Scribner's Sons, 1984. 1st ed. Advance review copy, slip laid in. VF in dj. *MORDIDA.* $40

WOOD TYPE OF THE ANGELICA PRESS. N.p.: The Angelica Press, 1976. Ltd to 200 numbered. 4 separate bound folio sections loosely inserted in specially constructed wooden box w/side hinges and closing latches. *OAK KNOLL.* $450

Wood, Walter. ADVENTURES WITH BIG FISH. London and Edinburgh: Jack, n.d. (30's?). 1st ed. Minor edgewear, else VG. *OLD LONDON.* $25

Wood, William. CAPTAINS OF THE CIVIL WAR, A CHRONICLE OF THE BLUE AND GRAY. NY, 1921. 1st ed. 423pp. Fldg maps. VG. *PRATT.* $22.50

Woodbury, Richard B. ALFRED E. KIDDER. NY: Columbia Univ Press, 1973. 1st ed. As New in rubbed dj. *PARMER.* $30

Woodcock, H.B.D. and W.T. Stearn. LILIES OF THE WORLD....NY, 1950. Cloth worn at corners, edges. Ex-lib. *SUTTON.* $56

Woodford, Jack. DANGEROUS LOVE. NY, (1950). 1st Avon paperback, 1st ptg. Avon Pocket Size Book #402. Paper starting to brown, else Fine. *McCLINTOCK.* $20

Woodford, Jack. PLOTTING: HOW TO HAVE A BRAIN CHILD. NY, 1939. 1st ed. Signed. VG. *McCLINTOCK.* $27.50

Woodford, M. H. A MANUAL OF FALCONRY. London: A&C Black, 1972. Reprint of 2nd ed. NF in dj. *OLD LONDON.* $20

Woodgate, W.B. BOATING (BADMINTON LIBRARY). Boston: Little, Brown & Co., and London: Longmans, Green & Co., 1888. 1st Amer ed. Minor edgewear, foxing, else VG-NF. *OLD LONDON.* $65

Woodhall, Barnes and Gilbert Beebe. PERIPHERAL NERVE REGENERATION, A FOLLOW-UP STUDY OF 3,656 WORLD WAR II INJURIES. Washington, 1956. 1st ed. *FYE.* $50

Woodley, Thomas Frederick. THADDEUS STEVENS. Harrisburg, 1934. 1st ed. VG+. *PRATT.* $60

Woodrell, Daniel. MUSCLE FOR THE WING. NY: Henry Holt, 1988. 1st ed. VF in dj. *MORDIDA.* $30

Woodrell, Daniel. UNDER THE BRIGHT LIGHTS. NY: Henry Holt, 1986. 1st ed. VF in dj. *MORDIDA.* $30

Woodrell, Daniel. WOE TO LIVE ON. NY: Henry Holt, 1987. 1st ed. VF in dj. *MORDIDA.* $25

Woodruff, C.E. THE EFFECTS OF TROPICAL LIGHT ON WHITE MEN. NY: Rebman, 1905. 1st ed. Cvr mod. worn, contents VG. *SMITHFIELD.* $28

Woodruff, George Coyne. HISTORY OF HILLSIDE, NJ AND VICINITY. Hillside, 1934. 1st ed. 278pp + 54pp ads. *HEINOLDT.* $25

Woodruff, Hiram. THE TROTTING HORSE OF AMERICA. Ed by Charles J. Foster. NY: J.B. Ford, 1868. 1st ed. Little cvr wear, staining, foxing, o/w VG. *DIAMOND.* $60

Woods, Daniel B. SIXTEEN MONTHS AT THE GOLD DIGGINGS. NY: Harper & Brothers, 1851. 1st ed. 199pp,6,(2) ads. Orig lt blue blindstamped cl (some lt wear to extrems). Some foxing. Inscribed. *MOTT.* $400

Woods, Edgar. ALBEMARLE COUNTY IN VIRGINIA. (Michie, c. 1901). 1st ed. Good. *BOOK BROKER.* $85

Woods, Edgar. ALBEMARLE COUNTY IN VIRGINIA...WHAT IT WAS BY NATURE...AND OF SOME OF THE MEN WHO MADE IT. (Charlottesville, Michie, 1901). 1st ed. (4),412pp. Orig cl, sm paper label on lower spine. Howes W652. *GINSBERG.* $100

Woods, James. RECOLLECTIONS OF PIONEER WORK IN CALIFORNIA. SF: Joseph Winterburn & Co, 1878. 260pp. Blind and gold stamped cl, overall wear. *DAWSON'S.* $55

Woods, John. TWO YEARS' RESIDENCE IN THE SETTLEMENT OF THE ENGLISH PRAIRIE, IN THE ILLINOIS COUNTRY....London, 1822. 1st ed. (4),310pp. 3 maps, 2 fldg. Orig boards, lightly chipped at crown, ptd paper label on spine, cl slipcase. Howes W654. *GINSBERG.* $1250

Woods, Joseph. LETTERS OF AN ARCHITECT FROM FRANCE, ITALY, AND GREECE. 2 vols. London: John and Archer Arch, 1828. 1st ed. xv,(i),465pp; xi,(iii),450pp. 20 plts w/occasional foxing. Orig grn cl rubbed and bumped, cl split and chipped at spines, hinges cracked, bkpl. VG. *BLUE MOUNTAIN.* $385

Woods, Leonard. A SERMON, PREACHED AT HAVERILL, (Mass.) IN REMEMBRANCE OF MRS. HARRIET NEWELL...Boston: Samuel T. Armstrong, 1814. 250 pp, full lea. VG. *NUTMEG.* $20

Woods, Stuart. DEEP LIE. NY: Norton, 1986. 1st ed. Fine in dj. *ELSE FINE.* $40

Woods, Stuart. DEEP LIE. NY: W.W. Norton, 1986. 1st ed. Fine in dj. *MORDIDA.* $30

Woods, Stuart. GRASS ROOTS. NY: Simon & Schuster, 1989. 1st ed. Remainder streak on bottom edge o/w Fine in dj. *MORDIDA.* $25

Woods, Stuart. RUN BEFORE THE WIND. NY: Norton, 1983. 1st ed. VF in dj. *ELSE FINE.* $45

Woods, Stuart. UNDER THE LAKE. NY: Simon & Schuster, 1987. 1st ed. Remainder stamp on bottom edge o/w Fine in dj. *MORDIDA.* $25

Woods, Stuart. WHITE CARGO. NY: Simon & Schuster, 1988. 1st ed. Fine in dj. *MORDIDA.* $25

Woods, William Crawford. KILLING ZONE. NY: Harpers, (1970). 1st ed. 179pp. NF in sl worn dj. *AKA.* $40

Woodward, Arthur. FEUD ON THE COLORADO. Westernlore, 1955. 1st ed. Signed. Fine in VG+ dj. *FIVE QUAIL.* $45

Woodward, Arthur. THE DENOMINATORS OF THE FUR TRADE. Pasadena: Socio-Technical Pub, 1970. 1st ed. VF in VF dj. *OREGON.* $50

Woodward, Edward. THE HOUSE OF TERROR. NY: Mystery League, 1930. 1st ed. VF; dj w/faint age darkening to spine. *ELSE FINE.* $35

Woodward, Joseph et al. THE MEDICAL AND SURGICAL HISTORY OF THE WAR OF REBELLION, 1861-65. THE THREE SURGICAL VOLUMES. Washington, 1870-83. 1st ed. Vols 1 & 2, 1st ptg. Orig grn cl. Inner hinges cracked as usual in this heavy set. 4" of outer hinge of one vol cracked, o/w VG to Fine. *FYE.* $1,500

Woodward, Joseph et al. THE MEDICAL AND SURGICAL HISTORY OF THE WAR OF THE REBELLION. (1861-65). (6 vols). Washington: GPO, 1875-1888. 1st and only eds, mixed issues. Cvrs rubbed, somewhat stained; some wear to cl at joints. Occasional dampstaining & minor flaws, else VG. *BLUE MOUNTAIN.* $1250

Woodward, Joseph et al. THE MEDICAL AND SURGICAL HISTORY OF THE WAR OF REBELLION, 1861-65. 6 vols. Washington, 1870-88. 1st ed. Some vols are the second issue. Orig grn cloth. VG. *FYE.* $2500

Woodward, R. Pitcher. ON A DONKEY'S HURRICANE DECK. NY: Blanchard, 1902. 1st ed. Signed. VG. *AARD.* $85

Woodward, Samuel et al. REPORTS AND OTHER DOCUMENTS RELATING TO THE STATE LUNATIC HOSPITAL AT WORCESTER, MASS. Boston, 1837. 1st ed. Cloth backed boards, 200pp. Ex-lib. No marks on title page, outer hinges cracked w/tears on backstrip. Contents Fine. Rare. *FYE.* $350

Woodworth, Jim. THE KODIAK BEAR—ALASKAN ADVENTURE. Harrisburg, PA: The Stackpole Company, 1958. 1st ed. Fine in VG+ dj. *GREAT EPIC.* $95

Woodworth, John et al. CHOLERA EPIDEMIC OF 1873 IN THE UNITED STATES. Washington, 1875. 1st ed. 1025pp. Front hinge cracked. *FYE.* $125

Wooley, Mary and John. SOUTH SEA LETTERS. Chicago: New Voice Press, (1906). 236pp. Cl and boards, a little soiled. Unopened. *SCHOYER'S.* $30

Woolf, Cecil and John Bagguley (eds). AUTHORS TAKE SIDES ON VIETNAM. London: Peter Owen, (c 1967). Price clipped, white dj sl soiled, o/w Fine. *HELLER.* $100

Woolf, Douglas. SIGNS OF A MIGRANT WORRIER. Eugene: Coyote's Journal, 1965. 1st ed. Wraps, Fine but for rust seepage from staples onto front wrap near spine. *BEASLEY.* $25

Woolf, Douglas. YA! AND JOHN-JUAN. NY: H&R, (1971). 1st ed. Inscribed. Fine in NF dj. *LOPEZ.* $45

Woolf, Douglas. YA! AND JOHN-JUAN. NY: Harper, 1971. 1st ed. Inscribed. Fine in Fine dj. *BEASLEY.* $25

Woolf, Leonard. DOWNHILL ALL THE WAY. London: Hogarth Press, 1967. 1st ed. Blue cl, corners bumped. VG in rubbed dj. *SCHOYER'S.* $25

Woolf, Virginia. A HAUNTED HOUSE AND OTHER SHORT STORIES. NY: Harcourt, (1944). 1st Amer ed. Fine in dj w/sl chipped corners and spine extrems. *CAPTAIN'S BOOKSHELF*. $50

Woolf, Virginia. A WRITER'S DIARY. Ed by Leonard Woolf. NY, 1954. 1st ed. Lower edges little rubbed. Dj spine sl sunned, chip; price clipped. *POLYANTHOS*. $65

Woolf, Virginia. A WRITER'S DIARY. NY, 1954. 1st ed. Leonard Woolf (ed). Lower edges little rubbed. Fine in dj (spine very sl sunned, top spine sl chipped). *POLYANTHOS*. $100

Woolf, Virginia. BEAU BRUMMEL. NY: Rimmington & Hooper, 1930. Ltd ed of 550, of which 500 were for sale. A folio, quarter-bound in red cloth and paper over boards, with paper label in cover. Copy Number 1 of the ed. Extraordinary, immaculate copy, nearly perfect: spine minutely faded, o/w bk and slipcase are As New—fresh, unrubbed, unfaded, in fldg chemise and cl slipcase, w/leather spine label. Beautiful copy, signed. *LOPEZ*. $3500

Woolf, Virginia. BETWEEN THE ACTS. NY, 1941. 1st ed. Extrems sl rubbed. Fine in dj, spine little sunned, extrems sl rubbed, price clipped. *POLYANTHOS*. $100

Woolf, Virginia. FLUSH. NY: HB, 1933. 1st US ed. Spine lettering a trifle rubbed, fore-edge has small damp stain. NF. *ARCHER*. $30

Woolf, Virginia. FLUSH. London: Hogarth Press, 1933. 1st ed, lg-paper ed. Vanessa Bell (illus). Usual lt foxing to edges of pgs & dj, o/w Fine in dj sl torn at base of spine. *JAFFE*. $175

Woolf, Virginia. FLUSH: A BIOGRAPHY. London: Hogarth Press, 1933. Ordinary ed. Grn cl, photo frontis, 2 illus. Errata slip. VG. *SCHOYER'S*. $30

Woolf, Virginia. MONDAY OR TUESDAY. NY, 1921. 1st ed. Ex-trems, little chipped; uncut, NF. *POLYANTHOS*. $95

Woolf, Virginia. ON BEING ILL. (London): Ptd and pub by Leonard & Virginia Woolf at The Hogarth Press, 1930. 1st ed. #243 of 250 signed. Orig 1/4 vellum, grn linen. NF, unopened, in VG dj. *CHAPEL HILL*. $2,000

Woolf, Virginia. ORLANDO. NY: Crosby Gaige, 1928. 1st ed. #457 of 861 signed. Orig black cl, teg. Top of spine chipped, 1/2" tear top rear gutter, else VG. *CHAPEL HILL*. $650

Woolf, Virginia. ORLANDO. NY: Crosby Gaige, 1928. 1st ed. One of 861, signed. Black cl, teg. VG to Fine. *SECOND LIFE*. $850

Woolf, Virginia. ORLANDO. NY: Crosby Gaige, 1928. NF. 1st ed. #388 of 861 signed. *CHAPEL HILL*. $750

Woolf, Virginia. ORLANDO: A BIOGRAPHY. NY: Crosby Gaige, 1928. One of 861 signed. Top corners and head of spine bumped, else NF. *CAPTAIN'S BOOKSHELF*. $475

Woolf, Virginia. REVIEWING. London: Hogarth Press, 1939. Light staining on rear w/some fading there, o/w VG w/ephemeral sheet laid in listing other titles in the "Hogarth Sixpenny Pamphlets" series. *LOPEZ*. $45

Woolf, Virginia. THE CAPTAIN'S DEATH BED AND OTHER ES-SAYS. London: Hogarth Press, 1950. 1st ed. Dj a bit soiled, o/w Fine. *JAFFE*. $125

Woolf, Virginia. THE CAPTAIN'S DEATH BED AND OTHER ES-SAYS. London: Hogarth, 1950. 1st ed. VG in sl spine-darkened dj. *LOPEZ*. $65

Woolf, Virginia. THE MOMENT AND OTHER ESSAYS. NY, 1948. 1st ed. Extremities minimally rubbed. Fine in dj (very sl sunned, few tiny edge nicks). *POLYANTHOS*. $75

Woolf, Virginia. THE MOMENT AND OTHER ESSAYS. NY: Har-court, Brace, (1948). Top edge dusty, else Fine in faded pink dj (shows minimal wear). 1st Amer ed. One of 3500. *CHAPEL HILL*. $75

Woolf, Virginia. THE SECOND COMMON READER. NY: Har-court, (1932). 1st Amer ed. Advance rev copy with publisher's slip tagged to front dj flap. Head of spine chipped, dj defective. Withal Fine. *MUELLER*. $50

Woolf, Virginia. THE VOYAGE OUT. NY: George Doran, (1920). 1st US ed, 1st bk. Sl soiled. Good, tight. *SECOND LIFE*. $250

Woolf, Virginia. THE VOYAGE OUT. NY: Harcourt, (1926). 1st Harcourt ed. Just About Fine (large owner sig) in lightly edgeworn dw. Uncommon. *CAPTAIN'S BOOKSHELF*. $225

Woolf, Virginia. THE WAVES. London: Hogarth Press, 1931. 1st ed. One of 7113 ptd. Base of spine faded, o/w VG in dj (darkened, lt wear head of spine, piece at base of spine detached but present). *JAFFE*. $225

Woolf, Virginia. THE YEARS. NY: Harcourt Brace, (1937). 1st US ed. Blue cl, little worn, soiled, else VG, tight. *SECOND LIFE*. $45

Woolf, Virginia. THREE GUINEAS. London: The Hogarth Press, 1938. 1st ed, 1st binding. Lemon yellow cl, dec dj (some tape repairs and minor chipping). VG in Good dj. *JUVELIS*. $150

Woolf, Virginia. THREE GUINEAS. NY: Harcourt, (1938). 1st Amer. ed. Advance rev copy with publisher's rubber stamp on ffep. Head of spine damaged, dj defective. Withal Fine. *MUELLER*. $50

Woolf, Virginia. THREE GUINEAS. NY: Harcourt, Brace, (1938). 1st Amer. ed. Fine in NF dj, very sl sunned on spine. *LOPEZ*. $125

Woolf, Virginia. TO THE LIGHTHOUSE. NY: Harcourt Brace, (1927). 1st Amer ed. Very sl foxing to pg edges, o/w bright, NF in dj (modestly tanned on spine, o/w crisp and VG). *LOPEZ*. $750

Woolley, C. Leonard. A FORGOTTEN KINGDOM. Baltimore, MD: Penguin, 1953. 1st ed. 24 plts. Dj torn, o/w VG. *WORLDWIDE*. $16

Woolley, C. Leonard. DEAD TOWNS AND LIVING MEN. NY, 1929. Illus. *O'NEILL*. $45

Woolley, C. Leonard. DIGGING UP THE PAST. London: Benn, 1930. 1st ed. 31 plts. VG. *WORLDWIDE*. $16

Woolley, C. Leonard. UR EXCAVATIONS. VOL. V. THE ZIG-GURAT AND ITS SURROUNDINGS. London & Phila, 1939. 1st ed. Sl rubbed, o/w NF ex-lib w/o lib markings on outside. *WORLDWIDE*. $350

Woolman, John. THE JOURNAL OF...Boston: J.R. Osgood, 1871. John G. Whittier (intro). 1st ed thus. Spine faded (light chipping at top, edge wear). Non-authorial presentation. *CONNOLLY & WADE*. $35

Woolner, Amy. THOMAS WOOLNER, R.A.—HIS LIFE IN LET-TERS. NY: Dutton, 1917. 1st US ed. Fine-. *AARD*. $30

Woolrich, Cornell. BLACK ALIBI. NY: Simon & Schuster, 1942. 1st ed. Slight touch of rubbing to gold spine lettering, else Fine in light-ly worn VG dj w/small circular scuff to front panel, small chip, rub-bing to extremities. Scarce. *BETWEEN COVERS*. $350

Woolrich, Cornell. BLACK ALIBI. NY: Simon & Schuster, 1942. 1st ed. VF in dj (light stain rear panel, creasing there, o/w also Fine). *LOPEZ*. $650

Woolrich, Cornell. CHILDREN OF THE RITZ. Sydney: Cornstalk Publishing, 1927. 1st Australian ed. Mildly foxed on eps, pg edges, and one signature is loose. Binding a bit frayed, soiled but still close to VG, lacking dj. *LOPEZ*. $150

Woolrich, Cornell. DEAD MAN BLUES. Phila & NY: J.B. Lippin-cott Co., 1948. 1st ed. Fine in bright, attractive dj. *BERNARD*. $250

Woolrich, Cornell. HOTEL ROOM. NY, 1958. 1st ed. Fine in dj (spine sl sunned). *POLYANTHOS*. $75

Woolrich, Cornell. INTO THE NIGHT. NY: Mysterious Press, 1987. 1st ed. Unfinished unpublished novel by the author completed by Lawrence Block & signed by him. Fine in dj. *SILVER DOOR*. $37.50

Woolrich, Cornell. NIGHTWEBS. NY: Harper & Row, 1971. 1st ed. VF in dj. *MORDIDA*. $75

Woolrich, Cornell. RENDEZVOUS IN BLACK. NY: Rinehart, 1948. 1st ed. Fine but for light shelf wear, in lightly used dj (tears). *BEASLEY.* $100

Woolrich, Cornell. SAVAGE BRIDE. NY: Fawcett Publications, 1950. 1st ed. Pb orig. Gold Medal no. 136. Fine, unread, in wrappers. *MORDIDA.* $65

Woolrich, Cornell. THE DANCING DETECTIVE. Phila & NY: J.B. Lippincott Co., (1946). 1st ed. NF in bright, attractive dj. *BERNARD.* $250

Woolrich, Cornell. THE DOOM STONE. NY: Avon, 1960. 1st ed. Pb orig. Avon T-408. VF, unread, in wrappers. *MORDIDA.* $85

Woolrich, Cornell. THE TEN FACES OF CORNELL WOOLRICH. NY: Simon and Schuster, 1965. 1st ed. Fine in dj, couple of closed tears. *MORDIDA.* $75

Woolrich, Cornell. THRILLERS 4. London: Zomba Books, 1983. Omnibus ed. Stamp, o/w Fine in dj. *MORDIDA.* $35

Wooster, David. THE GOLD RUSH LETTERS OF DAVID WOOSTER...1850-1855. Mt. Pleasant, MI: Cumming Press, (1972). 1st ed, ltd to 487. VF. *OREGON.* $35

Worcester, A. SMALL HOSPITALS. ESTABLISHMENT AND MAINTENANCE. NY, 1905. 114pp. Scarce. *FYE.* $100

Wordsworth, Christopher. ATHENS AND ATTICA: NOTES OF A TOUR; WITH MAPS & PLANS. London, 1855. 3rd ed, rev. Near-mint. *O'NEILL.* $110

Work, Frederick J. (ed.) FOLK SONGS OF THE AMERICAN NEGRO, NO. 1. Nashville: Work Bros. & Hart, 1907. 1st ed. Wraps. 48pp. VG w/a few corner chips. *BEASLEY.* $100

Work, John. JOURNAL OF...CHIEF TRADER OF THE HUDSON'S BAY CO. DURING HIS EXPEDITION....Cleveland: Clark, 1923. 1st ed. One of 1000 ptd. Orig cl. Howes W675. *GINSBERG.* $175

Workman, Boyle. THE CITY THAT GREW. LA, 1936. Author's autographed ed. 3rd ptg. Spine faded, numbered (no lib markings), o/w VG. *DIAMOND.* $25

Wormington, H.M. PREHISTORIC INDIANS OF THE SOUTHWEST. Denver, 1947. Stiff wraps. Some cover wear, else VG. *FIVE QUAIL.* $10

Worsdworth, William. THE EXCURSION. London: Longman, Hurst, Rees, Orme, and Brown, 1814. Large paper copy. Modest foxing, prev owner's name, date, and bkpl on first blank. Recently rebacked in attractive three-quarter calf, preserving orig marbled paper boards and marbled endpapers. *LOPEZ.* $1,350

Worsley, Frank A. ENDURANCE. AN EPIC OF POLAR ADVENTURE. NY: J. Cape, (1931). 1st Amer ed. Faded spines/boards. VG-. *BLUE DRAGON.* $75

Worsley, Frank A. ENDURANCE. NY: Jonathan Cape, 1931. 1st Amer ed. Spine and boards faded, owner's bkpl. Clean. *PARMER.* $150

Worsley, Frank A. UNDER SAIL IN THE FROZEN NORTH. Phila: David McKay Co, (1927). VG+. *PARMER.* $75

Worsley, Peter. THE TRUMPET SHALL SOUND. London: Mac-Gibbon & Keel, 1957. 1st ed. VG in chipped dj. *ACADEMIC.* $22

Worthen, W.E. (ed.) APPLETONS' CYCLOPAEDIA OF DRAWING...New, enl ed. NY: D. Appleton. 1869. 120 plts (some double-page), 3 color plates, 1 orig mounted photo. 1/2 brn calf over brn cl. *KARMIOLE.* $150

Wortley, Emmeline Stuart. TRAVELS IN THE UNITED STATES, ETC., DURING 1849 AND 1850. NY, 1851. 1st Amer ed. 463pp. Orig cl, lightly chipped at crown of spine. Howes W687. *GINSBERG.* $125

Wortley, Lady Emmeline Stuart. TRAVELS IN THE UNITED STATES...1849 AND 1850. London: Richard Bentley, 1851. 3 vols.

1st ed. Orig emb cl. Hinge w/superficial cracks, few spots on cl. Beautiful, solid. *PIRAGES.* $650

Wouk, Herman. THE CAINE MUTINY. GC: Doubleday, 1951. 1st ed. NF, light edgewear, chip at dj spine head. *ELSE FINE.* $160

Wray, Leonard. THE PRACTICAL SUGAR PLANTER. London: Smith, Elder and Co, 1848. 1st ed. Orig emb cl, w/illus of sugar cane plant at center of each cvr; several pp unopened. 19 plts (2 fldg). Owner inscrip. Thin cracks in hinges (but no hint of looseness), sm spot front cvr, sl wear, fade, but binding very solid. Scattered foxing in text, but generally excellent internally. Quite Good. *PIRAGES.* $500

Wren, Lassiter and Randle McKay. THE SECOND BAFFLE BOOK. Doubleday, Doran, 1929. 1st ed. Cvrs rubbed. VG. *BEBBAH.* $15

Wren, M.K. A MULTITUDE OF SINS. GC: Doubleday Crime Club 1975. 1st ed. Fine in dj. *MORDIDA.* $40

Wren, M.K. CURIOSITY DIDN'T KILL THE CAT. GC: Doubleday Crime Club, 1973. 1st ed. Adv rev copy, slip laid in. Fine in dj. *MORDIDA.* $40

Wren, M.K. NOTHING'S CERTAIN BUT DEATH. GC: Doubleday Crime Club, 1978. 1st ed. Inscribed by Wren and the cat. Fine in dj. *MORDIDA.* $35

Wren, M.K. OH, BURY ME NOT. GC: Doubleday Crime Club, 1976. 1st ed. Fine in price-clipped dj. *MORDIDA.* $35

Wren, M.K. SEASONS OF DEATH. GC: Doubleday Crime Club, 1981. 1st ed. Signed. Emb stamp o/w Fine in dj. *MORDIDA.* $35

Wren, M.K. WAKE UP, DARLIN' COREY. GC: Doubleday Crime Club, 1984. 1st ed. Adv rev copy, slip laid in. Fine in dj. *MORDIDA.* $35

Wren, P.C. ROUGH SHOOTING. London: John Murray, (1938). 1st UK, ed. Spine faded o/w VG in dj sl chipped at spine ends & with abrasions at top edge of front panel, still an attractive dj. *BERNARD.* $50

Wriedt, Dr. Christian. HEREDITY IN LIVE STOCK. London: Macmillan, 1930. 1st ed. Fldg chart. Blue cl, gilt. Fine in VG dj. *CONNOLLY & WADE.* $35

Wright (Mdm. Frances D'Arusmont). VIEWS OF SOCIETY AND MANNERS IN AMERICA...IN A SERIES OF LETTERS...DURING THE YEARS 1818, 1819, AND 1820....London: Longman, et al, 1821. 1st ed. x,523pp. Modern 1/2 calf. Howes C-74. *SECOND LIFE.* $600

Wright, A.A. and A.H. HANDBOOK OF FROGS AND TOADS. Ithaca, 1942. 2nd ed. 88 plts. Dj taped to pastedown, worn. *SUTTON.* $35

Wright, A.H. and A.A. HANDBOOK OF SNAKES OF THE UNITED STATES AND CANADA. NY, 1957. 1st ed. 70 maps (1 fold-out). 2 vols. Lt scuffing. *SUTTON.* $98

Wright, Austin Tappan. ISLANDIA. NY: Rinehart, (1942). 1st ed. Front hinge tender, else Fine in VG, edgeworn price-clipped dw. (Together with) AN INTRODUCTION TO ISLANDIA, a 61pp bklet in lightly rubbed cream boards. *CAPTAIN'S BOOKSHELF.* $200

Wright, Austin Tappan. ISLANDIA. Farrar, 1942. 1st ed. VG in chipped, torn dj. *MADLE.* $95

Wright, Bruce S. BLACK DUCK SPRING. NY: E.P. Dutton & Co, 1966. 1st ed. Fine in VG+ dj. *BACKMAN.* $25

Wright, Bruce S. HIGH TIDE AND AN EAST WIND. Harrisburg: 1954. 1st ed. Fine in Good dj. *ARTIS.* $35

Wright, Charles. BLOODLINES. Middletown: Wesleyan, (1975). 1st ed. Fine in very lightly rubbed dj. Contemp presentation. *CAPTAIN'S BOOKSHELF.* $125

Wright, Charles. CHINA TRACE. Middletown: Wesleyan, (1977). 1st ed. Fine in dw. Review copy, slip laid in. *CAPTAIN'S BOOKSHELF.* $50

Wright, Charles. COLOPHONS. POEMS. Iowa City: Windhover Press, (1977). 1st ed. Ltd to 200 ptd on Barcham Green's Dover paper & signed. Cl-backed dec boards. Fine. *JAFFE*. $100

Wright, Charles. COLOPHONS: POEMS. Iowa City: The Windover Press, (1977). Cl backed boards, paper spine label. One of 200 signed. Fine. *CAPTAIN'S BOOKSHELF*. $75

Wright, Charles. FIVE JOURNALS. NY: Red Ozier Press, 1986. 1st ed, regular issue. One of 75 bound in wrappers & signed by Wright out of a total ed of 100. Orig wraps. VF. *JAFFE*. $175

Wright, Charles. FOUR POEMS OF DEPARTURE. Portland: Trace Editions, 1983. 1st ed. 1/75 signed; this copy being inscribed. Fine in wrappers. *CAPTAIN'S BOOKSHELF*. $75

Wright, Charles. HARD FREIGHT. Middletown: Wesleyan, (1973). 1st ed. Fine in spine-faded dj. Inscribed. Owners sig. *CAPTAIN'S BOOK-SHELF*. $125

Wright, Charles. THE GRAVE OF THE RIGHT HAND. Middletown: Wesleyan, (1970). 1st ed. Fine in dj w/chips. *CAPTAIN'S BOOKSHELF*. $50

Wright, Charles. THE GRAVE OF THE RIGHT HAND. Middletown: Wesleyan, (1970). 1st ed. Fine in price-clipped dj. Signed, dated. *CAPTAIN'S BOOKSHELF*. $75

Wright, Charles. THE GRAVE OF THE RIGHT HAND. Toronto: New Press, (1970). 1st ed. Set of gathered, unbound signatures issued, presumably, for review purposes. *CAPTAIN'S BOOKSHELF*. $100

Wright, Charles. THE JOURNAL OF THE YEAR OF THE OX. Iowa City: Windhover Press, 1988. 1st ed. One of 150 (entire ed) signed. Orig black cl w/ptd label on spine. Fine. *JAFFE*. $125

Wright, Charles. THE OTHER SIDE OF THE RIVER. NY: Random House, (1984). 1st ed. Fine in dj. Contemp presentation inscrip, additional sig. *CAPTAIN'S BOOKSHELF*. $60

Wright, Charles. THE OTHER SIDE OF THE RIVER. NY: Random House, (1984). Uncorrected proof. Fine in wrappers. *CAPTAIN'S BOOKSHELF*. $50

Wright, Charles. THE OTHER SIDE OF THE RIVER. NY: Random House, (1984). Uncorrected proof. Signed. Fine in wraps. *DORN*. $60

Wright, Charles. THE SOUTHERN CROSS. NY: Random House, (1981). 1st Amer ed. Signed. Fine in dj. *DORN*. $35

Wright, Charles. THE SOUTHERN CROSS. NY: Random House, (1981). 1st ed. Fine in dj. Signed. *CAPTAIN'S BOOKSHELF*. $45

Wright, Charles. THE SOUTHERN CROSS. Poems. NY: Random House, (1981). Uncorrected proof. Fine in wrappers. Signed. *CAPTAIN'S BOOKSHELF*. $65

Wright, Charles. ZONE JOURNALS. NY: Farrar Straus & Giroux, (1988). 1st ed. VF in dj. Signed. *CAPTAIN'S BOOKSHELF*. $40

Wright, Charles. ZONE JOURNALS. NY: FS&G, (1988). 1st ed. Fine in dw. Contemp presentation inscrip. *CAPTAIN'S BOOKSHELF*. $40

Wright, Dare. THE DOLL AND THE KITTEN. NY: Doubleday, (1960). 4th ed. Cl, pict boards. VG+. Sm closed tears in dj. *ACADEMIC LIBRARY*. $40

Wright, E. W. (ed). LEWIS & DRYDEN'S MARINE HISTORY OF THE PACIFIC NORTHWEST: AN ILLUSTRATED REVIEW. NY, 1961. Ltd to 750. Orig cl. Howes W693, reprint ed. *GINSBERG*. $175

Wright, E. W. (ed). LEWIS & DRYDEN'S MARINE HISTORY OF THE PACIFIC NORTHWEST: AN ILLUSTRATED REVIEW. Portland, OR: Lewis & Dryden Pub. Co, 1895. 1st ed. (xxiv),494 pp. Frontis. Orig morocco, joints a bit worn, as is usual, but Fine. *LEF-KOWICZ*. $750

Wright, E.W. (ed). LEWIS & DRYDEN'S MARINE HISTORY OF THE PACIFIC NORTHWEST. Portland: The Lewis & Dryden Printing Company, 1895. 1st ed. Full leather, gilt titles and cover

dec; aeg. Marbled eps. xxiii,494pp. Some wear to orig leather at corners, spine expertly rebacked. *PARMER*. $475

Wright, Eddie. THOUGHTS ABOUT THE VIETNAM WAR. NY: Carlton Press, (1986). 1st ed. Fine in Fine dj. *LOPEZ*. $65

Wright, Eric. A BODY SURROUNDED BY WATER. Toronto: Collins Crime Club, 1987. 1st ed. VF in dj. *MORDIDA*. $45

Wright, Eric. SMOKE DETECTOR. Toronto: Collins Crime Club, 1984. 1st ed. Fine in dj. *ELSE FINE*. $30

Wright, Eric. SMOKE DETECTOR. Toronto: Collins Crime Club, 1984. 1st ed. Fine in dj, tiny tear top of spine. *MORDIDA*. $45

Wright, Frances. A FEW DAYS IN ATHENS; BEING THE TRANS-LATION OF A GREEK MANUSCRIPT DISCOVERED IN HERCULANEUM. Boston: J.P. Mendum, 1850. Signature, bkpl. Good. *ARCHAEOLOGIA*. $65

Wright, Frank Lloyd. A TESTAMENT. NY: Horizon Press, (1957). 1st ed. Stained at top w/slight damage to head of spine, in pict dj soiled and chipped w/small pieces torn from tip. Lt foxing, top of hinges starting. Good. *BLUE MOUNTAIN*. $85

Wright, Frank Lloyd. AN AMERICAN ARCHITECTURE. NY, 1955. NF. *POLYANTHOS*. $75

Wright, Frank Lloyd. ARCHITECTURE: MAN IN POSSESSION OF HIS EARTH. GC: Doubleday, 1962. 1st ed. Edgewear o/w Fine in sl edgeworn dj w/short closed tear. *AKA*. $75

Wright, Frank Lloyd. FRANK LLOYD WRIGHT, AN AUTOBIOG-RAPHY. NY: Duell, Sloan & Pearce. (1943). 1st Amer ed of revised autobio. Rust cloth stamped in silver. Dj sl soiled, chipped. *KARMIOLE*. $150

Wright, Frank Lloyd. MAN IN POSSESSION OF HIS EARTH, WITH A BIOGRAPHY BY IOVANNA L. WRIGHT. NY, 1962. NF. *POLYANTHOS*. $45

Wright, Frank Lloyd. THE NATURAL HOUSE. NY: Horizon, 1954. 1st ed. Nick on bottom edge, else NF lacking dj. *CAPTAIN'S BOOK-SHELF*. $150

Wright, G. Frederick. THE ICE AGE IN NORTH AMERICA AND ITS BEARINGS UPON THE ANTIQUITY OF MAN. NY: D. Appleton, 1891. 3rd ed. Fldg maps. Early inscrip. VG. *WEBER*. $100

Wright, Hamilton et al. TO THE MOON. NY: Meredith Press, 1968. 1st ed. VG in dj. *KNOLLWOOD*. $45

Wright, Harold Bell. THE WINNING OF BARBARA WORTH. Chicago, 1911. 1st ed. Red cloth, 511pp. NF. *FIVE QUAIL*. $25

Wright, Harold Bell. THE WINNING OF BARBARA WORTH. Chicago: Book Supply, 1911. 1st ed. VG to Fine in VG to Fine dj. *BOOK MARKET*. $150

Wright, Helen et al (eds). THE LEGACY OF GEORGE ELLERY HALE, EVOLUTION OF ASTRONOMY AND SCIENTIFIC IN-STITUTIONS, IN PICTURES AND DOCUMENTS. Cambridge, MA: Massachusetts Institute of Technology, 1972. VG in dj w/1" tear. *KNOLLWOOD*. $45

Wright, Helen. PALOMAR, THE WORLD'S LARGEST TELE-SCOPE. NY: Macmillan, 1952. 1st prtg. VG in sl chipped dj. *KNOLLWOOD*. $35

Wright, Helen. SWEEPER IN THE SKY, THE LIFE OF MARIA MITCHELL. NY: Macmillan, 1949. 1st prtg. 3 photo plts. Good in chipped dj; owner's name. *KNOLLWOOD*. $45

Wright, Henry H. A HISTORY OF THE SIXTH IOWA IN-FANTRY. Iowa City, 1923. 1st ed. 539pp. Minor shelf wear o/w VG+. *PRATT*. $80

Wright, James. SAINT JUDAS. Middletown: Wesleyan, (1959). 1st ed. NF in dj. Signed. *LOPEZ*. $300

Wright, James. THE GREEN WALL. New Haven: Yale Univ Press, 1957. 1st ed, 1st bk. Owner's sig. Fine in sl used dj w/wear spine head. *CAPTAIN'S BOOKSHELF*. $225

Wright, John C. THE CROOKED TREE; INDIAN LEGENDS OF NORTHERN MICHIGAN. Harbor Springs, MI, (1917). 3rd ed. 30 plts. VG in VG+ dj. *BOHLING*. $37

Wright, Julia. AMONG THE ALASKANS. Phila: Presbyterian Board, (1883). Frontis map. Rubberstamp. 1st ed. *OREGON*. $90

Wright, Kenneth (pseud of Lester Del Rey). THE MYSTERIOUS PLANET. Phila: Winston, 1953. 1st ed. Fine; some spine fade, tear to bright dj. *ELSE FINE*. $50

Wright, L.R. AMONG FRIENDS. GC: Doubleday, 1984. 1st ed. VF in dj. *MORDIDA*. $25

Wright, L.R. SLEEP WHILE I SING. London: Collins, 1987. 1st British ed. Review copy, signed. Pub's slip laid in. Fine in dj. *SILVER DOOR*. $35

Wright, L.R. SLEEP WHILE I SING. NY: Viking, 1986. 1st ed. VF in dj. *MORDIDA*. $30

Wright, L.R. THE SUSPECT. NY: Viking, 1985. 1st ed. VF in dj. *MORDIDA*. $37.50

Wright, Louis B. and Julia H. MacLeaod. THE FIRST AMERICANS IN NORTH AFRICA. Princeton: Princeton Univ Press, 1945. 1st ed. Almost Fine. *AARD*. $25

Wright, Mdm. Frances D'Arusmont. COURSE OF POPULAR LECTURES AS DELIVERED BY FRANCES WRIGHT....NY: Free Enquirer, 1830. 3rd ed. Sl worn linen backed boards w/chipped paper label. *SECOND LIFE*. $325

Wright, Muriel H. GUIDE TO THE INDIAN TRIBES OF OKLAHOMA. Norman: Univ of OK, 1957. No 33 in Civilization of Amer Indians Series. Cloth. NF in Good+ dj. *CONNOLLY & WADE*. $35

Wright, Nathan Jr. READY TO RIOT. NY: HRW, (1968). 1st ed. Fine in Fine dj. *LOPEZ*. $45

Wright, Richard. AMERICAN HUNGER. NY: H&R, (1977). 1st ed. Fine in NF dj. *LOPEZ*. $25

Wright, Richard. BLACK BOY. NY: Harper, (1945). 1st ed. Spine torn, paper soiled, browning w/age. Only Good, in Good dj. *LOPEZ*. $20

Wright, Richard. BLACK BOY. NY: Harper, (1945). 1st ed. Fine in NF dj, tape repaired at top of spine. Photo laid in. *UNGER*. $100

Wright, Richard. EIGHT MEN. Cleveland: World, (1961). 1st ed. NF in VG dj. *LOPEZ*. $65

Wright, Richard. LETTERS TO JOE C. BROWN. Kent: Kent State Univ Libraries, 1968. Ed by Thomas Knipp. Pamphlet. NF in wrappers. *LOPEZ*. $40

Wright, Richard. NATIVE SON. NY & London: Harper & Bros., 1940. 1st ed. in 2nd state (gray) binding. Bkpl o/w Fine in VG+ dj w/chip at top edge of front panel; sl worn spine ends. Attractive. *BERNARD*. $60

Wright, Richard. NATIVE SON. NY, London: Harper & Brothers, 1940. 1st ed. Orig cl. Owner sig. VF in excellent price-clipped dj (spine sl faded, 2 sm water spots, chipping). *PIRAGES*. $125

Wright, Richard. NATIVE SON. NY: Harper & Brothers, 1940. 1st issue, in 1st issue dj. VG. Lt soiling to spine area, in dj (chipped, tanned spine but still Good). *LOPEZ*. $200

Wright, Richard. THE LONG DREAM. NY: Doubleday, 1958. 1st ed. VG. *SMITH*. $80

Wright, Richard. THE OUTSIDER. NY: Harper, 1953. 1st ed. Fine, lt wear to dj spine ends. *ELSE FINE*. $75

Wright, Richard. UNCLE TOM'S CHILDREN. NY: Harper, 1938. 1st ed. Slight stain lower cover; piece missing from ffep (still present). Good in worn dj. *LOPEZ*. $275

Wright, Richardson L. and Bassett Digby. THROUGH SIBERIA. NY: McBride, Nast & Co. 1913. 1st ed. *KARMIOLE*. $30

Wright, Robert M. DODGE CITY THE COWBOY CAPITAL AND THE GREAT SOUTHWEST. (Wichita?), n.d. (ca. 1930). Reprint. Orig grn cl printed in gilt on spine & black on cvr w/Indian & buffalo on cvr in black & red. Very sl spine tip wear. Several small cvr stains, o/w VG+. Howes W706. *DIAMOND*. $75

Wright, Robert M. DODGE CITY THE COWBOY CAPITOL. N.p, n.d., later ed. Dk grn pict cl. Fine. *VARNER*. $100

Wright, S. Fowler. ARRESTING DELIA. NY: Macaulay, 1933. 1st Amer ed. Name, front hinge cracked o/w VG in dj w/chipped spine ends, wear. *MORDIDA*. $20

Wright, S. Fowler. DAWN. NY: Cosmopolitan, 1929. 1st ed. Blindstamped, some spine lean else about VG in dj (chipping, fading, staining). *OTHER WORLDS*. $25

Wright, S. Fowler. THE THRONE OF SATURN. Sauk City: Arkham House, 1949. 1st Amer ed. VG+/NF in Fine dj. *OTHER WORLDS*. $45

Wright, S. Fowler. THE WORLD BELOW. Longmans, 1930. 1st US ed. NF in sl chipped, rubbed dj. *MADLE*. $65

Wright, S. Fowler. VENGEANCE OF GWA. London: Books of To-Day, (1945). 1st thus. (Orig pub as by Anthony Wingrave). Some edge staining else VG+ in worn dj, chipped. *OTHER WORLDS*. $25

Wright, Sean and John Farrell. THE SHERLOCK HOLMES COOKBOOK. NY: Drake, 1976. 1st ed. Fine in dj. *MORDIDA*. $45

Wright, Solomon A. MY RAMBLES AS EAST TEXAS COWBOY, HUNTER, FISHERMAN, TIE CUTTER. Austin, TX: Folklore Society, 1942. 1st ed. Frank Dobie (intro). B.E. Lewis (illus). Fine in Fine dj. *OREGON*. $60

Wright, Solomon A. MY RAMBLES AS EAST TEXAS COWBOY, HUNTER, FISHERMAN, TIE-CUTTER. Austin: Texas Folklore Society, 1942. NF in dj. *LAURIE*. $60

Wright, Thomas. NARRATIVES OF SORCERY AND MAGIC, FROM THE MOST AUTHENTIC SOURCES. NY: Redfield. 1852. 1st ed. 420,(12)pp. Orig blue blind-stamped cloth, gilt; spine faded, spine extrems bit worn, sl foxing. Ffep lacking. *KARMIOLE*. $100

Wright, Thomas. THE LIFE OF SIR RICHARD BURTON. London: (Everett), 1906. 1st ed. 2 vols. 64 plts. Orig red cl (lt wear; ex-lib markings); teg, others untrimmed. *BOOK BLOCK*. $70

Wright, W.J. GREENHOUSES THEIR CONSTRUCTION & EQUIPMENT. NY: Orange Judd, 1946. Dj worn, else VG. *AMERICAN BOTANIST*. $18

Wright, Willard Huntington. THE CREATIVE WILL. London, 1916. (Author later adopted pseud "S.S. Van Dyne" for mystery novels.) NF. *POLYANTHOS*. $30

Wright, Willard Huntington. WHAT NIETZSCHE TAUGHT. NY: Huebsch, 1915. 1st ed. Some minor foxing to eps, but VG+. *LAME DUCK*. $100

Wright, William. THE GRIZZLY BEAR. NY, 1913. VG. *ARTIS*. $40

Wright, William. THE GRIZZLY BEAR. Scribner, 1909. 1st ed. Frontis, 23 plts. Gilt stamped pict cl. Corner wear, marginal dampstaining. G+. *OREGON*. $85

WRITERS TAKE SIDES. NY: League of American Writers, 1938. 1st ed. Wraps. Fine but for light crease on rear wrap. *BEASLEY*. $75

Wroth, Lawrence C. (ed.) A HISTORY OF THE PRINTED BOOK, Being the Third Number of the Dolphin. NY: LEC, 1938. Ed ltd to 1800. *KARMIOLE*. $185

Wulffen, Erich. WOMAN AS A SEXUAL CRIMINAL. NY: Falstaff Press, 1935. Rear cvr sl bumped, o/w VG. *DIAMOND*. $45

Wunderlich, Carl. ON THE TEMPERATURE IN DISEASES: A MANUAL OF MEDICAL THERMOMETRY. London, 1871. 1st Eng trans. 468pp. 40 woodcuts, 7 lithographs. *FYE*. $300

Wurdemann, Audrey. BRIGHT AMBUSH. John Day Co, (1934). 1st ed, 1st bk. VG+ in chipped dj. *AUTHORS OF THE WEST*. $25

Wurtz, A. THE ATOMIC THEORY. London: Kegan, Paul, 1880. 1st Eng ed. 339pp. Fold-out pl. Dec red cvrs. *BOOKCELL.* $40

Wyatt, R.E.S. THE INS AND OUTS OF CRICKET. London: Bell, 1936. 1st ed. VG in Good dj. *OLD LONDON.* $30

Wyatt, Thomas. MEMOIRS OF THE GENERALS, COMMODORES...WHO DISTINGUISHED THEMSELVES IN THE AMERICAN ARMY AND NAVY DURING THE WARS OF THE REVOLUTION AND 1812, AND WHO WERE PRESENTED WITH MEDALS...Phila: Carey, 1848. 315pp. 1st ed. 82 engr. Orig gold dec red cloth w/dec gilt spine. Very Nice. *GINSBERG.* $175

Wyatt, Will. THE SECRET OF THE SIERRA MADRE: THE MAN WHO WAS B. TRAVEN. GC: Doubleday, 1980. 1st ed. Dj. VG. *AKA.* $20

Wycherley, George. BUCCANEERS OF THE PACIFIC. Indianapolis: The Bobbs-Merrill Company, 1928. Front hinge beginning, some foxing. *PARMER.* $65

Wycherley, R. E. STONES OF ATHENS. Princeton, NY: 1978. Dj rubbed. *SCHOYER'S.* $30

Wycherley, R.E. HOW THE GREEKS BUILT CITIES. London: Macmillan, 1979. 2nd ed. 52 figs, 16 plts. Dj. Good. *ARCHAEOLOGIA.* $35

Wyeth, Andrew. ANDREW WYETH. Greenwich: NY Graphic Soc, 1970. 1st ed. Cl. VG in VG dj. *CONNOLLY & WADE.* $35

Wyeth, Andrew. FOUR SEASONS. NY, (1962). Fine. *POLYANTHOS.* $95

Wyeth, George. SURGERY OF NEOPLASTIC DISEASES BY ELECTROTHERMIC METHODS. NY, 1926. 1st ed. 137 illus. *FYE.* $75

Wyeth, John Allan. LIFE OF GENERAL NATHAN BEDFORD FORREST. Harper, 1904 (1899). Cvr sl spotted, tear to bottom spine. Nearly VG. *BOOK BROKER.* $100

Wyeth, John. A TEXT-BOOK ON SURGERY. 1891. 2nd ed. 1/4 leather, 887pp. 772 woodcut illus. VF. *FYE.* $100

Wyeth, John. ESSAYS UPON THE SURGICAL ANATOMY AND HISTORY OF THE COMMON, EXTERNAL AND INTERNAL CAROTID ARTERIES, AND THE SURGICAL ANATOMY AND HISTORY OF THE INNOMINATE AND SUBCLAVIAN ARTERIES. Phila, 1878. 1st ed. Disbound. Woodcut illus. *FYE.* $75

Wykes, A. SNAKE MAN, THE STORY OF C.J.P IONIDES. NY, (1961). Illus. NF in VG+ dj. *MIKESH.* $15

Wylde, A.B. '83 TO '87 IN THE SOUDAN WITH AN ACCOUNT OF SIR WILLIAM HEWETT'S MISSION TO KING JOHN OF ABYSSINIA. London: Remington & Co, 1888. 2nd ed. 2 vols. Brn cl, gilt spine titles. 347pp; 314pp. Fldg map. Shelfwear, soil. Interior VG, unopened. *PARMER.* $150

Wylie, A. SECTARIANISM IS HERESY, IN THREE PARTS, IN WHICH ARE SHEWN ITS NATURE, EVILS, AND REMEDY. Bloomington, IN, 1840. Wraps. Little worn, soiled; foxing. *BOHLING.* $125

Wylie, Elinor. NETS TO CATCH THE WIND. London: Knopf, 1928. 1st UK ed. Very Nice in dj. *SECOND LIFE.* $50

Wylie, Philip. FISH AND TIN FISH. Toronto, NY: Farrar & Rinehart, (1944). 1st ed. VG+ in dj (sl wear). *BERNARD.* $125

Wylie, Philip. GENERATION OF VIPERS. NY; Farrar & Rinehart, (1942). Advance copy. Sl rubbed, but Fine. Ptd wraps. *JAFFE.* $125

Wylie, Philip. THE BIG ONES GET AWAY. NY, Toronto: Farrar & Rinehart, (1940). 1st ed. VG in dj (chipping, few internally mended tears), still attractive. *BERNARD.* $150

Wylie, Philip. THE DISAPPEARANCE. NY, 1951. 1st ed. VG in bit chipped dj. *PETTLER.* $30

Wyllie, John. TUMOURS OF THE CEREBELLUM. London, 1908. 1st ed. Scarce. *FYE.* $125

Wyllys, Rufus Kay. ARIZONA. THE HISTORY OF A FRONTIER STATE. Phoenix: Hobson & Herr, (1950). 1st ed. 8 plts. VF in VG dj. *OREGON.* $55

Wyman, L.E. and E.F. Burnell. FIELD BOOK OF BIRDS OF THE SOUTHWESTERN UNITED STATES. Boston, 1925. 1st ed. Marginal dampstaining. *SUTTON.* $20

Wyman, Morrill. AUTUMNAL CATARRH (HAY FEVER). NY: Hard and Houghton, 1872. 1st ed. 3 colored maps. Gilt beveled red cl cvr, stained, faded. Contents VG. *SMITHFIELD.* $125

Wyman, Walker. NOTHING BUT PRAIRIE & SKY. Norman: Univ of OK, (1954). 1st ed. Double pp map. Fine in Fine dj. *OREGON.* $35

Wymper, Charles. EGYPTIAN BIRDS. A&C Black, 1909. 1st ed. 20s Series. VG-NF. *OLD LONDON.* $200

Wyndham, Francis. THE OTHER GARDEN. Mt. Kisco, NY: Moyar Bell, 1988. Uncorrected proof of Amer ed. Fine in pink wraps w/dj wrapped around. *STAHR.* $25

Wyndham, Horace. FAMOUS TRIALS RE-TOLD. London: Hutchinson, n.d. 1st ed. VG+. *ARCHER.* $15

Wyndham, John. THE MIDWICH CUCKOOS. Ballantine, 1957. 1st ed. Near VG in frayed dj. *MADLE.* $50

Wyndham, John. THE MIDWICH CUCKOOS. NY: Ballantine, 1957. 1st ed. Name on fep, else VF in dj. *ELSE FINE.* $125

Wyndham, Richard. THE GENTLE SAVAGE. NY: Morrow, 1936. 1st ed. Color frontis. Sl rubbed, spine faded, o/w VG. *WORLDWIDE.* $35

Wynmalen, Henry. EQUITATION. London: Country Life, 1938. 1st ed. VG in Fair dj. *OCTOBER FARM.* $25

Wynn, Marcia Rittenhouse. DESERT BONANZA: STORY OF EARLY RANDSBURG MOHAVE DESERT MINING CAMP. Culver City: M.W. Samelson, 1949. 1st ed. Signed. Brown cl. Fine. Scarce. *CONNOLLY & WADE.* $75

Wynne, James. REPORT ON THE VITAL STATISTICS OF THE UNITED STATES, MADE TO THE MUTUAL LIFE INSURANCE COMPANY OF NEW YORK. NY, 1857. 1st ed. 1/2 lea, 218pp. Backstrip missing, front board detached, lib bkpl. Contents Fine. *FYE.* $75

Wynne, John J. THE JESUIT MARTYRS OF NORTH AMERICA. NY: Universal Knowledge Foundation, (1925). Lib stamp. VG. *NUTMEG.* $20

Wynter, H. and A. Turner. SCIENTIFIC INSTRUMENTS. Scribner's, 1975. Near New w/dj. *BOOKCELL.* $185

WYOMING, A GUIDE TO ITS HISTORY, HIGHWAYS, & PEOPLE. NY: Oxford, (1946). 2nd ptg. American Guide Series. Large fldg map in rear pocket. VG in Good+ dj. *OREGON.* $40

Wythes, Joseph H. THE MICROSCOPIST. Phila: Lindsay and Blakiston, 1853. 2nd ed. Good; scattered spotting. *KNOLLWOOD.* $75

X

X MARKS THE SPOT. CHICAGO GANG WARS IN PICTURES. n.p., 1930. Wraps, 8 1/2" x 11", 64pp. Good to VG. *BEASLEY.* $100

Xantus, John. LETTERS FROM NORTH AMERICA. Detroit: Wayne State Univ, 1975. 1st ed thus. Theodore and Helen B. Schoenman (trans, ed). VF in Fine dj. *CONNOLLY & WADE.* $37.50

Xantus, John. THE FORT TEJON LETTERS. 1857-1859. Tucson: Univ of AZ Press, 1986. New in dj. *PARMER.* $27

Xantus, John. TRAVELS IN SOUTHERN CALIFORNIA. Detroit: Wayne State Univ, 1976. 1st ed thus. Theodore and Helen B. Shoenman (trans, ed). Fine in Fine dj. CONNOLLY & WADE. $35

Xenophon. THE ANABASIS. Athens: LEC, 1969. 1/1500. Trans by Henry C. Dakyns. Illus, signed by A. Tassos. Fine in slipcase. CAPTAIN'S BOOKSHELF. $100

Xongo-Tee-Foh-Tchi (pseud). NAPOLEON IN THE OTHER WORLD. London: H. Colburn, 1827. 1st ed. 8vo, ix,406pp, frontis. Contemp boards stained & sl worn. Rebacked w/new cl & spine label. Inner margin of one page reinforced, else VG. DIAMOND. $75

Y

Yadin, Yigael. HAZOR. THE REDISCOVERY OF A GREAT CITADEL OF THE BIBLE. NY: Random House, 1975. 1st US ed. NF. WORLDWIDE. $25

Yaggy, L.W. and T.L. Haines. MUSEUM OF ANTIQUITY. SF: Law, King, & Law, 1884. 7 plts. Good+. OREGON. $35

Yarbro, Chelsea Quinn. THE PALACE. NY: St. Martin's, (1978). 1st ed. Fine in dj, short closed tears. OTHER WORLDS. $40

Yashima, Mitsu and Taro. PLENTY TO WATCH. Viking, 1954. Illus by Taro Yashima, who has inscribed this copy and painted full-page illus of bird & eggs in nest. Marked also w/his chop. VG+ in VG w/chips, light soil. BEBBAH. $32

Yashima, Taro. BLUE UMBRELLA. NY: Viking, 1958. 1st ed. Inscribed in both English and Japanese w/orig drwg. VG. SMITH. $100

Yates, Elizabeth. HOWARD THURMAN. PORTRAIT OF A PRACTICAL DREAMER. NY: John Day, 1964. 1st ed. Fine but for owner's name, trace of wear at spine ends, in VG dj. BEASLEY. $40

Yates, Raymond F. THE BOYS' BOOK OF ROCKETS. NY: Harper & Brothers, n/d (1947). Ex-lib (#, bkpl, stamps), worn, fraying. Internally clean. KNOLLWOOD. $24

Yavis, Constantine G. GREEK ALTARS: ORIGINS AND TYPOLOGY, INCLUDING THE MINOAN-MYCENAEAN OFFERTORY APPARATUS. Saint Louis: Saint Louis Univ Press, 1949. 93 figs. Wraps. Signature at title page. Good. ARCHAEOLOGIA. $85

Yazzie, Ethelou (ed). NAVAJO HISTORY. Many Farms: Navajo Community College Press, 1971. Vol 1 in a projected series. Fine in NF dj. LOPEZ. $50

Ybarra, T.R. YOUNG MAN OF CARACAS. Ives Washburn: NY, 1941. 1st ed. Frontis, 7 photo plts. Dj chipped on edges, else VG. Blue cl. VG. CONNOLLY & WADE. $30

YEARBOOK OF THE U.S. DEPARTMENT OF AGRICULTURE, 1910. Washington, 1911. 49 plts (8 colored). Cl, lt wear. SUTTON. $35

Yeats, Jack Butler. THE SCOURGE OF THE GULPH. London: Elkin Mathews, (1901). 1st ed, trade issue. Blue ptd wrappers illus by Yeats and colored by hand. NF. JUVELIS. $75

Yeats, William Butler. A VISION. London, 1926. Privately printed for subscribers only. Ltd ed, 198/600 signed. Uncut, partly unopened. Vellum spine little sunned, sides spine tiny fox points, 2 top corners sl creased, sl edge soiled. Fine in dj (spine sunned, little soiled, tiny nick). POLYANTHOS. $500

Yeats, William Butler. AUTOBIOGRAPHIES: REVERIES OVER CHILDHOOD AND YOUTH, AND THE TREMBLING OF THE VEIL. NY: Macmillan, 1927. 1/250 numbered, signed. Offsetting on ffeps; previous owner's pencil name, o/w NF. LOPEZ. $425

Yeats, William Butler. DEIRDRE. London: Bulklen; Dublin: Maunsel, 1907. 1st ed. Cl backed boards. Very Nice, tight. SECOND LIFE. $95

Yeats, William Butler. DRAMATIS PERSONAE. Dublin, Ireland: The Cuala Press, 1935. Title pg vignette. Tan cl backed ptd blue paper covered boards, bumped. Ptd paper label on spine. Fep creased. Bkpl of Marion Weeks, signed by her. One of ltd ed of 400. Fine, unopened. BLUE MOUNTAIN. $250

Yeats, William Butler. FOUR PLAYS FOR DANCERS. NY: Macmillan, 1921. 1st Amer ed. Edmund Dulac (illus). Orig cl-backed illus grey boards, paper spine label. VG in dj, some wear top edge. CHAPEL HILL. $195

Yeats, William Butler. LATER POEMS. London: Macmillan, 1922. 1st ed. One of 1500 ptd. Blind-stamped grn cl, plain brn ptd dj. Front inner hinge strained, owner sig, o/w VG in scarce dj, chipped at extrems. JAFFE. $375

Yeats, William Butler. NEW POEMS. Dublin: The Cuala Press, 1938. 1st ed. Ltd ed, 450. Fine in glassine dj. POLYANTHOS. $225

Yeats, William Butler. REVERIES OVER CHILDHOOD AND YOUTH. NY, 1916. 1st ed. Spine little sunned, scattered light foxing some pages. Fine in VG box. POLYANTHOS. $100

Yeats, William Butler. STORIES OF MICHAEL ROBARTES AND HIS FRIENDS; AN EXTRACT FROM A RECORD MADE BY HIS PUPILS: AND A PLAY IN PROSE. Dublin, Ireland: The Cuala Press, 1931. Tan cl backed ptd blue paper covered boards, bumped. Ptd paper label on spine. Title vignette, 2plts. Bkpl removed from front pastedown. One of ltd ed of 450. Fine, unopened. BLUE MOUNTAIN. $275

Yeats, William Butler. THE GREEN HELMET AND OTHER POEMS. NY: Macmillan, 1912. 1st Amer ed. Dec boards. Fine. JAFFE. $150

Yeats, William Butler. THE TOWER. London: Macmillan and Co, Ltd, 1928. 1st ed. Fine in grn gilt stamped cl. Grn dj repeating Moore's cover design. JUVELIS. $300

Yeats, William Butler. THE WINDING STAIR AND OTHER POEMS. London: Macmillan, 1933. 1st ed. Pict cl. Fine in dj sl chipped at head of spine. JAFFE. $275

Yeats, William Butler. THE WINDING STAIR AND OTHER POEMS. London: Macmillan and Co, Ltd, 1933. 1st ed. Fine in grn gilt stamped cl and dj repeating Sturge Moore design. JUVELIS. $350

Yeats, William Butler. THE WINDING STAIR. NY: The Fountain Press, 1929. Ltd ed, 323/600 (of 642) signed. Printed by W.E. Rudge. Uncut. Fine. POLYANTHOS. $300

Yee, Chiang (I. Chiang.) THE SILENT TRAVELLER. A CHINESE ARTIST IN LAKELAND. NY: Charles Scribner's Sons. (1938). 1st Amer ed. Dj chipped. 1st bk of "The Silent Traveller" series. KARMIOLE. $35

Yee, Chiang. THE SILENT TRAVELLER IN SAN FRANCISCO. NY: Norton, 1964. 1st ed. NF in same dj. CONNOLLY & WADE. $25

Yeo, Eileen and E.P. Thompson. THE UNKNOWN MAYHEW. NY: Pantheon, 1971. Stated 1st US ed. Dj. VG. AKA. $20

Yeoman, R.S. A GUIDE BOOK OF UNITED STATES COINS. CATALOG AND PRICE LIST—1616 TO DATE. Racine, WI: Whitman Pub Co. 1946. 254,(2)pp. Index. Red cl, gilt. The rare first year of pub of the Bible for American coins. KARMIOLE. $200

Yeomans, P.A. WATER FOR EVERY FARM. Sydney: Murray, 1968. Dj w/light wear; contents VG. AMERICAN BOTANIST. $28

Yerby, Frank. A WOMAN CALLED FANCY. NY: Dial, 1951. 1st ed. Fine; lt wear dj extrems. ELSE FINE. $35

Yerby, Frank. AN ODOR OF SANCTITY. NY: Dial, (1965). 1st ed. Fine in VG, sl soiled, predominately white dj. LOPEZ. $40

Yerby, Frank. JUDAS, MY BROTHER. NY: Dial, (1968). 1st ed. Fine in NF dj. LOPEZ. $30

Yerby, Frank. PRIDE'S CASTLE. NY: Dial, (1949). 1st ed. Fine in NF dj, spine ends nicked. UNGER. $65

Yerby, Frank. THE DEVIL'S LAUGHTER. NY: Dial, 1953. 1st ed. Fine; minor wear to dj corners. *ELSE FINE.* $35

Yerby, Frank. THE DEVIL'S LAUGHTER. NY: Dial, 1953. 1st ed. Fine in dj. *LOPEZ.* $65

Yerby, Frank. THE OLD GODS LAUGH. NY: Dial, 1964. 1st ed. Fine in NF dj. *LOPEZ.* $45

Yerby, Frank. THE SARACEN BLADE. NY: Dial, 1952. 1st ed. Owner name, o/w VG in dj. *LOPEZ.* $45

Yerby, Frank. THE TREASURE OF PLEASANT VALLEY. NY: Dial, (1955). 1st ed. Fine in NF edge-nicked dj. *UNGER.* $65

Yerby, Frank. THE TREASURE OF PLEASANT VALLEY: A NOVEL ABOUT THE GOLD RUSH. NY: Dial, 1955. 1st ed. Name, else Fine in VG+ dj w/slight wear at extremities. *BETWEEN COVERS.* $65

Yerkes, Robert. PSYCHOLOGICAL EXAMINING IN THE UNITED STATES ARMY. Washington, 1921. 1st ed. 890pp. Ex-lib. *FYE.* $125

Yeutter, Frank. JIM KONSTANTY. Barnes, 1951. 1st ed. Good+ in VG dj. 1st ed. *PLAPINGER.* $27.50

Yevtushenko, Yevgeny. ALMOST AT THE END. NY: Holt, 1987. 1st ed. Rmdr mark top edge, else Fine in price clipped dj. Signed. *LAME DUCK.* $45

Yevtushenko, Yevgeny. BRATSK STATION. NY: Praeger, 1966. 1st US ed. NF in price clipped dj. *LAME DUCK.* $35

Yevtushenko, Yevgeny. SELECTED POEMS. NY: Dutton, 1962. Trans w/intro by Robin Milner-Gulland and Peter Levi, S.J. 1st Amer ed. Fine in sl rubbed dj. Richard Eberhart's owner sig. *CAPTAIN'S BOOKSHELF.* $60

Yoakum, H. HISTORY OF TEXAS FROM ITS FIRST SETTLE-MENT IN 1685...TO THE UNITED STATES IN 1846. NY: Redfield, 1856. 2 vols: 482,(2); 576pp. 3 maps, 2 fldg, 1 in facsimile, fldg facsimile, 4 plts. Orig cl, nice set. Most copies of 1855 orig ed were destroyed by fire soon after pub. Howes Y10. *GINSBERG.* $500

Yolen, Jane. THE GIRL WHO CRIED FLOWERS. David Palladini, illus. NY: Crowell, (1974). 1st ed. Fine in price-clipped dj showing very light wear, short tear. *CAPTAIN'S BOOKSHELF.* $40

Yonge, James. THE JOURNAL OF JAMES YONGE (1647-1721) PLYMOUTH SURGEON. London: Longmans, Green and Co., Ltd., 1963. VG in worn dj. *PARMER.* $45

Yorinks, Arthur. HEY, AL. Richard Egielski (illus). NY: FS&G, (1986). 1st ed. Signed by artist, author. Fine in Fine dj. *ACADEMIC LIBRARY.* $40

Yorinks, Arthur. IT HAPPENED IN PINSK. Richard Egielski (illus). NY: FS&G, (1983). 1st ed. Signed by author, illus. Fine in Fine dj. *ACADEMIC LIBRARY.* $35

Yost, Karl and F.G. Renner. A BIBLIOGRAPHY OF THE PUB-LISHED WORKS OF CHARLES M. RUSSELL. Univ of NE, 1971. 1st ed. Fine in VG dj. *VARNER.* $65

Yost, Karl and F.G. Renner. A BIBLIOGRAPHY OF THE PUB-LISHED WORKS OF CHARLES M. RUSSELL. Univ of NE Press, (1971). 1st ed. 42 plates (18 color). New in dj. *AUTHORS OF THE WEST.* $75

Yost, Karl. CHARLES M. RUSSELL, THE COWBOY ARTIST. Trail's End, Pasadena, CA (1948), 1st ed. Ltd to 500. *HEINOLDT.* $95

Yost, N.S. BOSS COWMAN....ED LEMMON 1857-1946. Univ of NE, 1969. 1st ed. Fine in Fine dj. *VARNER.* $35

Yost, N.S. MEDICINE LODGE. THE STORY OF A KANSAS FRONTIER TOWN. Chicago: Sage Swallow, (1970). 1st ed. Double pp map. VF in Fine dj. *OREGON.* $17.50

Yost, N.S. THE CALL OF THE RANGE. Sage, 1966. 1st ed. Fine in VG dj. *VARNER.* $50

Youatt, William. SHEEP: THEIR BREEDS, MANAGEMENT, AND DISEASES. NY: Moore, (1848). 1st ed? 159pp. Pub's cl, water stained. *SECOND LIFE.* $75

Youatt, William. THE HORSE. (London: Charles Knight, 1847). viii, 581pp. A New Edition. Contemp smooth half calf, textured cl sides, raised bands, dec spine, morocco label. Armorial bkpl. End papers rather foxed, first few and last few leaves sl affected, o/w clean and unworn. *PIRAGES.* $165

Young, Andrew McLaren et al. THE PAINTINGS OF JAMES MCNEILL WHISTLER. Text. (Plates). New Haven: Pub for The Paul Mellon Centre for Studies in British Art by Yale Univ Press. 1980. 1st ed. 2 vols. Djs. Fine. *KARMIOLE.* $150

Young, Art. ART YOUNG, HIS LIFE AND TIMES. NY: Sheridan House, 1939. 1st ed. Very close to Fine in lightly used dj. *BEASLEY.* $45

Young, Art. ON MY WAY. NY: Horace Liveright, (1928). 303pp. Cover lightly sprung. #160/1000 for friends of author & publisher. No copies of this ed were for sale. *AKA.* $75

Young, Arthur. TRAVELS IN FRANCE DURING THE YEARS 1787, 1788, 1789. Intro by M. Betham Edwards. London: George Bell, 1890. 3rd ed. 12mo, liii,366pp,24pp ads, frontis. Dec blind stamped cl. Minor shelf wear, o/w VG. *DIAMOND.* $25

Young Bear, Ray. WINTER OF THE SALAMANDER. SF: H&R, (1980). 1st ed. Fine in NF dj. *LOPEZ.* $65

Young, Charles A. THE SUN. London: Kegan, Paul, Trench & Co, 1883 (1881), 2nd ed. Good in worn red cl; corners bumped, worn to boards, top, bottom spine fraying, nick. *KNOLLWOOD.* $30

Young, Collier (pseud of Robert Bloch). THE TODD DOSSIER. Delacorte, 1969, 1st ed. Ex-lib but Fine in VF dj. *MADLE.* $75

Young, Edward. NIGHT THOUGHTS...WITH THE LIFE OF THE AUTHOR, AND NOTES CRITICAL AND EXPLANATORY. London: by C. Whittingham for T. Heptinstall, 1798. 364pp (incl index). Engraved frontis portrait, pict title, engraved plts. Contemp calf awkwardly rebacked, red leather label on spine. Scattered foxing, else Good. *WREDEN.* $95

Young, Egerton Ryerson. BY CANOE AND DOG-TRAIN AMONG THE CREE & SALTEAUX INDIANS. London: Charles H. Kelly, 1895. 19th thousand. Bkpl. VG. *DIAMOND.* $35

Young, Egerton Ryerson. BY CANOE AND DOG-TRAIN AMONG THE CREE AND SALTEAUX INDIANS. NY: Hunt & Eaton, 1891. Mark Guy Pearse (intro). 1st ed. Bound in buckram. Cover wear, but still clean, tight. *LAURIE.* $75

Young, Egerton Ryerson. STORIES FROM INDIAN WIGWAMS AND NORTHERN CAMPFIRES. NY: Hunt & Eaton. 1893. 1st ed. 294pp. *KARMIOLE.* $50

Young, Filson. CHRISTOPHER COLUMBUS, AND THE NEW-WORLD OF HIS DISCOVERY. Phila: Lippincott, 1906. 2 vols. 4 fldg maps. 11 plts. Cl bit soiled. *KARMIOLE.* $60

Young, Ford E., Jr. THE THIRD DAY AT GETTYSBURG. Bethesda, (1981). 1st ed. Dj. VG+. *PRATT.* $27.50

Young, Ford E., Jr. THE THIRD DAY AT GETTYSBURG. Bethesda, MD, (1981). 1st ed. Fine in NF dj. *McGOWAN.* $35

Young, Georgie. A MAGDALEN'S LIFE. N,p, n.d. (Grand Rapids, MI, 1889?). Grn cl stamped in gilt and blind, rubbed on corners. VG. *SCHOYER'S.* $75

Young, Gordon. DAYS OF '49. NY: Doran, (1925). Grn stamped cl. Inscribed. *DAWSON'S.* $35

Young, Hugh Hampton. GENITAL ABNORMALITIES, HER-MAPHRODITISM & RELATED ADRENAL DISEASES. 379 plts. Baltimore: The Williams & Wilkins Co. 1937. 1st ed. Blue cl, gilt spine. Dj. Fine. *KARMIOLE.* $125

Young, James C. MARSE ROBERTS, KNIGHT OF THE CONFEDERACY. NY, (1929). 2nd ptg. 362pp. VG. *PRATT.* $35

Young, John D. JOHN D. YOUNG AND THE COLORADO GOLD RUSH. Ed by Dwight Smith. Chicago: Lakeside Classic, 1969. As opposed to the usual Lakeside reprint, this account by Young is here published for the first time. 1st ed. VF. *OREGON.* $40

Young, John D. JOHN D. YOUNG AND THE COLORADO GOLD RUSH. Chicago, 1969. Ed by Dwight L. Smith. 1st ed. Lakeside Classic #67. Fine. *PRATT.* $37.50

Young, John P. JOURNALISM IN CALIFORNIA: PACIFIC COAST AND EXPOSITION BIOGRAPHIES. SF: Chronicle, (1915). 1st ed. Marbled e.p. Frontis, 51 plts. Grey cl, gilt. Fine. *CONNOLLY & WADE.* $75

Young, John Richard. SCHOOLING FOR YOUNG RIDERS. Norman: Univ of OK Press, 1970. 1st ed. VG in Good+ dj. *OCTOBER FARM.* $25

Young, O.E., Jr. THE MINING MEN. Kansas City, MO, 1974. 1st ed. Fine in Fine dj. *VARNER.* $30

Young, Otis E. THE FIRST MILITARY ESCORT ON THE SANTA FE TRAIL 1829: FROM THE JOURNAL REPORTS OF MAJOR BENNETT RILEY AND LIEUTENANT PHILIP ST. GEORGE COOKE. Glendale: Arthur H. Clark, 1952. 1st ed. VG. *LAURIE.* $100

Young, Paul. IMAGES. LA: Nash, 1969. 1st ed, 1st bk. VG. *SMITH.* $20

Young, Philip. HISTORY OF MEXICO...1520, TO THE PRESENT TIME, 1847; INCLUDING...THE WAR WITH THE UNITED STATES....Cincinnati: James, 1847. 1st ed. 564pp. 9 maps, plans, 2 fldg. Contemp half morocco. *GINSBERG.* $450

Young, S. Hall. ALASKA DAYS WITH JOHN MUIR. NY: Fleming H. Revell, (1915). 226pp. Map, 12 illus. Dec blue cl. VG-. *BLUE DRAGON.* $50

Young, S.P. and E.A. Goldman. THE PUMA. Washington, DC: Amer Wildlife Inst, 1946. 1st ed. VG+. *MIKESH.* $45

Young, S.P. and H.H.T. Jackson. THE CLEVER COYOTE. Washington DC: W.L. Mgt. Institute, 1951. 1st ed. NF. *MIKESH.* $45

Young, S.P. THE BOBCAT IN NORTH AMERICA, ETC. Washington DC: Amer. W.L. Institute, 1958. 1st ed. Wm. G. Sheldon's copy. NF. *MIKESH.* $30

Young, S.P. THE LAST OF THE LONERS, A NARRATIVE OF NORTH AMERICAN WOLVES IN LEGEND & HISTORY. London, etc., 1970. 1st ed. Fine in Fine dj. *MIKESH.* $35

Young, Scott. MURDER IN A COLD CLIMATE. NY: Viking, (1989). 1st US ed. VF in VF dj. *UNGER.* $30

Young, S.P. and E.A. Goldman. THE PUMA. Washington, DC: Amer Wildlife Inst, 1946. 1st ed. *ARTIS.* $30

Young, Stark. FELICIANA. NY: Scribner's, 1935. 1st ed. Owner name, address, brief note, review tipped in at rear, else Fine in dj. *CHAPEL HILL.* $60

Young, Stark. IMMORTAL SHADOWS. NY: Scribner's, 1948. 1st ed. Inscribed. Orig grn cl. Fine in VG dj. *CHAPEL HILL.* $100

Youngblood, Charles L. A MIGHTY HUNTER. THE ADVENTURES OF CHARLES YOUNGBLOOD. Chicago: 1890. 2nd issue of rare 1882 ed. Fine. *BOOK MARKET.* $175

Youngblood, Charles L. MIGHTY HUNTER. THE ADVENTURES OF CHARLES L. YOUNGBLOOD. Chicago: Rand, 1890. Reprint on wood pulp paper of 1882 orig ed. 362,(4)pp. Frontis, 47 plts. Orig pict cl. Howes Y34. *GINSBERG.* $200

Younghusband, Sir Francis. KASHMIR. A&C Black, 1909. 1st ed. 20s Series. Minor ex-lib markings, else Good. *OLD LONDON.* $55

Yount, John. WOLF AT THE DOOR. NY: R-H, (1967). 1st ed. Fine in dj. Author's 1st book. *WOOLMER.* $75

Yourcenar, Marguerite. COUP DE GRACE. Trans by Grace Frick in collaboration w/author. 1st Amer ed. Name ffep else VG in edge worn dj w/sticker residue bottom of front panel. *DORN.* $30

Yourcenar, Marguerite. THE ABYSS. NY: FSG, (1976). Inscribed in 1981. 1st ed. Fine in Fine dj. *LOPEZ.* $85

Yourcenar, Marguerite. THE ALMS OF ALCIPPE. NY: Targ Editions, 1982. Edith R. Farrell (trans). 1st ed. 1/250 signed. Fine in glassine dj. *JUVELIS.* $75

Yoyotte, Jean. TREASURES OF THE PHARAOHS. Geneva: Skira, 1968. 1st Eng ed. 120 illus. Dj sl rubbed, frayed, o/w NF. *WORLDWIDE.* $85

Yumato, J.M. THE SAMURAI SWORD, A HANDBOOK. Rutland, VT & Tokyo: Tuttle, 1958. Illus. VG. *MIKESH.* $30

Yun, Leong Gor. CHINATOWN INSIDE OUT. Brattleboro, VT (1936). Dj frayed. *HEINOLDT.* $12

Z

Zabriskie, George A. PERRY'S EXPEDITION TO JAPAN, 1853-1854. Ormond Beach, Florida, 1951. 26pp. 1st ed. Orig cl, dj. One of 750. Signed on presentation leaf. *GINSBERG.* $75

Zackel, Fred. COCAINE AND BLUE EYES. Coward, McCann, 1978. 1st ed. VF in dj. *STAHR.* $20

Zaehnsdorf, J.W. THE ART OF BOOKBINDING: A PRACTICAL TREATISE. London: George Bell & Sons, 1897. 3rd ed. Frontis. 8 color plts & diagrams. Front, rear hinges started, binding crack. *AKA.* $100

Zahl, Paul. CORO-CORO: THE WORLD OF THE SCARLET IBIS. Indianapolis: Bobbs-Merrill, (1954). 1st ed. *SILVER.* $30

Zangwill, Israel. THE MASTER. NY, 1895. 1st ed. Illus. Dec cvrs, gilt. Spine sl sunned. Fine. *POLYANTHOS.* $35

Zappa, Frank. THE REAL FRANK ZAPPA BOOK. Poseidon Press, 1989. 1st ed. VF in dj. Signed. *STAHR.* $45

Zeigler, Tom and Hal Barnell. ZEN OF BASE AND BALL. Simon & Schuster, 1964. 1st ed. VG in Fine dj. *PLAPINGER.* $25

Zeigler, Zirlin and Greenberg (eds). POETS ON STAGE. (NY): Release Press, (1978). 1st ed. Pub as Some #9. *CAPTAIN'S BOOKSHELF.* $35

Zelazny, Roger. EYE OF CAT. NY: Timescape Books, (1982). 1st ed. Remainder mark, o/w Fine in Fine dj and signed. *LOPEZ.* $30

Zelazny, Roger. ROADMARKS. NY: Ballantine/Del Rey, (1979). 1st ed. Fine in dj and signed. *LOPEZ.* $35

Zelazny, Roger. THE COURTS OF CHAOS. Doubleday, 1978. 1st ed. Fine in price-clipped dj. *STAHR.* $35

Zelazny, Roger. THIS IMMORTAL. NY: Ace, 1966. Wraps. 1st ed. Author's 1st book. Fine w/owner's date inside. *BEASLEY.* $20

Ziegler, Ernst. A TEXT-BOOK OF GENERAL PATHOLOGICAL ANATOMY AND PATHOGENESIS. NY, 1883-1884. 1st Amer ed. 2 vols. 371pp, 365pp. Woodcut illus. *FYE.* $75

Ziemssen, Hugo von (ed). ACUTE INFECTIOUS DISEASES AND CHRONIC INFECTIOUS DISEASES. NY, 1874-75. 1st Eng trans. 3 vols. 708, 751, 672pp. *FYE.* $100

Zilboorg, Gregory. THE MEDICAL MAN AND THE WITCH DURING THE RENAISSANCE. Baltimore, 1935. 1st ed. *FYE.* $50

Zimmerman, Bill. AIRLIFT TO WOUNDED TREE. Chicago: Swallow Press, 1976. 1st ed. Fine in Fine dj. *CONNOLLY & WADE.* $25

Zimmerman, Bruce. BLOOD UNDER THE BRIDGE. NY: Harper & Row, 1989. 1st ed. VF in dj. *MORDIDA.* $25

Zimmerman, Bruce. THICKER THAN WATER. NY: Harper Collins, 1991. 1st ed. VF in dj. *MORDIDA*. $20

Zimmerman, Leo and Ilza Veith. GREAT IDEAS IN THE HISTORY OF SURGERY. Baltimore, 1961. 1st ed. Signed. Head of spine and near board have been repaired. Contents Fine. *FYE*. $100

Zimmerman, Paul. THE LOS ANGELES DODGERS. Coward McCann, 1960. 1st ed. Fine in Fine dj. *PLAPINGER*. $25

ZION, GRAND CANYON, BRYCE, CEDAR BREAKS, AND KAIBAB. Kansas City, 1929. Red stiff pict wraps. 56pp. Some sunfade and minor flaws on cover, else VG. *FIVE QUAIL*. $17.50

Zollers, George D. THRILLING INCIDENTS ON SEA AND LAND: THE PRODIGAL'S RETURN. Mt. Morris, IL, 1892. 1st ed. VG. *McGOWAN*. $85

Zollinger, Norman. LAUTREC. NY: E.P. Dutton, 1990. 1st ed. Inscribed. VF in dj. *MORDIDA*. $20

Zolotow, Charlotte. BUT NOT BILLY. Harper & Row, (1983). Stated 1st ed. Illus by Kay Chorao and signed by author. Fine in Fine dj. *BEBBAH*. $25

Zornow, William Frank. KANSAS. A HISTORY OF THE JAYHAWK STATE. Norman: Univ of Oklahoma Press, 1957. 1st ed. 8 maps. Fine in VG dj. *CONNOLLY & WADE*. $37.50

Zubro, Mark Richard. WHY ISN'T BECKY TWITCHELL DEAD? NY: St. Martin's Press, 1990. 1st ed. VF in dj. *MORDIDA*. $20

Zuckerkandl, Otto. ATLAS AND EPITOME OF OPERATIVE SURGERY. Phila, 1898. 1st Eng trans. 24 color lithographic plts, 217 engrvs. *FYE*. $100

Zugsmith, Albert. THE BEAT GENERATION. Bantam, 1959. 1st ed. Fine in wraps. Price marked out on front cover. *STAHR*. $20

Zukofsky, Louis. "A"-24. NY: Grossman, (1972). 1st ed. Orig blue cl. Couple bumps bottom edge, but VG in dj. *CHAPEL HILL*. $40

Zukofsky, Louis. 16 ONCE PUBLISHED, A SELECTION BY HIS WIFE. (Edinburgh): Wild Hawthorn Press, 1962. 1st ed. Dec wraps sl soiled, but VG. *JAFFE*. $45

Zukofsky, Louis. ARISE, ARISE. NY: Grossman, 1973. 1st ed, hb issue, dj. VF. *JAFFE*. $35

Zukofsky, Louis. PREPOSITIONS. London, 1967. 1st ed. Ltd ed, 94/150 signed. Sl offsetting small areas front and rear feps. Fine in price clipped dj. *POLYANTHOS*. $100

Zukofsky, Louis. PREPOSITIONS. London: Rapp & Carroll, (1967). 1st ed. 1/150 signed. Fine in price-clipped dj. *CAPTAIN'S BOOKSHELF*. $75

Zukofsky, Louis. SOME TIME. SHORT POEMS. Stuttgart: Jonathan Williams, 1956. 1st ed, regular issue. One of 300. Owner sig. Orig wraps (sewn as issued) sl foxed, o/w VG. *JAFFE*. $175

Zumbo, Jim. HUNTING AMERICA'S MULE DEER. Tulsa: Winchester Press, 1981. 1st ed. Signed, slipcased. Fine/VG in VG+ slipcase. (Unknown if box is orig). *BACKMAN*. $35

Zupko, R.E. BRITISH WEIGHTS & MEASURES...TO THE 17TH CENTURY. Univ of WI Press, 1977. Near New w/dj. *BOOKCELL*. $27

Zwerin, Mike. LA TRISTESSE DE SAINT LOUIS: JAZZ UNDER THE NAZIS. NY: Morrow, (1985). 1st ed. Fine in Fine dj (tiny tear). *AKA*. $25

Zwinger, Ann. A DESERT COUNTRY NEAR THE SEA...CAPE REGION OF BAJA CALIFORNIA. NY: Harper, (1983). 1st ed. Fine in Fine dj. *BOOK MARKET*. $25

Zwinger, Ann. WIND IN THE ROCK. NY, 1978. 1st ed. VG+. *FIVE QUAIL*. $25